Geological Survey of Canada

Geology of Canada, no. 2

GEOLOGY OF THE CONTINENTAL MARGIN OF EASTERN CANADA

edited by

M.J. Keen and

G.L. Williams

1990

This is volume I-1 of the Geological Society of America's Geology of North America series produced as part of the Decade of North American Geology project.

Available in Canada through

authorized bookstore agents and other bookstores

or by mail from

Canadian Government Publishing Centre
Supply and Services Canada
Ottawa, Canada K1A 0S9

and from

Geological Survey of Canada offices:

601 Booth Street
Ottawa, Canada K1A 0E8

3303-33rd Street N.W.,
Calgary, Alberta T2L 2A7

100 West Pender Street
Vancouver, B.C. V6B 1R8

A deposit copy of this publication is also available for reference
in public libraries across Canada

Cat. No. M40-49/2E
ISBN 0-660-13130-7

Price subject to change without notice

Technical editor
P.J. Griffin

Technical assistance
M.A. Best

Design and layout
M.J. Kiel

Cartography
Cartographic Section, GSC, Ottawa
The Cartography-Drafting Unit, Atlantic Geoscience Centre, GSC, Dartmouth
Illustration Unit, Bedford Institute of Oceanography, Dartmouth

Cover
CSS Hudson undertaking a geological and geophysical survey in a fiord along the southeastern coast
of Baffin Island. Photo by R. Bélanger, Bedford Institute of Oceanography, Dartmouth.

Printed in Canada

PREFACE

The Geology of North America series has been prepared to mark the Centennial of the Geological Society of America. It represents the co-operative efforts of more than 1000 individuals from academia, state and federal agencies of many countries, and industry to prepare syntheses that are as current and authoritative as possible about the geology of the North American continent and adjacent oceanic regions.

This series is part of the Decade of North American Geology (DNAG) Project which also includes eight wall maps at a scale of 1:5 000 000 that summarize the geology, tectonics, magnetic and gravity anomaly patterns, regional stress fields, thermal aspects, seismicity, and neotectonics of North America and its surroundings. Together, the synthesis volumes and maps are the first co-ordinated effort to integrate all available knowledge about the geology and geophysics of a crustal plate on a regional scale.

The products of the DNAG Project present the state of knowledge of the geology and geophysics of North America in the 1980s, and they point the way toward work to be done in the decades ahead.

From time to time since its foundation in 1842 the Geological Survey of Canada has prepared and published overviews of the geology of Canada. This volume represents a part of the seventh such synthesis and besides forming part of the DNAG Project series is one of the nine volumes that make up the latest *Geology of Canada.*

J.O. Wheeler
General Editor for the volumes
published by the
Geological Survey of Canada

A.R. Palmer
General Editor for the volumes
published by the
Geological Society of America

CONTENTS

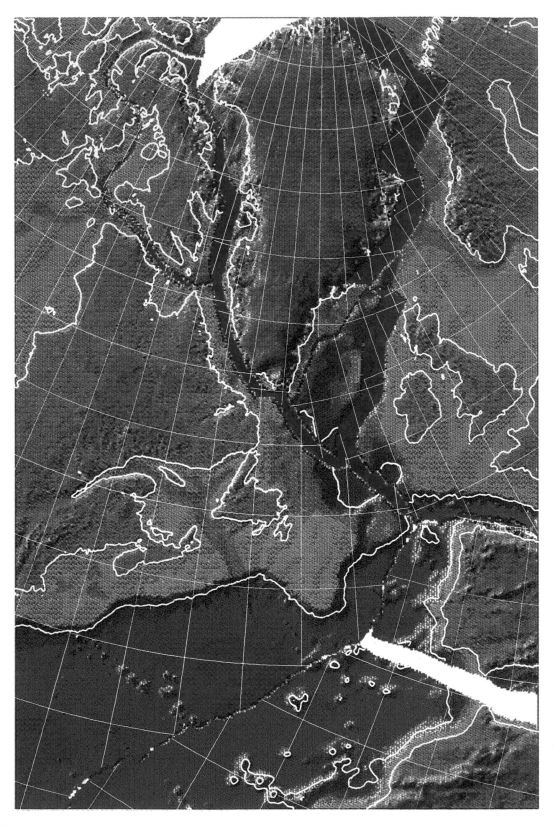

Shaded relief map of a reconstruction of the North Atlantic at chron MO (118 Ma, Aptian) using gridded bathymetry and elevation data from ETOPO5, illuminated from the northwest. The dark blue regions show where plates overlap (implying later extension), and the blank regions where they fail to meet (indicating later compression).

Figure was compiled by S.P. Srivastava, W.R. Roest, and S. Lévesque.

ETOPO5 is a digital data file accessible through the National Geophysical Data Center in Boulder, Colorado

FOREWORD

The continental margin of eastern Canada extends from Georges Bank at 41 degrees North to Nares Strait at 80 degrees North, almost half the distance from the Pole to the equator. It is a classical example of a passive or "Atlantic" type of continental margin with a geological history reflecting at least two "Wilson Cycles". The first gave birth to the Iapetus Ocean, and the second to the modern Atlantic and its neighbours. This margin ties the glacial history of the Canadian landmass to the adjacent ocean basins, and so to the world's oceans. Two of the basins offshore eastern Canada, the Jeanne d'Arc Basin off Newfoundland and the Scotian Basin off Nova Scotia, contain substantial resources of oil and gas. An understanding of the geology of the margin bears directly on the evolution of the whole of the North Atlantic and of the Arctic, and on the generation of hydrocarbons.

This volume is in a sense a very personal one, because most contributors have worked together for many years at the Atlantic Geoscience Centre or at Dalhousie University. We have lived in exciting times. Twenty years ago it would have been impossible to produce a major publication on the geology of the continental margin of eastern Canada; indeed in 1970 only 2000 words were devoted to all of Canada's offshore in the Geological Survey's *Geology and Economic Minerals of Canada*. The size of this volume is largely the result of the impetus from the successful search for hydrocarbons off eastern Canada, the development of increasingly sophisticated methods for acquiring, analyzing and interpreting data, and new ideas. The work spans many conventional boundaries, and several contributions are from teams of scientists. Teamwork will surely be more important in the future, although the impetus may be different. In the years to come the way the world is managed will depend on our knowledge of how it works as a physical system: the oceans and their margins will be important parts of new investigations.

We acknowledge elsewhere the help of many individuals in the preparation of this volume, but we want to recognize here the vision of early pioneers. Some enlarged the world's intellectual store in their search for new knowledge. Others had the imagination and courage to lease, survey and drill on the new frontiers off eastern Canada. Some had the foresight to initiate programs and provide facilities in Halifax and Dartmouth, Nova Scotia. Ronald Hayes founded oceanography at Dalhousie University in 1960, and Ewart Blanchard started geophysics. Bedford Institute of Oceanography was founded by William van Steenburgh in 1962, and the first Director was Bill English. Many of the contributors to this volume have benefited over the years from the work of these talented individuals. We hope that those who started it all will be pleased with this book.

This is the second volume in the *Geology of Canada* series to be published. The original guidelines for the series identified our audience as the entire earth science community — geologists, geochemists, geophysicists, oceanographers, and students — and the series was to be of interest to all. We have tried to meet those lofty goals, and only regret that it has taken so long.

Acknowledgments

Many worked to produce this volume — at sea or on the ice, in the laboratory, or in production of the book itself. We thank you all.

We are in debt to the officers and crews of the many research vessels — the HUDSON, BAFFIN, DAWSON and smaller vessels from Bedford Institute of Oceanography, and of ships not now in service — such as the SACKVILLE and KAPUSKASING. The Polar Continental Shelf Project helped us in our work in the Arctic, and it is a pleasure to say "thank you" to their Director of many years, George Hobson. The pilots of the submersible PISCES IV took some of us to the seafloor to view the rocks at first hand. The technical support staff at the Atlantic Geoscience Centre and the staff associated with specific scientific topics were always magnificent.

The volume represents the sustained efforts of numerous authors, primarily from the Atlantic Geoscience Centre. We would like to thank them for their perseverence especially since most of the chapters were completed by 1987.

The 1:5 million scale maps are a major component of this volume; the responsibility for their compilation fell to Gordon Cameron and Margie Best. They did an excellent job. We thank them and the many contributors who are acknowledged on the individual maps and who provided information for the maps ahead of publication, especially Paul Hoffman, John Adams, Andy Okulitch and Hank Williams. The staff of the Geophysics Division of the Geological Survey of Canada helped magnificently in the preparation of the gravity and magnetic maps.

Many individuals in GSC helped with the preparation of the manuscripts. Typing was done by Nelly Koziel, Jane Dawe and Patricia Dennis at AGC in Dartmouth and staff of the Word Processing Centre in Ottawa; drafting and illustrations were by Gary Cook, Art Cosgrove, Gary Grant, Ken Hale, and Francis Kelly at the Bedford Institute of Oceanography in Dartmouth and the Geoscience Information Division (GID) of the Geological Survey in Ottawa. Margie Best (AGC, Dartmouth) and Mike Kiel and Peter Griffin (GSC, Ottawa) provided editorial support and guidance. Thank you.

Numerous reviewers provided prompt, helpful and constructive criticism. Richard Haworth, formerly with the Atlantic Geoscience Centre and now with the British Geological Survey, helped in the early stages and was responsible for initial plans for the volume. J.O. Wheeler, the general editor of the Geology of Canada series, reviewed all the chapters.

Although the *Geology of Canada* is produced and published by the Geological Survey of Canada, additional support from the following contributors through the Canadian Geological Foundation assisted in defraying special costs related to the volume on the Appalachian Orogen in Canada and Greenland: Alberta Energy Co. Ltd., Bow Valley Industries Ltd., B.P. Canada Ltd., Canterra Energy Ltd., Norcen Energy Resources Ltd., Petro-Canada, Shell Canada Ltd., Westmin Resources Ltd., J.J. Brummer, D.R. Derry (deceased), and R.E. Folinsbee.

Finally, we acknowledge our particular debt to Basil Cooke, Professor Emeritus of Geology at Dalhousie University, and a friend and colleague of many contributors. He was our principal reviewer and read all the manuscripts and made innumerable helpful suggestions. Many, many thanks.

M.J. Keen and G.L. Williams
Atlantic Geoscience Centre
Geological Survey of Canada
Bedford Institute of Oceanography
Dartmouth, Nova Scotia

INTRODUCTION

Early seismic work on Sable Island. Geophysical Services Inc.'s party 412 at work for Mobil Oil during the first reflection survey carried out on Sable Island during the summer of 1960. Photo by Maurice Crosby, Halifax, Nova Scotia.

Chapter 1

GEOLOGICAL AND HISTORICAL PERSPECTIVE

Chapter 1

GEOLOGICAL AND HISTORICAL PERSPECTIVE

M.J. Keen and D.J.W. Piper

with contributions by J.S. Bell and K. Moran

INTRODUCTION

The continental margin of eastern Canada and the floors of the seas which border it (Fig. 1.1) are keys to understanding the opening of the North Atlantic during the Mesozoic and Cenozoic and to determining the relationships between the Precambrian and Paleozoic rocks on the opposing continents. Eastern Canada lay in the middle of the super-continent Pangea when the North Atlantic began to open some 200 million years ago, eventually separating the Appalachian-Caledonide Orogen. This represented the first part of a "Wilson Cycle" of opening and closing of an ocean, which had occurred once before in the history of the Appalachians with the creation and destruction of the Iapetus Ocean. The North Atlantic opened from south to north in the Mesozoic and Cenozoic, as reflected in the sedimentary sequences of the margins (including Eastern Canada), and ended in the Arctic Ocean. Thus, oceanographic events and seafloor spreading off eastern Canada have been linked to events to the north in the Arctic, and to the south in the Central Atlantic, as well as to those of the conjugate margins of western Africa, Europe and Greenland (see Chapters 2 and 8). The eastern Canadian margin is a classical example of an Atlantic type, passive continental margin.

The initial rifting of the North Atlantic, at least in part, was controlled by the grain of the crustal framework within which the rifting developed. In eastern Canada this framework included the Appalachians in the south and the Canadian Shield in the north. This effect can be seen on the southern margin of the Grand Banks, where the offset of the modern margin mirrors the ancient offset at the St. Lawrence re-entrant of the Appalachians. The offset in the margin at the Cartwright Fracture Zone is colinear with the Precambrian Grenville Front on land (see Fig. 2.2). Faults bounding the sedimentary basins which developed within this crustal framework may extend right through the crust, but the mechanism of initial rifting is not yet understood.

The sedimentary basins off eastern Canada are part of a system of basins extending from the southeastern United States to northern Baffin Bay (see Chapters 5, 6 and 7). They developed during the initial Mesozoic and Cenozoic rifting and during seafloor spreading. The sediments of the Jeanne d'Arc Basin, east of Newfoundland, are more than 20 km thick, and those of the Scotian Basin 15 to 20 km thick (see Map 1707A, in pocket). Oil and gas have been discovered in some of the basins off eastern Canada. The Hibernia field, in the Jeanne d'Arc Basin, is one of the world's giant fields, with reserves in the range of 103 to 143 million cubic metres of oil (650 to 900 million barrels).

The southern oceans surrounding Antarctica started to cool significantly at about 40 Ma. Glaciations began in the Oligocene in Antarctica, and intensified in the Middle Miocene (Chapter 10). The effects of cooling in the northern hemisphere became apparent on land about 10 Ma, with glaciation in Alaska and the development of sub-Arctic flora in Iceland. The Laurentide ice-sheet, which occupied much of Canada and the northern United States east of the Cordilleras, was the largest in the northern hemisphere, perhaps because of the transport of moist air into the high latitudes through the Labrador Sea. When the Laurentide ice-sheet melted, its products had only a few routes for escape: through the Mackenzie River into the Arctic Ocean; through rivers draining the Great Lakes — the Mississippi into the Gulf of Mexico and the St. Lawrence into the Atlantic; and through Hudson Strait into the Labrador Sea. Consequently, an understanding of the Quaternary history of the continental margin of eastern Canada is needed to interpret the deglaciation of North America. Evidence of the first drift ice, sea ice, or icebergs from the Greenland or Laurentide ice-sheets, is seen in sediments of the Arctic Ocean which are about 4 Ma, and in the Labrador Sea and Baffin Bay about 3 Ma (Chapter 10).

The processes that have sculptured the margin since deglaciation have been controlled by two important parameters, climate and sea level. Marine geological processes on the continental shelf are primarily controlled in the south by waves and currents, but are dominated in the north by ice, and other effects of a cold climate such as permafrost on land and ice-scoured and ice-rafted sediments offshore. The shelves to the south are relatively shallow, and the late Wisconsinan and Holocene rises in sea level following deglaciation transgressed an exposed shelf. In the north, the shelves are deeper and in most places they have not been exposed subaerially since at least the Tertiary.

Keen, M.J. and Piper, D.J.W.
1990: Geological and historical perspective, Chapter 1, in Geology of the Continental Margin of Eastern Canada, M.J. Keen and G.L. Williams (ed.); Geological Survey of Canada, Geology of Canada, no. 2 p. 5-30 (also Geological Society of America, The Geology of North America, v. I-1).

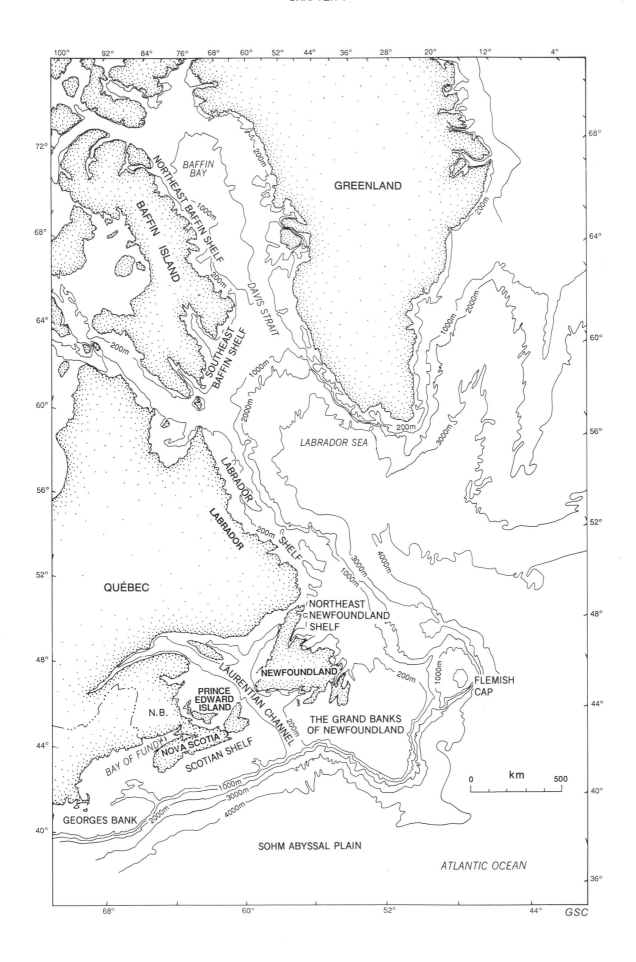

Proper planning for development of resources in the coastal regions and offshore must take into account the surficial sediments and modern processes. Aggregate will be needed for construction, and cannot be extracted indiscriminately from beaches. The need for development will result in conflict with environmental concerns, and the environment will cause some problems for development: iceberg scour is a hazard to pipelines and seabed well completions (Chapters 10, 13, 14).

The major shelves include from south to north: Georges Bank, Scotian Shelf, the Grand Banks of Newfoundland, Northeast Newfoundland Shelf, Labrador Shelf, Southeast Baffin Shelf and Northeast Baffin Shelf (Fig. 1.1).

The Scotian Shelf, situated southeast of Nova Scotia, is about 750 km long and between 128 and 224 km wide. It covers an area of about 960 000 km². As of late 1987, over 115 wells had been drilled on the shelf, with several major gas discoveries and one oil discovery. The Grand Banks of Newfoundland are located to the south and east of Newfoundland and are separated from the Scotian Shelf by the Laurentian Channel. The Grand Banks are up to 720 km long, 480 km wide and have an area of some 180 000 km². Exploration in this domain has focussed on the Jeanne d'Arc Basin (Map 1706A, in pocket) where several major oil and gas finds have been found. As its name implies, the Northeast Newfoundland Shelf lies to the northeast of Newfoundland. It is an elongate, relatively narrow shelf with an area of about 120 000 km². Exploration there has been intermittent with no significant discoveries. The Labrador Shelf represents the western margin of the Labrador Sea. With an area of about 140 800 km² and as wide as 320 km, the Labrador Shelf extends from the Northeast Newfoundland Shelf to Hudson Strait (about 1100 km to the north). The Southeast Baffin Shelf lies between Hudson Strait and Davis Strait. North from Davis Strait to latitude 78°N lies Baffin Bay with an area of about 690 000 km²; its length is 1350 km long with a width ranging from 110 to 650 km. Several gas discoveries have been made on the Labrador Shelf, however, the lack of success in finding any oil and the high cost of development have led to a slowdown in drilling. In the Davis Strait region three wells have been drilled, with one discovering gas and condensate.

This volume describes the geology of the continental margin of eastern Canada, the contiguous seas and the eastern Canadian Arctic. The rifting and seafloor spreading of this pivotal region tie the Atlantic to the Arctic: the sediments tell us of glacial and deglaciation events that have affected much of North America in the late Quaternary. Modern processes exhibit the spectrum from those typical of temperate regions to those typical of the high Arctic.

A major part of this publication is the accompanying maps and pocket figures. The 1:5 000 000 maps and figures, all plotted on a Lambert Conic Conformal Projection, are: Bathymetry; Geology; Tectonics; Depth to Basement; Gravity; Magnetics; Crustal thickness, Seismicity and Stress Orientations; Quaternary Geology; Well Locations; Subsurface Quaternary Features; and Surficial

Features. The three other pocket figures are the correlation chart, a 1:2 000 000 Coastal Features plot, and Seismic Profiles. The compilation of these pocket figures represents a contribution as impressive as that for the chapters. The figures are an integral aspect of the volume and are referred to continually in the text.

The area dealt with in this volume is vast. We have tried to cover it adequately, but inevitably there are gaps in the record.

EXPLORATION OF THE CONTINENTAL MARGIN

Oil was discovered in 1979 in the Hibernia P-15 well (Fig. 1, in pocket) in the Jeanne d'Arc Basin beneath the Grand Banks of Newfoundland. Thirty years earlier, the existence of the sedimentary basins off the east coast of Canada was only vaguely known; and even as recently as 1970, the previous edition of the Geology of Canada contained only a few paragraphs on offshore eastern Canada. This reflects the exponential growth in our knowledge of the geology of this area over the last 25 years. This growth has taken many forms, including as examples: our knowledge of the history of opening of the oceanic basins; our understanding of the development of the Mesozoic-Cenozoic basins and our knowledge of the sedimentary strata that fill them; our ability to model the rifting of the continental margins; and our understanding of the processes which led to the formation of the unconsolidated sediments on the shelves. Substantial advances really began in the 1950s; earlier studies had been rather sporadic, although some had, in retrospect, remarkable insight. An example is Spencer's delineation of submarine valleys from wire-line soundings in 1903 (Fig. 1.2). Details of the history of exploration are given in Table A.1 in the Appendix.

Studies in the 19th century (Upham, 1894) and the early part of the 20th century were pertinent to the research on the glacial history of the region, and gave the first clues to the existence of the sedimentary basins offshore. During those early years, United States scientists examined material collected primarily by fishermen in their trawls and concluded that Cretaceous and Tertiary sedimentary rocks extended all the way from Florida to the Grand Banks of Newfoundland (Dahl, 1925). The shelf off the Atlantic Provinces appeared to be a submerged part of the Atlantic coastal plain of the eastern United States. A glacial origin for the Laurentian Channel (Fig. 1.1) was proposed in 1931 by Shepard. The characteristics of sediment samples from the Labrador Sea and Baffin Bay were described in 1932 following the expedition by the United States Coast Guard in the vessel MARION; this work anticipated the importance of ice rafting as a process.

The magnitude of the sedimentary basins was appreciated when the pace of investigations offshore accelerated in the 1950s. Lamont Geological Observatory of Columbia University made seismic refraction observations off Nova Scotia and Newfoundland and, as a result, suggested that a substantial thickness of sediments lay beneath the shelf and slope, analogous to those beneath the coastal plain onshore and offshore the United States to the south (Officer and Ewing, 1954). Lamont scientists discovered the East Coast Magnetic Anomaly (ECMA) (Maps 1706A and 1709A, in pocket). The ECMA is a prominent

Figure 1.1. Bathymetry of the continental margin of eastern Canada and the contiguous ocean basins. After Canadian Hydrographic Service Map 850-A (in pocket).

BULL. GEOL. SOC. AM.

VOL. 14, 1902, PL. 19

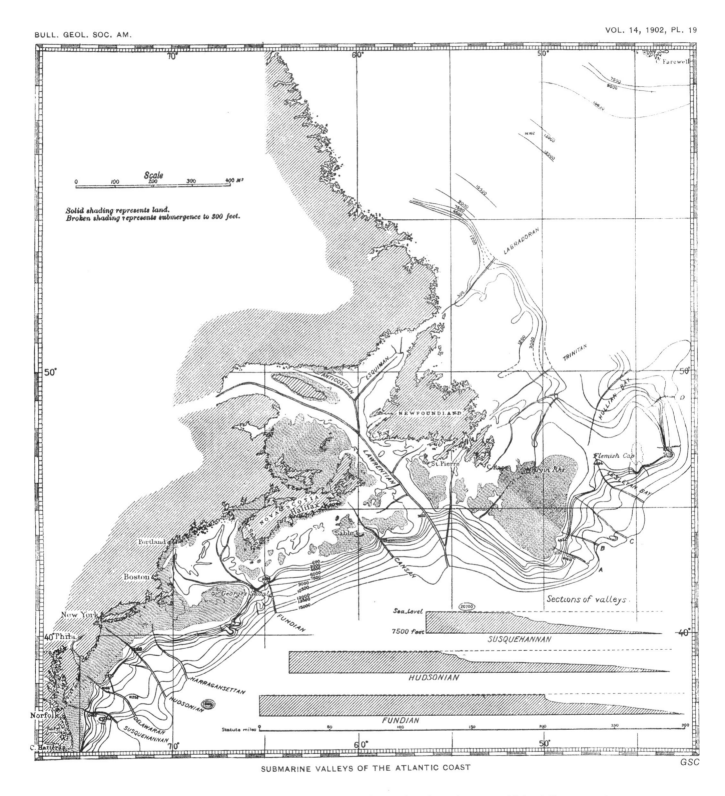

SUBMARINE VALLEYS OF THE ATLANTIC COAST

GSC

Figure 1.2. Submarine valleys on the continental margin of northeastern United States and eastern Canada, delineated by J.W. Spencer from early soundings (Spencer, 1903).

anomaly, which is now known to extend from the southeastern United States to the southern margin of the Grand Banks, and from the eastern Grand Banks to the north. No definitive explanation for this anomaly has yet been given. The Dominion Observatory of Canada investigated the seismic structure beneath the Gulf of St. Lawrence, to determine if the circular form of the southern coastline of the gulf reflects a meteorite impact (Willmore and Scheidegger, 1956). It does not, but that could not be said with assurance for some time.

Petroleum exploration of the sedimentary basins began in 1958 when Mobil Oil Canada Ltd. sought exploration permits on 0.5 million hectares around Sable Island, located on the Scotian Shelf. In 1960, industry began seismic surveys off the east coast, with the first exploration drilling in 1965. The Geological Survey of Canada started aeromagnetic surveys offshore in 1958, and initiated co-operative geophysical surveys with the Canadian Hydrographic Service in 1959. The National Aeronautical Establishment and the Geological Survey carried out aeromagnetic reconnaissance flights over the Labrador Sea and Baffin Bay, and suggested that the shelves of these regions, like those to the south, had thick sedimentary sequences beneath them (Godby et al., 1966; Hood, 1971). Marine magnetometer surveys in Hudson Bay led to similar conclusions, although the sediments of Hudson Bay are Paleozoic, whereas those of the Labrador Shelf are principally Mesozoic and Cenozoic (Hood, 1964). Exploration by industry came to fruition, in 1971 with the first significant oil and gas discovery off Nova Scotia in the Sable Island E-48 well, and then in 1979 with the discovery of oil and gas on the Grand Banks of Newfoundland in the Hibernia P-15 well (Fig. 1, in pocket).

The Mesozoic and Cenozoic sedimentary basins of the east coast overlie Precambrian and Paleozoic rocks. These older rocks usually outcrop in a narrow strip between the feather edge of the Cenozoic sediments and the coast. Exploration of the Paleozoic has been aided by advances in both high-resolution seismic systems and in sampling by rock-core drilling systems, which could be deployed by oceanographic vessels.

Exploration was also accompanied by conceptual advances. The discovery of seafloor spreading and plate tectonics in the 1960s led to our present understanding of the histories for the North Atlantic Ocean, Labrador Sea, and Arctic Ocean. Advances in biostratigraphy, lithostratigraphy and paleoecology allowed our understanding of the origin of the sedimentary basins along the continental margin of eastern Canada to be tied to the spreading of the ocean floors and to the changing configuration of the oceans themselves. Models of extension for the initiation of the sedimentary basins of the margins have led to successful prediction of subsidence and thermal history (see Chapter 9). The passive margins were recognized as an early part of the Wilson Cycle, of opening and closing of an ocean, as we see in the Paleozoic in the Appalachians. Phenomena first comprehended on the present passive margins have been recognized on ancient margins. Examples of these are the quantitative predictions of subsidence rates, and the recognition of a breakup unconformity between synrift and postrift sediments. The role of the lithosphere in the early extension leading to the sedimentary basins of the passive margin off eastern Canada is a topic of current research, and is part of an attempt to put basin formation in the global context of the driving forces of plate tectonics, and of the relationship between the lithospheric plates and the earth's mantle as a whole.

Investigations of the surficial sediments of the continental margin off eastern Canada accompanied the search for oil and gas, partly as a consequence of the need to define the potential impact of development upon the environment and the constraints which the environment would place upon development. These investigations were aided in the 1970s by the development of a variety of high-resolution seismic systems, of which the Huntec "Deep Tow" system was particularly successful (Hutchins et al., 1976). This gives a vertical resolution in surficial sediments of about 10 cm in seismic profiling and led to the delineation of a variety of glacial and postglacial deposits on continental shelves. Such seismic profiles can be used to precisely place sediment cores in a stratigraphic framework. Advances in technology led also to the recognition of ice scour, and to the ability to map the seabed with swath-mapping systems such as the U.K. GLORIA in deep water. As another example, these techniques allowed the effects of the 1929 earthquake of the Grand Banks to be described in detail (Piper et al., 1988). Conceptual advances in understanding sedimentation in a glaciomarine environment have made it possible to attempt to correlate land and offshore Quaternary stratigraphy. Interest in the effects of industrial development also led to the modelling of sediment transport, for example in the Bay of Fundy and on the Scotian Shelf, in order to predict the effect of structures on sediment accumulation.

The need to predict the potentially negative consequences of the exploitation of hydrocarbons led in the 1970s to an increased interest in the geology of the coastlines, from both the physical descriptions and the processes. These studies were given impetus by the oil spills from the vessels ARROW in 1970 and KURDISTAN in 1979, by the need to plan for development in the Beaufort Sea, with the possibilities of tankers passing through the Northwest Passage into the Atlantic, and by the need to plan for the development of harbours and terminals in the Arctic Islands. These investigations led, for example, to the recognition of the importance of gravel beaches on Canada's eastern seaboard, and to the importance of periglacial phenomena in the development of beaches in the Canadian Arctic.

INVESTIGATIONS AT SEA
The approach
Acquisition of geological and geophysical data in the ocean basins is quite different from acquisition of these data on land. Ships make convenient platforms, but weather conditions and difficulties of positioning are constraints. Land-based geologists are usually in contact with the subject of their study but marine geologists and geophysicists seldom are. For them, the seafloor is generally a distant and invisible target. Ice, in its various forms of sea ice in a coastal zone, icebergs, or permanent pack ice in the Arctic, provide special challenges for a geologist interested in the seafloor. Consequently, methods have had to be developed for many difficult circumstances. For example, geological mapping in icebound channels of the Arctic Islands will be difficult until a suitable icebreaker or submersible is available; until then the investigator is forced to use the leads in the

ice which develop from time to time as the window through which to peer. In this case, a small inflatable boat must be transported from lead to lead by helicopter.

The general approach to geological and geophysical investigations in the ocean basins, whether they be of the coastal zone or the open ocean, is similar whatever the particular problem. The investigations proceed from regional to detailed, from small to large scales of mapping, in terms of area and of depth below the seafloor. As a simple example, investigations of the surficial sediments on a continental shelf will proceed in something like the following order: regional bathymetry, with depths measured on lines spaced 1 to 20 km apart, spacing depending on depth, with closer spacing in shallower water, sidescan sonar mapping with systems of steadily decreasing swath width and increasing resolution, finally focussing on the details of features delineated in the coarse surveys; seismic reflection surveys conducted in the same sort of conceptual framework, finally focussing on the details of individual features to be sampled; photography, as an extension of sidescan sonar at the level of resolution not easily attained with acoustic systems; sampling, with drills, corers, manned and unmanned submersibles, or with other sampling devices. Mapping of this nature leads to specific questions to be resolved by dedicated surveys, or to experiments designed to investigate a particular process identified in the surveys. Processes may be modelled theoretically in the laboratory; samples and records will be studied in the laboratory; both sorts of investigations lead to scientific insight and a new set of questions to be answered.

Navigation

A key concern to offshore surveys is navigation. We have to know where the ship is and where the instruments deployed from the vessel are. The instruments may be far from the vessel, at the end of a long cable, or on the seafloor. These two sets of problems are both solved by triangulation, but use different physical properties. Electromagnetic waves propagate well in air, but poorly in water, and acoustic waves propagate well in water, but poorly in air. Consequently, positioning a vessel generally depends on observing electromagnetic waves from satellites or shore-based transmitters, whereas positioning an instrument usually depends on observing acoustic waves from acoustic transmitters on ships or on the seafloor.

Many positioning techniques have been used by vessels in the acquisition of the data used in this volume. Astronomical positioning and radar ranging onto the nearest land were used during the older surveys, but the Global Positioning System in its current experimental mode has been used in acquiring the latest data. The error in the first case may be 20 nautical miles, but only 20 m in the second case. The standard techniques used in the last decade have combined the radio-aid LORAN-C with the Transit Satellite System. This satellite navigational system allows a position to be obtained every few hours, but the position obtained depends on knowing the course and speed of the vessel during the 20 minutes required to receive information from the satellite. LORAN-C allows interpolation between satellite fixes, and determination of the speed and course during the observation of the satellite. LORAN-C has been used mainly in "range-range" mode, in which distances are established between a station on shore and a vessel by comparing the time of start of transmission of a

signal and the time of receipt on board. This requires an extremely accurate clock on the vessel, but is more accurate than using the system in "hyperbolic" mode, and only two shore stations are needed, rather than three. This is important in remote areas, such as much of the continental margin off eastern Canada.

The Global Positioning System will revolutionize navigation of vessels at sea, allowing positions to be established continuously to within 20 m anywhere on the globe.

Instruments on the seafloor, or on cables attached to a vessel, have been positioned acoustically using a number of systems. Acoustic beacons may be placed on the seafloor and the measuring instrument positioned with reference to them. Acoustic transmitters on instruments may be triggered by a transmitter on the vessel; the arrival time of a signal from the instrument gives the range, and the difference in arrival time at different receivers on the vessel gives the direction of the instrument.

MORPHOLOGY
Measuring depth

The bathymetry shown in Map 850-A (in pocket) is based substantially on systematic surveys made by the Canadian Hydrographic Service, supplemented by soundings provided by a variety of other agencies, such as the International Hydrographic Bureau in Monaco, the Geological Survey of Canada, and oil companies who collect soundings as a part of their seismic surveys. Figure 1.3 shows the quality and coverage of bathymetric data.

The systematic reconnaissance bathymetric surveys are substantially complete for the regions south of Davis Strait except in the nearshore areas, but are absent in large parts of the areas to the north. In those areas, the bathymetry is known from geophysical surveys by a number of agencies and from tracks of opportunity. In inter-island channels of the Canadian Arctic Archipelago, many of the existing bathymetric data have been obtained by spot measurements through the permanent and semi-permanent sea ice. Systematic surveys will not be conducted in the northern regions until the Global Positioning System is available. Many coastal areas have not been surveyed to modern standards and there are still fiords where there is only a single line of soundings obtained by a ship of opportunity. The systematic surveys in the southerly regions are of the whole inner part of the continental margin of eastern Canada, approximately to the foot of the slope, and of the whole of the Labrador Sea. Soundings were obtained on single lines, the line spacing increasing with water depth. No systematic bathymetric surveys have been made using multi-beam mapping systems.

The accuracy with which bathymetric features are located varies with the navigational systems used in the different surveys, and on the different tracks of opportunity. Features may be systematically mislocated on the shelves by as much as 200 to 300 m on account of systematic errors in positioning, but may not be relatively misplaced by more than a few tens of metres. It is possible but unlikely that new seamounts will be discovered in deep water between the continental slope east of the Grand Banks and the Mid-Atlantic Ridge. Some features of relatively low relief on the present bathymetric map, such as valley patterns in deep water, will change substantially

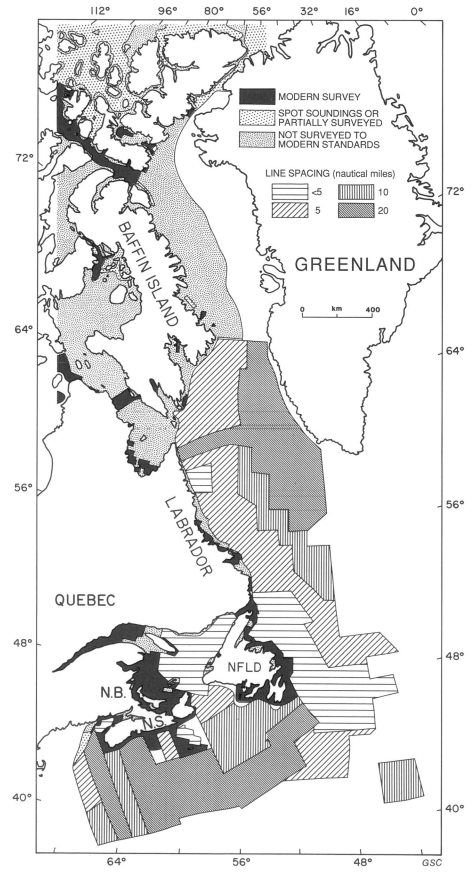

Figure 1.3. Quality and coverage of bathymetric data used to prepare the Map 850-A of eastern Canada.

when surveyed by swath mapping systems. However, the major features of Map 850-A of the continental margin of eastern Canada should not change significantly.

Geomorphological evolution
The oceanic basins

The morphology of the northwest Atlantic and the adjoining seas and margins (shown in Map 850-A, in pocket and in Fig. 1.1 and 1.4), is generally typical of an oceanic basin which has developed by rifting of a continent, followed by seafloor spreading and subsidence. The North Atlantic started with rifting at about 200 Ma, with subsequent spreading at a rate of about 1 cm per year to the east and west of the Mid-Atlantic Ridge (Chapter 8). The thermal contraction of the lithosphere is reflected in the overall increase in water depths from the ridge to the continental margins. Initial volcanic morphology is partially masked

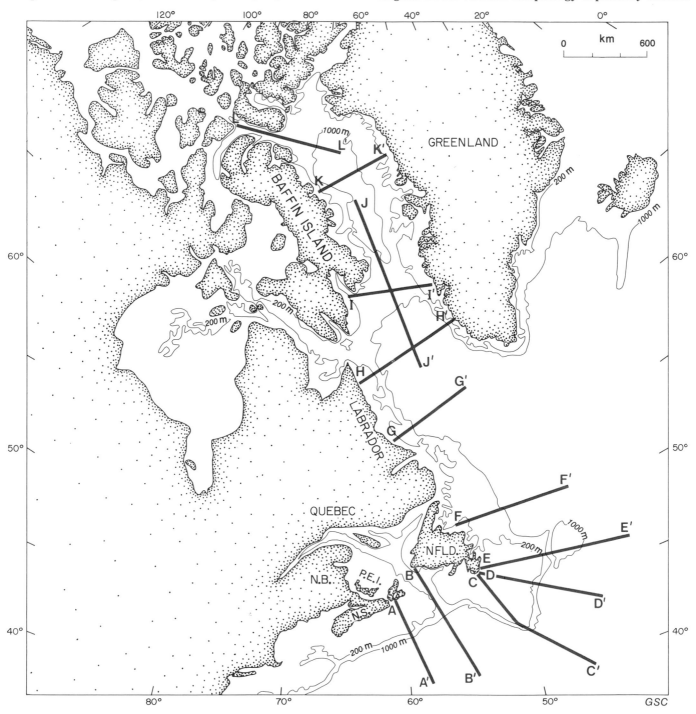

Figure 1.4. Typical bathymetric profiles of the continental margin of eastern Canada and the contiguous ocean basins.

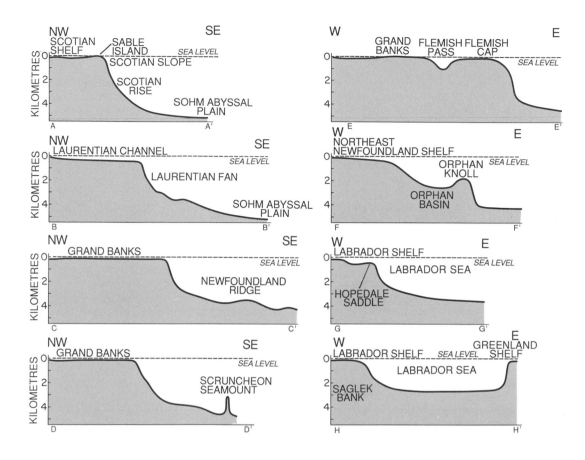

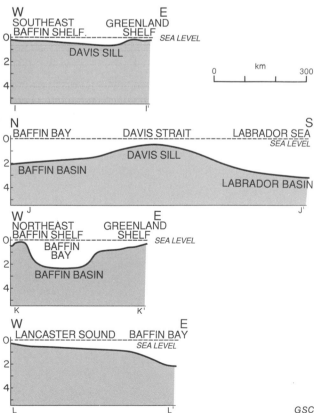

GSC

by a veneer of pelagic sediments, which thickens away from the ridge. Sedimentary basins developed at the margins by the accumulation and progradation of continental detritus, evaporites, carbonates and organic matter over regions of attenuated continental crust and early oceanic crust. The continental margins are now composed of shelves, slopes and rises, which extend into the abyssal oceanic plains. Fracture zones developed during the initial formation of the North Atlantic as offsets in what were then the continental margins, and their traces, as transform faults, now cross the ocean basin disrupting the morphology. Lines or groups of seamounts, representing volcanic eruptions that perhaps reflect the traces of hot spots, or the products of leaky transform faults, rise from the ocean crust above the level of the surrounding ocean floor, or were buried beneath a later sedimentary cover (Chapters 2, 10).

The North Atlantic, Labrador Sea and Baffin Bay did not develop in one single episode of opening, synchronous throughout the whole region. Rifting and seafloor spreading took place later in the northern part than in the south. Furthermore, spreading in the Labrador Sea and Baffin Bay stopped at about 35 Ma, so that these regions remain small oceanic basins, now defunct in terms of active spreading, although earthquakes still occur along the "extinct" axis of the Labrador Sea (Srivastava, 1978).

The shallow waters of Davis Strait separate Baffin Bay and Labrador Sea. The origin of the strait is still an enigma (Srivastava, 1983); it possibly contains continental rocks as well as Tertiary igneous rocks with equivalent volcanic rocks on land in western Greenland and Baffin Island and

15

offshore on the Southeast Baffin Shelf. The Ungava Transform Fault (Map 1706A, in pocket) is purported to run through Davis Strait, largely on geometrical grounds — it is needed in continental reconstructions. Whatever its origin, the effect of the strait on bathymetry is to raise the general level of the oceanic crust at the northern end of the Labrador Sea, so that the seafloor slopes downward from Davis Strait south to the North Atlantic.

Oceanic crust in the Labrador Sea is overlain by pelagic sediments and, over much of the northern Labrador Sea, by turbidites. The present seafloor is cut by the Northwest Atlantic Mid-Ocean Canyon (NAMOC), which developed in the late Cenozoic as the conduit for debris from the Laurentide ice-sheet transported through Hudson Strait. The route of this channel is offset substantially by the Charlie-Gibbs Fracture Zone, before it passes through the Newfoundland Basin to end in the Sohm Abyssal Plain. This channel rather remarkably connects the drainage from the interior of the North American continent to the abyssal plains of the western North Atlantic thousands of kilometres to the southeast (Chapters 2, 8 and 10).

Baffin Bay is a small oceanic basin created in the Tertiary and now separated from the oceanic basins to the south by Davis Strait, so that sediments derived from the margins of the bay are trapped on its floor (Chapter 7). It has received detritus from the Arctic Archipelago and northwestern Greenland, most recently through the mechanism of rafting by icebergs and sea ice. Icebergs have also scoured the seafloor in many parts of the adjacent continental shelves. The floor of the deeper parts of Baffin Bay is rather smooth, as a result of deposition of turbidites, and does not reflect the underlying rough topography of the oceanic crust seen in the multichannel seismic profiles.

The gross morphology, which can be associated with the history of opening of the western North Atlantic, cannot yet be wholly explained in a quantitative manner. For example, depths to the top of the oceanic crust in the western North Atlantic and Labrador Sea, when corrected for the effect of loading by sediments and values of heat flow, appear to be affected by factors such as the formation of the Bermuda Swell and the passage of former hot spots (Louden et al., 1985, 1987). These problems are now being addressed.

The continental margin

Origin

The tectonic style of the continental margin off eastern Canada has been governed by rifting and transform faulting (Map 1706A, in pocket). Rifting is represented by Georges Bank, Bay of Fundy, Scotian Margin, Grand Banks (except for its southwestern margin), most of the Labrador Sea, and at least parts of Baffin Bay. Transform faulting is represented by the southwestern margin of the Grand Banks, offset elements of the margins of the Labrador Sea, such as those northwest of Orphan Knoll and east of Hamilton Bank, and possibly by parts of the margin of Baffin Bay. Other parts of the margin may be transform faults but are not yet recognized as such. Some of the dominant morphological elements directly reflect their origins. Flemish Cap and Orphan Knoll are fragments of continental crust, separated from today's continental shelves. Their structural relationships to the other parts of the margin are not yet known. Orphan Basin (Map 1707A, in pocket), located between the continental slope off northeastern Newfoundland and the ocean basin proper, is underlain by abnormally stretched continental crust. The margins of the Labrador Sea are asymmetrical, with that off Labrador relatively wide and with low gradients on its continental slope, and that off Greenland relatively narrow, with a steep slope. The origin of this asymmetry is not clear, and it may reflect initial rifting or the action of currents subsequent to the formation of the Greenland margin. A comparable situation occurs in Baffin Bay; the shelf off Baffin Island is narrow, and that off Greenland is wide. A complex of rift basins occurs beneath the wide margins, but not beneath the narrow margins. These basins are not always mirrored in the present surface morphology of the continental shelves of the region (see Chapters 2, 9, and 10).

This tectonic style has controlled development of the margins, which are generally overlain by seaward-thickening sedimentary wedges forming today's shelves and slopes. These sedimentary wedges have been modified by currents and glacial action.

Continental shelves

The present continental shelves tend to be shallower in the south than in the north. The Scotian Shelf and Grand Banks of Newfoundland are dominated by the 100 m contour, whereas the Labrador Shelf is dominated by the 200 m contour (Map 850-A, in pocket). The Northeast Newfoundland Shelf lies between 200 and 500 m, as does much of the Southeast Baffin Shelf and the shelf off Greenland north of Disko Island. The most pronounced change in depth occurs at a latitude of about 48.5°N. Its cause is not known; present speculation is that it resulted from tectonic phenomena related to the opening of the Labrador Sea and Baffin Bay or from phenomena related to glacial loading or erosion.

The continental shelves of eastern Canada consist predominantly of transverse troughs, marginal channels and shallow banks. These troughs and channels are substantially due to glacial erosion, which overdeepened and straightened former river channels and accentuated cuestas. The Laurentian Channel and Northeast Channel (Fundian Channel in Map 850-A, in pocket) are excellent examples of transverse troughs. Marginal channels are well developed off Labrador; the mid-shelf basins of the Scotian Shelf, such as Emerald Basin (see Chapter 10) appear to be equivalent features, although less spectacularly developed. These channels have been eroded along the contact of the feather edge of the Mesozoic-Cenozoic sediments and the underlying Precambrian or Paleozoic rocks. The commonality in all these features is glacial erosion as the latest process in their sculpturing, but this was commonly a matter of accentuating earlier features such as Tertiary fluvial drainage patterns.

The pre-Mesozoic bedrock lies directly beneath relatively thin Quaternary sediments on the inner parts of the shelves, and over large areas of regions such as the Gulf of Maine, the Gulf of St. Lawrence, the inner shelf east of Newfoundland, Foxe Basin and Hudson Bay (Map 1705A, in pocket). The details of the morphology of these regions depend not only on the surficial cover, but also on the nature of the bedrock. For example, the floor of the southern Gulf of St. Lawrence is relatively smooth, reflecting the relatively soft and easily eroded Carboniferous sediments beneath, whereas much of the Gulf of Maine is hummocky, due to the presence of older, metamorphosed Paleozoic rocks.

Continental slopes and rises

The most conspicuous parts of the slopes and rises, which are due to relatively recent building of the sedimentary wedges out into the oceanic basins, are the lobes off Lancaster Sound (associated with Bylot Basin), off Hudson Strait (associated with Saglek Basin, see Fig. 1.7), and the largely Quaternary lobe of the Laurentian Fan off the Laurentian Channel (Map 850-A, in pocket). Several other major features are due to sedimentation controlled by the Western Boundary Undercurrent, notably the Gloria Drift and the spur off Eirik Ridge in the eastern Labrador Sea, and Hamilton Spur in the western Labrador Sea (Kidd and Hill, 1986). Eirik Ridge is a ridge in oceanic basement representing a transform fault off Kap Farvel, Greenland, which was once colinear with the Cartwright Fracture Zone off Labrador; a sediment drift has developed north of this ridge as a consequence of the Western Boundary Undercurrent which hugs the seabottom off southeastern and southwestern Greenland. The present Sackville Spur developed with the initiation of the Labrador Current — a surface current — in the Middle Miocene, although an older drift may lie beneath the present one (Kennard et al., in press).

Sea levels were lowered during glacial stages in the Pleistocene. Unconsolidated sediment was available to be redeposited by a variety of phenomena near the edge of the continental shelf. Waves of the lowered surf zone eroded terraces and built coastal landforms and submarine canyons were cut in many areas of the margin, particularly off shallow banks. Submarine canyons could also have been formed in the Tertiary during episodes of lower sea level. At such times, drainage systems on the shelves cut some of the transverse troughs as well as submarine canyons. This was accompanied by erosion over extensive areas of the shelves and redeposition elsewhere.

Submarine canyons are absent but transverse troughs are well developed in Baffin Bay. The absence of submarine canyons may be a reflection of the mechanism of transportation of debris from glaciers to the seafloor in high latitudes. Tidewater glaciers in these latitudes have cold bases, and dissipate as icebergs rather than by melting at ice fronts. As a consequence, the sediments are dispersed by ice rafting; they do not accumulate in a concentrated way with the possibility of forming turbidity currents. Another explanation for the absence of submarine canyons is that basins in the fiords trapped most of the sediment load.

The morphology of the slopes off the major transverse troughs, such as the Laurentian Channel, is very irregular, as a result of gullying and sediment failure. The absence of submarine canyons on small scale maps is deceptive, because the slope is commonly in fact dissected by relatively shallow gullies, originating in water depths of some hundreds of metres. These gullies appear to originate in front of lobes of glacial till on the uppermost slopes; they are probably the equivalents of outwash channels, maintained by turbidity currents derived from the ice margin. The till lobes represent deposition from grounded ice sheets that terminated in (present) water depths of several hundreds of metres. Where the slope is smooth, as off the western end of the Scotian Shelf, this may be on account of Quaternary sediments blanketing an older gullied morphology (Chapter 10).

Although this volume is mainly devoted to the continental margin, some striking features of the land may be directly related to the evolution of the oceanic basins and margins. The mountains of Baffin Island rise to heights greater than 2000 m above sea level, and the Torngat Mountains in northern Labrador to greater than 1500 m. Elevations of this sort are predicted in Chapter 9 as a consequence of small scale convection during rifting, persisting for time scales in the order of one thermal time constant after rifting, before slowly decaying. Refinements of these predictions will no doubt be pursued in the years to come, and the results tied firmly to the evidence of initiation of uplift in the offshore stratigraphic record.

THE LITHOSPHERE

Types of data

Our knowledge of the framework of the lithosphere comes from a variety of sources: seismic refraction experiments; seismic reflection profiles; seismicity; heat flow; and measurements of the magnetic and gravity fields. Other types of observations, of stress, for example, are clearly related. Theoretical modelling of lithosphere and crustal processes constrains values of physical parameters — such as viscosity — which cannot be inferred directly from observations (see Chapters 2 and 9).

Seismic refraction

Seismic refraction experiments have been conducted in the region in many ways, with the methods used at sea and the techniques of interpretation becoming successively more sophisticated. Early experiments by the (then) Lamont Geological Observatory, for example, used two ships, one for shooting with explosives, and the second for receiving using a single hydrophone deployed from the vessel. A number of refraction lines were obtained by Dalhousie University exploiting the particular configuration of the coastline of eastern Canada to cross parts of the Appalachians by recording on land, and shooting at sea (Ewing et al., 1966). The results were limited mainly by navigational uncertainties and by the absence of recording stations between the ends of lines on land. Work in the open ocean away from land was made possible later using moored recording sonobuoys and expendable free-floating sonobuoys. Ocean-bottom seismometers were developed in the 1970s and these are now deployed using arrays of as many as 20 on the seafloor at any one time (Heffler and Barrett, 1979). Sources have changed from explosives to airguns, and the present practice (in 1987) is to use an airgun with up to 190 litres of air at pressures of 10 MPa at the greatest ranges. The greater density of data which can be obtained with airguns fired every 100 to 500 m at these sorts of volumes and pressures, is important when applying modern processing methods and allows greater resolution in interpretations. Improvements in navigational facilities over the years have led to ranges being found from direct measurements of seismometer and vessel position using navigational aids such as LORAN-C, satellite navigation and dopplar sonar. They would before have been found from the arrival times of water waves at the seismometer (I. Reid, pers. comm., 1987).

The techniques for processing and interpretation of seismic refraction data have changed in comparable ways in terms of sophistication. Early data were interpreted in terms of refraction in layers with plane interfaces, using first arrivals as the principal sources of information. The experiments mentioned above, in which stations were established on land with a vessel shooting at sea, had the advantage that three components of ground motion could be measured, and Poisson's ratio determined for crust and mantle. These — now old — observations have recently become a useful source of information for comparison with the results of more modern experiments (I. Reid, pers. comm., 1987). Modern methods of computer processing correct data for different sources of noise, such as the effects of topography, and permit data enhancement by time series analysis. Interpretation, rather than concentrating on times of first arrivals, now makes use of the entire wave train and attempts to produce velocity-depth models which account for time and amplitudes of all observed phases. As a result, it is becoming possible to put closer constraints on lithosphere structure (see Chapter 2).

Deep seismic reflection

A number of deep multichannel seismic reflection profiles were obtained in the southern part of the region between 1984 and 1986 (Fig. 1.5). The profiles extend in depth up to 20 seconds of two-way reflection time, about 60 km if the average velocity is 6 km/s (Keen and Kay, 1986). They image the lithosphere beneath the

Appalachians, some of the sedimentary basins and the continental margin to depths of many tens of kilometres.

Seismicity

The earthquakes shown in Map 1710A (in pocket) were detected using the Standard Canadian and World Wide Networks. As seismicity is a potential constraint to offshore development because of such effects as the shaking of the seafloor and sediment instability, it is discussed in Chapter 14.

Gravity

The gravity map included in this volume (Map 1708A, in pocket) has been prepared from the data in the Canadian National Gravity Data Base, and from other sources listed in the legend to that map. The National Gravity Data Base contains all information collected by the Geological Survey of Canada that meets the standards established for the data base. Canadian measurements have been made in a variety of ways over the years, the quality depending on the gravimeters used and the navigational facilities available at the time. Bouguer anomalies are shown on land and free air anomalies offshore.

Early surveys were made with a Graf-Askania GSS-2 (shipborne) sea gravimeter and in some areas of the shelf with a Lacoste-Romberg bottom gravity meter. The most recent surveys have been made with a Bodenseewerk KSS-30 sea gravimeter and a Lacoste-Romberg Straight Line (SL-1) gravimeter. A multiparameter survey in 1984 on the continental shelf between Newfoundland and Nova Scotia showed the sorts of capabilities now routinely available in terms of positioning, measurement of gravity, bathymetry, and magnetic field (Macnab et al., 1985). The survey relied on a navigational system in which LORAN-C, in range-range mode, was integrated with the Transit Satellite Navigation System; this produced positional accuracies estimated to be 150 m or better. The navigational system also provided the Eotvos corrections for the

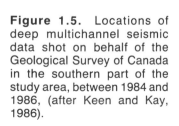

Figure 1.5. Locations of deep multichannel seismic data shot on behalf of the Geological Survey of Canada in the southern part of the study area, between 1984 and 1986, (after Keen and Kay, 1986).

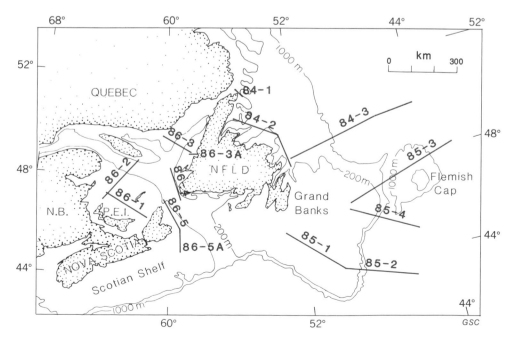

two gravity meters on board, a KSS-30 and an SL-1. The values of the standard deviation of the gravity values at about 120 crossover points were about 1.8 and 1.0 mGal respectively. The standard deviation for depth was about 2 m, and for the magnetic field about 35 nT.

A gravity survey was conducted in a coastal bay off Nova Scotia with a KSS-30 meter, using a high precision navigational system. The organization of this survey allowed many opportunities for checking the gravity meter's drift at a shore station, and for correcting for tides. The accuracy of the measurements was estimated to be about 0.3 mGal; however, this survey raised the question that the phenomenon limiting the accuracy of gravity surveys at sea may be occasional displacements of the sea surface caused, for example, by solitons. These could displace the sea surface by about 10 cm and so cause errors of about 1 mGal (Loncarevic and Woodside, 1984).

Magnetic field

The magnetic field map (Map 1709A, in pocket) represents measurements made mainly from the air over the landmass of Canada and from vessels offshore. Airborne surveys have recently also been conducted offshore, in the Gulf of Maine, and south and northeast of Newfoundland.

The measurements from vessels were made using proton precession magnetometers, with the sensors towed two ship-lengths astern the vessel. The standards set for these surveys may have been inadequate, resulting in uncertainties of a few tens of nanoteslas between tracks from the same vessel with different azimuths, and between tracks from different vessels. This does not affect qualitative comparisons between tracks along constant azimuths, for the purpose of delineating lineations associated with the oceanic crust, for example. The marine measurements have been made over a period of about 20 years, and the earth's main field has changed substantially over that time. Corrections for this have been made by using the International Geomagnetic Reference Field. Serious problems arise from the diurnal variations in the earth's field, and from magnetic storms and similar phenomena. Land stations do not provide adequate corrections for these temporal variations in the field, because the amplitudes and phases of the corrections change with the substantial distances involved. A few surveys have been conducted with a moored magnetometer in the survey area providing corrections, but this is expensive, and has not been standard practice. Consequently, most of the observations of the magnetic field made at sea have not been corrected for diurnal variations, but observations made at times of severe disturbances have been eliminated.

Anomalies from the shipborne surveys greater than some tens of nanoteslas are portrayed accurately in Map 1709A. Smaller anomalies in areas of shipborne surveys may not be real.

Airborne surveys are more satisfactory, because they are completed in a shorter time. Diurnal variations are more easily corrected as flight lines and tie lines are completed more quickly. Fewer surveys have to be patched together from year to year, and so the secular variation does not cause so much noise. An aeromagnetic survey flown south of Newfoundland had an accuracy of about 0.1 nT, known from crossovers, so that significant vertical derivatives could be computed. This figure should be compared with the value of 35 nT from a seaborne magnetic survey in the same area (B.D. Loncarevic, pers. comm., 1987).

Capabilities in processing and in interpreting potential field data are now at a high level. It is routine to filter the data in a variety of ways, to produce vertical derivative maps, and to illustrate the results as though the anomalies were illuminated from specific directions.

The physical properties of rocks and water lead to very different gravity and magnetic anomalies. Magnetic properties vary by orders of magnitude, but densities by only a factor of three. The gravity values are filtered in their acquisition more heavily than are the magnetic field values. Gravity anomalies on land are from observations on an 8 km grid. The onshore magnetic field is measured essentially continuously along lines about 1 km apart. Gravity values at sea are measured on lines with spacings of 1 to 20 km, and each gravity value is averaged along track for a distance of about 4 km; this is needed to average out a ship's motion. Magnetic field values are measured along the same tracks, but essentially continuously, with no averaging. Consequently, the magnetic and gravity anomaly maps often reflect different geological phenomena. For example, at the continental margin the gravity anomalies show the change from continent to ocean relatively clearly, but the magnetic anomalies less clearly.

Heat flow

Measurement of heat flow by conduction to the earth's surface from the interior demands measurement of the temperature gradient and the thermal conductivity. Interpretation of the values of heat flow depends on being able to correct for past surface temperature fluctuations which may have been caused by changing bottom-water temperatures, in the case of measurements made at the seafloor, or by changing air temperatures in the case of measurements made at the earth's surface on land. Interpretation also depends on being able to assume that heat is transferred only by conduction, not by some other process such as advection of fluids. Values of heat flow on the continental margin and in the contiguous oceanic basins off eastern Canada have been found from probes penetrating a few metres into sediment, and from temperature and conductivity measurements in offshore exploration wells and in one hole drilled by the Ocean Drilling Program (ODP).

Modern heat flow probes measure temperature with as many as 9 sensors spaced over 4 m, and measure conductivity by observing the dissipation of a pulse of heat injected into the sediment (Louden et al., 1987). Earlier observations, such as those of Lewis and Hyndman (1976), used probes fitted with about four sensors, and these probes could measure only temperature. Conductivity had to be estimated from measurements made on sediment cores obtained separately. As a consequence of the few sensors and relatively inadequate information on conductivity, non-linear heat flow gradients suggestive of a temperature disturbance, due to some cause other than conductive heat flow, were difficult to observe. Nevertheless, Pye and Hyndman (1972) obtained the first measurements in the Labrador Sea and Baffin Bay with instruments of this sort and their values in the Labrador Sea are generally similar to those obtained later by Louden et al. (1985).

Heat flow values using modern techniques have been obtained in fiords of Newfoundland by Wright et al. (1984) and in the Labrador Sea and the Sohm Abyssal Plain by Louden et al. (1985, 1987). The instrumentation used by Louden et al. (1985, 1987) is typical of modern heat flow instruments. They used a "violin bow" heat flow probe with a sensor string 4 m long with nine equally spaced thermistors. The instrument could measure thermal conductivity in situ, and the data could be both recorded internally and be telemetred to the surface. The thermal gradient is reduced by sedimentation — new material being relatively cold, and is increased by heating on account of sediment which is radiogenic. These effects in the Sohm Abyssal Plain were both about 8% of the measured gradient, and approximately cancelled each other. These sorts of corrections vary from site to site, and substantial variations commonly occur in shallow waters on account of temporal variations in the temperatures of bottom waters. The vertical resolution of the observations by Wright et al. (1984) in Newfoundland fiords allowed perturbations due to seasonal changes in bottom water temperatures to be observed.

Heat flow has been estimated on the continental margins by measuring temperatures in offshore exploration wells, usually determining the conductivities from the lithology (see Chapter 9). The principal problem in obtaining values of heat flow from deep wells is the disturbance in temperature caused by the drilling itself, so that when possible, temperatures are measured at intervals of months and years after drilling in order to obtain equilibrium temperatures. This is obviously a problem in offshore wells because of the difficulty and expense of keeping a well open after completion of drilling. Heat flow has been measured in this way in one offshore well on Sable Island (Hyndman et al., 1979). In all other cases the temperature gradients have been estimated from the bottomhole temperatures measured during drilling, and corrections made for the disturbances due to the operations themselves (Issler, 1984; Reiter and Jessop, 1985). The data set of Reiter and Jessop is among the best published for any continental margin, although the values they used for thermal conductivities have been challenged (Issler and Beaumont, 1986; Reiter and Jessop, 1986).

Heat flow was measured in site 646 of Leg 105 of the Ocean Drilling Program south of Greenland. Temperature gradients were measured successfully at two locations in the bottom of the hole before the section below the instrument was cored. Conductivity was measured using the sediment core recovered. The values obtained were in agreement with that predicted from the age of the oceanic crust at that site (Srivastava et al., 1987).

Stress

J.S. Bell

Information on the present day, in situ stress regime of the continental margin of eastern Canada, has been provided by first motion studies of earthquakes and analysis of the drilling records of exploration wells. The earthquake data give stress information between crustal depths of 6 and 16 km (Stein et al., 1979) whereas the well data extend only to 6 km at most below the seafloor (Ervine and Bell, 1987). Ideally, first motion studies give principal stress orientations if some assumptions are made (Zoback and Zoback, 1980). Most earthquakes off eastern Canada, however, are of relatively small magnitude and do not generate records suitable for clear cut first motion analysis, so that the data suite is limited. Much more information on principal stress orientations has been provided by borehole breakouts. These are elliptically caved intervals in wells that form in response to anisotropic stress. In vertical holes, their long axes are aligned with the direction of the smaller horizontal principal stress (Bell and Gough, 1979). Stress orientations from these sources confirm that offshore eastern Canada (Fig. 1.6) forms part of the North American stress province (Zoback and Zoback, 1980).

In situ stress magnitudes have been determined from geophysical logs and from pressure measurements made while drilling (Ervine and Bell, 1987). Most of the Mesozoic and Tertiary rocks are now at their maximum depth of burial, so that the vertical stress acting on them at a given depth is likely to be close to the weight of the overburden. This is determined by integrating density log values. Horizontal stress magnitudes are best obtained through controlled hydraulic fracturing. Formation leak-off tests involve a similar process in that a micro-fracture is initiated in the rocks surrounding the well bore. Provided that the tensile strength of the rock interval is negligible, the leak-off pressure is likely to be close to the magnitude of the smaller horizontal principal stress (Ervine and Bell, 1987). Mesozoic and Tertiary clastic rocks from the offshore basins give consistent values which are compatible with those measured elsewhere by hydraulic fracture techniques. Provided that the formation fluid pressure within the rocks in which leak-off occurs is known, the magnitude of the larger horizontal principal stress can be estimated. Formation pressures are frequently measured by drill stem tests and repeat formation tests and can be inferred from mudweights. Suites of data for estimating the magnitudes of all three principal stresses are available from many of the oil industry wells drilled in the 1970s and 1980s.

Present lithosphere framework

The present lithosphere framework is shown in the maps portraying the geology, tectonics, depth to basement, gravity, magnetics, and crustal thickness, seismicity, and stress orientations (Maps 1705A-1710A, in pocket). Seismic profiles are shown in pocket Figures 6 and 5.52.

The crustal thickness map (Map 1710A) is based on seismic refraction measurements with gravity observations used to interpolate between the seismic lines. The map shows clearly the change from continental crustal thicknesses of more than 30 km to oceanic crustal thicknesses of less than 10 km. The 10 km contour has been used on the tectonic element map (Map 1706A) as a "proxy" for the ocean-continent boundary, but as this is based on our present knowledge, this generality may be inaccurate. The transition zone between crust of continental thickness and crust of oceanic thickness is relatively wide across the margin off Nova Scotia, and relatively narrow across many other parts of the margin, off Labrador, for example. This probably reflects the processes of initial rifting and extension; an extreme example occurs off Newfoundland beneath the East Newfoundland Basin (Orphan Basin), where a large tract of the margin has a crustal thickness of 15 km; this area appears to be extended continental crust (Keen et al., Chapter 2). The map shows that the Appalachians are underlain by a central belt of very thick crust, where thicknesses are greater than 45 km. These values are based on refraction results which, by today's standards, are inadequate in their resolution.

The transition between continental and oceanic crust is reflected in the gravity field (Map 1708A) by the belt of free air anomalies as high as about 100 mGal (reds and light purples) at the edge of the continental margin. This belt is relatively continuous and linear off Nova Scotia, parts of Labrador, and southwestern Greenland, but is broken and discontinuous around the Grand Banks and in northern and eastern Baffin Bay; this reflects the greater complexity of the crust in those regions.

Different gravity levels and patterns on the continent are associated with different geological regions, as can be seen by comparing the gravity map with the tectonic ele-

Figure 1.6. Principal horizontal stresses in northeastern North America. The figure shows the azimuths of maximum horizontal compression as bars. The bars with crosses at each end are the deviatoric extension axes (mostly from normal faulting earthquake mechanisms). The map is a polar projection chosen to reduce the plotted angular discrepancies between azimuths that are parallel on a sphere (from Adams, 1985, updated to November 1986).

ment map (Map 1706A). For example, gravity values are consistently higher in the Appalachian region than in the Grenville Province of the Canadian Shield. Gravity values suggest that the boundary between these regions in eastern Canada extends almost as far southeast as the Cabot Strait where the boundary appears to be almost a right angle (Stockmal et al., 1987). Some major geological features can be traced with ease: sedimentary basins can be delineated on the Grand Banks, in Hudson Strait, Cumberland Sound, Frobisher Bay, Lancaster and Jones sounds, and in Melville Bugt off western Greenland; the Orpheus anomaly extends from the line of the Cobequid-Chebucto Fault to the east of Nova Scotia as far as the eastern side of the Laurentian Channel; and the Grenville Front is marked by the easterly belt of values as low as about -125 mGal, colinear with the Cartwright Fracture Zone of the Labrador Sea.

The gravity anomalies in the oceanic basins beyond the continental margins show lineations and fracture zones in the Labrador Sea (compare the tectonic and gravity maps). The extinct spreading axis of the Labrador Sea is visible on the gravity and seismicity maps, aligned with the Cumberland Sound and Frobisher Bay grabens. Suggestions of former spreading axes and fracture zones can be seen in Baffin Bay. The Charlie-Gibbs Fracture Zone, a feature which spans the North Atlantic Ocean and which offsets the Mid-Atlantic Ridge, strikes just north of east from the northern side of Orphan Basin. Gravity patterns north of this fracture zone and east of the southern tip of Greenland appear merely mottled, and may simply reflect noise here; the data come from a variety of sources in these mottled regions (see Map 1708A).

The magnetic anomaly map (Map 1709A) shows some of the same features as the gravity map, as would be expected. Different geological regions of the continent landward of the margin can be distinguished, for example, the Grenville Province from other Precambrian provinces to the north. Comparisons of the tectonic, gravity, and magnetic maps are helpful here. Similarly, the lineations and fracture zones of the Labrador Sea can be distinguished, but more clearly on the magnetic map than on the gravity map. The large magnetic anomaly north of Disko Island, Greenland, coincides approximately with the large gravity anomaly in the region; the origins of both are still obscure.

The magnetic anomaly on the margin off Nova Scotia is a continuation of the East Coast Magnetic Anomaly (ECMA in Map 1706A) which is well developed off the eastern United States. The anomaly disappears towards the southern margin of the Grand Banks, perhaps on account of the great thickness of sediments in the eastern part of the Scotian Basin, but this has not been quantitatively demonstrated. A similar set of anomalies occurs northeast of Newfoundland and Labrador; this is much more discontinuous than the East Coast Magnetic Anomaly, possibly reflecting the juxtaposition of different parts of the Appalachians and the Canadian Shield against oceanic crust at the continental margin.

The crustal stress map summarizes principal horizontal stress directions obtained from well data and earthquake records (Map 1710A). Figure 1.6 shows that the lithosphere of eastern Canada is under generally northeast-southwest directed compressive stress and appears to be part of the North American mid-continent

stress province (Zoback and Zoback, 1980). This vast region, corresponding approximately to cratonic North America, is similarly compressed. Zoback and Zoback (1980) believed that this regional stress orientation was most consistent with basal drag on the lithosphere, due to southwestward motion of the North American plate over a stationery asthenosphere. McGarr (1982) noted that this would correspond to northeastward basal drag on the plate and cited supporting evidence. Gough (1984) also favoured northeastward asthenospheric drag beneath the mid-continent stress province, because the active extensional stress provinces to the southwest appeared to preclude alternate kinematic scenarios.

Seismicity does not appear to be related to the present overall stress field in any simple way. The pattern of earthquakes on the seismicity map can only be securely related to known geological features over the extinct axis of the mid-ocean ridge of the Labrador Sea. This is discussed in greater detail in Chapter 14.

Geological observations on the continental shelf provide additional perspectives on rocks better known on land. Widespread Lower Paleozoic carbonates on the Labrador and Baffin shelves are represented by only rare outliers on the Canadian Shield. The Silurian-Devonian section southeast of the Avalon Peninsula of Newfoundland is a non-volcanic Avalonian sequence of a type not known elsewhere in the Appalachians. As well, the productive coalfields of Cape Breton Island extend far beyond the Gulf of St. Lawrence and the Cabot Strait (see Chapter 4).

THE SEDIMENTARY BASINS
Types and sources of data
Our present knowledge of the sedimentary basins of the margin off eastern Canada (Fig. 1.7) comes primarily from the seismic reflection surveys and exploration wells of the petroleum industry, and from geological and geophysical mapping of bedrock outcropping at or near the seafloor primarily by the Geological Survey of Canada (Map 1707A, in pocket). Information on the oceanographic framework and the oceanic crust comes from the holes drilled in Baffin Bay, Labrador Sea and the northwestern Atlantic by the Deep Sea Drilling Project and the Ocean Drilling Program (Chapters 3 to 8).

Offshore exploration wells
The first exploration well offshore eastern Canada was spudded in 1943 in Hillsboro Bay, Prince Edward Island, in the Carboniferous basin of the Gulf of St. Lawrence (Howie and Cumming, 1963). The first stratigraphic tests in the Mesozoic-Cenozoic basins of the continental margin were the core holes drilled in 1965 by American Petroleum Corporation (now Amoco) and Imperial Oil on the Grand Banks (Williams and Brideaux, 1975) and by Mobil Oil near Sable Island. This was followed by the drilling of the Tors Cove D-52 and Grand Falls H-09 wells on the Grand Banks in 1966 (Bartlett and Smith, 1971) and the Sable Island C-67 well on Scotian Shelf in 1967. By the end of 1986, about 260 wells had been drilled off eastern Canada (Fig. 1, in pocket), including Hudson Bay; well cuttings, logs, cores, and other data from these wells are available for examination, after a maximum two year period of confidentiality, at the Bedford Institute of Oceanography.

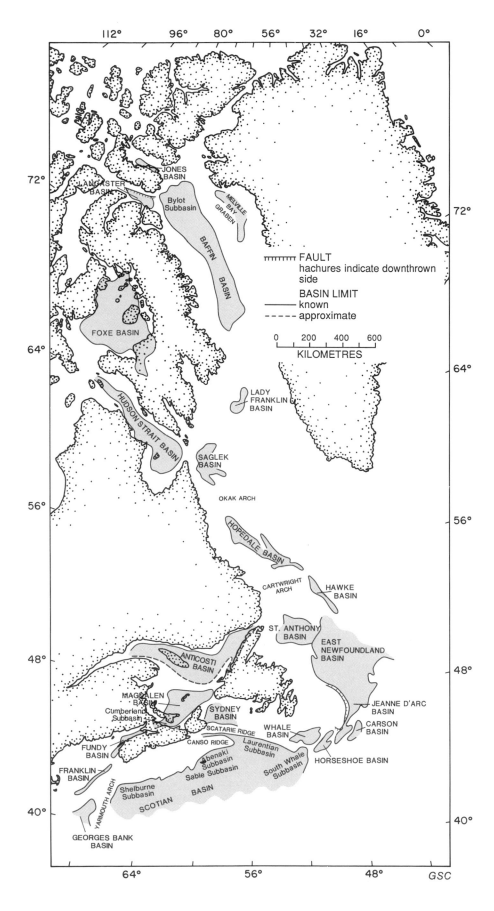

Figure 1.7. Sedimentary basins of offshore eastern Canada. After depth to basement Map 1707A (in pocket). General locations of subbasins within Scotian Basin are also indicated.

This lithological data base is impressive and has provided the largest body of subsurface data available to the public on the eastern margin of the continent north of the Gulf of Mexico. As a result, stratigraphic units described from the Scotian Shelf have been extended to the south, down the United States margin, where for many years the only deep stratigraphic data available were from five Continental Offshore Stratigraphic Test (COST) wells.

The wells, and therefore most data, are concentrated in the prospective parts of the sedimentary basins. The deepest well to date was drilled to 6284 m below sea level on the Scotian Shelf, in 114 m of water (Southwest Banquereau F-34). Although this is impressive, the basins may be more than 20 km deep in places so the stratigraphy has to be assembled from wells drilled in different parts of the basin. The most abundant sample materials are well cuttings which provide data on lithology and facies variations, the age of formations, their depositional environments and the type and degree of maturation of contained organic material. Well cutting samples are augmented by sidewall cores with most wells having 200 to 300 of these valuable samples. In addition, about 7100 m of core has been cut, but this is only a small fraction of the total section drilled. The number of wells is low, considering the size of the region. As an example, 130 wells had been drilled in the Scotian Basin by the end of 1986; this is a density of about one well per 1000 km^2 for the basin (see Chapter 12). These wells, however, have yielded an abundance of data on the geological history of the area and its petroleum potential.

Only a few wells have been drilled off the shelf; these include Blue H-28, drilled in a water depth of 1486 m northeast of Newfoundland, and Shubenacadie H-100 in a water depth of 1475 m and Tantallon M-41 in a water depth of 1511 m both on the Scotian Slope (Fig. 1, in pocket). The continental rise extends down to water depths of about 5 km, so that this large part of the margin has in effect not been sampled by deep industry drilling.

The data available from the offshore wells have provided information in many fields. They include: biostratigraphy, lithostratigraphy, temperature and heat flow regimes, maturation, hydrocarbon geochemistry, stress regime, and the oil and gas potential of the margin. They provide the calibration for the interpretation of the hundreds of thousands of kilometres of seismic data and the "ground truth" for the numerical modelling of the basins. A record of volcanism has been determined and a possible meteorite crater, the Montagnais Structure, identified (see Chapter 5, Part 2). More detailed large scale geological and geophysical surveys were conducted around the sites of many wells before they were drilled, so that the safety of the operation could be assessed. The results of these surveys provide additional information on the local bedrock geology, on modern sediments and on modern processes.

Deep Sea Drilling Project and Ocean Drilling Program

The Deep Sea Drilling Project, through Leg 12, and the Ocean Drilling Program, through Leg 105, have drilled several deep core holes in the Labrador Sea and one in Baffin Bay (Fig. 1, in pocket). The results of Leg 12 provided the basis for the calibration for the magnetic

anomaly record in the Labrador Sea, and basic lithostratigraphic information of the oceanic basin. Leg 105 was directed to more specific questions, concerning, for example, paleo-oceanography and the relationship of the Labrador Sea and Baffin Bay to the North Atlantic and Arctic oceans. Other legs were valuable in a variety of ways and are described principally in Chapter 8.

Industry seismic reflection data

Industry has acquired over one million line kilometres of multichannel seismic reflection profiles, providing coverage of the entire east coast offshore, including Baffin Bay and Hudson Bay, since the first seismic surveys on the Scotian Shelf in 1960. These lines form a dense net over the sedimentary basins on the continental shelf; many lines extend over the continental slopes and some extend onto the rise. Most of the older data were recorded to 5 to 7 seconds in terms of two-way reflection times; the more recent data have been recorded to 8 to 12 seconds. Consequently, an excellent data set exists for the study of many aspects of offshore sedimentary basins. The data are limited only in the sense that they do not completely penetrate the deeper parts of the basins, and rarely cross the continent-ocean transition.

Geological mapping: pre-Quaternary units exposed at the seafloor

Pre-Quaternary units may be unconsolidated or consolidated sedimentary rocks or crystalline basement. Such rocks have been mapped using potential field measurements, described earlier in this chapter, shallow single channel and high resolution seismic reflection systems, drilling devices and sidescan sonar.

Seismic reflection profiling is the most successful technique for mapping these pre-Quaternary units offshore, especially where the units are predominantly sedimentary. It reveals the lateral distribution of the rock as well as any folding or faulting. Rock core drilling provides information on the lithostratigraphy, biostratigraphy, paleoenvironments, petroleum potential and maturation history. Potential field data are also used extensively. Magnetics are most useful where the contrast in magnetic signature is significant, as in crystalline basement, basalts, or across major faults. Magnetic field observations led to the delineation of Tertiary basalts offshore Greenland and Baffin Island. Gravity is useful in shallow water, where multiple reflections obscure seismic targets. This has been demonstrated in the coastal waters of Nova Scotia, where high precision gravity measurements allow easy recognition of granites, slates and quartzites.

High resolution seismic systems have included single channel systems with a single hydrophone or single short array and an airgun or sparker, multichannel systems suitable for investigations down to 1 or 2 seconds of equivalent depth (about 1 or 2 km), and the high resolution Huntec Deep-Tow system. A regional geophysical survey establishes the geological framework; the Huntec Deep-Tow seismic system delineates sites where bedrock is at a sufficiently shallow depth for sampling with a rock-core drill; the drill is then used to obtain samples of the target. Sidescan sonar, photography and submersible observations are supplementary methods which have been used to advantage in particular situations (see Chapter 10 for accounts of mapping systems). In areas such as Hudson Strait and Baffin Bay where industry data are minimal, the sole sources of information for geological mapping have been seismic and sample data obtained on cruises run by the Atlantic Geoscience Centre.

Present sedimentary basins

The sedimentary basins off eastern Canada are shown in Figure 1.7, in the geology, tectonic, and depth-to-basement maps (Maps 1705A, 1706A, and 1707A, in pocket), and in the seismic cross-sections (Fig. 6, 5.52, in pocket). The basins are of three distinct ages: (1) mainly Early Paleozoic — the Anticosti Basin in the northern Gulf of St. Lawrence, parts of basins on the southern Grand Banks, Hudson Bay and Hudson Strait, and Foxe basin, and the grabens off southeastern Baffin Island; (2) Carboniferous — Magdalen Basin in the Gulf of St. Lawrence, and the Minas and Cumberland subbasins, the Sydney Basin east of Cape Breton Island, and the St. Anthony Basin northeast of Newfoundland; and (3) Mesozoic-Cenozoic — the whole continental margin and the Bay of Fundy.

The depth to basement map shows depths to "seismic basement", the depth to the deepest seismic horizon within a sedimentary basin from which reflected energy is detected. This is an arbitrary horizon because the deepest horizon detected depends on the seismic system and upon the nature of the sediments in the basin. One example is from the Mesozoic-Cenozoic basins of the margin off Nova Scotia and Newfoundland. The basins are deep and the lower parts are occupied by salt which masks seismic energy. The only seismic profiles to penetrate to the base of these basins are the few, deep multichannel seismic profiles extending to 20 seconds in two-way reflection travel time. Consequently, judgement has to be used in mapping the greatest thicknesses, and discrepancies can be expected between the depth to basement map (Map 1707A) and other maps of the same sort (Tucholke and Fry, 1985).

The sedimentary basins which dominate the maps on account of their thicknesses and areal extent are the Carboniferous Magdalen, Sydney and St. Anthony basins and the Mesozoic-Cenozoic basins.

Early Paleozoic basins are epicratonic, and generally are relatively undeformed (Chapter 12). The Carboniferous basins formed as "successor" basins following the development of the Appalachians, and are also relatively undeformed: their tectonic origin is not yet understood. The Magdalen Basin could, for example, be a foreland basin, the product of thrusting from the southeast which loaded and depressed the crust now beneath the Gulf of St. Lawrence, or could be a "pull-apart" basin, the consequence of extension and wrench faulting, or both, one superimposed on the other.

Mesozoic-Cenozoic basins formed as a consequence of the rifting of the North Atlantic, seafloor spreading, and subsidence. Most Mesozoic-Cenozoic basins are bounded on their landward side by hinge zones, regions from which they step down towards the oceanic basins. They are separated from one another by arches or fracture zones. The deformation within the Mesozoic-Cenozoic basins is due to extension and to subsidence and, in the southerly basins, to deformation by salt movement. The oldest sediments in the basins are generally continental clastics. Deposition in

the Scotian Basin followed that predicted by Falvey (1974) for Atlantic-type continental margins. During the rift valley stage, deposition of the continental clastics of the Eurydice Formation and the evaporites of the Argo Formation was followed locally by volcanism (Wade and MacLean, Chapter 5). The succeeding beds include evaporitic dolostones (Iroquois Formation) and continental clastics (Mohican Formation). Locally a major unconformity, the breakup unconformity, separates the Eurydice and Argo formations from the Iroquois and Mohican formations. The post breakup sequences are in ascending order: Middle to Upper Jurassic clastics and carbonates, Lower Cretaceous fluvial-deltaic sediments, Upper Cretaceous marine shales, chalks and limestones, and Tertiary clastics. Contrary to earlier beliefs, several major hiatuses can be recognized in these sequences. The most prospective sequences for petroleum exploration in the Scotian Basin are the Upper Jurassic-Lower Cretaceous clastics, especially where the reservoirs are overpressured.

The Mesozoic-Cenozoic sequences in the basins of the Grand Banks have been grouped into six regional seismic sequences which evolved through two episodes of rifting and subsidence (Grant and McAlpine, Chapter 6). These sequences are, in ascending order: an aborted rift sequence of redbeds, evaporites, and carbonates; an epeiric basin sequence of marine shales and limestones; a late rift sequence of shallow to nonmarine clastics; a transition to drift sequence I of siliciclastics; a transition to drift sequence II of marine shales and some chalks; and a passive margin sequence of fine grained clastics. The major unconformity is the Late Jurassic-Early Cretaceous Avalon Unconformity which spans 50-60 Ma of deformation, uplift and erosion, and includes at least four lesser erosional events. Most of the reservoir rocks occur in the late rift sequence. The Jeanne d'Arc Basin of the Grand Banks may be cut by a series of transverse faults associated with its extension and with its deepening to the north, but these structures are not clearly understood.

Igneous rocks are found mainly associated with times of rifting or of subsequent plate re-organizations. Examples of igneous rocks associated with rifting are the Lower Jurassic basalts and associated dykes of Nova Scotia and Newfoundland, and the Lower Tertiary basalts and associated dykes of southern Baffin Island, Davis Strait and western Greenland. Plate re-organization led to Cretaceous volcanism on the Scotian Shelf, and to the Newfoundland Seamounts east of the Grand Banks.

The other Mesozoic-Cenozoic basins of offshore eastern Canada generally show less complete sequences.

Major oil and gas discoveries in offshore eastern Canada have been made in the Mesozoic-Cenozoic basins. The principal source rocks are the Upper Jurassic shales assigned to the Verrill Canyon Formation in Scotian Basin (Chapter 5) and the Egret Member of the Rankin Formation in Jeanne d'Arc Basin (Chapter 6). Reservoir rocks are generally Late Jurassic to Early Cretaceous in age. They include the Mic Mac, Missisauga and Logan Canyon formations in Scotian Basin, the Jeanne d'Arc, Hibernia, Catalina, Eastern Shoals, Avalon and Ben Nevis formations in Jeanne d'Arc Basin, and the Bjarni Formation in Hopedale Basin. Other reservoir rocks may occur in the Tertiary, especially to the north (Chapter 7).

SURFICIAL SEDIMENTS

Mapping

The same sort of approach used for mapping bedrock out-cropping at or near the seafloor has been used to map surficial sediments (Fig. 2, 3, in pocket). The Huntec Deep-Tow seismic system in conjunction with single channel seismic, sidescan sonar and other acoustic systems has been used to establish the regional stratigraphic framework of the surficial sediments in a particular area, and to establish the seismic facies. The lithology, biostratigraphy, paleo-ecology and geotechnical properties of the sediments are determined from piston cores and other types of samples. In early investigations on the Scotian Shelf, echo sounding records obtained by the Canadian Hydrographic Service were useful; the character of the seafloor could be established from the nature of the reflections, and in some cases the units beneath could be delineated to depths of a few tens of metres where they were relatively soft, and easily penetrated by the sounder (Piper et al., Chapter 10).

The slopes and the oceanic basins have been investigated using techniques similar to those used on the shelves, but with two major differences. Areal coverage of a region is more easily obtained in deep water than in shallow with sidescan sonar systems, and so a variety of such systems have been used in particular investigations on the slopes. However, no instrumentation with which to obtain very high resolution seismic information is presently in use in water depths greater than about 500 m, the useful limit of the Huntec Deep Tow System. Consequently, seismic stratigraphy is limited to a resolution of metres or tens of metres, rather than tens of centimetres.

The sidescan systems used have included GLORIA, the long range sidescan system with a swath width of about 70 km and a horizontal resolution of some 100 m, and SEAMARC I, a deeply towed system with a swath width of 5 km and a horizontal resolution of about 2 m. These have been used principally to map morphological features on the slopes, on the Laurentian Fan, for example (see Chapters 11 and 14).

Samples from the slopes and deeper water have been obtained principally with piston corers, with cores of 20 m obtained in 1987. However, the sampling by the Deep Sea Drilling Project (DSDP) and the Ocean Drilling Program (ODP) in Labrador Sea and in Baffin Bay has yielded useful information for those deep water areas, and has provided reference sections with which to compare more limited data obtained in other ways.

Engineering properties

K. Moran

Geotechnical measurements define the physical character and behaviour of sediments when loaded or disturbed, and so contribute to the solutions of geological problems, and to the design and construction of offshore structures. For example, what was the thickness of ice sheets on the shelves during the Pleistocene? The solution may be found in the present physical properties of the sediments loaded by the ice. An engineering problem may be the construction of an artificial island for use in exploration or production drilling. The response of the seafloor to the load of the island, and to environmental loads of ice, wind and sea transmitted to the seafloor through the island, must be predicted to ensure satisfactory construction.

The measurement of geotechnical properties has been done typically by testing samples collected from beneath the seafloor with traditional rotary coring and wireline sampling techniques, methods adapted for use in the Gulf of Mexico in the 1960s. These methods are limited in value because the samples may be significantly disturbed due to stress relief during sample recovery. Obtaining samples with minimal disturbance for laboratory testing is also expensive, so that many investigations have utilized methods that measure the properties in situ. The following techniques have been used in the Canadian offshore. A cone penetrometer is continuously pushed into the sediment to obtain a profile of the penetration resistance at its tip, the friction along its sides, and the sediment pore pressure response. The penetrometer gives a continuous stratigraphic record with depth and good estimates of density and strength. A second method utilizes a pressuremeter as a self-boring instrument which cuts its own hole to the required test depth. This instrument has an inflatable membrane which, when expanded, produces a stress-strain curve for the sediment. The pressuremeter consequently measures in situ lateral stress, elastic shear modulus, peak shear strength and pore pressure. A simpler instrument, the in situ vane, can be pushed into the seabed and rotated to obtain the undrained shear strength. These and other methods establish geotechnical properties in only one small region, that of the site or borehole under investigation, and the results have to be extrapolated. This necessitates a knowledge of the geology of the surrounding area, so reasonable limits of extrapolation are known. This is done in a variety of ways, and in particular with the use of seismic methods (see Chapter 14).

Studies of coastal regions

Coastal regions are studied in two ways. First coastal features and deposits have to be mapped, and second, coastal processes, both past and present, have to be understood. The difficulties are sometimes severe; for example, it is not easy to establish the influence of waves on sediment transport because waves destroy instruments. Furthermore, it is difficult to tie shore processes to those of the inner shelf because most oceanographic vessels cannot easily work close to shore, and because seismic systems are plagued by multiple reflections in shallow water. These difficulties are compounded in areas of ice (see Chapters 11 and 14).

Coastal mapping usually proceeds from small to large scale, using the information from satellites and aircraft at successively lower elevations, and any topographic, bathymetric and geological maps which may be available. Conventional coastal mapping uses the visual information from satellites, for example, but other parts of the electromagnetic spectrum are useful for special purposes. Satellite images are only useful for mapping in certain situations, because the coastal zone is usually so narrow. These data, however, are useful for the study of sea ice and suspended sediment concentrations offshore, and regional studies of landforms onshore. The scale of aerial photographs available routinely in Canada is 1:60 000 in northern regions, and 1:10 000 in southern regions. Aerial oblique video-photography is usually obtained from heights of about 200 m. The results of mapping from these "remotely sensed" data are used to select representative areas in which to conduct site-specific investigations of the morphology and sediments of the region, of the shoreline stability, and of the processes at work.

Studies of processes represent attempts to understand the dynamics of the coastal region itself, and its relationship to the land on the one hand and the offshore on the other. This involves the monitoring of sediment transport across the coastal zone and along the shore and of processes within the region of breaking waves and on the beach. An example of an instrument of this type is RALPH, which measures the interaction between the sea and seafloor (Fig. 1.8). Processes in Arctic regions are dominated by sea ice and the presence of permafrost. Consequently, studies of the thermal regime and of the mechanics of sea ice and its interaction with the coast have to be made, in addition to the measurements typical of studies in southerly regions. The most important part of the thermal regime is the upper few metres, within which annual thaw occurs (see Chapters 11 and 14).

Processes in the open sea

Information concerning processes affecting the seafloor at the present time come from mapping, observations of processes, and from experiments and modelling.

Mapping at various scales produces information on bedforms, and on phenomena such as ice scour by modern and old icebergs. The most useful techniques for such observations are sidescan imaging and seismic profiling; the resolution which is useful depends on the scale of the features. Photography using cameras on deeply towed sledges has been useful in studies of bedforms such as ice scours and in studies of sediment winnowing by bottom currents. Mapping, which is repeated at various time intervals, shows changes in bedforms, for example, the annual rate of production of new ice scours and the rate at which old ones are degraded (see Chapter 11).

Field observations and laboratory experiments attempt to establish the types of processes involved in sedi-

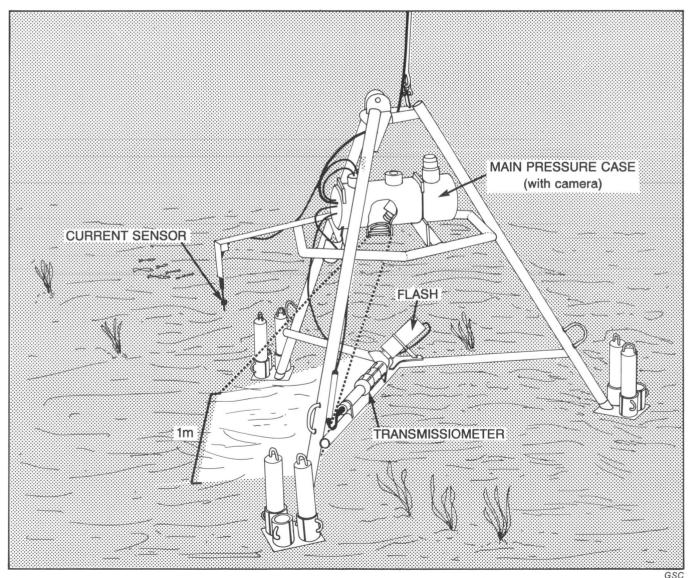

GSC

Figure 1.8. RALPH: an instrument for measuring the interaction between the sea and the seafloor.

ment transport and relate the processes observed at the seafloor to driving mechanisms such as waves and currents. Repeated mapping is one example of this sort of work, but experiments and observations of many types have been made. Radioactive tracers have been used to map the dispersion of sediment in mobile bedforms (Long, 1986). Instruments have been deployed on the seabed to measure and observe a number of parameters simultaneously. Examples of observations of this sort and their purpose are: photographs of the seafloor, often in time-lapse mode, show mobility and type of bedforms under the prevailing wind and currents; currents at various heights above the seabed indicate stress at the seafloor; optical transparency provides information on suspended sediment; and height to the sea surface shows tides and waves. Submersibles provide an opportunity to observe processes at first hand, but only in fair weather.

The difficulties of making these sorts of observations should not be underestimated. Practical difficulties arise from the fact that the sea is an unkind environment; much of the monitoring equipment is by nature fragile, and the quantities of data to be stored and recovered are potentially enormous. The instrumentation may also interfere with the very processes that it is intended to measure.

Quaternary sediments and modern processes

The distribution of Quaternary sediments on the continental shelf is shown in Map 1711A (in pocket). Buried Pleistocene moraines, channels and other features resulting from glaciations are shown in Figure 3 — Subsurface Quaternary features (in pocket). Many such features pose constraints to offshore development. The texture of surface sediment, which in places may form a thin veneer over mapped Quaternary sediments of different composition, and seabed features such as sandy bedforms and iceberg scours that were developed by modern processes are illustrated in Figure 2 — Surficial features (in pocket). The figures extend beyond the nearshore zone only to the edge of the continental shelf, reflecting the lack of systematic data in deep and very shallow water.

Glacial till and other ice-contact deposits have been mapped across much of the continental shelves off eastern Canada, reflecting the former presence of ice sheets that reached the edge of the continental shelf. In most places this till appears to date from the last (Wisconsinan) glaciation, although remnants of earlier glaciations may be present. In most areas, the deposits record recession of ice sheets. Prominent moraines have developed where the grounding line of a floating ice margin has remained stationary for a long time, and glaciomarine sediments were deposited seaward. On the continental slope, proglacial muds accumulated in most areas seaward of the ice margin, although sands and gravels may have been deposited where subglacial meltwater discharged, and poorly sorted diamicts accumulated as a result of sediment supply from melting icebergs.

Glacial ice thus covered almost all the continental shelf off eastern Canada as recently as 50 000 BP. This ice extended south of latitude 45 degrees North and so approached the warm mid-latitudes dominated by the effects of the Gulf Stream, which would have brought large amounts of moisture to the southern ice sheets. The Labrador Sea was probably an important route for storms to nourish the more northern areas of ice.

By contrast, the shelf off the eastern United States has almost no record of glacial sediment; till is found only on the inner shelf from Georges Bank to New York. To the south, the surficial sediments of the shelf are Pleistocene fluvial deposits reworked during the rise of sea level in the Holocene.

The glacial till is generally overlain by thick glaciomarine silts and muds — the deposits of fine grained glacial outwash into the sea. On some shallow outer banks on the continental shelf, fluvioglacial outwash has been mapped in the subsurface, and some subsurface channels may be of fluvial origin. Most subsurface channels, however, are probably in part of subglacial origin.

On the shallower southern shelves, the late Wisconsinan Holocene rise in sea level has had a major influence on regional sediment distribution. Sorted sands and gravels on bank tops resulted from unmixing of glacial deposits in the coastal zone as the sea transgressed the area. The thin glacial till and glaciomarine silts on the inner shelf were largely removed by coastal erosion as sea level rose. Fine grained postglacial sediments accumulated in basins. In more northern latitudes, where the shelves are deeper, there has been less modification of the glacial deposits, although postglacial muds do occur in deeper basins.

Deglaciation occurred later to the north than to the south, so that equivalent facies are younger in the north. Deglaciation also took place first on the outer parts of the continental shelves, so that deposits across a shelf may be diachronous. Earlier glaciations probably resulted in a similar distribution of facies to that mapped for the Wisconsinan, but these sediments were largely removed by glacial erosion as the Wisconsinan ice advanced. The thickness and physical behaviour of the ice sheets that once extended across the continental shelves is not well constrained by the mapped distribution of glacial sediments, and many questions remain as to what degree well known terrestrial glaciation features can be used as analogues of Pleistocene glaciation offshore.

Figure 2 (Surficial Features) and Figure 4 (Coastal Geology) show the effects of modern processes on the framework of Quaternary deposits. Map 1711A (Quaternary geology) shows the distribution of mappable lithological units. Figure 2 shows the character of the thin layer of sediment at the seabed — analogues to soil on land. In many areas, this "soil" is derived from the underlying Quaternary units and has similar textural characteristics — sand and gravel on the outer banks of the Scotian Shelf or mud in deep basins. Elsewhere, the Quaternary lithostratigraphic units have an erosional surface overlain by a veneer of younger sediment, resulting from iceberg rafting and scouring or from sediment reworking during the late Wisconsinan-Holocene rise in sea level. The widespread distribution of gravel-sized clasts reflects the glacial origin of much of the sediment, and is characteristic of formerly glaciated shelves. However, on northern shelves, modification of seabed sediments is dominated by the ploughing effects of scouring by grounded icebergs. Shallower draft modern icebergs produce scours to water depths of a few hundred metres; deeper draft Pleistocene icebergs have produced scours to water depths of 700 m in places. This activity has resulted in a distinctive pattern of grooves and pits on the seafloor, to depths of several metres. The southern continental shelves are dominated by currents rather than by the effects of ice. Predominantly tidal currents in the Bay of Fundy and predominantly storm-driven currents on the banks of the Scotian Shelf and the Grand Banks have formed a variety of sandy bedforms. Other features on the seabed are the result of subsurface processes, such as the crater-like pockmarks which result from the venting of subsurface fluids and gases (King and MacLean, 1970).

Figure 4 (in pocket), which depicts coastal features, can be regarded as a snapshot of a continuing process of sea level adjustment following glaciation. In many southern parts of the region, relative sea level is rising following glacial retreat. For example, on the Atlantic coast of Nova Scotia, this may be as much as 4 mm a year. In more northern areas, the north shore of the Gulf of St. Lawrence, and the Labrador and Baffin coasts as examples, relative sea level is falling.

The character of the coastline is also affected by the tidal range — microtidal in the Gulf of St. Lawrence, macrotidal in the Bay of Fundy, Ungava Bay and the bays of southeastern Baffin Island (see Fig. 14.1, Chapter 14). Exposure to storm waves and the length of the ice-free season affects the extent to which the coastline is eroded and reworked by waves.

Much of the coastline of eastern Canada has only a limited supply of unconsolidated sediment from local glacially derived sources, till and fluvioglacial deposits. Most rivers deliver little sediment to the shoreline, since sediment is largely trapped in thalweg (valley trend) irregularities upstream. The glacier-fed rivers entering the fiords of Baffin Island are a significant exception; these have built prominent sandur (outwash plain) deltas. With the exception of parts of the Gulf of St. Lawrence and the Bay of Fundy, bedrock is resistant and relatively unimportant as a source of sediment. Irregular glacial erosion of this bedrock results in an irregular, highly compartmentalized coastline, in which longshore transport of sediment is unimportant. The coastline of eastern Canada is predominantly rocky; beaches are generally small and gravelly. The southwestern Gulf of St. Lawrence, fringed by soft Carboniferous bedrock and with a relatively stable sea level, is one of the few areas of extensive sandy beaches with significant longshore drift. This causes severe siltation of fishing harbours.

ACKNOWLEDGMENTS

We thank C. Amos, H.B.S. Cooke, C.E. Keen, C.F.M. Lewis, Bernie MacLean, Brian MacLean and J.A. Wade, who critically reviewed all or substantial parts of the chapter, and R. Macnab, B. Smith, I. Reid, K. Louden, G. Cameron and M. Best, who helped in its preparation.

REFERENCES

Adams, J.
1985: Canadian crustal stress data — a compilation to 1985; Earth Physics Branch, Open File 85-31, 77 p.

Bartlett, G.A. and Smith, L.
1971: Mesozoic and Cenozoic history of the Grand Banks of Newfoundland; Canadian Journal of Earth Sciences, v. 8, p. 65-84.

Bell, J.S. and Gough, D.I.
1979: Northeast-southeast compressive stress in Alberta; Earth and Planetary Science Letters, v. 45, no. 2, p. 382-475.

Dahl, W.H.
1925: Tertiary fossils dredged off the northeastern coast of North America; American Journal of Science, Series 5, v.10, p. 213-218.

Dawson, J.O.
1868: Acadian Geology (second edition); MacMillan and Company, London, 694 p.

Ervine, W.R. and Bell, J.S.
1987: Subsurface in-situ stress magnitudes from oil well drilling records: an example from the Venture area, offshore eastern Canada; Canadian Journal of Earth Sciences, v. 24, p. 1748-1759.

Ewing, G.N., Dainty, A.M., Blanchard, J.E., and Keen, M.J.
1966: Seismic studies of the eastern seaboard of Canada: the Appalachian system; Canadian Journal of Earth Sciences, v. 3, p. 89-109.

Falvey, D.A.
1974: The development of continental margins in plate tectonic theory; Australian Petroleum Exploration Association Journal, v. 14, p. 95-106.

Godby, E.A., Baker, R.C., Bower, M.E., and Hood, P.J.
1966: Aeromagnetic reconnaissance of the Labrador Sea; Journal of Geophysical Research, v.71, p. 511-517.

Gough, D.I.
1984: Mantle upflow under North America and plate dynamics; Nature, v. 311, p. 428-433.

Heffler, D.E. and Barrett, D.L.
1979: OBS development at Bedford Institute of Oceanography; Marine Geophysical Reserches, v. 4, p. 227-245.

Hood, P.J.
1964: Sea magnetometer reconnaissance of Hudson Bay; Geophysics, v. 29, p. 916-921.

Hood, P.J. (ed.)
1971: Offshore Eastern Canada Symposium; Geological Survey of Canada, Paper 71-23, 652 p.

Howie, R.D. and Cumming, L.M.
1963: Basement features of the Canadian Appalachians; Geological Survey of Canada, Bulletin 89, 18 p.

Hutchins, R.W., McKeown, D.L., and King, L.H.
1976: A deep tow high resolution seismic system for continental shelf mapping; Geoscience Canada, v. 3, p. 95-100.

Hyndman, R.D., Jessop, A.M., Judge, A.S., and Rankin, D.S.
1979: Heat flow in the Maritime Provinces of Canada; Canadian Jounal of Earth Sciences, v. 16, p. 1154-1165.

Issler, D.R.
1984: Calculation of organic maturation levels for offshore eastern Canada — implications for general application of Lopatin's method; Canadian Journal of Earth Sciences, v. 21, p. 477-488.

Issler, D.R. and Beaumont, C.B.
1986: Estimates of terrestrial heat flow in offshore eastern Canada: discussion; Canadian Journal of Earth Sciences, v. 23, p. 2083-2085.

Keen, C.E. and Kay, W.
1986: Deep marine multichannel seismic data from the northeast Newfoundland continental margin — Lithoprobe East; Geological Survey of Canada, Open File 1281.

Kennard, L., Schafer, C., and Carter, L.
in press: Late Cenozoic evolution of Sackville Spur: A sediment drift on the Newfoundland Continental Slope; Canadian Journal of Earth Sciences.

Kidd, R.B. and Hill, P.R.
1986: Sedimentation on mid-ocean drifts; in North Atlantic Paleoceanography, ed. C.P. Summerhayes and N.J. Shackleton; Geological Society, Special Publication no. 21, p. 87-102.

King, L.H. and MacLean, B.
1970: Pockmarks on the Scotian Shelf; Geological Society of America, v. 81, p. 3141-3148.

Lewis, J.F. and Hyndman, R.D.
1976: Oceanic heat flow measurements over the continental margins of eastern Canada; Canadian Journal of Earth Sciences, v. 14, p. 1031-1038.

Loncarevic, B.D. and Woodside, J.M.
1984: Coastal geophysics: gravity measurements in Mahone Bay, N.S. with a shipborne seagravimeter: Canadian Geophysical Union, Program with Abstracts, 20 May — 1 June, 1984, Dalhousie University, Halifax, Nova Scotia, p. 20.

Long, B.
1986: Techniques of tracers; in Sediment Transport and Industry Needs, ed. D.O. Hodgins, D.A. Huntley, W.D. Finn, B. Long, G. Drapeau and A.J. Bowen; Environmental Studies Revolving Funds, Report 027, p. 151-214.

Louden, K.E., Fang, C., and Wright, J.A.
1985: Heat flow and depth versus age in the Labrador Sea; EOS, Transactions of the American Geophysical Union, v. 66, p. 1059.

Louden, K.S., Wallace, D.O., and Courtney, R.C.
1987: Heat flow and depth versus age for the Mesozoic NW Atlantic Ocean: results from the Sohm Abyssal Plain and implications for the Bermuda Rise; Earth and Planetary Science Letters, v. 83, p. 109-122.
Macnab, R., Loncarevic, B.D., Cooper, R.V., Girouard, P.R., Hughes, M.D., and Shouzhi, F.
1985: A regional marine multiparameter survey south of Newfoundland; in Current Research, Part B, Geological Survey of Canada, Paper 85-1B, p. 325-332.
McGarr, A.
1982: Analysis of states of stress between provinces of constant stress; Journal of Geophysical Research, v. 87, p. 9279-9288.
Officer, C.B. and Ewing, M.
1954: Geophysical investigations in the emerged and submerged Atlantic coastal plain: Part 7. Continental shelf, continental slope, and continental rise south of Nova Scotia; Geological Society of America Bulletin, v. 65, p. 653-670.
Piper, D.J.W., Shor, A.N., and Hughes Clarke, J.E.
1988: The 1929 Grand Banks earthquake, slump and turbidity current; Geological Society of America, Special Paper, 229, p. 77-92.
Pye, G.D. and Hyndman, R.D.
1972: Heat-flow measurements in Baffin Bay and the Labrador Sea; Journal of Geophysical Research, v. 77, p. 938-944.
Reiter, M. and Jessop, A.M.
1985: Estimates of terrestrial heat flow in offshore eastern Canada; Canadian Journal of Earth Sciences, v. 22, p. 1503-1517.
1986: Estimates of terrestrial heat flow in offshore eastern Canada:Reply; Canadian Journal of Earth Sciences, v. 23, p. 2085-2086.
Shepard, F.P.
1931: Saint Lawrence (Cabot Strait) submarine trough; Geological Society of America Bulletin, v. 42, p. 853-8654.
Spencer, J.W.
1903: Submarine valleys off the American coast and in the North Atlantic; Geological Society of America Bulletin, v. 14, p. 207-226.
Srivastava, S.P.
1978: Evolution of the Labrador Sea and its bearing on the early evolution of the North Atlantic; Geophysical Journal, v. 52, p. 313-357.
1983: Davis Strait; structures, origin and evolution; in Structure and Development of the Greenland-Scotland Ridge — New Methods and Concepts, ed. M.H.P. Bott et al.; Nato Conference Series IV, Marine Sciences, v. 8, p. 159-189.
Srivastava, S.P., Arthur, M., and Clement, B., et al.
1987: Proceedings of the Ocean Drilling Program, Part A, Initial Report, Leg 105, 917 p.
Stein, S., Sleep, N.H., Geller, R.J., Wang, S., and Kroeger, G.C.
1979: Earthquakes along the passive margin of eastern Canada; Geophysical Research Letters, v. 6, p. 537-540.

Stockmal, G.S., Colman-Sadd, S.P., Keen, C.E., O'Brien, S.J., and Quinlan, G.
1987: Collision along an irregular margin: A regional plate tectonic interpretation of the Canadian Appalachians; Canadian Journal of Earth Sciences, v. 24, p. 1098-1107.
Tucholke, B.E. and Fry, V.A.
1985: Basement structure and sediment distribution in the Northwest Atlantic Ocean; American Association of Petroleum Geologists, v. 69, p. 2877-2897.
Upham, W.
1894: The fishing banks between Cape Cod and Newfoundland; American Journal of Science, Series 3, v. 47, p. 123-129.
Williams, G.L. and Brideaux, W.W.
1975: Palynological analysis of Late Mesozoic-Cenozoic rocks of the Grand Banks of Newfoundland; Geological Survey of Canada, Bulletin 236, 162 p.
Willmore, P.L. and Scheidegger, A.E.
1956: Seismic observations in the Gulf of St.Lawrence; Transactions of the Royal Society of Canada, series 3, v. 50, p. 21-38.
Wright, J.A., Keen, C.E., and Keen, M.J.
1984: Marine heat flow along the north-east coast of Newfoundland: Geological Survey of Canada, Paper 84-1B, p. 93-100.
Zoback, M.L. and Zoback, M.D.
1980: State of stress in the conterminous United States; Journal of Geophysical Research, v.85, p. 6113-6156.

Authors' addresses.

M.J. Keen
Atlantic Geoscience Centre
Geological Survey of Canada
Bedford Institute of Oceanography
P.O. Box 1006
Dartmouth, Nova Scotia
B2Y 4A2

D.J.W. Piper
Atlantic Geoscience Centre
Geological Survey of Canada
Bedford Institute of Oceanography
P.O. Box 1006
Dartmouth, Nova Scotia
B2Y 4A2

Printed in Canada

Chapter 2

TECTONIC AND GEOPHYSICAL OVERVIEW

Chapter 2

TECTONIC AND GEOPHYSICAL OVERVIEW

**C.E. Keen, B.D. Loncarevic, I. Reid, J. Woodside,
R.T. Haworth and H. Williams**
with a contribution on Igneous Rocks
by G. Pe-Piper, D.J.W. Piper, M.J. Keen, and N.J. McMillan

INTRODUCTION

The tectonic history of offshore eastern Canada can best be described within the context of the Wilson Cycle of ocean opening and closing. The Appalachian Orogen (Fig. 2.1, 2.2, 2.11) records a clear history of Late Precambrian rifting and the development of a Paleozoic passive continental margin bordering the Iapetus Ocean, the Paleozoic equivalent of the Atlantic Ocean. Iapetus closed in the Ordovician and this closing destroyed the passive margin. The resulting subduction and accretion are recorded in the Paleozoic rocks of the region. Ordovician destruction of the passive margin was accompanied by the westward obduction of ophiolitic material and of sedimentary rocks of the passive margin itself. Deformational events which created the Appalachians persisted in pulses throughout the Paleozoic. During that time several large suspect or exotic terranes were accreted to North America, to the east of the obducted thrust sheets. In addition, the peculiar geometry of plate interactions led to the creation of the late Paleozoic sedimentary basins within the Gulf of St. Lawrence. Mesozoic rifting and later seafloor spreading created the North Atlantic Ocean (Fig 2.3). This new cycle produced the contemporary passive margins, which now dominate the offshore region. The rifted margin off Nova Scotia, the transform margin south of the Grand Banks, the rifted margin east of the Grand Banks, and the rifted margin northeast of Newfoundland were all formed during the Mesozoic.

North of the Appalachian Orogen, along the coasts of Labrador and Baffin Island, Precambrian rocks of the Grenville, Nain, and Churchill provinces and Makkovik Subprovince are exposed (Fig. 2.2, 2.4, 2.5). This region was not involved in the Paleozoic cycle of opening and closing of the Iapetus Ocean. Precambrian rocks extend offshore from Labrador, Baffin Island and western Greenland (see Chapter 7), but the characteristics of Precambrian structures beneath these adjacent offshore regions are uncertain. There is a large time gap between the Precambrian events and the Mesozoic-Cenozoic development of the offshore region and the modern margin cuts indiscriminately across the Precambrian structural provinces. Therefore, the Precambrian history of the region will not be discussed in this chapter, however, it is briefly mentioned in Chapter 7. Paleozoic sedimentary rocks that have been sampled probably represent sediments of a shallow inland seaway that existed between Greenland and North America during that time (see Chapter 4).

The Mesozoic-Cenozoic history of this northern region is, by comparison, well-documented. Plate motion between Greenland and North America and the development of the sedimentary basins began in the Early Cretaceous. Final continental break-up of these plates and the onset of seafloor spreading formed the Labrador Sea, Baffin Bay, and Davis Strait, starting in the Late Cretaceous. However, the evidence for seafloor spreading in this region has been challenged (Umpleby, 1979; Grant, 1980). The plate motions between the Canadian Arctic Islands and Northern Greenland (the Nares Strait region) are also the subject of considerable controversy (Dawes and Kerr, 1982a), and the relationship between the tectonics of the Baffin Bay-Labrador Sea region and the tectonics of the Canadian Arctic Islands and the Arctic Ocean is unclear.

The continental margins of eastern Canada, their relationship to earlier continental evolution and to ancient passive margins, and their link to the unknown history of the Arctic Ocean, provide an opportunity to study exten-

Figure 2.1. Map of offshore eastern Canada with geographic names, selected bathymetric contours, the approximate location of the oceanic-continental boundary (in red), and locations of offshore well sites. The two dashed lines of latitude indicate the northern extent (62°N) of the southern area, show in Figures 2.2, 2.3, 2.14, and 2.16; and the southern extent of the northern area (58°N), shown in Figures 2.4, 2.15 and 2.17. The dots and numbers represent the locations of the following deep exploratory wells: 1. Hellefisk 1, 2. Nukik 2, 3. Gjoa G-37, 4. Hekja A-72, 5. Snorri J-90, 6. Bjarni H-81, 7. Herjolf M-92, 8. Indian Harbour M-52, 9. Leif E-38, 10. DSDP 111, 11. Blue H-28, 12. Bonavista C-99, 13. Bittern M-62, 14. Twillick G-49, 15. Fox I-22, 16. Eurydice P-36, 17. Mic Mac J-77, 18. Wyandot E-53, 19. Missisauga H-28, 20. Bluenose G-47, 21. Triumph P-50, 22. DSDP 384. For precise geographic locations of the wells see Figure 1 (in pocket).

Keen, C.E., Loncarevic, B.D., Reid, I., Woodside, J., Haworth, R.T., and Williams, H.
1990: Tectonic and geophysical overview; Chapter 2 in Geology of the Continental Margin of Eastern Canada, M.J. Keen and G.L. Williams (ed.); Geological Survey of Canada, Geology of Canada, no. 2, p. 31-85, [also Geological Society of America, The Geology of North America, V.I.-1].

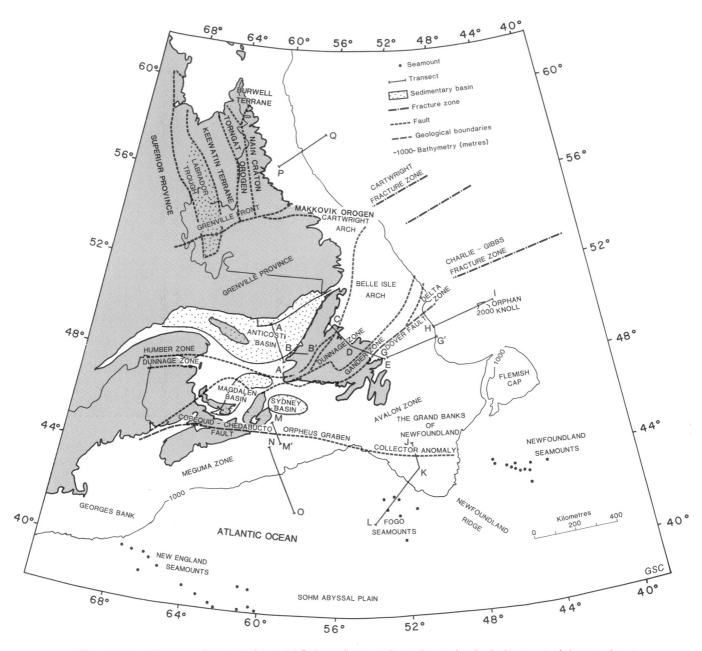

Figure 2.2. Principal Precambrian and Paleozoic tectonic and geophysical elements of the southern portion of the study region. The locations of the transects (Fig. 2.20-2.22) are shown as solid lines designated by letters.

sional tectonic regimes which have global relevance, and in this chapter we provide a brief overview of the Phanerozoic evolution of the region. Many of the points only mentioned here are described more fully elsewhere in this volume. A summary of the geophysical characteristics of the region is also given in this chapter, because they are closely related to the overall tectonic development of the offshore region. The observations allow us to illustrate the relationship of near surface geology to crustal or lithospheric properties, although the nature of these relationships is not fully understood. This important aspect of geological evolution should be explored more fully in the next decade.

PALEOZOIC TECTONICS

The record of the Paleozoic margin of the Iapetus Ocean is contained in rocks of western Newfoundland (Fig. 2.2, 2.6) and their southern correlatives (Williams, in press). Development of that margin was initiated by the rifting of Grenville basement with coeval mafic dyke intrusion, mafic volcanism, and the accumulation of thick clastic sequences (Williams and Stevens, 1974). These events began in the Proterozoic, as indicated by isotopic dating of mafic dykes and rift related granitic rocks (Pringle et al., 1971; Stukas and Reynolds, 1974).

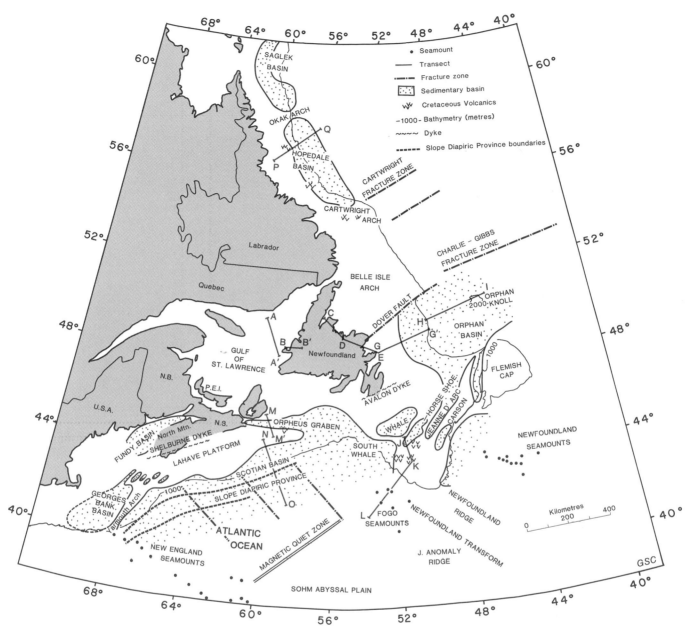

Figure 2.3. Principal Mesozoic-Cenozoic tectonic and geophysical features of the southern portion of the study region (basin outlines are approximate). The locations of the transects (Fig. 2.20-2.22) are shown as solid lines designated by letters.

A thin sequence of mainly carbonate rocks formed on the continental shelf from Early Cambrian to latest Early Ordovician (Rodgers, 1968). These sediments thicken eastward and record an upward transition from immature arkosic sandstones to mature quartz sandstones, and then to limestones and dolomites. Rocks deposited on the continental slope and rise are now preserved in allochthonous sequences structurally above the carbonate shelf.

Destruction of the ancient passive margin by the closing of the Iapetus Ocean began towards the end of the Early Ordovician with a series of accretionary events that lasted throughout the Paleozoic (Williams, 1979; Colman-Sadd, 1982; Fig. 2.6). During the Cambrian and Early

Ordovician, the Iapetus Ocean was consumed by eastward subduction of the oceanic lithosphere. This was accompanied by the development of an island arc/backarc region to the east of the subduction zone. These plate motions culminated during the Taconic Orogeny in the Middle Ordovician, when the North American passive margin collided with the island arc (Colman-Sadd, 1982). The passive margin was overridden by thrust sheets comprising a variety of rock types in separate slices. The structurally lowest slices consist of sedimentary rocks from the nearby continental margin, and the highest slices, ophiolitic, represent farther-travelled oceanic crust and mantle. The structural pile was assembled from the east, possibly

Figure 2.4. Principal tectonic and geophysical features of the northern portion of the study region.

through peeling of successively landward sections from the top of the subducting plate. These thrust sheets form the Taconic allochthons which overlie parts of the ancient margin.

The development of these Taconic allochthons provided an additional load on the lithosphere, causing a flexural response which resulted in formation of the Anticosti foreland basin in the northern Gulf of St. Lawrence. Similar foreland basins are found along the length of the Appalachian Orogen; an example is the Appalachian

Figure 2.5. Various stages of continental break-up off eastern Canada. The solid red lines are incipient or active mid-ocean ridges. The dashed red lines are fracture zones. Red stipple denotes oceanic crust. Triangles are seamounts. The lighter, solid and dashed lines outline the approximate edge of the shelf on the western and eastern sides of the Atlantic, respectively. N.R. = Newfoundland Ridge; F.C. = Flemish Cap; O.K. = Orphan Knoll; C.G.F.Z. = Charlie-Gibbs Fracture Zone; N.F.Z. = Nares Strait Fracture Zone.

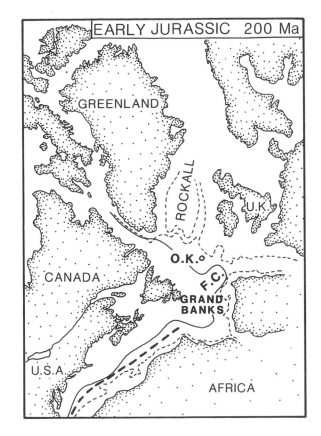

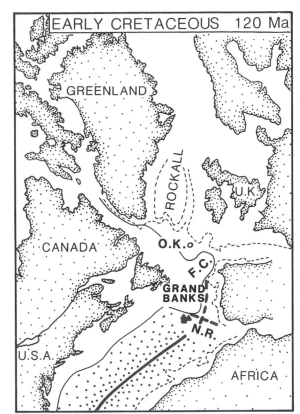

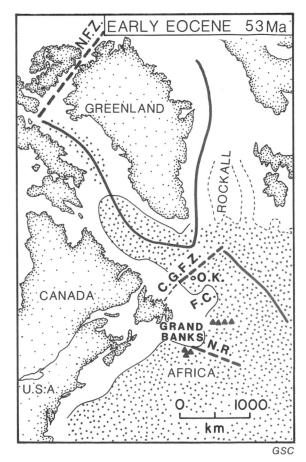

GSC

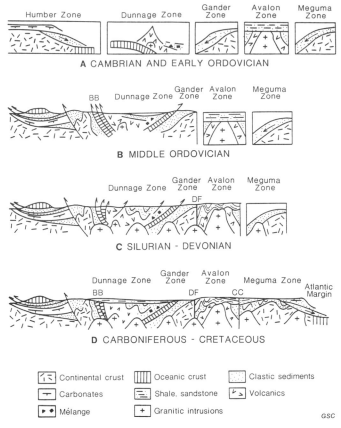

Figure 2.6. Schematic portrayal of the tectonic development of the Canadian Appalachian Orogen and Atlantic Margin. BB = Baie Verte-Brompton Line, DF = Dover Fault, CC = Cobequid-Chedabucto Fault (or Glooscap Fault). A: Cambrian to Early Ordovician: The Appalachian Orogen with Humber, Dunnage, Gander, Avalon and Meguma zones being discrete entities. B: Middle Ordovician: Collision of Humber Zone with the Dunnage and the Dunnage with Gander Zone. Avalon and Meguma zones remain as discrete entities. C: Silurian to Devonian: Collision of Avalon Zone with Gander Zone to leave only the Meguma as a separate zone. D: Carboniferous to Cretaceous: Meguma Zone is now part of the Appalachian Orogen.

Basin in the United States (Quinlan and Beaumont, 1984). The Taconic Orogeny and later compressional events controlled the stratigraphy of these foreland basins.

In Newfoundland, the North American margin of Iapetus is succeeded to the east by three large composite terranes or zones (Williams and Hatcher, 1982, 1983). All are of unknown paleogeography with respect to North America. From west to east, these are the Dunnage, Gander and Avalon zones (Fig. 2.2). An additional zone, the Meguma, occurs in mainland Nova Scotia, on the southeastern margin of the Appalachian Orogen.

Volcanic rocks of the Dunnage Zone overlie an ophiolitic substrate. Accordingly, the Dunnage is an example of one (or more) early Paleozoic island arc and oceanic volcanic islands built upon the crust of Iapetus. Its collision with the passive margin resulted in the Taconic Orogeny. The intensity of Taconic deformation diminishes eastward

across the Dunnage Zone. Recent studies indicate that the Dunnage Zone may be allochthonous on a crust of continental aspect (Karlstrom, 1983; Colman-Sadd and Swinden, 1984). Zones east of the Dunnage are of continental affinity.

The Gander Zone contains a thick clastic sequence of Ordovician and earlier age. This zone may represent part of a continental block, initially lying east of the Iapetus Ocean and of Dunnage island arc and backarc zone. It may therefore have been accreted to North America during the Taconic Orogeny. The Gander has been viewed as a miogeoclinal apron along the west flank of the Avalon Zone, although adjacent Avalonian volcanics seem an unlikely source for Gander greywackes and quartzites. Although the Gander Zone may have once bordered a continental craton, it is not linked to one now. Possibly the offshore Delta Zone (Fig. 2.2) is a continental remnant linked to the Gander Zone (Haworth, 1980).

The Avalon Zone is defined from its thick Upper Precambrian sedimentary and volcanic sequences, and its overlying Cambrian shales with their faunas of Atlantic or European affinities. Its basement is probably of the same age as the Grenville Structural Province (Olszewski and Gaudette, 1982; Farrar and Glover, 1983). The stratigraphy and structure of the Avalon Zone are well known in places but the significance of the zone in the Appalachian Orogen remains a mystery. Its setting in the Late Precambrian has been interpreted as either an archipelago of volcanic islands related to subduction and a Pan-African orogenic cycle that pre-dated the opening of Iapetus (Rast, 1980; O'Brien et al., 1983), or one of volcanoes and sedimentary basins related to rifting and the initiation of Iapetus (Strong, 1979).

The Meguma Zone has about 10 km of marine greywackes and shales of Cambrian and Early Ordovician age. These sedimentary rocks were derived from a gneissic source of continental dimensions that lay to the southeast (Schenk, 1981). The zone is interpreted as a continental embankment and is underlain by gneisses, which have an isotopic age of 1180 Ma (Keppie et al., 1983).

Stratigraphic and sedimentological analyses of the Appalachian Orogen indicate that it built outward from the miogeocline (Humber Zone) on its western margin in three accretionary events. These occurred in the Early to Middle Ordovician, the Silurian-Devonian, and the Carboniferous-Permian. These times of accretion coincide with the three main orogenic episodes affecting the system, respectively the Taconian, Acadian and Alleghanian orogenies (Williams and Hatcher, 1982, 1983). The boundaries between the first accreted western zones, the Humber-Dunnage and the Dunnage-Gander boundaries, are nearly horizontal or moderately dipping zones marked by ophiolites and melanges. These features imply subduction and obduction (e.g. Williams and St. Julien, 1982). Later boundaries between eastern zones, the Gander-Avalon and the Avalon-Meguma boundaries, are steep ductile shears and brittle faults, implying transcurrent movements.

The Middle Ordovician Taconic Orogeny was followed by a rather long quiescent period until the widespread orogenic episode in the Devonian — the Acadian Orogeny. Only the most westerly parts of the ancient North American margin and some easterly parts of the Avalon Zone escaped Acadian deformation. Its effects were most intense east of the Taconic deformed zone and its timing probably corresponds to the time of Avalonian accretion. Large granitic plutons were emplaced at this time in all the zones east of the North American margin. The mechanism which caused this plutonism is still under debate. The chemistry of the granitic plutons is incompatible with the plutonism of island arcs, so that they were not generated in that type of subduction (Strong, 1980; Fyffe et al., 1981; Hanmer, 1981).

Most geological models for the development of the Canadian Appalachians focus on the history of the evolution and destruction of Iapetus from the late Precambrian to the Ordovician. The Silurian-Carboniferous history is less well known. The conflict between geological and paleomagnetic models is rather severe, and the few mid-Paleozoic poles from the Canadian Appalachians only add to the confusion (Kent and Opdyke, 1978; Morel and Irving, 1978; Irving and Strong, 1984). Whereas paleomagnetic data favour a wide Ordovician ocean, the appearance of cosmopolitan faunas and synchronous ophiolite emplacement suggests narrowing and destruction of the ocean at that time (McKerrow and Cocks, 1976; Spjeldnaes, 1978). Possibly a middle Paleozoic ocean existed to the east of the Dunnage Zone, separating the Gander-Avalon and/or Avalon-Meguma zones. The boundaries separating these zones, however, imply transcurrent rather than collisional motion (Arthaud and Matte, 1977). Significant transcurrent motions between the zones in the late Paleozoic would remove the requirement for a succession of Paleozoic ocean basins. Restricted upper Paleozoic marine deposits and the limited extent of late Paleozoic (Alleghanian) deformation in the Canadian Appalachians may signify the narrowness of the remaining seaways and perhaps the final structural tightening of these and other weak crustal areas.

In the Late Devonian-Carboniferous, the deposition of primarily terrestrial sedimentary rocks was widespread in New Brunswick, but elsewhere in eastern Canada it was largely confined to rift basins. Volcanic rocks have been drilled in the Magdalen Basin, the Carboniferous basin in the Gulf of St. Lawrence, at a depth of about 3000 m (Howie and Barss, 1975). This basin developed in a "rift" that crosscuts most early Paleozoic features. Recent attempts to model the evolution of the basin invoke the creation of a depocentre by transcurrent movement along a sigmoidal fault (Bradley, 1982). Whatever the cause of the depocentre, the deposition is episodic (G. Quinlan, Memorial University of Newfoundland, pers. comm., 1982).

In Newfoundland, Carboniferous rocks are found only within a narrow rift basin close to and paralleling the Paleozoic miogeocline and the Baie Verte-Brompton Line. The rocks continue offshore, northeast of Newfoundland, with fold trends that become progressively more oblique to the Paleozoic margin and more nearly parallel to the present Labrador margin. Fauna from the basin have been interpreted as suggesting that a Carboniferous ocean existed in that area (Jansa et al., 1978), but anything more than a local seaway is difficult to reconcile with other data. A depositional gap during most of the Permian may mark a period of uplift prior to the opening of the present Atlantic Ocean.

MESOZOIC-CENOZOIC TECTONICS

The beginning of Mesozoic continental break-up is marked by the development of rift basins (Fig. 2.7) with concomitant volcanism and mafic dyke intrusion. These basins generally formed within half-grabens, bounded by normal faults. They contain nonmarine and shallow marine sediments whose thickness ranges from about 1 to 6 km. The volcanism associated with the rifting appears to have been sporadic and localized. The sedimentary stratigraphy of some offshore rift basins shows a well-developed break-up unconformity, marking the time of final continental break-up and this may imply uplift towards the end of rifting. In other basins deposition and subsidence was continuous throughout both the rift and post-rift phases. The post-rift phase was generally a time of passive subsidence and sedimentation, in response to cooling and thermal contraction of the lithosphere. The thickness of the Mesozoic-Cenozoic sediments now exceeds 10 km in some of the deeper basins.

Although subsidence and sedimentation were fairly continuous, several regional unconformities occur in the Mesozoic and Cenozoic (see Chapters 5 to 7). McWhae (1981) suggested that five unconformities can be recognized along the entire eastern Canadian margin but they are not uniformly well-developed. Some of these may be related to major tectonic events, such as rifting on a regional scale, orogenesis on a continental scale, or global changes in eustatic sea level. No comprehensive studies are available of the seismic stratigraphy of the region and its relationship to eustatic sea level changes (Vail et al., 1977) or to major tectonic events.

The deep sedimentary basins along the eastern Canadian margin are separated from one another by platforms, regions of little sediment cover (Fig. 2.3). For example, the Yarmouth Arch separates Georges Bank Basin from the Scotian Basin, and the Okak Arch separates the Hopedale and Saglek basins. This alternation of basins and platforms is one of the most distinctive features of the continental margin and requires an explanation in terms of the tectonic development of the region.

In most basins the landward side is delineated by a hinge zone which separates the basin from the "coastal plain" sediments lying farther inland. The coastal plain sediments comprise a relatively thin wedge, which progressively onlaps the continent. The hinge zone appears to be a zone of normal faulting, across which sediment thicknesses change rapidly. The boundaries, which are normal to the margins and which separate basins and platforms, also appear to be zones of steep faults. Beneath the continental slope and rise the basins merge with the sediments overlying oceanic crust.

Normal faulting accompanied rifting. Some basins are underlain by a series of normal faults, stepping down toward the ocean basins, whereas others appear to consist of isolated half grabens. Examples of the latter include the basins on the Grand Banks, the Orpheus Graben on the Scotian Shelf (Loncarevic and Ewing, 1966), and the Melville Bay Graben (see Fig. 2.4) off West Greenland. Many normal faults lie beneath the sediments in Georges Bank Basin, Orphan Basin (also referred to as East Newfoundland Basin), and the basins of the Labrador and Baffin Bay margins. Scotian Basin may be anomalous in that few nor-

DEVELOPMENT OF SEDIMENTARY BASINS

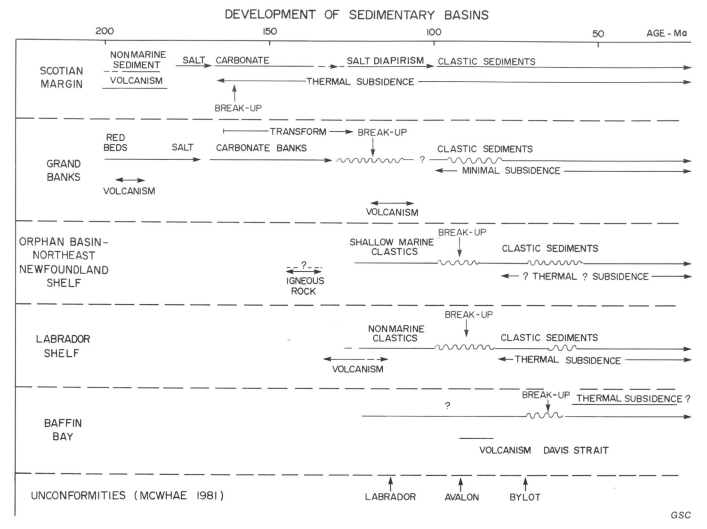

Figure 2.7. Schematic illustration of the evolution of sedimentary basins on the margins of eastern Canada. The evolution is depicted for five segments of the margin; Scotian Margin, Grand Banks, Orphan Basin-Northeast Newfoundland Shelf, Labrador Shelf, and Baffin Bay. The times of final continental break-up are shown by vertical arrows, and the presence of a break-up unconformity is indicated by a wave line. Sediment types, presence of volcanism, and subsidence are indicated. Three of the regional unconformities of McWhae (1981), are indicated at the bottom of the figure.

mal faults have been mapped in basement but this may be partly due to poor resolution through the great thickness of the sedimentary cover.

The normal faults on each margin segment exhibit similar trends and sense of displacement, and may be controlled by the geometry of earlier faulting (Bally, 1982). This polarity is apparent in some margin segments off eastern Canada, but their ancestral controls are unclear. A good example occurs on the Labrador margin (McWhae, 1981). Basement structures in that region show both northwest-trending down to basement normal faults, and northeast-trending transform faults, perpendicular to the margin. These trends are compatible with lineaments (high angle faults, master joints and dykes; McWhae, 1981) in the adjacent Canadian Shield.

Vertical tectonics and volcanism during rifting

The stratigraphy of the offshore rift basins is derived mainly from seismic reflection and well data, collected as part of the program of petroleum exploration in the region. This information allows the history of vertical motions of the margins to be determined. Vertical tectonics are important in understanding the processes responsible for continental break-up and rifting. Rift phase volcanic rocks have also been discovered offshore, as well as on the adjacent continent. The role and importance of volcanism in the rifting of continents is unclear, perhaps because much of the evidence is buried beneath great thicknesses of sediment. Most of the data concerning offshore rift basins have been described in regional syntheses published by Cutt and Laving (1977), Umpleby (1979) and McWhae (1981) for the Labrador and Baffin Bay margins; by Amoco and Imperial (1973), Jansa and Wade (1975), Given (1977), and Wade (1981) for the Grand Banks and Scotian margin, and by Ballard and Uchupi (1975), Wade (1981), and Scholle and Wenkam (1982) for the Gulf of Maine. The biostratigraphy and depositional environment are described by Gradstein et al. (1975), Gradstein and Williams (1976, 1981), Barss et al. (1979), and Gradstein and Srivastava (1980). The sediments of the Baffin Bay region have not been sampled by deep drilling, so that much of the timing of tectonic events in that area is speculative.

The following paragraphs give a brief description of the vertical evolution and rift phase volcanic activity of the various segments of the margin during rifting, from the oldest in the south to the youngest in the north. This evolution is illustrated in Figure 2.7.

The earliest rifting was that between Africa and North America, creating the rifted margin off Nova Scotia and the United States and the transform margin along the southern edge of the Grand Banks (Fig. 2.5). Rifting began in the Late Triassic and affected the margin of eastern Canada from the northern Grand Banks to the Gulf of Maine, a distance of about 2000 km. Narrow, elongate rift basins were created. The oldest sediments of rift origin are Upper Triassic nonmarine clastics which have been sampled in the Bay of Fundy, the Gulf of Maine, the Orpheus Graben on the Scotian Shelf, and some of the basins of the Grand Banks. Nonmarine deposition was followed in the Late Triassic-Early Jurassic by the development of an extensive salt basin, which grew southward as the Tethyan Sea flooded the region (Jansa et al., 1980). The salt is over 2 km thick beneath the basins of the Grand Banks and the Scotian Basin, but salt of this age is thin or absent beneath the Georges Bank Basin; the Yarmouth Arch may mark the southwestern extent of these deposits. The most northerly occurrence of salt is in the region of the Jeanne d'Arc Basin on the Grand Banks.

In most of this region the salt is unconformably overlain by carbonates, which developed as more open marine conditions were established. These carbonates occur as banks and build-ups, and can be used to estimate the position of the former shelf edge (Jansa, 1981). Carbonate deposition persisted throughout most of the Jurassic, although the Middle and Late Jurassic were dominated by clastics, such as the Middle Jurassic Mohican Formation found in the Scotian Basin. Both the change from salt to carbonate deposition and the onset of deposition of Mohican clastic rocks have been interpreted to mark the onset of seafloor spreading (Jansa and Wade, 1975; Given, 1977). In both cases an Early to Middle Jurassic age for final continental separation is indicated. The stratigraphy indicates that a break-up unconformity developed on the Scotian margin during this time between the Argo salt and the overlying carbonates or clastics.

Lower Jurassic mafic volcanics and dykes are observed in southern Nova Scotia and in eastern Newfoundland, and can be traced offshore by geophysical means. In western Nova Scotia the tholeiitic North Mountain Basalt rests conformably on nonmarine Upper Triassic sediments (Poole et al., 1970). The basalts have been traced offshore beneath the Bay of Fundy and Gulf of Maine (King and MacLean, 1976). Early Jurassic dykes, such as the Shelburne Dyke in Nova Scotia and the Avalon dyke (referred to as the Avalon aeromagnetic lineament by Hodych and

Hayatsu, 1980) in eastern Newfoundland (which can be traced aeromagnetically for over 100 km), trend subparallel to the present margin (Papezik and Hodych, 1980). The northeast trend of these dykes is compatible with many of the other magnetic trends indicative of dykes on the Northeast Newfoundland Shelf (Haworth and Keen, 1979). Elsewhere, particularly within the deeper sedimentary basins, there is no specific evidence of Triassic or Lower Jurassic volcanic rocks, but in most cases they would be too deeply buried to detect.

In summary, rifting on the Scotian margin was accompanied by basin subsidence, which allowed several kilometres of sediments to accumulate. Early rift stage sediments are nonmarine; later deposition is shallow marine, suggesting that the shelf region slowly subsided from a starting elevation above sea level. Volcanism accompanied rifting, and its age suggests that rifting started at about 200 Ma. The duration of the rift phase can thus be estimated at about 20 Ma.

Whereas rifting ended in the Gulf of Maine and on the Scotian margin with the onset of Early to Middle Jurassic seafloor spreading, the development of rift basins persisted until the Cretaceous on the Grand Banks. During the Jurassic and Early Cretaceous, the southern margin of the Grand Banks remained an active transform fault and the eastern margin experienced continental rifting between Iberia and North America. This complex situation culminated in mid-Cretaceous time, as seafloor spreading began east of the Grand Banks and the African and North American continents were decoupled.

The Scotian Basin extends into the southwestern region of the Grand Banks, which experienced a rift-drift history similar to that of the Scotian margin (Fig. 2.3); post-rift subsidence was coeval with the start of seafloor spreading in the Early to Middle Jurassic and continued to the present. On the remainder of the Grand Banks, the rift basins continued to subside during the Jurassic, but in the Early Cretaceous a major erosional unconformity developed, perhaps in response to uplift resulting from rifting between Iberia and North America. Mesozoic sediments older than Late Cretaceous were eroded, except in the deep basins. Both the Labrador and Avalon unconformities (Fig. 2.7) have been identified in the Jeanne d'Arc Basin and appear to merge over much of the Grand Banks.

Lower Cretaceous alkaline volcanic rocks (Fig. 2.3) occur in some of the wells on the Grand Banks (Gradstein et al., 1977; Jansa and Pe-Piper, 1985). These volcanic rocks lie near the boundary of the Avalon and Meguma zones suggesting reactivation along that zone of weakness. Oceanic volcanism of comparable age is observed in the Fogo Seamounts, the Newfoundland Ridge, and the Newfoundland Seamounts, which collectively encircle the southeastern tip of the Grand Banks (Fig. 2.2; Keen et al., 1977; Sullivan and Keen, 1978; Tucholke and Ludwig, 1982).

Vertical tectonics on much of the Grand Banks were marked by uplift and erosion throughout the Early Cretaceous, and also by pronounced subsidence in the basins, in which lower Mesozoic sediments are preserved. Unlike the Scotian margin, there is little evidence for Early Jurassic volcanism; however, the Lower Cretaceous volcanic rocks which have been sampled are probably associated with rifting between Iberia and North America.

The Grand Banks mark the transition from Triassic rifting to the south to Early Cretaceous rifting to the north. The margin northeast of Newfoundland was formed by rifting between Europe and North America. In Orphan Basin (East Newfoundland Basin), basement faulting, subsidence and sedimentation appear to have started in the Early Cretaceous, although rifting may have begun as early as in the Jurassic (Umpleby, 1979). Whereas nonmarine Jurassic sediments were sampled at DSDP Site 111 on Orphan Knoll, no Mesozoic sediments older than Early Cretaceous have been observed elsewhere in the region (Parsons et al., 1985). In the well Blue H-28 in the Orphan Basin, Lower Cretaceous shallow marine sediments overlie Paleozoic sediments. There is a pronounced mid-Cretaceous break-up unconformity (Avalon Unconformity, Fig. 2.7) between the Lower Cretaceous sediments and the overlying Cenozoic post-rift sediments.

Jurassic rifting is suggested by the occurrence of Jurassic lamprophyre dykes and mafic intrusions in northeastern Newfoundland (Strong and Harris, 1974). Offshore, the well Bonavista C-99 ended in Jurassic aplite. However, more observations are needed to determine if rift sediments of Jurassic age, as opposed to igneous rocks, were deposited in this region.

On the Labrador margin, Precambrian and Paleozoic basement rocks are disrupted by normal faults which developed during the Early Cretaceous. Subaerial volcanic rocks and terrestrial clastic sediments filled the rift basins, which lie beneath the present shelf and slope (Gradstein and Williams, 1976, 1981; Cutt and Laving, 1977; Umpleby, 1979). The volcanism appears to have occurred first, in the Berriasian to Hauterivian, although minor volcanic activity may have persisted until the Aptian. The distribution of the volcanic rocks is not well known, but they have been encountered in five of the wells drilled on the Labrador Shelf (see Chapter 7). The overlying Hauterivian to lower Cenomanian sediments have been tilted by normal faults that were active during the deposition of the sediments (McWhae, 1981). Most of these Lower Cretaceous sediments are nonmarine, and are preserved in the regions between basement highs. This reflects the presence of the mid-Cretaceous erosional unconformity (Avalon Unconformity; Fig. 2.7), which separates the predominantly nonmarine rift stage sediments from the marine post- rift sediments of Cenozoic age. Seafloor spreading appears to have begun in this region in the Late Cretaceous. However, the post-rift subsidence of the margin did not begin until the Early Tertiary (Royden and Keen, 1980). This delay in subsidence is compatible with significant uplift just prior to seafloor spreading.

By comparison with the Scotian margin, both the Orphan Basin (East Newfoundland Basin) and the basins of the Labrador margin exhibit long rift phases, about 50 Ma. They are also both characterized by pronounced break-up unconformities (Avalon Unconformity) and the delayed post-rift subsidence suggests that significant uplift was associated with these break-up features.

The Baffin Bay enigma

The history of the regions north of the Labrador margin is less well documented. Recent reviews include those of Grant (1980), Henderson et al. (1981), McWhae (1981), Srivastava et al. (1981), and Srivastava (1983). Baffin Bay and Davis Strait are thought to have formed by plate tectonic motion between Greenland and North America, with seafloor spreading starting in the latest Cretaceous or Paleocene (Fig. 2.5). The timing approximately corresponds to a major change in the direction of motion of Greenland relative to North America (Srivastava et al., 1981) and is correlative with the emplacement of Paleocene basalts found in the Davis Strait region (Johnson et al., 1982). The main phase of the Eurekan Orogeny to the north also corresponds to the opening of Baffin Bay (McWhae, 1981). Plate motions ceased at about 38 Ma, in the Late Eocene.

There are some who do not believe that Baffin Bay was formed by seafloor spreading (see Umpleby, 1979; Grant, 1980). Disputes arise over Davis Strait, the positive bathymetric feature between the Labrador Sea and Baffin Bay, and the Nares Strait to the north, which is a major plate boundary in plate tectonic reconstructions (Fig. 2.1, 2.5).

Various models for the origin of Davis Strait have been proposed, none of which are entirely convincing: an Icelandic type hot spot, a leaky transform fault system, and a mixture of continental crustal fragments and oceanic material (Keen and Barrett, 1972; Hyndman, 1973; Srivastava, 1978, 1983). Paleocene volcanics observed on land on both sides of Davis Strait can be traced offshore, but pre-rift Paleozoic sediments are also found in the nearshore regions of the strait (MacLean and Falconer, 1979). A large basement high trends northeast across the strait which may be a piece of continental crust rifted away from Baffin Island (Srivastava, 1983).

Nares Strait has recently received much attention, with the publication of a volume devoted to its probable origin (Dawes and Kerr, 1982a). The arguments centre on whether or not there was substantial transform movement along the strait during plate tectonic motion between Greenland and North America. Some correlations of geological units across the strait suggest that there was little motion (Christie et al., 1981; Dawes and Kerr, 1982b), although most plate tectonic reconstructions require over 100 km of left lateral motion. Some of the most recent concepts of thin-skinned tectonics may resolve this argument; the surface geology may not reflect plate motions, as has recently been suggested by Keen and Peirce (1982), Hugon (1983), and Miall (1983). Furthermore, new evidence on plate motions in the Arctic Ocean which better constrain the motion of Greenland still require some transform motion along Nares Strait, as well as oblique compression and subduction across it (Jackson and Koppen, 1985).

In addition to problems of the origin and tectonic significance of Davis Strait and Nares Strait, there are other major lineaments whose roles during the Mesozoic-Cenozoic are unclear. These include major physiographic features, such as the half grabens or grabens of Lancaster, Frobisher and Cumberland sounds, along which some extensional or transcurrent movement may have occurred (Kerr, 1981; Hamilton, 1983).

The rift phase sediments on the margins around Baffin Bay include nonmarine to shallow marine sediments of Early Cretaceous to Paleocene age. These have been observed only on the adjacent land mass: in west Greenland (Henderson et al., 1976); in Eclipse Trough on Bylot Island (Miall et al., 1980); and in small outliers on Baffin Island (Srivastava et al., 1981). Normal faults in places bound the troughs in which these sediments are preserved, and in west Greenland faulting is believed to have occurred sporadically throughout the Cretaceous and Early Tertiary (Rosenkrantz and Pulvertaft, 1969). This suggests a long rift phase in the Baffin Bay region. McWhae (1981) proposed that a break-up unconformity, the Bylot Unconformity of early Paleocene age, marks the transition from the rift to the post-rift phase (Fig. 2.7) but this is not well documented.

Volcanism in the region is centred in Davis Strait, where Paleocene volcanic rocks are widespread onshore and offshore. A Late Cretaceous or Early Tertiary volcanic event was also observed in wells (Fig. 1, in pocket and Fig. 2.1) such as Nukik 2 and Hellefisk 1 on the Greenland Shelf, and Hekja A-72, Gjoa G-37, and Raleigh N-18 on the western margin of the strait (Johnson et al., 1982). This may mark a period of renewed rift activity in the region.

An important element in the evolution of the margins of the Baffin Bay region is the observation of post-rift uplift along the shoulders of the rifted margin (MacLean and Falconer, 1979). Marine rocks of Cretaceous and Paleogene age are now found some 600 m above sea level along the coast of eastern Baffin Island. This post-rift uplift may also occur along the Labrador coast, but the only evidence at present is the elevation of the land mass. Post-rift uplift is an unusual feature of rifted continental margins and is discussed in some detail in Chapter 7.

Post-rift subsidence history

After seafloor spreading began, the sedimentary basins of the margin continued to subside, in some cases after a period of uplift marked by a break-up unconformity. Their development is, in general, characterized by subsidence and almost continuous sedimentation. This is demonstrated by the subsidence curves for Scotian Shelf, Labrador Shelf, and Orphan Basin (Fig. 2.8, 2.9, 2.10). The subsidence history, derived from the biostratigraphy for selected wells, is best defined for the Scotian Basin (Keen, 1979; Royden and Keen, 1980). The subsidence curves exhibit the familiar exponential shape, indicative of cooling and thermal contraction of the lithosphere (Fig. 2.8). A time constant of about 60 Ma for lithospheric cooling is compatible with that of the oceanic lithosphere and with many other continental regions (Sclater et al., 1980). The subsidence of the Labrador margin is similar, although the curves (Fig. 2.9) show considerable scatter, probably because of variations in paleo-water depth which were not included in the analysis (Royden and Keen, 1980). Post-rift sedimentation of the Labrador margin was delayed for about 10 Ma after seafloor spreading began, probably because this margin was uplifted just before the commencement of seafloor spreading.

The subsidence history of Orphan Basin (Fig. 2.10) is not compatible with a simple model of a cooling lithosphere (Keen and Barrett, 1981). The basin did not undergo significant subsidence until the Eocene, when subsidence was extremely rapid. This was followed by anomalously slow subsidence in the later Tertiary (Ruffman and Van Hinte, 1973). This unusual behaviour may be related to the proximity of a transform margin represented by the Charlie-Gibbs Fracture Zone along the northern boundary of the basin. In this case the two plates would remain coupled so that the basin would continue to be actively rifted during continent-continent motion. Only final continental separation would have allowed rapid foundering of the basin. This proposal is analogous in some respects to continued

rifting of the Grand Banks until the Cretaceous. However, the mechanical and thermal processes involved are unclear.

TECTONIC INHERITANCE AND CONTRASTING TECTONIC STYLES

Tectonic inheritance

Several geological boundaries in eastern Canada have either been the locus of continued tectonic activity throughout the Phanerozoic or have propagated as a result of orogenesis (Fig. 2.2, 2.3).

Mesozoic-Cenozoic rifting cut across the Appalachian Orogen (Fig. 2.11) of northeastern Newfoundland and the Grenville Province of Labrador. Some Paleozoic zone boundaries and Precambrian structural features propagated eastward and their prolongations coincide with offsets in the present margin and major oceanic fracture zones. Most obvious is the prolongation of the Dover Fault into the Charlie-Gibbs Fracture Zone (Fig. 2.2). The importance of the Dover Fault as a Paleozoic zone boundary is apparent from the contrasting surface geology of the Avalon and Gander zones as well as their deep crustal contrasts. Similarly, the prolongation of the Precambrian Grenville Front is expressed in the margin offset at the Cartwright Arch and its seaward prolongation into the Cartwright Fracture Zone. In general, boundaries between basins and platforms can be traced seaward into oceanic fracture zones, even though the boundaries do not correspond to any well-defined older lineament (e.g. Fig. 2.12). Surprisingly, the fundamental Avalon-Meguma zone boundary is not expressed in a rift or transform margin, although it localized the Fundy Rift Basin, the Orpheus Graben, and the mid-Cretaceous volcanism on the Grand Banks (Fig. 2.2).

The important southern transform margin of the Grand Banks does not appear to have developed along a pre-existing lineament. Also, normal faults within the Orphan Basin appear to be perpendicular to the northeasterly trend of Avalon structures. These exceptions suggest that extensional forces during rifting controlled the locus of continental break-up, and that although pre-existing boundaries were convenient, they were not essential for the development of Mesozoic rift structures.

The Tail of the Bank at the Grand Banks transform margin is a modern promontory that parallels the Paleozoic St. Lawrence Promontory of the Appalachian Orogen (Fig. 2.11; Williams and Doolan, 1979). Furthermore, the "transform" linking the St. Lawrence Promontory to the Quebec Reentrant lies along the prolongation of the older Labrador Trough, which may represent a much older Early Proterozoic continental margin. Although inheritance and ancestral controls are implied among these features, no observable structural breaks can be traced from one to another.

Finally, some features have maintained tectonic activity over long periods but have never developed into continental margins. For example, the St. Lawrence River valley has evidence of incipient rifting prior to the opening of Iapetus and the Atlantic, and it continues to be a zone of high earthquake activity.

On a more global scale for the entire North Atlantic region, there is an obvious spatial relationship between the distribution of rocks affected by the Grenville Orogeny,

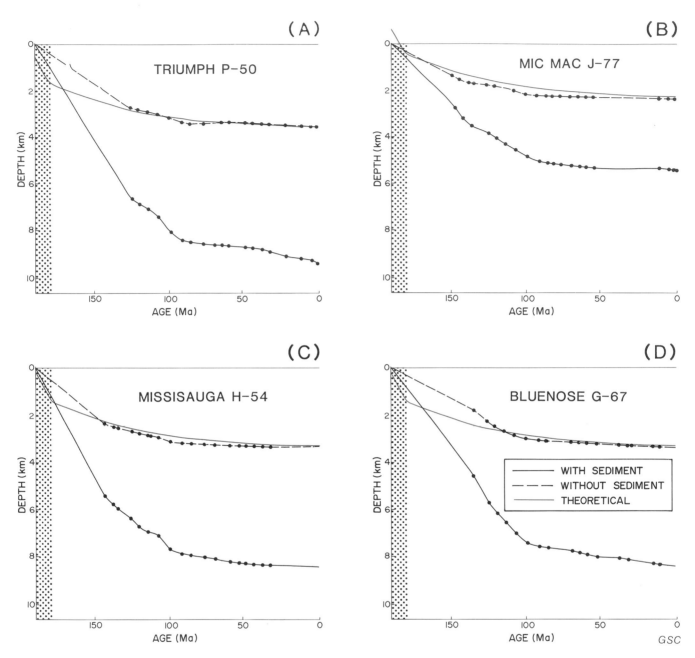

Figure 2.8. Subsidence curves for the Scotian Shelf (well locations are shown in Figure 1, in pocket). The dots are the observations. Two subsidence curves are shown in each example; one represents the total subsidence of the shelf, the other has been corrected for the effects of sediment loading so that only the subsidence due to tectonic processes is represented. The red line was computed from a model in which the lithosphere is stretched during rifting by an amount given by b = 2, and during the post-rift phase the lithosphere cools towards thermal equilibrium. The time of rifting is represented by the shaded region. After Royden and Keen (1980).

those affected by Paleozoic orogenies, and the location of present continental margins (Williams, 1984). Thus tectonic patterns in the North Atlantic may have been determined by events that began before 1000 Ma.

Tectonic styles

Comparisons of continental margin segments and of conjugate margins reveal some interesting differences in their behaviour during rifting. For example, basement normal faults, stepping down towards the ocean basin, are observed on many margin segments including those of Baffin Bay, Labrador, the Orphan Basin, and Georges Bank. Basement normal faults, however, have not been observed except locally beneath the Scotian Basin. Instead there is a hinge zone in the latter region, beyond which the basement appears to be unfaulted. This apparent absence of normal faults may be caused in part by the blanketing

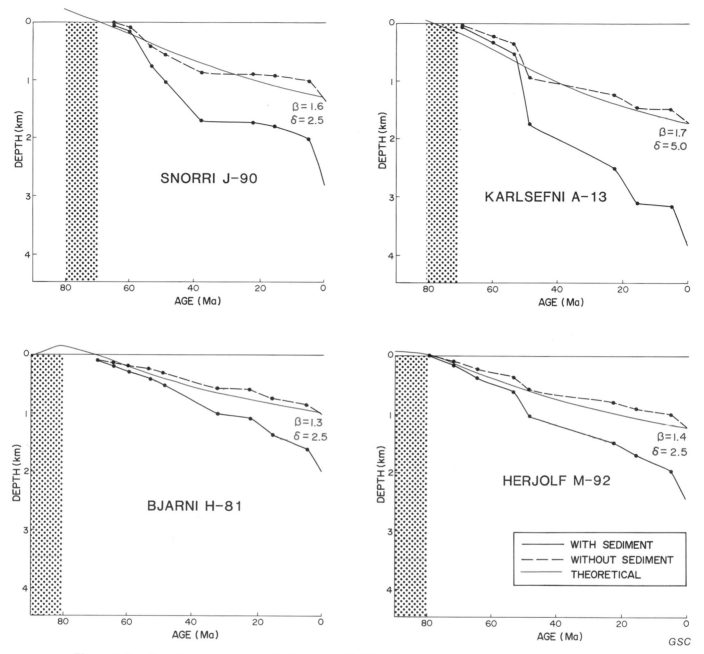

Figure 2.9. Subsidence curves for the Labrador Shelf (well locations are shown in Figure 1, in pocket). Curves are as described in Figure 2.8. In this case values for crustal stretching (b) and for sub-crustal lithospheric stretching (?) are given beside each example. After Royden and Keen (1980).

effect of the thick sedimentary sequence, and the presence of a highly reflective salt layer just above basement. However, good quality seismic reflection data have been collected in the region so that numerous normal faults should have been observed if present. This same absence of normal faults also occurs on the margin to the south, as in the Baltimore Canyon Trough off the eastern United States (LASE Study Group, 1986), so that this feature of the Scotian Basin is not an isolated, anomalous example. If normal faults are present, they must be small by comparison with those observed beneath the other margin segments listed above.

The reasons why the style of faulting should differ are not clearly established. However, several factors can be suggested. All the margins where normal faults are clearly observed lie within basement rocks of Precambrian age, either Canadian Shield rocks of the Labrador and Baffin Island margins or in the Avalon Zone. Conversely, the rifted basement rocks of the Scotian Basin comprise metasediments of the Paleozoic Meguma Group and granitic intrusions. Thus there may be a correlation between extensional faulting and factors such as the age, pre-rift tectonic fabric, or mechanical strength of the basement rocks. In some regions where Paleozoic faults or major

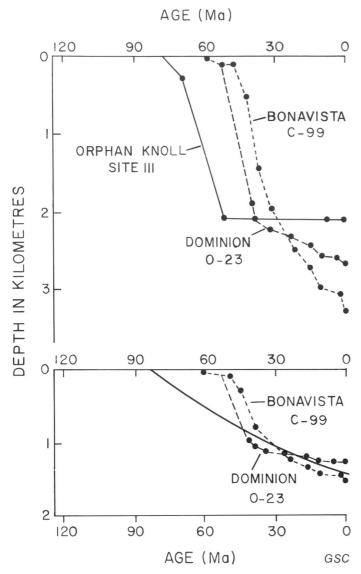

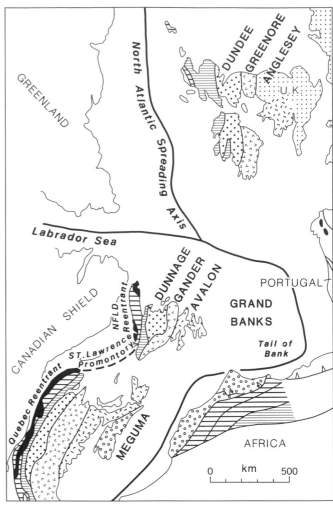

Figure 2.10. Subsidence curves for the Orphan Basin region (well locations are shown in Figure 1, in pocket). The upper diagram shows subsidence at DSDP Site 111 on Orphan Knoll, and for the wells Bonavista C-99 and Dominion O-23 on the Northeast Newfoundland Shelf. The lower diagram shows the subsidence curves for Bonavista C-99 and Dominion O-23 after the correction has been applied to remove the effect of sediment loading. The solid red line is theoretical subsidence predicted by the depth-dependent extension model of rifting (see Keen and Barrett, 1981).

Figure 2.11. Relative position of the continents before rifting. The geological correlation of major Paleozoic tectonic elements and promontories and re-entrants in the Canadian Appalachians are shown. The position of impending continental break-up in the Mesozoic is indicated by a heavy solid line. After Williams (1984).

MIOGEOCLINES

Moderately deformed

Intensely deformed

ALLOCHTHONOUS ROCKS

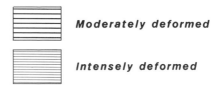

(above exposed miogeoclines)

SUSPECT TERRANES

COVER ROCKS

GSC

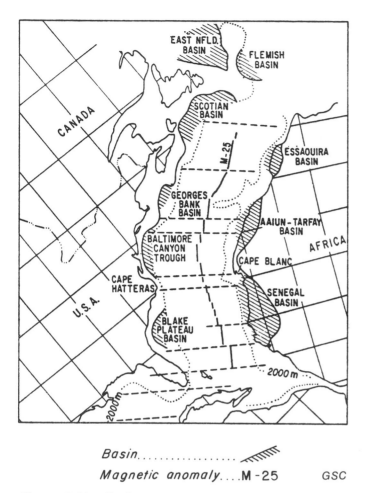

Basin.................

Magnetic anomaly....M-25   GSC

Figure 2.12. Basins and platforms around the central North Atlantic. The plates have been restored to their relative positions in the late Jurassic-Early Cretaceous (after Jansa and Weideman, 1982).

structural boundaries have been subjected to Mesozoic extension, the same fault planes or boundaries may be reactivated, but this may depend on the direction of extension with respect to the trends of these earlier boundaries. This could explain why south of the Grand Banks the Appalachian Orogen was split longitudinally, whereas to the north, rifting cut across the orogen, as described earlier.

The absence of faulting beneath the deeper parts of the Scotian Basin makes it difficult to explain the observed crustal thinning by extension of the crust and lithosphere during rifting (see Chapter 9). However, it is possible that instead of many small normal faults, there is a single large fault block, whose fault plane flattens to form a décollement surface beneath the Scotian Basin. Within the fault block there may be ductile deformation and normal faults which are too small to be mapped. This concept is compatible with the ideas of detachment fault systems developed from geological mapping of the Basin and Range Province in the United States (Wernicke and Burchfiel, 1982). Large, presently active fault systems within the Aegean region also support this suggestion (Jackson and McKenzie, 1983).

The role of transcurrent faulting in forming the present margins is not well understood. Major transform margins such as those of the southern Grand Banks, the northern boundary of the East Newfoundland Basin, and the region near the Cartwright Arch off Labrador (Fig. 2.3) are the most obvious examples of transform margin segments. The transform margin south of the Grand Banks is the best known and is used as the example in the following discussion. Many less obvious examples probably exist and there may be many small transform segments along predominantly rifted margin segments, such as the Labrador and the Scotian margins, particularly where oceanic transforms intersect the margin (Fig. 2.2, 2.3).

The intersection between rifted and transform margin segments in the southeastern Grand Banks region is complex. There is no clear evidence for any landward prolongation of the transform margin of the southern Grand Banks (Haworth and Keen, 1979). As described earlier, the major Paleozoic boundaries in this region do not coincide with the transform. Instead it would appear that the northwestern part of the southern Grand Banks margin experienced rifting during the Early Jurassic and forms the northern extremity of the Scotian Basin (Fig. 2.3). Any transcurrent motion in this region was probably small and is not defined by observational data. At the same time linear rift basins formed on the Grand Banks in response to extension. All these can, in some respects, be considered to be failed Early Jurassic rifts — an attempt of the rift system to propagate northeastward across the Grand Banks.

At the end of the rift phase, continental break-up occurred southeast of the Scotian Basin and new oceanic crust was formed. Continent-continent transform motion would have continued along the southern Grand Banks margin. This change from the rift to the post-rift phase is marked by a change in tectonic style which occurs near the eastern limit of the South Whale Subbasin along the transform margin (Fig. 2.3). This position probably marks the first occurrence of oceanic crust adjacent to the transform margin. East of the South Whale Subbasin, the margin is characterized by the proximity of the Fogo Seamounts, by a volcanic ridge which parallels the margin near the foot of the slope and appears to mark the ocean-continent boundary, and by the absence of a thick sedimentary basin on the adjacent shelf. These characteristics are markedly different from those of the Scotian Basin. This suggested history for the formation of the transform margin is consistent with observations but has not been rigorously tested. The development of other transform segments may be somewhat different.

One interesting hypothesis related to the formation of a transform margin proposes that rifting was caused by upwelling mantle plumes, situated at the present junctions between rifted and transform margin segments (Kinsman, 1975). The plumes created an incipient triple junction, radiating outward from the centre of the proposed plume. This scenario would apply, for example, to the mouth of the Laurentian Channel, lying between the rifted Scotian margin and the Grand Banks transform. According to this suggestion the third arm of the triple junction, the Laurentian Channel, is now a failed rift. The presence of plumes during rifting is difficult to substantiate. Any plume-related volcanism in the Laurentian Channel area would now be buried beneath the thick sedimentary cover and so has not been detected. Furthermore, there is no evidence that the Laurentian Channel is a failed rift.

Major transcurrent faults of late Paleozoic age may be responsible for the development of the Magdalen Basin in the Gulf of St. Lawrence (Bradley, 1982). Such basins are presumed to be extensional in origin, and result where the fault system is not linear. The role of large offsets along such faults in controlling the tectonic development of the region during the late stages of the Appalachian Orogen is largely speculative at present. Further geological and geophysical studies of the Gulf of St. Lawrence region would be important in this respect.

Detailed studies of conjugate margins, margins which were juxtaposed prior to rifting, have yet to be made. However, it is instructive to compare the first order properties of margins now on opposite sides of the ocean basins. In the Labrador Sea the margin off Labrador is occupied by two thick sedimentary basins, underlain by thinned crust. The margin off West Greenland is by comparison sharp, and has the properties of a platform, rather than a basin. The Orphan Basin is a broad sedimentary basin, while its counterparts off the British Isles are relatively sharp platformal margins. The Scotian Basin and the LaHave Platform off Nova Scotia can be matched with a platformal area and the Essaouira Basin of the west African margin (Fig. 2.12; Jansa and Weidman, 1982). Thus it would appear that continental break-up was in places asymmetric and that the final split occurred near one side of the rift basin. This asymmetry has yet to be explained satisfactorily, although there are suggestions that it may be a result of asymmetric thinning of the lithosphere during extension (Keen, 1985; see Chapter 9).

Finally, variations in tectonic style at contemporary margins may help us to understand the controlling elements in the observed variations in overthrust belts above ancient passive margins, like that which once bordered the early Paleozoic Iapetus Ocean (Fig. 2.6). An example of such a control may be a well-developed hinge line, which could act as a barrier to thrusting. Similarly, platformal margin segments may hinder overthrusting, and an example of this may be the Long Range Mountains of western Newfoundland. In general, re-entrants of the Appalachian Orogen are marked by wide zones of thrusting; ancient promontories have exposed basement and lack a wide thrust zone (Thomas, 1977). Segments of margins which are starved, such as that in the region of the Orphan Basin might be expected to respond differently to thrusting than heavily sedimented regions such as the Scotian Basin. Certainly, the sedimentary thicknesses available to form the thrust sheets would differ. The thermal age of the margin at the initiation of thrusting may also be important, as the mechanical strength of the lithosphere will depend largely on its thermal state. Differences between different thrust-and-fold belts — such as the degree to which basement is involved in thrusting, the allochthonous nature of thrusting and the horizontal distances over which allochthonous terranes move — are fundamental questions in understanding orogenesis.

GRAVITY AND MAGNETIC ANOMALIES

During the past two decades, gravity and magnetic data have been collected from Georges Bank to the Arctic channels, with the majority of surveys in the Labrador Sea and the Arctic (Fig. 2.13). Free-air gravity and magnetic anomalies are shown in Figures 2.14 to 2.17 (see Maps 1708A and 1709A, in pocket).

Major Precambrian and Paleozoic features

One of the major contributions of the study of the gravity and magnetic anomaly fields has been in delineating the offshore extent of Appalachian and Precambrian geologi-

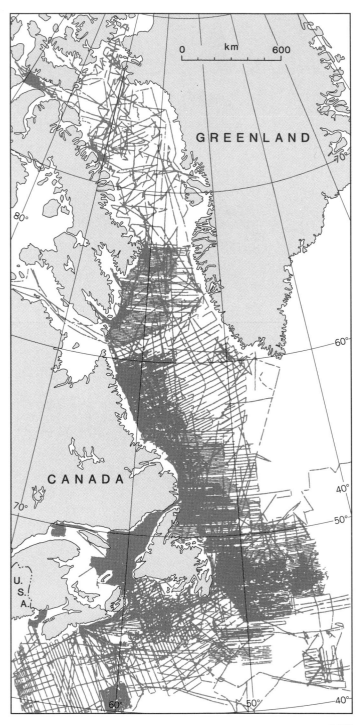

GSC

Figure 2.13. Track chart, showing coverage of magnetic and gravity anomaly measurements off eastern Canada.

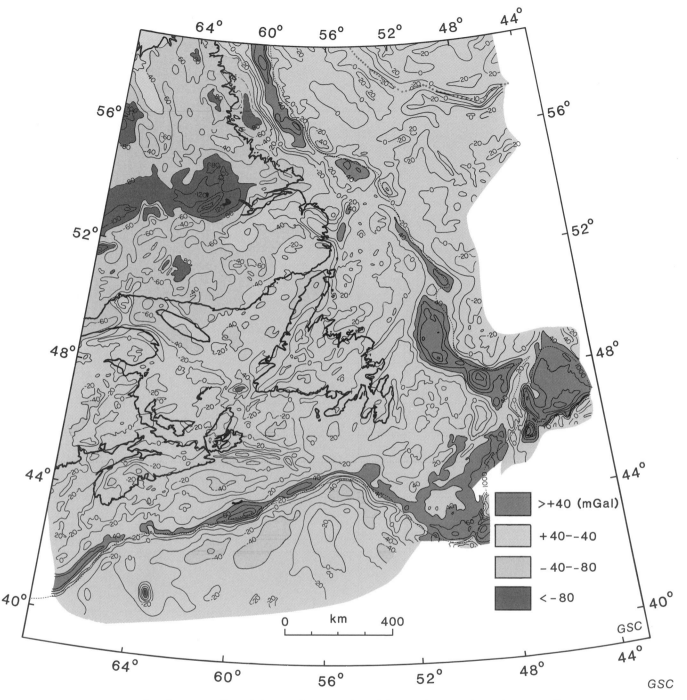

Figure 2.14. Gravity anomalies of the southern portion of the study area: free air at sea, Bouguer on land. Contour interval is 20 mGal. Four patterns have been used to indicate anomaly amplitudes. Note the positive anomalies along the edge of the shelf, and the corresponding negative anomalies on the slope and rise. The transition to large negative anomalies in the northern Gulf of St. Lawrence and in western Newfoundland appears to be associated with the ancient passive margin at the edge of the Grenville Province. Dotted lines denote central gravity lows. Data are from Srivastava (1979); Gravity Map of Canada (Earth Physics Branch, 1980); Shih et al. (1981); and Haworth and Jacobi (1983).

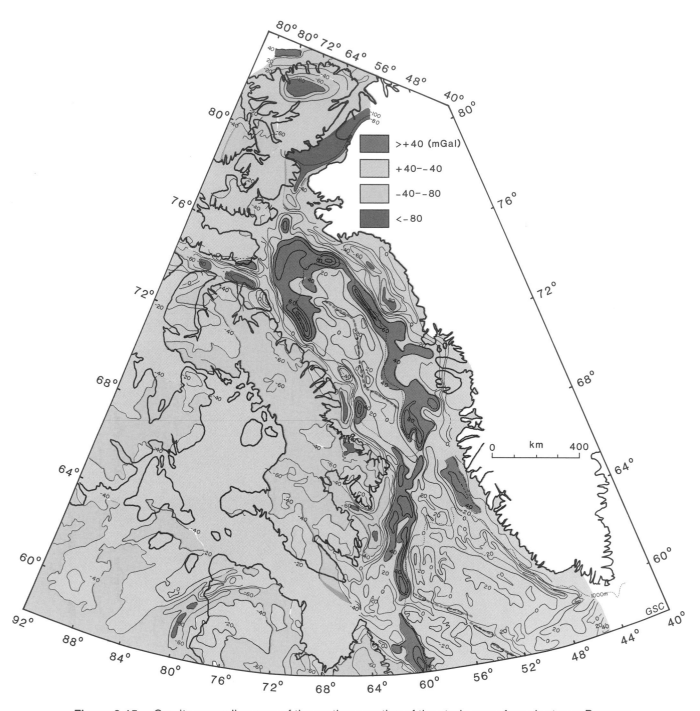

Figure 2.15. Gravity anomalies map of the northern portion of the study area: free air at sea, Bouguer on land. Contour interval is 20 mGal. Dotted lines denote central gravity lows. (Credits as for Fig. 2.14).

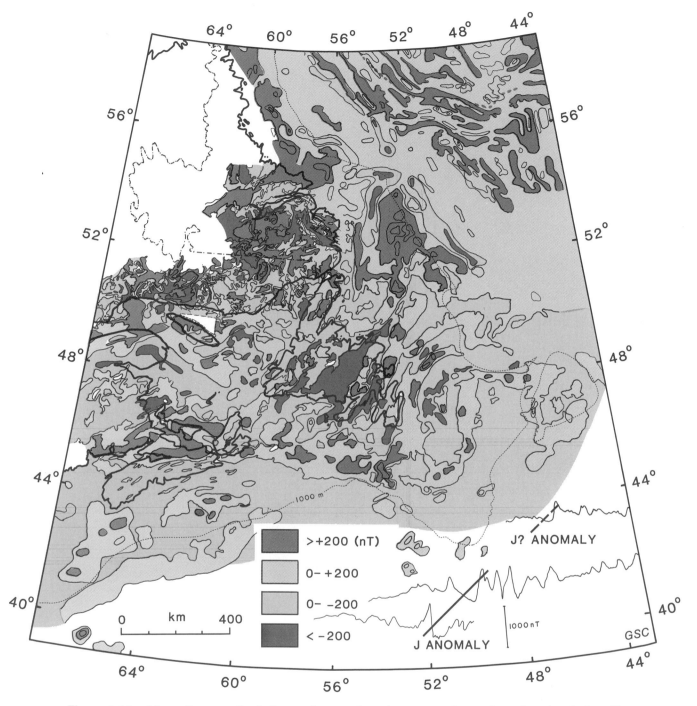

Figure 2.16. Magnetic anomalies in the southern region, shown as contours where data density is sufficient and in profile form where data are sparse. Four patterns have been used to indicate anomaly amplitudes. The contoured data are derived from Haworth and MacIntyre (1975); the Magnetic Anomaly Map of Canada (McGrath et al., 1977); and Haworth and Jacobi (1983). The profiles were obtained from data reported by Keen et al. (1977); Srivastava (1978, 1979); and Shih et al. (1981). The position of the J-Anomaly is indicated. In the Labrador Sea the trends of lineated oceanic anomalies are shown. The position of the extinct Mid-Labrador Sea Ridge is shown by a red dotted line.

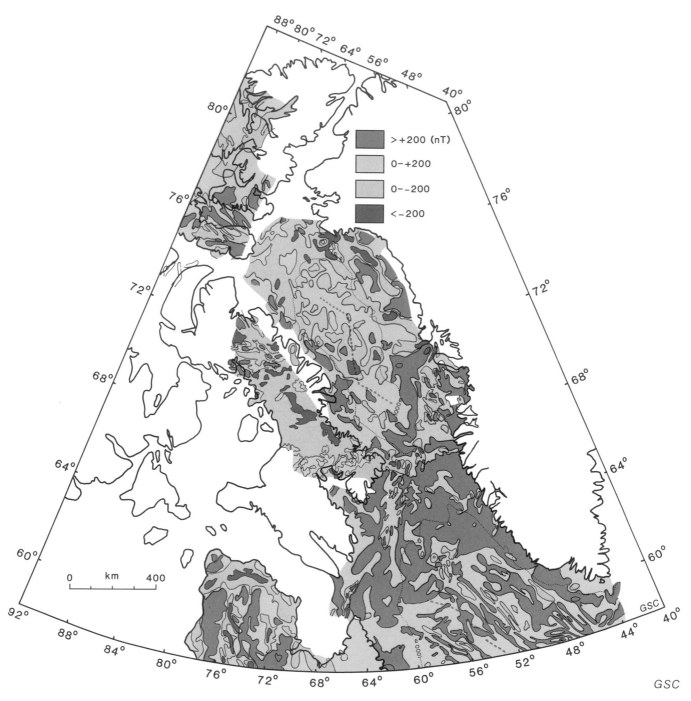

Figure 2.17. Magnetic anomalies of the northern region. The red dotted line represents the extinct Mid-Labrador Sea and Baffin Bay ridges. See Figure 2.16 for further information.

cal zones and structural provinces (e.g. Haworth, 1975; Haworth and Jacobi, 1983).

A prominent gravity gradient generally follows the western Appalachian Miogeocline from the southern United States into Canada (Haworth et al., 1980; Thomas, 1983). This gradient runs through the Gaspésie Peninsula, east across the Gulf of St. Lawrence and thence along the Humber Zone in western Newfoundland. There is a gravity low over the foreland, northwest of the limit of deformation. Quinlan and Beaumont (1984) used this gravity signature as an independent verification of their model of Appalachian foreland basins, developed by lithospheric flexure in response to overthrusting of a Cambrian-Ordovician continental margin by a wedge, tectonically assembled from the east. The gravity gradient, however, does not coincide with the western limit of Appalachian deformation. In places it is distorted by the large positive gravity anomalies over ophiolite bodies associated with Taconic allochthons such as ophiolites in western Newfoundland, including the Bay of Islands, and in the Hare Bay region. Thus it appears that the gradient may reflect either the structure of the ancient passive margin, or the later overthrusting of that margin, or both. But the controlling structures are unclear. The Paleozoic margin probably extends north from Newfoundland almost as far as the Cartwright Fracture Zone (Haworth et al., 1976), as indicated by the geophysical trends.

The Meguma and Avalon zones of the Appalachian Orogen are well defined by their gravity and magnetic signatures. To the south, the Meguma exhibits a distinctive pattern of elongate NNE-SSW magnetic anomalies (Zietz et al., 1980) which terminate along the Cobequid-Chedabucto Fracture Zone. These magnetic anomalies are thought to originate in pyrrhotite-rich zones within the Halifax Formation of the Meguma Group (McGrath et al., 1973). Potential field data suggest that Meguma rocks with their associated granitic intrusives extend to the edge of the continent, although the thick sediments obscure the magnetic signature of the Meguma near the shelf edge. The Devonian granites beneath the Scotian Shelf are associated with gravity lows (-20 to -40 mGal) and a smooth magnetic field. This geophysical signature has been interpreted to reflect granitic batholiths similar to those throughout southern Nova Scotia (McGrath et al., 1973; Watts, 1974; Haworth and MacIntyre, 1975; King and MacLean, 1976). This is confirmed by the presence of granitic rocks in the wells Ojibwa E-07 and Mohawk B-93 (see Chapter 5).

Strong, positive magnetic anomalies along the southeast coast of New Brunswick and eastward along the Cobequid-Chedabucto Fracture Zone mark the junction between the Meguma and the Avalon zones. East from Nova Scotia, the Cobequid-Chedabucto Fracture Zone is best defined by the gravity anomalies across the Orpheus Graben, a narrow, east-west trending, sedimentary basin exceeding 6 km in depth (Loncarevic and Ewing, 1966). A gravity low of about -45 mGal occurs over the graben and positive values of greater than +20 mGal are present over the ridges lying north and south of the graben. The magnetic anomaly marking the boundary between the Avalon and Meguma zones continues eastward across the southern Grand Banks towards the Newfoundland Seamounts as the Collector Anomaly (Fig. 2.2; Haworth, 1975); this appears in Figure 2.16 as a line of positive areas. North

from this anomaly trend, a series of curved magnetic anomaly trends extends across the Grand Banks and into the Orphan Basin. The Collector Anomaly derives its name from the way it appears to 'collect' the sinuous magnetic anomalies to the north of it across the Grand Banks. These magnetic highs and lows are equated with alternating volcanic and sedimentary belts within the Avalon Zone (Haworth and Lefort, 1979).

The northern limit of the Avalon Zone follows a fault-controlled line of stepped offsets (Fig. 2.2) from the Gulf of St. Lawrence to south central Newfoundland, where it follows the Hermitage and Dover faults through Newfoundland and the Charlie-Gibbs Fracture Zone to the shelf edge (Haworth and Lefort, 1979). Miller (1977) and Miller et al. (1985) examined some of these trends on land and their extension into the nearshore region.

Three major Paleozoic sedimentary basins occur within the Gulf of St. Lawrence region: Anticosti, Magdalen, and Sydney (Fig. 2.2), with free-air gravity anomaly lows of about -40 mGal, -40 mGal, and -20 mGal, respectively. Magnetic anomalies over the basins are generally of long wavelength and low amplitude (Haworth and MacIntyre, 1977), as might be expected over basins as deep as these are: Magdalen, 12 km; Anticosti and Sydney, 6 km (Jansa and Wade, 1975; see Chapter 4).

A short review of the geology and geophysics of part of the Magdalen Basin was made by Watts and Haworth (1974). Salt diapirism within the Carboniferous-Permian sediments was shown to be responsible for a local magnetic anomaly high of 100 nT and a corresponding Bouguer anomaly low of -40 mGal just east of the Magdalen Islands. The salt structures occur over a ridge near the centre of the basin. The structural trends of the basin are similar to those to the northeast and southwest, and continuity could be inferred from the continuous Cape Breton-Newfoundland Ridge across Cabot Strait (e.g. Sheridan and Drake, 1968).

Anticosti Basin lies just outside the Appalachian deformed zone and shoals rapidly to the north. This can be seen on the magnetic anomaly map (Haworth and MacIntyre, 1977) where there is a continuous and rapid northerly change to shorter wavelengths (less than 10 km) and higher amplitudes (of the order of ±500 nT). The gravity field does not change appreciably across the shoaling basin, which is in keeping with the age and type of sediments. The Cambrian to Silurian sedimentary rocks have densities probably similar to that of the underlying Grenville basement, and the general isostatic balance is achieved.

The intersection of the Grenville Front with the continental margin creates a major offset in geomorphology and in trends of gravity and magnetic anomalies at the Cartwright Fracture Zone (or Cartwright Arch). As a geological boundary between the thicker Grenville and thinner Superior provinces, the Grenville Front has a distinctive gravity low of less than -40 mGal. Large positive gravity and magnetic anomalies occur over the Cartwright Arch just south of the Cartwright Fracture Zone. A major change in trend and offset of the seafloor spreading magnetic anomalies coincides with the Cartwright Fracture Zone offshore. The complexity of the region of the Cartwright Arch may derive from the convergence and interaction of a number of trends there: the N-S

Appalachian trends, the E-W trend of the Grenville Front, and the fundamental NW-SE and NE-SW trending lineaments (correlating with many fractures, faults, and dykes) noted, for example, by McWhae (1981) in the Precambrian basement of Labrador.

Little is known about the pre-rift geology of the shelves off Baffin Island. Along the margin of Baffin Island, gravity and magnetic anomalies have been used to delineate the seaward extension of Paleozoic rocks (Grant, 1975b; MacLean and Falconer, 1979). The structural grain of Baffin Island appears to be roughly northwest-southeast (Fahrig et al., 1971; McWhae, 1981; Rice and Shade, 1982) or parallel to the direction of opening of Baffin Bay. This makes separation of pre-rift and rift-related geological features difficult.

Shelf edge gravity anomalies

The east coast margin includes both rifted and transform types, and a positive free-air anomaly which follows the morphologic shelf break along the continental margin from Georges Bank to Hudson Strait reflects these differences (Fig. 2.14). Like a topographic ridge, this ridge of positive gravity varies along its length in amplitude and width. These variations can be linked to the intersection of the margin by oceanic fracture zones and to sedimentary thicknesses. They can also be classified according to the style of rifting, resulting in deep basins or platforms, along particular sections of the margin. As important indicators of the state of isostatic balance along the margin, the gravity variations are strongly controlled by the flexure of the lithosphere during margin evolution (Beaumont et al., 1982; Karner and Watts, 1982).

Along the rifted Scotian margin, the shelf edge free-air anomaly maximum varies in amplitude from about +10 mGal southeast of the southern tip of Nova Scotia to over +100 mGal southeast of Sable Island (Map 1708A, in pocket) where the positive band is 100 km wide.

Flanking the positive anomaly over the shelf break are two broad lows: one of -20 to -40 mGal on the inner and middle shelf (Stephens et al., 1971; McGrath et al., 1973; Haworth and MacIntyre, 1975); the other, near the foot of the slope, with values up to about -60 mGal. A right-lateral offset between these gravity lows at the foot of the slope (Fig. 2.14) may correspond to a fracture zone whose landward prolongation separates the LaHave Platform from the Scotian Basin. A similar offset occurs off Georges Bank.

Gross features of the gravity field across the Scotian margin have been shown to be similar to those predicted by a simple model for the rifting and thermomechanical evolution of the margin (Beaumont et al., 1982). Such modelling is discussed in detail in Chapter 9. Over the Scotian margin, a gravity high of perhaps 60 mGal is expected over the locus of maximum loading by sediments of the flexed plate. Flanking gravity lows, about -20 to -40 mGal, correspond to mass deficits in downflexed regions where lower density sediments replace crust and crust replaces mantle (Beaumont et al., 1982; see Chapter 9). It is therefore inferred that a major component of the flanking low is caused by flexure. However, geological «noise», such as granitic intrusions beneath the Scotian Shelf may modify the gravity signature. The change in amplitude and wavelength of the gravity signature between the LaHave Platform and the Scotian Basin to the

northeast is attributed to the flexural response to the greater sediment load beneath the shelf in the Scotian Basin.

The southwestern margin of the Grand Banks is a transform margin (Keen and Keen, 1974). The shelf edge gravity anomaly is not well defined. It has a smaller amplitude with localized high values. Transform margins do not undergo the same stretching and rifting as rifted margins and deep sedimentary basins have not developed. Consequently the transform margins do not exhibit the flexural characteristics of the neighbouring rifted margins. This supports the contention that the juxtaposition of oceanic and continental crust alone does not cause the characteristic shelf edge anomaly of rifted margins; flexure of the lithosphere under sedimentary loading is also an important component of the gravity signature. The southern flank of Flemish Cap and the southeastern margin of Baffin Island may also be transform margins, but their characteristics are poorly defined at present.

The Newfoundland Ridge (Fig. 2.3), extending southeastward along what has been interpreted as a mid-Cretaceous leaky transform fault, is considered to be a volcanic edifice built of oceanic crust (Sullivan and Keen, 1978). The Tail of the Banks produces the largest free-air anomaly in this area (+80 to +100 mGal) and may be a part of this volcanic province. The Grand Banks themselves are predominantly positive with relative lows over the Mesozoic basins which cut across them (Fig. 2.14; Haworth and MacIntyre, 1975).

Between Flemish Cap and Hudson Strait, the margin shows considerable variability in the character of the gravity field and in the stretching history of the margin during initial continental break-up. Greatest stretching of the continental crust within the Avalon Zone appears to have been in the Orphan Basin. This is in contrast to the region between the Charlie-Gibbs and Cartwright fracture zones, where the basement is formed from the other Appalachian terranes, and where the ocean-continent boundary is sharp. A straight, narrow, free-air anomaly high of about 40 mGal follows the shelf break along this latter margin, and the absence of a well-developed sedimentary basin (with its accompanying lithospheric flexure) makes this margin appear gravitationally similar to that of the southern Grand Banks, although it is a rifted and not a transform margin.

In the region of the Orphan Basin a striking free-air anomaly of +40 to +120 mGal occurs just landward of the shelf break. It is arcuate and concave seaward. This gravity anomaly near the shelf edge is anomalous, in amplitude (greater than 100 mGal), in position (landward of the shelf edge), and in the absence of flanking gravity lows (Fig. 2.14). The absence of gravity lows is most puzzling; without them it is difficult to envisage how the sediment load and the varying distribution of crust and mantle densities across the shelf edge are isostatically compensated. The origin of this gravity high is one of the more problematic features of the margin and may be related to the other anomalous features of the region.

Such peculiar edge anomalies appear elsewhere in the world, as over the Mackenzie Delta in the Beaufort Sea (Sobczak, 1975a, b), and may signal anomalous stretching during the rifting phase of margin development. The Orphan Basin anomaly has been attributed to a thick wedge of sediments built out over the thinned but rigid continental crust (Walcott, 1972; LeBis, 1975; Keen and Barrett, 1981).

There are several anomalous features of the Orphan Basin region in addition to this gravity anomaly: the extensive zone of rifted continental crust; the presence of continental fragments; and the variable nature of post-rift subsidence (Fig. 2.10).

The Labrador margin between the Cartwright Fracture Zone and Hudson Strait consists of two large sedimentary basins, in contrast to the conjugate margin west of Greenland which is narrow and without extensive basins. A ridge of positive free-air anomalies (in places greater than +80 mGal) follows the shelf break, and north of 56°N lies obliquely across the ends of the magnetic seafloor spreading anomalies (compare Fig. 2.15 and 2.17, noting the convergence in Fig. 2.15 of the axial trend (dashed) and the marginal high). Over the inner part of the shelf, there is a strong gravity gradient between the shelf-edge positive anomaly and the negative anomalies of the continental craton. The positive anomalies appear to lie across a zone of rapid thinning of continental crust beneath the deep sedimentary basins, bounded by an intermittent, fault-controlled basement high along the continental slope (Hinz et al., 1979). Like Orphan Basin, Labrador Basin does not appear to have a flanking gravity low seaward of the shelf-edge high; this is difficult to explain in terms of the mode of isostatic compensation.

Differences in the gravity signature between the Scotian margin and those to the north are possibly related to the age and origin of the basement rocks underlying the different margins and to the age and duration of rifting (Royden and Keen, 1980). Early Jurassic rifting southeast of Nova Scotia affected rocks of the Appalachian Orogen, whereas Late Cretaceous rifting in the Labrador Sea affected the Precambrian lithosphere. The period between initiation of rifting and commencement of seafloor spreading was more than twice as long for the northern margins as for the Scotian margin (Fig. 2.7). Furthermore, the oceanic lithosphere created in the north is relatively young and therefore hotter and lighter than that to the south.

Following the rifting of the Archean craton shared by Labrador and Greenland (Bridgwater et al., 1973; Baer et al., 1974) north of the Cartwright Fracture Zone, asymmetries developed not only in the evolution and structure of the conjugate margins but in the geophysical characteristics of the Labrador Sea on either side of the spreading centre. The spreading centre, as indicated by a linear gravity minimum (locally approaching free air anomalies lower than -40 mGal) and magnetic lineations (Fig. 2.15, 2.17), is closer to Greenland than to Labrador. In Baffin Bay it is closer to Baffin Island than Greenland. Asymmetries in ocean basin evolution resulted in more positive gravity (by 20 to 40 mGal) on the Greenland side of the Mid-Labrador Sea Ridge (Vogt et al., 1982). On the southwest margin of Greenland, a narrow positive free air anomaly, locally greater than +80 mGal, lies just landward of the shelf break. A narrow, negative free-air anomaly which is less than -60 mGal over the slope between 60°N and 62°N broadens northward and diminishes in amplitude to greater than -40 mGal. The unusual presence of the edge anomaly over an apparently unthinned shelf, lacking a sediment load similar to those present on the Labrador side, has not yet been explained. Large volumes of volcanic rocks are, present beneath the

southwestern margin, however, so that similar rocks could be the source of the shelf edge gravity high to the northwest. The broadening of both the positive and negative free-air anomalies northward appears to correspond to a broader transition region between oceanic and continental crust, with a more disturbed, faulted basement shown in seismic reflection profiles (Hinz et al., 1979). Seismic and gravity studies along a transect across the southwestern margin of Greenland near 60°N (Stergiopoulos, 1984) suggest a narrow ocean/continent transition zone, only 40 km wide, with a crust which is thin — less than 5 km.

The Davis Strait region linking the Labrador Sea and Baffin Bay is also complex and poorly understood. The shelf edge southeast of Baffin Island is geomorphologically indistinct and lacks a prominent edge anomaly. The 600 m seafloor contour coincides, approximately, with the seaward edge of a linear strip of positive free-air anomalies, 100 km wide, running from Hudson Strait to Baffin Bay. Values vary from +20 to +100 mGal within this strip. The local highs may be caused either by crustal attenuation and volcanism within the pull-apart basins of a major wrench fault system — the Hudson Fracture Zone, trending northeast (Klose et al., 1982) — or by Tertiary volcanic rocks associated with transform faulting and rifting at the northwest end of the Labrador Sea. Faulting is common in this zone and there is at least one prominent structural high oriented northeast- southwest (Srivastava et al., 1981; Srivastava, 1983). The gravity low associated with the old Labrador Sea spreading centre extends northwestwards almost as far as the 1000 m bathymetric contour, indicating that the zone of major transform motion, the Ungava Transform (Fig. 2.4), lies landward of that contour (Klose et al., 1982; Menzies, 1982). A relative low, less than -40 mGal off Cumberland Sound, lies along the northwestern edge of the band of high free-air anomalies well into Davis Strait. To the northwest, gravity lows extend into the grabens of Cumberland Sound, Frobisher Bay and Hudson Strait, suggesting that part of the Labrador Sea rifting extended beyond the transform fault boundary. The opening of the Labrador Sea may have been facilitated in part by reactivation of extensional faulting which had earlier formed Cumberland Sound and Frobisher Bay. These grabens may represent a failed third arm of a triple junction off southeastern Baffin Island.

The shelf edge in Baffin Bay is marked in general by a strong gradient between the negative anomalies on Baffin Island and the predominantly positive to slightly negative values in the oceanic basin. The transition from continental to oceanic crust northeast of Baffin Island is relatively narrow (about 30 km; Keen et al., 1976; Jackson et al., 1977). The strong gravity gradient across the northeast margin of Baffin Island, in the order of 1 to 2 mGal/km, is attributed to the juxtaposition of mountainous terrain on Baffin Island and shallow oceanic crustal structure, separated by an unusually steep gradient of the M-discontinuity beneath a narrow shelf (Jackson et al., 1977). A major offset in the shelf edge at 69°N may be caused by a transform fault system trending NNE across Baffin Bay at about 65°W (Menzies, 1982; Rice and Shade, 1982), parallel to predominant bathymetric trends. Over the northwestern end of Baffin Bay a broad positive free-air anomaly, greater than +40 mGal, corresponds to a region of thicker sedimentation perhaps up to 7 km (Keen and Barrett, 1972) supported and underlain by oceanic crust (Keen et al., 1974).

The margin conjugate to Baffin Island on the Greenland side is much broader. The shelf edge off west Greenland has a ridge of high free-air anomalies, in places greater than 80 mGal. The deep graben in Melville Bay generates a free-air anomaly low of -60 to -80 mGal, and probably contains a minimum of 7 km of sediments (Keen and Barrett, 1972, 1973). The structure of the graben with its thick sediments is undoubtedly the cause of the low gravity values. A basement ridge at the west side of the graben rises to within 700 m of the seafloor (Keen and Barrett, 1973) and marks the continuation from the south of the positive gravity anomaly of the shelf edge. South of the Melville Bay Graben, a broad region of high gravity values coincides with the region of Tertiary volcanism.

The interpretation of the structural geology of the northern end of Baffin Bay is clouded by the controversy over the nature of Nares Strait, discussed previously in this chapter. The current status of the conflict between those who think that major displacement has occurred along Nares Strait and those who disagree with that view has been discussed by Dawes and Kerr (1982a) and more recently by Jackson and Koppen (1985). Free-air anomalies in Lancaster Sound are less than -80 mGal, probably because it is a half-graben (e.g. Kerr, 1980; McWhae, 1981). Across Nares Strait from Greenland to Ellesmere Island, the free-air gravity anomaly decreases to -100 to -120 mGal, corresponding to a thickening of the continental crust along the Ellesmere Island side of the strait. The anomaly and structure are comparable to those across zones of collided continental crust elsewhere (Jackson and Koppen, 1985).

East Coast Magnetic Anomaly and magnetic expression of the ocean-continent boundary

The East Coast Magnetic Anomaly (ECMA, see Map 1706A) lies roughly parallel to the shelf break from the Blake Plateau, offshore Florida in the south, to the Scotian margin in the north (Taylor et al., 1968; Klitgord and Behrendt, 1979; Sheridan et al., 1979). It is less prominent east of Nova Scotia as its amplitude decreases. Where present, it crosses bathymetric trends and is not correlative with the shelf edge gravity anomalies. It is offset by fracture zones along its course, and off Nova Scotia its offsets coincide with those of the shelf-edge gravity anomaly. The source of the East Coast Magnetic Anomaly is thought to be located at the ocean-continent boundary and might arise from a combination of relief on magnetic basement and contrasting magnetization between continental and oceanic crust (e.g. Keen, 1969; Keen et al., 1974; Sheridan et al., 1979). Alternatively, Nelson et al. (1985a, b) interpreted the anomaly as the magnetic signature of a Carboniferous suture, at which Mesozoic continental break-up and seafloor spreading was localized. As the equivalent of the East Coast Magnetic Anomaly occurs over parts of the eastern Atlantic margin (Emery and Uchupi, 1965), the suture must have been split in two during break-up for this interpretation to be valid.

If the East Coast Magnetic Anomaly is associated with a late Paleozoic suture, its disappearance on the Scotian margin and its absence on margins to the north might therefore indicate the absence of the suture in this region. Alternatively, break-up may have occurred west of the suture, and therefore its magnetic signature should lie wholly on the eastern Atlantic margin or in the eastern continental interior. Whatever the underlying cause of this anomaly, most workers believe that it marks the present ocean-continent transition, and so it is a useful marker in rift stage reconstructions of the continental positions. The estimated age of this anomaly off Nova Scotia based on calculated spreading rates for the magnetic quiet zone is 175 Ma or Middle Jurassic (Barrett and Keen, 1976).

Various other changes in the character of the magnetic anomalies, including termination of trends and lineations, may be used to mark the transition zone between continents and oceans. The continent-ocean boundary may be considered to lie landward of the oldest seafloor spreading, magnetic lineations and seaward of trends arising from pre-rift geological features of the continental shelf. Over the Grand Banks and eastern Newfoundland, the seaward termination of the sinuous magnetic highs and lows associated with the Avalon basement should mark the edge of rifted continent — in this case the outer margin of Orphan Basin and Flemish Cap. Likewise, oceanic seafloor spreading anomalies can be followed landward to the continental slope off northern Labrador where their amplitudes are greatly diminished (Srivastava, 1978); this indicates that the oceanic crust ends landward of the 2000 m contour, almost as far landward as the gravity high marking the Labrador Basin and the region of greatest thinning of continental crust (Fig. 2.15, 2.17).

Apart from the sinuous anomalies over the Avalon basement, the Grand Banks are magnetically subdued. Local anomalies in excess of 600 nT mark the locations of volcanics along the southern Grand Banks. The transition from this relatively smooth field to a more variable field, in excess of 200 nT, east of the Grand Banks is considered to mark the ocean-continent transition there (Sullivan, 1983). South of the Newfoundland Seamounts the oldest oceanic crust is interpreted to be of J-Anomaly age (115 Ma). This is based on correlations made between the ocean-continent boundary there and the buried J-Anomaly Ridge south of the Newfoundland Ridge. North of the Newfoundland Seamounts the boundary is offset 50 km eastward from the J-Anomaly to the south.

Between the Charlie-Gibbs and Cartwright fracture zones, a series of large positive magnetic anomalies (locally greater than 800 nT) follow the shelf edge and locally resemble the East Coast Magnetic Anomaly. Most of the shelf region here exhibits positive magnetic anomalies, and many appear to connect to the south with linear highs in the Appalachian Dunnage Zone of Newfoundland. This might suggest Paleozoic basic and ultrabasic rocks as the magnetic source (Haworth and Miller, 1982). Fenwick et al. (1968) showed that the shelf edge anomalies could be explained by the juxtaposition of a 30 km thick continental crust composed of basic and ultrabasic rocks, the Dunnage Zone, with thinner oceanic crust, about 10 to 12 km thick. In this case the significance of the anomaly would be the same as the East Coast Magnetic Anomaly, despite the source and appearance being different. The ocean-continent transition zone here is thought to be narrow and to occur beneath the lower continental shelf (Fenwick et al., 1968; Srivastava, 1978). The largest positive anomalies are just south of the Cartwright Fracture Zone, over the Cartwright Arch, where drilling (e.g. the wells Bjarni H-81 and Leif M-48) has sampled Lower Cretaceous volcanic rocks (Umpleby, 1979; see Chapter 6).

Along the Labrador margin north of the Cartwright Fracture Zone, the magnetic field is relatively subdued between the oceanic lineations and a number of irregular patches of positive anomalies over the continental shelf. A sudden deepening of magnetic basement corresponds to a sharp boundary between high frequency magnetic anomalies and smoother variations east of the marginal trough along the inshore portion of the Labrador Shelf (Hood and Bower, 1973). The shelf anomalies are likely caused by volcanism associated with rifting of the Labrador Sea or, closer inshore, by the offshore extension of Precambrian lavas and crystalline basement. Lower Cretaceous volcanics were drilled in seven wells in the southern Hopedale Basin (see Chapter 6). Helikian (Middle Proterozoic) intrusions are common in east-central Labrador north of the Cartwright Arch, as are isolated patches of supracrustal volcanic rocks (Greene, 1974; Ryan, 1981).

The Ungava Transform Fault Zone southeast of Baffin Island is marked by a linear pattern of relatively high-frequency anomalies similar in orientation and location to the positive gravity anomalies associated with the same zone. This pattern extends northeast past Disko Island (Hood and Bower, 1975) and therefore includes regions of Tertiary volcanics in the Davis Strait region. Magnetic basement, which is difficult to distinguish as crystalline basement or volcanics, deepens gradually to the southeast from Baffin Island (Klose et al., 1982).

Magnetic data from Baffin Bay are difficult to interpret. Among the problems have been the large diurnal variations which have been observed to exceed the amplitude of anomalies being measured at sea (Jackson et al., 1979). About a dozen aeromagnetic lines across Baffin Bay were described by Hood and Bower (1973, 1975) and by Keen et al. (1974). A magnetic edge effect between continental and oceanic crust (Hood and Bower, 1973) and the boundary inferred from gravity data (Ross, 1973) correspond closely (Keen et al, 1974). The survey reported by Jackson et al. (1979) provided confirmation of the oceanic character of Baffin Bay by revealing typical seafloor spreading lineations, which are thought to correlate with magnetic anomalies 13 to 24 (38 to 60 Ma). The lineations lie slightly oblique to gravity trends; however, the area surveyed likely has oblique spreading (Srivastava et al., 1981), and may be just northwest of a major transform fault in central Baffin Bay (Menzies, 1982; Rice and Shade, 1982) making it difficult to identify trends and anomalies with certainty. To the north and south of the area of detailed survey, the trend of the central gravity low is more nearly perpendicular to the presumed spreading direction.

Magnetic signature of basalts

Many of the magnetic anomalies observed on the margins result from volcanic intrusion and extrusion, as noted above. The importance of many of the volcanic rocks is their relationship to the rifting process which constituted the first stage of continental break-up and margin evolution.

Volcanism in Nova Scotia in the Early Jurassic occurred first in the Bay of Fundy region and later to the east, when the centre of rifting shifted to the eastern side of Nova Scotia. The magnetic signature of these volcanic rocks is not distinctive. The long linear high over the North Mountain of western Nova Scotia is only slightly more prominent than the long linear magnetic anomalies produced by pyrrhotite-rich zones in the Lower Ordovician Halifax Formation (Meguma Group) of southern Nova Scotia (see GSC aeromagnetic map NK/NL 20-AM and McGrath et al., 1973). The North Mountain Basalt can be followed offshore using magnetic anomalies (King and MacLean, 1976). The Shelburne Dyke of southwestern Nova Scotia is difficult to determine on aeromagnetic maps, but can be traced on ship-towed magnetometer crossings. In contrast, the Avalon Dyke is a magnetically prominent feature.

The Cobequid-Chedabucto Fracture Zone is the locus of the Collector Anomaly of Haworth (1975). The sources of the string of magnetic highs which lie along the Collector trend are probably volcanic rocks. The shear zone may have been reactivated as a leaky transform during the rifting of the Iberian Peninsula from the eastern Grand Banks (Haworth, 1975; Sullivan, 1983). The Newfoundland Seamounts which formed along the extension of this zone into the East Newfoundland Basin are mid-Cretaceous in age (Fig. 2.3). Sullivan and Keen (1977) suggested a similar age for the source of the Collector Anomaly.

Extensive volcanism is the probable source of several large, isolated magnetic anomalies along the margin of the southern Grand Banks. A leaky transform is again suggested as the cause of volcanic features such as the Fogo Seamounts (Hall et al., 1977), and the J-Anomaly Ridge (Fig. 2.3). The J-Anomaly Ridge extends southwest from the Tail of the Bank and is built over a thickened section of oceanic crust in a manner hypothesized to be analogous to the Reykjanes Ridge south of Iceland (Tucholke and Ludwig, 1982). The Newfoundland Ridge, extending southeastwards from the Tail of the Bank, might similarly be compared to the Iceland-Faeroes Ridge, another transverse aseismic feature (Keen and Haworth, 1985). Acceptance of the latter two hypotheses is not universal because controversy remains concerning the nature of the underlying crust (e.g. Grant, 1977, 1979; Gradstein, 1977). However, drilling at Deep Sea Drilling Project (DSDP) Site 384 on the J-Anomaly Ridge yielded typical mid-oceanic ridge, tholeiitic basalts which probably formed in the Barremian, between 115 and 121 Ma (Tucholke and Vogt, 1979). The large positive J-Anomaly of up to 1000 nT is thought to result from an increase in magnetic intensity (Rabinowitz et al., 1979) but this has not been established.

Significant periods of volcanism accompanied the initial rifting of the Labrador Sea margins in the Late Jurassic and Early Cretaceous (Johnson et al., 1982). Samples of these volcanic rocks were recovered during exploratory drilling for hydrocarbons as well as during scientific dredging. High positive magnetic anomalies along the margins of both sides of the Labrador Sea are chiefly related to these volcanics. Paleocene volcanic rocks have also been recovered from the western and eastern margins of the Labrador Sea (see Chapter 4). These volcanic rocks are linked to a period of reorientation of the spreading axis (Srivastava, 1978; Johnson et al., 1982). In all cases, localized positive magnetic anomalies exceed 500 nT over the volcanics.

On Southeast Baffin Shelf, the volcanic rocks probably were emplaced along major fractures associated with the Ungava Transform Fault Zone (MacLean et al., 1982). Here the large magnetic variations over the volcanics (up to 2000 nT over wavelengths less than 5 km according to MacLean et al., 1978), and the buried northeast-southwest trending ridges in which they are chiefly found, are also correlated with positive gravity anomalies (Klose et al., 1982; MacLean et al., 1982).

DEEP STRUCTURE FROM SEISMIC OBSERVATIONS

Seismic refraction studies have been extensively carried out in offshore eastern Canada for over three decades (Fig. 2.18). The initial work was carried out principally by Lamont Geological Observatory, largely on and around the margins off Nova Scotia and Newfoundland (Officer and Ewing, 1954; Press and Beckmann, 1954; Bentley and Worzel, 1956; Ewing and Ewing, 1959; Sheridan and Drake, 1968), and by the Dominion Observatory, (now part of the Geological Survey of Canada), and associated organizations (Willmore and Scheidegger, 1956; Willmore and Tolmie, 1956). From about 1962, the main participants in seismic refraction studies were Dalhousie University and Bedford Institute of Oceanography, later the Atlantic Geoscience Centre (Barrett et al., 1964; Berger et al., 1966; Dainty et al., 1966; Ewing et al., 1966; Keen and Loncarevic, 1966; Fenwick et al., 1968). Studies were extended to the Labrador Sea and Baffin Bay (Keen and Barrett, 1972; van der Linden, 1975; Jackson et al., 1977), and improved techniques were developed and applied in several regions (Jackson et al., 1975; Keen et al., 1975; Keen and Barrett, 1981; Keen and Cordsen, 1981). Figure 2.19, which shows the crustal thickness over the whole margin off eastern Canada, summarizes some of the results of this work and of associated gravity and magnetic studies.

At the same time the advances in understanding, brought about largely by the advent of plate tectonic theories, enabled a systematic approach to the geodynamic modelling and interpretation of the continental margins; this gave an added direction to the experimental work (Keen and Barrett, 1981). Across passive continental margins such as those of eastern Canada, continental crust thins toward the ocean-continent boundary (Fig. 2.19), with volcanism and intrusion becoming progressively more dominant until the crust is purely oceanic. Furthermore, ancient analogues of these margins have been recognized within the continental orogens and cratons. We can classify offshore eastern Canada into five general regimes of crustal structure: (1) continental cratons; (2) the Appalachian Orogen; (3) the thinned continental crust of the continental shelves; (4) transitional crust at the ocean-continent boundary; and (5) normal oceanic crust. In this section we review the results of seismic refraction studies of each of these regimes, emphasizing particularly the major differences between them.

The western part of the region, which forms the starting point for the Phanerozoic history, is occupied by the Precambrian Grenville and Churchill provinces (Fig. 2.2, 2.4). Results from seismic refraction studies in the Grenville Province and in the older Superior Province to the northwest were reported by Mereu and Jobidon (1971) and Berry and Fuchs (1973). The crustal structure of these two provinces is similar, the principal difference being that the Superior is thinner than the Grenville crust (34 as opposed to 39 km); the crust at the Grenville Front between the two is several kilometres thicker than either. The variation has been ascribed to Precambrian collisional tectonics involving the Grenville Province (Burke and Dewey,

1973). The velocity structure of the cratons may be approximated by a 2-layer crust, with an upper crustal velocity of about 6.2 km/s increasing to 6.6 km/s at a depth of 15-20 km. Velocity gradients within the layers are relatively small and there is some evidence for one or two low-velocity channels. There does not appear to be a significant thickness of deep crustal material of velocity 7 km/s or greater. Elsewhere in the cratons, however, such high velocity layers are present (Hajnal et al., 1985).

The crustal structure of the Appalachian Orogen is significantly different. Seismic refraction results from this area were summarized by Dainty et al. (1966); there has been little recent deep seismic refraction work in the northern Appalachians. Within the orogenic zone, in the Gulf of St. Lawrence or the Dunnage Zone of Newfoundland, the crust is typically 45 km thick and includes a basal crustal layer with velocity in the region of 7.3 km/s, underlain by high velocity mantle, 8.5 km/s (Ewing et al., 1966). In contrast, this layer is not seen on profiles of Grenvillian crust along the northwest coast of Newfoundland or, on the other side of the orogen, beneath the Avalon and Meguma zones (Barrett et al., 1964). The main crustal velocities are typically 6.1-6.3 km/s, which are normal for continental crust, although a more complex velocity structure for the Newfoundland tectonic zones, with high velocities in the upper crust, has been attributed to vestiges of an old subducting slab of oceanic lithosphere (Sheridan and Drake, 1968; Haworth et al., 1978).

Marine deep seismic reflection data have been collected recently across the Appalachian Orogen northeast of Newfoundland, with the aim of relating deep crustal structure to near surface geology (Keen et al., 1986). These data, when combined with the other geophysical data in the region, will allow a more complete definition of crustal geometry at depth than was previously possible. Preliminary results are shown in Figure 2.23a-c (major reflectors are indicated by circled letters). The extent of the geologically defined zones is indicated above the line drawing; below, an interpretation of the major lower crustal units is given. These data will be discussed later; they are more completely described in Williams (in press).

Seaward of the Appalachian Orogen and the Precambrian cratons, variations in crustal structure are controlled primarily by the Mesozoic extensional tectonics associated with formation of the continental margins. Across the continental shelves of the rifted margins, the crust (not including the rift and post-rift sediments) thins to about one half its normal thickness of 35-45 km. The thinning increases toward the ocean-continent transition and the crustal velocities change, suggesting that major changes in composition are associated with that region. Crustal velocities of 7.2 to 7.4 km/s are common, similar to the high velocity layer in the Appalachians.

Farther seaward, oceanic crust is found, and typically comprises oceanic layer 2 (5-5.5 km/s) and layer 3 (6.5-7 km/s) with a total thickness of about 6 km. The oceanic crust may be overlain by more than 4 km of sediments beneath the lower continental slope and rise.

There does not appear to be striking modification to the oceanic crust produced adjacent to the margin. In general its thickness and velocity structure are «normal». However, subtle but important differences in the oceanic crust have been defined in a region adjacent to the rifted margin of the eastern United States (LASE Study Group, 1986).

Figure 2.18. Seismic refraction lines on and around the margin of eastern Canada, 1956-1983. Lines are numbered according to text references as follows: 1. Bentley and Worzel, 1956; 2. Willmore and Scheidegger, 1956; 3. Ewing and Ewing, 1959; 4. Barrett et al., 1964; 5. Press and Beckmann, 1954; 6. Officer and Ewing, 1964; 7. Dainty et al., 1966; 8. Ewing and Hobson, 1966; 9. Fenwick et al., 1968; 10. Sheridan and Drake, 1968; 11. Mayhew et al., 1970; 12. Berry and Fuchs, 1973; 13. Keen and Barrett, 1972; 14. van der Linden, 1975; 15. Jackson et al., 1975; 16. Jackson et al., 1977; 17. Keen and Barrett, 1981; 18. Keen and Cordsen, 1981; 19. Srivastava et al., 1982; 20. Stergiopoulos, 1984.

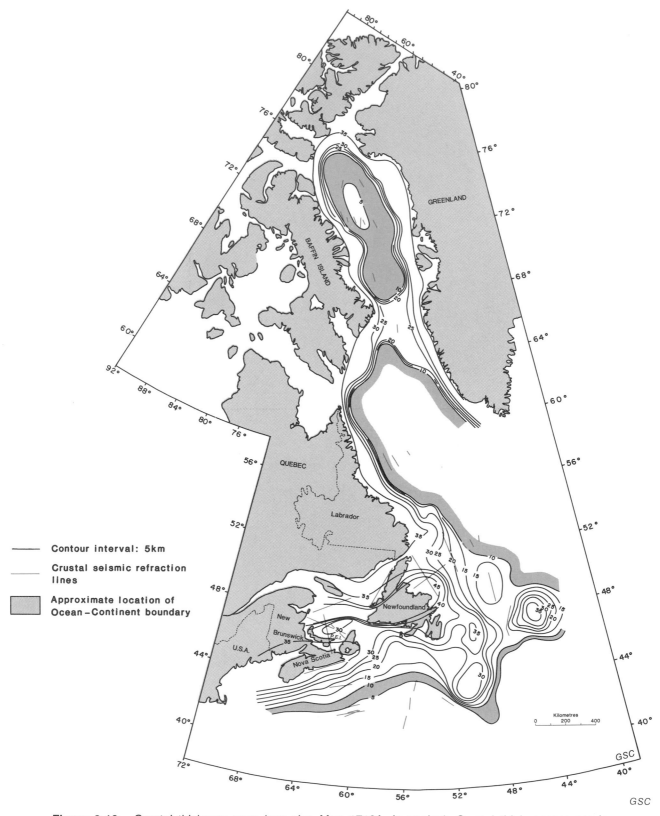

Figure 2.19. Crustal thickness map (see also Map 1710A, in pocket). Crustal thicknessess are in kilometres, and do not include sediments or water. The red shaded area is the approximate location of the transition from oceanic to continental crust (crustal thickness 5-10 km). Seismic refraction lines used as control are indicated; sources are listed in Figure 2.18.

Similar differences may occur off eastern Canada, but more elaborate experiments will be required to observe them.

There are, however, three regions where oceanic crust is anomalous. First, the oceanic crust adjacent to the transform margin south of the Grand Banks consists of about 6 km of « layer 2 » material, with little or no corresponding « layer 3 ». Either the proximity of the transform or the volcanism associated with the Fogo Seamounts may be related to this peculiarity. Second, Davis Strait has crustal thicknesses of 18 to 30 km, with velocities of 6.2 to 6.8 km/s (Keen and Barrett, 1972; Srivastava et al., 1982). This region may have both continental and oceanic affinities, with continental fragments juxtaposed against oceanic material, formed as part of the « Icelandic type » volcanic activity along this part of the margin (Srivastava, 1983). Third, the oceanic crust in Baffin Bay is only about 4 km thick (Keen and Barrett, 1972; Jackson et al., 1979). This may be due to the slow rate of seafloor spreading at which Baffin Bay is believed to have formed (Reid and Jackson, 1981). A similar phenomenon may occur in parts of the Labrador Sea.

TRANSECTS

A brief summary of the first-order tectonic and geophysical features of offshore eastern Canada is provided here, using illustrations of the structure along several cross sections traversing the contemporary margins and the Appalachian Orogen. These transects were first compiled and described by Keen and Haworth (1985). Figures 2.20 to 2.22 are simplified versions of those originals. Three kinds of crust are shown on each transect: continental, transitional, and oceanic. The transitional crust includes both the categories of thinned continental crust and transitional crust described earlier. Above the crust, the syn-rift sediments (in red) and post-rift sediments are depicted, with a break-up unconformity shown where appropriate. Some of the deep exploratory wells used to determine the sedimentary characteristics are also shown.

In many ways, these transects illustrate the discussion already presented in this chapter. Therefore, rather than repeat that discussion we shall attempt to synthesize the various geophysical and tectonic aspects of the region, and show how the deep crustal structure reflects the near surface geology.

Rifted margins

The rifted margin off Nova Scotia is the best understood of the rifted margins of eastern Canada, in part because of the greater number of observations available. This margin was formed within the Meguma Zone of the Appalachian Orogen. The hinge line is well developed and occurs between the wells Wyandot E-53 and Micmac J-77 and H-86. However, few normal faults are observed across the shelf. A thick sedimentary wedge consisting of both syn- and post-rift sediments now occupies this margin. No break-up unconformity is observed. Salt diapirs are numerous, particularly beneath the slope where they form the Slope Diapiric Province (formerly termed the Sedimentary Ridge Province). Carbonate build-ups are common and probably represent the position of an earlier, Jurassic, shelf edge.

The crystalline continental crust thins across the shelf by about a factor of two. Seismic velocities increase as the ocean-continent boundary is approached, and beneath the continental slope velocities of 7.4 km/s are observed. Normal oceanic crust occurs beyond the Slope Diapiric Province (see Chapter 5), but whether it exists beneath these salt structures is unknown.

The ocean-continent transition is also coincident with the East Coast Magnetic Anomaly. This anomaly is small by comparison with its amplitude farther south. Other magnetic anomalies are associated with rapid changes in basement depth, such as that in the Orpheus Graben. The latter feature is also marked by a gravity low. The major gravity feature is the high near the edge of the shelf, however, which is flanked on each side by lows.

The rifted margin northeast of Newfoundland and across the Orphan Basin was formed within crust of the Avalon Zone. It is significantly wider than that off Nova Scotia. The hinge line is not well defined but numerous normal faults have been mapped within the Orphan Basin, where sediments are thinner and faults are more easily seen. The sediments comprise syn- and post-rift deposits, but here there is a well-developed break-up unconformity, of mid-Late Cretaceous age.

The transitional crust within the Orphan Basin is thin (15 to 20 km) and consists of two layers, an upper layer of velocity 6.1 km/s and a lower, high velocity layer, 7.4 km/s. The nature of the crust beneath the continental fragment of Orphan Knoll is unknown, but drilling indicates that this is a continental feature. Just seaward of Orphan Knoll the transition to oceanic crust occurs; this transition appears to be sharp and may be marked by a major fault. Why Orphan Knoll and other similar continental fragments occur is not understood. They may develop as a result of a jump in the locus of rifting, in this case from the Orphan Basin to the ocean-continent transition, leaving Orphan Knoll as a positive feature. If so, a change in the age of rift sediments across the knoll should be indicative of such a jump.

In this region the physiographic shelf edge and slope bear little relationship to the location of the ocean-continent transition. The Orphan Basin has not received sufficient sediment to extend the shelf over the thinned continental region. This isolates the large shelf edge gravity anomaly from the ocean-continent transition. The anomaly here is very large because it is not associated with the transition; its location and size support the idea that a large part of the anomaly is caused by the isostatic response of the lithosphere to sediment loading. There are problems in fully explaining this anomaly, however, because it is not apparently flanked by gravity lows, as one would expect if the region were in regional isostatic equilibrium. This problem requires more study before a full understanding of the gravity field is reached. A smaller positive anomaly occurs across the ocean-continent boundary, east of Orphan Knoll.

Unlike the margins to the south, the Labrador rifted margin formed within the Precambrian craton. The hinge line is fairly well developed; it occurs on the cross section landward of the well Snorri J-90. Numerous normal faults have been mapped on this margin (McWhae, 1981), although on our cross section only a few were visible beneath the thick sediments. The sediments comprise rift

Figure 2.20. Transects on the Scotian margin and the southern margin of the Grand Banks. The Scotian Margin transect (MM-NO) crosses a mature rifted margin, now occupied by over 10 km of sediment. The Orpheus Graben, which developed at the Avalon-Meguma boundary, is one of the few well developed Triassic grabens on the Scotian Shelf. Farther seawards the Slope Diapiric Province (previously termed the Sedimentary Ridge Province), encompassing numerous salt diapirs, lies beneath the continental slope near the transition from oceanic to continental crust. Deep exploratory wells are shown by vertical lines. The lithostratigraphy used to construct the transect is controlled by data from these wells and by seismic reflection data (Jansa and Wade, 1975; Barss et al., 1979; Barss et al., 1980; Wade, 1981). The A* and b deep water horizons are derived from seismic-stratigraphy (Tucholke and Mountain, 1979). The deep structure of the margin was deduced from seismic refraction data reported by Barrett et al. (1964), Berger et al. (1966), Dainty et al. (1966), Keen et al. (1975), and Keen and Cordsen (1981). Gravity and magnetic anomalies were obtained from the data of Stephens and Cooper (1973); Haworth and MacIntyre (1975); and Shih et al. (1981). Crustal velocities of some layers are indicated in kilometres per second. Solid boundaries are approximate; dashed boundaries are more assumed.

The southern Grand Banks transect (JKL) crosses Horseshoe Basin, one of the deep, linear basins common on the Grand Banks. The Avalon-Meguma boundary occurs near the Twillick G-49 well, where mid-Cretaceous volcanics have been sampled. Two of the Fogo Seamounts, one of which is now buried by sediments, occur on oceanic crust. The stratigraphy was derived from studies of the well data and from seismic reflection profiles (Jansa and Wade, 1975; Grant, 1977; Barss et al., 1979; Barss et al., 1980; Wade, 1981). The wells are shown as solid vertical lines. "U" is the Early Cretaceous unconformity discussed in the text. Above it lie Upper Cretaceous and Cenozoic sediments. The deep structure along this transect was derived from seismic refraction data reported by Press and Beckman (1954); Bentley and Worzel (1956); Keen and Keen (1974); and Jackson et al. (1975). Gravity and magnetic data were taken from Haworth and MacIntyre (1975) and Shih et al. (1981).

GSC

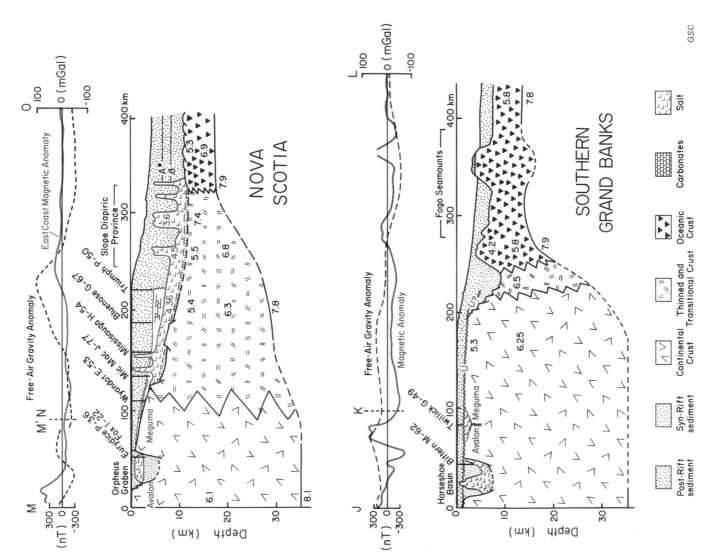

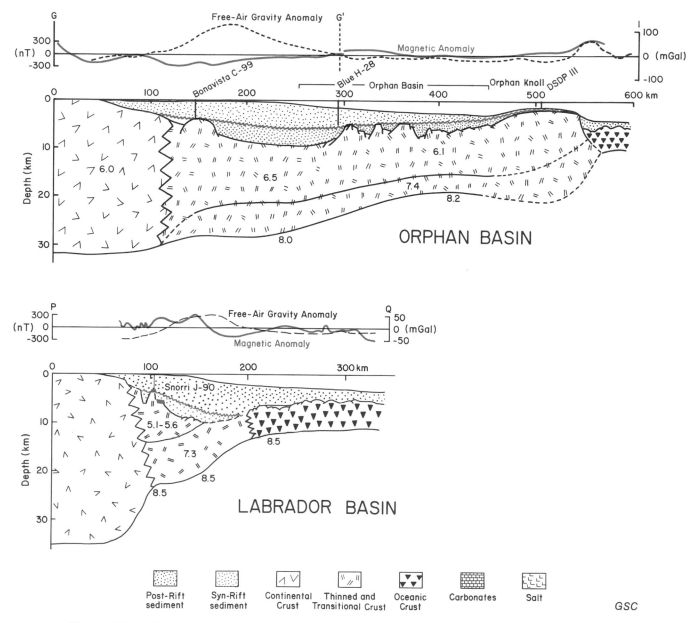

Figure 2.21. Transects across Northeast Newfoundland Shelf, Orphan Basin and Labrador margin (Fig. 2.3).

On the Orphan Basin transect (G-I), the stratigraphy was obtained from two deep exploratory wells. Blue H-28 and Bonavista C-99, shown as vertical lines. The stratigraphy from these wells and from DSDP Site 111 were extrapolated to other parts of the transect using seismic reflection data (Ruffman and van Hinte, 1973; Grant, 1975a; Gradstein and Williams, 1981). The Cretaceous marker (wavy red line) corresponds to a mid-Cretaceous unconformity in Blue H-28. The deep crustal structure of this region was derived from Dainty et al. (1966), Fenwick et al. (1968), Sheridan and Drake (1968), and Keen and Barrett (1981). Gravity and magnetic data were compiled from Haworth (1977).

The Labrador transect (PQ) crosses a rifted margin which is somewhat younger than the Scotian Margin. The stratigraphy is derived from studies of the exploratory wells such as Snorri J-90, shown by a vertical line, and from seismic reflection data (Gradstein and Williams, 1976; Hinz et al., 1979; Umpleby, 1979). The deep crustal structure was derived from seismic refraction data reported by van der Linden (1975). Gravity and magnetic data were obtained from the compilations by Srivastava (1978, 1979).

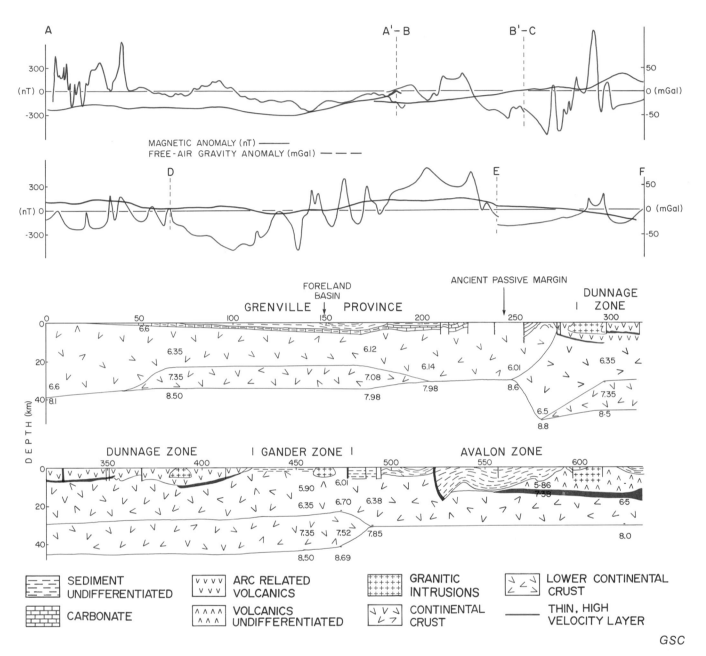

Figure 2.22. Transect across Appalachian Orogen in Newfoundland, shown in two sections with no vertical exaggeration. Although much of the detailed surface geology is lost at this scale, the correlation is evident between zone boundaries defined by surface geology and significant changes in crustal structure. A deep layer (>20 km) of anomalously high velocity (red), labelled lower continental crust is found beneath the Gulf of St. Lawrence, and also beneath the Dunnage and Gander zones northeast of Newfoundland where it is abruptly truncated at their boundary with the Avalon Zone. A shallower layer of high velocity rocks (red) is apparently continuous with exposed ophiolites occupying a synformal structure beneath the Dunnage Zone. A similar layer beneath the Avalon Zone has no demonstrable continuity with the Dunnage layer. The deep crustal structure was derived from seismic refraction data reported by Press and Beckman (1954), Dainty et al. (1966), Ewing et al. (1966), Fenwick et al. (1968), Sheridan and Drake (1968), Berry and Fuchs (1973), and Hobson and Overton (1973). Gravity and magnetic data were obtained from contour maps by Weaver (1967), Haworth and MacIntyre (1975), Hood and Reveler (1977), and Miller and Deutsch (1978).

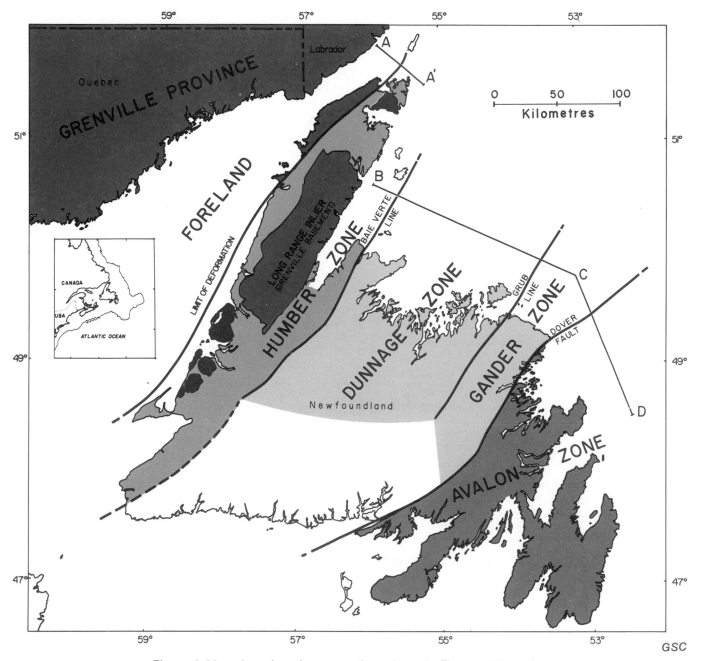

Figure 2.23a. Location of cross-sections shown in Figure 2.23b and c.

Figure 2.23b and c. Interpretation of deep marine seismic reflection data across the Appalachian Orogen (after Keen et al., 1986). The circled letters denote the major reflectors as follows: A, West-dipping faults cutting Moho; B, Moho below Grenville crust; C, the top of basement of the ancient Grenville passive margin; D, wedge of dipping reflectors which mark a change in seismic character in the lower crust; E, Moho below the eastern Dunnage and Gander zones, which terminates abruptly below the Dover Fault; F, Moho(?) below the Avalon Zone; G, Arcuate reflectors perhaps marking the basement to Precambrian-Early Paleozoic sedimentary basins within the Avalon Zone. The zones and boundaries between zones defined from near surface geology are shown above the line drawing. GRUB Line denotes Gander River Ultrabasic Belt. The deep crustal units, defined by the seismic data, are shown below the line drawing. Two seismic sections are shown at the bottom of the figure.

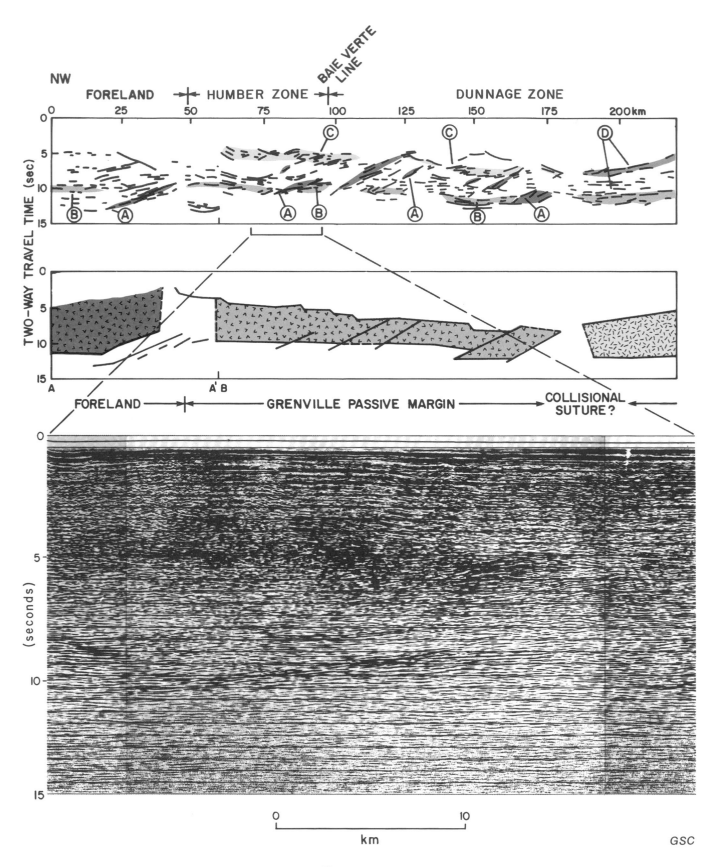

Figure 2.23b

GSC

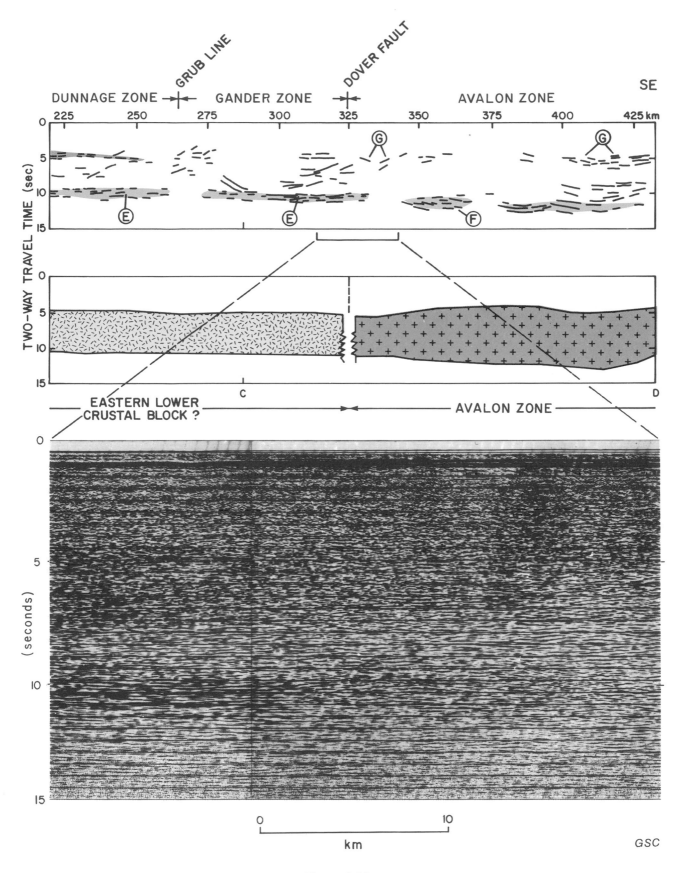

Figure 2.23c

and post-rift deposits, separated by a well-developed break-up unconformity of mid-Late Cretaceous age. Lower Cretaceous volcanic rocks have intruded the thinned Precambrian crust. The transition to oceanic crust is interpreted here to occur near the foot of the continental slope.

The transitional crust of the Labrador margin has been thinned by at least a factor of two and like the Orphan Basin, a high velocity, lower crustal layer is observed. A large positive gravity anomaly occurs over the shelf edge and, again, there does not appear to be a flanking gravity low on the seaward side of the margin. Thus the mode of isostatic balance of the margin is not clear. The magnetic anomalies are subdued beyond the edge of the shelf. This is typical of much of the Labrador margin, and has been used as an argument for the occurrence of transitional crust much farther seaward than is shown here. There is a magnetic high at the edge of the shelf but, unlike the East Coast Magnetic Anomaly, this anomaly cannot be traced continuously along the margin. Just beyond the eastern end of this cross section seafloor spreading magnetic anomalies were clearly observed.

While some important differences were observed between these rifted margin segments, there are also striking similarities. First, there has been crustal thinning beneath all the marginal sedimentary basins. This suggests there may be a common origin for crustal changes and basin development. Whatever caused the crustal thinning and the formation of the sedimentary basins may be directly linked to the fundamental rifting processes. This will be discussed in detail in Chapter 7. Second, the prevalence of the high velocity, lower crustal layer within the transition zone must also signal compositional changes which occurred during continental break-up. There is growing evidence that this layer, widely observed elsewhere on rifted margins, is the product of basaltic melt produced during rifting, which has migrated from the deeper mantle to crustal levels where it has intruded and underplated the thinned continental crust (LASE Study Group, 1986). The occurrence of a similar layer beneath continental regions may have a similar origin, as discussed below.

Transform margins

Only one transform margin, that south of the Grand Banks, has been studied in any detail. Continental basement beneath this region comprises rocks of the Meguma and Avalon zones. Faulting on the Grand Banks resulted in a number of elongate half grabens, which are aligned perpendicular to the strike of the transform margin. Except in these grabens, sediments are thin over the southern Grand Banks adjacent to the transform, and only post-rift sediments of Late Cretaceous or Tertiary age are observed. Below these post-rift sediments is a break-up unconformity ('U'; the Avalon Unconformity) bounding basement and the rift basins. The exception to this sequence is the part of the Scotian Basin adjacent to the transform and which was discussed earlier.

The contact between the Avalon and Meguma zones appears to have been reactivated during rifting to the east, between Iberia and North America, and Early to mid-Cretaceous volcanism occurred near this boundary on the Grand Banks and in the Orpheus Graben. Volcanism also occurred on oceanic crust and formed the Fogo Seamounts

and the J-Anomaly Ridge along the southeastern part of the transform margin (Fig. 2.3).

The ocean-continent transition appears to be much sharper across the transform margin than across the rifted margins and there is no broad zone over which the crystalline continental crust has been thinned. The narrow ocean-continent transition and the absence of a wide zone of thinned crust is compatible with the hypothesis that extensional forces caused the thinning observed at rifted margins. These extensional or 'pull-apart' forces would not have occurred across the transform. The absence of a thick, post-rift sedimentary sequence on the transform margin further supports this hypothesis.

Other important contrasts with the rifted margins are the absence of large shelf edge gravity anomalies and the absence of any consistent magnetic signature at the ocean-continent transition. There may be no gravity anomaly because there are no thick sedimentary sequences across the margin, eliminating the need for isostatic adjustment to sediment loading. Magnetic and gravity anomalies occur over the inferred Avalon-Meguma boundary, where they are also associated with volcanic rocks. These are part of the Collector Anomaly, described by Haworth (1975).

The Newfoundland Appalachians

Figure 2.22 illustrates the structure across the Grenville Province, including the ancient passive margin or miogeocline (the Humber Zone), and the Dunnage, Gander, and Avalon zones. It was drawn before the deep seismic reflection results, shown in Figure 2.23, were available and it is instructive to compare the two cross sections. We first describe the results shown in Figure 2.22.

Grenvillian crust underlies at least the westernmost 250 km in the Gulf of St. Lawrence and western Newfoundland. The crust thins to the east where it has a thickness of 30 to 40 km. Grenvillian crust is overlain by carbonates which formed part of the sedimentary sequence of the ancient passive margin. These are in turn overlain by sediments of the Anticosti Basin within the Gulf of St. Lawrence (Fig. 2.2). This basin probably developed in the depression created by the load imposed on the lithosphere by the development of a thrust-and-fold belt across the miogeocline (Beaumont, 1978). The miogeocline (Humber Zone), situated between 175 and 280 km on the cross section, is now occupied by allochthonous sediments and oceanic crust thrust upon the ancient passive margin. The sediments originally deposited on that margin were also deformed and incorporated into the thrust slices. The thickness of the crust increases significantly near the boundary of the miogeocline (Humber Zone) and the Dunnage Zone.

Beneath the Dunnage Zone the lower crustal, high velocity layer reappears, increasing the crustal thickness to about 45 km. This crust is underlain by high velocity mantle, with a compressional wave velocity of 8.5 km/s. A similar crustal structure is observed beneath the Gander Zone. Within the Dunnage Zone, a second region of high velocities is observed within the upper crust at depths of less than 10 km. This thin, high velocity layer has been associated with the ophiolitic substrate of the Dunnage Zone (Haworth et al., 1978). No similar upper crustal, high velocity layer has been observed beneath the Gander Zone.

The crustal thickness abruptly decreases and the lower crustal layer disappears east of the Dover Fault, at the Gander-Avalon boundary. Crustal thicknesses in the Avalon Zone are inferred to be about 35 km, although this needs confirmation. An upper, thin, high velocity layer like that in the Dunnage Zone was observed in the Avalon Zone. The two layers, however, may not be related (but see Haworth et al., 1978).

The edge of the Paleozoic North American margin is expressed by the major eastward increase in gravity, at the location of the major change in crustal thickness. Whether this gravity signature is directly related to the change in crustal thickness has yet to be demonstrated, but this would appear to be a reasonable explanation. The gravity anomalies are subdued across the remainder of the orogen, although the gravity trends in the Avalon Zone are characteristic of that region, as described earlier. The magnetic anomalies are largest across the Dunnage and Gander zones. A large magnetic anomaly marks the boundary between the Humber and the Dunnage. The alternating belts of volcanic and sedimentary rocks of the Avalon Zone are expressed as high and low magnetic anomalies.

Although our knowledge of the crustal structure across the Appalachians is incomplete, it is clear that striking changes in crustal structure and magnetic and gravity signature can be roughly related to the major changes in surface geology. It is less clear what these changes signify in terms of collisional tectonics. If the Dunnage Zone is an oceanic terrane, why is it now underlain by rocks exhibiting velocities of 6.2 km/s? Perhaps the Dunnage Zone is allochthonous and is underlain by Grenvillian crust of the ancient passive margin (Karlstrom, 1983) or continental crust of presently unknown affinity. The upper layer of high velocity might then mark the base of the Dunnage Zone: the lower layer of high velocity could result from melting, or metamorphism of the lower continental crust as it sank beneath the allochthonous load. This would imply that the Gander Zone, and possibly the Avalon Zone, also have shallow roots. Alternatively, the Gander Zone may partly lie beneath the Dunnage, as suggested by Colman-Sadd and Swinden (1984).

Some of these questions have been addressed by the deep seismic reflection data shown in Figure 2.23a-c. Interpretation of these data (Keen et al., 1986) suggests that the ancient Grenville margin continues about 75 km eastward beneath the Dunnage Zone. Similarly, the lower crust beneath the Gander Zone underlies the eastern part of the Dunnage. These two lower crustal units appear to meet and possibly form a suture below the central Dunnage Zone. The results suggest that the Gander and Dunnage zones have shallow roots, although there is no evidence that they have been horizontally transported over several hundred kilometres, as has been suggested for the southern Appalachians (Cook et al., 1979). The Avalon Zone appears to be separated from the rest of the Appalachians by a vertical fault (the Dover Fault) which penetrates the entire crust. Thus the geological development of the Avalon Zone was probably separate from that of the other zones in the Appalachians. More data of this kind are essential to understanding Appalachian tectonics, particularly the controlling processes which lie at depth within the lithosphere.

CONCLUSIONS

More than 30 years of research, together with an aggressive exploration program in the search for hydrocarbons, have brought together a wealth of information on the continental margin of eastern Canada. Portions of this margin are among the most studied and best understood passive margins in the world — yet the more we study it, the more questions are posed.

It is clear from our studies that a 'typical' margin section does not exist. As soon as the observations are refined, the density of data is increased, or new tools of investigation are applied, the geological diversity is revealed in its true scale. The methods of geological and geophysical investigations at sea average the observations over large areas, thus making it possible to reach some conclusions regarding the global processes. Applying these global models to specific geographic localities invariably leads to discrepancies between models and observations. On a detailed scale, we know that the geological complexity is the result of the combination of specific tectonic forces and local history of development, in many places obliterated by subsequent geological events.

Knowledge of the geology of the east coast margin has advanced considerably since the comprehensive reviews of Keen et al. (1971) and Haworth and Keen (1979). In spite of that progress, much has to be done with an increased emphasis on northern studies. Equally impressive advances are anticipated in the reviews to be published in the next decade.

ACKNOWLEDGMENTS

We thank all our colleagues at the Atlantic Geoscience Centre who contributed to an understanding of this region. In particular we thank R. Jackson, W. Kay, and K. Shih for their assistance in compiling many of the maps and transects shown. G. Stockmal reviewed a draft of the manuscript and made many helpful comments.

REFERENCES

Amoco-Imperial Oil
1973: Regional geology of the Grand Banks; Bulletin of Canadian Petroleum Geology, v. 21, p. 479-503.

Arthaud, F. and Matte, P.
1977: Late Paleozoic strike-slip faulting in southern Europe and northern Africa: Result of a right-lateral shear zone between the Appalachians and the Urals; Geological Society of America Bulletin, v. 88, p. 1305-1320.

Baer, A.J., Emslie, R.F., Irving, E., and Tanner, J.G.
1974: Grenville geology and plate tectonics; Geoscience Canada, v. 1, no. 3, p. 54-60.

Ballard, R.D. and Uchupi, E.
1975: Triassic rift structure in the Gulf of Maine; American Association of Petroleum Geologists Bulletin, v. 59, p. 1041-1072.

Bally, A.W.
1982: Musings over sedimentary basin evolution; Philosophical Transactions of the Royal Society of London, A, v. 305, p. 325-338.

Barrett, D.L. and Keen, C.E.
1976: Mesozoic magnetic lineations: the Magnetic Quiet Zone and seafloor spreading in the northwest Atlantic; Journal of Geophysical Research, v. 81, p. 4875-4884.

Barrett, D.L., Berry, M., Blanchard, J.E., Keen, M.J., and McAllister, R.E.
1964: Seismic studies on the eastern seaboard of Canada; the Atlantic coast of Nova Scotia; Canadian Journal of Earth Sciences, v. 1, p. 10-22.

Barss, M.S., Bujak, J.P., Wade, J.A., and Williams, G.L.
1980: Age, stratigraphy, organic matter type and colour, and hydrocarbon occurrences in 47 wells, offshore eastern Canada; Geological Survey of Canada, Open File 714, 6 p.

Barss, M.S., Bujak, J.P., and Williams, G.L.
1979: Palynological zonation and correlation of 67 wells, eastern Canada; Geological Survey of Canada, Paper 78-24, p. 1-118.

Beaumont, C., Keen, C.E., and Boutilier, R.
1982: On the evolution of rifted continental margins: comparison of models and observations for the Nova Scotia margin; Geophysical Journal of the Royal Astronomical Society, v. 70, no. 3, p. 667-716.

Bentley, C.R. and Worzel, J.L.
1956: Geophysical investigations in the emerged and submerged Atlantic coastal plain X. Continental slope and continental rise south of the Grand Banks; Geological Society of America Bulletin, v. 67, p. 1-18.

Berger, J., Cok, A.E., Blanchard, J.E., and Keen, M.J.
1966: Morphological and geophysical studies on the eastern seaboard of Canada: the Nova Scotia Shelf; ed. G.D. Garland; Royal Society of Canada, Special Publication 9, p. 102-113.

Berry, M.J. and Fuchs, K.
1973: Crustal structures of the Superior and Grenville Provinces of the northeastern Canadian Shield; Seismological Society of America Bulletin, v. 63, p. 1393-1432.

Bradley, D.C.
1982: Subsidence in late Paleozoic basins in the northern Appalachians; Tectonics, v. 1, p. 107-123.

Bridgwater, D., Watson, J., and Windley, B.F.
1973: The Archaean craton of the North Atlantic region; Philosophical Transactions of the Royal Society of London, A, v. 273, p. 493-512.

Burke, K. and Dewey, J.F.
1973: Plume generated triple junctions: Key indicators in applying plate tectonics to old rocks; Journal of Geology, v. 81, no. 4, p. 405-433.

Christie, R.D., Dawes, P.R., Frisch, T.O., Higgins, A.K., Hurst, J.M., Kerr, J.W., and Peel, J.S.
1981: Geological evidence against major displacement in the Nares Strait; Nature, v. 291, p. 478-480.

Colman-Sadd, S.P.
1982: Two stage continental collision and plate driving forces; Tectonophysics, v. 90, p. 263-282.

Colman-Sadd, S.P. and Swinden, H.S.
1984: A tectonic window in central Newfoundland? Geological evidence that the Appalachian Dunnage Zone may be allochthonous; Canadian Journal of Earth Sciences, v. 21, p. 1349-1367.

Cook, F., Albaugh, D.S., Brown, L.D., Kaufman, S., Oliver, J.E., and Hatcher, R.D., Jr.
1979: Thin-skinned tectonics in the crystalline southern Appalachians; COCORP seismic-reflection profiling of the Blue Ridge and Piedmont; Geology, v. 7, p. 563-567.

Cutt, B.J. and Laving, J.G.
1977: Tectonic elements and geologic history of the South Labrador and Newfoundland continental shelf, eastern Canada; Bulletin of Canadian Petroleum Geology, v. 25, p. 1937-1058.

Dainty, A.M., Keen, C.E., Keen, M.J., and Blanchard, J.
1966: Review of geophysical evidence on crust and upper mantle structure on the eastern seaboard of Canada: in The Earth beneath the Continents; American Geophysical Union, ed. J.S. Steinhart and J.J. Smith; Monograph 10, p. 349-369.

Dawes, P.R. and Kerr, J.W. (editors)
1982a: Nares Strait and the Drift of Greenland — A Conflict in Plate Tectonics; Meddelelser om Gronland, Geoscience 8: 386 p.
1982b: The case against major displacement along Nares Strait; in Nares Strait and the Drift of Greenland — A Conflict in Plate Tectonics, ed. P.R. Dawes and J.W. Kerr; Meddelelser om Gronland, Geoscience v. 8: 369-386.

Earth Physics Branch
1980: Gravity map of Canada; Energy Mines and Resources, Canada, Gravity Map Series 80-1.

Emery, K.O. and Uchupi, E.
1965: Structure of Georges Bank; Marine Geology, v. 3, p. 349-358.

Ewing, G.N. and Hobson, G.D.
1966: Marine seismic refraction investigation over the Orpheus gravity anomaly off the east coast of Canada; Geological Survey of Canada, Paper 66-38, 10 p.

Ewing, G.N., Dainty, A.M., Blanchard, J.E., and Keen, M.J.
1966: Seismic studies on the eastern seaboard of Canada: The Appalachian System, I; Canadian Journal of Earth Sciences, v. 3, p. 89-109.

Ewing, J. and Ewing, M.
1959: Seismic refraction measurements in the Atlantic Ocean basins, in the Mediterranean Sea, on the Mid-Atlantic Ridge, and in the Norwegian Sea; Geological Society of America Bulletin, v. 70, p. 291-318.

Fahrig, W.F., Irving, E., and Jackson, G.D.
1971: Paleomagnetism of the Franklin diabases; Canadian Journal of Earth Sciences, v. 8, no. 4, p. 455-467.

Farrar, S.S. and Glover, L., III
1983: Grenville basement in the Piedmont east of the pre-Appalachian (pre-Caledonian) edge (?) of the North America craton; Geological Society of America, Abstracts with Programs, v. 15, no. 3, p. 123.

Fenwick, D.K.B., Keen, M.J., Keen, C.E., and Lambert, A.
1968: Geophysical studies of the continental margin northeast of Newfoundland; Canadian Journal of Earth Sciences, v. 5, p. 483-500.

Fyffe, L.R., Pajari, G.E., Jr. and Cherry, M.E.
1981: The Acadian plutonic rocks of New Brunswick; Maritime Sediments and Atlantic Geology, v. 17, p. 23-36.

Given, M.M.
1977: Mesozoic and Early Cenozoic geology of offshore Nova Scotia; Bulletin of Canadian Petroleum Geology, v. 25, p. 63-91.

Gradstein, F.M. and Srivastava, S.P.
1980: Aspects of Cenozoic stratigraphy and palaeoceanography of the Labrador Sea and Baffin Bay; Palaeogeography, Palaeoclimatology and Palaeoecology, v. 30, p. 261-295.

Gradstein, F.M. and Williams, G.L.
1976: Biostratigraphy of the Labrador Shelf; Geological Survey of Canada, Open File 349, 39 p.
1981: Stratigraphic charts of the Labrador Sea and Newfoundland shelves; Geological Survey of Canada, Open File 826, 5 p.

Gradstein, F.M., Grant, A.C., and Jansa, L.F.
1977: Grand Banks and J-Anomaly Ridge: a geological comparison; Science, v. 197, p. 1074-1076.

Gradstein, F.M., Williams, G.L., Jenkins, W.A.M., and Ascoli, P.
1975: Mesozoic and Cenozoic stratigraphy of the Atlantic continental margin, eastern Canada; in Canada's Continental Margins and Offshore Petroleum Exploration, ed. C.T. Yorath, E.R. Parker and D.J. Glass; Canadian Society of Petroleum Geologists, Memoir 4, p. 103-131.

Grant, A.C.
1975a: Structural modes of the western margin of the Labrador Sea; in Offshore Geology of Eastern Canada, Volume 2, Regional Geology, ed. W.J. M. van der Linden and J.A. Wade; Geological Survey of Canada, Paper 74-30, p. 217-231.
1975b: Geophysical results from the continental margin of southern Baffin Island; in Canada's Continental Margins and Offshore Petroleum Exploration, ed. C.J. Yorath, E.R. Parker, and D.J. Glass; Canadian Society of Petroleum Geologists, Memoir 4, p. 411-431.
1977: Continental crust beneath the Newfoundland Ridge: evidence from multi-channel seismic reflection data; Nature, v. 270, p. 22-25.
1979: Geophysical observations bearing upon the origin of the Newfoundland Ridge; Tectonophysics, v. 59, p. 71-81.
1980: Problems with plate tectonics: Labrador Sea; Bulletin of Canadian Petroleum Geology, v. 28, p. 252-275.

Greene, B.A.
1974: An outline of the geology of Labrador; Newfoundland Department of Mines and Energy, Mineral Development Division, Information Circular, No. 15, 64 p.

Hajnal, Z., Fowler, C.M.R., Mereu, R.F., Kanasewich, E.R., Cumming, G.L., Green, A.G., and Mair, A.
1985: An initial analysis of the Earth's crust under the Williston Basin: 1979 COCRUST experiment; Journal of Geophysical Research, v. 89, p. 9381-9400.

Hall, J.M., Barrett, D.L., and Keen, C.E.
1977: The volcanic layer of the ocean crust adjacent to Canada — a review; in Volcanic Regimes in Canada, ed. W.R.A. Baragar, L.C. Coleman, and J.M. Hall; Geological Association of Canada, Special Paper 16, p. 425-444.

Hamilton, W.
1983: Cretaceous and Cenozoic history of the northern continents; Annals of the Missouri Botanical Garden, v. 70, p. 449-458.

Hanmer, S.
1981: Tectonic significance of the northeastern Gander Zone, Newfoundland: an Acadian ductile shear-zone; Canadian Journal of Earth Sciences, v. 18, p. 120-135.

Haworth, R.T.
1975: The development of Atlantic Canada as a result of continental collision — evidence from offshore gravity and magnetic data; <u>in</u> Canada's Continental Margins and Offshore Petroleum Exploration, ed. C.J. Yorath, E.R. Parker, and D.J. Glass; Canadian Society of Petroleum Geologists, Memoir 4, p. 59-77.
1977: The continental crust northeast of Newfoundland and its ancestral relationship to the Charlie Fracture Zone; Nature, v. 266, p. 246-249.
1980: Appalachian structural trends northeast of Newfoundland and their trans-Atlantic correlation; Tectonophysics, v. 64, p. 111-130.

Haworth, R.T. and Jacobi, R.D.
1983: Geophysical correlation between the geological zonation of Newfoundland and the British Isles; <u>in</u> Contributions to the Tectonics and Geophysics of Mountain Chains, ed. R.D. Hatcher Jr., H. Williams and I. Zietz; Geological Society of America, Memoir 159, p. 25-31.

Haworth, R.T. and Keen, C.E
1979: The Canadian Atlantic margin: a passive continental margin encompassing an active past; in Crustal Properties Across Passive Margins, ed. C.E. Keen; Tectonophysics, v. 59, p. 83-126.

Haworth, R.T. and Lefort, J.P.
1979: Geophysical evidence for the extent of the Avalon Zone in Atlantic Canada; Canadian Journal of Earth Sciences, v. 16, p. 552-567.

Haworth, R.T. and MacIntyre, J.B.
1975: The gravity and magnetic fields of Atlantic offshore Canada; Geological Survey of Canada, Paper 75-9, 22 p.
1977: Gravity and magnetic fields of the Gulf of St. Lawrence, Canada; Geological Survey of Canada, Paper 75-42, 11 p.

Haworth, R.T. and Miller, H.G.
1982: The structure of Paleozoic oceanic rocks beneath Notre Dame Bay, Newfoundland; <u>in</u> Major Structural Zones and Faults of the Northern Appalachians, ed. P. St. Julien and J. Béland; Geological Association of Canada, Special Paper 24, p. 149-173.

Haworth, R.T., Daniels, D.L., Williams, H., and Zietz, I.
1980: Bouguer gravity anomaly map of the Appalachian Orogen; Memorial University of Newfoundland, Map No. 3 (1:1 000 000).

Haworth, R.T., Grant, A.C., and Folinsbee, R.A.
1976: Geology of the continental shelf off southeastern Labrador; in Report of Activities, Part C, Geological Survey of Canada, Paper 76-1C, p. 61-70.

Haworth, R.T., Lefort, J.P., and Miller, H.G.
1978: Geophysical evidence for an east-dipping Appalachian subduction zone beneath Newfoundland; Geology, v. 6, p. 522-526.

Henderson, G., Rosenkrantz, A., and Schiener, E.J.
1976: Cretaceous-Tertiary sedimentary rocks of West Greenland; <u>in</u> Geology of Greenland, ed. A. Escher and W.S. Watt; Geological Survey of Greenland, Copenhagen, p. 340-362.

Henderson, G., Schiener, E.J., Rissum, J.B., and Croxton, C.A.
1981: The West Greenland Basin; in Geology of the North Atlantic Borderlands, ed. J.W. Kerr and A.J. Fergusson; Canadian Society of Petroleum Geologists, Memoir 7, p. 399-428.

Hinz, K., Schluter, H.V., Grant, A.C., Srivastava, S.P., Umpleby, D., and Woodside, J.
1979: Geophysical transects of the Labrador Sea: Labrador to southwest Greenland; <u>in</u> Crustal Properties across Passive Margins, ed. C.E. Keen; Tectonophysics, v. 49, p. 151-183.

Hobson, G.D. and Overton, A.
1973: Sedimentary refraction seismic surveys, Gulf of St. Lawrence; <u>in</u> Earth Science Symposium on Offshore Eastern Canada, ed. P.J. Hood; Geological Survey of Canada, Paper 71-23, p. 325-336.

Hodych, J.P. and Hayatsu, A.
1980: K-Ar isochron age and paleomagnetism of diabase along the trans-Avalon aeromagnetic lineament — evidence of Late Triassic rifting in Newfoundland; Canadian Journal of Earth Sciences, v. 17, p. 491-499.

Hood, P.J. and Bower, M.E.
1973: Low-level aeromagnetic surveys of the continental shelves bordering Baffin Bay and the Labrador Sea; Geological survey of Canada, Paper 71-23, p. 573-598.
1975: Aeromagnetic reconnaissance of Davis Strait and adjacent areas; <u>in</u> Canada's Continental Margins and Offshore Petroleum Exploration, ed. C.J. Yorath, E.R. Parker, and D.J. Glass; Canadian Society of Petroleum Geologists, Memoir 4, p. 433-451.

Hood, P.J. and Reveler, D.A.
1977: Magnetic anomaly maps of the Atlantic Provinces; Geological Survey of Canada, Open File 496.

Howie, R.D. and Barss, M.S.
1975: Upper Paleozoic rocks of the Atlantic Provinces, Gulf of St. Lawrence and adjacent continental shelf; <u>in</u> Offshore Geology of Eastern Canada, Volume 2, Regional Geology, ed. W.J.M. van der Linden and J.A. Wade; Geological Survey of Canada, Paper 74-30, v. 2, p. 35-50.

Hugon, H.
1983: Ellesmere-Greenland Fold Belt: structural evidence for left-lateral shearing; <u>in</u> Continental Tectonics: Structure, Kinematics and Dynamics, ed. M. Friedman and M.N. Toksoz; Tectonophysics, v. 100, p. 215-225.

Hyndman, R.D.
1973: Evolution of the Labrador Sea; Canadian Journal of Earth Sciences, v. 10, p. 637-644.

Irving, E. and Strong, D.F.
1984: Evidence against large-scale Carboniferous strike-slip faulting in the Appalachian-Caledonian orogen; Nature, v. 30, p. 762-764.

Jackson, H.R. and Koppen, L.
1985: The Nares Strait gravity anomaly and its implications for crustal structure; Canadian Journal of Earth Sciences, v. 22, p. 1322-1328.

Jackson, H.R., Keen, C.E., and Barrett, D.L.
1977: Geophysical studies of the eastern continental margin of Baffin Bay and in Lancaster Sound; Canadian Journal of Earth Sciences, v. 14, p. 1991-2001.

Jackson, H.R., Keen, C.E., Falconer, R.K.H., and Appleton, K.P.
1979: New geophysical evidence for sea-floor spreading in central Baffin Bay; Canadian Journal of Earth Sciences, v. 16, p. 2122-2135.

Jackson, H.R., Keen, C.E., and Keen, M.J.
1975: Seismic structure of the continental margins and ocean basins of southeastern Canada; Geological Survey of Canada, Paper 74-51, 13 p.

Jackson, J. and McKenzie, D.
1983: The geometrical evolution of normal fault systems; Journal of Structural Geology, v. 5, p. 471-482.

Jansa, L.F.
1981: Mesozoic carbonate platforms and banks of the eastern North American margin; Marine Geology, v. 44, p. 97-117.

Jansa, L.F. and Pe-Piper, G.
1985: Early Cretaceous volcanism on the northeastern American margin and implications for plate tectonics; Geological Society of America Bulletin, v. 96, no. 1, p. 83-91.

Jansa, L.F. and Wade, J.A.
1975: Geology of the continental margin off Nova Scotia and Newfoundland; <u>in</u> Offshore Geology of Eastern Canada, Volume 2, Regional Geology, ed. W.J.M. Van der Linden and J.A. Wade; Geological Survey of Canada, Paper 74-30, v. 2, p. 51-105.

Jansa, L.F.and Wiedmann, J.
1982: Mesozoic-Cenozoic development of the eastern North American and northwest African continental margins: a comparison; <u>in</u> Geology of the Northwest African Continental Margin, ed. U. von Rad, K. Hinz, M. Sarnthein, and E. Siebold, p. 215-269.

Jansa, L.F., Bujak, J.P., and Williams, G.L.
1980: Upper Triassic salt deposits of the western North Atlantic; Canadian Journal of Earth Sciences, v. 17, p. 547-559.

Jansa, L.F., Mamet, B., and Roux, A.
1978: Viséean limestones from the Newfoundland Shelf; Canadian Journal of Earth Sciences, v. 15, p. 1422-1436.

Johnson, G.L., Srivastava, S.P., Campsie, J., and Rasmussen, M.
1982: Volcanic rocks in the Labrador Sea and environs and their relation to the evolution of the Labrador Sea; <u>in</u> Current Research, Part B, Geological Survey of Canada, Paper 82-1B, p. 7-20.

Karlstrom, K.E.
1983: Reinterpretation of Newfoundland gravity data and arguments for an allochthonous Dunnage Zone; Geology, v. 11, p. 263-266.

Karner, G.D. and Watts, A.B.
1982: On isostasy at Atlantic-type continental margins; Journal of Geophysical Research, v. 87, p. 2923-2948.

Keen, C.E.
1979: Thermal history and subsidence of rifted continental margins — evidence from wells on the Nova Scotian and Labrador shelves; Canadian Journal of Earth Sciences, v. 16, p. 502-522.
1985: The dynamics of rifting: deformation of the lithosphere by active and passive driving forces; Geophysical Journal of the Royal Astronomical Society, v. 80, p. 101-120.

71

Keen, C.E. and Barrett, D.L.
1972: Seismic refraction studies in Baffin Bay: an example of a developing ocean basin; Geophysical Journal of the Royal Astronomical Society, v. 30, p. 253-271.
1973: Structural characteristics of some sedimentary basins in northern Baffin Bay; Canadian Journal of Earth Sciences, v. 10, p. 1267-1279.
1981: Thinned and subsided continental crust on the rifted margin of eastern Canada: crustal structure, thermal evolution and subsidence history; Geophysical Journal of the Royal Astronomical Society, v. 65, p. 443-465.

Keen, C.E. and Cordsen, A.
1981: Crustal structure, seismic stratigraphy, and rift processes of the continental margin off eastern Canada: Ocean bottom seismic refraction results off Nova Scotia; Canadian Journal of Earth Sciences, v. 18, p. 1523-1538.

Keen, C.E. and Haworth, R.T.
1985: D-2 Transform margin south of Grand Banks: offshore eastern Canada; Geological Society of America, Centennial Continent/Ocean Transect #2, scale 1:500 000.

Keen, C.E. and Keen, M.J.
1974: The continental margins of eastern Canada and Baffin Bay; in The Geology of Continental Margins, ed. C.A. Burk and C.L. Drake; Springer Verlag, New York, p. 381-389.

Keen, C.E. and Loncarevic, B.D.
1966: Crustal structure on the eastern seaboard of Canada: Studies on the continental margin; Canadian Journal of Earth Sciences, v. 3, p. 65-76.

Keen, C.E. and Peirce, J.W.
1982: The geophysical implications of minimal Tertiary motion along Nares Strait; in Nares Strait and the Drift of Greenland: A Conflict in Plate Tectonics; ed. P.R. Dawes and J.W. Kerr; Meddelelser om Gronland, Geoscience, v. 8, p. 327-337.

Keen, C.E., Colman-Sadd, S.P., Keen, M.J., Miller, H., Nichols, B., O'Brien,S.J.,Quinlan, G., Reid, I., Stockmal, G.S., Williams, H., and Wright, J.
1986: A deep seismic reflection profile across the northern Appalachians; Geology, v. 14, p. 141-145.

Keen, C.E., Hall, B.R., and Sullivan, K.D.
1977: Mesozoic evolution of the Newfoundland Basin; Earth and Planetary Science Letters, v. 37, p. 307-320.

Keen, C.E., Keen, M.J., Barrett, D.L., and Heffler, D.E.
1975: Some aspects of the ocean-continent transition at the continental margin of eastern North America; in Offshore Geology of Eastern Canada, Volume 2. Regional Geology, ed. W.J.M. Van der Linden and J.A. Wade; Geological Survey of Canada, Paper 74-30, v. 2, p. 189-197.

Keen, C.E., Keen, M.J., Ross, D.I., and Lack, M.
1974: Baffin Bay: Small ocean basin formed by sea-floor spreading: American Association of Petroleum Geologists Bulletin, v. 58, p. 1089-1108.

Keen, M.J.
1969: Magnetic anomalies off the eastern seaboard of the United States: a possible edge effect; Nature, v. 222, p. 72-74.

Keen, M.J., Loncarevic, B.D., and Ewing, G.N.
1971: Continental margin of Eastern Canada: Georges Bank to Kane Basin; in The Sea: Ideas and Observations, v. 4, New Concepts of Sea-Floor Evolution. Part II: Regional Observations Concepts, ed. A.E. Maxwell; New York, Wiley — Interscience, p. 251-291.

Kent, D.V. and Opdyke, N.D.
1978: Paleomagnetism of Devonian Catskill redbeds: evidence for motion of coastal New England — Canadian maritime region relative to cratonic North America; Journal of Geophysical Research, v. 8, p. 4441-4450.

Keppie, J.D., Odom, L., and Cormier, R.F.
1983: Tectonothermal evolution of the Meguma terrane: Radiometric controls; Geological Society of America, Abstracts with Programs, v. 15, no. 3, p. 136.

Kerr, J.W.
1980: Structural framework of Lancaster Sound aulacogen, arctic Canada; Geological Survey of Canada, Bulletin 319, 24 p.
1981: Evolution of the Canadian Arctic Islands — A transition between the Atlantic and Arctic Oceans; in The Ocean Basins and Margins, ed. A.E.M. Nairn, M. Churkin, Jr., and F.G. Stehli; 5, The Arctic Oceans, Plenum Press Publishing Co., p. 105-199.

King, L.H. and MacLean, B.
1976: Geology of the Scotian Shelf; Geological Survey of Canada, Paper 74-31, 31 p.

Kinsman, D.J.J.
1975: Rift valley basins and sedimentary history of trailing continental margins; in Petroleum and Global Tectonics, ed. A.G. Fischer and S. Judson; Princeton University Press, p. 83-128.

Klitgord, K. and Behrendt, J.C.
1979: Basin structure of the U.S. Atlantic margin; in Geological and Geophysical Investigations of Continental Margins, ed. J.S. Watkins, L. Montadert and P. Dickenson; American Association of Petroleum Geologists, Memoir 29, p. 85-112.

Klose, G.W., Malterre, E., McMillan, N.J., and Zinkan, C.G.
1982: Petroleum exploration offshore southern Baffin Island; in Arctic Geology and Geophysics, ed. A.F. Embry and H.R. Balkwill; Canadian Society of Petroleum Geologists, Memoir 8, p. 233-244.

LASE Study Group
1986: Deep structure of the US east coast passive margin from large aperture seismic experiments (LASE); Marine and Petroleum Geology, v. 3, p. 234-242.

LeBis, A.P.
1975: Investigation of a gravity high — offshore Newfoundland; in Canada's Continental Margins and Offshore Petroleum Exploration, ed. C.J. Yorath, E.R. Parker and D.J. Glass; Canadian Society of Petroleum Geologists, Memoir 4, p. 169-180.

Loncarevic, B.D. and Ewing, G.N.
1966: Geophysical study of the Orpheus Gravity Anomaly; Proceedings, VII World Petroleum Congress, Mexico City, p. 827-835.

MacLean, B. and Falconer, R.K.H.
1979: Geological-geophysical studies in Baffin Bay and Scott Inlet-Buchan Gulf and Cape Dyer-Cumberland Sound areas of the Baffin Island Shelf; in Current Research, Part B, Geological Survey of Canada, Paper 79-1B, p. 231-244.

MacLean, B., Falconer, R.K.H., and Clarke, D.B.
1978: Tertiary basalts of western Davis Strait: bedrock core samples and geophysical data; Canadian Journal of Earth Sciences, v. 15, p. 773-780.

MacLean, B., Srivastava, S.P., and Haworth, R.T.
1982: Bedrock structures off Cumberland Sound, Baffin Island Shelf: Core sample and geophysical data; in Arctic Geology and Geophysics, ed. A.F. Embry and H.R. Balkwill; Canadian Society of Petroleum Geologists, Memoir 8, p. 279-295.

Mayhew, M.A., Drake, C.L., and Nafe, J.E.
1970: Marine geophysical measurements on the continental margins of the Labrador Sea; Canadian Journal of Earth Sciences, v. 7, p. 199-214.

McGrath, P.H., Hood, P.J., and Cameron, G.W.
1973: Magnetic surveys of the Gulf of St. Lawrence and the Scotian Shelf; in Earth Science Symposium on Offshore Eastern Canada, ed. P.J. Hood; Geological Survey of Canada, Paper 71-23, p. 339-358.

McGrath, P.H., Hood, P.J., and Darnley, A.G.
1977: Magnetic anomaly map of Canada; Geological Survey of Canada, Map 1255A, third edition.

McKerrow, W.S. and Cocks, L.R.M.
1976: Progressive faunal migration across the Iapetus Ocean; Nature, v. 263, p. 304-306.

McWhae, J.R.H.
1981: Structure and spreading history of the northwestern Atlantic region from the Scotian Shelf to Baffin Bay; in Geology of the North Atlantic Borderlands, ed. J.W. Kerr and A.J. Fergusson; Canadian Society of Petroleum Geologists, Memoir 7, p. 299-332.

Menzies, A.W.
1982: Crustal history and basin development of Baffin Bay; in Nares Strait and the Drift of Greenland: A Conflict in Plate Tectonics, ed. P.R. Dawes and J.W. Kerr; Meddelser om Gronland, Geoscience, v. 8, p. 295-312.

Mereu, R.F. and Jobidon, G.
1971: A seismic investigation of the crust and Moho on a line perpendicular to the Grenville Front; Canadian Journal of Earth Sciences, v. 8, p. 1553-1583.

Miall, A.D.
1983: The Nares Strait problem: A re-evaluation of the geological evidence in terms of a diffuse oblique-slip plate boundary between Greenland and the Canadian Arctic Islands; in Continental Tectonics: Structure, Kinematics and Dynamics, ed. M. Friedman and M.N. Toksoz; Tectonophysics, v. 100, p. 227-239.

Miall, A.D., Balkwill, H.R., and Hopkins, W.R., Jr.
1980: Cretaceous and Tertiary sediments of Eclipse Trough, Bylot Island area, arctic Canada, and their regional setting; Geological Survey of Canada, Paper 79-23, 20 p.

Miller, H.G.
1977: Gravity zoning in Newfoundland; Tectonophysics, v. 38, p. 317-326.

Miller, H.G. and Deutsch, D.R.
1978: The Bouguer anomaly field of the Notre Dame Bay area, Newfoundland; Earth Physics Branch, Gravity Map Series 163.

Miller, H.G., Goodacre, A.K., Cooper, R.V., and Halliday, D.
1985: Offshore extensions of the Avalon Zone of Newfoundland; Canadian Journal of Earth Sciences, v. 22, p. 1163-1170.

Morel, P. and Irving, E.
1978: Tentative paleocontinental maps for the Early Phanerozoic and Proterozoic; Journal of Geology, v. 86, p. 535-561.

Nelson, K.D., Arnow, J.A., McBride, J.H., Willemin, J.H., Huang, J., Zheng, L.,Oliver, J.E., Brown, L.D., and Kaufman, S.
1985a: New COCORP profiling in the southeastern United States. Part I: Late Paleozoic suture and Mesozoic rift basin; Geology, v. 13, p. 714-718.

Nelson, K.D., McBride, J.H., Arnow, J.A., Oliver, J.E., Brown, L.D., and Kaufman, S.
1985b: New COCORP profiling in the southeastern United States. Part II, Brunswick and east coast magnetic anomalies, opening of the north- central Atlantic Ocean; Geology, v. 13, p. 718-723.

O'Brien, S.J., Wardle, R.J., and King, A.F.
1983: The Avalon Zone: a Pan-African terrane in the Appalachian Orogen of Canada; Geological Journal, v. 18, p. 195-222.

Officer, C.B. and Ewing, M.
1954: Geophysical investigations in the emerged and submerged Atlantic coastal plain, Part VII, continental shelf, continental slope, and continental rise south of Nova Scotia; Geological Society of America Bulletin, v. 65, p. 653-670.

Olszewski, W.J., Jr. and Gaudette, H.E.
1982: Age of the Brookville gneiss and associated rocks, southeastern New Brunswick; Canadian Journal of Earth Sciences, v. 19, p. 2158-2166.

Papezik, V.S. and Hodych, J.P.
1980: Early Mesozoic diabase dikes of the Avalon Peninsula, Newfoundland: Petrochemistry, mineralogy and origin; Canadian Journal of Earth Sciences, v. 17, p. 1417-1430.

Parsons, L.M., Masson, D.G., Pelton, C.D. and Grant, A.C.
1985: Seismic stratigraphy and structure of the east Canadian continental margin between 41 and 52°N; Canadian Journal of Earth Sciences, v. 22, p. 686-703.

Poole, W.H., Sanford, B.V., Williams, H., and Kelley, D.G.
1970: Geology of southeastern Canada; in Geology and Economic Minerals of Canada, ed. R.J.W. Douglas; Geological Survey of Canada, Economic Geology Report 1 (fifth edition), p. 229-304.

Press, F. and Beckmann, W.
1954: Geophysical investigations in the emerged and submerged Atlantic coastal plain, Part VIII, Grand Banks and adjacent shelves; Geological Society of America Bulletin, v. 65, p. 299-314.

Pringle, I.R., Miller, J.A., and Warrell, D.M.
1971: Radiometric age determination from the Long Range Mountains, Newfoundland; Canadian Journal of Earth Sciences, v. 8, p. 1325-1330.

Quinlan, G. and Beaumont, C.
1984: Appalachian thrusting, lithospheric flexure, and the Paleozoic stratigraphy of the eastern interior of North America; Canadian Journal of Earth Sciences, v. 21, p. 973-996.

Rabinowitz, P.D., Cande, S.C., and Hayes, D.E.
1979: The J-anomaly in the central North Atlantic Ocean; in Initial Reports of the Deep Sea Drilling Project, ed. B.E. Tucholke et al.; U.S. Government Printing Office, Washington, Volume 43, p. 879-885.

Rast, N.
1980: The Avalonian plate in the northern Appalachians and Caledonides; in Proceedings, The Caledonides in the U.S.A., ed. D.R. Wones; Virginia Polytechnic Institute and State University, Memoir 2, p. 63-66.

Reid, I. and Jackson, H.R.
1981: Oceanic spreading rate and crustal thickness; Marine Geophysical Researches, v. 5, p. 165-172.

Rice, P.D. and Shade, B.D.
1982: Reflection seismic interpretation and sea-floor spreading history of Baffin Bay; in Arctic Geology and Geophysics, ed. A.F. Embry and H.R. Balkwill; Canadian Society of Petroleum Geologists, Memoir 8, p. 245-265.

Rodgers, J.
1968: The eastern edge of the North America continent during the Cambrian and Early Ordovician; in Studies of Appalachian Geology, Northern and Maritime, ed. E-an Zen, W.S. White, J.B. Hadley and J.B. Thompson Jr.; Interscience Publishers, New York, p. 141-149.

Rosenkrantz, A. and Pulvertaft, T.C.R.
1969: Cretaceous-Tertiary stratigraphy and tectonics in northern west Greenland; American Association of Petroleum Geologists, Memoir 12, p. 883-898.

Ross, D.I.
1973: Free air and simple Bouguer gravity maps of Baffin Bay and adjacent continental margins; Geological Survey of Canada, Paper 73-37, 11 p.

Royden, L. and Keen, C.E.
1980: Rifting process and thermal evolution of the continental margin of eastern Canada determined from subsidence curves; Earth and Planetary Science Letters, v. 51, p. 343-361.

Ruffman, A. and Van Hinte, J.E.
1973: Orphan Knoll, a 'chip' off the North American 'plate'; in Earth Science Symposium on Offshore Eastern Canada, ed. P.J. Hood; Geological Survey of Canada, Paper 71-23, p. 407-449.

Ryan, A.B.
1981: Volcanism, sedimentation, plutonism, and Grenvillian deformation in the Helikian basins of central Labrador; in Proterozoic Basins of Canada, ed. F.H.A. Campbell; Geological Survey of Canada, Paper 81-10, p. 361-378.

Schenk, P.E.
1981: The Meguma Zone of Nova Scotia — a remnant of western Europe, South America or Africa; in Geology of the North Atlantic Borderlands; ed. J.W. Kerr and A.J. Fergusson; Canadian Society of Petroleum Geologists, Memoir 7, p. 119-148.

Scholle, P.A. and Wenkam, C.R.
1982: Geological studies of the Cost Nos. G-1 and G-2 wells, United States North Atlantic outer continental shelf; United States Geological Survey, Circular 861, 193 p.

Sclater, J.G., Jaupart, C., and Galson, D.
1980: The heat flow through oceanic and continental crust and the heat loss of the earth; Review of Geophysics and Space Physics, v. 18, p. 269-311.

Sheridan, R.E. and Drake, C.L.
1968: Seaward extension of the Canadian Appalachians; Canadian Journal of Earth Sciences, v. 5, p. 337-373.

Sheridan, R.E., Grow, J.A., Behrendt, J.C., and Bayer, K.C.
1979: Seismic refraction study of the continental edge off the eastern United States; Tectonophysics, v. 59, p. 1-26.

Shih, K.G., Macnab, R., and Halliday, D.
1981: Multiparameter survey data from the Scotian margin; Geological Survey of Canada, Open File 750, 5 p.

Sobczak, L.W.
1975a: Gravity anomalies and passive continental margins; in Canada's Continental Margins and Offshore Petroleum Exploration, ed. C.J. Yorath, E.R. Parker, and D.J. Glass; Canadian Society of Petroleum Geologists, Memoir 4, p. 743-761.
1975b: Gravity anomalies and deep structure of the continental margin of Banks Island and the MacKenzie Delta; Canadian Journal of Earth Sciences, v. 12, p. 378-394.

Spjeldnaes, N.
1978: Faunal provinces and the Proto-Atlantic; in Crustal Evolution of Northwestern Britain and Adjacent Regions, ed. D.R. Bowes, and B.E. Leake; Geological Journal, Special Issue 10, p. 139-150.

Srivastava, S.P.
1978: Evolution of the Labrador Sea and its bearing on the early evolution of the North Atlantic; Geophysical Journal of the Royal Astronomical Society, v. 52, p. 313-357.
1979: Marine gravity and magnetic anomalies maps of the Labrador Sea; Geological Survey of Canada, Open File 627, 2 p.
1983: Davis Strait: Structures, origin and evolution; in Structure and Development of the Greenland-Scotland Ridge, ed. M.H.P. Bott, S. Saxov, M. Talwani, and J. Thiede; Plenum Press, New York, p. 159-190.

Srivastava, S.P., Falconer, R.K.H., and MacLean, B.
1981: Labrador Sea, Davis Strait, Baffin Bay: geology and geophysics — a review; in Geology of the North Atlantic Borderlands, ed. J.W. Kerr and A.J. Fergusson; Canadian Society of Petroleum Geologists, Memoir 7, p. 333-398.

Srivastava, S.P., MacLean, B, MacNab, R.F., and Jackson, H.R.
1982: Davis Strait: structure and evolution as obtained from a systematic geophysical survey; in Arctic Geology and Geophysics, ed. A.F. Embry and H.R. Balkwill; Canadian Society of Petroleum Geologists, Memoir 8, p. 267-278.

Stephens, L.E. and Cooper, R.V.
1973: Results of underwater gravity surveys over the southern Nova Scotia continental shelf; Gravity Map Series, Earth Physics Branch No. 149, p. 1-10.

Stephens, L.E., Goodacre, A.K., and Cooper, R.V.
1971: Results of underwater gravity surveys over the Nova Scotia continental shelf; Gravity Map Series, Earth Physics Branch No. 123, 9 p.

Stergiopoulos, A.B.
1984: Geophysical crustal studies off the southwest Greenland margin; M.Sc. Thesis, Dalhousie University, Halifax, Nova Scotia, 250 p.

Strong, D.F.
1979: Proterozoic tectonics of northwestern Gondwanaland: New evidence from eastern Newfoundland; Tectonophysics, v. 54, p. 81-101.
1980: Granitoid rocks and associated mineral deposits of eastern Canada and western Europe; in The Continental Crust and its Mineral Deposits, ed. D.W. Strangway; Geological Association of Canada, Special Paper 20, p. 741-769.

Strong, D.F. and Harris, A.
1974: The petrology of Mesozoic alkaline intrusives of central Newfoundland; Canadian Journal of Earth Sciences, v. 11, p. 1208-1219.

Stukas, V. and Reynolds, P.H.
1974: ^{40}Ar/^{39}Ar dating of the Long Range dikes, Newfoundland; Earth and Planetary Science Letters, v. 22, p. 256-266.

Sullivan, K.D.
1983: The Newfoundland Basin: Ocean-continent boundary and Mesozoic sea?floor spreading history; Earth and Planetary Science Letters, v. 62, p. 321-339.

Sullivan, K.D. and Keen, C.E.
1977: Newfoundland seamounts: petrology and geochemistry; in Volcanic Regimes in Canada, ed. W.R.A. Baragar, L.C. Coleman, and J.M. Hall; Geological Association of Canada, Special Paper 16, p. 461-476.
1978: On the nature of the crust in the vicinity of the Newfoundland Ridge; Canadian Journal of Earth Sciences, v. 15, p. 1462-1471.

Taylor, P.T., Zietz, I., and Dennis, L.S.
1968: Geologic implications of aeromagnetic data for the eastern continental margin of the United States; Geophysics, v. 33, p. 755-780.

Thomas, M.D.
1983: Tectonic significance of paired gravity anomalies in the southern and central Appalachians; in Contributions to the Tectonics and Geophysics of Mountain Chains, ed. R.D. Hatcher, Jr., H. Williams, and I. Zietz; Geological Society of America, Memoir 158, p. 113-124.

Thomas, W.A.
1977: Evolution of Appalachian-Ouachita salients and recesses from re-entrants and promontories in the continental margin; American Journal of Science, v. 277, p. 1233-1278.

Tucholke, B.E. and Ludwig, W.J.
1982: Structure and origin of the J-Anomaly Ridge, western North Atlantic Ocean; Journal of Geophysical Research, v. 87, p. 9389-9407.

Tucholke, B.E. and Mountain, G.S.
1979: Seismic stratigraphy, lithostratigraphy and paleosedimentation patterns in the North American basin; in Deep Drilling Results in the Atlantic Ocean: Continental Margins and Paleoenvironment, M. Talwaine, W. Hay and W.B.F. Ryan, ed.; Maurice Ewing Series 3, American Geophysical Union, Washington, p. 53-86.

Tucholke, B.E. and Vogt, P.R.
1979: Western North Atlantic: sedimentary evolution and aspects of tectonic history; in Initial Reports of the Deep Sea Drilling Project, ed. B.E. Tucholke et al.; United States Government Printing Office, Washington, Volume 43, p. 791-825.

Umpleby, D.C.
1979: Geology of the Labrador Shelf; Geological Survey of Canada, Paper 79-13, 34 p.

Vail, P.R., Mitchum, R.M., Todd, R.G., Widmier, J.M., Thompson, S., Sangree, J.B., Bubb, J.N., and Hatlelid, W.G.
1977: Seismic stratigraphy and global changes of sea level; in Seismic Stratigraphy — Application to Hydrocarbon Exploration, ed. C.E. Payton; American Association of Petroleum Geologists, Memoir 26, p. 49-212.

van der Linden, W.J.M.
1975: Crustal attenuation and sea-floor spreading in the Labrador Sea; Earth and Planetary Science Letters, v. 27, p. 409-423.

Vogt, P.R., Kovacs, L.C., Bernero, C., and Srivastava, S.P.
1982: Asymmetric geophysical signatures in the Greenland-Norwegian and southern Labrador seas and the Eurasian Basin; Tectonophysics, v. 89, p. 95-160.

Wade, J.A.
1981: Geology of the Canadian Atlantic margin from Georges Bank to the Grand Banks; in Geology of the North Atlantic Borderlands, ed. J.W. Kerr and A.J. Fergusson; Canadian Society of Petroleum Geologists, Memoir 7, p. 447-460.

Walcott, R.I.
1972: Gravity, flexure and the growth of sedimentary basins at a continental edge; Geological Society of America Bulletin, v. 83, p. 1845-1848.

Watts, A.B.
1974: A gravity survey of the continental shelf south of Cape Sable, Nova Scotia; Canadian Journal of Earth Sciences, v. 11, p. 1329-1334.

Watts, A.B. and Haworth, R.T.
1974: Geological interpretation of Bouguer anomaly and magnetic anomaly maps east of the Magdalen Islands, southern Gulf of St. Lawrence; Geological Survey of Canada, Paper 74-55, 9 p.

Weaver, D.F.
1967: A geological interpretation of the Bouguer anomaly field of Newfoundland; Dominion Observatory, Energy Mines and Resources, v. 35, p. 223-251.

Wernicke, B. and Burchfiel, B.C.
1982: Modes of extensional tectonics; Journal of Structural Geology, v. 4, p. 105-115.

Williams, H.
1979: The Appalachian Orogen in Canada; Canadian Journal of Earth Sciences, v. 16, p. 792-807.
1984: Miogeoclines and suspect terranes of the Caledonian-Appalachian Orogen: Tectonic patterns in the North Atlantic region; Canadian Journal of Earth Sciences, v. 21, p. 887-901.

Williams, H. (ed.)
in press: The Appalachian/Caledonian region: Canada and Greenland; Geological Survey of Canada, Geology of Canada, no. 5, (also Geological Society of America; The Geology of North America, v. F-1). (in press)

Williams, H. and Doolan, B.L.
1979: Evolution of Appalachian-Ouachita salients and recesses from reentrants and promontories in the continental margin; American Journal of Science, v. 279, p. 92-95.

Williams, H. and Hatcher, R.D. Jr.
1982: Suspect terranes and accretionary history of the Appalachian Orogen; Geology, v. 10, p. 530-536.
1983: Appalachian suspect terranes; in Contributions to the Tectonics and Geophysics of Mountain Chains, ed. R.D. Hatcher Jr., H. Williams and I. Zietz; Geological Society of America, Memoir 159, p. 33-53.

Williams, H. and St.-Julien, P.
1982: The Baie Verte-Brompton line: Early Paleozoic continent-ocean interface in the Canadian Appalachians; in Major Structural Zones and Faults of the Northern Appalachians, ed. P. St.-Julien and J. Béland; Geological Association of Canada, Special Paper 24, p. 177-207.

Williams, H. and Stevens, R.K.
1974: The ancient continental margin of eastern North America; in Geology of Continental Margins, ed. C.A. Burk and C.L. Drake; Springer-Verlag, New York, p. 781-796.

Willmore, P.L. and Scheidegger, A.E.
1956: Seismic observations in the Gulf of St. Lawrence; Transactions of the Royal Society of Canada, v. 50, series III, p. 21-30.

Willmore, P.L. and Tolmie, R.
1956: Geophysical observations on the history and structure of Sable Island; Transactions of the Royal Society of Canada, v. 50, series III, p. 13-20.

Zietz, I., Haworth, R.T., Williams, H., and Daniels, D.L.
1980: Magnetic anomaly map of the Appalachians; Memorial University of Newfoundland, Map 2 (1:1 000 000).

Author's addresses

C.E. Keen
Atlantic Geoscience Centre
Geological Survey of Canada
Bedford Institute of Oceanography
P.O. Box 1006
Dartmouth, Nova Scotia
B2Y 4A2

B.D. Loncarevic
Atlantic Geoscience Centre
Geological Survey of Canada
Bedford Institute of Oceanography
P.O. Box 1006
Dartmouth, Nova Scotia
B2Y 4A2

I. Reid
Atlantic Geoscience Centre
Geological Survey of Canada
Bedford Institute of Oceanography
P.O. Box 1006
Dartmouth, Nova Scotia
B2Y 4A2

J. Woodside
Vrije Universiteit
Instituut voor Aardwetenschappen
De Boelelaan 1085
10081 HV Amsterdam
The Netherlands

R.T. Haworth
British Geological Survey
Keyworth
Nottinghamshire NG1Z5GG
England

H. Williams
Department of Earth Sciences
Memorial University of Newfoundland
St. John's, Newfoundland
A1B 3X5

IGNEOUS ROCKS OF THE CONTINENTAL MARGIN

Georgia Pe-Piper, D.J.W. Piper, M.J. Keen and *N.J. McMillan*

INTRODUCTION

In ancient orogens, igneous rocks are important sources of information on tectonic evolution. Igneous activity is generally a direct reflection of tectonic processes and different igneous products are formed in different tectonic environments. Igneous activity associated with the rifting and drifting of the North Atlantic Ocean, the Labrador Sea, Baffin Bay and the Arctic Ocean provides a record of these tectonic processes on the Canadian continental margin and in adjacent oceanic basins (Fig. 2.24).

Different parts of the Canadian margin have had different histories of continental breakup and seafloor spreading. For convenience, this account of the associated igneous rocks is divided into two areas. The Scotian and Grand Banks margins show igneous activity associated with the Triassic and earliest Jurassic rifting of the central North Atlantic, and seafloor spreading which began in the early Jurassic (see Chapter 5). The East Newfoundland, Labrador and Baffin margins record Cretaceous rifting of Iberia from the Grand Banks and the opening of the Labrador Sea and Baffin Bay (see Chapters 6 and 7).

In both areas, a rather similar sequence of igneous rocks occurs. The earliest igneous rocks are alkaline intrusions developed during the earliest stages of rifting. These are followed by tholeiitic basalts associated with the main phase of rifting; this phase terminates with the onset of continental drift. In some areas, long, wide, coast-parallel dykes formed during the main rift phase. Extensive tholeiitic basalt sheets locally occur offshore, buried beneath younger sediments. Later igneous activity (usually minor) is associated either with final differentiation of residual magma masses, or with re-activation of old faults.

We follow McHone and Butler (1984) in recognizing igneous provinces consisting of groups of igneous rocks related primarily by age and geographic distribution and secondarily by magmatic association. Different igneous provinces usually reflect different tectonic origins. Jansa and Pe-Piper (Fig. 1, 1986; 1988) have summarized the tectonic associations of igneous rocks on the eastern Canadian continental margin.

The geochemical character of the igneous rocks may be a guide to petrogenesis and thus to tectonic setting. Alkali rocks of seamounts and minor rift zones in continents are a product of partial melting of deeper mantle than the tholeiitic rocks of rifting continental margins and mid-ocean ridges. The most useful rocks for geochemical assessment are primitive basalts that have experienced little fractionation in crustal magma chambers. The abundance of incompatible elements such as potassium, rubidium, barium, thorium and the rare earth elements (REE) and ratios of isotopes of strontium, neodymium and lead can be used to infer the mineralogical and chemical character of source mantle rocks (Thompson et al., 1984). The variable character of the mantle may then be related to tectonic history. Deep mantle plumes or hot spots (Morgan, 1983) produce voluminous volcanic products. Mantle-derived magma from these hotspots is enriched in many incompatible elements (LeRoex et al., 1984). Enrichment in incompatible elements may also result from other processes (Fitton and Dunlop, 1985) and local mantle upwelling might result from processes other than hotspot activity.

Few Mesozoic and Cenozoic igneous products are exposed on land. Voluminous rift-related basalts and associated dykes of Triassic to Early Jurassic age outcrop in the Atlantic provinces; similar rocks occur farther southwest along the United States continental margin and on the conjugate margin in west Africa. Youngest Cretaceous and Early Tertiary rift-related basalts outcrop in west Greenland and Baffin Island. Otherwise, data on igneous activity are based on dredging or drilling the most recent lavas on seamounts and oceanic crust at the base of Deep Sea Drilling Project (DSDP) holes, or analysis of cuttings samples from exploration wells. Thus, the data base is limited, particularly for geochemical studies.

EARLY MESOZOIC IGNEOUS ROCKS OF THE SCOTIAN MARGIN

Igneous rocks associated with Triassic to Early Jurassic rifting in eastern Canada comprise dykes throughout the Atlantic Provinces and lava flows of the North Mountain Basalt around the Bay of Fundy and in wells on the Grand Banks (Table 2.1). Farther south, in the eastern United States Appalachians, similar dykes and lava flows occur. In addition, there are several plutons of Triassic age in New England. McHone and Butler (1984) recognized two distinct igneous provinces: the coastal New England province and the Eastern North America dolerite (i.e. continental tholeiite) province.

Coastal New England igneous province

In coastal New Hampshire and southern Maine there are three syenite to alkali granite plutons yielding dates close to the Permian-Triassic boundary (Foland and Faul, 1977; McHone and Butler, 1984). Associated dykes occur at Seabrook in New Hampshire (Bellini et al., 1982), dated between 212 and 236 Ma. The dykes are olivine-normative tholeiite with considerable enrichment in incompatible elements.

The oldest Triassic igneous activity on the Canadian margin is a high-alumina olivine tholeiite with flat REE spectra and depletion in incompatible elements found as a dyke in the Northumberland Strait F-25 well (Pe-Piper and Jansa, 1986; Fig. 1, in pocket), and dated at 214 Ma. It is thus similar in age to the volcanism of the Coastal New England province.

Eastern North America continental tholeiite province

The Eastern North America province, largely of Late Triassic to earliest Jurassic age, is represented in eastern Canada by mafic rocks occurring as both dykes and flows (Fig. 2.25a). Three large dykes, each about 100 km long, occur in Atlantic Canada (Fig. 2.24): the Avalon (Hodych and Hyatsu, 1980; Papezik and Hodych, 1980), Shelburne

(Papezik and Barr, 1981) and Caraquet (Burke et al., 1973; Greenough and Papezik, 1986). These large dykes are tens of metres wide and show evidence for multiple injection of magma, possibly over many million years (Greenough and Papezik, 1986). Smaller dykes include the George Island dyke in Prince Edward Island. Radiometric data (Table 2.1) suggest ages between 160 and 215 Ma, with the most reliable data clustering around 191 to 201 Ma.

The North Mountain Basalt around the Bay of Fundy is a thick succession of 16 or more subaerial flows on the southern margin of the Bay of Fundy half graben. Volcanic necks occur on the northern side of the Minas Basin (Stevens, 1980). K-Ar isochron dating gave an age of 191 $\pm$2 Ma (Early Jurassic) (Hyatsu, 1979). The North Mountain Basalt has also been sampled in the Chinampas N-37 well in the Bay of Fundy (Jansa and Pe-Piper, 1986). Lavas of probable Triassic-Early Jurassic age occur in the Glooscap C-63 well on the Scotian Shelf and the Cormorant N-83 and Spoonbill C-30 wells on the Grand Banks. Basalt flows were also encountered in a well on Nantucket Island (Folger et al., 1978).

All the analyzed dykes from Atlantic Canada and most lavas are of quartz-normative tholeiite composition (Dostal and Dupuy, 1984; Greenough and Papezik, 1986), although some lavas are olivine-normative tholeiites. They have the geochemical character of continental tholeiites, with variable abundance of elements such as titanium, potassium and thorium (Fig. 2.26a). This variability has been generally interpreted as resulting from variable crustal contamination of primary tholeiitic magma (Dostal and Dupuy, 1984), an interpretation that is confirmed by isotopic data (Lambert et al., 1988).

Similar tholeiitic dykes and minor extrusive equivalents occur over a large area of the eastern Appalachians of the United States (Weigand and Ragland, 1970; Smith et al., 1975; McHone and Butler, 1984). They range in composition from quartz-normative to olivine-normative tholeiite and rare nepheline-normative alkali rocks (Hermes et al., 1984). Most rocks show ages between 170 and 200 Ma, with a peak at about 190 Ma (McHone and Butler, 1984). Although there are some regular variations in composition of these rocks in space and time (Weigand and Ragland, 1970; Smith et al., 1975), no satisfactory theory has been put forward to account for these variations. The dyke orientations provide information on the stress field during rifting (May, 1971; de Boer and Snider, 1979; Ragland et al., 1983).

On the conjugate margin in Morocco, there was extensive Late Triassic tholeiitic volcanism (dated around 196 Ma), both olivine and quartz normative, in the High Atlas (Manspeizer et al., 1978). Lowest Jurassic subalkaline quartz tholeiites occur in the Middle Atlas, and mostly date between 180 and 194 Ma. Minor Upper Jurassic diabase sills yield dates between 135 and 155 Ma. Manspeizer et al. (1978) suggested that the voluminous magmatic

---

Figure 2.24. Wells containing igneous rocks on the eastern Canadian margin with generalized onshore occurrences of Mesozoic igneous rocks and major seamount chains. After Figure 1 of Jansa and Pe-Piper (1986). Late Jurassic to Cretaceous hotspot tracks as proposed by Duncan (1984) are also shown.

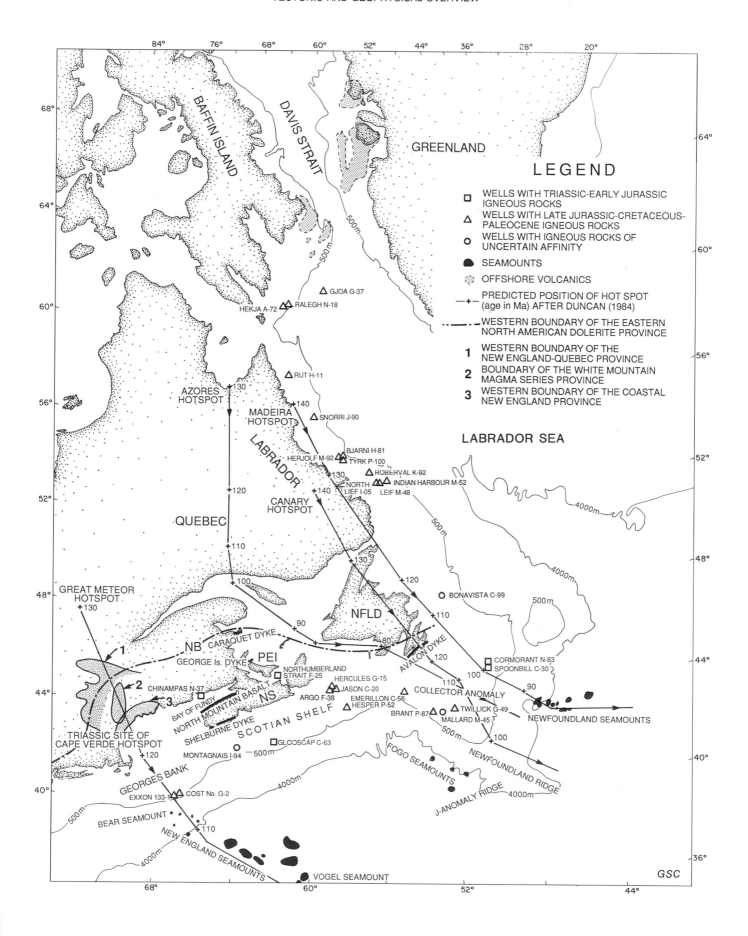

Table 2.1. Occurrence, type and age of offshore igneous rocks on the eastern Canadian margin

Location	Rock type	Age (Ma)	Reference
TRIASSIC-EARLY JURASSIC			
Northumberland Strait F-25	diabase dykes	214 ± 9 239 ± 10	Pe-Piper and Jansa, 1986
Chinampas N-37	basalt	not determined	Mobil et al., 1975
Glooscap C-63	basalt	not determined	Husky Bow Valley et al., 1984
Spoonbill C-30	basalt	not determined	Amoco et al., 1973 Jansa and Pe-Piper, 1986
Cormorant N-83	basalt	not determined	Amoco et al., 1972

In addition, there are offshore extensions of the North Mountain Basalt and major dykes which outcrop on land.

Location	Rock type	Age (Ma)	Reference
LATE JURASSIC-CRETACEOUS			
Scotian Shelf			
Argo F-38	<100 m of volcaniclastics and pyroclastics; overlying 15 m of basalt	Aptian	Jansa and Pe-Piper, 1985
Hercules J-15	82 m of volcaniclastics and pyroclastics; overlying 23 m of basalt	119 ± 5	Jansa and Pe-Piper, 1985
Hesper I-52	20 m diabase sill	112 ± 5 125.9 ± 3.2	Jansa and Pe-Piper, 1985
Jason C-20	85 m of volcaniclastics and pyroclastics; overlying 14 m of basalt (3 flows)	Aptian	Jansa and Pe-Piper, 1985
Grand Banks			
Brant P-87	55 m of basalt and pyroclastics; 123 m of diabase sills or flows	135 ± 6	Jansa and Pe-Piper, 1988
Emerillon C-56	21 m diorite dyke	96.4 ± 3.8	Jansa and Pe-Piper, 1988
Twillick G-49	15 m porphyritic diabase	117 ± 5	Jansa and Pe-Piper, 1988
Mallard M-45		uncertain	
Newfoundland Seamounts			
Newfoundland Seamounts	alkali basalts and trachytes	97.7 ± 1.5	Sullivan and Keen, 1977
Labrador Shelf			
Snorri J-90	290 m of volcanic rock	110 ± 12	Eastcan et al., 1975
Herjolf M-92	258 m of basalt	121 ± 5	Johnson et al., 1982 Umpleby, 1979
Roberval K-92	>365 m of alkali basalts	122 129	Eastcan et al., 1979
Bjarni H-81	>288 m of alkali basalts	122 ± 6 139 ± 7	Johnson et al., 1982
Leif M-48	>61 m of alkali basalts	104 ± 5 131 ± 6	Umpleby, 1979
North Leif I-05	>70 m of alkali basalt		
Indian Harbour M-52	mafic to intermediate lapilli tuffs	90 ± 4	Johnson et al., 1982; Umpleby, 1979
Rut H-11	15 m of tuff over diabase	59	Balkwill and McMillan, Part 1 of Chapter 7
Southeast Baffin Shelf			
Gjoa G-37	tholeiitic basalt	56 ± 3	Klose et al., 1982
Hekja A-72	1021 m of tholeiitic basalt	105 119	Klose et al., 1982
Ralegh N-18	tholeiitic basalt	83 ± 2	Canterra et al., 1982
Southeast Baffin Shelf outcrops	basalt	not determined	MacLean et al., 1982

Onshore igneous occurrences are described in more detail in the volume on the Appalachian region of Canada to be published by the Geological Survey of Canada as Geology of Canada, no. 5. Igneous rocks from the offshore of northeastern United States are reviewed by Jansa and Pe-Piper (1986, 1988). Igneous rocks from offshore Greenland have been described by Rolle (1985).

activity resulted from the onset of seafloor spreading at about 195 Ma. However, most estimates place the opening of the Atlantic Ocean at about 170-175 Ma (Klitgord and Schouten, 1986), so that the onset of seafloor spreading was marked by the cessation of most igneous activity on the continental margin.

White Mountain igneous province

The White Mountain igneous province consists of a number of alkali granite and syenite plutons concentrated in eastern New Hampshire. They yield radiometric ages between 155 and 200 Ma (Foland and Faul, 1977; McHone and Butler, 1984). The individual plutons show no systematic spatial or temporal pattern that might be produced as a result of hot spot motion (McHone, 1981). No representatives of this province are known on the continental margin.

LATER MESOZOIC IGNEOUS ROCKS OF THE CENTRAL NORTH ATLANTIC

Ocean crust

The products of normal seafloor spreading of Mesozoic age in the North Atlantic Basin have not been sampled off eastern Canada. The J-anomaly Ridge, which parallels the continental margin beneath the Sohm Abyssal Plain (Map 1706A, in pocket) probably formed as a result of a temporary increase in volcanism at the spreading centre 112 to 117 Ma. The feature may be analogous to the modern Reykjanes Ridge (Vogt and Tucholke, 1979; Emery and Uchupi, 1984). Basalts drilled on the J-anomaly Ridge on Leg 43 of DSDP are normal mid-ocean ridge type tholeiites (Houghton, 1979).

Seamount chains

Three linear seamount chains occur off the continental margin of eastern Canada (Fig. 2.24): the New England, Fogo and Newfoundland Seamounts. Only highly altered volcanic rocks have been recovered from the Fogo Seamounts, but samples from the other two chains have been dated as Cretaceous. The New England Seamounts are a northwest-trending chain of seamounts nearly 2000 km long and 100-200 km wide. There is a slight change in trend of the chain at Vogel Seamount. Dredge samples have been dated by the $^{40}Ar/^{39}Ar$ method by Duncan (1984) and show a systematic progression in age from 103 Ma at Bear Seamount in the northwest to 82 Ma at Nashville Seamount in the southeast. Samples have been analyzed chemically from DSDP sites (Houghton, 1979) and dredge hauls, in both cases sampling only the uppermost part of the volcanic pile. The rocks are alkali basalts, basanites and tephrites (Fig. 2.25b), with substantial enrichment in incompatible elements (Fig. 2.26b). Lead isotopic data show characteristics similar to the St. Helena type of oceanic island volcanism (Lambert et al., 1988). Geochemically, therefore, the rocks have the character of mantle plume-related volcanism (Pe-Piper and Jansa, 1987).

Three of the Newfoundland Seamounts have been sampled by dredging, yielding alkali basalts and sodic trachyandesite (Sullivan and Keen, 1977) (Fig. 2.25b). The trachyandesite was dated as 98 Ma. The geochemical character of the volcanic rocks is typical of that of other seamounts, with an alkali basalt differentiation series. Trace element and isotopic data (Lambert et al., 1988) show source mantle enrichment for some samples.

Sullivan and Keen (1977) suggested that the Fogo Seamount chain continues to the thick volcanic basement of the Southeast Newfoundland Ridge and that both are developed along the reactivated transform fault marking the northern boundary of the Central Atlantic Ocean. Grant (1979) provided an alternative interpretation that the Southeast Newfoundland Ridge consists of subsided continental basement.

Jurassic volcanism on Georges Bank

Basalt, diabase, tuff and volcaniclastic sediments have been intersected by two wells on Georges Bank (Amato and Simonis, 1980; Jansa and Pe-Piper, 1988). Biostratigraphic data indicate a Callovian age; radiometric dates indicate an age of about 140 Ma (consistent with the time scale of van Hinte, 1976, but not with the time scale used in this volume).

Geochemically, the rocks are trachybasalts with substantial enrichment in incompatible elements, as might be expected if the mantle was enriched as a result of mantle plume activity (Pe-Piper and Jansa, 1987), although such an interpretation is not supported by the isotopic data (Lambert et al., 1988).

Correlative buried volcanic features have been identified seismically near Bear Seamount on the continental slope off Georges Bank (see Part 1 of Chapter 5).

Mid-Cretaceous igneous activity on the continental shelf

Volcanic rocks and associated intrusions of mid-Cretaceous age are widespread on the Scotian Shelf (Jansa and Pe-Piper, 1985) and Grand Banks (Jansa and Pe-Piper, 1988). Volcanic cones of alkali basalt and associated pyroclastic and hyaloclastic rocks have been intersected in several wells on the Scotian Shelf (Table 2.1). Diabase sills and dykes were found in other wells on both the Grand Banks and Scotian Shelf. Biostratigraphic and radiometric data (Jansa and Pe-Piper, 1988) indicate that the main volcanic activity occurred in the Barremian-Aptian, about 120 Ma. Later (96 Ma) diorite dykes occur in the Emerillon C-56 well on the Grand Banks. Most of the volcanic centres lie within the Orpheus Graben on the Scotian Shelf or along the Collector Anomaly on the Grand Banks, and are interpreted as resulting from re-activation of these major fault zones as a result of plate re-organization when Iberia began to drift away from the Grand Banks (Jansa and Pe-Piper, 1988). Geochemically, the rocks are basalts, trachybasalts and trachyandesites (Fig. 2.25b), and show rather low enrichment in light Rare Earth Elements (REE) (Fig. 2.26b), suggesting a distinctive mantle source beneath the modern continental margin that was different from mantle-plume enriched mantle beneath the New England Seamounts (Pe-Piper and Jansa, 1987).

Lamprophyre dykes of similar age occur on the United States continental margin in the Baltimore Trough area (Schlee et al., 1976; Jansa and Pe-Piper, 1988). These are mostly basanite-tephrites (Fig. 2.25b) apparently derived from source mantle enriched in light REE and incompatible elements, quite different from that beneath the Canadian margin (Pe-Piper and Jansa, 1987).

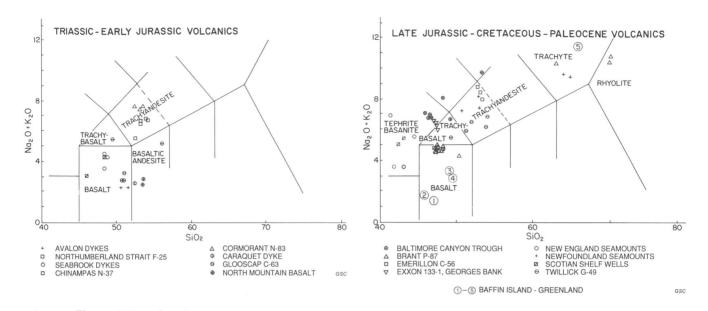

Figure 2.25. Geochemical analyses of offshore igneous rocks and selected onshore Mesozoic rocks plotted on a Zanettin (1984) diagram of total alkalis versus silica.
(a) Triassic and Early Jurassic volcanics
(b) Late Jurassic to Paleocene volcanics
Data from Clarke (1977), Jansa and Pe-Piper (1986) and unpublished data of L.F. Jansa and G. Pe-Piper.

New England-Quebec igneous province

The New England-Quebec igneous province (McHone and Butler, 1984) consists of alkalic stocks and small plutons in the Monteregian Hills of southwestern Quebec and over a wide area of New England. Lamprophyric dykes also occur throughout this area. Radiometric dates lie between 85 and 135 Ma, with most between 110 and 125 Ma (McHone and Butler, 1984). Geochemically, these intrusions are typical continental peralkaline rocks (Eby, 1985). The location of many intrusions appears to be controlled by graben-forming faults (Philpotts, 1974).

Cenozoic igneous activity

Cenozoic volcanic activity is known from Bermuda (Hall et al., 1977) and Eocene intrusive rocks occur in Virginia (Dennison and Johnson, 1971). No Cenozoic volcanism is known from the Canadian margin of the central North Atlantic. Melt rocks associated with an early Tertiary impact structure at the Montagnais I-94 well site on the southwest Scotian Shelf (Jansa and Pe-Piper, 1987) were initially misinterpreted as volcanic rocks.

ORIGIN OF THE CRETACEOUS VOLCANISM — HOT SPOT OR FRACTURE REACTIVATION

Mantle plumes and the associated hot-spot volcanism are widely accepted as important in the development of linear seamount chains and the doming of continental crust (particularly at triple junctions) during rifting. The lineament extending from the White Mountains of New Hampshire to the New England Seamounts (Fig. 2.24) has been widely interpreted as resulting from passage of the North American plate across a hot spot (Crough, 1981; Morgan, 1983).

The New England Seamounts have also been interpreted to result from volcanism along a leaky fracture zone (Uchupi et al., 1970), with the observed sequence of ages resulting from southeasterly propagation of the tip of the leaky fracture (Jansa and Pe-Piper, 1988).

This debate about the origin of the New England Seamounts may also be extended to questions about the origin of other linear volcanic features on the continental margin, such as the Newfoundland Seamounts. Duncan (1984) demonstrated that the predicted tracks of hot spots bordering the central and southern Atlantic Ocean match observed seamount trends and ages (Fig. 2.24). He related the New England Seamounts and Corner Seamounts to the present Great Meteor Seamount; and the Newfoundland Seamounts to the present Canary hotspot. Backtracking the present Cape Verde hotspot brings it to beneath the Georges Bank in the Late Jurassic and to the White Mountains in the Triassic.

The continental area continuing the trend of the New England Seamounts has an unusual thermal and igneous history, and is a zone of modern seismic activity (Sbar and Sykes, 1973). High heat flow in Permian time reset radiometric ages (Zartman et al., 1970). Igneous intrusions of Permian-Triassic and Cretaceous age are widespread (McHone and Butler, 1984) and the related high heat flow produced thermal maturation anomalies in Paleozoic strata (Nowlan and Barnes, 1987). These phenomena may result principally from deep-seated tectonic features allowing access to mantle derived magmas (McHone and Butler, 1984), or from the successive action of the Cape Verde and Great Meteor hotspots (Crough, 1981).

The case for fault reactivation is much stronger for the Cretaceous volcanism of the Scotian Shelf and Grand Banks located along major faults and for which there is no

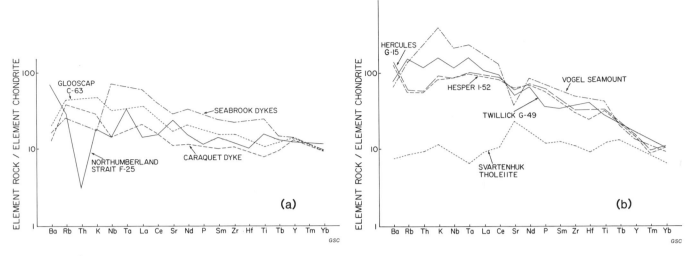

Figure 2.26. Incompatible trace element data from offshore volcanic rocks and selected onshore rocks, with elements normalized to chondrite values and plotted in order of decreasing incompatibility, following Thompson et al. (1984).
(a) Triassic and Early Jurassic volcanics
(b) Late Jurassic to Paleocene volcanics
Data from Jansa and Pe-Piper (1986); Clarke et al. (1983) and unpublished data of L.F. Jansa and G. Pe-Piper.

spatial or geochemical evidence for mantle plume activity (Jansa and Pe-Piper, 1985). The Newfoundland Seamounts lie along the continuation of the volcanic trend on the continental shelf, at the juncture of the Avalon and Meguma zones of the Appalachians (Keen et al., this chapter), and thus probably also result from volcanism along a reactivated fracture. Geochemically, they show less evidence for incompatible element enrichment, characteristic of hot-spot volcanism, than do rocks associated with the New England Seamount Chain.

There is also a good case for fracture reactivation for the lamprophyre dykes in the Baltimore Canyon Trough. Although these rocks show substantial enrichment in incompatible elements, they do not lie along any predicted hot spot tracks, and there is no spatially related igneous activity that might be related to the same hypothetical hotspot.

There is a close parallelism between major volcanic events in the linear zones of volcanism and major changes in plate motion. For example, separation and drifting of Iberia from the Grand Banks at about 115 Ma corresponds to the main phase of volcanism on the Scotian Shelf; and separation and drifting in the Labrador Sea began at about the time that volcanism ceased at the southeastern end of the New England Seamounts and dykes were emplaced at the Emerillon C-56 well on the Grand Banks (Jansa and Pe-Piper, 1988).

In summary, the main features of uplift and volcanism are probably related to the movement of hot spots. The fortuitous passage of the New England area over both the Cape Verde and Great Meteor hotspots resulted in a long history of igneous activity in that area. However, the timing and location of intrusion and volcanism is also closely related to the regional stress in the lithosphere, which is only in part a consequence of hot spot activity and is highly dependent on plate configurations. For this reason there is

a close correlation between changes in plate movement and changes in igneous activity, and some voluminous volcanism may be unrelated to hot spot activity.

RIFTING OF THE LABRADOR SEA

Igneous events in northern Newfoundland and southern Labrador

Small mafic and ultramafic intrusions in central Newfoundland (Fig. 2.24) are the first igneous events associated with the rifting of the Grand Banks and Labrador Sea. The Budgell Harbour gabbro (Helwig et al., 1974) yielded radiometric dates of 135-155 Ma (Strong and Harris, 1974). It is associated with a radiating pattern of lamprophyric dykes.

At Ford's Bight, on the coast of central Labrador (Fig. 2.24), breccia, biostratigraphically dated as Early Jurassic to Early Cretaceous, is cut by lamprophyre-carbonatite dykes (King and McMillan, 1975). Radiometric ages range from 129 ± 6 to 145 ± 6 Ma (Umpleby, 1979).

Dyke swarms in southwest Greenland

In southwestern Greenland, there is a large coast-parallel dyke swarm of Late Jurassic age (Watt, 1969). There are also scattered alkalic intrusions (lamprophyre dykes, kimberlite sills and a carbonatite complex) of Jurassic to Early Cretaceous age (Larsen and Moller, 1968; Larsen et al., 1983).

Cretaceous volcanism on Labrador Shelf

Basalts underlie Cretaceous sedimentary rocks in seven wells in southern Hopedale Basin of the Labrador Shelf. Radiometric ages range from 131 to 105 Ma (Neocomian to Albian). The basalts are several hundred metres thick — basalt is over 365 m thick in the Roberval K-92 well. The basalts appear to have been extruded terrestrially, and have red weathered tops to flows. They are reported to have an alkaline character (Balkwill and McMillan, Part 1 of Chapter 7). The Indian Harbour M-52 well contains younger weathered basic lapilli tuffs, dated at 90 ± 4 Ma (Umpleby, 1979).

In Saglek Basin, basalt flows and pyroclastic beds were sampled in the Rut H-11 well. An intrusive diabase was dated radiometrically at 59 Ma (Paleocene), but the main volcanic sequence may be older. Seismic anomalies suggest that these volcanics are both thick and widespread beneath the northern Labrador Shelf.

Hinz et al. (1979) identified a prominent flat-lying reflector over parts of the continental margin of the northern Labrador Sea, which was tentatively interpreted as Paleocene basalt flows. This reflector is similar to that identified as basalt flows on the Voring Plateau in the Norwegian Sea (Leg 104 Scientific Party). It appears to be overlain by shale of the Markland Formation of Late Cretaceous age (Balkwill and McMillan, Part 1 of Chapter 7).

Cretaceous-Paleocene volcanism on Southeast Baffin Shelf

Seismic reflection profiles suggest that there are great thicknesses of volcanic rocks beneath the Southeast Baffin Shelf, where olivine tholeiitic basalts have been encountered in the three wells drilled. Basalt over 1020 m thick and dated radiometrically as Early Cretaceous (105-119 Ma) was recovered from the Hekja A-72 well. Late Cretaceous basalts occur in the Ralegh N-18 well (83 Ma). The upper parts of the volcanic succession at Gjoa G-37 are intercalated with Paleogene strata, and have been radiometrically dated at 56 Ma, but the lower parts are probably of Late Cretaceous age. Near-surface outcrops of basalt have also been sampled by MacLean et al. (1982) on Southeast Baffin Shelf.

Early Paleocene volcanism in Davis Strait

Youngest Cretaceous and Early Tertiary volcanic rocks, largely tholeiitic basalts, occur in central West Greenland and in the Cape Dyer region of Baffin Island (MacLean et al., Part 2 of Chapter 7). Basalts extend over large areas of Davis Strait — their extent has been mapped principally from their magnetic signature (Park et al., 1971). The volcanic pile is up to 6 km thick in West Greenland. Clarke (1977) described a sequence of five units, from oldest to youngest (Fig. 2.25b): 1. subaqueous volcanic breccias and flows; 2. subaerial olivine tholeiites and picritic tholeiites; 3. subaerial feldspar-phyric tholeiites; 4. trachyte and intermediate to acid pyroclastic rocks; and 5. lamprophyre dykes. Radiometric ages for units 1 to 4 range from 51 to 63 Ma suggesting an Early Paleogene age. The lamprophyres are much younger (31-40 Ma, Parrott and Reynolds, 1975).

The early olivine tholeiites (Fig. 2.26b) are very primitive and essentially of mid ocean ridge basalt composition. Trace elements (O'Nions and Clarke, 1972; Keen and Clarke, 1974; Clarke et al., 1983) suggest enriched source mantle of the type found in hot spots. Carter et al. (1979) found isotopic compositions similar to those of Iceland and

characteristic of plume-related mid-ocean ridge basalt as defined by LeRoex et al. (1984). The feldspar-phyric tholeiites and more felsic rocks represent differentiation by settling of olivine phenocrysts in magma chambers near the base of the crust (Clarke, 1977).

Tholeiitic basalts occur in two wells on the West Greenland Shelf (Rolle, 1985). Thick subaqueous basalts in the Nukik 2 well are probably of Maastrichtian or Early Paleocene age, yielding radiometric ages of 62-68 Ma. Thick subaerial basalts in the Hellefisk 1 well are Early Paleocene, yielding radiometric ages of 53-54 Ma.

Hot spots, transform faults and the evolution of the Labrador Sea

The absence of well-defined seamount chains and the paucity of geochemical data for much of the volcanic activity around the Labrador Sea (with the notable exception of the West Greenland Paleocene volcanism) makes evaluation of the role of hot spots and fracture zones more difficult than in the central Atlantic region.

Duncan (1984) has related the Jurassic alkaline intrusive activity in northern Newfoundland and the Newfoundland Seamounts to the Canary Islands hot spot. Morgan (1983) correlated the West Greenland alkalic intrusions of Jurassic and Early Cretaceous age with the Madeira hotspot (Fig. 2.24).

The Thulean volcanic province (Hall, 1981), extending through Davis Strait and Greenland to Iceland and Scotland, is interpreted as resulting from the Iceland hotspot (Hyndman, 1973), and Keen and Clarke (1974) identified trace element data to support this hypothesis.

The origin of the thick volcanic sequence on Southeast Baffin Shelf is linked to the complex structural history of the northern Labrador Sea and Davis Strait (Keen et al., this Chapter); it is probably related to pull-apart basins (Klose et al., 1982) or leaky transform motion. In the absence of geochemical data from Southeast Baffin Shelf, it is difficult to evaluate the possible role of hot spots in Davis Strait but it is unlikely that the voluminous volcanism in Davis Strait and Southeast Baffin Shelf are not in some way related.

REFERENCES

Amato, R.V. and Simonis, E.K.
1980:   Geologic and operational summary, COST No. 2 G-2 well, Georges Bank area, North Atlantic Ocean; United States Geological Survey, Open File Report 80-269, 116 p.

Amoco et al.
1972:   Cormorant N-83: well history report by Amoco Canada Ltd.; Canada Oil and Gas Lands Administration, Department of Energy, Mines and Resources Canada.
1973:   Spoonbill C-30: well history report by Amoco Canada Ltd.; Canada Oil and Gas Lands Administration, Department of Energy, Mines and Resources Canada.

Bellini, F.X., Corkum, D.H., and Stewart, A.J.
1982:   Geology of foundation excavations at Seabrook Station, Seabrook, New Hampshire; in Geotechnology in Massachusetts, ed. O.C. Farquar; University of Massachusetts, Amherst, Massachusetts, p. 109-117.

Burke, K.B.S., Hamilton, J.B., and Gupta, V.K.
1973:   The Caraquet dyke: its tectonic significance; Canadian Journal of Earth Sciences, v. 10, p. 1760-1768.

Canterra et al.
1982:   Ralegh N-18: well history report by Canterra Energy Ltd.; Canada Oil and Gas Lands Administration, Department of Energy, Mines and Resources Canada.

Carter, S.R., Evensen, N.M., Hamilton, P.J., and O'Nions, R.K.
1979: Basalt magma sources during the opening of the North Atlantic; Nature, v. 281, p. 28-30.

Clarke, D.B.
1977: The Tertiary volcanic province of Baffin Bay; Geological Association of Canada, Special Paper 16, p. 445-460.

Clarke, D.B., Muecke, G.K., and Pe-Piper, G.
1983: The lamprophyres of Ubekendt Ejland, west Greenland: products of renewed partial melting or extreme differentiation; Contributions to Mineralogy and Petrology, v. 83, p. 117-127.

Crough, S.T.
1981: Mesozoic hotspot epeirogeny in eastern North America; Geology, v. 9, p. 2-6.

de Boer, J.Z. and Snider, F.G.
1979: Magnetic and chemical variations of Mesozoic diabase dikes from eastern North America: evidence for a hot spot in the Carolinas; Geological Society of America Bulletin, v. 90, p. 185-198.

Dennison, J.J. and Johnson, R.W., Jr.
1971: Tertiary intrusions and associated phenomena near the Thirty eighth Parallel Fracture Zone in Virginia and West Virginia; Geological Society of America Bulletin, v. 82, p. 501-508.

Dostal, J. and Dupuy, C.
1984: Geochemistry of North Mountain basalts (Nova Scotia, Canada); Chemical Geology, v. 45, p. 245-261.

Duncan, R.A.
1984: Age progressive volcanism in the New England Seamounts and the opening of the Central Atlantic Ocean; Journal of Geophysical Research, v. 89, p. 9980-9990.

Eastcan et al.
1975: Snorri J-90: well history report by Eastcan Ltd.; Canada Oil and Gas Lands Administration, Department of Energy, Mines and Resources Canada.
1979: Roberval K-92: well history report by Eastcan Ltd.; Canada Oil and Gas Lands Administration, Department of Energy, Mines and Resources Canada.

Eby, G.N.
1985: Monteregian Hills II. Petrography, major and trace element geochemistry and strontium isotope chemistry of the eastern intrusions: Mounts Shefford, Brome and Megantic; Journal of Petrology, v. 26, p. 418-448.

Emery, K.O. and Uchupi, E.
1984: The Geology of the Atlantic Ocean; Springer Verlag, 1050 p.

Fitton, J.G. and Dunlop, H.M.
1985: The Cameroon line, West Africa and its bearing on the origin of oceanic and continental alkali basalt; Earth and Planetary Science Letters, v. 72, p. 23-38.

Foland, K.A. and Faul, H.
1977: Ages of White Mountain intrusives — New Hampshire, Vermont and Maine, U.S.A.; American Journal of Science, v. 280-A, p. 888-904.

Folger, D.W., Hathaway, J.C., Christopher, R.A., Valentine, R.C., and Poag, C.W.
1978: Stratigraphic test well, Nantucket Island, Massachusetts; United States Geological Survey, Circular 773, 28 p.

Grant, A.C.
1979: Geophysical observations bearing upon the origin of the Newfoundland Ridge; Tectonophysics, v. 59, p. 71-81.

Greenough, J.D. and Papezik, V.S.
1986: Petrology and geochemistry of early Mesozoic Caraquet dyke, New Brunswick, Canada; Canadian Journal of Earth Sciences, v. 23, p. 193-201.

Hall, J.M.
1981: The Thulean volcanic line; Canadian Society of Petroleum Geologists, Memoir 7, p. 231-244.

Hall, J.M., Barrett, D.L., and Keen, C.E.
1977: The volcanic layer of the ocean crust adjacent to Canada — A review; Geological Association of Canada, Special Paper 16, p. 425-444.

Helwig, J.A., Aronson, J., and Day, D.S.
1974: A late Jurassic mafic pluton in Newfoundland; Canadian Journal of Earth Sciences, v. 11, p. 1314-1319.

Hermes, O.D., Rao, J.M., Dickenson, M.P., and Pierce, T.A.
1984: A transitional alkalic dolerite dike suite of Mesozoic age in southeastern New England; Contributions to Mineralogy and Petrology, v. 86, p. 386-397.

Hinz, K., Schluter, H.U., Grant, A.C., Srivastava, S.P., Umpleby, D., and Woodside, J.
1979: Geophysical transects of the Labrador Sea: Labrador to Southwest Greenland; Tectonophysics, v. 59, p. 151-183.

Hodych, J.P. and Hyatsu, A.
1980: K-Ar isochron age and paleomagnetism of diabase along the trans-Avalon aeromagnetic lineament — evidence of Late Triassic rifting in Newfoundland; Canadian Journal of Earth Sciences, v. 17, p. 491-499.

Houghton, R.L.
1979: Petrology and geochemistry of basaltic rocks recovered on Leg 43 of the Deep Sea Drilling Project; in Initial Reports of the Deep Sea Drilling Project, Volume 43, eds. B.E. Tucholke, P.R. Vogt et al.; United States Government Printing Office, Washington, v. 43, p. 721-738.

Husky Bow Valley et al.
1984: Glooscap C-63 well history report by Husky Bow Valley Ltd.; Canada Oil and Gas Lands Administration, Department of Energy, Mines and Resources Canada.

Hyatsu, A.
1979: K-Ar isochron age of the North Mountain Basalt, Nova Scotia; Canadian Journal of Earth Sciences, v. 16, p. 973-975.

Hyndman, R.D.
1973: Evolution of the Labrador Sea; Canadian Journal of Earth Sciences, v. 10, p. 637-644.

Jansa, L.F. and Pe-Piper, G.
1985: Early Cretaceous volcanism on the northeastern American margin and implications for plate tectonics; Geological Society of America Bulletin, v. 96, p. 83-91.
1986: Geology and geochemistry of middle Jurassic and Early Cretaceous igneous rocks on the eastern North American continental shelf; Geological Survey of Canada, Open File 1351, 71 p.
1987: Identification of an underwater extraterrestrial impact crater Nature, v. 327, p. 612-614.
1988: Middle Jurassic to Early Cretaceous igneous rocks along Eastern North American Margin; Bulletin of the American Association of Petroleum Geologists, v. 72, p. 347-366.

Johnson, G.L., Srivastava, S.P., Campsie, J., and Rasmussen, M.
1982: Volcanic rocks in the Labrador Sea and environs and their relation to the evolution of the Labrador Sea; in Current Research, Part B, Geological Survey of Canada, Paper 82-1B, p. 7-20.

Keen, M.J. and Clarke, D.B.
1974: Tertiary basalts in Baffin Bay: geochemical evidence for a fossil hot spot; in Geodynamics of Iceland and the North Atlantic Area, ed. L. Kristjansson; D. Reidel Publishing Co., Dordrecht, The Netherlands; p. 127-137.

King, A.F. and McMillan, N.J.
1975: A mid-Mesozoic breccia from the coast of Labrador; Canadian Journal of Earth Sciences, v. 12, p. 44-51.

Klitgord, K. and Schouten, H.
1986: Plate kinematics of the central Atlantic; in The Geology of North America, Volume M: The Western North Atlantic Region, ed. P.R. Vogt and B.E. Tucholke; Geological Society of America, The Geology of North America, v. M, p. 351-378.

Klose, G.W., Malterre, E., McMillan, N.J., and Zinkan, C.G.
1982: Petroleum exploration offshore southern Baffin Island, northern Labrador Sea, Canada; in Arctic Geology and Geophysics, ed. A.F. Embry and H.R. Balkwill; Canadian Society of Petroleum Geologists, Memoir 8, p. 233-244.

Lambert, R.St J., Pe-Piper, G., and Jansa, L.F.
1988: Sr, Nd and Pb isotopic data for Mesozoic volcanic suites on the eastern North American continental margin; Geological Association of Canada — Mineralogical Association of Canada, Joint Annual Meeting, St. John's, v. 13, p. A71.

Larsen, L.M., Rex, D.C., and Secher, K.
1983: The age of carbonatites, kimberlites and lamprophyres from southern West Greenland: recurrent alkaline magmatism during 2500 million years; Lithos, v. 16, p. 215-221.

Larsen, O. and Moller, J.
1968: Potassium-argon age studies in West Greenland; Canadian Journal of Earth Sciences, v. 5, p. 683-691.

Leg 104 Scientific Party
1986: Dipping reflectors in the Norwegian Sea — ODP Leg 104 drilling results; Journal of the Geological Society of London, v. 143, p. 911-912.

LeRoex, A.P., Dick, H.J.B., Erlank, A.J., Reid, A.M., Frey, F.A., and Hart, S.R.
1984: Geochemistry, mineralogy, and petrogenesis of lavas erupted along the Southwest Indian Ridge between the Bouvet Triple Junction and 11° East; Journal of Petrology, v. 24, p. 267-318.

MacLean, B., Srivastava, S.P., and Haworth, R.T.
1982: Bedrock structures off Cumberland Sound, Baffin Island Shelf: core sample and geophysical data; Canadian Society of Petroleum Geology, Memoir 8, p. 279-295.

Manspeizer, W., Puffer, J.H., and Cousminer, H.L.
1978: Separation of Morocco and eastern North America: a Triassic-Liassic stratigraphic record; Geological Society of America Bulletin, v. 89, p. 910-920.

May, P.R.
1971: Pattern of Triassic-Jurassic diabase dikes around the North Atlantic in the context of predrift positions of continents; Geological Society of America Bulletin, v. 82, p. 1285-1291.

McHone, J.G.
1981: Comment on « Mesozoic hotspot epeirogeny in eastern North America »; Geology, v. 9, p. 341-343.

McHone, J.G. and Butler, J.R.
1984: Mesozoic igneous provinces of New England and the opening of the North Atlantic Ocean; Geological Society of America Bulletin, v. 95, p. 757-765.

Mobil et al.
1975: Chinampas N-37: well history report by Mobil Canada Ltd.; Canada Oil and Gas Lands Administration, Department of Energy, Mines and Resources Canada.

Morgan, W.J.
1983: Hotspot tracks and the early rifting of the Atlantic; Tectonophysics, v. 94, p. 123-139.

Nowlan, G.S. and Barnes, C.R.
1987: Thermal maturation of Paleozoic strata in eastern Canada from conodont colour alteration index (CAI) data with implications for burial history, tectonic evolution, hotspot tracks and mineral and hydrocarbon exploration; Geological Survey of Canada, Bulletin 367, 47 p.

O'Nions, R.K. and Clarke, D.B.
1972: Comparative trace element geochemistry of Tertiary basalts from Baffin Bay; Earth and Planetary Science Letters, v. 15, p. 436-446.

Papezik, V.S. and Barr, S.M.
1981: The Shelburne dike, an early Mesozoic diabase dike in Nova Scotia: mineralogy, chemistry and regional significance; Canadian Journal of Earth Sciences, v. 18, p. 1346-1355.

Papezik, V.S. and Hodych, J.P.
1980: Early Mesozoic diabase dikes of the Avalon Peninsula, Newfoundland: petrochemistry, mineralogy and origin; Canadian Journal of Earth Sciences, v. 17, p. 1417-1430.

Park, I., Clarke, D.B., Johnson, J., and Keen, M.J.
1971: Seaward extension of the West Greenland Tertiary volcanic province; Earth and Planetary Science Letters, v. 10, p. 235-238.

Parrott, R.J.E. and Reynolds, P.H.
1975: Ar40/Ar39 geochronology: age determinations from the Labrador Sea area; Geological Society of America, Abstracts with Program, v. 7, p. 835.

Pe-Piper, G. and Jansa, L.F.
1986: Triassic olivine-normative diabase from Northumberland Strait, eastern Canada; Canadian Journal of Earth Sciences, v. 23, p. 1013-1021.

1987: Geochemistry of Late Jurassic-Early Cretaceous igneous rocks on the eastern North American margin; Geological Society of America Bulletin, v. 99, p. 803-813.

Philpotts, A.R.
1974: The Monteregian Province; in The Alkaline Rocks, ed. H. Sorenson; John Wiley and Sons, New York, p. 293-310.

Ragland, P.C., Hatcher, R.D., and Whittington, D.
1983: Juxtaposed Mesozoic diabase dykes sets from the Carolinas: A preliminary assessment; Geology, v. 11, p. 394-399.

Rolle, F.
1985: Late Cretaceous-Tertiary sediments offshore central West Greenland: lithostratigraphy, sedimentary evolution, and petroleum potential; Canadian Journal of Earth Sciences, v. 22, p. 1001-1019.

Sbar, M.L. and Sykes, L.R.
1973: Contemporary compressive stress and seismicity in eastern North America: an example of intraplate tectonics; Geological Society of America Bulletin, v. 84, p. 1861-1882.

Schlee, J., Behrendt, J.C., Grow, J.A., Robb, J.M.N., Mattick, R.E., Taylor, P.T., and Lawson, B.J.
1976: Regional geologic framework off northeastern United States; American Association of Petroleum Geologists Bulletin, v. 60, p. 926-951.

Smith, R.C., Rose, A.W., and Lanning, R.M.
1975: Geology and geochemistry of Triassic diabase in Pennsylvania; Geological Society of America, v. 86, p. 943-955.

Stevens, G.
1980: Trip 8: Mesozoic vulcanism and structure — Northern Bay of Fundy region, Nova Scotia; Geological Association of Canada-Mineralogical Association of Canada Joint Annual Meeting, Fieldtrip Guidebook, Halifax, Nova Scotia, 41 p.

Strong, D.F. and Harris, A.
1974: The petrology of Mesozoic alkaline intrusives of central Newfoundland; Canadian Journal of Earth Sciences, v. 11, p. 1208-1219.

Sullivan, K.D. and Keen, C.E.
1977: Newfoundland Seamounts: petrology and geochemistry; Geological Association of Canada, Special Paper 16, p. 461-476.

Thompson, R.N., Morrison, M.A., Hendry, G.N., and Parry, S.J.
1984: An assessment of the relative roles of crust and mantle in magma genesis: an elemental approach; Philosophical Transactions of the Royal Society of London, Series A, v. 310, p. 549-590.

Uchupi, E., Phillips, J.D., and Prada, K.E.
1970: Origin and structure of the New England Seamount Chain; Deep Sea Research, v. 17, p. 483-494.

Umpleby, D.
1979: Geology of the Labrador Shelf; Geological Survey of Canada, Paper 79-13, 39 p.

van Hinte, J.E.
1976: A Jurassic time scale; American Association of Petroleum Geologists Bulletin, v. 60, p. 489-497.

Vogt, P.R. and Tucholke, B.E.
1979: The New England Seamounts: testing origins; Initial Reports of the Deep Sea Drilling Project, v. 43, p. 847-856.

Watt, W.S.
1969: The coast parallel dike swarm of southwest Greenland in relation to the opening of the Labrador Sea; Canadian Journal of Earth Sciences, v. 6, p. 1320-1321.

Weigand, P.W. and Ragland, P.C.
1970: Geochemistry of Mesozoic dolerite dykes from eastern North America; Contributions to Mineralogy and Petrology, v. 29, p. 195-214.

Zanettin, B.
1984: Proposed new chemical classification of volcanic rocks; Episodes, v. 7, p. 19-20.

Zartman, R.E., Hurley, P.M., Krueger, H.W., and Giletti, B.J.
1970: A Permian disturbance of K-Ar radiometric ages in New England: Its occurrence and cause; Geological Society of America Bulletin, v. 81, p. 3359-3374.

Authors' addresses.

G. Pe-Piper
St. Mary's University
Halifax Nova Scotia
B3H 3C3

D.J.W. Piper
Atlantic Geoscience Centre
Geological Survey of Canada
Bedford Institute of Oceanography
P.O. Box 1006
Dartmouth, Nova Scotia
B2Y 4A2

M.J. Keen
Atlantic Geoscience Centre
Geological Survey of Canada
Bedford Institute of Oceanography
P.O. Box 1006
Dartmouth, Nova Scotia
B2Y 4A2

N.J. McMillan
Institute of Sedimentary and Petroleum Geology
Geological Survey of Canada
3303-33rd Street N.W.
Calgary, Alberta
T2L 2A7

Chapter 3

BIOSTRATIGRAPHY AND RELATED STUDIES

Chapter 3

BIOSTRATIGRAPHY AND RELATED STUDIES

G.L. Williams, P. Ascoli, M.S. Barss,
J.P. Bujak, E.H. Davies, R.A. Fensome
and M.A. Williamson

INTRODUCTION

The biostratigraphy of offshore eastern Canada has been tabulated principally from a study of the exploratory wells drilled in the Magdalen, Scotian, Jeanne d'Arc, East Newfoundland, Hopedale and Saglek basins (Fig. 3.1a, b). The sedimentary rocks of these and the other offshore basins represent most periods of the Phanerozoic (Fig. 3.2) and were deposited in a wide range of paleoenvironments from continental to abyssal. The samples available for study may be dredge or grab samples, but are more commonly from core holes or exploratory wells. Core hole samples are of two types: those obtained by drills lowered over the sides of ships such as the Bedford Institute's drill (see Chapter 1), or those obtained by a drillship such as the cores taken by CALDRILL in 1965 (Williams and Brideaux, 1975). Well samples are of three types: conventional core which is rare, sidewall cores which are more commonly available, and cuttings which are the normal type available.

The necessity to use cuttings for most analyses has placed a heavy dependence on the highest occurrence of taxa in the various biostratigraphic zonal schemes. Thus, the last appearance datum of taxa (termed the LAD by Berggren and Van Couvering, 1978) is the basis for most operational zonations. This does not allow development of zonations based on evolutionary sequences or lineages. The first appearance datum of taxa (termed the FAD by Berggren and Van Couvering, 1978) is rarely used because of the inadequate sidewall and conventional core control. Unlike cuttings, which may be contaminated by mixing, these samples provide reliable data on first appearances.

The multiple authorship of this chapter reflects the range of expertise. The individual contributions are as follows: M.S. Barss, Late Paleozoic spores and pollen; P. Ascoli, Mesozoic-Cenozoic foraminifers and ostracodes and Late Jurassic-Early Cretaceous calpionellids; M.A. Williamson, Late Jurassic-Cretaceous foraminifers, J.P. Bujak, Mesozoic-Cenozoic dinoflagellates, pollen and spores; E.H. Davies, Mesozoic dinoflagellates, pollen and spores; R.A. Fensome, Mesozoic dinoflagellates, pollen and

spores; and G.L. Williams, Mesozoic-Cenozoic dinoflagellates, pollen and spores.

Fossil groups

Acritarchs and chitinozoans, two groups of organic-walled microfossils, are used for correlation of the Lower Paleozoic rocks in offshore eastern Canada. The oldest such rocks dated with any precision are Tremadocian rocks from the Grand Banks and Labrador Shelf. Upper Paleozoic rocks of the Grand Banks and Labrador Shelf also contain organic-walled microfossils, primarily spores (Fig. 3.3). These palynomorphs have allowed correlation with the Devonian-Carboniferous onshore sequences of Nova Scotia and New Brunswick.

The Mesozoic-Cenozoic sedimentary rocks extend the full length of the continental margin of eastern Canada. They are the most frequently encountered rocks penetrated by exploration wells and, consequently, have been studied in greatest detail. The three groups of microfossils generally used to provide age control are the palynomorphs, foraminifers and ostracodes. Palynomorphs include spores, pollen and dinoflagellates. The foraminifers include planktonics, calcareous benthics and agglutinated benthics. Other groups that are used occasionally are calcareous nannoplankton, calpionellids and diatoms (Fig. 3.3).

The reliance for age control on any one group generally reflects the environment of deposition. Spores and pollen provide control for terrestrial, marginal marine and inner neritic sediments; ostracodes are invaluable for sediments deposited in marginal marine to inner neritic environments; foraminifers and dinoflagellates are used for neritic sediments, and nannofossils and foraminifers are most useful in bathyal and abyssal environments. Integration of the data on the individual groups has provided a zonation at least to the age level for most of the Mesozoic and to the subepoch level for the Cenozoic. A more precise zonation scheme is not always feasible with the sample control available.

HISTORICAL REVIEW

The biostratigraphic zonations presented here are in part regional and in part cosmopolitan. Geochronological terminology is the same as that used in the Decade of North American Geology time scale (Palmer, 1983), which is based primarily on the European geochronological scale. This chapter reviews, but does not provide a detailed

Williams, G.L., Ascoli, P., Barss, M.S., Bujak, J.P. Davies, E.H. Fensome, R.A., and Williamson, M.A.
1990: Biostratigraphy and related studies, Chapter 3, in Geology of the Continental Margin of Eastern Canada, M.J. Keen and G.L. Williams (ed.); Geological Survey of Canada, Geology of Canada, no. 2, p. 87-137 (also Geological Society of America, the Geology of North America, v. I-1).

cataloguing of, existing microfossil zonations for the Phanerozoic of offshore eastern Canada. For a more complete discussion the reader is referred to Hacquebard (1972), Williams (1975), Ascoli (1976), or Williams and Bujak (1985) or see Tables 3.1 and 3.2.

A formal zonation for the Early Paleozoic has not been proposed. Instead, the ages are based on a comparison of acritarchs and chitinozoans with coeval assemblages from sections in Europe and eastern North America. The European stratigraphic terminology is used in all cases. Control in the Devonian-Carboniferous is based on the spore zonations of Barss and Hacquebard (1967) and Barss (in Hacquebard, 1972), which were erected for onshore sedimentary basins in Nova Scotia and New Brunswisk.

The Mesozoic-Cenozoic zonations are generally regional (Tables 3.1, 3.2). The palynomorph zonation developed by Williams (1975) and Bujak and Williams (1977) is applicable mainly to the Scotian Shelf. It has been used to correlate Grand Banks' wells, but is not suitable for wells east and north of the Avalon Uplift (Map 1706A, in pocket). The study of these latter wells is helping to refine palynological zonations in the Late Jurassic-Early Cretaceous of the Jeanne d'Arc Basin (this chapter). The informal palynomorph zonation for the Tertiary of the Labrador Shelf, proposed in Gradstein and Williams (1976) and modified in Williams and Bujak (1977a), has been refined through the application of the Rank and Scaling Program (RASC) by Gradstein and Agterberg (1982) and D'Iorio (1986).

Independent zonations for Mesozoic-Cenozoic foraminifers have followed a threefold subdivision based on planktonic foraminifers, calcareous benthic foraminifers, and agglutinated benthic foraminifers. Ascoli (1976) presented such a zonal scheme for the Bathonian-Late Miocene of the Scotian Shelf, primarily using assemblage zones. The planktonic foraminiferal zonation was based in part on the stratigraphic ranges of taxa in Postuma (1971). The zonation of Ascoli (1976) was emended in subsequent publications (Ascoli, 1981, 1984; Ascoli et al., 1984). A revision of the zonations is presented in this chapter. Gradstein and Agterberg (1982) established a zonation, using planktonic and benthic foraminifers, for the Tertiary of the Scotian Basin.

Foraminiferal zonations for the Mesozoic of the Grand Banks have been proposed by Exton and Gradstein (1984), who defined three zones in the Early Jurassic; Gradstein (1976, 1978), who defined eight zones in the Jurassic; and Williamson (1987), who defined eleven zones in the Cretaceous. Gradstein and Agterberg (1982) recognized nine subdivisions of the Tertiary of the northern Grand Banks and Labrador Shelf, based on optimum sequences and taxa. The work of Gradstein and Agterberg (1982) was expanded by Gradstein (1985) to include additional wells.

Gradstein and Williams (1976) published a zonation for the latest Cretaceous-Tertiary of the Labrador Shelf. The foraminiferal zonation was refined by Gradstein and Srivastava (1980) and Gradstein and Agterberg (1982). D'Iorio (1986), using the foraminiferal data of Gradstein and the palynological data of Williams, determined the optimum sequence for 78 taxa and defined nine events in the Tertiary of the Labrador Shelf. This demonstrates the effectiveness of quantitative stratigraphic techniques in refining qualitative zonations.

Ostracodes have also been used for zoning the Mesozoic of the Scotian Shelf and the Grand Banks, most notably by

Ascoli (1976, 1981). The paucity of ostracodes in the Tertiary prevents their use for zonation of that period.

Other zonations for the Mesozoic-Cenozoic of offshore eastern Canada are more specific in application. Jansa et al. (1980) applied the Tethyan late Tithonian-earliest Berriasian calpionellid zonation of Remane (1964) to coeval sections in some Scotian Shelf-Grand Banks wells. Ascoli et al. (1984) extended this study into the Late Berriasian-Early Valanginian.

Nannoplankton have been used extensively by oil company micropaleontologists for zonation of the Mesozoic-Cenozoic, but the findings have not been published. The only published contribution is by Doeven (1983), who subdivided the Albian-Maastrichtian into 16 zones. Both qualitative and quantitative techniques were used to order the data.

The other microfossils used for stratigraphic studies in the Cenozoic of offshore eastern Canada are diatoms. Thomas and Gradstein (1981) reported the occurrences of species of *Coscinodiscus* in the Tertiary of 16 wells. Their findings are discussed more fully in the section on other microfossil groups.

PALEOZOIC

Early Paleozoic

Lower Paleozoic rocks occur extensively in offshore eastern Canada, but are precisely dated in only a few places. Age determinations must be made on core and cuttings samples whose small size precludes the practical utility of macrofossils for age correlation and results in the use of microfossils.

Conodonts are perhaps the most useful microfossils in Early Paleozoic biostratigraphy. Large samples, unfortunately, are typically required for adequate recovery of specimens; so, the use of conodonts has been limited in the offshore setting. Greater success has been achieved with organic-walled microfossils, acritarchs and chitinozoans. These groups can be recovered from a few grams of rock and show rapid evolution which makes them useful guide fossils.

The age significance of the acritarch assemblages has been demonstrated in studies of Grand Banks and Labrador Shelf wells. The oldest known sedimentary rocks are in the Hopedale E-33 well (Fig. 3.1a,b), where the interval 1985-1995 m is Tremadoc, the assemblages comparing favorably with Tremadoc assemblages described by Martin (1968). Three wells on the Labrador Shelf (Freydis B-87, Hopedale E-33 and Indian Harbour M-52) and three wells on the Grand Banks (Cumberland B-55, Linnet E-63 and Phalarope P-62) encountered Ordovician rocks (Jenkins, 1984; Jenkins in Barnes et al., 1981; King et al., 1986). Lower Ordovician rocks in the interval 3952-3957 m (12 966-12 982 ft) in Indian Harbour M-52 contained scolecodonts, conodonts and acritarchs. In Phalarope P-62, between 2969 and 3074 m (9740 and 10 085 ft), the Tremadoc-Arenig acritarchs showed affinities with coeval assemblages from Morocco and Bohemia (Jenkins, 1984). In Freydis B-87, the chitinozoans and acritarchs indicate a Caradoc-Late Ashgill age for the interval 1932.4 to 2313.4 m (6340-7590 ft). This is at variance with the middle to late Caradoc age given by Jenkins (in Barnes et al., 1981). The environment of deposition during the Ordovician was presumed to be marine.

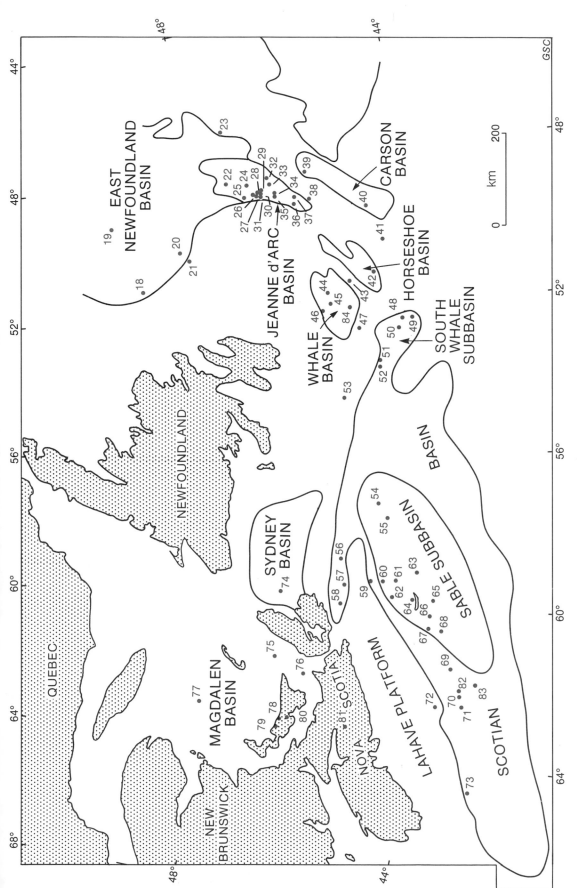

Figure 3.1a. Location map, southern area of study (Scotian Shelf, Gulf of St. Lawrence, Bay of Fundy, Grand Banks, offshore northeast Newfoundland) showing position of wells for which biostratigraphic data are provided. The wells are numbered accordingly: Acadia K-62, 83; Adolphus D-50, 24; Argo F-38, 56; Ben Nevis I-45, 32; Bittern M-62, 42; Bjarni H-81, 8; Blue H-28, 19; Bonnition H-32, 39; Bradelle L-49, 77; Brant P-87, 50; Cartier D-70, 11; Coot K-56, 46; Cormorant N-83, 37; Cree E-35, 67; Cumberland B-55, 20; Dauntless D-35, 54; Dominion O-23, 22; East Point E-49, 75; Egret K-36, 34; Egret N-46, 35; Eider M-75, 45; Eurydice P-36, 58; Fox I-22, 57; Freydis B-87, 15; Gabriel C-60, 23; Gannet O-54, 47; Gjoa G-37, 1; Glooscap C-63, 82; Green Gables No. 1, 78; Gudrid H-55, 9; Hare Bay E-21, 17; Hebron I-13, 33; Hekja A-72, 2; Herjolf M-92, 7; Hermine E-94, 53; Heron H-73, 49; Hibernia B-08, 28; Hibernia K-18, 27; Hibernia O-35, 30; Hibernia P-15, 29; Hopedale E-33; 6, Indian Harbour M-52, 14; Irishtown No. 1, 79; Iroquois J-17, 62; Jaegar A-49, 41; Karlsefni A-13, 3; Kittiwake P-11, 51; Leif E-38, 12; Linnet E-63, 21; Mic Mac H-86, 60; Missisauga H-54, 61; Moheida P-15, 70; Mohawk B-93, 73; Murre G-67, 36; Naskapi N-30, 72; Nautilus C-92, 26; North Sydney P-05, 74; Northumberland Strait F-25, 76; Onondaga E-84, 66; Osprey H-84, 40; Phalarope P-62, 43; Primrose A-41, 63; Puffin B-90, 52; Razorbill F-54, 84; Roberval K-92, 10; Sable Island C-67, 64; Sachem D-76, 55; Sandpiper 2J-77, 44; Skolp E-07, 4; Snorri J-90, 5; Spoonbill C-30, 38; Stewiake borehole, 81; Tors Cove D-52, 48; Triumph P-50, 65; Tyrone No. 1, 80; Verrazano L-77, 16; Wenonah J-75, 68; Wyandot E-53, 59.

Other questionable Ordovician rocks have been encountered in the Gudrid H-55 and Roberval K-92 wells on the Labrador Shelf. Dolomite sequences in these wells contain organic-walled microfossils ranging in age from Devonian through Carboniferous (Visean and Westphalian) to Mesozoic (Jenkins, 1984). The Carboniferous age was confirmed by Barss et al. (1979) and Barss (pers. comm.) who interpreted the dolomite in Gudrid (2677.8-2677.9 m; 8785.3-8785.6 ft) and Roberval (3578.7-3870.3 m) to be Westphalian D-Stephanian. Detailed palynological and petrographical studies indicated, however, that the palynomorphs were contaminants.

Legault (1982) noted several acritarch species and two chitinozoan species in a dredge sample from Orphan Knoll. Legault regarded the palynomorph assemblages as being Late Ordovician (Caradoc-Ashgill).

No data have been published on the composition of the chitinozoan-acritarch assemblages which occur in the Grand Banks cores described by Jenkins (in Barnes et al., 1981) and King et al. (1986). These authors have stated, however, that the microfossil assemblages show affinity with coeval European assemblages, so control is presumably by extrapolation from the type sections.

Late Paleozoic

The biostratigraphy of Upper Paleozoic rocks in the study region is based primarily on spores. The zonation utilized (Fig. 3.4) was originally proposed in Barss and Hacquebard (1967) and Hacquebard (1972). The zonation was established using samples from surface sections, whose lithostratigraphy is discussed in Chapter 4.

Horton Group

Devonian-Tournaisian rocks of Atlantic Canada include the Horton Group which outcrops in New Brunswick and Nova Scotia; lateral equivalents occur in southwestern Newfoundland (Chapter 4). The rocks were named the Horton Bluff Series by Dawson (1873). Bell (1929) shortened this to Horton Series, which is now termed the Horton Group to comply with the North American Commission on Stratigraphic Nomenclature (1983). Although a type section was not designated, it has been assumed to be Horton Bluff in Kings County, Nova Scotia. Rocks older than those at Horton Bluff were included in the Horton Group by Hacquebard (1972). The two oldest spore zones of the Horton are the A and B zones of Devonian age (Hacquebard, 1972). The alphabetic system of naming zones in Hacquebard (1972) is confusing, because the same letters repeat for the Horton, Windsor-Canso-Riversdale-Cumberland, and Pictou groups. Accordingly, in this chapter, we have named the zones after a diagnostic species (Fig. 3.4). The types of zones were not specified by Hacquebard (1972) but they appear to fall within the definition of Oppellian zones or concurrent range zones (see North American Commission on Stratigraphic Nomenclature, 1983).

In parts of the Cumberland Subbasin, the *Emphanisporites annulatus* Zone (previously Zone A) is recognized in rocks formerly assigned to the River John Series of the Horton Group. The *Hystrichosporites multifurcatus* Zone (previously Zone B) is recognized in the Memramcook Formation, also of the Horton Group, in the Moncton Subbasin of southeast New Brunswick.

The remaining five zones of the Horton Group are, in ascending order: the *C, D, E, F,* and *G* zones (Fig. 3.4). The lower four zones are of restricted regional occurrence. Rocks assigned to the youngest zone, the *Vallatisporites vallatus* Zone (Zone G), occur over much of Atlantic Canada. This includes western Newfoundland, Cape Breton, mainland Nova Scotia, and the Moncton Subbasin of New Brunswick. In parts of Atlantic Canada, oil shales occur in the Carboniferous (Tournaisian) part of the Horton Group; an example is the Albert Formation (Williams et al., 1985). The spores of the Albert Formation suggest a Tournaisian age (Utting, 1987).

Rocks of equivalent age to the Horton Group probably occur offshore in the Gannet O-54, Phalarope P-62 and Sandpiper 2J-77 wells on the Grand Banks (Fig. 3.5). The oldest zone, the *Emphanisporites annulatus* Zone, occurs in Phalarope P-62. Rocks assigned to the next youngest zone, the *Hystrichosporites multifurcatus* Zone, are present in Gannet O-54 and Phalarope P-62; in Phalarope the Devonian rocks are immediately overlain by Jurassic rocks. The occurrence of the other zones is shown in Figure 3.5.

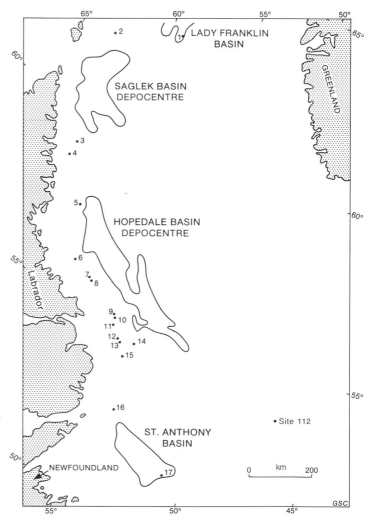

Figure 3.1b. Location map, northern area of study (Labrador margin) showing position of wells and DSDP site 112 for which biostratigraphic data are provided. The numbering of wells is presented in Figure 3.1a.

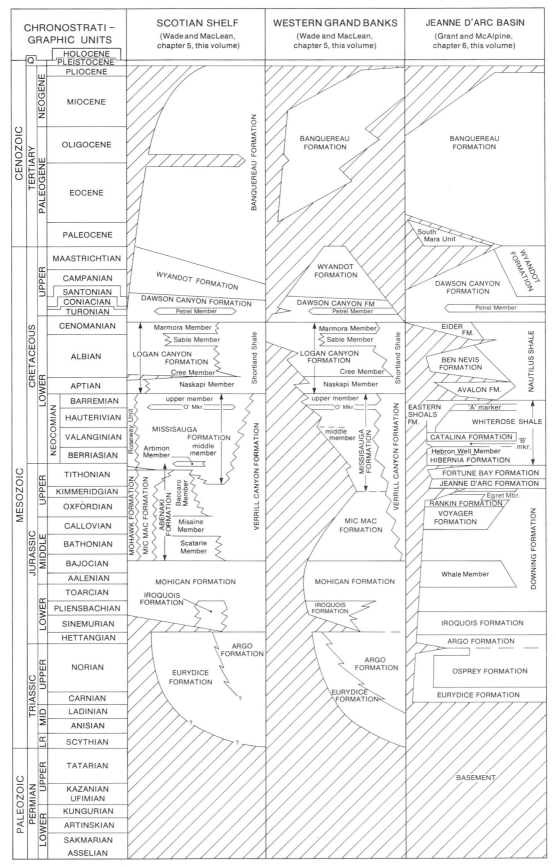

Figure 3.2. Lithostratigraphic units of offshore eastern Canada, after Wade and MacLean (Chapter 5) and Grant and McAlpine (Chapter 6). For Labrador Shelf see Figure 5 (in pocket).

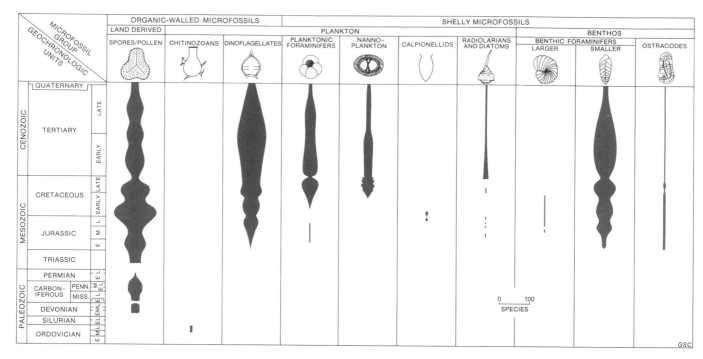

Figure 3.3. Microfossil species diversity in the Phanerozoic of offshore eastern Canada (adapted and updated from Gradstein et al., 1975).

Table 3.1. Published palynological zonations for the Mesozoic-Cenozoic offshore

Age/Region	Scotian Shelf	Grand Banks	Labrador Shelf
Tertiary	Williams et al., 1974 Gradstein et al., 1975 Williams, 1975	Jenkins et al., 1974 Gradstein et al., 1975	Gradstein and Williams, 1976 Williams and Bujak, 1977a Gradstein and Agterberg, 1982 D'Iorio, 1986
Cretaceous	Williams et al., 1974 Gradstein et al., 1975 Williams, 1975 Bujak and Williams, 1978	Gradstein et al., 1975 Williams, 1975 Williams and Brideaux, 1975 Davies, 1986 van Helden, 1986	Gradstein and Williams, 1976
Jurassic	Williams et al., 1974 Gradstein et al., 1975 Williams, 1975 Bujak and Williams, 1977 Barss et al., 1979 Davies, this chapter	Gradstein et al., 1975 Bujak and Williams, 1977 Barss et al., 1979 Jansa et al., 1980 Davies, 1986 van Helden, 1986	
Triassic	This chapter	Gradstein et al., 1975 Walton and Berti, 1976 Bujak and Williams, 1977 Jansa et al., 1976,1977,1980 Barss et al., 1979	

Table 3.2. Published foraminiferal-ostracode zonations for the Mesozoic-Cenozoic offshore

Age/Region	Scotian Shelf	Grand Banks	Labrador Shelf
Tertiary	Ascoli, 1976 Gradstein and Agterberg, 1982	Jenkins et al., 1974 Ascoli, 1976 Gradstein et al., 1975 Gradstein, 1976, 1985 Gradstein and Agterberg, 1982 Gradstein and Agterberg, 1985	Gradstein and Williams, 1976 Gradstein and Srivastava, 1980 Gradstein and Agterberg, 1982 d'Iorio, 1986
Cretaceous	Williams et al., 1974 Gradstein et al., 1975 Ascoli, 1976 Ascoli et al., 1984	Jenkins et al., 1974 Gradstein, 1975, 1976 Gradstein et al., 1975 Ascoli, 1976 Jansa et al., 1980 Ascoli et al., 1984 Agterberg et al., 1985 Williamson, 1987	Gradstein and Williams, 1976 Gradstein and Srivastava, 1980 Gradstein in Srivastava, 1986
Jurassic	Williams et al., 1974 Gradstein et al., 1975 Ascoli, 1976, 1981 Ascoli et al., 1984	Gradstein, 1975, 1976, 1978 Gradstein et al., 1975 Ascoli, 1976, 1984, this chapter Jansa et al., 1980 Ascoli et al., 1984 Williamson, 1987	

Windsor to Pictou groups

The remaining Carboniferous rocks of the Maritime Provinces include in ascending order: the Windsor, Canso, Riversdale, Cumberland, and Pictou groups (the type sections of these groups are described in Chapter 4). The palynological zonation is as presented in Barss and Hacquebard (1967) for the Pictou Group, in Hacquebard (1972) for all the groups, and in Utting (1980) for the Windsor Group and the boundary beds between the Windsor and Canso groups (Fig. 3.4).

Utting (1980), in a study of core samples from a borehole at Stewiacke, Nova Scotia, proposed a threefold subdivision of the Windsor Group (Fig. 3.4) and the boundary beds between the Windsor and the Canso groups. Utting termed the three assemblage zones: I, II, and III. The zones can be correlated with the five macrofossil subzones A-E proposed by Bell (1929). Assemblage zone I is coeval with Bell's subzones A and B; assemblage zone II is coeval with subzones C, D, and E; and assemblage zone III is equivalent to beds which occur above the uppermost marine carbonate of E. The zonation has been tentatively correlated with the Visean spore zones of Britain. Further work has shown that this threefold zonation can be recognized throughout Atlantic Canada (Utting, 1987).

Barss (in Belt, 1965) defined six miospore zones in the Windsor-Canso-Riversdale-Cumberland groups: the A, B, C, D, E, and F zones (Fig. 3.4). The zones are named after diagnostic species in this paper. Hacquebard (1972), gave characteristic species for each zone and considered it impractical to separate zones B and C.

The spore-pollen zonation for the Pictou Group presented by Barss and Hacquebard (1967) lists the five zones (Fig. 3.4). All the zones were named after genera with one or more species first appearing in the named zone.

Barss and Hacquebard (1967) stated that each zone is referred to by the name of its most characteristic miospore species. The three oldest zones can be correlated with the three floral zones which Bell (1938) recognized in the Sydney Basin. Thus, the *Vestispora* and *Torispora* zones are Westphalian C in age and the *Thymospora* Zone is Westphalian D. The *Potonieisporites* Zone is characterized by the first appearance of striate bivesiculate pollen grains, together with other species characteristic of the Westphalian. Barss and Hacquebard (1967), therefore, considered the zone to be Stephanian. The youngest zone, the *Vittatina* Zone, contains several taxa known only from the Permian.

Rocks of Early Carboniferous (Visean) age occur extensively on the continental margin of eastern Canada (see Chapter 4). They underlie most of the Gulf of St. Lawrence and have also been recorded in wells on the Labrador Shelf and Grand Banks. In the Gulf of St. Lawrence, Barss et al. (1979) provided detailed biostratigraphy on six wells. These are Green Gables No. 1, Irishtown No. 1 and Tyrone No. 1, which are on Prince Edward Island, and the offshore wells Bradelle L-49, East Point E-49 and Northumberland Strait F-25. All six wells contain Visean-lower Namurian rocks which can be included in the *Rugospora* Zone (Fig. 3.5). Another well, North Sydney P-05, located offshore in the Sydney Basin, also reached total depth in Visean-lower Namurian rocks.

Two Grand Banks wells, Gannet O-54 and Sandpiper 2J-77, penetrated rocks assigned to the *Rugospora* Zone (Barss et al., 1979). The single occurrence of Visean rocks on the Labrador Shelf is in Verrazano L-77 (Fig. 3.5).

The offshore occurrences of Upper Carboniferous-Permian rocks are less extensive. Rocks included in the *Vestispora* or *Torispora* zones of Westphalian C age occur in two Gulf of St. Lawrence wells (Bradelle L-49 and North Sydney P-05) and in one Grand Banks well (Hermine E-94). The *Thymospora* Zone has been recognized with certainty in the North Sydney P-05 well (Fig. 3.5). The zone is also believed to be present in dolomites in the Labrador Shelf wells, Roberval K-92 and Gudrid H-55 (Barss et al., 1979). There is, however, a divergent view on the age of the Carboniferous dolomite in these two wells. Jenkins (1984) lithologically equated the dolomite with Ordovician rocks in other wells on the Labrador Shelf. He did not dispute the evidence of the Carboniferous palynomorphs but believed they were contaminants. As stated previously, detailed palynological and petrographical studies tend to support the views of Jenkins. The youngest zones, the *Potonieisporites* Zone (Stephanian) and the *Vittatina* Zone (Early Permian), have been positively recognized only in the Gulf of St. Lawrence.

Two other groups of microfossils used for age control in the Carboniferous of offshore eastern Canada are the foraminifers and the algae. Jansa et al. (1978) analyzed

three limestone cores recovered by the Bedford Institute drill from the Northeast Newfoundland Shelf. The foraminiferal assemblages are diagnostic, being from zones 15 and 16 (Mamet, 1970) of Late Visean age. Both Jansa et al. (1978) and Jansa and Mamet (1984) demonstrated that the foraminiferal and algal assemblages in the core from the Northeast Newfoundland Shelf show North American and not European affinities. This is of considerable importance in Carboniferous reconstructions of the North Atlantic.

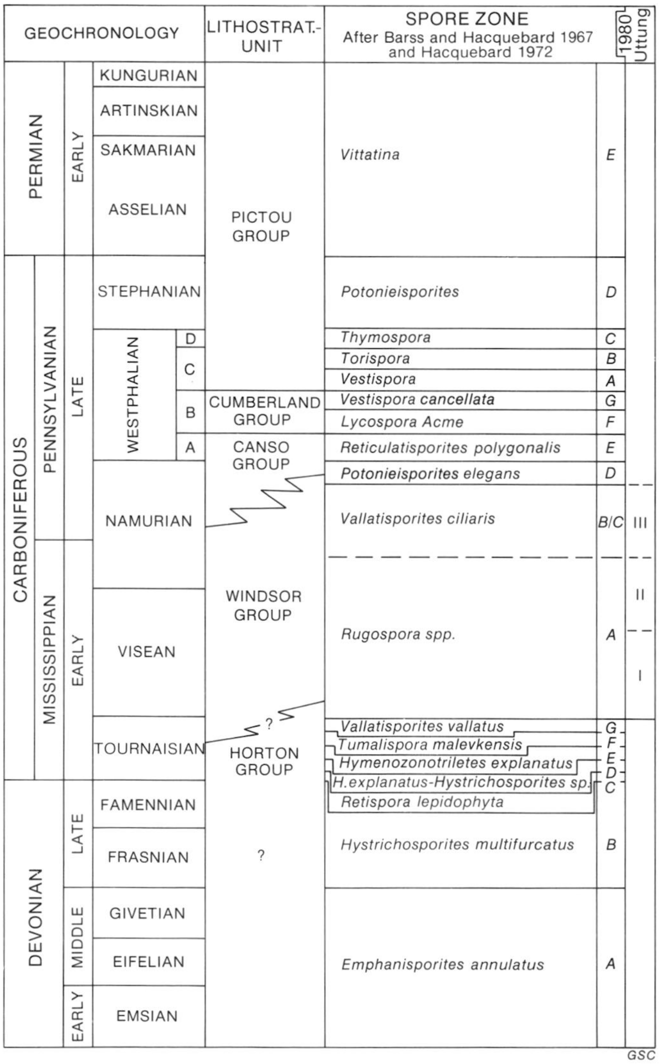

MESOZOIC-CENOZOIC PALYNOLOGY

The exploration for hydrocarbons on the continental margin of eastern Canada over the last two decades has revealed the widespread occurrence of Mesozoic-Cenozoic sediments. The nature of the samples recovered has resulted in a general reliance on palynology and foraminifers and ostracodes for age control. The regional zonations have been provisionally correlated with European stratotypes. This is especially true for the palynology, because detailed Mesozoic-Cenozoic zonations were not available when the initial investigations began in the early 1970s. In the last ten years, however, several palynological zonations have been erected, especially for the Mesozoic-Cenozoic of the North Sea and related areas, by Davey (1979a, 1982), Costa and Downie (1979), Bujak et al. (1980), Riley and Fenton (1982), Woollam and Riding (1983), and Riding (1984). Such works have provided some of the motivation for reappraisal of the palynological zonation of offshore eastern Canada, as demonstrated by Davies (1986) and van Helden (1986).

Scotian Shelf-Grand Banks

Control of the offshore Mesozoic-Cenozoic sequences is not possible from nearby onshore sections, since there are few known outcrops of that age in Atlantic Canada. All the onshore occurrences are of nonmarine to possibly innermost neritic sediments of Early Cretaceous age. Terasmae and Scott (in Stevenson, 1959), Stevenson and McGregor (1963), Lin (1971), and Davies et al. (1984) described spore and pollen assemblages from nonmarine Lower Cretaceous sediments of Hants and Halifax counties, Nova Scotia. The age of the samples analyzed by Davies et al. (1984) was Aptian-early Albian. Such sparse control is of minimal help in correlating the offshore sediments.

Triassic

The oldest known Mesozoic rocks in offshore eastern Canada are of Late Triassic age. They occur in the Whale, Horseshoe and Carson basins of the Grand Banks. A biostratigraphic zonation for these nonmarine sediments was first presented in Gradstein et al. (1975). They dated the lowermost part of Bittern M-62 as middle Triassic and assigned it to the *Klausipollenites* assemblage (Fig. 3.6). Walton and Berti (1976) recognized two Triassic assemblages. The older included the spore genera *Protodiploxypinus* and *Cucullispora*; the younger included the spore species *Patinasporites densus* and *Camarosporites secatus*. Comparison of the taxa with assemblages from the European stratotypes indicated that they were of Carnian age. The assemblages are known from the Sandpiper 2J-77 well in Whale Basin, the Bittern M-62 well in Horseshoe Basin, and Osprey H-84 in Carson Basin (Fig. 3.7). According to

GEOCHRONOLOGY			LITHOSTRAT.-UNIT	SPORE ZONE After Barss and Hacquebard 1967 and Hacquebard 1972		Utting 1980
PERMIAN	EARLY	KUNGURIAN	PICTOU GROUP	*Vittatina*	E	
		ARTINSKIAN				
		SAKMARIAN				
		ASSELIAN				
CARBONIFEROUS	PENNSYLVANIAN	STEPHANIAN		*Potonieisporites*	D	
		WESTPHALIAN D		*Thymospora*	C	
		WESTPHALIAN C	CUMBERLAND GROUP	*Torispora*	B	
				Vestispora	A	
		WESTPHALIAN B		*Vestispora cancellata*	G	
				Lycospora Acme	F	
		WESTPHALIAN A	CANSO GROUP	*Reticulatisporites polygonalis*	E	
				Potonieisporites elegans	D	
		NAMURIAN		*Vallatisporites ciliaris*	B/C	III
	MISSISSIPPIAN	EARLY VISEAN	WINDSOR GROUP	*Rugospora spp.*	A	II
						I
		TOURNAISIAN	HORTON GROUP	*Vallatisporites vallatus*	G	
				Tumalispora malevkensis	F	
				Hymenozonotriletes explanatus	E	
				H. explanatus-Hystrichosporites sp.	D	
				Retispora lepidophyta	C	
DEVONIAN	LATE	FAMENNIAN	?	*Hystrichosporites multifurcatus*	B	
		FRASNIAN				
	MIDDLE	GIVETIAN		*Emphanisporites annulatus*	A	
		EIFELIAN				
	EARLY	EMSIAN				

GSC

Figure 3.4. Palynological zonation of the Devonian-Carboniferous of eastern Canada (adapted from Barss and Hacquebard, 1967; Hacquebard, 1972; Utting, 1980).

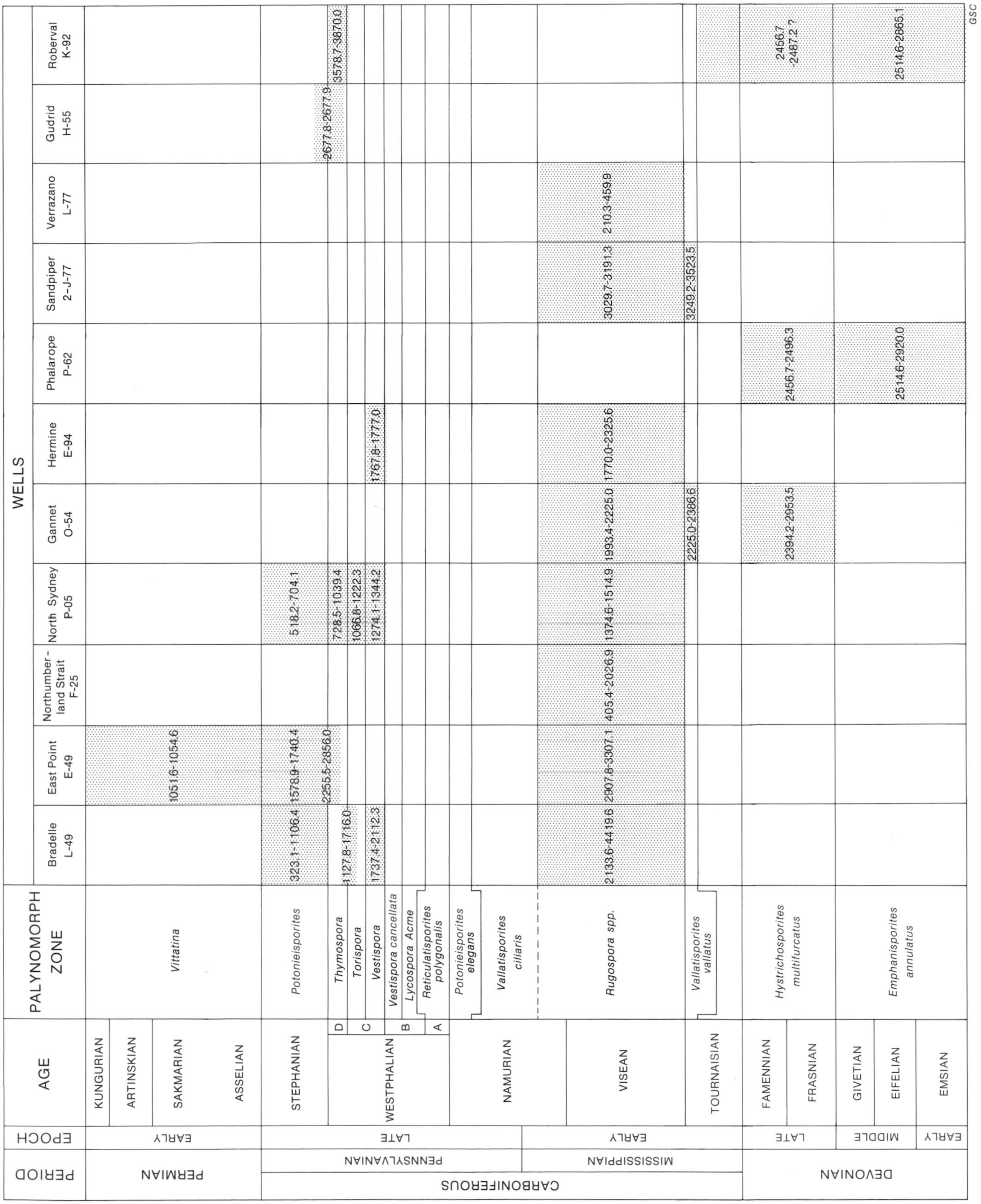

Figure 3.5 — Occurrence of Viséan to Permian rocks in wells, eastern Canada (intervals in metres). Rotated stratigraphic chart.

PERIOD	EPOCH	AGE	PALYNOMORPH ZONE
PERMIAN	EARLY	KUNGURIAN	Vittatina
		ARTINSKIAN	
		SAKMARIAN	
		ASSELIAN	
CARBONIFEROUS (PENNSYLVANIAN)	LATE	STEPHANIAN	Potonieisporites
		WESTPHALIAN D	Thymospora
		WESTPHALIAN C	Torispora
		WESTPHALIAN C	Vestispora
		WESTPHALIAN B	Vestispora cancellata / Lycospora Acme
		WESTPHALIAN A	Reticulatisporites polygonalis
			Potonieisporites elegans
		NAMURIAN	Vallatisporites ciliaris
CARBONIFEROUS (MISSISSIPPIAN)	EARLY	VISEAN	Rugospora spp.
		TOURNAISIAN	Vallatisporites vallatus
DEVONIAN	LATE	FAMENNIAN	Hystrichosporites multifurcatus
		FRASNIAN	
	MIDDLE	GIVETIAN	Emphanisporites annulatus
		EIFELIAN	
	EARLY	EMSIAN	

Well intervals (metres):

- **Bradelle L-49:** 323.1–1106.4; 1578.9–1740.4; 2255.5–2856.0; 1127.8–1716.0; 1737.4–2112.3; 2133.6–4419.6
- **East Point E-49:** 1051.6–1054.6
- **Northumberland Strait F-25:** 405.4–2026.9; 2907.8–3307.1
- **North Sydney P-05:** 518.2–704.1; 728.5–1039.4; 1066.0–1222.3; 1274.1–1344.2
- **Gannet O-54:** 1993.4–2225.0; 2225.0–2386.6; 2384.2–2953.5
- **Hermine E-94:** 1767.8–1777.0; 1770.0–2325.6
- **Phalarope P-62:** 2456.7–2496.3; 2514.6–2920.0
- **Sandpiper 2-J-77:** 3029.7–3191.3; 3249.2–3623.5
- **Verrazano L-77:** 210.3–459.9
- **Gudrid H-55:** 2677.8–2677.9
- **Roberval K-92:** 3578.7–3870.0; 2456.7 / 2487.2 ?; 2514.6–2865.1

GSC

Figure 3.5. Occurrence of Viséan to Permian rocks in wells located in Prince Edward Island and offshore eastern Canada. Location of individual wells is shown in Figures 3.1a and b. Intervals are in metres.

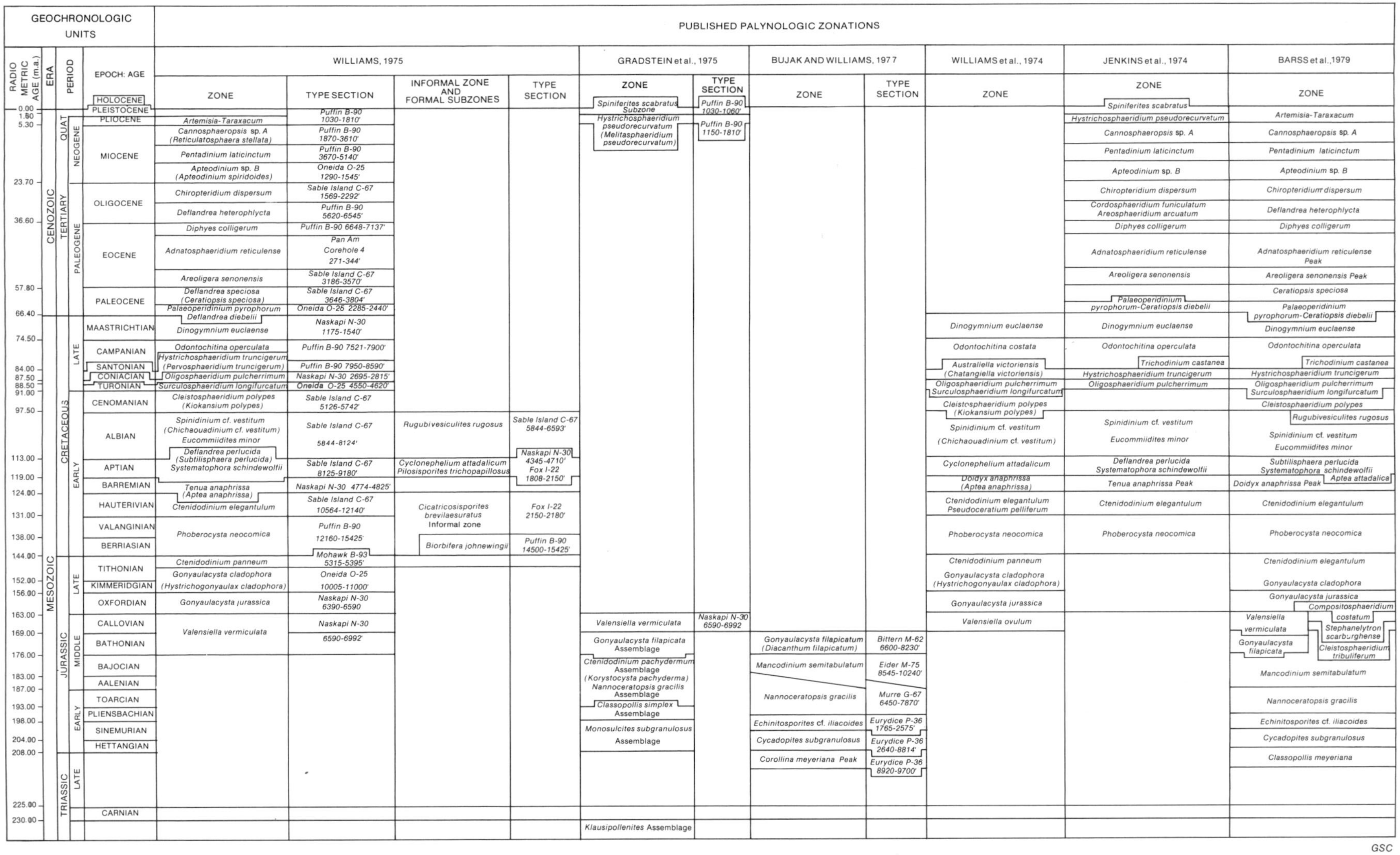

Figure 3.6. Published palynological zonations for the Mesozoic-Cenozoic rocks of offshore eastern Canada. Details of the type sections for each zone and subzone are also included. Depths are in feet.

GSC

98

Walton and Berti (1976), the assemblages were diagnostic of the Eurydice and Argo formations (equivalent to the Kettle redbeds and Osprey evaporites of Jansa et al., 1977).

Distinctive Carnian-Norian assemblages in two Grand Banks wells (Osprey H-84 and Spoonbill C-30) have been assigned to the *Porcellispora longdonensis* assemblage (Barss et al., 1979). Carnian-Norian rocks are also present in the Glooscap C-63 well in the Scotian Basin. Overlying the Carnian-Norian in Osprey H-84 is an interval with abundant specimens of *Corollina meyeriana*. This can be correlated with the *Corollina meyeriana* Peak Zone of Bujak and Williams (1977). These authors regarded the zone as Rhaetian-early Hettangian. The *C. meyeriana* Zone also occurs in Argo F-38 and Eurydice P-36 in Scotian Basin, Sandpiper 2J-77 and Coot K-56 in Whale Basin, Osprey H-84 in Carson Basin, and Spoonbill C-30 in Jeanne d'Arc Basin (Barss et al., 1979).

Jurassic

Jurassic rocks occur extensively on the Scotian Shelf and Grand Banks, although there are some major unconformities and hiatuses, especially on the Grand Banks. The dinoflagellate zonations which have been widely applied are those of Williams (1975), as emended by Gradstein et al. (1975), Bujak and Williams (1977) and Davies (1985, 1986). Some of the zonations are shown in Figure 3.6.

Five of the six zones formally erected by Bujak and Williams (1977) were assemblage zones as defined in Article 21 of the American Commission on Stratigraphic Nomenclature (1961). Each assemblage was named for a taxon not found in sediments above the zone. The single peak zone is as defined in the American Commission on Stratigraphic Nomenclature (1961). The zone is named after a species that attained its maximum absolute abundance in that zone.

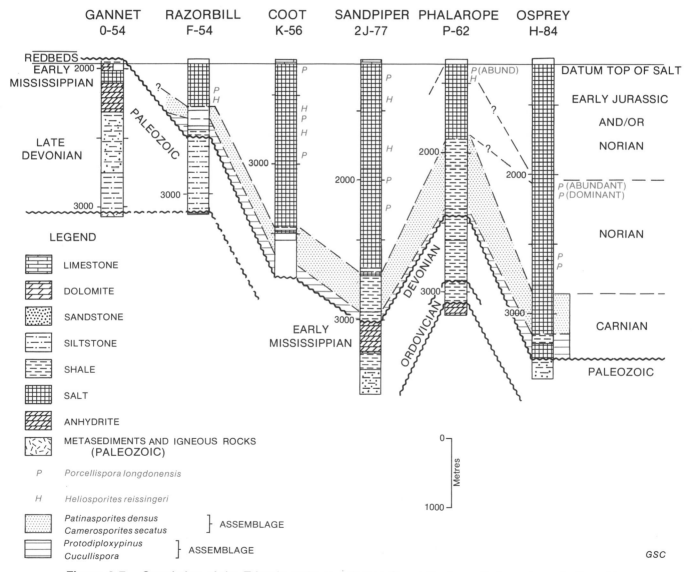

Figure 3.7. Correlation of the Triassic rocks in selected Grand Banks wells based on stratigraphic ranges of spores and pollen (after Walton and Berti, unpublished data, 1976).

99

The three Liassic zones proposed by Bujak and Williams (1977) are based exclusively on spores and pollen. Those authors gave the following age assignments to the zones: the *Classopollis meyeriana* Peak Zone, Rhaetian to early Hettangian; the *Cycadopites subgranulosus* Zone, Late Hettangian to early Sinemurian; the *Echinitosporites* cf. *E. iliacoides* Zone, Sinemurian to Pliensbachian. In a comparison with the miospore zonation for outcrop sections in Portugal (Davies, 1985, fig. 5a) the above zones may be assigned the following ages (Fig. 3.8): the *Classopollis meyeriana* Peak Zone, Rhaetian to Hettangian; the *Cycadopites subgranulosus* Zone, Sinemurian to early Pliensbachian; and the *Echinitosporites* cf. *E. iliacoides* Zone, late Pliensbachian to early Toarcian. The younger age assignments seem to be more correct.

Predominantly marine dinoflagellate assemblages first appear in the *Nannoceratopsis gracilis* Zone which was believed to be late Pliensbachian to Aalenian (Bujak and Williams, 1977). It now appears to be Toarcian to Aalenian, when calibrated with the Portuguese and northwest European zonations. The succeeding *Mancodinium semitabulatum* Zone, which was dated as Aalenian-Bajocian (Bujak and Williams, 1977), appears to be Aalenian when compared with the European zonations (Fig. 3.8). The youngest zone proposed by Bujak and Williams was the Bathonian *Diacanthum* (as *Gonyaulacysta*) *filapicatum* Zone, which we believe may include part of the Bajocian.

Davies, in a re-evaluation of four wells (Acadia K-62, Glooscap C-63, Moheida P-15, and Mohican I-100) on the Scotian Shelf, has identified Early Jurassic dinocyst species including *Dapcodinium priscum*, *Eyachia prisca* and *Liasidium variabile*.

The data from the Scotian Basin conclusively prove, for the first time, the presence of marine Lower Jurassic rocks in that area. They are also the basis for the Sinemurian

to early Oxfordian zonation proposed by Davies in Figure 3.8, which is correlated with existing European zonations (Woollam and Riding, 1983; Riding, 1984; Davies, 1985). The zones are: the *Liasidium variabile* Zone (late Sinemurian-early Pliensbachian), the *Echinitosporites* sp. A zone (late Pliensbachian-early Toarcian), the *Dapcodinium semitabulatum* Zone (late Toarcian-Aalenian), the *Nummus* spp. Peak Zone (Bajocian), the *Ctenidodinium sellwoodii* Zone (latest Bajocian-earliest Callovian) and the *Adnatosphaeridium caulleryi* Zone (Callovian-early Oxfordian). Each zone can be subdivided as shown in Figure 3.8.

Williams (1975) recognized four assemblage zones in the Middle to Late Jurassic of the Scotian Shelf (Fig. 3.6). The four zones allowed recognition of the Bathonian-Callovian, the Oxfordian, the Kimmeridgian, and the Tithonian. Williams' incorrect usage of the Tithonian Age has resulted in some confusion. His two youngest zones, *Rhynchodiniopsis* (as *Gonyaulacysta*) *cladophora* and *Ctenidodinium panneum* zones, are based on correlation with coeval sediments from southern England. Therefore, the *R. cladophora* Zone equates with the Kimmeridgian of southern England and the *C. panneum* Zone is more correctly referred to the Portlandian.

Barss et al. (1979) refined the Jurassic zonation by erecting three informal zones as shown in Figure 3.6 and demonstrated the presence of Middle and Upper Jurassic rocks in several Scotian Shelf wells. The continuity of the section is unusual, especially in the Late Jurassic.

Two Liassic dinoflagellate assemblages occur in wells from the Grand Banks (Barss et al. 1979; Jansa et al., 1980). The older assemblage, which contains *Dapcodinium priscum*, was found in the Sandpiper 2J-77 well; it can be assigned a Sinemurian age based on correlations to Portugal (Davies, 1985) and northwestern Europe (Woollam and

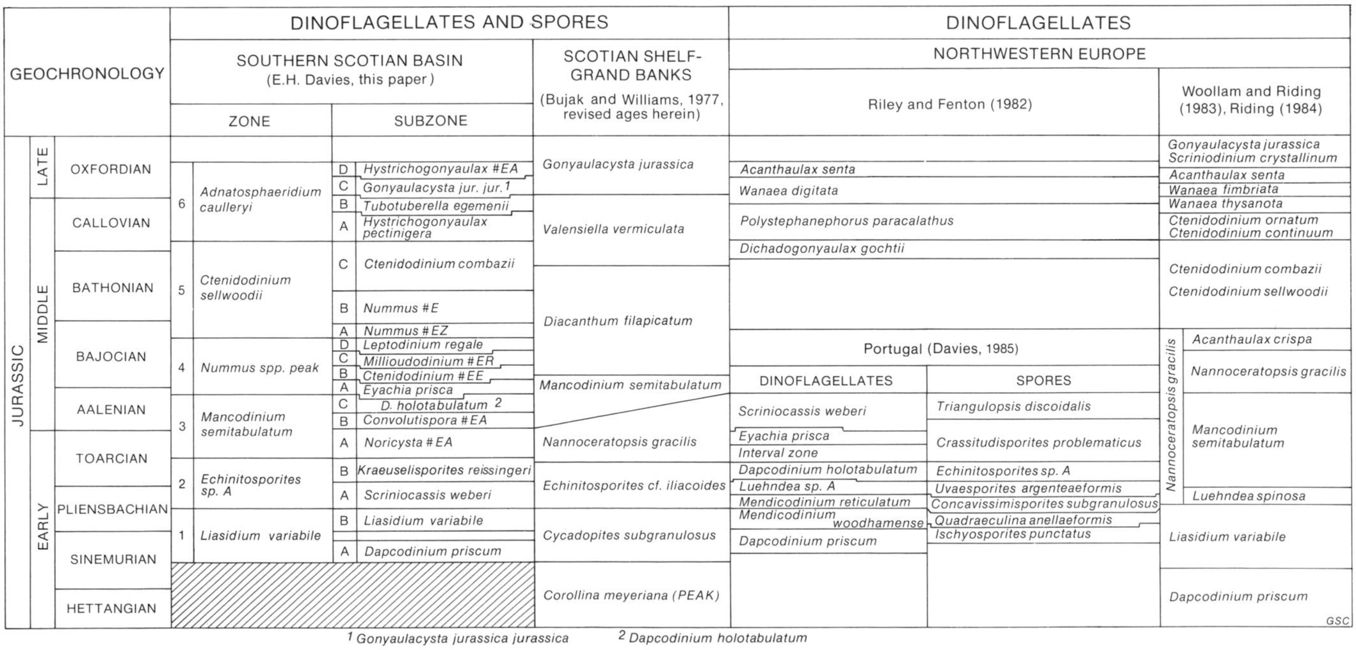

Figure 3.8. Correlation of the palynomorph zonations for the Early to Middle Jurassic of the Scotian Shelf with palynomorph zonations for northwestern Europe (after Davies, 1985).

Riding, 1983; Riding, 1984). The second assemblage, with *Luehndea spinosa*, occurs in the Cormorant N-83, Bittern M-62, and Heron H-73 wells; it can be assigned a late Pliensbachian age (Davies, 1985).

The Jurassic section in the Grand Banks wells is often incomplete because of the Cimmerian unconformity. In extreme cases — as in Tors Cove D-52, Osprey H-84 and Spoonbill C-30 — Lower Jurassic rocks may be directly overlain by Upper Cretaceous rocks. More or less complete Upper Jurassic sequences are present in the Jeanne d'Arc Basin as typified in wells of the Hibernia field.

Biostratigraphic studies of the Late Jurassic have received added impetus with the discovery of the Hibernia field. The concentration of wells in a relatively small area and the availability of extensive sidewall cores and conventional cores have provided an opportunity for detailed zonations and correlations. This is demonstrated in Figure 3.9, which presents the palynological zonation developed by Davies (1986). Both the Kimmeridgian and the Portlandian can be subdivided in this zonation (Fig. 3.9). The above palynological zonation provides detailed control in the Hibernia wells and throughout the Jeanne d'Arc Basin. Van Helden (1986) has also proposed a zonation for some of the reservoir intervals in the Hibernia wells (Fig. 3.10). The sequence includes the oldest reservoir sandstone, which was termed the Jeanne d'Arc member of the Mic Mac Formation (Arthur et al., 1982) and is now termed the Jeanne d'Arc Formation (Chapter 6). In the Jurassic, van Helden recognized two zones: the *Rhynchodiniopsis* (as *Gonyaulacysta*) *cladophora* Assemblage Zone of Williams (1975), which he also believed was Kimmeridgian, and the *Amphorula metaelliptica* Assemblage Zone, which he considered to be Portlandian-early Berriasian.

The *Rhynchodiniopsis cladophora* Assemblage Zone includes shales, sandstones and limestones underlying the Jeanne d'Arc member (Arthur et al., 1982) subsequently named the Jeanne d'Arc Formation (Chapter 6). The *Amphorula metaelliptica* Assemblage Zone includes the Jeanne d'Arc Formation and the overlying shale sequence, the Fortune Bay Shale. The other zones of van Helden (1986) are discussed in the following section.

Cretaceous

Lower Cretaceous rocks are not uniformly distributed on the Scotian Shelf and Grand Banks. The maximum thicknesses occur at the delta fronts such as in the Scotian Basin and Jeanne d'Arc Basin, where the total thickness of the Missisauga and Logan Canyon formations can be in excess of 3000 m. On LaHave Platform and Grand Banks, the formations are considerably thinner or absent. Upper Cretaceous rocks are almost invariably marine and have a ubiquitous distribution, reflecting the major transgressive phase in the Mesozoic-Cenozoic of the region. The thicknesses are generally much less, however, than those for the Lower Cretaceous sequences.

The palynological zonation applied to the Cretaceous rocks of the Scotian Basin has been that of Williams (1975). He erected eleven zones and three subzones which only have regional applicability (Fig. 3.6). Each zone is named after a species that does not occur in sediments younger than the zone. Recognition of the *Rugubivesiculites rugosus* Subzone, of late Albian age, is possible only where sidewall or conventional cores are available, since it is defined

on the base or oldest occurrence of the index species. Two informal spore zones were also defined in the Early Cretaceous.

All the age assignments in Williams (1975) were provisional. Subsequent studies indicate that the correct assignments may differ by up to an age. Several of the Cretaceous zones can be adjusted by up to half an age, so that the top of the *Odontochitina operculata* Zone should more correctly fall in the early Maastrichtian, the top of the *Pervosphaeridium* (as *Hystrichosphaeridium* and *Cordosphaeridium*) *truncigerum* Zone would be early Campanian.

Other reviews of palynological zonations for the offshore Cretaceous are listed in Table 3.1. Williams and Brideaux (1975) published the results of an analysis of eight shallow coreholes, located on the Grand Banks. The Cretaceous section was Late Albian to Maastrichtian. Although Williams and Brideaux did not propose a formal zonation, they did recognize diagnostic biostratigraphic divisions based on the spore and pollen or dinoflagellate and acritarch assemblages (Fig. 3.11). The biostratigraphic divisions closely approximated concurrent range zones, except for those divisions separated by large gaps in geological time. Also, the divisions generally equated with age or epoch boundaries.

Bujak and Williams (1978) made only minor revisions to the zonation of Williams (1975). They defined the *Cerbia tabulata* (as *Cyclonephelium attadalicum*) Zone as a peak zone and noted the inconsistency of the *Biorbifera johnewingii* Subzone. The tentative ages of the zones were based on detailed comparisons with palynomorph assemblages from European surface sections, including the stratotypes.

The need for more detailed control in the Jeanne d'Arc Basin, where most of the reservoir intervals are Late Jurassic or Early Cretaceous, has resulted in the publication of revised zonations. Van Helden (1986) recognized two dinocyst assemblage zones in the Berriasian-Valanginian of the basin (Fig. 3.10). The oldest zone, the *Endoscrinium campanulum* Zone, encompasses the lower part of the Hibernia member (Arthur et al., 1982), subsequently named the Hibernia Formation (Chapter 6) plus the underlying shale unit, the Fortune Bay Shale. The *Endoscrinium campanulum* Zone was considered to be Late Berriasian to early Valanginian. Van Helden (1986) included the upper part of the Hibernia member in the *Phoberocysta neocomica* Zone (pars.) of Williams (1975); he considered the lower part of the zone to be Valanginian.

Davies (1986) proposed a detailed zonation for the Berriasian-Turonian of the Hibernia field in the Jeanne d'Arc Basin. The zones are based on analyses of seven wells. The zones, their ages and their occurrences in the Hibernia wells, are shown in Figure 3.9. Using this zonation, it is possible to correlate "Avalon sands" in the Hibernia field (Fig. 3.12). This demonstrates the true ages and relationships of the main Avalon zone of Benteau and Sheppard (1982). The exercise also draws attention to the need for detailed biostratigraphic studies of the reservoir sands in the Jeanne d'Arc Basin.

Tertiary

The Tertiary sediments on the Scotian Shelf and Grand Banks are all included in the Banquereau Formation (Fig. 3.2), which is a clastic sequence of mudstones, sandstones

AGE		ZONE	SUBZONE		HIBERNIA WELLS						
					G-55	I-46	J-34	O-35	P-15	K-18	B-08
TURONIAN	14	Surculosphaeridium longifurcatum	B	Surculosphaeridium longifurcatum	1620	1701.3	1710	1720	1920	1990	2015
			A	Florentinia ferox	?	1751	1790	1810	1950	2025	
CENOMANIAN	13	Kiokansium polypes	B	Cyclonephelium vannophorum	1650	1798.3	1870		2010	2055	
			A	Matonisporites excavatus	1724	1825	1900	1900	2190		2110
ALBIAN	12	Spinidinium sp. A.	C	Aptea polymorpha	1770	1874	1920		2190+	2145	2115
			B	Parvosaccites rugosus	1800	1888	2030	1971	2310	2175	2130
			A	Nodosisporites babsei	1825	1902	2070	2002		2230	
	11	Stellatopolis sp. A.	B	Plicatella jansonia	1950		2150+	2045	2340	2275	
			A	Nodosisporites costatus	2000	1925	2350+	2110	2400?		
APTIAN	10	Parvosaccites amplus	C	Parvosaccites amplus	2130	2125	2430+	2200?	2430		
			B	Cerbia tabulata	2175	2160	2503+	2230	2440	2286	2135
			A	Callialasporites turbatus	2269	2299	?	2290	2455	2294.8	2145
BARREMIAN	9	Subtilisphaera terrula	D	Muderongia imparilis	2414	2358.35	2620	2320	2460	2300	2150
			C	Concavissimisporites longiverrucatus	2480	?		2386		2352	?
			B	Hystrichogonyaulax sp. cf. H. cladophora	2510	2416	2635	?			2155
HAUTERIVIAN			A	Canningia sp. cf. C. reticulata	2600			2440			2165
	8	Muderongia staurota	C	Heslertonia heslertonensis	2640	2472.8		2530	2490		
			B	Phoberocysta #EB			2655	2620	2550	2450	2255
			A	Achomosphaera neptunii	2725	2473.4	2720	2700?	2675	2540	2315
VALANGINIAN	7	Pseudoceratium pelliferum	D	Surculosphaeridium sp. III	2857	2478.2	2760	2840		2600	2555
			C	Ctenidodinium elegantulum	2973?	2496.9			2730	2660	2675
			B	Oligosphaeridium diluculum	3080	2551.2	2800	2870	2820	2780	2740
			A	Pilosisporites ericus	?	2594.8	2960	3050	2940	2875	2830
	6	Cerebropollenites macroverrucosus	B	Ischyosporites tuberculatus	3200	2640.5	3070	3095	3060	3025	2895
BERRIASIAN			A	Cicatricosisporites magnus	?	2826.55+	?	3310	3291	3235	3040
			C	Muderongia mcwhaei	3352 3392	2830.8	3150	3490	3480	3450	3245
			B	Striatella #EJ		3000	3425?	4005	3720	3630	3400
TITHONIAN	5	Ctenidodinium panneum	A	Amphorula #EA		?	3500? 3711 TD	4185	3820	3745	3492.9
	4	Glossodinium dimorphum				3125 3250		4245	3895	3875	3650
KIMMERIDGIAN	3	? Subtilisphaera paeminosa		Cantulodinium #EA							
			C	Cribroperidinium #E2				4365	3955	3960	3780
			B	Muderongia #EA				4455	4045	4060	3810
			A					4545	4075	4120	3990
	2	Pilosisporites sp. A.	C	Imbatodinium kondratjevii				4635	4195	4330	4140
			B	Meiourogonyaulax callomonii				4755	4395	4510	4355
	1	Hystrichodinium #DA	A	Cribroperidinium systremmatum				4788 TD	4405 TD	4675	4435 TD
										4905 5035 TD	

Note: For G-55 column "fault to basement"; for I-46 "fault to Triassic".

GSC

Figure 3.9. Proposed palynological zonation of the Late Jurassic (Kimmeridgian) to Late Cretaceous (Turonian) of Hibernia wells in Jeanne d'Arc Basin. The columns to the right give the depth, in metres, to the "top" of each zone or subzone in the Hibernia wells. The red stipple indicates absence or uncertainty of zones.

and siltstones. Thicknesses of the Tertiary section vary considerably from a few hundred metres as in Cree E-35 in the Scotian Basin to several thousand metres as in Dominion O-23 in the Jeanne d'Arc Basin. There is a significant increase in thickness northwards on the Northeast Newfoundland Shelf. This is discussed in the section on the Labrador Shelf.

The palynological zonation generally followed for the Cenozoic of the Scotian Shelf-southwestern Grand Banks is that of Williams (1975), who erected 11 zones (Fig. 3.6). In the same paper, Williams also informally subdivided the early Oligocene and the Plio-Pleistocene.

Williams and Brideaux (1975), in their analyses of the eight shallow coreholes from the Grand Banks, recognized several biostratigraphic divisions in the Cenozoic (Fig. 3.11). The dinoflagellates allowed recognition of 12 age-diagnostic divisions; the spores and pollen allowed recognition of 14 age-diagnostic divisions. The detailed spore-pollen zonation has not been applied to the explora-

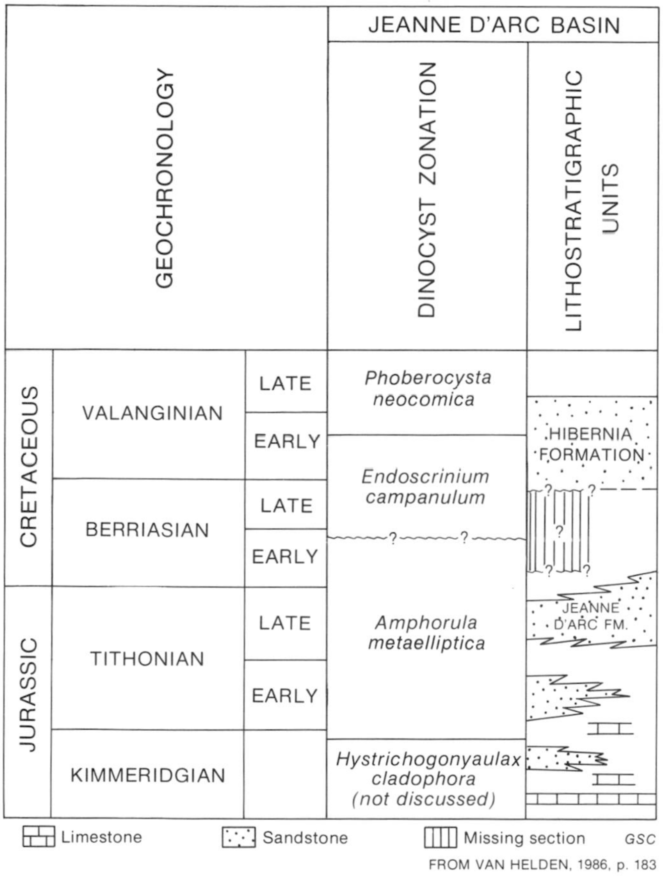

GEOCHRONOLOGY			DINOCYST ZONATION	LITHOSTRATIGRAPHIC UNITS
CRETACEOUS	VALANGINIAN	LATE	Phoberocysta neocomica	
		EARLY	Endoscrinium campanulum	HIBERNIA FORMATION
	BERRIASIAN	LATE		
		EARLY	? ?	
JURASSIC	TITHONIAN	LATE	Amphorula metaelliptica	JEANNE D'ARC FM.
		EARLY		
	KIMMERIDGIAN		Hystrichogonyaulax cladophora (not discussed)	

JEANNE D'ARC BASIN

Limestone   Sandstone   Missing section   GSC

FROM VAN HELDEN, 1986, p. 183

Figure 3.10. The stratigraphic ranges of selected dinocyst species in the Late Jurassic (Kimmeridgian) to Early Cretaceous (Valanginian) of the Jeanne d'Arc Basin, according to van Helden (1986). The proposed zonation of van Helden (1986) is related to the lithostratigraphic units recognized in Arthur et al. (1982).

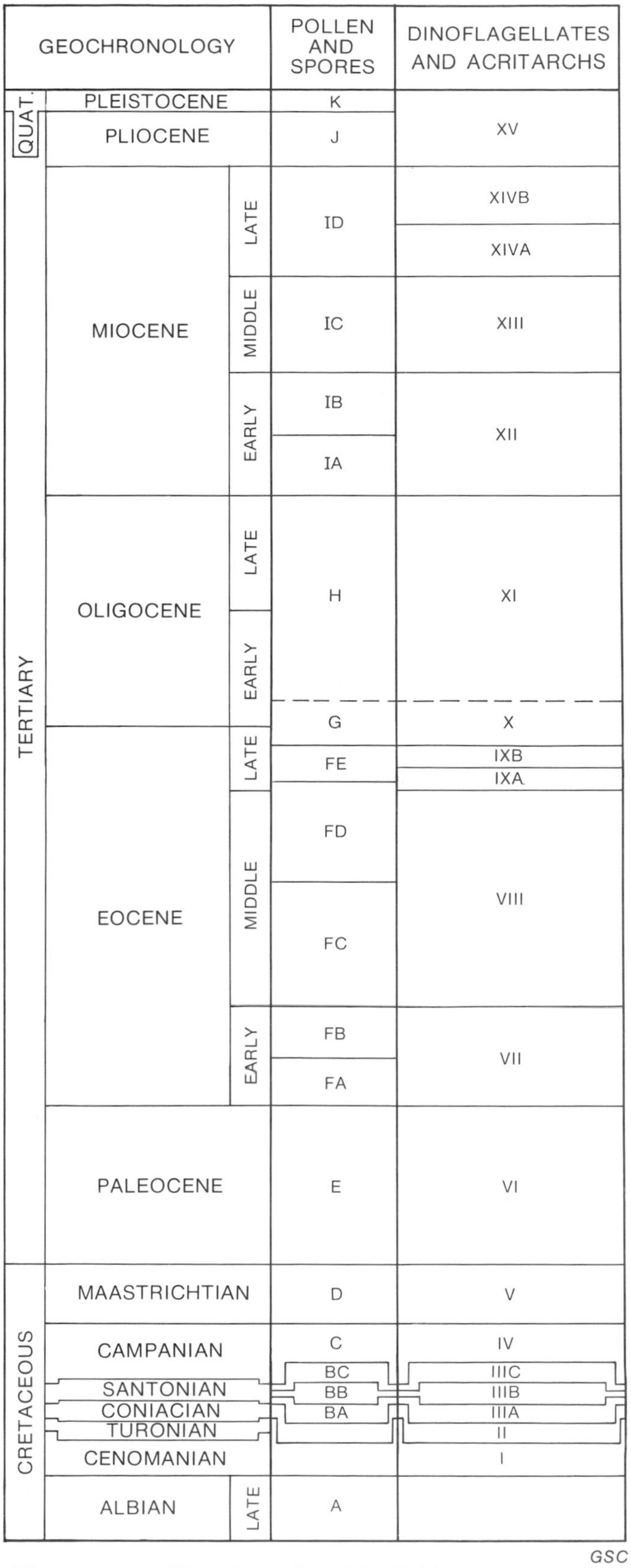

GEOCHRONOLOGY			POLLEN AND SPORES	DINOFLAGELLATES AND ACRITARCHS
QUAT.	PLEISTOCENE		K	
	PLIOCENE		J	XV
TERTIARY	MIOCENE	LATE	ID	XIVB
				XIVA
		MIDDLE	IC	XIII
		EARLY	IB	XII
			IA	
	OLIGOCENE	LATE	H	XI
		EARLY		
			G	X
	EOCENE	LATE	FE	IXB
				IXA
		MIDDLE	FD	VIII
			FC	
		EARLY	FB	VII
			FA	
	PALEOCENE		E	VI
CRETACEOUS	MAASTRICHTIAN		D	V
	CAMPANIAN		C	IV
	SANTONIAN		BC	IIIC
	CONIACIAN		BB	IIIB
	TURONIAN		BA	IIIA
	CENOMANIAN			II
				I
	ALBIAN	LATE	A	

GSC

Figure 3.11. The biostratigraphic divisions — based on ranges of spores, pollen, dinocysts and acritarchs — recognized in the Late Albian to Pleistocene of the Grand Banks by Williams and Brideaux (1975). The samples analyzed were cores from a series of shallow coreholes drilled in 1965

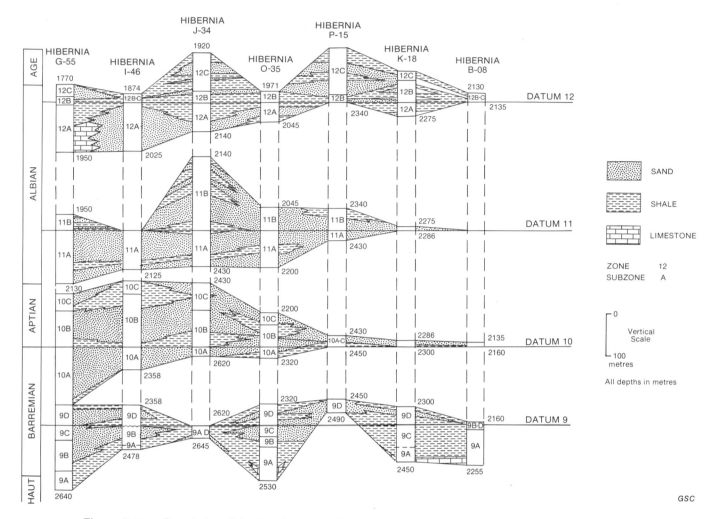

Figure 3.12. Correlation of the "Avalon sands" in wells in the Hibernia field. The datum lines are: Datum 9 (within the Barremian), Datum 10 (base of Aptian), Datum 11 (within the Albian), Datum 12 (within the Albian). The alphanumeric symbols represent the subzones shown in Figure 3.9. The analyses and compilation were carried out by E. H. Davies.

tory wells, in part because nearly all the samples from the Upper Cretaceous-Tertiary sections are cuttings samples, in part because of the tendency not to undertake detailed analyses of the fine fractions (ca. 20-30 µm) of palynology samples.

Labrador Shelf

The geological evolution of the Labrador Sea began in the Late Jurassic or Early Cretaceous with rifting between Canada and Greenland. The classical rift-drift model (Srivastava, 1978) assumes that the area is a failed oceanic basin, with the initial phase of rifting in the Early Cretaceous being accompanied by volcanism; these volcanics are called the Alexis Formation (Fig. 5, in pocket). The overlying synrift deposits of the Bjarni Formation are predominantly coarse clastics. In the Late Cretaceous, the rifting phase gave way to drifting with deposition of a fine to coarse clastic sequence, the Markland Formation. Srivastava (1978) stated that rifting occurred between the Early Cretaceous and Campanian. The duration of drifting

in the southern Labrador Sea was Campanian (anomaly 32) to late Eocene. In the northern Labrador Sea, drifting commenced in the Maastrichtian.

The structural elements of the Labrador Shelf from south to north include the Hopedale Basin and Saglek Basin. Lady Franklin Basin is located farther north off southeast Baffin Island. Individual wells are identified according to basin in the following two sections.

Cretaceous

There is no formal palynological zonation for the Cretaceous of the Labrador Shelf. Gradstein and Williams (1976) defined two assemblages: the *Cerebropollenites mesozoicus* assemblage which they dated Barremian-Albian; and the *Amphidiadema nucula-Leberidocysta* (as *Hexagonifera*) *chlamydata* assemblage of Maastrichtian age. The *C. mesozoicus* assemblage occurs in several wells in Hopedale Basin, including Bjarni H-81, Skolp E-07 and Snorri J-90. This assemblage, which is typical of the Bjarni Formation, is believed to be Barremian-Aptian by later workers (Barss et al., 1979). The spore assemblage is dominated by cicatricose spores. There are a few marginal marine dinoflagellate taxa, including *Muderongia asymmetrica* (Davies, pers. comm.).

Cretaceous rocks of post-Aptian and pre-Maastrichtian age are rarely encountered in wells drilled on the Labrador Shelf. Two exceptions are Freydis B-87 and Skolp E-07. In Freydis B-87, a spore assemblage overlying the *Cerebropollenites mesozoicus* assemblage, has been dated as late Albian (Barss et al., 1979). This is overlain by an assemblage containing both spores and dinocysts, which is probably late Albian to Cenomanian. The sediments containing this assemblage represent some of the oldest marine Cretaceous rocks in the Labrador Sea. In Skolp E-07, a late Albian-Cenomanian palynomorph assemblage is probably coeval, but is devoid of dinoflagellates. The interval 1786.1 to 1795.3 m (5860-5890 ft) in Freydis B-87 contains species which elsewhere characterize the Turonian. Probable Coniacian-Santonian assemblages occur in Freydis B-87 and Skolp E-07. The dinoflagellate assemblages of the Coniacian and Santonian show close affinities with assemblages from Graham Island (Manum and Cookson, 1964) and from Bylot Island (Ioannides, 1986). Ioannides regarded his Interval I as Santonian-early Campanian, perhaps a more correct age for the Labrador Shelf assemblages.

In Skolp E-07 a diverse dinoflagellate assemblage at 1645-1835 m appears to be Santonian-early Campanian. The assemblage shows some affinities with those from arctic islands (McIntyre, 1975). The overlying sediments from 446.5 to 495.3 m (1465 to 1625 ft) are probably Campanian. Campanian rocks are also found on the Baffin Island Shelf (Chapter 7), Bylot Island (Ioannides, 1986), and the West Greenland Shelf (Rolle, 1985).

The succeeding *Amphidiadema nucula-Leberidocysta* (as *Hexagonifera*) *chlamydata* assemblage has been regarded as Maastrichtian (Gradstein and Williams, 1976). The widespread occurrence of this assemblage and underlying Campanian assemblages indicate that there was a major marine transgression in the Labrador Sea during the Campanian-Maastrichtian. This is particularly true of the southern and central parts of Hopedale Basin. In Skolp E-07, in Hopedale Basin, the Maastrichtian can be subdivided into two informal zones. The late Maastrichtian contains species of *Laciniadinium* which are common in Arctic assemblages (Ioannides, 1986). Their absence from other wells may denote missing section or a restricted occurrence of these species.

Tertiary

The Tertiary rocks of the Labrador Shelf form a thick sequence of clastic sediments. These may be several kilometres thick, especially under the outer shelf. Formal Tertiary lithological units, in ascending order, are: the Cartwright Formation, Kenamu Formation, Mokami Formation, and Saglek Formation (Fig. 5, in pocket). The sediments tend to become coarser upwards and there has been repeated recycling. This dilutes the microfossil concentrations and aggravates the problem of reworking. Consequently, it is often difficult to recognize which palynomorphs are *in situ* and which are reworked.

The informal palynomorph zonation that has been used for the Tertiary of the Labrador Shelf is shown in Figure 3.13 (Gradstein and Williams, 1976; Williams and Bujak, 1977a). The informal subdivisions, termed assemblages, are based on the stratigraphic distribution of dinoflagellates and spores. The Tertiary palynomorph subdivisions can be recognized in part or in total in most of

GEOCHRONOLOGY			ASSEMBLAGE	LABRADOR SHELF WELLS									
				Freydis B-87	Indian Harbour M-52	Leif E-38	Leif M-48	Cartier D-70	Gudrid H-55	Bjarni H-81	Herjolf M-92	Snorri J-90	Karlsefni A-13
CENOZOIC	PLEISTOCENE PLIOCENE		*Tsugaepollenites igniculus*	451.1 -515.1	304.8 -579.1	344.4 -585.2	393.2 -576.1			381.0 -731.5	487.7 -801.6	393.2 -576.1	536.5 -1243.6
	MIOCENE	LATE MIDDLE	*Operculodinium centrocarpum*	542.5 -823.0		606.6 -874.8	731.5 -880.9	591.3 -1109.5	506.0 -713.2	871.7 -972.3	823.0 -1106.4	731.5 -880.9	1264.9 -1917.2
		EARLY	*Epicephalopyxis indentata*	841.3 -1036.3		779.4 -890.0 T.D.	880.9 -1155.2	1143.0 -1213.1	731.5 -1423.4	1024.1 -1307.6	1127.8 -1350.3	880.9 -1155.2	1942.8 -2008.6
	OLIGOCENE	LATE	*Cordosphaeridium fibrospinosum- Deflandrea sp.*	1045.5 -1054.6			1173.5 -1194.8	1271.0 -1277.1	?	1328.9 -1368.6	?	1173.5 -1194.8	
		EARLY	*Wetzeliella ovalis*	1066.8 -1077.5			1200.9 -1237.5		1450.8 -1645.9	?		1200.9 -1237.5	
	EOCENE	LATE MIDDLE	*Wetzeliella lunaris*	1097.3 -1338.1	1447.8 -2490.2		1255.8 -1511.8	1301.5 -1700.8	1670.3 -2090.9	1389.9 -1825.8	1402.1 -1777.0	1255.8 -1511.8	2048.3 -2767.6
		EARLY	*Areoligera senonensis*	1356.4 -1411.2	2508.5 -3038.9		1527.0 -1722.1	1728.2 -1761.7	2109.2 -2228.1	1831.8 -1917.2	1798.3 -2142.7	1527.1 -1722.1	2792.0 -3774.0
	PALEOCENE	LATE	*Deflandrea speciosa*	1429.5 -1466.1	3057.1 -3121.2		1742.5 -1752.6	1783.1 -1859.3	2243.3 -2377.4	1938.5 -1947.7	2164.1 -2173.2	1741.0 -1752.6	3794.8 -3925.8
		EARLY	*Eisenackia circumtabulata*		3139.4 -3148.6		1767.8		?	1969.0 -2039.1	2194.6 -2203.7	1767.8	
			P. pyrophorum	1484.4 -1493.5	3166.9 -3176.0			1883.7 -1905.0	2395.7 -2432.3	2054.4 -2063.5	2225.0 -2325.6	1791.0 -1836.4	3947.2 -4108.7

GSC

Figure 3.13. The Cenozoic palynomorph assemblages recognized by Gradstein and Williams (1976) and Williams and Bujak (1977) and their occurrences in some Labrador Shelf wells. The wells are ordered sequentially from south to north. All depths are in metres.

the Labrador Shelf-Davis Strait wells, although there are often gaps. The *Alisocysta* (as *Eisenackia*) *circumtabulata* assemblage of middle Paleocene age occurs in only six wells. These are Gjoa G-37 in the Saglek Basin tectonically but in the Davis Strait geographically, and Bjarni H-81, Herjolf M-92, Hopedale E-33, Indian Harbour M-52 and Leif M-48, which are all in the Hopedale Basin of the Labrador Shelf. Documented hiatuses in the Tertiary occur in the early Oligocene (Bjarni H-81, Herjolf M-92, Karlsefni A-13 and Leif E-38), in the middle to late Oligocene (Herjolf M-92, Gjoa G-37), in the Oligocene (Hekja A-72, Hopedale E-33), and probably in the Miocene. Williams (pers. comm.), in a palynological study of six wells, has noted that middle to upper Oligocene sediments are absent in Cartier D-70, Hekja O-71, Herjolf M-92, Karlsefni A-13 and Roberval K-92. From a study of multichannel seismic data, Grant (1980) postulated a Late Miocene regional unconformity on the Labrador Shelf. This is difficult to substantiate with the palynomorph data because of the sparse assemblages in the Neogene. There is some support, however, in the Bonavista C-99 well on the Northeast Newfoundland Shelf where middle Miocene sediments appear to be overlain by Pliocene sediments.

Concerns over the low resolution of the biostratigraphic control in the Tertiary of the Labrador Shelf have led to the evaluation of other approaches (Gradstein and Agterberg, 1982). This has resulted in the development of a quantitative stratigraphic correlation method, the Ranking and Scaling Program (RASC). The Ranking and Scaling Program orders species occurrences into an optimum sequence and spaces them relatively according to time. Application of RASC to the palynology data for the Tertiary of the Labrador Shelf orders the species as shown in Figure 3.14. This provides an optimum sort of 43 taxa, with four taxa being reworked. The consistent positioning of the reworked taxa suggests that there is a time relationship between reworked material and *in situ* assemblages. A dendrogram based on 38 taxa yields a more precise zonation than the subjective zonation of Gradstein and Williams (1976). This is now being applied to Labrador Shelf wells.

MESOZOIC-CENOZOIC FORAMINIFERS AND OSTRACODES

During the last decade, major advances have been made in the utilization of foraminiferal and ostracode zonations of the Mesozoic-Cenozoic of offshore eastern Canada. Because foraminifers and ostracodes are predominantly marine, they have not provided age control in the Triassic. The zonations will, therefore, deal with the Jurassic, Cretaceous and Tertiary, with geographic separation as for the section on palynomorphs. The forced, almost exclusive reliance on cuttings samples has placed a heavy reliance on the last appearance datum (LAD) or "top" of individual species. This has been negated to some extent by the integration of the individual zonations. There are, however, several instances of discrepancies between the data from the foraminifers, ostracodes and palynomorphs, an inevitable consequence of the sample types. One example has been the availability of palynology slides from sidewall cores, which were too small to be processed for foraminifers and ostracodes. Such differences are noted here, but detailed comparisons of zonations of individual wells can be found in the following publications: Gradstein, 1975,

SEQUENCE POSITION	FOSSIL NUMBER	RANGE	PALYNOMORPH TAXON
1	115	0 - 2	Pinus
2	173	1 - 3	Tsugaepollenites igniculus
3	1	2 - 6	Abies
4	182	2 - 5	Osmundacidites
5	230	4 - 6	Chatangiella (reworked)
6	7	5 - 8	Alnipollenites verus
7	34	5 - 8	Caryapollenites simplex
8	104	7 - 9	Osmundacidites DA
9	175	8 - 10	Ulmipollenites DA
10	166	9 - 11	Triporopollenites
11	12	10 - 12	Aquilapollenites (contaminant)
12	469	11 - 13	Systematophora ancyrea
13	519	12 - 14	Veryhachium trispinosum
14	159	13 - 16	Triatriopollenites
15	125	13 - 16	Podocarpidites DA (reworked)
16	59	15 - 17	Deltoidospora
17	129	16 - 18	Polypodiacidites DA
18	378	17 - 19	Lingulodinium machaerophorum
19	204	18 - 20	Areoligera coronata (reworked)
20	98	19 - 22	Nyssapollenites
21	504	18 - 22	Epicephalopyxis indentata
22	236	21 - 23	Chatangiella victoriensis (reworked)
23	65	22 - 24	Extratriporopollenites (reworked)
24	333	23 - 25	Hystrichokolpoma rigaudiae
25	37	24 - 26	Cicatricosisporites
26	401	25 - 27	Operculodinium centrocarpum
27	422	26 - 28	Phthanoperidinium
28	271	27 - 29	Dapsilidinium pastielsii
29	348	28 - 30	Impletosphaeridium transfodum
30	277	29 - 32	Deflandrea phosphoritica
31	511	29 - 32	Pediastrum
32	198	31 - 33	Apectodinium homomorphum
33	318	32 - 34	Glaphyrocysta ordinata
34	491	33 - 35	Wetzeliella articulata
35	477	34 - 37	Thalassiphora patula
36	397	34 - 38	Oligosphaeridium complex
37	331	35 - 38	Hystrichokolpoma cinctum
38	222	37 - 39	Ceratiopsis dartmooria
39	226	38 - 40	Ceratiopsis speciosa
40	192	39 - 41	Alisocysta circumtabulata
41	412	40 - 42	Palaeoperidinium pyrophorum
42	405	41 - 43	Palaeocystodinium

GSC

Figure 3.14. Optimum ordering of palynomorph taxa for the Tertiary of the Labrador Shelf. This has been generated from the Ranking and Scaling program (RASC) as described by Gradstein and Agterberg (1982).

1976, 1978; Gradstein et al., 1975; Ascoli, 1976, 1981, 1984; Jansa et al., 1980; Thomas and Gradstein, 1981; Ascoli et al., 1984; and Williamson, 1987.

Scotian Shelf—Grand Banks

Jurassic

In the east coast offshore, the oldest Jurassic sediments in which foraminifers have been found are of Pliensbachian age on the Grand Banks. Gradstein et al. (1975) outlined an eightfold zonation based on foraminifers which spans the Pliensbachian to Tithonian.

The first detailed foraminiferal zonation for the Jurassic of the Grand Banks was published by Gradstein (1976). In his study of six wells (Cormorant N-83, Eider M-75, Egret K-36, Bittern M-62, Heron H-73 and Murre G-67), eight zones were defined (Fig. 3.15). Chronostratigraphically, the assemblages were referenced to coeval assemblages from northwestern Europe, Poland and U.S.S.R. Exton and Gradstein (1984) emended the foraminiferal zonation and utilized ostracode taxa for the Pliensbachian-

GEOCHRONOLOGY			NERITIC	
			SHALLOW-DEEP	VERY SHALLOW
JURASSIC	LATE	TITHONIAN		Anchispirocyclina lusitanica
		KIMMERIDGIAN	Epistomina mosquensis	Pseudocyclammina jaccardi
		OXFORDIAN		
	MIDDLE	CALLOVIAN	Reinholdella crebravar	
		BATHONIAN	'Globigerina' bathoniana	
		BAJOCIAN	Garantella ssp.	
		AALENIAN		
	EARLY	TOARCIAN	Lenticulina d'orbignyi	
		PLIENSBACHIAN	Involutina liassica	
		SINEMURIAN- HETTANGIAN		

GSC

Figure 3.15. Foraminiferal zonation for the Jurassic of the Grand Banks, based on wells in the South Whale Subbasin and Jeanne d'Arc Basin, as erected by Gradstein (1976).

AGE			SPECIES AM-MONITE ZONE	FORAMINIFER - OSTRACODE ZONES		
				Lusitanian Basin	Grand Banks	Mainly W. Europe
JURASSIC	MIDDLE	AALENIAN	concavum	Lenticulina d'orbignyi	Lenticulina d'orbignyi	Lenticulina d'orbignyi
			murchisonae			
			opalinum			
	EARLY	TOARCIAN L	levesquei	Bairdiacypris sp.	Bairdiacypris sp.	Vaginulina clathrata group
			thouarsense			
		M	variabilis		—?—	
			bifrons			
		E	falciferum			
			tenuicostatum			
		PLIENSBACHIAN L	spinatum	Frondicularia terquemi	Involutina liassica	Marginulina prima plex. interrupta
			margaritatus			
		E	davoei			
			ibex		—?—	
			jamesoni			
		SINEMURIAN L	raricostatum			Dentalina matutina
			oxynotum			
			obtusum			

GSC

Figure 3.16. Foraminiferal-ostracode zonation for the Sinemurian-Aalenian of Grand Banks, Lusitanian Basin of western Portugal, and western Europe (adapted from Exton and Gradstein, 1984) and its relationship to the standard ammonite zonations.

Aalenian of the Grand Banks. Portuguese surface sections provided the control (Fig. 3.16).

The zonation generally used for the Scotian Shelf Jurassic is that of Ascoli (1976, 1981) and Ascoli et al. (1984); an updated version is given in Figure 3.17. The fourfold zonation includes planktonic foraminifers, calcareous benthic foraminifers, agglutinated benthic foraminifers and ostracodes. The zonation reflects the variable environments of deposition. All the zones were assemblage zones as defined in the American Commission on Stratigraphic Nomenclature (1961). Each assemblage zone is named after one, two, or three "zone markers" which have their highest stratigraphic occurrences in that zone.

According to Ascoli (1976), there are two planktonic foraminiferal zones in the Middle-Late Jurassic. This zonation (Fig. 3.17) is used in this chapter.

The calcareous benthic foraminiferal zonation outlined in Ascoli (1976) is derived from the studies of Simon and Bartenstein (1962), Ohm (1967), Bartenstein (1976a, b, c) and Van Hinte (1976). The five zones approximately equate with the stages: Bathonian, Callovian, Oxfordian, Kimmeridgian ("*sensu gallico*") and Tithonian. The zones, as revised herein, are presented in Figure 3.17. The epistominids are important in providing control in the Middle and Late Jurassic and also in the Early Cretaceous (Ascoli, 1981, 1984). Calibration of the stratigraphic ranges of the epistominids with the standard calpionellid biozonation of the Tethyan domain (Jansa et al., 1980) means that age assignments in the latest Jurassic-earliest Cretaceous sections of offshore eastern Canada have a high degree of precision.

The Jurassic zonation based on agglutinated benthic foraminifers does not permit subdivision of the Middle Jurassic. In the Late Jurassic, three and commonly four zones can be recognized (Fig. 3.17).

The ostracode zonation for the Middle and Late Jurassic was based mostly on the studies of Oertli (1957, 1959, 1985), Simon and Bartenstein (1962) and Bate and Robinson (1978) on the European sections. The fourfold subdivision of the Jurassic has been modified herein, with zones denoting the ages Bathonian through Tithonian (Fig. 3.17). Each of the three Late Jurassic ages can be further subdivided into "early" and "late."

The lateral distribution of the Late Jurassic zones — the calcareous benthic foraminifers, the arenaceous benthic foraminifers and the ostracodes — are documented in Ascoli (1981). All the Middle and Late Jurassic zones occur in wells in the Scotian Basin, LaHave Platform, Carson Basin and Jeanne d'Arc Basin.

The cosmopolitan nature of the Jurassic zonation has been demonstrated by several authors (Jansa et al., 1980; Ascoli, 1984; Ascoli et al., 1984). The Late Jurassic-Early Cretaceous zonations based on calcareous and agglutinated benthic foraminifers and ostracodes can be recognized in the Continental Offshore Stratigraphic Test (COST) G-1 and G-2 wells in the Georges Bank Basin, in the COST B-3 well in the Baltimore Canyon Trough, in the Bonnition H-32 well in the Carson Basin, and in the Hibernia P-15 well in Jeanne d'Arc Basin.

The results of more detailed biostratigraphic studies in Jeanne d'Arc Basin are incorporated in the foraminiferal zonations presented here. The studies also confirmed the presence of the Late Jurassic foraminiferal zone markers recognized by Moullade (1984) in deep-water oceanic sediments.

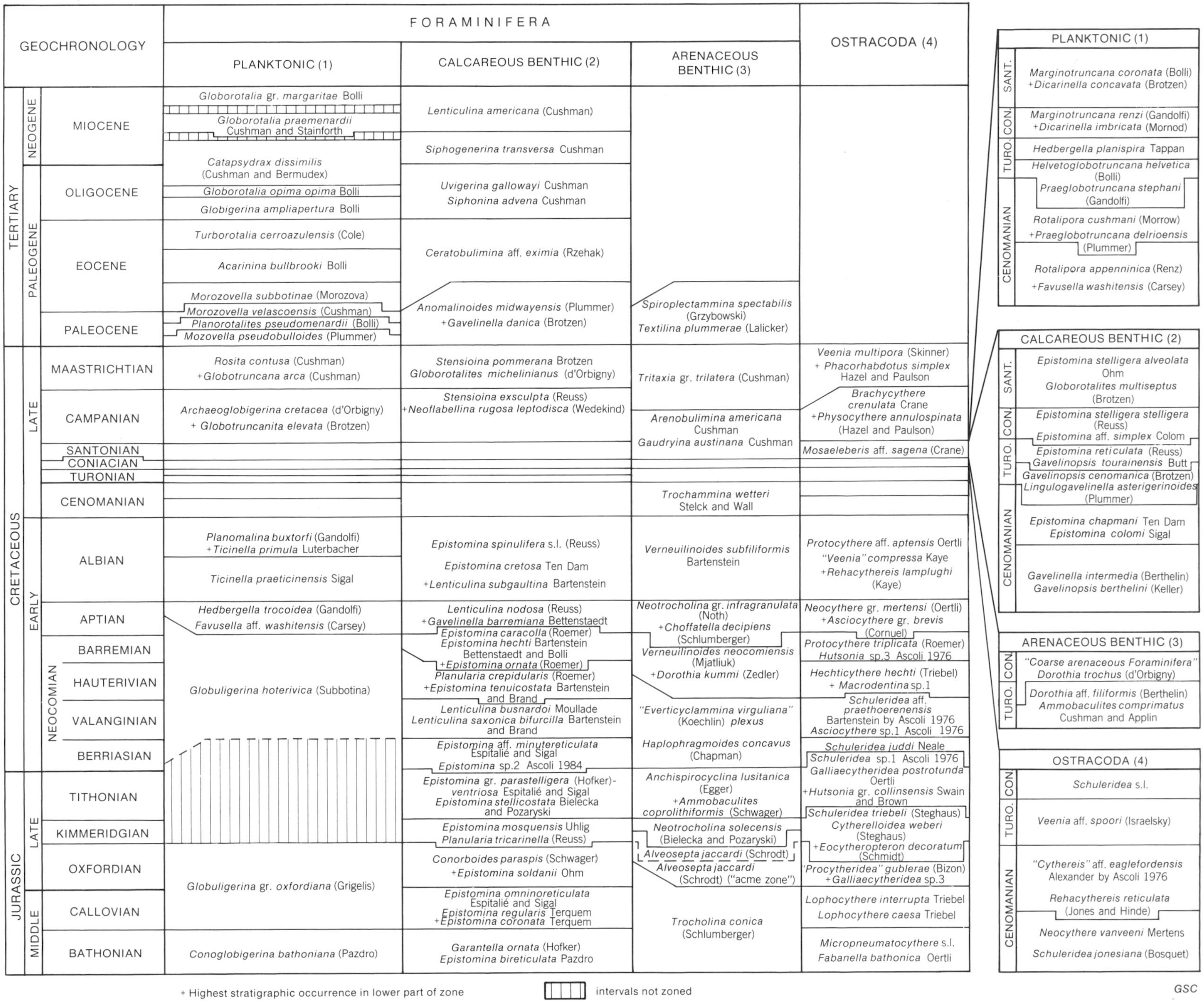

Figure 3.17. Foraminiferal-ostracode zonations for the Mesozoic-Cenozoic of the Georges Bank, Scotian, Jeanne d'Arc, and Carson basins as erected by Ascoli (1976, 1981, 1984, this chapter). The zonations for the Cenomanian-Santonian are shown in the far right column.

Williamson (1987) has also re-evaluated the foraminiferal assemblages of Jeanne d'Arc Basin and applied quantitative stratigraphic techniques. He determined the highest or youngest occurrences of 113 foraminiferal taxa in 13 wells, including Hibernia B-08, K-18, G-55, O-35 and P-15, Hebron I-13 and Ben Nevis I-45. The stratigraphic relationships of the taxa were investigated with the aid of the Ranking and Scaling Program, which provides an optimum and scaled optimum sort of the taxa (Fig. 3.18). The RASC-derived zonation permitted recognition of 11 zones, 2 of which were in the Late Jurassic of Kimmeridgian and Tithonian age. These two oldest zones are characterized by calcareous benthic foraminifers, including species of *Epistomina* and *Lenticulina*. The zonation differs from other studies of Ascoli (1976), Gradstein (1976) and Ascoli et al. (1984). In the early Kimmeridgian, two of the index species were previously used as index species in the Callovian (*Epistomina regularis*) and the Tithonian (*Lenticulina quenstedti*).

Cretaceous

The generally accepted foraminiferal-ostracode zonation for the Scotian Basin is that of Ascoli (1976 and this chapter). His planktonic foraminiferal zonation was based on the cosmopolitan zonations proposed by Bolli (1966) and others; it has been updated in this chapter to take into account the zonation proposed by Caron (1985).

Ten planktonic foraminiferal zones, whose boundaries are usually coincident with stage boundaries, were recognized in the Cretaceous (Ascoli, 1976). The oldest zone, the *Caucasella hoterivica*, was of Valanginian-Barremian age; it is now known as the *Globuligerina hoterivica* Zone. This lack of detailed control in the Neocomian generally reflects the dominance of shallow water sediments in the wells. The other zones allowed recognition of most of the Cretaceous. Ascoli (this chapter) is proposing a series of emendations to this zonation. The Albian is subdivided into early-middle Albian and late Albian, with further subdivision of the late Albian possible. Both the early to middle Cenomanian zone and the late Cenomanian zone can be further subdivided. The Turonian, Coniacian, Santonian, Campanian and Maastrichtian can all be subdivided into early and late. The currently accepted zonation is shown in Figure 3.17. Most of the planktonic foraminiferal zones are recognizable in most offshore wells, ranging from the Baltimore Canyon Trough in the south to the East Newfoundland Basin in the north.

The calcareous benthic foraminiferal zonation (Ascoli, 1976 and this chapter) permits a fourteenfold subdivision of the Cretaceous (Fig. 3.17). The Neocomian zonation is primarily based on the dominance of epistominid species (Ascoli, 1984). Succeeding zones equate with the remaining ages of the Cretaceous and allow subdivision of the Aptian, Cenomanian, Campanian and Maastrichtian.

In the Cretaceous, agglutinated benthic foraminifers were most abundant in littoral and inner neritic environments. They are particularly useful for providing age control and correlation in the clastic reservoir sequences of the Missisauga and Logan Canyon formations of Scotian Basin and the coeval sequences in Jeanne d'Arc Basin. The agglutinated benthic foraminiferal zones proposed by Ascoli (1976) and modified slightly in Ascoli et al. (1984) provided an eightfold subdivision of the Cretaceous. This has been emended herein as shown in Figure 3.17.

Ascoli (1976) also proposed an ostracode zonation for the Cretaceous of offshore eastern Canada. The dominant taxa in the Early Cretaceous showed distinct affinities with coeval European assemblages, based on the work of Oertli (1958) and Simon and Bartenstein (1962). The Late Cretaceous taxa had North American affinities, showing similarities to assemblages described by Howe and Laurencich (1958), Hazel and Paulson (1964) and Crane (1965). The ten zones of Ascoli (1976) allow recognition of most of the Cretaceous stages.

In this chapter, the ostracode zonation for the Cretaceous has been emended, with 11 zones now being recognized (Fig. 3.17). It is also possible to subdivide the Hauterivian, Aptian, Albian, late Santonian-early Campanian, and late Campanian-Maastrichtian. The ostracode zonation is particularly useful for zonation and correlation of deltaic, lagoonal and inner neritic sediments.

The need for a detailed zonation and correlation of the reservoir sands in Jeanne d'Arc Basin motivated Ascoli to undertake analyses of the foraminifers and ostracodes in the Early Cretaceous intervals in 11 wells off east Newfoundland. The results are incorporated into the revised zonation included in this chapter.

Williamson (1987), using the Ranking and Scaling Program (RASC) to generate an optimum and a scaled optimum sequencing of stratigraphically significant foraminiferal taxa, has also studied several wells in Jeanne d'Arc Basin. In the Cretaceous, there are nine distinct clusters or groups which are termed RASC zones (Fig. 3.18). Each zone is defined by the youngest or highest occurrence of key taxa. The zones are equivalent to assemblage zones of conventional stratigraphic practice or interval zones of the North American Stratigraphic Code (Article 45, Section 3, 1983).

The individual taxa diagnostic of the RASC zones are often the same as the index species used by Ascoli. RASC Zones IX through VI are dominated by calcareous benthic foraminifers which sometimes allow correlation with the European stratotypes and the zonation of Ascoli (1976 and this chapter). There are some critical differences, however, in the stratigraphic ranges of the 32 species common to both zonations. Only eleven have the same "tops" (youngest occurrence or Last Appearance Datum, LAD). Sixteen species show differences in their LAD of up to one stage, four differ by two stages, and one differs by three stages. Williamson (1987) considered three species — *Ammobaculites coprolithiformis*, *Lenticulina guttata* and *Conorboides valendisensis* — as characterizing the Berriasian-Valanginian. Ascoli does not extend *A. coprolithiformis* above the Early Tithonian, and has recorded *L. guttata* and *C. valendisensis* as high as the Late Hauterivian.

Diagnostic taxa of Williamson's RASC zones VIII and V also include agglutinated foraminifers, such as *Choffatella decipiens* (RASC Zone V). RASC Zones IV through I are generally dominated by planktonic foraminifers first described from European or other North American sections. The calcareous benthic foraminifers are of secondary importance in the younger zones.

The most complete RASC zonations in the 13 wells were in the Ben Nevis I-45 and Hibernia K-18. RASC Zone VI of Barremian age is missing in Hibernia P-15, O-35, and G-55, and Hebron I-13. RASC Zone IV of Aptian age has not been recognized in Hibernia B-08 and Nautilus C-92. Some of these conclusions are at variance with other

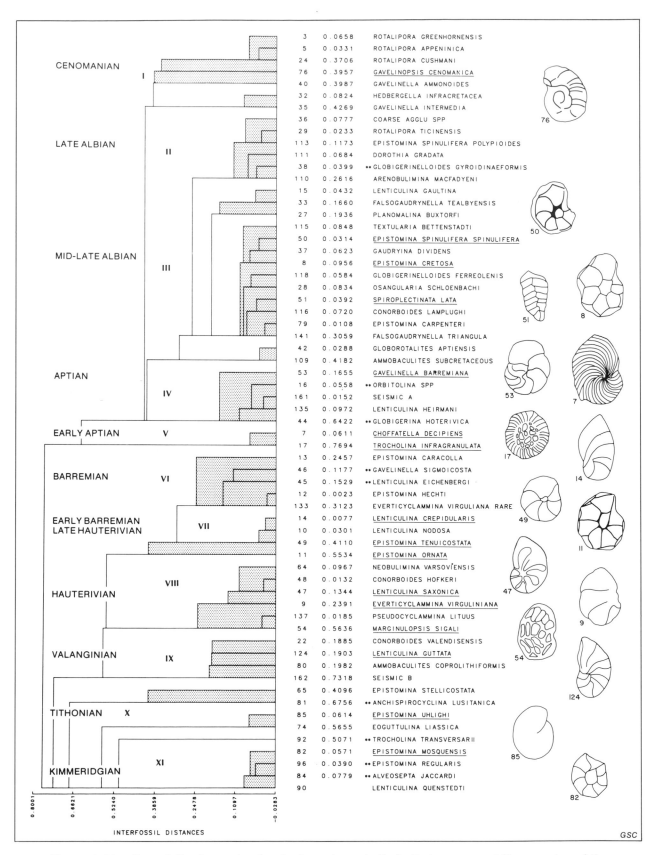

3	0.0658	ROTALIPORA GREENHORNENSIS
5	0.0331	ROTALIPORA APPENINICA
24	0.3706	ROTALIPORA CUSHMANI
76	0.3957	GAVELINOPSIS CENOMANICA
40	0.3987	GAVELINELLA AMMONOIDES
32	0.0824	HEDBERGELLA INFRACRETACEA
35	0.4269	GAVELINELLA INTERMEDIA
36	0.0777	COARSE AGGLU SPP
29	0.0233	ROTALIPORA TICINENSIS
113	0.1173	EPISTOMINA SPINULIFERA POLYPIOIDES
111	0.0684	DOROTHIA GRADATA
38	0.0399	**GLOBIGERINELLOIDES GYROIDINAEFORMIS
110	0.2616	ARENOBULIMINA MACFADYENI
15	0.0432	LENTICULINA GAULTINA
33	0.1660	FALSOGAUDRYNELLA TEALBYENSIS
27	0.1936	PLANOMALINA BUXTORFI
115	0.0848	TEXTULARIA BETTENSTADTI
50	0.0314	EPISTOMINA SPINULIFERA SPINULIFERA
37	0.0623	GAUDRYINA DIVIDENS
8	0.0956	EPISTOMINA CRETOSA
118	0.0584	GLOBIGERINELLOIDES FERREOLENSIS
28	0.0834	OSANGULARIA SCHLOENBACHI
51	0.0392	SPIROPLECTINATA LATA
116	0.0720	CONORBOIDES LAMPLUGHI
79	0.0108	EPISTOMINA CARPENTERI
141	0.3059	FALSOGAUDRYNELLA TRIANGULA
42	0.0288	GLOBOROTALITES APTIENSIS
109	0.4182	AMMOBACULITES SUBCRETACEOUS
53	0.1655	GAVELINELLA BARREMIANA
16	0.0558	**ORBITOLINA SPP
161	0.0152	SEISMIC A
135	0.0972	LENTICULINA HEIRMANI
44	0.6422	**GLOBIGERINA HOTERIVICA
7	0.0611	CHOFFATELLA DECIPIENS
17	0.7694	TROCHOLINA INFRAGRANULATA
13	0.2457	EPISTOMINA CARACOLLA
46	0.1177	**GAVELINELLA SIGMOICOSTA
45	0.1529	**LENTICULINA EICHENBERGI
12	0.0023	EPISTOMINA HECHTI
133	0.3123	EVERTICYCLAMMINA VIRGULIANA RARE
14	0.0077	LENTICULINA CREPIDULARIS
10	0.0301	LENTICULINA NODOSA
49	0.4110	EPISTOMINA TENUICOSTATA
11	0.5534	EPISTOMINA ORNATA
64	0.0967	NEOBULIMINA VARSOVIENSIS
48	0.0132	CONORBOIDES HOFKERI
47	0.1344	LENTICULINA SAXONICA
9	0.2391	EVERTICYCLAMMINA VIRGULINIANA
137	0.0185	PSEUDOCYCLAMMINA LITUUS
54	0.5636	MARGINULOPSIS SIGALI
22	0.1885	CONORBOIDES VALENDISENSIS
124	0.1903	LENTICULINA GUTTATA
80	0.1982	AMMOBACULITES COPROLITHIFORMIS
162	0.7318	SEISMIC B
65	0.4096	EPISTOMINA STELLICOSTATA
81	0.6756	**ANCHISPIROCYCLINA LUSITANICA
85	0.0614	EPISTOMINA UHLIGHI
74	0.5655	EOGUTTULINA LIASSICA
92	0.5071	**TROCHOLINA TRANSVERSARII
82	0.0571	EPISTOMINA MOSQUENSIS
96	0.0390	**EPISTOMINA REGULARIS
84	0.0779	**ALVEOSEPTA JACCARDI
90		LENTICULINA QUENSTEDTI

Chronostratigraphy labels (left column): CENOMANIAN (I), LATE ALBIAN (II), MID-LATE ALBIAN (III), APTIAN (IV), EARLY APTIAN (V), BARREMIAN (VI), EARLY BARREMIAN LATE HAUTERIVIAN (VII), HAUTERIVIAN (VIII), VALANGINIAN (IX), TITHONIAN (X), KIMMERIDGIAN (XI)

INTERFOSSIL DISTANCES scale: 0.8001, 0.6821, 0.5240, 0.3859, 0.2478, 0.1097, -0.0283

GSC

Figure 3.18. Foraminiferal zonation for the Late Jurassic-Early Cretaceous and Cenomanian of the Jeanne d'Arc Basin. The dendrogram shows the Ranking and Scaling (RASC) interval zones and their relationship to the chronostratigraphy; shaded areas denote RASC biozones. The zones or clusters are named after the taxa underlined. Asterisks indicate unique events. After Williamson (1987).

studies. Ascoli has not recorded Barremian to Cenomanian sediments in Hibernia B-08. Davies (Fig. 3.9) also shows gaps in the Albian.

Application of the RASC zonation to the Hibernia wells has provided age control for the sand units named in Arthur et al. (1982). The Hibernia member (now the Hibernia Formation) and Catalina or "C" member (now the Catalina Formation) both occur within RASC Zone IX, so are assumed to be Berriasian-Valanginian. The Avalon member (now the Avalon Formation) occurs within RASC Zone IV, indicating a middle to late Aptian age.

Biostratigraphically, it is also possible to recognize two of the unconformities. Within RASC Zone VII is a pre-Aptian unconformity, which is recognized in Ben Nevis I-45, Hebron I-13, Hibernia G-55, O-35, P-15, K-18, B-08, and Nautilus C-92. The Avalon unconformity is associated with RASC Zone IV (early Albian) in the wells examined.

The Ranking and Scaling Program has also been applied to the Late Cretaceous foraminifers of the Grand Banks (Agterberg et al., 1985). The optimum sequence for the planktonic and benthic foraminifers is shown in Figure 3.19.

Tertiary

Biostratigraphic studies of the Tertiary rocks of offshore eastern Canada have been more detailed than lithostratigraphic studies. This is especially true for the Banquereau Formation in Scotian Basin.

Ascoli (1976) presented a planktonic foraminiferal zonation based on the studies of previous workers, includ-

ing Bolli (1966) and Stainforth et al. (1975). The zones did not allow recognition of the intervals, the late early Eocene, late early Miocene, and late middle Miocene-base late Miocene. In this chapter, the above zonation has been refined with 11 Tertiary zones being recognized and the early early Eocene now being defined (Fig. 3.17).

The zonation based on the calcareous benthic foraminifers (Ascoli, 1976) is shown in Figure 3.17.

The significance of the agglutinated foraminifers declines in the Tertiary clastic sequences of the southern basins of offshore eastern Canada. Only one zone, of Paleocene-early Eocene age, was defined by Ascoli (1976). This contrasts sharply with utilization of agglutinated foraminifers in the zonation of the Tertiary of Hopedale and Saglek basins, where these taxa are more diverse.

Gradstein and Agterberg (1982) published some models of Cenozoic foraminiferal stratigraphy for the northwestern Atlantic Margin; the findings for the Scotian Shelf and Grand Banks are presented here. An optimum sequence of 206 Tertiary foraminiferal taxa from 22 wells was generated and the average distance between successive events in the optimum sequence was determined through use of the Ranking and Scaling Program. The number of planktonic and benthic foraminifers decreases northwards with 75 planktonic taxa on the Scotian Shelf decreasing to 30 on the Labrador Shelf. Inversely, the number of agglutinated foraminifers increases northwards.

Latitudinal changes in relative abundances of the three groups of foraminifers resulted in two distinct RASC zonations. The southern zonation was based on six wells from the Scotian Basin: Mohican I-100, Triumph P-50, Wenonah J-75, Kittiwake P-11, Brant P-87 and Heron H-73. The zonation provides a twelvefold integrated subdivision of the Tertiary when combined with Ascoli's (1976) findings. The clusters, which are related to the standard planktonic foraminiferal zonation of Stainforth et al. (1975), are shown in Figure 3.20. According to Gradstein and Agterberg (1982), the clusters can be equated with assemblage zones.

The planktonic foraminiferal assemblages of offshore eastern Canada have also been related to the standard planktonic zonation (Gradstein and Agterberg, 1982). The zonation for the 6 southern wells differs from that for the 16 northern wells. A major hiatus in the wells equates with the *Cassigerinella chipolensis* and *Globigerina ampliapertura* standard zones. This indicates that part or all of the early Oligocene is missing in the southern wells. Locally, there are also gaps in the Eocene section. Whether this reflects sediment starvation or a eustatic sea-level drop is not known. The impoverished or absent *Globorotalia acostaensis* Zone would suggest higher latitude cooling or a eustatic sea-level drop.

The 16 northern wells include the Osprey H-84 well in the Carson Basin and the Egret N-46, Egret K-36 and Dominion O-23 wells in the Jeanne d'Arc Basin (Gradstein and Agterberg, 1982). Details of the zonation as applied to the wells in these basins were not provided. However, Gradstein (1985) presented a zonation of the Tertiary of two other wells in Jeanne d'Arc Basin: the Hibernia P-15 and Adolphus D-50. The more complete zonation is in Adolphus D-50 where the ten zones are recognized. According to Gradstein (1985), in the Hibernia P-15 well there are middle and upper Eocene, Oligocene and lower and middle

SEQUENCE POSITION	FOSSIL NUMBER	RANGE	FOSSIL NAME
1	5	0 - 5	*Stensioina pommerana*
2	4	0 - 6	*Globotruncana arca*
3	3	0 - 6	*Globotruncana stuarti*
4	105	0 - 5	*Loxostoma gemmum*
5	6	4 - 6	*Globotruncanella havanensis*
6	8	5 - 8	*Globigerinelloides messinae*
7	16	5 - 8	*Rugoglobigerina rugosa*
8	13	7 - 9	*Globotruncana linneiana*
9	12	8 - 10	*Globotruncana stuartiformis*
10	11	9 - 11	*Globotruncana fornicata*
11	14	10 - 12	*Globotruncana cretacea*
12	15	11 - 13	*Globotruncana marginata*
13	26	12 - 16	*Globotruncana angusticarinata*
14	108	12 - 19	*Gavelinella minima*
15	56	12 - 16	*Gaudryina austinana*
16	20	15 - 17	*Globotruncana coronata*
17	23	16 - 18	*Stensioina exculpta*
18	55	17 - 19	*Globotruncana carinata*
19	109	18 - 20	*Coarse agglutinated spp.*
20	24	19 - 21	*Hedbergella amabilis*
21	22	20 - 22	*Sigalia deflaensis*
22	54	21 - 23	*Globotruncana concavata*
23	72	22 - 24	*Globotruncana renzi*
24	110	23 - 25	*Globotruncana imbricata*
25	70	24 - 26	*Hedbergella bosquensis*
26	112	25 - 28	*Globotruncana helvetica*
27	30	25 - 29	*Praeglobotruncana stephani*
28	71	26 - 29	*Globotruncana schneegansi*
29	31	28 - 30	*Praeglobotruncana turbinata*
30	27	29 - 32	*Rotalipora cushmani*
31	131	29 - 32	*Gavelinopsis cenomanica*

GSC

Figure 3.19. Optimum ordering of foraminiferal taxa for the Late Cretaceous of the Grand Banks. After Agterberg et al. (1985).

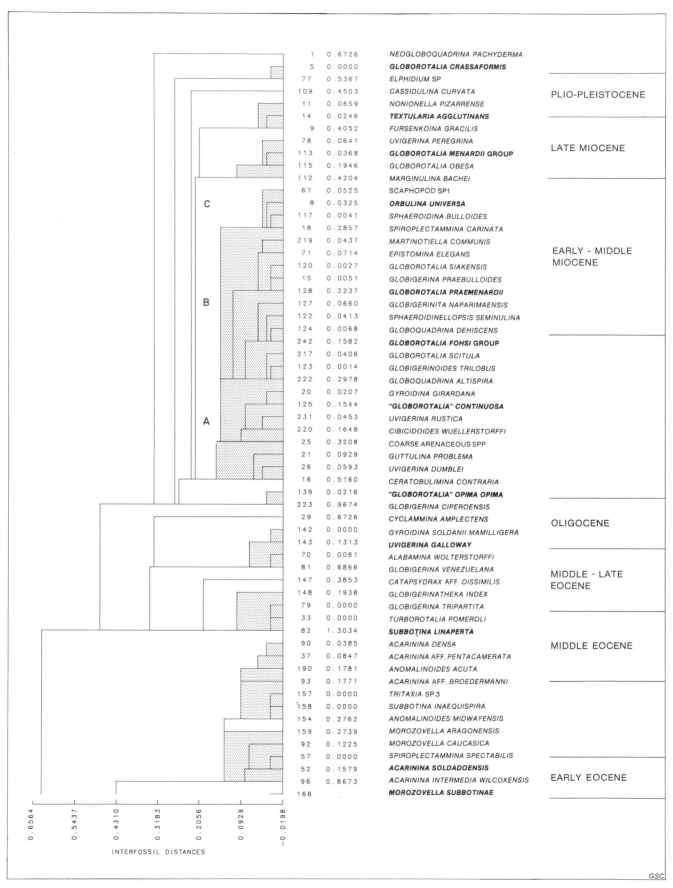

1	0.6726	*NEOGLOBOQUADRINA PACHYDERMA*
5	0.0000	**GLOBOROTALIA CRASSAFORMIS**
77	0.5367	*ELPHIDIUM SP*
109	0.4503	*CASSIDULINA CURVATA*
11	0.0659	*NONIONELLA PIZARRENSE*
14	0.0246	**TEXTULARIA AGGLUTINANS**
9	0.4052	*FURSENKOINA GRACILIS*
78	0.0641	*UVIGERINA PEREGRINA*
113	0.0368	**GLOBOROTALIA MENARDII** GROUP
115	0.1946	*GLOBOROTALIA OBESA*
112	0.4204	*MARGINULINA BACHEI*
67	0.0525	SCAPHOPOD SP1
8	0.0325	**ORBULINA UNIVERSA**
117	0.0041	*SPHAEROIDINA BULLOIDES*
18	0.2857	*SPIROPLECTAMMINA CARINATA*
219	0.0437	*MARTINOTIELLA COMMUNIS*
71	0.0714	*EPISTOMINA ELEGANS*
120	0.0027	*GLOBOROTALIA SIAKENSIS*
15	0.0051	*GLOBIGERINA PRAEBULLOIDES*
128	0.2237	**GLOBOROTALIA PRAEMENARDII**
127	0.0660	*GLOBIGERINITA NAPARIMAENSIS*
122	0.0413	*SPHAEROIDINELLOPSIS SEMINULINA*
124	0.0068	*GLOBOQUADRINA DEHISCENS*
242	0.1582	**GLOBOROTALIA FOHSI** GROUP
217	0.0406	*GLOBOROTALIA SCITULA*
123	0.0014	*GLOBIGERINOIDES TRILOBUS*
222	0.2978	*GLOBOQUADRINA ALTISPIRA*
20	0.0207	*GYROIDINA GIRARDANA*
125	0.1544	**"GLOBOROTALIA" CONTINUOSA**
231	0.0453	*UVIGERINA RUSTICA*
220	0.1648	*CIBICIDOIDES WUELLERSTORFFI*
25	0.3206	COARSE ARENACEOUS SPP
21	0.0929	*GUTTULINA PROBLEMA*
26	0.0593	*UVIGERINA DUMBLEI*
16	0.5160	*CERATOBULIMINA CONTRARIA*
139	0.0216	**"GLOBOROTALIA" OPIMA OPIMA**
223	0.9674	*GLOBIGERINA CIPEROENSIS*
29	0.6726	*CYCLAMMINA AMPLECTENS*
142	0.0000	*GYROIDINA SOLDANII MAMILLIGERA*
143	0.1313	**UVIGERINA GALLOWAY**
70	0.0061	*ALABAMINA WOLTERSTORFFI*
81	0.6866	*GLOBIGERINA VENEZUELANA*
147	0.3853	*CATAPSYDRAX AFF. DISSIMILIS*
148	0.1938	*GLOBIGERINATHEKA INDEX*
79	0.0000	*GLOBIGERINA TRIPARTITA*
33	0.0000	*TURBOROTALIA POMEROLI*
82	1.3034	**SUBBOTINA LINAPERTA**
90	0.0385	*ACARININA DENSA*
37	0.0847	*ACARININA AFF. PENTACAMERATA*
190	0.1781	*ANOMALINOIDES ACUTA*
93	0.1771	*ACARININA AFF. BROEDERMANNI*
157	0.0000	*TRITAXIA SP.3*
158	0.0000	*SUBBOTINA INAEQUISPIRA*
154	0.2762	*ANOMALINOIDES MIDWAYENSIS*
159	0.2739	*MOROZOVELLA ARAGONENSIS*
92	0.1225	*MOROZOVELLA CAUCASICA*
57	0.0000	*SPIROPLECTAMMINA SPECTABILIS*
52	0.1579	**ACARININA SOLDADOENSIS**
96	0.8673	*ACARININA INTERMEDIA WILCOXENSIS*
166		**MOROZOVELLA SUBBOTINAE**

PLIO-PLEISTOCENE

LATE MIOCENE

EARLY - MIDDLE MIOCENE

OLIGOCENE

MIDDLE - LATE EOCENE

MIDDLE EOCENE

EARLY EOCENE

C

B

A

0.6564 0.5437 0.4310 0.3183 0.2056 0.0929 -0.0198

INTERFOSSIL DISTANCES

GSC

Figure 3.20. Optimum ordering of foraminiferal taxa for the Cenozoic of the Scotian Basin. The dendrogram shows the RASC "zones" or clusters and their relationship to the geochronology. The zones or clusters are named after those taxa which are in bold type. After Gradstein and Agterberg (1982).

Miocene sediments. In Adolphus D-50, the Oligocene is thin and probably incomplete.

The ostracodes, because of their low numbers and inconsistent occurrences, have not been used to zone the Tertiary of offshore eastern Canada.

Northeast Newfoundland Shelf — Labrador Shelf

This geographic area includes the East Newfoundland Basin, a Cretaceous-Tertiary successor basin on the Northeast Newfoundland Shelf, the Hopedale, Saglek and Lady Franklin basins of the Labrador Sea, and the Deep Sea Drilling Project (DSDP) site 112 in the Labrador Sea (Fig. 3.1b). Previous micropaleontological studies of Mesozoic-Cenozoic rocks from these areas have emphasized differences between the assemblages of these latitudes and those farther south on the Grand Banks and Scotian Shelf. Such differences reflect paleoclimatic and paleoenvironment control and have made the development of regional zonations necessary.

Cretaceous

The oldest known marine Cretaceous rocks of the Northeast Newfoundland and Labrador shelves occur in the Freydis B-87 well; they have been interpreted to be mid-Cretaceous on the foraminifers. The palynomorphs indicate a late Albian-Cenomanian age (Gradstein in Srivastava, 1986). In the same well, overlying marine sediments contain Coniacian-Santonian foraminifers. The oldest foraminiferal assemblages assigned to a formal zonation are Maastrichtian. Gradstein and Williams (1976) defined a *Glomospira corona* assemblage which they regarded as latest Cretaceous-Paleocene. This was refined in Gradstein and Srivastava (1980), who recognized two zones in the Maastrichtian (Fig. 3.21).

Tertiary

The Tertiary rocks of the East Newfoundland, Hopedale and Saglek basins can attain thicknesses of over 4800 m, as in Blue H-28. The predominantly clastic sediments generally coarsen upwards. The foraminiferal assemblages show marked differences from those to the south, with agglutinated taxa becoming more abundant (Gradstein and Berggren, 1981) at the expense of planktonic and calcareous benthic foraminifers.

A foraminiferal zonation of the Labrador Shelf Tertiary, based on benthic taxa, was outlined in Gradstein and Williams (1976). In a biostratigraphic study of three Labrador Shelf wells (Leif E-38, Leif M-48 and Bjarni H-81), they proposed an eightfold subdivision of the Tertiary (Fig. 3.21). The ages were confirmed by correlation with the Egret K-36 well in Jeanne d'Arc Basin. Emendations to the benthic zonation and a zonation based on planktonics were published by Gradstein and Srivastava (1980) and Gradstein and Agterberg (1982).

The initial attempts to subdivide the Tertiary of the Labrador Shelf were hindered by the low species diversity, the low numbers of individuals per gram of sample in the coarser clastics, and the high degree of reworked material in the Neogene. Accordingly, the Ranking and Scaling Program has been applied to obtain an optimum sequence and to scale that sequence (Gradstein and Agterberg, 1982).

The resulting zonation for the northern area was based on data from 16 wells on the Labrador Shelf and northern Grand Banks. Labrador Shelf wells included Karlsefni A-13 in Saglek Basin, and Snorri J-90, Herjolf M-92, Bjarni H-81, Gudrid H-55, Cartier D-70, Leif E-38, Leif M-48, Indian Harbour M-52 and Freydis B-87 in Hopedale Basin. On the northern Grand Banks, the wells were Bonavista C-99 and Cumberland B-55 in East Newfoundland Basin, Dominion O-23, Egret K-36 and Egret N-46 in Jeanne d'Arc Basin, and Osprey H-84 in Carson Basin.

Sorting of those foraminifers which occurred in at least five wells gave an optimum sequence of 41 taxa. The original database included 555 last occurrences of 157 benthic and planktonic foraminifers. In the final sort, only six planktonic taxa remained. These occurred in nine, clearly separate clusters, which approximate the assemblage zones of Gradstein and Williams (1976).

Gradstein (1985) generated an optimum sequence for the Tertiary of 21 northern wells. The additional wells included Hibernia B-08, Hibernia K-18, Hibernia O-35 and Hibernia P-15, Adolphus D-50, and Flying Foam I-13 in Jeanne d'Arc Basin; Blue H-28 in East Newfoundland Basin; and Hare Bay E-21 in St. Anthony Basin.

The revised optimum sequence and scaled optimum sequence based on the latest or youngest occurrence of 54 taxa, primarily foraminifers, is shown in Figure 3.22. It is possible to recognize ten, sharply defined, stratigraphically successive dendrogram clusters, based on the optimum sequences (Gradstein, 1985).

Different RASC computer runs were used to determine if the extra wells (21 versus 16) provided a refined zonation, and if there was one preferred zonation. The results showed that there was little difference in rank for the optimum sequences, regardless of whether the Labrador Shelf and Grand Banks were treated separately, and only one species changed rank significantly in the optimum sequence based on 21 rather than 16 wells.

Scaling of the ranked optimum sequences has highlighted some differences between the Labrador Shelf and the northern Grand Banks. These are as follows: on the Grand Banks there appears to be a distinct zone between the *Gavelinella beccariiformis* Zone (Paleocene) and the *Subbotina patagonica* Zone (early Eocene); the *Subbotina patagonica* and *Acarinina densa* zones (early to middle Eocene) are not well developed on the Labrador Shelf; the *Cyclammina amplectens* Zone (middle to late Eocene) is more distinct on the Labrador Shelf; the *Turborotalia centralis* (late Eocene) and *Turrilina alsatica* (Oligocene) zones are separated by the *Ammodiscus latus* Zone on the Grand Banks; and the *Turrilina alsatica* Zone is better defined on the Grand Banks.

Any discussion of the Tertiary foraminiferal zonations of the Labrador Shelf would not be complete without reference to the agglutinated benthic foraminifers. Gradstein and Williams (1976) first noted the dominance of agglutinated foraminifers in the "uniform shale" of McWhae and Michel (1975) and the Cartwright Formation of Umpleby (1979). Taxa of this group are common in the Maastrichtian to Late Eocene-Oligocene and appear to have occupied water depths from about 200 m to over 4 km (Gradstein and Berggren, 1981).

The stratigraphic utility of agglutinated foraminifers has long been a contentious issue. However, in an analysis

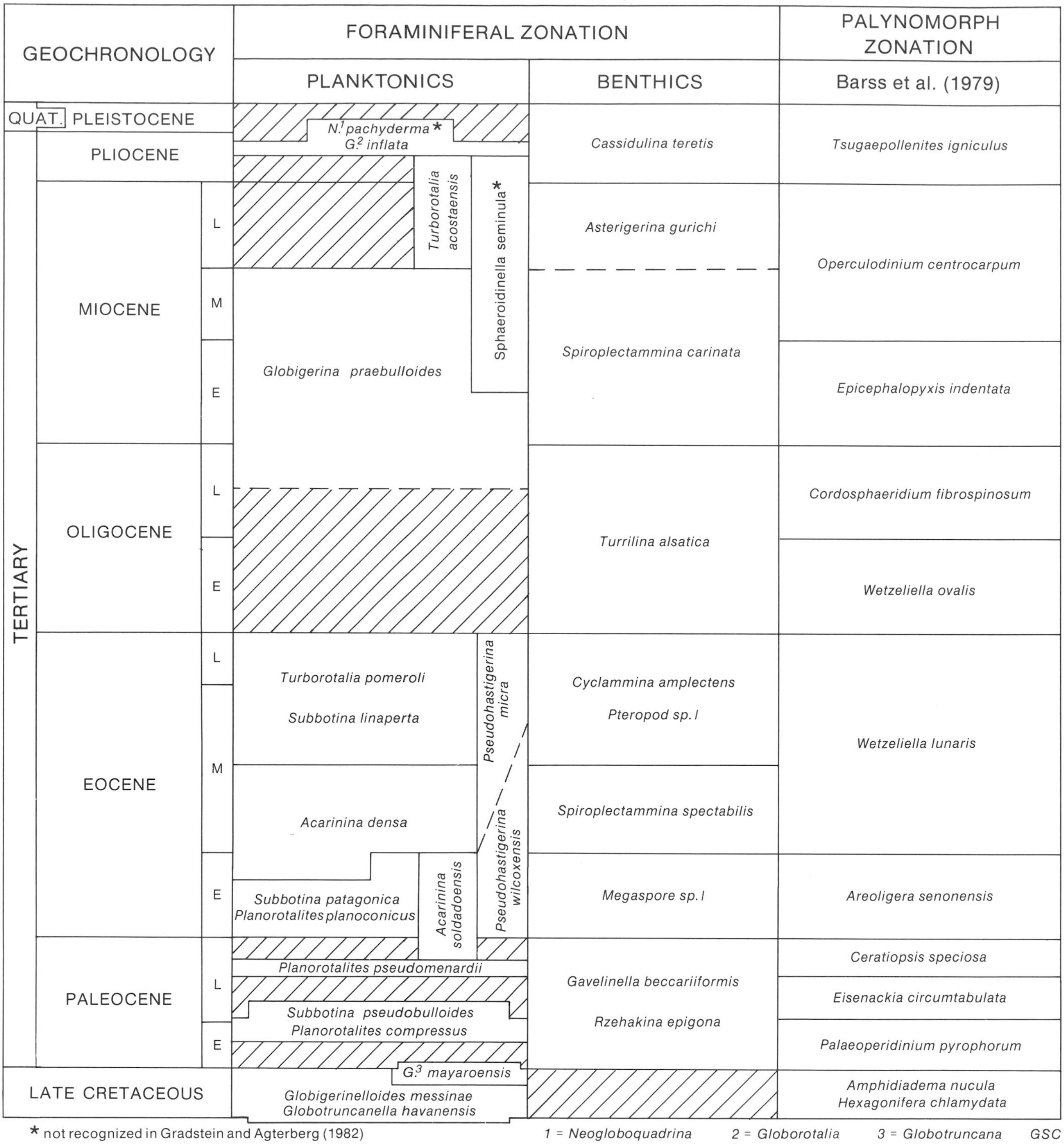

GEOCHRONOLOGY		FORAMINIFERAL ZONATION			PALYNOMORPH ZONATION
		PLANKTONICS		BENTHICS	Barss et al. (1979)
QUAT. PLEISTOCENE		N.[1] pachyderma * G.[2] inflata		Cassidulina teretis	Tsugaepollenites igniculus
PLIOCENE			Turborotalia acostaensis	Asterigerina gurichi	Operculodinium centrocarpum
MIOCENE	L		Turborotalia acostaensis	Asterigerina gurichi	Operculodinium centrocarpum
MIOCENE	M	Globigerina praebulloides	Sphaeroidinella seminula *	Spiroplectammina carinata	Epicephalopyxis indentata
MIOCENE	E	Globigerina praebulloides	Sphaeroidinella seminula *	Spiroplectammina carinata	Epicephalopyxis indentata
OLIGOCENE	L			Turrilina alsatica	Cordosphaeridium fibrospinosum
OLIGOCENE	E			Turrilina alsatica	Wetzeliella ovalis
EOCENE	L	Turborotalia pomeroli Subbotina linaperta	Pseudohastigerina micra	Cyclammina amplectens Pteropod sp. l	Wetzeliella lunaris
EOCENE	M	Acarinina densa	Pseudohastigerina micra / Pseudohastigerina wilcoxensis	Spiroplectammina spectabilis	Wetzeliella lunaris
EOCENE	E	Subbotina patagonica Planorotalites planoconicus	Acarinina soldadoensis / Pseudohastigerina wilcoxensis	Megaspore sp. l	Areoligera senonensis
PALEOCENE	L	Planorotalites pseudomenardii Subbotina pseudobulloides Planorotalites compressus		Gavelinella beccariiformis Rzehakina epigona	Ceratiopsis speciosa
PALEOCENE	L	Planorotalites pseudomenardii Subbotina pseudobulloides Planorotalites compressus		Gavelinella beccariiformis Rzehakina epigona	Eisenackia circumtabulata
PALEOCENE	E	Planorotalites pseudomenardii Subbotina pseudobulloides Planorotalites compressus		Gavelinella beccariiformis Rzehakina epigona	Palaeoperidinium pyrophorum
LATE CRETACEOUS		G.[3] mayaroensis Globigerinelloides messinae Globotruncanella havanensis			Amphidiadema nucula Hexagonifera chlamydata

(Note: left column has TERTIARY spanning PLIOCENE through PALEOCENE)

* not recognized in Gradstein and Agterberg (1982)   1 = Neogloboquadrina   2 = Globorotalia   3 = Globotruncana   GSC

Figure 3.21. Foraminiferal and palynomorph zonations for the latest Cretaceous-Cenozoic of the Labrador and Northeast Newfoundland shelves, as proposed in Gradstein and Srivastava (1980), Gradstein and Agterberg (1982), and Barss et al. (1979).

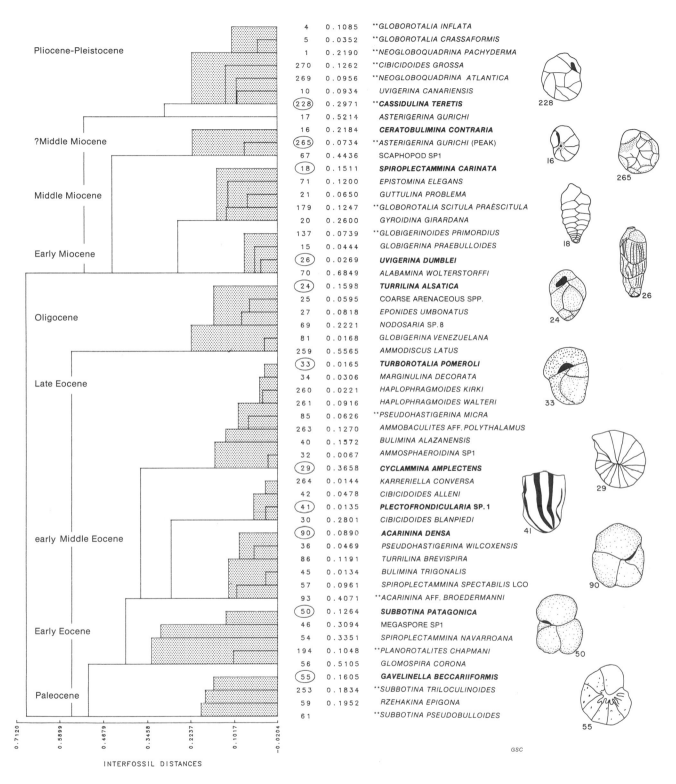

4	0.1085	**GLOBOROTALIA INFLATA
5	0.0352	**GLOBOROTALIA CRASSAFORMIS
1	0.2190	**NEOGLOBOQUADRINA PACHYDERMA
270	0.1262	**CIBICIDOIDES GROSSA
269	0.0956	**NEOGLOBOQUADRINA ATLANTICA
10	0.0934	UVIGERINA CANARIENSIS
(228)	0.2971	**CASSIDULINA TERETIS
17	0.5214	ASTERIGERINA GURICHI
16	0.2184	CERATOBULIMINA CONTRARIA
(265)	0.0734	**ASTERIGERINA GURICHI (PEAK)
67	0.4436	SCAPHOPOD SP1
(18)	0.1511	SPIROPLECTAMMINA CARINATA
71	0.1200	EPISTOMINA ELEGANS
21	0.0650	GUTTULINA PROBLEMA
179	0.1247	**GLOBOROTALIA SCITULA PRAESCITULA
20	0.2600	GYROIDINA GIRARDANA
137	0.0739	**GLOBIGERINOIDES PRIMORDIUS
15	0.0444	GLOBIGERINA PRAEBULLOIDES
(26)	0.0269	UVIGERINA DUMBLEI
70	0.6849	ALABAMINA WOLTERSTORFFI
(24)	0.1598	TURRILINA ALSATICA
25	0.0595	COARSE ARENACEOUS SPP.
27	0.0818	EPONIDES UMBONATUS
69	0.2221	NODOSARIA SP.8
81	0.0168	GLOBIGERINA VENEZUELANA
259	0.5565	AMMODISCUS LATUS
(33)	0.0165	TURBOROTALIA POMEROLI
34	0.0306	MARGINULINA DECORATA
260	0.0221	HAPLOPHRAGMOIDES KIRKI
261	0.0916	HAPLOPHRAGMOIDES WALTERI
85	0.0626	**PSEUDOHASTIGERINA MICRA
263	0.1270	AMMOBACULITES AFF. POLYTHALAMUS
40	0.1572	BULIMINA ALAZANENSIS
32	0.0067	AMMOSPHAEROIDINA SP1
(29)	0.3658	CYCLAMMINA AMPLECTENS
264	0.0144	KARRERIELLA CONVERSA
42	0.0478	CIBICIDOIDES ALLENI
(41)	0.0135	PLECTOFRONDICULARIA SP.1
30	0.2801	CIBICIDOIDES BLANPIEDI
(90)	0.0890	ACARININA DENSA
36	0.0469	PSEUDOHASTIGERINA WILCOXENSIS
86	0.1191	TURRILINA BREVISPIRA
45	0.0134	BULIMINA TRIGONALIS
57	0.0961	SPIROPLECTAMMINA SPECTABILIS LCO
93	0.4071	**ACARININA AFF. BROEDERMANNI
(50)	0.1264	SUBBOTINA PATAGONICA
46	0.3094	MEGASPORE SP1
54	0.3351	SPIROPLECTAMMINA NAVARROANA
194	0.1048	**PLANOROTALITES CHAPMANI
56	0.5105	GLOMOSPIRA CORONA
(55)	0.1605	GAVELINELLA BECCARIIFORMIS
253	0.1834	**SUBBOTINA TRILOCULINOIDES
59	0.1952	RZEHAKINA EPIGONA
61		**SUBBOTINA PSEUDOBULLOIDES

Pliocene-Pleistocene

?Middle Miocene

Middle Miocene

Early Miocene

Oligocene

Late Eocene

early Middle Eocene

Early Eocene

Paleocene

0.7120 0.5899 0.4679 0.3458 0.2237 0.1017 -0.0204

INTERFOSSIL DISTANCES

GSC

CENOZOIC ZONATION GRAND BANKS/LABRADOR

Figure 3.22. Scaled optimum sequence for 54 microfossil taxa, primarily foraminifers, in 21 wells located on the Labrador Shelf and Grand Banks. The interfossil distances are given along the X-axis. The distance between two events is given along the Y-axis. Unique events are denoted with asterisks. The shading denotes the ten zones named for the species underlined. The exception is the *Turborotalia pomeroli-Cyclammina amplectens* Zone, which is named for two species. After Gradstein (1985).

of ten Labrador Shelf wells and some North Sea wells, Gradstein and Berggren (1981) have demonstrated that these taxa can be used to zone Paleogene sediments.

Miller et al. (1982) compared the agglutinated foraminifers of Labrador Shelf and Northeast Newfoundland Shelf with coeval DSDP and North Sea assemblages. DSDP Site 112, which is in the southern Labrador Sea, was selected for the comparison. Site 112 reached total depth in Paleocene basalt, which is overlain by Eocene and Oligocene sediments. Of the 43 species and 23 genera of agglutinates identified, 20 species were also recorded in the central North Sea, Labrador Shelf, Northeast Newfoundland Shelf and western Greenland (Gradstein and Berggren, 1981). In the Eocene, it was possible to recognize four agglutinate assemblages, all of which had stratigraphic significance. The foraminiferal assemblages in the Oligocene were dominated by calcareous benthic taxa, with a maximum of two agglutinated species in any one sample. The Eocene agglutinates of Site 112 can be correlated with the Labrador Shelf and North Sea and demonstrate the practical utilization of such taxa for biostratigraphic control. In all three areas, the disappearance or suppression of the agglutinates at the Eocene-Oligocene boundary is taken to reflect changes in hydrographic properties associated with the development of a more vigorous abyssal circulation and the psychrosphere.

The application of quantitative stratigraphic methodology to the zonation of the Tertiary of the Labrador Shelf-northern Grand Banks has resulted in a more refined zonation. It has also provided a means for objectively relating a biozonation to geochronology, so that their relationships become evident.

OTHER MICROFOSSIL GROUPS

Jurassic—Cretaceous calpionellids

Calpionellids have been recorded from uppermost Jurassic-lowermost Cretaceous rocks of offshore eastern Canada by several authors (Jenkins et al., 1974; Gradstein et al., 1975; Jansa et al., 1980; Ascoli et al., 1984). The significance of such discoveries is that they allow precise correlation with the European surface sections, including the stratotypes, for the late Tithonian to middle Valanginian. This was demonstrated in a comparison of the assemblages in Bonnition H-32, Mohican I-100 and Moheida P-15 with coeval European assemblages. In Bonnition H-32 and Mohican I-100, the calpionellids occurred in upper Tithonian-lowermost Berriasian rocks. In Moheida P-15, they occurred in lower Berriasian rocks (Fig. 3.23).

Jansa et al. (1980) did not erect a calpionellid zonation for offshore eastern Canada, but utilized the zonation established for the Tithonian-Valanginian of the Mediterranean region by Remane (1964). This zonation is keyed to the standard Tethyan ammonite zonation, so that the ages are known with greater precision than for the other microfossil zonations. Remane (1964) recognized five zones labelled A through E (Fig. 3.23). Allemann et al. (1971) modified this zonation by combining zones B and C. This is now the "Standard Calpionellid Zonation," which can be further subdivided, with as many as eight subzones being recognized in both the Mediterranean and offshore eastern Canada. Its relationship to the coeval ammonite and nannoplankton zonations are given in Remane (1978). In this chapter, we accept the zonation of Remane (1964) and retain zones B and C.

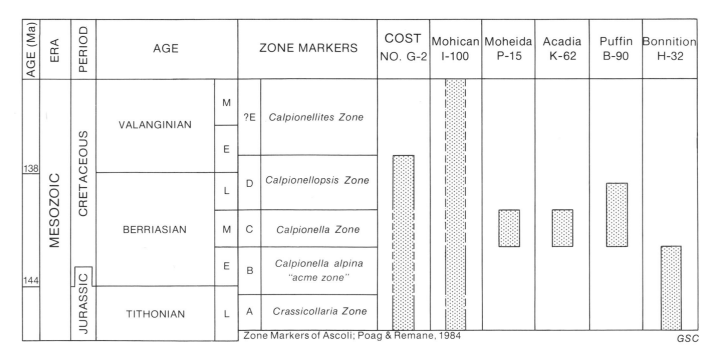

Figure 3.23. Calpionellid zones recognized in Georges Bank (COST G-2), Scotian Shelf (Mohican I-100, Moheida P-15, Acadia K-62), and Grand Banks (Puffin B-90, Bonnition H-32) wells. After Jansa et al. (1980) and Ascoli et al. (1984).

The cosmopolitan nature of the calpionellid zones is reflected in Ascoli et al. (1984). These authors recognized one or more of the zones in the wells mentioned above plus the Puffin B-90 well on the Grand Banks, the Acadia K-62 well on the Scotian Shelf, and the COST G-2 well in Georges Bank Basin (Fig. 3.23). The practical applicability of the zonation in subsurface sections was increased by using "tops" or LADs to define each zone, rather than "bases" or FADs as used by Remane (1964, 1978). The precision of the calpionellid zones allows recalibration of the foraminiferal, ostracode and palynomorph zonations across the Jurassic-Cretaceous boundary.

Calpionellids are stenotopic, planktonic organisms which are restricted to deeper water, tropical seas. Therefore, their presence in the Upper Jurassic-Lower Cretaceous rocks of the Northwest Atlantic gives an indication of the extent of the proto-Atlantic at that time. This has important implications for reconstructions of the North Atlantic.

Cretaceous calcareous nannoplankton

The utilization of nannoplankton for zonation of the Mesozoic-Cenozoic rocks of offshore eastern Canada has been limited in the past. This partly reflects their absence or rarity in shallow water to nonmarine environments. Thus, they are of little value in correlation of the reservoir rocks in the Late Jurassic-Early Cretaceous, although Upshaw et al. (1974) listed some stratigraphically useful species in the Early Cretaceous. Nannoplankton have been used to zone some Jurassic rocks on the Grand Banks, but the data have not been published. The most detailed published zonation is for the Late Cretaceous (Doeven, 1983). Upshaw et al. (1974) also provided lists of diagnostic nannoplankton taxa in the Cretaceous-Tertiary.

The nannoplankton zonation for the Albian-Maastrichtian is based on conventional and probabilistic techniques and on the analyses of 11 Scotian Shelf wells, 4 Grand Banks wells, and 1 Labrador Shelf well (Doeven, 1983). The fourteenfold zonation utilizes four types of stratigraphic events: the earliest occurrence of a taxon (lowest occurrence), the earliest consistent occurrence of a taxon (subbottom occurrence), the latest consistent occurrence of a taxon (subtop occurrence), and the latest occurrence of a taxon (highest occurrence). The conventional zones with ages are shown in Figure 3.24. Doeven's zonation was based in part on previous nannoplankton zonations such as Verbeek (in Manivit et al., 1977) and Sissingh (1977).

A proposed probabilistic zonation was developed using the Ranking and Scaling (RASC) computer program as outlined in Gradstein and Agterberg (1982). Although the probabilistic zonation provided a more detailed subdivision, there was remarkable agreement between the two zonations. The only serious discrepancy was in the relative positions of two species.

Comparison of the nannoplankton zonation with the palynomorph and foraminiferal zonations shows some differences in stadial correlation. However, these may not be as critical as implied in Doeven (1983). According to Doeven, each palynomorph zone corresponds exactly to one stage. Williams (1975), in erecting the palynomorph zonation, deliberately referred to age in parenthetic fashion in

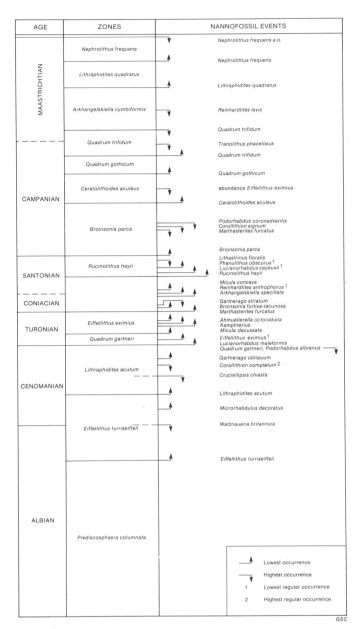

Figure 3.24. Nannoplankton zonation for the Albian-Maastrichtian of the Canadian Atlantic margin proposed by Doeven (1983).

all text-figures. This practice, perpetuated in Barss et al. (1979), was intended to convey the provisional age assignments for all the proposed zones. Unfortunately, later authors have invariably assumed that all ages with reference to the palynomorph zonation are definitive. As stated previously, this is not the case.

Doeven (1983) provided plots of the palynomorph, foraminiferal and nannoplankton zonation in six wells. These were Missisauga H-54, Mohawk B-93, Primrose A-41, Triumph P-50, and Wyandot E-53 on Scotian Shelf and Indian Harbour M-52 on Labrador Shelf. The major discrepancies are in the Coniacian-Santonian, where the three zonations rarely agree. The Coniacian is probably the most difficult age to delineate in the Cretaceous. Its duration is short (1 Ma) and knowledge of the microfossil assemblages is limited.

One significant result from application of the nannoplankton zonation has been the recognition of several hiatuses. These occur within the Late Cretaceous-Early Tertiary. Coniacian and lower Santonian rocks are missing in Triumph P-50, whereas in other wells, as at Primrose A-41 and Sachem D-76, all of the Turonian may be missing. In Onondaga E-84, upper Campanian-lowest Maastrichtian rocks may be absent. The Late Cretaceous-Early Tertiary hiatus may represent a period of time of about 2 Ma as in Adolphus D-50, to about 27 Ma as in Heron H-73. The hiatuses may represent major transgressive-regressive phases in the Late Cretaceous or may merely denote nondeposition.

Tertiary diatoms

Diatoms are occasionally common in Tertiary sediments of offshore eastern Canada, particularly in Labrador Shelf and Grand Banks wells (Thomas and Gradstein, 1981). Almost invariably, the diatoms are pyritized and appear to represent the internal mold of the space between the two siliceous frustules comprising the test of a whole specimen. The four taxa identified are all included in the genus *Coscinodiscus*. In the 16 Labrador Shelf-Grand Banks wells studied, the diatoms show maximum concentrations or peaks in the late Paleocene-early Eocene. A single peak also occurs in the late Oligocene-early Miocene in Dominion O-23 located in the Jeanne d'Arc Basin (Fig. 3.25). In southern Grand Banks and Scotian Shelf wells, diatoms are generally rare although they may be more abundant as in the Oligocene-Miocene of Kittiwake P-11.

The peak occurrences are not always related to deeper water, but may denote neritic environments. The peaks are believed to reflect diatom blooms, resulting from higher nutrient levels in the surface waters (Thomas and Gradstein, 1981). This agrees with their Late Paleocene-Early Eocene and Oligocene-Miocene age, times of maximum northward incursion of lower latitude surface waters (Gradstein and Srivastava, 1980).

PALEOENVIRONMENTS AND RELATIONSHIPS TO LITHOSTRATIGRAPHY AND EUSTATIC FLUCTUATIONS

The spatial and temporal distribution of the various microfossil groups in the Mesozoic-Cenozoic of offshore eastern Canada can be used to determine the paleoenvironments. Spores and pollen permit recognition of nonmarine deposits, whereas dinoflagellates and acritarchs can be used to recognize neritic or deeper environments. Ostracodes are particularly useful in lagoonal, marginal marine and neritic environments. Benthic foraminifers provide detailed control in marine domains ranging from inner neritic to bathyal. Other groups such as planktonic foraminifers, calcareous nannoplankton and calpionellids are becoming increasingly useful when calibrating water depths and climatic conditions.

Synthesis of the paleoecologic data derived from the various microfossil groups can be related to the lithostratigraphy and often shows the relationship of regional sea-level fluctuations to the worldwide eustatic sea-level curve of Vail et al. (1984) and Haq et al. (1987). This is presented on a modest scale in this chapter.

Regional paleoenvironments and their relationship to paleogeography and paleo-oceanography are presented in Chapter 8. Detailed paleoenvironmental fluctuations are discussed in Chapters 5, 6 and 7.

Triassic

The Triassic rocks of eastern Canada are predominantly nonmarine. On the Scotian Shelf, they occur in the Eurydice P-36 and Argo F-38 wells in Orpheus Graben; the microfossil assemblages in these two wells consist exclusively of spores and pollen. The Triassic and overlying Lower Jurassic rocks contain the pollen *Classopollis*, which probably occupied upland slopes and lowlands near the coast and preferred well-drained soils and a warm climate (Srivastava, 1976). The lithology of these rocks, which constitute the Eurydice Formation, is discussed in Chapter 5.

In the Carson Basin on the Grand Banks, the thick Triassic sequences are included in the Kettle redbeds and Osprey evaporites. The only microfossils present in these units are terrestrial spores and pollen (Jansa et al., 1977). The Kettle redbeds are nonmarine. The Osprey evaporites are primarily marginal marine deposits (Fig. 3.26).

Jurassic

The Jurassic is represented by generally neritic marine environments (Fig. 3.27). In Scotian Basin, the Argo Formation (Fig. 3.2), which is generally Early Jurassic in age,

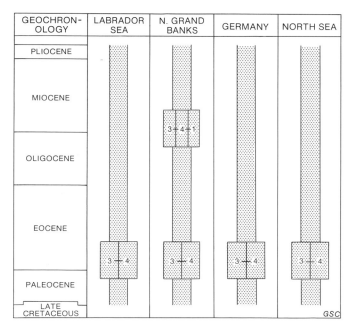

Figure 3.25. Schematic plot of stratigraphic occurrence and composition of diatom abundance peaks in wells of offshore eastern Canada and Europe. The boxes represent the peaks, the numbers in the boxes represent the number of dominant species present. From Thomas and Gradstein (1980).

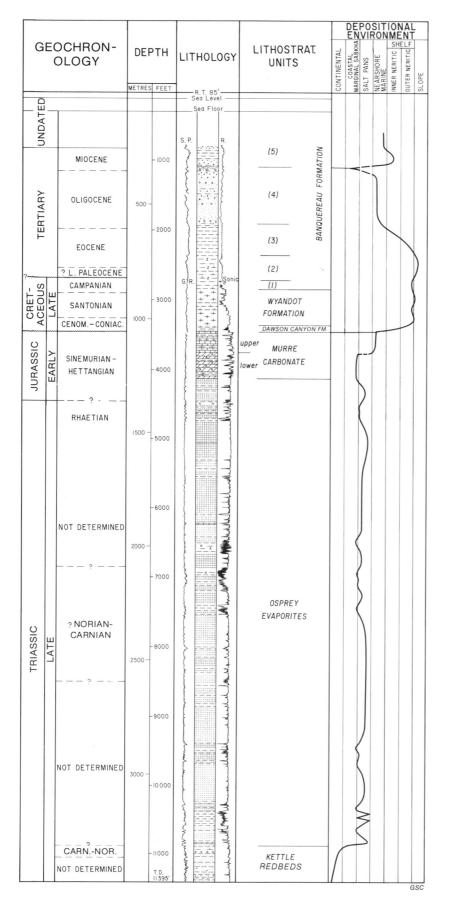

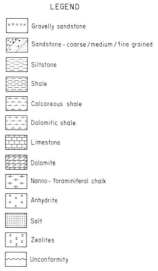

Figure 3.26. Stratigraphy and depositional environments in Osprey H-84, Carson Basin. The mechanical logs shown are gamma ray (G.R.), resistivity (R), sonic, and spontaneous potential (S.P.). The Banquereau Formation is subdivided into five lithological units. After Jansa et al. (1980).

LEGEND

∘∘∘∘	Gravelly sandstone
	Sandstone - coarse / medium / fine grained
	Siltstone
	Shale
	Calcareous shale
	Dolomitic shale
	Limestone
	Dolomite
+++	Nanno - foraminiferal chalk
∧∧∧	Anhydrite
	Salt
z z z	Zeolites
	Unconformity

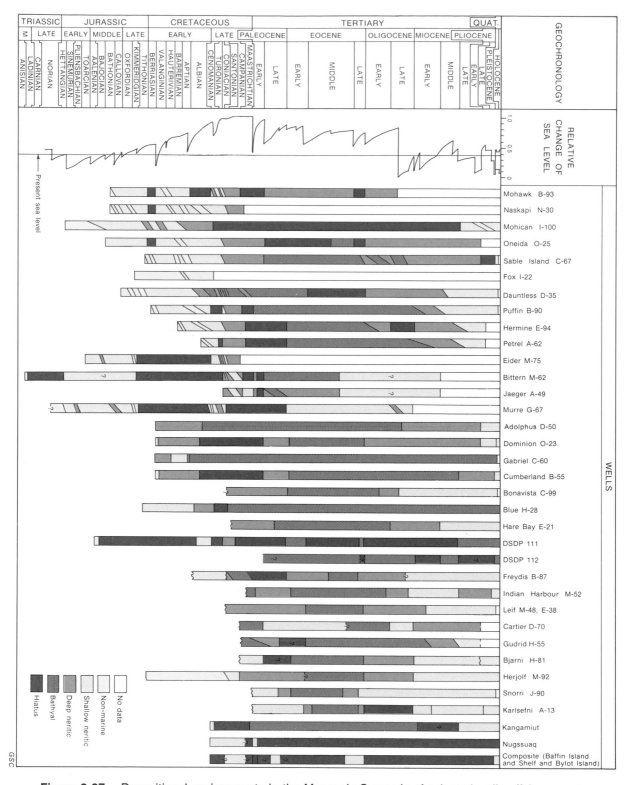

Figure 3.27. Depositional environments in the Mesozoic-Cenozoic of selected wells offshore eastern Canada. The wells are arranged approximately from south to north. Also included are DSDP Sites 111 and 112, and Kangamiut No. 1 and Nugssuaq from the western Greenland region (Fig. 1, in pocket). After Gradstein et al. (1975), and Gradstein in Srivastava (1986).

consists predominantly of relatively pure halite (Chapter 5). The Argo Formation is overlain by dolomitic rocks of the Iroquois Formation or clastic rocks of the Mohican Formation. These Lower to Middle Jurassic rocks were deposited in nonmarine to neritic environments and often contain diverse dinocyst assemblages.

An inner to outer neritic environment is indicated for the Bathonian-Callovian clastic sediments of the overlying Mic Mac Formation, which contain abundant foraminifers; these include the lenticulinids, and epistominids and few planktonics. The partly coeval Abenaki Formation, predominantly a carbonate unit, contains many species of *Trocholina* and agglutinated foraminifers, rare lenticulinids and ostracodes, which indicate a littoral to inner neritic environment. A higher concentration of lenticulinids and epistominids in the Callovian of Mohican I-100 and Wyandot E-53 suggests deeper water, inner to outer neritic environments farther out in Scotian Basin.

Oxfordian-Lower Kimmeridgian clastic sediments of the Mic Mac Formation contain abundant agglutinated foraminifers and ostracodes in Mohawk B-93 and Naskapi N-30 on LaHave Platform. Based on the microfossils, the environment is interpreted as littoral to inner neritic. Coeval limestones of the Abenaki Formation in Oneida O-25 and Dauntless D-35, towards the depocentre of Scotian Basin, were deposited in deeper water. This is suggested by the abundance of epistominids and the presence of rare planktonic specimens of *Globuligerina* gr. *oxfordiana*. A deepening of the environments agrees with the worldwide marine transgression shown by Haq et al. (1987).

Clastic sediments assigned to the Mic Mac Formation were deposited in littoral to inner neritic environments in the Late Kimmeridgian-Tithonian. Episodes of terrestrial deposition are evident in some wells such as Wyandot E-53. In wells towards the depocentre of the basin, where the coeval sediments are included in the Abenaki Formation or the clastic Missisauga Formation (Dauntless D-35), the environment was inner to outer neritic. More open-ocean, warm-water conditions are indicated in Mohican I-100 and Moheida P-15, from which calpionellid assemblages have been described (Jansa et al., 1980; Ascoli et al., 1984).

Neritic conditions with occasional marginal marine episodes prevailed in the Grand Banks basins during the Jurassic. This is shown in Eider M-75 (Gradstein, 1975) and Murre G-67 (Jansa et al., 1976) where argillaceous and carbonate lithologies are predominant. Stam (1986) recognized an ecological zonation in the benthic foraminifers for the Middle and Late Jurassic of the Grand Banks and Portugal (see Chapter 8). In Eider M-75, the inner neritic environments of the Early Jurassic are replaced by deeper water neritic environments during the Bajocian-Bathonian. The Callovian-Kimmeridgian was a time of inner neritic deposition. In the Egret K-36 well in Jeanne d'Arc Basin, the Oxfordian-Kimmeridgian is represented by marginal marine to nonmarine sediments, with slightly deeper water marine environments in the Portlandian. Some information on Late Jurassic paleoenvironments in the Jeanne d'Arc Basin is given by Williamson (1987). He stated that his zones XI (Kimmeridgian) and X (Tithonian) represented periods of middle neritic deposition, with water depths between 50-100 m.

Poag (1985), Poag and Schlee (1984) and Schlee et al. (1985) have had some measure of success in correlating the Jurassic sequences in the COST B-3 (Baltimore Canyon Trough), COST G-1 (Georges Bank Basin) and Mohawk B-93 (LaHave Platform) with the sequence stratigraphy of Vail et al. (1977; Fig. 3.28).

Early Cretaceous

The Early Cretaceous was predominantly a time of nonmarine to inner neritic deposition in offshore eastern Canada. This depositional system is well demonstrated in the Scotian Basin. There, the variable, generally thick clastic sequences of the Missisauga and Verrill Canyon formations are present in Sable Island C-67 and Onondaga E-84, respectively. In Sable Island C-67, the sparse foraminiferal assemblages in the Berriasian-Valanginian contain a high percentage of agglutinated foraminifers. Updip wells, such as Mic Mac H-86 and Mohawk B-93, contain spores and pollen but are devoid of foraminifers. The sediments deposited at that time are assumed to be marginal marine to nonmarine. Generally deeper water environments, with some episodes of outer neritic deposition, were present in wells towards the depocentre of the Scotian Basin, e.g., Mohican I-100, Oneida O-25, Dauntless D-35 and Puffin B-90 (Fig. 3.27). These deeper water assemblages are characterized by abundant calcareous foraminifers, especially epistominids and lenticulinids.

The Hauterivian-Barremian was a period of more stable conditions, with widespread inner neritic to littoral environments, as indicated by abundant *Trocholina* spp. and "complex" agglutinated foraminifers, including *Choffatella* spp. Outer neritic conditions prevailed at Oneida O-25, with nonmarine episodes in updip wells such as Mic Mac H-86.

A marine transgression, denoted by the Naskapi Member of the Logan Canyon Formation, occurred over most of the Scotian Shelf in the Aptian. This agrees with the global eustatic rise in sea level shown by Haq et al. (1987). The foraminiferal assemblages are rich in *Trocholina*, gavelinellids and, occasionally, epistominids. Some continental episodes are indicated in Sable Island C-67 where there are numerous spores, pollen and coal fragments. This would indicate a major regression towards the end of the Aptian. In Mic Mac H-86 and Wyandot E-53, the Aptian appears to be represented by continental deposits.

The major marine transgression in the Albian (Vail et al., 1977; Haq, et al., 1987) is indicated by planktonic and benthic foraminifers and numerous dinocyst taxa in such wells as Mohican I-100, Oneida O-25 and Dauntless D-35. The foraminiferal assemblages are dominated by *Ticinella* and the benthic gavelinellids, epistominids and lenticulinids. Shallower water, inner neritic conditions prevailed for some of the Albian in updip wells such as Naskapi N-30 and even in wells such as Sable Island C-67 and Puffin B-90 (Ascoli, 1976).

The Early Cretaceous paleoenvironments in Puffin B-90 ranged from outer neritic in the Berriasian-Valanginian to coastal or lower delta plain in the Hauterivian-Barremian, to nearshore marine to inner neritic in the Aptian-Albian (Jenkins et al., 1974). The Lower Cretaceous lithostratigraphic units present in this well, in ascending order, are: Verrill Canyon Formation,

121

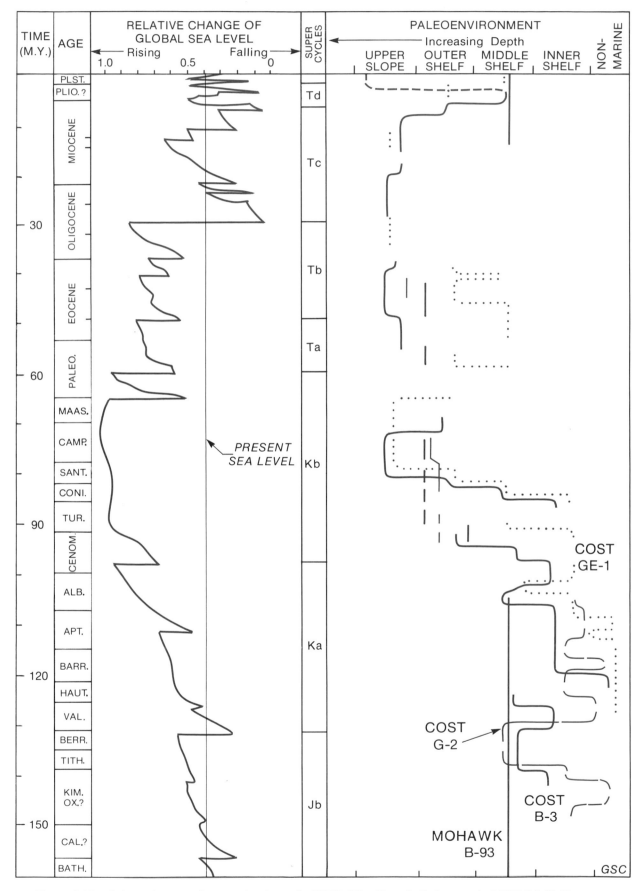

Figure 3.28. Paleoenvironmental curves for the wells COST GE-1 (Georgia Embayment), COST B-3 (Baltimore Canyon Trough), COST G-2 (Georges Bank Basin) and Mohawk B-93 (LaHave Platform) plotted against the relative sea-level curve of Vail et al. (1977). After Poag and Schlee (1984).

Missisauga Formation, and Logan Canyon Formation. Predominantly continental environments prevailed in the vicinity of the Mic Mac H-86 and Wyandot E-53, with occasional littoral interludes indicated by shallow-water ostracodes.

Lower Cretaceous rocks are commonly missing over large areas of the Grand Banks. Where present, as in Jeanne d'Arc Basin, they represent littoral, sublittoral brackish, and lagoonal to neritic environments. Williamson (1987) stated that the Berriasian-Valanginian (Zone IX) was a time of littoral to inner neritic deposition. During the Hauterivian and Barremian (Zones VIII, VII, and VI), the dominant environment was inner to middle neritic with water depths of 0-100 m based upon calcareous and agglutinated foraminifers. There was some shallowing in the Aptian (Zones V and IV) as indicated by *Choffatella decipiens* and *Trocholina infragranulata*. This was followed by a major transgression in the Albian, when water depths were 100-200 m or outer neritic.

A slightly different history is shown for Egret K-36 (Gradstein et al., 1976) also in Jeanne d'Arc Basin. In that well, the Berriasian to Hauterivian is nonmarine to marginal marine, with spores and a few ostracodes being the only microfossils present; the Barremian-Aptian is marginal marine to possibly inner neritic with the foraminifers including *Choffatella* spp. and *Everticyclammina* spp.; the Albian is marginal marine. This shallowing in the Albian presumably reflects tectonic adjustment on the basin's margin.

Deeper water conditions prevailed in Carson Basin in the Berriasian. This is indicated by the presence of calpionellids in Bonnition H-32.

Lower Cretaceous rocks on the Labrador Shelf are either igneous or sedimentary nonmarine to shallow marine. The igneous rocks are included in the Alexis Formation (Fig. 5, in pocket) which also contains clay and sand stringers. The continental to shallow marine clastic sequences are placed in the Bjarni Formation, which contains spores and pollen, with a few dinoflagellate taxa. This indicates deposition in fluvial to lacustrine to inner neritic environments.

Late Cretaceous

The Late Cretaceous represented a time of worldwide marine transgressions as documented in Vail et al. (1977), Vail and Mitchum (1979), and Haq et al. (1987). In the Scotian Basin, the Cenomanian was a time of intermittent transgression and the onset of deposition of the Dawson Canyon Formation, a shale mudstone sequence with some limestone and sandstone. Several wells towards the depocentre of the basin, including Dauntless D-35, Cree E-35 and Mohican I-100, contain abundant planktonic and calcareous benthic foraminifers which indicate an outer neritic environment. Other wells — such as Naskapi N-30 on LaHave Platform, and Oneida O-25, Onondaga E-84 and Sable Island C-67 in Sable Subbasin — contain few planktonic but numerous agglutinated foraminifers and occasional thick-shelled ostracodes, which indicate inner neritic to littoral environments. In Mic Mac H-86, the Cenomanian may even be represented by nonmarine to littoral deposits. The apparent absence of rocks of this age in Puffin B-90 may equate with the Cenomanian unconformity in the COST B-3 and B-2 wells of the Baltimore Canyon Trough (Poag and Schlee, 1984).

Deeper water conditions prevailed in Scotian Basin in the Turonian. The abundant planktonic foraminifers and the rare to abundant calcareous benthic and agglutinated foraminifers confirm the widespread inner to outer neritic environments in all wells studied. The apparent absence of Turonian sediments in Puffin B-90 and Mohican I-100 may represent nondeposition in the former and subsequent uplift, erosion and subsidence in the latter. The low volume of terrigenous material being brought into the basin is reflected in the development of the thin limestone beds, which form the Petrel Member of the Dawson Canyon Formation and are found in most wells on the Scotian Shelf.

Paleoenvironments in the Coniacian were essentially unchanged from those in the Turonian. There must have been some subsidence, however, because outer neritic to bathyal conditions are indicated in Sable Island C-67 and Dauntless D-35 in Sable Subbasin. These deeper water paleoenvironments coincide with the onset of deposition of the Wyandot Formation, a chalky carbonate. Within the Coniacian, the Mesozoic agglutinated foraminifers disappear in Scotian Basin.

The Santonian-Maastrichtian was an interval of continuing outer neritic to bathyal deposition which, depending on lithology and age, may be assigned to the Dawson Canyon Formation, Wyandot Formation or Banquereau Formation (Fig. 3.2). These sediments are invariably rich in planktonic foraminifers, calcareous benthic foraminifers and thin-shelled ostracodes. Water depths attained a maximum in the Scotian Basin as indicated by the assemblages in Puffin B-90, Mic Mac H-86 and Naskapi N-30 (Fig. 3.27).

In the Campanian, foraminifers and ostracodes attained their maximum abundance in numbers of specimens and species, with planktonics being more abundant than benthics and calcareous benthics far outnumbering agglutinated foraminifers. Benthic foraminifers and ostracodes are less abundant in the Maastrichtian.

Poag and Schlee (1984), in a study of United States Atlantic margin wells, related the stratigraphy to the major global unconformities (Fig. 3.28) of Vail et al. (1977). In comparative data for Mohawk B-93 on LaHave Platform, Poag and Schlee stated that, in the Cretaceous, they recognized biostratigraphic gaps in the late Albian-middle Cenomanian, late Cenomanian, late Turonian-early Coniacian, late Coniacian-early Santonian, late Santonian, and Maastrichtian-middle Paleocene (Fig. 3.29). Our data do not supply that degree of resolution.

The Late Cretaceous paleoenvironments of the Grand Banks basins are not as well known as those in the Scotian Basin. Gradstein et al. (1975) displayed depositional environments in some of the wells, in a manner similar to that in Figure 3.27. The paleoenvironments in the Whale, Horseshoe and Jeanne d'Arc basins ranged from shallow marine through marine. Shallow marine comprised marginal marine to inner neritic sediments deposited in water depths of less than 100 m. Marine was equivalent to outer neritic, with water depths between 100-200 m. This indicates that water depths were somewhat shallower than in the Scotian Basin.

Some paleoenvironmental data appeared in the individual well reports published by the Geological Survey of Canada in the 1970s. Late Cretaceous foraminiferal assemblages in Murre G-67 in Jeanne d'Arc Basin, particularly in the Turonian, indicated shallow marine paleoenvironments (Jansa et al., 1976). The apparent absence of Santonian-Maastrichtian sediments may reflect subsequent uplift and erosion or more probably nondeposition.

The Upper Cretaceous rocks are of Turonian to early Maastrichtian age in Egret K-36 (Gradstein et al., 1976), also in Jeanne d'Arc Basin. The deepest water conditions existed in the Turonian where they were outer neritic to bathyal. Inner neritic (up to 100 m depth) water conditions existed throughout the rest of the Late Cretaceous. The condensed Campanian-Maastrichtian sequence may represent deeper water deposits.

Paleoenvironmental curves for Adolphus D-50 farther north in Jeanne d'Arc Basin indicate that water depths were bathyal throughout the Late Cretaceous (Gradstein in Srivastava, 1986). There appears to have been no breaks in the sequences.

Gradstein (1975) recorded a condensed Upper Cretaceous sequence in Eider M-75, with the probable absence of Turonian and Maastrichtian sediments. Water depths were interpreted as inner to outer neritic (up to 200 m).

An incomplete Upper Cretaceous sequence in Osprey H-84 in Carson Basin was deposited in an outer neritic to slope setting, suggesting a close parallel with the Scotian Basin. The open marine, relatively shallow shelf environment in the Cenomanian-Coniacian gave way to deeper neritic to epibathyal (upper slope) conditions in the Santonian-early Campanian (Jansa et al., 1977).

Farther north in East Newfoundland Basin (in Cumberland B-55 and Blue H-28 wells), the condensed and incomplete Upper Cretaceous sediments were deposited in outer neritic to bathyal environments. Gabriel C-60, to the east in the Flemish Basin, contains about 30 m of fault-bounded Campanian-Maastrichtian sediments. These bathyal sediments are underlain by bathyal sediments of Aptian age and overlain by bathyal Lower Eocene sediments. Presumably, the hiatuses represent nondeposition.

The Upper Cretaceous rocks of the Labrador Shelf are predominantly marine shales of the Markland Formation, with a proximal sandstone facies of the Freydis Member of the Markland Formation. The rocks generally represent an incomplete sequence, with the oldest marine sediments being Campanian or Maastrichtian in most wells (Gradstein in Srivastava, 1986). Exceptions are Skolp E-07 in Saglek Basin and Freydis B-87 in Hopedale Basin. In Freydis B-87, upper Albian-Cenomanian rocks contain dinocysts indicative of shallow marine environments. The environment has been interpreted as marginal marine to shallow neritic (Gradstein in Srivastava, 1986). The presence of Turonian sediments has not been confirmed. Coniacian-Santonian sediments in Freydis B-87 and Skolp E-07 were predominantly deposited in shallow neritic environments with water depths up to 100 m (Fig. 3.27).

A marine transgression starting in the Campanian, but much more widespread in the Maastrichtian, inundated most of the Labrador Shelf. Several wells, including Bjarni H-81, Cartier D-70, Freydis B-87 and Leif M-48, in Hopedale Basin, and Snorri J-90 in Saglek Basin, contain Maastrichtian sediments which were deposited in deep neritic to bathyal environments (Fig. 3.27). The transgression and increase in water depths must, therefore, have been relatively rapid. As with the southern part of the margin, water depths attained their Cretaceous maximum in the Campanian-Maastrichtian.

Tertiary

The Tertiary sediments were generally deposited in upward shallowing paleoenvironments in offshore eastern Canada. In the Paleocene-Eocene of the Scotian Basin (Ascoli, 1976), the high species diversity of the planktonics, which is characteristic of the Campanian-Maastrichtian, does not occur. The Paleocene-early Eocene assemblages contain few planktonic and calcareous benthic foraminifers and rare to frequent agglutinated foraminifers and radiolarians. This indicates that the environment was inner to outer neritic with the shoreline being much closer, that there was a change in the Carbonate Compensation Depth, or that there was a difference in the diagenesis of the sediments. At Sable Island C-67 in the Sable Subbasin, the few calcareous foraminifers suggest outer neritic waters with low calcium carbonate concentrations (Fig. 3.27).

Eocene sequences are rarely complete in Scotian Basin wells. The well diversified planktonic and benthic foraminiferal assemblages in the middle and late Eocene were interpreted by Ascoli (1976) as living in outer neritic to bathyal waters. This is supported by the lower number of calcareous benthic foraminifers and the sparsity of agglutinated foraminifers. The deep water environments in the Eocene may be reflected in condensed rather than incomplete sequences. This is the case in Missisauga H-54 where closely spaced sidewall cores were available. Palynological analyses of these sidewall cores revealed the presence of a complete Eocene sequence. Without such control, the Eocene would have been assumed to be incomplete.

The Oligocene sediments of the Scotian Shelf contain numerous calcareous benthic foraminifers, especially of the genera *Lenticulina* and *Sigmomorphina*. Planktonic foraminifers from these sediments are less abundant and agglutinated foraminifers are rare. Radiolarians may be abundant. The environment was presumably outer neritic to upper bathyal, somewhat shallower than in the Eocene. This apparent major discrepancy with the eustatic sea-level curve may simply reflect the lack of precision of the stratigraphic control. Vail et al. (1977) indicated a major regressive phase in the late Oligocene (Chattian). This may affect the Scotian Shelf, since in several wells the late Oligocene is missing (Barss et al., 1979).

Scotian Basin microfaunal assemblages show some significant changes in the Miocene. The early Miocene assemblages contain radiolarians (locally abundant) and diatoms and are probably outer neritic to bathyal. Cooler water conditions would explain the reduction in size of the planktonics during this time. Shallowing in the middle and late Miocene is indicated by the reduction in planktonics and the absence of radiolarians and diatoms. The worldwide

Figure 3.29. Schematic stratigraphy of the four wells COST GE-1 (Georgia Embayment), COST B-3 (Baltimore Canyon Trough), COST G-2 (Georges Bank Basin), and Mohawk B-93 (LaHave Platform) plotted against the seismic unconformities recognized in three east coast offshore basins and the unconformities recognized by Vail and Mitchum (1979). Blank areas represent missing section. The unconformities in the four wells show good agreement with Vail and Mitchum's data. The diagonally hachured sections represent questionable data. After Poag and Schlee (1984).

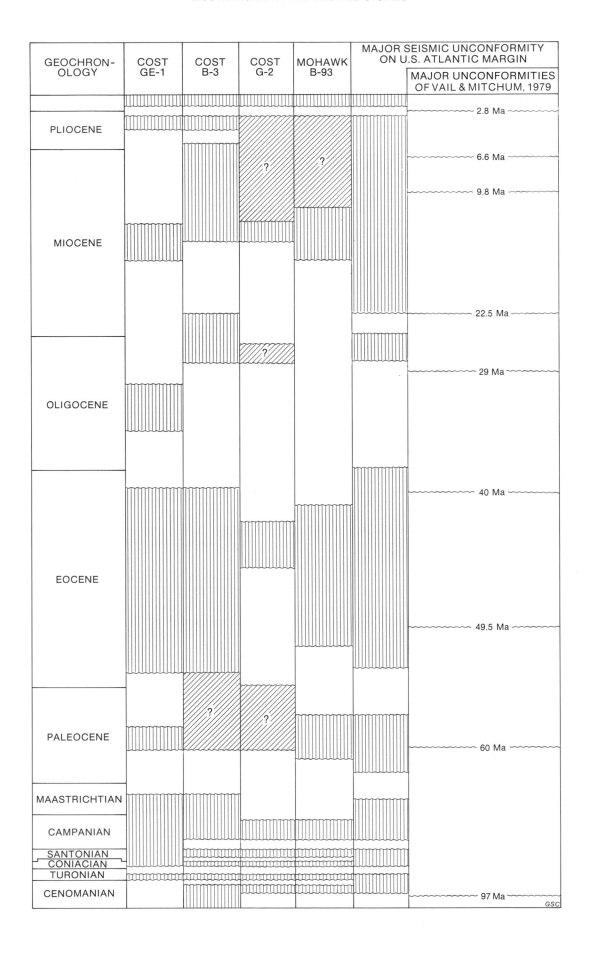

eustatic sea-level drop must have affected the Scotian Basin in the late Miocene as shown by the possible occurrence of nonmarine sediments in Dauntless D-35 in Sable Subbasin.

Shallowing of the sea continued in the Plio-Pleistocene, with littoral to inner neritic conditions existing in much of the basin. Nonmarine deposition was particularly extensive during glaciation (see Chapter 10). Foraminiferal assemblages are dominated by species of shallow-water benthics such as those of the families *Elphidiidae* and *Nonioniidae*.

The global cycles of relative change of sea level are perhaps best known for the Tertiary (Vail et al., 1977). Several of these have been recognized by Poag and Schlee (1984) in wells on the U.S. Atlantic margin (Fig. 3.28). Poag and Schlee also included Mohawk B-93 on the Scotian Shelf in which they recognized the following biostratigraphic gaps in the Tertiary: early-middle Paleocene, late Paleocene-early Eocene, middle Eocene-middle Miocene, late Pliocene-early Pleistocene.

Paleocene sediments are in part or completely missing in several of the Grand Banks' basins, including the Horseshoe, Whale and Jeanne d'Arc. Eocene sediments are more widespread, occurring in Jaeger A-49 on the Avalon uplift, Bittern M-62 in Horseshoe Basin, and Egret K-36 and Murre G-67 in Jeanne d'Arc Basin (Map 1706A, in pocket). Water depths range from less than 100 m in Murre G-67 to bathyal in Bittern M-62. In Murre G-67, lower Eocene sediments immediately overlie the Senonian. The Eocene includes a basal conglomerate and coarse sandstone, laid down under high energy, nearshore or nonmarine conditions. Also present are mudstones and sandstones deposited in littoral to inner neritic environments. This interpretation is borne out by the contained foraminifers. In Egret K-36, middle Eocene sediments unconformably overlie lower Maastrichtian rocks. A radiolarian bed in the middle Eocene presumably denoted a clastic-starved, outer neritic paleoenvironment.

The Osprey H-84 well in Carson Basin exhibited outer neritic to bathyal environments in the late Paleocene-Eocene, which persisted until rapid shallowing in the late Eocene-Oligocene (Fig. 3.26). This is paralleled by a reduction in foraminiferal taxa with only one planktonic *Globigerina* and benthics such as *Spiroplectammina* spp. and *Nonion affine*.

A general shallowing in the Oligocene is indicated in several wells in the Grand Banks basins (Gradstein et al., 1975). In Murre G-67 in Jeanne d'Arc Basin, the early Oligocene foraminiferal assemblages indicate deeper marine, possibly outer shelf conditions. Shallowing in the late Oligocene was accompanied by the disappearance of planktonic foraminifers and can be related to the worldwide lowering of sea level (Haq et al., 1987).

The sand-mudstone sequence of the Miocene contains glauconite, some molluscs, radiolarians and sponge spicules. It is interpreted as having been deposited, in part, in very shallow marine waters with periodic high energy.

Other Jeanne d'Arc Basin wells showing a shallowing trend in the Tertiary are Adolphus D-50 and Dominion O-23. In both wells, deposition in the late Paleocene-Eocene was in a predominantly bethyal environment. Shallowing in the Oligocene was most marked in Dominion O-23 where there was inner to outer neritic deposition. This extended into the Miocene with shallowing in the late Miocene and Plio-Pleistocene.

The Tertiary sediments of some wells in the East Newfoundland Basin (Gabriel C-60 and Blue H-28) appear to have been deposited in bathyal environments. Coeval sediments in other wells, at least in the East Newfoundland Basin, show intervals of shallowing (Gradstein in Srivastava, 1986). In Cumberland B-55, there is a marked shallowing phase in the Oligocene and Pleistocene. This is more pronounced than in Bonnition H-32, where the onset of gradual shallowing in the Oligocene persists through the Miocene to the Plio-Pleistocene, with deposition being marginal marine to inner neritic.

The Tertiary paleoenvironments of the Hopedale and Saglek basins show a gradual shallowing, with episodes of subaerial erosion. According to the agglutinated foraminiferal assemblages the late Paleocene-Eocene, when part of the Cartwright and Kenamu formations were deposited, was a period of bathyal deposition in most of the wells with some shallowing in the late Eocene (Gradstein in Srivastava, 1986, Fig. 3.27). This contrasts with the palynological data which suggest shallow-water conditions. In wells such as Indian Harbour M-52 and Bjarni H-81 in Hopedale Basin, shallowing first occurred in the Oligocene during deposition of the Mokami Formation. This resulted in deposition of shallow neritic deposits of the Saglek Formation in the Miocene over most of the Labrador Shelf, with further shallowing in the Plio-Pleistocene. Consequently, most of the coarse clastics represent marginal marine deposition in the Plio-Pleistocene, although inner neritic deposition persisted in the vicinity of Hare Bay E-21, Cartier D-70 and Gudrid H-55.

The shallowing of the environments on the Labrador Shelf in the Neogene is widespread in offshore eastern Canada. The onset of this trend is in the Oligocene as predicted by the worldwide eustatic sea-level curve. The finite relationship to the curve of Vail et al. (1977) cannot be determined, however, because of the degree of resolution. Future studies may resolve this dilemma, especially through utilization of quantitative stratigraphy.

DINOFLAGELLATE CYST PALEOPROVINCIALISM

The dinoflagellate assemblages in the Mesozoic-Cenozoic rocks of offshore eastern Canada show temporal and spatial fluctuations. Some of these assemblage fluctuations may be local, merely reflecting paleoenvironment control or changes. Other fluctuations have greater significance, however, and reflect regional differences or provinciality. It is our contention, after comparing coeval assemblages, that Mesozoic-Cenozoic dinocyst paleoprovinces can be recognized and defined on a worldwide basis.

Our conclusions regarding distribution patterns of Mesozoic-Cenozoic dinoflagellates apply only to the cysts. Evitt (1981, 1985) succinctly summarized some of the problems relating to interpretations based on the dinoflagellate fossil record. Because only the encysted stage is known to be preserved and because the number and percentage of fossil dinoflagellate species which encyst is unknown, the data for this group will always be incomplete. Evitt (1985) issued a timely warning to fossil dinoflagellate workers when: determining population size and assemblage composition, determining the evolutionary succession of characters or taxa, judging the role of dinoflagellates in the ecological setting, estimating rates of speciation and extinction, and qualifying simple statements about the dinoflagellate fossil record.

The cautionary advice of Evitt (1981, 1985) suggested that quantitative data based on fossil dinoflagellate cysts should be interpreted with circumspection. This has been an influencing factor in our decision to base recognition of paleoprovincialism in Mesozoic-Cenozoic dinocysts on qualitative data, that is species presence. Our findings demonstrate provinciality and, that this, at least in the Cretaceous, is related to climatic conditions. The major controlling climatic conditions appear to be water temperature and circulation patterns. Other controls may be water depth, salinity, light, and local nutrient supply.

Climatic control of Recent dinocyst assemblages has been demonstrated by Wall et al. (1977) and Harland (1983). Wall et al. (1977) in a study of modern marine sediments from the North and South Atlantic Oceans and adjacent seas, noted that distribution patterns of dinocysts varied in an inshore-offshore direction and with latitude, with water currents being a major controlling factor. Some species were limited to tropical-subtropical regions, whereas others were found only in temperate latitudes. The latitudinal trend was most obvious in nearshore environments, although it was recognizable in the offshore assemblages. Harland (1983) analyzed bottom sediments from the North Atlantic and adjacent seas. The 42 taxa could be grouped into latitudinal-climatic and onshore-offshore categories. The latitudinal-climatic categories were tropical, temperate, and arctic; the onshore-offshore categories were inner neritic, outer neritic, and oceanic. The distribution patterns were also related to oceanic currents. The studies of Wall et al. (1977) and Harland (1983) obviously indicated provincialism in Recent dinoflagellate cyst assemblages and make it possible to recognize tropical-subtropical, temperate, and boreal provinces. As shown in the present investigation, the findings of Wall et al. and Harland can be related to distribution patterns of fossil dinocysts, which seem to reflect a similar provincialism.

We have followed previously established criteria for recognition of paleoprovincialism. Sylvester-Bradley (1971) defined faunal provinces as "the major continental or oceanic units into which the world's faunas can be divided." Campbell and Valentine (1977) believed that the modern provinces "are distinctive biodistributional regions within which the faunal communities maintain a relatively narrow range of species composition, but between which there are important compositional differences at the species level in at least a number of communities." Campbell and Valentine defined paleoprovinces as "regions within which fossil communities maintain a characteristic species composition and between which they tend to differ significantly." They were not concerned about the distinction between a province or a subprovince. Valentine (1968) defined a marine province as simply a collection of communities associated in space and time. When discussing microfossil assemblages, we prefer to use the term in the sense of Valentine.

Jurassic

The oldest unequivocal dinoflagellate cysts in the Mesozoic sediments of offshore eastern Canada are Early Jurassic and occur in both Scotian Shelf and Grand Banks wells. Representatives of *Dapcodinium*, *Luehndea*, *Maturodinium*, *Nannoceratopsis* and *Rhaetogonyaulax* were found in these strata. The overall composition of the assemblages compares closely with that from coeval rocks in England (Woollam and Riding, 1983; Riding, 1984), Portugal (Davies, 1985), and Svalbard (Bjaerke, 1980). This may demonstrate their cosmopolitan nature or may reflect the areas studied.

The Middle Jurassic assemblages described from offshore eastern Canada contain only a few species. These include species of *Aldorfia*, *Ctenidodinium*, *Diacanthum* and *Valensiella*. The assemblages show close affinities with coeval European assemblages as described for England (Sarjeant, 1979; Riley and Fenton, 1982; Woollam and Riding, 1983; Riding, 1984) and France (Sarjeant, 1979). In contrast, coeval assemblages in the Canadian Arctic (Johnson and Hills, 1973; Davies and Norris, 1980; Davies, 1983) show only moderate affinities with relatively few species in common with offshore eastern Canada.

The Late Jurassic data were obtained primarily from the Scotian Shelf and Jeanne d'Arc Basin. Common genera in the Late Jurassic of the Scotian Shelf are *Ambonosphaera*, *Ctenidodinium*, *Dichadogonyaulax*, *Endoscrinium*, *Epiplosphaera*, *Gonyaulacysta*, *Lanterna*, *Leptodinium*, *Senoniasphaera*, and *Systematophora*. These taxa are also diagnostic of coeval European assemblages as described in Riley (1977), Rawson and Riley (1982), Woollam and Riding (1983), and Riding (1984). A few of the species are known from the Canadian Arctic (Johnson and Hills, 1973; Davies, 1983), but the differences are more pronounced than the similarities. Scotian Shelf assemblages bear little similarity to Late Jurassic assemblages of western Canada (Pocock, 1972, 1976) or of California (Warren, 1967).

The Late Jurassic dinocyst assemblages of Jeanne d'Arc Basin have been described in this chapter and by van Helden (1986). Common or significant taxa include *Cribroperidinium systremmatum*, *Imbatodinium kondratjevii*, *Rhynchodiniopsis cladophora*, *Scriniodinium inritibilum*, *Muderongia simplex*, *Muderongia* sp. A of Davey (1979a), *Amphorula metaelliptica*, and *Amphorula* sp. These assemblages show some elements of the boreal assemblages as described in Williams and Bujak (1985).

Cretaceous

Major changes in the regional affinities of the fossil dinoflagellate assemblages of eastern Canada first become evident in the Cretaceous, possibly reflecting the development of the proto-Gulf Stream. The provincialism in dinocysts ranging in age from Berriasian to Maastrichtian (135-65 Ma) is shown in Figures 3.30 to 3.38. The data are plotted on the palinspastic reconstructions by Firstbrook et al. (1979), from whom the relative ages are derived. These Lambert equal area polar projections, which are based on those by Smith and Briden (1977), were chosen because the oceans are illustrated effectively and they emphasize the importance of the polar regions in paleooceanography. The recognition of boreal, temperate, and tropical dinocyst assemblages is based in part on Williams and Davies (1982) and Williams and Bujak (1985).

The Neocomian dinocyst assemblages of offshore eastern Canada can be collectively termed "north temperate." As shown in Figures 3.30 and 3.31, coeval assemblages of similar composition have been described from eastern England (Duxbury, 1977; Davey, 1979a). There are some differences, however, between assemblages of Scotian Basin and those of Jeanne d'Arc and East Newfoundland

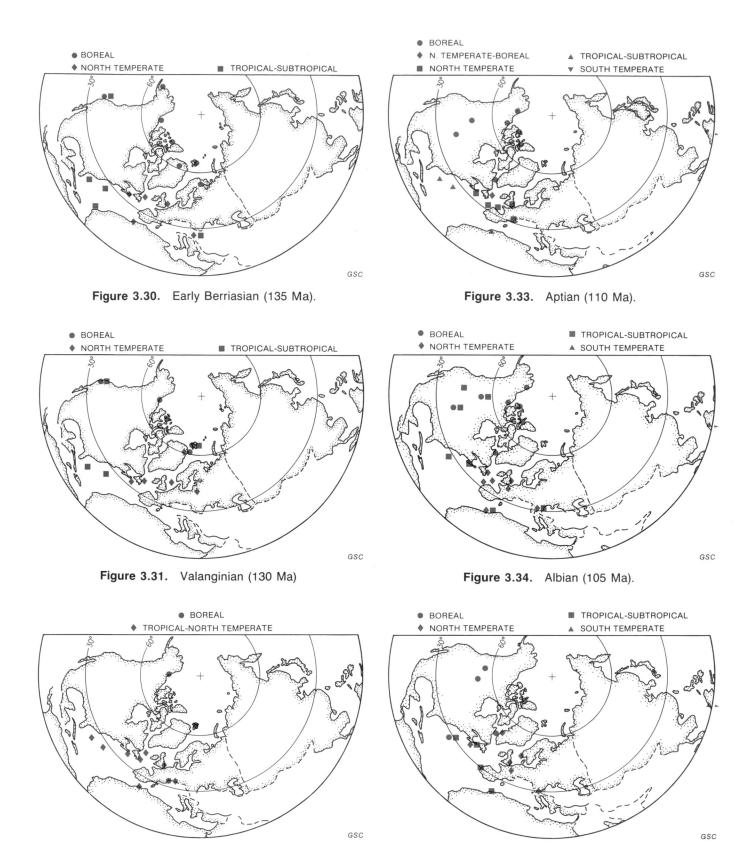

Figure 3.30. Early Berriasian (135 Ma).

Figure 3.31. Valanginian (130 Ma)

Figure 3.32. Barremian (120 Ma).

Figure 3.33. Aptian (110 Ma).

Figure 3.34. Albian (105 Ma).

Figure 3.35. Cenomanian (95 Ma).

Figure 3.30-3.38. Provincialism in dinocysts from Early Berriasian to Maastrichtian. The data for these eight figures are plotted on the palinspastic reconstructions of Firstbrook et al. (1979): the relative ages are also derived from that publication.

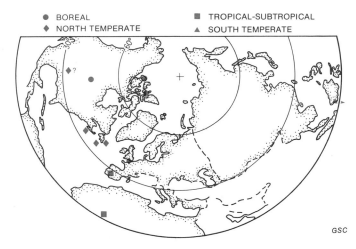

Figure 3.36. Santonian (85 Ma).

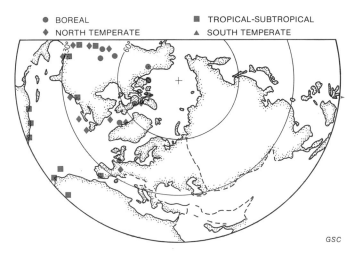

Figure 3.37. Campanian (70 Ma).

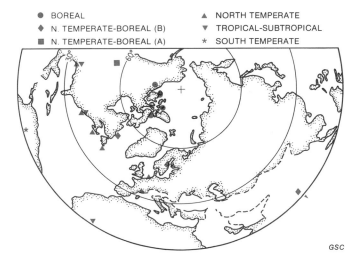

Figure 3.38. Maastrichtian (65 Ma).

basins. The latter have more species in common with coeval assemblages from Speeton in northern England. Species common to Speeton and offshore eastern Newfoundland include: *Achomosphaera neptunii*, *Gonyaulacysta fastigiata*, *G. ordocava*, and *Kleithriasphaeridium fasciatum*.

Only two distinct dinocyst assemblages were recognized in the Barremian (Fig. 3.32). The assemblages of offshore eastern Canada are included in the tropical to north temperate assemblage which is also known from elsewhere in the North Atlantic (Habib, 1975, 1977, 1978), and England (Davey, 1979a; Duxbury, 1977). This suggests that the proto-Gulf Stream was a major factor in controlling dinocyst distribution patterns in the North Atlantic in the Barremian. As in the Neocomian, however, the assemblages in Jeanne d'Arc Basin are more closely related to coeval Speeton Clay assemblages (Duxbury, 1977) than are those of the Scotian Shelf. This may reflect local paleogeographic conditions rather than regional affinities.

Provinciality in dinocyst assemblages in the Aptian (Fig. 3.33) is more pronounced than in the Barremian. Offshore eastern Canada is included in the temperate assemblage, which is also known from the Bay of Biscay (Davey, 1979b), France (Davey and Verdier, 1974), England (Duxbury, 1983), and offshore Portugal (Masure, pers. comm., 1984).

The East Newfoundland Basin assemblages exhibit some unique characteristics. The assemblage includes *Cerbia tabulata*, *Gardodinium trabeculosum*, *Gonyaulacysta exsanguia*, *Hystrichosphaerina schindewolfii*, *Subtilisphaera perlucida*, and *Tanyosphaeridium boletum*. The similarity with the assemblages described from England (Duxbury, 1977, 1983) is striking.

The coeval tropical assemblages from Morocco (Below, 1981) and the southern North Atlantic (Habib, 1977, 1978) contain elements of the temperate assemblages, possibly reflecting more uniform climatic conditions or an evolutionary burst in the dinoflagellates, as reflected by their cysts, in the Aptian-Albian.

The Albian dinocysts can be grouped into four distinct, and presumably provincial, assemblages (Fig. 3.34): the tropical-subtropical, the north temperate, the south temperate, and the boreal. Scotian Shelf assemblages show closest affinity with the assemblages described from the North Atlantic (Habib, 1977, 1978) which are tropical-subtropical. East Newfoundland Basin assemblages are more compatible with coeval assemblages from the Bay of Biscay (Davey, 1979b), France (Davey and Verdier, 1971, 1973) and England (Duxbury, 1983), which we regard as north temperate. The more ubiquitous distribution of the tropical assemblages suggests that more uniform climatic conditions or more active northward moving ocean currents existed along the western margin of the North Atlantic.

The dinoflagellate assemblages do not indicate a direct seaway between offshore eastern Canada and the Arctic in the Albian, although there may have been some connection between the Labrador Shelf and the Arctic and Western Interior. This is indicated by the presence of the *Muderongia asymmetrica* assemblage in Albian rocks from all three areas (Brideaux, 1977; G.L. Williams, personal observations).

In the Cenomanian, the dinoflagellate assemblages of offshore eastern Canada appear to represent mixed north temperate to tropical-subtropical assemblages (Fig. 3.35). The Cenomanian assemblages are difficult to categorize, however, with apparent mixing of boreal and tropical-subtropical assemblages in the western North Atlantic to the south of offshore eastern Canada (Habib, 1977).

The next interval with sufficient data is the Santonian (Fig. 3.36). The dinocysts of the offshore eastern Canadian Santonian can all be grouped into the north temperate assemblage. Similar assemblages have been described from Germany (Yun, 1981), southern England (Clarke and Verdier, 1967) and France (Foucher in Robaszynski et al., 1980). The apparent southerly migration of temperate assemblages suggests possible cooling, which is at variance with Frakes (1979). Alternatively, it may indicate more cosmopolitan assemblages, resulting from a major eustatic rise in sea level.

Labrador Shelf dinocyst assemblages became prominent in the Campanian (Fig. 3.37). During that time, the coeval assemblages for most of offshore eastern Canada could be included in the north temperate assemblage. The exceptions are the mixed boreal-temperate Bylot Island assemblages, which compare most favorably with coeval assemblages from west Greenland.

Lentin and Williams (1980), in a study of the distribution patterns of Campanian peridiniacean dinoflagellates, recognized three assemblages which seemed to reflect regional differentiation rather than local paleoecological control. These assemblages, which seemed to show a relationship to climatic belts, were named the Malloy or tropical-subtropical suite, the Williams or warm temperate suite, and the McIntyre or boreal suite. The Scotian Shelf-Grand Banks assemblages are characteristic of the Williams suite. The Bylot Island-west Greenland assemblages are intermediate between the Williams and McIntyre suites.

The youngest Cretaceous plot of dinocyst assemblages is for the Maastrichtian. The complexity of the assemblages is shown in Figure 3.38. The Bylot Island taxa are included in the boreal assemblage which has also been described from the Canadian Arctic (McIntyre, 1975; Doerenkamp et al., 1976). The Labrador Shelf dinocysts are included in the north temperate-boreal B assemblage, which shows remarkable similarity to assemblages from the Australian Late Cretaceous. This appears to reflect climatic control because both areas were roughly equidistant from the paleoequator during the Maastrichtian, that is around the 50° latitude. Troncoso (1977) described a Maastrichtian southern hemisphere assemblage from Chile, which shows affinities with the north temperate-boreal assemblage of the Labrador Shelf. Again, it may represent the southern hemisphere latitudinal equivalent, since Chile lay between 40 and 60°S during the Maastrichtian.

The Grand Banks — Scotian Shelf dinocysts of the Maastrichtian are herein included in the north temperate assemblage. This assemblage also characterized the Maastrichtian of Denmark (Wilson, 1971; Hansen, 1977) and southern France (Wilson, 1971).

Cenozoic

The Cenozoic was a time of increasing provincialism, reflecting increasing climatic differentiation and the continuing separation of Europe and North America. In the Paleogene, Scotian Shelf assemblages show marked affinity with coeval assemblages from offshore Florida

JOIDES coreholes (unpublished data). Grand Banks taxa show affinities with the Scotian Shelf and English assemblages (Williams and Brideaux, 1975; Bujak et al., 1980). The dinocyst zonation proposed for southern England by Bujak et al. (1980) can be applied with modifications, probably reflecting paleoenvironmental variations, to the Grand Banks.

During the late Eocene-early Oligocene, differences between the Grand Banks, Scotian Shelf and offshore Florida became apparent. These became more pronounced in the late Oligocene, with the disappearance of certain tropical species from the Grand Banks. We regard this as marking the onset of cooler water conditions on the Grand Banks.

Williams and Bujak (1977b) documented the affinities of selected species in the late Eocene-Oligocene. One of the species, *Areosphaeridium diktyoplokus*, occurred in upper Eocene sediments of the Grand Banks and southern England but was absent from coeval Scotian Shelf and offshore Florida sediments. *Areosphaeridium multicornutum* occurred in the Oligocene of the Grand Banks, southern England, offshore Florida, and offshore northwest Africa, but was absent from coeval Scotian Shelf sediments. *Distatodinium paradoxum* was ubiquitous to the Scotian Shelf, Grand Banks and southern England, but absent from more southerly areas such as offshore Florida. Such fluctuations suggest both local environmental and regional control.

The stratigraphic ranges of four other species were plotted for five regions: offshore Florida, offshore west Africa, Scotian Shelf, Grand Banks, and Labrador Shelf (Fig. 3.39). Almost invariably, species appeared later and became extinct earlier on the Grand Banks than on the Scotian Shelf. Two such species are *Homotryblium floripes* and *Polysphaeridium zoharyi*, which have not been recorded from any Labrador Shelf well.

Warmer water conditions seem to have persisted into the middle and possibly late Miocene on the Scotian Shelf. This is confirmed by comparing the Scotian Shelf assemblages with coeval assemblages from offshore Florida. In the latter, the tropical species such as *Polysphaeridium zoharyi* do not become extinct but appear to persist without breaks until the present.

The Neogene assemblages of Scotian Shelf and Grand Banks show some similarities with many of the index species being common to both areas. Often, however, the stratigraphic ranges of individual taxa show subtle differences in the two areas. Such differences cannot be resolved without more adequate Neogene control than that shown in Williams and Bujak (1985).

The Cenozoic dinocyst assemblages of Labrador Shelf and offshore northeast Newfoundland show some significant differences from those of the Grand Banks-Scotian Shelf (Gradstein and Williams, 1976; Williams and Bujak, 1977a). The Paleocene assemblages compare favorably with those of Europe, Scotian Shelf and Grand Banks. In the Eocene, there is less affinity with Scotian Shelf and Grand Banks assemblages, but there is some similarity with southern England and the North Sea. Oligocene and Neogene assemblages appear to be unique to the Labrador Shelf, probably reflecting the onset of much cooler conditions. It is more likely that similar Neogene assemblages will be found in more northerly areas such as Baffin Bay and the Arctic Islands.

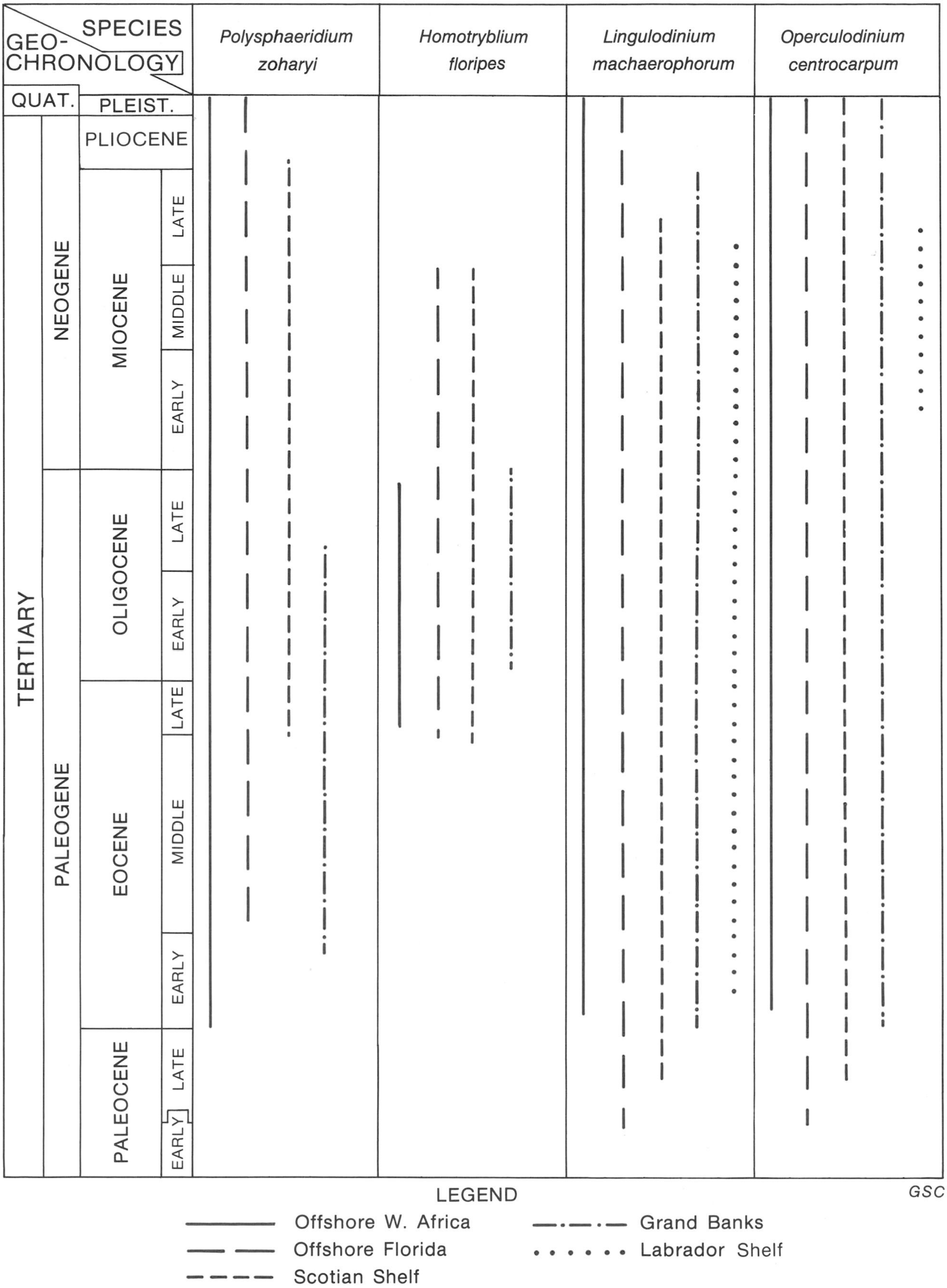

Figure 3.39. Variations in stratigraphic ranges of four dinocyst species which occur in the Cenozoic of the North Atlantic margin (after Williams and Bujak, 1977b).

The Mesozoic-Cenozoic dinocyst assemblages of off-shore eastern Canada show spatial and temporal distribution patterns, which can be compared with those for coeval assemblages from other regions of North America, Europe, Africa, Asia and Australia. When plotted on palinspastic reconstructions for the Cretaceous, the distribution patterns delineate dinocyst paleoprovinces. These paleoprovinces appear to reflect climatic and paleocurrent control of the dinocyst assemblages and support the presence of a proto-Gulf Stream as early as the Neocomian. This has no implications regarding the distribution patterns of thecate dinoflagellates in the Mesozoic-Cenozoic. As Evitt (1985) has explained, such conclusions cannot be determined from the fossil record where we appear to have only the encysted stage preserved.

CONCLUSIONS AND RECOMMENDATIONS

Detailed biostratigraphic zonation of the Phanerozoic rocks of offshore eastern Canada has been accomplished using various groups of microfossils. The fossil groups and the ages covered are as follows: acritarchs and chitinozoans (Early Paleozoic), foraminifers (Carboniferous, Jurassic-Tertiary), ostracodes (Jurassic-Cretaceous), dinoflagellates (Jurassic-Tertiary), spores (Late Paleozoic), spores and pollen (Late Triassic-early Cretaceous), calpionellids (Late Tithonian-Berriasian), calcareous nannoplankton (Late Cretaceous), and diatoms (early Tertiary).

The major zonations now in use are primarily qualitative, providing control down to the age level. This is satisfactory for regional control but is often insufficiently refined to allow correlation of reservoir sands in the Hibernia and Venture fields. It is also inadequate to allow recognition of several of the unconformities and, hence, correlation with eustatic sea-level curves.

The second phase of zonation, utilizing quantitative techniques, holds considerable long-term potential. Initial results have provided refinement of the palynology zones in the Tertiary of the Labrador Shelf, an alternative foraminiferal zonation of the Late Jurassic-Early Cretaceous of the Jeanne d'Arc Basin, and a foraminiferal zonation of the Tertiary of the Scotian margin, Grand Banks and Labrador Shelf. Invariably, the technique utilized has been the Ranking and Scaling Correlation (RASC) program. As with other techniques, however, care must be exercised in filtering out noise, such as reworking, caving, missing section or faulting.

Future developments in producing more detailed zonations should include application of the graphic correlation method as originated by Shaw (1964) and applied by Miller (1977) and Edwards (1984). This approach will be invaluable if related to correlative horizons using electric logs' character and seismology. Inclusion of other data such as organic geochemistry and vitrinite reflectance data will allow predictions on maturation and development of geohistory models.

Detailed biostratigraphic zonations are also necessary if we are to delineate stratigraphic plays. All exploration in offshore eastern Canada has been directed towards structural traps. Stratigraphic traps, potentially greater sources of hydrocarbons, have not been pinpointed because of inadequate control. The complexity and number of reservoir sands at Venture and Hibernia indicate that the potential for stratigraphic traps may be considerable.

Detailed quantitative zonations may provide the key to many of these plays.

Another major development in future years will be the refinement of the paleoecological data by using other groups of microfossils. There needs to be more emphasis on age control based on nannofossils. Less well known but equally useful groups, such as calcareous dinoflagellates, radiolarians, silicoflagellates, and otoliths, should be utilized for specific parts of the section. Otoliths, for example, may provide the most detailed subdivision of the Tertiary of northern waters, such as the Labrador Shelf. These microfossil groups also allow more precise delineation of paleoenvironments, so that paleogeographic reconstructions will be less speculative. Such refinement enables the geologist to map the extent of hydrocarbon source rocks and, hence, predict with more accuracy possible plays.

An exciting consequence of the recent biostratigraphic studies has been the recognition of regional differences in acritarch, dinocyst, spore and foraminiferal assemblages. Correlation of the data has emphasized the provinciality of some of the assemblages and their affinities with other areas. A good example is the resemblance of the Campanian-Maastrichtian dinocyst assemblages of the Labrador Shelf to coeval assemblages of Australasia.

Paleo-oceanographic studies hold particular promise because several major currents influenced offshore eastern Canada. The geological history of the North Atlantic Ocean and Labrador Sea cannot be deciphered without biostratigraphy and, in as much as this is critical to paleo-oceanographic modelling, it highlights the importance of biostratigraphy. Both Gradstein and Srivastava (1980) and MacLean and Williams (1980) have demonstrated the possibility of a Baffin Bay seaway connecting the Arctic and North Atlantic oceans in the Campanian-Maastrichtian. Similar studies of Cretaceous dinocyst distribution patterns have emphasized the long-term role of the proto-Gulf Stream in the late Mesozoic and Cenozoic. Future studies should help our understanding of the evolution of the Labrador Current.

A high priority for the next decade is correlation of the eastern Canadian shelf and the deep-sea stratigraphy. This will be accomplished through analyses of wells on the slope and Ocean Drilling Program sites. It will also facilitate correlation with the European type sections. Integration of seismic stratigraphy and biostratigraphy must be accelerated, so that the applicability of eustatic sea-level curves to a classic Atlantic margin can be determined with a high degree of accuracy. Lastly, paleoclimatological models should be developed by relating the occurrences of the microfossil taxa to occurrences of extinct taxa and such parameters as the oxygen isotope data.

ACKNOWLEDGMENTS

The authors are indebted to B. van Helden, who made data available, C. W. Poag, A.G. Smith and F. M. Gradstein, who gave permission for the reproduction of some text-figures, and A. Berti, who provided information on the Triassic palynological zonation. We are especially grateful to Basil Cooke, Evan Kidson, Bruce Masters and Merrell Miller, who spent many hours reviewing the paper. Their guidance and constructive criticism have led to immeasurable improvements. Thanks are also extended to M.A. Best for providing editorial assistance and producing several of the text-figures and to the Word Processing Center at Amoco Production for typing several versions of this chapter.

REFERENCES

Agterberg, F. P., Gradstein, F. M., Lew, S. N., and Thomas, F. C.
1985:   Nine databases with applications of ranking and scaling of stratigraphic events; in Quantitative Stratigraphy, ed. F. M. Gradstein et al.; D. Reidel Publishing Company, Dordrecht, p. 473-564.

Allemann, F., Catalano, R., Fares, F., and Remane, J.
1971:   Standard calpionellid zonation (Upper Tithonian-Valanginian) of the Western Mediterranean Province; Proceedings Second Planktonic Conference, Roma, 1970, v. 2, p. 1337-1340.

American Commission on Stratigraphic Nomenclature
1961:   Code of Stratigraphic Nomenclature; American Association of Petroleum Geologists Bulletin, v. 45, p. 645-665.

Arthur, K. R., Cole, D. R., Henderson, G.G.L., and Kushnir, D. W.
1982:   Geology of the Hibernia discovery; in the Deliberate Search for the Subtle Trap, ed. M.T. Halbouty; American Association of Petroleum Geologists, Memoir 32, p. 181-196.

Ascoli, P.
1976:   Foraminiferal and ostracod biostratigraphy of the Mesozoic-Cenozoic, Scotian Shelf, Atlantic Canada; in First International Symposium on Benthonic Foraminifera of Continental Margins, Part B, Paleoecology and Biostratigraphy, ed. C. T. Schafer and B.R. Pelletier; Maritime Sediments, Special Publication no. 1, p. 653-771.

1981:   Foraminiferal-ostracod Late Jurassic biozonation of the Scotian Shelf; Geological Survey of Canada, Open File 753, 32 p.

1984:   Epistominid biostratigraphy across the Jurassic-Cretaceous boundary on the northwestern Atlantic Shelf; in Benthos '83, Second International Symposium on Benthic Foraminifera, ed. H. J. Oertli, Pau and Bordeaux, April 1983, p. 27-34.

Ascoli, P., Poag, C. W., and Remane, J.
1984:   Microfossil zonation across the Jurassic-Cretaceous boundary of the Atlantic margin of North America; in Jurassic-Cretaceous Biochronology and Paleogeography of North America, ed. G.E.G. Westermann; Geological Association of Canada, Special Paper 27, p. 31-48.

Barnes, C. R., Norford, B. S., and Skevington, D.
1981:   The Ordovician System in Canada: Correlation Chart and Explanatory Notes; International Union of Geological Sciences, publication no. 8, 27 p.

Barss, M. S. and Hacquebard, P. A.
1967:   Age and the stratigraphy of the Pictou Group in the Maritime Provinces as revealed by fossil spores; in Collected Papers on Geology of the Atlantic Region — Hugh Lilly Memorial Volume, ed. E.R.W. Neale and H. Williams; Geological Association of Canada, Special Paper 4, p. 267-282.

Barss, M. S., Bujak, J. P., and Williams, G. L.
1979:   Palynological zonation and correlation of 67 wells, eastern Canada; Geological Survey of Canada, Paper 78-24, 118 p.

Bartenstein, H.
1976a: Foraminiferal zonation of the Lower Cretaceous in northwest Germany and Trinidad, West Indies — an attempt; Neues Jahrbuch für Geologie und Palaontologie, Monatshefte, v. 3, p. 187-191.

1976b: Benthonic index Foraminifera in the Lower Cretaceous of the northern hemisphere between east Canada and northwest Germany; Erdol und Kohle-Erdgas, v. 29, p. 254-256.

1976c: Practical applicability of a zonation with benthonic foraminifera in the worldwide Lower Cretaceous; Geologie en Mijnbouw, v. 55, p. 83-86.

Bate, R.H. and Robinson, J.E., editors
1978:   A stratigraphical index of British Ostracoda; Geological Journal, Special Issue, no. 8, 538 p.

Bell, W. A.
1929:   Horton-Windsor district, Nova Scotia; Geological Survey of Canada, Memoir 155, 268 p.

1938:   Fossil flora of Sydney coalfield, Nova Scotia; Geological Survey of Canada, Memoir 215, 334 p.

Below, R.
1981:   Dinoflagellaten-zysten aus dem oberen Hauterive bis unteren Cenoman Sudwest-Marokkos; Palaeontographica, Abt. B, v. 176, p. 1-145.

Belt, E. S.
1965:   Stratigraphy and paleogeography of Mabou Group and related Middle Carboniferous facies, Nova Scotia, Canada; Geological Society of America Bulletin, v. 76, p. 777-802.

Benteau, R. T. and Sheppard, M. G.
1982:   Hibernia — a petrophysical and geological review; Journal of Canadian Petroleum Technology, v. 21, p. 59-72.

Berggren, W. A. and Van Couvering, J. A.
1978:   Biochronology; in the Geologic Time Scale, ed. G.V. Cohee, M.F. Glaessner and H.D. Hedberg; The American Association of Petroleum Geologists, Studies in Geology, no. 6, p. 39-55.

Bjaerke, T.
1980:   Mesozoic palynology of Svalbard IV, Toarcian dinoflagellates from Spitsbergen; Palynology, v. 4, p. 57-77.

Bolli, H. M.
1966:   Zonation of Cretaceous to Pliocene marine sediments based on planktonic Foraminifera: Boletin Informativo Asociacion Venezolana de Geologia, Mineria Petroleo, v. 9, p. 3-32.

Brideaux, W.W.
1977:   Taxonomy of Upper Jurassic-Lower Cretaceous microplankton from the Richardson Mountains, District of Mackenzie, Canada; Geological Survey of Canada, Bulletin 281, p. 1-89.

Bujak, J. P. and Williams, G. L.
1977:   Jurassic palynostratigraphy of offshore eastern Canada; in Stratigraphic Micropaleontology of Atlantic Basin and Borderlands, ed. F. M. Swain; Elsevier Scientific Publishing Company, New York, p. 321-339.

1978:   Cretaceous palynostratigraphy of offshore southeastern Canada; Geological Survey of Canada, Bulletin 297, 19 p.

Bujak, J. P., Downie, C., Eaton, G. L., and Williams, G. L.
1980:   Dinoflagellate cyst zonation of the Eocene, southern England; in Dinoflagellate Cysts and Acritarchs from the Eocene of Southern England, ed. J.P. Bujak et al.; The Palaeontological Association, Special Papers in Palaeontology, no. 24, p. 15-26.

Campbell, C. A. and Valentine, J. W.
1977:   Comparability of modern and ancient marine faunal provinces: Palaeobiology, v. 3, p. 49-57.

Caron, M.
1985:   Cretaceous planktic foraminifera; in Plankton Stratigraphy, ed. H. M. Bolli, J.B. Saunders, and K. Perch-Nielsen; Cambridge Earth Science Series, Cambridge University Press, Cambridge, England, p. 17-86.

Clarke, R.F.A. and Verdier, J.-P.
1967:   An investigation of microplankton assemblages from the Chalk of the Isle of Wight, England; Verhandelingen der Koninklijke Nederlandsche Akademie van Wetenschappen, Afdeeling Natuurkunde, Eerste Reeks, v. 24, p. 1-96.

Costa, L. I. and Downie, C.
1979:   The distribution of the dinoflagellate Wetzeliella in the Palaeogene of northwestern Europe; Palaeontology, v. 19, p. 591-614.

Crane, M. J.
1965:   Upper Cretaceous ostracodes of the Gulf Coast area; Micropaleontology, v. 11, p. 191-254.

Davey, R. J.
1979a: The stratigraphic distribution of dinocysts in the Portlandian (latest Jurassic) to Barremian (Early Cretaceous) of northwest Europe; American Association of Stratigraphic Palynologists, Contributions Series 5B, p. 49-81.

1979b: Marine Apto-Albian palynomorphs from Holes 400A and 402A, IPOD Leg 48, northern Bay of Biscay; in Initial Reports of the Deep Sea Drilling Project, Volume XLVIII, ed. L. Montadert et al.; United States Government Printing Office, Washington, v. 48, p. 547-577.

1982:   Dinocyst stratigraphy of the latest Jurassic to Early Cretaceous of the Haldager No. 1 borehole, Denmark; Geological Survey of Denmark, Series B, no. 6, p. 1-57.

Davey, R. J. and Verdier, J.-P.
1971:   An investigation of microplankton assemblages from the Albian of the Paris Basin; Verhandelingen der Koninklijke Nederlandsche Akademie van Wetenschappen, Afdeling Natuurkunde, Eerste Reeks, v. 26, p. 1-1 58.

1973:   An investigation of microplankton assemblages from latest Albian (Vraconian) sediments; Revista Española Micropaleontologia, v. 5, p. 173-212.

1974:   Dinoflagellate cysts from the Aptian type sections at Gargas and La Bedoule, France; Palaeontology, v. 17, p. 623-653.

Davies, E. H.
1983:   The dinoflagellate Oppel-zonation of the Jurassic-Lower Cretaceous sequences in the Sverdrup Basin, arctic Canada; Geological Survey of Canada, Bulletin 359, p. 1-59.

1985:   The miospore and dinoflagellate cyst Oppel-Zonation of the Lias of Portugal; Palynology, v. 9, p. 105-132.

1986:   The correlation and geohistory of the Hibernia Field; in Canadian Society of Petroleum Geologists Convention, Program with Abstracts, Calgary, Alberta, p. 36.

Davies, E. H. and Norris, G.
1980:   Latitudinal variations in encystment modes and species diversity in Jurassic dinoflagellates; in The Continental Crust and its Mineral Deposits, ed. D.W. Strangway; Geological Association of Canada, Special Paper 20, p. 361-373.

Davies, E. H., Akande, S. O., and Zentilli, M.
1984: Early Cretaceous deposits in the Gays River lead-zinc mine, Nova Scotia; in Current Research, Part A, Geological Survey of Canada, Paper 84-1A, p. 353-358.

Dawson, J. W.
1873: Report on the fossil plants of the Lower Carboniferous and Millstone Grit formations of Canada; Geological Survey of Canada, Separate Report 430, 47 p.

D'Iorio, M. A.
1986: Integration of foraminiferal and dinoflagellate data sets in quantitative stratigraphy of the Grand Banks and Labrador Shelf; Bulletin of Canadian Petroleum Geology, v. 34, no. 2, p. 277-283.

Doerenkamp, A. S., Jardine, S., and Moreau, P.
1976: Cretaceous and Tertiary palynomorph assemblages from Banks Island and adjacent areas (N.W.T.); Bulletin of Canadian Petroleum Geology, v. 24, p. 372-399.

Doeven, P. H.
1983: Cretaceous nannofossil stratigraphy and paleoecology of the northwestern Atlantic; Geological Survey of Canada, Bulletin 356, 69 p.

Doeven, P.H., Gradstein, F.M., Jackson, A., Agterberg, F.P., and Nel, L.D.
1982: A quantitative nannofossil range chart; Micropaleontology, v. 28, p. 85-92.

Duxbury, S.
1977: A palynostratigraphy of the Berriasian to Barremian of the Speeton Clay of Speeton, England; Palaeontographica, Abt B, v. 160, p. 17-67.
1983: A study of dinoflagellate cysts and acritarchs from the Lower Greensand (Aptian to Lower Albian) of the Isle of Wight, southern England; Palaeontographica, Abt B, v. 186, p. 18-80.

Edwards, L. E.
1984: Insights on why graphic correlation (Shaw's method) works; Journal of Geology, v. 92, p. 583-587.

Evitt, W. R.
1981: The difference it makes that dinoflagellates do it differently; International Commission on Palynology, Newsletter, v. 4, no. 1, p. 6-7.
1985: Sporopollenin dinoflagellate cysts: their morphology and interpretation; American Association of Stratigraphic Palynologists Foundation, 333 p.

Exton, J. and Gradstein, F. M.
1984: Early Jurassic stratigraphy and micropaleontology of the Grand Banks and Portugal; in Jurassic-Cretaceous Biochronology and Paleogeography of North America; ed. G.E.G. Westermann; Geological Association of Canada, Special Paper 27, p. 13-30.

Firstbrook, P. L., Funnell, B. M., Hurley, A. M., and Smith, A. G.
1979: Paleoceanic reconstructions 160-0 Ma; National Science Foundation, 41 p.

Frakes, L.A.
1979: Climate Throughout Geological Time; Elsevier Scientific Publishing Company, New York, 310 p.

Gradstein, F. M.
1975: Biostratigraphy (foraminifera) and depositional environment of Amoco IOE Eider M-75, Grand Banks of Newfoundland; Geological Survey of Canada, Open File 334, 17 p.
1976: Biostratigraphy and biogeography of Jurassic Grand Banks Foraminifera; in First International Symposium on Benthonic Foraminifera of Continental Margins Part B, Paleoecology and Biostratigraphy, ed., C.T. Schafer and B.R. Pelletier; Maritime Sediments, Special Publication no. 1, p. 557-583.
1978: Jurassic Grand Banks foraminifera; Journal of Foraminiferal Research, v. 8, no. 2, p. 97-109.
1985: Ranking and scaling in exploration micropaleontology; in Quantitative Stratigraphy, ed. F.M. Gradstein et al.; D. Reidel Publishing Company, Dordrecht, p. 109-160.

Gradstein, F. M. and Agterberg, F. P.
1982: Models of Cenozoic foraminiferal stratigraphy northwestern Atlantic Margin; in Quantitative Stratigraphic Correlation, ed., J. M. Cubitt and R. A. Reyment; John Wiley and Sons, Ltd., Chichester, p. 119-173.
1985: Quantitative correlation in exploration micropaleontology; in Quantitative Stratigraphy, ed., F.M. Gradstein et al.; D. Reidel Publishing Company, Dordrecht, p. 309-357.

Gradstein, F. M. and Berggren, W. A.
1981: Flysch-type agglutinated Foraminifera and the Maastrichtian to Paleogene history of the Labrador and North seas; Marine Micropaleontology, v. 6, p. 211-268.

Gradstein, F. M. and Srivastava, S. P.
1980: Aspects of Cenozoic stratigraphy and paleoceanography of the Labrador Sea and Baffin Bay; Palaeogeography, Palaeoclimatology and Palaeoecology, v. 38, p. 261-295.

Gradstein, F. M. and Williams, G. L.
1976: Biostratigraphy of the Labrador Shelf; Geological Survey of Canada, Open File 349, 39 p.

Gradstein, F. M., Williams, G. L., Jenkins, W.A.M., and Ascoli, P.
1975: Mesozoic and Cenozoic stratigraphy of the Atlantic continental margin, eastern Canada; in Canada's Continental Margins and Offshore Petroleum Exploration, ed., C.J. Yorath, E.R. Parker and D. J. Glass; Canadian Society of Petroleum Geologists, Memoir 4, p. 103-131.

Gradstein, F. M., Jenkins, W.A.M., and Williams, G. L.
1976: Biostratigraphy and depositional history of Amoco Imp Skelly B-1 Egret K-36, Grand Banks, Newfoundland; Geological Survey of Canada, Open File 396, 23 p.

Grant, A. C.
1980: Problems with plate tectonics: the Labrador Sea; Bulletin of Canadian Petroleum Geology, v. 28, p. 252-278.

Habib, D.
1975: Neocomian dinoflagellate zonation in the western North Atlantic; Micropaleontology, v. 21, p. 373-392.
1977: Comparison of Lower and Middle Cretaceous palynostratigraphic zonations in the western North Atlantic; in Stratigraphic Micropaleontology of Atlantic Basin and Borderlands, ed. F. W. Swain; Elsevier Scientific Publishing Company, New York, p. 341-367.
1978: Palynostratigraphy of the Lower Cretaceous section at Deep Sea Drilling Project Site 391, Blake-Bahama Basin, and its correlation in the North Atlantic; in Initial Reports of the Deep Sea Drilling Project, Volume XLIV, ed., B.E. Tucholke et al.; United States Government Printing Office, Washington, v. 44, p. 887-897.

Hacquebard, P. A.
1972: The Carboniferous of eastern Canada; Compte Rendu, Septième Congrès International de Stratigraphie et de Géologie du Carbonifère, Krefeld, p. 69-90.

Hansen, J. M.
1977: Dinoflagellate stratigraphy and echinoid distribution in Upper Maastrichtian and Danian deposits from Denmark; Geological Society of Denmark Bulletin, v. 26, p. 1-26.

Haq, B.U., Hardenbol, J., and Vail, P.R.
1987: Chronology of fluctuating sea levels since the Triassic; Science, v. 235, p. 1156-1167.

Hardy, I. A.
1975: Lithostratigraphy of the Banquereau Formation of the Scotian Shelf; in Offshore Geology of Eastern Canada, ed., W.J.M. van der Linden and J.A. Wade; Geological Survey of Canada, Paper 74-30, v. 2, p. 163-174.

Harland, R.
1983: Distribution maps of Recent dinoflagellate cysts in bottom sediments from the North Atlantic Ocean and adjacent seas; Palaeontology, v. 26, p. 321-387.

Hazel, J. E. and Paulson, O. L., Jr.
1964: Some new ostracode species from the Austinian and Taybran (Coniacian and Campanian) rocks of the East Texas Embayment; Journal of Palaeontology, v. 38, p. 1047-1064.

Howe, H. V. and Laurencich, L.
1958: Introduction to the study of Cretaceous Ostracoda; Louisiana State University Press, 536 p.

Ioannides, N. S.
1986: Dinoflagellate cysts from some Upper Cretaceous-Lower Tertiary sections, Bylot and Devon islands, District of Franklin, arctic Canada; Geological Survey of Canada Bulletin 371, 99 p.

Jansa, L. F. and Mamet, B. L.
1984: Offshore Visean of eastern Canada; paleogeographic and plate tectonic implications; in Ninth International Congress on Carboniferous Stratigraphy and Geology, Atlantic Coast Basins, ed., H.H.J. Geldsetzer; Southern Illinois University Press, Compte Rendu, v. 3, pt. 1, Carbondale, Illinois, p. 205-214.

Jansa, L. F. and Wade, J. A.
1975: Geology of the continental margin off Nova Scotia and Newfoundland; in Offshore Geology of Eastern Canada, Volume 2, Regional Geology, ed., W.J.M. van der Linden and J.A. Wade; Geological Survey of Canada, Paper 74-30, v. 2, p. 51-105.

Jansa, L. F., Bujak, J. P., and Williams, G. L.
1980: Upper Triassic salt deposits of the western North Atlantic; Canadian Journal of Earth Sciences, v. 17, p. 547-559.

Jansa, L. F., Gradstein, F. M., Harris, I. M., Jenkins, W.A.M., and Williams, G. L.
1976: Stratigraphy of the Amoco-IOE Murre G-67 well, Grand Banks of Newfoundland; Geological Survey of Canada, Paper 75-30, 14 p.

Jansa, L. F., Gradstein, F. M., Williams, G. L., and Jenkins, W.A.M.
1977: Geology of the Amoco Imp. Skelly A-1 Osprey H-84 well, Grand Banks, Newfoundland; Geological Survey of Canada, Paper 77-21, 17 p.

Jansa, L. F., Mamet, B. L., and Roux, A.
1978: Visean limestones from the Newfoundland Shelf; Canadian Journal of Earth Sciences, v. 15, p. 1422-1436.

Jansa, L. F., Remane, J., and Ascoli, P.
1980: Calpionellid and foraminiferal-ostracod biostratigraphy at the Jurassic-Cretaceous boundary, offshore eastern Canada; Revista Italiana di Paleontologia e Stratigrafia, v. 86, n. 1, p. 67-126.

Jenkins, W.A.M.
1984: Ordovician rocks in the Eastcan et al. Freydis B-87 and other wells in offshore Atlantic Canada; Canadian Journal of Earth Sciences, v. 21, p. 864-868.

Jenkins, W.A.M., Ascoli, P., Gradstein, F. M., Jansa, L. F. and Williams, G. L.
1974: Stratigraphy of the Amoco IOE A-1 Puffin B-90 well, Grand Banks of Newfoundland; Geological Survey of Canada, Paper 74-61, 12 p.

Johnson, C. D. and Hills, L. V.
1973: Microplankton zones of the Savik Formation (Jurassic), Axel Heiberg and Ellesmere Islands, District of Franklin; Bulletin of Canadian Petroleum Geology, v. 21, p. 178-218.

King, L.H., Fader, G.B., Jenkins, W.A.M., and King, E.L.
1986: Occurrence and regional geological setting of Paleozoic rocks on the Grand Banks of Newfoundland; Canadian Journal of Earth Sciences, v. 23, p. 504-526.

Legault, J. A.
1982: First report of Ordovician (Caradoc-Ashgill) palynomorphs from Orphan Knoll, Labrador Sea; Canadian Journal of Earth Sciences, v. 19, p. 1851-1856.

Lentin, J. K. and Williams, G. L.
1980: Dinoflagellate provincialism with emphasis on Campanian peridiniaceans; American Association of Stratigraphic Palynologists, Contributions Series, no. 7, p. 1-47.

Lin, C. I.
1971: Cretaceous deposits in the Musquodoboit River Valley, Nova Scotia; Canadian Journal of Earth Sciences, v. 8, p. 1152-1154.

MacLean, B. and Williams, G. L.
1980: Upper Cretaceous rocks in Baffin Bay; in Geological and Mineralogical Associations of Canada, Annual Meeting, Halifax, Program with Abstracts, p. 69.

Mamet, B.
1970: Carbonate microfacies of the Windsor Group (Carboniferous), Nova Scotia and New Brunswick; Geological Survey of Canada, Paper 70-21, 121 p.

Manivit, H., Perch-Nielsen, K., Prins, B., and Verbeek, J.W.
1977: Mid-Cretaceous calcareous nannofossil biostratigraphy; Proceedings of the Koninklijke Nederlandse Akademie van Wetenschappen, Series B, pt. 3, v. 80, p. 169-181.

Manum, S. and Cookson, I. C.
1964: Cretaceous microplankton in a sample from Graham Island, arctic Canada, collected during the second "Fram"-Expedition (1898-1902), with notes on microplankton from the Hassel Formation, Ellef Ringnes Island; Schrifter utgitt av Det Norske Videnskaps-Akademi i Oslo, I. Mat-Nuturv. Klasse, Ny Series 17, p. 1-35.

Martin, F.
1968: Les Acritarches de l'Ordovicien et du Silurien belges: determination et valeur stratigraphique; Institut Royal des Sciences Naturelles de Belgique, Memoir 160, 175 p.

McIntyre, D.J.
1975: Morphologic changes in *Deflandrea* from a Campanian section, District of Mackenzie, N.W.T., Canada; Geoscience and Man, v. 11, p. 61-76.

McIver, N. L.
1972: Mesozoic-Cenozoic stratigraphy of the Nova Scotia Shelf; Canadian Journal of Earth Sciences, v. 9, p. 54-70.

McWhae, J.R.H., Elie, R., Laughton, K.C., and Gunther, P.R.
1980: Stratigraphy and petroleum prospects of the Labrador Shelf; Bulletin of Canadian Petroleum Geology, v. 28, p. 460-488.

McWhae, J.R.H. and Michel, W.F.E.
1975: Stratigraphy of Bjarni H-81 and Leif M-48, Labrador Shelf; Bulletin of Canadian Petroleum Geology, v. 23, p. 361-382.

Miller, F. X.
1977: The graphic correlation method in biostratigraphy; in Concepts and Methods of Stratigraphy, ed. E.G. Kauffman and J.E. Hazel; Dowden, Hutchinson and Ross, Stroudsburg, Pennsylvania, p. 165-186.

Miller, K.G., Gradstein, F.M., and Berggren, W.A.
1982: Late Cretaceous to early Tertiary agglutinated benthic foraminifera in the Labrador Sea; Micropaleontology, v. 28, p. 1-30.

Moullade, M.
1984: Interêt des petits Foraminifères benthiques "profonds" pour la biostratigraphie et l'analyse des paleoenvironnements océaniques mesozoiques; in Benthos '83, ed. H.J. Oertli; Second International Symposium on Benthic Foraminifera, France, p. 429-464.

North American Commission on Stratigraphic Nomenclature
1983: North American Stratigraphic Code; American Association of Petroleum Geologists Bulletin, v. 67, p. 841-875.

Oertli, H. J.
1957: Ostracodes du Jurassique Supérieur du Bassin de Paris (sondage Vernon I); Revue Institut Francais du pétrole, v. 12, p. 647-695.
1958: Les Ostracodes de l'Aptien-Albien d'Apt; Revue Institut Francais du pétrole, v. 13, p. 1499-1537.
1959: Malm-Ostrakoden aus dem schweizemschen Juragebirge; Memoires de la Société Helvetique des Sciences Naturelles, v. 83, p. 1-44.
1985: Atlas des ostracodes de France (Paléozoique-Actuel); Bulletin Centres Recherches Exploration-Production Elf-Aquitaine, Mémoire 9, p. 1-396.

Ohm, U.
1967: Zur Kenntnis der Gattungen *Reinholdella, Garantella* und *Epistomina* (Foraminifera); Palaeontographica, Abt. A, v. 127, p. 103-188.

Palmer, A.R.
1983: The Decade of North American Geology 1983 Geologic Time Scale; Geology, v. 11, p. 503-508.

Poag, C.W.
1985: Depositional history and stratigraphic reference section for central Baltimore Canyon Trough; in Geologic Evolution of the United States Atlantic Margin, ed. C.W. Poag; Van Nostrand Reinhold Company, Inc., New York, p. 217-264.

Poag, C.W. and Schlee, J.S.
1984: Depositional sequences and stratigraphic gaps on submerged United States Atlantic margin; in Interregional Unconformities and Hydrocarbon Accumulation, ed. J.S. Schlee; American Association of Petroleum Geologists, Memoir 36, p. 165-182.

Pocock, S.A.J.
1972: Palynology of the Jurassic sediments of western Canada, Part 2, Marine Species; Palaeontographica, Abt B, v. 137, p. 85-153.
1976: A preliminary dinoflagellate zonation of the uppermost Jurassic and lower part of the Cretaceous Canadian Arctic, and possible correlation in the Western Canada Basin; Geoscience and Man, v. 15, p. 101-114.

Postuma, J.A.
1971: Manual of Planktonic Foraminifera; Elsevier Science Publishers, Amsterdam, 420 p.

Rawson, P.F. and Riley, L.A.
1982: Latest Jurassic-Early Cretaceous events and the "Late Cimmerian Unconformity" in North Sea area; American Association of Petroleum Geologists Bulletin, v. 66, p. 2628-2648.

Remane, J.
1964: Untersuchungen zur systematik und Stratigraphie der Calpionellen in den Jura-Kreide-Grenzschichten des Vocontischen Troges; Palaeontographica, Abt A, v. 123, p. 1-57.
1978: Calpionellids; in Introduction to Marine Micropaleontology, ed. B.U. Haq and A. Boersma; Elsevier Scientific Publishing Company, New York, p. 161-170.

Riding, J.B.
1984: Dinoflagellate cyst range-top biostratigraphy of the uppermost Triassic to lowermost Cretaceous of northwest Europe; Palynology, v. 8, p. 195-210.

Riley, L.A.
1977: Stage nomenclature at the Jurassic-Cretaceous boundary, North Sea Basin; Norsk Petroleums Forening, Mesozoic Northern North Sea Symposium Proceedings, v. 4, p. 1-11.

Riley, L.A. and Fenton, J.P.G.
1982: A dinocyst zonation for the Callovian to Middle Oxfordian succession (Jurassic) of northwest Europe; Palynology, v. 6, p. 193-202.

Robaszynski, F. and Amédro, F. coordinators, and Foucher, J.C., Gaspard, D., Magniez-Jannin, F., Manivit, H., and Sornay, J.
1980: Synthese biostratigraphique de l'Aptien au Santonien du Boulonnais a partir de sept groupes paléontologoques: foraminifers, nannoplancton, dinoflagellées et macrofaunes; Revue de Micropaleontologie, v. 22, no. 4, p. 195-321.

Rolle, F.
1985: Late Cretaceous-Tertiary sediments offshore central West Greenland: lithostratigraphy, sedimentary evolution, and petroleum potential; Canadian Journal of Earth Sciences, v. 22, p. 1001-1019.

Sarjeant, W.A.S.
1979: Middle and Upper Jurassic dinoflagellate cysts: The world excluding North America; American Association of Stratigraphic Palynologists, Contributions Series no. 5B, p. 133-157.

Schlee, J.S., Poag, C.W., and Hinz, K.
1985: Seismic stratigraphy of the continental slope and rise seaward of Georges Bank; in Geologic Evolution of the United States Atlantic Margin, ed. C.W. Poag; Van Nostrand Reinhold Company, Inc., New York, p. 265-292.

Shaw, A.B.
1964: Time in Stratigraphy; McGraw Hill Publishing Company, New York, 365 p.

Simon, W. and Bartenstein, H. (ed.)
1962: Leitfossilien der Mikropalaeontologie; Gebrüder Borntraeger, Berlin, v. 1-2, 432 p.

Sissingh, W.
1977: Biostratigraphy of Cretaceous calcareous nannoplankton; Geologie en Mijnbouw, v. 56, p. 37-65.

Smith, A.G. and Briden, J. C.
1977: Mesozoic and Cenozoic Paleocontinental Maps; Cambridge University Press, Cambridge, 63 p.

Srivastava, S.K.
1976: The fossil pollen genus *Classopollis*; Lethaia, v. 9, p. 437-457.

Srivastava, S.P.
1978: Evolution of the Labrador Sea and its bearing on the early evolution of the North Atlantic; Royal Astronomical Society, Geophysical Journal, v. 52, p. 313-357.

1986: Geophysical maps and geological sections of the Labrador Sea; Geological Survey of Canada, Paper 85-16, 11 p.

Stainforth, R.M., Lamb, J.L., Luterbacher, M. Beard, J.H., and Jeffords, R.M.
1975: Cenozoic planktonic foraminiferal zonation and characteristics of index forms; University of Kansas Paleontological Contributions, Art 62, 425 p.

Stam, B.
1986: Quantitative analysis of Middle and Late Jurassic Foraminifers from Portugal and its implications for the Grand Banks of Newfoundland; Utrecht Micropaleontological Bulletin, no. 34, 167 p.

Stevenson, I.M.
1959: Shubenacadie and Kennetcook map-areas, Colchester, Hants and Halifax Counties, Nova Scotia; Geological Survey of Canada, Memoir 302, 88 p.

Stevenson, I.M. and McGregor, D.C.
1963: Cretaceous sediments in central Nova Scotia, Canada; Geological Society of America Bulletin, v. 74, p. 355-356.

Sylvester-Bradley, P.C.
1971: Dynamic factors in animal palaeogeography; in Faunal Provinces in Space and Time, ed. F.A. Middlemiss, P.F. Rawson, and G .Newall; Geological Journal Special Issue no. 4, p. 1-18.

Thomas, F.C. and Gradstein, F.M.
1981: Tertiary subsurface correlations using pyritized diatoms, offshore eastern Canada; in Current Research, Part B, Geological Survey of Canada, Paper 81-1B, p. 17-23.

Troncoso, A.
1977: Étude palynologique de la limite Crétacé-Tertiaire dans la région de Magellan, Chili austral; PhD thesis, L'Université Louis Pasteur, Strasbourg, France, 153 p.

Umpleby, D.C.
1979: Geology of the Labrador Shelf; Geological Survey of Canada, Paper 79-13, 34 p.

Upshaw, C.F., Armstrong, W.E., Creath, W.B., Kidson, E.J., and Sanderson, G.A.
1974: Biostratigraphic framework of Grand Banks; American Association of Petroleum Geologists Bulletin, v. 58, p. 1124-1132.

Utting, J.
1980: Palynology of the Windsor Group (Mississippian) in a borehole at Stewiacke, Shubenacadie Basin, Nova Scotia; Canadian Journal of Earth Sciences, v. 17, p. 1031-1045.

1987: Palynology of the Lower Carboniferous Windsor Group and Windsor-Canso boundary beds of Nova Scotia and their equivalence in Quebec, New Brunswick and Newfoundland; Geological Survey of Canada Bulletin 374, 93 p.

Vail, P.R. and Mitchum, R.M., Jr.
1979: Global cycles of relative changes of sea level from seismic stratigraphy; in Geological and Geophysical Investigations of Continental Margins, ed. J.S. Watkins, L. Montadert and P.W. Dickerson; American Association of Petroleum Geologists, Memoir 29, p. 469-472.

Vail, P.R., Hardenbol, J., and Todd, R.G.
1984: Jurassic unconformities, chronostratigraphy, and sea-level changes from seismic stratigraphy and biostratigraphy; in Interregional Unconformities and Hydrocarbon Accumulation, ed. J.S. Schlee; American Association of Petroleum Geologists, Memoir 36, p. 129-144.

Vail, P.R., Mitchum, R.M., Jr., and Thompson, S. III
1977: Global cycles of relative changes of sea level; in Seismic Stratigraphy — Applications to Hydrocarbon Exploration, ed. C.E. Payton; American Association of Petroleum Geologists, Memoir 26, p. 83-97.

Valentine, J.W.
1968: Climatic regulation of species diversification and extinction; Geological Society of America Bulletin, v. 79, p. 273-275.

van Helden, B.G.T.
1986: Dinoflagellate cysts at the Jurassic-Cretaceous boundary, offshore east Newfoundland, eastern Canada; Palynology, v. 10, p. 181-200.

Van Hinte, J.E.
1976: A Jurassic time scale; American Association of Petroleum Geologists Bulletin, v. 60, p. 489-497.

Wall, D., Dale, B., Lohmann, G.P. and Smith, W.K.
1977: The environmental and climatic distribution of dinoflagellate cysts in modern marine sediments from regions in the North and South Atlantic oceans and adjacent seas; Marine Micropaleontology, v. 2, p. 121-200.

Walton, H.S. and Berti, A.A.
1976: Upper Triassic and Lower Jurassic palynology of the Grand Banks area, eastern Canada; Joint Meeting of the American Association of Stratigraphic Palynologists and Commission Internationale de Microflore du Paleozoique, Abstracts, p. 27-28.

Warren, J.S.
1967: Dinoflagellates and acritarchs from the Upper Jurassic and Lower Cretaceous rocks on the west side of the Sacramento Valley, California; PhD thesis, University of Stanford, California, 409 p.

Williams, G.L.
1975: Dinoflagellate and spore stratigraphy of the Mesozoic-Cenozoic, offshore eastern Canada; in Offshore Geology of Eastern Canada, Volume 2, Regional Geology, ed. W.J.M. van der Linden and J.A. Wade; Geological Survey of Canada, Paper 74-30, v. 2, p. 107-161.

Williams, G.L. and Brideaux, W.W.
1975: Palynologic analyses of Upper Mesozoic and Cenozoic rocks of the Grand Banks, Atlantic continental margin; Geological Survey of Canada, Bulletin 236, 162 p.

Williams, G.L. and Bujak, J.P.
1977a: Cenozoic palynostratigraphy of offshore eastern Canada; in Contributions of Stratigraphic Palynology (with emphasis on North America), Volume 1, Cenozoic Palynology, ed. W.C. Elsik; American Association of Stratigraphic Palynologists, Contributions Series, no. 5A, p. 14-47.

1977b: Distribution patterns of some North Atlantic Cenozoic dinoflagellate cysts; Marine Micropaleontology, v. 2, p. 223-233.

1985: Mesozoic and Cenozoic dinoflagellates; in Plankton Stratigraphy, ed. H.M. Bolli, J.B. Saunders and K. Perch-Nielsen; Cambridge University Press, Cambridge, p. 847-964.

Williams, G.L. and Davies, E.H.
1982: Cretaceous dinoflagellates and provincialism; Journal of Paleontology, v. 56, Part 2/3, suppl. 2, p. 30.

Williams, G.L., Fyffe, L.R., Wardle, R.J., Colman-Sadd, S.P., and Boehner, R.C. (eds.)
1985: Lexicon of Canadian Stratigraphy: Volume VI: Atlantic Canada; Canadian Society of Petroleum Geologists, 572 p.

Williams, G.L., Jansa, L.F., Clark, D.F., and Ascoli, P.
1974: Stratigraphy of the Shell Naskapi N-30 well, Scotian Shelf, eastern Canada; Geological Survey of Canada, Paper 74-50, 12 p.

Williams, V.E.
1986: Palynological study of the continental shelf sediments of the Labrador Sea; Ph.D. thesis, University of British Columbia, Vancouver, British Columbia, 214 p.

Williamson, M.A.
1987:   A quantitative foraminiferal biozonation of the Late Jurassic and
          Early Cretaceous of the East Newfoundland Basin; Micropaleon-
          tology, v. 33, no. 1, p. 37-65.
Wilson, G.J.
1971:   Observations on European Late Cretaceous dinoflagellate cysts;
          in Proceedings of the Second Planktonic Conference, ed. A.
          Farinacci; Roma 1970, Edizioni Tecnoscienza, v. 2, p. 1259-1275.
Woollam, R. and Riding, J.B.
1983:   Dinoflagellate cyst zonation of the English Jurassic; Institute of
          Geological Sciences, Report no. 83/2, 42 p.
Yun, H-S.
1981:   Dinoflagellaten aus der Oberkreide (Santon) von Westfalen;
          Palaeontographica, Abt B, v. 177, p. 1-89.

Authors' addresses

G.L. Williams
Atlantic Geoscience Centre
Geological Survey of Canada
Bedford Institute of Oceanography
P.O. Box 1006
Dartmouth, Nova Scotia
B2Y 4A2

P. Ascoli
Atlantic Geoscience Centre
Geological Survey of Canada
Bedford Institute of Oceanography
P.O. Box 1006
Dartmouth, Nova Scotia
B2Y 4A2

M.S. Barss
6095 Coburg Road, Apt. 506
Halifax, Nova Scotia
B3H 4K1

J.P. Bujak
Bujak Davies Group
4-4640 Manhatten Road S.E.
Calgary, Alberta
T2G 4B5

E.H. Davies
Bujak Davies Group
4-4640 Manhatten Road S.E.
Calgary, Alberta
T2G 4B5

R.A. Fensome
Atlantic Geoscience Centre
Geological Survey of Canada
Bedford Institute of Oceanography
P.O. Box 1006
Dartmouth, Nova Scotia
B2Y 4A2

M.A. Williamson
Shell Canada Limited
P.O. Box 100, Station 'M'
Calgary, Alberta
T2P 2H5

Printed in Canada

REGIONAL GEOLOGY

REGIONAL GEOLOGY AT SEA
Rock cores are obtained with the Bedford Institute of Oceanography's Rock-Core Drill. Photo courtesy of Bedford Institute of Oceanography Photo Services.

Chapter 4

PALEOZOIC GEOLOGY

Chapter 4

PALEOZOIC GEOLOGY

J.S. Bell and R.D. Howie

INTRODUCTION

Paleozoic rocks are widely distributed on the seafloor and beneath Mesozoic and Cenozoic rocks on the continental margins of eastern Canada (Fig. 4.1). Offshore wells have encountered an unmetamorphosed carbonate-clastic platform sequence and metamorphosed clastic and volcanic sequences, which locally contain Paleozoic granitoid intrusions. These sequences are locally overlain by upper Paleozoic clastics, carbonates and evaporites.

The Gulf of St. Lawrence is underlain by lower Paleozoic platform sequences and upper Paleozoic rocks. The southern Labrador Shelf, Davis Strait, southeast of Baffin Island and, possibly, the western margin of Baffin Bay are also underlain by the lower Paleozoic platform sequence. Deformed lower Paleozoic metasediments are present on the Grand Banks and Northeast Newfoundland Shelf, where they are overlain locally by upper Paleozoic units. Lower Paleozoic metasediments intruded by Devonian granites form the basement of Georges Bank, the Scotian Shelf and, possibly, the southernmost part of the Grand Banks.

The information compiled here has been obtained largely from grab samples, shallow cores, single channel seismic records, samples and logs from exploration wells, plus preliminary interpretation of multichannel seismic reflection profiles. Well information is described in detail in this chapter because much of it has not been previously compiled. Well locations are indicated in Figure 1 (in pocket). The structural database has been interpreted so that the inferred regional trends are compatible with potential field data and onshore geological information. All well depths are listed as depths below the Kelly Bushing or rotary table, so that they can be readily identified on downhole log records.

DISTRIBUTION OF PALEOZOIC ROCKS

In the nearshore areas, seismic reflection and sidescan sonar mapping, augmented by grab samples and short cores, have shown that folded metasediments of the lower Paleozoic Meguma Group are present on the Scotian Shelf (King and MacLean, 1976). Several anticlines and syn-clines can be recognized in seafloor mapping of the outcrop and attitudes of the Meguma Group (see Fig. 4.7). Northeast-trending Acadian folds, which affect the Meguma Group onshore, continue offshore at least as far south as the onlap edge of the Mesozoic sediments. These folds give rise to linear magnetic anomalies that can be traced offshore and swing southwards across part of the Georges Bank. Devonian granite intrusions, which are widespread onshore, also outcrop on the seafloor where they can be identified using magnetic and gravity data. Exploration well data suggest that the metasedimentary Meguma Group, intruded by Devonian (Acadian) granites, continues beneath the Mesozoic and younger sequences of the Scotian Shelf (Jansa and Wade, 1975). This group may extend eastwards across the southern part of the Grand Banks (Haworth and Lefort, 1979).

South of the Orpheus Graben (Fig. 4.1), basement appears to be the Meguma Group. North of the graben, and also perhaps within it, upper Paleozoic sediments are widespread.

The Gulf of St. Lawrence is entirely underlain by Paleozoic rocks. The St. Lawrence Platform crosses the northern part of the gulf and dips southward to form Anticosti Basin which is filled by more than 7000 m of lower Paleozoic strata. The northern flank of the basin contains a Cambrian carbonate-clastic shelf sequence which outcrops on Anticosti Island, mainland Quebec and southeastern Labrador. The southern flank of the Anticosti Basin is exposed in western Newfoundland where it includes clastic, carbonate, and volcanic rocks and exotic blocks and klippen of Early Cambrian to Silurian age (Williams, 1979). Lower Paleozoic rocks may well extend beneath the southern part of the Gulf of St. Lawrence and underlie the thick upper Paleozoic succession of the Magdalen Basin.

The Magdalen Basin contains Middle or Upper Devonian-Permian nonmarine sediments, conglomerates, sandstones, siltstones and shales, and marine carbonates, volcanics and evaporites, probably embracing the Horton, Windsor, Canso, Riversdale and Pictou groups. Devonian-Carboniferous rocks occur directly east of Cape Breton on the Scotian Shelf and also in the subsurface on the southern Grand Banks, but it is not known if they are physically continuous between the two areas. The Pennsylvanian Pictou Group outcrops on the seafloor east of Cape Breton (Hacquebard, 1983), in Placentia Bay, Newfoundland (King et al., 1986; Barss, internal Eastern Petroleum Geology Paleontology Report EPGS-PAL.36-79MSB, 1979) and in the Hermine E-94 well on the western Grand Banks (see Fig. 4.12). There is a reasonable possibility that the Pictou

Bell, J.S. and Howie, R.D.
1990: Paleozoic geology, Chapter 4 in Geology of the Continental Margin of Eastern Canada, M.J. Keen and G.L. Williams (ed.); Geological Survey of Canada, Geology of Canada, no. 2, p. 141-165: (also Geological Society of America, The Geology of North America, v. I-1).

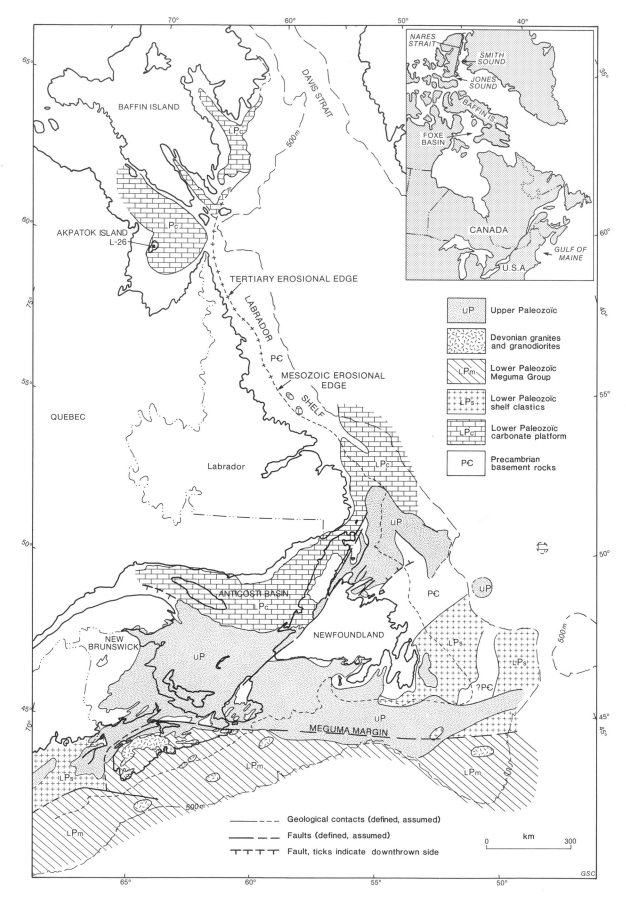

Figure 4.1. Distribution of Paleozoic rocks on the continental margin of eastern Canada.

Group is continuously present between these three areas (Avery and Bell, 1985) (Fig. 4.1).

Eight exploration wells on the southern Grand Banks encountered Paleozoic sedimentary rocks (Avery and Bell, 1985). Lower Paleozoic clastics occur at Phalarope P-62, Razorbill F-54 and possibly Murre G-67. Upper Paleozoic continental deposits are present in five wells and several coreholes. The upper Paleozoic subcrop configuration appears to define an east-trending synclinorium or structural basin (Fig. 4.1), which rests unconformably on lower Paleozoic rocks (Avery and Bell, 1985).

East of the Avalon Peninsula, cores from a gently folded clastic sequence have been dated as early Paleozoic (King et al., 1986). There, redbeds of possible Devonian age (King et al., 1986) appear to rest unconformably on the older sediments (Durling et al., 1987).

Upper Paleozoic rocks outcrop on the seafloor in the Notre Dame Bay area of northeast Newfoundland (Haworth et al., 1976a, b) and include salt diapirs in a sequence which extends to the northeast beneath the overlapping Mesozoic rocks. Pennsylvanian continental clastic rocks were drilled at the Verrazano L-77 and Hare Bay E-21 wells. According to seismic, magnetic and gravity data, they overlie a diapirically deformed, salt-bearing interval.

On the southern Labrador Shelf Mesozoic rocks overlie lower Paleozoic carbonates. Limestones in Freydis B-87, Indian Harbour M-52, Hopedale E-33 and Roberval K-92 wells have been dated as Ordovician. These carbonates extend from the Strait of Belle Isle as far north as Gudrid H-55 and, from indications on reflection seismic profiles, probably form a semi-continuous blanket. A northerly outlier exists in the vicinity of Hopedale E-33. Other Paleozoic

sediments are not known to occur on the Labrador Shelf between latitudes 56°N and 60°N, although Tucholke and Fry (1985) and Grant and McAlpine (Chapter 6) have suggested that Paleozoic rocks may be present. However, in the northern part of the Labrador Shelf, all wells which extend beneath Mesozoic units terminate in Precambrian granites or gneisses, and there are no obvious suggestions on reflection seismic profiles of any Paleozoic subcrop (H.R. Balkwill, pers. comm., 1984). Ordovician limestones, which outcrop extensively in Foxe Basin and on parts of the adjacent west side of Baffin Island, may underlie Hudson Strait and Ungava Bay and also occur farther north on the Southeast Baffin Shelf between Frobisher Bay and Cumberland Sound where these limestones have been sampled by shallow core-hole drilling at several localities (MacLean et al., 1977; MacLean, 1978; MacLean and Williams, 1983; B. MacLean, pers. comm., 1987). On the basis of seismic reflection, magnetic and gravity data and observations made from a submersible vessel (MacLean et al., 1982), these strata are also inferred to outcrop on the seafloor in Frobisher Bay and outer Cumberland Sound and to extend northward along the shelf toward Cape Dyer (MacLean et al., 1982). How far seaward these Ordovician carbonates extend beneath the onlapping Mesozoic cover is not known, since none of the three wells drilled (on the Southeast Baffin Shelf) in Davis Strait penetrated beds older than Cretaceous.

In Baffin Bay, lower Paleozoic carbonate rocks may be present locally on the shelf between Cape Dyer and Bylot Island near the northwestern end of Baffin Island (B. MacLean, pers. comm., 1986). An acoustically fast, pre-Mesozoic sedimentary section is suggested by seismic reflection and refraction lines (MacLean et al., 1984), but no direct evidence is available. MacLean et al. (1984)

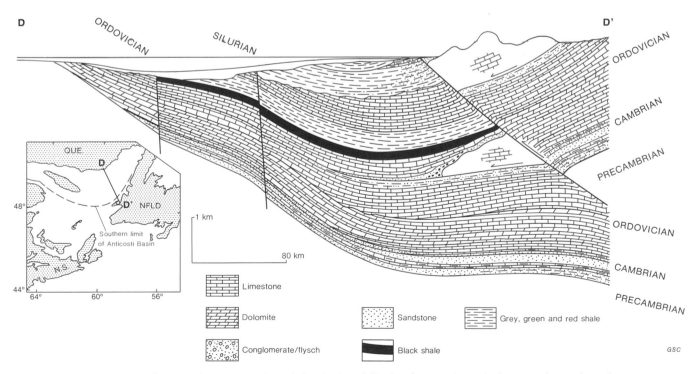

Figure 4.2. Structural cross-section of the Anticosti Basin. System boundaries are shown in red.

believed that seismic reflection and magnetometer data may indicate that lower Paleozoic bedrock occurs in Jones Sound about 250 km north-northwest of Bylot Island, but there is no confirmation of this.

STRATIGRAPHY

Lower Paleozoic platform facies

The northern rim of the Canadian Maritime region is underlain by unmetamorphosed lower Paleozoic carbonates and clastics which form the St. Lawrence Platform along the northern margin of the Gulf of St. Lawrence. Between the Gaspésie Peninsula and northwestern Newfoundland, the succession thickens southwards into a foreland basin, the Anticosti Basin. The same rocks are exposed along the southern coastline of Quebec and southeastern Labrador, on Anticosti Island and in northwestern Newfoundland. Shallow core samples have also been obtained from offshore western Newfoundland (Haworth et al., 1976b). These sections and outcrops, augmented by well and reflection seismic data, provide the information for the structural cross section presented in Figure 4.2. It illustrates the Anticosti Basin in the area of greatest control, and shows that it is a typical foreland basin, which is likely to have subsided in response to crustal loading initiated by overthrusting (Quinlan and Beaumont, 1984).

Figure 4.3 illustrates the stratigraphic succession of the Anticosti Basin. In the western part around Anticosti Island, platform carbonates dominate the Ordovician-Silurian succession whereas the eastern part contains older rocks in which the post-Grenvillian succession contains uppermost Precambrian clastics and volcanics at its base. These are overlain by Cambrian and Ordovician carbonates, followed by Ordovician and Silurian clastics (Fig. 4.4). B.V. Sanford (pers. comm., 1985) has defined six unconformity-bound sequences or cycles in the Anticosti Basin (Fig. 4.3).

These cycles can be recognized along the St. Lawrence Platform from Michigan, U.S.A. to Newfoundland. They are delineated on the basis of rich assemblages of shelly macrofossils and age-diagnostic conodonts (B.V. Sanford, pers. comm., 1985).

The shelf carbonates of the St. Lawrence Platform extend eastwards through the Strait of Belle Isle onto the southern part of the Labrador Shelf, where they were identified in six wells (Fig. 4.5). Their present extent is limited (Fig. 4.1) and only Ordovician rocks have been identified. Freydis B-87 well ended in 75 m of Ordovician limestone, informally designated the Freydis limestone. This is overlain by 333 m of Ordovician siltstones, limestones, sandstones and shales, described informally as the Freydis sandstone (Eastcan Exploration Ltd., 1976a).

The Freydis limestone consists of light grey to dark brown micritic limestone, with thin shale intervals. Core no. 2 (2307.2-2313.3 m) sampled dark brown, micritic limestone with pyrite and cephalopod fragments. Bedding is defined by finely undulating argillaceous laminae. Ditch cuttings contained pelecypod and echinoid fragments.

The Freydis sandstone can be subdivided into a lower siltstone unit (2167.3-2238.6 m), a middle limy unit (2103.0-2167.3 m) and an upper siltstone unit (1906.1-2103.0 m). The lower siltstone unit is made up largely of red calcareous siltstone with thin beds of fine grained sandstone and shale. The middle limy unit con-

tains light brown argillaceous limestones interbedded with calcareous siltstones containing pelecypod fragments. The upper siltstone unit consists of grey to greenish grey calcareous siltstone, fine grained sandstone and shale. Core no. 1 (1934.8-1941.2 m) recovered calcareous sandstones with interbedded shales, the sandstones being light grey, fine grained and micaceous. The core yielded abundant pelecypod fragments together with echinoid plates, solitary corals and material which may be algal. Brachiopod shell fragments were identified in ditch cuttings.

The well history report of Freydis B-87 (Eastcan Exploration Ltd., 1976a) summarizes three biostratigraphic studies. Compagnie Française du Pétrole dated the interval 1937.2 to 1940.9 m as Late Ordovician. Robertson Research (North America) Ltd. suggested that the interval 1914.1-1981.1 m was Late Ordovician (Édenian-Richmondian) and that the interval 1981.1-2313.3 m was Middle Ordovician (Trentonian). INRS Pétrole assigned the following ages: 2246.4 m – Middle Ordovician to Early Caradocian, equivalent to the Mingan Formation and the Trenton Group; 2209.7 m – Late Ordovician, equivalent to the Becancour Formation, Quebec; 1940.0 m – Late Ordovician, equivalent to the Vauréal Formation, Anticosti Island. Jenkins (1984), using the known stratigraphic ranges of seven species of acritarchs and chitinozoa, dated the Freydis sandstone above 2164 m as Caradocian to late Ashgillian (Late Ordovician). Jenkins (1984) could not date precisely the lower part of the succession (Freydis limestone and basal Freydis sandstone), but stated that it was clearly Ordovician in age.

At Indian Harbour M-52 well, a lower Paleozoic carbonate sequence lies below the Mesozoic section (BP Canada, 1978). It can be divided into a lower dolomite unit (3700.1-3957.9 m) in which the well ends, a middle limestone unit (3528.2-3700.1 m) and an upper chert unit (3484.3-3528.2 m). The upper chert unit consists of hard, dark grey chert or fine grained quartzite. The ditch cuttings exhibit conchoidal fractures but also a sugary texture, which suggests that the rock may have been originally a fine grained sandstone or siltstone. The middle limestone unit consists of light grey to buff, aphanitic to microcrystalline limestone beds which are locally dolomitic, interbedded with calcareous shales and shelly limestones and thin volcanic beds which may be tuffs. Pelecypod, brachiopod, ostracod, crinoid, bryozoan and algal fragments have been recognized in ditch cuttings. The lower dolomite unit is dominated by hard, grey to brown, microcrystalline dolomite that contains aphanitic limestone intervals similar to those in the overlying unit. Thin volcanic beds, and beds which may be tuffs, were recovered in side wall cores. Cores from the lowest drilled beds (3951.8-3957.9 m) consist of grey, aphanitic, mottled and bioturbated dolomitic limestone containing foraminifera, algae, calcispheres, ostracods, brachiopods and trilobites, and a thin bed of microcrystalline nodular dolomite. Conodonts from the basal core (3954-3957 m) yielded an Arenigian-Early Llanvirnian age (Jenkins, 1984).

Hopedale E-33 well encountered a thin, gas-bearing limestone sequence (1976.5-2000.5 m) of Ordovician age. This rests on metamorphic rocks interpreted as Precambrian (Chevron Standard Ltd., 1978). Side wall cores indicate that the limestone is pale brown, microcrystalline and pelletoidal, with abundant small shell fragments at

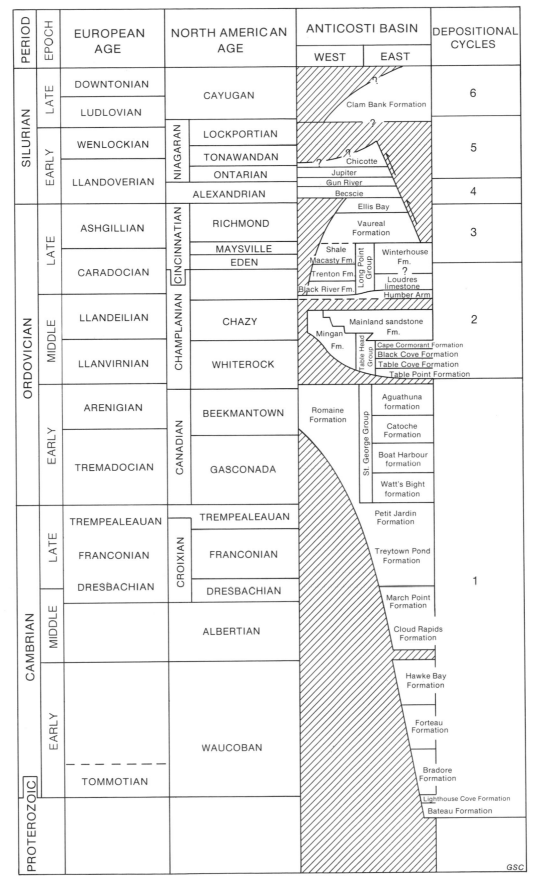

Figure 4.3. Lower Paleozoic unconformity-bounded sequences and megacycles of Anticosti Basin. The depositional cycles are as defined by B.V. Sanford (pers. comm., 1985).

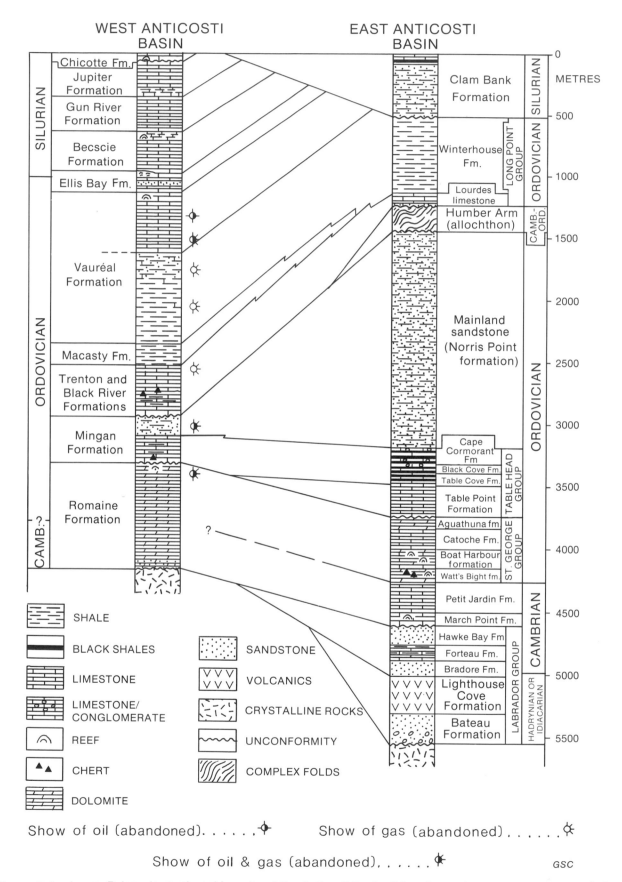

Figure 4.4. Lower Paleozoic stratigraphic units of the Anticosti Basin. Oil and gas shows are based on well data.

several levels, including ostracods, brachiopods, gastropods and calcispheres. Ordovician fossils have been recovered from the limestone (Jenkins, 1984).

Gudrid H-55 well penetrated a gas-bearing dolomite sequence, 141.4 m thick, resting on granite of presumed Precambrian age and overlain by Upper Cretaceous shales (Eastcan Exploration Ltd., 1976b). The dolomite beds are white to buff, micro- to medium crystalline, porous and fractured with minor dolomitic shale interbeds. Core no. 1 (2675.7-2680.7 m) consists of a buff greybrown, fine to medium crystalline dolomite with leached fossil, interfossil and intracrystalline porosity, and was originally a micritic limestone containing oncolites and crinoids (Umpleby, 1979). A similar sequence of dolomite and shale was encountered at the nearby Roberval K-92 well between 3543 and 3874 m. Roberval K-92 terminated in dolomite. Core no. 6 (3578-3582.5 m) consists of hard fractured, buff and sucrosic microcrystalline dolomite and grey blue-green silty shale; core no. 7 (3870-3874 m) consists of grey to brown, sucrosic and cryptocrystalline dolomite with vuggy and fracture porosity. Possible stromatoporoid outlines were observed. Tyrk P-100 also encountered a thin sequence of buff dolomite (1702-1706 m) beneath early Cretaceous volcanics and resting on granite (Eastcan Exploration Ltd., 1979).

The age of the dolomite is somewhat controversial. Palynomorphs of Viséan and Westphalian age have been recovered from samples identified as portions of the Gudrid H-55 Core no. 1 (Eastcan Exploration Ltd., 1976; Umpleby, 1979). Although there is no argument about the age of the fossils, there is some doubt that they were in situ (Jenkins, 1984). If the dolomites are Pennsylvanian, they are unlike any other Pennsylvanian rocks on either side of the Atlantic Ocean. In terms of lithology and location, they are more likely to be early Paleozoic and thus laterally continuous with the Ordovician carbonates described above.

If the dolomite sections drilled at Gudrid H-55 and Roberval K-92 wells are early Paleozoic, a subcrop of shelf carbonates can be mapped across the southern part of the Labrador Shelf. This subcrop outline is compatible with the reflection character associated with carbonates that is displayed on seismic lines traversing the region (H.R. Balkwill, pers. comm., 1985). On this basis, the limestones at Hopedale E-33 are believed to represent a subcropping outlier.

Orphan Knoll to the southeast (Fig. 4.1) may represent a laterally displaced segment of this lower Paleozoic carbonate platform from the region northeast of Newfoundland. Limestone was recovered from a bedrock pinnacle

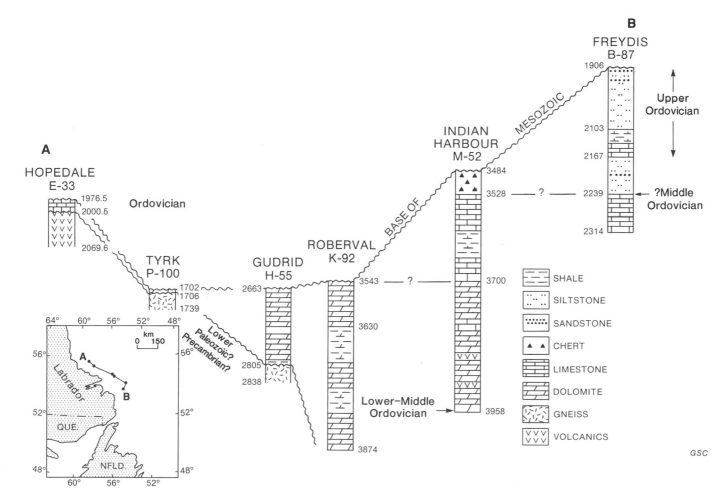

Figure 4.5. Ordovician carbonate units, and possible correlation in Labrador Shelf wells. Depths shown are in metres below rotary table.

and dated as Late Ordovician (Late Caradocian-Ashgillian) from acritarchs and chitinozoa (Legault, 1982).

The Labrador Shelf wells north of Hopedale E-33 have not encountered lower Paleozoic rocks and the extensive seismic coverage does not contain any clearcut indications that such rocks are present (H.R. Balkwill, pers. comm., 1985).

Carbonate rocks outcrop on the seafloor in Ungava Bay and Hudson Strait (B. MacLean, pers. comm., 1987). Lithologic correlations with exposed sections in northern Hudson Bay and with the section drilled in the Akpatok Island L-26 well in Ungava Bay suggest they are of Ordovician and Silurian ages (Fig. 4.1).

In Davis Strait, Ordovician limestones outcrop on the seafloor between Frobisher Bay and Cumberland Sound (MacLean et al., 1977, 1978). Five shallow core holes recovered grey to brown, micritic limestones with abundant skeletal remains including fragments of corals, bryozoa, echinoderms, articulate brachiopods, cephalopods, graptolites, sponges, trilobites and radiolaria. Jenkins (in MacLean et al., 1977) identified chitinozoa and scolecodonts which suggest a Late Ordovician age (Caradocian). Bolton considered a coral from site 5 to be early Middle to Late Ordovician (in MacLean et al., 1977). The lithology and faunas imply carbonate shelf deposition in nearshore to epibathyal environments. Data from seismic profiles suggest that Ordovician limestones are also present on the seafloor in Frobisher Bay and in the outer part of Cumberland Sound (Srivastava et al., 1981). Grant (1975) and MacLean and Falconer (1979) inferred from geophysical data that lower Paleozoic strata may extend northward on the shelf toward Cape Dyer. Similar limestones outcrop onshore in the Foxe Basin and on parts of western Baffin Island (MacLean et al., 1977).

Lower Paleozoic carbonates may also occur beneath Mesozoic rocks on the continental shelf along the west side of Baffin Bay. A pre-Mesozoic sequence with strong internal reflections can be seen on many seismic lines. Bedrock beneath Jones Sound also may be Paleozoic in age, based on its acoustic and magnetic character (MacLean et al., 1984).

A complex succession of lower Paleozoic platform and platform margin deposits outcrop onshore on both sides of Nares Strait (Peel and Christie, 1982; Hurst and Kerr, 1982). In all likelihood similar successions underlie the offshore but no samples have been recovered. Newman (1977) using gravity modelling indicated that there is probably a sequence of high density sediments more than 2 km thick beneath Smith Sound at the southern end of Nares Strait.

Lower Paleozoic clastic facies

In contrast to the (widespread) carbonates of the St. Lawrence Platform, the Labrador Shelf and the Davis Strait region, all the lower Paleozoic rocks identified on the Grand Banks are clastics. Eastward and offshore of the Avalon Peninsula, King et al. (1986) cored Ordovician and Silurian sandstones and siltstones from a gently folded sequence on the Avalon Platform, which they estimated to be about 7000 m thick (Fig. 4.6). The Ordovician rocks include dark grey, fine grained and fissile laminated shales, grey siltstones, and greyish green, fine grained, burrowed and bioturbated sandstones. The Silurian rocks include grey, laminated, fissile siltstones, with burrows and fragments of brachiopods and bryozoa, light grey calcareous siltstones which are laminated and bioturbated and contain well sorted beds of fossil fragments, and nonfossiliferous, bioturbated, siltstones. The biota suggest deposition in a variety of marine shelf environments.

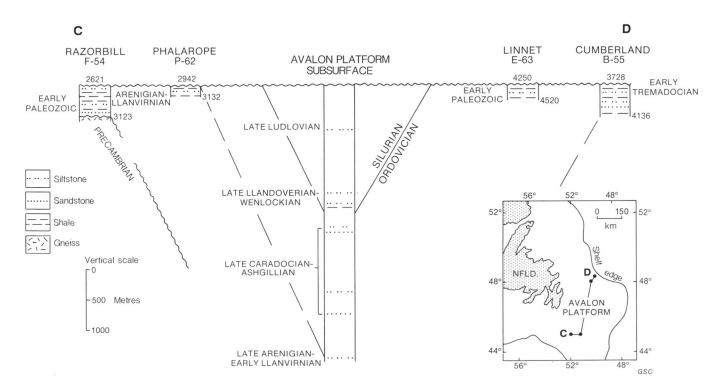

Figure 4.6. Ordovician and Silurian units in Grand Banks wells. Depths shown are in metres below rotary table.

Dating of fourteen cores was based on the acritarchs and chitinozoa (W.A.M. Jenkins, pers. comm., 1986).

Northeast of the Avalon Platform, lower Ordovician (Tremadocian) shales were also encountered in the Cumberland B-55 well (Jenkins, 1984), beneath overlying Mesozoic and Tertiary rocks (Fig. 4.6). Linnet E-63 well may also have ended in lower Paleozoic shales and slates (Leavitt, pers. comm., 1985).

South of the Avalon Platform, lower Ordovician (Arenigian-Llanvirnian) shales and siltstones occur between 2942 and 3132 m in the Phalarope P-62 well (Jenkins, 1984). The indurated pre-Jurassic grey and green shale sequence in Razorbill F-54 (2621.3-3123.6 m), which overlies a Precambrian granite (Fig. 4.6), is early Paleozoic (W.A.M. Jenkins, pers. comm., 1979). This may also be the age of the basal quartzites (3237.0-3372.3 m) in Murre G-67 (Avery and Bell, 1985).

The Jaeger A-49 well in the southern part of the Grand Banks, ended in granite dated as 376 ± 17 Ma, the same age as the numerous Devonian granitic batholiths and stocks associated with the Acadian Orogeny and which outcrop onshore from New England to Newfoundland. The granite in the Jaegar well is probably intruded into lower Paleozoic metasediments, which are included in the Meguma Group in Figure 4.1.

Along the northern part of the Scotian Shelf, metasediments of the Meguma Group, intruded by Acadian granites, outcrop on the seafloor in nearshore areas (King and MacLean, 1976). These rocks are also present beneath the Mesozoic and Cenozoic sequences of the Scotian Shelf (Jansa and Wade, 1975). Metaquartzites and schists have

been identified from the basal ditch cuttings recovered from the Fox I-22, Naskapi N-30 and Wyandot E-53 wells. Pink metaquartzites and slates were cored at Argo F-38. All these metasediments are assigned to the Meguma Group (Fig. 4.7), the upper part of which is early Ordovician (Tremadocian) in southern Nova Scotia (Schenk, 1981).

Onshore, the metamorphic grade of the Meguma Group ranges from low greenschist facies in the east to amphibolite facies in the southwest (Keppie, 1982), but no such lateral changes in metamorphic grade can be defined in the offshore area. Subsurface Acadian intrusions are present locally. The wells Crow F-52, Erie D-26 and Ojibwa E-07 ended in granite, and Mohawk B-93 ended in granodiorite (Fig. 4.7).

The Meguma Group is also believed to extend beneath Mesozoic rocks on the continental shelf west and south of Nova Scotia (Ballard and Uchupi, 1975). Truncation of a characteristic magnetic signature (Kane et al., 1972) defines the western margin of the Meguma Group north of latitude 43°N (Fig. 4.7). South of this latitude the margin is not as well defined and magnetic trends are truncated against an east-west lineament (Map 1709A, in pocket). South of the lineament, on Georges Bank, the magnetic signature resembles that of the Meguma Group and is so interpreted here. Thus, the metamorphosed dolomite, quartzites and phyllites which occur between 4755 and 4898 m (total depth) in the COST G-1 well, are assigned to the Meguma Group. A 450-550 Ma K-Ar age determination for a phyllite at 4892 m suggests that this well terminated in Cambrian-Ordovician strata (Scholle and Wenkam, 1982).

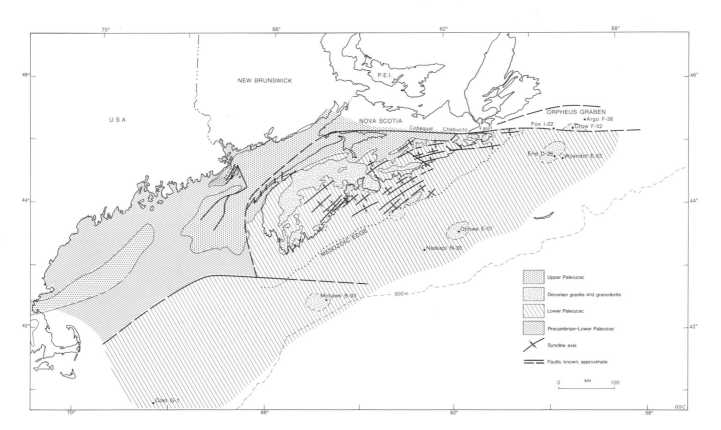

Figure 4.7. Pre-Mesozoic subcrop map of the Scotian Shelf. Lower Paleozoic rocks represent the Meguma Group.

Ballard and Uchupi (1975) interpreted the northern part of the Gulf of Maine as underlain by Cambrian-Ordovician strata that were deposited in the Appalachian geosyncline and suggested that the southern part contains a basement sequence consisting of Avalon platform rocks. Both sequences are equivalent to the succession exposed in the Avalon Zone of Newfoundland (Williams, 1979). We consider them to be lower Paleozoic clastic facies and map them as lower Paleozoic clastic rocks (Fig. 4.7).

Upper Paleozoic strata

Upper Paleozoic rocks are widely distributed in Quebec and the Atlantic Provinces. Deposits of late Devonian and Carboniferous successor basins rest unconformably on rocks deformed during the Acadian Orogeny and considered as basement in Quebec, central and southern New Brunswick, northern Nova Scotia, and western Newfoundland, whereas Permian strata outcrop in Prince Edward Island (Poole, 1967). The major late Paleozoic depocentre is the Magdalen Basin (Map1707A, in pocket) which occupies the southern half of the Gulf of St. Lawrence and extends into adjacent onshore areas of Quebec and the Atlantic Provinces.

Volcanism appears to have accompanied the development of this basin (Fig. 4.8). In several Atlantic provinces, the basal successions of the post-Acadian successor basins contain mineralogically bimodal volcanic sequences overlain by thick deposits of nonmarine and shallow marine sediments (Blanchard et al., 1984). Bradley (1982) attributed this phenomenon to crustal thinning associated with the formation of pull-apart basins. Recent radiometric age determinations made on volcanic rocks from Cape Breton Island suggest the volcanism and associated faults are progressively younger from east to west (Blanchard et al., 1984). In Gaspésie, New Brunswick and Maine, late Paleozoic volcanic rocks appear to get younger from west to east. From Late Devonian to mid-Carboniferous time, the overall pattern of volcanism appears to show migration from the margin to the centre of the Magdalen Basin. On Îles de la Madeleine, basalts erupted onto a thick sequence of evaporites during Viséan time and were later deformed by salt tectonics (Barr et al., 1985).

Reflection seismic profiles show that the upper Paleozoic thicknesses are in excess of 12 000 m in the Magdalen Basin, and document extensive, now diapirically deformed, Windsor Group salt deposits within the section. No wells drilled in the Magdalen Basin penetrate rocks beneath the salt and most end in overlying continental redbeds. Consequently, only limited inferences can be made about older rocks in the basin. Upper Paleozoic rocks are widely distributed on land around the margins of the basin, and it is likely that they are representative of the rock sequences present offshore. A brief description of the onshore sequences is thus warranted.

The oldest strata lying on basement in the Magdalen Basin are the coarse- to fine-grained clastics of the Horton Group. The Horton, as originally defined, is of Tournaisian

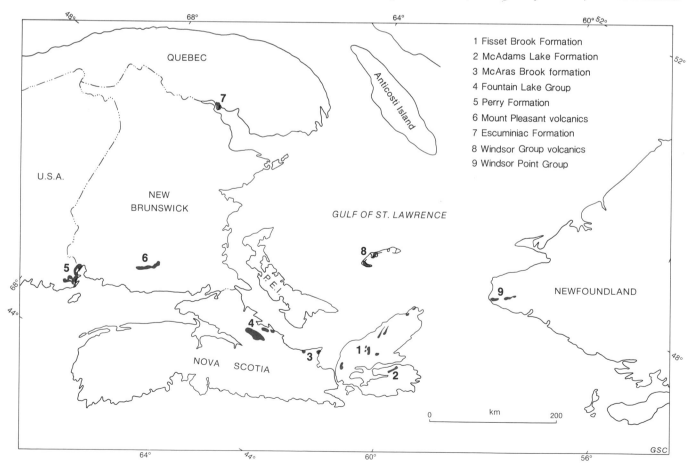

Figure 4.8. Devonian and Carboniferous volcanic rocks, Gulf of St. Lawrence (adapted from Blanchard et al., 1984).

age (Bell, 1929) and includes the feldspathic conglomerates, sandstones, siltstones, shales and rare ferruginous limestone lenses exposed at Horton Bluff in central Nova Scotia. Following Kelley (1967), Howie and Barss (1975) included all post-Acadian Orogeny sequences of middle Devonian to early Viséan age in the Horton Group, and noted that its thickness may exceed 4000 m in the deepest parts of the Magdalen Basin. Onshore, measured sections range from a few tens of metres to 3291 m in western Cape Breton (Kelley, 1967).

In the Atlantic Provinces, basal rocks of the Horton Group are polymictic conglomerates that are interpreted as having accumulated in fault-controlled piedmont environments (Howie and Barss, 1975). These conglomerates pass upwards into locally cyclical sandstone and shale sequences characterized by the presence of angular quartz fragments and erect plant stems, laminated shales containing ostracods and fish beds, and black carbonaceous oil shales. Coal also occurs locally and volcanic rocks are interbedded with Horton Group conglomerates in several areas (Howie and Barss, 1975; Blanchard et al., 1984).

Continental and marine sedimentary rocks of the Windsor Group overlie the Horton Group and are widely distributed across the Atlantic Provinces. Onshore, the Windsor consists of conglomerate, red sandstone, red and grey siltstone, limestone, dolomite, halite, sylvinite, carnallite and anhydrite (Schenk, 1967; Howie and Barss, 1975; Anderle et al., 1979; Kingston and Dickie, 1979; Crosby, 1985). The Windsor Group records the transgression of eastern Quebec and the Atlantic Provinces by a shallow sea in which marine carbonates and extensive evaporite deposits accumulated. Bordering former highland areas, the Windsor Group consists of conglomerates and sandstones which pass laterally into finer grained clastics, reefal carbonates and evaporites (Howie and Barss, 1975). Rocks within the group range in age from middle Viséan to early Namurian (Bell, 1929; Mamet, 1970).

The type section of the Windsor Group is exposed in the Minas Subbasin (Wade et al., 1977) along the Avon River, near Windsor, Nova Scotia. There, it comprises at least 473 m of red sandstone, red and grey siltstone, limestone, minor amounts of dolomite and gypsum, but no salt (Bell, 1929, 1958). The group is usually poorly exposed at the surface due to the dissolution and rapid weathering of the evaporitic components, but is well preserved in the subsurface. Near Stewiacke, Nova Scotia, at the eastern end of the Minas Subbasin, several coreholes penetrate complete, relatively undeformed, Windsor evaporites. The data have been used to construct a composite reference section (Fig. 4.9) that serves to illustrate the lithologic character and structural configuration of the rocks in this area (Fig. 4.10).

Windsor Group sedimentary rocks are present in many of the onshore subbasins flanking the Gulf of St. Lawrence, but the most extensive and thickest Windsor succession underlies the Gulf of St. Lawrence. There, wells and seismic profiles document a vast blanket of salt-dominated deposits which have been deformed into a forest of salt diapirs (Howie, 1984). Swells, ridges, domes and variously shaped diapiric structures extend across an area of some 60 000 km² and involve Windsor Group rocks 5000 m or more thick.

Wells drilled on structures in the Gulf of St. Lawrence, Prince Edward Island, Cape Breton Island, New Brunswick and Nova Scotia penetrate up to 2134 m of Windsor clastics and evaporites (Howie and Cumming, 1963; Howie and Hill, 1972). In the Cumberland Subbasin, the Wallace Station no. 1 (see Fig. 4.16) drillhole penetrated 3567 m of highly contorted rocks of the Windsor Group (Howie, 1986b). Salt is mined at Pugwash and brined from several wells south of Amherst, Nova Scotia (Prud'homme, 1986). Economically exploitable potash beds form part of the evaporitic sequence at three localities in the Moncton Subbasin of southern New Brunswick (Kingston and Dickie, 1979; Barnett, 1984).

The Windsor Group is overlain by Namurian-Lower Westphalian strata of the Canso and Riversdale groups. In its type section at Plaster Cove on the Strait of Canso, northwest of Port Hawkesbury, Nova Scotia (Bell, 1944), the Canso Group is 623 m thick and consists of thinly laminated, nonmarine, red and green shales, sandstones and minor interbeds of limestone. This sequence on Cape Breton Island contains Namurian plants (Bell, 1944). Outside the type area, the Canso Group includes conglomerate,

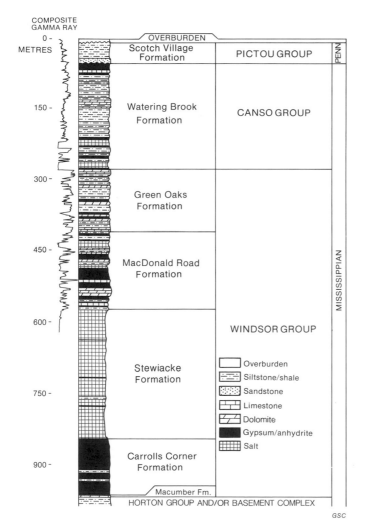

Figure 4.9. Stratigraphy of the Windsor Group in the Stewiacke area, Minas Subbasin, Nova Scotia (adapted from Giles and Boehner, 1979; gamma-ray log was adapted from St. Joseph Explorations Ltd.).

153

tuff, basic and acidic intrusives, and extrusives (Poole et al., 1970b) and locally, gypsum and minor intervals of salt (Boehner, 1983a, b).

The thickness of the Canso Group varies across the Atlantic Provinces. In the Antigonish area of northern Nova Scotia, Bell (1958) estimated it to be about 1830 m thick. In southern New Brunswick, Gussow (1953) reported it to be 1912 m thick. On Cape Breton Island, the Port Hood no. 1 well encountered 1290 m of strata assigned to the Canso Group (Howie and Cumming, 1963).

The Riversdale Group, at the type section at Riversdale, Nova Scotia (see Fig. 4.16), consists of 915 m of red and grey continental sandstones, siltstones and shales. Although diagnostic megafossils are absent in the type area, the section appears to be of Early Westphalian age (Bell, 1944). Elsewhere, the Riversdale Group is late Namurian to early Westphalian (Howie and Barss, 1975). It consists of fine- to coarse-grained sandstone, shale, siltstone and conglomerate with local, basal quartz-pebble conglomerate (Poole et al., 1970a). In the Antigonish area the Riversdale Group is 1159 m thick (Bell, 1944); in southern New Brunswick it is 1890 m thick (Gussow, 1953).

Biostratigraphic evidence suggests that the Canso and Riversdale groups at the type localities may represent largely coeval facies. Spore assemblages recovered from the Riversdale Group correlate with assemblages obtained from the Canso Group (Howie and Barss, 1975). Also, in several offshore wells, similar assemblages have been identified in fine grained clastic sequences, which appear to be Canso and do not contain sandstone, and conglomerate-rich intervals typical of the Riversdale Group (M.S. Barss, pers. comm., 1985). This suggests that sequences with Riversdale lithologies were restricted to marginal near-source areas and were replaced basinward by shale-rich intervals typical of the Canso Group.

The youngest upper Paleozoic rocks in the Atlantic Provinces are assigned to the Cumberland and Pictou groups. The Cumberland Group is only present in northwestern Nova Scotia, with the type section being in the vicinity of Joggins. There, it consists of approximately 2700 m of nonmarine red and grey conglomerate, sandstone, shale and coal of Westphalian age (Bell, 1944). It rests conformably, unconformably, and disconformably on older upper Paleozoic rocks and regionally overlaps the pre-Carboniferous basement complex. According to Howie and Barss (1975), spore assemblages indicate that the upper beds of the Cumberland Group are coeval with the lower beds of the Pictou Group.

The Pictou Group is a sequence of nonmarine, dark red sandstone, grey sandstone, arkosic grit, dark red shale, mudstone, grey shale, and coal of Westphalian to Wolfcampian (Permian) age (Bell, 1944). These rocks rest unconformably on older Paleozoic rocks, as well as on lower beds of the Cumberland Group, and onlap the basement.

In the type section on West Branch River John, Nova Scotia, the Pictou Group is about 2250 m thick. It is up to 3300 m thick in southern New Brunswick (Gussow, 1953) and may be 5000 m thick in southeastern Prince Edward Island. A composite section compiled from the East Point E-47 and E-49 wells indicates that about 4000 m of Pictou redbeds may be offshore, northeast of Prince Edward Island. East of the Magdalen Islands, the Pictou Group may reach 5000 m in thickness based on seismic interpretations (SAREP, unpublished report, 1970).

Upper Paleozoic rocks are presumed to underlie the Bay of Fundy. They outcrop along the southern coast of New Brunswick and on Grand Manan Island (Howie and Barss, 1975), and are believed to lie beneath Triassic strata in the central part of the bay, where they may overstep, or be faulted against, the Meguma Group (Fig. 4.7).

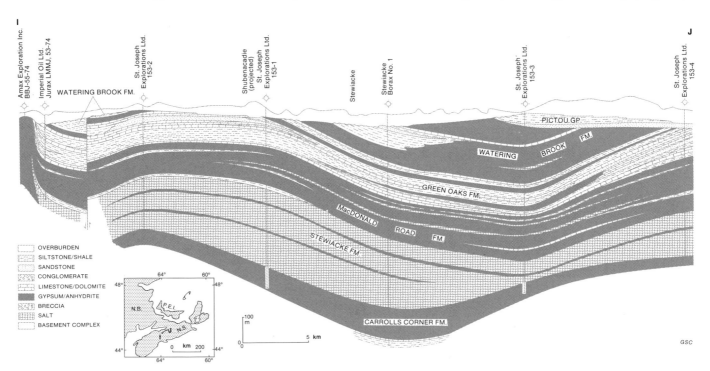

Figure 4.10. Carboniferous cross section I-J, Minas Subbasin, Nova Scotia. Note that the exaggerated vertical scale has increased the apparent dip of the relatively flat-lying strata. Stratigraphic terminology after Giles and Boehner (1979).

Carboniferous-Permian sediments are mapped within a seismically-defined graben extending northeast across the Gulf of Maine (Ballard and Uchupi, 1975) from onshore outcrops in New England (Fig. 4.7).

Upper Paleozoic rocks are also present on the continental shelf east of Cape Breton and in the Sydney Basin (Fig. 4.1). Two wells, North Sydney P-05 and North Sydney F-24, penetrated Upper Carboniferous rocks of the Canso, Riversdale and Pictou groups, encountering continental shales, siltstones, sandstones, conglomerates and coal beds. These overlie Lower Carboniferous continental conglomerates (Murphy Oil Company Limited, 1974; Shell Canada Resources Ltd., 1976; Barss et al., 1979). In the Sydney Basin the Pictou Group is about 2237 m thick (Hacquebard, 1983). If the unfossiliferous redbeds penetrated in offshore drilling, which may extend into the Permian, are included, the entire section could be about 4500 m thick. Upper Carboniferous (Westphalian B to D) shales, siltstones, sandstones and coal were also cored at three locations on the seafloor in Placentia Bay, Newfoundland (Barss, 1979; King et al., 1986).

On the southern part of the Grand Banks, five wells encountered upper Paleozoic rocks beneath the Mesozoic (Fig. 4.11). Late Viséan-Westphalian spores were recovered from Hermine E-94 (Barss et al., 1979) which ended in halite, anhydrite, dolomite and shale of the Windsor Group (2455.2-3267.7 m) (Howie, 1974). The Windsor Group is overlain by red shales and sandstones of the Canso Group (2106.2-2455.2 m), red sandstones, conglomerates, shales and dolomite of the Riversdale Group (1709.9-2106.2 m), and red sandstones and shales of the Pictou Group (1641.3-1709.9 m). The dipmeter log suggests that an angular unconformity separates the Riversdale Group from the overlying Pictou Group. A discordance at the same level is present onshore in Sydney Basin (Keppie, 1982). Gannet O-54 ended in Precambrian metasediments (3039.6-3047.8 m); these are overlain by upper Devonian shales and sandstones of the Horton Group (2345.3-3039.6 m) and anhydrite, halite, dolomite and

shale of the Lower Carboniferous Windsor Group (1987.2-2345.3 m) (Barss et al., 1979). Sandpiper 2J-77 ended in Lower Carboniferous shales and sandstones (3264.1-3525.3 m) of the Horton Group; these are overlain by anhydrite, shale and dolomite (3002.3-3264.1 m) of the Windsor Group (Barss et al., 1979). Murre G-67 encountered red slates between 3157.7 and 3237.0 m, which have not been dated, but are lithologically similar to the Horton Group. Phalarope P-62 was drilled through a sequence of red shales, siltstones and sandstones which may be Devonian or Carboniferous in age and which overlies Ordovician Shales.

Early Carboniferous palynomorphs were recovered from Pan American corehole 10C (Fig. 4.12), southeast of the Avalon Peninsula (Howie and Barss, 1975). King et al. (1986) reported an Ordovician-Devonian age for a red siltstone core recovered from east of the Avalon Peninsula (core 77-011-28A). Four other cores in the area also recovered redbeds, suggesting a Devonian-Carboniferous age (Fig. 4.1 and 4.12).

Northeast of Newfoundland, upper Paleozoic strata are widely distributed in the Notre Dame subbasin (named proposed by authors) and Belle Isle Subbasin (Fig. 4.13) of the St. Anthony Basin (Haworth et al., 1976a, b; Cutt and Laving, 1977).

By using data collected from magnetic, gravity and reflection seismic surveys and bedrock coring, Haworth et al. (1976a, b) mapped the geology of the shelf and seafloor northeast of Newfoundland (Fig. 4.13), where they found upper Paleozoic rocks. Haworth et al. (1976a, b) identified in core samples granite of possible Devonian age, and mapped its extent from magnetic lows. A Lower Mississippian unit, equivalent to the Anguille Group, was mapped on the basis of its seismic character. Cored sandstone was lithologically similar to rocks in the onshore Lower Carboniferous Cape Rouge Formation. This unit is overlain by a Mississippian unit, equivalent to the Codroy and Windsor groups, which was mapped on the basis of its nonmagnetic character and the lack of seismic penetration

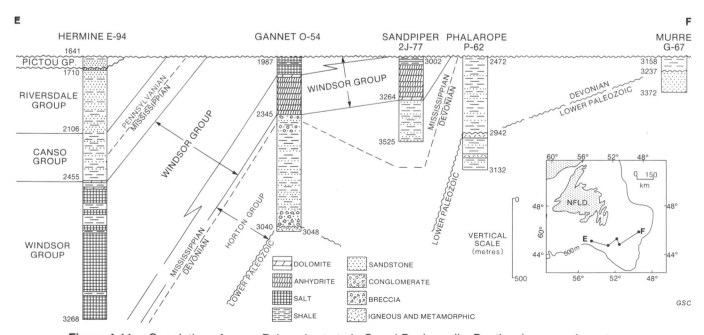

Figure 4.11. Correlation of upper Paleozoic strata in Grand Banks wells. Depths shown are in metres below rotary table.

155

(Haworth et al., 1976a, b). The correlation is based on the three limestone cores obtained from the unit (Haworth et al., 1976b), and its age was determined from the spore assemblages (Haworth et al., 1976a). Above the limestone lies a Mississippian-Pennsylvanian unit which exhibits good reflectivity. It consists of grey, red and brown sandstone, conglomerate and shale similar to the Barachois Group (Canso-Riversdale groups of western Newfoundland) that may be in part Permian (Haworth et al., 1976b). Salt diapirism was recognized locally (Fig. 4.13) and interpreted as due to the presence of Mississippian salt (Haworth et al., 1976a, b).

Farther offshore, on the southern Labrador Shelf, Cutt and Laving (1977) defined the Belle Isle Subbasin (Fig. 4.13). Their unit 2 is a seismically reflective, folded sequence with clear evidence of salt diapirism. It is in angular unconformable contact with overlying Cretaceous and Tertiary strata and from seismic interval velocities probably consists largely of carbonates. Cutt and Laving (1977) favoured a Carboniferous, or possibly Triassic and Jurassic, age for the sequence. Although this late Paleozoic subbasin may extend farther to the southwest, it cannot be recognized there for lack of reliable seismic data.

Two wells were subsequently drilled in the Belle Isle Subbasin (Fig. 4.13). Verrazano L-77 was drilled to a depth of 460 m; the section penetrated consists of alternating beds of light grey, fine- to medium-grained sandstone with siliceous cement and traces of kaolinite, pyrite, coal, mica and glauconite, and brown, red and dark grey, indurated silty to sandy shale with minor amounts of hard dolomitic limestone (Eastcan Exploration Ltd., 1977c). M.S. Barss (pers. comm., 1985) recovered palynomorphs of late Viséan to early Namurian age. Hare Bay E-21 penetrated 1473 m of Pennsylvanian and possibly Permian rocks between 3401 and 4874 m (total depth). These rocks overlie a salt-bearing sequence. The upper Paleozoic strata consist of an interbedded sequence of tight, well cemented, sandstones and indurated shales and siltstones, which are predominantly red-brown, with green mottling between 3401 and 3405 m. Below this interval, the predominant colour is grey. Several coals and a few limestone beds were encountered (BP Canada, 1979).

M.S. Barss (pers. comm., 1985) identified late Viséan palynomorphs from the 5505-5675 m interval in the Blue H-28 well (Fig. 4.13) about 200 km southeast of Hare Bay E-21. This suggests that the sandstone and shale sequence at Blue H-28 from 5505 m to 6103 m (total depth) is Carboniferous and may correlate with the upper Windsor Group and basal Canso Group. Organic concentrations from 5700 to 5840 m contained coal particles with vitrinite reflectance levels greater than 5.0% Ro. Although these high-rank coal fragments were about 0.2 mm in size, it is not known if they originated from in situ coal seams, coal stringers or existed as disseminated particles (M.P. Avery, pers. comm., 1986).

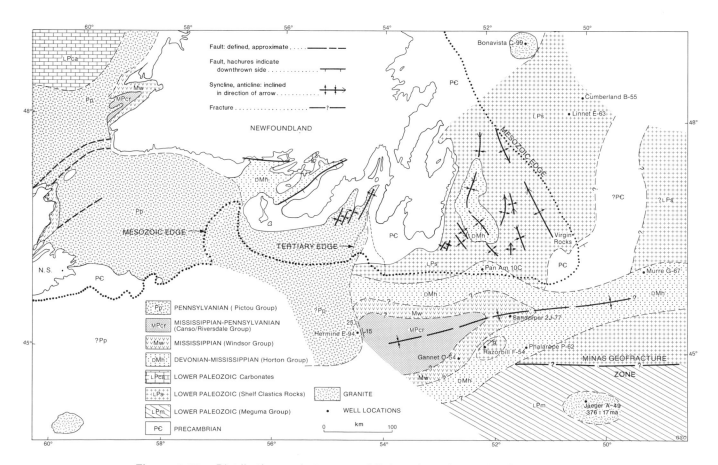

Figure 4.12. Distribution and structure of Paleozoic rocks on the Grand Banks.

STRUCTURAL GEOLOGY

In this section, the regional tectonics are described in terms of the Paleozoic megasequences recognized in the basins of offshore eastern Canada. The discussion is limited to the deformation which occurred prior to Mesozoic time.

The approximate extent of Paleozoic rocks is portrayed on geological maps, which combine seafloor outcrop patterns with subcrop configurations of units buried beneath Mesozoic and Tertiary rocks (Fig. 4.7, 4.12, 4.13, 4.14). The subcrop patterns utilize bed attitudes derived from dipmeter logs, but are simplified. Mesozoic and later structures have been omitted. The possibility for continuity between wells has been emphasized. It is clear that the true configurations are far more complex, especially in the Grand Banks area (see, for example, Wade 1981, Fig. 5). In the outcrop areas, these structural summary maps depict Paleozoic rock distribution and structures on the seafloor; in the subcrop areas, they portray a simplified

picture of how the Paleozoic sequences might have appeared prior to Mesozoic burial.

Detailed seismic interpretation might increase our understanding of the extent and configuration of buried Paleozoic units, but without more well control many uncertainties remain.

Early Paleozoic structures

The northern flank of the Anticosti Basin is now a south-dipping, southward thickening homocline (Fig. 4.2) and it appears likely that this tilting occurred in response to margin subsidence during accumulation of the lower Paleozoic rocks. The southern margin, preserved in western Newfoundland, contains evidence of northwestward Taconic overthrusting (Williams, 1979), which foreland basin modelling (Beaumont, 1981) suggests would have contributed to basin subsidence. The emplacement of these Taconic klippen and associated mélanges in western Newfoundland is discussed in detail in Chapter 2.

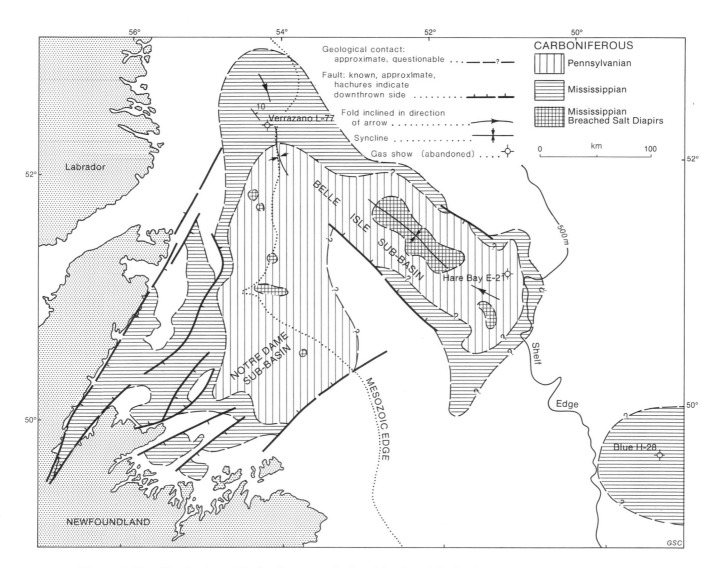

Figure 4.13. Distribution of Carboniferous rocks in subbasins of the St. Anthony Basin, offshore northeast Newfoundland. A time-structure map was made available by BP Canada and their partners for the compilation.

On the southern Labrador Shelf, dipmeter data show that the Ordovician carbonates are folded into a northwest-trending anticlinorium (Fig. 4.14). Northeasterly dipping carbonates at Roberval K-92, Gudrid H-55 and Indian Harbour M-52 are replaced to the southwest by Precambrian gneisses at Cartier D-70. The carbonates at Freydis B-87, on the other hand, dip to the southwest. A pre-Cretaceous anticlinorium with lower Paleozoic sediments eroded from the crest agrees with the available evidence, although the subcrop configuration may be more complex (Fig. 4.14). However, the folding may not be Paleozoic. The strike of the carbonates is approximately parallel to the present shelf margin, so that they could have been tilted during the early stages of Mesozoic rifting of the Labrador Sea (Grant, 1975; Srivastava et al., 1981).

In Davis Strait, single channel reflection seismic lines show that the Ordovician limestones are folded about north-south axes. It appears that this deformation occurred before burial beneath Mesozoic and Tertiary rocks (MacLean et al., 1977, 1978).

On the Avalon Platform, between the Avalon Peninsula and Virgin Rocks, single channel reflection seismic lines indicate that Ordovician and Silurian rocks are gently folded approximately along north-trending axes (Durling et al., 1987; King et al., 1986). Grant (1972) illustrated this type of folding in his line G-H. The folding is open and appears to be similar in style to the Acadian folding, which has given rise to the north-south trending inliers of lower Paleozoic shelf deposits that onshore overlie the Precambrian sediments on the Avalon Peninsula (McCartney, 1969; Keppie, 1982). Offshore, folded Ordovician and Silurian beds are truncated and unconformably overlain by redbeds of probable Devonian age on the Avalon Platform. This implies the folding is of Acadian age (Fig. 4.12). Faults may also be present, but few offsets can be recognized on the single channel seismic reflection profiles (Durling et al., 1987). On the southern Grand Banks, only three wells penetrate lower Paleozoic rocks and thus the data are inadequate to determine the nature of deformation or its timing.

Acadian folding, however, appears to have affected the Meguma Group on the Scotian Shelf. This is demonstrated be the east-northeast-trending anticlines and synclines which have been mapped on the seafloor (Fig. 4.7), using seismic reflection, sidescan sonar, gravity and bottom core

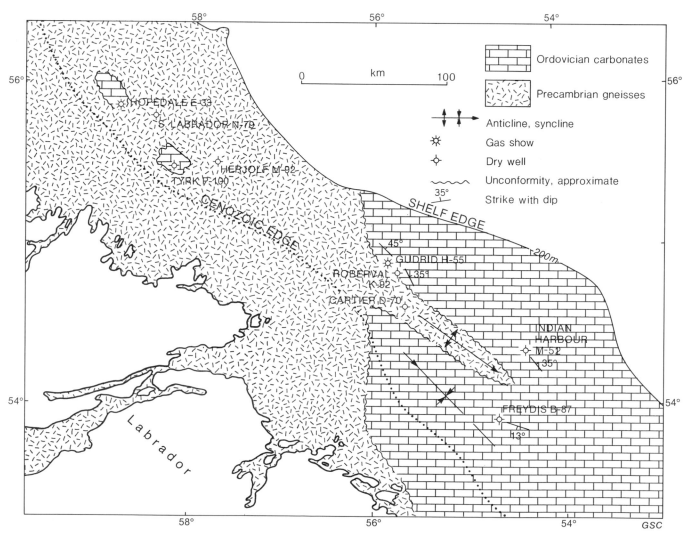

Figure 4.14. Pre-Mesozoic subcrop map of the southern Labrador Shelf.

samples (King and MacLean, 1976). Evidence of folding was also encountered in several wells. Dipmeter records from Wyandot E-53 and Fox I-22 document a northwest strike for the Meguma metasediments and suggest that, on a small scale, the beds are folded in a complex manner. This also appears to be the case at Argo F-38. In Nova Scotia, the Meguma Group is intruded by granites which post-date folding and have yielded radiometric ages ranging between 300 and 372 Ma (Cormier and Smith, 1973; Clarke and Halliday, 1980; Reynolds et al., 1981; MacDonald and Clarke, 1985).

A K-Ar age determination of 359 ± 12 Ma was obtained from a biotite concentrate recovered from ditch cuttings of granodiorite over the interval 2319.4-2322.5 m in Ojibwa E-07 (L.F. Jansa, per. comm., 1985). All granitic rocks encountered in the subsurface on the Scotian Shelf are believed to be Acadian intrusions similar to those which outcrop onshore in Nova Scotia.

Late Paleozoic structures

The thickest and most widespread upper Paleozoic deposits in eastern Canada are those which fill the Magdalen Basin in the Gulf of St. Lawrence and extend onto surrounding land areas (Fig. 4.15). Seismic profiles and salt thickness estimates indicate that the basin contains up to 12 km of upper Paleozoic sediments, with the axial area located east of Îles de la Madeleine.

Lower Paleozoic and older rocks beneath the Gulf of St. Lawrence are masked by a thick accumulation of overlying, and presumably onlapping, sediments. Complex faulting of pre-upper Paleozoic units, which has led to the development of horsts and grabens, is characteristic of the onshore structural regime (Keppie, 1982). Similar features can be recognized on seismic lines which cross nearshore areas north of Cape Breton and in Northumberland Strait. A comparably faulted terrain is believed to underlie the Magdalen Basin, but such faults are not illustrated in Figure 4.15 because of the poor quality of the seismic data. Figure 4.15 shows a preliminary appraisal of the pre-Horton structural surface in the Gulf of St. Lawrence and indicates the probable extent and gross geometry of the basin fill. The basin axis trends northeasterly and the depocentre lies close to Îles de la Madeleine.

Seismic reflection profiles also illustrate the wide extent of upper Paleozoic salt deposits in the Magdalen Basin. Locally, basement faults can be recognized beneath the Windsor Group salt-rich section. Extensive salt flowage and intrusive diapirism into overlying strata may also be associated with adjustments within the basement. Figure 4.16 illustrates a preliminary interpretation of the extent and thickness of the Cumberland and Pictou groups in the Gulf of St. Lawrence. Again, the depositional axis is centred around Îles de la Madeleine and the eastern part of Prince Edward Island; the map also outlines the salt

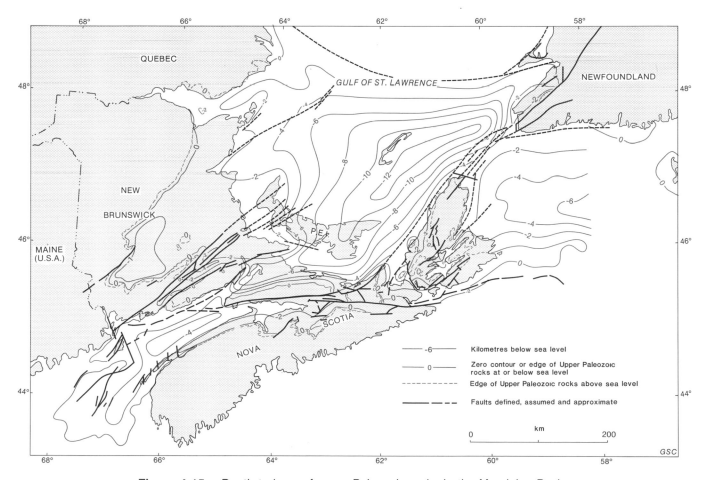

Figure 4.15. Depth to base of upper Paleozoic rocks in the Magdalen Basin.

159

diapir field of the Windsor Group in the southeastern part of Îles de la Madeleine (Howie, 1984). The regional structure is illustrated in the generalized cross-section in Figure 4.17. At the west end, the section passes through the Brion Island No. 1 well, which ended in a salt pillow of the Windsor Group. Three diapiric structures off the line of section are illustrated by dashed lines and, in the deeper part of the basin, diapirs recognized on seismic lines are shown penetrating sediments of the Windsor, Canso, Riversdale and most of the Pictou groups. The eastern margin of the basin is faulted and is only slightly affected by salt diapirism. The Magdalen Basin appears to be separated from the Sydney Basin by a basement arch complex (Map 1707A, in pocket) which is assumed to be uplifted Precambrian and Lower Cambrian rocks (Howie, 1984).

The Sydney Basin offshore contains thick sequences of the Pictou Group. These rocks outcrop on the seafloor and have been encountered in the North Sydney F-24 and North Sydney P-05 wells (Fig. 4.16), and in offshore holes drilled as part of a coal exploration program (Hacquebard, 1983). Clastics of the Canso and Riversdale groups were also encountered in the two North Sydney wells, but it is not known how far east these rocks extend or what underlies them. The limited seismic data do not suggest that the Sydney Basin is diapirically deformed and it is not clear

if the Windsor and Horton groups extend from Cape Breton to the southern Grand Banks.

Pre-Mesozoic rocks on the Grand Banks exhibit considerable structural relief due to the formation of a series of rapidly subsiding Mesozoic rift basins (Amoco and Imperial, 1973; see Chapter 6). Upper Paleozoic rocks were encountered in Hermine E-94, Gannet O-54, Razorbill F-54, Sandpiper 2J-77 and Phalarope P-62 wells and Pan American corehole 10C (Fig. 4.12) and the distribution of the subcrop units suggests an east-trending structural basin, 150 km wide, south of the Avalon Peninsula. This basin contains rocks coeval with the Horton, Windsor and Canso and Riversdale groups (Avery and Bell, 1985). Discordant dips in the Hermine E-94 well suggest that west-dipping sandstones of the Pictou Group rest unconformably on east-dipping sandstones and conglomerates of the Riversdale Group. These Pictou sandstones may represent the eastern edge of a blanket of Upper Carboniferous rocks extending east from Cape Breton across the Sydney Basin (Avery and Bell, 1985).

Upper Paleozoic redbeds probably also outcrop on the seafloor east of the Avalon Peninsula, southeast Newfoundland (Fig. 4.12). Single-channel seismic records suggest that the redbeds fill a mildly downwarped syncline

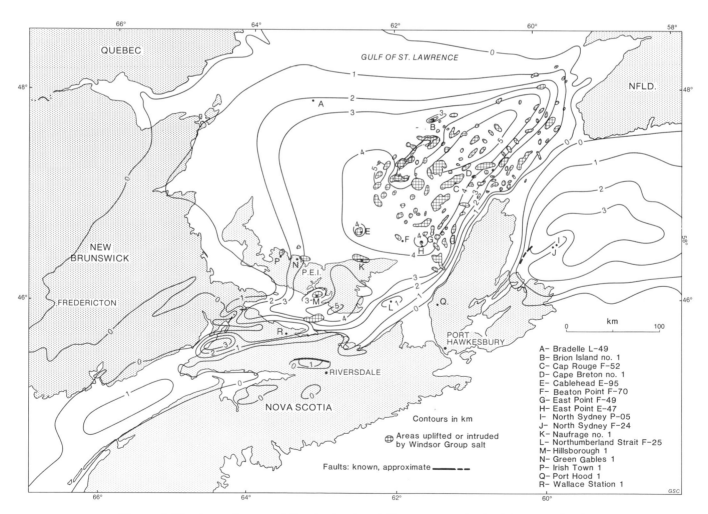

Figure 4.16. Isopach map of Cumberland and Pictou groups in the Magdalen Basin.

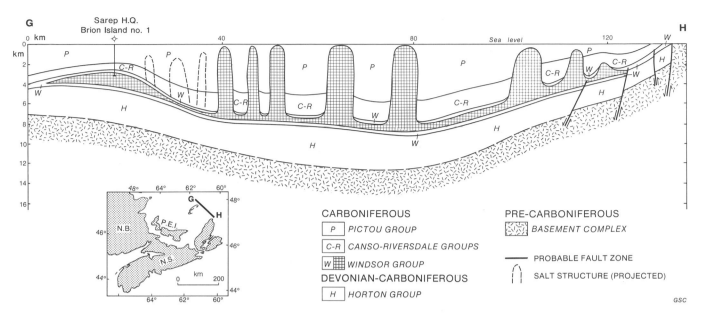

Figure 4.17. Section showing salt structures in Magdalen Basin (adapted from Murphy Oil Co. Ltd., unpublished report, 1972 and Catalina Exploration and Development Ltd., unpublished internal report, 1971).

and rest unconformably on more tightly folded lower Paleozoic rocks (Durling et al., 1987). This north-trending syncline, which is interpreted to contain Devonian continental clastics, appears to be separated from the more extensive late Paleozoic basin to the south.

Carboniferous sediments fill the St. Anthony Basin on the Northeast Newfoundland Shelf and extend across the southern part of the Labrador Shelf. They are folded, faulted and intruded by salt (Haworth et al., 1976a, b). In the southern part of the basin (Fig. 4.13), several northeast-trending faults are associated with similarly trending folds. Farther north where Upper Carboniferous rocks outcrop, folds are interpreted to trend northerly and north-northwesterly, although the seismic line spacing of 15 to 35 km means that structural continuity cannot be mapped with certainty. Some of the folds that affect the uppermost Mississippian-Pennsylvanian unit are truncated by flat-lying Cretaceous and Tertiary rocks that overstep the Notre Dame subbasin on the outer shelf (Fig. 4.13). Salt diapirs are also present, including several collapse structures, which may be due to salt withdrawal. Folding is clearly pre-Cretaceous and could have occurred in late Paleozoic time, especially if it is related to salt movement at depth. Haworth et al. (1976b) showed a spatial configuration of folds, faults, and outcrop pattern compatible with an interpretation that the uppermost Mississippian-Pennsylvanian unit rests unconformably on older previously deformed Carboniferous rocks. If this is correct, their map documents mid-Carboniferous folding, faulting and erosion, in addition to later folding which also affected the uppermost Mississippian-Pennsylvanian unit.

On the southern Labrador Shelf, Carboniferous rocks also occur in the Belle Isle Subbasin beneath the Cretaceous and Tertiary wedge (Cutt and Laving, 1977). The rocks fill a subcropping structural basin, which may extend southwestwards to join the Notre Dame Subbasin (Fig. 4.13). Whereas single channel seismic reflection profiles have sketchily documented the structure of the Notre Dame Subbasin at relatively shallow depth, multichannel seismic reflection data have revealed the configuration of the Belle Isle Subbasin in considerable detail. Cutt and Laving (1977) estimated that the sediments preserved in the Belle Isle Subbasin are more than 4500 m thick. Figure 4.13 illustrates a subcropping basin about 100 km wide and over 200 km long, with its long axis aligned northwesterly (Fig. 4.13). Numerous salt-cored diapirs are present, many of which exhibit solution collapse (Cutt and Laving, 1977, their Fig. 4.6). These diapirs penetrate upward to a pre-Mesozoic paleosurface, or were exposed to erosion at this surface. A northeast-trending anticline, possibly with a diapir in its core, crosses the southeastern end of the Belle Isle Subbasin near the Hare Bay E-21 well. Otherwise, the trough exhibits rather uniform flexure, although the northeastern flank is more steeply dipping than the southwestern side. The salt diapirs are concentrated in the centre of the basin.

Post-depositional and syn-depositional subsidence may have affected the Carboniferous rocks in the Belle Isle Subbasin. There may also have been an intra-Carboniferous unconformity as previously suggested for the St. Anthony Basin. The seismic profiles in Cutt and Laving (1977, Fig. 6, 7) indicate discordancies between reflections. It is not clear how the Notre Dame Subbasin and Belle Isle Subbasin are connected, if indeed they are. They appear to be separate structural basins divided by a northwest-trending high which is approximately parallel to the present shelf edge (Fig. 4.13). As with the sub-Cretaceous anticlinorium involving Ordovician carbonates to the north, this high and the Belle Isle Subbasin may be Mesozoic rift-associated structures.

Carboniferous sediments have also been identified below 5505 m in the Blue H-28 well which was drilled in 1500 m of water off the Northeast Newfoundland Shelf (Fig. 4.13). The structural setting of these sediments is unknown (see Grant and McAlpine, Chapter 6).

TECTONICS

At least four Paleozoic megasequences can be identified on the continental margin of eastern Canada: a lower Paleozoic shelf carbonate-clastic sequence; a lower Paleozoic clastic sequence; a Meguma turbidite sequence with Acadian granite intrusions; and an upper Paleozoic redbed and evaporite sequence, which is largely continental (Fig. 4.1).

The lower Paleozoic shelf carbonate-clastic sequence is an eastward continuation of the St. Lawrence Platform assemblages of central Canada and the Michigan Basin. These rocks were deposited on an early Paleozoic passive margin and accumulated around the western rim of the Cambrian-Ordovician Iapetus Ocean (Rodgers, 1968; Keen et al., Chapter 2). They extend into the southern part of the Labrador Shelf and may once have joined up with the carbonates in the Davis Strait area. Onshore in Newfoundland, equivalent units lie within the Humber Zone (Williams, 1979). During Cambrian and Early Ordovician time, the Iapetus Ocean floor was consumed by eastward subduction of the oceanic lithosphere. In Middle Ordovician time, the North American passive margin collided with an island arc and was overridden by Taconic thrust sheets containing a variety of rock types (Colman-Sadd, 1982). These Taconic allochthons loaded the lithosphere and generated a flexural response which initiated the subsidence and infilling of the Anticosti Basin (Keen et al., Chapter 2). Onshore, in Newfoundland, the Humber Zone is succeeded southeastwards by the Dunnage, Gander and Avalon zones (Fig. 4.18). These zones are of unknown paleogeography with respect to cratonic North America.

Regional offshore geophysical data (Haworth, 1981) suggest that the Dunnage and Gander zones extend northeastwards across the Northeast Newfoundland Shelf. No wells drilled in the areas concerned have penetrated Lower Paleozoic rocks. All the lower Paleozoic shelf clastics encountered in wells on the Northeast Newfoundland Shelf and on the Grand Banks lie within the offshore extension of the Avalon Zone where they probably represent the upper part of the lower Paleozoic sequence onshore (Durling et al., 1987). The Meguma Group appears to be exotic (Schenk, 1981), so the Minas Geofracture Zone would initially have been a plate collision scar. According to Schenk (1981), the portion of eastern Canada's continental margin now underlain by the Meguma Group and overlying related strata originated either in northern South America or northwest Africa. It accreted to North America near the end of Early Devonian time. Granitoid plutons were subsequently emplaced in all the tectonic zones east of the early Paleozoic North American margin during the Devonian Acadian Orogeny. The emplacement mechanism is still under debate (see Chapter 2).

Upper Paleozoic redbeds and evaporites rest unconformably on all three lower Paleozoic sequences identified here, and occupy a series of "successor basins". The largest and deepest is the Magdalen Basin. The sequence is also present in several structural depressions preserved offshore of Newfoundland, but is not found on the Labrador Shelf.

Haworth (1981) correlated Caledonide and Appalachian features using the regional geophysical characteristics of the tectonic zones recognized in both orogens. This approach relies on fitting major lineaments, rather than matching speculative palaeogeographies or interpreted boundaries. Haworth found that the two sides of the Atlantic Ocean could not be fitted without introducing a major right lateral flexure between the orogenic systems (Fig. 4.18). This flexure parallels a swing across the

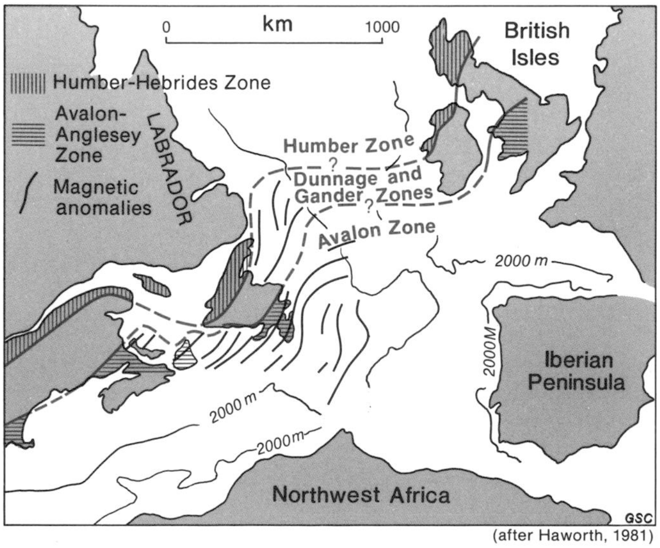

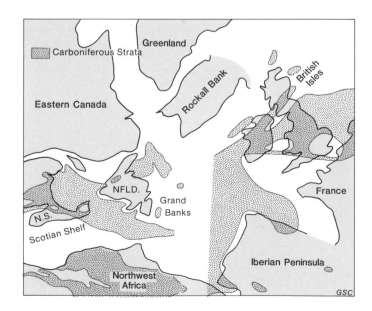

Figure 4.18. Appalachian-Caledonide structural configuration of the North Atlantic area prior to rifting of Iapetus (after Haworth, 1981).

Figure 4.19. Carboniferous strata (red stipple) of the North Atlantic area in pre-drift configuration (after Wilson, 1981; Ziegler, 1982).

Grand Banks of northwest-trending magnetic lineations that are attributable to Acadian structures. The early Paleozoic data described here are compatible with Haworth's reconstruction and are not sufficient to suggest modifications. It is hoped that the emerging understanding of early Paleozoic accretionary tectonics combined with deep seismic reflection information will permit correlation of these zones with increased precision in future years.

No flexure is needed to correlate upper Paleozoic strata. Figure 4.19 illustrates the extent of Carboniferous rocks on both North Atlantic margins. As Cutt and Laving (1977) showed, the Belle Isle Subbasin is situated almost opposite an evaporite-bearing sequence identified by Bailey (1975) on the west Irish Shelf. Wilson (1981) demonstrated that the fit is good and no major offsets appear to be required.

ACKNOWLEDGMENTS

The authors express their gratitude to BP Canada Resources Inc. and to Petro Canada Inc. and their operating partners, who provided seismic interpretations of parts of the Labrador Shelf. Unpublished information was also made available by Mobil Oil Canada Ltd., M.S. Barss and B. MacLean. We appreciate the assistance of R.C. Boehner, K.S. Crosby, W.A.M. Jenkins, J.D. Keppie, A.F. King, H.G. Miller, P.E. Schenk, P. Sherrington and H. Williams and the ongoing help of our colleagues: A.C. Grant, G.B. Fader, L.F. Jansa, C.E. Keen, B.V. Sanford, S.P. Srivastava and G. Stockmal. This chapter has been reviewed by B.V. Sanford and H. Williams.

REFERENCES

Amoco Canada Petroleum Company Ltd. and Imperial Oil Ltd.
1973: Regional geology of the Grand Banks; Bulletin of Canadian Petroleum Geology, v. 21, p. 479-503.

Anderle, J.P., Crosby, K.S., and Waugh, D.C.E.
1979: Potash and Salt Springs, New Brunswick; Economic Geology, v. 74, p. 389-396.

Avery, M.P. and Bell, J.S.
1985: Vitrinite reflectance measurements from the South Whale Basin, Grand Banks, Eastern Canada and implications for hydrocarbon exploration; in Current Research, Part B, Geological Survey of Canada, Paper 85-1B, p. 51-57.

Bailey, R.J.
1975: Sub-Cenozoic geology of the British continental margin (50°N to 57°N) and the reassembly of the North Atlantic Late Paleozoic supercontinent; Geology, v. 3, p. 591-594.

Ballard, R.D. and Uchupi, E.
1975: Triassic rift structure in Gulf of Maine; American Association of Petroleum Geologists Bulletin, v. 59, p. 1041-1072.

Barnett, D.E.
1984: Potash production in New Brunswick; Fertilizer International, September 6, no. 186, p. 38-43.

Barr, S.M., Brisebois, D., and MacDonald, A.S.
1985: Carboniferous volcanic rocks of the Magdalen Islands, Gulf of St. Lawrence; Canadian Journal of Earth Sciences, v. 22, p. 1679-1688.

Barss, M.S., Bujak, J.P., and Williams, G.L.
1979: Palynological zonation and correlation of sixty-seven wells, Eastern Canada; Geological Survey of Canada, Paper 78-24, 118 p.

Beaumont, C.
1981: Foreland basins; Geophysical Journal of the Royal Astronomical Society, v. 65, p. 291-329.

Bell, W.A.
1929: Horton-Windsor district, Nova Scotia; Geological Survey of Canada, Memoir 155, 268 p.

1944: Carboniferous rocks and fossil floras of northern Nova Scotia; Geological Survey of Canada, Memoir 238, 277 p.
1958: Possibilities for occurrence of petroleum reservoirs in Nova Scotia; Nova Scotia Department of Mines, Miscellaneous Publication, 177 p.

Blanchard, M-C., Jamieson, R.A., and More, E.B.
1984: Late Devonian-Early Carboniferous volcanism in western Cape Breton Island, Nova Scotia; Canadian Journal of Earth Sciences, v. 21, p. 762-774.

Boehner, R.C.
1983a: Windsor Group salt and potash in Nova Scotia, Canada; Sixth International Symposium on salt, The Northern Ohio Geological Society Inc., v. 1, p. 99-113.
1983b: Carboniferous, basin studies, salt, potash, celestite and barite: New exploration potential in the Sydney Basin, Cape Breton Island Nova Scotia Department of Mines and Energy; Eighth Annual Open House and Review of Activities, November 28-29; Information Series No. 7, p. 75-77.

BP Canada
1978: Indian Harbour M-52: well history report, BP Columbia et al.; Canada Oil and Gas Lands Administration, Department of Energy, Mines and Resources Canada, 21 p.
1979: Hare Bay E-21: Well History Report, by BP Columbia et al.; Canada Oil and Gas Lands Administration, Department of Energy, Mines and Resources Canada, 79 p.

Bradley, D.C.
1982: Subsidence in late Paleozoic basins in the Appalachians; Tectonics, v. 1, p. 107-123.

Chevron Standard Ltd.
1978: Hopedale E-33: Well History Report by, Chevron et al.; Canada Oil and Gas Lands Administration, Department of Energy, Mines and Resources, Canada, 26 p.

Clarke, D.B. and Halliday, A.N.
1980: Strontium isotope geology of the South Mountain batholith, Nova Scotia; Geochimica et Cosmochimica Acta, v. 44, p. 1045-1058.

Colman-Sadd, S.P.
1982: Two stage continental collision and plate driving forces; Tectonophysics, v. 90, p. 263-282.

Cormier, R.F. and Smith, T.E.
1973: Radiometric ages of granitic rocks, southwestern Nova Scotia; Canadian Journal of Earth Sciences, v. 10, p. 1201-1210.

Crosby, K.S.
1985: Millstream potash exploration program, Lower Millstream, New Brunswick; in Geological Association of Canada-Mineralogical Association of Canada, Program with Abstracts, v. 10, p. A12.

Cutt, B.J. and Laving, J.G.
1977: Tectonic elements and geologic history of the South Labrador and Newfoundland continental shelf, eastern Canada; Bulletin of Canadian Petroleum Geology, v. 25, p. 1037-1058.

Durling, P.D., Bell, J.S., and Fader, G.B.
1987: The geological structure of the Paleozoic rocks on the Avalon Platform, offshore Newfoundland; Canadian Journal of Earth Sciences, v. 24, n. 7, p. 1412-1420..

Eastcan Exploration Ltd.
1976a: Freydis B-87: Well History Report, by Eastcan et al.; Canada Oil and Gas Lands Administration, Department of Energy, Mines and Resources Canada, 42 p.
1976b: Gudrid H-55: Well History Report, by Eastcan et al.; Canada Oil and Gas Lands Administration, Department of Energy, Mines and Resources Canada, 42 p.
1976c: Verrazano L-77: Well History Report, Eastcan et al.; Canada Oil and Gas Lands Administration, Department of Energy, Mines and Resources Canada, 32 p.
1979: Tyrk P-100: Well History Report by Eastcan et al.; Canada Oil and Gas Lands Administration, Department of Energy, Mines and Resources Canada,, 126 p.

Giles, P.S. and Boehner, R.C.
1979: Carboniferous stratigraphy of the Shubenacadie and Musquodoboit basins, central Nova Scotia; Nova Scotia Department of Mines and Energy, Open-File Report 410.

Grant, A.C.
1972: The continental margin off Labrador and eastern Newfoundland: morphology and geology; Canadian Journal of Earth Sciences, v. 9, p. 1394-1430.
1975: Geophysical results from the continental margin off southern Baffin Island; in Canada's Continental Margins and Offshore Petroleum Explorated, ed. C.J. Yorath, E.R. Parker and D.J. Glass; Canadian Society of Petroleum Geologists, Memoir 4, p. 411-431.

Gussow, W.C.
1953: Carboniferous stratigraphy and structural geology of New Brunswick, Canada; American Association of Petroleum Geologists Bulletin, v. 37, no. 7, p. 1713-1816.

Hacquebard, P.A.
1983: Geological development and economic evaluation of the Sydney Coal Basin, Nova Scotia; in Current Research, Part A, Geological Survey of Canada, Paper 83-1A, p. 71-81.

Harland, W.B., Cox, A.V., Llewellyn, P.G., Pickton, C.A.G., Smith, A.G., and Walters, R.
1982: A geologic time scale. Cambridge Earth Science Series, Cambridge University Press, 131 p.

Haworth, R.T.
1981: Geophysical expression of Appalachian-Caledonide structures on the continental margins of the North Atlantic; in Geology of the North Atlantic Borderlands, ed. J.W. Kerr and A.J. Ferguson; Canadian Society of Petroleum Geologists, Memoir 7, p. 429-446.

Haworth, R.T. and Lefort, J.P.
1979: Geophysical evidence for the extent of the Avalon Zone in Atlantic Canada; Canadian Journal of Earth Sciences, v. 16, p. 552-567.

Haworth, R.T., Grant, A.C., and Folinsbee, R.A.
1976a: Geology of the continental shelf of southeastern Labrador; in Report of Activities, Part C, Geological Survey of Canada, Paper 76-1C, p. 61-70.

Haworth, R.T., Poole, W.H., Grant, A.C., and Sanford, B.V.
1976b: Marine geoscience survey northeast of Newfoundland; in Report of Activities, Part A, Geological Survey of Canada, Paper 76-1A, p. 7-15.

Howie, R.D.
1974: Report on the stratigraphic analysis of the Paleozoic section the Elf Hermine E-94; Geological Survey of Canada, Eastern Petroleum Geology Subdivision, unpublished Report No. EPGS-STRAT.1-74RDH.

1984: Carboniferous evaporites in Atlantic Canada; Neuvième Congrès International de Stratigraphie et de Géologie du Carbonifère, Southern Illinois University Press, v. 3, p. 131-142.

1986a: Windsor Group salt in the Minas Subbasin of Nova Scotia; Geological Survey of Canada, Paper 85-10, 29 p.

1986b: Windsor Group salt in the Cumberland Subbasin of Nova Scotia; Geological Survey of Canada, Paper 85-11, 11 p.

Howie, R.D. and Barss, M.S.
1975: Upper Paleozoic rocks of the Atlantic provinces, Gulf of St. Lawrence and adjacent continental shelf; in Offshore Geology of Eastern Canada, Volume 2, Regional Geology, ed. W.J.M. Van der Linden and J.A. Wade; Geological Survey of Canada, Paper 74-30, v. 2, 35-50.

Howie, R.D. and Cumming, L.M.
1963: Basement features of the Canadian Appalachians; Geological Survey of Canada, Bulletin 89, 18 p.

Howie, R.D. and Hill, J.V.
1972: Developments in Eastern Canada in 1971; American Association of Petroleum Geologists Bulletin, v. 56, no. 7, p. 1193-1204.

Hurst, J.M. and Kerr, J.W.
1982: Upper Ordovician to Silurian facies patterns in eastern Ellesmere Island and western North Greenland and their bearing on the Nares Strait lineament; in Nares Strait and the Drift of Greenland: A Conflict in Plate Tectonics, ed. P.R. Dawes and J.W. Kerr; Meddelelser om Gronland, Geoscience 8, p. 137-146.

Jansa, L.F. and Wade, J.A.
1975: Geology of the continental margin off Nova Scotia and Newfoundland; in Offshore Geology of Eastern Canada, Volume 2, Regional Geology, ed. W.J.M. Van der Linden and J.A. Wade; Geological Survey of Canada, Paper 74-30, v. 2, p. 51-105.

Jenkins, W.A.M.
1984: Ordovician rocks in the Eastcan et al. Freydis B-87 and other wells in offshore Atlantic Canada; Canadian Journal of Earth Sciences, v. 21, p. 864-868.

Kane, M.F., Yellin, M.J., Bell, K.G., and Zietz, I.
1972: Gravity and magnetic evidence of lithology and structure in the Gulf of Maine region; United States Geological Survey, Professional Paper 726-B, 22 p.

Kelley, D.G.
1967: Baddeck and Whycocomagh map-areas with emphasis on Mississippian stratigraphy on central Cape Breton Island, Nova Scotia (11K/2 and 11F/14); Geological Survey of Canada, Memoir 351, 65 p.

Keppie, J.D.
1982: Tectonic map of the province of Nova Scotia; Department of Mines and Energy, Nova Scotia.

King, L.H., Fader, G.B., Jenkins, W.A.M., and King, E.L.
1986: Occurrence and regional setting of Lower Paleozoic sediments on the Grand Banks of Newfoundland; Canadian Journal of Earth Sciences, v. 23, p. 504-526.

King, L.H. and MacLean, B.
1976: Geology of the Scotian Shelf; Geological Survey of Canada, Paper 74-31, 31 p.

Kingston, P.W. and Dickie, D.E.
1979: Geology of New Brunswick potash deposits; Canadian Mining and Metallurgical Bulletin, v. 72, no. 802, p. 134-141.

Legault, J.A.
1982: First report of Ordovician (Caradoc-Ashgill) palynomorphs from Orphan Knoll, Labrador Sea; Canadian Journal of Earth Sciences, v. 19, p. 1851-1856.

MacDonald, M.A. and Clarke, D.B.
1985: The petrology, geochemistry and economic potential of the Musquodoboit batholith, Nova Scotia; Canadian Journal of Earth Sciences, v. 22, no. 11, p. 1633-1642.

MacLean, B.
1978: Marine geological-geophysical investigations in 1977 of the Scott Inlet and Cape Dyer-Frobisher Bay areas of the Baffin Island continental shelf; in Current Research, Part B, Geological Survey of Canada, Paper 78-1B, p. 13-20.

MacLean, B. and Falconer, R.K.H.
1979: Geological-geophysical studies in Baffin Bay and Scott Inlet-Buchan Gulf and Cape Dyer – Cumberland Sound area of the Baffin Island shelf; in Current Research, Part B, Geological Survey of Canada, Paper 79-1B, p. 231-244.

MacLean, B. and Williams, G.L.
1983: Geological investigations of Baffin Island Shelf in 1982; in Current Research, Part B, Geological Survey of Canada, Paper 83-1B, p. 309-315.

MacLean, B., Falconer, R.K.H., and Clarke, D.B.
1978: Tertiary basalts of western Davis Strait: bedrock core samples and geophysical data; Canadian Journal of Earth Sciences, v. 15, p. 773-780.

MacLean, B., Jansa, L.F., Falconer, R.K.H., and Srivastava, S.P.
1977: Ordovician strata on the southeastern Baffin Island shelf revealed by shallow drilling; Canadian Journal of Earth Sciences, v. 14, p. 1925-1939.

MacLean, B., Srivastava, S.P., and Haworth, R.T.
1982: Bedrock structures off Cumberland Sound, Baffin Island shelf: sample an geophysical data; in Arctic Geology and Geophysics, ed. A.F. Embry and H.R. Balkwill; Canadian Society of Petroleum Geologists, Memoir 8, p. 279-295.

MacLean, B., Woodside, J.M., and Girouard, P.
1984: Geological and geophysical investigations in Jones Sound, District of Franklin; in Current Research, Part A, Geological Survey of Canada, Paper 84-1A, p. 359-365.

Mamet, B.L.
1970: Carbonate microfacies of the Windsor Group (Carboniferous), Nova Scotia and New Brunswick; Geological Survey of Canada, Paper 70-21, 121 p.

McCartney, E.D.
1969: Geology of the Avalon Peninsula, southeast Newfoundland; in North Atlantic — Geology and Continental Drift, ed. W.M. Kay; American Association of Petroleum Geologists, Memoir 12, p. 115-129.

Murphy Oil Company Ltd.
1974: North Sydney P-05: Well History Report by Murphy et al., Canada Oil and Gas Lands Administration, Department of Energy, Mines and Resources Canada, 29 p.

Newman, P.H.
1977: The offshore and onshore geology and geophysics of the Nares Strait region; its tectonic history and significance in regional tectonics; M.Sc. thesis, Dalhousie University, Halifax, Nova Scotia, 153 p.

Peel, J.S. and Christie, R.L.
1982: Cambrian-Ordovician platform stratigraphy: correlations around Kane Basin; in Nares Strait and the Drift of Greenland: A Conflict in Plate Tectonics, ed. P.R. Dawes and J.W. Kerr; Meddelelser om Gronland, Geoscience 8, p. 117-136.

Poole, W.H.
1967: Tectonic evolution of Appalachian region of Canada; in Geology of the Atlantic Region, ed. E.R.W. Neale and H. Williams; Geological Association of Canada, Special Paper 4, p. 9-51.

Poole, W.H., Sanford, B.V., Williams, H., and Kelley, D.G.
1970a: Geology of southeastern Canada; in Geology and Economic Minerals of Canada, ed. R.J.W. Douglas; Geological Survey of Canada, Economic Geology Report 1, 5th Edition, p. 228-304.

1970b: Geotectonic correlation chart for southeastern Canada, chart II; in Geology and Economic Minerals of Canada, ed. R.J.W. Douglas; Economic Geology Report 1, 5th Edition, Geological Survey of Canada, Maps and Charts.

Prud'homme, M.
1986: Salt Mineral Report 34, Canadian Minerals Yearbook 1985; Energy, Mines and Resources Canada, Mineral Policy, p. 51-1 to 51-12.

Quinlan, G.M. and Beaumont, C.
1984: Appalachian thrusting, lithospheric flexure, and the Paleozoic stratigraphy of the Eastern Interior of North America; Canadian Journal of Earth Sciences, v. 21, no. 9, p. 973-996.

Reynolds, P.H., Zentilli, M., and Muecke G.K.
1981: K-Ar and ^{40}Ar/^{39} geochronology of granitoid rocks from southern Nova Scotia; its bearing on the geological evolution of the Meguma Zone of the Appalachians; Canadian Journal of Earth Sciences, v. 18, no. 2, p. 386-394.

Rodgers, J.
1968: The eastern edge of the North America continent during the Cambrian and Early Ordovician; in Studies in Appalachian Geology: Northern and Maritime, ed. E-an Zen, W.S. White, J.B. Hadley and J.B. Thompson Jr.; Interscience Publishers, New York, p. 141-149.

Schenk, P.E.
1967: The significance of algal stromatolites to palaeoenvironmental chronostratigraphic interpretations of the Windsorian stage (Mississippian), Maritime provinces; in Geology of the Atlantic Region, ed. E.R.W. Neale and H. Williams; Geological Association of Canada, Special Paper 4, p. 229-243.
1981: The Meguma Zone of Nova Scotia — a remnant of Western Europe, South America, or Africa?; in Geology of the North Atlantic Borderlands, ed. J.W. Kerr and A.J. Ferguson; Canadian Society of Petroleum Geologists, Memoir 7, p. 119-148.

Scholle, P.A. and Wenkam, C.R. (ed.)
1982: Geological studies of the COST Nos. G-1 and G-2 wells, United States North Atlantic outer continental shelf: United States Geological Survey, Circular 861, 193 p.

Shell Canada Resources Ltd.
1976: North Sydney F-24: Well History Report by Shell et al.; Canada Oil and Gas Lands Administration, Department of Energy, Mines and Resources Canada, 23 p.

Srivastava, S.P., Falconer, R.K.H., and MacLean, B.
1981: Labrador Sea, Davis Strait, Baffin Bay: geology and geophysics — a review; in Geology of the North Atlantic Borderlands, ed. J.W. Kerr and A.J. Ferguson; Canadian Society of Petroleum Geologists, Memoir 7, p. 333-398.

Tucholke, B.E. and Fry, V.A.
1985: Basement structure and sediment distribution in northwest Atlantic Ocean; American Association of Petroleum Geologists Bulletin, v. 69, no. 12, p. 2077-2097.

Umpleby, D.C.
1979: Geology of the Labrador Shelf; Geological Survey of Canada, Paper 79-13, 34 p.

Wade, J.A.
1981: Geology of the Canadian Atlantic margin from Georges Bank to the Grand Banks; in Geology of the North Atlantic Borderlands, ed. J.W. Kerr and A.J. Ferguson; Canadian Society of Petroleum Geologists, Memoir 7, p. 447-460.

Wade, J.A., Grant, A.C., Sanford, B.V., and Barss, M.S.
1977: Basement structure, eastern Canada and adjacent areas; Geological Survey of Canada, Map 1400A, 4 sheets, scale 1:2 000 000

Williams, H.
1978: Tectonic lithofacies map of the Appalachian Orogen; Memorial University of Newfoundland, Map No. 1A.
1979: Appalachian Orogen in Canada; Canadian Journal of Earth Sciences, v. 16, p. 792-807.

Wilson, L.M.
1981: Circum-north Atlantic tectono-stratigraphic reconstruction; in Geology of the North Atlantic Borderlands, ed. J.W. Kerr and A.J. Ferguson; Canadian Society of Petroleum Geologists, Memoir 7, p. 167-184.

Ziegler, P.A.
1982: Geological atlas of western and central Europe; Shell Internationale Petroleum, Maatschappij B.V., Elsevier Science Publishing Co., New York, 130 p.

Authors' addresses

J.S. Bell
Institute of Sedimentary and Petroleum Geology
Geological Survey of Canada
3303-33rd Street N.W.
Calgary, Alberta
T2L 2A7

R.D. Howie
Atlantic Geoscience Centre
Geological Survey of Canada
Bedford Institute of Oceanography
P.O. Box 1006
Dartmouth, Nova Scotia
B2Y 4A2

Chapter 5

THE GEOLOGY OF THE SOUTHEASTERN MARGIN OF CANADA

Chapter 5

THE GEOLOGY OF THE SOUTHEASTERN MARGIN OF CANADA

J.A. Wade and B.C. MacLean

INTRODUCTION

The Georges Bank and Scotian basins, two sedimentary basins offshore Nova Scotia, are described in this chapter. Georges Bank Basin (Part 1) lies beneath the outer continental shelf and slope south-southwest of southern Nova Scotia. Scotian Basin (Part 2) extends northeast from Georges Bank Basin to the western part of the Grand Banks. The geological interpretation of these basins is based primarily on data acquired from the petroleum industry.

Although all but their earliest geological histories are similar and both areas were washed by the same seas, sedimentary rocks within the basins commonly differ greatly reflecting variations in subsidence rates and sediment supply. Both basins have been the focus of petroleum exploration for more than two decades. No hydrocarbons have been discovered in Georges Bank Basin whereas several gas and oil discoveries have been made in the Scotian Basin.

Throughout this chapter, absolute age dates are not related to the Decade of North American Time Scale (Palmer, 1983). This scale does not include the Rhaetian Stage of the Triassic System and it adjusts the absolute ages of earlier Mesozoic stages. For example, the boundary between the Triassic and Jurassic systems is 208 Ma rather than 195 Ma (van Eysinga, 1983). Thus if the Decade of North American Geology Time Scale were used major discrepancies with biostratigraphic dating would result requiring reinterpretation of certain geological events in terms of absolute age. Therefore, the stratigraphic tables and ages given in the text are related to biostratigraphic zonations and not to absolute age.

Metrication in the petroleum industry in Canada was initiated in mid-1978. Exploratory data acquired prior to that, which includes 80 Scotian Basin wells, are in Imperial units. Metrication of depth data in these wells is a possible source of error. Therefore, throughout Part 2 of this chapter, when referring to data acquired in Imperial units the metric units are given first with Imperial equivalents following in parenthesis. For data acquired after metrication, only the metric values are given.

Physiography

The topography of the mainland areas of Nova Scotia and Newfoundland is dominated by a peneplain which probably has been developing since the late Paleozoic. This peneplain is composed of a series of highlands and uplands with intervening lowland areas. It has an average elevation of less than 300 m. Elevations are generally highest in the northwest and the surface slopes gently southeastward to the Atlantic Ocean, reflecting the gradual regional tilting of this part of the continental margin.

Georges Bank, the most southerly of the "Canadiantype" banks along the Atlantic margin of North America, extends from Great South Channel on the west to Northeast Channel on the east. The average water depth on the bank is less than 100 m with a small area, Georges Shoal, being less than 30 m. A series of basins with water depths greater than 200 m lie between Georges Bank and the coasts of Maine and Nova Scotia (Fig. 5.1).

The continental shelf southeast of Nova Scotia, the Scotian Shelf, has an average width of 200 km and an average water depth of about 125 m. South of Newfoundland, the Grand Banks are up to 480 km wide and have an average water depth of about 90 m. Between the Scotian Shelf and the Grand Banks is the Laurentian Channel, a broad, silled, glacially modified channel. The Scotian Shelf and Georges Bank are separated by a second but smaller glacial channel – the Northeast Channel.

The Scotian Shelf is divisible into three physiographic zones. The inner zone, extending from the shore line to the edge of the coastal plain sequences, is characterized by rough topography. The middle zone consists of generally broad basins and, south of Cape Breton Island, a series of deep irregular channels marking ancient drainage courses (Piper et al., Chapter 10). The outer region contains a series of smooth sandy banks delineated by the 100 m isobath.

The boundary between the continental shelf and the slope lies approximately at the 200 m isobath where the gradient of the seafloor changes abruptly to more than 1:40. The average gradient of the slope off Georges Bank is about 1:13 and much of its surface is incised with submarine canyons. The slope is also intersected by the western end of the New England Seamount Chain. West of

Wade, J.A. and MacLean, B.C.
1990: The geology of the southeastern margin of Canada, Chapter 5 in Geology of the Continental Margin of Eastern Canada, M.J. Keen and G.L. Williams (ed.); Geological Survey of Canada, Geology of Canada, no. 2, p. 167-238 (also Geological Society of America, the Geology of North America, v. I-1).

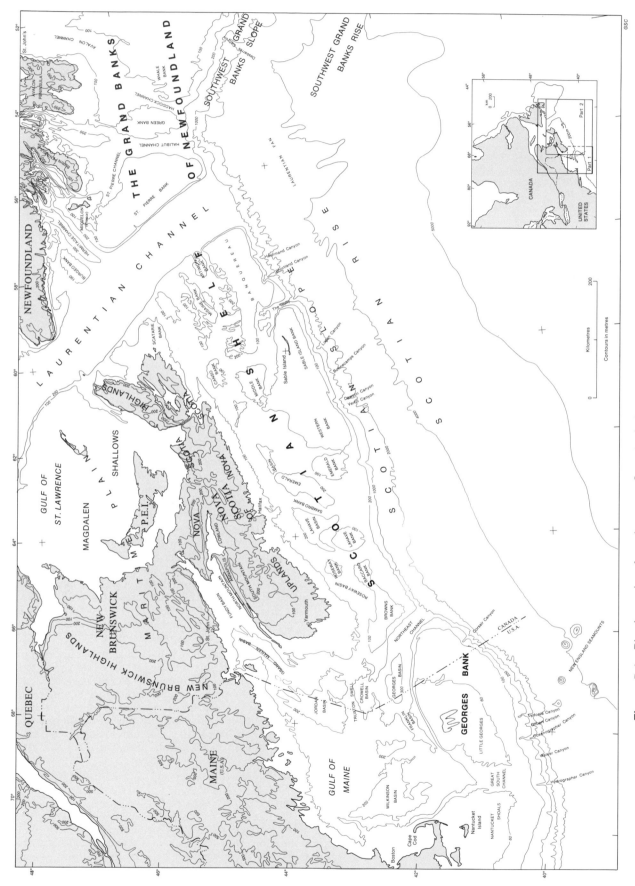

Figure 5.1 Physiography of southeastern Canada. Index map shows areas described by Parts 1 and 2 of this chapter.

Hydrographer Canyon, at the mouth of Great South Channel, the slope broadens and the gradient is only about 1:25.

The continental slope adjacent to the Scotian Shelf and the southwestern Grand Banks lies roughly between the 200 and 4000 m isobaths. Between the 200 and 2000 m isobaths, the average gradient is about 1:17 whereas below

2000 m the gradient decreases to about 1:35. The eastern part of the Scotian Slope and the southwest Grand Banks Slope are cut by numerous transverse canyons which were probably formed during the Pleistocene. The largest of these features is The Gully which incises the shelf to the east of Sable Island.

PART 1: THE STRATIGRAPHY OF GEORGES BANK BASIN AND RELATIONSHIPS TO THE SCOTIAN BASIN

J.A. Wade

Georges Bank Basin underlies the central and western parts of Georges Bank and the adjacent slope. Basic data for the interpretation of the geology in this area are numerous multichannel reflection seismic profiles (Fig. 5.2) that provided information on the structural framework, the timing of tectonic events and the areal extent of lithostratigraphic units. They were used to construct a suite of structure and isopach maps of the major stratigraphic subdivisions. The quality of the data ranges from fair to very good with much of the poorer quality data being those recorded in the early 1970s. Due to their various sources, the data are inconsistent in both vertical and horizontal scale and in the methods used in processing. Furthermore the scale of presentation of much of the data, from microfilm original, is generally small. As a result correlation was often tenuous.

The amount of stratigraphic data available is relatively limited for so large an area. Two Continental Offshore Stratigraphic Tests (COST) and eight industry exploratory wells have been drilled in a small area of the outer part of Georges Bank as well as a shallow core hole on Nantucket Island off Cape Cod, Massachusetts (Fig. 5.2). This well control is supplemented by a small amount of shallow core and dredge sample data from Georges Bank and two industry wells on the western Scotian Shelf.

The COST G-1 and G-2 wells provide ties to the seismic grid (Ditty, 1980; Waetjen, 1980; Taylor and Anderson, 1982) which is also tied to the Scotian Shelf data through the Mohawk B-93 and Bonnet P-23 wells (designated Bonnet F-23 in Figure 1, in pocket) using synthetic seismograms and acoustic logs. These four wells, together with limited data from the industry wells on Georges Bank, yield lithologic and biostratigraphic control on eight seismic horizons, some of which are only semi-regional in nature. Biostratigraphic dating of the horizons in the COST wells is based on extensive studies of Foraminifera and Ostracoda by P.A. Ascoli and is summarized in Table 5.1. Age control in the Mohawk well was provided by Ascoli (1976), Barss et al. (1979) and Doeven (1983).

Many accounts have been published of various aspects of the geology of the Georges Bank area, however, only a relatively few deal specifically with regional syntheses, for example, Schultz and Grover (1974), Schlee et al. (1976), Wade (1977), Austin et al. (1980), Manspeizer (1981), Klitgord et al. (1982), Schlee and Fritsch (1983), Schlee et al. (1985) and Schlee and Klitgord (1988). Reports edited by

Amato and Bebout (1980), Amato and Simonis (1980) and Scholle and Wenkam (1982) on detailed analyses and interpretation of data from the COST G-1 and G-2 wells are most useful.

TECTONIC ELEMENTS

Three of the major tectonic elements which occur in the subsurface of Georges Bank, namely Georges Bank Basin, Yarmouth Arch and Long Island Platform, were first described by Schultz and Grover (1974). These major features (Fig. 5.3) are outlined by an unconformity surface which separates essentially undeformed Jurassic and younger sediments of the continental margin sedimentary wedge from a block-faulted basement complex with grabens containing what is interpreted as lower Mesozoic or older sedimentary fill.

Georges Bank Basin is the name given to a semi-enclosed Jurassic depocentre which occurs beneath the central and southwestern part of Georges Bank and the adjacent continental slope. Its western flank is designated the Long Island Platform. The Yarmouth Arch marks its eastern limit. The axis of the basin strikes N 30°E and plunges to the southwest (Fig. 5.3). The southern extremity of the basin is not seen on the seismic data. During its earliest development a southern boundary may have lain beneath the present-day continental slope or rise, but during most of its history it was an embayment in open connection with the evolving Atlantic Ocean.

Georges Bank Basin had its most rapid period of development during the Early and Middle Jurassic when more than 4 km of siliciclastic and carbonate rocks with some evaporite facies were deposited. These are overlain by up to 4-5 km of younger Jurassic, Cretaceous and Tertiary strata.

Schultz and Grover (1974) showed Georges Bank Basin to be composed of Jurassic through Tertiary sediments, unconformably overlying a block-faulted basement. Schlee et al. (1976) and Wade (1977 and 1978) followed this original concept of the basin. Klitgord et al. (1982), Schlee and Fritsch (1983) and Klitgord and Hutchinson (1985) provided additional detail on the tectonic development of Georges Bank, including the delineation and naming of many of the grabens beneath the breakup or postrift unconformity. These authors also included all these features in an expanded definition of Georges Bank Basin. Since the seismic control indicated in Figure 5.2 is not as

Table 5.1 Foraminiferal, ostracode and calpionellid zonation of the COST G-1 and G-2 wells, Georges Bank Basin. Biostratigraphy by P.A. Ascoli.

COST NO. G-1

AGE		FORAMINIFERAL ASSEMBLAGES	OSTRACOD ASSEMBLAGES
CRETACEOUS	E. CAMPANIAN	1060 (ft.) *Kyphopyxa christneri* 314 (m)	1030 (ft.) 314 (m) *Brachycythere crenulata*
	SANTONIAN	1226 374 *Marginotruncana coronata*	*Brachycythere crenulata*
	CONIACIAN	1360 415 *Marginotruncana renzi*	1510 460 *Schuleridea s.l.*
	TURONIAN	1930 588 *Helvetoglobotr. helvetica*	1870 570 *"Veenia" aff. spoori*
	CENOMANIAN	2127 *Rotalipora cushmani* 648; 2260 *Gavelinella intermedia* 692	2127 ?*"Cythereis"* aff. *eaglefordensis* 648 + *Schuleridea jonesiana*
	APTIAN	2353 717 *Lenticulina nodosa*	2350 716 *Rehacythereis* aff. *semiaperta*
	BARREMIAN	3420 1042 *Epistomina caracolla*	
	HAUTERIVIAN	4646 *Epistomina tenuicostata* 1416	3580 1091 *Hechticythere hechti*
	VALANGINIAN	5050 (lower part) 1539	5080 1548
	BERRIASIAN	*Everticyclammina virguliana*	*Schuleridea* aff. *praethoerenensis*
JURASSIC	TITHONIAN	5330 1625 *Epistomina uhligi*	5380 1640 *Schuleridea sp. 1 Ascoli 1976*
	KIMMERIDGIAN	5810 1771 *Neotrocholina solecensis*	5810 1771 *Schuleridea triebeli*
	OXFORDIAN	9597 *Reinholdella* aff. *crebra* 2925	9140 2786 *Eocytheropteron decoratum* (lower part)
	CALLOVIAN	10 060 3006 *Epistomina coronata*	10 000 3048 *Lophocythere interrupta*
	BATHONIAN		10 390 3167 *Fabanella bathonica*
	(NOT DATABLE)		12 310 3752
	BAJOCIAN		14 690 4478 *Glyptocythere polita*
	(NOT DATABLE)		14 830 4520
			16 071 (T.D.) 4898

COST NO. G-2

AGE		FORAMINIFERAL ASSEMBLAGES	OSTRACOD ASSEMBLAGES	CALPIONELLID ZONES
	(NOT EXAMINED)	1100 (ft.) 335 (m)		
	TURONIAN	2120 646 *Helvetoglobotr. helvetica*		
CRETACEOUS	CENOMANIAN	2270 692 *Rotalipora cushmani* + *Gavelinella intermedia*	2270 6921 *"Cythereis"* aff. *eaglefordensis* + *Schuleridea jonesiana*	
	APTIAN	2330-2420 710-738 *Lenticulina nodosa*	2330-2420 710-738 *Schuleridea derooi*	
	BARREMIAN	2960 *Conorotalites bartensteini* 902; 3290 *Epistomina caracolla* 1003	3680 *Protocythere triplicata* 1122 (lower part)	
	HAUTERIVIAN	3919 1194 *Epistomina tenuicostata*	4010 *Hechticythere hechti* 1222; 4780 *Hutsonia capelensis* 1457	
	VALANGINIAN	5440 1658 *Lenticulina busnardoi*	5427 1654 *Schuleridea praethoerenensis*	
	BERRIASIAN	5590 1704 *Epistomina* aff. *minutereticulata*	5590 1704 *Schuleridea juddi*	5530 1685 *Calpionellopsis*; 5560 1695 (No Calpionellids); 5710 1740 ? *Calpionella alpina* ("acme")
JURASSIC	TITHONIAN	5856 1785 *Epistomina uhligi*	5856 1785 *Schuleridea sp. 1 Ascoli 1976*	5770 1841 *Crassicollaria*; 6040
	KIMMERIDGIAN	6370 *Planularia tricarinella* 1941; 7690 *Alveosepta jaccardi* 2344	6245 *Schuleridea triebeli* 1903; 7498 *Eocytheropteron decoratum* 2285	
	OXFORDIAN	8690-9677 2639-2949 *Alveosepta jaccardi* ("acme"); 10,199 *Epistomina soldanii* 3109	9677 2949 *Terquemula multicostata*	
	CALLOVIAN		11 299 3444 .*Nophrecythere* cf. *cruciata cruciata*	
	(NOT DATABLE)		12 550 3825	
			21 874 (T.D.) 6667	

GSC

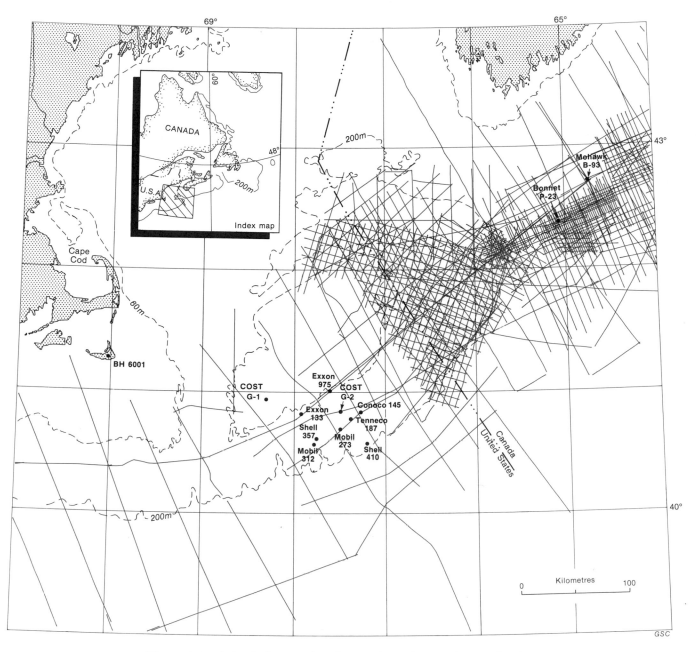

Figure 5.2 Seismic lines and well control, southwest of Nova Scotia.

extensive as that available to the United States Geological Survey, and as the sediments filling the grabens are environmentally and structurally unrelated to those above the unconformity, the following discussion is confined mainly to the post-rift sediments.

The Long Island Platform forms the western and northwestern flank of Georges Bank Basin. It is slightly arcuate in trend and is readily discernible in Figure 5.3 as a zone up to 100 km wide in which the gradient of the basement is about 35 m/km to the southeast. This is in contrast to a gradient of about 100 m/km within the central part of the basin. The flexure separating these basement gradients cuts indiscriminately across the complex of basement grabens, strengthening the argument that the pre- and

post-unconformity systems are not structurally related. The eastern limit of the platform is near longitude 67°W, where it intersects with the Yarmouth Arch.

Klitgord and Hutchinson (1985) and Schlee and Klitgord (1988) used the term "Gulf of Maine platform" for the area north of Georges Bank Basin in which metasedimentary and plutonic Paleozoic rocks and lower Mesozoic sedimentary rocks of the Fundy Basin are at or near the seafloor. As these sequences form the basement complex to Georges Bank Basin, the Gulf of Maine Platform does not have the same relationship to the basin as does the Long Island Platform and it is not included in Figure 5.3.

The Yarmouth Arch is a buried complex of approximately north-northeast-trending basement elements

173

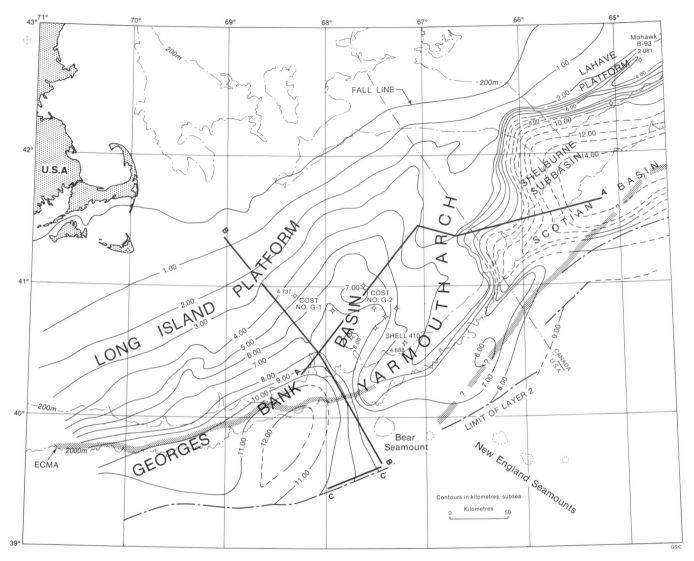

Figure 5.3 Depth to the Breakup Unconformity and major tectonic elements, Georges Bank Basin. The mapped horizon is indicated in Figure 5.5. (Scotian Basin Contours are on the base of Mesozoic-Cenozoic sediments. Shaded area is positive axis of the East Coast Magnetic Anomaly (ECMA). Section A-A' is shown in Figure 5.4, B-B' in Figure 5.6 and C-C' in Figure 5.10

which form the eastern limit of Georges Bank Basin and the western limit of the Scotian Basin. The Yarmouth Arch complex consists of several blocks (Fig. 5.3). The most northerly is the segment originally named "Yarmouth Arch" by Schultz and Grover (1974). Its surface is characterized by a strong and distinct seismic event indicative of high velocity contrast. The arch has a smooth surface. In cross-section it stands well above the base of sediments in Georges Bank Basin (Fig. 5.4). Furthermore, the dip of its axis is less than that in the basin suggesting the arch remained relatively positive as the basin subsided.

Southeast of the southern extremity of this segment of the arch is a second segment. It is a relatively indistinct block having a very weak acoustic surface. Between this and the volcanic cones of the New England Seamount Chain, beneath the continental slope, is a third basement segment. Seismic data indicate that it too was an early,

relatively positive feature limiting communication between the Georges Bank and Scotian basins. Lower(?) and lower Middle Jurassic strata pinch out on the flanks of the third segment whereas the remainder of the Jurassic thins across it. In this chapter the three segments are collectively referred to as Yarmouth Arch.

Large amplitude, linear magnetic anomalies trend south from the vicinity of Yarmouth, Nova Scotia toward the Yarmouth Arch and suggest a possible structural relationship between the two areas. The surface of the Yarmouth Arch plunges from the Fall Line to a depth of 7 km in a distance of 265 km. The Yarmouth Arch was most prominent during the early history of the area when it served as a distinct barrier to the westward extension of the Late Triassic and Early Jurassic salt basin from the Tethys Sea and during the Early and Middle Jurassic when it separated the carbonate prone sediments of

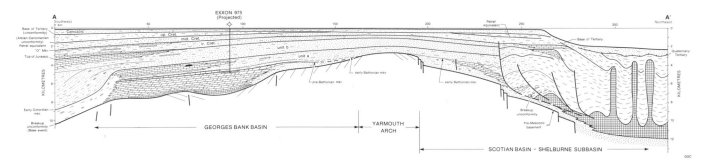

Figure 5.4 Geological cross-section A-A' from Georges Bank Basin to the Scotian Basin showing stratigraphic relationships. Location of section is shown in Figure 5.3. Lithology is described in Figure 5.6.

Georges Bank Basin from the predominantly clastic sediments of the Scotian Basin. It maintained a mild influence on later units as can be seen from stratigraphic thicknesses, facies changes and erosional patterns (Fig. 5.4).

The Scotian Basin extends beneath the continental shelf, slope and rise east from the Yarmouth Arch to the western Grand Banks. It consists of a complex of interconnected depocentres flanked by more stable platforms and is described in detail in Part 2 of this chapter. The Shelburne Subbasin, the most westerly of these depocentres lies directly east of Yarmouth Arch and south of LaHave Platform (Fig. 5.3). Depth to basement in the Shelburne Subbasin may be greater than 14 km (Wade and MacLean, Part 2, this chapter).

EARLY GEOLOGICAL DEVELOPMENT

At the onset of the Mesozoic the Georges Bank area was part of a broad lowland, within the supercontinent Pangaea, on the northwest side of a developing rift system which trended southwestward from the Tethys Sea. Rifting, the first stage of continental breakup, started some time between Late Permian and Late Triassic with the formation of a rift-valley system which progressively widened and lengthened during the early part of the Mesozoic. Adjacent to this central rift, in response to tensional or transcurrent forces, a complex of half grabens developed within the basement terrane. These rift basins are of the "Newark" type (Manspeizer, 1981), and were the site of deposition for large quantities of coarse grained fluvial to fine grained lacustrine sediments. The major rock types in the exposed Newark-type basins are red-brown arkosic sandstones, conglomerates and mudstones and grey to black shales with subordinate evaporites and coal lenses. Similar facies are expected to occur in some of the grabens of the Long Island Platform.

Tholeiitic basalts occur extensively in the upper part of the rift basin sequences (Klein, 1962; Van Houten, 1977; Manspeizer, 1981). Most of the lavas were emplaced as multiple subaerial flows but some were deep water (lacustrine) pillow lavas, fissure eruptions and volcanic breccias (Manspeizer, 1981). A thick succession of 16 or more subaerial flows, the North Mountain Basalt, occurs in Nova Scotia along the southern margin of the Bay of Fundy half graben. The flows occur just above the Triassic-Jurassic boundary as determined from reptile and dinosaur remains (P. Olsen and N. Shubin, pers. comm., 1986). K-Ar age determinations from the North Mountain Basalt range from 191 ± 2 Ma (Hayatsu, 1979) to 202 Ma

(Wark and Clarke, 1980). The Shelburne Dyke, extending for more than 140 km across the southwestern part of Nova Scotia (Papezik and Barr, 1981), is tentatively dated, using the K-Ar isochron method, at 201 Ma (Hodych and Hayatsu, 1980). A well drilled on Nantucket Island, Massachusetts, encountered weathered basalts with a maximum age of 183 ± 8 Ma. Because of alteration, this is considered to be a minimum age for these volcanics (Folger et al., 1978). These data clearly indicate one or more very early Jurassic igneous episodes at about 190-200 Ma.

Seismic profiles clearly show that the basalt in the Nantucket Island borehole unconformably overlies northerly dipping graben-fill sediments and that some deformation and erosion occurred prior to the emplacement of the flows. This angular relationship was observed in many areas of Georges Bank Basin. The underlying sediments, therefore, cannot be younger than earliest Jurassic. Sediments, which outcrop directly above the basalt at locations around the Bay of Fundy, contain locally abundant assemblages of Early Jurassic reptile and dinosaur remains. Sparse palynomorph assemblages from these beds indicate a Late Triassic-Early Jurassic age (J.P. Bujak, pers. comm., 1979). This is consistent with the conclusion of Manspeizer (1981) that the volcanics were emplaced during the Hettangian or Sinemurian.

Collectively, these data indicate that the strata in Georges Bank Basin are separated by an unconformity from mildly deformed Triassic or lowermost Jurassic rocks beneath it. The postrift strata are seen on seismic profiles to onlap the unconformity from a southerly direction. This regional onlap marks the transformation from a series of independent centres of continental deposition to a single depositional basin and, as such, probably indicates the timing of the onset of seafloor spreading and initiation of marine sedimentation in this sector of the North Atlantic.

Rocks of oceanic basement (seismic Layer 2), which occur on the seaward ends of some of the seismic lines, show the hyperbolic character typical of this reflector. In general, Layer 2 lies seaward of the zone of peak intensity of the East Coast Magnetic Anomaly (ECMA) as delineated from residual total field aeromagnetic anomaly maps. This anomaly, therefore, must underlie the outer rim of the continental block (Fig. 5.3). It is generally accepted that the East Coast Magnetic Anomaly (ECMA) is associated with the transition from continental crust to oceanic crust, perhaps representing an edge effect between the two or a linear zone of intrusion of oceanic magma into continental crust (Rabinowitz, 1974).

The East Coast Magnetic Anomaly trends beneath the edge of Georges Bank as far east as the New England Seamount Chain. At this point, which also coincides with the end of the Yarmouth Arch, it may swing north and join the series of positive magnetic anomalies which run south-southwest from the vicinity of Yarmouth, Nova Scotia. Alternatively, there may be a right-lateral offset in the ECMA at its intersection with the New England Seamount Chain with the anomaly trending northeast between there and the Shelburne Subbasin (Fig. 5.3). In Shelburne Subbasin, the ECMA may again be offset, this time by an apparent left-lateral transform fault. East of this area the positive magnetic anomaly is much weaker and bears little similarity to the strong anomaly south of Georges Bank (Wade and MacLean, Part 2 of this chapter). Both the East Coast Magnetic Anomaly and the apparent transform coincide with the deepest part of Shelburne Subbasin, an area with thick salt deposits which considerably predate the breakup unconformity, the onset of seafloor spreading and

formation of oceanic crust. However, calculations of depths to a possible magnetic source for several peaks along the trend of the ECMA yielded depths of only 6 to 8 km (T.W. Eby, pers. comm., 1985) which would place the magnetic source within the Cretaceous sedimentary section in Shelburne Subbasin. These relationships require a reinterpretation of what the anomaly is, the timing of continental breakup, or both.

LITHOSTRATIGRAPHY

As mentioned above, the interpretation of the stratigraphy of the study area is developed through the study of seismic data together with limited well control. As a result, interpretation and discussion are based primarily on gross seismostratigraphic units with an informal correlation made to Scotian Shelf nomenclature. The generalized stratigraphy is illustrated in Figure 5.5.

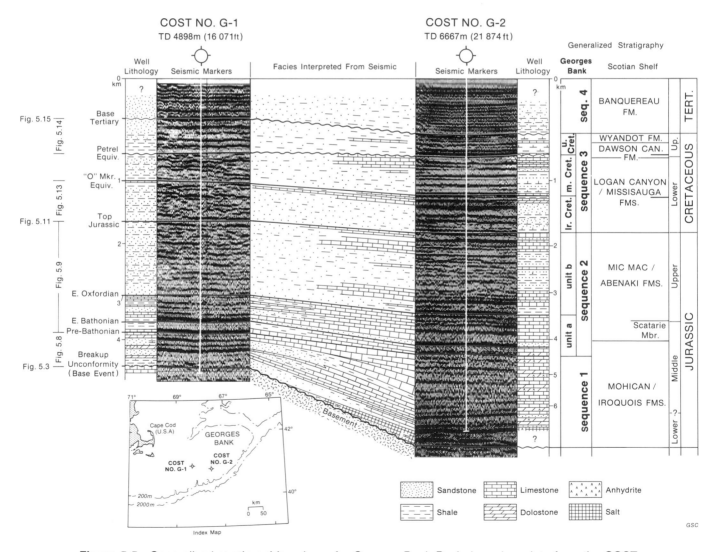

Figure 5.5 Generalized stratigraphic column for Georges Bank Basin based on data from the COST G-1 and G-2 wells and showing the relationship with Scotian Basin stratigraphy. Figure numbers to the left indicate maps of individual sequences.

Breakup unconformity or base-event

A persistent seismic marker occurs at the base of the Georges Bank Basin sedimentary sequence (Schultz and Grover, 1974; Schlee et al., 1976; Wade, 1977). As described above, it represents a major regional unconformity separating two distinctly different stratigraphic sequences. It correlates with the base of Unit 1 of Ballard and Uchupi (1975) and with horizon K of Schlee et al. (1976). This event is now widely accepted to represent the "breakup unconformity" defined by Falvey (1974) as marking the onset of sea-floor spreading. Since it represents the deepest, regionally consistent mappable marker, following the concepts of Grant (1984) and Grant and McAlpine (Chapter 6), it also may be referred to as the base-event. Schlee and Klitgord (1988) referred to this marker as the "postrift unconformity".

Within Georges Bank Basin, the breakup unconformity clearly separates two distinctly different stratigraphic sequences (Fig. 5.4, 5.6). The unconformity marks, essentially, a peneplaned surface developed across a variable landscape consisting of grabens, half grabens, horsts and ridges. The rocks which occur in the grabens appear, from their seismic character, to consist of up to three different types of sedimentary strata. The intervening horsts may consist of igneous or metasedimentary rocks.

Because of the major differences in the rocks beneath and above the unconformity, only the latter, which were deposited as the result of regional subsidence of the margin, are mapped as comprising Georges Bank (sedimentary) Basin. The rocks below the unconformity consist of a variable basement complex within which are isolated, sediment-filled grabens. Some of these contain extensive thicknesses of high velocity Paleozoic metasediments whereas others contain lower velocity synrift sediments of probable earliest Mesozoic age.

The age-range of the hiatus represented by the breakup unconformity is unknown and can be inferred only from the limited direct data. Three wells in the area have penetrated the breakup unconformity. Mohawk B-93, on the western Scotian Shelf, encountered Bathonian clastics, including a 10 m thick basal arkose, overlying a pink granodiorite at a subsea depth of 2081 m. The latter is compositionally similar to the granites of southwestern Nova Scotia which have a mean age of 367 Ma (Reynolds et al., 1981). The COST G-1 well, drilled on the western flank of Georges Bank Basin, encountered the unconformity at about 4737 m subsea after penetrating nearly 200 m of conglomeratic basal clastics (Fig. 5.5). The oldest datable

sediments, which are about 250 m above the unconformity, are Bajocian (Table 5.1) (P. Ascoli, pers. comm., 1983). Slate, schist, metaquartzite and phyllite occur beneath the base-event (Lachance, 1980; Arthur, 1982a). The beds beneath the unconformity yielded K-Ar dates in the range of 550-450 Ma. The character of material suggests that the 550 Ma age (Cambrian) most probably represents the correct "metamorphic" age (Steinkraus, 1980). On seismic profiles, these beds are characterized by a series of gently dipping, low frequency reflections of a type that prevail beneath much of the southern part of Georges Bank. The Shell Block 410 well, drilled to a total depth of 4720 m subsea on the outer part of Georges Bank (Fig. 5.2) appears from logs and seismic data to have penetrated the base-event at a depth of about 4688 m subsea. No age data are available from this well and no sample descriptions were released for the section below 4600 m. Log data, however, indicate approximately 70 m of basal clastics overlying the unconformity. The clastics are in sharp contact with thick overlying carbonate beds.

The data from these wells indicate that the basement rocks are probably early Paleozoic in age. Seismic profiles show they are locally inset with sedimentary strata which, since they are related to the rifting phase of breakup and are older than the dated volcanics (190-200 Ma), probably represent Triassic to Lower Jurassic graben fill. The maximum established age of the sediments above the unconformity is Bajocian but, as is shown in Figure 5.5, in the COST G-2 well the equivalent of the dated beds is more than 500 m above the unconformity. However, since the onset of sedimentation in the Scotian Basin is roughly coincident with the cessation of volcanism in the Early Jurassic, a hiatus of only a few million years is suspected.

Pre-breakup unconformity sequences

Rocks occurring beneath the breakup unconformity are interpreted to be of three different types and ages. Those which lack coherent seismic reflections are probably igneous rocks or a highly deformed crystalline basement complex. They usually occur as horsts or beneath grabens. Rocks which exhibit weak to prominent, low frequency, gently to steeply dipping reflections, of the type occurring at the base of the G-1 well (which are dated as Cambrian) are interpreted to be similar lower Paleozoic metasediments. They may occur within grabens or adjacent to grabens with younger sediment fill. Well bedded, highly reflective, gently to moderately dipping beds occupy some of the grabens. They are most prominent in the grabens of

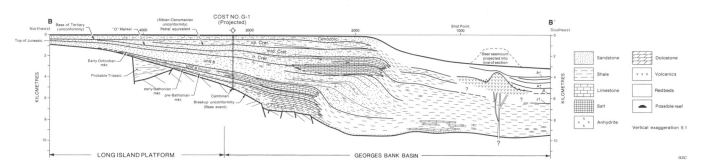

Figure 5.6 Geological cross section B-B', Georges Bank Basin, based on USGS line 20. Location of section is shown in Figure 5.3.

the Long Island Platform (Figs. 5.6, 5.7) and underlie the basalt in the Nantucket Island borehole. From their stratigraphic position and similarity to the Eurydice Formation on Scotian Shelf and the Wolfville and Blomidon formations in and adjacent to the Bay of Fundy (Wade and MacLean, Part 2, of this chapter), they are interpreted to be mainly Triassic in age. The distribution and sediment fill in the grabens of the Long Island Platform is discussed by Klitgord et al. (1982) and Klitgord and Hutchinson (1985). Across these various units beneath the base-event, the postrift Jurassic and younger strata above the unconformity form relatively gently dipping and undisturbed basin fill (Fig. 5.6).

East of the Yarmouth Arch, in the Scotian Basin, the Eurydice Formation grades laterally and vertically into the salt of the Argo Formation which consistently has a minimum age of Sinemurian (Fig. 7 of Wade, 1981). This thick salt sequence is not known west of Scotian Basin. In

Georges Bank Basin the coeval redbed deposition may have occurred in local grabens but, in general, the area stood above the level of the invading Tethys Sea and so did not receive the thick evaporitic facies. The distribution and generalized facies of these pre-breakup rocks are shown in Figure 5.7.

Diapiric and pillowed salt occurs in a structural complex at 42°N and 67°W beneath northern Georges Bank (Fig. 5.7) which roughly coincides with the northeastern end of the Yarmouth sag of Schlee and Klitgord (1982, their Fig. 4). The seismic character of the sediments in this "basin" differs somewhat from that of the interpreted Triassic to Lower Jurassic strata described above. Considering the location of the graben, the thickness of the sediments it contains and their structural isolation from the Scotian Basin, they are interpreted to be upper Paleozoic clastics and evaporites. Carboniferous salt is abundant in the Magdalen Basin to the northeast (Howie and Barss,

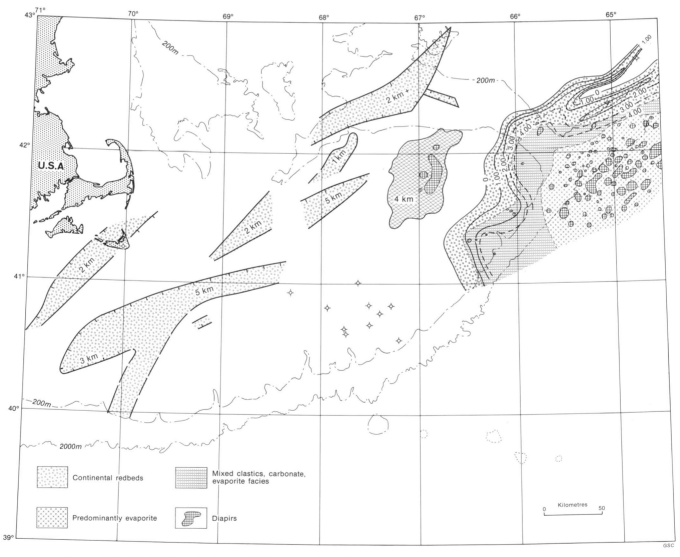

Figure 5.7 Distribution, facies and thickness of pre-breakup sediments. Some of the grabens south of Cape Cod are modified from Klitgord and Hutchinson (1985). The 4 km-thick structural basin (at approx. 42°N, 67°W) contains sediments and evaporites of possible late Paleozoic age. Sediments in the northeast corner are contoured in kilometres.

1975). Alternatively, it is possible that this graben may initially have been connected to the Scotian Basin and later isolated due to development of the Yarmouth Arch. In the latter case the salt would be Late Triassic or Early Jurassic in age and equivalent to the Argo Formation.

Post-breakup unconformity sequences

To facilitate discussion of the stratigraphy of Georges Bank Basin the postrift sedimentary wedge has been subdivided into four informal sequences:

1) the upper Lower and lower Middle Jurassic; 2) the Middle and Upper Jurassic; 3) the Cretaceous; and 4) the Cenozoic. Sequences 2 and 3 are further subdivided into five units (Fig. 5.5).

Sequence 1: upper Lower Jurassic to lower Middle Jurassic

The maximum age of the breakup unconformity has been inferred from its position relative to the Lower Jurassic volcanic event. It is mapped regionally using the base-event reflection. The sediments immediately overlying this reflector form the initial deposits in Georges Bank Basin. Sequence 1, the first major sedimentary sequence, extends from the unconformity to a distinctive seismic reflection which, through ties to G-1 and G-2 and other wells, is interpreted to be at or near the base of the Bathonian (Table 5.1, Fig. 5.5). This reflection onlaps the base-event reflection along an irregular trend which serves to outline the major structural elements in Georges Bank Basin (Fig. 5.8).

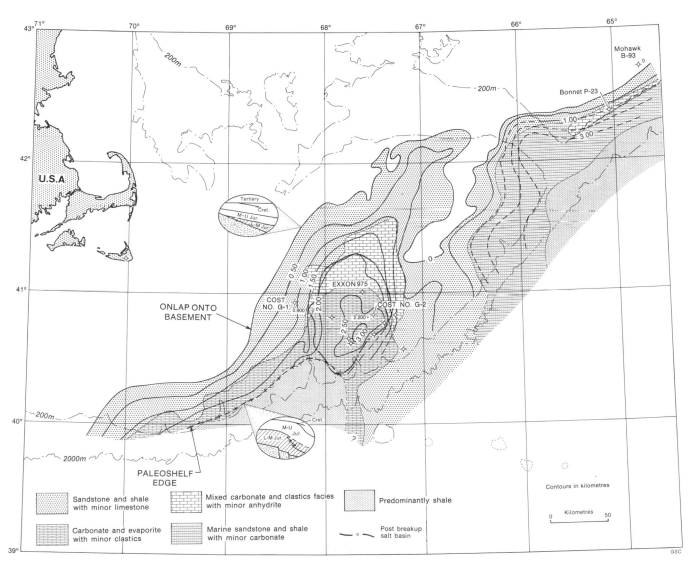

Figure 5.8   Isopach map and generalized facies of sequence 1 (Breakup Unconformity to pre-Bathonian marker). The mapped interval is hachured in the inset "windows" (see Fig. 5.5). Area outlined with red line and circles is post-breakup salt basin (in centre of figure).

The COST G-1 well, drilled on the flank of the early basin, encountered 900 m of sequence 1 unconformably overlying the basement complex. The lower part of the sequence consists of nonmarine beds containing coarse grained to conglomeratic sandstones which are overlain by red-brown and dark grey shales. The balance of sequence 1 is a mixed dolostone-anhydrite facies indicative of sedimentation in a stable, shallow marine to tidal flat environment.

The COST G-2 well, drilled near the axis of Georges Bank Basin, encountered approximately 2200 m of this Lower to Middle Jurassic sequence but did not reach the base-event. The lowermost 13 m is halite and anhydrite which may equate to the nonmarine beds in the G-1 well (Fig. 5.5). The seismic character of the evaporite is mappable over an extensive area of the early basin axis where it fills topographic lows (Fig. 5.4, 5.8). The top of the salt appears conformable with the overlying carbonate facies. The average thickness of the evaporite facies as interpreted from seismic profiles is about 300 m but, locally, it may be twice this thickness. The occurrence of salt above the breakup unconformity in Georges Bank Basin indicates that this evaporite is not equivalent to the Argo Formation salt of the Scotian Basin. Instead it probably represents a local evaporitic facies, possibly part of a sabkha, associated with the initial marine influxes into Georges Bank Basin sometime during the Sinemurian-Pliensbachian.

An alternate interpretation has been presented by Schlee and Klitgord (1988) who placed their postrift unconformity above the salt. It is possible that the base-event is not everywhere the breakup unconformity and that this unconformity may occur at the top of the salt (where salt exists). Such an interpretation still demonstrates that there was general emergence of the Georges Bank area during deposition of the thick Eurydice and Argo formations to the east but, if the salt of Georges Bank Basin is equivalent to the uppermost part of the Argo Formation, the breakup unconformity would have to be above rather than beneath the Georges Bank Basin salt.

The pre-Bathonian section above the anhydrite and halite in the G-2 well consists of a variable mix of interbedded dolostone and anhydrite which grades upward into interbedded limestone and dolostone or anhydritic dolostone (Fig. 5.5). Both the carbonate and evaporite facies are interpreted to grade landward into thick clastic facies (Fig. 5.4, 5.6, 5.8).

The other available wells encountered variations of the facies seen in the two COST wells. They confirm the widespread nature of the dolostone-anhydrite environment in Georges Bank Basin and the increasing content of clastics in a landward direction (Fig. 5.8).

In the two COST wells where age control exists, the lower part of sequence 1 is barren of foraminifers and ostracodes and cannot be dated. The age of the oldest rocks above the sequence is probably Bathonian. Within the sequence there is a thin zone which has been dated as Bajocian (Table 5.1) (P. Ascoli, pers. comm., 1983). This indicates a pre-Bathonian age for the top of sequence 1. The maximum age of its base, controlled by the age of the breakup unconformity and the associated volcanics, is about late Sinemurian to Pliensbachian.

Manspeizer and Cousminer (1988), however, considered this part of the Georges Bank Basin stratigraphy to be Carnian-Norian in age. Their interpretation is based on palynomorphs recovered from a thin layer of dark organic shale between 4440.0 and 4441.5 m (14 567.0 and 14 571.9 ft) in a core from the COST G-2 well. Similar forms in a core from 4034.0 to 4050.6 m (13 235.0 to 13 289.5 ft) are considered reworked. The only way to rationalize the Manspeizer and Cousminer age interpretation, considering the lithological differences between Georges Bank Basin and Scotian Basin, is to invoke the Yarmouth Arch as a narrow but complete barrier between the Scotian and Georges Bank basins, and their counterparts on the African Margin, with evaporitic (Tethyan) deposition to the northeast and marine deposition to the southwest from a source which would have to be of "Pacific" origin.

Ages for the lower strata in Georges Bank Basin also have been interpreted on the basis of seismostratigraphy and sedimentation rates (Poag, 1982, 1985). Although the results lead to an aesthetic picture, it must be remembered that the ages assigned to the older units are mainly unsupported (Table 5.1) (P. Ascoli, pers. comm., 1983). For comparison, the intervals dated Rhaetian to Bajocian by Poag were interpreted by Ascoli to be Pliensbachian to Bajocian.

The facies variations within and between the wells indicate that the initial deposition in Georges Bank Basin was in a small, semi-restricted, shallow, quiet water basin with a broad flanking alluvial plain. The seismic character is used to map the distribution of the facies which are shown as "regional averages" in Figure 5.8. Above the base-event there are a series of high amplitude reflections that onlap local highs within the basin as well as the Long Island Platform to the west and north. These are interpreted as the basal clastic and evaporite beds discussed above. They grade upward into somewhat discontinuous reflections of lower amplitude which are indicative of the limestone-dolostone-anhydrite facies. In a trend along the western flank of the basin and across its mouth, there is a carbonate front (Fig. 5.4, 5.6, 5.8) which probably resulted in periodic restriction during the early part of basin development and the deposition of the evaporitic facies. The basin expanded through time, and became less restricted, resulting in a widespread normal marine carbonate facies toward the top of the unit.

In the central part of the basin, just beneath the top of the carbonate prone interval near its interface with the interpreted mixed facies of carbonate and clastic components, there is a low velocity amplitude anomaly, approximately 10 km in diameter, which has been modelled as porous carbonate or salt (Anderson and Taylor, 1981). The feature was drilled by Exxon in their Corsair Canyon Block 975 well (Fig. 5.4, 5.8). Data from this well indicate anhydrite overlain by approximately 76 m of grey micritic limestone with leached vugs filled with salt, a 12 m thick salt bed and 14 m of red brown shale. No similar features are seen elsewhere in the seismic data. The restricting mechanism for this small halite deposit is not apparent although a nearby seismic line suggests it overlies a basement graben which may have had a brief period of reactivation during the early part of the Middle Jurassic.

The facies and thickness of pre-Bathonian sediments seaward of the carbonate front are unknown. A deep seismic marker, correlated with the J_3 reflector (top Lower Jurassic) of Klitgord et al. (1982), occurs on several profiles showing that distal equivalents of sequence 1 are present in that area.

To the northeast, in Scotian Basin, the Eurydice and Argo formations are overlain by the clastic Mohican Formation and, locally, by a dolostone facies, the Iroquois Formation (McIver, 1972; Given, 1977). The age of the Iroquois Formation is late Sinemurian to early Pliensbachian (G.L. Williams, pers. comm., 1986) and the Mohican Formation is late Sinemurian to early Bajocian (E.H. Davies, pers. comm., 1986). Based on extensive correlations and regional considerations, therefore, the pre-Bathonian sequence 1 on Georges Bank is interpreted to include, at least, the Pliensbachian to Bajocian Stages and possibly also the uppermost Sinemurian. It is correlated with parts of the Iroquois and Mohican formations of the Scotian Shelf.

Based on the preceding discussion, it is concluded that while deposition in the deeper grabens of Scotian Basin progressed from basal clastics through salt of the Eurydice and Argo formations, the area of Georges Bank Basin and the Long Island and LaHave platforms were emergent and subject to erosion with only limited areas receiving terrestrial deposition. Breakup occurred about 190-200 Ma. This was marked by local volcanism, subsidence, and the onset of marine deposition in a broad shallow shelf environment in Georges Bank Basin. In the Scotian Basin the shelf environment was narrower and thick siliciclastic basinal facies prevailed in the more rapidly subsiding subbasins.

Sequence 2: Middle and Upper Jurassic

The second major sequence in Georges Bank Basin lies between the pre- Bathonian reflector discussed above and a widespread reflector approximately at the top of the Jurassic (Fig. 5.5). This upper reflector, which is the most extensive seismic horizon in the study area, extends from an erosional or depositional edge along the inner platforms, through a paleoshelf break at a carbonate front, to distal slope or deep basin environments. Over much of the shelf, the top Jurassic reflection emanates from a carbonate facies which grades gradually landward into sandstone and basinward into shale.

The interval between the pre-Bathonian and top Jurassic seismic events consists of lower and upper "semi-regional" seismostratigraphic units designated as units a and b (Fig. 5.5). The two are discernible in paleoshelf and deep basin facies but are seismically indistinguishable in the proximal alluvial facies.

From well control and seismic character the lithology of unit a is predominately carbonate with some interbedded clastics. Minor anhydrite occurs in its lowermost part beneath a distinctive, 100 m thick, clastic bed. The clastic bed is characterized by red-brown sandstone and shale and marks a minor regressive period. It is also the source of a prominent seismic reflector. These clastics are in the lower part of the Bathonian interval and may be correlative with the uppermost part of the Mohican Formation on the LaHave Platform (Table 5.1, Fig. 5.5). Regionally, the carbonate content appears to increase seaward to a carbonate front across the outer part of Georges Bank Basin (Fig. 5.4, 5.6, 5.9). This carbonate correlates with the lower part of the Abenaki Formation on the LaHave Platform. From ties to the COST wells, the age of unit a is Bathonian to Early Oxfordian (Fig. 5.5). The trace of the Lower Oxfordian carbonate front is shown in Figure 5.9.

Seismically, unit a, which is 1007 m thick in COST G-2 and 830 m thick in COST G-1, is composed of regularly bedded, relatively high amplitude reflections that overstep sequence 1 and transgress the Long Island Platform and the Yarmouth Arch. Seaward, toward the "mouth" of Georges Bank Basin, this unit slightly oversteps the pre-Bathonian shelf break and forms its own distinct shelf edge and slope with a relief of about 1.5 to 2.0 km (Fig. 5.4, 5.6, 5.9).

Small bioherms or patch reefs may be associated with the upper reflections of unit a. Two such features have been interpreted within the zone of predominantly carbonate facies. They are located in Figure 5.9, and projected onto the section in Figure 5.4 as a small black mound to the southwest (left) of the Exxon 975 well.

In the Exxon Block 133 well, located between the G-1 and G-2 wells (Fig. 5.9), a series of diabase flows or sills are interbedded with limestone beds between 4044.7-4117.8 m in the upper part of unit a. A 1 m core was cut in diabase at 4111 m. No age was reported. The seismic event that marks the top of unit a is locally of variable intensity, possibly due to associated volcanic beds. Basalt was not found in the G-1 well but thin beds of tuffaceous sediment were reported in the coeval interval in the G-2 well (Simonis, 1980). The projected position of the basalt is also shown in Figure 5.4 southwest (left) of the well.

Two buried volcanic cones or seamounts occur seaward of the Early Oxfordian shelf break, on the paleoslope (Fig. 5.10). They lie southwest of Bear Seamount, which is the northwesternmost seamount in the New England Seamount Chain (Fig. 5.9, 5.11). The bases of the buried seamounts cannot be resolved clearly on the existing seismic line but they are approximately at the stratigraphic level of the Early Oxfordian marker of the shelf which, in turn, ties into the J_2 Marker of Shor and Uchupi (1984) of the slope. The overlying Upper Jurassic J_1 and Lower Cretaceous seismic markers onlap the cones whereas on the seismic line of Figure 5.10, the middle and upper Cretaceous units are draped over them. These features, together with the basalt in the Exxon 133 well and the tuffs in G-2, suggest that an early Late Jurassic episode of volcanism affected both the shelf and slope parts of Georges Bank Basin. The volcanism was probably associated with movement along the Azores Fracture Zone.

Schlee et al. (1985) interpreted the buried seamounts as basement highs and map a third such feature west of Bear Seamount. The seismic section in Figure 5.10 clearly indicates discontinuous, horizontal, primary reflections beneath the "highs". These reflections are in turn underlain by an unconformity surface, possibly J_3, beneath which are prominently dipping beds. The continuity of seismic reflections beneath these features precludes their interpretation as basement highs and, in turn, supports the interpretation of volcanic seamount cones extruded on the seafloor during the early Late Jurassic.

The age of unit b, the upper unit in sequence 2, is from Early Oxfordian to latest Jurassic or earliest Cretaceous. Unit b is 1417 m and 1703 m thick in the G-1 and G-2 wells, respectively, and has a more varied facies than the underlying unit a. Clastics predominate in the central and inner part of the shelf, and carbonates increase in the outer paleoshelf region (Fig. 5.11). The contact with the underlying carbonate is gradational seaward of the G-2 well with the carbonate beds persisting upward. Landward, however, although apparently conformable, the contact between the underlying carbonates and overlying clastics is sharp. Unit b is correlated with the upper part of the Mic Mac Formation in the Scotian Basin (Fig. 5.5).

There has been some erosion on the top of sequence 2 in a band up to 50 km wide running from south of Nantucket Island eastward to the western extremity of the Scotian Shelf. East of this, deposition appears to have been continuous with a gradual onlap of basement (Fig. 5.9). No hiatus was observed at this horizon in the Georges Bank wells indicating, therefore, differential uplift or tilting of the Long Island Platform.

In the G-2 well, unit b consists of approximately 535 m of mixed clastic and carbonate facies overlying the Lower Oxfordian carbonates of unit a. These are succeeded by

800 m of white, light grey and red sandstones, grey, maroon and red shales and minor limestone and coal. The uppermost part of the unit consists predominately of micritic to chalky limestone (Fig. 5.5). Environmental interpretation of the clastic facies, from microfossils, indicates a regression from a marginal marine environment at this location (P. Ascoli, pers. comm., 1983). In G-1 and Exxon 133 wells unit b consists almost entirely of clastics, whereas in the Shell Block 410 well there are interbedded sandstones, shales and limestones.

Seismically, over much of the area, unit b is relatively transparent with only scattered discontinuous high amplitude reflections. At the "mouth" of Georges Bank Basin a series of strong progradational reflections are built out over the carbonate front delineated by the Early Oxfordian seismic marker, and form a distinctive deltaic seismic sig-

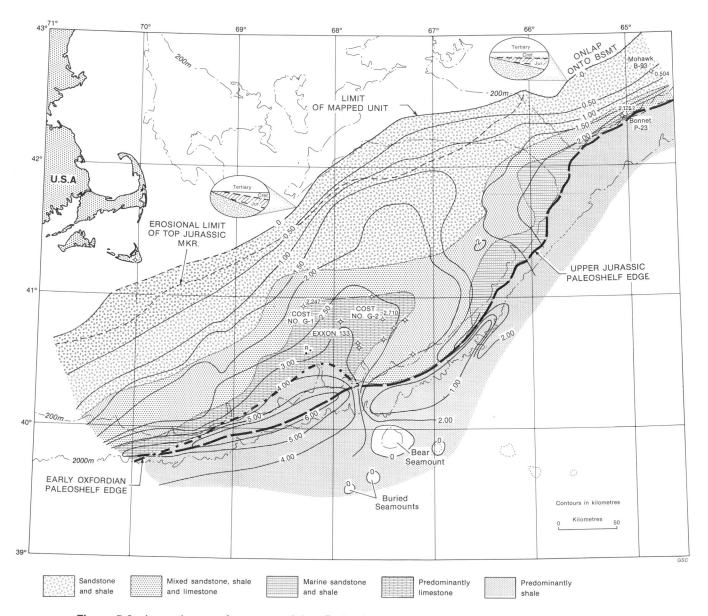

Figure 5.9 Isopach map of sequence 2 (pre-Bathonian to top Jurassic) with generalized facies of unit a (Bathonian to Early Oxfordian). R = possible reef. Mapped interval is hachured in the inset "windows" (see Fig. 5.5).

nature. The progradational beds grade outward and upwards into parallel, lower frequency and more continuous reflections as the facies change upwards to limestone. The limestone forms a prominent uppermost Jurassic carbonate shelf and front beneath the present day upper slope (Fig. 5.4, 5.6). The clastic outpourings, which may attain a thickness of 4 km, are mirrored to the east of the Yarmouth Arch in the Shelburne Subbasin and indicate a significant change in the type and the rate of local sediment supply.

This Oxfordian deltaic facies has been discussed in detail by Mattick (1982). He described a lower oblique — progradational seismic facies overlain by a sigmoid — progradational seismic facies which he suggested are characteristic of fluvial deltas and associated coastal-plain sediments. However, in correlating to the COST G-2 well he noted that the lower zone was carbonate and the upper was predominantly clastic and concluded that the oblique facies "represents limestone beds deposited in a high-energy environment, perhaps an oolitic limestone", and the sigmoid facies was the result of a later influx of clastics. His interpretation is followed by Klitgord et al. (1982) and Schlee and Fritsch (1983). These authors apparently do not take into account the magnitude of the carbonate front, the degree of subsequent infilling with clastics nor the lateral facies changes which occur within Upper Jurassic strata in this area.

The Bonnet P-23 well, on the LaHave Platform, encountered approximately 2175 m of the equivalent Middle and Upper Jurassic sequence 2 in predominantly carbonate facies. At Mohawk B-93, the coeval section consists of 504 m of predominately clastic facies overlying granitic basement rocks (Fig. 5.9, 5.11).

Regional contours on the top Jurassic seismic horizon indicate a smooth surface dipping southward to an abrupt shelf break just seaward of the present day feature (Fig. 5.11). The trace of the shelf break then, as now, was sigmoidal from Georges Bank to Browns Bank. However, in detail, considerable structural complexity affects this surface east of the Yarmouth Arch. This is caused by an abundance of down-to-the-basin faulting in the thick sandstone-shale sequences in the Shelburne Subbasin (Fig. 5.4, 5.11). The trace of the faults is parallel or subparallel to the eastern flank of the arch and the southern

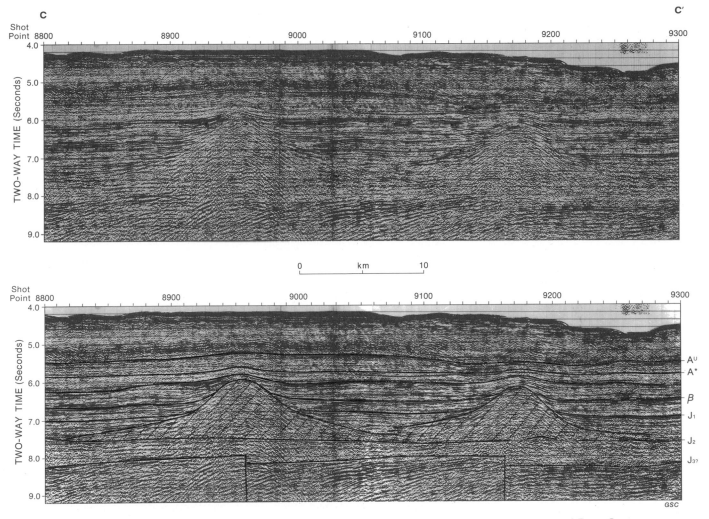

Figure 5.10 Section C-C', portion of USGS Line 13 across two buried seamounts west of Bear Seamount. Location shown in Figure 5.3. Lower panel shows interpretation with horizons indicated on right side. Seismic horizons are identified in the text.

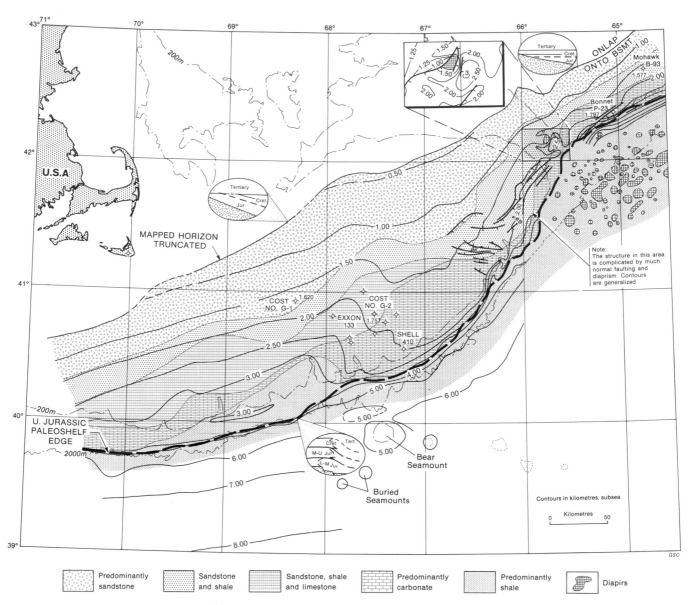

Figure 5.11 Contours on the top of the Jurassic with generalized unit b (Upper Jurassic) facies of sequence 2. The mapped horizon is indicated in the inset "windows" (see Fig. 5.5).

Legend:
- Predominantly sandstone
- Sandstone and shale
- Sandstone, shale and limestone
- Predominantly carbonate
- Predominantly shale
- Diapirs

edge of the LaHave Platform. The faulting is attributed to mobile salt of the Argo Formation which occurs at depth in this subbasin, the paucity of carbonates in the thick regressive clastic facies, and possibly overpressured formations at depth.

Seaward of the Upper Jurassic shelf edge, where they are not complicated by seamounts, the Middle and Upper Jurassic strata are regularly bedded deep-water facies that distally onlap Layer 2 basement. They are equivalent to the lower part of the Verrill Canyon Formation in the Scotian Basin.

The combination of onlap of the basement and some erosion on the top of the Middle and Upper Jurassic rocks result in irregularities in the thickness of sequence 2 on the Long Island Platform. The sequence thickens rapidly from about 1 km over the southern end of the Yarmouth Arch to more than 6 km along the basin axis beneath the upper part of the present day slope, a distance of only

30 km (Fig. 5.9). This rapid thickening stems from the progradation of the underlying Oxfordian carbonate front and the development, seaward, of the Upper Jurassic shelf edge.

In summary, upper Middle and Upper Jurassic strata beneath Georges Bank consist of a lower platformal carbonate (unit a) which is overlain by a thick, regressive clastic succession (unit b) that developed a small, but thick, deltaic complex at the mouth of Georges Bank Basin. During the latest Jurassic, the outer shelf facies was predominantly limestone that developed a prominent carbonate front (Fig. 5.4, 5.6, 5.9, 5.11). The facies and depositional environments are similar to those occurring in the Sable Island area of the Scotian Basin during this time. Correlation is with the upper part of the Mohican Formation and the Abenaki and Mic Mac formations of the Scotian Shelf.

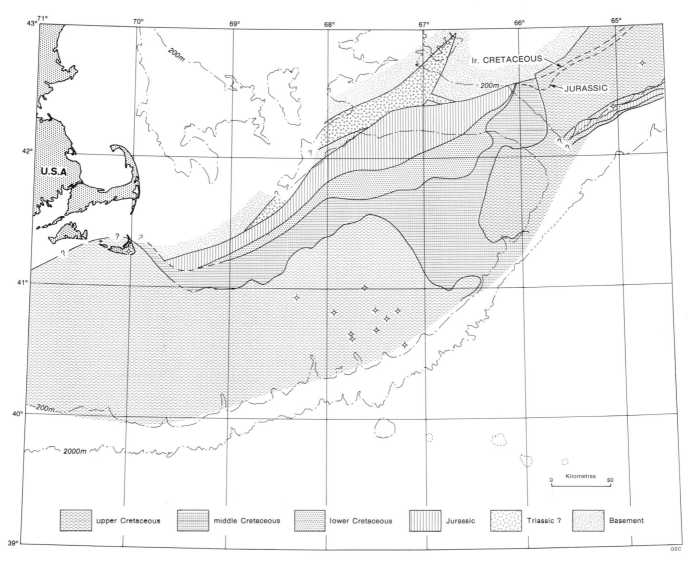

Figure 5.12 Geological map at the base of the Tertiary.

Sequence 3: Cretaceous

The entire Cretaceous System in Georges Bank Basin is included in sequence 3. It is divided, by two seismic markers, into three units which, informally, are referred to as, the lower, middle and upper Cretaceous units (Fig. 5.5). The lower Cretaceous unit extends from the top Jurassic seismic event to a reflector which is equated to the "O" Marker, a series of thin transgressive limestone beds within the Missisauga Formation of the Scotian Shelf (Wade and MacLean in Part 2 of this chapter). The "O" Marker equivalent occurs at about the top of the Hauterivian in the COST G-1 well and the base of the Barremian in COST G-2 (Table 5.1, Fig. 5.5). The middle Cretaceous unit extends to a seismic reflection from an unconformity between the Aptian and the Cenomanian (Table 5.1). In the outer parts of the basin a thin limestone bed lies about 30 m above the unconformity which is approximately equivalent to the Petrel Member of the Dawson Canyon Formation of the Scotian Shelf (Fig. 5.5). The reflection marking the top of the middle Cretaceous unit is consid-

ered to be the Petrel equivalent marker. The upper Cretaceous unit ranges from the Petrel equivalent marker to a widespread Cretaceous-Tertiary unconformity (Fig. 5.5).

Beneath most of Georges Bank, the Cretaceous units have undergone postdepositional tilting and erosion so that the oldest is the most widespread and the youngest the most limited in extent (Fig. 5.12). However, south of Cape Cod, and on the western Scotian Shelf, the three units appear successively transgressive, with each unit overstepping the underlying one and onlapping the basement. The Cretaceous facies on the Long Island Platform indicate that extensive nonmarine deposits occur considerably to the south of shallow marine conditions on the LaHave Platform so that, in effect, an embayment existed to the east of the Yarmouth Arch. This suggests a Cretaceous flexure, in the vicinity of Northeast Channel and the eastern flank of the Yarmouth Arch, which resulted in the deposition of continental facies on the Long Island Platform concurrent with subsidence and marine deposition in the Shelburne Subbasin.

Lower Cretaceous

In dip section the lower Cretaceous unit is uniformly wedge-shaped from a proximal erosional edge offlapping the Jurassic to a maximum thickness in excess of 1 km along the basin axis near the paleoshelf edge (Fig. 5.6). It is 587 m and 527 m thick in the G-1 and G-2 wells, respectively. The unit is very thin or absent in a narrow zone along the upper paleoslope and thickens to more than 1 km on the middle to lower slope (Fig. 5.13). Distally, the upper reflector (approximately Hauterivian-Barremian) is correlated with the oceanic horizon β whereas the lower reflector (approximately at the top of the Jurassic) correlates with the J_1 horizon of Klitgord et al. (1982).

Seismically this lower Cretaceous unit consists of low to moderate amplitude reflections which grade from discontinuous to semicontinuous in a seaward direction. This is consistent with a sandstone and shale facies over much of Georges Bank that grades laterally to limestone and shale toward the paleoshelf edge. The lithologies of the

deep-water facies are unknown but they are interpreted from the seismic data to include turbidites that grade upwards into deep-water limestone or marl beds that are coeval with the equivalent "O" Marker limestone beds on the shelf.

Along the southwestern edge of Georges Bank the shelf break of this lower Cretaceous unit usually occurs slightly landward of that of the Upper Jurassic with a distinct step seaward from the younger to the older shelf break. Elsewhere the two edges are nearly coincident (Fig. 5.6). However, in some areas, there appears to have been outbuilding at the shelf edge during lower Cretaceous deposition as the unit is locally overthickened at its shelf break.

Although predominantly a clastic facies which was deposited in nonmarine to inner neritic environments, the lithologies at the COST wells indicate a somewhat transgressive upward facies with the occurrence of minor limestone beds at the upper seismic marker. This lower

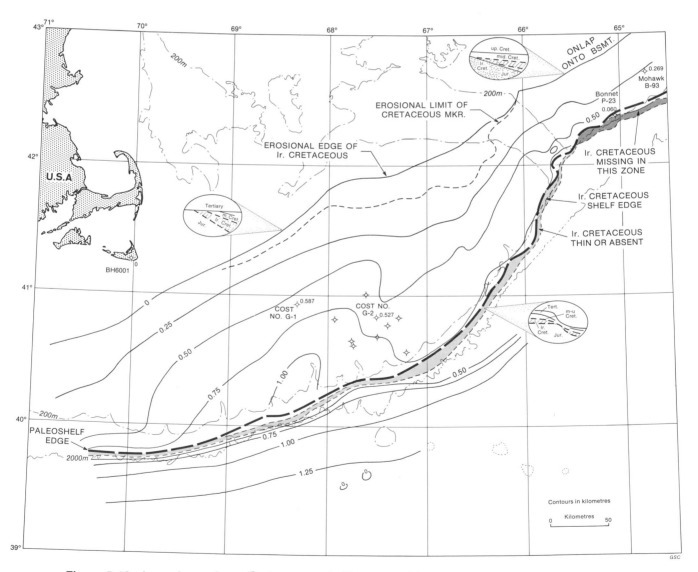

Figure 5.13 Isopach map-lower Cretaceous unit. The mapped interval is hachured in the inset "windows" (see Fig. 5.5).

Cretaceous unit is equivalent to that part of the Scotian Shelf Missisauga Formation below the "O" Marker which shows a similar trend in lithologies.

Contours on the top of the lower Cretaceous unit dip uniformly to the south across the Long Island Platform. A remnant small low, marking the axis of Georges Bank Basin, is flanked to the east by a broad nose reflecting the Yarmouth Arch. To the east of the arch, the contours again display an arcuate trend from eastern Georges Bank, across Northeast Channel and onto the western Scotian Shelf. The dip is to the southeast and south. Thus, during that part of the Early Cretaceous the depositional environment appears to have been quite uniform across Georges Bank and the Scotian Shelf.

Middle Cretaceous

The middle Cretaceous unit, occurring as it does between seismic markers approximately equivalent to the "O" Marker and Petrel Member, includes the stratigraphic equivalents of the upper part of the Missisauga Formation and a condensed Logan Canyon Formation (Fig. 5.5). The Aptian-Cenomanian unconformity at the top of this unit is widespread, occurring in the two COST wells and the Mohawk well. No Albian section is reported from these wells (Ascoli, 1976; Barss et al., 1979; P. Ascoli, pers. comm., 1983). The unit is wedge-shaped in dip section ranging from an updip zero edge on the Long Island Platform to a maximum of about 1000 m along the basin axis at the paleoshelf break. Along strike the unit thickens in two places, one coincident with the axis of Georges Bank Basin and the other in the Shelburne Subbasin. In between, over the Yarmouth Arch, the middle Cretaceous unit is thin but this is due partly to erosion (Fig. 5.4).

In the G-2 well, the middle Cretaceous unit is 533 m thick and consists of grey mudstone, interbedded with siltstone and sandstone, with minor thin limestone beds becoming more frequent toward the top. Shoreward in G-1, where it is 350 m thick, the facies are coarser sandstones interbedded with shale. In the Mohawk well the middle Cretaceous unit is mainly shale and is 301 m thick. Seaward from Mohawk, beneath the outer Scotian Shelf, it has been truncated by a phase of shelf edge erosion during the Tertiary.

Seismically, this unit is characterized by weak to moderate amplitude, somewhat discontinuous reflections. Continuity increases toward the shelf break. The unit is traced with difficulty beneath the slope and it is tentatively tied to the beds occurring between oceanic reflections β and A*. In the most distal occurrences, for example south of Bear Seamount, the middle Cretaceous unit is over 600 m thick (Fig. 5.6).

The seaward end of Figure 5.6 intersects the south flank of Bear Seamount. Although seismic data from the upper slope are poor, the top of the volcanic rocks appear to occur between the "O" Marker and the Petrel equivalent events. The reflection marking the top of the Jurassic extends for some distance beneath the interpreted volcanic apron. If it formed at or near the time of deposition of the "O" Marker, the seamount would have stood well above sea level. Alternatively, if the volcanic activity occurred as late as Turonian, the seamount only grew to about sea level. The first correlation agrees well with Vogt and Tucholke (1979) who, based on postulated movement over a hot-spot, inferred that volcanic activity in the vicinity of

Bear Seamount took place about 120 Ma. However, the 30 to 40 Ma difference in age between Bear Seamount and the two buried seamounts described previously (Fig. 5.10) indicates that their origins are more likely the result of volcanism associated with periodic movement along the Azores Fracture Zone, and not the result of a hot-spot.

Upper Cretaceous

The upper unit of sequence 3 lies between the unconformity at the base of the Cenomanian (Petrel equivalent marker) and an erosional unconformity at the top of the Cretaceous (Fig. 5.5). It is equivalent to the Dawson Canyon Formation and possibly the Wyandot Formation of the Scotian Shelf. Poag and Schlee (1984) identified three other unconformities within this upper Cretaceous unit in Georges Bank Basin. The upper Cretaceous unit is relatively thin and discontinuous. Its distribution is restricted to the southwestern part of Georges Bank Basin along a basin axis that trended N 60°E, and to the western end of the Scotian Basin (Fig. 5.14). The unit is 84 m thick in the Nantucket borehole and 369 m and 294 m thick in the G-1 and G-2 wells, respectively. It has a maximum thickness of about 1 km in a small area near the shelf break. This unit also is very thin or locally absent on the upper paleoslope but thickens distally to more than 1 km. The lithology at the control wells is light grey calcareous claystones and clayey siltstones which grade upwards into medium- to coarse-grained, unconsolidated sandstones. In the Mohawk B-93 well the upper Cretaceous unit is 425 m thick and is composed almost entirely of shale. There, too, the unit is in unconformable contact with the overlying Tertiary.

Micropaleontological evidence from the control wells indicates that the hiatus between Cretaceous and Tertiary strata ranges from Santonian-early Campanian to Paleocene, with Upper Paleocene sediments overlying the unconformity (Ascoli, 1976; Poag, 1982; P. Ascoli, pers. comm., 1983; Poag and Schlee, 1984). Erosion during the hiatus may have removed as much as 1 km of Cretaceous sediment from the area of the Yarmouth Arch.

With the exception of situations such as depositional thinning due to onlap onto the basin margin or the Yarmouth Arch, the Jurassic and Cretaceous reflectors in Georges Bank Basin are very uniform. There is no evidence of syndepositional movement on a local scale or, more regionally, on the scale of individual crustal blocks. However, during the hiatus between the Cretaceous and Tertiary there was minor structural adjustment of the Georges Bank region at the basement level which resulted in reactivation of basement faults and which is reflected throughout the sedimentary section by small highs and lows.

Sequence 4: Cenozoic

The post-Cretaceous strata across Georges Bank are included in sequence 4. They form a wedge-shaped cap on the outer shelf. They consist primarily of Tertiary rocks with a thin variable cover of unconsolidated Quaternary sediments. The Tertiary strata increase in thickness from their erosional edge along the inner margin of Georges Bank to about 1 km at the shelf break (Fig. 5.15). The Cretaceous-Tertiary unconformity forms a relatively smooth surface, with the exception of an area southeast of

Cape Cod, where a 300 m deep saucer-shaped depression is indicated on two seismic lines. It was excavated through the Mesozoic strata so the infilling Tertiary sediments lie partly on the basement complex (Fig. 5.12, 5.13). Because of the spacing of the deep reflection profiles, the outlet from this basin was not detected but it may be in the vicinity of Great South Channel. The base of sequence 4 is flat beneath Northeast Channel but it has been thinned by more than 200 m due to cutting of the channel during the late Cenozoic. Towards the channel mouth a large salt diapir has pierced the Jurassic and Cretaceous rocks and intrudes the Tertiary sediments.

Detailed lithological control from sequence 4 on Georges Bank is limited to the COST wells and even there only the lowermost part was sampled. In G-2, glauconitic sand between 381.0 m and 399.3 m was interpreted by Simonis (1980) as marking the Cretaceous-Tertiary unconformity. In the Nantucket Island borehole, sequence 4 is 128 m thick and consists of an upper 85 m of medium- to

very coarse-grained sandstone and a lower zone of green-sand with a matrix of silt and clay-sized glauconite that overlies the unconformity (Folger et al., 1978).

In the Mohawk B-93 well on LaHave Platform, a major episode of shelf-edge erosion is dated as probably Late Eocene (Ascoli, 1976; Barss et al., 1979). Seismic data indicate that at the same time, several major channels were incised across the western Scotian Shelf. Some of these are more than 300 m deep and cut entirely through lower Tertiary strata and into Upper Cretaceous strata. The erosion was followed by a period of strong outpouring of clastic sediments and the construction of a new shelf edge during the late Tertiary. This period of erosion, however, was not recognized on southern Georges Bank where the Tertiary, although relatively thin, is continuous from outer shelf to lower slope.

A thick lens of Quaternary sediments is interpreted to occur on the lower continental slope and upper rise across the area. It appears to thin to zero near the base of the

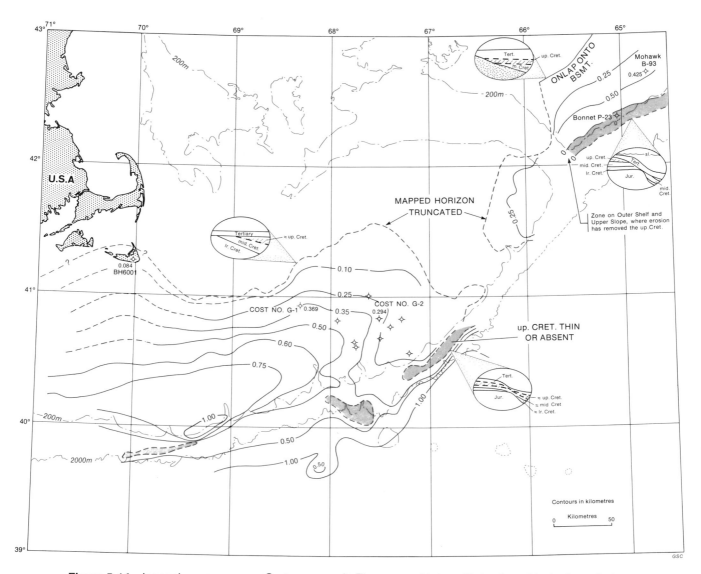

Figure 5.14 Isopach map — upper Cretaceous unit. The mapped interval is hachured in the inset "windows" (see Fig. 5.5).

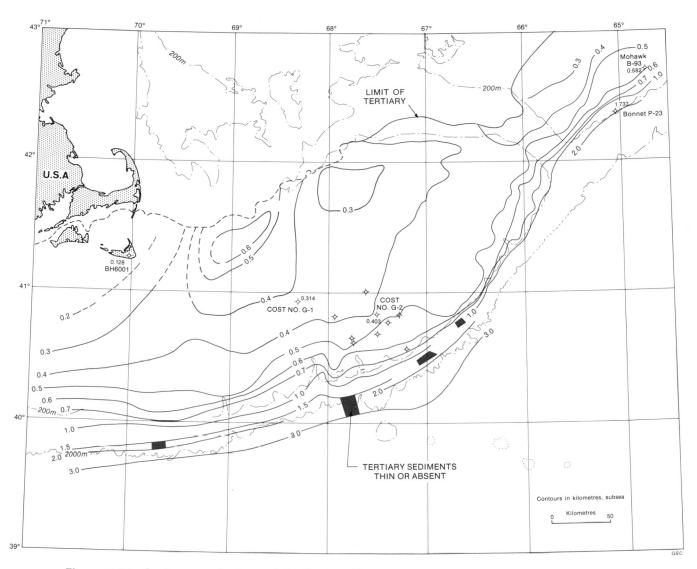

Figure 5.15 Contours on the base of the Tertiary. The mapped horizon is indicated in Figure 5.5.

upper slope off Georges Bank but forms part of the thick outer shelf wedge on the western LaHave Platform. Two main areas of accumulation of Quaternary sediments were noted in the seismic data. The larger occurs off the mouth of Northeast Channel (right hand side of Fig. 5.4). The other lies off Great South Channel. The maximum thickness in each area is greater than 800 m. These accumulations confirm the active nature of the two channels during the Pleistocene low stand of sea level.

OIL AND GAS POTENTIAL

The sedimentary basins off the east coasts of New England and Nova Scotia have been the site of active exploration for oil and gas for more than two decades. The first permits for petroleum exploration on Georges Bank were issued in 1964 by the Government of Canada and covered the portion of the bank east of an equidistance line between Nova Scotia and Cape Cod. Extensive seismic surveys have been run in this area but no wells have been drilled.

A consortium of oil companies conducted a regional seismic program on Georges Bank in 1974, prior to the drilling of the COST G-1 and G-2 stratigraphic tests in Georges Bank Basin in 1976 and 1977 respectively. In December 1979, the United States Department of the Interior sold 63 tracts for petroleum exploration and between mid-1981 and late-1982 eight exploratory wells were drilled. No occurrences of hydrocarbons were reported.

Portions of two sedimentary basins, Georges Bank Basin and Scotian Basin, underlie Georges Bank. As described above they differ significantly in sedimentary facies and structural style. Georges Bank Basin developed as a sag in a relatively stable platform, following continental breakup. Carbonate prone sedimentation prevailed throughout much of its early history, indicating a combination of stability and few major clastic sources. Subsequent clastic facies show little variation or structure.

Studies of the organic matter type, source-rock quantity and level of maturation have been conducted for the

189

G-1 and G-2 wells (Miller et al., 1982; Arthur, 1982b). Type II kerogen is prevalent in the clastic facies of both wells with some Types I and II in the carbonates. However, the percentage of extractable hydrocarbons is low and the overall source-rock quality can be classed as only poor to fair. Corrected geothermal gradients of 21.3°C/km and 26.6°C/km in the G-1 and G-2 wells, respectively, are somewhat lower than the 2.6 to 3.4°C/100 m occurring in wells in the Sable Island area of the Scotian Shelf (Nantais, 1983). In spite of this, vitrinite reflectance and other maturation indicators show a fully mature section has been penetrated in both COST wells, and that the base of the fully mature section occurs at about 4500-5000 m in that part of the basin.

Therefore, it is concluded that most of the oil and gas potential is likely to occur in Middle Jurassic to Lower Cretaceous strata in the outer part of Georges Bank Basin, near the present day shelf edge and upper slope, in conjunction with thicker marine facies, the various carbonate fronts and associated small prograding clastic wedges. Stratigraphic traps may be the most common type of trap in this part of the basin.

By contrast, beneath eastern Georges Bank, the Shelburne Subbasin of the Scotian Basin is interpreted to contain thick sandstone facies intertonguing with marine shale, deposited over a thick and mobile salt unit, which has resulted in the development of large listric faults and numerous diapiric structures. In this setting, source and reservoir rock relationships should be enhanced and numerous structures should be available to migrating hydrocarbons. Also, the presence of marine Jurassic clastic facies occurring at depths shallower than in the Sable Subbasin may increase the possibility of oil occurrence in the eastern area of Georges Bank.

ACKNOWLEDGMENTS

The author acknowledges the contributions of H.B.S. Cooke and K. Klitgord for scientific review. Special thanks are due to P. Ascoli for his extensive studies of ostracodes and foraminifers which resulted in a time framework for the COST wells from which the seismic data, used in this study, were calibrated.

PART 2: ASPECTS OF THE GEOLOGY OF THE SCOTIAN BASIN FROM RECENT SEISMIC AND WELL DATA

J.A. Wade and B.C. MacLean

The Scotian Basin extends from the eastern part of Georges Bank to the central Grand Banks, a distance of 1200 km, and from the edge of the submerged rocks of the coastal plain to the continental rise, an area of about 300 000 km². The physiography of this part of eastern Canada is illustrated in Figure 5.1.

Figure 5.16 and Figure 1 (in pocket) show the location of all wells drilled in the exploration for petroleum in the Scotian Basin through the end of 1986. Control for the interpretation of the stratigraphy of the Scotian Basin is based on results from the wells numbered 1 through 120 inclusive. Of these, 15 are on the western Grand Banks, 2 are in the Bay of Fundy and the remainder are on the Scotian Shelf and Slope. The well data were tied to a grid of more than 170 000 km of industry reflection seismic data which were used to provide a regional geological interpretation. Few seismic data and no well control are available for a large area centred on St. Pierre Bank due to a moratorium on petroleum exploration pending settlement of a boundary dispute between Canada and France. Facies data and contours across this area are based on the projection of regional trends.

TECTONIC DEVELOPMENT

The history of the development of the Scotian Basin in the context of plate tectonics and the development of the North Atlantic Ocean has been described by Jansa and Wade (1975a).

The Scotian Basin is part of an accreted wedge of Mesozoic-Cenozoic sediments deposited on the eastern flank of the Appalachian Orogen. The latter consists, in this area, of low grade metasedimentary strata of the Cambro-Ordovician Meguma Group. The extent of the Meguma Group beneath the Scotian Basin and its relationship to rocks of the Avalon Platform to the north, in the context of mode of emplacement, oceanic contacts, subduction zones, transform faults, etc. are not well known.

The Scotian Basin is a complex of interconnected Mesozoic-Cenozoic depocentres resulting from sedimentation associated with the development of the North Atlantic ocean basin. The depocentres are flanked to the north by more stable platforms. Regional data indicate that deposition in the Scotian Basin started in the Middle Triassic, before any other basin on the continental margin of eastern Canada, with the possible exception of the Jeanne D'Arc Basin to the east of Newfoundland. Seismic time contours on the basement surface provide details of the basin margins and serve to outline the major subbasins (Fig. 5.17). Depth to basement contours in the subbasins are extrapolated from geophysical data and regional depositional patterns (Fig. 5.18, in pocket). They compare with a 7-8 km/s intermediate crustal layer identified in refraction studies by Officer and Ewing (1954), Dainty et al. (1966), Keen et al. (1975) and Keen and Cordsen (1981). Regional data suggest that the earliest form of the basin was probably a northeast-trending complex of grabens which were floored with redbeds and filled variably with redbeds and salt. The scale of the figures does not allow delineation of the numerous smaller structures related to basement. Following the onset of plate separation in the late Early Jurassic, the regional depositional units were

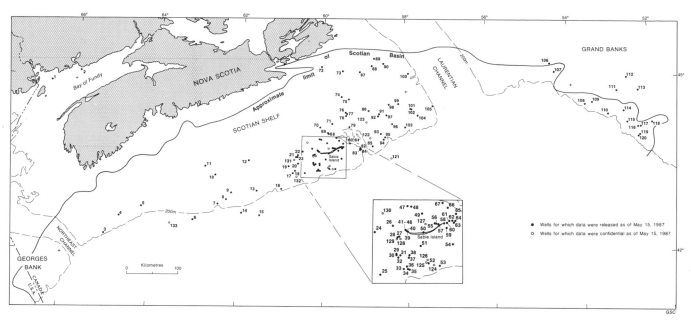

Wells		
No.	**Name**	**Status**
1.	Chinampas N-37	P & A
2.	Cape Spencer No. 1	P & A
3.	Bonnet P-23	P & A
4.	Mohawk B-93	P & A
5.	Montagnais I-94	P & A
6.	Albatross B-13	P & A
7.	Mohican I-100	P & A
8.	Moheida P-15	P & A
9.	Glooscap C-63	P & A
10.	Naskapi N-30	P & A
11.	Sambro I-29	P & A
12.	Ojibwa E-07	P & A
13.	Oneida O-25	P & A
14.	Acadia K-62	P & A
15.	Shubenacadie H-100	P & A
16.	Evangeline H-98	P & A
17.	Alma K-85	Del. G
18.	Alma F-67	DISC. G
19.	Demascota G-32	P & A
20.	Cree E-35	P & A
21.	Cohasset A-52	Del. O
22.	Cohasset P-42	P & A
23.	Cohasset D-42	DISC. O
24.	Cohasset L-97	P & A
25.	Wenonah J-75	P & A
26.	Migrant N-20	P & A
27.	Thebaud P-84	DISC. G,C
28.	Thebaud I-94	Del. G,C
29.	Onondaga B-96	P & A
30.	Onondaga O-95	P & A
31.	Onondaga F-75	P & A
32.	Onondaga E-84	DISC. G
33.	Glenelg E-58 and E-58A	Del. G
34.	Glenelg J-48	DISC. G
35.	Glenelg H-38	P & A
36.	Glenelg N-49	Del. G
37.	Marmora C-34	P & A
38.	Marmora P-35	P & A
39.	Sable Island O-47	DISC. G
40.	Sable Island E-48	DISC. G,C,O
41.	Sable Island H-58, 1a H-58	Del. G,C,O
42.	Sable Island 2H-58	Del. G,C,O
43.	Sable Island 3H-58	Del. G,O
44.	Sable Island 4H-58	Del. G,O
45.	Sable Island 5H-58	Del. G,C,O
46.	Sable Island 6H-58	P & A
47.	Penobscot B-41	P & A
48.	Penobscot L-30	P & A
49.	South Desbarres O-76	P & A
50.	Sable Island C-67	P & A
51.	Intrepid L-80	DISC. G
52.	Triumph P-50	P & A
53.	Chebucto K-90	DISC. G
54.	Eagle D-21	P & A
55.	Olympia A-12	DISC. G,C
56.	West Venture N-01	P & A
57.	West Venture N-91	DISC. G
58.	West Venture C-62	DISC. G,C
59.	South Venture O-59	DISC. G,C
60.	Venture B-52	Del. G,C
61.	Venture B-43	Del. G,C
62.	Venture D-23	DISC. G,C
63.	Venture H-22	DISC. G,C
64.	Venture B-13	DISC. G,C
65.	Arcadia J-16	DISC. G,C
66.	Citnalta I-59	DISC. G,C

Wells		
No.	**Name**	**Status**
67.	Uniacke G-72	DISC. G,C
68.	Abenaki J-56	P & A
69.	Abenaki L-57	P & A
70.	Dover A-43	P & A
71.	Iroquois J-17	P & A
72.	Eurydice P-36	P & A
73.	Fox I-22	P & A
74.	Erie D-26	P & A
75.	Wyandot E-53	P & A
76.	Mic Mac D-89	P & A
77.	Mic Mac J-77	P & A
78.	Mic Mac H-86	P & A
79.	Missisauga H-54	P & A
80.	Bluenose G-47	P & A
81.	Bluenose 2G-47	P & A
82.	Primrose F-41	P & A
83.	Primrose N-50	DISC. G,O
84.	Primrose A-41, 1a A-41	P & A
85.	Southwest Banquereau F-34	P & A
86.	Tuscarora D-61	P & A
87.	Crow F-52	P & A
88.	Argo F-38	P & A
89.	Hercules G-15	P & A
90.	Jason C-20	P & A
91.	Chippewa G-67	P & A
92.	Chippewa L-75	P & A
93.	Sauk A-57	P & A
94.	Banquereau C-21	DISC. G
95.	North Banquereau I-13	P & A
96.	Louisbourg J-47	P & A
97.	Huron P-96	P & A
98.	West Esperanto B-78	P & A
99.	Esperanto K-78	P & A
100.	Adventure F-80	P & A
101.	Hesper P-52	P & A
102.	Hesper I-52	P & A
103.	South Griffin J-13	P & A
104.	Sachem D-76	P & A
105.	Dauntless D-35	P & A
106.	Hermine E-94	P & A
107.	Emerillon C-56	P & A
108.	Puffin B-90	P & A
109.	Kittiwake P-11	P & A
110.	Tern A-68	P & A
111.	Petrel A-62	P & A
112.	Gannet O-54	P & A
113.	Merganser I-60	P & A
114.	Shearwater J-20	P & A
115.	Brant P-87	P & A
116.	Gull F-72	P & A
117.	Tors Cove D-52	P & A
118.	Mallard M-45	P & A
119.	Heron H-73	P & A
120.	Heron J-72	P & A
121.	Tantallon M-41	P & A
122.	Citadel H-52	P & A
123.	Peskowesk A-99	P & A
124.	West Chebucto K-20	P & A
125.	North Triumph B-52	Del. G
126.	North Triumph G-43	DISC. G
127.	West Olympia O-51	DISC. G
128.	Thebaud C-74	Del. G
129.	Thebaud I-93	Del. G
130.	Kegeshook J-67	P & A
131.	Panuke B-90	DISC. O
132.	Merigomish C-52	P & A
133.	Shelburne G-29	P & A

Wells	
No.	**Name**
68.	Abenaki J-56
69.	Abenaki L-57
14.	Acadia K-62
100.	Adventure F-80
6.	Albatross B-13
18.	Alma F-67
17.	Alma K-85
65.	Arcadia J-16
88.	Argo F-38
94.	Banquereau C-21
80.	Bluenose G-47
81.	Bluenose 2G-47
3.	Bonnet P-23
115.	Brant P-87
2.	Cape Spencer No. 1
53.	Chebucto K-90
1.	Chinampas N-37
91.	Chippewa G-67
92.	Chippewa L-75
122.	Citadel H-52
66.	Citnalta I-59
21.	Cohasset A-52
23.	Cohasset D-42
24.	Cohasset L-97
22.	Cohasset P-42
20.	Cree E-35
87.	Crow F-52
105.	Dauntless D-35
19.	Demascota G-32
70.	Dover A-43
54.	Eagle D-21
107.	Emerillon C-56
74.	Erie D-26
99.	Esperanto K-78
72.	Eurydice P-36
16.	Evangeline H-98
73.	Fox I-22
112.	Gannet O-54
33.	Glenelg E-58 and E-58A
35.	Glenelg H-38
34.	Glenelg J-48
36.	Glenelg N-49
9.	Glooscap C-63
116.	Gull F-72
89.	Hercules G-15
106.	Hermine E-94
119.	Heron H-73
120.	Heron J-72
102.	Hesper I-52
101.	Hesper P-52
97.	Huron P-96
51.	Intrepid L-80
71.	Iroquois J-17
90.	Jason C-20
130.	Kegeshook J-67
109.	Kittiwake P-11
96.	Louisbourg J-47
118.	Mallard M-45
37.	Marmora C-34
38.	Marmora P-35
113.	Merganser I-60
132.	Merigomish C-52
76.	Mic Mac D-89
78.	Mic Mac H-86
77.	Mic Mac J-77
26.	Migrant N-20
79.	Missisauga H-54

Wells	
No.	**Name**
4.	Mohawk B-93
8.	Moheida P-15
7.	Mohican I-100
5.	Montagnais I-94
10.	Naskapi N-30
95.	North Banquereau I-13
125.	North Triumph B-52
126.	North Triumph G-43
12.	Ojibwa E-07
55.	Olympia A-12
13.	Oneida O-25
29.	Onondaga B-96
32.	Onondaga E-84
31.	Onondaga F-75
30.	Onondaga O-95
131.	Panuke B-90
47.	Penobscot B-41
48.	Penobscot L-30
123.	Peskowesk A-99
111.	Petrel A-62
84.	Primrose A-41, 1a A-41
82.	Primrose F-41
83.	Primrose N-50
108.	Puffin B-90
50.	Sable Island C-67
40.	Sable Island E-48
41.	Sable Island H-58, 1a H-58
42.	Sable Island 2H-58
43.	Sable Island 3H-58
44.	Sable Island 4H-58
45.	Sable Island 5H-58
46.	Sable Island 6H-58
39.	Sable Island O-47
104.	Sachem D-76
11.	Sambro I-29
93.	Sauk A-57
114.	Shearwater J-20
133.	Shelburne G-29
15.	Shubenacadie H-100
49.	South Desbarres O-76
103.	South Griffin J-13
59.	South Venture O-59
85.	Southwest Banquereau F-34
121.	Tantallon M-41
110.	Tern A-68
128.	Thebaud C-74
129.	Thebaud I-93
28.	Thebaud I-94
27.	Thebaud P-84
117.	Tors Cove D-52
52.	Triumph P-50
86.	Tuscarora D-61
67.	Uniacke G-72
64.	Venture B-13
61.	Venture B-43
60.	Venture B-52
62.	Venture D-23
63.	Venture H-22
25.	Wenonah J-75
124.	West Chebucto K-20
98.	West Esperanto B-78
127.	West Olympia O-51
57.	West Venture N-91
58.	West Venture C-62
56.	West Venture N-01
75.	Wyandot E-53

P & A - plugged and abandoned
Del. - delineation well
DISC. - discovery well

G - gas
C - condensate
O - oil

GSC

Figure 5.16 Wells drilled in the Scotian Basin through the end of 1986. The wells are listed numerically and alphabetically. The numerical list includes the well status.

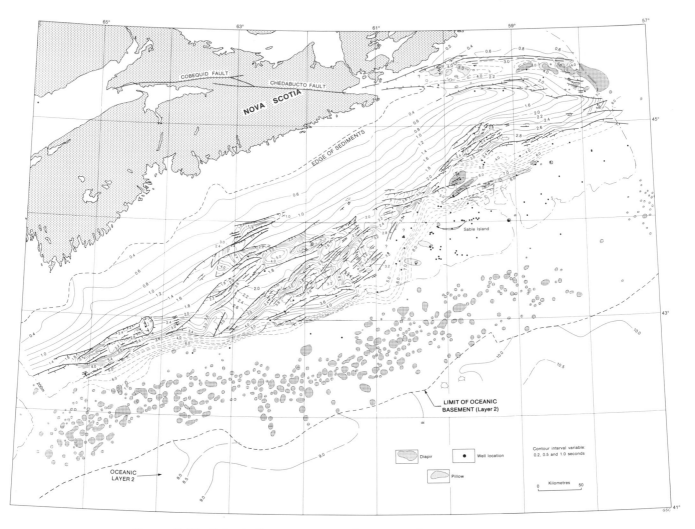

Figure 5.17 Seismic time contours on basement, Scotian Shelf and Rise.

lens-shaped in cross-section with the thickest sediments accumulating in outer shelf-upper slope environments (Fig. 5.19, inset).

Figure 5.19 is a regional geological cross-section which is a composite of portions of several industry seismic profiles. This interpretation differs considerably from Continent-Ocean Transect D-3 (Keen and Haworth, 1985). Transect D-3 was based on seismic data collected in 1972 and interpretations published in the mid-1970s. Figure 5.19 is based on seismic data acquired in 1980-81, and on wells drilled through 1984. The major difference is in the depth of the base of Mesozoic sediments. Transect D-3 indicates a maximum depth of about 10 km in the vicinity of the Triumph P-50 well as compared to about 18 km. Furthermore, the transect indicates the presence of a 1.5 km thick carbonate bank to the shelf edge whereas, in fact, the carbonate bank is not present in this part of the basin. These differences will be of particular significance to those concerned with modelling the development of the margin or the level of organic matter maturity within the basin.

The Scotian Basin (Fig. 5.18, in pocket) is flanked to the southwest by the Yarmouth Arch (Fig. 5.3) and to the northeast by the Avalon Uplift. The Yarmouth Arch, as discussed earlier in this chapter, appears to have been a relatively positive element throughout the Mesozoic and Cenozoic and formed the westerly limit of the major Triassic-Jurassic salt basin. The Avalon Uplift on the other hand, is a Late Jurassic (Late Cimmerian) element, probably formed in conjunction with the initiation of seafloor spreading between the Grand Banks and western Europe. It cut across the trend of the Jurassic basin, elevating parts of it, and resulting in significant erosion and sediment reworking during the Early Cretaceous with deposition westward into the Scotian Basin and northeastward into the Jeanne d'Arc Basin.

The LaHave Platform and Canso Ridge form the northwestern flank of the Scotian Basin. A comparison of Figures 5.17 and 5.18 shows the basement surface here to be generally less than 4 km deep. Regionally it is a seaward-dipping surface broken into a complex of horsts and grabens by numerous northeast trending normal faults. Many of the graben features are, in fact, half grabens bounded on the south by major faults. The sizes of the grabens vary; some are small and shallow, others contain considerable thicknesses of redbeds and a few are

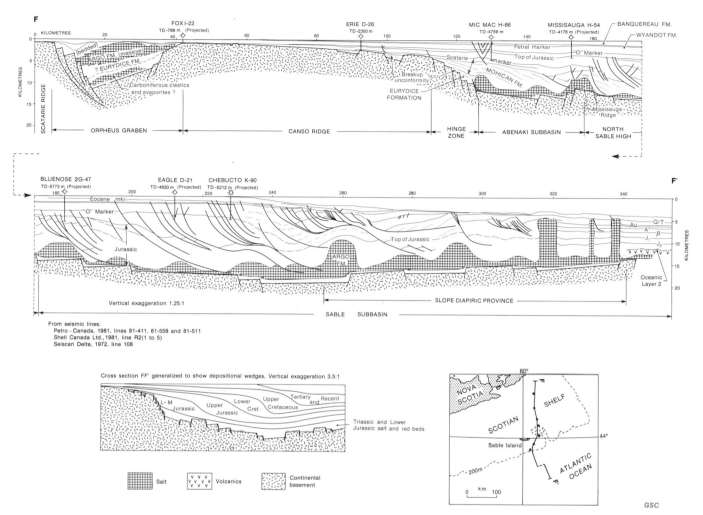

Figure 5.19 Regional geological cross section F-F' across the Scotian Shelf and slope. Location also shown in Figure 5.18 (in pocket).

interpreted to also contain salt. This surface was peneplaned at the breakup unconformity prior to the slow transgression during the Jurassic.

The extent of the Triassic graben system beneath the Burin Platform, which forms the northern flank of the basin, is unknown. Carboniferous strata, however, are known to locally underlie the 1 to 2 km of Mesozoic and Cenozoic sediments in this area.

A prominent Early Jurassic (post-breakup) basement hinge zone trends northeasterly along the flank of the basin. The hinge zone consists of a series of faults or flexures across which the depth to basement increases rapidly from approximately 4 km on the platforms to 10 km or more in the subbasins (Fig. 5.18, in pocket). The hinge zone does not follow a single fault. Rather it passes from one fault to another, or cuts obliquely across fault trends, indicating that it developed after rifting and is related to independent crustal downwarp probably resulting from processes associated with the early stages of seafloor spreading.

The development of basement structures due to crustal adjustments must also have occurred southeast of the

hinge zone, but the structures are too deep to be detected directly. Their presence is inferred from associated salt structures and from faulting in the overlying strata. On the platformal areas, movements as young as Tertiary are recognized on some normal faults involving basement. Basement related structures, such as those drilled by the Mohawk B-93, Naskapi N-30, Erie D-26 and Wyandot E-53 wells, occur where closures resulted from combinations of early differential vertical movement and subsequent compaction drape near the boundaries between horst blocks and adjacent grabens (Fig. 5.17, 5.19).

From west to east, the subbasins of the Scotian Basin are: Shelburne, Sable, Abenaki, Laurentian and South Whale. As can be seen from Figure 5.18, these are not isolated basins but rather they are interconnected areas of thick sediments. In these subbasins, prolonged subsidence has resulted in the accumulation of more than 12 km of strata and maximum thicknesses may approach 18 km. The distribution of salt suggests that the subbasins were, initially, the loci of evaporite deposition with each subbasin accumulating, before breakup, thick sequences of

193

redbeds and evaporites that thinned across the intervening highs. All the subbasins had periods of rapid subsidence and it is these stages of their development that differentiate them from each other. For example, rapid subsidence immediately following Early Jurassic salt deposition in the Abenaki Subbasin is in contrast with prolonged rapid subsidence during the Jurassic and Early Cretaceous in the Sable and South Whale subbasins. The subsidence in Sable Subbasin continued into the late Early Cretaceous. Deposition in Shelburne Subbasin was most rapid during the Jurassic and relatively slow during the Cretaceous and Tertiary.

The Mohican Graben (the Mohican Basin of Given, 1977) and the Orpheus Graben are two other areas with very thick pre-breakup sediment fill. Mohican Graben is a southwest-plunging structural complex within the LaHave Platform. The graben-fill sediments dip southerly. The largest faults occur along its southern flank apparently juxtaposing salt against older redbeds. Stratigraphic control, provided by the Mohican I-100 and Glooscap C-63 wells, and some seismic data show the early graben fill, including salt, to be very thick and capped in part with basaltic flows. These were onlapped, following breakup, by the Mohican and Iroquois formations and graben fill was completed during this time.

The Orpheus Graben is an easterly plunging feature lying between Canso and Scatarie ridges. Its northern side is a portion of the Cobequid-Chedabucto fault zone. Seismic and well data show that the Orpheus Graben contains two areas with up to 10 km of Lower Jurassic, Upper Triassic and possibly Paleozoic strata with an intervening, 3 km high, arch. Most of the sediments are interpreted to be thick redbed and evaporite facies. These are separated by the breakup unconformity from relatively thin Mesozoic and Cenozoic clastics and minor carbonates. Extensive salt flowage occurred during deposition of the Mohican-Iroquois facies, possibly associated with periodic reactivation of the fault system during later stages of continental breakup. Salt pillows and diapirs are most common in the two areas with thickest sediments and the salt movement has resulted in locally thick accumulations of sediments in withdrawal synclines. Thin, conformable basalt beds occur above a local unconformity at the top of the Missisauga Formation.

A major zone of diapiric structures trending from eastern Georges Bank to the western Grand Banks was referred to by Jansa and Wade (1975b) as the Sedimentary Ridge Province. The abundance of seismic data now available irrefutably demonstrates that the structures are not ridges but rather discrete, roughly circular features (Fig. 5.18, in pocket). As a result this trend is now referred to as the "Slope Diapiric Province".

As discussed in Part 1 of this chapter, the East Coast Magnetic Anomaly (ECMA) is a strong positive anomaly which is prominent along the eastern margin of the United States as far north as the New England Seamount Chain. The East Coast Magnetic Anomaly may be offset across the seamount chain and continue as a strong positive anomaly into the Shelburne Subbasin. There it appears to break up into a series of short segments, possibly due to a second transform zone, and then continues to the east and northeast as a much reduced anomaly. The anomaly has been interpreted as marking the transition from continental crust to oceanic crust (Rabinowitz, 1974). However, the seg-

ment in the Shelburne Subbasin is well landward of the limit of oceanic Layer 2 (Fig. 5.18, in pocket) as observed on seismic profiles. Due to its reduced amplitude, the trace of the anomaly along the Scotian margin is somewhat uncertain. Keen et al. (1975) depicted the ECMA as following an arcuate trend, entirely within the continental realm, from the Shelburne Subbasin to the central part of the Sable Subbasin (Fig. 5.18, in pocket).

Seismic interpretation of the Montagnais structure

A unique basement feature, named the Montagnais structure after the Montagnais I-94 well drilled on its crest, occurs on the western LaHave Platform (Fig. 5.16, 5.18). The well is located 47 km northeast of the Mohawk B-93 well which bottomed in granite. Montagnais I-94 encountered lower Tertiary strata overlying a 30 m (100 ft.) thick glassy, possibly volcanic bed at a depth of 653 m (2142 ft). A second similar layer, 34 m (112 ft) thick, was encountered at 953 m (3128 ft) below a section of atypical but possibly Upper Cretaceous sediments. A third unit, consisting of glassy volcanics grading downward into rhyolite was encountered between 1100 and 1141 m (3608 and 3745 ft) within metasediments interpreted to be Meguma Group. Whole rock K-Ar radiometric dating indicated an early Eocene age for the deepest glassy/rhyolitic beds (L.F. Jansa, pers. comm., 1984)

Two origins have been suggested for the Montagnais structure: igneous, according to Jansa and Wade (1975a); and impact crater, according to Jansa and Pe-Piper (1987). The bases for the two interpretations are discussed below.

Seismic interpretation shows that the roughly circular Montagnais structure is located over an inferred west-dipping fault that marks the abrupt eastern termination of the Mohawk graben complex (Fig. 5.17, 5.18). It also shows the structure developed during the Late Cretaceous and Paleogene mainly through uplift and erosion.

Adjacent to the structure, the Jurassic, Cretaceous and Tertiary shelf sediments are relatively flat-lying with parallel bedding. In the mid-Late Cretaceous the structure started to rise, possibly due to deep igneous intrusion associated with the underlying faulting. As a result, all of the Mesozoic sediments were eroded from the central core, an area approximately 15 km in diameter, and a major unconformity, dated as Turonian in the nearby Mohawk B-93 well, incised irregular channels around the structure. In places these channels cut nearly to basement (Fig. 5.20). The erosion appears to have been followed by a period of extrusive acidic volcanism which formed an irregular apron of lava or volcaniclastics around the core and partially filled the channels. On the seismic profiles this volcanic apron has a chaotic internal character. A period of transgression resulted in the deposition of flat-lying, marine Upper Cretaceous beds which fill much of the remaining channels and onlap the volcanic apron. They onlap and thin on the flanks of the central core indicating differential subsidence. Sediments between 700 and 760 m (2300 and 2500 ft), i.e. between the upper glassy intervals in the well, contain both Eocene and Albian to Cenomanian palynomorphs (E.H. Davies, pers. comm., 1984).

Marine sedimentation continued into the early part of the Tertiary. A major unconformity during the Eocene resulted in a small western valley and a very large eastern

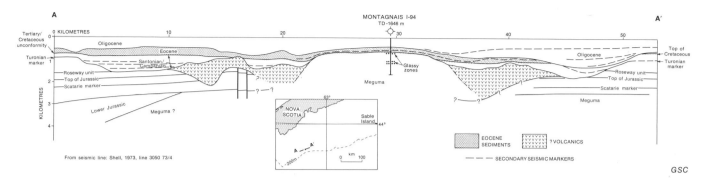

Figure 5.20 Geological cross section A-A' across the Montagnais structure, LaHave Platform. Location also shown in Figure 5.18, in pocket.

valley which cut deeply into the preceding sequences (Fig. 5.20). A regional Eocene-Oligocene unconformity overprints the Eocene one. The valleys cut by this last event were completely filled by probable Miocene sediments. There was some continued differential uplift of the structure because the Eocene-Oligocene unconformity is high over the structure.

Consequently, the combination of seismic interpretation and stratigraphic data from wells indicates the structure formed during the early Late Cretaceous, probably through basement uplift, erosion and volcanism, followed by successive periods of sedimentation and uplift resulting in erosion. The last apparent movement of the structure occurred in the Eocene-Oligocene.

This 50 Ma of structural development, rather than the split second in geological time for an astrobleme, is not the only argument against an impact origin. A second argument relates to the geometry of the structure. The Montagnais structure bears no resemblance in cross-section to other documented impact craters as there are no obvious crater rims and the central high is proportionally too large and too high for the rest of the feature. In Figure 5.20 the entire feature is approximately 50 km across with the central high being about 15 km in diameter. Typically, the central high in an impact crater is lower than the surrounding rim. At Montagnais, the central high is at least 300 m higher than the outer walls of the Late Cretaceous channels and the surface of the Meguma Group is more than 1200 m higher than regional basement.

Jansa and Pe-Piper (1987) proposed that the Montagnais structure was formed by a meteor impact into a shallow sea. Their interpretation is based mainly on the results of detailed petrographic studies and chemical analyses of cuttings samples from the well. Petrography indicates the presence of high pressure lamellae in quartz and feldspar grains. The geochemical analyses of the amygdaloidal glassy material show SiO_2 in excess of 70% associated with feldspars of bytownite composition. Such associations cannot occur in igneous rocks formed through normal geological processes (L.F. Jansa, pers. comm., 1986). Also, the melt rocks contain iridium levels which are somewhat higher than normal but consistent with known impact products. The radiometric age of the melt rocks, together with an interpretation of biostratigraphic data, indicate the event is Eocene in age. Jansa and Pe-Piper interpreted the glassy intervals as melted Meguma Group rocks and considered that the best explanation for their origin is a

meteor impact during the Eocene. However, an explanation is still required for the occurrence of three different zones of impact melt over an interval of 447 m and separated by unaltered sedimentary rocks.

A final resolution of the problem regarding the origin of the Montagnais structure is unlikely until there is a satisfactory explanation for the apparent differences between the geophysical and geochemical interpretations, including the origin of the unique "volcanic" rocks and the possibly abnormal iridium levels. No other features of this type have been observed in the Scotian Basin.

Other occurrences of volcanic rocks

Seamounts, and buried features resembling seamounts, occur at both ends of the Scotian Basin. The New England Seamounts (Fig. 5.1), which are aligned with the Azores Fracture Zone, lie off the southwestern end of the Yarmouth Arch. These are interpreted to have last experienced active volcanism in the Cenomanian/Turonian (Vogt and Tucholke, 1979). However, some data also suggest initial volcanic episodes may be early Late Jurassic (see Part 1 of this chapter).

The Fogo Seamounts lie off the southwestern flank of the Grand Banks (Fig. 5.18, in pocket), at the eastern end of the Scotian Basin, and are probably associated with the Newfoundland Transform (Map 1706A, in pocket). These seamounts have not been dated, but the J-Anomaly Ridge 150 km to the southeast has a minimum age of 104±6 Ma (Houghton et al., 1979). The ridge is overlain by carbonates dated as Aptian (Gradstein et al., 1977).

Volcanic and volcaniclastic rocks occur within the sedimentary sequences over extensive areas on the Canso Ridge and on the eastern flank of the South Whale Subbasin. The petrography and origin of these rocks have been described in some detail by Jansa and Pe-Piper (1985, 1986, 1988).

LITHOSTRATIGRAPHY

This section presents a summary of the stratigraphy of the Scotian Basin and describes new aspects of the geology, relating them in particular to the large amount of currently available seismic data. Previous accounts of the stratigraphy can be found in McIver (1972), Jansa and Wade (1975b), Given (1977) and Eliuk (1978).

Summary

The Mesozoic-Cenozoic stratigraphy of the Scotian Basin is illustrated diagrammatically in Figure 5.21. The oldest Mesozoic sediments are continental redbeds and evaporites of the Eurydice and Argo formations, respectively, with the evaporites being common in the Orpheus Graben and in the subbasins south of the Early Jurassic hinge zone. Salt deposition ceased abruptly in the Early Jurassic and was succeeded by continental clastics and evaporitic dolostones of the Mohican and Iroquois formations, respectively. During the Middle and Late Jurassic, a complex of clastic and carbonate facies developed along the margin of the basin. These are the Mohawk, Mic Mac, Abenaki and Verrill Canyon formations. The Early Cretaceous was characterized by the thick fluvial-deltaic Missisauga and Logan Canyon formations, whereas the Late Cretaceous consists of transgressive marine shales and minor limestones of the Dawson Canyon Formation and chalk and marl of the Wyandot Formation. The remainder of the sediments are included in the Banquereau Formation which consists of mudstones, sandstones and conglomerates, deposited during the latest Cretaceous and the Paleogene transgression and subsequent Neogene regression.

Basement rocks

The Mesozoic, and in part the Cenozoic, sedimentary rocks of the Scotian Basin overlie a crystalline basement complex except in the Burin Platform where they are locally deposited on upper Paleozoic sedimentary strata. Basement refers to "petroleum basement" which, on the Scotian Shelf, consists of Paleozoic metasedimentary rocks with some plutonic granites. The basement complex has been encountered in only eight wells and all these occurrences are on the LaHave Platform and Canso Ridge. Five wells, Argo F-38, Fox I-22, Montagnais I-94, Naskapi N-30 and Wyandot E-53, encountered schists, phyllites and quartzites which are tentatively correlated to the Cambro-Ordovician Meguma Group of Nova Scotia. The Mohawk B-93 and Ojibwa E-07 wells bottomed in coarse grained, biotitic granite with up to 40% orthoclase whereas the Crow F-52 well encountered granite which was similar in composition but finer in texture. K-Ar dating of biotite from the granites in the Ojibwa E-07 well yielded an age of 359 ± 12 Ma which is close to the mean age of 367 Ma reported for the South Mountain Batholith of southwestern Nova Scotia (Reynolds et al., 1981). Petrographic analysis shows that these granites are also similar to the granites on the mainland of Nova Scotia (S. Woodend, pers. comm.).

Rocks of the Meguma Group can sometimes be distinguished from the granites on the basis of seismic signature. On shallow platforms or ridges below undisturbed sediments the granites produce a crisp, clean, strong reflector, whereas, the response from Meguma basement is a broad, weak event which is often difficult to follow. Both types of basement present a generally smooth surface that slopes seaward to the hinge zone at approximately 30 m/km indicative of a tilted peneplain. Steeply dipping events from within basement, particularly on the LaHave Platform, give clues to internal structures or intrusions. However the basement surface is difficult to pick on seismic profiles where it lies beneath thick graben fill consisting of Eurydice or Argo formations. Wave path distortion through disturbed evaporite beds and the similarities in the seismic velocities of clastics (4900 m/s) and of the Meguma Group (5500 m/s) combine to reduce reflection amplitude and continuity. North of the Chedabucto-Cobequid fault zone basement rocks of the Scatarie Ridge and Burin Platform form part of the Avalon Terrane

Upper Triassic and lower Lower Jurassic rocks

During the Triassic, the rifting phase of continental breakup resulted in the formation of a complex of northeasterly trending horsts and grabens on the margin of the Scotian Basin. These grabens became the site of locally very thick accumulations of red clastic sediments deposited under seasonally arid conditions in fluvial and lacustrine environments (Klein, 1962; Jansa and Wade, 1975b; Manspeizer, 1981). Dating of these sequences is difficult but some beds have been dated as Late Triassic (Barss et al., 1979; J.P. Bujak, pers. comm., 1979). Older Triassic or even Permian rocks may occur in some of the grabens but these beds have not been drilled.

Eurydice and Argo formations

The oldest dated Mesozoic sequences in the Scotian Basin are late Norian (i.e. Rhaetian) to Hettangian-Sinemurian. They consist of red clastics of the Eurydice Formation and coeval evaporites of the Argo Formation. The type sections of both formations are in the Orpheus Graben (Jansa and Wade, 1975b; Wade, 1976). Although one or both of the formations occur in all the early formed grabens in the Scotian Basin, regional stratigraphic control is limited. Along the margin of the basin they are separated from overlying formations by the breakup unconformity.

The type section of the Eurydice Formation is from 2393-2965 m (7850-9728 ft) in the Eurydice P-36 well, where it consists of 45% red to red-brown, slightly silty shale with minor amounts of green shale, 45% thin red sandstone and siltstone beds and minor amounts of limestone and evaporite. The total thickness of Eurydice facies at this location is interpreted, from seismic data, to be greater than 3 km. Coarser clastics are more abundant in other wells where the formation is encountered. For example, in Sambro I-29, where 1580 m (5185 ft) of Eurydice Formation were penetrated between 1489 and 3070 m (4886 and 10 071 ft), the proportions of sandstone, siltstone and shale are similar (37% very fine- to medium-grained, red, argillaceous sandstone, 28% red siltstone and 35% red shale). An estimated 1600 m of the Eurydice Formation occurs below the bottom of this well. At the hinge zone on the western LaHave Platform, the Eurydice Formation is interpreted to be several thousand metres thick in tilted fault blocks.

The Argo Formation (McIver, 1972) overlies and interfingers with the Eurydice Formation in many of the deeper grabens. Its type section (Wade, 1976) is between 2305-3085 m (7563 and 10 122 ft) in the Argo F-38 well. The Argo Formation consists of a series of massive beds of salt which are colourless to pale orange, coarsely crystalline and separated by zones of red shale. The lithologic variations suggest brief periods in which thick beds of salt were deposited, interspersed with extended periods when there was little or no deposition (Wade, 1981). In the type section, the boundary between the Eurydice and Argo formations is placed between an underlying red-brown, saline

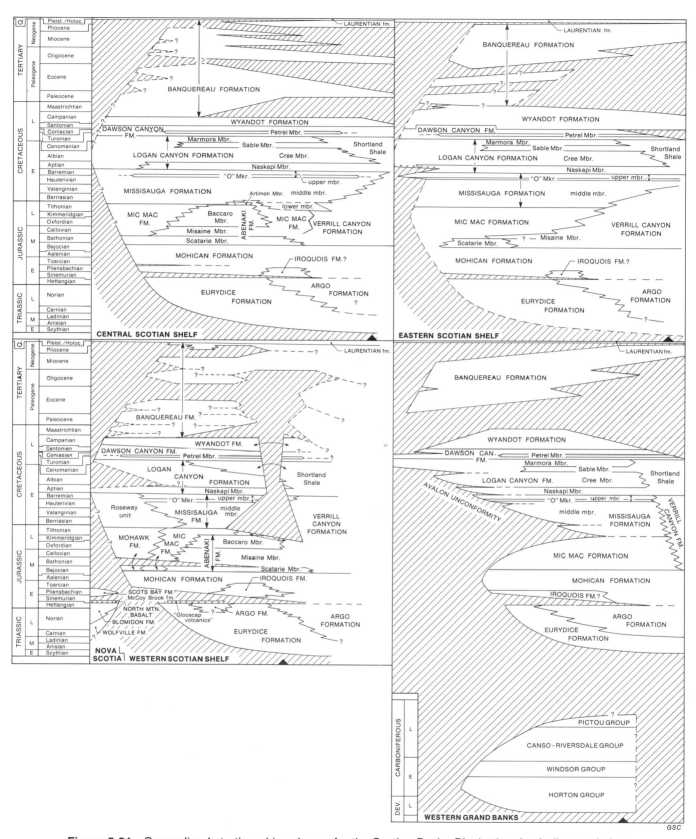

Figure 5.21   Generalized stratigraphic columns for the Scotian Basin. Black triangles indicate relative position of present day shelf break.

shale sequence and a 7-m thick, dark brown, bituminous, dolomitic and argillaceous sequence which passes upward into halite. Toward the top of the formation there are more frequent interbeds of shale or dolomite. The contact with overlying formations is commonly unconformable.

In the Eurydice P-36 well the gamma ray and sonic curves suggest the presence of potash-bearing beds in the Argo Formation. In the intervals 942 to 957 and 1984 to 2181 m (3090 to 3140 and 6510 to 7155 ft) there are numerous beds, 1-3 m (3-10 ft) thick, with gamma ray counts as high as 240 API units and acoustic transit times of 243 to 249μs/m (74-76μs/ft) (Fig. 5.22). This is most consistent with the presence of sylvite (KCl) and carnallite (KCl-$MgCl_2$-$6H_2O$) which have gamma ray counts of 200-500 API units and sonic transit times of 243 to 256μs/m (74-78μs/ft) (Wade, 1976). Potash salts in this well are in keeping with its location in the western part of the Orpheus Graben where periods of complete evaporation were most likely. Although not recognized in other wells encountering the Argo Formation, potash salts probably also occur in other locally restricted areas along the margins of the Argo salt basin.

An anomalous situation in the evaporite sequences of the Argo Formation is the deficiency of anhydrite. In the normal evaporation of seawater, calcium carbonate and calcium sulphate are significant early products. Their absence regionally, relative to hundreds of metres of pure halite, indicates that the salt was precipitated from brines already depleted of carbonate and sulphate minerals (Jansa et al., 1980). Only two wells, both in the South Whale Subbasin, have penetrated more than 35m of anhydrite in the Argo Formation and they were in relatively thin beds within the salt section.

The seismic expression of the Eurydice and Argo formations varies considerably across the area. Within the shallow grabens near Wyandot E-53, the Eurydice Formation is represented by strong, often hummocky and discontinuous, reflectors lying disconformably above the basement. This is characteristic of weakly layered, probably alluvial clastics. In the Mohican Graben the formation is much thicker and is associated with evaporites of the Argo Formation which caused later disturbance of the fill sequences. The internal seismic expression shows this disturbance with weaker and shorter reflector segments. As noted earlier, where the Eurydice Formation is either excessively thick or deep it is commonly seismically indistinguishable from basement. For example, at the Moheida P-15 well the seismic character of the formation is weak and discontinuous, with only subtle hints as to internal forms, and no apparent reflector at the top of the suspected basement horst.

The seismic expression of the Argo Formation varies from a sequence of strong parallel reflectors indicating interbedded salt and redbeds, such as occur in Eurydice P-36, to classic examples of reflection-free diapiric structures. The variations in appearance are directly related to the thickness of the salt beds and to the amount of salt in the total sequence. Where the salt beds are thin, and a relatively small component of the total section, the adjacent beds are less prone to disturbance and internal reflections can be seen. Thick salt beds produce few coherent internal reflectors and are susceptible to flowage and diapirism (halokinesis). In the Orpheus Graben the transition from bedded to massive salt occurs very rapidly with the massive salt facies dominating the central part of the graben.

The Argo Formation extends from a depositional limit on the flank of the Yarmouth Arch in the southwest to a structural limit on the eastern flank of the South Whale Subbasin (Fig. 5.23). During the Early Jurassic, salt deposition was continuous through the rift basins of the Grand Banks into the East Newfoundland Basin. Landward, deposition was controlled by the larger grabens. The seaward limit of the salt is mapped as coinciding with the northern limit of the seismic event marking oceanic Layer 2 (Fig. 5.18, in pocket) although, for some distance seaward, salt may underlie this layer (Wade, 1981) (Fig. 5.19).

East of 58°W, the apparent variation in the density of diapirs is generally a function of available seismic data. However, one large area, centred on 54°W and 44°30'N in South Whale Subbasin, appears, with one exception, to be devoid of diapirs. Unlike other salt free areas in Figure 5.23 this is due to very thick ?Lower Jurassic sediments whose seismic character ranges from poorly to clearly defined dipping events. This suggests either the presence of interbedded salt with insufficient evaporite in the section to allow the development of diapirs or the movement of salt away from an area with thick overlying sediments.

Neither the original thickness of the undeformed salt, nor the present distribution of the Argo Formation, are known with certainty. This is due to its depth, as well as to extensive flowage of salt mainly into the distal parts of the Scotian Basin. The regions affected by large scale salt withdrawal are characterized by thick infilling sedimentary units or by large, deeply soled listric faults; whereas areas of salt concentration are distinguished by numerous diapiric structures. The most spectacular of these is the Slope Diapiric Province (Figs. 5.17, 5.23). In this area, salt originally deposited at or near sea level is at a present depth of 13 km or more (Fig. 5.18, in pocket).

The type section of the Eurydice Formation is dated palynologically as Rhaetian-early Hettangian to late Hettangian-early Sinemurian (Barss et al., 1979). In areas where the Argo Formation is present, the Eurydice sediments interfinger with and are laterally equivalent to the salt. In Eurydice P-36 the Argo Formation and mixed Argo-Eurydice facies are late Sinemurian-early Pliensbachian (Barss et al., 1979). In the Mohican Graben, these facies are dated Late Triassic-Hettangian (E.H. Davies, pers. comm., 1984) and are overlain by subaerial basalts.

Wolfville and Blomidon formations

The Wolfville and Blomidon formations occur in the Annapolis Lowland of western Nova Scotia (Fig. 5.1) and at various localities on the margin of the Fundy Basin. In their type sections these formations consist of a fining upward sequence of soft red conglomerate, grit, sandstone and shale totalling more than 1000 m in thickness. They lie between the Paleozoic basement complex and a series of lava flows, the North Mountain Basalt (Fig. 5.21). Based on the presence of reptilian bones, fish scales and plant fragments (Klein, 1962), and through correlation to similar sequences in Morocco and southwestern Europe (Jansa et al., 1980), the redbed facies have long been regarded as

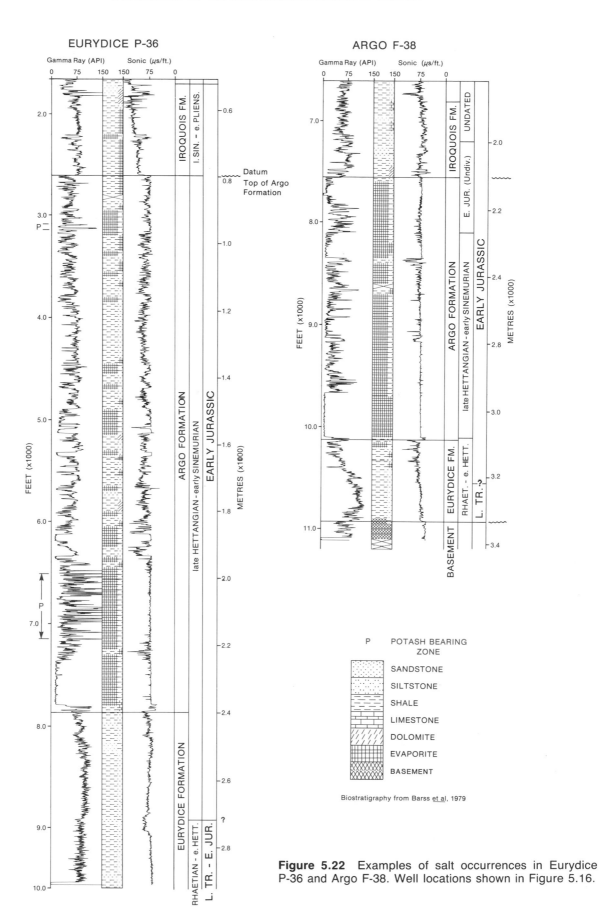

Figure 5.22 Examples of salt occurrences in Eurydice P-36 and Argo F-38. Well locations shown in Figure 5.16.

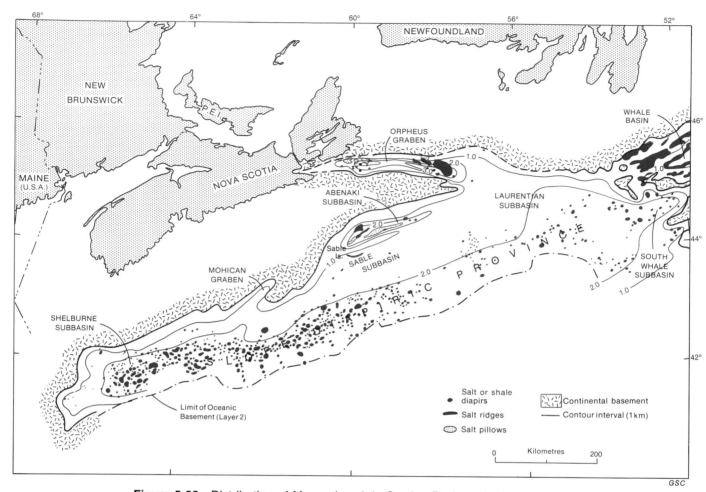

Figure 5.23 Distribution of Mesozoic salt in Scotian Basin and adjacent areas.

Triassic. Recent interpretations based on reptile and dinosaur remains indicate the occurrence of beds as old as late Middle Triassic and place the Triassic-Jurassic boundary in the upper part of the Blomidon Formation (P. Olsen and N. Shubin, pers. comm., 1986). Attempts at dating the Wolfville and Blomidon formations using palynology from Chinampas N-37 in the Bay of Fundy indicate a general Rhaetian age (J.P. Bujak, pers. comm., 1980). These data show that the Wolfville and Blomidon formations are correlative with the Eurydice Formation.

North Mountain Basalt

A succession of 16 or more subaerial flows, the North Mountain Basalt, outcrops extensively in Nova Scotia. Its thickness in outcrop is from 175-425 m. The North Mountain Basalt is also known, from drilling and seismic profiles, to occur in the subsurface of the Bay of Fundy. Although stratigraphic relationships are uncertain, the basalt is structurally conformable with the underlying Blomidon Formation and is unconformably overlain by the Scots Bay Formation. K-Ar ages for the North Mountain Basalt range from 191 ± 2 Ma (Hayatsu, 1979) to 202 Ma (Wark and Clarke, 1980).

A 152-m thick basalt sequence lies between the Mohican Formation and the underlying Argo and Eurydice for-

mations in the Glooscap C-63 well (Fig. 5.24) where is it referred to as "Glooscap volcanics". On the basis of its stratigraphic position relative to the Argo Formation and the breakup unconformity this basalt is correlated with the North Mountain Basalt. The basaltic layer can be traced as a bright seismic event across much of the Mohican Graben, where it appears to conform with the top of the underlying beds, but it is onlapped from southwest to northeast by clastics of the overlying Mohican Formation. Therefore, the breakup unconformity appears to follow the top of the volcanic rocks. These volcanics do not occur in the nearby Mohican I-100 well and seismic data indicate that they end, or originate, at a zone of faulting along the north flank of the Moheida Ridge (Fig. 5.18, in pocket). Holser et al. (1988) reported a radiometric age of 176 ± 7 Ma for these volcanics but they did not comment on the quality of the sample or the reliability of the date.

The breakup unconformity

Across Georges Bank Basin to the southwest, the breakup unconformity is marked by a strong, regionally mappable seismic event separating areally restricted, mildly deformed Upper Triassic to Lower Jurassic strata from undeformed Lower Jurassic and younger rocks. The unconformity can be traced across the LaHave Platform and the

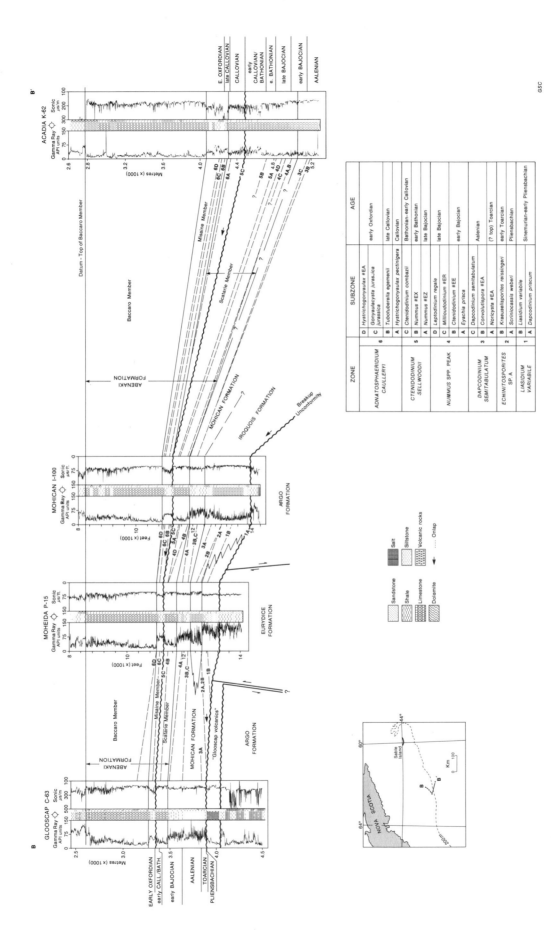

Figure 5.24 Geological cross section B-B', LaHave Platform, showing details of the Mohican and Iroquois formations. Biozonations by E.H. Davies. Location also shown in Figure 5.18, in pocket.

ZONE		SUBZONE		AGE
ADNATOSPHAERIDIUM CAULLERYI	6	D	Hystrichogonyaulax #EA	early Oxfordian
		C	Gonyaulacysta jurassica jurassica	late Callovian
		B	Tubotuberella egemenii	Callovian
		A	Hystrichogonyaulax pectinigera	Bathonian–early Callovian
CTENIDODINIUM SELLWOODII	5	C	Ctenidodinium combazii	early Bathonian
		B	Nummus #EX	late Bajocian
		A	Nummus #EZ	late Bajocian
NUMMUS SPP. PEAK	4	D	Leptodinium regale	
		C	Milioudodinium #ER	
		B	Ctenidodinium #EE	early Bajocian
		A	Eyachia priaca	
DAPCODINIUM SEMITABULATUM	3	C	Dapcodinium semitabulatum	Aalenian
		B	Convolutispora #EA	(? top) Toarcian
		A	Noricysta #EA	early Toarcian
ECHINITOSPORITES SP. A	2	B	Kraeuselisporites reissingeri	Pliensbachian
		A	Scriniocassis weberi	
LIASIDIUM VARIABLE	1	B	Liasidium variabile	Sinemurian–early Pliensbachian
		A	Dapcodinium priscum	

GSC

201

Canso Ridge where it has a similar appearance. In Mohican and Orpheus grabens, very thick sections of Eurydice and Argo formations lie beneath the breakup unconformity. It is generally unrecognizable in subbasins of Scotian Basin but is assumed to occur at about the top of the Argo Formation.

Iroquois and Mohican formations

Locally, on the Scotian Shelf and Grand Banks, the Argo and Eurydice formations are overlain unconformably by dolomitic rocks of the Iroquois Formation. Elsewhere they are overlain by a clastic sequence, the Mohican Formation, or a facies transitional between the two (Fig. 5.21).

The type section of the Iroquois Formation is between -1774 and -2013 m (-5819 and -6604 ft)[1] in Iroquois J-17 (McIver, 1972). The age of the Iroquois Formation in the type section is late Sinemurian-early Pliensbachian (G.L. Williams, pers. comm., 1986). In wells on the LaHave Platform it is ?late Sinemurian to Toarcian (E.H. Davies, pers. comm., 1986). The thickest occurrence of Iroquois Formation is interpreted to be in the Bonnet P-23 well at the southwestern edge of the Scotian Shelf (Fig. 5.16). There, just over 800 m of dolostone were encountered and described as rose, cream, tan or white, micro- to coarsely crystalline with intervals of fair to good intercrystalline and vuggy porosity (Petro-Canada, 1984). The base of the formation was not drilled but seismic data indicate the total thickness of the Iroquois Formation at Bonnet P-23 to be approximately 1600 m. Thick developments of the formation occur as far east as Albatross B-13.

In several wells in the Scotian Basin, a dolomitic unit directly overlying the salt in diapiric structures has been referred to as Iroquois Formation. Jansa and Wade (1975b) interpreted this unit to be a caprock facies and subsequent petrographic analysis of thin sections supported this interpretation (L.F. Jansa, pers. comm., 1980). P. Adams (pers. comm., 1986) reported aspects of caprock facies in all wells in which the dolomite was associated with salt. Analyses of palynomorph assemblages from the type section indicated a normal occurrence of Early Jurassic assemblages. However, the dolomitic facies in the Primrose N-50 well exhibited an unusual mixing of species and extreme to total carbonization of older forms (G.L. Williams, pers. comm., 1986). This "caprock" unit is particularly prominent in wells such as Adventure F-80, Huron P-96, Primrose N-50 and others on the Scotian Shelf and Gull F-72, Heron J-72, Merganser I-60, Petrel A-62, Tors Cove D-52 and others in the South Whale Subbasin. This facies is not related to the Iroquois Formation.

Mohican Formation is the name proposed by Given (1977) for the texturally immature clastic unit lying above the Iroquois Formation dolostone and below the Abenaki Formation limestone and its equivalents. The type section of the Mohican Formation is between -3839 and -4084 m (-12 595 and -13 399 ft) in the Oneida O-25 well, and it consists of dolomitic siltstones and fine grained sandstones

interbedded with red, red-brown and green shales. The base of the formation was not penetrated. Barss et al. (1979) dated the type section as Callovian. Recent palynological studies by E.H. Davies (pers. comm., 1986) show the age of the Mohican Formation in the Mohican I-100 well to be Aalenian-early Bajocian (Fig. 5.24).

The post-breakup surface along the margin of the Scotian Basin was a complex of fault blocks. The Mohican Formation completed the process of filling the rift grabens and overlapped the basement highs. Figure 5.25 illustrates the thickness of Middle Jurassic and older sediments on the Scotian Shelf in areas where the Scatarie marker occurs. In this figure, much of the irregularity on the LaHave Platform is due to Mohican and older graben fill sediments because the post-Mohican sediments thicken uniformly to the southeast. On seismic sections from the LaHave Platform, the top of the Mohican is picked directly below the event corresponding to the Scatarie Member of the Abenaki Formation. Where the Mohican Formation is thin over basement highs, it is commonly characterized by strong subparallel reflections indicating intervals with an increased content of limestone or siltstone. Particularly convincing evidence that these reflectors are carbonates occurs south of the Ojibwa E-07 well in two strong reflective segments within the Mohican Formation. Where the Mohican Formation thickens into grabens, the internal reflections are weaker and less continuous. The beds filling the grabens onlap the graben sides producing parallel and subparallel seismic reflections of varying amplitudes. The onlap of the breakup unconformity by the Mohican and Iroquois formations, across the LaHave Platform, is shown clearly in Figure 5.24.

Extremely thick "molasse type" sequences were built out across the hinge zone from the LaHave Platform and Canso Ridge, and show sigmoidal and complex sigmoidal-oblique patterns on the seismic records. The reflections lose their strength and continuity in the seaward direction due to decreasing sand-shale ratios. A distinct unconformity has been identified on seismic profiles within the upper part of the Mohican facies in the area of the Mic Mac wells (Fig. 5.19) indicating a significant hiatus in basin subsidence.

The fact that the Iroquois Formation is really a facies unit coeval with the lower part of the Mohican Formation is documented by the lithologic and biostratigraphic correlation between the Glooscap C-63, Moheida P-15, Mohican I-100 and Acadia K-62 wells (Fig. 5.24). The Iroquois Formation is best developed along the outer edge of the LaHave Platform where the environment was favourable for carbonate deposition. In Mohican I-100 it is a dolomitized oolitic and pelletoid grainstone indicating deposition in a warm, shallow, agitated marine environment. Landward of this, it is represented by a microcrystalline dolomitic mudstone with some nodular anhydrite indicative of a possible sabkha environment. Farther landward still, at Glooscap C-63, the Iroquois facies is absent and the entire section, between the base of the Abenaki Formation and the breakup unconformity at the top of the volcanic rocks, is included in the Mohican Formation (Fig. 5.24). This interval consists of white to red sandstones which are thinly bedded, poorly sorted and interbedded with red siltstones and shales. A few thin beds of dolostone occur in the lower part of the formation. Seismic profiles show that a lower facies of the Mohican Formation lies beneath the

---

[1] McIver (1972), who designated type sections for many of the formations in the Scotian Basin, used '−' to indicate a sea-level datum. That system is followed here when referring to McIver's type sections. Other depths used in this chapter are drilling depths which are read directly from well logs.

dolostones in the graben south of the Glooscap well (Fig. 5.24). This is another indication that the Iroquois Formation is a relatively localized facies controlled by the paleotopography.

Detailed palynozonation of the Mohican Formation in the Glooscap C-63 well indicates that it is Pliensbachian to early Bajocian making it essentially coeval to the Mohican and Iroquois formations in the Mohican I-100 and Moheida P-15 wells (Fig. 5.24). The maximum thickness of these formations in the Mohican Subbasin is interpreted to be more than 1600 m. However, seaward from the Mohican Subbasin, across the Moheida Ridge and towards the Acadia K-62 well, the Mohican Formation is a rapidly thickening, prograding, predominantly clastic (molasse) sequence more than 2000 m thick. Its upper part contains interbeds of brown oolitic limestone. It is overlain by a greatly overthickened Scatarie Member (Fig. 5.24). In this area a strong, low frequency reflection 1400 m below the bottom of Acadia K-62, and above interpreted salt, may be from the Iroquois facies.

Beneath the eastern Scotian Shelf, the Mohican Formation also varies greatly in thickness as it prograges

southward across the hinge zone and onto the top of the evaporite facies in the Abenaki Subbasin. North of the hinge zone its thickness increases from the depositional edge to about 300 m. It is about 500 m thick in the western end of the Abenaki Subbasin but, as the subbasin plunges to the east, the Mohican thickens to more than 4000 m. In an area both to the west and east of the Iroquois J-17 well there is a thin but strong reflection at the base of the Mohican sequence which is interpreted to be from a carbonate bed, possibly the Iroquois Formation. The Mohican and Iroquois formations cannot be traced beneath the Sable Subbasin because of their great depth. Regional facies distributions, and projections of subsidence, however, indicate that at least 2 km of sediments of late Sinemurian to Aalenian age probably occur there.

Figures 5.26 and 5.27 are cross-sections which cross the hinge zone in the vicinity of Cohasset L-97, and show the clastic facies of the Mohican Formation prograding into the Sable Subbasin. There is a very strong reflector just above basement at the edge of a salt pillow, that is interpreted as a volcanic bed (Fig. 5.52, in pocket, Section D-D'; 3.20 sec at S.P. 3350 and Fig. 5.26). A bright reflection

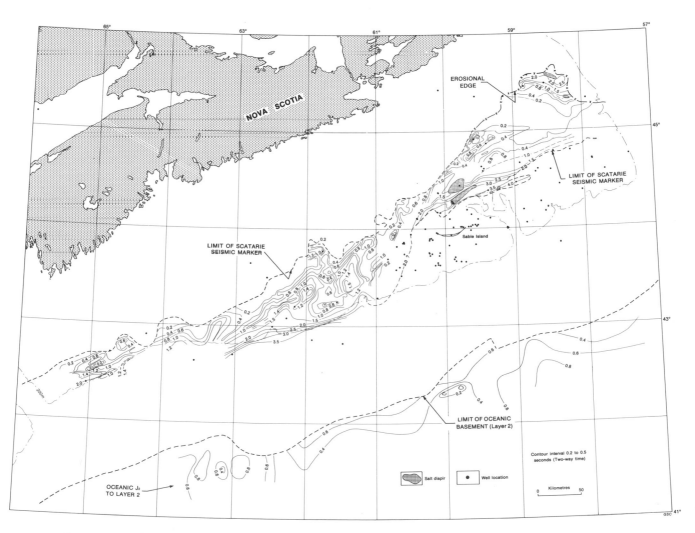

Figure 5.25 Seismic isochron map-Scatarie marker to basement and J_2 to oceanic Layer 2. Contour interval variable

above the salt pillow is shown as a thin unit of Iroquois facies. The Cohasset L-97 well (Fig. 5.52 in pocket, Section E-E', and Fig. 5.27), bottomed in a dolomitic facies of Middle Jurassic age (R.A. Fensome, pers. comm., 1986) which is interpreted to be within the upper part of the Mohican Formation. The age and stratigraphic position of this dolomitic facies precludes its correlation with the Iroquois Formation.

Lower Jurassic stratigraphy of the LaHave Platform is summarized as consisting of continental clastics, the product of tectonic adjustments induced by continental breakup, interfingering with supratidal evaporitic dolostones which grade seaward into dolomitized shallow marine carbonates and beyond that into thick, marine clastics. Eastward, in the area of transition from the platform to the subbasins, the depositional environment was generally not favourable for extensive development of the Iroquois facies and a thick clastic wedge of Mohican Formation prograded over the underlying redbeds and evaporites. Regionally, the Mohican Formation overlies the breakup unconformity and in the Abenaki Subbasin a second unconformity was noted within the Mohican Formation. The extent of the latter unconformity across the Abenaki and Sable subbasins is unknown. The overall age of the Iroquois and Mohican formations is ?late Sinemurian to early Bajocian (E.H. Davies, pers. comm., 1986; G.L. Williams, pers. comm., 1986).

Scots Bay and McCoy Brook formations

In the Scots Bay region of Nova Scotia, and at other localities around the Bay of Fundy, and offshore in the Chinampas N-37 and Cape Spencer No. 1 wells, sediments which are coeval with the lower part of the Mohican Formation rest unconformably on the North Mountain Basalt. These sediments, the Scots Bay and McCoy Brook formations (Fig. 5.21), consist of a series of red eolian sandstones; light grey-green calcareous, lacustrine, sandstones, siltstones and mudstones; red to grey sandstones and mudstones; and minor light grey, arenaceous limestone and siliceous limestone with large chert concretions. A sparse pollen assemblage suggested that the Triassic-Jurassic boundary occurred within the Scots Bay Formation just above the North Mountain Basalt (J.P. Bujak, pers. comm., 1979). However, recent discoveries of locally abundant dinosaur and reptile bones in the McCoy Brook formation on the north shore of Minas Basin indicate an Early Jurassic age for this formation (P. Olsen and N. Shubin, pers. comm., 1986). From this macrofossil evidence, and the position of the formations above the basalt flows and the breakup unconformity, they are interpreted to be mid-Early Jurassic in age and therefore coeval with the lower part of the Mohican Formation.

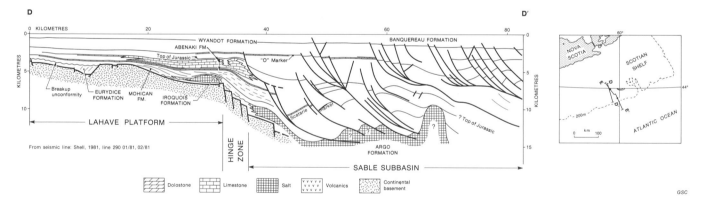

Figure 5.26 Geological cross section D-D', LaHave Platform to Sable Subbasin. Location also shown in Figure 5.18, in pocket.

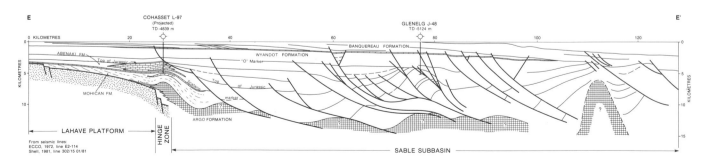

Figure 5.27 Geological cross section E-E', LaHave Platform to Sable Subbasin. Seismic detail of carbonate bank in Cohasset L-97 is shown in Figure 5.32. Line of section is also in Figures 5.18 (in pocket) and 5.26. Legend in Figure 5.26.

Western Bank Group

The Western Bank Group (McIver, 1972) includes four facies-dependent, Middle and Upper Jurassic formations deposited as normal marine conditions were established across the basin. The group is characterized by a continental clastic facies designated the Mohawk Formation; shallow marine sandstones, shales and limestones of the Mic Mac Formation; a shelf carbonate facies, the Abenaki Formation and a basinal shale facies, the Verrill Canyon Formation (Fig. 5.21). Much has been learned from seismic data gathered in the late 1970s and early 1980s about the thickness and facies distribution of this group of formations.

Abenaki Formation

The Abenaki Formation, named and described by McIver (1972), is predominantly a limestone unit. The type section is from -2858 to -3821 m (-9375 to -12 535 ft) in the Oneida O-25 well on the LaHave Platform. Regional correlations with Jurassic limestone facies on the Grand Banks were discussed by Jansa and Wade (1975b). A comprehensive description of the Abenaki Formation and its four mem-

bers, the Artimon, Baccaro, Misaine and Scatarie, was published by Eliuk (1978).

Although it forms a distinctive lithologic complex and a prominent seismic sequence, the Abenaki Formation of the type section is limited in areal extent (Fig. 5.28). The best developments are at the hinge between LaHave Platform and Sable Subbasin (Fig. 5.26, 5.27, Fig. 5.52, in pocket) where the formation was penetrated by the Demascota G-32 and Cohasset D-42 and L-97 wells. In a southwesterly direction the Abenaki Formation follows the hinge zone to the southern extremity of the Scotian Basin. To the north and east of the Cohasset wells the formation interfingers with the clastic and carbonate facies of the Mic Mac Formation. It is now recognized that the thick carbonate units seen as intermittent strong reflections on seismic profiles from the eastern part of the Scotian Shelf are not Abenaki Formation, as such, but rather a series of localized limestone facies. These facies commonly cap prograding clastic wedges within the Mic Mac Formation. Where seen, the contact between the Abenaki Formation and the underlying Mohican clastics is sharp and apparently conformable.

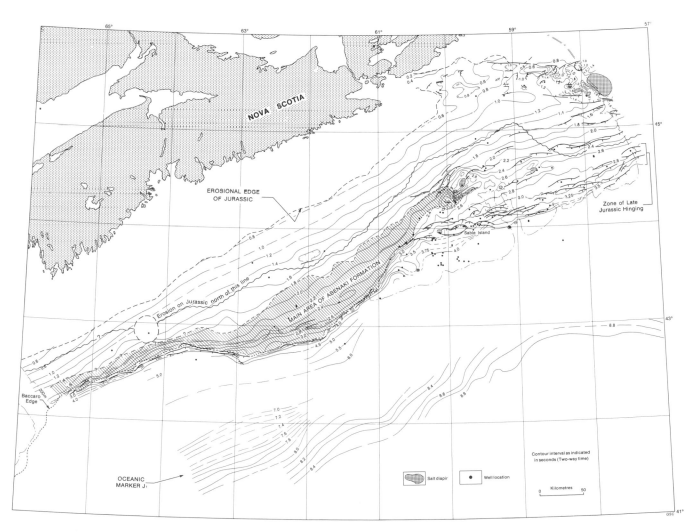

Figure 5.28 Seismic time-structure map, top Jurassic and oceanic equivalents. Main area of Abenaki Formation and Baccaro carbonate edge are indicated.

The age of the Abenaki Formation in the type section is Callovian to Berriasian-Valanginian (Barss et al., 1979) or Callovian to Tithonian (Ascoli, 1976). Recent studies by E.H. Davies (pers. comm., 1986) indicate that the lower limit may be as old as early Bajocian (Fig. 5.24). A consideration of all data suggests the upper limit is very near the Jurassic-Cretaceous boundary.

The lowermost subdivision of the Abenaki Formation is the Scatarie Member. It is the most extensive of the members of the Abenaki Formation, extending from north and east of the Erie D-26 and Wyandot E-53 wells on the Canso Ridge to west of the Bonnet P-23 well on the LaHave Platform. In cross-section it is, in essence, a seaward-thickening wedge, which ranges from a depositional edge along the northern flank of the basin to more than 600 m in thickness in the Acadia K-62 well (Fig. 5.24). At this location there is an unconformity within the Scatarie Member and seismic and biostratigraphic data show a lower limestone unit, which thins onto the Moheida Ridge, and an upper wedge that is not present in other wells in the area. In Abenaki Subbasin this upper unit is represented by a shale and sandstone facies which is included in the Mic Mac Formation.

The Scatarie Member is predominantly an oolitic limestone. Eliuk (1978) described four facies within the Scatarie Member that together indicate deepening upward transgressive cycles which he interpreted as being related to eustatic sea level changes. Each cycle is 10 to 60 m thick and up to four cycles have been encountered in wells. Lithologic variations occur in the proximal and distal areas. In Acadia K-62 the lithology of the lower wedge is brown to grey-brown oolitic limestone interbedded with fine grained white sandstone. Seismic profiles reveal this wedge to overlie prograding clastics in the Mohican Formation. The age of the Scatarie Member is from Bajocian to early Callovian (Ascoli, 1976; Barss et al., 1979; E.H. Davies, pers. comm., 1986).

The seismic response from the Scatarie limestone is generally a strong reflector in both the shelf and basinal areas. This is due to its position between the Misaine and Mohican clastics. In Abenaki Subbasin the reflector ends abruptly at the shaleout edge of the Scatarie, but it can extend for great distances seaward of the edge of the Baccaro Member south of LaHave Platform (Fig. 5.26, 5.27, 5.29, 5.30).

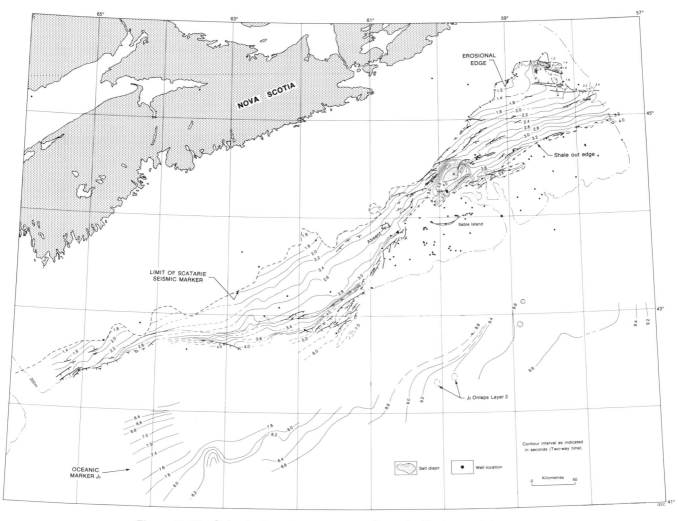

Figure 5.29 Seismic time-structure map, Scatarie Marker and J_2.

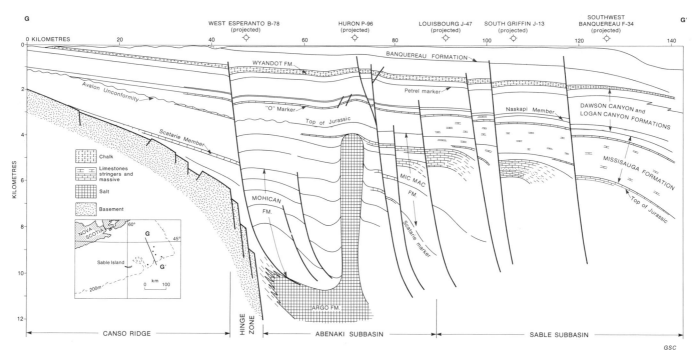

Figure 5.30 Geological cross-section G-G' showing development of limestone facies in the Mic Mac Formation. Location also shown in Figure 5.18, in pocket.

Eliuk (1978) speculated that a slope facies equivalent to the Scatarie Member occurred in the bottom of Cohasset D-42. The correlation of seismic profiles through this area confirms that the Scatarie facies is indeed present, however it was not penetrated by the well. A change in the character of the seismic reflector, in conjunction with a change in depositional dip, does take place near the seaward limit of the Scatarie seismic event in the Cohasset area indicating the presence of deeper water (Fig. 5.27, 5.29).

The Misaine Member is a transgressive shale facies that overlies the Scatarie Member limestone. It is thickest in the Acadia K-62 well (218 m) whereas in the Wyandot E-53 well on the Canso Ridge it is less than 15 m thick. The member is predominantly a dark grey, slightly calcareous shale with minor interbeds of siltstone and very fine grained sandstone. The Misaine shale, occurring as it does between thick carbonate units, generates a good, regional seismic reflection. Changes in the amplitude and sharpness of this reflection are variously attributed to changes in the thickness of the Misaine Member or to changes in the limestone content of the adjacent units. Generally, the age of the member is from Callovian to early Oxfordian. However, it may be in part younger on the western LaHave Platform due to persistence of the shale facies at the expense of overlying carbonates (Fig. 5.21).

The Baccaro is the thickest member of the Abenaki Formation but is relatively limited in areal extent. It occurs only in a zone 15 to 25 km wide along the hinge to the west of the Abenaki J-56 and L-57 wells broadening between Oneida O-25 and Mohican I-100 and then narrowing again westward from Albatross B-13 (Fig. 5.16, 5.28, 5.31). The member is thickest along the extreme edge of the Late Jurassic shelf where Bonnet P-23 and Acadia K-62 encountered thicknesses of 1087 and 1180 m, respectively.

The Baccaro Member is a complex of environmentally controlled carbonate types (Eliuk, 1978). The most prominent is the extensive bank facies of oolitic limestone that characterizes the lower part of the Baccaro over much of the LaHave Platform. Due to regression, however, this bank facies was later limited to a zone near the paleoshelf edge. Nowhere has the Baccaro Member been found to be a reef, although wells such as Demascota G-32 and Cohasset D-42 drilled at the carbonate front, encountered a significant increase in skeletal limestones. Shoreward, these lithologies are replaced by Eliuk's "moat" and "ridge" facies of argillaceous limestone and mixed carbonates and clastics, respectively. Basinward of the carbonate front are the coeval shales of the Verrill Canyon Formation. The age of the Baccaro is Oxfordian to Tithonian from foraminifers and ostracodes (Ascoli, 1976).

The seismic expression of the Baccaro Member is complex. There is a strong, sharp reflection from the top of the member and several weaker, subparallel reflections from within it. These overlie the pair of strong events representing the Misaine and Scatarie members. Shoreward, the strong reflection from the top of the Baccaro Member weakens as the limestone interfingers with clastics (Fig. 5.32a). Deeper Baccaro events maintain their subparallel patterns but become progressively weaker landward. The weakened upper reflection has been mapped regionally as a time-line equivalent to the top of the Jurassic (Fig. 5.28). The regional continuity of this seismic horizon, which is tied to most of the wells on the Scotian Shelf, supports the dating of Ascoli (1976) but raises doubts about the accuracy of the palynological age of the Baccaro Member as presented by Barss et al. (1979).

The seismic expression of the Baccaro carbonate front is variable. Near Cohasset L-97, the top bright seismic event maintains its character until the edge of the carbonate bank is reached. At this point it and the weaker

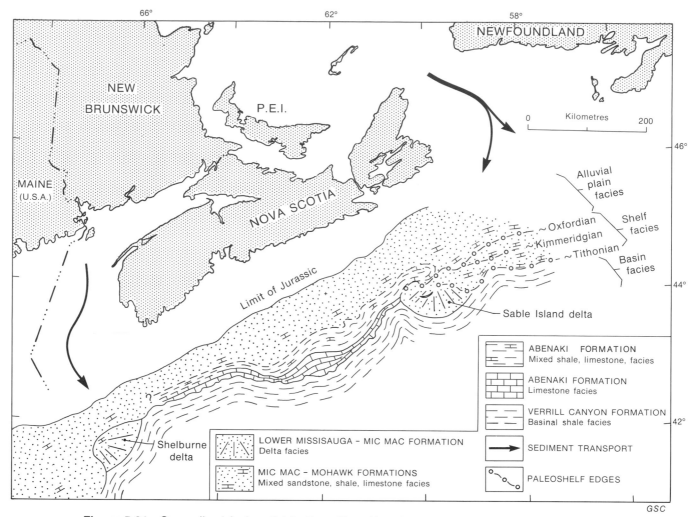

Figure 5.31 Generalized facies distribution, Abenaki and equivalent formations, Scotian Shelf.

internal Baccaro events end abruptly. Bright reflections from limestone stringers can be followed from the Baccaro edge out into the clastic basin (Fig. 5.32a). Southwest from Oneida O-25, the reflection from the top of the limestone is continuous over the smooth bank edge and down the gentle paleoslope (Fig. 5.32b).

In the area from Cohasset L-97 to Penobscot L-30, which is transitional between LaHave Platform and Abenaki Subbasin, the lower part of the Baccaro Member is interbedded with tongues of shale. These represent the transition between the stable carbonate platform to the west and a mixed facies of clastics and carbonates to the east. The eastward limit of the Baccaro Member is taken to be where the carbonate starts to break up, and the equivalent section thickens and progrades basinward (Fig. 5.33). This occurs southeast of a line from Cohasset L-97 to Abenaki J-56 and then northward to the limit of carbonate deposition (Fig. 5.31). This shaling-out is recognized in Penobscot L-30 where a 300-m shale unit lies between two carbonate zones. Farther east, the entire section equivalent to the Abenaki Formation consists of a mixed sandstone-shale-limestone facies of the Mic Mac Formation. Although carbonate units within the Mic Mac Formation are similar to parts of the Baccaro Member they

are discontinuous, apparently forming local outer shelf banks (Fig. 5.30).

There is no Abenaki Formation to the east and northeast of Sable Island as was indicated by Jansa and Wade (1975b), Eliuk (1978) and others. Eastward, from Penobscot L-30 to the vicinity of the Uniacke G-72 well, the reflection from the limestone at the top of the Jurassic maintains its strength whereas lower limestone reflectors are seen to "peel" away below it into the underlying clastics. From Uniacke G-72 to South Venture O-59 additional limestone beds are developed in successive fault slices (Fig. 5.33). In the Banquereau area of the eastern Scotian Shelf, the equivalent of the Abenaki Formation consists, seismically, of relatively weak, subparallel reflections which prograde seaward. The only limestones are in the Scatarie Member, which rapidly shales out south of the Canso Ridge, and in locally thick sequences within the Mic Mac Formation where they are expressed as intermittent

Figure 5.32 Seismic sections showing the relationships of Jurassic markers and the nature of the carbonate front at Cohasset L-97 (a) and Albatross B-13 (b).

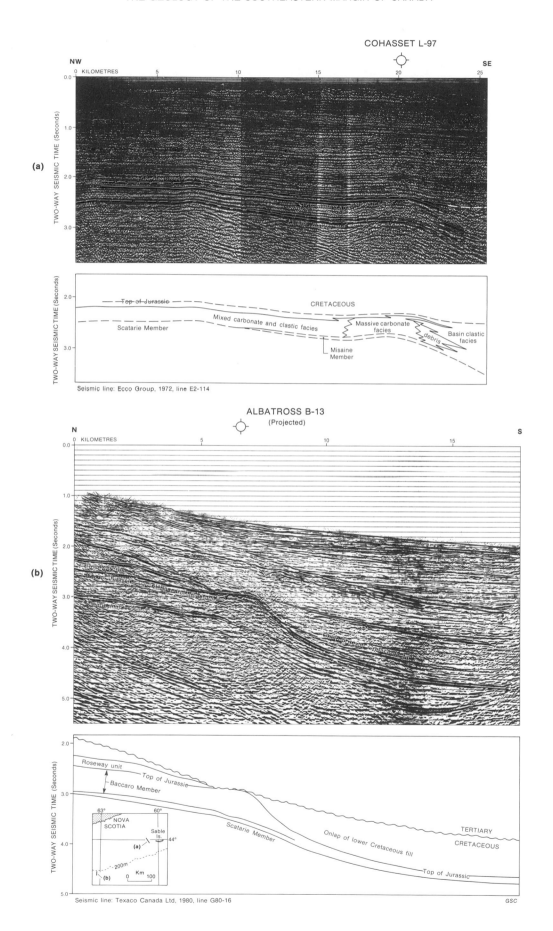

COHASSET L-97

(a)

Seismic line: Ecco Group, 1972, line E2-114

ALBATROSS B-13
(Projected)

(b)

Seismic line: Texaco Canada Ltd, 1980, line G80-16

GSC

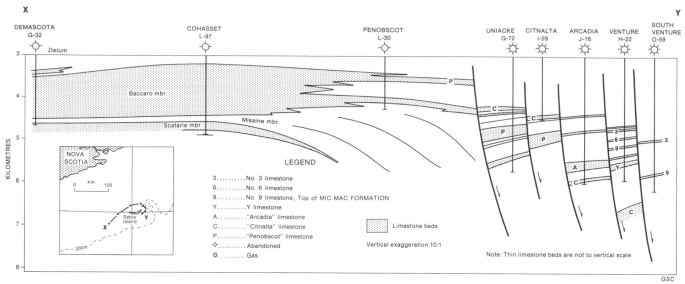

Figure 5.33 Schematic diagram illustrating the breakup of the Abenaki Formation near Sable Island.

strong reflectors which climb stratigraphically as they progress seaward. The limestones are thus progressively younger southward from the Canso Ridge and the carbonate environment was restricted to areas near the outbuilding paleoshelf edges (Fig. 5.31).

Eliuk (1978) erected the Artimon Member as the uppermost member of the Abenaki Formation and designated its type section between 3401-3515 m (11 157 and 11 532 ft) in Demascota G-32. This member is characterized by an abundance of lithistid sponges in grey to brown argillaceous limestone encased in Verrill Canyon Formation shale. The Artimon Member has only been found in three wells and there is some uncertainty as to its age. In its type section the Artimon is poorly expressed on seismic records. In this location, Eliuk (1978) reported the presence of Valanginian-Hauterivian nannofossils in the Artimon Member, whereas P. Ascoli (pers. comm., 1979) dated this interval Tithonian-Berriasian; R.A. Fensome (pers. comm., 1985) as Berriasian- Valanginian and Jansa et al. (1982) dated it as Tithonian to Berriasian-Valanginian. In Cohasset D-42, where the interval designated as Artimon is Kimmeridgian (Barss et al., 1979; P. Ascoli, pers. comm., 1980) it is characterized on seismic records by a strengthening of the reflection immediately above the top Jurassic event. In its third location, in the Moheida P-15 well, the Artimon Member correlates seismically with the "O" Marker and it is dated as Hauterivian (P. Ascoli, pers. comm., 1979).

The relationships of the Artimon Member with the Missisauga and Verrill Canyon formations are described at the end of the section on the Missisauga Formation and its equivalents.

Eliuk (1978) also described three types of shelf-edge morphologies relative to the Abenaki Formation and designated them "platform", "ramp", and "prograding". The platform type is typical of the Abenaki on the LaHave Platform and shows the most abrupt change seaward from carbonate bank to the adjacent slope and basin clastic facies (Fig. 5.26, Fig. 5.52, in pocket). In the past, the sea-

ward front of the Abenaki Formation has been considered the paleoshelf edge (McIver, 1972; Jansa and Wade, 1975b; Given, 1977; Eliuk, 1978; McWhae, 1981). However, from detailed study of a large amount of seismic data, the morphology of the carbonate platform appears to have varied across the area. In the vicinity of the Demascota G-32 and Cohasset D-42 wells, drilled at the carbonate front, there was only minor seafloor relief during deposition of the carbonate and the coeval seaward sequences of shale and sand (Fig. 5.27, 5.32a). In other words, the Upper Jurassic facies of the Sable Island delta appears to have almost kept up with the flanking carbonate deposition resulting in a gradual increase in the gradient of the seafloor to a shelf break approximately 20 km to the south of the carbonate front (Fig. 5.28). Farther to the west, however, seismic data indicate that the carbonate front stood in considerable relief above coeval basin sediments and did form the Upper Jurassic shelf edge and upper slope (Fig. 5.32b).

The ramp and prograding morphologies are related, but are interpreted as a phenomenon of the Mic Mac Formation rather than of the Abenaki Formation (Fig. 5.19, 5.30). These morphologies are found throughout the Abenaki and Sable subbasins and reflect the greater rate of subsidence of the depocentre in these areas, the strong influx of siliciclastics, and the limited environment for carbonate deposition. This is seen specifically in the aforementioned zone east and south of the Penobscot wells where a prominent series of prograding beds occurs beneath the eastward thinning limestone tongues of the Baccaro Member. These clearly indicate a major outpouring of clastics into the Sable Subbasin at the site of the Sable Island delta. Concurrently, down-to-the-basin faulting resulted in stratigraphic units thickening rapidly in a southward direction. In the Sable Island area this is best seen in an overlying unit, such as the lower member of the Missisauga Formation, which is less than 300 m thick in Citnalta I-59 but nearly 1000 m thick in the Venture field only 10 km to the south.

Mohawk and Mic Mac formations

There are several siliciclastic facies which are equivalent to the Abenaki Formation (Fig. 5.21, 5.31). The Mic Mac Formation (McIver, 1972) is the updip facies of the Baccaro Member. The type section, between -3086 and -4382 m (-10 125 and -14 375 ft) in Mic Mac H-86, consists of approximately 55% shale and siltstone, 35% sandstone, and 10% carbonate. The depositional environment is interpreted as that of a shallow marine back-bank (McIver, 1972). Studies of foraminifers and ostracodes indicate the age is Bathonian-Callovian to Tithonian (Ascoli, 1976). Therefore, the top of the Mic Mac Formation is slightly below the Cretaceous-Jurassic boundary.

The Mohawk Formation (McIver, 1972), as redefined by Given (1977), is predominantly a sandstone unit representing the more continental facies of the Mic Mac Formation beneath the western Scotian Shelf. The type section is between -1578 and -2081 m (-5177 and -6827 ft) in Mohawk B-93 where the lithology is approximately 47% fine- to coarse-grained feldspathic sandstone and siltstone, 41% interbeds of green, red and grey shale and 12% light brown, micritic to oolitic limestone. The age is Bathonian to Berriasian-Valanginian (Barss et al., 1979) and Batho-

nian to Late Kimmeridgian-Tithonian (P. Ascoli, pers. comm., 1980).

The mixed sandstone-shale-limestone facies, described above in conjunction with the breakup of the carbonate bank, is widespread beneath the southeastern Scotian Shelf. Although this neritic facies differs in both lithology and depositional environment from the type section of the Mic Mac Formation, it is included in this formation. Several wells have been drilled into its upper part but it has not been fully penetrated. These sediments were deposited in a strand plain environment which was undergoing relatively rapid subsidence seaward of a broad alluvial plain system. The isochron map of the interval top Jurassic to Scatarie (Fig. 5.34) shows about 1 second of thickening of the section southward from the Canso Ridge. In the outer part of Sable Subbasin, south of the limit of the Scatarie Member limestone, the equivalent interval thickens by an additional 2 seconds.

In Sable Subbasin, the Mic Mac Formation consists of a series of thick, seaward and upward building sequences interpreted to consist of a limestone-sandstone topset, giving way to a sandstone-shale foreset and a shale-sandstone bottomset. Consequently, as each sequence builds seaward

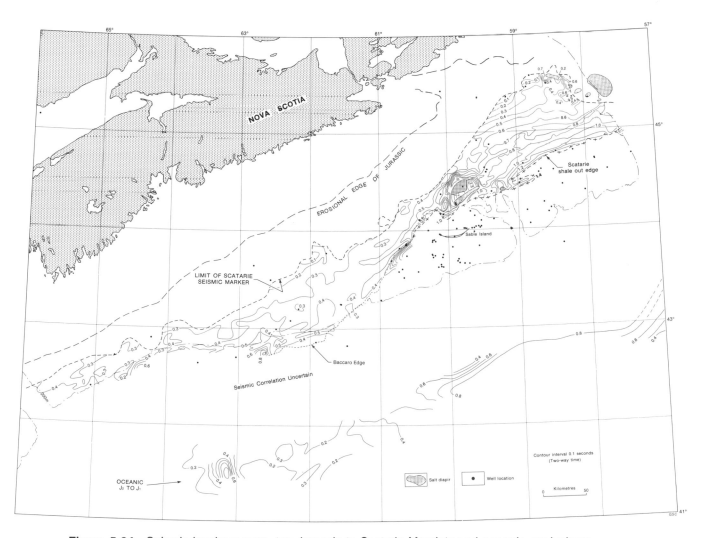

Figure 5.34 Seismic isochron map, top Jurassic to Scatarie Member and oceanic equivalents.

over the previous one, the topset limestone beds are progressively younger (Fig. 5.30).

The upper 1000 m of the neritic facies of the Mic Mac Formation have been encountered in wells drilled in the Venture area. The top of the formation has been placed arbitrarily at the top of the No. 9 Limestone (see Fig. 5.36) of Kimmeridgian-Tithonian age (P. Ascoli, pers. comm., 1982) which lies at a depth of about 5100 m in the Venture H-22 well. In this area, the lithology is predominantly dark grey shale with thin interbeds of siltstone and sandstone and occasional thin limestone beds. The depositional environment is outer neritic.

The form of the Jurassic sedimentary wedge is illustrated in Figure 5.35. The wedge thickens gradually seaward from an onlap edge on the LaHave Platform to the Hinge Zone where it expands rapidly. In the Sable Island area, it is in excess of 5 seconds two-way time (14 km) in thickness but distally thins, south of the Slope Diapiric Province, to less than one second two-way time (2 km). This figure, like Figure 5.25, includes the pre-Jurassic graben fill sequences which account for some of the thick areas on the platform.

In summary, the Abenaki and equivalent formations are interpreted as forming a thick outer shelf carbonate bank complex which developed on the stable LaHave Platform and was flanked to the east by thicker alluvial plain, deltaic or paralic equivalent sequences in the more rapidly subsiding subbasins. Distally, all of these units pass to shales of the Verrill Canyon Formation. This formation is described following the section on the Missisauga Formation and its equivalents.

Avalon Unconformity

During the latest Jurassic, the eastern margin of Canada was affected by the breakup of the Iberian and North American plates. Most strongly affected was the area of the Grand Banks south of Newfoundland where there was uplift, deformation and extensive erosion of Jurassic sediments. The breakup unconformity in this area was named the Avalon Unconformity (Jansa and Wade, 1975b). In the Scotian Basin, the Avalon Unconformity was observed across the inner part of the Canso Ridge, the Orpheus Graben, Burin Platform, the western flank of the Laurentian Subbasin and the eastern flank of the South Whale Subbasin.

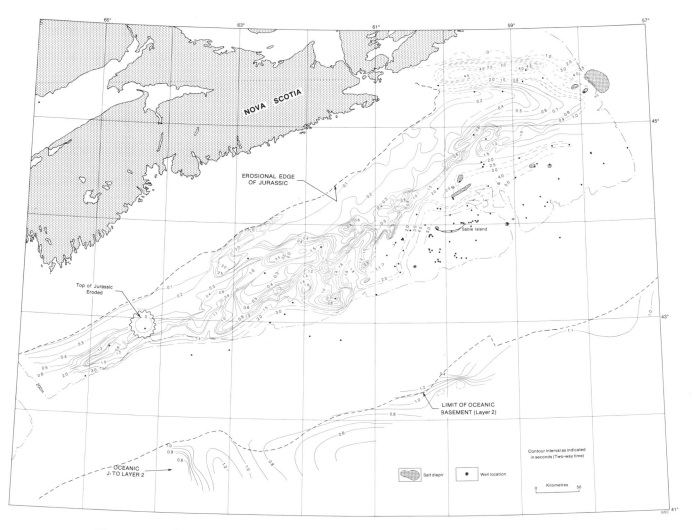

Figure 5.35   Seismic isochron map, top Jurassic to Basement and oceanic equivalents.

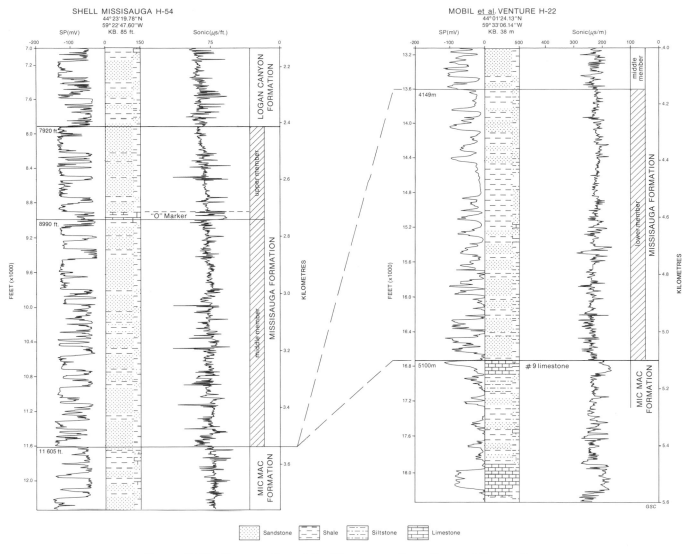

Figure 5.36 Type section of the Missisauga Formation and its members.

Seismic profiles collected during the early stages of exploration of the Grand Banks and adjacent areas, together with data from wells, showed a profound angular unconformity separating deformed pre-unconformity Jurassic and older sediments and evaporite facies from undeformed Cretaceous and younger sediments. Other Cretaceous unconformities were also recognized. Following the discovery of oil and gas at Hibernia in 1979, there was a dramatic increase in the acquisition of seismic data and exploratory drilling in the Jeanne d' Arc Basin (Grant et al., 1986). Interpretation of these data indicated the presence of additional unconformities in the Upper Jurassic to Upper Cretaceous section, several of which have been referred to as the Avalon Unconformity.

The first description of Mesozoic unconformities in the subsurface of the Grand Banks was by Bartlett and Smith (1971). Based on an integrated analysis of lithic and faunal data from the Grand Falls H-09 (Fig. 1, in pocket) and Tors Cove D-52 wells, these authors recognized a minimum of seven unconformity bounded sequences including three within the Cretaceous. The oldest recognized unconformity was between Middle(?) and Upper Jurassic rocks and Lower Cretaceous rocks.

Sherwin (1973) noted the occurrence of a strong unconformity which he interpreted to be within the lower Upper Cretaceous, near the top of the Lower Cretaceous, which was "accompanied by thinning of Cenomanian strata and apparent attenuation of some Lower Cretaceous stages ...". He related the development of this unconformity to a global event near the Lower-Upper Cretaceous boundary.

Amoco and Imperial (1973) described "... a major angular unconformity of from Early to Middle Cretaceous age" separating relatively flat-lying Lower Cretaceous sediments from deformed Jurassic rocks which were preserved in structural basins bounded by faulted basement blocks. They correlated a Lower Cretaceous sandstone interval above the unconformity with the Missisauga Formation of the Scotian Shelf. These authors also named the basal transgressive clastic sediments overlying the mid-Cretaceous unconformity the Eider Unit and suggested a correlation to the Logan Canyon Formation of the Scotian Shelf.

213

Upshaw et al. (1974) integrated lithostratigraphic and biostratigraphic data from the Grand Banks and recognized that the deposition of the post unconformity sequence began in the latest Jurassic or earliest Cretaceous. These authors also recognized a series of lesser unconformities associated with transgressive and regressive cycles that eventually inundated the Grand Banks and they documented the diachroneity of the Eider Unit and the overlying Petrel Limestone.

Jansa and Wade (1975a,b) also described the prominent angular unconformity separating deformed pre-unconformity Jurassic from undeformed post-unconformity Cretaceous strata on the Grand Banks. They named it the Avalon Unconformity. These authors attributed the development of the unconformity to the Late Cimmerian Orogeny associated with the decoupling of the eastern margin of the Grand Banks from the Iberian Peninsula during latest Jurassic or earliest Cretaceous time. They also recognized a reduction in the hiatus away from the Grand Banks.

McWhae (1981) correlated a series of unconformities along the Atlantic margin from the Scotian Shelf to Baffin Bay and referred to a mid-Cretaceous (100-85 Ma) unconformity as the Avalon Unconformity. However, the Labrador Unconformity in McWhae's Figure 7 equates to the Avalon Unconformity in this chapter.

A key feature in understanding the Avalon Unconformity is a large structural element, the Avalon Uplift (Wade, 1973) whose development coincided with the deformation of the Jurassic sediments. Subsequently, the western flank of the Avalon Uplift was onlapped by progressively younger Cretaceous strata and, on the axis of the uplift, Cenomanian clastics completed the transgression (Barss et al., 1979). The strata immediately above the Avalon Unconformity all overlie deformed Jurassic or older rocks which had been peneplaned by erosion. This indicates that the main tectonic event occurred earlier, rather than later, in the Cretaceous.

Local unconformities within the Lower Cretaceous section are found in the outer part of the South Whale Subbasin, where salt diapirs are prevalent. A period of salt movement in this area during the Early Cretaceous resulted in the formation of large withdrawal synclines. Thick lenses of Lower Cretaceous fill onlap the flanks of these synclines and occasionally exhibit some erosion. The other intra-Cretaceous unconformities, described by Bartlett and Smith (1971) and others, are the result of fluctuating shorelines as the Avalon Uplift was slowly covered. These unconformities are onlapped by overlying sediments and exhibit little or no associated deformation or erosion.

The data quality and quantity are still insufficient to establish with certainty the maximum age of the Avalon Unconformity. However, on the southeastern part of the Scotian Shelf, where there is no longer any angularity associated with the unconformity, it lies within the lowermost part of the Cretaceous section. Across the eastern end of the Abenaki Subbasin the top Jurassic reflector is eroded marking the western limit of influence of the Avalon Uplift (Fig. 5.28, 5.30). Thus it is concluded that the deformation associated with the breakup of North America and Iberia was a relatively short-lived and locally severe event at about the beginning of the Cretaceous. The subsidence of the Avalon Uplift was relatively slow and intermittent resulting in a series of smaller unconformities

some of which are difficult to distinguish from local movements.

Nova Scotia Group

McIver (1972) included the thick, regressive, Lower Cretaceous siliciclastic Missisauga and Logan Canyon formations in the Nova Scotia Group. The Missisauga Formation was deposited by a major river system which probably drained much of the northeastern part of the Canadian Shield during the Early Cretaceous. It is characterized by a broad alluvial plain facies with adjacent delta and prodelta facies. The deltaic sequences are best known in the Sable Island area but probably also occur in parts of the Laurentian and South Whale subbasins. The Logan Canyon Formation consists of thick paralic facies with fining upward sandstone sequences and decreased sandstone-shale ratios which indicate a regional reduction in the elevation of source areas and deposition in a more mature system.

Missisauga Formation

The contact between the Mic Mac and Missisauga formations is generally conformable except in proximal areas of the LaHave Platform where erosion, associated with the Early Cretaceous regression, cut into the uppermost Jurassic sediments. This area of erosion is illustrated in Figure 5.28 which also shows the area of influence of the Avalon Unconformity by the seaward shift of the area of erosion across the eastern end of the Abenaki Subbasin.

Two type sections of the Missisauga Formation were designated by McIver (1972). The "updip" facies is represented by the interval between -2388 to -3511 m (-7835 and -11 520 ft) in Missisauga H-54, where the formation is a thick, dominantly sandstone sequence that was deposited in an alluvial plain environment. The type section of the "downdip" facies was designated in Cree E-35 between -2551 and -3719 m (-8370 and -12 200 ft). In this section the sandstones are thinner, less massive and the sand-shale ratio much less than in the updip section, reflecting the greater distance from source. Deposition was in a lower delta plain to inner neritic environment. A similar downdip facies is recognized in the Banquereau area with a reference section between 3918 and 4980 m in Southwest Banquereau F-34. In this area the coarse clastic content in the section is somewhat reduced and there is a corresponding increase in shale content. Deposition was in a marine shelf environment.

The Missisauga Formation is variable in thickness, because of its fluvial-deltaic nature. It ranges from a zero edge on the Avalon Uplift in the east and across the Burin and LaHave platforms to a thickness of more than 2000 m in the depocentre of the Sable Subbasin. The formation is less than 500 m thick on the LaHave Platform where it contains an increased amount of shale and carbonate. The maximum thickness drilled is more than 2100 m in the Venture area where the average rate of deposition for the formation is calculated at more than 8 cm/ka.

The age of the Missisauga Formation in McIver's type sections is Berriasian-Valanginian to Barremian, although uppermost Jurassic rocks occur in the basal part of the formation in many wells (Barss et al., 1979). A Hauterivian-Barremian age was reported for the Missisauga Formation in Southwest Banquereau F-34 (Petro-

Canada, 1983). In this well the Missisauga Formation overlies the Verrill Canyon Formation. This relationship is consistent with the seaward thickening observed on seismic data.

A consistent differentiation of the Missisauga and Mic Mac formations is not always easy. The correlation of facies-dependent formations which have gradational contacts inevitably involves diachronism. For example, the seismic reflection from the top of the type section of the Mic Mac Formation, if correlated through the Missisauga well, 22 km south, results in a tie more than 200 m below the base of the type section of the overlying Missisauga Formation. Therefore, McIver's description is followed and the base of the Missisauga Formation is picked at the shift from massive sandstones (Missisauga Formation) to thinner or more argillaceous sandstones (Mic Mac Formation) or at a significant increase in shale interbeds.

Jansa and Wade (1975b) described the "O" Marker, a transgressive limestone unit within the Missisauga, which, across much of the Scotian Shelf, divides the main alluvial and delta plain facies into an upper and lower sequence. These were the informal upper and lower units of Given (1977). Drilling since 1978, in the area of the Sable Island delta, has revealed a third facies. Therefore, a threefold subdivision of the Missisauga Formation into a lower member, a middle member, which equates to Given's lower unit, and an upper member is introduced here (Fig. 5.36).

The type section for the lower member of the Missisauga Formation is between 4149 and 5100 m in Venture H-22. It consists of a series of fine grained to pebbly, often coarsening upward sandstone beds and minor thin limestone beds within a section of grey marine shale. The base of the member is picked above a distinctive, local limestone bed which marks the top of the Kimmeridgian (P. Ascoli, pers. comm., 1982). The top of the member is picked at the top of a prominent shaly sequence which is dated as Berriasian-Valanginian (J.P. Bujak, pers. comm., 1979). It is overlain by thick, clean fine- to coarse-grained sandstones of the middle member of the Missisauga Formation. A complete section of the Missisauga Formation in the Venture B-43 well is shown later in Figure 5.49. The depositional environment of the lower member is delta front, including possible barrier bar, beach and tidal channel deposits grading upward into prodelta facies. This member probably is restricted to the region south of the outer zone of Late Jurassic hinging (Fig. 5.28). To the north of this area the lower member is much thinner and grades into a delta plain facies, which makes it difficult to differentiate from the middle member.

Sediments of the lower member were transported via local distributary systems to small clastic fans or active fault zones. The best documented example of such point concentrated deposition is in the Venture area where the lower Missisauga section expands across growth faults from less than 300 m in Citnalta to approximately 1000 m in the Venture field. In a west-east direction, the lower member extends at least from Cree to Bluenose 2G-47.

In summary, the Sable Island delta (lower member facies) is interpreted as developing in an area with rapid subsidence and a high rate of clastic deposition east of the Jurassic carbonate bank and within the zone of Late Jurassic-Early Cretaceous syndepositional faulting. The delta front-prodelta facies of the lower member of the Mis-

sisauga Formation spread southwestward to the Abenaki carbonate front (Fig. 5.31). Thus at the end of the Jurassic, from east to west, the continental shelf-slope break occurred at the front of a prograding mixed clastic and carbonate Mic Mac facies, the seaward bulge of the Sable Island delta, and the Abenaki carbonate front.

The type sections of the middle and upper members of the Missisauga Formation are included in the type section of the updip facies designated by McIver in the Missisauga H-54 well (Fig. 5.36). The middle member lies between 3537 and 2740 m (11 605 and 8990 ft) whereas the upper member, including the "O" Marker, occurs between 2740 and 2414 m (8990 and 7920 ft). A similar subdivision occurs in McIver's downdip section with the base of that section being the top of the lower member.

The Missisauga Formation is expressed on seismic profiles as parallel, continuous reflectors with occasional local depositional details such as shallow channels being visible. Beneath the eastern part of the Scotian Shelf, reflections from the top of and from within the formation are generally weak but they strengthen to the west, over the LaHave Platform, as the sequence thins and its carbonate content increases. The strongest internal reflector is the "O" Marker which, over most of the shelf, generates a single reflection but in the Banquereau area changes into a number of strong diverging loops.

The "O" Marker is a series of thin oolitic to skeletal and sandy limestone beds of Hauterivian to Barremian age which occur in the upper part of the Missisauga Formation (Jansa and Wade, 1975b; Barss et al., 1979). As such it provides a mappable horizon which, over much of the area, simulates the top of this formation. The time-structure map on the "O" Marker (Fig. 5.37) shows a gentle dip as far as the basement hinge zone. South of the hinge, the surface is more irregular, reflecting the effect of underlying mobile salt and of syndepositional extensional tectonics before plunging to depth over the paleoshelf edge.

Although the "O" Marker represents a minor transgressive episode in a regionally regressive period, it can be used to interpret the paleogeography of that time. Over much of the Scotian Shelf it covered a broad, essentially flat, delta plain. Proximally, on the Canso Ridge, the "O" Marker onlaps the Avalon Unconformity (Fig. 5.37). At its updip edge on the LaHave Platform it oversteps the Jurassic and onlaps the basement. Distally it forms a clinoform surface indicative of a change in water depth and probably marks the late Neocomian slope (Fig. 5.19, inset). Farther seaward, the marker disappears as the facies grades laterally into deeper water shales.

Locally, on the LaHave Platform, however, the "O" Marker downlaps westward onto Jurassic strata. The isochron map (Fig. 5.38) shows the southwestward thinning and its relationship to the underlying Baccaro carbonate front. It is apparent that, during deposition of the "O" Marker, portions of the outer LaHave Platform were sediment starved resulting in the downlap relationship. In local areas, such as north of Evangeline H-98, the marker is missing at the Jurassic paleoshelf break but reoccurs in the wedge of infilling sediments in front of the carbonate. This wedge eventually thins as it forms what appears to be a bottomset system.

In the southwestern part of the Sable Subbasin, in the vicinity of the Alma K-85 and F-67 and Wenonah J-75 wells, where deposition was relatively continuous, the

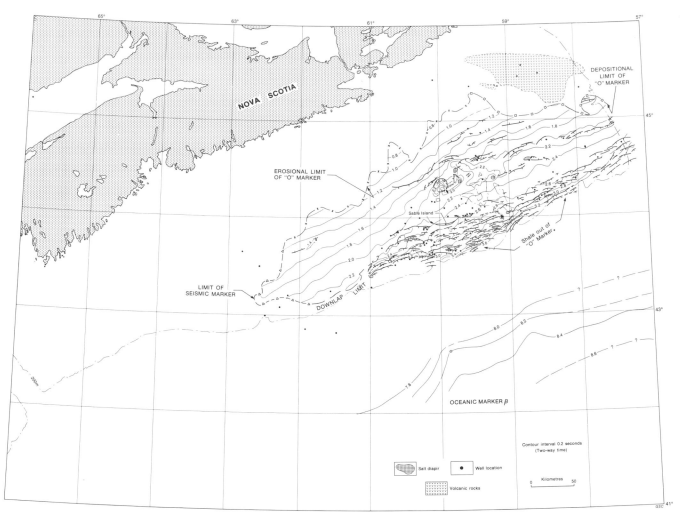

Figure 5.37 Seismic time-structure map, "O" Marker and Horizon β.

shape of this Lower Cretaceous unit is a sigmoidal lens. South of Sable Island, the amount of downlapping is less significant and the section between the "O" Marker and the top of the Jurassic is a seaward thickening wedge. Correlations in this area are difficult, since they are based on a specific reflective bed which is involved in a series of large listric faults, probably related to deep salt movement.

These differences in the geometry of the lower and middle members of the Missisauga Formation can be attributed to supply-subsidence relationships. West of the Sable Island delta, in the Oneida area, during the Early Cretaceous, there was insufficient sediment supply to maintain basin fill which resulted in downlap on the Jurassic shelf. In the Alma-Glenelg area the "O" Marker shales out as it plunges to depth across the paleoslope. Section E-E' (Fig. 5.27 and Fig. 5.52, in pocket) which is an interpretation of a seismic section across the Glenelg structure, shows the Hauterivian shelf edge south of the well to have a topographic relief of approximately 3 km suggesting about this amount of thinning between the "O" Marker and top Jurassic. In the area of maximum sediment supply, the Sable Island delta, however, the shelf

break occurs much farther seaward and the "O" Marker disappears through facies change beneath the present day continental slope (Fig. 5.19).

In the Banquereau area the change in geometry is related to the period of Late Jurassic to Early Cretaceous hinging, as well as to the relative supply-subsidence relationships that controlled the thickness of the middle and lower Missisauga units in the Sable Island region. The extent of the marker in this area is a product of oversupply which resulted primarily in outbuilding with a minimum of upbuilding and a rapid regression of the shelf edge.

Figure 5.37 is a time-structure map on the "O" Marker which, like the maps of the top of the Jurassic and the Scatarie (Fig. 5.28, 5.29), shows areas of salt tectonics and two zones of extensional faulting. The northern zone of faulting, although still apparent at the "O" Marker level, shows less throw than at the deeper horizons. The southern zone of flexure is shifted south of that observed on the top Jurassic map, reflecting the seaward progression of the margin faulting with the outbuilding of the Cretaceous continental shelf.

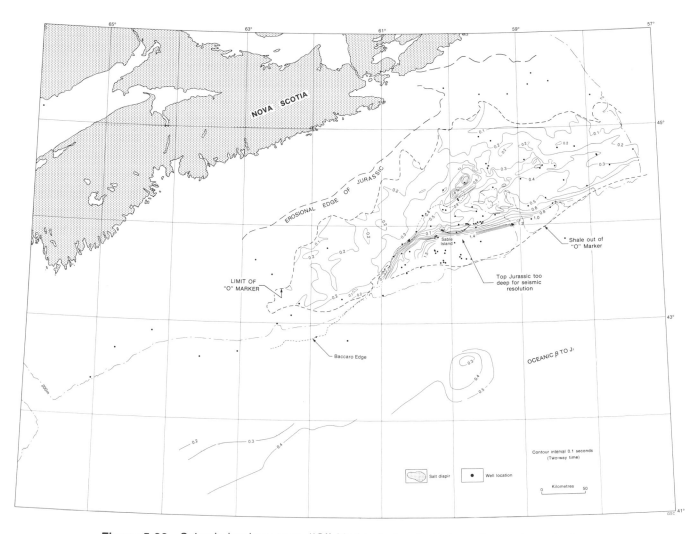

Figure 5.38 Seismic isochron map, "O" Marker to top Jurassic and oceanic equivalents.

Roseway Unit

In the Mohawk B-93 well, within the interval 1340 to 1609 m (4396 to 5280 ft), the lithology is skeletal to oolitic limestone (45%); grey shale and siltstone (34%) and sandstone-siltstone (21%). This section contains all of the palynozones of the type Missisauga Formation (Barss et al., 1979; G.L. Williams, pers. comm., 1985) and it is therefore coeval to the Missisauga Formation. Since stratigraphic control is still limited to the Mohawk well, the informal designation of the Roseway Unit proposed by Wade (1977) is followed for this Missisauga equivalent section.

The seismic expression of the Roseway Unit in the Mohawk area is two prominent, strong reflections. The top is time-equivalent with the top of the Missisauga Formation as mapped to the east, confirming the palynological interpretation. The lower reflection is time equivalent with the top of the Jurassic. South of Mohawk B-93, the Roseway Unit thickens somewhat but it maintains its seismic character. Eastward, towards the Mohican and Moheida wells, the upper Roseway reflection reduces in amplitude and the Roseway Unit is characterized by a series of semi-parallel reflections of varying strengths. At

these wells, it correlates with a series of thin, silty and glauconitic limestone interbeds in a generally shaly Missisauga section which originally was interpreted as part of the Naskapi Member of the Logan Canyon Formation. This facies is 30 m thick in Mohican I-100 whereas in Moheida P-15, the limestones occur over a 150 m interval.

The seismic and well data indicate that significant facies changes occur within the Missisauga Formation as one goes farther from the main area of sandstone deposition and into more stable marine conditions (Fig. 5.39). The thick, predominantly sandstone sequence at Cree E-35 grades into a shale section with limestone interbeds at Oneida O-25, Moheida P-15 and Mohican I-100. This, in turn, becomes a predominantly limestone facies at Mohawk B-93. These changes are an amplification of the facies change originally described by McIver (1972).

It has been pointed out that Eliuk (1978) described and named the Artimon Member of the Abenaki Formation, a Lower Cretaceous lithistid sponge-rich, argillaceous limestone interval observed in the Demascota G-32, Cohasset D-42 and Moheida P-15 wells. Westward from Moheida, this member correlates stratigraphically with the lower part of the Roseway Unit and, eastward, it correlates with

217

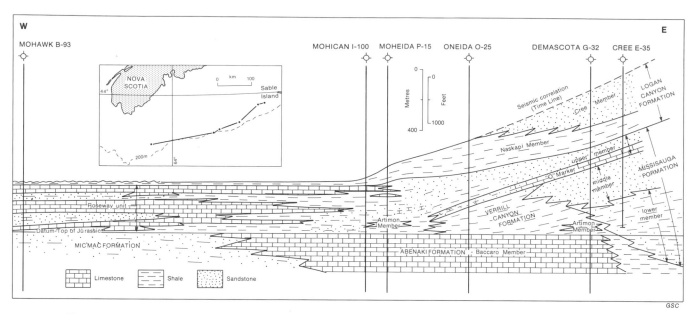

Figure 5.39 Facies relationships within the Missisauga Formation on the LaHave Platform. No horizontal scale.

the "O" Marker (Fig. 5.39). The facies and depositional environment of the Artimon Member show more affinity with the Roseway Unit or the Verrill Canyon Formation than with the Abenaki Formation. The Kimmeridgian to Hauterivian age variations between the three occurrences of the Artimon Member suggest that it is an environmentally controlled facies rather than a regional, chronostratigraphically significant unit. As such, and since it is mainly of Early Cretaceous age and encased in shales of the Verrill Canyon Formation, it is more probably a facies of that formation.

Verrill Canyon Formation

The basinal facies equivalent of the Missisauga, Mic Mac and Abenaki formations is named the Verrill Canyon Formation (McIver, 1972). As such, its age range is Callovian to Barremian. The designated type section is a shale tongue between -2498 and -2858 m (-8195 and -9375 ft) in the Oneida O-25 well and has an age range of Berriasian-Barremian (Ascoli, 1976). It is underlain by a complete section of Abenaki Formation and overlain by an attenuated Missisauga section. Seismic profiles clearly show the type section to be in a shelf rather than a basin environment. Many other stratigraphic intervals referred to as Verrill Canyon Formation (Canada Oil and Gas Lands Administration, 1987) are now known to be shale tongues within the delta front-prodelta facies of the Missisauga Formation.

There is no distinctive seismic reflection associated with the top of the Verrill Canyon Formation and no recognizable character from within. Its occurrence is interpreted where gradual basinward weakening of the discontinuous, semi-parallel reflectors within the distal parts of the Missisauga Formation give way to a zone with no coherent or continuous reflectors.

Glenelg J-48 penetrated a 900 m thick basinal shale equivalent of the lower part of the Missisauga Formation.

This shale is dark grey to dark olive grey, carbonaceous and occasionally calcareous, and contains minor interbeds of very fine grained argillaceous sandstone and siltstone. This shale is considered a portion of the Verrill Canyon Formation. Below 4120 m there is a zone containing an abundance of planktonic foraminifera which indicate deeper water, but the overall depositional environment of the Verrill Canyon Formation in Glenelg is neritic (P. Ascoli, pers. comm., 1985). A lithologically similar section, 1300 m thick, encountered at the bottom of the Southwest Banquereau well, is also interpreted to be part of the Verrill Canyon Formation. The regional depositional environment of this formation is one of outer neritic, prodelta and basinal.

The Jurassic part of the Verrill Canyon Formation may never be completely drilled in the Sable Subbasin because of its great depth. However, it may be within reach on the western flank of the Shelburne Subbasin and on the eastern flank of the South Whale Subbasin, where the Upper Jurassic formations are shallower.

Logan Canyon Formation

The upper formation of the Nova Scotia Group is designated the Logan Canyon Formation (Fig. 5.21). Two major shale tongues, the Naskapi Shale and the Sable Shale Member, were described by McIver (1972). Jansa and Wade (1975b) designated McIver's Naskapi Shale as the basal unit of the Logan Canyon Formation and named it the Naskapi Member. They referred to the second shaly sequence, which occurs toward the top of the formation, as the Sable Member. The sandstone and shale sequence between the Naskapi and Sable members was unnamed as was the shale-sandstone section above the Sable Member.

It is proposed that the Logan Canyon Formation be subdivided into four members; Naskapi, Cree, Sable and Marmora. The type section of the Logan Canyon Formation and its members is between 1472 and 2582 m (4831 and

8470 ft) in the Cree E-35 well (Fig. 5.40). The formation consists of an alternation of thick shale and sandstone-shale units deposited during periods of relatively greater or lesser quartz clastic deposition in a broad coastal plain and shallow shelf environment. The age of the type section is Aptian to early Cenomanian (Barss et al., 1979) or Aptian to late Cenomanian (P. Ascoli, pers. comm., 1978).

On seismic records, the Logan Canyon Formation is characterized by a series of subparallel, fairly continuous reflections which lose their strength and continuity westward over the LaHave Platform and seaward into the Sable Subbasin. In the subbasins there is insufficient seismic character associated with the Naskapi and Sable members to permit their recognition as seismostratigraphic units, although it is possible to follow related seismic time lines for short distances from well ties. On the LaHave Platform the reflections are more continuous allowing correlations over greater distances. The Petrel to "O" Marker isochron map (Fig. 5.41) consists primarily of the Logan Canyon Formation (Fig. 5.21). Of particular interest are the areas with thick sediment associated with salt withdrawal in the Abenaki Subbasin and the area, south of the Alma F-67 and Glenelg J-48 wells, where the unit is very thick due to outbuilding beyond the upper Missisauga shelf edge.

Distally, the sandstones of the Logan Canyon Formation change to a shale facies. McIver (1972) and Given (1977) considered the Dawson Canyon Formation to include the downdip facies of the Logan Canyon Formation. Jansa and Wade (1975b) considered the Dawson Canyon to be a separate formation, deposited over the Logan Canyon Formation and its equivalents in response to the Late Cretaceous global rise in sea level. They proposed the name Shortland Shale for the basinal shale facies of the Logan Canyon Formation. This concept reduces the age range of the Dawson Canyon Formation as defined by McIver, from Barremian-Santonian (about 34 Ma) to Cenomanian-Santonian (about 8 Ma). It also restricts the Dawson Canyon Formation to the Gully Group, thereby simplifying the proposed stratigraphic subdivision.

Each member of the Logan Canyon Formation thickens and the relative amount of shale increases seaward across the Abenaki and Sable subbasins. Westward of these subbasins the Logan Canyon thins and changes to a predominantly shale facies with minor sandstone and siltstone beds. This change reflects deposition in a marine environment peripheral to the main area of coarse clastic discharge. Again, this creates difficulty in identifying individual formations on the western LaHave Platform. Only 170 m of section equivalent to the Logan Canyon Formation has been recognized in the Mohawk well where it consists of light grey silty, glauconitic mudstone with thin interbeds of siltstone and very fine grained calcareous sandstone.

The Naskapi Member is the lower transgressive shale unit of the Logan Canyon Formation, which, beneath the eastern part of the Scotian Shelf is readily identified as a thick shale interval between the massive sandstone sequences of the Missisauga Formation and the interbedded sandstone-shale sequences of the Cree Member of the Logan Canyon Formation. Its type section is between 2582 and 2408 m (8470 and 7900 ft) in the Cree well (Fig. 5.40). It consists of distinctively varicoloured shales ranging from yellowish brown to green-grey to reddish brown.

Interbedded silty and sandy zones are common. Isopachs show the member to be a seaward thickening wedge with the thickest sections drilled being near the shelf edge in the Sable Subbasin. In the South Whale Subbasin, 79 m of the Naskapi Member were encountered in Puffin B-90 with lesser amounts in the Brant P-87, Tern A-68 and Emerillon C-56 wells. The member becomes increasingly sandy along the northern edge of the Abenaki Subbasin and over most of the Canso Ridge it is lithologically indistinguishable from the adjacent sandstone sequences.

The interpretation of microfossils and well samples indicates that the depositional environment of the Naskapi Member is one of tidal flat to marginal marine. Thus, the member represents a transgressive episode from the underlying delta plain environment of the upper member of the Missisauga Formation.

The seismic reflection associated with the top of the Naskapi Member is seen to downlap the top Roseway reflection, when correlating from Naskapi N-30 to Mohican I-100 and then westward toward Mohawk B-93. Differentiation of the Naskapi and Roseway units on the basis of age is difficult, partly because of a lack of well control but also because the Naskapi Member is Aptian and the Roseway Unit is Barremian to earliest Aptian. On the LaHave Platform, therefore, the best tool to discriminate between the two is seismic data. Biostratigraphic data (Barss et al., 1979; Ascoli, 1976) clearly indicate that biozones representing the Naskapi Member occur in the Mohawk well beneath an unconformity and overlying the biozones indicative of the Missisauga Formation.

Correlating eastward from Mohican I-100 to Demascota G-32 and Cree E-35, the Naskapi time-line rises gradually, as the Naskapi and Missisauga sections thicken, until it is about 250-300 m higher than the lithologic pick (Fig. 5.39). This again indicates the earlier influence of the deltaic facies in the Sable Subbasin and the diachronous nature of the lithostratigraphic units.

Basalt flows and volcaniclastics are interbedded with sediments of the Naskapi Member in five wells on the northeastern part of the Scotian Shelf. From the continuity of the seismic reflections, the basalts at the Argo F-38, Hercules G-15 and Jason C-20 wells appear as a series of thin flows over an area 50x150 km (Fig. 5.37). They probably originated at tensional fractures along the south flank of the Orpheus Graben. The flows were later disturbed by salt tectonics and by faulting. The seismic data do not confirm the presence of volcanic cones at the Argo F-38 and Jason C-20 wells as postulated by Jansa and Pe-Piper (1985). At both Hesper wells a single 18-m thick basalt layer, also in the Naskapi Member, produces a strong, bright reflector. It is relatively flat-lying and appears confined to a single listric fault slice. Jansa and Pe-Piper (1985) suggested that this Scotian Shelf volcanism was related to a period of mid-plate volcanism which was widespread in the western North Atlantic Ocean during the Early Cretaceous.

The type section of the Cree Member of the Logan Canyon Formation is from 2408 to 1805 m (7900 to 5922 ft) in the Cree E-35 well (Fig. 5.40). It occurs below the base of the Sable Member shale and above the top of the Naskapi Member shale. The member consists of sandstone beds interbedded with medium to dark grey shales and occasional thin beds of siltstone. The lower sandstones are medium- to coarse-grained, coarsening upward, but toward the top of the member they are fine- to medium-grained.

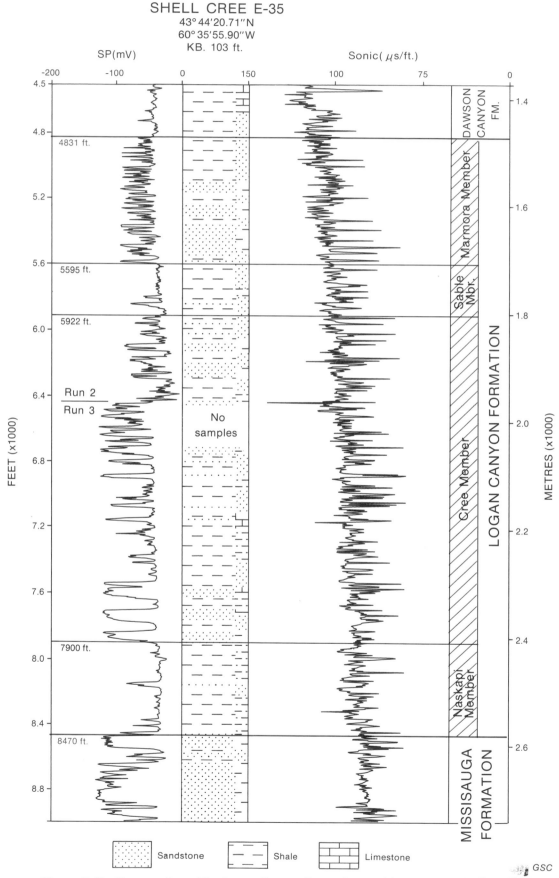

Figure 5.40 Type section of the Logan Canyon Formation and its members in Cree E-35.

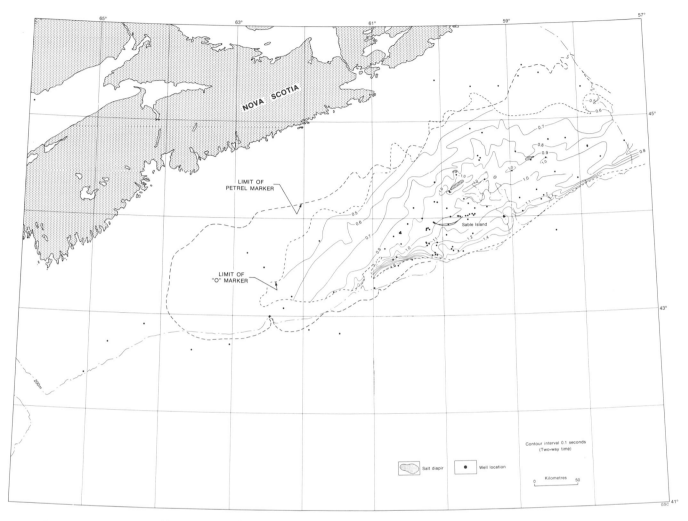

Figure 5.41 Seismic isochron map, Petrel marker to "O" marker.

The sandstone beds thin both in an upward and seaward direction. From biostratigraphic data, the Cree Member is interpreted to be late Aptian to late Albian in age.

The Sable Member, the second regional shaly unit in the Logan Canyon Formation, has its type section between 1805 and 1705 m (5922 and 5595 ft) in Cree E-35 (Fig. 5.40). Although predominantly a shale facies resulting from a period of more rapid transgression, it contains, depending on basin position, a varying number of thin sandstone and siltstone beds. Across the inner part of the Abenaki Subbasin and on the Canso Ridge the member is dominated by sandstones and it can no longer be mapped as a separate unit.

The Marmora Member of the Logan Canyon Formation lies above the Sable Member and is overlain by the Dawson Canyon Formation. A type section is proposed in the interval 1705 to 1472 m (5595 to 4831 ft) in Cree E-35. The Marmora Member continues the trend of the Cree Member with upward thinning and fining sand beds. The contact of the Logan Canyon Formation with the overlying Dawson Canyon Formation is gradational in many wells, and it is picked at the top of the discernibly sandy section.

The age on the Scotian Shelf, from foraminifera and ostracodes, is late Albian to late Cenomanian (P. Ascoli, pers. comm., 1978) whereas palynomorphs indicate a late Albian to early Cenomanian age (Barss et al., 1979).

The informal name "Eider Unit" was proposed by Amoco and Imperial (1973) for the basal transgressive "... marginal to shallow marine sand-shale sequence ..." overlying the mid-Cretaceous unconformity on the Grand Banks. Disregarding the interpretation of Upshaw et al. (1974), Jansa and Wade (1975b) equated the Eider Unit with the upper sandstone sequence of the Logan Canyon Formation and designated it the "Eider Member". Subsequent dating of the sandstone interval indicated a broad range of ages, as would be expected in a basal transgressive sequence. One of the largest is from the Berriasian to Cenomanian in the Pelican well on the central Grand Banks (Barss et al., 1979). More commonly, however, the unit is confined to parts of the Albian and Cenomanian (Barss et al., 1979). Seismic time-line correlation between the wells is at odds with the biostratigraphy and further study is required before the relationship between the Eider

221

Unit and corresponding Scotian Shelf units can be defined. Therefore, the informal Eider Unit of Amoco and Imperial (1973) is retained for these sequences. The Eider Unit is a coarse to medium grained friable sandstone, grading upward into a fine grained glauconitic sandstone with interbeds of calcareous mudstones and marls (Jansa and Wade, 1975b).

Continental equivalents of the Logan Canyon Formation are known from six scattered localities in Nova Scotia (Fig. 5.42). The lithology includes interbedded red, grey and white clay, quartzose sand and lignite (Lin, 1971). Contained palynomorphs include diverse assemblages of subtropical terrestrial flora (spores) and fresh water algal cysts (dinoflagellates) and indicate a late Aptian-early Albian age (E.H. Davies, pers. comm., 1982 and 1983; Davies et al., 1984) making them equivalent to a part of the Cree Member. In addition, the occurrence at Diogenus Brook included a 23 m interval dated as Valanginian making it the only occurrence of Neocomian (Missisauga equivalent) sediments found in in the Maritime Provinces (E.H. Davies, pers. comm., 1983). Samples from localities 7 and 8 in Figure 5.42, where Cretaceous sediments were suspected, were barren.

Gully Group

The Gully Group (McIver, 1972) overlies the Nova Scotia Group and consists of the Dawson Canyon, Wyandot and Banquereau formations. These formations reflect the onset of the Late Cretaceous global transgression that lasted into the Oligocene and they include some of the deepest water facies deposited beneath the Scotian Shelf. The Banquereau Formation also includes sediments which were deposited during a series of sea-level fluctuations in the mid-Tertiary as well as sediments of the final pre-Pleistocene regression. Lithologies include shale, mudstone, chalk and marl as well as coarser clastics ranging from siltstone to conglomerate.

Dawson Canyon Formation

The Dawson Canyon Formation consists predominantly of grey marine shale or mudstone with occasional thin beds of siltstone, sandstone and limestone. One persistent series of thin, limestone beds, designated the Petrel Member (Amoco and Imperial, 1973; Jansa and Wade, 1975b), form a regional seismic marker within the Dawson Canyon Formation. The type section of the Dawson Canyon Formation

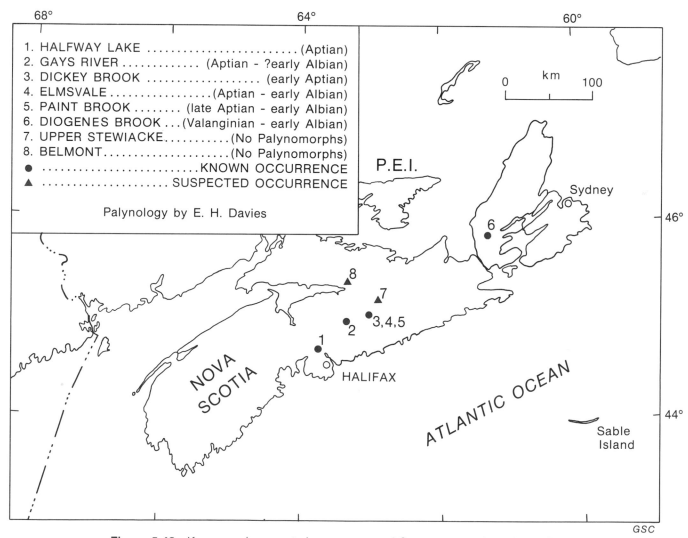

1. HALFWAY LAKE .... (Aptian)
2. GAYS RIVER .... (Aptian - ?early Albian)
3. DICKEY BROOK .... (early Aptian)
4. ELMSVALE ....(Aptian - early Albian)
5. PAINT BROOK .... (late Aptian - early Albian)
6. DIOGENES BROOK ...(Valanginian - early Albian)
7. UPPER STEWIACKE...........(No Palynomorphs)
8. BELMONT....................(No Palynomorphs)
● ....KNOWN OCCURRENCE
▲ .... SUSPECTED OCCURRENCE

Palynology by E. H. Davies

Figure 5.42 Known and suspected occurrences of Cretaceous rocks in Nova Scotia.

is between -1017 and -1288 m (-3335 and -4225 ft) in the Missisauga H-54 well (McIver, 1972) with the Petrel Member occurring between 1212 and 1228 m (3975 and 4030 ft). Eastward from the type section, the part of the formation above the Petrel grades from predominantly shale to predominantly limestone. The age of the Dawson Canyon Formation is Cenomanian to Santonian (Barss et al., 1979) and early Cenomanian to Santonian (Doeven, 1983). The age of the Petrel Member is Turonian. The thickness of the Dawson Canyon Formation varies from more than 500 m in the South Whale Subbasin and on the LaHave Platform, to over 200 m on the Canso Ridge, to just over 100 m in the sediment starved outer part of the Sable Subbasin.

At the type locality, the top of the Dawson Canyon Formation appears on the seismic data as a relatively strong and clean reflection which deteriorates both to the north and to the south. Below this event is a zone of weak but continuous energy which thins and downlaps to the south onto the reflection from the Petrel Member.

The Petrel Member limestone generates a strong regional marker which can be followed over most of the Scotian Shelf and the Grand Banks. Its seismic expression varies with its thickness: the seismic reflection deteriorates as the limestone thins and it broadens into two where the Petrel Member is thickest. The member thickens regionally from southwest to northeast. Beneath the easternmost part of the Scotian Shelf, the Petrel Member is continuous with the thick overlying Wyandot Formation making separation of the two difficult.

Figure 5.43 is the time-structure map of the Petrel marker. The northern limit occurs where the event subcrops at the seafloor or, in the eastern portion of the map area, where Tertiary channels have cut it out. In the Orpheus Graben, there are three areas where erosional cutout occurs over diapirs. The southern limit occurs where the marker has been cut off either by erosion associated with Wyandot downlap, or by erosion at the Tertiary shelf edge. The fault patterns identified on the deeper maps are still present at the Petrel level. The northern fault trend is largely unchanged, and the southern one is again southward relative to the deeper events. Few of the salt structures beneath the shelf pierce this level.

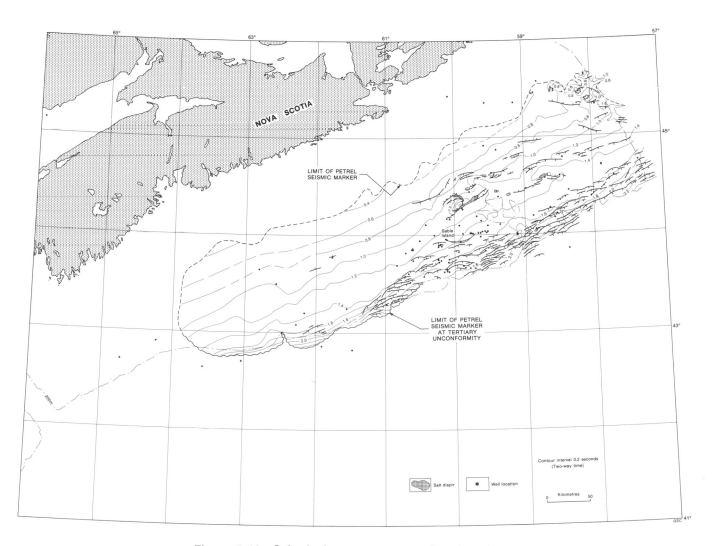

Figure 5.43   Seismic time-structure map, Petrel marker.

Wyandot Formation

McIver (1972) gave the name Wyandot Chalk to, "perhaps the most distinctive and widely recognized lithologic unit on the shelf ...". Its type section was designated in the Mic Mac H-86 well and its age was given as Santonian to early Campanian. Jansa and Wade (1975b) expanded McIver's unit to 689-835 m (2260-2738 ft) in order to incorporate the adjacent marls and chalky mudstones and referred to it as the Wyandot Formation. Barss et al. (1979) interpreted the age range of the Wyandot Formation to be Campanian to Maastrichtian whereas Doeven (1983), using nannofossils, indicated a range from Santonian to Maastrichtian.

In the Mic Mac area, the Wyandot appears on seismic profiles as several strong events, but more commonly it produces one strong and clean reflection. Although a lithologically distinctive unit, seismic data show that the Wyandot Formation may be diachronous in the Abenaki and Sable subbasins. In these eastern shelf regions the data show there was regression during deposition of the upper part of the formation. That is, the chalks and marly facies developed in the bottom set position of prograding sequences. The chalks grade upslope into calcareous shales or mudstones and then, farther upslope, to mudstones. The topset beds in these sequences can be sufficiently calcareous to produce a strong reflection, similar to the true Wyandot event, thus making local character ties difficult. Care must be taken when correlating the Wyandot event landward that a reflection from one of the progradations is not be mistaken for the event. Well data show that the more eastern occurrences of the Wyandot Formation are Campanian-Paleocene in age, as compared to Santonian-Campanian west of Sable Island. This is consistent with the Late Cretaceous-Paleogene paleogeography, which indicates continued subsidence accompanied by an easterly shift in the depocentre resulting in southeasterly progradation during this time.

Figure 5.44 is the time-structure map of the Wyandot Formation. To the north, the event fades but it eventually subcrops the Quaternary. Locally it is cut by Tertiary channels. To the south, Tertiary shelf-edge erosion cuts into the Wyandot and the incised nature of that shelf edge is apparent on the map. The same tectonic elements are apparent on the Wyandot surface as were seen on the Petrel structure map, although some of the faulting has died out. North of Oneida O-25, in the eastern extremity of the Mohican Graben, there is a broad area where erosion

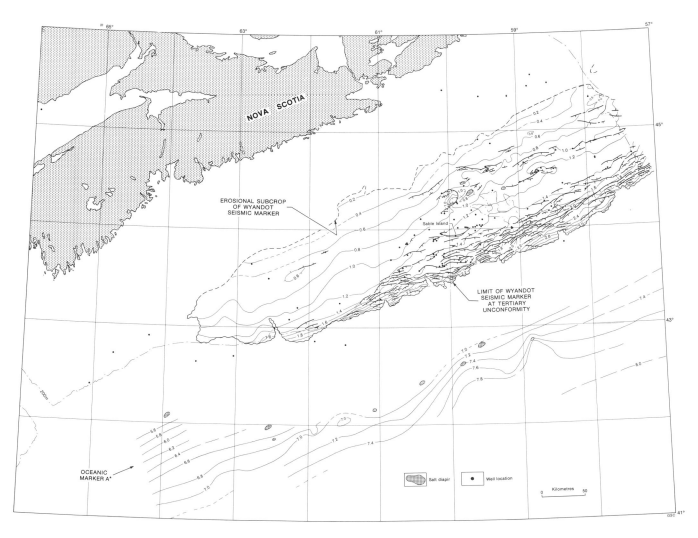

Figure 5.44 Seismic time-structure map, Wyandot marker and oceanic Horizon A*.

has cut into but not through the Wyandot. This shows on the Wyandot to Petrel isochron (Fig. 5.45) as a north-trending thin area.

Extensive correlation studies by Hardy (pers. comm., 1979) indicated that the main chalky facies of the Wyandot Formation extends from west of Naskapi N-30 on LaHave Platform east to Puffin B-90 in the South Whale Subbasin. Several lithostratigraphic subunits of the Wyandot Formation, both above and below the main chalk unit, occur only beneath the eastern Scotian Shelf. The thickness of the Wyandot Formation increases eastward from an average of about 50 m on the LaHave Platform to nearly 400 m at the Dauntless D-35 well with the thickest sections being beneath the extreme eastern end of the Scotian Shelf. This is due in part to an increase in the thickness of the limestone facies and a corresponding decrease in the shale of the Dawson Canyon Formation. These studies also confirmed the more active subsidence of the Laurentian Subbasin during the Late Cretaceous.

The Wyandot Formation is intersected, immediately east of Dauntless D-35, by a major Paleocene unconformity that erodes gradually to the level of the Petrel reflector and then rises again beneath St. Pierre Bank. Two other major

unconformities in the area are dated by their occurrence in the Dauntless well as Oligocene and Miocene. All three unconformities are related to an ancestral Laurentian Channel which was active during the Tertiary (Fig. 5.46). Over most of the South Whale Subbasin, the Wyandot appears to have been eroded during the early part of the Tertiary and the presence of an immediately overlying Eocene chalky facies makes recognition of the Wyandot on seismic records difficult.

Biostratigraphy has shown that a hiatus of varying duration occurs at the top of the Wyandot Formation in several wells in the Scotian Basin (Ascoli, 1976; Barss et al., 1979; Doeven, 1983). Some workers have construed this to indicate a regional unconformity at the top of the Cretaceous. However, the top of the Wyandot Formation is not coincident with the end of the Cretaceous Period. Furthermore, the regional depositional environment is marine and in many wells the stratigraphy is continuous from the Cretaceous into the Tertiary. A possible explanation for this apparent inconsistency is found in the seismic data. In some areas, the Wyandot reflector is characterized by a rough or irregular seismic signature. This develops coincidentally with an impinging bottomset bed, i.e. at the

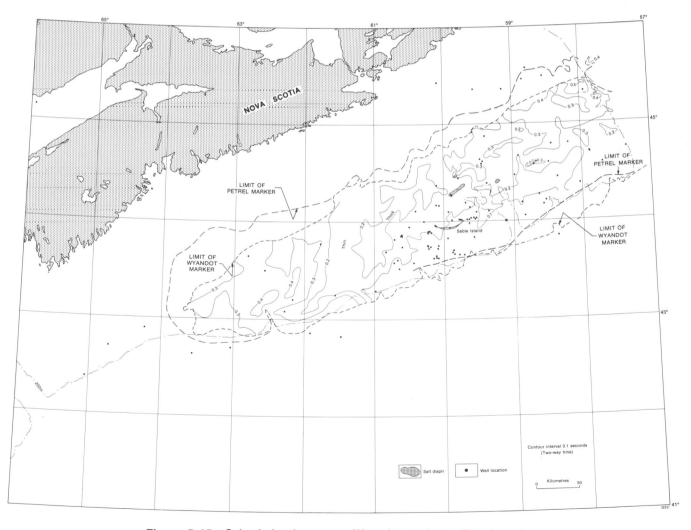

Figure 5.45 Seismic isochron map, Wyandot marker to Petrel marker.

225

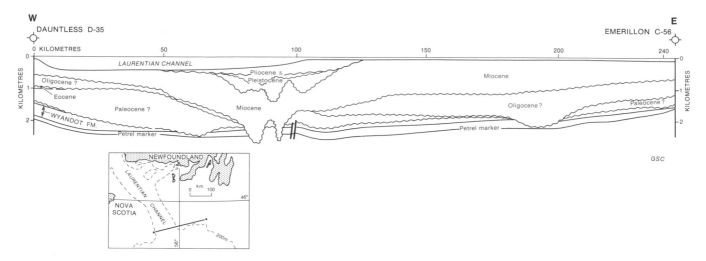

Figure 5.46 Cretaceous, Tertiary and Quaternary unconformities beneath the Laurentian Channel.

base of a prograding or downlapping sequence, and may indicate rip-up or local scouring by bottom following currents and the development of localized unconformities. Another explanation for the inconsistency may be that extremely condensed sequences occur in front of the downlapping beds and these are not detected in the biostratigraphic sampling of well cuttings.

Sedimentation rates during the deposition of the Wyandot were among the lowest experienced on the Scotian Shelf. The average thickness of the formation is 135 m which was deposited over 15 Ma for a depositional rate (compacted) of 0.9 cm/ka.

Banquereau Formation

The Cretaceous sediments and the entire Tertiary sedimentary succession above the Wyandot have been designated the Banquereau Formation (McIver, 1972). The type section is between -165 and -1355 m (-540 and -4445 ft) in the Sable Island C-67 well. The lithology of this formation is predominantly mudstone which grades upward into sandstone and conglomerate. The age range of the formation is from Campanian-Maastrichtian to Pliocene. The thickness of the Banquereau Formation ranges from a zero edge along the middle part of the shelf to more than 1500 m in some wells in the Sable Subbasin. The time-structure on the Wyandot Formation (Fig. 5.44) approximates the isochron map of the Banquereau Formation in all but the extreme outer part of the shelf where a narrow but thick prism of Holocene sediment caps the present day shelf edge.

Hardy (1975) proposed an informal four-fold subdivision of the Banquereau Formation and detailed a series of lateral and vertical facies changes, resulting from the filling of the Sable Subbasin, followed by Neogene regression. Correlation of the stratigraphy with the seismic data is difficult and, because of the variable nature of the units, as discussed below, it can be followed only locally.

The seismic character of this formation resembles that of the underlying formations in that it consists of generally continuous events which prograde seaward. However, there are some differences. Channel cut and fill sequences and shelf edge unconformities are apparent on the strike

lines. Interpretation is complicated at the present shelf edge because multiples from a dipping seafloor cut across the primary reflections and simulate unconformities.

Several major subaqueous unconformities, probably associated with sea-level fluctuations, developed in outer shelf and upper slope environments during deposition of the Banquereau Formation (Fig. 5.21, 5.46). On the outer LaHave Platform and in the Sable Subbasin, six major unconformities were noted in wells and on seismic data: within the ?upper Miocene, where major channelling is observed; between Oligocene and probable Miocene beds; between the Eocene and lower Upper Oligocene, where major channelling is also seen; within the Eocene; between the Paleocene and Eocene; and between Campanian-Maastrichtian and Paleocene-Eocene strata. The last unconformity is present on a large high which is onlapped by lower Tertiary beds. At its crest sediments as young as mid- to Late Oligocene may overlie beds as old as Campanian.

Quaternary

King (1970) subdivided the Quaternary stratigraphy of the Halifax-Sable Island area into five formations beginning with till and passing upward through individual silt, sand, clay, and sand and gravel units. Jansa and Wade (1975a) introduced the name Laurentian Formation to include the thick wedge of ?Upper Pliocene and Quaternary sediments that occurs along the outer shelf edge and upper slope. Quaternary stratigraphy is described in Chapter 10.

Distal equivalents of Scotian Shelf formations

In spite of the large amount of seismic and well data currently available from the Scotian Shelf there are some aspects of the regional stratigraphy that are still poorly known. One example is the correlation between the proximal and distal facies of the formations in the Scotian Basin. This is due in part to the lack of well data seaward of the Slope Diapiric Province and in part to the difficulty in tying seismic reflections from the shelf to the basin across a zone of strong dipping multiples, deep Tertiary unconformities, ancient faults, and the myriad of diapiric structures beneath the slope and their chaotic effect on the intruded sediments. The diapirism is largely a post-depositional complication. If the diapirs were not there the regional seismic markers would probably continue uninterrupted across the slope.

Many of the regional seismic reflectors on the Scotian Shelf result from periods of carbonate deposition, for example, the Eocene chalk, Wyandot, Petrel, "O" Marker, approximate top of Jurassic and Scatarie. The ages of these units are well known. Changes in lithology, resulting in regional seismic reflectors in a shelf environment, should also be discernible in coeval sequences in the oceanic realm, at least where these are composed of hemipelagic sediments. In the distal realm, many of the regional reflections have been tied to limy beds in wells drilled in the Deep Sea Drilling Project (DSDP). These have been correlated into the area of the Scotian Rise. Using the shelf and deep water seismic and well data, a reasonable correlation between shelf and oceanic markers has been established (Wade, 1978; Ewing, 1984; Swift, 1985). These correlations are summarized in Table 5.2.

Table 5.2 Correlation of shelf and oceanic markers, based on shelf and deep water seismic and well data.

Shelf unit	Deep-sea unit
Eocene-Oligocene (unconformity?)	Horizon A^u (Oligocene)
Wyandot Formation	Horizon A* (Maastrichtian) Crescent Peaks Member-Plantagenet Formation)
"O" Marker	Horizon β (Barremian) (top Blake Bahama Fm)
Top Jurassic	J$_1$ (Tithonian)
Scatarie Member	J$_2$ (Callovian-E. Oxfordian)
North Mountain Basalt	Layer 2 (top oceanic basalts)

The deepest of the oceanic markers is the irregular series of hyperbolic reflections that mark the top of Layer 2 (Fig. 5.17, 5.19). If Layer 2 represents the top of oceanic crust, its landward edge should be coeval with the breakup event and therefore be about the same age as the Glooscap and North Mountain basalts. There are some areas on the Scotian Shelf with several kilometres of sedimentary strata beneath the breakup unconformity. The diffracted nature of the Layer 2 reflection obscures underlying reflections but, at its landward edge in Scotian Basin, which approximates the 4000 m isobath, sedimentary horizons including salt can be seen, or inferred from relative depths, to lie well below the level of Layer 2 (Fig. 5.19). The extent of these sediments and transitional crust beneath Layer 2 cannot be determined from existing seismic data. The northern limit of Layer 2 and the associated ocean-continent transition zone as mapped from reflection seismic lies considerably seaward of both the ocean-continent boundary shown on map 1710A (in pocket) and the East Coast Magnetic Anomaly.

The first regional sedimentary reflector above Layer 2 has been tentatively correlated with J$_2$, a reflector from within the Jurassic on the slope off Georges Bank (Klitgord et al., 1982; Uchupi and Shor, 1983). As described in Part 1 of this chapter, the J$_2$ reflection can be tied to an Early Oxfordian-Callovian event from Georges Bank Basin. This reflection has been correlated to a major regional reflection of similar age on the Scotian margin which is generated from the Scatarie Member limestone of the Abenaki Formation. J$_2$ is best developed off the LaHave Platform in the area where the Scatarie can be recognized south of the hinge zone (Fig. 5.29). South of the Sable Subbasin, J$_2$ is weaker because of its distance from the edge of the Scatarie and is discontinuous due to irregularities in Layer 2.

The sediments below J$_2$, in the distal part of Scotian Basin, fill depressions in the highly irregular surface of Layer 2 (Fig. 5.25). Just beyond the Slope Diapiric Province this sedimentary unit is about 2000 m thick but it thins to 0 over Layer 2 highs.

The second regional sedimentary reflector from the deep Scotian Basin is correlated to J$_1$ which has been dated as Tithonian. The stratigraphic control for J$_1$ comes from DSDP Site 105 off North Carolina where the reflection represents the top of a sequence of reddish brown argillaceous limestones and calcareous claystones, the Cat Gap Formation (Jansa et al., 1979). In Scotian Basin, the J$_1$ event, like J$_2$, is strongest off LaHave Platform. It becomes weaker across the projection of the Sable Island delta and it onlaps possible continental basement beneath the Laurentian Fan. This reflector is considered coeval to the widespread reflector on Scotian Shelf which marks the maximum transgressive pulse near the top of the Jurassic and which is dated as Tithonian (Fig. 5.28). Correlation of J$_1$ with the Tithonian shelf marker is favoured because carbonate deposition was most widespread at this time.

A third regional oceanic marker in this area is correlated to Horizon β which is dated Barremian. It has been drilled in a number of DSDP wells in the western Atlantic and consistently ties to the top of the Blake-Bahama Formation (Jansa et al., 1979) which consists of an interbedded sequence of limestone, marly limestone and sandy limestone to calcareous claystone. South of the Scotian Shelf, the reflection designated Horizon β is weaker than J$_1$ suggesting a more subtle lithological contrast but the reflection is still considered to be indicative of an increase in limestone content. Again, an excellent correlation can be made between β and the prominent Hauterivian-Barremian limestone "O" Marker on the Scotian Shelf (Fig. 5.37).

The β to J$_1$ (Fig. 5.38) interval corresponds to the lower part of the major deltaic sequence in the Sable Island area and probably consists of fine grained clastic sediments with considerably less carbonate than the carbonate-rich, coeval Blake-Bahama Formation. A seismic profile along geological strike beneath the upper rise, seaward from the delta, shows a marked increase in the thickness of this interval, from less than 1000 to more than 3000 m, indicative of the large volumes of terrigenous material transported through the prodelta into the bathyal environment.

As described above, a slow regional transgression is indicated by the distribution of the alluvial plain, delta plain and delta front facies of the Logan Canyon Formation. These interfinger seaward with the Shortland Shale.

They are succeeded by a more transgressive period represented by the Dawson Canyon Formation and culminate with the Wyandot Formation.

Two regional Upper Cretaceous seismic reflections, from the Petrel Member and the Wyandot Formation, occur on the shelf. Toward the shelf break, the two tend to converge and in many instances the Wyandot appears to truncate the Petrel and survive into the realm of the slope diapirs. In other areas both reflectors are truncated by a major Eocene unconformity.

In North Atlantic Basin, a very widespread sequence of black carbonaceous clays, the Hatteras Formation, overlies Horizon β. This formation is, in turn, overlain by the Plantagenet Formation, a thin, variegated clay, rich in zeolites and other minerals (Jansa et al., 1979). A prominent oceanic reflector, Horizon A*, is associated with a marly limestone to calcareous ooze, the Crescent Peaks Member, which lies near the top of the variegated clays. The probable age of the reflector is Maastrichtian (Jansa et al., 1979) and hence it is correlative with the uppermost part of the Wyandot Formation (Fig. 5.44). West of 62°W, Horizon A* produces a moderately strong reflection. East of this it can be traced with some difficulty as far as South Whale Subbasin. The interval between horizons β and A*, which correlates approximately with the interval between "O" Marker to Wyandot, thickens gradually from about 600 m off the LaHave Platform to 1400 m beneath the Laurentian Fan. It thins to the northeast of the fan then thickens rapidly to more than 1500 m in the South Whale Subbasin. South of Sable Island there appears to be an unconformity associated with Horizon A* related to post-depositional scouring and deposition of thick lenses of younger sediment.

One of the strongest and most widespread of the oceanic reflections is Horizon Aᵘ which is from an Oligocene unconformity (Tucholke and Mountain, 1979). In the Scotian Basin a prominent reflection from an Eocene-Oligocene unconformity has been correlated with Horizon Aᵘ.

Along the Scotian Margin, the interval A* to Aᵘ is generally 150-300 m thick. South of Sable Island, however, the interval forms a lens of sediment up to 1200 m thick which, from its orientation and thickness, is interpreted to be a turbidite fan deposited at the mouth of a submarine canyon. As mentioned above, this lens developed partly at the expense of the underlying unit which appears to have undergone some erosion. The unit above Aᵘ thins across the lens.

The Shubenacadie H-100 well, on the upper slope off the LaHave Platform, was drilled to test a similar turbidite fan which is predominantly Maastrichtian-Paleocene in age (Shell, 1983). Figure 5.47 is a seismic dip section near the Shubenacadie well illustrating the Upper Cretaceous-Quaternary stratigraphy. No Oligocene has been reported from this well, but sediments of this age occur in the Oneida O-25 well, 48 km to the north (Ascoli, 1976; Barss et al., 1979) and are interpreted to occur on the flanks of the fan.

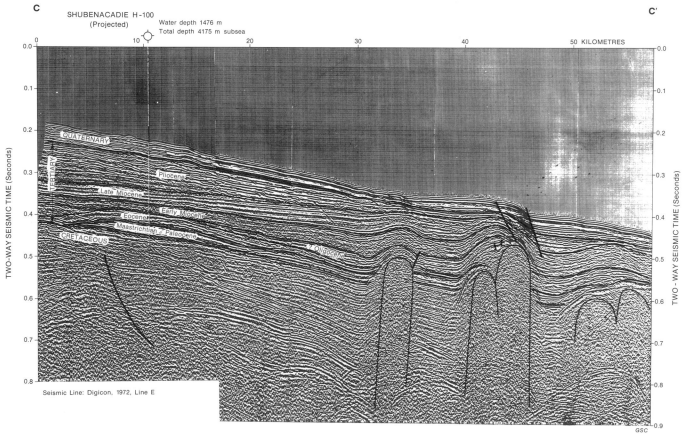

Figure 5.47 Seismic section C-C' from the Scotian Slope near Shubenacadie H-100 showing subdivision of the Tertiary. Location also shown in Figure 5.18, in pocket.

Other reflectors occur beneath the mid and upper slope, landward of the Slope Diapiric Province, separating wedges of upper Tertiary and Pleistocene sediments. Many deep water unconformities occur in this part of the section with the most prominent interpreted as: approximately mid-Paleocene-Early Eocene; Late or Middle Eocene-Early Oligocene; Late Oligocene-Early Miocene; Middle Miocene-Late Miocene; Late Miocene-possible Pliocene; and Pliocene-probable Pleistocene.

STRUCTURE

The discussion of structure is divided into two sections, one dealing with salt related structures, the other with syn-sedimentary and normal faults affecting the sedimentary section. Throughout this discussion it should be remembered that the origins of these structures are commonly interrelated because, in many instances, salt movement is a fundamental cause of normal faulting and growth faulting.

Salt structures

Numerous diapiric and pillow structures occur within the subbasins of the Scotian Basin (Fig. 5.23). Several of these have been drilled in the search for oil and gas. In most instances these are halokinetic structures with a core of Argo Formation salt but some may be lutokinetic and some a combination of both. Because of their similar style they are described together.

Four distinctive types of diapiric structures occur in the Scotian Shelf area.

Type 1.

In the southwestern part of the Abenaki Subbasin three salt diapirs (Fig. 5.28), including the very large Abenaki and Iroquois structures, rise from a depth of about 6 km almost to the seafloor. The Abenaki structure is elongate, being up to 35 km long and 6 km wide, with its long axis trending southwest. A salt ridge trends from the Abenaki diapir southwest to the Penobscot B-41 and L-30 wells. The Iroquois diapir is up to 24 km long and 14 km wide. The third, unnamed diapir, is roughly circular and much smaller with a diameter of 4 km. It is located centrally on the 80 km long northeast-trending Missisauga salt ridge (Fig. 5.18, in pocket, and Fig. 5.29). Collectively these features contain a large volume of salt.

To the north and west, this group of diapirs are flanked by large withdrawal synclines which can be seen on all of the time structure maps. Salt movement occurred in two distinct stages. In approximately Middle Jurassic time there was large scale movement of salt off the flank of the Canso Ridge and contemporaneous infilling with clastics of the Mohican and Mic Mac formations. This period of salt withdrawal resulted in the formation of secondary structures such as the arcuate graben paralleling the hinge zone which is shown in the top Jurassic map (Fig. 5.28). This period of salt movement was effectively over by the end of the Jurassic.

A second period of salt movement associated with these diapirs took place during the Tertiary, in the area north of the Abenaki and west of the Iroquois structures, resulting in a large, nearly circular withdrawal syncline which was filled with sediments probably of Neogene age. At that time the salt stocks in all three large diapirs may have reached the seafloor and experienced a prolonged period of simultaneous growth and dissolution until they were capped by Pleistocene sediments.

In the central part of Abenaki Subbasin, in the area of the Chippewa G-67 and L-75 and Huron P-96 wells, the diapirs are smaller in volume and they appear to rise in clusters from a large salt mass at depth. The depth to basement in the Huron-Chippewa area is greater than in the Iroquois area reflecting the eastward plunge of the subbasin. These diapirs show the same mid-Jurassic period of development as well as late Tertiary growth but no large, late, rim syncline was observed indicating less localized salt withdrawal during the Neogene.

Type 2.

In Sable and South Whale subbasins, diapirs are much smaller in cross-section and volume than Abenaki and Iroquois but, in the case of structures such as Primrose, Gull-Tors Cove and Shearwater, they rise much higher in the section. The salt at Primrose has risen as much as 16 km and it may be detached from regional salt, as is suggested by the small rim syncline associated with this structure.

Hundreds of diapiric structures occur within the Slope Diapiric Province of the Scotian Basin. As has been mentioned, this province was initially called the Sedimentary Ridge Province by Jansa and Wade (1975b). Using a sparse seismic grid, these authors interpreted linear diapirs, trending parallel to the basin axis, as having formed during the seaward movement of salt and the overlying sedimentary wedge. The diapirs are now recognized as being circular structures (Fig. 5.17, 5.19). They vary in size and form, and in some instances may be cored with a combination of salt and shale. They rise from very great depths and some are still growing, reaching almost to the seafloor where they cause subtle but discernible highs. The concentration of salt and mobile shales is still attributed to the mass seaward flow of salt away from the major basin depocentres, the shelf edge sedimentary prism and the development of large listric fault systems (Fig. 5.19).

Type 3

A third area of diapiric and pillowed salt structures was found in the Sable Subbasin seaward of the Abenaki front and southwest of Sable Island. It contains complex pillow and fault-controlled structures, some of which have been drilled at Glenelg J-48, Alma F-67 and Chebucto K-90 and diapiric and faulted structures drilled at Onondaga E-84 and Wenonah J-75. These features are interpreted to be part of a large structural system which developed parallel or subparallel to the Abenaki carbonate front. They originated through an interaction between basement subsidence, salt tectonics and down-to-basin faulting. The style of these structures, however, is different from the salt structures described previously, probably due to differences in the nature of the Argo Formation and the basement topography. The lack of numerous diapirs on the north flank of the Sable Subbasin indicates either the flowage of salt into the Slope Diapiric Province or only sufficient salt to facilitate large scale gravity faulting but not enough to produce diapirs.

To elaborate, a series of major listric faults extend eastward from the Abenaki carbonate front (Fig. 5.28, 5.37). These appear to have developed in conjunction with an underlying zone of basement faulting with considerable vertical offset which led to a thick salt filled graben to the south. The listric faults are interpreted to coalesce at depth, possibly at or near the top of the salt, and the fault sole can be mapped for some distance seaward. A little to the east, similar faulting developed in conjunction with linear salt pillowing and the Lower Cretaceous strata onlap the north flank of the developing structures. In this area the fault sole clearly follows the salt facies. Farther east again, at Wenonah J-75, salt diapirs apparently developed from a "pillow ridge". Various aspects of these styles of structures are illustrated in Figures 5.26 and 5.27 and in Figure 5.52 (in pocket).

An unusual salt-related structure in this area occurs in the Onondaga wells. There, the salt is clearly diapiric for it occurs within Hauterivian sediments of the Missisauga Formation (P. Ascoli, pers. comm., 1986). The structure was originally thought to be an intermediate level piercement similar to the West Sable structure (Smith, 1975). However, seismic data now available clearly show that the salt occurs in conjunction with a fault plane and that it is underlain by a great thickness of sediments interpreted to be Middle and Late Jurassic, or older. The salt is now interpreted to have moved up a fault zone and to have formed a diapir or a pillow in rocks of much younger age and is completely detached from the regional Argo Formation. Salt structures of somewhat similar origin have been described in the southern North Sea (Jenyon, 1985). Alternatively, the salt at Onondaga may have been part of a normal diapir which, in the Early Cretaceous, was severed by a major listric fault slice with only the cap surviving within the structural complex.

Type 4.

In Abenaki Subbasin, salt pillows are seen on seismic data and are suspected to occur at depth, commonly in conjunction with growth faults. Because of their great depth, the true structural aspects of these features are not known and some of them may, in fact, may be diapiric in their relationship to the deep beds. South of the Abenaki to Chippewa trend of diapiric structures is the Missisauga Ridge, a northeast-striking salt pillow ridge. The Missisauga Ridge may mark the southern flank of the Abenaki Subbasin and the northern flank of the North Sable High (Fig. 5.18, in pocket, and Fig. 5.19). The ridge may have developed because of basement tilting and the pressure of sediment loading at the north flank of the Abenaki Subbasin.

Large salt masses also occur in the Orpheus Graben (Fig. 5.17). There, salt diapirs and pillows are less than 1 km below sea level and some are more than 5 km thick. The large amount of salt, relative to post-salt sediment in this basin, readily indicates how thick the salt was initially and allows the interpretation of equally thick salt deposits in the axial grabens of the rift system seaward of the present day shelf.

Faults

The time-structure maps (Fig. 5.28, 5.29, 5.37, 5.43, 5.44) show two major fault zones in the area east of longitude 61°W. Both trend east-northeast and are separated by a relatively undisturbed zone about 50 km wide. Westward, these fault trends merge into one as the basement hinge swings southward. The northern faults are just south of the hinge area and mark the northern edge of the Abenaki Subbasin (Fig. 5.18, 5.30). These faults sole at a depth of about 10 km on top of the salt and show relatively continuous movement from mid- Jurassic to the Tertiary.

Individual listric faults in the southern series were not active over such a long period and they affected successively younger sediments in a seaward direction (Fig. 5.19). The range of ages affected by the entire fault zone is, however, similar to that of the northern faults. The extent and magnitude of listric faulting is difficult to interpret from the relatively limited seismic coverage. Line spacings of 8 km or more make correlation of faults uncertain since the apparent direction and magnitude of movement varies depending on the position of seismic data within the fault slice.

The major listric fault systems which are developed in the western Sable Subbasin, south of the carbonate front, are seen to sole at progressively shallower depths in a seaward direction (Fig. 5.27; Fig. 5.52, in pocket). The deepest set, stratigraphically, is developed at or near the Abenaki carbonate front and soles, generally, at about 12-14 km. The second set, some 10-15 km to the south, soles at about 10-12 km and the third, developed south of the shelf edge, soles at about 8-10 km. The relationship of these faults to the Slope Diapiric Province is unknown but it is suspected that the successive levels of faulting may relate to major episodes of salt movement away from the hinge zone or to periods of growth in the Slope Diapiric Province. The timing of the major movements are approximately Late Jurassic, Early Cretaceous, and Late Cretaceous.

The seismic correlation of specific reflectors across the large listric faults at structures such as Glenelg and Alma is uncertain but large amounts of growth are indicated. For example, the main bounding fault of the Glenelg structure carries Lower Cretaceous beds to depths greater than 9 km, more than 4 km deeper than their occurrence in the Glenelg J-48 well (Fig. 5.27). The resultant increase in maturation of the Lower Cretaceous marine shales may extend to overmaturity. At the same time, it is possible that oil generation will be enhanced on the north flank of the structure as regional, marginally mature, marine beds are carried down into the zone of peak generation.

East of Sable Island near the Primrose structure, and to the south, the depth of the deepest mappable fault sole has a reflection time greater than 8.0 seconds. This yields a depth to the top of the Argo salt of more than 16.0 km and possibly as much as 20.0 km. The general style of the faulting in this area is one of relatively closely spaced, deeply soled, listric faults rising to the approximate level of the Wyandot Formation (Fig. 5.30). Across this area the density of faults and their accumulated throws illustrate the significant extension in the outer shelf region (Fig. 5.28, 5.37, 5.43, 5.44).

OVERPRESSURES

Overpressured conditions prevail when subsurface formation fluids are under a pressure greater than normal hydrostatic. Hydrostatic pressure (approximately 10.5 kPa/m) is defined as the pressure exerted by a column of water, containing 80 000 ppm total disolved solids, which is in open communication with the surface. Overpressures are known from many sedimentary basins around the world. The most commonly proposed causes of formation overpressuring are disequilibrium compaction, clay diagenesis, aquathermal pressuring, osmosis, tectonism and hydrocarbon generation (Fertl, 1976; Gretener, 1981).

Abnormally high formation pressures were found at depth in the Sable Island area and in parts of the Abenaki Subbasin. The Sable Island overpressured zone was encountered in a number of early wells. Although it was often accompanied by a gas show, it was considered to be the limit of the exploitable hydrocarbon bearing section because the occurrence of overpressure was thought, at the time, to indicate an absence of reservoirs. In 1979, Mobil and partners drilled into the overpressured section to evaluate seismic reflectors in a deep rollover structure at the Venture D-23 location. They found a thick series of uppermost Jurassic sandstone reservoirs in the lower member of the Missisauga Formation containing gas and condensate at a formation pressure nearly twice hydrostatic. Subsequent deep drilling discovered overpres-

sured gas in six other structures and established that the area of the overpressure system is at least 10 000 km² and is roughly centred on Sable Island. However, with subsequent occurrences encountered in the West Esperanto, Hesper and Louisbourg wells it is now known that overpressures also underlie the Abenaki Subbasin (Fig. 5.48). It is not known if the two systems are connected. In the Sable Island area the overpressured system is more than 1500 m thick and its base has not been encountered.

The cause of the Scotian Shelf overpressuring is not yet fully understood. In the Gulf of Mexico, and in many other basins of the world, overpressure is a common phenomenon resulting from incomplete compaction of sediment during rapid deposition, thermal expansion of fluids, clay mineral diagenesis and other causes. Physical and chemical phenomena accompanying the overpressures in the Gulf Coast area include sharply reduced shale resistivity, density and velocity, increased shale porosity, and reduced formation water salinity. Inherent in the development of Gulf Coast type overpressure is a general scarcity of porous reservoir beds.

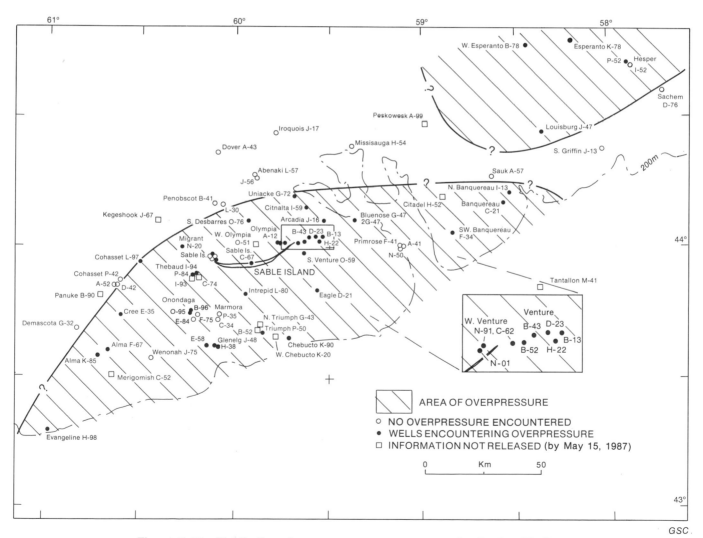

GSC

Figure 5.48 Distribution of overpressure occurences on the Scotian Shelf.

VENTURE B-43

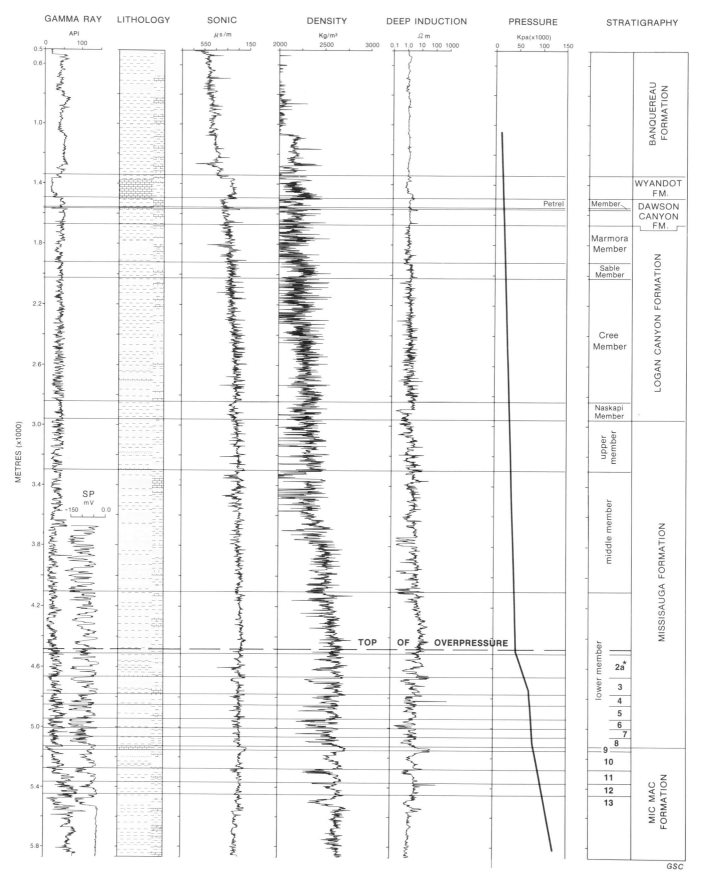

GAMMA RAY	LITHOLOGY	SONIC	DENSITY	DEEP INDUCTION	PRESSURE	STRATIGRAPHY
API		μs/m	Kg/m³	Ω m	Kpa(x1000)	

GSC

Overpressured formations encountered in the Scotian Basin are different. They contain abundant reservoir beds and the shales involved are fully lithified. Consequently, bulk density and sonic velocity data show only gradual change with increased fluid pressure although shale resistivity is considerably reduced (Fig. 5.49). This indicates that the reduction is not due to increased porosity but rather to a change in the conductivity of the pore fluid. Petrographic studies demonstrate that some sandstones have been cemented and have subsequently developed secondary porosity. Therefore, the Sable Island overpressure system developed after shale diagenesis was complete and may result from a mechanism such as thermal expansion of pore fluids or gas generation in an effectively sealed system.

Structures such as Thebaud, Venture and South Venture contain gas in both normally and overpressured reservoirs. Pressure versus depth plots of wells drilled into the overpressured system reveal the presence of a distinct transition zone between the hydrostatic and "hard" overpressure regimes. (Hard overpressure is defined as pressure requiring a drilling mud density of at least 2036 kg/m^3 (17 lb/gal) to control.) The transition zone is indicative of incomplete reservoir communication or of a series of imperfect horizontal seals. It is therefore speculated that the relatively few and small underfilled gas reservoirs in the overlying hydrostatic regime in the Sable Subbasin are indicative of almost perfect seals which have kept most of the gas in the overpressured regime since its generation. The transition zone is considered related to a gas migration front in a dynamically expanding system fueled by the generation of gas.

Figure 5.50 is a plot of pressure versus depth for five wells in the Venture field. The pressure data used are from formation tests and have been extrapolated to maximum. The hydrostatic pressure gradient above the overpressured zone is 10.7 kPa/m. This is slightly higher than normal and is attributed to the high density (high salinity) formation fluids in the Missisauga Formation in this area. In the overpressure system of the Venture field, three zones, with different pressure gradients, each contain a series of reservoirs and seals. In the interval between 4450 and 4750 m, which includes the #2 and #3 reservoir series (Mobil, 1984), the pressure rises rapidly with a gradient of greater than 100 kPa/m, indicating effective seals and the virtual isolation of reservoirs. From 4750-5100 m, which includes the #4 to #8 reservoir series, the gradient is only about 20 kPa/m, indicating interconnected permeable reservoirs. Below 5100 m is the zone with hard overpressure in which the pressure gradient is about 50 kPa/m. The top of the hard overpressure is coincident with the #9 limestone member which, from the pressure differential across it, obviously forms a better than average seal.

Maturation studies of the Sable Subbasin area by Nantais (1983) indicated that the onset of maturation of the dominantly terrestrial organic matter in the Mic Mac and Missisauga deltaic system occurred at a temperature of about 75°C and at a depth of 2000 to 2500 m. Over much of this area, the top of the Missisauga Formation is just now reaching the onset of maturity. However, in the area

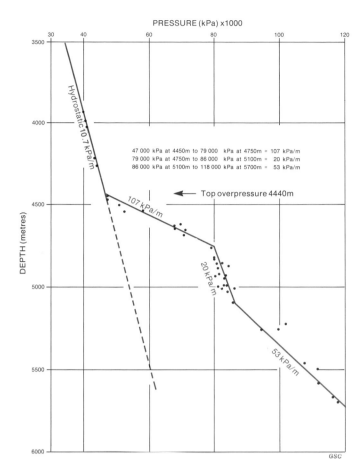

Figure 5.50 Plot of pressure versus depth for five wells in the Venture field.

of Sable Island, the lower member of the Missisauga reached this stage during the Late Cretaceous and is currently at its peak. In some areas, the Mic Mac Formation has been in the overmature zone for the last 10-20 Ma. Therefore, gas generation from these formations has started only relatively recently after full lithification of the sediments and after cessation of much of the faulting. With adequate seals, the gas would remain trapped adjacent to the source rocks and the active gas generation would result in overpressuring.

Hydrocarbon generation from Middle Jurassic source rocks began even earlier and was escalated by rapid burial during the Late Jurassic and Cretaceous. This rapid burial also caused excessive thermal expansion of fluids and increased the level of overpressuring. It is felt that the original top of the overpressured system was deeper than it is now and that it subsequently has been forced upward and laterally to its present configurations by the higher pressures at depth.

With one exception, the top seal on the Scotian Basin overpressure system consists of Missisauga and Mic Mac Formation shale intervals and the Verrill Canyon Formation. The seal is not the same bed throughout the basin but varies in depth and stratigraphic position from structure to structure. The lateral seals probably occur at the down-to-basin faults which form the updip limit of many of the hydrocarbon prospects. The top of the overpressure system,

Figure 5.49 Venture B-43 well logs and pressure plot showing the log response in the overpressure zone. *Informal terminology of Mobil Oil Canada, Ltd.

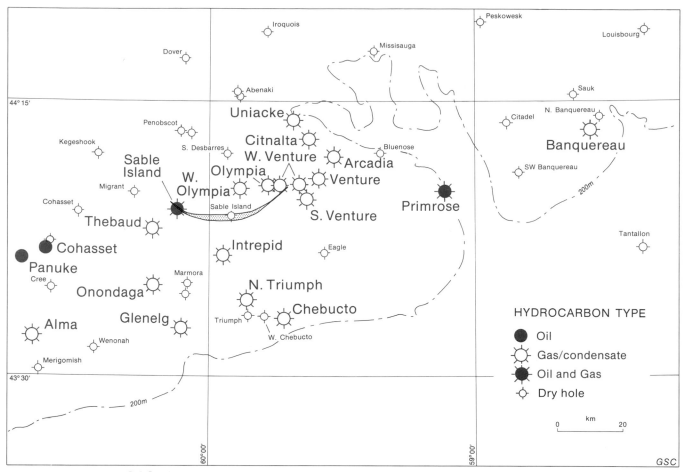

GAS AND OIL DISCOVERIES-SABLE ISLAND AND ADJACENT AREA

Figure 5.51 Signifigant hydrocarbon discoveries in the Scotian Basin.

as observed in control wells, is shallowest to the southwest and becomes progressively deeper and older to the northeast. This suggests both lateral and vertical expansion of the overpressure system, a phenomenon which may be ongoing. Lateral migration occurs across the down-to-the-basin faults where porous beds are juxtaposed. Vertical migration occurs along the faults or through fractures generated when the local pressure exceeds the lithostatic pressure of the sealing beds, allowing the gas to move into adjacent hydrostatically pressured reservoirs.

The exception referred to above is at the Shubenacadie well, where the top of the overpressured regime was encountered at a depth of approximately 2740 m in Miocene sediments. Sediment characteristics in this well suggest that the most likely generating mechanism is disequilibrium compaction.

OIL AND GAS OCCURRENCES

Exploratory drilling for oil and gas in the Scotian Basin commenced in 1966 when Amoco Canada and Imperial Oil Limited drilled the Tors Cove D-52 well to a depth of 1473 m (4834 ft) on the crest of a salt diapir in the South Whale Subbasin. A small amount of gas was recovered from wireline tests of the caprock facies at 1183 and 1189 m (3880 and 3900 ft). In 1967, Mobil drilled the Sable Island C-67 well to a depth of 4604 m (15 106 ft) within the overpressured lower member of the Missisauga Formation. Small amounts of gas and oil were recovered from a bottom-hole test. The first significant discovery in the basin was made in 1969 by Shell in the Onondaga E-84 well. This well encountered approximately 40 m of interpreted gas pay in the upper member of the Missisauga Formation overlying a salt structure. By the end of 1986 there were 22 discoveries of some significance in Scotian Basin. All of these were in Sable Subbasin (Fig. 5.51). The discoveries are described in more detail by Grant et al. (1986) and in Chapter 12 of this volume.

Studies of organic matter from the Scotian Shelf wells show that terrestrially dominated (Type III) kerogen is prevalent in the Logan Canyon, Missisauga and Mic Mac formations (Barss et al., 1980). The organic carbon content in these formations is generally low. However, analysis of some deeper wells in the Sable Subbasin indicate extensive intervals within the lower member of the Missisauga Formation in which the organic carbon content is in excess of 2.0%. Further studies may prove these zones to be equivalent to the rich Kimmeridgian source rocks of the Grand Banks. Hydrocarbon extract data indicate that the Verrill Canyon Formation (and equivalent shales within the Mic Mac and Missisauga formations) are the source rocks for most of the discovered hydrocarbons (Powell, 1982) with differences in product arising from variations in organic matter type and in the levels of maturation.

The thermal history of the formations on the Scotian Shelf has been developed from a variety of indicators including geothermal gradient, thermal alteration index (TAI), time temperature index (TTI), and vitrinite reflectance (Ro). Correlation of the other indices with measured values of Ro allows the interpretation of maturation levels in the wells where Ro data are not available. The geochemical and maturation data from the Scotian Shelf indicate that the onset of full maturity coincides with an Ro of 0.7%, equivalent to a TTI of 50 and a temperature of about 110°C. The transition to overmaturity occurs at an Ro of 1.3% which is equivalent to a TTI of 2895 and a temperature of about 180°C (Nantais, 1983). The most common maturation product of Scotian Shelf kerogen is gas and condensate but small accumulations of oil have been encountered in Cohasset D-42, Panuke B-90, Primrose N-50 and Sable Island E-48.

In the Sable Island area, the fully mature zone lies in the lower part of the Missisauga Formation and the transition to overmaturity occurs in the upper part of the Mic Mac Formation (Wade et al., 1989) where present day temperatures at 6 km are in excess of 170°C. Therefore more than half of the sedimentary section in the Sable Subbasin is in the overmature realm. Drilling results have confirmed the predicted gas and condensate products from the source rocks and their occurrence within and below the fully mature zone. No indications of major oil occurrences have been encountered in the deeper parts of the Sable Subbasin, but oil plays such as Cohasset D-42 may occur at intermediate depths where Upper Cretaceous marine source rocks are entering the oil window, or along the inner regions of the basin where Lower and Middle Jurassic source rocks are in a mature state.

The resources associated with the Scotian Shelf discoveries through the end of 1983 were estimated at more than 117×10^9 m^3 (4 Tcf) of gas, approximately 13×10^6 m^3 (90 Mbbl) of condensate and 1.5×10^6 m^3 (10 Mbbl) of oil (Wade et al., 1989). Discoveries made during 1984-85 approximately offset reductions in the estimated values of resources which followed stepout drilling. The discoveries and basin potential are described in more detail in Chapter 12.

ACKNOWLEDGMENTS

The authors acknowledge the contributions of their colleagues in the Eastern Petroleum Geology Subdivision both for their data and for stimulating discussions which have helped to formulate some of the interpretations presented. We thank H.B.S. Cooke for scientific review.

REFERENCES

Amato, R.V. and Bebout, J.W. (ed.)
1980: Geologic and Operational Summary, COST No. G-1 well, Georges Bank Area, North Atlantic OCS; United States Geological Survey, Open-File Report 80-268, 112 p.

Amato, R.V. and Simonis, E.K. (ed.)
1980: Geologic and operational summary, COST No. G-2 well, Georges Bank area, North Atlantic OCS; United States Geological Survey, Open-File Report 80-269, 116 p.

Amoco Canada Petroleum Company Limited and Imperial Oil Limited
1973: Regional geology of the Grand Banks; Bulletin of Canadian Petroleum Geology, v. 21, p. 479-503.

Anderson, R.C. and Taylor, D.J.
1981: Very high amplitude seismic anomaly in Georges Bank trough, Atlantic continental margin; American Association of Petroleum Geologists Bulletin, v. 65, p. 133-144.

Arthur, M.A.
1982a: Lithology and petrography of the COST Nos. G-1 and G-2 wells; in Geological Studies of the COST Nos. G-1 and G-2 Wells, United States North Atlantic Outer Continental Shelf, ed. P.A. Scholle and C.R. Wenkam; United States Geological Survey, Circular 861, p. 11-33.

1982b: Thermal history of the Georges Bank Basin; in Geological Studies of the COST Nos. G-1 and G-2 Wells, United States North Atlantic Outer Continental Shelf, ed. P.A. Scholle and C.R. Wenkam; United States Geological Survey, Circular 861, p. 143-152.

Ascoli, P.
1976: Foraminiferal and ostracod biostratigraphy of the Mesozoic-Cenozoic, Scotian Shelf, Atlantic Canada; Maritime Sediments, Special Publication No. 1, p. 653-771.

Austin, J.A., Uchupi, E., Shaughnessy, D.R., and Ballard, R.D.
1980: Geology of New England passive margin; American Association of Petroleum Geologists Bulletin, v. 64, p. 501-526.

Ballard, R.D. and Uchupi, E.
1975: Triassic rift structure in the Gulf of Maine: American Association of Petroleum Geologists Bulletin, v. 59, p. 1041-1072.

Barss, M.S., Bujak, J.P., Wade, J.A., and Williams, G.L.
1980: Age, stratigraphy, organic matter type and colour, and hydrocarbon occurrences in 47 wells, offshore eastern Canada; Geological Survey of Canada, Open File 714, 55 p.

Barss, M.S., Bujak, J.P., and Williams, G.L.
1979: Palynological zonation and correlation of sixty-seven wells, eastern Canada; Geological Survey of Canada, Paper 78-24, 118 p.

Bartlett, G.A. and Smith, L.
1971: Mesozoic and Cenozoic history of the Grand Banks of Newfoundland: Canadian Journal of Earth Sciences, v. 8, p. 65-84.

Canada Oil and Gas Lands Administration
1987: Offshore Schedule of Wells 1966-1986; Energy Mines and Resources, Canada, Indian and Northern Affairs, Canada, Ottawa.

Dainty, A.M., Keen, C.E., M.J., and Blanchard, J.E.
1966: Review of geophysical evidence on crust and upper-mantle structure on the eastern seaboard of Canada; in The Earth beneath the Continents, ed. J.S. Steinhart and T.J. Smith; American Geophysical Union, p. 349-369.

Davies, E.H., Akande, S.O., and Zentilli, M.
1984: Early Cretaceous deposits in the Gays River lead-zinc mine, Nova Scotia; in Current Research, Part A, Geological Survey of Canada, Paper 84-1A, p. 353-358.

Ditty, P.S.
1980: Seismic velocity and correlations; in Geologic and Operational Summary, COST No. G-1 Well, Georges Bank Area, North Atlantic Ocean, ed. R.V. Amato and J.W. Bebout; United States Geological Survey, Open-File Report 80-268, p. 59-67.

Doeven, P.H.
1983: Cretaceous nannofossil stratigraphy and paleoecology of the Canadian Atlantic Margin; Geological Survey of Canada, Bulletin 356, 70 p.

Eliuk, L.S.
1978: The Abenaki Formation, Nova Scotia Shelf, Canada — a depositional and diagenetic model for a Mesozoic carbonate platform; Bulletin of Canadian Petroleum Geology, v. 26, p. 424-514.

Ewing, J.I. and Rabinowitz, P.D. (ed.)
1984: Eastern North American Continental Margin and Adjacent Ocean Floor, 34 to 41°N and 68 to 78°W; Ocean Margin Drilling Program, Atlas 4, Marine Science International, Woods Hole, Massachusetts.

Falvey, D.A.
1974: The development of continental margins in plate tectonic theory; Australian Petroleum Exploration Association Journal, v. 14, p. 95-106.

Fertl, W.H.
1976: Abnormal Formation Pressures; Elsevier Scientific Publishing Co., New York, 382 p.

Folger, D.W., Hathaway, J.C., Christopher, R.A., Valentine, P.C. and Poag, C.W.,
1978: Stratigraphic test well, Nantucket Island, Massachusetts; United States Geological Survey Circular 773, p. 28

Given, M.M.
1977: Mesozoic and early Cenozoic geology of offshore Nova Scotia: Bulletin of Canadian Petroleum Geology, v. 25, p. 63-91.

Gradstein, F.M., Grant, A.C., and Jansa, L.F.
1977: Grand Banks and the J-Anomaly Ridge: A geological comparison; Science, v. 197, p. 1074-1076.

Grant, A.C.
1984: A seismic base-event map for the continental margin around Newfoundland; in Proceedings of the Canadian Meteorological and Oceanographic Society and Canadian Geophysical Union Joint Meeting, Halifax, Nova Scotia.

Grant, A.C., McAlpine, K.D., and Wade, J.A.
1986: The continental margin of eastern Canada: Geological framework and petroleum potential; in Future Petroleum Provinces of the World, ed. M.T. Halbouty; American Association of Petroleum Geologists, Memoir 40, p. 177-205.

Gretener, P.E.
1981: Pore pressure: fundamentals, general ramificationss and implications for structural geology (revised); American Association of Petroleum Geologists, Education Course Note Series no. 4, 131 p.

Hardy, I.A.
1975: Lithostratigraphy of the Banquereau Formation of the Scotian Shelf; in Offshore Geology of Eastern Canada, Volume 2, Regional Geology, ed. W.J.M. van der Linden and J.A. Wade; Geological Survey of Canada, Paper 74-30, v. 2, p. 163-174.

Hayatsu, A.
1979: K-Ar isochron age of the North Mountain Basalt, Nova Scotia; Canadian Journal of Earth Sciences, v. 16, p. 973-975.

Hodych, J.P. and Hayatsu, A.
1980: K-Ar isochron age and paleomagnetism of diabase along the trans-Avalon aeromagnetic lineament — evidence of Late Triassic rifting in Newfoundland; Canadian Journal of Earth Sciences, v. 17, p. 491-499.

Holser, W.T., Clement, G.P., Jansa, L.F., and Wade, J.A.
1988: Evaporite deposits of the North Atlantic Rift; in Developments in Geotectonics 22; Triassic-Jurassic Rifting. Continental Breakup and the Origin of the Atlantic Ocean and Passive Margins, ed. W. Manspeizer; Elsevier Scientific Publishing Co., The Netherlands, p. 525-556.

Houghton, R.L., Thomas, J.E., Diecchio, R.J., and Tagliacozzo, A.
1979: Radiometric ages of basalts from DSDP Leg 43: sites 382 and 385 (New England Seamounts), 384 (J-Anomaly), 386 and 387 (central and western Bermuda Rise); in Initial Reports of the Deep Sea Drilling Project, Volume 43, ed. B.E. Tucholke; U.S. Government Printing Office, Washington, v. 43, p. 739-753.

Howie, R.D. and Barss, M.S.
1975: Upper Paleozoic rocks of the Atlantic Provinces, Gulf of St. Lawrence and adjacent continental shelf; in Offshore Geology of Eastern Canada, Volume 2, Regional Geology, ed. W.J.M. van der Linden and J.A. Wade; Geological Survey of Canada, Paper 74-30, v. 2, p. 35-50.

Jansa, L.F. and Pe-Piper, G.
1985: Early Cretaceous volcanism on the northeastern American margin and implications for plate tectonics; Geological Society of America Bulletin, v. 96, pp. 83-91.
1986: Geology and geochemistry of Middle Jurassic and early Cretaceous igneous rocks on the eastern North American continental shelf; Geological Survey of Canada, Open File 1351, 104 p.
1987: Identification of an underwater extraterrestrial impact crater; Nature v. 327, no. 6/23, p. 612-614.
1988: Middle Jurassic to early Cretaceous igneous rocks along eastern North American continental margin; American Association of Petroleum Geologists Bulletin, v. 72, p. 347-366.

Jansa, L.F. and Wade, J.A.
1975a: Paleogeography and sedimentation in the Mesozoic and Cenozoic, southeastern Canada; in Canada's Continental Margins and Offshore Petroleum Exploration, ed. C.J. Yorath, E.R. Parker and D.J.Glass; Canadian Society of Petroleum Geologists, Memoir 4, p. 79-102.
1975b: Geology of the continental margin off Nova Scotia and Newfoundland; in Offshore Geology of Eastern Canada, Volume 2, Regional Geology, ed. W.J.M. van der Linden and J.A. Wade; Geological Survey of Canada, Paper 74-30, v. 2, p. 51-106.

Jansa L.F., Bujak, J.P., and Williams, G.L.
1980: Upper Triassic salt deposits of the western North Atlantic; Canadian Journal of Earth Sciences, v. 17, p. 547-559.

Jansa, L.F., Enos, P., Tucholke, B.E., Gradstein, F.M., and Sheridan, R.E.
1979: Mesozoic-Cenozoic sedimentary formations of the North American Basin, western North Atlantic; in Deep Drilling Results in the Atlantic Ocean, Continental Margins and Paleoenvironment, ed. M. Talwani, W. Hay and W.B.F.Ryan; Maurice Ewing Series 3, American Geophysical Union, Washington, D.C., p. 1-57.

Jansa, L.F., Termier, G., and Termier, H.
1982: Les biohermes a algues, spongiaires et coraux des series carbonates de la flexure bordiere du 'paleoshelf' au large du Canada oriental; Revue de Micropaleontologie, v. 25, p. 181-219.

Jenyon, M.K.
1985: Basin-edge diapirism and updip salt flow in Zechstein of southern North Sea; American Association of Petroleum Geologists Bulletin, v. 69, p. 53-64.

Keen, C.E., and Cordsen, A.
1981: Crustal structure, seismic stratigraphy, and rift processes of the continental margin off eastern Canada: ocean bottom seismic refractrion results off Nova Scotia; Canadian Journal of Earth Sciences, v. 18, p. 1523-1538.

Keen, C.E. and Haworth, R.T.
1985: D-3 rifted continental margin off Nova Scotia, offshore eastern Canada; Geological Society of America, Centennial Continent/Ocean Transect #3.

Keen, C.E., Keen, M.J., Barrett, D.L., and Heffler, D.E.
1975: Some aspects of the ocean-continent transition at the continental margin of eastern North America; in Offshore Geology of Eastern Canada, Volume 2, Regional Geology, ed. W.J.M. van der Linden and J.A. Wade; Geological Survey of Canada, Paper 74-30, v. 2, p. 189-197.

King, L.H.,
1970: Surficial geology of the Halifax-Sable Island map area; Marine Sciences Branch, Dept. of Energy, Mines and Resources, Ottawa, Marine Science Paper, 16 p.

Klein, G. de V.
1962: Triassic sedimentation, Maritime Provinces, Canada; Geological Society of America Bulletin, v. 73, p. 1127-1146.

Klitgord, K.D. and Hutchinson, D.R.
1985: Distribution and geophysical signatures of early Mesozoic rift basins beneath the United States continental margin; in Proceedings of the 2nd U.S. Geological Survey Workshop on the Early Mesozoic Basins of the Eastern United States, ed. G.R. Robinson and A.J. Froelich; United States Geological Survey, Circular 946, p. 45-61.

Klitgord, K.D., Schlee, J.S., and Hinz, K.
1982: Basement structure, sedimentation and tectonic history of the Georges Bank Basin; in Geological Studies of the COST Nos. G-1 and G-2 Wells, United States North Atlantic Outer Continental Shelf, ed. P.A. Scholle and C.R. Wenkham; United States Geological Survey, Circular 861, p. 160-186.

Lachance, D.J.
1980: Lithology; in Geologic and Operational Summary, COST No. G-1 well, North Atlantic OCS, ed. R.V. Amato and J.W. Bebout; United States Geological Survey, Open-File Report 80-268, p. 17-21.

LePichon, X., Sibuet, J.C., and Francheteau, J.
1977: The fit of the continents around the North Atlantic Ocean; Tectonophysics, v. 38, p. 169-209.

Lin, C.L.
1971: Cretaceous deposits in the Musquodoboit River Valley, Nova Scotia; Canadian Journal of Earth Sciences, v. 8, p. 1152-1154.

Manspeizer, W.
1981: Early Mesozoic basins of the central Atlantic passive margins; in Geology of Passive Continental Margins: History, Structure and Sedimentologic Record (With Special Emphasis on the Atlantic Margin); American Association of Petroleum Geologists, Education Course Note Series no. 19, 60 p.

Manspeizer, W. and Cousminer, H.L.
1988: Late Triassic-Early Jurassic synrift basins of the U.S. Atlantic margin; in Sheridan, R.E., and Grow, J.A. (ed), The Atlantic Continental Margin: U.S., Geological Society of America, The Geology of North America, v. I-2, p. 197-216.

Mattick, R.E.
1982: Significance of the Mesozoic carbonate bank-reef sequence for the petroleum geology of the Georges Bank Basin; in Geological Studies of the COST Nos. G-1 and G-2 wells, United States North Atlantic Outer Continental Shelf, ed. P.A. Scholle and C.R. Wenkam; United States Geological Survey, Circular 861, p.93-104.

McIver, N.L.
1972: Mesozoic and Cenozoic stratigraphy of the Nova Scotia Shelf; Canadian Journal of Earth Sciences, v. 9, p. 54-70.

McWhae, J.R.H.
1981: Structure and spreading history of the northwestern Atlantic region from the Scotian Shelf to Baffin Bay; in Geology of the North Atlantic Borderlands, ed. J.W. Kerr and A.J. Fergusson; Canadian Society of Petroleum Geologists, Memoir 7, p. 299-332.

Miller, K.G., Mountain, G.S., and Tucholke, B.E.
1985: Oligocene glacio-eustasy and erosion on the margins of the North Atlantic; Geology, v. 13, p. 10-13.

Miller, R.E., Lerch, H.E., Claypool, G.E., Smith, M.A., Owings, D.K., Ligon, D.T., and Eisner, S.B.
1982: Organic geochemistry of the Georges Bank basin COST Nos. G-1 and G-2 wells; in Geological Studies of the COST Nos. G-1 and G-2 Wells, United States North Atlantic Outer Continental Shelf, ed. P.A. Scholle and C.R. Wenkam; United States Geological Survey, Circular 861, p. 105-142.

Mobil Oil Canada Ltd.
1984: Mobil et al. Venture H-22: Well History Report; Canada Oil and Gas Lands Administration, Department of Energy, Mines and Resources, Ottawa, Canada.

Nantais, P.T.
1983: A reappraisal of the regional hydrocarbon potential of the Scotian Shelf; Geological Survey of Canada, Open File 1175, 83 p.

Officer, C.B. and Ewing, M.
1954: Geophysical investigations in the emerged and submerged Atlantic Coastal Plain, Part VII. Continental shelf, continental slope, and continental rise south of Nova Scotia; Bulletin of the Geological Society of America, v. 65, p. 653-670.

Palmer, A.R. (comp.)
1983: The decade of North American geology, 1983 geologic time scale; Geological Society of America.

Papezik, V.S. and Barr, S.M.
1981: The Shelburne dike, an early Mesozoic diabase dike in Nova Scotia: mineralogy, chemistry and regional significance; Canadian Journal of Earth Sciences, v. 18, p. 1346-1355.

Petro-Canada Inc.
1983: Southwest Banquereau F-34: Well History Report; Petro-Canada et al.; Canada Oil and Gas Lands Administration, Department of Energy, Mines and Resources, Ottawa, Canada.

1984: Petro-Canada et al., Bonnet P-23: Well History Report; Canada Oil and Gas Lands Administration, Department of Energy, Mines and Resources, Ottawa, Canada, 138 p.

Poag, C.W.
1982: Foraminiferal and seismic stratigraphy, paleoenvironments and depositional cycles in the Georges Bank Basin; in Geological Studies of the COST Nos. G-1 and G-2 Wells, United States North Atlantic Outer Continental Shelf, ed. P.A. Scholle and C.R. Wenkam; United States Geological Survey, Circular 861, p. 43-91.

Poag, C.W. (ed.)
1985: Geologic evolution of the United States Atlantic margin; Van Nostrand Reinhold Company Inc., New York, 383 p.

Poag, C.W. and Schlee, J.S.
1984: Depositional sequences and stratigraphic gaps on the submerged United States Atlantic margin; in Interregional Unconformities and Hydrocarbon Accumulation, ed. J.S. Schlee; American Association of Petroleum Geologists, Memoir 34, p. 165-182.

Powell, T.G.
1982: Petroleum geochemistry of the Verrill Canyon Formation; A source for Scotian Shelf hydrocarbons; Bulletin of Canadian Petroleum Geology, v. 30, p. 167-179.

Rabonowitz, P.D.
1974: The boundary between oceanic and continental crust in the western North Atlantic; in Geology of the Continental Margins, ed. C.A. Burk and C.L. Drake; Springer Verlag, New York, p. 67-84.

Reynolds, P.H., Zentilli, M., and Muecke, G.K.
1981: K-Ar and ^{40}Ar/^{39}Ar geochronology of granitoid rocks from southern Nova Scotia; Its bearing on the geological evolution of the Meguma Zone of the Appalachians; Canadian Journal of Earth Sciences, v. 18, p. 386-394.

Schlee, J.S. and Fritsch, J.
1983: Seismic stratigraphy of the Georges Bank Basin complex, Offshore New England; in Studies in Continental Margin Geology, ed. J.S. Watkins and C.L. Drake; American Association of Petroleum Geologists, Memoir 34, p. 223-251.

Schlee, J.S. and Klitgord, K.D.
1982: Geologic setting of the Georges Bank Basin; in Geological Studies of the COST Nos. G-1 and G-2 Wells, United States North Atlantic Outer Continental Shelf, ed. P.A. Scholle and C.R. Wenkam; United States Geological Survey, Circular 861, p. 4-10.

1988:: Georges Bank basin: A regional synthesis; in Sheridan, R.E., and Grow, J.A., (ed). The Atlantic Continental Margin, U.S., Geological Society of America, The Geology of North America, v. I-2. p. 243-268.

Schlee, J.S., Behrendt, J.C., Grow, J.A., Robb, J.M., Mattick, R.E., Taylor, P.T., and Lawson, B.J.
1976: Regional geologic framework off northeastern United States; American Association of Petroleum Geologists Bulletin, v. 60, p. 926-951.

Schlee, J.S., Poag, C.W., and Hinz, K.
1985: Seismic stratigraphy of the continental slope and rise seaward of Georges Bank; in Geologic Evolution of the United States Atlantic Margin, ed. C.W. Poag; Van Nostrand Reinhold Company, New York, p. 256-292.

Scholle, P.A. and Wenkam, C.R. (ed.)
1982: Geological Studies of the COST Nos. G-1 and G-2 Wells, United States North Atlantic Outer Continental Shelf; United States Geological Survey, Circular 861, 193 p.

Schultz, L.K. and Grover, R.L.
1974: Geology of Georges Bank Basin; American Association of Petroleum Geologists Bulletin, v. 58, p. 1159-1168.

Shell Canada Resources Limited
1983: Shell et al. Shubenacadie H-100: Well History Report; Canada Oil and Gas Lands Administration, Department of Energy Mines and Resources, Ottawa, Canada.

Sherwin, D.F.
1973: Scotian Shelf and Grand Banks; in The Future Petroleum Provinces of Canada — Their Geology and Potential, ed. R.G. McCrossan; Canadian Society of Petroleum Geologists, Memoir 1, p. 519-559.

Shor, A.N. and Uchupi, E. (ed.)
1984: Eastern North American Continental Margin and Adjacent Ocean Floor, 39° to 46° and 54° to 64°W; Ocean Margin Drilling Program, Atlas 2, Marine Science International, Woods Hole, Massachusetts, 35 p.

Simonis, E.K.
1980: Lithologic description; in Geologic and Operational Summary, COST No. G-2 Well, Georges Bank Area, North Atlantic OCS, ed. R.V. Amato and E.K. Simonis; United States Geological Survey, Open-File Report 80-269, p. 14-19.

Smith, H.A.
1975: Geology of the West Sable Structure; in Canada's Continental Margins and Offshore Petroleum Exploration, ed. C.J. Yorath, E.R. Parker, and D.J. Glass; Canadian Society of Petroleum Geologists, Memoir 4, p. 133-153.

Steinkraus, W.E.
1980: Biostratigraphy; in Geologic and Operational Summary, COST No. G-1 Well, Georges Bank Area, North Atlantic OCS, ed. R.V. Amato and J.W. Bebout; United States Geological Survey, Open-File Report 80-268, p. 39-52.

Swift, S.A.
1985: Cenozoic geology of the continental slope and rise off western Nova Scotia; Ph.D. thesis, Massachusetts Institute of Technology, Woods Hole Oceanographic Institution, Paper 85-34, 188 p.

Taylor, D.J. and Anderson, R.C.
1982: Geophysical studies of the COST Nos. G-1 and G-2 wells; in Geological Studies of the COST Nos. G-1 and G-2 Wells, United States North Atlantic Outer Continental Shelf, ed. P.A. Scholle and C.R. Wenkam; United States Geological Survey, Circular 861, p. 153-159.

Tucholke, B.E. and Mountain, G.S.
1979: Seismic stratigraphy, lithostratigraphy and paleosedimentation patterns in the North American basin; in Deep Drilling Results in the Atlantic Ocean; Continental Margins and Paleoenvironments, ed. M. Talwani, W. Hay and W.B.F. Ryan; American Geophysical Union, M. Ewing Series, v. 3, p. 58-86.

Uchupi, E. and Shor, A.N. (ed.)
1983: Eastern North American Continental Margin and Adjacent Ocean Floor, 39° to 46° and 64° to 74°W; Ocean Margin Drilling Program, Atlas 3, Marine Science International, Woods Hole, Massachusetts, 38 p.

Upshaw, C.F., Armstrong, W.E., Creath, W.B., Kidson, E.J., and Sanderson, G.A.
1974: Biostratigraphic framework of Grand Banks; American Association of Petroleum Geologists Bulletin, v. 58, pt. 2, p. 1124-1132.

Van Eysinga, F.W.B.
1983:   Geological Time Table; Elsevier Scientific Publishing Co., The Netherlands.

Van Houten, F.B.
1977:   Triassic-Liassic deposits of Morocco and eastern North America; a comparison; American Association of Petroleum Geologists Bulletin, v. 61, p. 79-99.

Vogt, P.R and Tucholke, B.E.
1979:   The New England Seamounts: testing origins; in Initial Reports of the Deep Sea Drilling Project, Volume 43, ed. B.E. Tucholke et al.; U.S. Government Printing Office, Washington, p. 847-856.

Wade, J.A.
1973:   Regional Geology of the Mesozoic-Cenozoic sediments off Nova Scotia and Newfoundland; Geological Survey of Canada, Paper 73-1, Part B, p. 99.

1976:   Early Mesozoic evaporite deposits in eastern Canada; in Evaporite Deposits of Canada Phase 1 – An Overview, ed. B.V. Sanford, Internal Report for the Geological Survey of Canada; Energy Mines and Resources, Ottawa, p. 137-151.

1977:   Stratigraphy of Georges Bank Basin: interpreted from seismic correlation to the western Scotian Shelf; Canadian Journal of Earth Sciences, v. 14, p. 2274-2283.

1978:   The Mesozoic-Cenozoic history of the northeastern margin of North America; Offshore Technology Conference Proceedings, v. 3, p. 1849-1859.

1981:   Geology of the Canadian Atlantic Margin from Georges Bank to the Grand Banks; in Geology of the North Atlantic Borderlnds, ed. J.W. Kerr and A.J. Fergusson; Canadian Society of Petroleum Geologists, Memoir 7, p. 447-460.

Wade, J.A., Campbell, G.R., Procter, R.M., and Taylor, G.C.
1989:   Petroleum resources of the Scotian Shelf; Geological Survey of Canada, Paper 88-19, 26 p.

Wark, J.M. and Clarke, D.B.
1980:   Geochemical discriminators and the paleotectonic environment of the North Mountain basalts, Nova Scotia; Canadian Journal of Earth Sciences, v. 17, p. 1740-1745.

Waetjen, H.H.
1980:   Seismic velocity and reflection correlation; in Geologic and Operational Summary, COST No. G-2 Well, Georges Bank Area, North Atlantic OCS, ed. R.V. Amato and E.K. Simonis; United States Geological Survey, Open-File Report 80-269, p. 37-44.

Authors' addresses

J. A Wade
Atlantic Geoscience Centre
Geological Survey of Canada
Bedford Institute of Oceanography
P.O. Box 1006
Dartmouth, Nova Scotia
B2Y 4A2

B.C. MacLean
Institute of Sedimentary and Petroleum Geology
Geological Survey of Canada
3303-33rd Street N.W.
Calgary, Alberta
T2L 2A7

Printed in Canada

Chapter 6

THE CONTINENTAL MARGIN AROUND NEWFOUNDLAND

Chapter 6

THE CONTINENTAL MARGIN AROUND NEWFOUNDLAND

A.C. Grant and K.D. McAlpine

INTRODUCTION

This chapter describes the geology of the continental margin around Newfoundland, including the Grand Banks and the Northeast Newfoundland Shelf, and the adjacent continental slope and rise (CHS Map 850-A, in pocket). The area of the continental shelf from the Laurentian Channel to southern Labrador, and including Flemish Cap, is about 450 000 km^2. The adjacent slope and rise is similar in area (Fig. 6.1). Continental crust, composed of Paleozoic and Precambrian igneous and sedimentary rocks, underlies the shelf and extends seaward beneath the slope and rise. The major subsurface geological elements of the region are a series of interconnected Mesozoic sedimentary basins (Fig. 6.2). These basins and intervening basement highs are truncated by a prominent peneplain commonly termed the Avalon Unconformity (Jansa and Wade, 1975), which is related to a regional late Mesozoic arch, the Avalon Uplift. The peneplain is blanketed by a generally thin cover of undeformed Upper Cretaceous and Tertiary sediments. These sediments thicken seaward through the slope and rise and eventually prograde onto oceanic crust. The configuration of the continent/ocean boundary around the Newfoundland continental margin is complex and variable and the exact location of this transition is unknown in many areas.

Much of our knowledge of this region derives from industrial geophysical surveys and drilling for petroleum. Geophysical surveys have been carried out on the shelf, slope and rise; drilling has been concentrated in the several sedimentary basins on the shelf. Accordingly, our knowledge is more extensive for these sedimentary basins, and they are discussed in some detail in the first part of this chapter. In the second part of this chapter, these results are extrapolated to off-shelf regions using geophysical control.

The well data used in this chapter are those released to the public by the Canada Oil and Gas Lands Administration (COGLA) and the Canada-Newfoundland Offshore

Petroleum Board (CNOPB) after a 2 year period of confidentiality for wildcat wells, or a 90 day period for delineation wells (Fig. 6.1). The industrial geophysical data are mainly multichannel reflection records, which are held confidential for 5 years by COGLA and CNOPB. To year end 1986, results are released for 80 wells out of a total of 95 drilled or drilling off the Island of Newfoundland, and released multichannel seismic coverage amounts to about 310 000 km. These data have been complemented by deep reflection seismic studies carried out by the Geological Survey of Canada, and by data drawn from relevant studies by various government and university research groups.

Exploration history

Systematic geophysical and marine geological investigations of the eastern margin of North America were first carried out in the 1950s by Canadian and American governments and university research agencies. These deep refraction, potential field, and bottom sampling surveys indicated a thick sedimentary wedge lying offshore, and this stimulated the interest of the petroleum industry. Exploration for petroleum on the Grand Banks began with geophysical reconnaissance surveys in 1964, and a shallow corehole project by Amoco Canada (then Pan American Petroleum Corporation) and Imperial Oil in 1965. This work outlined the principal basins in the area (Fig. 6.2). In 1966 the first two deep wildcat wells (Tors Cove D-52 and Grand Falls H-09) were drilled on the Canadian continental margin; the first well, on a diapiric salt structure, recovered a small amount of free gas, providing early proof of the favourable hydrocarbon potential of this area. In the ten year period from 1966 to 1975, exploratory wells were drilled at 41 locations on the continental shelf around Newfoundland, with 13, 10, and 10 wells located in the South Whale Subbasin and Whale and Jeanne d'Arc basins, respectively (Fig. 6.2). The results from this first phase of exploration were disappointing, although in the Jeanne d'Arc Basin some oil was found in the Adolphus 2K-41 well, and good potential source rocks were encountered in other wells, as documented by Bujak et al. (1977a, b) and Swift and Williams (1980). Other reviews of results from this period of exploration have been published by Amoco and Imperial (1973), Sherwin (1973), Upshaw et al. (1974), Gradstein et al. (1975), Jansa and Wade (1975), Swift et al. (1975), Williams and Brideaux (1975) and McWhae (1981).

Grant, A.C. and McAlpine, K.D.
1990: The continental margin around Newfoundland; Chapter 6 in Geology of the Continental Margin of Eastern Canada, M.J. Keen and G.L. Williams (ed.); Geological Survey of Canada, Geology of Canada, no. 2, p. 239-292 (also Geological Society of America, the Geology of North America, v. I-1).

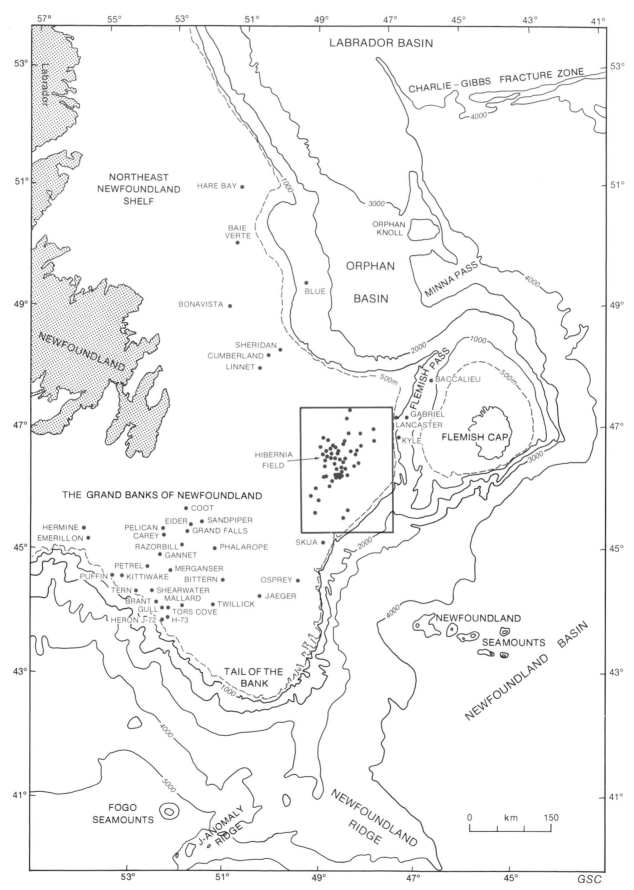

Figure 6.1. Bathymetry of the continental margin around Newfoundland (contours in metres). Well locations in red (see Fig. 6.6 for names of wells in the Jeanne D'Arc Basin, Hibernia field areas). Dashed red line is the 500 m water depth contour. Complete well names and locations are given in Figure 1 (in pocket).

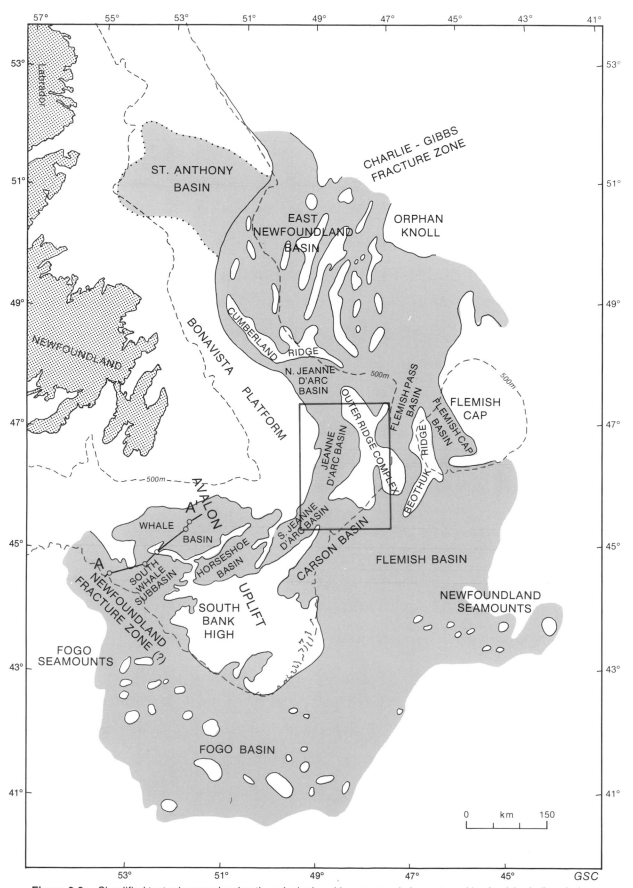

Figure 6.2. Simplified tectonic map showing the principal positive structural elements and basins (shaded) underlying the continental margin around southeast Newfoundland. Dashed red line is the 500 m water depth contour. Dashed black line is the landward edge of Cretaceous-Tertiary sediments. A-A' is line of cross section in Figure 6.4. Rectangle (red) encloses area of Figure 6.6.

243

The second round of exploration off Newfoundland commenced in 1979, and the third well spudded that year was the Hibernia P-15 oil discovery in Jeanne d'Arc Basin. Capable of producing 3180.0 m³ (20 000 barrels) per day (Benteau and Sheppard, 1982), this ranked as the best oil well discovered in Canada to that time. The nine additional wells drilled on the Hibernia structure have delineated a field with recoverable oil reserves in the order of 79.5 to 127.2 x 10⁶ m³ (500 to 800 million barrels) (CNOPB, 1986), which places Hibernia in the "giant" class (more than 79.5 x 10⁶ m³ (500 million barrels)). The geology of the Hibernia field and the Jeanne d'Arc Basin has been discussed by McKenzie (1980), Arthur et al. (1982), Benteau and Sheppard (1982), McMillan (1982), Handyside and Chipman (1983), Hubbard et al. (1985), Grant et al. (1986a, b), Enachescu (1987), and Tankard and Welsink (1988). Of the 40 wells drilled off Newfoundland since 1979, 34 are in Jeanne d'Arc Basin; the others are located to the east in the Carson and Flemish Pass basins and to the north in the East Newfoundland Basin. Geophysical exploration has continued throughout the region, and it is anticipated that additional wells will eventually be drilled in the Horseshoe and Whale basins and the South Whale Subbasin on the southern Grand Banks.

Regional setting

The continental margin off eastern Canada is regarded as a classic "Atlantic-type" margin, where a prism of sediments accumulated in the Mesozoic and Cenozoic as the adjacent oceans widened and deepened. On the Scotian Shelf, the Grand Banks and east of Newfoundland these sediments onlap Paleozoic and Precambrian rocks of the Appalachian Orogen; to the north, off Labrador and Baffin Island, they onlap Paleozoic strata and crystalline rocks of the Canadian Shield (Map 1706A, in pocket). The stratigraphic range of the Mesozoic sediments beneath the Scotian Shelf and the Grand Banks contrasts with that beneath the Labrador Shelf (Fig. 6.3), presumably because of differences in the seafloor spreading histories of these regions. Whereas in the Atlantic north of the Bahamas seafloor spreading is inferred to have begun in the Early Jurassic, seafloor spreading apparently did not begin in the Labrador Sea until the Late Cretaceous, and possibly progressed northward to Baffin Bay by the Eocene (Srivastava, 1978; McWhae, 1981; Gradstein et al., Chapter 8).

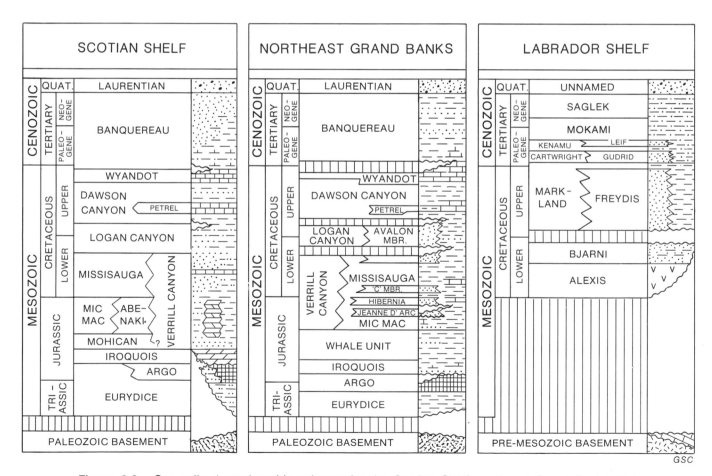

Figure 6.3. Generalized stratigraphic columns for the Scotian Shelf, northeast Grand Banks and Labrador Shelf regions (after Grant et al., 1986a). This diagram is for comparison only; see diagrams elsewhere in this chapter and volume (Fig. 5, in pocket) for current stratigraphy.

The continental margin around Newfoundland lies between these two seafloor spreading regimes, and as a result the region has a complex geological history reflected in the regional physiography (Fig. 6.1) and the changing trends of basement structure (Fig. 6.2). The northeast-southwest trending basins on the Grand Banks began to develop during the Late Triassic to Early Jurassic by rifting between North America and Africa. However, the underlying continental crust has a long and complex history of construction that began in the Proterozoic and included accretion of a series of exotic terranes onto the North American Craton. The rocks of the Appalachian Orogen record three main Paleozoic tectonic episodes, the Taconian, Acadian and Alleghenian orogenies, that culminated respectively in the Middle Ordovician, Devonian and Permian. An overview of the pre-Mesozoic history of the margin is provided in Chapter 2. The Mesozoic basins on the Grand Banks may be related to reactivated Paleozoic structures, because they are approximately parallel to structural trends of the Appalachian Orogen exposed onshore in Newfoundland, and they contain Carboniferous clastics and evaporites (see Chapter 4). Nova Scotia and northern Africa began to separate during the Early Jurassic (Wade and MacLean, Chapter 5), but this rifting was aborted north of the Newfoundland Fracture Zone, and the Grand Banks experienced only epeirogenic subsidence to the Late Jurassic. Updoming of the Grand Banks in the latest Jurassic initiated a second period of rifting that culminated in separation of Iberia from the Grand Banks in the late Early Cretaceous (Masson and Miles, 1984). The eastern margin of the Grand Banks formed at this time (Fig. 6.2), and this was the final principal event in formation of the prominent peneplain on the Grand Banks that is referred to as the Avalon Unconformity. East of Newfoundland the trend of basement structures swings from northeast-southwest to north-south (Fig. 6.2), expressing mid-Cretaceous separation of Europe from North America (Masson and Miles, 1984; Srivastava and Tapscott, 1986). Keen et al. (1987a) suggested that the structural complexity of the East Newfoundland Basin relates to extensional tectonics associated with transform motion along the Charlie-Gibbs Fracture Zone.

Seismic refraction measurements made in 1986 and earlier show that the continental crust beneath the southern Grand Banks is about 32 km thick and has a simple structure (I. Reid, pers. comm., 1987). Relatively thin sediments and "basement" (probably Paleozoic igneous or metasedimentary rocks) overlie a single, main crustal layer. The crust thins toward the southwestern margin of the Grand Banks starting at a distance of about 70 km from the margin. Deep multichannel (LITHOPROBE) seismic lines show easterly dipping faults extending deep within the crust on the west sides of the Whale Basin and the southern extension of the Jeanne d'Arc Basin. Keen et al. (1987b) suggested these faults may extend to near MOHO depths and may be planes of crustal extension that led to the formation of these basins. A deep reflection profile across the northern Jeanne d'Arc Basin shows that the Mesozoic-Cenozoic section at that location may be 20 km thick, but the western bounding fault and the MOHO reflector cannot be traced beneath this basin.

The crust beneath the East Newfoundland Basin (Orphan Basin in Chapter 2) (Fig. 6.2) is about 15 km thick, and is interpreted as continental crust thinned by extension (Keen and Barrett, 1981). The basement is dissected by normal faults (Grant, 1975), which appear to detach at a sub-horizontal décollement at mid-crustal depths (Keen et al., 1987a).

The Cretaceous and older rocks in the basins on the Grand Banks and east of Newfoundland (Fig. 6.2) contain the targets of petroleum exploration. The general Mesozoic sequence in these basins (Fig. 6.3) consists of Triassic to Early Jurassic redbeds and evaporites, Jurassic carbonates and shales, and Cretaceous marine clastics. Flowage of the buried salt in the basins has resulted in extensive disturbance of the younger sediments, and most of the wells have been drilled on salt-related structures. The peneplain truncating these basins and the adjacent basement areas is blanketed by Upper Cretaceous and Cenozoic clastics and chalky limestones, which thin to zero landward and onto Flemish Cap, but thicken substantially to the northeast in the East Newfoundland Basin. These sediments are essentially undeformed except for local piercement by salt and minor faulting in the areas of the sub-unconformity basins.

The Grand Banks basins are approximately parallel to the structural trends of the Appalachian Orogen exposed onshore, but north of the Grand Banks the basin axes swing to the north and cut across the northeast trend of the Appalachian Orogen. Basement trends there are parallel to the present physiographic margin (Fig. 6.2), and presumably relate genetically to the formation of the Labrador Sea and the northern North Atlantic Ocean. These contrasting relationships to basement geology complicate attempts to resolve the tectonic timetable and to relate Mesozoic syntectonic sediments to variously aligned tensional regimes that resulted in rifting and continental break up. Similarly, alignment of Mesozoic basins with Caledonian geology can be demonstrated in the North Sea, Celtic Sea, Hebrides (Ziegler, 1975; Pegrum and Mounteney, 1978; Naylor and Shannon, 1982), and east Greenland (Surlyk, 1977), whereas southwest of Ireland the basins have a dominant northwest-southeast alignment (Masson and Miles, 1986a, b) that is oblique to basement structure. It is not yet clear how plate tectonic models are relevant at the scale of these local problems, but we show later that the plate tectonic framework is a useful first-order reference for interpreting the sedimentary sequence of the region.

GRAND BANKS BASINS

Structure

The post-Paleozoic geological record of the basins beneath the Grand Banks is essentially a history of intra-cratonic development. The buried peneplain beneath the continental margin is a first-order geological feature of this region. Beneath the central part of the Grand Banks, erosion associated with the Avalon Uplift began in the Late Jurassic and cut deeply into Jurassic rocks in the sub-unconformity basins (Fig. 6.2, 6.4). To the southwest and northeast, progressively younger strata are present beneath this erosional surface in the South Whale Subbasin and Jeanne d'Arc Basin respectively. Since the early 1970s this surface has been referred to as the "Avalon Unconformity". It was first described in detail by Amoco and Imperial (1973), and subsequently discussed by Jansa and Wade (1975), McWhae (1981) and Arthur et al. (1982).

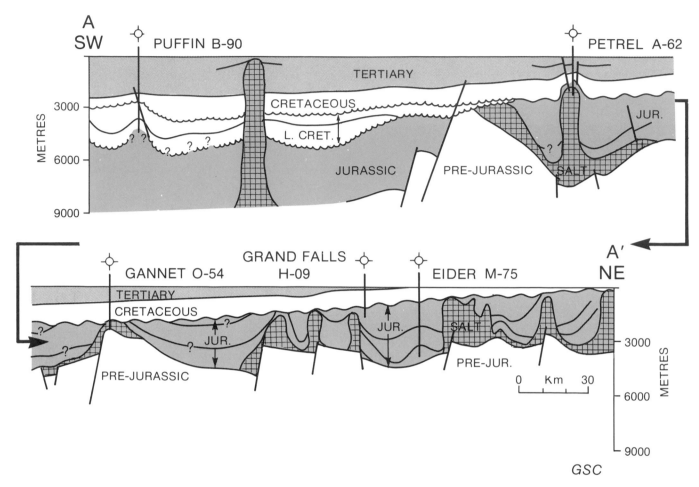

Figure 6.4. Geological-geophysical cross-section of the southern Grand Banks (location shown in Figure 6.2). Note that the prominent unconformity over most of the line of section separating Jurassic and Cretaceous rocks represents the combination of the two unconformities shown just south of the Petrel A-62 well. From Amoco and Imperial (1973).

These papers presented different interpretations regarding the age of the Avalon Unconformity, which has led to some confusion in the use of the term. The differences arise because several erosional surfaces in the sedimentary basins coalesce at the basin margins to form the interbasin peneplain. In Jeanne d'Arc Basin four major erosional events can be identified ranging from late Kimmeridgian to Albian-Cenomanian (Fig. 6.5). The peneplain thus reflects 50 to 60 Ma of deformation, uplift and erosion; if the term "Avalon Unconformity" is to be retained, it should probably be applied in this context rather than to any one event.

The structural elements of the Mesozoic and Cenozoic sediments within the basins on the Grand Banks are dominated by the effects of salt flowage (Fig. 6.4). The structures include salt diapirs, salt pillows, turtle structures and rollover anticlines associated with listric normal faults. The seismic expression of these structures has been illustrated by Amoco and Imperial (1973). In the initial phase of drilling (1966 to 1975), most of the wells were located on the structurally complex and relatively shallow salt structures, and because of the abbreviated and anomalous stratigraphy at these sites it was difficult to reconstruct the geological history of the Grand Banks basins. Drilling results since 1979 from the thicker and more complete section in Jeanne d'Arc Basin have greatly increased our knowledge of depositional and structural relationships on the Grand Banks, and therefore the structure and stratigraphy of Jeanne d'Arc Basin are reviewed here as the most complete record of Grand Banks subsurface geology.

Figure 6.6 shows sediment thickness in the Jeanne d'Arc Basin and the major tectonic elements: the stable Bonavista Platform to the west consists of pre-Mesozoic rocks; the Outer Ridge Complex is a structural high forming the east flank of the basin and is underlain in large part by complexly deformed Jurassic sediments. The thickness of sediments in this figure in the centre of the basin is conservative because basement lies below the depths recorded on the industry seismic records from which the figure was constructed. Deep multichannel seismic data recorded to 20 seconds show that the Jeanne d'Arc Basin

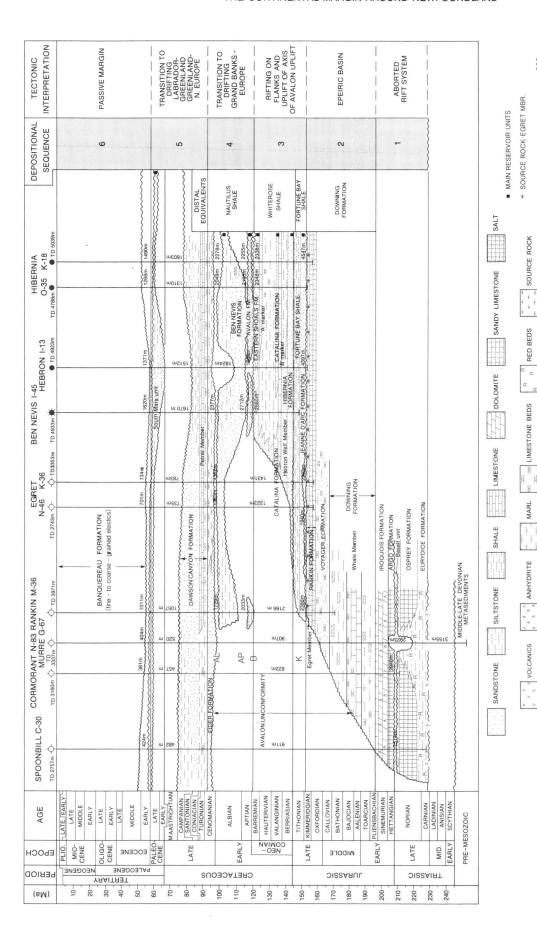

Figure 6.5. Time-stratigraphic section of the Jeanne d'Arc Basin showing lithostratigraphic framework and major depositional sequences. Well locations are in Figure 6.6. The Avalon unconformity, a prominent peneplain buried beneath the central Grand Banks, records the net effect of at least four erosional events that are identified by well and seismic data. The times of these events are Kimmeridgian (K), late Barremian (B), late Aptian (AP) and late Albian-Cenomanian (AL). The numbers beneath wells at stratigraphic hiatuses are depths in metres where these breaks were encountered.

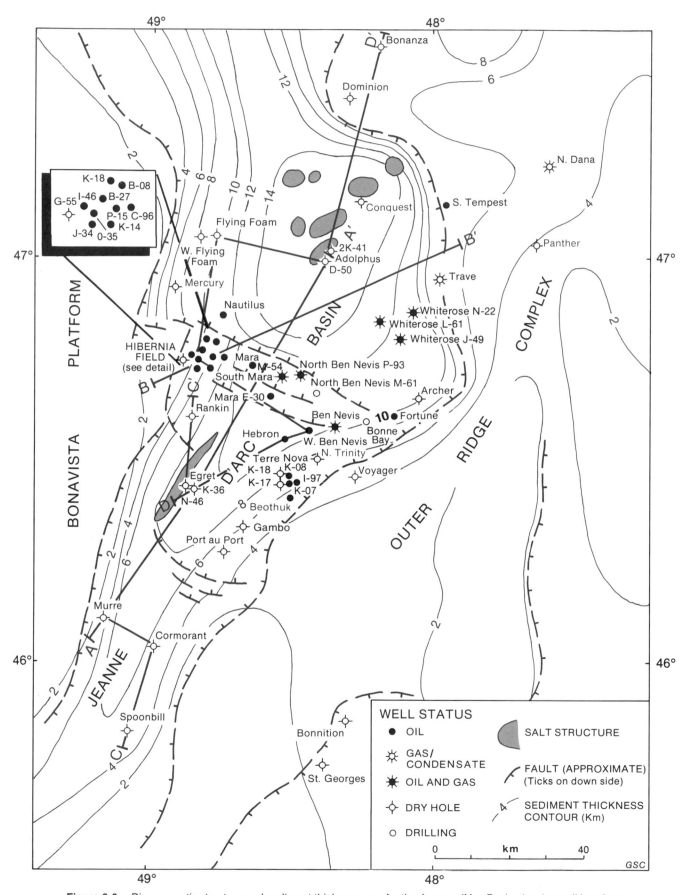

Figure 6.6. Diagrammatic structure and sediment thickness map for the Jeanne d'Arc Basin showing well locations (from Grant et al., 1986a). Complete well names and locations are given in Figure 1 (in pocket).

is in fact 20 km deep (Keen et al., 1987a). Figure 6.7 is a seismic section that follows the axis of the basin, from the Murre G-67 well in the south, across a major trans-basin fault, through the Egret K-36 well and then a zone of trans-basin faulting to the Adophus D-50 well drilled on a salt diapir in the depocentre of the basin. The trans-basin seismic section (Fig. 6.8) extends from the Hibernia rollover structure against the Bonavista Platform to the Outer Ridge Complex in the vicinity of the South Tempest G-88 and Trave E-87 wells.

To understand the stucture of the Jeanne d'Arc Basin it is important to distinguish the effects of regional versus local tectonism. The principal regional controls are the periods of relative subsidence of the basin; local structures relate mainly to salt flowage. In some respects, the sediments in the basin can be viewed as "floating" on a substrate of salt. Much of the structural disruption in the marginal areas of the basin is the product of compensatory movement for salt flowage in the axial part of the basin.

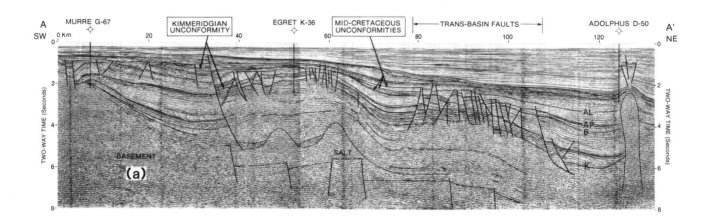

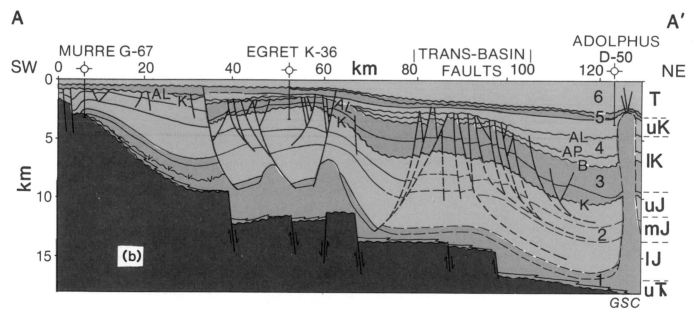

Figure 6.7. Seismic line (a) and geological interpretation (b) approximately along the axis of the Jeanne d'Arc Basin (AA', Fig. 6.6). Notable seismic features discussed in the text are: the Kimmeridgian unconformity, which exhibits prominent channelling in the vicinity of the Egret K-36 well; the three mid-Cretaceous unconformities that bound two onlapping-fill seismic sequences; the trans-basin fault zone extending from the Hibernia field to the Ben Nevis I-45 well; the large fault about 15 km south of the Egret K-36 well that offsets the Kimmeridgian unconformity about 1.2 seconds and overlies an important basement fault. (Seismic line NF 79-112, courtesy of Geophysical Service Incorporated). The Mesozoic-Cenozoic stratigraphic record is divided into six depositional sequences (1 to 6) that can be related to the geological history of the Newfoundland continental margin. Ages are denoted by letters in Figure 6.6b. See Figure 6.5 for explanation of unconformities lettered K, B, AP and AL.

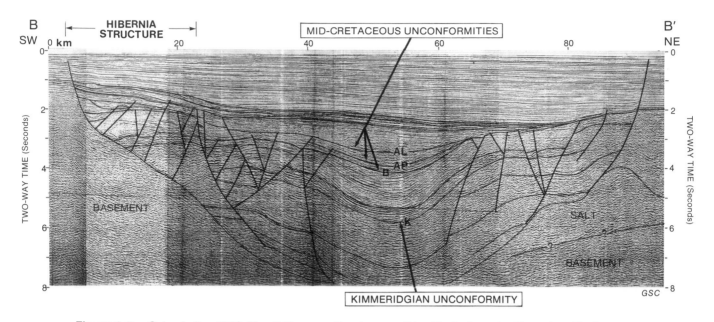

Figure 6.8. Seismic line (BB', Fig. 6.6) across the Jeanne d'Arc Basin from the Bonavista Platform to the Outer Ridge Complex in the vicinity of the Trave E-87 well. The Bonavista Platform is composed of Paleozoic metasediments and igneous rocks. The Outer Ridge Complex includes structured Jurassic sedimentary rocks equivalent to those in the basin and is underlain partially by salt. The Hibernia structure is a large rollover anticline adjacent to a major listric normal fault that delineates the western flank of the basin. The westward thickening of the Cretaceous section at Hibernia indicates the period of maximum fault growth. (Seismic line NF 79-114, courtesy of Geophysical Service Incorporated)

The pattern of faulting in the basin expresses this relationship in three main sets of faults: listric-type faults approximately parallel to the margins of the basin; high-angle normal faults approximately parallel to the margins of the basin; and trans-basin faults, orthogonal to the other two sets, that are planes of adjustment for differential lateral movement on listric faults. The principal trans-basin faults appear to be located over zones of normal faulting of the basement. Among the most spectacular products of salt flowage are the diapiric structures near the Adolphus wells and the salt wall in the vicinity of the Egret wells (Fig. 6.6).

A strong, sloping seismic reflection, which can be mapped along much of the west side of Jeanne d'Arc Basin, is related to a fault plane on which the overlying sediments have slid towards the axial zone of the basin. This surface tends to become nearly horizontal at depth. Three main zones of detachment can be mapped, which, from south to north, are separated by two zones of trans-basin faults (Fig. 6.6).

On the east side of Jeanne d'Arc Basin a "basement" surface is more difficult to delineate. A surface of detachment can be discerned in some areas, but rotational movement on this fault is not prominent. There is extensive evidence of tensional conditions in the form of numerous normal faults, including "keystone" stuctures, suggesting that there has been westward displacement of the sedimentary section toward the axial zone of the basin. Locally, this zone of faulting appears to involve salt flowage.

The structural high forming the eastern flank of Jeanne d'Arc Basin was called the Outer Ridge Complex by McKenzie (1980). This area is not analogous to the stable Bonavista Platform on the west side of the basin, formed from pre-Mesozoic rocks. The portion of the Outer Ridge Complex bordering the northeastern segment of Jeanne d'Arc Basin is underlain by deformed Jurassic sediments that are stratigraphically equivalent to those in the basin (Fig. 6.8). To the south, these deformed sediments terminate against older and seismically "harder" media. The latter are presumed to be rocks of the Appalachian System.

Post-Cretaceous subsidence of the main part of the Grand Banks has been relatively uniform, and apart from a few salt structures that pierce the Tertiary cover, the underlying basins have been essentially stable. Toward the margins of the Grand Banks, however, Tertiary subsidence is more pronounced; it has affected the axial zone of the northern part of the Jeanne d'Arc Basin, and is pervasive to the north, east of the Bonavista Platform.

Stratigraphy

Stratigraphically, the continental margin around Newfoundland is a zone of transition, with pre-Tertiary stratigraphy similar to that of the Scotian Shelf, and Tertiary sediments east of Newfoundland similar to those off Labrador (Fig. 6.3). Despite more than two decades of petroleum exploration on the Grand Banks a formal stratigraphic nomenclature has not been proposed, whereas by contrast, formal lithostratigraphic schemes were advanced for the Scotian Shelf and the Labrador Shelf within a decade of the first wells being drilled (McIver, 1972; Umpleby, 1979). This reflects not only the complex geological history of the Grand Banks on account of its pivotal position between the comparatively simple passive margins to the southeast and northwest, but also reflects the fact that all the early wells were drilled on or near the axis of the Avalon Uplift and on diapiric salt structures where much of the section was missing.

Before the discovery of the Hibernia oil field in 1979, Scotian Shelf stratigraphic nomenclature was extended to the Grand Banks. Figure 6.9 shows the chronological development of lithostratigraphic terminology applied to this area. Earlier descriptions of the stratigraphic record were given by Bartlett and Smith (1971) and Sherwin (1973).

Discovery of the Hibernia oil field initiated the current period of intense exploration in Jeanne d'Arc Basin, and the recent wells have penetrated a more complete stratigraphic record, particularly a more fully developed Cretaceous section. Four new lithostratigraphic units were informally introduced by Arthur et al. (1982) for the productive reservoirs in Jeanne d'Arc Basin. Grant et al. (1986a, b) synthesized previous stratigraphic usages with unpublished biostratigraphic analyses, but did not introduce any new units. In this chapter we used the lithostratigraphic nomenclature as illustrated in Figure 6.10.

Pre-Mesozoic basement

Pre-Mesozoic rocks have been encountered in shallow core holes and in oil exploratory wells on the continental margin around Newfoundland, and have been detected by geophysical methods. These rocks include Precambrian and Paleozoic sedimentary, metasedimentary and igneous rocks.

Carboniferous clastic and evaporite rocks have been drilled at several locations in Whale Basin and South Whale Subbasin (Barss et al., 1979), and in the Blue H-28 well in East Newfoundland Basin (M.S. Barss, pers. comm., 1983). These occurrences indicate that the subunconformity basins on the Grand Banks (Fig. 6.2) originated at least as early as the late Paleozoic, and their trends probably reflect the geological fabric of the older, Appalachian "basement" rocks (e.g. Haworth, 1981).

The geology and distribution of these rocks are discussed in detail in Chapter 4.

Mesozoic igneous rocks

Mesozoic igneous rocks occur at scattered locations offshore and onshore Newfoundland (Fig. 6.11, Table 6.1). Radiometric and stratigraphic dating of these occurrences suggest two distinct episodes of volcanic activity that record the major periods of rifting associated with continental breakup and attendant relaxation of tensional conditions.

The basalt flows at the Cormorant N-83 and Spoonbill C-30 wells and the diabase dykes on the Avalon Peninsula of Newfoundland are about 200 Ma old. They apparently belong to the period of igneous activity that preceded (for about 20 Ma) the onset of Middle Jurassic (180 Ma) seafloor spreading in the central North Atlantic (Pe-Piper and Jansa, 1986). Late Triassic to Early Jurassic volcanic rocks have been described also from Connecticut and Nova Scotia (Hodych and Hayatsu, 1980).

All the other igneous rocks discovered around Newfoundland are of Early Cretaceous age. Volcanic rocks of

similar age occur extensively on the Labrador margin (see Chapter 7) and have been reported as far north as the Sverdrup Basin (Balkwill and Fox, 1982). These rocks may relate to the initiation of rifting in the Labrador Sea in Berriasian-Valanginian time. Volcanic activity on the Newfoundland margin apparently ceased at the end of the Early Cretaceous, marking the release of tensional stresses in the region.

Mesozoic-Cenozoic stratigraphy

The comprehensive geological and geophysical data base, that has accumulated since the 1979 discovery of the Hibernia field, forms the basis for the following account of the tectonostratigraphic development of the Grand Banks.

The biostratigraphic ages assigned to the depositional sequences and lithostratigraphic units described are a synthesis of ages from diverse sources and disciplines. Most reliance was placed on palynological assemblages after Barss et al. (1979), supplemented by extensive unpublished data provided by E.H. Davies. Age interpretations from ostracodes and foraminifers were also relied on for supporting evidence (P. Ascoli, pers. comm., 1986). A detailed synthesis of the biostratigraphic (palynology) and lithostratigraphic correlation of seven wells from the Hibernia field by Davies (1986; see also Chapter 3) and Davies and McAlpine (unpublished results) was extended to several other wells in Jeanne d'Arc Basin using various combinations of seismic, lithostratigraphic and biostratigraphic techniques. The geochronology used in this chapter is based on the Decade of North American Geology time scale (Palmer, 1983).

We have recognized several regionally correlatable seismic sequences bounded by widely persistent primary seismic events. Correlation of litho- and biostratigraphic data bases with these geophysical sequences has provided a framework for dividing the stratigraphic record into six distinctive depositional sequences that may be correlated approximately with rifting and spreading events, and compared with homotaxial sedimentary sequences in other basins bordering the Atlantic Ocean.

The strata within each sequence are the product of a unique tectonic episode in the record of construction of the continental margin of eastern Canada. In brief, the Mesozoic-Cenozoic sequences of the basins offshore Newfoundland evolved through two periods of rifting and subsidence associated with seafloor spreading. The two periods of subsidence are separated by a tectonically quiet period and are followed by a two-phase transition to passive margin subsidence (Fig. 6.5 and 6.7).

The sequences that follow are approximately correlative to the four megasequences on the Grand Banks proposed by Hubbard et al. (1985). They are also consistent with the scenario for the development of sedimentary basins around the North Atlantic discussed by Masson and Miles (1986b). However, our interpretation of the time of initiation of the second period of rift subsidence (Kimmeridgian) differs from that of Tankard and Welsink (1988) who begin this rift phase in the Callovian. Their account is based on their interpretation of a "major late Callovian unconformity" and their use of the simple-shear model of Wernicke (1985) to explain basin development by crustal extension, wherein lower-plate ductile deformation precedes upper-plate brittle deformation by 5-10 Ma. We

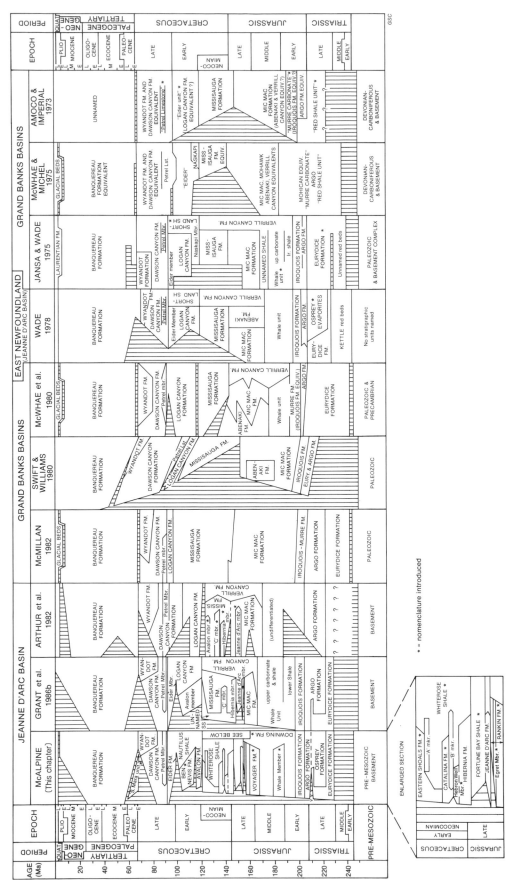

Figure 6.9. Comparison of stratigraphic terminology used by various authors for Mesozoic rocks on the Grand Banks. (See Figure 6.10 for details in Jeanne d'Arc Basin).

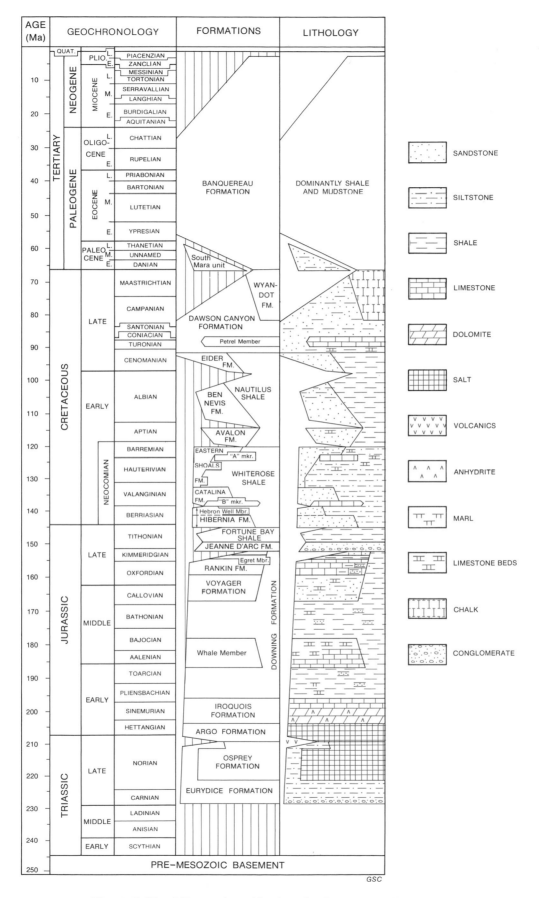

Figure 6.10. Lithostratigraphic chart for the Jeanne d'Arc Basin.

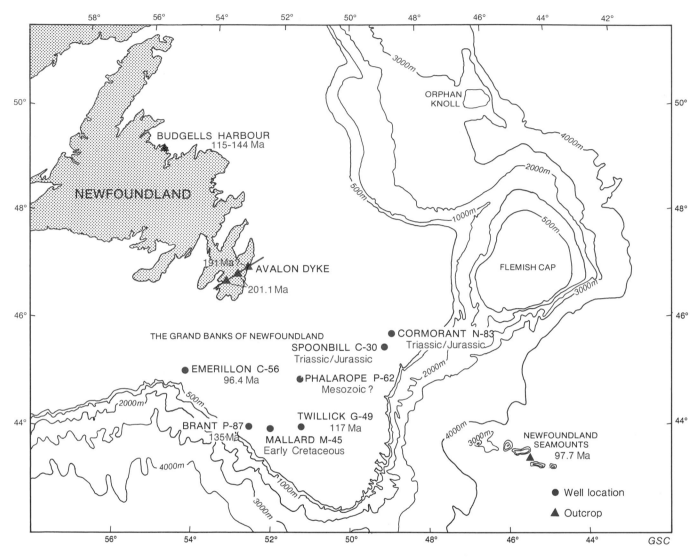

Figure 6.11. Locations of known Mesozoic igneous rocks. Numbers denote absolute radiometric ages in millions of years. Dots and triangles denote subsurface borehole and surface locations respectively.

see little direct evidence to document a late Callovian tectonic event and we cannot fully endorse Wernicke's model to explain the formation of the Grand Banks basins. We prefer to interpret our depositional sequences based on style of sedimentation and infer that the Kimmeridgian unconformity and accompanying accumulation of coarse clastics signals the onset of the second rifting phase.

Sequence 1 — Aborted Rift; Late Triassic to Early Jurassic

Sequence 1, overlying pre-Mesozoic basement, is Late Triassic to Early Jurassic in age and consists of red beds, evaporites, and carbonates deposited in a formerly coherent rift system that developed between North America-Greenland and Europe-Africa and extended into the area of the present North Sea. Similar facies are present on the Scotian Shelf, and in the Celtic Sea, the Southwest Approaches of the British Isles and southern North Sea basins.

The Eurydice, Osprey, Argo and Iroquois formations make up this first sequence (Fig. 6.5, 6.10, 6.12). Their dominant lithologies are red clastics (Eurydice Formation), halite (Osprey and Argo formations), and anhydritic dolomite and oolitic and skeletal limestones (Iroquois Formation). These rocks record a vertical sequence of depositional environments reflecting a gradual influx of normal marine water from the Tethys. The environments we interpret from these lithologies are arid continental, restricted evaporite basins followed by coastal sabkhas, tidal flats and restricted lagoons, and finally a shallow neritic sea. A thin unit of subaerial basalt flows has been drilled in the Cormorant N-83 and Spoonbill C-30 wells between the Osprey and Argo salts. This basalt can be followed as a prominent seismic event over much of the southern part of the basin. From their stratigraphic position the basalts appear to be latest Triassic in age, and to be part of a widespread igneous event related to early rifting.

Table 6.1. Summary of Mesozoic igneous activity onshore and offshore Newfoundland.

LOCATION	ROCK, TYPE	AGE	METHOD	REMARKS	REFERENCE
J-ANOMALY RIDGE (DSDP Site 384)	Basalt (abyssal tholeiite)	106 ± 4 Ma	Whole rock K/Ar	Consistent with nannofossil age	Houghton et al. (1979)
		88 ± 5 Ma	Whole rock $^{40}Ar/^{39}Ar$	Consistent with Van Hinte (1976)	
NEWFOUNDLAND SEAMOUNTS	Alkali basalts and trachyte	97.7 ± 1.5 Ma	Whole rock $^{40}Ar/^{39}Ar$	Dredge sample	Sullivan and Keen (1977)
GRAND BANKS					
Emerillon C-56	Dioritic dyke	96.4 ± 3.8 Ma	Whole rock K/Ar	2975-2996 m	Jansa and Pe-Piper (1986)
Twillick G-49	Porphyritic diabase subaerial flow	117 ± 5 Ma	Whole rock K/Ar	1286-1301m	Amoco (1974)
Brant P-87	Basalt flows and pyroclastics Diabase sills or flows	Barremian 135 ± 6 Ma	Biostratigraphy Whole rock K/Ar	2843-2898 m 3460-3588 m	Amoco (1974)
Cormorant N-83	Subaerial basalt flow	Tr/J	Biostratigraphy	2940-2975m	Grant et al. (1986a)
Spoonbill C-30	Subaerial basalt flow	Tr/J	Biostratigraphy	1514-1565m	Grant et al. (1986a)
Mallard M-45	Rhyolyte, trachyte, andesite, basalt flows and pyroclastics	Neocomian	Biostratigraphy	2268-3149m	Amoco (1973b)
Phalarope P-62	Mafic dyke or sill	Mesozoic?	Petrologic affinity	3074-3087m intrusive in Paleozoic metased	Hada , (personal communication, 1976)
ONSHORE NEWFOUNDLAND					
Avalon Peninsula aeromagnetic lineament	Diabase dykes	191? Ma 201.1 ± 2.6 Ma	K/Ar isochron K/Ar isochron	2 outcrop samples 7 outcrop samples Precambrian host rock	Hodych and Hayatsu (1980)
Budgells Harbour a) Lamprophyre dykes	Lamprophyre dykes	115 ± 20 Ma 129 ± 7 Ma 144 ± 12 Ma	Horneblende K/Ar Biotite K/Ar Biotite K/Ar	3 outcrop samples Ordovician host rock	Wanless et al.(1965 and 1967) Strong and Harris (1974)
b) stock	Alkaline ultramafic pluton	135 ± 8 Ma 139 ± 9 Ma	Biotite K/Ar Biotite K/Ar	2 outcrop samples Ordovician host rock	Helwig et al. (1974)

GSC

Sequence 2 — Epeiric Basin; Early to Late Jurassic

During the Early Jurassic, continental and marine clastics dominated deposition on the Scotian Shelf and northwest African margin, which may reflect rifting and the initiation of seafloor spreading in that area. However, rifting apparently was aborted north of the Newfoundland Fracture Zone along the southwestern edge of the Grand Banks, inferred by Auzende et al. (1970) to be a transform margin. Sequence 2 consists predominantly of shallow marine shales and limestones of Early to Late Jurassic age that were deposited in a broad epeiric sea that flooded the old rifted topography. Remnants of these deposits are present in the basins of the Grand Banks, Celtic Sea, southern England, and the southern North Sea.

Five regionally mappable stratigraphic units within the sequence are divided into 3 formations and 2 members (Fig. 6.5, 6.10, 6.12). All formation contacts appear gradational and conformable on a regional scale, although local unconformities may be present due to mobilization of the underlying salt.

The Downing Formation is a thick heterogeneous unit that exhibits a gross lithofacies pattern consisting of a lower shale, a middle limestone (Whale Member) and an upper shale. The relative development of these facies varies regionally and lithostratigraphic boundaries are probably diachronous within the unit. The lower shale is grey, variably calcareous and marly and locally silty. Skeletal-pelletoidal wackestones and packstones with rare oolite-rich beds dominate the Whale Member. The upper

shale is grey and calcareous and contains occasional beds of siltstone and fine grained sandstone which become more frequent in the upper part of the formation. The depositional environment suggested by these rocks is that of a low energy epicontinental sea in a tectonically quiet setting dominated by eustatic sea-level changes. The limestones were deposited under shallower, higher energy conditions during a regressive period in the early Middle Jurassic. The upper contact with the Voyager Formation, encountered in the Murre G-67 and Rankin M-36 wells, is gradational (Fig. 6.12).

The Voyager Formation consists of fine- to medium-grained quartzose sandstone, with subordinate oolitic limestone, reddish-brown shale, and coal, which indicate a nearshore to marginal marine environment. Sediment accumulation rates were low, indicating shallowing and infilling of the epicontinental sea.

The Upper Jurassic Rankin Formation consists of shallow water, oolitic limestones and subordinate very fine to fine grained quartz sandstones. Sandstones and shales are more dominant north of the trans-basin fault system between the Hibernia and Ben Nevis fields. The Egret Member of the Rankin Formation is a distinctive shale unit of middle Kimmeridgian age, 75-150 m thick. Its lithology is shale, grey to brown, carbonaceous, and calcareous. Interbeds of marl are common in some areas. Organic carbon content is very high, between 3 and 9 per cent. The environment indicated is that of restricted shallow neritic and brackish lagoons. As discussed later, this

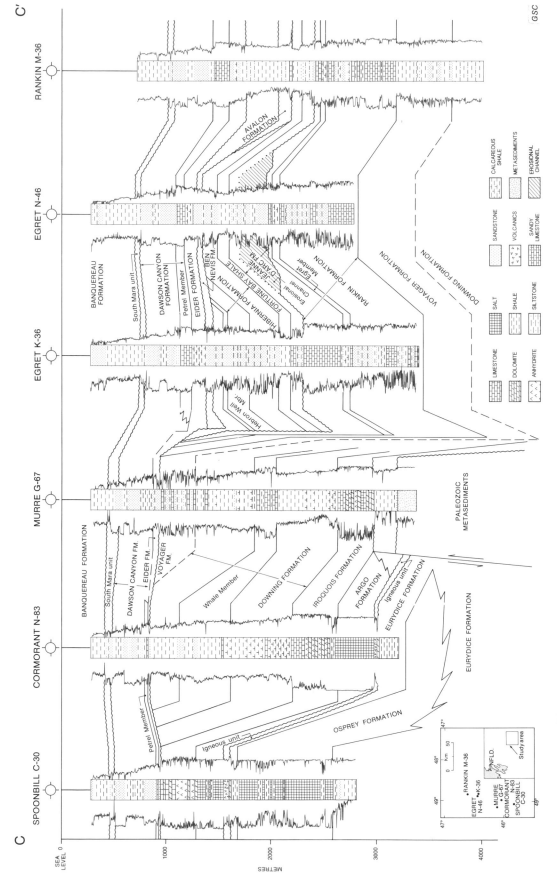

Figure 6.12. Electric log and lithostratigraphic correlation from Spoonbill C-30 to Rankin M-36. The large fault between Murre G-67 and Egret K-36 has a throw of over 2 km (see Fig. 6.7).

is the oil source rock for the Jeanne d'Arc Basin. Petrographic and geochemical data indicate that the Egret Member thickens northeastward in the basin, where it was deposited in a more open marine environment. In the Eider M-75 well in the Whale Basin to the southeast coeval sediments are continental. This is the first indication of regional up-doming of the Avalon Uplift.

Sequence 3 — Late Rift; Latest Jurassic and Neocomian

The base of sequence 3 is a major Late Jurassic unconformity of middle Kimmeridgian age. This unconformity relates to the initiation of the Avalon Uplift, and by inference to the renewal of rifting between North America and Europe which continued through the Neocomian. Regional rifting and subsidence were coincident with the vertical uplift. Previous shale and carbonate-dominated deposition in an epeiric sea was replaced by a clastic dominated rift sequence in the developing graben on the flanks of the Avalon Uplift. These included the South Whale Subbasin and Carson and Jeanne d'Arc basins. However, uplift outstripped trough development on the axis of the Avalon Uplift, which was eroded. Hubbard et al. (1985) suggested that Early Cretaceous subsidence in Jeanne d'Arc Basin was influenced by a northwest-trending rift system that they named the Labrador Rift system. The major northwest-trending trans-basin fault south of the Egret wells has a throw of about 2 km and overlies a major basement fault (Fig. 6.7). Movement on both faults began near the base of sequence 3 in the earliest Cretaceous. This coincides with the initiation of rifting and volcanic activity on the Labrador Shelf (see Chapter 7). Thus the timing and the orientation of this fault parallel to the Mesozoic basins of the Labrador Shelf suggest an overprinting of the Grand Banks-Iberia and Labrador Sea tensional regimes which enhanced subsidence and complicated the stratigraphy of the Lower Cretaceous rift sequence.

In Jeanne d'Arc Basin average sedimentation rates of 11 or 12 cm/ka during the Middle to early Late Jurassic almost doubled to 20 cm/ka at the onset of sequence 3. Basin subsidence was initially fast, but soon slowed. This initially high rate of subsidence and the associated coarse clastic sedimentation is also recorded in the marginal basins of Iberia and the Celtic Sea. These sediments are homotaxially equivalent to the Missisauga Formation of the Scotian Shelf. The basin was filled by a variety of sediments: fluvial fan and fan-delta deposits of the Jeanne d'Arc Formation; coastal plain-delta top and delta front-prodelta sediments of the Hibernia Formation; interdistributary bay and shallow marine shoreface facies of the Catalina Formation; and estuarine to tidal flat sandstones and siltstones of the Eastern Shoals Formation (Fig. 6.5, 6.10, 6.13).

The source area for these sediments was the Avalon Uplift to the south and the Bonavista Platform and Outer Ridge Complex to the west and east. The sediments fine upward overall, and are interpreted as reflecting gradual peneplanation of the source areas and exposure and erosion of progressively older and finer-grained Jurassic rocks.

Two limestone markers occur within sequence number 3; the oolitic and bioclastic limestones of the 'B' and 'A' markers.

The sandstone units are vertically isolated, one from another, by the Fortune Bay and Whiterose shales deposited when the source areas were relatively low or during periods of high sea levels and associated marine transgressions. Of these shales the Fortune Bay Shale, laterally continuous, is important because it is the sealing caprock for overpressure in the basin.

Sequence 4 — Transition to Drift — Phase I; Barremian to Cenomanian

The siliciclastic units of sequence 4 (Fig. 6.5, 6.10, 6.13) were probably deposited during the transition from rifting to continental separation and formation of oceanic crust between the Grand Banks and Iberia. Incipient spreading may have occurred between the Grand Banks and northern Europe at this time.

The late Lower Cretaceous sequence is coeval with and stratigraphically similar to the Logan Canyon Formation of the Scotian Shelf. Basin subsidence and sediment accumulation had waned during the Neocomian. In the latest Barremian and Aptian subsidence began slowly to increase, but the hinterland was still low-lying and initial sediments of the Avalon Formation were fine grained estuarine sandstones and lagoonal and tidal flat shales. The base of this sequence is an easily recognizable seismic event. Although often erosional at the basin margins and over local structures, it generally represents a surface of seismic onlap (Fig. 6.7).

In several wells a red mudstone unit occurs in the lower part of the Avalon Formation just above the Barremian unconformity. This red mudstone is locally emergent, contains rootlets, and represents a period of very slow, possibly intermittent deposition. It is equivalent to the Naskapi Member of the Logan Canyon Formation. The Avalon Formation as discussed here is equivalent to the Avalon member as it was informally defined in the Chevron Hibernia P-15 well (Arthur et al., 1982).

A period of basin deformation is recorded by the trans-basin fault trend and the sediments of the Ben Nevis Formation. A cross section (Fig. 6.7) shows that most fault movement was during the Albian, which lies between the middle and upper unconformities within sequence 4. These unconformities are late Aptian and late Albian in age. This is the last period of deformation to affect the Jeanne d'Arc Basin and corresponds in time (about 110 Ma) to the beginning of spreading between the Grand Banks and Iberia (see Chapter 8). The late Aptian unconformity shows well developed angularity both near the basin margins and over structures. There is no apparent seismic evidence of tectonic movements involving basement during this period; all of the disruption in the sedimentary section can be accounted for by salt flowage. Many of the faults of the trans-basin trend appear to be listric at depth, but the seismic data involved are difficult to interpret (Fig. 6.7). Although some faults may sole out in salt, most appear to be restricted to younger strata and sole out in overpressured Jurassic shales.

The Ben Nevis Formation is a syntectonic deposit related to this phase of basin development. Facies analysis indicates that the Ben Nevis Formation consists of shallow estuarine channel and tidal flat sands. Sediment was supplied from the margins and down the axis of the basin and locally from high standing fault blocks. Reworking and

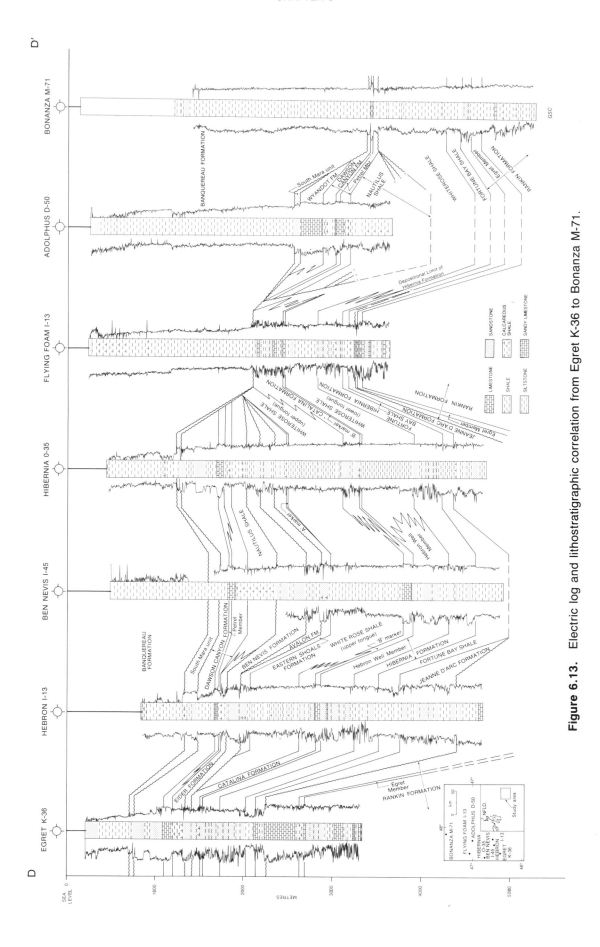

Figure 6.13. Electric log and lithostratigraphic correlation from Egret K-36 to Bonanza M-71.

winnowing of sands on these blocks, especially along the trans-basin trend, was an important factor in producing reservoir quality sands.

The late Albian unconformity at the top of the Ben Nevis Formation was less erosive than the late Aptian unconformity. Angularity is observed only at the basin margins and over the most prominent basin structures. In a sense the unconformity represents a base-level surface caused by syntectonic infill and bevelling of the Albian structures. In the basin depocentre prominent seismic onlap can be observed over this surface indicating that the basin was subsiding faster than sediment was filling it. The southern part of the basin was tectonically stable. There the Eider Formation consists of brown and reddish, medium- to coarse-grained sandstones and conglomerates deposited in a continental to marginal marine environment. Farther north, marls and shallow water shales and siltstones of the Nautilus Shale were deposited.

Sequence 5 — Transition to Drift — Phase II; Late Cretaceous and Paleocene

Sequence 5 records the final transition phase to a passive continental margin setting. Complete separation of the Grand Banks and northern Europe probably occurred during this period. Sediment supply was intermittent and produced overlapping deltaic sequences with distal turbidites. Deep water chalky limestones were deposited when subsidence outstripped sediment supply. The Late Cretaceous and Tertiary unconformities correspond respectively in time to the break-up between Labrador and Greenland and Greenland and north Europe.

Transgressive marine sediments of Turonian and Cenomanian age in the lower part of the Dawson Canyon Formation consist mainly of shales with minor siltstone and sandstone deposited in a neritic environment. The chalky Petrel Member was deposited in an outer neritic environment at the end of this period. During the Senonian (Coniacian-Maastrichtian) prograding clinoforms observed on seismic lines indicate sediment influx from the west which formed an offlapping clastic wedge (Fig. 6.8). Equivalent sediments in the basin depocentre are chalky, outer neritic limestones of the Wyandot Formation.

The top of the Late Cretaceous is an unconformity with prominent channelling into the underlying Dawson Canyon Formation (Fig. 6.8). The overlying South Mara unit of Paleocene age consists of delta front sands and prodelta turbidites.

Sequence 6 — passive margin; Tertiary

By Eocene time sediment supply had dwindled and the Grand Banks were surrounded by oceanic crust of the proto-Atlantic Ocean. Thermal subsidence and seaward tilting of the passive margin led to deposition of deep neritic shales of the Banquereau Formation.

Sequence 6 is dominated by fine grained, neritic sediments deposited in a true passive margin setting. Paleoenvironmental data from the Tertiary sections in East Newfoundland Basin wells indicate a change in Oligocene time from deep neritic and bathyal depositional conditions to shallow neritic environments (Gradstein and Williams, 1981). Sea level was again lower in Middle to Late Miocene time and much of the Grand Banks may have been exposed

subaerially. At the present time, the erosional and depositional record of this regression cannot be distinguished unequivocally from the subsequent effects of Pleistocene lowerings of sea level. The thickest section of Tertiary sediments occurs in East Newfoundland Basin where it locally exceeds 4 km, as observed in the Sheridan J-87 well.

Discussion

In summary, the Mesozoic stratigraphy offshore Newfoundland developed as a complicated response to the protracted rifting and break-up of the supercontinent Pangea between the Late Triassic and the end of the Cretaceous. The Cenozoic stratigraphy, by contrast, is a relatively simple response to passive margin subsidence following break-up. The sediments record two periods of rift tectonics that are separated by a period of tectonic stability. The final period of rifting was followed by a two-stage transition to the tectonic setting of a passive margin.

The sedimentary record can be satisfactorily described within a framework of six depositional (seismic-stratigraphic) sequences that are related to the formation of the Atlantic Ocean and the Labrador Sea. The first depositional sequence (Aborted Rift) includes redbeds, evaporites and marginal marine carbonates deposited in an apparently coherent rift system of Late Triassic to Early Jurassic age that spanned Pangea and predated the formation of oceanic crust.

The North American and African plates began to separate during the Early Jurassic (see Chapters 2 and 5), but north of the Newfoundland Fracture Zone rifting was aborted before the formation of oceanic crust. The second depositional sequence (Epeiric Basin) comprises normal marine shales and limestones with minor fine grained siliciclastics deposited in an epeiric sea that transgressed the old rifted terrain.

Updoming of the Avalon Uplift and a second phase of rifting started in the latest Jurassic and this rifting persisted until the end of the Neocomian. Associated deposition on the flanks of the Avalon Uplift and in the developing graben was dominated by sands and muds of the third depositional sequence (Late Rift) that contains many of the proven petroleum reservoirs of the Jeanne d'Arc Basin. Erosion of the central Avalon Uplift took place throughout deposition of the late rift sequence and was a principal event in the formation of the prominent peneplain referred to as the Avalon Unconformity.

Depositional sequences 4 and 5 (Transition to Drift — Phase I and Phase II) occupy the periods Barremian to Cenomanian and the Late Cretaceous to Paleocene respectively. These complex sequences were deposited in a rapidly changing tectonic setting with numerous attendant unconformities, and they record the formation of oceanic crust north from the Newfoundland Fracture Zone to the Labrador Sea. Sequence 4 consists of shallow to marginal marine siliciclastic rocks deposited in lagoonal, intertidal and estuarine environments. The deeper marine rocks of sequence 5 were deposited as offlapping deltaic lobes with distal turbidites. Deep water chalky limestones were deposited during periods of marine transgression.

The sediments of sequence 6 (Passive Margin) were deposited in a passive margin setting after the Newfoundland margin had been surrounded by oceanic crust. Fine grained, deep neritic clastics predominated.

OFF-SHELF AREAS

Drilling for petroleum on the continental margin around Newfoundland has been confined to the areas of the principal sedimentary basins, and except for wells in Flemish Pass and the Blue H-28 well in the East Newfoundland Basin, to water depths of less than 400 m on the continental shelf (Fig. 6.1). Sites 111 and 384 of the Deep Sea Drilling Project (DSDP) on Orphan Knoll and J-anomaly Ridge (Laughton et al., 1972; Tucholke and Vogt, 1979), and dredge samples from the flanks of Orphan Knoll, Flemish Cap and the Newfoundland Seamounts are the only additional points of stratigraphic control in the slope-rise zone around Newfoundland. Interpretations of the geology of this zone therefore have been derived mainly from geophysical data and are presented in this chapter in the form of maps and cross-sections.

The maps of the subsurface are based primarily on industrial multichannel seismic data, complemented by assorted lines of single channel seismic data in deeper water and in nearshore areas of thin sediment cover. Structure maps have been drawn for "basement" and for a horizon in the overlying sediments referred to as a "base event", and thickness maps have been prepared for the sediments relative to these surfaces and the seafloor. The cross-sections are line drawings of seismic records across the continental margin, selected to illustrate predominant styles of structure and deposition. Because the maps and sections cover a large area with many geological complexities, interpretations are speculative or preliminary in many instances.

Regional maps

Basement structure and the distribution of the overlying sediments are portrayed using two types of maps, a "base event" map (Fig. 6.14) and a "basement" map (Fig. 6.15). These maps have been converted from reflection time of the seismic markers to depth in metres using velocity control from wells in the region, velocity data derived from processing multichannel seismic records, and velocities from sonobuoy observations (Tucholke and Fry, 1985). The base event map (Fig. 6.14) depicts the deepest seismic horizons that are regionally mappable; this surface corresponds approximately to the base of the Late Cretaceous. The basement map (Fig. 6.15) shows depths to the deepest detectable seismic reflectors; it depicts the basement structures that controlled the deposition of younger sediments, and in that sense may be provisionally regarded as a map of "economic basement". These two markers, base event and basement, are the most reasonably mappable seismic horizons over this large and geologically complex region.

Base event

Within the area of well control in the basins on the Grand Banks, the base event (Fig. 6.14) generally represents a regional unconformity of approximately mid-Cretaceous age. In the marginal zones of the basins this is an angular unconformity that truncates progressively older strata toward the basin edges, and coincides with the peneplain (Avalon Unconformity) on basement in intrabasin areas. The identification of this marker becomes uncertain outside the area of well control; for example, beneath the

deeper parts of the basins it may trace a horizon representing a depositional equivalent of the unconformity. However, despite the disparate origins of the horizons composing the map, it nonetheless provides a datum surface from which to assess aspects of regional geology both above and below. Regionally, it indicates the approximate form of the base of the Upper Cretaceous-Cenozoic sedimentary sequence, and therefore is a datum for mapping the thickness of these overlying deposits (Fig. 6.16). The base event is also a datum surface from which to estimate the thickness of the underlying Mesozoic sediments; total sediment thickness is presented in Figure 6.17. In Figure 6.26 the base event is used as a datum for mapping the underlying geology on the basis of seismic reflection character.

To the extent that the base event surface (Fig. 6.14) approximates the base of the Upper Cretaceous section, it indicates the post mid-Cretaceous subsidence history of the continental margin around Newfoundland. Figure 6.16 shows the degree to which this subsidence has been accompanied by accumulation of sediments. In general, these maps show that the present shallow water areas of the region (Fig. 6.1) have been relatively high since the Late Cretaceous, while surrounding areas have subsided. The Grand Banks and the Northeast Newfoundland Shelf form a continuous positive element; the part of this high beneath the Grand Banks is the Avalon Uplift (Jansa and Wade, 1975). Flemish Cap is a prominent high to the east, connected to the Grand Banks by an east-west saddle. Orphan Knoll is a relatively positive crustal unit to the north of Flemish Cap. Comparison of the base event surface (Fig. 6.14) and present bathymetry (Fig. 6.1) shows that the area of greatest post-Late Cretaceous subsidence east of Newfoundland has been buried by outbuilding of the continental shelf. More than 7 km of post-base event sediments have accumulated in this zone (Fig. 6.16). In the southern part of this basin it is apparent that the western bank of Flemish Pass has been built up by post-Cretaceous sedimentation. In contrast, the irregular physiography of the southern part of Flemish Pass reflects the thin sediment cover on irregular, buried topography along the saddle connecting the Grand Banks and Flemish Cap.

Around the southern margin of the Grand Banks the base event surface lies at depths of 6 to 8 km (Fig. 6.14). Sediment accumulation (Fig. 6.16) is most extensive beneath the southwestern flank of the Grand Banks, in the area of South Whale Subbasin, which thus appears to have experienced some subsidence in Late Cretaceous-Cenozoic time. The Whale, Horseshoe, Carson basins and the southern extension of the Jeanne d'Arc basin are not seen on the base event surface, and therefore have been an integral part of the Grand Banks cratonic block since the mid-Cretaceous.

Basement

The basement map (Fig. 6.15) generally depicts depths to the "deepest detectable" seismic reflectors. Some of the maximum depths recorded on the map are by extrapolation from these deepest reflectors on the basis of dips in the overlying sedimentary section. Probably the most important constraint regarding interpretation of a seismic basement map is that the depth of seismic penetration may be

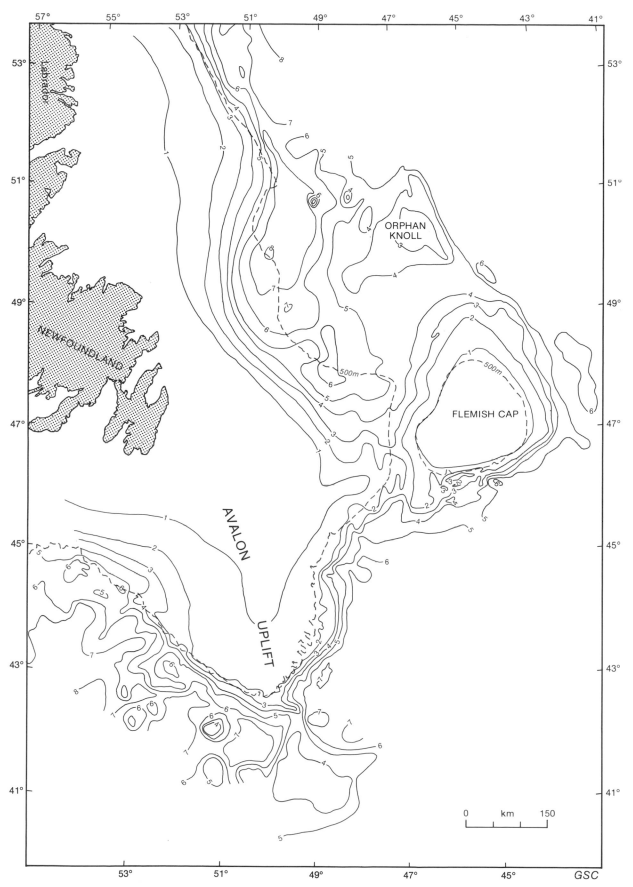

Figure 6.14. Base event map for the continental margin around Newfoundland, contoured in kilometres below sea level. Red dashed line is the 500 m water depth contour.

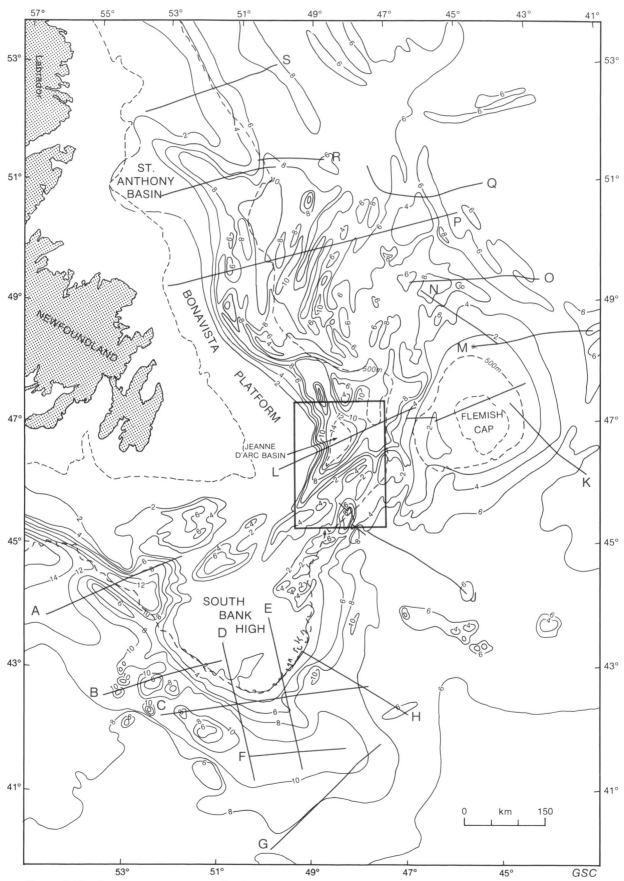

Figure 6.15. Basement structure map for the continental margin around Newfoundland (contoured in kilometres below sea level). Rectangle (red) encloses area of Figure 6.6. Red dashed line is 500 m water depth contour. Black dashed line is landward edge of Cretaceous — Tertiary sediments. Lettered lines are locations of cross-sections in Figures 6.18 to 6.25.

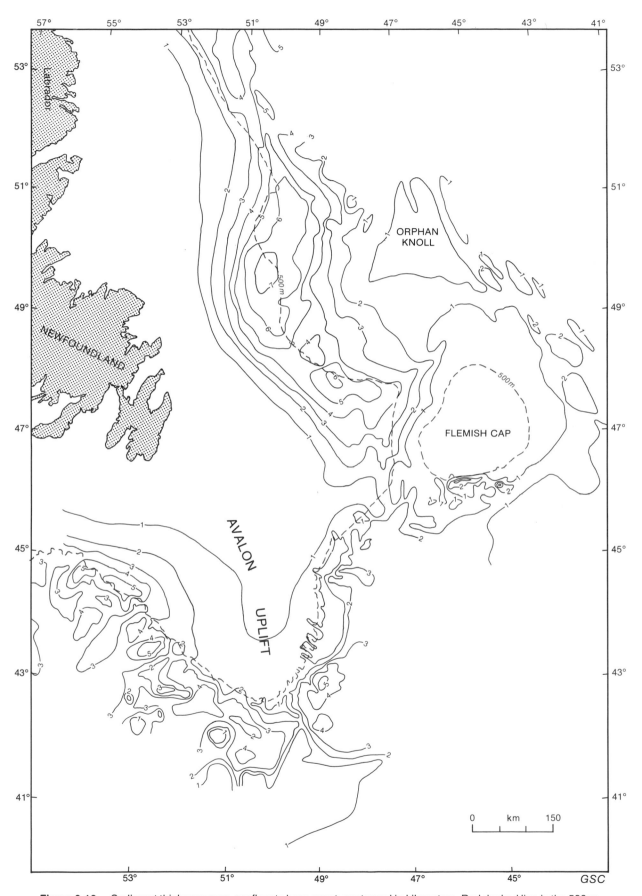

Figure 6.16. Sediment thickness map, seafloor to base event, contoured in kilometres. Red dashed line is the 500 m water depth contour.

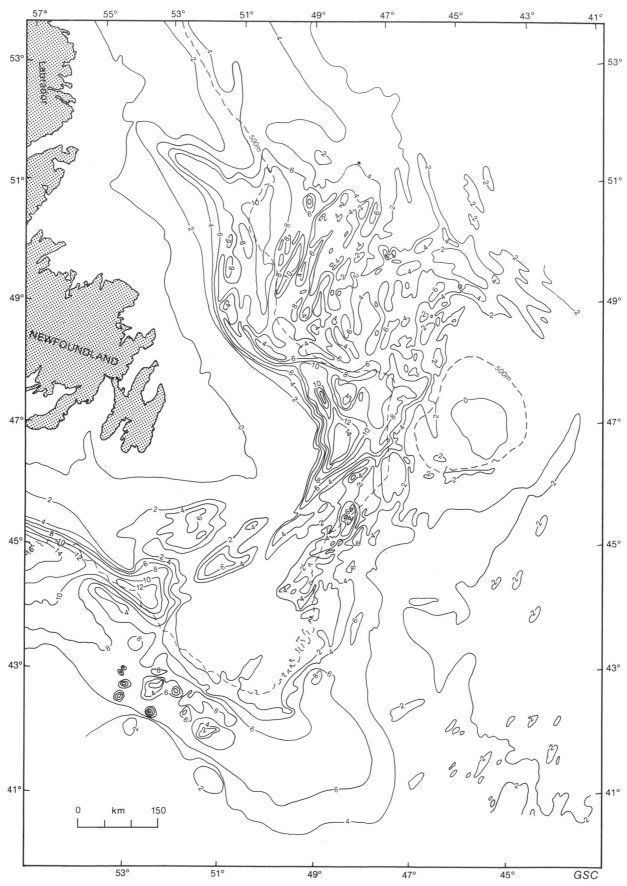

Figure 6.17. Sediment thickness map, seafloor to basement, contoured in kilometres. Red dashed line is the 500 m water depth contour.

a function of the degree of structural disturbance; for example, a surface on deformed sedimentary strata may be interpreted as acoustic basement if reflections from the strata are weak. Because absolute depths recorded on the map are subject to the constraint of record quality, the most useful feature of this map may be to illustrate trends of basement structure that controlled younger sedimentary basins. Geologically, the basement mapped in Figure 6.15 may range in age from Precambrian to Tertiary.

The basement map of the continental margin around Newfoundland (Fig. 6.15) shows the same positive features obvious on the base event map (Fig. 6.14), although the zone of the Avalon Uplift is broken by fault-bounded basins that separate the South Bank High from the Bonavista Platform, and the Orphan Knoll structure is less prominent. Flemish Cap and the regional basement high to the west, the Bonavista Platform, are peneplaned areas of Precambrian and Paleozoic bedrock. Northeast of Newfoundland the Bonavista Platform terminates at the St. Anthony Basin, which contains Carboniferous rocks (Cutt and Laving, 1977). The peneplanation of these basement features may date in part from the Paleozoic, with further truncation during several periods of erosion in Mesozoic time. Widespread burial of this surface began in the Late Cretaceous following Early to mid-Cretaceous uplift. The total thickness of sediments covering basement is mapped in Figure 6.17.

The Jeanne d'Arc Basin appears to contain the thickest accumulation of Mesozoic-Cenozoic sediments in the region — as much as 20 km (Fig. 6.15, 6.17; Keen et al., 1987a). It extends north-northwest, as shown by the 10 km depth contour, to north of latitude 48°N, and is separated from the East Newfoundland Basin to the north by the Cumberland Ridge. The deepest parts of the East Newfoundland Basin lie between 49 and 51°N and west of longitude 49°W, as defined by two linear depressions more than 10 km deep. The 8 km depth contour extends northwest into the area of the (Carboniferous) St. Anthony Basin. Southwest of the Grand Banks the South Whale Subbasin is at least 12 km deep, and the Laurentian Subbasin adjacent to the west may be more than 16 km deep (Wade and MacLean, Chapter 5). The extent and depth of the basin south of the Grand Banks, here named the "Fogo Basin", are conservatively defined by the 10 km depth contour. This is the largest of the basins in the Grand Banks region and its depth may be substantially greater than shown in Figure 6.15 because available seismic data do not penetrate to the base of the sedimentary section.

The basement structures beneath the continental margin around Newfoundland are in general elongate, and trend northeasterly beneath the Grand Banks, but between latitudes 47 and 49°N there is a notable kink in the structural fabric, with basement features there aligned north-south to northwest-southeast (Fig. 6.15). North of 49°N structural trends are predominantly north-south. The trends of the basins on the Grand Banks have been compared to those of the Appalachian Orogen on land, suggesting that the basins are successor features on Hercynian structures. However, it is not clear that this relationship is valid to the north. There, structures in the 47-49°N "kink-zone" lie nearly at right angles to projected Appalachian trends, and apparently are superimposed on the older geology.

In contrast to the mainly linear form of basement structures east of the Bonavista Platform, several nearly circular and conical features have been mapped in the East Newfoundland Basin (Fig. 6.15). One of these structures, at approximately latitude 51°N, longitude 49°W, projects above the seafloor. These features are interpreted to be seamounts. To the south, concentrations of seamounts occur in deep water southeast and southwest of the Grand Banks (Fig. 6.15).

The basinal areas beneath the continental margin around Newfoundland have undergone different styles, rates and degrees of subsidence. Two types of tectonic setting for these basins can provisionally be defined: intracratonic and pericratonic. The Whale, Horseshoe and Jeanne d'Arc basins are examples of intracratonic subsidence. Relative to the Grand Banks cratonic block, the South Whale Subbasin and Fogo and Carson basins are in a pericratonic setting. This type of subsidence presumably occurs in areas of transition from continental to oceanic crust and will be enhanced by sediment loading.

In the northern part of the study region (Fig. 6.15) a relatively subdued basement depression occurs in the transition zone between continental and oceanic crust inferred by Parson et al. (1985) and Keen et al. (1987a) to lie east of Orphan Knoll. The limited subsidence along this segment of the craton may reflect low sedimentation because it lies far from land. According to the tectonic setting defined above, the basement structures to the west, between Orphan Knoll and the Bonavista Platform, are the result of intracratonic subsidence. Clearly, however, the structure of this area differs from that of the intracratonic basins on the Grand Banks to the south, posing the question of whether the contrast relates primarily to fundamental differences in the underlying geology, or to differences in timing, degree or mechanism of subsidence (Keen et al., Chapter 2 and 1987a, b). The spatial relationship of the East Newfoundland Basin to the Bonavista Platform to the west is not unlike the situation of the nominally pericratonic South Whale Subbasin and Fogo Basin relative to the Grand Banks cratonic block. This raises some doubts as to whether pericratonic basins in this region necessarily define transition from continental to oceanic crust.

Profiles of the margin around Newfoundland

The history of seafloor spreading described earlier in this chapter leads us to anticipate different types of margins around the Grand Banks and Orphan Basin (see also Chapters 2 and 8). A transform margin might be expected southwest of the Grand Banks, and rifted margins to the east. Evidence of continent-continent motion along the trace of the Charlie-Gibbs Fracture Zone on the northern side of the East Newfoundland Basin might still exist. In this section diagrammatic cross sections of the margins are presented to illustrate the variety of structural styles (Fig. 6.18 to 6.25). The figures are based on selected multichannel seismic sections. They complement the transects of the margins described in Chapter 2. The locations of the sections are shown in Figure 6.15.

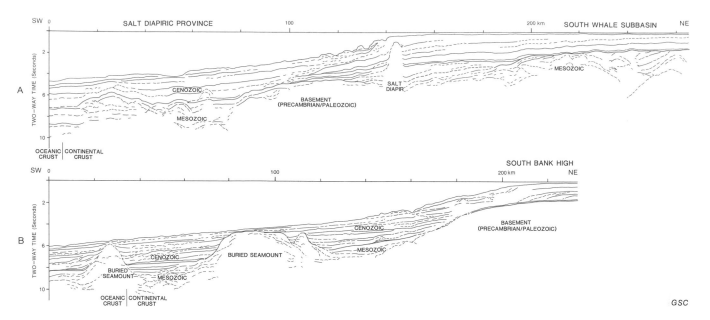

Figure 6.18. Cross-sections (A, B) of the southwest margin of the Grand Banks. Locations shown in Figure 6.15. Red reflector is base event mapped in Figure 6.14. (A, part of seismic line 112, 1972, courtesy of Geophysical Service Incorporated; B, part of seismic line 111, 1972, courtesy of Seiscan-Delta Limited)

Southwest Grand Banks

Sections A and B (Fig. 6.18) cross the southwestern margin of the Grand Banks in two different structural settings. Section A extends southwesterly off the Grand Banks from the South Whale Subbasin, and section B extends seaward from the basement block forming the South Bank High (Jansa and Wade, 1975) to the zone of seamounts southwest of the Grand Banks (Fig. 6.15).

The South Whale Subbasin is the eastern extremity of the Scotian Basin (Fig. 6.15), and diapiric structures on section A (Fig. 6.18) indicate that the Slope Diapiric Province of the Scotian Basin extends eastward into the South Whale Subbasin (see Chapter 5). The Fogo Seamounts, southwest of the Grand Banks (section B) may be the result of the same mid-Cretaceous volcanic event that produced the Newfoundland seamounts southeast of the Grand Banks (Fig. 6.15), where dredged volcanic rocks have been dated at about 100 Ma (Sullivan, 1978). Radiometric ages of 135 and 117 Ma have been reported for volcanic rocks in the Brant P-87 and Twillick G-49 wells on the Grand Banks (Amoco Canada Petroleum Company Ltd., 1973a, 1974), and an age of 106 Ma has been determined for basalt in Deep Sea Drilling Project Site 384 on the J-anomaly Ridge (Houghton et al., 1979). The strong reflections at the base event on the deep water portion of section A may indicate the presence of volcanics, although they are not thick enough to prevent deeper penetration. On section B, in the area of the seamounts, the volcanics may be sufficiently thick to prevent deeper penetration.

Sections A and B (Fig. 6.18) cross the inferred transform margin of the Grand Banks (see, for example, Auzende et al., 1970; LePichon and Fox, 1971). Jansa and Wade (1975) suggested that this transform fault began to develop about 170 Ma (Middle Jurassic) with the initiation of continental drift. They noted, however, that the fault

had not been recognized on processed seismic profiles across its inferred location.

Seismic refraction observations in this area now being analyzed indicate that transition from continental crust (about 27 km thick) to oceanic crust (about 8 km thick) occurs beneath the foot of the continental slope over a distance of 20 to 30 km (I. Reid, pers. comm., 1987). This is a very rapid transition relative to crustal structure usually observed at rifted margins. An interpretation of these observations by I. Reid (pers. comm., 1987) is that towards the margin the crust was thinned by flow in the lower crust and lithosphere. This caused subsidence of the margin with less erosion of the Paleozoic layer near the margin during the subsequent Avalon Uplift than away from it, in accord with the refraction observations. The inferred margin fault in this model delineates the original continental shear, which truncates the upper crustal layers. The 20-30 km transition between this fault and the ocean-continent boundary may be a zone where the continental crust flowed or deformed due to tectonic or lithostatic stresses at the margin. The oceanic crust appears to be little influenced by this setting (in contrast to oceanic transforms), apart from the presence of the volcanic seamounts which may be due to irregularities in the spreading process along the margin.

An alternative explanation for the origin of this segment of the continental margin is that it reflects a zone of differential down-warping of two adjacent crustal segments, and if this is true there is no need to invoke large transverse displacements. The peneplanation, volcanism and downwarping may be related events. Such an explanation implies that the crust on the oceanic side of the inferred transform margin is composed of severely thinned continental crust. These two interpretations have different implications regarding the location of the continent-ocean boundary. Geophysical data available at this time are not sufficient to show appreciable difference between the deep structure of the southwest margin of the Grand Banks and that of the southeast margin (I. Reid, pers. comm., 1987). The question might be resolved by drilling into the crust on the seaward side of the supposed continent-ocean boundary.

In summary, there is no direct evidence of transform motion along the Newfoundland Fracture Zone. The most compelling indirect evidence comes from plate reconstructions of the Atlantic Ocean (e.g. Klitgord and Schouten, 1986).

Newfoundland Ridge

Sections C, D, E, F and G (Fig. 6.19) cross the inferred transform margin of the Grand Banks farther to the southeast, and the Newfoundland Ridge. The Newfoundland Ridge is an anomalous feature that poses additional problems for transform models of this part of the margin. The ridge is a physiographic feature that extends about 900 km southeast from the Tail of the Bank (Fig. 6.1). Watson and Johnson (1970) interpreted single channel seismic profiles from the ridge as showing buried basement blocks, which they considered to be volcanic in origin because of associated magnetic anomalies. Because of the alignment of this ridge with the southwestern margin of the Grand Banks, some workers have concluded that it represents a fracture zone on the seaward extension of the supposed transform fault (Auzende et al., 1970; LePichon and Fox, 1971).

More recently, with collection of multichannel seismic data from the Newfoundland Ridge, it is apparent that the "basement" blocks of Watson and Johnson (1970) are composed of layered rocks (Fig. 6.19). Grant (1979) compared the seismic character of these media with that of Mesozoic strata on the adjacent Grand Banks and proposed that the Newfoundland Ridge is a remnant of a former sedimentary basin, the Fogo Basin. The line drawings of seismic records in Figure 6.19 show planar reflectors to depths approaching 4 seconds (2-way travel time) in the crustal blocks. Structures at approximately 200 km on line E and 70 km on line F are interpreted as piercement structures relating to flowage of evaporites or shale. These structures are distinguished from seamounts, such as those at 160 km on line F and on the western ends of lines B (Fig. 6.18) and C (Fig. 6.19), by associated rim-synclines. The structural trend of the Fogo Basin as defined by subsurface reflectors is about northwest-southeast, somewhat oblique to the physiographic trend of the Newfoundland Ridge. The absence of a significant gravity anomaly over the Newfoundland Ridge (Fig. 6.19, G) supports the interpretation that it consists of substantially lighter material than would compose a ridge of oceanic crust (Grant, 1979).

The magnetic anomalies over the ridge suggest a significant component of igneous rock. However, drilling on the Grand Banks has shown that there is considerable variability in magnetic expression of volcanics, so these anomalies may likewise represent only extrusive volcanics at the level of the mid-Cretaceous unconformity. Deep Sea Drilling Project Site 384, on the J-anomaly Ridge that projects southwestward from the Newfoundland Ridge (Fig. 6.1), bottomed in altered diabasic basalt, overlain by Aptian reefal carbonates (Tucholke and Vogt, 1979). Gradstein et al. (1977) noted that the subsidence history at this location matches that of wells drilled on the Grand Banks in the South Whale Subbasin. Consequently it is concluded here that the region south and west of the Grand Banks, including the Newfoundland Ridge and the J-anomaly Ridge, and the area traversed by the profiles in Figure 6.19, has experienced mid-Cretaceous volcanism and subsidence.

Newfoundland Basin

Sections H and J in Figure 6.20 cross the northern and southern portions of the southeast margin of the Grand Banks (Fig. 6.15). These two sections show similar structural relationships beneath the slope-rise zone, but the landward end of section H extends on to the South Bank High whereas section J crosses the Carson Basin on the Grand Banks. These relationships are somewhat analogous to those of sections A and B (Fig. 6.18) on the southwest margin of the Grand Banks. Several seismic units can be defined in the slope-rise zone on these sections and they are provisionally dated in the diagrammatic section in Figure 6.21a, following the work of Parson et al. (1985). However, the irregular basement depicted in this diagram is not apparent on the seismic records from the slope-rise zone along the southeast margin of the Grand Banks. As indicated in sections H and J (Fig. 6.20) and in section C of Figure 6.19, the seismic reflection data available do not show a strong basal reflection. A sonobuoy on line J (Fig. 6.20) recorded a velocity of 5.0 km/s at the level of the deepest, continuous event in the area. Grant (1979) has noted that refraction velocities in this area are not diagnostic of crustal origin, as refraction velocities of "crustal" range (greater than 5.0 km/s) have been recorded in areas of vastly different "basement" seismic reflection character. He concluded that this area of the slope-rise zone is probably underlain by foundered continental crust.

The Carson Basin is somewhat analogous to the South Whale Subbasin (Fig. 6.15) in that it extends seaward beneath the continental slope. Section J (Fig. 6.20) shows that the present shelf edge lies roughly 30 km landward of a major deflection in the underlying seismic reflector interpreted as the approximate mid-Cretaceous unconformity. Landward from this break the unconformity surface shows irregularities due to faulting, warping and erosion, and these irregularities appear to reflect collapse of the underlying margin on listric faults directed seaward. The landward limit of these fault planes is arcuate in plan view and concave seaward. The relief on the unconformity has a dendritic pattern, indicative of cutting by erosional processes. Downslope from this zone a seismic unit can be identified that may be the depositional record of the clastic material transported through this drainage system. This unit is up to 0.4 seconds thick (2-way travel time), with an undulating surface. Relative to the overlying sequence it is strongly reflective, with somewhat irregular internal reflectors (Fig. 6.20, J). The base of the unit is a strong, continuous and smooth reflector, with local irregularities that may represent erosional depressions. Extrapolation from the Bonnition H-32 well shows that this seismic unit provides a marker in the slope-rise section that is later than mid-Cretaceous in age.

Section J (Fig. 6.20) is typical for the area described above. Transects of this zone eventually reach irregular seismic basement to the southeast, which may rise

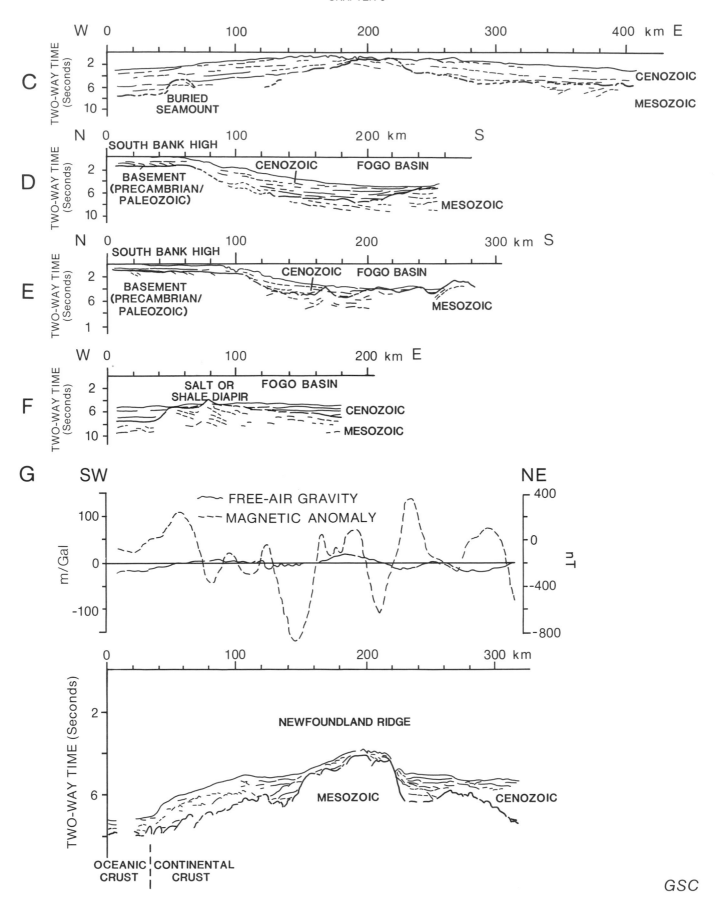

Figure 6.19. Cross sections (C to G) of the southern Grand Banks margin and the Newfoundland Ridge. Locations shown in Figure 6.15. Red reflector is base event mapped in Figure 6.14. (C, D and E are parts of 1972 lines 112, 114 and 115 respectively, and line F is 1972 line 116, courtesy of Seiscan-Delta Limited. Line G is after Figure 5 of Sullivan and Keen, 1978).

GSC

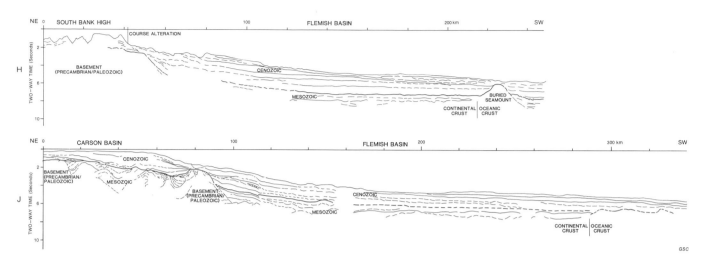

Figure 6.20. Cross sections (H, J) of the southeast margin of the Grand Banks. Locations shown in Figure 6.15. Red reflector is base event mapped in Figure 6.14. (H, courtesy of Institute of Oceanographic Sciences, U.K., as reported in Parson et al., 1985. From the shelf seaward cross section J includes part of line NF 79-103, 1980, courtesy of Geophysical Service Incorporated; parts of lines E-614, 1971 and G-564, 1973 courtesy of Mobil Oil Corporation; part of line NF 79-107D, 1980 courtesy of Geophysical Service Incorporated; part of line S-215, 1977 courtesy of Texaco Exploration Canada Limited; southeast portion is courtesy of Institute of Oceanographic Sciences, U.K., as reported in Parson et al., 1985).

abruptly to extend above the seafloor in the form of seamounts. The landward edge of irregular basement has been mapped by Parson et al. (1985); the zone of foundered continental crust southeast of the Grand Banks, as inferred on the basis of seismic character, narrows to the northeast and ends at the eastern extremity of Flemish Cap (Fig. 6.15). Section K (Fig. 6.21b) shows exposed basement on the southeast flank of Flemish Cap, and shows an irregular basement surface on the seaward end of the section.

Flemish Cap

Cross-sections L and M (Fig. 6.22) provide transects of the Jeanne d'Arc Basin and Flemish Pass on the west side of Flemish Cap, and the eastern flank of Flemish Cap; cross-section N (Fig. 6.23) shows the north flank of Flemish Cap. The core of Flemish Cap is composed in part of granitic rock of Late Proterozoic (Hadrynian) age (Pelletier, 1971). King et al. (1985) concluded that these rocks are part of the Avalon Zone of the Appalachian Orogen.

Seismic data from Flemish Cap (sections K to N) indicate that the central, "basement" core of the cap is encircled by a veneer of outward dipping sedimentary strata, which generally are truncated at the flank of the cap. The depositional, erosional, and structural aspects of these sediments suggest that Flemish Cap has been a relatively positive crustal element through Cenozoic and at least part of Mesozoic time. Because Flemish Cap lies far out on the continental margin, remote from sediment sources, the sediments on the cap probably reflect slow deposition in shallow water, with frequent lacunae. Sen Gupta and Grant (1971) reported Cretaceous foraminifers in a limestone specimen dredged from the southern flank of Flemish Cap. Sections from the western and northern flanks of Flemish Cap (L, M, Fig. 6.22; N, Fig. 6.23) indicate that

the veneer of sediments in those areas is Neogene-Quaternary in age, based on extrapolation from exploratory wells on the Grand Banks.

The veneer of sediments on the cap is underlain by a prominent unconformity. In the central area of the cap, where this surface is exposed at the seafloor, seismic data occasionally show sub-bottom reflectors, indicating that the area of the "granitic core" probably includes sedimentary strata. The irregular character of the magnetic and gravity fields over this area also reflects the complex origin of these basement rocks. Toward the flanks of the cap, seismic data show that the unconformity is underlain in some areas by folded and faulted sedimentary strata, particulary in the western and northern quadrants of the cap. In the southwestern quarter of the cap more than 3 km of sediment are present in a north-trending half-graben basin bounded to the west by the faulted flank of Beothuk Ridge. The sediments in this graben are essentially undeformed, but they are underlain by deformed strata. If the latter are analogous to the deformed strata in Flemish Pass that have been sampled by the Gabriel C-60 well, they are Early Cretaceous in age, and the undeformed sediments in the graben may then be Late Cretaceous.

The sedimentary section beyond the northern flank of Flemish Cap is disrupted by faults, which bound rotated blocks that have been displaced northward. As is the case for western Flemish Cap, the age of the sediments forming these blocks and the timing of their displacement is uncertain. By analogy with events in Jeanne d'Arc Basin, the faulting and displacement may have occurred in late Early Cretaceous time. The younger sediments in these rotated blocks may therefore be Early Cretaceous in age, equivalent to disrupted sediments in Flemish Pass.

Section N (Fig. 6.23) shows a sediment drift at the present flank of Flemish Cap, and a buried sediment drift at

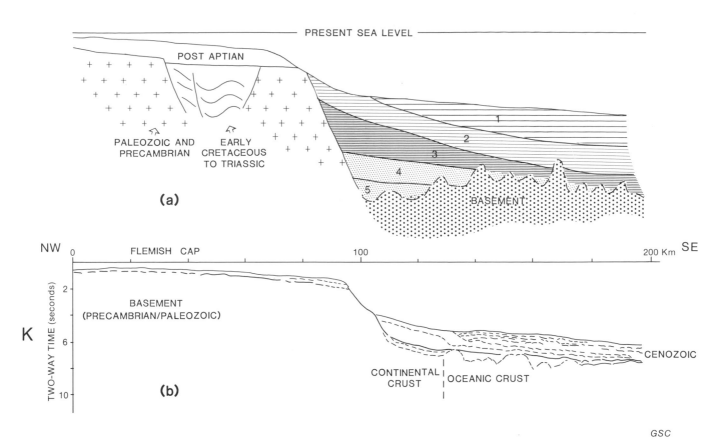

PRESENT SEA LEVEL

POST APTIAN

PALEOZOIC AND PRECAMBRIAN   EARLY CRETACEOUS TO TRIASSIC

1
2
3
4
5
BASEMENT

(a)

NW   FLEMISH CAP   100   200 Km   SE

K   TWO-WAY TIME (seconds)

BASEMENT (PRECAMBRIAN/PALEOZOIC)

CENOZOIC

CONTINENTAL CRUST   OCEANIC CRUST

(b)

GSC

Figure 6.21.   a) Schematic model illustrating seismic stratigraphy of the continental margin east of New-foundland. Crosses mark continental basement; coarse stipple covers basement of uncertain affinities and possible oceanic basement. Interpreted age-range of the numbered seismic sequences is as follows: 1, Oligocene-Quaternary; 2, Cenomanian-Eocene; 3, Albian-Campanian; 4, Barremian-Albian; 5, Neocomian-Barremian (after Parson et al., 1985).
b) Cross section (K) of the southeast flank of Flemish Cap. Location shown in Figure 6.15. Red reflector is base event mapped in Figure 6.14. (Courtesy of Institute of Oceanographic Sciences, U.K., as reported in Parson et al., 1985).

the foot of the slope off Flemish Cap. Sackville Spur (Fig. 6.1) is the most prominent physiographic example of a sediment drift in this area. It may reflect depositional conditions peculiar to a lower stand of sea level, as occurred several times in the Pleistocene (Grant, 1972). The presence of such sediment drifts in the subsurface may suggest that similar depositional relationships existed in the Tertiary (L.R. Kennard, pers. comm., 1977). The buried sediment drift shown in Section N is tentatively attributed to lower sea-level conditions in Late Miocene time.

There is little evidence of a sedimentary section beneath the unconformity on the east flank of Flemish Cap (Fig. 6.21b, K and Fig. 6.22, M). Furthermore, the sedimentary section above basement in the slope-rise zone is somewhat thinner than is observed to the south (Fig. 6.20), in part because some deep units are missing.

Orphan Basin — Orphan Knoll

Sections across the East Newfoundland Basin and Orphan Knoll (Fig. 6.24, P) show a series of "basement" irregulari-ties, which represent north- to northeast-trending linear ridges (Fig. 6.15). Reflection seismic records across these

features in some cases show internal reflectors, whereas others show no apparent seismic penetration. This differ-ence depends to some extent upon factors such as record quality, line orientation, and the thickness of the overlying sedimentary section. However, examination of all avail-able seismic data reveals consistent properties associated with specific structures and regional patterns in these properties are apparent. In general, there is a roughly north-south dividing line between basement structures that show seismic penetration and those that do not, with the seismically "harder" structures lying west of longitude 49°W. This difference in seismic character is tentatively interpreted as denoting older rocks to the west. To the north, both classes are replaced by "basement" structures with irregular surfaces and no apparent seismic penetra-tion. Circular structures in this area are interpreted to be seamounts.

The two sections in Figure 6.24 cross the continent-ocean transition zone as defined by interpretations that place this boundary immediately east of Orphan Knoll. Grant (1975) noted, however, that the reflection seismic character of supposed oceanic crust east of Orphan Knoll is indistinguishable from that of some of the crustal structures west of Orphan Knoll, where a continental origin is assumed. The continental nature of Orphan Knoll itself was confirmed by Deep Sea Drilling Project Site 111 (Laughton et al., 1972). The location of the continent-ocean boundary in this region can be defined indirectly using magnetic anomalies. A large positive magnetic anomaly a few kilometres east of Orphan Knoll runs approximately north-northeast and lies west of Anomaly 34 (Srivastava and Tapscott, 1986). A reconstruction of the North Atlantic based on magnetic data matches this anomaly with a similar anomaly on Goban Spur, southwest of Ireland. Deep sea drilling showed that the Goban Spur anomaly is bounded to the east (continent-side) by continental rocks and to the west by oceanic rocks (Scrutton, 1985). Assuming this anomaly marks the continent-ocean boundary east of Orphan Knoll, it can be traced south to the east of Flemish Cap, but available magnetic data are not good enough to trace it off the southeastern margin of the Grand Banks.

The sections north and south of Orphan Knoll (Fig. 6.24, Q; Fig. 6.23, O) each show a basement high, with deeper water to the east, as well as various changes in seismic reflection character from west to east. "Basement" is not visible to the west in these sections, but an irregular deep reflector is apparent to the east. The basement structures in the northernmost section (Fig. 6.24, Q)

appear to be rotated blocks, with rotation having taken place on east-dipping fault surfaces.

Section P (Fig. 6.24) illustrates the character of the westernmost ridge in the East Newfoundland Basin. The surface of this feature appears to be approximately a continuation of the peneplaned surface of the Bonavista Platform to the west. There appears to have been differential movement of this block relative to the Bonavista Platform, but its surface has been bevelled to the same level after this movement.

South Labrador

The cross-sections (R, S) in Figure 6.25 illustrate the characteristics of the southwestern margin of the Labrador Sea, which is discussed in detail in Chapter 7. These sections show a planar unconformity dipping gently seaward, with gradual transition to an irregular "basement" surface in the slope-rise zone. Basement of the latter type is usually considered typical of oceanic crust. However, Grant (1975, 1980) pointed out that the magnetic character of the rocks in this area does not appear to correlate with seismic character, and it was not clear that the linear magnetic anomalies in this region can be sensibly interpreted in terms of seafloor spreading. Obviously this question is relevant to interpretation of the nature and location of the

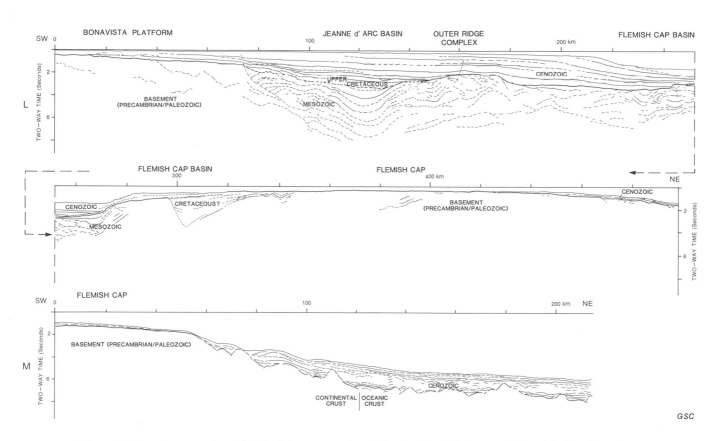

Figure 6.22. Cross sections (L, M) of the eastern Grand Banks, Flemish Pass and Flemish Cap. Location shown in Figure 6.15. Red reflector is base event mapped in Figure 6.14. (L, part of line NF 79-114, 1980 courtesy of Geophysical Service Incorporated; part of line 14, 1971 courtesy of Canadian Superior Oil Limited; part of line 32, 1972 courtesy of Geophysical Service Incorporated. M, courtesy of Institute of Oceanographic Sciences, U.K., as reported in Parson et al., 1985).

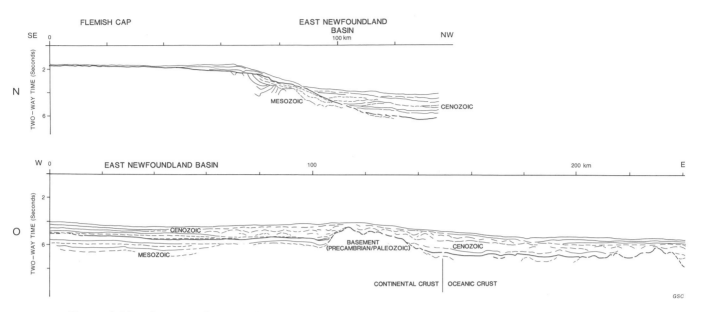

Figure 6.23. Cross sections (N, O) of the northeast flank of Flemish Cap and through Minna Saddle. Locations shown in Figure 6.15. Red reflector is base event mapped in Figure 6.14. (Courtesy of Institute of Oceanographic Sciences, U.K., as reported in Parson et al., 1985).

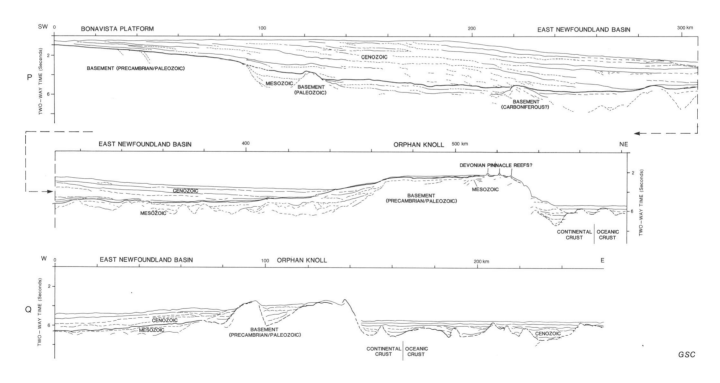

Figure 6.24. Cross sections (P, Q) of the East Newfoundland Basin and Orphan Knoll. Locations shown in Figure 6.15. Red reflector is base event mapped in Figure 6.14. (P, part of line 22, 1971 courtesy of Geophysical Service Incorporated; part of line 120, 1972 courtesy of Seiscan-Delta Limited. Q, courtesy of Institute of Oceanographic Sciences, U.K., as reported in Parson et al., 1985).

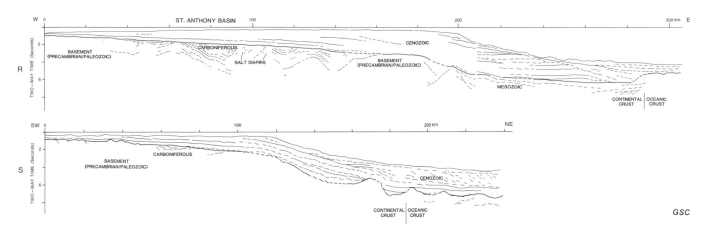

Figure 6.25. Cross sections (R, S) of the continental margin northeast of Newfoundland. Locations shown in Figure 6.15. Red reflector is base event mapped in Figure 6.14. (R, part of line 14, 1971 courtesy of Geophysical Service Incorporated; part of line R20250, Imperial Oil, 1972 courtesy of Esso Resources Canada Limited. S, line 121, 1972 courtesy of Seiscan-Delta Limited).

continent-ocean boundary in this region. Srivastava and Tapscott (1986) illustrated the evidence for the identification of anomaly 34 in the area of these profiles.

Beneath the unconformity on the continental shelf northeast of Newfoundland, seismic data show substantial thicknesses of sedimentary strata. The Hare Bay E-21 well (Fig. 6.1), in the St. Anthony Basin near section R (Fig. 6.25), terminated at 4874 m in Carboniferous beds (B.P. Exploration Canada Ltd., 1979). Carboniferous rocks have also been recovered from shallow drillholes to the west, close to shore (Haworth et al., 1976a, b; Barss et al., 1979). Diapiric structures affecting these sediments northeast of Newfoundland have been attributed to salt flowage (Grant, 1975; Cutt and Laving, 1977). Cretaceous and Tertiary sediments overlying the unconformity thicken gradually seaward. In the Hare Bay E-21 well the oldest sediments above the unconformity are Campanian (F.M. Gradstein, pers. comm., 1979).

Geology

The base event map (Fig. 6.14) is used as a datum for interpreting subcrop geology from seismic character (Fig. 6.26). The units in Figure 6.26 are intentionally broad because of the interpretive nature of this diagram, especially in off-shelf areas; the profiles in the preceeding section indicate the subsurface relationships of these units. Subcrop interpretation is constrained by well data in the area of exploratory drilling, but is increasingly interpretative with distance from well control. Geology of "basement" has been inferred by extrapolating from land geology, incorporating information from offshore samples, and by interpreting geophysical character (mainly seismic and magnetic). On Flemish Cap and at Virgin Rocks seismic profiling and bedrock coring have confirmed that Precambrian rocks are exposed at the seafloor (Lilly, 1966; Pelletier, 1971; King et al., 1985). King et al. (1986) have mapped Paleozoic strata west of Virgin Rocks, and Haworth et al. (1976a, b) have mapped Precambrian and Paleozoic rocks northeast of Newfoundland. The volcanic origin of several of the seamounts south of the Grand Banks has been confirmed by dredging (Sullivan, 1978).

Figure 6.26 shows Mesozoic sediments subcropping in the basins beneath the central Grand Banks. Considerable section was eroded from this zone as a result of Cretaceous uplift (the Avalon Uplift). Locally, Triassic-Jurassic evaporites reach the base event surface at piercement structures in these basins and in the South Whale Subbasin and the northern extension of the Jeanne d'Arc Basin, and Triassic redbeds are exposed in some areas along the margins of the Whale and Horseshoe basins and the southern extension of the Jeanne d'Arc Basin. The margins of the basins on the Grand Banks (Fig. 6.26) are generally drawn along faults; in some areas the seismic data indicate that sedimentary strata extend beyond these faults, so that parts of the peneplain between the basins in Figure 6.26 probably are underlain by Mesozoic or Paleozoic sedimentary rocks.

In deeper parts of the region, such as the East Newfoundland Basin and the slope-rise zone south of the Grand Banks (Fig. 6.15), dipping and truncated seismic reflectors in basement structures indicate that the basement rocks are composed of deformed sediments and that considerable section has been removed by erosion. The Blue H-28 exploratory well bottomed in Carboniferous strata (M.S. Barss, pers. comm., 1983) on the south end of an elongate ridge (Fig. 6.26). Accordingly, this feature is considered to be composed of Carboniferous rocks (Fig. 6.26). An interpreted seamount occurs on this same ridge about 100 km to the north-northeast; a closer contour interval would define this structure. The seamount slightly west of 51°N, 49°W is superimposed on the base event surface (Fig. 6.14), and therefore is assumed to postdate this surface. Examples of apparent changes in geology along structural trends in Figure 6.26 express the fact that the structural trends mapped in Figure 6.15 are superimposed on older geology. Contacts between basement rock units subcropping at the base event surface might provisionally be projected along the axes of the deeps between these basement highs (Fig. 6.15). Jurassic rocks may occur in some of these deeps, but their extent is obscured by the overlying Cretaceous strata.

Triassic-Jurassic rocks are inferred to extend as a component of "basement" northward through Orphan Knoll

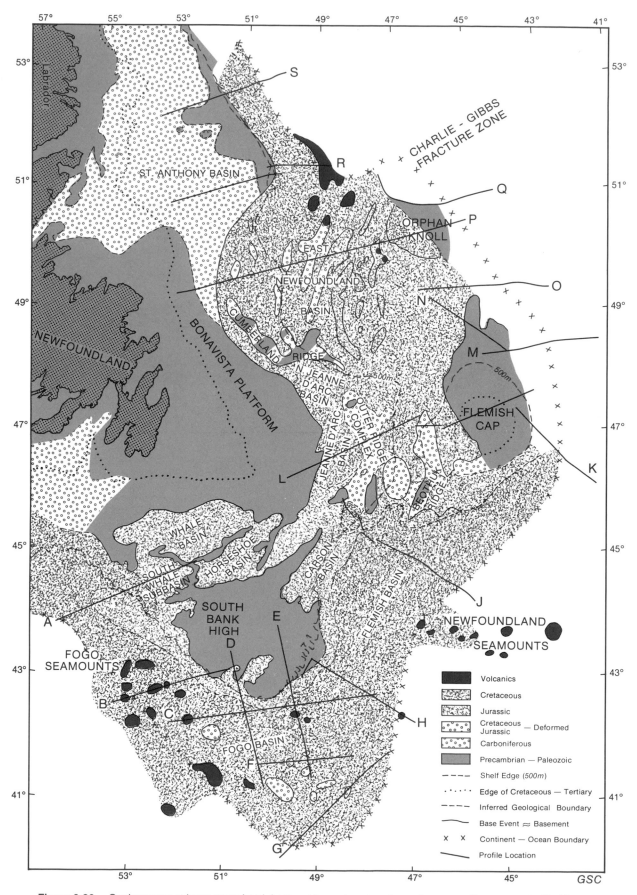

Figure 6.26. Geology map at base event level. Lettered lines show locations of cross sections presented in Figures 6.18 to 6.25. Red dashed line is the 500 m water depth contour.

(Fig. 6.26). Jurassic (Bajocian) sediments drilled on Orphan Knoll support this interpretation (Laughton et al., 1972). Structures on seismic records from the East Newfoundland Basin possibly related to salt flowage may also support this interpretation, although salt, if present, could be older than Triassic-Jurassic; Carboniferous salt occurs in the St. Anthony Basin on the shelf northeast of Newfoundland (Haworth et al., 1976a, b; Cutt and Laving, 1977). Alternatively, evaporites in this area might be Permian in age, by analogy with Zechstein evaporites in northwest Europe (Zeigler, 1981).

Multichannel seismic data show gently dipping reflectors beneath the base event surface on the Newfoundland Ridge. Grant (1979) compared the character of these reflectors to that of Mesozoic strata on the Grand Banks. This interpretation contrasts with earlier suggestions (e.g. Auzende et al., 1970; Watson and Johnson, 1970; Sullivan and Keen, 1978) that the Newfoundland Ridge is composed of oceanic crust, and it poses important constraints on pre-drift reconstructions of this part of the North Atlantic.

Although substantial amounts of section have been removed by erosion, Figure 6.26 shows remnants of a northeast-trending Jurassic seaway that extended across the Grand Banks, and turned northward to the east of Newfoundland. Jansa and Wade (1975) and Swift and Williams (1980) have sketched the original boundaries of this seaway, showing the South Bank High and Flemish Cap as positive areas to the southeast and east. Figure 6.26 shows Jurassic rocks flanking the South Bank High to the south, indicating that this may have been an insular feature in Jurassic time, and that the Jurassic seaway extended south of the Grand Banks through Fogo Basin to Carson Basin. Late Jurassic fauna in the Bonnition H-32 well have more "open Atlantic" affinities than coeval fauna in the Jeanne d'Arc Basin (P. Ascoli, pers. comm., 1986).

Orphan Knoll is depressed now relative to Flemish Cap and the south Grand Banks, but Carboniferous (continental) clastics recovered at DSDP Site 111 (Laughton et al., 1972), Ordovician limestone in a dredge haul (Legault, 1982), and physiographic evidence of a pre-Jurassic (Devonian?) landscape surviving there (Parson et al., 1984) indicate that Orphan Knoll may be an ancient continental landmass. As drawn in Figure 6.26 the axis of Jurassic deposition may extend northward on the west side of Orphan Knoll. It is not apparent from basement seismic character that the Jurassic seaway extended eastward between Flemish Cap and Orphan Knoll, but it is emphasized that differential vertical displacements throughout this region, which appear to be at least partly independent of pre-existing geology, have obscured and complicated the evidence. To the west, Jurassic rocks occur beneath Cretaceous strata southwest of Cumberland Ridge, and are suspected at depth between basement highs north of Cumberland Ridge.

The identification of geological units in Figure 6.26 is particularly speculative in the area of complex geology southwest of Flemish Cap. Apart from some relatively small zones of highly reflective basement tentatively designated "Paleozoic-Precambrian", seismic data indicate that the basement media in this area are mainly composed of deformed sedimentary rocks. Grant (1972) compared the seismic character of rocks underlying Beothuk Ridge to that of Carboniferous strata in the St.

Anthony Basin northeast of Newfoundland. No sample data have been acquired to refute this suggestion, hence the indication (Fig. 6.26) that Carboniferous rocks occur beneath the southwest flank of Flemish Cap. Obviously there is a need for bedrock sampling to resolve the geology of this area.

The continent-ocean crustal boundary drawn in Figure 6.26 is the minimum seaward extent of interpreted "continental" character on reflection seismic data (see profiles in Fig. 6.18 to 6.25). Southeast and southwest of the Grand Banks this boundary tends to lie seaward of that interpreted from refraction seismic data (e.g. I. Reid, pers. comm., 1987), and raises the question of whether refraction seismic velocities are necessarily diagnostic of crustal origin.

Seamounts occur within areas of inferred continental crust in the East Newfoundland Basin and flank the Fogo Basin south of the Grand Banks (Fig. 6.26). Possibly the latter are emplaced in fault zones bounding Fogo Basin.

PETROLEUM GEOLOGY

Discoveries

Several known and potential hydrocarbon plays have been recognized in the basins on the Grand Banks. These include rollover anticlines associated with listric faults, complex trans-basin fault trends, block-faulted basement structures, halokinetic structures, and stratigraphic traps related to both unconformities and depositional pinchouts. However, significant hydrocarbon accumulations have only been found in Jeanne d'Arc Basin. The 35 wildcat wells drilled there have yielded 15 discoveries for a success ratio approaching one in two (Table 6.2 and Fig. 6.6; see Chapter 12).

Rollover anticlines are of special significance in the Jeanne d'Arc Basin, because the Hibernia oil field is located on one (Fig. 6.8). Subsequent discoveries at Hebron I-13 and Ben Nevis I-45 (Fig. 6.6) are on structural closures related to slippage on low angle faults dipping from the southeast flank of the basin. The Hibernia and Ben Nevis structures also lie at opposite ends of a trans-basin fault trend, which appears to be an important factor both in trap formation and hydrocarbon migration for these accumulations. The exploration successes at Nautilus C-92, South Mara C-13, Mara M-54, West Ben Nevis B-75 and North Ben Nevis P-93 confirm the importance of this trend.

The remaining oil discoveries are located on the faulted eastern flank of the basin proximal to the Outer Ridge Complex (Fig. 6.6). Terra Nova K-08 and Beothuk M-05 are associated with a low-angle listric fault south of the trans-basin fault trend. To the northeast the Whiterose N-22, Trave E-87 and South Tempest G-88 discoveries are on fault blocks that may have been displaced as a result of salt flowage, although deep structural relationships in this area are not readily apparent on available seismic data. Seismic data indicate that the North Dana I-43 well, on the Outer Ridge Complex, is probably located on a block-faulted basement structure. More data on oil discoveries and reserves can be found in Chapter 12.

All proven reservoir beds occur in Upper Jurassic and Lower Cretaceous rift and rift-drift transition sandstones. These reservoirs occur in the Jeanne d'Arc, Hibernia, Catalina, Eastern Shoals, Avalon, and Ben Nevis formations (Fig. 6.10). In the Hibernia P-15 discovery well, the

Table 6.2. Oil and gas discoveries offshore Newfoundland.

WELL (date)	INTERVAL (m)	OIL RATE (m3/d)	GAS RATE (x10³m3/d)	GRAVITY (°API)	REMARKS
Hibernia P-15 (1979)	2422-2443	185.4	11.3	32.2	Avalon Fm.
	3742-3746	321.3	59.5	34.5	Hibernia Fm.
	3805-3822	592.1	124.6	35.5	"
	3841-3845	343.4	51.0	34.7	"
	3852-3858	422.4	53.8	34.9	"
	3898-3905	No flow; rec. saltwater			"
	4113-4129	127.2	14.2	32.1	Jeanne d'Arc Fm;
	4113-4134	89.7	5.7	33.5	overpressured res.
Ben Nevis I-45 (1980)	2378-2446	4 tests; no flow, rec. oil and water			Ben Nevis Fm.
	2891-2894	41.5	291.7	48.1	Eastern Shoals Fm.
	4112-4477	6 tests; fm. tight, rec. trace oil and gas			Hibernia Fm.
	4535-4550	253.7	339.5	38.9	overpressured res.
Hebron I-13 (1981)	1866-1876	121.1	5.7	19.0	Ben Nevis Fm.
	1905-1916	110.2	2.8	13.6	"
	2923-2940	491.4	42.5	29.0	Hibernia Fm.
	3842-3857	848.3	82.1	31.0	Jeanne d'Arc Fm;
	4368-4381	592.2	110.5	36.0	overpressured res.
South Tempest G-88 (1981)	3826-3834	23.1	45.3	39.4	Rankin Fm;
	4041-4049	30.5	8.5	40.7	overpressured res.
	4109-4117	198.7	141.6	42.0	
Nautilus C-92 (1982)	3285-3300	334.0	53.8	31.0	Avalon Fm;
	3325-3336	418.1	68.0	31.3	overpressured res.
	3982-4001	trace condensate	152.9	-	Catalina Fm; overpressured res
North Dana I-43 (1983)	4537-4548	45.3 (condensate)	354.0	51.5	Rankin Fm; overpressured res.
Terra Nova K-08 (1984)	3329-3336	173.8	28.3	35.1	Jeanne d'Arc Fm.
	3380-3397	542.8	73.6	34.9	"
	3410-3423	615.6	73.6	34.6	"
	3530-3544	104.3	8.5	35.1	"
Trave E-87 (1984)	2144-2150	11.8 (condensate)	195.4	71.5	Hibernia Fm.
	2232-2238	82.8 (condensate)	506.9	69.3	"
South Mara C-13 (1984)	2952-2958	275.7	59.5	34.7	Press report
	2926-2932	104.9 (condensate)	399.3	58.7	"
Whiterose N-22 (1985)	2663-2680	107.3 (condensate)	606.1	54	Press report
	2689-2695	25.9 (condensate)	102.0	54	"
	2724-2727	no data	39.6		"
	3542-3554	87.0	11.3	32	"
	3565-3572	57.4	8.5	32	"
Beothuk M-05 (1985)	2740-3061	4 tests; 3 yielded oil Best flow 227.7		31	Press report
Mara M-54 (1985)	1851-1857	98.6	2.8	21.6	Press report
	2403-2408	122.4	8.5	21.5	"
	2704-2708	Minor amounts oil and water		11	"
West Ben Nevis B-75 (1985)	2002-2015	97.3	5.7	28.1	Press report
	2044-2065	rec formation water			"
	2445-2465	340.1	19.8	22.8	"
	4498-4507	954.7	144.4	33.7	"
North Ben Nevis P-93 (1985)	3062-3067	91.6 (condensate)	475.8	-	Press report
	3080-3085	319.6	11.3	34	"
	3091-3095	449.0	25.5	34	"
Fortune G-57 (1986)	3989-4002	215.4	70.8	36	Press report
	4030-4040	107.9	14.2	34.8	"
	4400-4452	786.0	152.9	35.5	"

Jeanne d'Arc Formation consists of fluvial sandstones and conglomerates, with clasts as large as 10 cm in diameter. The average porosity is 10% in this zone. Shallower reservoir beds are finer grained, generally coarse to fine sandstones. Average values of porosities in the Hibernia, Catalina, Avalon and Ben Nevis formations range from 17 to 21%. Potential reservoir quality rocks have also been encountered in clastics and carbonates in the lower part of the Mesozoic section, but in most of the basin these lie beyond the reach of the drill.

Hydrocarbon generation, migration and accumulation

The Jeanne d'Arc Basin is the site of most of the major oil discoveries off eastern Canada. The commercial reserves in this basin reflect the combination of a rich oil-prone source rock (the Egret Member of the Rankin Formation), sufficient thermal maturation, good reservoir beds and hydrocarbon trapping mechanisms, proper timing of trap formation, and good migration pathways. This favourable set of conditions comes from the particular tectonic history of the area following the formation of the source rock, and the resultant stratigraphic record. Similarly favourable conditions have not been found elsewhere off eastern Canada. Although good reservoir rocks are present beneath the Scotian and Labrador shelves, mature oil source rocks have not been found. Potential oil-prone Tertiary source rocks are ubiquitous, but they are usually immature or are not associated with good reservoir beds. Over the axis of the Avalon Uplift the interval containing the Egret Member source rock of the Jeanne d'Arc Basin has been stripped by erosion and coeval rocks in the Eider M-75 well were deposited in a continental to marginal marine environment and are of non-source quality. It has been postulated that, by analogy to the Jeanne d'Arc Basin, Upper Jurassic source rocks could occur in the South Whale Subbasin, but this has not been confirmed (Powell, 1985).

All the hydrocarbons discovered to date in Jeanne d'Arc Basin appear to be of one genetic family that can be typed geochemically to the Egret Member, a calcareous shale and limestone sequence of Kimmeridgian age. This source rock is a distinctive and correlatable unit with geochemical parameters and organic petrographic characteristics different from any other potential source rock encountered in the basin. The hydrocarbon discoveries appear to occur in a predictable geographic pattern related to the subsidence and maturation history of the source rock.

Potential hydrocarbon source rocks in Jeanne d'Arc Basin were described by Bujak et al. (1977a, b). They showed that good potential oil source rocks were deposited in the Late Jurassic, Late Cretaceous and the Tertiary (Fig. 6.27). Lower Cretaceous rocks are a potential gas source. Although the Lower Jurassic Iroquois Formation in the Cormorant N-83 and Murre G-67 wells has a high percentage of amorphous organic material, the potential source rocks are thin and the total organic carbon content is low. The Upper Cretaceous and Tertiary section is generally immature to marginally mature in this basin. Thus the Upper Jurassic rocks have the best potential as a source for oil. This interval is evident in the Egret K-36 and Flying Foam I-13 wells (Fig. 6.27). It coincides with the Egret Member of the Rankin Formation.

Swift and Williams (1980) tentatively correlated geochemically the small amount of oil recovered at the Adolphus 2K-41 well — located on a salt diapir in the deepest part of Jeanne d'Arc Basin — to the Upper Jurassic potential source rock identified at Egret K-36. The Egret Member source rock interval is about 75 to 100 m thick, and appears to be widely correlatable (Fig. 6.28). Further biostratigraphic studies are required to establish whether or not the unit is a coeval deposit. The Flying Foam I-13, North Dana I-43, Terra Nova K-08, and Trave E-87 wells are the only other wells for which data have been released (to year end, 1986), which reached the source rock, although seismic data suggest that several wells in the southern half of the basin may have encountered it (the data on these wells are not yet public).

The Egret Member consists predominantly of shale which is grey or occasionally brown, blocky and calcareous. In the south the member contains interbeds of marl. Carbonaceous material is common and the shale is commonly resinous or waxy. Thinner source beds also occur in a zone up to about 400 m thick, bracketing the main source rock. However, all source beds lie below the Kimmeridgian unconformity within the Rankin Formation. Lithofacies analysis of this broader interval reveals a general but clear geographic distribution. The south is dominated by microcrystalline, light grey to brown, argillaceous and locally oolitic and pelletoidal limestone. The north and northeast is dominated by grey shales grading to siltstone and fine grained sandstone.

Wireline logs respond distinctively to the Egret Member source rock and are useful for identification (Fig. 6.29). The unit is characterized by higher sonic transit time, lower density and higher resistivity than other shaley intervals in the sedimentary sequence. This distinctive log signature is caused by the high organic carbon content and indigenous hydrocarbons in the source unit, and is amplified by undercompaction due to overpressure.

RockEval pyrolysis data also aid identification of the source rock and yield quantitative geochemical parameters that characterize its quality (Fig. 6.30). RockEval is a means of analyzing the organically derived material present in all sedimentary rocks by heating a rock sample to mimic natural thermal maturation. The first two parameters in Figure 6.30 are indices of maturity that generally increase systematically with depth. However, the last four parameters exhibit anomalous readings over the source rock interval. These parameters show that the source rock is very rich in oil-prone type II and type I kerogen and has a very high potential for generating oil. Similar RockEval results for several other wells in the basin indicate that the Egret Member source rock is unique. These results are another example of the fact that prolific marine oil source rocks are not distributed haphazardly in the geological record, but tend to occur in conjunction with worldwide transgressions, when various factors combined to minimize water circulation and led to anoxic conditions favourable to the preservation of organic matter. Such conditions were prevalent during the global highstands of the Late Jurassic and Late Cretaceous. Other notable examples of Late Jurassic oil source rocks occur in the North Sea, West Siberian Basin and Saudi Arabia (Demaison and Moore, 1980).

Geochemical data indicate that all the oils analyzed to date belong to the same genetic family and have a common

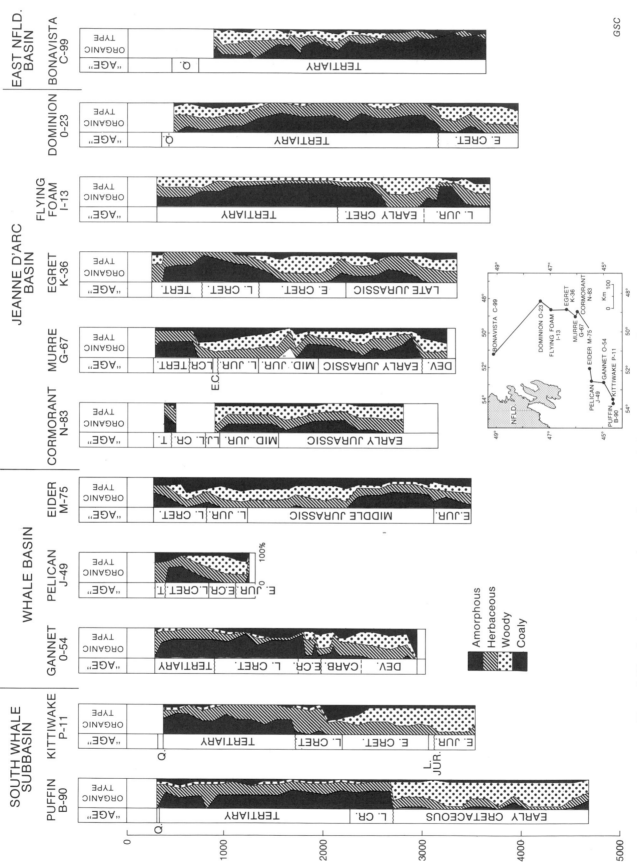

Figure 6.27. Organic matter type by organic petrography in wells drilled on the Grand Banks. The nature of hydrocarbons generated depends on organic matter type. Amorphous organic matter has the highest potential to generate oil while herbaceous, woody and coaly organic matter increasingly produce gas. Organic maturity and amount of organic matter are other factors critical to the ability of a potential source rock to generate hydrocarbons. The combination of these factors in the Late Jurassic suggests this interval has the highest oil source potential. (after Bujak et al., 1977a, b).

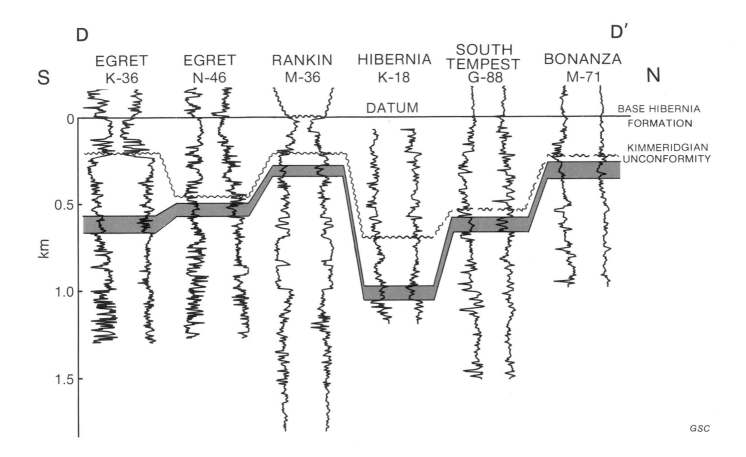

Figure 6.28. Gamma ray and sonic logs for Egret K-36 to Bonanza M-71 showing the Egret Member source rock correlation. Source rock in red. Well locations and line of section DD' are shown in Figure 6.6.

source. Figures 6.31 and 6.32 show examples of two geochemical correlation techniques. Figure 6.31 is a ternary diagram of the normalized composition of C7 compounds in oils from 7 wells in Jeanne d'Arc Basin (Powell, 1984). The large parallelogram covers the same field as the small one in the triangle and the tight-knit group suggests that the oils belong to one family. Figure 6.32 shows fingerprints of sterane biomarkers separated by gas chromatography and mass spectrometry from an extract of the oil source rock and two oils from widely spaced wells. Their striking similarity again indicates that the oils are of one genetic family and that their source was the Egret Member.

Other geochemical data show that, although the oils are similar, they differ in degree of maturity, even in separate pools within a single well. Figure 6.33 is a cross-plot of the ratios of 20S to 20R C_{29} sterane biomarkers and $14\beta17\beta$ to 20R C_{29} sterane biomarkers. On both axes 20R is the same biological compound that isomerizes during maturation to two more stable geological compounds, 20S and $14\beta17\beta$. Both ratios are 0 at the origin, i.e., the time of deposition, and maturity increases upward to the right.

The cross-plots for all oils from the Hebron I-13 well show medium maturity characteristics. The vertical range of drill stem tests (DSTs) in this well is 2500 m and the oils are in at least 3 physically distinct reservoirs. This indicates that the oils entered the reservoirs during the same

phase of migration and that extensive vertical migration occurred. A similar effect is evident for the Hibernia P-15 oils, although the oils there appear to be, on the whole, less mature.

Interesting trends in maturity have shown up in some wells. The oils from Ben Nevis I-45, for instance, show increasing maturity from DST 11 at about 2400 m in the sands of the Ben Nevis Formation to DST 3 at about 4400 m in the Hibernia sands. In other words the oil in the deeper reservoir is more mature. Gasoline range data show similar and also reverse maturity trends in several other wells.

Various scenarios can be envisaged to explain these phenomena, but it is evident that different episodes of oil migration and emplacement have caused vertical variations in maturity between pools. All oil discoveries have been made in the Upper Jurassic to Lower Cretaceous rift and rift-drift transition sequences 3 and 4; the source rock is located very near the top of the stable epeiric basin sequence 2. Therefore, the oil has migrated long distances vertically.

The main mechanism for oil migration appears to be periodic leakage along faults and fractures that have opened sporadically in response to the buildup of abnormally high fluid pressures. Overpressured zones were encountered in the first six discovery wells in Jeanne d'Arc Basin (Fig. 6.34). Three of these wells had to be suspended

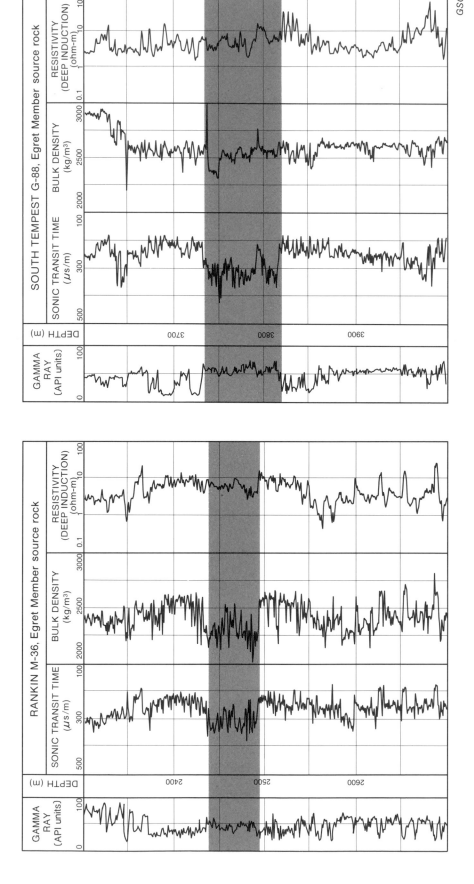

Figure 6.29. Composite log of Egret Member oil source rock for two wells in the Jeanne d'Arc Basin. Well locations in Figure 6.6. The source rock (in red) shows lower sonic velocity, lower density, and higher resistivity than non-source rocks of similar mineralogy and compaction. This distinctive petrophysical signature is characteristic of the Egret Member and this phenomenon can be used to identify and correlate it throughout the basin.

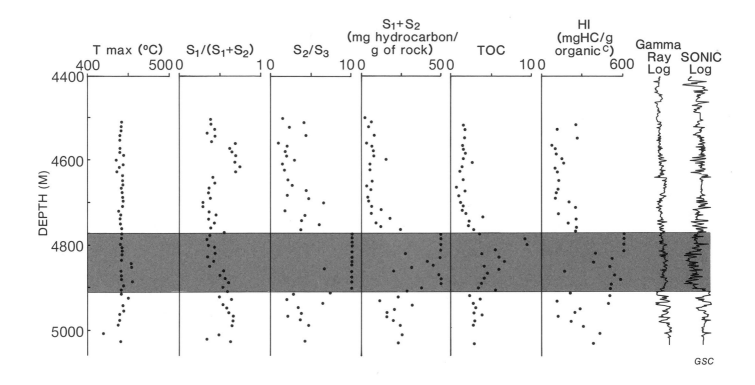

Figure 6.30. RockEval pyrolysis data for the Hibernia K-18 well in the Jeanne d'Arc Basin (see Fig. 6.6), source rock interval coloured red. Pyrolysis consists of heating a rock sample in the absence of oxygen until thermal decomposition of the dispersed organic matter occurs. S1 is indicative of free hydrocarbons that are indigenous or migrated into the sample. S2 represents hydrocarbons produced by thermal conversion of the organic matter and S3 is a measure of the organic carbon dioxide released. TOC is the weight per cent of organic material. HI is the hydrogen index or ratio of S2/TOC. Tmax and S1/(S1 + S2) are organic maturity indicators. The S2/S3 and HI parameters classify kerogen type and the high values over the source rock interval indicate Type I kerogen with a lesser amount of Type II kerogen. The high values of S1 + S2 indicate a good oil generating potential.

short of projected total depth when pressures approached the limits of blow-out prevention. Hydrocarbons have been discovered in both the normally pressured and overpressured hydrodynamic regimes. In Jeanne d'Arc Basin, the top of the overpressured zone occurs generally at or near the top of the laterally continous Fortune Bay Shale. In all cases studied, the overpressures are associated with shale compaction anomalies observed in plots of sonic transit time as a function of depth (Fig. 6.35). Shale transit times in the overpressured zones are considerably above values for normally pressured zones at equivalent depth. This reflects a significant increase in the porosity of the shales, which is due to the inability of the interstitial fluids to escape freely, leading to undercompaction. Consequently, the fluids must support part of the overburden stress and their pressure rises above normal hydrostatic levels. Undercompaction can occur if the sedimentary load increases too rapidly, or if the transmissibility of the rock is too low for fluid to escape.

The primary cause of the undercompaction is probably rapid loading during the initial phase of the second period of rift subsidence. Pressure versus depth plots in many wells show that the pressure within the sealed zone increases more rapidly than would be expected by simple loading, probably because of thermal expansion and hydrocarbon generation. This means that at depth the compressional strength of the shales steadily decreases until they become mobile, causing faults and fractures in the overlying section which become avenues for pressure and fluid escape and oil migration. This process is cyclic because the faults close again after pressure reduction.

Preliminary studies show some evidence of a break in the normal rate of smectite-illite transformation in clays associated with the top of the overpressure zone (L.F. Jansa, pers. comm., 1985). This retardation of clay mineral diagenesis may be a direct consequence of the lack of dewatering in the undercompacted zones and supports the theory that rapid burial causes relatively early development of overpressure.

The timing of hydrocarbon generation and migration in the Jeanne d'Arc Basin has been estimated by determining when the source rock reached thermal maturity. The present-day relationship between maturity and depth was determined from vitrinite reflectance (Ro) measurements for 13 wells in the area. The maturation histories of these wells were estimated by computing time-temperature indices (TTIs) based on biostratigraphic (burial history) and geothermal information (Ervine, 1985). The onset of oil

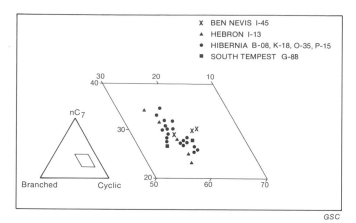

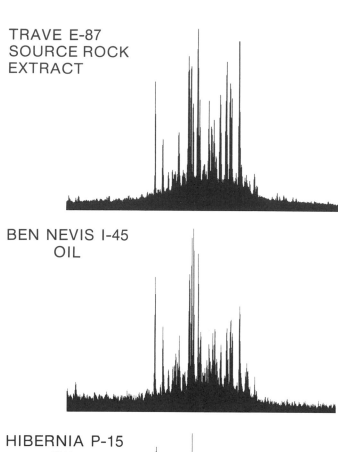

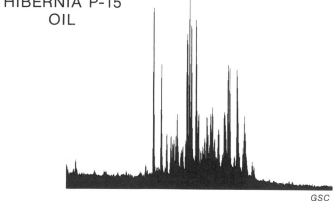

Figure 6.31. Ternary diagram of normalized composition of C7 compounds (hectane) in oils from 7 wells in the Jeanne d'Arc Basin. Well locations in Figure 6.6.

generation for Type II kerogen should occur when the value of Ro is about 0.5. Oil generation reaches a peak at about an Ro value of 0.8, and ends when the value is about 1.2 (Dow, 1977). Correlation beween TTI and Ro values for the 13 wells gives equivalent TTI values of 2, 25, and 240 for onset, peak, and end of oil generation, enabling calculation of thermal maturity in wells where Ro measurements are not available. Plots of these TTI values on diagrams showing burial history curves and temperature grids indicate the times and depths at which the Upper Jurassic source rock had the potential for generating oil at each well location. In the most mature source rock section drilled until now the top of the "oil generative window" (a TTI value of 2) was not reached until the Albian, and peak generation (a TTI value of 25) occurred during the Eocene. Most of the recognized structural and stratigraphic traps in Jeanne d'Arc Basin were formed prior to and during the mid-Cretaceous period of tectonic activity. Therefore, all these traps are prospective for hydrocarbon accumulations where they are suitably located with respect to the Upper Jurassic source rock.

Many of the oil discoveries in Jeanne d'Arc Basin are located on, or adjacent to, the zone of trans-basin faults trending east-southeast from the Hibernia field. Both oil and gas have been discovered on the west side of the basin north of this zone. The reason for this pattern appears to lie in the maturation history of the Egret Member source rock.

A map of the present day thermal gradient of the basin (Fig. 6.36) resembles the map of sediment thickness (Fig. 6.6). The highest thermal gradients are associated with diapiric salt structures that penetrate the sedimentary section to at least the Upper Cretaceous level. This relates to the relatively high thermal conductivity of the salt compared to the low conductivity of the adjacent thick Mesozoic sediments. This effect is probably enhanced by the vertical migration of hot fluids around the diapirs. The low thermal gradients of basin margin wells are thought to reflect the thin Mesozoic-Cenozoic section. Present day thermal gradients, therefore, appear to be structurally controlled and reflect conductivity contrasts.

Figure 6.32. Comparison of the distribution of steranes obtained by GC-MS from an extract of the Egret source rock at the Trave E-87 well and from produced oils at the Ben Nevis I-45 and Hibernia P-15 wells. Well locations in Figure 6.6.

These thermal gradients show good correlation with present-day maturation profiles, based on vitrinite reflectance. High maturation profiles characterize wells with high thermal gradients and vice versa. Figure 6.37 is a map of depth to the top of the oil generative window corresponding to a vitrinite reflectance of 0.5%. It shows that the top of the oil window is deeper where thermal gradients are lower. The same relationship is evident on the map of the base of the oil window, which corresponds to a vitrinite reflectance of 1.35% (Fig. 6.38). These figures provide an understanding of the present day three dimensional configuration of the theoretical oil window.

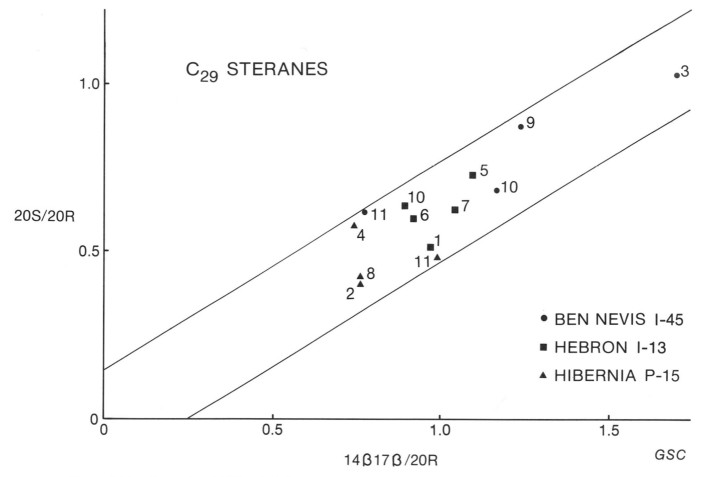

Figure 6.33. Crossplot of 20S to 20R C_{29} sterane biomarkers and $14\beta17\beta$ to 20R C_{29} sterane biomarkers for 3 wells in Jeanne d'Arc Basin. Well locations in Figure 6.6. Numbers refer to drillstem tests.

Since the structural configuration of Jeanne d'Arc Basin was established prior to Late Cretaceous time, the dominant process has been burial beneath a continuously accreting blanket of prograding latest Mesozoic and Tertiary sediments. Today's thermal gradient configuration is therefore likely to have existed throughout the last 100 Ma. If so, the oil generative window that can now be mapped can be assumed to have risen stratigraphically through the section during this period.

Figure 6.39 is a schematic structure map of the top of the source rock that also indicates where the source rock intersects the oil generative window. It is obvious from this map that the "sweet spot" in Jeanne d'Arc Basin is the trans-basin fault trend where many of the oil discoveries represented by the black dots are located, including the giant Hibernia oil field.

As indicated earlier, the main period of movement on the faults occurred during Albian time. At that time the oil generative zone was north of its present day position due to the subsidence pattern of the basin. Thus, there occurred a fortuitous timing of creation of structural traps, hydrocarbon generation and opening of pathways for oil migration. This, combined with an excellent oil-prone source rock, with good porous reservoirs above it, makes the Jeanne d'Arc Basin the best target for oil exploration presently known on the east coast of Canada.

SUMMATION

The plate tectonic framework for the North Atlantic region is a useful model for describing the tectonic and stratigraphic development of the continental margin around Newfoundland. The stratigraphic picture now emerging for the Jeanne d'Arc Basin may provide valuable control for refining the timing of events in the plate tectonic history and assessing their intensity. The geological data base for the Jeanne d'Arc Basin will continue to expand as oil companies follow-up on hydrocarbon discoveries in a variety of structural and stratigraphic settings. Government and industrial research is in progress on all aspects of these data, and results from this work are beginning to appear in the literature (e.g. Ervine, 1985; Hubbard et al., 1985; Avery et al., 1986; Grant et al., 1986a, b; Meneley, 1986; Enachescu, 1987; Grant, 1987; Keen et al., 1987a, b; Tankard and Welsink, 1988).

The regional synthesis of the slope and rise zone in this chapter is based mainly on extrapolation from geological control on the continental shelf using geophysical data. Possibly the most significant result of this synthesis is the indicated variety in the structure of the continental margin, and the general uncertainty in the nature and location of the continent-ocean crustal boundary. A detailed refraction survey on the southwestern margin of the Grand

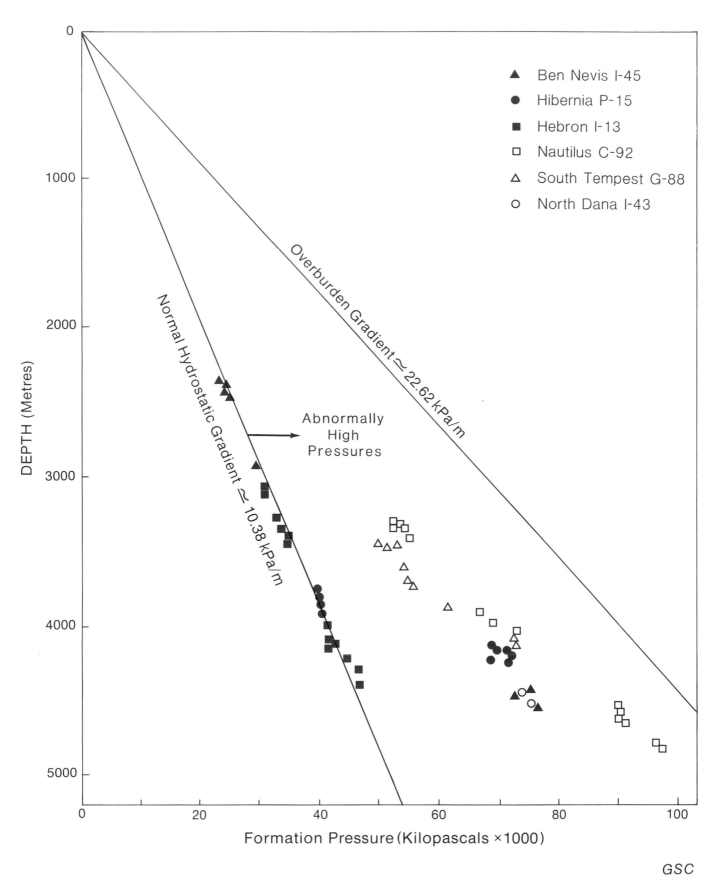

Figure 6.34. Plot of measured pressure versus depth for 8 discovery wells in Jeanne d'Arc Basin.

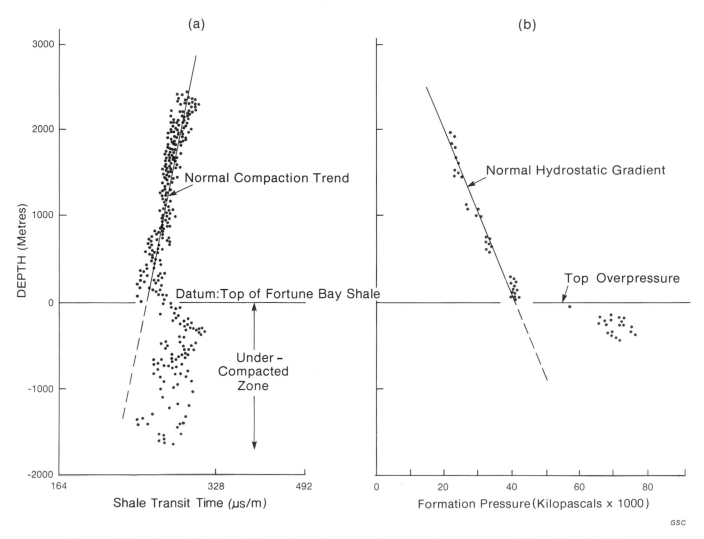

Figure 6.35. Plot of shale transit times (a) and measured pressure in porous rocks (b) for Hibernia B-08, K-18, O-35 and P-15.

Banks shows a surprisingly narrow (20 to 30 km) transition zone between continental- and oceanic-type crust (I. Reid, pers. comm., 1987). This result by itself does not answer the question of whether this was a transform-type margin in the past, but it demonstrates the intensity of refraction seismic coverage that must be focused on these problems to solve them.

Deep reflection (LITHOPROBE) seismic transects of the margin reported by Keen et al. (1987a) reveal additional complexities in the continent-ocean transition zone and, in particular, indicate deep crustal faults associated with some basins on the Grand Banks. These faults appear to flatten at, or near, MOHO depths, and may express crustal extension associated with the formation of these basins. Again, these results demonstrate the need for additional subsurface control of this type to address these crustal-scale problems.

It is clearly of some importance to resolve the questions reiterated above, in order to understand the geology of this region in particular and the processes that form continental margins in general. In view of the present momentum

of geological and geophysical research in this region, the prospects of learning something useful about these questions appear to be excellent.

As most of the geological and geophysical data in the region have been collected in the course of hydrocarbon exploration, it is appropriate to end this section with a comment on the areas and geological settings that may be most favourable for future exploration. The immediately obvious targets are the off-shelf areas of thickest sediments. In general, such areas have already been surveyed by industry, and graded as to their accessibility with current drilling and production technology. However, using the approach of our Figure 6.26, which demonstrates that some of the "basement" structures in these areas may be composed of potentially good source and reservoir rocks, it may be possible to further rank these areas in terms of hydrocarbon prospectivity. For example, a potential area for future exploration is the untested Fogo Basin south of the Grand Banks. Although it lies in relatively deep water, this may be the largest of the Mesozoic basins beneath the Newfoundland continental margin.

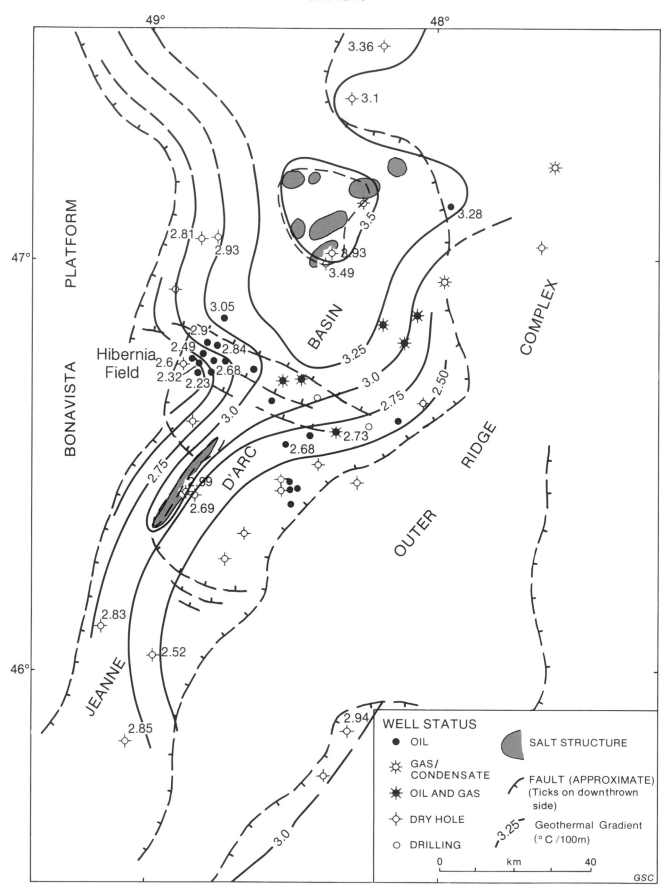

Figure 6.36. Geothermal gradient map of the Jeanne d'Arc Basin (degrees C/100 m).

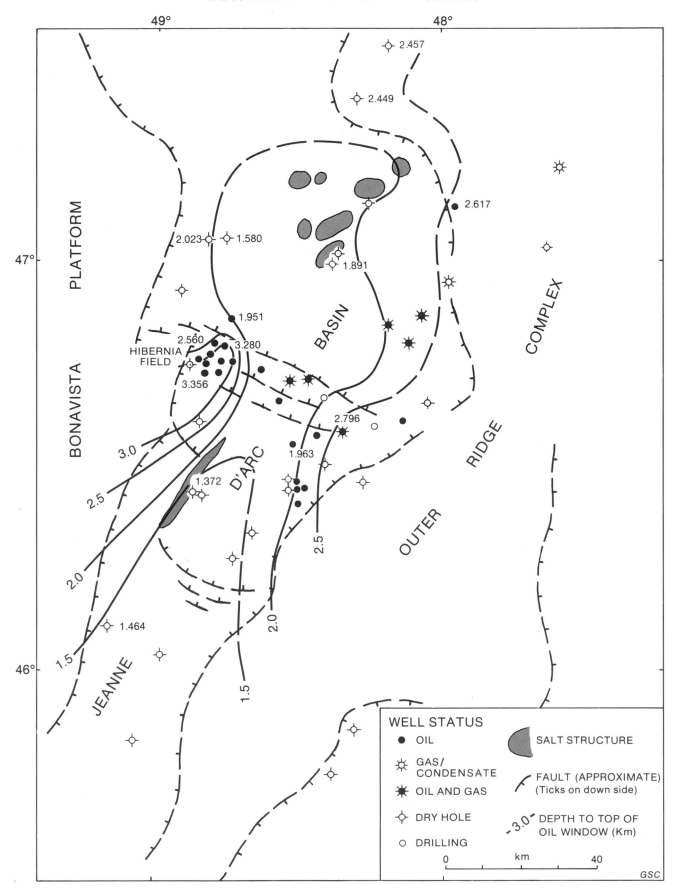

Figure 6.37 Depth to top of the oil window (0.5 Ro) in the Jeanne d'Arc Basin.

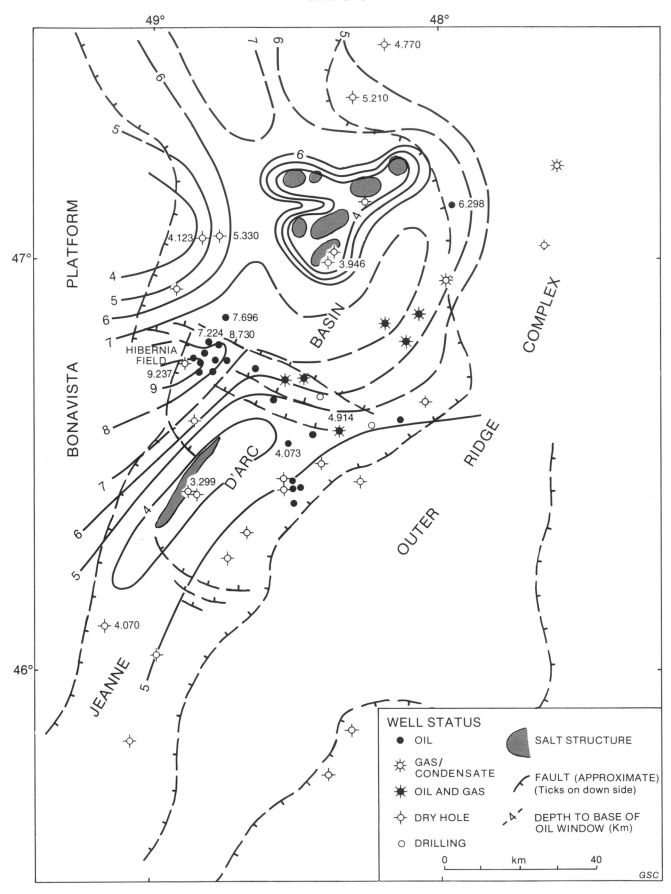

Figure 6.38. Depth to base of the oil window (1.35 Ro) in the Jeanne d'Arc Basin.

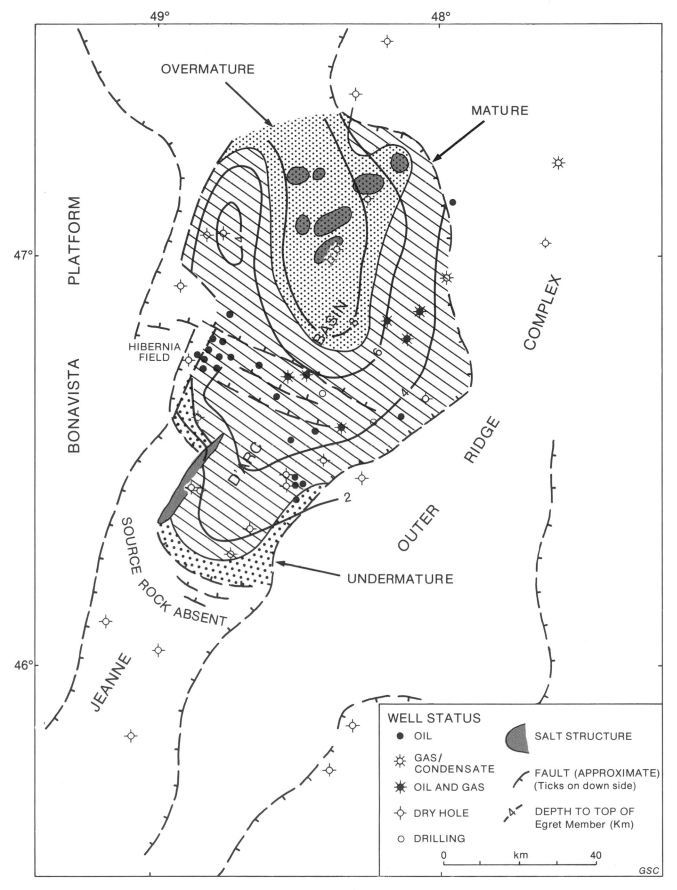

Figure 6.39. Depth to top of Egret Member oil source rock in the Jeanne d'Arc Basin. Small red dots indicate where source rock is overmature, hachuring where it is within the oil window, and large red dots where source rock has not reached sufficient organic maturity to generate oil.

On the continental shelf vast areas remain to be explored in a stratigraphic context, including areas that are structurally complex. Exploration for these more subtle traps will entail extensive, detailed geophysical surveying and judicious drilling. We anticipate that exploration on the margin around Newfoundland will continue to be scientifically exciting and ultimately will be economically rewarding.

ACKNOWLEDGMENTS

We have drawn extensively on the knowledge of our colleagues in the Eastern Petroleum Geology Subdivision (Atlantic Geoscience Centre) in preparing this chapter and we are pleased to acknowledge their contribution. E.H. Davies provided valuable biostratigraphic input in the early stages of this work.

REFERENCES

Amoco Canada Petroleum Company Ltd.
1973a: Amoco-Imperial-Skelly Brant P-87; Well History Report; Canada Oil and Gas Lands Administration, Energy, Mines and Resources Canada.
1973b: Amoco-Imperial-Skelly Mallard M-45; Well History Report; Canada Oil and Gas Lands Administration, Energy, Mines and Resources Canada.
1974: Amoco-Imperial-Skelly Twillick G-49; Well History Report; Canada Oil and Gas Lands Administration, Energy, Mines and Resources Canada.

Amoco Canada Petroleum Company Ltd. and Imperial Oil Ltd.
1973: Regional geology of the Grand Banks; Bulletin of Canadian Petroleum Geology, v. 21, p. 479-503.

Arthur, K.R., Cole, D.R., Henderson, G.G.L., and Kushnir, D.W.
1982: Geology of the Hibernia discovery; in The Deliberate Search for the Subtle Trap, ed. M.T. Halbouty; American Association of Petroleum Geologists, Memoir 32, p. 181-196.

Auzende, J.M., Olivet, J.L., and Bonnin, J.
1970: La marge du Grand Banc et la fracture de Terre-Neuve; Comptes Rendus de l'Académie des Sciences, Paris, Séries D, v. 271, p. 1063-1066.

Avery, M.P., Bell, J.S., and McAlpine, K.D.
1986: Vitrinite reflectance measurements and their implications for oil and gas exploration in the Jeanne d'Arc Basin, Grand Banks, eastern Canada; in Current Research, Part A; Geological Survey of Canada, Paper 86-1A, p. 489-498.

Balkwill, H.R. and Fox, F.G.
1982: Incipient rift zone, western Sverdrup Basin, Arctic Canada; in Arctic Arctic Geology and Geophysics, ed. A.F. Embry and H.R. Balkwill; Canadian Society of Petroleum Geologists, Memoir 8, p. 171-187.

Barss, M.S., Bujak, J.P., and Williams, G.L.
1979: Palynological zonation and correlation of sixty-seven wells, eastern Canada; Geological Survey of Canada Paper 78-24, 118 p.

Bartlett, G.A. and Smith, L.
1971: Mesozoic and Cenozoic history of the Grand Banks of Newfoundland; Canadian Journal of Earth Sciences, v. 8, p. 65-84.

Benteau, R.T. and Sheppard, M.G.
1982: Hibernia — a petrophysical and geological review; Journal of Canadian Petroleum Technology, v. 21, p. 59-72.

B.P. Exploration Canada Ltd.
1979: Hare Bay E-21, Well History Report; Canada Oil and Gas Lands Administration, Energy, Mines and Resources Canada, 77 p.

Bujak, J.P., Barss, M.S., and Williams, G.L.
1977a: Offshore eastern Canada — Part I, Organic type and colour and hydrocarbon potential; Oil and Gas Journal, v. 75, no. 14, p. 198-202.
1977b: Offshore eastern Canada — Part II, Organic type and colour and hydrocarbon potential; Oil and Gas Journal, v. 75, no. 15, p. 96-100.

Canada-Newfoundland Offshore Petroleum Board
1986: Decision 86.01: application for approval; Hibernia Canada-Newfoundland Benefits Plan, Hibernia Development Plan; Canada-Newfoundland Offshore Petroleum Board, St. John's, Newfoundland, June, 1986, 121 p.

Cutt, B.J., Laving, J.G.
1977: Tectonic elements and geologic history of south Labrador and Newfoundland continental shelf; Bulletin of Canadian Petroleum Geology, v. 25, p. 1037-1058.

Davies, E.H.
1986: The correlation and geohistory of the Hibernia field; Abstract in, Program and abstracts for the Canadian Society of Petroleum Geologists 1986 Convention, Calgary.

Demaison, G.J. and Moore, G.T.
1980: Anoxic environments and oil source bed genesis; American Association of Petroleum Geologists Bulletin, v. 64, n. 8, p. 1179-1209.

Dow, W.G.
1977: Kerogen studies and geological interpretations; Journal of Geochemical Exploration, v. 7, p. 79-99.

Enachescu, M.E.
1987: The tectonic and structural framework of the northwest Newfoundland continental margin; in Sedimentary Basins and Basin-Forming Mechanisms, ed. C. Beaumont and A.J. Tankard; Canadian Society of Petroleum Geologists, Memoir 12, p. 117-145.

Ervine, W.B.
1985: A synthesis of hydrocarbon maturation data for the East Newfoundland Basin; Geological Survey of Canada, Open File 1178, 105 p.

Gradstein, F.M. and Williams, G.L.
1981: Stratigraphic charts of the Labrador and Newfoundland shelves; Geological Survey of Canada, Open File 826.

Gradstein, F.M., Grant, A.C. and Jansa, L.F.
1977: Grand Banks and J-Anomaly Ridge; a geological comparison; Science, v. 197, p. 1074-1076.

Gradstein, F.M., Williams, G.L., Jenkins, W.A.M., and Ascoli, P.
1975: Mesozoic and Cenozoic stratigraphy of the Atlantic continental margin, eastern Canada; in Canada's Continental Margins and Offshore Petroleum Exploration, ed. C.J. Yorath, E.R. Parker and D.J. Glass; Canadian Society of Petroleum Geologists, Memoir 4, p. 103-131.

Grant, A.C.
1972: The continental margin off Labrador and eastern Newfoundland; morphology and geology: Canadian Journal of Earth Sciences, v. 9, p. 1394-1430.
1975: Structural modes of the western margin of the Labrador Sea; Geological Survey of Canada, Paper 74-30, p. 217-231.
1979: Geophysical observations bearing upon the origin of the Newfoundland Ridge; Tectonophysics, v. 59, p. 71-82.
1980: Problems with plate tectonics; the Labrador Sea; Bulletin of Canadian Petroleum Geology, v. 28, p. 252-278.
1987: Inversion tectonics on the continental margin east of Newfoundland; Geology, v. 15, p. 845-848.

Grant, A.C., McAlpine, K.D., and Wade, J.A.
1986a: The continental margin of Eastern Canada — geological framework and petroleum potential; in Future Petroleum Provinces of the World, ed. M.T. Halbouty; American Association of Petroleum Geologists, Memoir 40, p. 177-205.
1986b: Offshore geology and petroleum potential of Eastern Canada; Energy Exploration and Exploitation, v. 4, p. 5-52.

Handyside, D.D. and Chipman, W.I.
1983: A preliminary study of the Hibernia field; Journal of Canadian Petroleum Technology, v. 22, p. 67-78.

Haworth, R.T.
1981: Geophysical expression of Appalachian-Caledonide structures on the continental margins of the North Atlantic; in Geology of the North Atlantic Borderlands, ed. J.W. Kerr and A.J. Fergusson; Canadian Society of Petroleum Geologists, Memoir 7, p. 429-446.

Haworth, R.T., Poole, W.H., Grant, A.C., and Sanford, B.V.
1976a: Marine geoscience survey northeast of Newfoundland; in Report of Activities, Part A, Geological Survey of Canada, Paper 76-1A, p. 7-15.

Haworth, R.T., Grant, A.C., and Folinsbee, R.A.
1976b: Geology of the continental shelf off southeastern Labrador; in Current Research, Part C; Geological Survey of Canada, Paper 76-1C, p. 61-70.

Helwig, J., Aronson, J., and Day, D.S.
1974: A Late Jurassic mafic pluton in Newfoundland; Canadian Journal of Earth Sciences, v. 11, p. 1314-1319.

Hodych, J.P. and Hayatsu, A.
1980: K-Ar isochron age and paleomagnetism of diabase along the trans-Avalon aeromagnetic lineament; evidence of Late Triassic rifting in Newfoundland; Canadian Journal of Earth Sciences, v. 17, p. 491-499.

Houghton, R.L., Thomas, J.E., Diecchio, R.J., and Tagliacozzo, A.
1979: Radiometric ages of basalts from DSDP Leg 43: Sites 382 and 385 (New England Seamounts), 384 (J-Anomaly), 386 and 387 (Central and Western Bermuda Rise); in Initial Reports of the Deep Sea Drilling Program, Volume 43, ed. B.E. Tucholke et al.; United States Government Printing Office, Washington, v. 43, p. 739-753.

Hubbard, R.J., Pape, J., and Roberts, D.G.
1985: Depositional sequence mapping to illustrate the evolution of a passive continental margin; in Seismic Stratigraphy II, ed. O.R. Berg and D.C. Woolverton; American Association of Petroleum Geologists, Memoir 39, p. 93-115.

Jansa, L.F. and Pe-Piper, G.
1986: Geology and geochemistry of Middle Jurassic and early Cretaceous igneous rocks on the eastern North American Continental Shelf; Geological Survey of Canada, Open File 1351, 104 p.

Jansa, L.F., and Wade, J.A.
1975: Geology of the continental margin off Nova Scotia and Newfoundland; Geological Survey of Canada, Paper 74-30, p. 51-105.

Keen, C.E., and Barrett, D.L.
1981: Thinned and subsided continental crust on the rifted margin of eastern Canada: crustal structure, thermal evolution and subsidence history; Geophysical Journal of the Royal Astronomical Society, v. 65, p. 443-465.

Keen, C.E., Boutilier, R., de Voogd, B., Mudford, B., and Enachescu, M.
1987a: Crustal geometry and models of the evolution of the rift basins on the Grand Banks of Eastern Canada; constraints from deep seismic data; in Sedimentary Basins and Basin-Forming Mechanisms, ed. C. Beaumont and A.J. Tankard; Canadian Society of Petroleum Geologists, Memoir 12, p. 101-115.

Keen, C.E., Stockmal, G., Welsink, H., Quinlan, G., and Mudford, B.
1987b: Deep crustal structure and evolution of the rifted margin northeast of Newfoundland; results from LITHOPROBE EAST; Canadian Journal of Earth Sciences, v. 24, p. 1537-1549.

King, L.H., Fader, G.B., Poole, W.H., and Wanless, R.K.
1985: Geological setting and age of the Flemish Cap granodiorite; Canadian Journal of Earth Sciences, v. 22, p. 1286-1298.

King, L.H., Fader, G.B., Jenkins, W.A.M., and King, E.L.
1986: Occurrence and regional setting of Paleozoic sediments on the Grand Banks of Newfoundland; Canadian Journal of Earth Sciences, v. 23, p. 504-526.

Klitgord, K.D. and Schouten, H.
1986: Plate kinematics of the central Atlantic; in The Western North Atlantic region, ed. P.R. Vogt and B.E. Tucholke; Geological Society of America, The Geology of North America, Volume M, p. 351-378.

Laughton, A.S., Berggren, W.A., et al. (editors)
1972: Initial Reports Deep Sea Drilling Project, Volume 12; United States Government Printing Office, Washington, 1243 p.

Legault, J.A.
1982: First report of Ordovician (Caradoc-Ashgill) palynomorphs from Orphan Knoll, Labrador Sea; Canadian Journal of Earth Sciences, v. 19, p. 1851-1856.

LePichon, X. and Fox, P.J.
1971: Marginal offsets, fracture zones and the early opening of the North Atlantic; Journal of Geophysical Research, v. 76, p. 6294-6308.

Lilly, H.D.
1966: Late Precambrian and Appalachian tectonics in the light of submarine exploration on the Great Bank of Newfoundland and in the Gulf of St. Lawrence; preliminary views; American Journal of Science, v. 264, p. 569-574.

Masson, D.G. and Miles, P.R.
1984: Mesozoic seafloor spreading between Iberia, Europe and North America; Marine Geology, v. 56, p. 279-287.
1986a: Structure and development of the Porcupine Seabight sedimentary basin, offshore southwest Ireland; American Association of Petroleum Geologists Bulletin, v. 70, no. 5, p. 536-548.
1986b: Development and hydrocarbon potential of Mesozoic sedimentary basins around margins of North Atlantic; American Association of Petroleum Geologists Bulletin, v. 70, no. 5, p. 721-729.

McIver, N.L.
1972: Cenozoic-Mesozoic stratigraphy of the Nova Scotia shelf; Canadian Journal of Earth Sciences, v. 9, p. 54-70.

McKenzie, R.M.
1980: The Hibernia structure; Oilweek, December 15, 1980, p. 59.

McMillan, N.J.
1982: Canada's east coast: the new super petroleum province; Journal of Canadian Petroleum Technology, v. 21, p. 1-15.

McWhae, J.R.H.
1981: Structure and spreading history of the northwestern Atlantic region from the Scotian Shelf to Baffin Bay; in Geology of the North Atlantic Borderlands, ed. J.W. Kerr and A.J. Ferguson; Canadian Society of Petroleum Geologists, Memoir 7, p. 299-332.

McWhae, J.R.H. and Michel, W.F.E.
1975: Stratigraphy of Bjarni H-81 and Leif M-48, Labrador Shelf; Bulletin of Canadian Petroleum Geology, v. 23, p. 361-382.

McWhae, J.R.H., Elie, R., Laughton, K.C., and Gunther, P.R.
1980: Stratigraphy and petroleum prospects of the Labrador Shelf; Bulletin of Canadian Petroleum Geology, v. 28, p. 460-488.

Meneley, R.A.
1986: Oil and gas fields in the east coast and Arctic basins of Canada; in Future Petroleum Provinces of the World, ed. M.T. Halbouty; American Association of Petroleum Geologists, Memoir 40, p. 143-176.

Naylor, D. and Shannon, I.P.M.
1982: Geology of offshore Ireland and west Britain; London, Graham and Trotman, 161 p.

Palmer, A.R.
1983: The decade of North American geology, 1983 geologic time scale; The Geological Society of America.

Parson, L.M., Masson, D.G., Rothwell, R.G., and Grant, A.C.
1984: Remnants of a submerged pre-Jurassic (Duvonian?) landscape on Orphan Knoll, offshore eastern Canada; Canadian Journal of Earth Sciences, v. 21, p. 61-66.

Parson, L.M., Masson, D.G., Pelton, C.D., and Grant, A.C.
1985: Seismic stratigraphy and structure of the east Canadian continental margin between 41°N and 52°N; Canadian Journal of Earth Sciences, v. 22, p. 686-703.

Pegrum, R.M. and Mounteney, N.
1978: Rift basins flanking North Atlantic Ocean and their relation to North Sea area; American Association of Petroleum Geologists Bulletin, v. 62, no. 3, p. 419-441.

Pe-Piper, G. and Jansa, L.F.
1986: Triassic olivine-normative diabase from Northumberland Strait, eastern Canada; implications for continental rifting; Canadian Journal of Earth Sciences, v. 23, p. 1013-1021.

Pelletier, B.R.
1971: A granodioritic drill core from the Flemish Cap, eastern Canadian continental margin; Canadian Journal of Earth Sciences, v. 8, p. 1499-1503.

Powell, T.G.
1984: Hydrocarbon-source relationships, Jeanne d'Arc and Avalon basins, offshore Newfoundland; Geological Survey of Canada, Open File 1094, 12 p.
1985: Paleogeographic implications for the distribution of Upper Jurassic source beds, offshore eastern Canada; Bulletin of Canadian Petroleum Geology, v. 33, no. 1, p. 116-119.

Scrutton, R.A.
1985: Modelling of magnetic and gravity anomalies at Goban Spur, northeastern Atlantic; in Initial Reports of the Deep Sea Drilling Program, Volume 80, ed. P.C. de Graciansky et al.; United States Government Printing Office, Washington, v. 80, p. 1141-

Sen Gupta, B.K. and Grant, A.C.
1971: Orbitolina, a Cretaceous larger foraminifer, from Flemish Cap: paleoceanographic implications; Science, v. 173, p. 934-936.

Sherwin, D.F.
1973: Scotian Shelf and Grand Banks; in The Future Petroleum Provinces of Canada, ed. R.G. McCrossan; Canadian Society of Petroleum Geologists, Memoir 1, p. 519-559.

Srivastava, S.P.
1978: Evolution of the Labrador Sea and its bearing on the early evolution of the north Atlantic; Geophysical Journal of the Royal Astronomical Society, v. 52, p. 313-357.

Srivastava, S.P. and Tapscott, C.R.
1986: Plate kinematics of the North Atlantic; in The Western North Atlantic Region, ed. P.R. Vogt and B.E. Tucholke; Geological Society of North America, The Geology of North America, Volume M, p. 379-404.

Strong, D.F. and Harris, A.
1974: The petrology of Mesozoic alkaline intrusives of central Newfoundland; Canadian Journal of Earth Sciences, v. 11, p. 1208-1219.

Sullivan, K.D.
1978: The structure and evolution of the Newfoundland Basin, offshore eastern Canada; Ph.D. thesis, Dalhousie University, Halifax, Nova Scotia.

Sullivan, K.D. and Keen, C.E.

1977: Newfoundland Seamounts: petrology and geochemistry; in Volcanic Regimes of Canada, ed. W.R.A. Baragar, L.C. Coleman and J.M. Hall; Geological Association of Canada, Special Paper 16, p. 461-476.

1978: On the nature of the crust in the vicinity of the southeast Newfoundland Ridge; Canadian Journal of Earth Sciences, v. 15, p. 1462-1471.

Surlyk, F.

1977: Mesozoic faulting in East Greenland; in Fault Tectonics in N.W. Europe, ed. R.T.C. Frost and A.J. Dickers; Geologie en Mijnbouw, v. 56, p. 311-327.

Swift, J.H. and Williams, J.A.

1980: Petroleum source rocks, Grand Banks area; in Facts and Principles of World Petroleum Occurrence, ed. A.D. Miall; Canadian Society of Petroleum Geologists Memoir 6, p. 567-588.

Swift, J.H., Switzer, R.W., and Turnbull, W.F.

1975: The Cretaceous Petrel limestone of the Grand Banks, Newfoundland; in Canada's Continental Margins and Offshore Petroleum Exploration, ed. C.J. Yorath, E.R. Parker and D.J. Glass; Canadian Society of Petroleum Geologists, Memoir 4, p. 181-194.

Tankard, A.J. and Welsink, H.J.

1988: Extensional tectonics and stratigraphy of the Mesozoic Grand Banks of Newfoundland; in Triassic-Jurassic Rifting: Continental breakup and the origin of the Atlantic Ocean and passive margins, Part A, Developments in Geotectonics 22, ed. W. Manspeizer, Elsevier, p. 129-165.

Tucholke, B.E. and Fry, V.A.

1985: Basement structure and sediment distribution in the Northwest Atlantic Ocean; American Association of Petroleum Geologists Bulletin, v. 69, p. 2077-2097.

Tucholke, B.E. and Vogt, P.R.

1979: Western North Atlantic: sedimentary evolution and aspects of tectonic history; Initial Reports of the Deep Sea Drilling Project, v. 43, p. 791-825.

Umpleby, D.C.

1979: Geology of the Labrador Shelf; Geological Survey of Canada, Paper 79-13, 34 p.

Upshaw, C.F., Armstrong, W.E., Creath, W.B., Kidson, E.J., and Sanderson, G.A.

1974: Biostratigraphic framework of the Grand Banks; American Association of Petroleum Geologists Bulletin, v. 58, p. 1124-1132.

Wanless, R.K., Stevens, R.D., Lachance, G.R., and Edmonds, C.M.

1967: Age determinations and geologic studies — K-Ar Isotopic ages, Report 7; Geological Survey of Canada, Paper 66-17.

Wanless, R.K., Stevens, R.D., Lachance, G.R., and Rimsaite, R.Y.H.

1965: Age determinations and geological studies, Part 1 — Isotopic ages, Report 5; Geological Survey of Canada, Paper 64-17.

Watson, J.A. and Johnson, G.L.

1970: Seismic studies in the region adjacent to the Grand Banks of Newfoundland; Canadian Journal of Earth Sciences, v. 7, p. 306-316.

Wernicke, B.

1985: Uniform sense simple shear of the continental lithosphere; Canadian Journal of Earth Sciences, v. 22, p. 108-125.

Williams, G.L. and Brideaux, W.W.

1975: Palynological analysis of Late Mesozoic-Cenozoic rocks of the Grand Banks off Newfoundland; Geological Survey of Canada Bulletin 236, 162 p.

Ziegler, P.A.

1975: The geological evolution of the North Sea area in the tectonic framework of northwestern Europe; American Association of Petroleum Geologists Bulletin, v. 59, p. 1073-1097.

1981: Evolution of sedimentary basins in northwest Europe; in Petroleum Geology of the continental shelf of northwest Europe, ed. L.V. Illing and G.D. Hobson; Institute of Petroleum, London, p. 3-39.

Authors' addresses

A.C. Grant
Atlantic Geoscience Centre
Geological Survey of Canada
Bedford Institute of Oceanography
P.O. Box 1006
Dartmouth, Nova Scotia
B2Y 4A2

K.D. McAlpine
Atlantic Geoscience Centre
Geological Survey of Canada
Bedford Institute of Oceanography
P.O. Box 1006
Dartmouth, Nova Scotia
B2Y 4A2

Printed in Canada

Chapter 7

GEOLOGY OF THE LABRADOR SHELF, BAFFIN BAY, AND DAVIS STRAIT

Chapter 7

GEOLOGY OF THE LABRADOR SHELF, BAFFIN BAY, AND DAVIS STRAIT

H.R. Balkwill , N.J. McMillan, B. MacLean, G.L. Williams, and S.P. Srivastava

PART 1: MESOZOIC-CENOZOIC GEOLOGY OF THE LABRADOR SHELF

H.R. Balkwill and N.J. McMillan

INTRODUCTION

The Labrador Basin is an immense, oval tectonic depression in the southern part of the zone of extended cratonic and oceanic crust that connects the Atlantic and Arctic ocean basins (Fig. 7.1). The basin has topographically high, incised, glaciated rims of crystalline Precambrian rocks, which form the coastal margins of Labrador, southern Baffin Island and West Greenland. A wide expanse of deeply subsided oceanic crust, with an uneven basement surface, forms the floor of the basin. A narrow zone of differentially extended, faulted, seaward-inclined, cratonic basement separates the coastal basin rims from the oceanic basement floor.

Labrador Basin contains about four million cubic kilometres of Cretaceous, Tertiary, and Quaternary terrigenous clastic sediments. About half of this material comprises terrace prisms along the Labrador and Greenland cratonic margins; most of this is along the Labrador margin. The other half forms a thick blanket on the deep oceanic basement floor. These clastic sediments were derived from widespread erosion of central Canada, and local erosion of coastal uplands during late Phanerozoic separation of the North American and Greenland crustal plates, and subsidence of the oceanic realm that was generated between them.

Part 1 deals mainly with the upper Phanerozoic rocks comprising the shelf and slope sedimentary prism along the Canadian (Labrador) margin of the Labrador Basin. Except for isolated small outcrops of Lower Cretaceous sediments on Ford's Bight, southern Labrador (King and McMillan, 1975), all of the terrace prism is concealed by the waters of the Labrador Sea. As a consequence, the subsurface geology is interpreted mainly from 31 exploratory wells drilled by the Canadian petroleum industry, and a regional seismic grid of about about 80 000 line kilometres of multi-channel reflection seismic data acquired for petroleum exploration.

PREVIOUS WORK

The Atlantic Geoscience Centre of the Geological Survey of Canada (located at the Bedford Institute of Oceanography in Dartmouth) conducted reconnaissance seismic surveys across the Labrador continental margin in the period 1965-1969, and demonstrated the existence of a major sedimentary wedge. Many surveys have also been carried out subsequently on the Labrador shelf by this organization but these have been more directly concerned with the geology and engineering properties of the Quaternary sediments.

The Atlantic Geoscience Centre since 1971 has also undertaken extensive investigations of the bedrock geology and surficial sediments of the Southeast Baffin Shelf by means of geophysical surveys and shallow borehole sampling. Interest in the petroleum potential of these rocks led to the first permits to explore in 1966. Following extensive aeromagnetic surveys, reflection seismic shooting and bottom sampling, the first well (Leif E-38, Fig. 7.1) was spudded in 1971 (well data in Fig. 1, in pocket).

Grant (1972, 1975a and 1980b), Srivastava (1978), Keen (1979), Royden and Keen (1980), Srivastava et al. (1981), and Roots and Srivastava (1984) have discussed the geology of the Labrador Basin. Some regional multichannel reflection seismic lines acquired in 1977 (Hinz et al., 1979) are especially valuable because they are tied to Labrador Shelf wells and thus provide a means for transbasin stratigraphic correlation. The Labrador Shelf sedimentary terrace prism and its petroleum potential have been described by McMillan (1973), Cutt and Laving (1977), Umpleby (1979), Rashid et al. (1980), McWhae et al. (1980), Klose et al. (1982), and Meneley (1986). For southeast Baffin Shelf in addition to the above see MacLean et al (1977, 1978, 1982, 1986a, b).

Balkwill, H.R., McMillan, N.J., MacLean, B., Williams, G.L., and Srivastava, S.P.
1990: Geology of the Labrador Shelf, Baffin Bay, and Davis Strait, Chapter 7 in Geology of the Continental Margin of Eastern Canada, M.J. Keen and G.L. Williams (ed.); Geological Survey of Canada, Geology of Canada, no. 2, p. 293-348 (also Geological Society of America, The Geology of North America, v. I-1).

Figure 7.1 Major tectonic features and well locations, Labrador Shelf and Davis Strait. Partly after Wade et al. (1977), Sanford et al. (1979), and Balkwill (pers. comm., 1984).

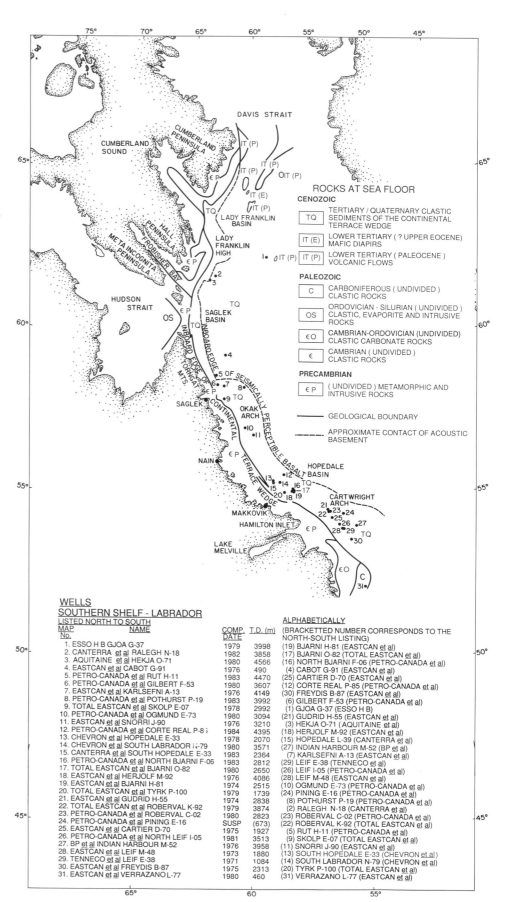

ROCKS AT SEA FLOOR

CENOZOIC

TQ — TERTIARY / QUATERNARY CLASTIC SEDIMENTS OF THE CONTINENTAL TERRACE WEDGE

IT (E) — LOWER TERTIARY (? UPPER EOCENE) MAFIC DIAPIRS

IT (P) — LOWER TERTIARY (PALEOCENE) VOLCANIC FLOWS

PALEOZOIC

C — CARBONIFEROUS (UNDIVIDED) CLASTIC ROCKS

OS — ORDOVICIAN - SILURIAN (UNDIVIDED) CLASTIC, EVAPORITE AND INTRUSIVE ROCKS

ЄO — CAMBRIAN-ORDOVICIAN (UNDIVIDED) CLASTIC CARBONATE ROCKS

Є — CAMBRIAN (UNDIVIDED) CLASTIC ROCKS

PRECAMBRIAN

Є P — (UNDIVIDED) METAMORPHIC AND INTRUSIVE ROCKS

——— GEOLOGICAL BOUNDARY

‑ ‑ ‑ APPROXIMATE CONTACT OF ACOUSTIC BASEMENT

WELLS

SOUTHERN SHELF - LABRADOR

LISTED NORTH TO SOUTH

MAP No.	NAME	COMP. DATE	T.D. (m)
1.	ESSO H B GJOA G-37	1979	3998
2.	CANTERRA et al RALEGH N-18	1982	3858
3.	AQUITAINE et al HEKJA O-71	1980	4566
4.	EASTCAN et al CABOT G-91	1976	490
5.	PETRO-CANADA et al RUT H-11	1983	4470
6.	PETRO-CANADA et al GILBERT F-53	1980	3607
7.	EASTCAN et al KARLSEFNI A-13	1976	4149
8.	PETRO-CANADA et al POTHURST P-19	1983	3992
9.	TOTAL EASTCAN et al SKOLP E-07	1978	2992
10.	PETRO-CANADA et al OGMUND E-73	1980	3094
11.	EASTCAN et al SNORRI J-90	1976	3210
12.	PETRO-CANADA et al CORTE REAL P-85	1984	4395
13.	CHEVRON et al HOPEDALE E-33	1978	2070
14.	CHEVRON et al SOUTH LABRADOR N-79	1980	3571
15.	CANTERRA et al SOUTH HOPEDALE E-33	1983	2364
16.	PETRO-CANADA et al NORTH BJARNI F-06	1983	2812
17.	TOTAL EASTCAN et al BJARNI O-82	1980	2650
18.	EASTCAN et al HERJOLF M-92	1976	4086
19.	EASTCAN et al BJARNI H-81	1974	2515
20.	TOTAL EASTCAN et al TYRK P-100	1979	1739
21.	EASTCAN et al GUDRID H-55	1974	2838
22.	TOTAL EASTCAN et al ROBERVAL K-92	1979	3874
23.	PETRO-CANADA et al ROBERVAL C-02	1980	2823
24.	PETRO-CANADA et al PINING E-16	SUSP	(673)
25.	EASTCAN et al CARTIER D-70	1975	1927
26.	PETRO-CANADA et al NORTH LEIF I-05	1981	3513
27.	BP et al INDIAN HARBOUR M-52	1976	3958
28.	EASTCAN et al LEIF M-48	1973	1880
29.	TENNECO et al LEIF E-38	1971	1084
30.	EASTCAN et al FREYDIS B-87	1975	2313
31.	EASTCAN et al VERRAZANO L-77	1980	460

ALPHABETICALLY

(BRACKETTED NUMBER CORRESPONDS TO THE NORTH-SOUTH LISTING)

(19) BJARNI H-81 (EASTCAN et al)
(17) BJARNI O-82 (TOTAL EASTCAN et al)
(16) NORTH BJARNI F-06 (PETRO-CANADA et al)
(4) CABOT G-91 (EASTCAN et al)
(25) CARTIER D-70 (EASTCAN et al)
(12) CORTE REAL P-85 (PETRO-CANADA et al)
(30) FREYDIS B-87 (EASTCAN et al)
(6) GILBERT F-53 (PETRO-CANADA et al)
(1) GJOA G-37 (ESSO H B)
(21) GUDRID H-55 (EASTCAN et al)
(3) HEKJA O-71 (AQUITAINE et al)
(18) HERJOLF M-92 (EASTCAN et al)
(15) HOPEDALE L-39 (CANTERRA et al)
(27) INDIAN HARBOUR M-52 (BP et al)
(7) KARLSEFNI A-13 (EASTCAN et al)
(29) LEIF E-38 (TENNECO et al)
(26) LEIF I-05 (PETRO-CANADA et al)
(28) LEIF M-48 (EASTCAN et al)
(10) OGMUND E-73 (PETRO-CANADA et al)
(24) PINING E-16 (PETRO-CANADA et al)
(8) POTHURST P-19 (PETRO-CANADA et al)
(2) RALEGH N-18 (CANTERRA et al)
(23) ROBERVAL C-02 (PETRO-CANADA et al)
(22) ROBERVAL K-92 (TOTAL EASTCAN et al)
(5) RUT H-11 (PETRO-CANADA et al)
(9) SKOLP E-07 (TOTAL EASTCAN et al)
(11) SNORRI J-90 (EASTCAN et al)
(13) SOUTH HOPEDALE E-33 (CHEVRON et al)
(14) SOUTH LABRADOR N-79 (CHEVRON et al)
(20) TYRK P-100 (TOTAL EASTCAN et al)
(31) VERRAZANO L-77 (EASTCAN et al)

The stratigraphic nomenclature used in this paper is presented in Figure 7.2 and in Figure 5 (in pocket). It is based upon the work of Umpleby (1979) and McWhae et al. (1980), which reflected the stages of subsurface control as exploration of the Labrador Shelf progressed. Umpleby's lithostratigraphic units were based mainly on well data, including cutting samples. McWhae et al. (1980) were able to use seismic data not available to Umpleby. They introduced seismic-stratigraphic sequences to the nomenclature, mapped depositional units, bounded by regional unconformities. With additional wells and improved seismic definition, it is possible now to refine stratigraphic increments beyond this distinction between formations made by McWhae et al. (1980).

DATA BASE

Thirty-one petroleum exploration wells have been drilled on the Labrador Shelf (Fig. 7.1). Leif E-38 and Cabot G-91 were abandoned in upper Tertiary sediments because of engineering difficulties. Verrazano L-77 was abandoned after spudding in and drilling several hundred metres of upper Paleozoic strata. Pining E-16 was suspended in upper Tertiary sediments. Eleven wells penetrated the sedimentary column ending in Precambrian basement; six wells were in Cretaceous or lower Tertiary basalts at total depth.

Only a few conventional cores have been taken in Labrador Shelf wells because of the great expense involved. Sample quality in some wells is poor because of extensive caving from poorly indurated upper Tertiary sediments. Samples were not recovered from the uppermost beds of wells (commonly upper Tertiary) in which surface casing was set.

The first industry seismic data were gathered in 1968. About 80 000 line kilometres of multi-channel reflection seismic data, and a relatively small amount of refraction data have been acquired. There is abundant seismic coverage in the Hopedale Basin and the southern Saglek Basin and significantly less coverage in the northern Saglek Basin and Cumberland Basin. These basins are defined in the next section.

Biostratigraphic determinations and age-assignments of Labrador Shelf strata resulted from studies of well samples by industry paleontologists, and some published reports (Barss et al., 1979; Gradstein and Srivastava, 1980; Gradstein and Williams, 1981).

Radiometric ages of igneous rocks, quoted in this report, are based on whole-rock K-Ar determinations by several laboratories.

TECTONIC SETTING

The Labrador Shelf has first-order attributes that characterize it as an Atlantic-type passive margin (Bally, 1981):
- a nearly flat continental shelf merges with a more steeply inclined continental slope (Fig. 7.3); the inner part of the shelf is an erosional surface developed on Precambrian basement; the outer shelf and slope are constructed of a thick prism of seaward-dipping Cretaceous and younger terrigenous clastics;
- the more landward part of the shelf prism lies on extended cratonic crust, locally containing large, elongate, fault-bounded wedges of Lower Cretaceous and

lower Upper Cretaceous syn-rift clastics; the outer part of the shelf prism lies on (and is intercalated with) thick Cretaceous and lower Tertiary basalts that represent transitional cratonic/oceanic crust, or oceanic crust;
- all of the late Phanerozoic structures can be interpreted as products of crustal (or supra-crustal) extension; there is no evidence of significant lateral compression.

Craton

Good exposures of Precambrian rocks in the incised, high-relief, glaciated uplands of Labrador and southern Baffin Island provide the main evidence for the possible ages and fabrics of pre-rift basement in the adjacent offshore cratonic margin. These Precambrian rocks have been assigned to the Grenville and Churchill provinces, Nain Craton, Burwell, North Keewatin and Hoare Bay terranes, Torngate Orogen, Dorset and Foxe fold belts and Baffin Batholith of the Canadian Shield (Taylor, 1981; P.F. Hoffman, pers. comm., 1987; Map 1705A, in pocket).

The Precambrian Grenville Province of southern Labrador comprises metasedimentary and plutonic rocks with radiometric ages of about 1000 Ma. Structures in this province have strongly developed eastward to southeastward striking foliation, and northward vergence. The Nain Craton, which forms the coast of central Labrador, has a northward-striking grain. These rocks include some very old (3600 Ma) Archean relicts, immersed in granitic gneisses that are products of late Archean (2500 Ma) orogeny. Archean basement is overlain locally by Lower Proterozoic supracrustal rocks that were folded and faulted during Early Proterozoic (1600 Ma) tectonism. Anorthosite batholiths, emplaced about 1400 Ma, occupy large areas of the south-central Nain Craton.

The Burwell and Hoare Bay terranes, Dorset Fold Belt and Baffin Batholith includes northernmost Labrador and all of southern Baffin Island. The rocks are mainly high-grade gneissic granites that were deformed and metamorphosed during late Archean tectonism (about 2500 Ma). These basement rocks have variable northwestward, northeastward, and northward-striking fabrics. The age, nature, and distribution of Precambrian tectonic provinces of West Greenland support the notion that the Canadian and Greenland margins were part of a continuous cratonic mass before separating in the Cretaceous and Tertiary (Escher and Watt, 1976).

Cratonic margin

A zone of rifted, seaward-flexed cratonic basement separates the high-standing uplands of coastal Labrador from the low-standing oceanic basement floor. This zone is broken by Cretaceous, rift-stage half grabens, infilled by disconnected wedges of Cretaceous basalt and synrift sediments. Along the entire shelf the rift zone is overlain by Upper Cretaceous and younger strata of the post-rift terrace wedge. The faulted and flexed zone of cratonic basement ranges in width from about 25 km, offshore from northern Labrador — where the sialic basement is abruptly flexed seaward — to about 125 km, offshore from southern Labrador, where the basement surface is broken by a wide zone of abundant small normal faults.

Regional divergences in the strike and design of the flexed and broken cratonic monocline allow delineation of

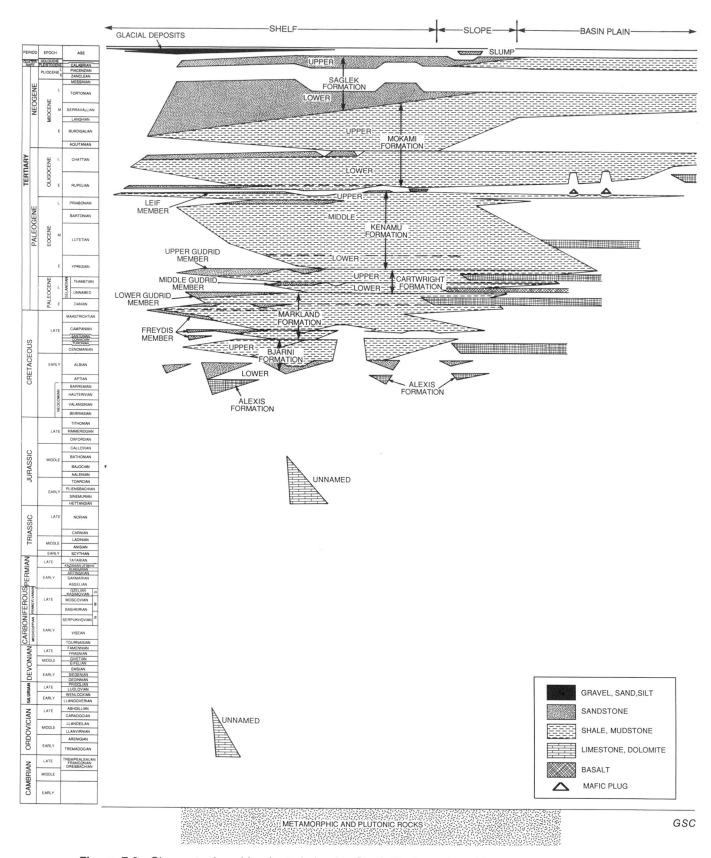

Figure 7.2 Chronostratigraphic chart, Labrador Shelf. Rock-stratigraphic nomenclature partly after McWhae et al. (1980). Biostratigraphy from Barss et al. (1979), Gradstein and Williams (1981), Bujak and Lee (pers. comm., 1983), Bujak (pers. comm., 1985), and unpublished petroleum industry reports.

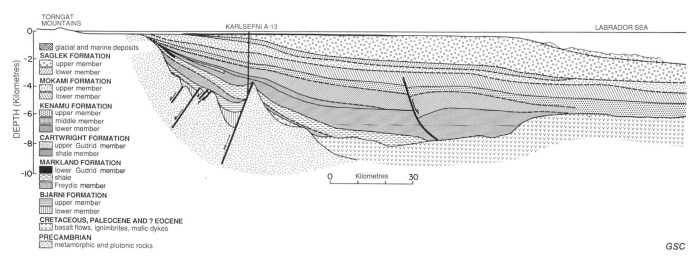

Figure 7.3 Geological cross-section through Karlsefni A-13, Saglek Bank, Labrador Shelf (based on interpretation of regional reflection seismic profiles). Note: landward (westward) dipping normal faults in Precambrian basement; seaward-dipping, listric, mid-Tertiary normal fault in middle part of shelf; large Quaternary slumps on modern-day continental slope; progressive landward (westward) onlap of basement hinge zone by Tertiary sequences; inner shelf pediment surface carved in Precambrian basement.

six tectonic domains along the Labrador-southern Baffin Island margin. Three of these are convex-seaward salients (arches), and three are concave-seaward re-entrants (basins). From south to north these salients and re-entrants, which are subparallel to the present coastline, are the Cartwright Arch, Hopedale Basin, Okak Arch, Saglek Basin, Lady Franklin High, and Cumberland Basin (Fig. 7.1).

The Cartwright Arch is a northeastward-plunging salient, lying seaward of the Precambrian Grenville Province. The inner part of the arch is a smooth, unbroken basement surface that dips gently seaward. The outer part of the arch is abruptly flexed basinward, plunging to a depth of about 8 km below sea level where it is onlapped by acoustic basement reflectors which, because of their high-amplitude, discontinuous, "ropy" seismic nature, are interpreted to be basalts.

The Hopedale Basin is a 500-km long, northeastward-facing re-entrant, underlain by a wide zone of rifted cratonic basement. Northwest-striking master faults of the rift domain are several kilometres long. They are linked to each other by relatively short, orthogonal, transfer faults. The master faults dip both landward and seaward, but within a given part of the system one dip direction or the other prevails, with the result that the structural depressions are mainly half-grabens, rather than grabens, and the intervening basement highs are rotated blocks rather than symmetrical horsts. Seismic geometry indicates that many of the faults are listric, and that sedimentary fill took place during growth of the faults. The Cretaceous-age basement faults provided a mechanism for brittle, northeast-southwest extension of the upper lithosphere, approximately orthogonal to the strike of the Labrador Shelf.

A northeastward-plunging cratonic basement salient, the Okak Arch, separates the Hopedale and Saglek basins. Saglek Basin consists of two segments, joined east of Hudson Strait. Where it merges with the northern flank of the Okak Arch, the southern Saglek Basin is underlain by

rifted cratonic basement resembling the floor of Hopedale Basin. Most of Saglek Basin is bounded on the landward side by a narrow zone of locally faulted, seaward-flexed Precambrian basement, which plunges as deep as 10 km below sea level to a basin floor composed of Late Cretaceous and Paleocene basalt. The eastern flank of the basin consists of westward, or landward sloping, oceanic basalt.

Lady Franklin High plunges southeastwards from the Precambrian rocks forming Hall Peninsula. This salient separates the northern part of Saglek Basin from structurally disrupted basement rocks forming the floor of Cumberland Basin. The latter is a broad, relatively high-standing tectonic domain that extends northeastward to Davis Strait. The basin floor is composed mainly of Paleocene basalt flows. The basaltic basement is abruptly interrupted by steeply dipping to near-vertical northeast-striking faults, and by ridges of mafic intrusive rock. The structural style of the Cumberland Basin supports interpretations that the region underwent significant early Tertiary transcurrent faulting (Klose et al., 1982; MacLean et al., 1982).

Oceanic basin floor

Kerr (1967), Umpleby (1979), and Grant (1980) offered "fixist" hypotheses for the tectonic initiation and evolution of central Labrador Basin. Integral to their hypotheses is the notion that large parts of the basin floor consist of sialic crust, engulfed and overlain by basalt. Gravity, magnetic, and seismic measurements, however, have been interpreted by a succession of geophysicists — Le Pichon et al. (1971), Laughton (1972), van der Linden (1975), Kristoffersen (1978), and Srivastava (1978) — to the point that the plate-tectonic model of lithospheric extension and spreading generation of new oceanic crust is now generally tentatively accepted.

Srivastava (1978) identified and correlated magnetic anomalies in the oceanic parts of the Labrador Basin with known anomalies in the northwest Atlantic, thus arriving

299

at a chronological scenario for the basin (Map 1706A, in pocket). The anomalies were re-correlated by Roots and Srivastava (1984). The oldest southern anomaly is correlated with anomaly 34 (Coniacian or Santonian); the oldest northern anomaly is correlated with anomaly 31 (Maastrichtian). The western part of the basin is divided by northeast-striking fracture zones, separating segments that are progressively younger northward. Additionally, Srivastava (1978) discerned a pronounced change in the direction of ocean spreading — from orthogonal-to-the-margin vectors to oblique-to-the-margin vectors — between anomalies 25 and 24 (approximately early Eocene). The absence of anomaly 13 (early Oligocene) in the Labrador Sea, and its continuation toward Iceland, provides an indication of the approximate end of Labrador Sea ocean spreading.

STRATIGRAPHY

The Labrador Shelf contains an assemblage of Mesozoic-Cenozoic sedimentary and volcanic rocks divisible into three megasequences. These chronologic stratigraphic divisions were deposited during three successive tectonic regimes: intra-cratonic rifting; cratonic separation of North America and Greenland and subsequent ocean spreading; and post-spreading massive subsidence of Labrador sea oceanic crust.

The oldest known rift deposits are Barremian sandstones (Fig. 7.2). These coarse grained, nonmarine sediments lie on Neocomian basalts, isolated Paleozoic erosional relicts, and Precambrian basement. The youngest rift deposits are Coniacian. Along the deeply subsided, seaward part of the shelf, thick piles of Cretaceous and early Tertiary basalt onlap the rift structures and synrift sediments.

From the Cenomanian to the Santonian the middle and outer parts of the extended margin were sediment starved. Small amounts of clastics were trapped in the inboard, early Late Cretaceous grabens. Because the lower Upper Cretaceous succession is thin and discontinuous, it is difficult to identify a specific "break-up unconformity" marking the stratigraphic response to initial generation of Labrador Basin oceanic crust. The oldest known post-rift beds are Santonian (Fig. 7.2).

The supply of clastics surged in the Campanian, following cratonic separation and development of a seaward gradient to the cratonic margin. Campanian and Maastrichtian pelites prograded seaward over the rift-age grabens and ridges, approximately to the position of the modern continental slope. In the outer parts of Saglek Basin these Upper Cretaceous beds are intercalated with basalt flows. The remainder of the ocean-spreading megasequence consists of successively prograding, seaward-thickening and seaward-inclined increments. These sequences are preceptible in well samples by their upward-coarsening, rhythmic nature, and by seismic reflector termination (onlap, downlap, or truncation) at their boundaries. Sequence boundaries are generally more obvious — both seismically and in well samples — along the inner parts of the terrace wedge. Most boundaries are paraconformable in the outer part of the shelf where lithological control is sponse.

The top of the ocean-spreading sequence is probably late Eocene. This level marks a widespread phase of shelf shallowing, coastal erosion, and seaward progradation of sand. Moreover, this stratigraphic level coincides with culmination of large-scale transcurrent faulting in the Cumberland Basin and intrusion of large mafic plugs in the Cumberland Basin and the northern Labrador Sea. It is also coeval with the postulated late Eocene (or early Oligocene) cessation of Labrador Basin ocean-spreading, inferred from correlation of oceanic magnetic anomalies (Srivastava, 1978).

The upper megasequence spans the interval from the early Oligocene to the Quaternary. Crustal dynamics during this phase were dominated by massive thermal subsidence of the Labrador Sea oceanic basin floor, accompanied by uplift of coastal margins. During this phase the cratonic margin was tilted seaward and received thick successions of coarse clastic detritus, generated by erosion of uplifted coastal highlands. The volume of clastics generated by coastal uplift and erosion greatly exceeded the rate of cratonic margin subsidence. As a result, the clastics prograded vigorously basinward, constructing the present-day outer continental shelf and slope. Fine grained fractions bypassed the shelf and slope and were deposited as a thick, widespread blanket on the floor of the basin.

There are no carbonate rocks, other than a few thin lenses and discontinuous shell beds, and no evaporite rocks in the three megasequences.

Paleozoic sedimentary rocks

Paleozoic rocks were encountered in six wells in the southern Hopedale Basin, lying as paleoerosional remnants on Precambrian basement. Paleozoic strata also underlie parts of Frobisher Bay, Cumberland Sound, and the interior part of Hudson Strait (Wade et al., 1977; Bell and Howie, Chapter 4). No formal stratigraphic names have been assigned to these rocks.

Paleozoic beds in the southern Hopedale basin are overlain in some wells by Early Cretaceous basalt, and in others by Lower Cretaceous sandstones or Upper Cretaceous shale. Not more than a few hundred metres of Paleozoic beds are present in any of the Hopedale Basin wells. It is commonly difficult to discern the Paleozoic rocks from Cretaeous basalt or Precambrian basement, because of the similarity in seismic reflection characteristics. The most common Paleozoic lithology is very fine-crystalline to micro-crystalline, light grey, tight dolomite. In Indian Harbour M-52 the dolomites are overlain by partly sandy micritic limestone. Calcareous siltstone and shales overlie the limestones in Freydis B-87.

Biostratigraphic evidence indicates that some Paleozoic carbonates and overlying pelites are Ordovician in age, ranging possibly from Early to early Late Ordovician (Jenkins, 1984; Bell and Howie, Chapter 4; Williams et al., Chapter 3). The age of dolomites in the Gudrid H-55 well is controversial: well-preserved Carboniferous (Westphalian) spores were recovered from core in that well (Barss et al., 1979, p. 91); likewise, Westphalian palynomorphs were recovered from Roberval K-92 (M.S. Barss, pers. comm., 1981). One biostratigrapher considers the paleoenvironmental assemblage and state of preservation of the Carboniferous spores to be inconsistent with the depositional and diagenetic nature of the dolomites and concluded that the spores are contaminants (Jenkins, 1984).

Paleozoic strata under the Labrador sea margin are probably remnants of a once-widespread, platform-deposited basement cover that was widely eroded prior to and during Early Cretaceous rifting. The Paleozoic rocks performed as passive riders during basement extension, exerting no obvious influence on the locations and styles of rift structures.

Synrift megasequences

The synrift megasequence comprises the Neocomian Alexis Formation, the?Neocomian-Albian Bjarni Formation, and Cenomanian-Campanian shales of the Markland Formation and the equivalent sandstones of the Freydis Member of the Markland Formation (Fig. 7.2).

Alexis Formation

Basalts, dated radiometrically by whole-rock K-Ar methods as Early Cretaceous in age (approximately 131-104 Ma: Berriasian-Albian at Leif M-48, Umpleby, 1979) or lying beneath Cretaceous sediments, were penetrated in seven wells in the southern Hopedale Basin. Umpleby (1979) applied the name Alexis Formation to these, the oldest known Mesozoic rocks of the Labrador Shelf. In the adjacent coastal region of Labrador, the only reported evidence of coeval mafic activity is a possible mid-Mesozoic lamprophyre dyke in Precambrian rocks of the Makkovik orogen (Wanless et al., 1974; King and McMillan, 1975).

Gabbro dykes which parallel the coast in the Precambrian rocks of southwest Greenland may be Oxfordian-Kimmeridgian in age (Watt, 1969). These rocks may represent incipient Labrador Basin rifting. Possibly, parts of the Alexis volcanic assemblage are as old as the Fords Bight and Greenland dykes — which suggests that Upper Jurassic sedimentary rocks may occupy the deep, undrilled parts of some synrift troughs.

The type section of the Alexis Formation is from 2515-2255 m in Bjarni H-81. It consists of repeated sequences of red and green weathered basalt, alternating with fresh amygdaloidal basalt and some intra-basaltic shale, siltstone, and sandstone (Umpleby, 1979) and were dated radiometrically as 122 ± 6 Ma. Basalts in other Hopedale Basin wells are lithologically similar to the Alexis Formation at Bjarni H-81. The thickest basaltic succession is 365 m at Roberval K-92. The Lower Cretaceous volcanics overlie Precambrian basement or Paleozoic carbonate strata, and are overlain by the Bjarni Formation or, in structurally high or more distal parts of the shelf, by marine shelf shales of the Upper Cretaceous Markland Formation or Paleocene Cartwright Formation. The alkali character of the Lower Cretaceous Alexis basalts in the rifted domain of the southern Hopedale Basin is in constrast to the tholeiitic character of the post-rift basalts of northern Saglek Basin and Cumberland Basin.

Onshore equivalents of the Alexis may be the Ford's Bight volcanics which consist of breccia cut by lamprophyre dykes (King and McMillan, 1975). According to Wanless et al. (1974), the age of these volcanics is 129 ± 6 Ma (Valanginian-Hauterivian); according to Geochron the age of these volcanics is 145 ± 6 Ma (Tithonian-Berriasian).

Bjarni Formation

The informal name "Bjarni sandstone" was applied by McWhae and Michel (1975) to the interval between 2150 and 2257 m in Bjarni H-81 in the Hopedale Basin. The interval is dominated by Lower Cretaceous gas-bearing sandstones, which overlie volcanics of the Alexis Formation. Umpleby (1979) formalized the name to Bjarni Formation and designated as the type section the interval 2614-3767 m in Herjolf M-92, which is adjacent to Bjarni H-81. According to Umpleby, the formation consists of predominantly nonmarine, coarse grained arkosic sandstones of Barremian to early Cenomanian age. The lowermost 217 m, which are dominated by shale and coal beds, he included in the Snorri Member of the Bjarni Formation.

The Bjarni Formation is discontinuous in the Hopedale Basin, mostly occupying the structurally low parts of large northwest-striking grabens and half-grabens in basement (Fig. 7.4 to 7.8). Large, northwest-striking normal faults commonly form the western or eastern, or both, boundaries of these subbasins, which are separated by narrow, structurally high, basement horst blocks. Basement in this context includes seismically inseparable combinations of Precambrian crystalline rock, Paleozoic strata and the Alexis Formation. The formation probably attains its greatest thickness north of Hopedale E-33, where in the regionally depressed area it may be over 2600 m thick. The Bjarni also occurs in the southern part of Saglek Basin.

In Hopedale and Saglek basins, the Bjarni Formation is overlain by Upper Cretaceous or younger rocks. Along the inner margins the lower Upper Cretaceous rocks are commonly sandstones, which are included in the Freydis Member of the Markland Formation (see Fig. 7.3). The Bjarni and Freydis cannot always be distinguished seismically. Towards the depocentres of the basins, in the middle and outer shelf areas, the Bjarni is overlain by Upper Cretaceous marine shales of the Markland Formation. In some parts of the inner shelf, the upper Markland shales overlap eastward-dipping beds of the Bjarni Formation landward.

The Bjarni Formation can be divided into lower and upper members in both basins. The lower Bjarni member consists of feldspathic, lithic, coaly, in part conglomeratic, fine- to coarse-grained, nonmarine quartzose sandstones, with poor to excellent intergranular porosity. The upper Bjarni member consists of sandy, clayey and carbonaceous, marine in part but predominantly nonmarine, siltstone and shale, with intercalated beds of feldspathic, partly porous sandstone.

In Hopedale Basin, the lower member is discernible on well logs and seismic profiles. The thickest drilled section is in Herjolf M-92, where it is 1137 m (2615-3752 m). At Herjolf the member consists of about 75% sandstone. This is a light grey to light orange, pebbly to silty to clayey, fine- to coarse-grained, poorly sorted, feldspathic quartzarenite, with the lower third having fair to excellent intergranular porosity. The cements include calcite, silica, clay and siderite. Interbedded shale and siltstone may be up to 25 m, but generally are only a few metres thick. There are some thin coal beds. Usually individual sandstones comprise the upper parts of repeated, upward-coarsening cycles; in less than 20% of the section the textures are progressively finer upwards. The North Leif I-05 has 343.5 m of the lower Bjarni member, with the base being at 3443.5 m and the

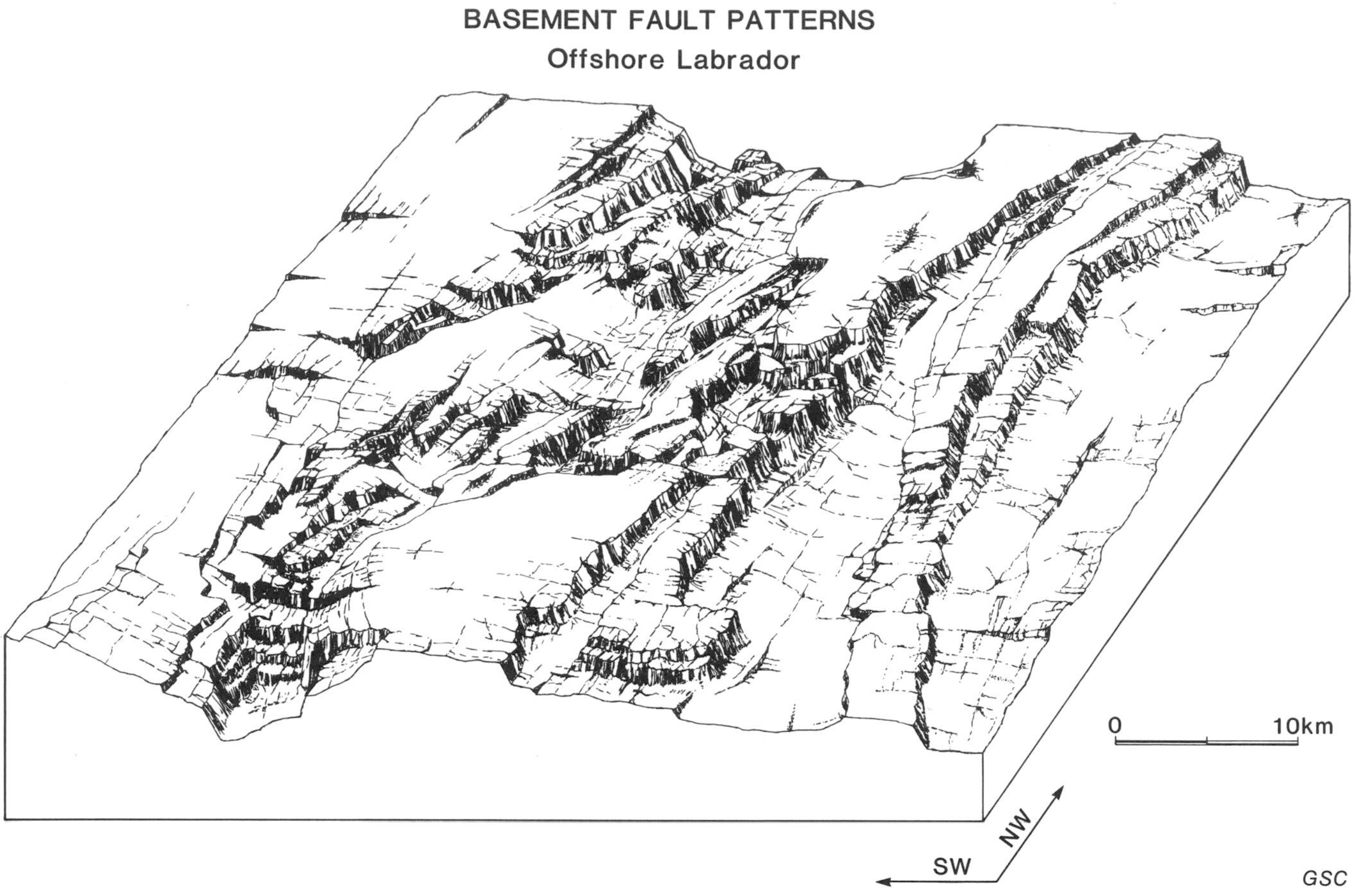

BASEMENT FAULT PATTERNS
Offshore Labrador

Figure 7.4 Westward view of Early Cretaceous normal faults in Precambrian basement, southern Hopedale Basin. There are long, northwest-striking, down-to-the-east master faults, and relatively shorter, southwest- striking, linking faults. Drawing by B. Petyhyrycz, based on detailed interpretation of the regional seismic grid.

seismically discernible contact with the upper member being at 3100 m. Incomplete sequences have been drilled at North Bjarni F-06. The former well is in the southern part of the Hopedale Basin; the latter well is in the central part of the Hopedale Basin.

The lower member cannot be mapped around or across Okak Arch, but is present in two wells — Skolp E-07 and Gilbert F-53 in the southern Saglek Basin. In Skolp E-07, the member overlies crystalline Precambrian basement and is 347 m thick, extending from 2620 to 2967 m. North of Skolp, the unit thins and is not recognized beyond 58°N.

As shown by its gently dipping seismic reflectors, the upper Bjarni member unconformably overlies and over-steps the tilted lower member in much of the Hopedale Basin. In other parts of the basin, the upper member is less widespread than the lower member (Fig. 7.9). Only a few wells penetrate both members and none of these are in the vicinity of Bjarni H-81. One well that does is North Leif I-05, where the upper member is 379 m (2721-3100 m).

In southern Saglek Basin, the upper member oversteps the lower member to rest directly on basement. The upper member, predominantly a marine shale, is 691 m thick in Skolp E-07, where it extends from 1782 to 2473 m.

Sedimentary rocks equivalent to the Bjarni Formation may be present in the northern part of Saglek Basin and

beneath Southeast Baffin Shelf, where they could be buried beneath or intercalated with Cretaceous and Lower Tertiary volcanic flows or mounds. A prominent seismic marker, which occurs beneath the mounds, is here termed the "mid-Cretaceous marker". Parallel-layered reflectors below it are probably Bjarni equivalent rocks. The presence of Lower Cretaceous rocks on the Southeast Baffin Shelf has been confirmed by MacLean et al. (1982, 1986a), MacLean and Williams (1983) and MacLean et al. (Part 2, this chapter). These rocks may be assignable to the Bjarni Formation.

Marine shales, probably coeval with the upper Bjarni member, are conformably overlain by shales of the Markland Formation in the intervolcanic depositional troughs of north Saglek Basin and Southeast Baffin Shelf.

The oldest age assigned to the Bjarni Formation by Umpleby (1979) was Barremian. This was based on the spore and pollen assemblages. However, the basal beds of the formation are clearly diachronous and could be Neocomian or even Jurassic where they are in structural lows. The youngest age for the Bjarni may be Cenomanian, although is generally thought to be late Albian. There is considerable debate on the age of the unconformity between the lower Bjarni member and the upper Bjarni member. If the upper member is probably middle to late

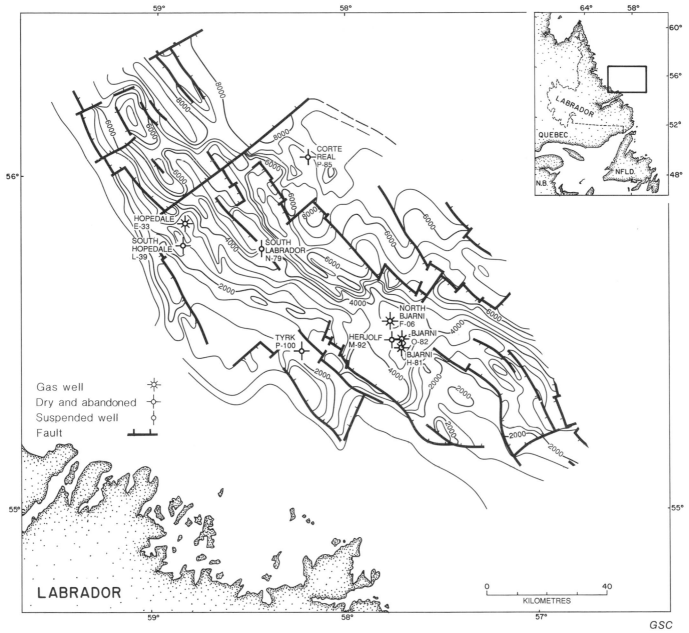

Figure 7.5 Basement structure map, south-central Hopedale Basin. Structural depth contours in metres below sea level. Note orthogonal pattern of normal faults in basement.

Albian, the unconformity in Hopedale Basin must be late middle or early late Albian.

The local paleotopographic relief on which the Bjarni was deposited was in the range of hundreds of metres. The basal beds of the lower Bjarni member consist of conglomeratic, nonmarine sandstones and fine grained clastics, where they are in fault contact with underlying rocks. This confirms that the beds were deposited contemporaneously with the ?Late Jurassic-early Cretaceous crustal rifting episode, which affected the Labrador Shelf. Basal conglomeratic beds, as at North Leif I-05, contain abundant weathered basalt clasts; these were apparently derived from erosion of the Alexis Formation outcropping in the hinterland.

The conglomeratic beds may be alluvial fan and scree slope deposits. The sandstones in the inner shelf grabens were presumably deposited by rivers confined to narrow valleys and with high gradients and braided patterns. There are few fining-upward cycles indicative of large meandering streams. The grabens narrow to the south toward the unrifted Precambrian hinge, indicating that the rivers drained to the north.

North Leif I-05 contains a thick succession of nonmarine shale of the lower Bjarni member. This probably represents deposition in a long-standing lake basin. Facies such as the sandstones at Herjolf M-92 may be proximal delta-front deposits (including turbidites) laid down in large, graben-defined lake basins or narrow elongate estuaries.

303

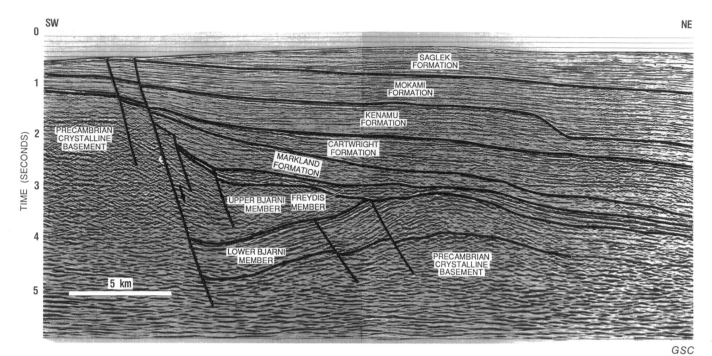

Figure 7.6 Seismic section (migrated), central Hopedale Basin. Two-way time (seconds).

Sandstones of the Bjarni Formation have been the most commonly pursued hydrocarbon objective in Labrador Shelf wells. The thick, locally porous sandstones are syngenetic with, and locally adjacent to very large rift structures, which were readily perceived from seismic profiles in early stages of exploration of the Hopedale Basin. Such structures in the inner part of the shelf lie in relatively shallow water (less than 200 m), at total depths that could be reached in one drilling season (approximately mid-July to mid-October). Moreover, excellent gas recoveries from the Lower member in early wells in Hopedale Basin (e.g. Bjarni H-81 and Hopedale E-33) encouraged further exploration of the formation in both Hopedale and Saglek basins. The North Bjarni F-06 gas field (Fig. 7.7), as an example, covers 31 km2. The net gas pay is 79.5 m out of a gross gas column of 177 m. The field contains calculated recoverable reserves of 13.6 x 106m^3 of condensate, and 50.4 x 109m^3 of natural gas (Meneley, 1986).

Freydis Member of the Markland Formation

Umpleby (1979) named a 55 m interval (1734-1789 m) in Freydis B-87, located in the Hopedale Basin, the Freydis Sand Member of the Cartwright Formation. McWhae et al. (1980) expanded Umpleby's type interval to include rocks between 1731 and 1875 m in Freydis B-87, and included these sandstone-dominated rocks in their newly named Markland Formation; they cited rocks in the Skolp E-07 well (1355-2427 m) as a reference section. From examination of lithology, seismic character, log signature, and biostratigraphy, it is suggested here that the contact between the Freydis Member and the Bjarni Formation in Skolp E-07 lies at 1782 m. The Freydis Member in Skolp E-07 therefore lies between 1355 and 1782 m and is 427 m thick. Further, the Freydis beds in Freydis B-87 is restricted here to the 60 m interval between 1728-1788 m on the basis of lithology, log and seismic character, and biostratigraphy;

this is approximately the same interval as Umpleby's originally designed Freydis Member.

The Freydis Member is confined to the inner part of the Upper Cretaceous succession of the Labrador shelf. The unit has two contrasting seismo-stratigraphic styles: 1) thick, narrow, half-graben confined wedges, at and near the regional contact of the terrace wedge with the Precambrian basement, both in the Hopedale and Saglek basins; and 2) narrow, relatively thin, seaward facing, sigmoidal prisms that locally overstep older beds both landward and seaward (Fig. 7.6).

Freydis beds occupying half-grabens are locally hundreds of metres thick (as at Skolp E-07 and Gilbert F-53) and have internal syntectonic bedding geometries resembling parts of the Bjarni Formation. Accordingly in some places, this results in only tenuous delineation of the Lower Cretaceous Bjarni Formation and the Upper Cretaceous Freydis Member. Where the Freydis beds are developed as seaward-facing sigmoidal wedges — as at Freydis B-87, Snorri J-90, and Tyrk P-100 — the interval is only a few tens to several tens of metres thick. The well lies in a succession confined in a half-graben, and this succession may be slightly thicker west of the well in the axial part of the structure. A thick succession occupies a half-graben offshore from Cape Chidley. If these beds can all be assigned to the Freydis Member as is possible from regional seismic correlation, the unit may be 1200 m thick.

The Freydis Member cannot be mapped with any confidence in the region northward from Hudson Strait. The locally thick wedges of the Freydis Member thin abruptly to a single seismic reflector; they apparently grade seaward to thin pelitic marine beds comprising the lower part of the Markland Formation. The contact of the Freydis (and equivalent Markland shales) with underlying Lower Cretaceous strata is a persistently strong seismic marker over wide parts of the Labrador Shelf. This contact has not

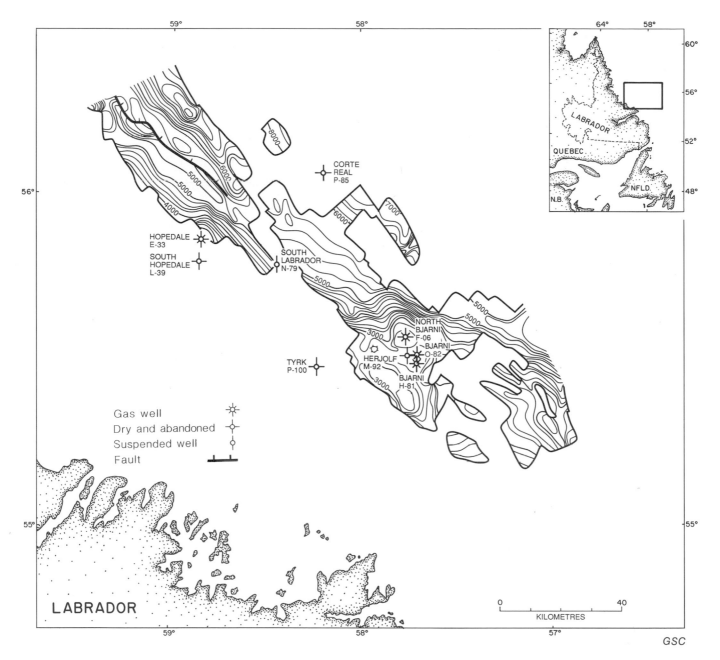

Figure 7.7 Structure map, top of lower Bjarni member, south-central Hopedale Basin. Structure depth contours in metres below sea level.

been drilled in the middle and outer parts of the shelf, so the lithologic nature of the contact is unknown. Possibly the single prominent distal Cretaceous seismic reflector at the Freydis level marks a thin limestone or calcite-cemented bed.

The thickest drilled Freydis section is at Skolp E-07 where it is 427 m. The member consists of shale, siltstone and sandstone, with log characteristics that suggest upward-coarsening cycles. The basal 80 m is brown-grey, soft sandy claystone. This is overlain by an intercalated sandstone-shale sequence. The sandstones are grey to brown-grey, partly pebbly, fine- to very coarse-grained, feldspathic and quartzose; they may be argillaceous, silty, carbonaceous, micaceous, or glauconitic, with a partly cal-

careous, cement. The shales are soft and brown- grey in colour. The thickest sandstones are in the uppermost 100 m. A core from the interval 1388 to 1397 m is a dark grey, argillaceous, micaceous, laminated quartz-sandstone. Freydis sandstones at Gilbert F-53, also in Saglek Basin, are arkosic, and have abundant lithic clasts.

Thin wedges of Freydis sandstone, as at Freydis B-87 (1728-1788 m) in the Hopedale Basin consist of light grey, fine- to coarse-grained, slightly glauconitic, quartzose sandstone and arkosic sandstone.

The Freydis Member thins seaward and is judged to grade into the marine shales of the lower part of the Markland Formation. The Freydis conformably overlies the

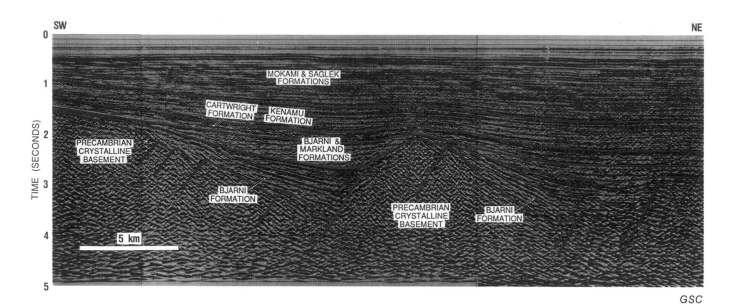

Figure 7.8 Seismic section (migrated), southern Hopedale Basin; two-way time (seconds). Note: landward (westward) dip of basement normal faults; antithetic dip of Bjarni reflectors toward basement normal faults; shoreward (westward) onlap of Cartwright Formation by basal reflectors of the Kenamu Formation; landward (westward) truncation of Mokami and Saglek reflectors at modern-day shelf surface.

Lower Cretaceous Bjarni Formation, or unconformably overlies older rocks, including in some places Precambrian basement. The unit is overlain most commonly by Upper Cretaceous marine shales of the Markland Formation. Along the western edge of the Cretaceous rocks, the Freydis Member is locally overstepped by Gudrid sandstones (Paleocene? and Eocene), as at Tyrk P-100.

The Freydis Member contains palynomorphs which indicate a Cenomanian-Campanian age (J. Bujak, pers. comm., 1985). Graben-confined Freydis beds in the Hopedale Basin are not younger than Coniacian. In Saglek Basin, at the Gilbert F-53 and Skolp E-07 wells, the upper Freydis beds are as young as early Campanian.

Foraminifera and palynomorphs from the Freydis beds confined to grabens indicate shallow marine to nonmarine environments. This, combined with the wedge-like internal geometry and coarse, carbonaceous lithology of the rocks, suggests that the deposits accumulated syntectonically during early Late Cretaceous rifting of the inner, shoreward parts of the embryonic shelf. Likely driving mechanisms for these mixed deltaic and shore-faced deposits include rivers, tides and waves. Sand-rich deposits of the Freydis Member comprising thin wedges have geometries and lithologies suggestive of locally active energy systems; these thick, massive clean sands may be deposits of small wave-dominated deltas and delta-margins, which locally may have contributed to thin sandstones forming distal fans downdip. Abundant fresh feldspar grains and lithic clasts of igneous and metamorphic rocks indicate derivation of coarse detritus from source terrains near the sites of Freydis deposition — to a large extent probably coastal uplands that developed contemporaneously with local Late Cretaceous rifting along the Labrador Shelf.

Drift-phase megasequence

Shale-dominated, seaward-prograding components of the Upper Cretaceous, Paleocene and Eocene drift-phase megasequence include the Markland, Cartwright, and Kenamu formations (Fig. 7.2). The distal facies of these formations, under the continental slope and on the basin plain, overlie (and are partly intercalated with) Paleocene and Eocene basalts.

Markland Formation

McWhae et al. (1980) gave the name Markland Formation to the widespread Upper Cretaceous and Lower Paleocene (Danian) succession on the Labrador Shelf, consisting mainly of marine shelf shales. The type section is the interval 1975-2150 m in Bjarni H-81 in the Hopedale Basin. The Markland Formation is an unconformity-bounded entity, and readily recognizable by seismo-stratigraphic and log analysis. Seismic and well analyses indicate that the Markland Formation has two recognizable members, both sandstone-dominated proximal facies: a locally thick (?)Cenomanian-Campanian unit, the Freydis Member; and a thinner, but locally prominent Danian unit, the lower Gudrid member (Fig. 7.2).

The Markland Formation is one of the most widespread lithostratigraphic units on the Labrador Shelf. It occurs throughout Hopedale Basin and in Saglek Basin where it is found on northern Labrador Shelf and Southeast Baffin Shelf. Shales of the formation commonly overstep the Bjarni Formation in grabens and the Freydis Member of the Markland, to lie directly on Precambrian basement, Paleozoic strata, or Cretaceous basalts. In those places the Markland shales are the oldest sediments of the Labrador Shelf terrace-wedge succession. The Markland Formation is intercalated with and lie beneath Late Cretaceous and Paleocene basalts in the northern part of Saglek Basin and

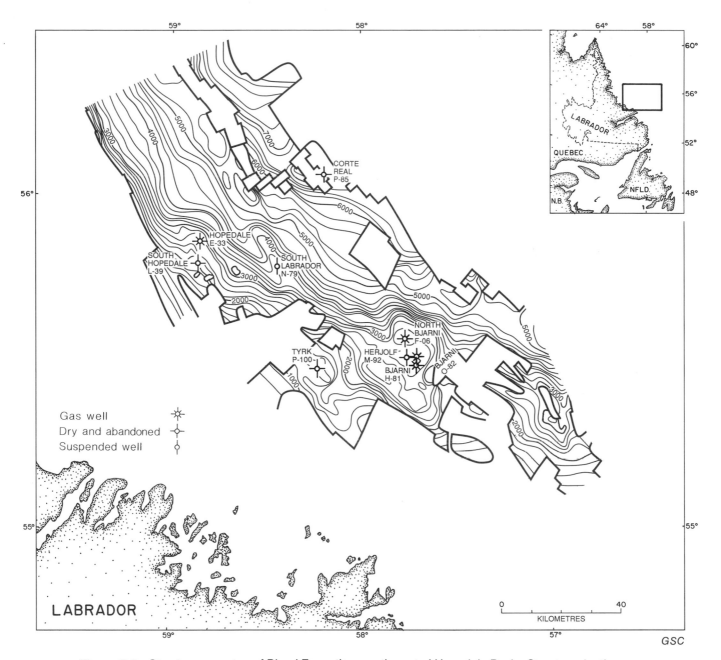

Figure 7.9 Structure map, top of Bjarni Formation, south-central Hopedale Basin. Structure depth contours in metres below sea level.

Southeast Baffin Shelf, making mapping of the unit difficult there. The formation tapers seaward and landward from a regional maximum; it forms an elongate prism superposed on the thick Bjarni Formation filling the grabens along the inner part of the Cretaceous shelf succession.

The thickest known section of the Markland Formation is at Gilbert F-53 (about 735 m) in southern Saglek Basin. In Hopedale Basin thick sections were drilled at South Labrador N-79 (622 m) and Herjolf M-92 (404 m). The Markland is relatively thin above the crests of structurally high basement horst blocks in the inner part of the shelf. It thins regionally seaward, with the result that it is absent on the crests of many horst blocks in the middle part

of the shelf. The formation cannot be discerned at the outer edge of the shelf succession; if it is present, it is probably so thin that it has no distinctive seismic expression. The lower part of the Gjoa G-37 well may have penetrated upper Markland shales, but this cannot be verified from present data.

The Markland Formation abruptly but conformably overlies the Lower Cretaceous Bjarni Formation in the central parts of many structural depressions. Towards the flanks of structural highs the basal Markland beds onlap or downlap the Bjarni Formation and older rocks, locally Paleozoic rocks, as in Gudrid H-55, or Cretaceous basalt as in Indian Harbour M-52 (Fig. 7.8). Seismic geometry indicates that the shales of the Markland Formation are distal

307

deposits or the inner shelf sandstone facies — the Freydis Member, an unnamed Maastrichtian sandstone, and the lower Paleocene lower Gudrid member (Fig. 7.2). Basal Markland rocks, occupying the lower parts of structural depressions, have not been drilled. The formation is overlain conformably in distal and middle parts of the shelf by shales of the Paleocene Cartwright Formation. The contact is marked abruptly by a velocity decrease on sonic logs and a resistivity increase in the basal Cartwright shales. The change in log character and the generally perceptible seismic reflector are reliable criteria for distinguishing the Markland and Cartwright shales; petrologically, the shales are similar. Shoreward, successively younger beds of the Cartwright Formation onlap the Markland (Fig. 7.6, 7.10).

Markland shales are generally dark grey, silty, partly carbonaceous and sideritic, partly micaceous, and commonly have fissile to splintery parting. Traces of fine grained glauconitic sandstone are present in some beds. The organic carbon content of the shales is generally less than 1.0 per cent; most of this is land-plant detritus.

Palynomorphs in the Markland Formation denote an age of Albian- Cenomanian to Danian. The foraminifers suggest an age of Cenomanian-Turonian to Danian. The dinoflagellates and foraminifers indicate deposition in marginal marine to middle shelf environments. The base of the formation is diachronous because of its onlapping character.

The indications of a generally shallow marine environment are supported by the following factors: the position of the formation above the nonmarine to marginal marine Bjarni Formation; local updip gradation to marginal marine sandstones of the Freydis Member; and the gentle seaward downlapping of seismic reflectors within the Markland.

The thin lower Markland Formation, including beds coeval with the Freydis Member, represents depositional starvation during early and middle-Late Cretaceous time. The amount of fine clastic material reaching the Labrador Shelf increased from the Campanian to the Maastrichtian and Danian. Consequently, Campanian and younger beds of the Markland onlap structural highs and are much more widely distributed than lower parts of the formation.

The Markland Formation shales are seals for Bjarni gas-bearing sandstones at North Bjarni F-06 and nearby wells. The shales contain mainly land-plant organic matter, and may be partly the source beds for the Bjarni gas.

The Gudrid members

The name Gudrid Sand Member was introduced by Umpleby (1979) for a 214 m interval in Gudrid H-55, located in Hopedale Basin. As originally defined, this member of the Cartwright Formation consisted of arkosic sand with an abundant clay matrix. Palynomorphs indicate a Paleocene-early Eocene age. McWhae et al. (1980) raised the unit to formational status, terming it the Gudrid Formation, and regarding it as coeval with the Cartwright Formation. They retained the interval 2179-2393 m in Gudrid H-55 as the type section.

Three levels of coastal marine sandstone development (Fig. 7.2) were recognized in the Paleocene and early Eocene, which equate with the Gudrid Formation, as defined by McWhae et al. (1980). Each of the sandstone facies lies at the top of an upward-coarsening succession. Since this is not the appropriate place to erect formal units, these sandstones are referred to as the lower, middle and upper Gudrid members. This is a confusing and unsatisfactory nomenclature that does not accord with the North American Commission on Stratigraphic Nomenclature

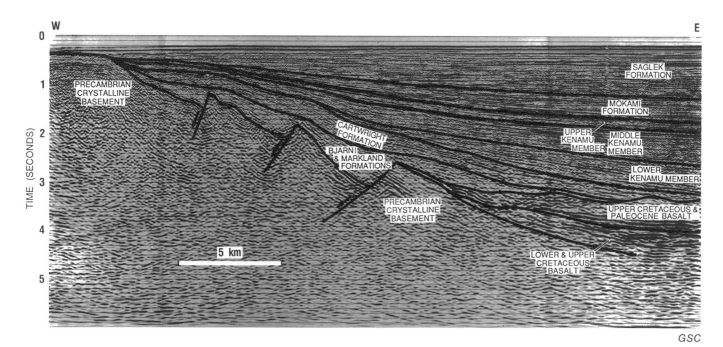

GSC

Figure 7.10 Seismic section (migrated), inboard part of Saglek Basin. Two-way time (seconds) along left margin.

(1983). Accordingly, a revision is necessary and the three Gudrid members are defined as follows:

— the lower Gudrid member is the coastal sand facies equivalent of the upper shales of the Markland Formation and so is included in that formation. It is probably of Danian age.

— the middle Gudrid member represents the coastal sand facies of the lower shales of the Cartwright Formation and is included in that formation. The age is middle to late Paleocene.

— the upper Gudrid member represents the coastal sand facies of the upper shales of the Cartwright Formation and is included in that formation. It is late Paleocene-early Eocene in age. The interval 2180-2280 m is included in Gudrid H-55, which is the upper part of the type section for the Gudrid Formation, in the upper Gudrid member.

Downdip from the middle and upper Gudrid coastal deltaic sandstones, lenticular and strong reflectors are interpreted as coeval shelf turbidite fans. For simplicity, the fans are referred to here as middle and upper Gudrid, on account of the deltas that apparently supplied them. A fan equivalent of the lower Gudrid has not been perceived. This explains why some regard the lower Gudrid as a member of the Markland Formation, and the middle and upper Gudrid as members of the Cartwright Formation.

Lower Gudrid member

The lower Gudrid member has been penetrated in inner shelf wells in southern Hopedale Basin, in Ogmund E-72 of northern Hopedale Basin and at Gilbert F-53 in southern Saglek Basin. The deposits in southern Hopedale Basin form a thin prism, asymmetric toward the basin re-entrant, covering a large area. The unit tapers updip to a feather edge because of truncation and overstepping by upper Gudrid or equivalent Paleocene or Eocene beds. Downdip, the lower Gudrid grades abruptly into Markland shelf shales. In Saglek Basin the lower Gudrid member is interpreted from seismic profiles to be a thin, greatly restricted, seaward-facing prism. The interval has not been drilled in northern Saglek Basin or beneath Southeast Baffin Shelf. The thickest section of the lower Gudrid is 212 m at Roberval K-92 (2468-2680 m); this is about 2 km downdip from a 130 m section draped over a basement horst block at Roberval C-02. At Cartier D-70, the lower Gudrid thins to 60 m.

In Gudrid H-55, the lower Gudrid includes light grey to light brown, fine- to coarse-grained, poorly sorted, partly pebbly, slightly clayey, feldspathic, quartz sandstones. The lower 50 m are cemented by dolomite. Levels in which dolomite cement is present are indicated by high values on the sonic and resistivity well logs. At Cartier D-70 the lower Gudrid is composed of light grey to light green, medium- to very coarse-grained quartzose sandstones with much feldspar, and some glauconite grains and some siderite and kaolinitic cement. Porosity is excellent throughout the succession.

The sandstones of the lower Gudrid member form asymmetric, seaward-facing wedges, the distal parts of which grade downdip into the upper shales of the Markland Formation. In landward positions, where most wells have penetrated the lower Gudrid unit, the nonmarine and shallow marine beds lie abruptly, with erosional unconformity, on the Markland shales. Although abrupt, the unconformity is judged to not represent much geological time. The lower Gudrid member and upper Markland Formation are regarded as the proximal and distal facies, respectively, of the same depositional sequence. In inner shelf positions, the lower Gudrid beds are abruptly onlapped by marine shelf shales composing the upper Cartwright Member of the Cartwright Formation. This abrupt contact marks a significant Paleocene hiatus. In mid-shelf positions, a succession of post-Danian-Paleocene rocks (middle Gudrid and equivalent lower Gudrid members) occupies a stratigraphic position at the level of this unconformity.

The age of the lower Gudrid member is uncertain. However, it can be interpreted in many seismic sections as an updip, shoreward, sandy facies equivalent of the upper shales of the Markland Formation. Since the uppermost Markland beds have been consistently dated as Danian, it is tentatively concluded that the lower Gudrid member is Danian. Further biostratigraphic studies are needed.

The sandstones of the lower Gudrid member have a characteristically blocky log character; they contain coal clasts, glauconite, and neritic fossils. Both the lower and upper Gudrid members have asymmetric, seaward facing, wedge-shaped seismic geometries, locally with oblique and sigmoidal internal reflectors. The lower Gudrid wedges pinch or grade downdip into Markland shales, in such a way as to prompt the suggestion that the steep, seaward-facing edge of the sandstones is a paleoslope, locally with relief of several tens of metres to possibly 200 m.

The lower Gudrid sandstones appear to be coastal sand bodies, partly delta- mouth and peripheral bar deposits, cleaned by waves and tides, that occupy shallow paleotopographic lows in the Danian coastal regime. The proximal delta plain facies and updip channel facies were largely eroded during mid-Paleocene time, as described in a later section.

At the southern margin of the Hopedale Basin, seaward of Hamilton Inlet (Fig. 7.1), a series of deltaic deposits include the underlying Freydis Member, and the lower, middle and upper Gudrid members. Also present is a locally well-developed Upper Eocene coastal sandstone, the Leif Member of the Kenamu Formation. This repeated Late Cretaceous to mid-Tertiary deltaic progradation eastward across the shallow marine shelf suggests that central Hamilton Inlet may have contained an important trunk stream, the ancestral Hamilton River, that transported coarse clastics from coastal uplands. The presence of reworked Mesozoic and Paleozoic fossils in pelitic shelf equivalents of the deltaic sandstones, indicates also that the "Hamilton River" system may have drained large areas of the adjacent interior part of the craton.

Cartwright Formation

Umpleby (1979) applied the name Cartwright Formation to the Upper Cretaceous, Paleocene, and Lower Eocene shales on the Labrador Shelf. He chose as a type section the interval 2393-2650 m in Gudrid H-55. Umpleby included two members in the Cartwright Formation. These were the Freydis Sand Member and the Gudrid Sand Member. McWhae et al. (1980) revised Umpleby's nomenclature. They restricted the Cartwright Formation to the Paleocene and Lower Eocene part of the succession, and included the Freydis Member in their Markland Formation. McWhae et al. (1980) designated the interval 1820-1975 m in the Bjarni H-81 well, the Hopedale Basin, as the type section for the Cartwright Formation.

The Cartwright Formation is a readily distinguishable unit in most wells and can be generally delineated seismically, thus providing a mappable, useful stratigraphic interval (Fig. 7.11). The intervals 2069 to 2453 m in Gilbert F-53 and 3036 to 3793 m in Karlsefni A-13 are thick sections and display on well logs the characteristic log styles of the Cartwright shales. In Saglek Basin, and northward to Southeast Baffin Shelf, the Cartwright Formation can be divided into lower and upper members, based on the presence of a prominent seismic and sonic log

marker. These members, and the sonic log marker that separates them, are conspicuously displayed by the logs for Gilbert F-53 and Karlsefni A-13. Beds at the top of the lower and upper Cartwright members are distal, silty facies of coastal sandstones informally referred to here as the middle and upper Gudrid members. The lower Gudrid member is the coastal facies sandstone interval at the top of the Markland Formation (described in the preceding section on the Markland Formation).

The Cartwright Formation extends parallel to the shelf off Labrador and southern Baffin Island forming an elongate prism, which thins landward by depositional onlap onto older rocks, and thins seaward by downlap onto and

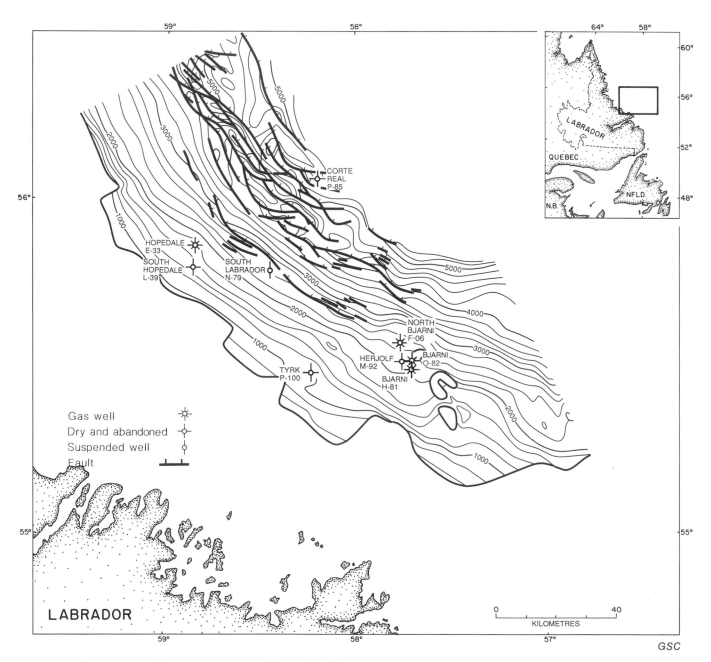

Figure 7.11 Structure map, top of Cartwright Formation, south-central Hopedale Basin. Structure contours in metres below sea level. Heavy lines denote seaward facing normal faults.

intercalation with large mounds of Paleocene volcanic rocks. In the central Hopedale Basin and parts of the Saglek Basin, the formation is fragmented by large, eastward-dipping listic normal faults (Fig. 7.3, 7.11, 7.12). Interpretation and correlation of seismic markers is very difficult through these arrays of faults. The faults, which penetrate the lower part of the Mokami Formation, may be products of large-scale, down-slope, supracrustal gravitational gliding of the sedimentary succession on a detachment surface above structural basement. Alternatively, the faults may be adjustments of the sedimentary succession to a phase of mid-Tertiary extension within the underlying crust. The latter interpretation is favoured here.

The Cartwright Formation is thickest in central Saglek Basin, offshore Hudson Strait. Basal beds lie deeper than the base of conventional seismic sections (6 seconds two-way time) in the middle and outer parts of the shelf where the formation is likely to be about 2500 m thick. At Rut H-11, the Cartwright is 913 m thick (3125-4038 m). At Gjoa G-37 it is over 1500 m thick (2337-3877 m), but this includes some thick basalt flows, a common occurrence on Southeast Baffin Shelf. In Hopedale Basin, the formation is much thinner, partly because the lower member is absent or only thinly developed in the inner parts of the shelf succession. The thickest measured section in this basin is in South Labrador N-79 where it is 495 m (2432-2927 m) thick. The Cartwright Formation generally thickens downdip (seaward) from the edge of the middle Gudrid member. In some places the Cartwright can be traced to the edge of the modern continental slope.

The Cartwright Formation in South Labrador N-79 is light to dark grey, soft to fissile, partly glauconitic, partly silty shale, with chips of brown, hard, silty, microcrystalline limestone. The lower part of the Cartwright Formation in Karlsefni A-13 consists of medium and dark grey shale with calcareous, partly glauconitic siltstones; traces of carbonaceous fragments are present on siltstone parting surfaces. Prominent sonic log peaks are interpreted to be calcareous and sideritic siltstone lenses. The upper part of the formation consists of medium to dark grey, silty, partly micromicaceous, partly fissile shale. Some beds are slightly calcareous; others are slightly glauconitic or pyritic. Foraminifera and broken pelecypod shells are common in the silty beds at the top of the formation.

The general colour, texture, and fabric of the Cartwright shales are similar to those of the Markland Formation; this explains why Umpleby (1979) regarded the Upper Cretaceous to Paleocene succession as a single unit. Nevertheless, the Cartwright Formation (as used here) is a recognizable entity from well log data and is an unconformity-bounded (depositional sequence) in landward positions.

In the middle part of the shelf, seismic reflectors in the lower part of the Cartwright Formation are conformable

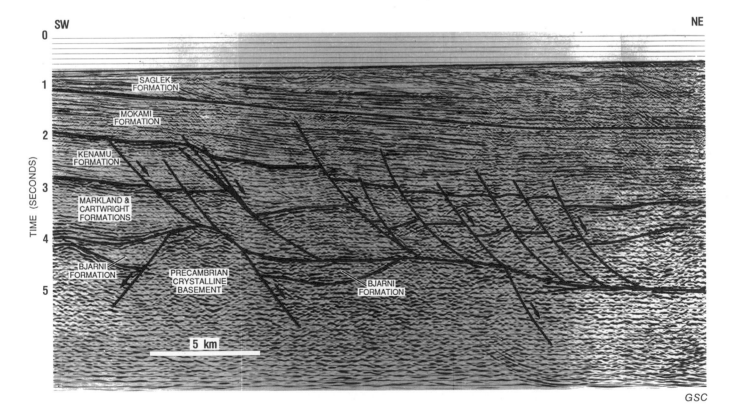

GSC

Figure 7.12 Seismic section (migrated) central Hopedale Basin. Two-way time (seconds) along left margin. Note: Listric geometry of mid-Tertiary seaward (eastward) facing normal faults; antithetic dip of Kenamu reflectors toward fault surfaces; depositional infilling of fault- associated topography by lower Mokami member; irregular, seaward (eastward) facing clinoforms in upper part of Saglek Formation; landward (westward) uniform dip of modern-day shelf surface.

with the reflector marking the contact between the Markland and Cartwright formations. Shoreward the basal Cartwright reflectors onlap the top of the Markland surface. The contact is an abrupt marker on sonic and resistivity logs. In some middle and outer parts of the Hopedale Basin, the lower Cartwright reflectors can be seen to downlap seaward on older rocks including the Markland Formation, volcanic ridges and Precambrian basement. In the middle and outer parts of Saglek Basin the contact between the Markland and the Cartwright is buried so deeply that it is below the bottom of the seismic section, conventionally recorded to six seconds. Along Southeast Baffin Shelf the lower Cartwright beds are intercalated with, or onlap Paleocene basalt flows (Fig. 7.10). An unconformity can be locally discerned, separating lower and upper Cartwright members. This unconformity can be traced up the regional dip to the sigmoidal wedge interpreted as the middle Gudrid member. Shoreward from the middle Gudrid wedge, the lower Cartwright is absent and upper Cartwright shales (or the equivalent upper Gudrid member) rest disconformably on, or onlap, the lower Gudrid member or shales of the Markland Formation. A coaly sandstone, which occurs below 2858 m in Hekja O-71, forms a prominent marker on seismic records. The sandstone and underlying shales gently onlap and eventually merge with the middle Gudrid marker just north of Hudson Strait, demonstrating that the base of the upper member is a diachronous contact.

To the west, the upper surface of the Cartwright Formation lies parallel to the beds of the overlying Kenamu. Lower Kenamu shales lie abruptly on the Cartwright Formation (Fig. 7.13). These Kenamu shales have relatively low velocity and low resistivity. The top of the Cartwright Formation is indistinct, seismically, beneath the Southeast Baffin Shelf.

Palynologists and micropaleontologists have dated the basal beds of the Cartwright as early Paleocene in Gilbert F-53, located in Saglek Basin. The early-late Paleocene boundary is picked at 2405 m, about 100 m below the boundary between the lower and upper Cartwright. The Paleocene-Eocene boundary is at 2025 m; this places the top of the Cartwright, at 2069 m, in the late Paleocene. The lower member in Gilbert contains numerous reworked late Cretaceous pollen. In Hopedale Basin, the Cartwright is Late Paleocene in the South Labrador N-79 well. This agrees with the age for the interval 2215-2289 m in North Bjarni F-06. The above indicate that the Cartwright Formation is of Late Paleocene age on most of the Labrador Shelf. The unconformity between the lower and upper members is presumably early late Paleocene.

The oldest sediments recovered from DSDP Site 112 (Fig. 1, in pocket) in the Labrador Sea are indurated red clays with authigenic calcite. The red colouring is due to hematite and ferromanganese oxides. The sediments have been baked by intrusive basaltic sills. Nannofossils from above these sediments have been dated as ?Late Paleocene to Early Eocene. Laughton (1972) calculated a middle to late Paleocene age for the basal sediments by using the average rate of sedimentation for the Eocene strata in the hole. Therefore, these sediments may be coeval with the Cartwright Formation.

Inner-shelf Gudrid sandstones (which locally are coal bearing) are seaward-facing, relatively thin sigmoidal wedges with interval reflectors resembling clinoform beds of deltas quite unlike the usual seismic character of turbidite fans — an interpretation favoured by some. Locally, the delta-like bodies merge downdip with elongate lensoid reflectors that are interpreted as sandy turbidite fans. In most places, however, the Gudrid deltaic sand bodies merge downdip with subparallel, layered reflectors representing shales of the Cartwright Formation. Paleotopographic relief from the tops of the delta-like bodies to the subjacent marine Cartwright shales can be estimated after correcting for the tilting imposed by subsequent deposition; the relief was probably not more than a few hundred metres, including the effects of differential compaction. Paleoecological characteristics of fossils in the Gilbert F-53 well suggest an outer neritic environment. This agrees with the interpretation that the Cartwright pelites accumulated as distal turbiditic muds, downdip from low-relief, seaward-facing, construction slopes of small Paleocene and Early Eocene deltas.

Gradstein and Srivastava (1980) concluded that Paleocene foraminiferal assemblages in Labrador shelf wells indicate incursions of temperate Atlantic water masses.

Middle Gudrid member

The interval here referred to as middle Gudrid can be traced seismically by means of the laterally correlative lower Cartwright member, from Hopedale Basin northward to wells on Southeast Baffin Shelf, where the gas-bearing sandstones have been referred to informally as the "Hekja sand" (Klose et al., 1982, p. 234).

The middle Gudrid has not been drilled in the Hopedale Basin but it is probably present in the mid-central part of the basin on account of the seismic geometry displayed within the Paleocene succession. The middle Gudrid wedge pinches updip rather abruptly; it does not extend landward as far as either the Markland Formation or the upper Gudrid member. Seaward, the wedge merges with a succession correlative with the lower Cartwright shales. Middle Gudrid (i.e. "Hekja") sands at Hekja O-71 are 86 m thick (3200-3286 m). From there the sands thin eastward to about 30 m (3485-3515 m) at Ralegh N-18. At Gjoa G-37 the sandstones are part of the intercalated Paleocene sedimentary and volcanic succession and no meaningful thickness can be determined.

Middle Gudrid beds at Hekja O-71 consist of light grey-brown, fine- to coarse-grained subangular, poorly sorted, slightly pyritic and slightly glauconitic, micaceous, partly arkosic, partly lithic, quartz sandstones with calcareous and kaolinitic cement. The sandstones have thin intercalations of black, brittle coal with vitreous lustre. The coal beds are indicated by extremely low-velocity intervals on the sonic logs. The various types of feldspars have undergone extensive dissolution and alteration, with the result that the sand is highly microporous and contains abundant kaolinite. The middle Gudrid member at Ralegh N-18, is medium- to coarse-grained, arkosic sandstone which may include as much as 30% feldspar and has abundant kaolinite in the matrix. Glauconite and shell fragments are also present.

Seismic evidence in the Hopedale Basin indicates that the middle Gudrid sandstones lie abruptly and paraconformably on lower Cartwright shales, which are the broadly coeval, downdip basinal or shelf succession. The unit is onlapped and overstepped shoreward on an erosional hia-

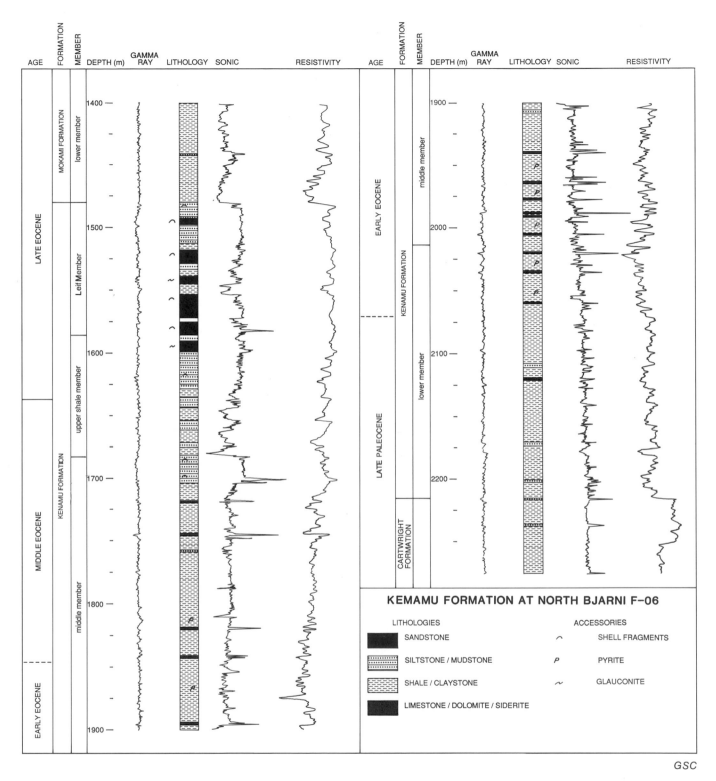

Figure 7.13 Log character and lithology of Kenamu Formation at North Bjarni F-06. Age assignments from Bujak and Lee (pers. comm., 1983).

tus by upper Cartwright shales. In some parts of Southeast Baffin Shelf, as in the vicinity of Ralegh N-18, the middle Gudrid sandstones onlap Paleocene basalt flows and are overstepped by upper Cartwright shales.

Klose et al. (1982) stated that the Hekja sands in Hekja O-71 were Paleocene. They placed the top of the Early Paleocene (Danian) at 3530 m. This is about 15 m below the base of beds here included in the middle Gudrid member.

The presence of poorly sorted, fine- to coarse-grained, coaly sandstones in the middle Gudrid at Hekja O-71, landward from finer grained, glauconitic, shelly, thinner sandstones at Ralegh N-18, suggests that the sandstones at the Hekja location comprise a lower delta-plain deposit, which grades eastward to shallow marine shoreface sandstones. Topset (delta-plain) and oblique forset (delta-front) reflectors are discernible in the Hopedale Basin; the forset beds merge downdip with a lens of prominent reflectors, interpreted as a shallow marine fan. The oblique progradational seismic character may be indicative of high-energy, sandy deposition. The fan may contain sand deposits fed by local erosion of the superadjacent delta during an abrupt lowering of sea level in the mid-Late Paleocene. This is substantiated by the studies of Gradstein and Williams (1976), who suggested there was a "middle" Paleocene hiatus on the Labrador Shelf. A possibility that the fan is at least partly sandstone is enhanced by the compactional drape observable in overlying shales.

The textural and mineralogical immaturity of the middle Gudrid sands of the Hekja region results from their derivation from nearby exposures of Precambrian crystalline rocks, probably from ancestral uplands of Baffin Island.

Upper Gudrid member

The term "upper Gudrid" member is used for coastal sand deposits and associated downdip shelf fans, which are the landward equivalent of the upper Cartwright Formation. Upper Gudrid sandstones are thick and well developed in the inner part of the southern Hopedale Basin, at such wells as Cartier D-70, Freydis B-87, and Gudrid H-55. From seismo-stratigraphic interpretation this arcuate mass of sand lies seaward from the mouth of Hamilton Inlet, which may have been an important Paleocene fluvial outlet for the sandy clastics. At Gudrid H-55, the upper Gudrid member is 100 m thick (2180-2280 m). Upper Gudrid beds are present also at Tyrk P-100 (73 m) in the central part of the basin and to the north in Snorri J-90 (24 m) and Ogmund E-72 (56 m). Some sandstones are present at the upper Gudrid level in Hekja O-71 and Ralegh N-18, but these are so poorly developed that they are included within the upper Cartwright shale-dominated succession. Slightly sandy siltstones are present at the same level in Gjoa G-37.

Upper Gudrid sandstones in the Gudrid H-55 well are composed of fine- to coarse-grained, subangular to subrounded, clear to white quartz sand, with the upper Gudrid sandstone. Barss et al. (1979) placed the Paleocene-Eocene boundary in Gudrid H-55 within the upper Gudrid interval. The unconformity separating the middle and upper Gudrid members is Late Paleocene, possibly mid-Late Paleocene. The age range for the upper Gudrid sandstones is therefore mid(?)? Late Paleocene-Early Eocene. This is consistent with correlation of the sandstones with the upper shale member of the Cartwright Formation on seismic records.

Upper Gudrid sandstones in the Gudrid H-55 well are composed of fine- to coarse-grained, subangular to subrounded, clear to white quartz sand, with abundant feldspar grains, some quartz pebbles and some glauconite. The beds are poorly cemented by kaolinite and have excellent porosity. In the nearby well, Cartier D-70, the upper Gudrid consists of light grey, fine grained, feldspathic, glauconitic quartz sandstone with calcite cement. The rocks have fair to good intergranular porosity. The gas-bearing upper Gudrid reservoir in Snorri J-90 (2491-2515 m) in the northern Hopedale Basin is composed of fine grained, feldspathic sandstone with zones of siderite cement (the cement appearing as prominent peaks on the sonic log), some pyrite, and zones of abundant kaolinite. The sandstones in the core from 2497 to 2504 m is also bioturbated in many places.

The upper Gudrid member penetrated in wells in the Hopedale Basin is the shoreward coarse grained facies of an Upper Paleocene depositional sequence. The sands lie disconformably on a Paleocene hiatus in the inner part of the shelf. In some places the hiatus separates lower and upper Gudrid members as at Gudrid H-55. In other wells upper Gudrid sandstones overlie upward coarsening, upper shales of the Cartwright Formation, and the contact represents little or no significant length of time, as at Freydis B-87. In some areas of the inner shelf the upper Gudrid beds have overstepped older units and lie unconformably on the Freydis Member of the Markland Formation, as at Tyrk P-100, or older units. Middle shelf, locally developed sand facies representing distal fans of the upper Gudrid may lie on the middle Gudrid deltaic sandstone. The upper surface of the Gudrid interval is onlapped landward by basal marine shales of Kenamu Formation.

Upper Gudrid sandstones are sparsely fossiliferous. The top of the Paleocene in the Roberval C-02 well has been placed at 2175 m by some oil company paleontologists. This is about 20 m above the top of Gudrid sandstones. In other wells, some paleontologists have assigned part of the upper Gudrid to the Lower Eocene. The boundary between the Eocene and Paleocene in Gudrid H-55 has been picked at about the middle of the upper Gudrid interval by Williams and Barss (Barss et al., 1979). The unconformity separating middle and upper Gudrid members is Late Paleocene (possibly mid-Late Paleocene). Therefore, the age range for the upper Gudrid sandstones is mid(?) – Late Paleocene-Early Eocene. This is consistent with correlation of the sandstones with the upper shale member of the Cartwright Formation on seismic records.

Seismic and log interpretations suggest that the upper Gudrid sandstones along the inner part of the Hopedale Basin are shallow marine, shoreface beds, locally contiguous with a system of small deltas. The sandy deltas, and peripheral shaly interdeltaic deposits (as at Tyrk P-100), formed a low seaward-facing slope, down which sands were fed to thin turbidite fans, elongated subparallel to the coast, on the subjacent shelf. A similar interpretation would explain the coeval sands in Hekja O-71 in Saglek Basin.

The features suggested here as turbidite fans have not been drilled. Their position, peripheral to the wedge-shaped deltaic and shoreface deposits, and geometry, the overlying shales are draped, indicate that the fans contain significant amounts of sandstone. The sandstones may be fine grained, however, and may have abundant shale interbeds. Identification of channels, updip from the suspected fans, carved in Cartwright shales and Precambrian basement, enhances the likelihood that the seismic entities are fans and that they probably contain sandstone. Moreover, the seismic data suggest the lower parts of feeder channels may be plugged with sandstone and the upper parts may be plugged with shale.

Kenamu, Mokami and Saglek formations — Status

Umpleby (1979) placed all the Labrador Shelf Tertiary rocks of Eocene age or younger in the Saglek Formation. This included a thick, monotonous sequence of mudstones which becomes sandier and siltier upwards. The type section was designated as the interval 1027-1131 m in Freydis B-87 in the southern Hopedale Basin. Two members, the Brown Mudstone Member and the Leif Sand Member, were included in the Saglek. According to the North American Stratigraphic Code (1983), Brown Mudstone Member is not a legitimate name.

The type section of the Brown Mudstone Member was given as the interval 1131-1321 m in Freydis B-87 in southern Hopedale Basin. The type section of the Leif Member was given as 2191-2394 m in Karlsefni A-13 in southern Saglek Basin. Umpleby stated that the Saglek Formation was Eocene-Miocene in age, and was overlain by unconsolidated sand and clay of Plio-Pleistocene age.

McWhae et al. (1980) revised the Saglek Formation to include only the uppermost pre-Quaternary part of the sequence. The older rocks they subdivided into the Kenamu Formation (Eocene) and the Mokami Formation (Late Eocene-Middle Miocene). Unfortunately, McWhae et al. proposed abandonment of the type section for the Saglek Formation and the Leif Member. According to Article 8e of the North American Stratigraphic Code (1983) a type section cannot be abandoned, although the lower or upper boundaries can be modified. Pending solution of the above dilemma, we have used the lithostratigraphic units of McWhae et al. (1980) and recognize all three formations — the Kenamu, the Mokami, and the Saglek — on the Labrador Shelf.

Kenamu Formation

McWhae et al. (1980) introduced the name Kenamu Formation for the thick, widespread, shale-dominated succession of Eocene age on the Labrador Shelf. The type section was taken as the interval 1222-1666 m in Leif M-48 in the southern part of Hopedale Basin. The formation consists of marine silty shale, shale, siltstone and fine grained sandstone, with thin, dolomitic limestone beds. McWhae et al. included the Brown Mudstone Member and Leif Member in the Kenamu Formation. They did not refer to the Brown Mudstone Member in their discussion of the lithostratigraphy, however, apart from recognizing it in Leif M-48. In Part 1 of this chapter we have followed the usage of McWhae et al. (1980), but also recognize three informal members within the Kenamu Formation throughout most parts of the Labrador and Southeast Baffin Shelf (Fig. 7.14):

1. The lower Kenamu member, slightly silty marine shales, which fine upward;
2. The middle Kenamu member, marine shales, which coarsen upward to siltstone, or locally, to fine grained marine sandstone;
3. The upper Kenamu member, dominantly marine siltstones, coarsening-upward in some places to shoreface and coastal sandstones; evidence from some wells indi-

cates that there may be at least two unconformities in the upper sandy sequence. The Leif sandstones, which can be regarded as informal, are included in this member. It is now apparent from well logs that sandstones may be developed at as many as three levels in the upper Kenamu succession: beneath the "top-of-Kenamu unconformity"; or beneath either of the two disconformities within the coarse grained succession. "Leif" is useful for referring to these sandstones, which are the most important mid-Tertiary hydrocarbon reservoirs in the Labrador terrace wedge.

The upper surface of the Kenamu Formation is a regional unconformity (probably partly subaerial). The surface is broken by arrays of seaward(eastward)-dipping listric normal faults (Fig. 7.12, 7.14).

The three members are discernible in the North Bjarni F-06 well in central Hopedale Basin (Fig. 7.13). The Kenamu Formation in this well is 735 m thick. The sequence can be subdivided as follows:

1. The lower Kenamu member is 201 m thick and consists of dark grey to dark brown-grey, partly fissile, slightly micro-micaceous shale. Chips of dark brown microcrystalline limestone coincide with high velocity peaks on sonic logs and are probably calcitic nodules.
2. The middle Kenamu member is 331 m thick and consists of dark grey to dark brown-grey, slightly micro-micaceous and silty shale with microcrystalline limestone chips. The uppermost 25 m are increasingly silty upwards.
3. The upper Kenamu member is 203 m thick and consists of grey, silty, calcareous shales in the lower part, with interbedded shales, siltstones and fine grained sandstone — the Leif Member with fair intergranular porosity. The sandstone is light grey and slightly calcareous because of the cement and shell fragments.

The North Bjarni F-06 well is a good reference (Fig. 7.13). It displays the three shale members of the Kenamu Formation as well as fine-grained sandstones of the Leif Member.

The Kenamu Formation is thickest — about 2200 m from seismic intervals — in the depocentre of Saglek Basin, east of Hudson Strait. It thins rapidly to the south, being only 131 m thick in Skolp E-07, and onlaps the northern flank of the Okak Arch. The formation also thins westward to the updip margin of the Tertiary terrace wedge, and eastward to north-central Labrador Sea. However, the middle and upper members extend underneath the present-day northern Labrador continental slope and continue, locally segmented by faulted blocks and mounds of oceanic basalt, underneath the Labrador Sea to the Greenland continental shelf. At Hekja O-71 the Kenamu Formation is 850 m thick (1730-2580 m); in nearby Ralegh N-18 it is 1170 m thick (1865-3035 m). In those wells the top of the lower member cannot be picked but the top of the middle member is easily determined. The thickest Kenamu sections drilled in the Hopedale Basin are at Indian Harbour M-52 (1032 m) and South Labrador N-79 (985 m). The formation does not appear to be much thicker than 1000 m anywhere in the Hopedale Basin.

In the middle part of the Hopedale Basin the upper Kenamu member is truncated by a locally abrupt, seaward-facing erosion surface which in some places probably has a relief of about 600 m (Fig. 7.6). The seaward-facing escarpment trends irregularly subparallel to the

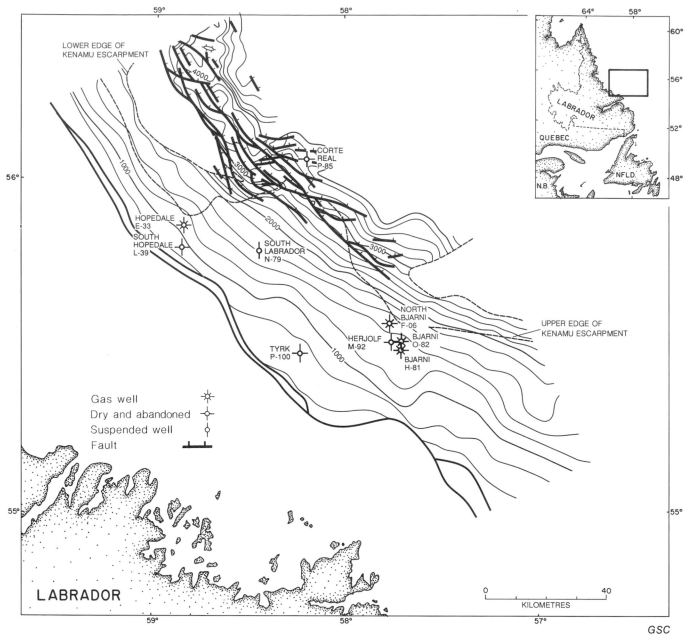

Figure 7.14 Structure map, top of Kenamu Formation, south-central Hopedale Basin. Structure contours in metres below sea level. See Figure 7.15 for seismic expression of Kenamu erosional escarpment.

present-day Hopedale Bight. The escarpment is near the western edge of the zone of Hopedale growth faults. It is not possible to trace this erosional surface into the growth-fault zone with any degree of confidence. However, tens to perhaps a few hundreds of metres of upper Kenamu beds must have been removed locally by the erosional event. This would explain the abrupt, irregular isopachs of the upper Kenamu member (Fig. 7.6).

The Leif sandstones are best developed in Hopedale Basin in the wells east of Hamilton Inlet, which are also, usually, the wells with thick lower and upper Gudrid sandstone. Only two wells, Corte Real P-85 and Indian Harbour M-52, have penetrated the stratigraphic level of the Leif sandstones in the outer part of the shelf. Neither well

encountered any significant thickness of Eocene sandstones. At Pothurst P-19, medium- to coarse-grained, well-sorted, quartzose glauconitic sandstones were encountered at 3980 m. These sandstones are at a seismic marker that is correlated with the top of the Kenamu Formation at Karlsefni A-13, and they may therefore represent the "Upper Leif" sandstones.

Carbonaceous and pyritic beds are common in the upper Kenamu in many wells. Thin coal beds are present in the upper part of the middle Kenamu member in Hekja O-71 and in Ralegh N-18, and coal was reported in samples at the level of the middle Kenamu member in Corte Real P-85.

Basal lower Kenamu beds onlap the Cartwright Formation in the vicinity of the hinge zones of Hopedale and Saglek basins (Fig. 7.6, 7.10). Landward from the hinge zones, the Kenamu strata locally overstep the Cartwright Formation onto older rocks. The contact is abrupt in the wells where the Kenamu Formation overlies the upper Gudrid member. Where the Kenamu lies disconformably on Cartwright shales, the contact in wells is marked by abrupt decreases in sonic velocity and in resistivity at the basal Kenamu shales. Seaward, the formation thins by downlap from the basin-axis prism. It oversteps the Cartwright Formation near the position of the present continental slope, at the transition zone between continental and oceanic crust, as determined from the marginal gravity anomaly and magnetic character. Towards the axis of Labrador Sea, the Kenamu Formation unconformably overlies oceanic crust, presumed to be Eocene and older.

The upper surface of the Kenamu Formation is one of the most easily discernible contacts of the Labrador Shelf succession, prominent in seismic records and in well logs. The surface provides a regional datum for intrabasin and basin-to-basin correlation from the northern Saglek Basin (Gjoa G-37) to the southern Hopedale Basin (Freydis B-87) — a distance of about 1200 km. The main reason that this upper surface is so visible is that it represents the top of an upward-coarsening sequence which is shelf-wide, and which is truncated in the inner and middle parts of the shelf by an unconformity. Siltstones and sandstones of the upper Kenamu (the Leif member in the broad sense) beneath the unconformity are overlain abruptly by basal marine shales of the lower Mokami member. The contact is demonstrated clearly and with consistent character in well logs, especially sonic logs: the sonic transit times in lower Mokami shales are conspicuously shorter than those in underlying upper Kenamu beds (Fig. 7.13).

On Southeast Baffin Shelf, southeast of Cumberland Sound, basal beds of the Mokami Formation downlap seaward and southeastward over the upper Kenamu. Locally, on some massive volcanic plugs in the outer part of the shelf, the Kenamu surface lies at or near the present day sea floor (Fig. 7.15). Downlap seaward by the Mokami on the Kenamu surface also occurs in the area south of Frobisher Bay. In central Saglek Basin the Mokami Formation onlaps the Kenamu landward. The Kenamu is onlapped by basal Mokami beds on the northern and southern flanks of Okak Arch.

Near the western edge of the Hopedale Basin, the reflectors marking the top of the Kenamu and the lower Mokami are subparallel. The basal Mokami beds must have formerly overstepped the Kenamu Formation landward from the present erosional limit of the terrace wedge, but the strata have been removed by subsequent erosion. In the southern part of Hopedale Basin the lower Mokami reflectors diverge seaward from the inner shelf hinge zone. Neither onlap nor downlap of the upper Kenamu surface can be discerned in the middle and inner shelf; some onlap may exist in parts of the outer shelf.

The palynomorphs and foraminifera of the lower Kenamu shales indicate an Early Eocene age. The middle member has been consistently dated as Middle Eocene. The age of the upper member is contentious.

Gradstein and Williams (1981) placed the top of the Kenamu Formation close to the Eocene-Oligocene boundary. In well history reports published by the operators, the

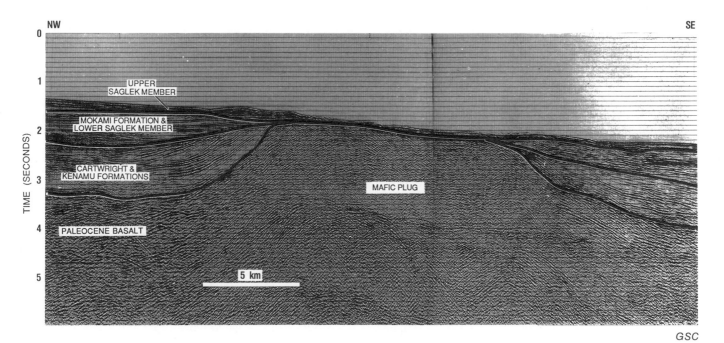

GSC

Figure 7.15 Seismic section (migrated), Southeast Baffin Shelf near Gjoa G-37. Two-way time (seconds) along left margin. Note: "ropy" mounded nature of Paleocene basalt reflectors; vague, diffuse nature of reflectors in mafic plug; truncation of Kenamu and Cartwright reflectors at the late Eocene unconformity; infilling of late Eocene-early Oligocene structural surface by lower Mokami member; thin, discontinuous distribution of upper Saglek member.

Eocene-Oligocene boundary is placed within the lower part of the Mokami Formation. Pending further studies, the Kenamu is being restricted to the Eocene, and the regional erosional hiatus between the Kenamu and Mokami is Late Eocene (Fig. 7.2).

Hinz et al. (1979) published interpretations of multichannel seismic reflection lines across the Labrador Sea. Their shelf marker horizon E approximates with the top of the Eocene, coinciding with our top of the Kenamu Formation (A.C. Grant, pers. comm., 1983).

Foraminifera and palynomorphs in the Kenamu Formation indicate that shales of the lower and middle members were deposited in outer neritic to bathyal water depths. Paleo-ecological studies of the upper Kenamu are not so definitive. Foraminifera indicate a deep marine environment, but the palynomorph assemblages suggest shallow marine and coastal environments. We accept the latter interpretation because of the reasons outlined in the following paragraph.

The most striking characteristics of the Kenamu Formation in the central and southern parts of Saglek Basin and throughout Hopedale Basin are the general tendencies for upward fining within the lower member, and upward coarsening within the middle and upper members (Fig. 7.13). These trends were noted in sonic logs. These characteristics were not seen in the Kenamu of the northern Saglek Basin, presumably because the succession there represents more proximal, coarser, and less well-graded deposits. The general textural style of the formation is taken to indicate gradual subsidence and deepening of the shelf from the onset of deposition to the top of the lower Kenamu, when the shelf was generally deeper than at any preceding time in its history. This was followed by gradual shallowing through depositional upbuilding during the progradation of the middle and upper members onto the submerged shelves off Labrador and southeast Baffin Island. Further shallowing led to the development of widespread coastal settings in the Late Eocene, as shown by the Leif sands. This is shown in general by the shallowing upwards which some fossils indicate, and the coarsening upwards observed in many wells on a regional scale. Other observations support this interpretation concerning the Kenamu:

1. Coal beds occur in the upper Kenamu member at Herjolf M-92, in Hekja O-71, and there is abundant carbonaceous detritus in upper Kenamu beds in many wells. Lower beds of the Kenamu in Ralegh N-18 are indicative of a paralic environment; the upper 250 m of the formation in the same well are devoid of foraminifera, suggesting a nonmarine environment.

2. A pronounced regional unconformity lies at the top of the Kenamu Formation; parts of this surface beneath the present outer shelf may represent a submarine unconformity. The distinctiveness of the surface, its relief, and the frequent presence of overlying nonmarine beds, however, suggests that the unconformity beneath the inner part of the present shelf at least was subaerial; it may have represented a brief phase of shelf emergence on the coastal plain — a climax to the shallowing trend of the Late Eocene.

3. The top of the Kenamu surface is tilted regionally seaward from an Eocene hinge zone of the inner shelf (Fig. 7.10); almost all the tilting resulted from post-Eocene

subsidence of the outer shelf. The shelf probably had a very low seaward gradient in Eocene time.

4. Seismic reflectors in the upper Kenamu member are smooth and subparallel. There is no evidence to indicate that the gradient of the Late Eocene shelf was interrupted by a high, seaward-facing bathymetric slope down which turbidity currents could have moved.

Most lines of evidence indicate therefore that the upper Kenamu beds are deposits of a shallow shelf or are coastal. The distribution of the sands and the inclination of internal seismic reflectors indicate that river systems contributed clastics to the shelf mainly from outlets near Cumberland Sound, Hudson Strait and Hamilton Inlet. Sand at Snorri J-90 in northern Hopedale Basin may have been derived from erosion of headlands of Precambrian basement during emergence of the Okak Arch in the Late Eocene. If the seaward gradient in the Late Eocene was as gradual as it appears to have been, tides and storm waves probably affected the deposition of coarse grained, sand-prone facies. In the case of the older coastal deposits, such as the sands of the three Gudrid members and the Freydis member, the prevailing southward directed flow of the ancestral Labrador current may have caused some preferential transport of sands to the southern shores of Saglek and Hopedale basins. This would make these prospective areas for sandstone reservoirs. The same may apply to the Kenamu sands which maybe the most prospective Eocene sandstone reservoirs.

Reworked Mesozoic and early Tertiary palynomorphs and foraminifera are present in the upper part of the Kenamu Formation. Kimmeridgian to Barremian fossils are reported, as well as reworked Late Cretaceous dinoflagellates near the top of the formation in North Bjarni F-06. It is unlikely that rocks of these ages survived the early Tertiary erosion of the Labrador coastal region. The Mesozoic fossils are therefore important indicators of mid-Tertiary erosion of Mesozoic strata in the interior of the craton. This supports the concept of a drainage system through Hudson Bay (McMillan, 1973; Hiscott, 1984). The possibility that some Mesozoic fossils originated locally cannot be discounted, since an outlier of this age has been found in Ford's Bight (King and McMillan, 1975).

Gradstein and Srivastava (1980) indicated that warm-temperate to temperate climatic conditions probably prevailed along the shelves of Labrador and southeastern Baffin Island in the Eocene. A climatic optimum was reached in the early or middle Eocene, about the time that the lower part of the middle Kenamu member was deposited. From then until late Eocene, the climate gradually cooled, a trend also seen in the Atlantic coastal plain of the United States (Powell and Baum, 1982).

Late Cretaceous-Eocene volcanic rocks

Along most of Saglek Basin, Cartwright Arch, Okak Arch, and Cumberland Basin, the lower (seaward) part of the rift-age rocks and structures are overlain by a mounded, landward-sloping, topographically irregular surface, containing ropy, discontinuous, variably strong and weak internal reflectors. The internal reflectors commonly have landward-facing, high-angle structures, resembling high deltaic clinoform beds. Rocks composing such mounded features were drilled at the Rut H-11, Hekja O-71, and Ralegh N-18 wells, where they were intercalated successions of fractured, microcrystalline, olivine basalt flows, vitric tuff beds, and Upper Cretaceous and Paleocene pelitic sedimentary rocks. Petrologic evidence indicates that all of the basalts were erupted subaqueously. About 1000 m of these rocks were drilled at Hekja O-71; a similar succession, about 1300 m thick ,was drilled at Gjoa G-37 (Klose et al., 1982).

Vitric tuff beds at Rut H-11 have been intruded by an ophitic diabase dyke, which yielded a whole rock K-Ar age of 59 Ma (Klose et al., 1982). The volcanic rocks lie below Danian marine shales of the uppermost Markland Formation. A radiometric age of 56 ± 3 Ma (late Paleocene-early Eocene, Klose et al., 1982) was obtained from the top of the Gjoa G-37 volcanic succession; basalts in Hekja O-71 were dated as 105 and 119 Ma (Klose et al., 1982). Although these and other basalts sampled in northern Labrador Basin wells are considerably altered (making whole-rock determinations uncertain), the ages are within constraints imposed by biostratigraphic determinations from the intercalated sedimentary rocks.

Basalts that outcrop at Cape Dyer, which are landward extensions of this volcanic domain, are mainly or entirely Paleocene, having radiometric ages of 58 ± 2 Ma (Clarke and Upton, 1971). Those basalts appear to have been fed by a swarm of diabase dykes. The brecciated flows have southwestward (landward) facing, giant, high-angle flow fronts, resembling immense crossbeds. The clinoform-like seismic structures observed at the base of the Labrador cratonic monocline are probably similar basalt flow fronts.

G. Rodrigue (pers. comm., 1984) conducted a preliminary petrologic study of the volcanic and volcaniclastic rocks of the Labrador margin. The Upper Cretaceous, Paleocene, and Eocene volcanic rocks from Saglek Basin wells, and Gjoa G-37, have a tholeiitic character, which contrasts with the alkali character of Hopedale Basin synrift volcanics assigned to the Alexis Formation. This petrologic contrast probably resulted from the contrasting tectonic environments that existed during volcanism. High-pressure, CO_2-rich volatiles, prevalent during rift-stage cratonic extension, produced the alkali basalts of Hopedale Basin. Low-pressure, H_2O-rich volatiles produced the ocean-spreading, drift-stage tholeiites forming the floor of Saglek Basin.

Wherever they can be seismically discerned, tholeiitic basalts onlap and cover rifted cratonic basement, concealing the nature and seaward limit of the continental/oceanic crustal boundary.

Volcanic plugs

MacLean et al. (1982) described some large "ridge" structures, revealed by shallow seismic profiles, in Cumberland Basin. The ridges lend a distinctive tectonic style to Cumberland Basin, unmatched in Saglek or Hopedale basins, but duplicated to some extent by the northern, deep part of Labrador Basin. Two of the ridges are long fault-bounded blocks of basalt, forming the outer margin of the Cumberland Basin trancurrent-fault domain. The other two ridges appear to have intruded Eocene and older parts of the succession, as large piercement masses. As illustrated by MacLean et al. (1982), the masses lack internal continuity. They have flat, abruptly truncated tops and the flanking sedimentary strata are upturned and truncated in fashions reminiscent of large salt diapirs. Samples from

one of these ridges consist of mafic volcanic rocks, Albian-Cenomanian sandstone and upper Paleocene and lower Eocene siltstone.

Another ridge, comparable in size and style to those in the Cumberland Basin is displayed spectacularly by seismic lines several kilometres east of the Gjoa G-37 well (Fig. 7.15). The style of the Gjoa structure supports the interpretation by MacLean et al. (1982) that some of the ridges are huge, intrusive volcanic plugs. The Gjoa well provides good stratigraphic control for correlating seismic reflectors on the flanks of the ridge. The Gjoa plug has a mainly flat top and moderately to steeply dipping flanks. The interior of the structure lacks systematic reflectors. The boundaries with flanking sedimentary rocks consist of a single strong reflector, or several layered, slightly undulatory strong reflectors. Sedimentary layers correlative with the Cartwright and Kenamu formations at Gjoa G-37 are tilted subparallel with the upturned flanks of the structure. These strata are truncated toward the crest of the structure by the top of the late Eocene Kenamu unconformity, which is slightly tilted away from the intrusion. This unconformity forms the present seafloor over part of the plug. Basal beds of the Mokami Formation onlap the tilted late Eocene unconformity, overstep dipping beds of the Cartwright and Kenamu formations, and lie directly on some parts of the fringe of the plug. Reflectors comprising the walls of the plug are seismically traceable through a structural depression to interlayered Paleocene basalt at Gjoa G-37. The walls of the plug are therefore partly or entirely composed of Paleocene basalt, upturned concordantly with the overlying Cartwright and Kenamu formations.

Truncation of Kenamu strata and onlap of basal Mokami shales at the flanks of the plugs, indicate that the plugs were emplaced in viscous fashion in the late Eocene or early Oligocene. MacLean et al. (1982) suggested that the plugs were emplaced by mantle leakage along a transform zone (Ungava Transform Zone) related to plate separation of Greenland and eastern Canada. The orientation of the structures and their age supports this view.

Post-drift megasequence

McWhae et al. (1980) divided Oligocene and younger, post-drift strata of the Labrador margin into a shale-dominated lower unit, the Mokami Formation, and a sandstone-dominated upper unit, the Saglek Formation. Four upward-coarsening sequences, separated by seismically perceptible regional unconformities, can be recognized in these formations. The approximate Mokami-Saglek boundary of McWhae et al. is a diachronous horizon in a mainly Miocene sequence (Fig. 7.2).

Mokami Formation

McWhae et al. (1980) designated the interval of Eocene-Miocene mudstonesbetween 997-1715 m in Snorri J-90 in Hopedale Basin as the type section of the Mokami Formation. The formation was named for Mokami Hill on the Labrador coast.

The Mokami Formation does not represent continuous deposition. For many years seismic interpreters have correlated and mapped a prominent intra-Mokami marker in Hopedale Basin. The marker, which can be recognized on logs from several wells, separates two regional sequences with different areas of distribution and different tectonic

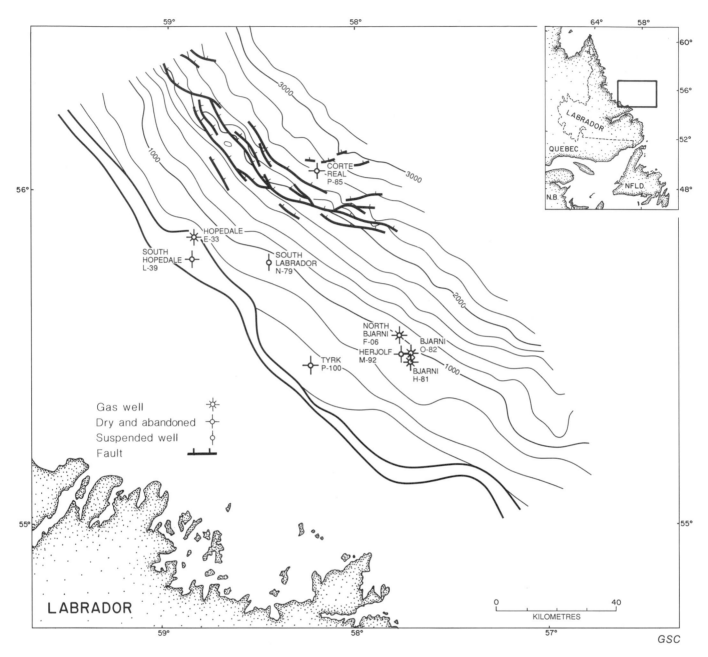

Figure 7.16 Structure map, top of lower member, Mokami Formation, south-central Hopedale Basin. Structure contours in metres below sea level. The number of faults and amount of structural relief are significantly less than at the early Tertiary levels (compare with Fig. 7.7).

significance (Fig. 7.16). The lower unit, the lower Mokami member, is a shale-dominated, unconformity-bounded stratigraphic sequence. Locally, an unconformity within the lower Mokami is prominent in the Hopedale Basin. The upper unit, the upper Mokami member, is the distal, shaly facies of a regional stratigraphic sequence that includes proximal coarse grained sands assigned to the lower part of the Saglek Formation (see Fig. 7.2 for relationship). The stratigraphic nomenclature needs revising formally to express these stratigraphic relationships. These units are referred to here informally as the lower Mokami member and upper Mokami member.

The lower Mokami member is a mudstone-dominated wedge that is thickest in the central parts of Saglek and Hopedale basins. It extends over all of the Labrador and southern Baffin Island shelves, disconformably overlying the Kenamu Formation. This contact can be recognized in most wells by a pronounced shift on sonic logs from relatively short travel times in the Kenamu Formation to longer travel times in the Mokami (Fig. 7.13). The disconformity marks a phase of regional emergence of the Labrador Shelf, with erosional truncation of the upper Kenamu beds in some areas, notably in the west central part of the Hopedale Basin. Basal Mokami beds onlap this surface landward (Fig. 7.6). The member thins landward by basal onlap, by truncation at its top, and by depositional thinning of internal increments, and thins seaward by basal downlap over the Kenamu Formation. It extends under the continental slope and merges with coeval sediments in central Labrador Basin, although it is locally absent on the crests and flanks of some high buried hills of oceanic basalt. In both the Hopedale (in the vicinity of Corte Real P-35) and Saglek basins (in the vicinity of Pothurst P-19), the lower member occupies structural depressions created by mid-Tertiary motion on seaward-dipping normal faults (Fig. 7.12).

The upper Mokami member is present mainly on the Labrador Shelf; landward it may onlap the lower member, seaward it extends in some places to the base of the continental slope where it terminates by downlap on the lower member, which is more widespread. Results from Site 112 of the Deep Sea Drilling Project show that the upper member is represented in the central Labrador Sea by thin pelagic deposits. Terrigenous clastics forming the upper member in the Saglek Basin prograded mainly southward across the shelf off southeastern Baffin Island. Beds coeval with the upper Mokami member in that area are mainly sandstones assigned to the lower part of the Saglek Formation (see Fig. 7.2 for relationship).

The Mokami Formation, particularly the upper member, is increasingly sandy northward through Saglek Basin to Southeast Baffin Shelf; there, the strata equivalent to the upper member are sandstone dominated and are therefore assigned to the lower part of the Saglek Formation. At Ralegh N-18 the interval between 1524 and 1865 m is classed with the lower member of the Mokami Formation.

In both the Hopedale and Saglek basins, the general lithological tendency within the lower and upper Mokami members is for upward- and landward-coarsening. In Hopedale Basin both members are almost entirely mudstones, moderately to poorly indurated, brown-grey and silty, with some thin siltstone beds, and zones of ironstone beds or nodules. Accessory glauconite, pyrite, carbonaceous detritus, and pelecypod fragments are present. A thick sequence of the lower Mokami in Corte Real P-95, central Hopedale Basin, includes thin beds of fine grained sandstone with poor intergranular porosity. Corte Real P-95 contains fine- to coarse-grained quartz sandstone with a clayey matrix that may be up to 15 m thick. The sandstones have poor to fair intergranular porosity. The contact with the lower member is marked by a 50 m thick interval of red clay. In northern Hopedale Basin at Snorri J-90, up to 15% of the upper member consists of fine- to medium-grained friable sandstones in beds 1 to 5 m thick. The sandstones are more abundant and coarser grained towards the top of the unit where they grade into overlying sandy beds of Saglek Formation. This coarsening upward trend is shown by both the lower and upper members throughout the area; there is also a tendency for both members to become coarser grained to the west.

Sandstones are much more prevalent in both the lower and upper Mokami members in Saglek Basin. At Karlsefni A-13 the upper part of the lower member contains some fine- to medium-grained, upward-coarsening, partly pebbly, porous sandstone beds as thick as 10 m; the upper member is mainly siltstone with about 25 per cent friable, porous sandstone interbeds and some relatively thin carbonaceous shales lignite beds. At Pothurst P-19, seaward of

the Karlsefni well, the lower and upper members contain beds of light grey, fine- to coarse-grained, cherty quartz sandstone with good intergranular porosity. Interbedded with the sandstones are mudstones, grey brown, sandy, silty, soft, and poorly indurated, with mollusc shells. Lower Mokami beds in wells of Southeast Baffin Shelf are almost 50 per cent fine- to coarse-grained friable sandstones.

The boundary between the upper Mokami and Saglek Formation may be an unconformity in the landward part of the shelf, but is generally transitional, the shaley beds of the Mokami passing gradually into the lower sandy beds of the Saglek. The base of the Saglek is usually picked at the level where the sand becomes dominant or at the base of a thick pebbly sandstone. This boundary cannot be discerned with confidence in seismic records, although in some areas the presence of oblique and sigmoidal reflectors, interpreted as foreset beds, allows approximate delineation of the transition.

Industry paleontologists have recently confirmed that the Mokami Formation ranges in age from late Eocene to, possibly, middle Miocene. The age range for the lower and upper members, and the two sub-sequences that make up the lower member, are poorly known. The middle part of the Tertiary is one of the more difficult parts of the stratigraphic column with respect to defining ages. More specifically the presence, absence and thickness of Oligocene sediments are inconsistently designated in older reports from one well to another, and even in reports on the same well by different paleontologists. This is not surprising. There is stratigraphic diachroneity because of onlap and downlap at the bases of sequences and erosional truncation at their tops. Furthermore, three regionally significant unconformities can be discerned seismically within the Mokami succession — and there may be other, locally important, rather subtle unconformities. Consequently, there may have been considerable reworking of older fossils into younger rocks in this part of the column; this, in addition to the uncertainties induced by downhole caving of the poorly indurated rocks, presents a formidable challenge to biostratigraphy.

It is concluded that the age of the lower Mokami member is late Eocene to Oligocene. This is based on Pothurst P-19, where an abrupt paleontological break at the level of the mid-Mokami (near 2800 m), separates from Oligocene marine rocks which have rich and diverse faunas from nonmarine Upper Oligocene strata. The onlap unconformity separating lower and upper Mokami members is locally conspicuous on seismic sections, but in other places no seismic discordance can be seen between the lower and upper members. Using regional stratigraphy as a guide, the hiatus represented by the unconformity is assumed to be mid-Late Oligocene.

The upper Mokami is late Oligocene to middle or late Miocene. The basal beds are younger landward because of onlap updip above the mid-Late Oligocene unconformity. The upper beds are younger seaward and southward in Saglek Basin, because of the gradational shale-sand facies transition to the lower Saglek Formation. The transitional contact between the upper Mokami and lower Saglek at Corte Real P-85, a mid-shelf well, is middle Miocene. At North Bjarni F-06, an inner shelf well, the Mokami-Saglek contact is Late Oligocene, demonstrating the seaward-younging diachroneity of the contact. At Ralegh N-18, on

Southeast Baffin Shelf, the Mokami-Saglek contact is late Oligocene. A large part of the lower Saglek member at this well is a coarse grained, proximal facies that is coeval with upper Mokami distal shales of southern Saglek Basin.

Foraminiferal assemblages indicate a deep neritic paleo-environment for the basal part of the lower Mokami member in the late Eocene. Beneath Southeast Baffin Island Shelf and in Saglek Basin, there was shallowing in the upper part of the lower member, with a nonmarine or marginal marine Oligocene setting at the boundary with the upper member. This and seismic evidence of a regional erosion surface, support the concept that most of the inner and central parts of the northern Labrador and Southeast Baffin shelves were emergent in the mid-Late Oligocene, so that there was subaerial erosion and the accumulation of nonmarine muds and peat in interfluvial lake basins. In inner shelf parts of Hopedale Basin, both the lower and upper members contain foraminiferal and palynomorph assemblages indicative of inner neritic depositional environments.

Parts of Mokami Formation contain abundant reworked Carboniferous and Cretaceous palynomorphs. These plus the large amounts of pelitic material were probably derived from continued erosion of interior parts of the large Hudson Bay drainage system. Alternatively the material is second or third cycle debris from paleo-outliers nearby. Coarse grained quartz and igneous clasts, which first appeared in the mid-Tertiary in the upper Mokami member, are evidence of the first phase of the uplift of coastal Labrador in the Late Oligocene to early Miocene. This uplift accelerated throughout Miocene time, producing the modern, incised topography of high relief of the Labrador and southern Baffin Island coasts. Offshore, it produced a coarse grained clastic wedge, the Saglek Formation, which forms the present-day outer shelf and slope.

The Late Eocene planktonic foraminiferal assemblages of the Labrador Shelf are low in species diversity and absolute numbers. Gradstein and Srivastava (1980) suggested that these assemblages indicated a phase of cooling, with increased cooling throughout the Oligocene and Neogene and the development of the cold Labrador Current of today.

Saglek Formation

Regional seismic correlation indicates that the Saglek Formation consists of two parts: a "lower Saglek", composed of conglomeratic sandstones lying at the top of an upward-coarsening sequence of upper Oligocene to upper Miocene sediments; and an "upper Saglek", composed of conglomeratic upper Miocene to Pliocene beds that lie on a pronounced regional unconformity on the upper Mokami-lower Saglek sequence. The unconformity separating the two Saglek members, first noted by Grant (1980), has great erosional relief and must mark a major tectonic event renewed uplift of the coastal regions. Moreover, the unconformity can be traced seaward to an important sequence boundary that extends across the Labrador Sea. Stratigraphic nomenclature should be revised formally to take these features into account.

The Saglek Formation represents the proximal coarse grained facies of two progradational wedges that are thick and widespread in Saglek and Hopedale basins. Maximum thicknesses occur beneath the present outer shelf in both basins (Fig. 7.3, 7.8, 7.10). In Saglek Basin, the formation is about 1900 m thick at Pothurst P-19, which is a mid-shelf well. There 900 m is included in the lower Saglek and about 1000 m in the upper Saglek. Thicknesses are somewhat less in Hopedale Basin. At Corte Real P-95 the formation is about 917 m thick (sea floor to 1355 m) with about 340 m assignable to the lower Saglek and 577 m to the upper Saglek. In Snorri J-90, the type section is about 730 m thick, of which the lower 430 m are considered to be lower Saglek. The lower Saglek thins landward because of updip erosional truncation of the top of the unit, below the Late Miocene unconformity, and in the central part of the Hopedale embayment, truncations at the modern sea floor. In some parts of the shelf the lower Saglek has been thinned erratically by deep erosional incision at this same mid-Saglek unconformity. Similarly, the upper Saglek is of variable thickness because it fills in a surface of high relief. The upper member is thin beneath landward-parts of the shelf and is thickest beneath the edge of the shelf.

Lower Saglek sandstones are widely distributed beneath Southeast Baffin Shelf; these sandstones are generally the proximal facies equivalent to the thick upper Mokami beds on the Labrador Shelf. The upper Saglek is more restricted in its distribution than the lower Saglek, because it fills structurally low areas.

The lower Saglek consists of light grey and brown, fine- to coarse-grained, pebbly, cherty feldspathic and lithic quartzose sandstones. There are also abundant mollusc shells, lignite and occasional glauconite grains, plus metamorphic and igneous rock fragments. The sandstones are weakly lithified and are very porous. In some wells including the type section at Snorri J-90, there are also some thick intervals of grey siltstone and silty claystone. The upper Saglek consists of quartzose conglomeratic sandstones, which are unconsolidated and lithic, with lignite fragments and broken pelecypod shells. Very coarse grained textures are typical of both members throughout the shelf.

The lower Saglek member represents the coarse grained, proximal coastal facies of an upward-coarsening sequence that has upper Mokami mudstones as the pelitic, distal shelf facies. Since in most parts of the shelf the contact is gradational, it is not represented by a regionally mappable seismic reflector. In some seismic sections oblique and sigmoidal reflectors are present at what is taken to be the transition from the Mokami to the lower Saglek. In wells of the inner shelf such as Gudrid H-55, the contact between sand and shale is abrupt, probably representing an unconformity where part of the shale succession had been eroded before the deposition of overlying sandstones. The boundary between the lower and upper Saglek members is locally an erosion surface with relief on seismic sections of a few hundred metres. The surface is most prominently developed beneath the shelf area east of Hudson Strait, where a channel about 40 to 50 km wide can be discerned on a seismic profile parallel to the trend of the shelf. The surface is also strongly developed in the central and southern parts of Hopedale Basin. Beneath the continental slope, the surface merges with a sequence boundary separating lower and upper Mokami members, from where it extends as a single prominent reflector beneath the Labrador Sea. Seismic reflectors within the lower Saglek member tend to be well-ordered and subparallel to each other, or low-angle, oblique and sigmoidal.

Reflectors in the upper Saglek are generally disordered, with large high-angle oblique styles, and much cut and fill.

The Saglek Formation is overlain unconformably by relatively thick Pleistocene deposits in some shelf areas near the mouth of Hudson Strait, Cumberland Sound, and Frobisher Bay.

McWhae et al. (1980) stated that the age of the Saglek Formation was probably mid-Late Miocene to Pliocene. A tentative age range has been assigned here of late Oligocene to late Miocene for the lower member and late Miocene to Pliocene for the upper member. Grant (1980) suggested from biostratigraphic data that the mid-Saglek unconformity is perhaps Late Miocene in age. Data from recently drilled wells do not refute this. The age of the Saglek Formation is difficult to determine in most wells, because surface casing is commonly set in the formation, so that no samples are collected. Furthermore, the unconsolidated sandstones cave badly and contain abundant reworked Carboniferous spores and Cretaceous-Tertiary spores and dinoflagellates.

The lower Saglek member is the coarse proximal facies of a clastic wedge that prograded seaward across the Labrador Shelf in the late Oligocene to middle Miocene. Seaward-dipping clinoforms, discernible in some seismic profiles, suggest that a shelf-long system of small deltas provided the clastics to the shelf. The geometry of the Saglek deposits indicates that the broad system of coalescing fan deltas probably were alluvial fans, with their apical, updip positions contiguous to the source area, the Torngat Mountains. The coarse, poorly sorted textures and compositional immaturity of the Saglek sediments support their derivation mainly from nearby terrains of relatively high relief, consisting of plutonic and metamorphic rocks. The reworked Carboniferous, Jurassic and Cretacous palynomorphs indicate that some sediment was supplied by erosion of sedimentary rocks of those ages. The numerous grey and black chert clasts are probably relicts of Paleozoic cherty carbonates (Williams, V.E., 1986).

Generally cool-water conditions prevailed during the Neogene in the Labrador Sea, with some possible mixing of the warm Gulf Stream and cold Labrador Current in southern areas during the mid-Pliocene (Gradstein and and Srivastava, 1980).

STRATIGRAPHIC EVOLUTION

Mesozoic-Cenozoic stratigraphic units chronicle the geological evolution of the shelf and the Labrador Sea. They indicate distinctive phases dominated by lateral stretching and rifting or by tectonic subsidence. The stratigraphic modifiers for both the rift and subsidence phases are the clastic sediments. These sediments are quantifiable in terms of amounts supplied and in terms of directions. The significance of fluctuations in eustatic sea level is uncertain (Vail et al., 1977).

In the Cretaceous, possibly from the Barremian to the Coniacian, lateral stretching of cratonic crust produced large horst and half-graben structures with their associated syntectonic clastic deposits. In Hopedale Basin, these clastics overlie Cretaceous basalts, which are of the Alexis Formation, probably interbedded with coeval sedimentary rocks. A thick, widespread blanket of ?Cretaceous and Tertiary basalts cover and mask the Cretaceous rift stage structures and sediments of all but the southern

part of Saglek Basin. The shoreward parts of the grabens are occupied by texturally and mineralogically immature lithic arenites, which are feldspar- and quartz-rich. These sediments were presumably derived by erosion of nearby highlands, including the horst blocks and unfaulted parts of the neighbouring craton. A poorly integrated network of short, high-gradient coastal rivers must have transported the coarse clastics into the grabens. Sediments confined to grabens beneath the middle and outer parts of the shelf have not been drilled. The regional facies geometry indicates that parts of these sections may be lacustrine or estuarine shales, with thin sandstones and possibly shallow marine shales.

Regional marine conditions were firmly established in the Hopedale Basin by late Albian time. Except for the innermost parts, marine deposition occurred on the shelf throughout the Late Cretaceous. The presence of Campanian and Maastrichtian marine faunas with European affinities in the West Greenland Basin (Henderson et al., 1981) probably indicates when the southern part of the Labrador Embayment (Cartwright Arch) was breached and transgressed by the North Atlantic. From that time on, Atlantic marine incursions dominated the environments of the Labrador Shelf. In the Cenomanian-Santonian, the middle and outer shelves were sediment starved, probably because of marine drowning of coastal rivers. Most of the meagre amounts of clastics which were available were trapped at that time in the grabens and small deltas to form the Freydis member along the inner shelf. The Cenomanian to Coniacian was considered to be a time of global marine eustatic transgression (Vail et al., 1977) with widespread early Late Cretaceous transgression of the Canadian craton (Jeletzky, 1971). It is uncertain to what extent sediment starvation of the early Late Cretaceous shelf is a consequence of a eustatic rise in sea level, and to what extent it may be a result of flooding from regional tectonic subsidence.

Early Late Cretaceous rifting is apparent in the inner part of the shelf where it is defined by thick sequences of the Freydis member. Rifting may also have taken place in the middle and outer shelf, but the event there may not be stratigraphically obvious because of acute sediment starvation.

Small grabens formed during deposition of the Bjarni Formation and Freydis member occur along the inner (updip) hinge zone of Saglek Basin; they are also present at the mouth of Cumberland Sound, at the hinge zone of Cumberland Basin (MacLean and Williams, 1983; MacLean et al., 1986a). The acoustic reflectors in deeper parts of Saglek and Cumberland basins are here interpreted as Late Cretaceous and Early Tertiary basalts. From that, it might be inferred that any remnants of Early Cretaceous grabens are buried so deeply by volcanic rocks, or were stretched so greatly before volcanic extrusion, that they cannot now be detected.

A surge of fine grained clastic sedimentation took place in the Campanian on the Labrador Shelf. From then until the late Tertiary, the shelf subsided episodically and received a thick succession of fine- to coarse-grained clastics. No carbonate rocks are known to have been deposited during that time.

The stratigraphy of the uppermost Cretaceous and Tertiary of the Labrador and Southeast Baffin shelves consists of stacked sequences which coarsen upward. This indicates shallowing of marine to nonmarine depositional settings. The succession indicates that the building of the shelf proceeded at a faster rate than that of tectonic subsidence and compaction. The episodic subsidence of the Labrador Shelf in the Tertiary is confirmed by the regional, partly subaerial, Late Eocene unconformity at the top of Kenamu Formation and the regional, partly subaerial, Late Miocene unconformity within Saglek Formation. These could be termed first-order interruptions of shelf construction.

Second-order interruptions in the interplay between sedimentation and subsidence are recorded by erosional unconformities in proximal, basin-margin facies — for example, those bounding the lower Gudrid member, and by nondepositional unconformities in distal, deep marine facies — as within the Mokami Formation. These interruptions therefore bound depositional sequences, and one of the most widespread separates lower Gudrid and upper Markland strata from younger Paleocene beds.

Depocentres were established in the central parts of Hopedale and Saglek basins by the Late Cretaceous and persisted with some gradual seaward offlap through the mid-Tertiary. Late Tertiary depocentres lie seaward of the earlier depocentres, with the Pliocene-Pleistocene depocentre being in the Labrador Sea Basin.

For each of the Late Eocene and Late Miocene unconformities that were recognized, evidence exists for lateral stretching of older rocks of the supracrustal succession prior to deposition of the succeeding supersequence. This has an important bearing on interpretations of crustal dynamics for the Labrador Sea.

A continued supply of mineralogically immature, feldspathic sands through the mid-Tertiary, indicates some erosion of the Labrador and Baffin uplands peripheral to the shelf areas. Four sets of observations suggest that most of the pelitic material probably came from geomorphologically mature terrains of low relief in the interior of the craton (McMillan, 1973; Hiscott, 1984). These are:

1. The immense volume of fine grained clastics requires erosion of large regions of low-relief which are geomorphologically mature, rather than small regions of nearby uplands.

2. The Tertiary pelites contain abundant reworked palynomorphs. Some of these such as the Carboniferous taxa are now known only from interior parts of the craton.

3. The regionally definable aspects of facies geometry in several sequences indicate that detritus was supplied to the shelf by large river and delta systems; large rivers imply large tributary drainage basins.

4. No comparable volumes of Upper Cretaceous and Tertiary clastics are present along the basins of the Atlantic Margin between Florida and the northern Baffin Bay. (see Chapter 2 and Watts, 1981 for representative cross-sections of these basins.)

The implication is that the Labrador Shelf was the principal Tertiary depocentre for eastward migrating fine grained clastic detritus from north-central North America. Thus, it complemented the systems that drained southward to the depocentres in the Gulf of Mexico, and those that drained northwestward to depocentres of the Arctic margin. The principal river systems contributing to the Labrador and southern Baffin margins occupied the areas now marked by Hamilton Inlet, Hudson Strait, Frobisher Bay, and Cumberland Sound. The Lower Tertiary succession beneath the Southeast Baffin Shelf consists of coarser grained clastics and was deposited in generally shallower water than coeval, equally thick strata on the Labrador Shelf. From this it can be inferred that the rivers draining the Baffin craton were shorter and of higher gradient than those to the south which drained the Labrador interior.

Large structural depressions resulting from seaward-extending faults within Eocene and older strata, created ephemeral, mid-shelf, sedimentary traps for the upper Eocene and Oligocene turbiditic clastics, as in the lower part of the Mokami Formation.

A fundamental change in the stratigraphic regime took place in the Oligocene, perhaps in the early Late Oligocene; this change is marked by the mid-Mokami unconformity. The upper Mokami contains fresh, coarse grained sandstones, grading upwards into the coarse sandstones of the lower Saglek member. These lithostratigraphic changes are taken as evidence of rejuvenated uplift of the coastal regions of Labrador and southern Baffin Island, accompanied by a major shift in the regional directions of clastic progradation. This phase of tectonic rejuvenation, with its associated depositional response, culminated in the accumulation of the thick, outer-shelf wedge of coarse grained upper Saglek clastics (Fig. 7.3).

Several authors have associated marine transgressive-regressive cycles of passive margins with the global eustatic sea level fluctuations, postulated by Vail et al. (1977). Some parts of the stratigraphy of the Labrador and southeast Baffin shelves appear to coincide with events predicted from the "Vail" sea-level curve. However, it can be argued that the coincidences result because biostratigraphic control for the Labrador Shelf needs refining, so that the stratigraphy can be subjectively adjusted to fit this curve. The magnitude of stratigraphic geometries within the Labrador Shelf Mesozoic-Cenozoic succession demonstrates that tectonic events have played a major role in shelf evolution, regardless of the influences of global sea-level fluctuation.

ACKNOWLEDGMENTS

Much of the interpretation presented here is the result of work between 1981 and 1984 by Petro-Canada geologists R. Cridland, D. Hunter, B. Petyhyrycz, and G. Sullivan, combined with concepts developed by geologists and geophysicists employed by other Labrador Group companies. We thank the Labrador Group of partners — AGIP Canada Ltd., Amerada Minerals Corporation of Canada Ltd., Canterra Energy Ltd., Gulf Canada Resources Ltd., Petro-Canada Resources, Ranchmen's Resources (1976) Ltd., and Suncor, Inc., for permission to publish this material.

PART 2: GEOLOGY OF BAFFIN BAY AND DAVIS STRAIT

B. MacLean, G.L. Williams and S.P. Srivastava

INTRODUCTION

Baffin Bay lies between latitudes 66°36'N and 78°N, longitudes 54°W and 79°W, north of the Davis Strait, and has an area of about 690 000 km². It extends for about 1350 km from north to south and varies in width from 110 to 650 km (Fig. 7.17).

The western and northwestern margins of the bay are formed by Baffin Island and the islands of the Canadian Arctic Archipelago; the eastern margin is formed by Greenland. Baffin Bay is connected to the north with the Arctic Ocean through Nares Strait, Lancaster and Jones sounds, and their tributary inter-island channels. Water depths in the bay exceed 2000 m in the central basin and gradually shallow to the north, about 700-800 m at the mouth of Lancaster Sound, and to less than 500 m near the entrance to Smith and Jones sounds. The connection with Davis Strait to the south is marked by an east-west sill at a depth of 500-600 m (Fig. 7.17, 7.18).

The Northeast Baffin Shelf forms the continental shelf along most of the west side of Baffin Bay. It is narrow, only about 50 km wide, and consists of a series of shallow banks, 200 m deep or less, separated by transverse troughs. The depths in the troughs may be greater than 800 m and the troughs represent submarine extensions of the numerous fiords of northeastern Baffin Island. Both troughs and fiords were probably formed by glacial erosion along preexisting Tertiary drainage systems (Fortier and Morley, 1956; Ives and Andrews, 1963; and Pelletier, 1966). The shelf break occurs at about 300 m off northeast Baffin Island but is not as pronounced a feature farther north.

The Northeast Baffin Shelf contrasts with the shelf south of Cape Dyer, which is wider, deeper, less dissected, and has a fairly well-defined continental slope; the latter area is referred to as the Southeast Baffin Shelf.

The West Greenland Shelf, which forms the eastern continental shelf of Baffin Bay, ranges from 135 to 200 km in width and is much wider than the Northeast Baffin Shelf. The shelf break occurs about 400 to 500 m. Like the Northeast Baffin Shelf, the West Greenland Shelf is cut by numerous transverse troughs, which also extend across the shelf from fiord mouths.

Interpretation of the regional geology of Baffin Bay (Fig. 7.19) is based primarily on geophysical evidence. This includes seaborne gravity, magnetic and seismic refraction and reflection data. Geological information includes lithostratigraphy and biostratigraphy which are derived from published studies of grab samples, core recovered from shallow drill holes, cores from ODP Site 645, and cuttings, sidewall cores, and conventional cores from eight offshore wells. The wells are: Hejka O-71, Gjoa G-37 and Ralegh N-18 on the southeast margin of Baffin Island, and Hellefisk 1, Ikermiut 1, Kangamiut 1, Nukik 1 and Nukik 2 on the west Greenland margin (Fig. 7.18). Geographically, only Hellefisk 1 lies in Baffin Bay; the other four wells off western Greenland are in Davis Strait; the three Canadian wells are in the northern Labrador Sea. A review of the onshore geology of Baffin Island and western Greenland provides a regional setting for the geology of Baffin

Bay. Papers on the regional geology and evolution of Baffin Bay and Davis Strait include: Keen and Barrett (1972), Keen et al. (1972), McMillan (1973), Keen et al. (1974), Hood and Bower (1975), Hyndman (1975), Jackson et al. (1979), Henderson et al. (1981), MacLean and Williams (1980 and 1983), MacLean et al. (1977, 1978, 1982, 1986b), Kerr (1981), Klose et al. (1982), McWhae (1981), Srivastava et al. (1981, 1982), Menzies (1982), Rice and Shade (1982), and Rolle (1985). An understanding of the regional geology must take into account the structure of the underlying crust and the tectonic setting.

CRUSTAL STRUCTURE

There are two theories on the nature of the crust underlying Baffin Bay, and these have a major impact on the interpretation of its evolution (see Chapter 2). The first — as advanced by Kerr (1967), Grant (1975b, 1980 and 1982) and van der Linden (1975) — postulates that the bay is underlain by foundered or attenuated continental crust, subsequently modified in the Tertiary by intrusion of basaltic rocks. According to this hypothesis, Baffin Bay does not represent an ocean basin formed by seafloor spreading, but resulted from vertical rather than lateral movements. If correct, this would support the contention that there was no major displacement along Nares Strait between Canada and Greenland in the Late Cretaceous-Early Tertiary (Dawes and Kerr, 1982). Several of the arguments advanced by Grant (1980, 1982) are based on interpretation of geophysical and stratigraphic data in the Labrador Sea. Two unconformities recognized on industry multichannel seismic lines were interpreted as Early Cretaceous and Late Miocene events (Grant, 1982). This interpretation implies vertical movement, incompatible with seafloor spreading models.

The second hypothesis on the nature of the crust in Baffin Bay — advanced by Keen et al. (1972, 1974), Srivastava (1978), Jackson et al. (1979), Menzies (1982), Rice and Shade (1982) — suggests that the bay represents an ocean basin formed by seafloor spreading, largely during the early Tertiary when Greenland and Baffin Island drifted apart. Most plate reconstructions imply a combination of translational and compressional motion between Greenland and Baffin Island as a result of seafloor spreading. Motions of this sort could also lead to stretching, attenuation and faulting of continental crust.

Formulation of the ocean crust hypothesis has been based on seismic, gravity and magnetic data. Seismic refraction data indicate variations in crustal thickness across the bay from 4 km in the west to about 7 km in the east. One possible explanation for this variation may be that the spreading rate was not constant, being faster to the west and slower to the east, so that more oceanic crust was generated on one margin. The absence of crustal velocities corresponding to oceanic layer 2 (between 4.5 and 5.5 km/s) is attributed to thinness of the crust or masking by overlying high velocity sediments (Keen and Barrett, 1972; Jackson et al., 1979). A diagramatic cross-section for

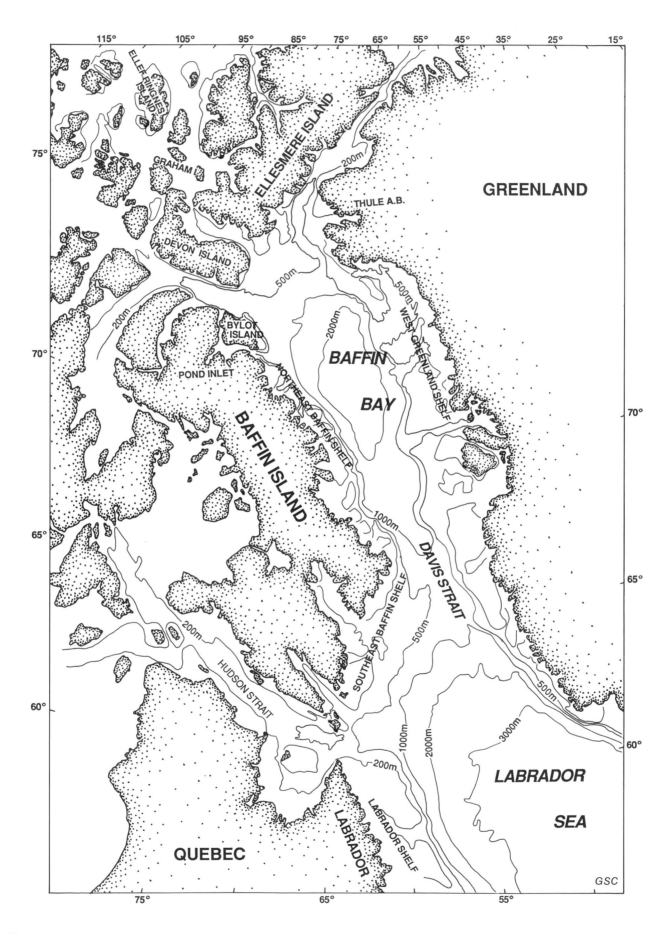

GSC

Baffin Bay based primarily on refraction data delineates six units and is presented in Figure 7.20 (Srivastava et al., 1981). This includes:

1) mantle, with velocities of 7.7-8.5 km/s.

2) problematic oceanic layers 2 and 3 (?) with velocities of 5.7-7.0 km/s.

3) basement rock (Precambrian?) under the western shelf and slope, with a velocity of 6.0-6.8 km/s.

4) consolidated slope sediments (presumably mainly Paleozoic or Mesozoic), with a velocity of 3.2-5.5 km/s.

5) consolidated sediments (Lower Tertiary?) in the deeper parts of the bay together with older sediments on the shelf, with a velocity of 3.2-4.4 km/s.

6) unconsolidated to semi-consolidated sediments (mainly Upper Tertiary-Quaternary) with a velocity of 2.0-3.2 km/s.

Multichannel seismic records indicate the presence of both flat and hummocky basement beneath Baffin Bay (McWhae, 1981; Srivastava et al., 1981). These data provide supporting evidence for an extinct ridge in central Baffin Bay. The velocity measurements from the refraction experiments of Keen and Barrett (1972) for the central part of the bay led to good agreement between the depths to the top of basement estimated from the refraction and reflection data. Information provided by these data on the make up of the basement rocks, however, is less definitive as a refraction velocity of 6.5 km/s obtained by Keen and Barrett (1972) near the centre of the bay (Fig. 7.20) can be interpreted as either continental or oceanic basement. The significance of these data has been extensively discussed by Keen and Barrett (1972) and by Srivastava et al. (1981) who in light of the various other geophysical data favoured an oceanic crust interpretation.

The existence of magnetic lineations in Baffin Bay, and their possible correlation with anomalies 13 through 21 (see Map 1706A, in pocket) of the Labrador Sea is supporting evidence for the presence of oceanic crust in the bay (Jackson et al., 1979; Srivastava et al., 1981). It was also concluded that Baffin Bay is underlain by a 130 km wide band of oceanic crust, which laterally becomes thinned continental crust on the eastern and western margins of the bay (Rice and Shade, 1982).

Refraction and earthquake seismicity data were used to examine the mantle and crustal structure of Baffin Bay (Menzies, 1982). He argued that oceanic crust in central Baffin Bay was separated from that of the Labrador Sea by a belt of continental crust spanning Davis Strait. Whether attenuated continental crust or oceanic crust underlies Davis Strait is still debatable in spite of the extensive seismic, gravity and magnetic data available for the region (Hood and Bower, 1975; Srivastava et al., 1982). Seismic refraction measurements in the central part of the strait (Keen and Barrett, 1972; Srivastava et al., 1982) indicate crustal thicknesses of 18-30 km. This is intermediate between oceanic crust (10 km) and continental crust (35 km). There are at least four possibilities to explain this variance. Davis Strait is underlain by: thickened oceanic

crust; thinned continental crust; crust intermediate in composition; or alternating oceanic and continental crust. Gravity data indicate positive anomaly bands on the shelves of the northern Labrador Sea and Davis Strait. A strong positive anomaly in Davis Strait is orientated northeast-southwest, coincident with the western edge of a structural high and probably denoting a volcanic sill. It has been suggested that the shallowing in Davis Strait indicates a "hot spot" or an upwelling convection plume associated with sea-floor spreading (Keen and Barrett, 1972; Hyndman, 1973; Keen et al., 1974). Grant (1980) preferred to regard this as evidence of recurrent volcanism.

The controversy relating to the amount of movement that has taken place between Greenland and North America along Nares Strait has been alluded to earlier. This has centred around differences between onshore geological studies which suggested less then 25 km of sinistral motion along the strait, and plate tectonic models which indicated 100 to 250 km of movement along the strait assuming rigid plate boundaries (Kerr, 1982; Srivastava and Falconer, 1982). For further insight into this problem the reader is also referred to the many other relevant papers in the volume edited by Dawes and Kerr (1982) and to Srivastava et al. (1981), Srivastava (1985) and Srivastava and Tapscott (1986). A possible solution to the problem is a proposal that the North American plate has been non-rigid and that oblique motion between Greenland and North America was partly taken up within the Canadian Arctic Archipelago, thus reducing the amount of displacement in Nares Strait from that required by earlier rigid-plate geophysical models (Srivastava, 1985).

The evolution of the Eurasian Basin, Labrador Sea, Norwegian-Greenland Sea and North Atlantic has been controlled by the relative motion between the North American, Greenland and Eurasian plates (Srivastava, 1985). Although the geophysical data from Baffin Bay and Davis Strait do not conclusively identify the type of crust present throughout those areas, they do indicate greater affinity with oceanic than continental crust (Srivastava et al., 1981). As those authors pointed out, regardless of the type of crust, the observations support the idea that the Baffin Bay-Davis Strait regions were subjected to tensional forces when Greenland and North America separated in response to active seafloor spreading in the Labrador Sea. The present writers concur with this view and, while recognizing the constraints outlined, on the basis of the various data available, favour the view that seafloor spreading has been a mechanism in the evolution of Baffin Bay and have employed that concept in preparing this chapter.

The history of the development of the North Atlantic as interpreted from geophysical measurements indicates that the Norwegian-Greenland Sea (e.g. Talwani and Eldholm, 1977; Vogt et al., 1981) and the Labrador Sea (e.g. Kristoffersen and Talwani, 1977; Srivastava, 1978; Srivastava et al., 1981; Srivastava and Falconer, 1982) evolved through seafloor spreading resulting from separation of Greenland from Eurasia and from North America. The chronology of events affecting Baffin Bay includes the development of graben and partial graben structures around the Labrador-Baffin Bay region due to crustal stretching as rifting commenced in the northern Labrador Sea-Davis Strait region during the Cretaceous (Srivastava, 1978; Srivastava and Falconer, 1982). Seafloor spreading, which began earlier in the southern Labrador Sea,

Figure 7.17 Generalized bathymetry of Baffin Bay-Davis Strait (adapted from Canadian Hydrographic Service Charts, 1985).

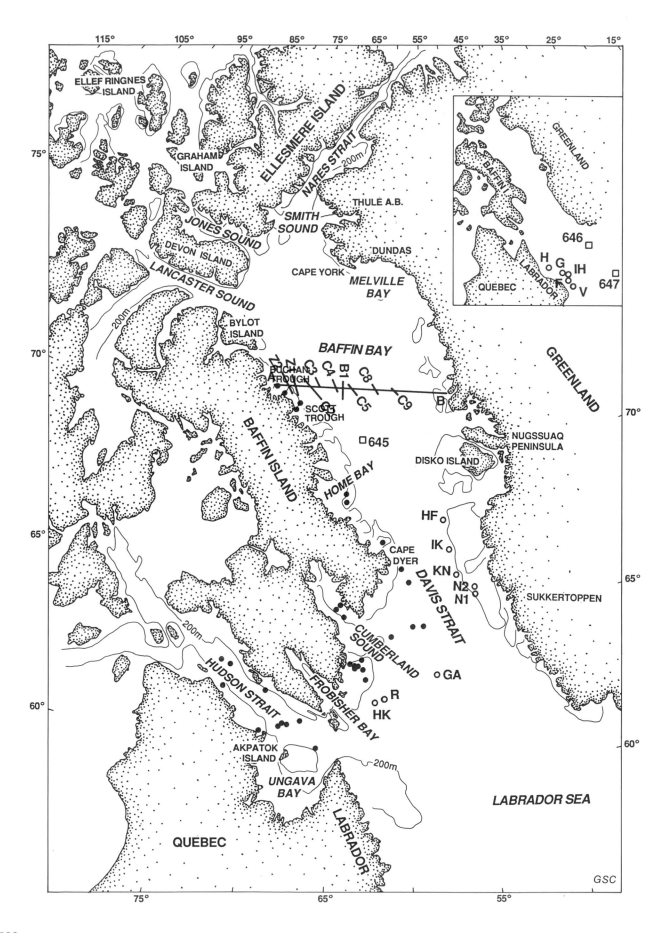

progressed northward into the northern Labrador Sea by the late Cretaceous and early Tertiary. Opening of Baffin Bay began during the Paleocene, accompanied by outpouring of basalt both onshore and offshore in the Davis Strait region. The opening of Baffin Bay continued until early Oligocene time. The movement between Greenland and North America included an initial rotational motion which resulted in compression between the Canadian Arctic Islands and northern Greenland. This phase was followed by translational motion as Greenland moved to the northeast in response to spreading between Eurasia and Greenland during the early Eocene.

TECTONIC SETTING

The regional tectonics of Baffin Bay are discussed in detail in Chapter 2 and are only briefly reviewed here. The major basin, Baffin Basin, fills most of central Baffin Bay (Fig. 7.21 and Map 1706A, in pocket). A major half-graben, the West Greenland Basin, lies on the western margin of Greenland and extends offshore. At its northern extremity, West Greenland Basin extends into the Melville Bay Graben, which occupies Melville Bugt. The Bylot Island Basin underlies the northwestern part of Baffin Bay. Eclipse Trough may be part of this. Cumberland Basin, which lies south of Baffin Bay, is considered by Balkwill and McMillan (Part 1 of this chapter, Fig. 7.1) to be the northernmost basin on the western margin of the Labrador Sea. It is presumably separated by Tertiary basalts from Baffin Basin.

Other grabens or partial grabens surround Baffin Bay and northern Labrador Sea. These include Lancaster Sound, Jones Sound, Cumberland Sound, Frobisher Bay and Hudson Strait (Map 1706A, in pocket).

The major fault patterns of the Baffin Bay region can be related to a seafloor spreading origin. The zone of magnetic anomalies running southwest from Disko Island to Hudson Strait can be related to a transform fault, the Ungava Transform Fault, whose direction is parallel to the Hudson Fracture Zone to the south (Hood and Bower, 1975).

The general configuration of the major fault patterns in the bay is northwest-southeast and northeast-southwest. This conforms to the regional pattern determined for the Labrador Shelf by McWhae (1981). However, there is a shift in orientation from south to north, with the northwest-southeast trend becoming more west-east as in Lancaster and Jones sounds. The original orientation is retained in the vicinity of Bylot Island, where the Eclipse Trough is one of a series of parallel northwest-trending horsts and grabens of the North Baffin Rift Zone. It is believed that block faulting has occurred periodically in this zone since the Precambrian (Jackson et al., 1975).

Figure 7.18 Index map of the Baffin Bay-Davis Strait region. Dots indicate shallow core hole sample locations. ODP Sites 645, 646, 647 and exploratory wells referred to in the text are indicated. Designations for the wells are as follows: F Freydis, G -Gudrid, GA — Gjoa, H — Hopedale, HF — Hellefisk, HK Hekja, IH — Indian Harbour, IK — Ikermiut, KN — Kangamiut, N2 Nukik 1 and 2, R — Raleigh, V — Verrazano.

ONSHORE GEOLOGY

This section provides a brief overview of the geological framework of the onshore regions surrounding Baffin Bay.

Precambrian

The landmasses surrounding Baffin Bay, namely Baffin Island, eastern Devon Island, Ellesmere Island and West Greenland consist predominantly of Precambrian igneous and metamorphic rocks (Fig. 7.19). These Archean and Proterozoic rocks were deformed during mid-Aphebian, Hudsonian and equivalent orogenies (Jackson and Taylor, 1972; Escher and Watts, 1976). Originally these represented a single cratonic area or shield. Rifting and drifting in the Precambrian established the structural trends which influenced later cycles (Bridgwater et al., 1973).

Rocks of the Canadian Shield bordering the west side of Baffin Bay have been assigned to the Churchill Structural Province (Taylor, 1971). The boundaries of the Churchill Province have since been extended to the southwest (Hoffman, 1987). He considered that it comprises two continental platforms bounded by Early Proterozoic suture zones. These rocks make up most of Baffin Island, eastern Devon Island and southeastern Ellesmere Island. Rock types include metamorphosed clastics, volcanics, granites and migmatites. In Greenland, Archean gneisses form an east-west belt, which outcrops on both coasts. In western Greenland the belt extends from near Frederikshab north to Søndre Strømfjord.

Paleozoic

Lower Paleozoic sedimentary rocks occur in western and northwestern Baffin Island, in northern Greenland, and are widely distributed in the Canadian Arctic Islands (Fig. 7.19). On Baffin Island, the strata consist of carbonate and detrital rocks primarily of Ordovician and Silurian age together with rocks of Cambrian age, locally in northwestern Baffin Island (Douglas, 1969; Trettin, 1969, 1975; Bolton et al., 1977).

Middle and Upper Ordovician rocks also occur on Akpatok Island in Ungava Bay (Workum et al., 1976), in Hudson Strait (Grant and Manchester, 1970; Grant, 1975b; MacLean and Williams, 1983; MacLean et al., 1986b), as outliers at the head of Frobisher Bay (Miller et al., 1954), and on the continental shelf between Frobisher Bay, Cumberland Sound, and Cape Dyer (MacLean et al., 1977; MacLean and Falconer, 1979; MacLean et al., 1982).

In Greenland, Paleozoic rocks are confined almost entirely to the north where up to 3500 m of Eocambrian to Devonian carbonate and clastic rocks extend northward into thicker folded rocks of the north Greenland geosyncline. This is considered to be an extension of the Franklinian geosyncline of the Canadian Arctic Islands (Dawes, 1976). A small outlier of Ordovician breccia near Sukkertoppen is the only other known occurrence of Paleozoic rocks on West Greenland (Stouge and Peel, 1979).

Although Upper Paleozoic rocks are not present onshore, reworked Carboniferous palynomorphs occur in the five wells drilled on the West Greenland Shelf (Rolle, 1985). Carboniferous palynomorphs have been recorded in carbonates from the Gudrid H-55 and Verrazano L-77 wells on the Labrador Shelf (Barss et al., 1979). Rolle (1985)

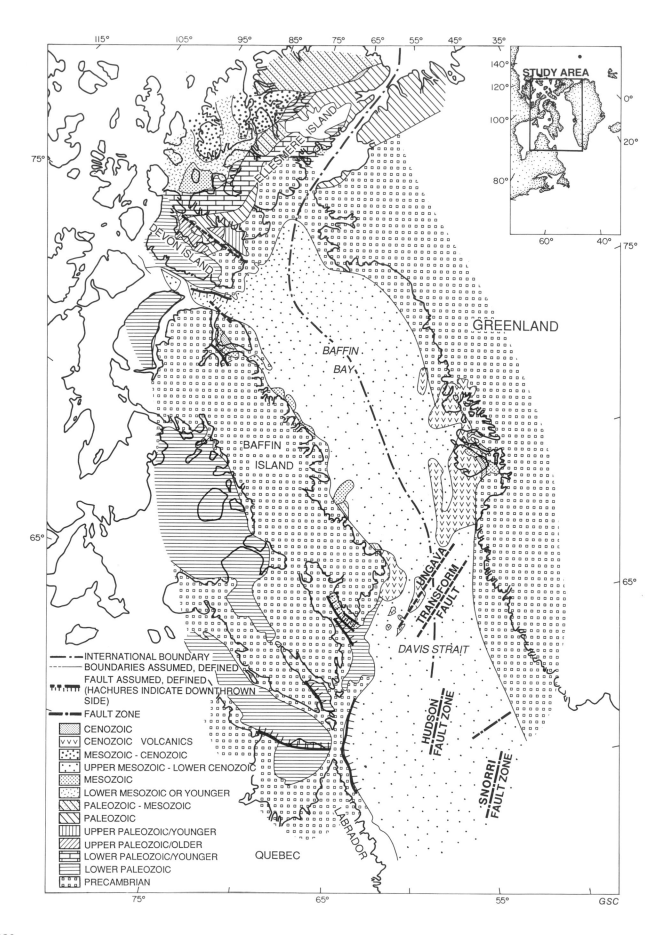

INTERNATIONAL BOUNDARY
BOUNDARIES ASSUMED, DEFINED
FAULT ASSUMED, DEFINED
(HACHURES INDICATE DOWNTHROWN SIDE)
FAULT ZONE

CENOZOIC
CENOZOIC VOLCANICS
MESOZOIC - CENOZOIC
UPPER MESOZOIC - LOWER CENOZOIC
MESOZOIC
LOWER MESOZOIC OR YOUNGER
PALEOZOIC - MESOZOIC
PALEOZOIC
UPPER PALEOZOIC/YOUNGER
UPPER PALEOZOIC/OLDER
LOWER PALEOZOIC/YOUNGER
LOWER PALEOZOIC
PRECAMBRIAN

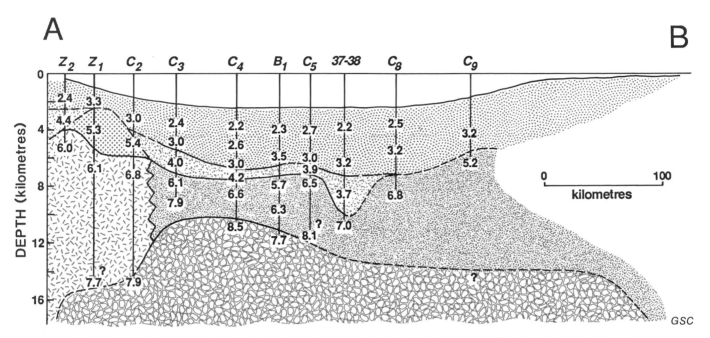

Figure 7.20 Cross-section A-B showing seismic velocity distribution across Baffin Bay (see Fig. 7.18 for location) (adapted from Srivastava et al., 1981).

postulated that a major sedimentary basin existed between Canada and Greenland during that time.

Mesozoic-Cenozoic sedimentary rocks

Cretaceous and Tertiary sediments outcrop on Bylot Island and in the adjacent Pond Inlet area on northeastern Baffin Island (Jackson and Davidson, 1975; Jackson et al., 1975; Miall et al., 1980; Ioannides, 1986) (Fig. 7.19). Most of the sediments, including those at Pond Inlet, were deposited in Eclipse Trough. At Pond Inlet about 3000 m of mudstones, sandstones, and locally some interbedded coal seams were included in the Hassel, Kanguk and Eureka Sound formations by Miall et al. (1980). In Eclipse Trough, these formations, previously recognized in the Sverdrup Basin, are assigned the following ages: Hassel Formation, Albian-Cenomanian; Kanguk Formation, Campanian-Maastrichtian; and Eureka Sound Formation, Paleocene-Eocene.

In the vicinity of Pond Inlet, the Hassel Formation consists predominantly of fluvial sandstones, with thin coal seams, which unconformably overlie Precambrian rocks. The Hassel Formation is believed to be equivalent to the Bjarni Formation, the base of which is marked by the Labrador Unconformity (McWhae, 1981). The Albian-Cenomanian age of the Hassel suggests that it was deposited during the rifting stage of opening of Labrador Sea and Baffin Bay.

The Kanguk Formation disconformably overlies the Hassel Formation. The Avalon Unconformity recognized on the Grand Banks is placed at the Hassel-Kanguk boundary (McWhae, 1981). The Kanguk consists of a lower mudstone member and an upper sandstone member, which

together are about 1150 m thick (Miall et al., 1980). The mudstone member, which is Campanian-Maastrichtian, was deposited during a widespread marine transgression. The overlying sandstone member represents a regressive phase and may mark the tectonic phase associated with the initiation of drifting. The Kanguk is Santonian-Early Paleocene, with the Bylot Unconformity separating it from the overlying Eureka Sound Formation (McWhae, 1981).

In Eclipse Trough, the Eureka Sound Formation was divided into four members by Miall et al. (1980): a lower marine sandstone member, lower marine mudstone member, upper nonmarine sandstone member (the thickest unit) and an upper marine mudstone member. The maximum thickness of the formation on Bylot Island is 1600 m. The formation was of Late Paleocene- ?Early Eocene age (Miall et al., 1980). The top of the Eureka Sound, according to McWhae (1981), is bounded by the Early Oligocene Baffin Bay Unconformity. This may denote cessation of seafloor spreading in Baffin Bay.

Tertiary sedimentary rocks occur in two other areas on Baffin Island. The first, 240 km south of Pond Inlet, consists of an isolated outcrop of lacustrine to marginal marine Paleogene sediments, which overlie Precambrian rocks (Andrews et al., 1972). The second consists of Paleocene sedimentary rocks which overlie the Precambrian and are overlain by volcanic rocks in a discontinuous belt, 85 km by 10 km, along the coast northwestward from Cape Dyer. These terrestrial sediments include sandstone, shale, minor coal and conglomerate, with some tuffaceous beds (Clarke and Upton, 1971).

The other major occurrence of onshore Cretaceous-Tertiary sediments in the Baffin Bay region is in the West Greenland Basin, between latitudes 68.50°N and 72.15°N (Rosenkrantz and Pulvertaft, 1969; Henderson et al., 1976, 1981). In the Nugssuaq Embayment, Lower Cretaceous to Lower Paleocene clastics overlie Precambrian rocks (Henderson, 1976; Rolle, 1985). The eastern margin of the basin

Figure 7.19 Generalized geological map of Baffin Bay and adjacent areas (adapted from Map 1705A, in pocket).

331

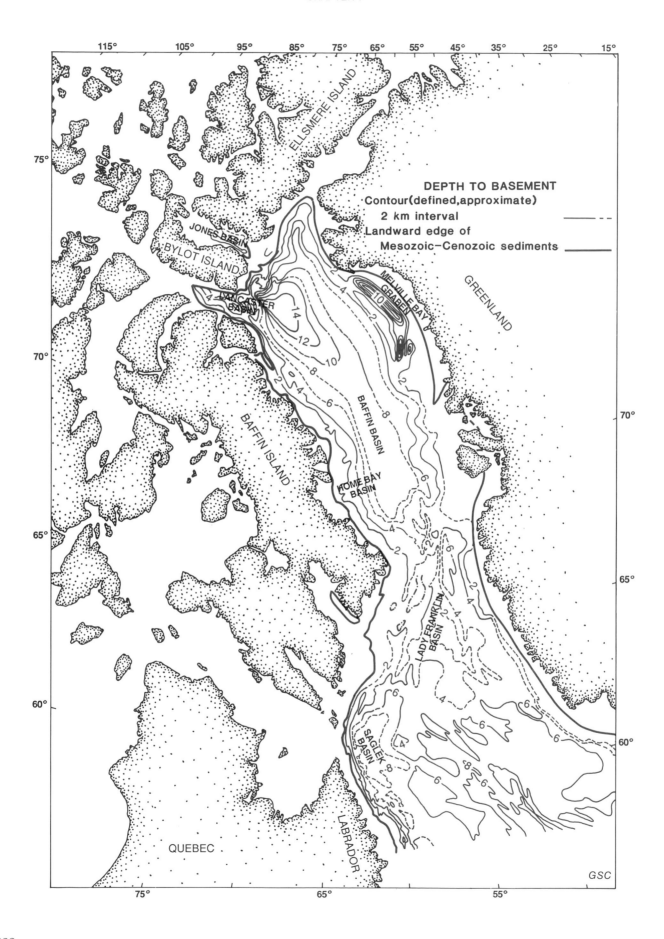

is defined by a series of north-south faults with downthrow to the west. The faulting is in part syndepositional, but appears to predate some of the Early Tertiary basalts. A transition was noted from southeast to northwest from fluviatile to marine sediments, with a total maximum thickness of 2000 m (Henderson et al., 1981). The facies recognized were: 1. upper delta plain-fluvial (generally Late Albian-Cenomanian); 2. delta plain and distributary flood basin (generally Cenomanian-Early Campanian); 3. delta front with bar sands (generally Cenomanian-Early Campanian); 4. prodelta muds (generally Late Campanian- Maastrichtian). The older Cretaceous sediments of the Nugssuaq Embayment — type 1 of Henderson et al. (1981) — appear to correlate lithologically and temporally with the Hassel and Bjarni formations. The basal unconformity would therefore be the Labrador Unconformity. It is difficult, however, to place the Avalon Unconformity without more information. The younger Cretaceous sediments (types 2-4 of Henderson et al., 1981) presumably equate with the Kanguk Formation.

The Paleocene sediments are assumed to be coeval with those of the Eureka Sound Formation and are separated from the underlying Cretaceous sediments by the Bylot Unconformity. This is confirmed by Rosenkrantz and Pulvertaft (1969), who also noted that faulting had occurred intermittently in the Cretaceous and Tertiary, with 400 m of movement between deposition of the Maastrichtian and Danian sediments. It was also noted that a major regional unconformity marks the base of the Tertiary sediments and in the Disko-Nugssuaq area oversteps the Cretaceous beds southwards (Henderson et al., 1981).

Mesozoic-Cenozoic igneous rocks

Jurassic-Early Cretaceous alkaline intrusions outcrop on the southern coast of Greenland as kimberlite sills, lamprophyre dykes and a carbonatite complex in the vicinity of Sukkertoppen (Larsen et al., 1983). Rolle (1985) noted the similarity in age with the intrusives of northeast Newfoundland, which he suggested were associated with the formation of the Labrador Shelf basins.

Volcanic sequences composed predominantly of basalt occur in the Cape Dyer area of eastern Baffin Island (Clarke and Upton, 1971) and in the Disko Island area of West Greenland (Clarke and Pedersen, 1976). The Baffin Island occurrences form a narrow, discontinuous belt along the coast northwest from Cape Dyer. They are of Paleocene age (Clarke and Upton, 1971). The subaqueous breccia, subaerial flows, and tuffaceous beds appear to have originated from a source to the northeast.

The Lower Tertiary volcanic rocks of West Greenland have been studied by Rosenkrantz and Pulvertaft (1969) and Clarke and Pedersen (1976). There, the onset of volcanism was marked by tuffaceous layers in the deltaic to shallow marine Danian sediments of the Nugssuaq embayment and Disko Island. This was followed by emplacement of subaqueous basalt breccias and pillow lavas, which locally are 600-700 m thick and appear to have had a source in the west. The overlying sequence of subaerial neritic and olivine-rich basalts contain an upper unit dominated by tholeiites. Intercalated with the upper part of the volcanic sequence are nonmarine clastic sediments, that contain Eocene plants (Clarke and Pedersen, 1976; Escher and Watts, 1976). The volcanic pile is cut by dykes which are more numerous in the lower part of the sequence. Some of these dykes served as feeders to the lavas. The composite thickness of the lava approaches 8000 m. The age of most of the basalts lies between 63 and 56 Ma (Early Paleocene-Early Eocene); they were probably emplaced during the initial phases of opening of Baffin Bay-Davis Strait (Parrott and Reynolds, 1975; Srivastava, 1978; Srivastava et al., 1981; Johnson et al., 1982).

OFFSHORE GEOLOGY

Sedimentary thicknesses in Baffin Bay are not well known. In the northern part, there is a marked change in structural style near the entrance to Lancaster Sound. Undeformed prograding sediments to the east pass westwards into sequences highly deformed by Paleozoic or early Mesozoic structures. It was suggested that this change occurred near the transition from continental to oceanic crust (Keen et al., 1974). Sedimentary rocks, which are interpreted to be Paleozoic or younger on the basis of seismic data, occur in fault-controlled basins in Lancaster Sound where they are 7 km thick, Jones Sound where they are 5 km thick, and Smith Sound where they are 5 km thick (Keen et al., 1974; MacLean et al., 1984). It is thought that Lancaster Sound may represent a Precambrian aulacogen that was reactivated during the Mesozoic-Cenozoic (Jackson et al., 1977).

In Melville Bay, geophysical data indicate the presence of a deep graben, 400 km long and 50-75 km wide, containing a sedimentary section up to 10 km thick (Hood and Bower, 1970, 1973; Keen et al., 1972, 1974; Ross and Henderson, 1973; Denham, 1974; Henderson, 1976). The succession includes a thin layer of acoustically transparent material that unconformably overlies folded and faulted strata (Manchester and Clarke, 1973). Cretaceous and Tertiary strata equivalent to those of onshore West Greenland are probably represented here, as well as Quaternary sediments (Henderson, 1973; Clarke and Pedersen, 1976).

Seismic reflection and refraction data indicate that sediment thickness in Baffin Bay is greatest in the north, where it amounts to 14 km (Fig. 7.21). This decreases to less than 2 km in Davis Strait. The greater sediment thickness in the north probably reflects a high rate of sediment transport into northern Baffin Bay, through an ancestral Lancaster Sound fluvial drainage system, which Fortier and Morley (1956) and Pelletier (1966) believed developed in the Tertiary. In the central part of the northern half of the bay, the upper 2-3 km of the stratigraphic sequence consists of unconsolidated and semi-consolidated, flat-lying sediments having velocities of 1.9 to 3.2 km/s, which are underlain by more disturbed sedimentary rocks with velocities of 3.9 to 4.2 km/s (Keen and Barrett, 1972; Keen et al., 1974). Deposition of the latter may have occurred while spreading was taking place, whereas the undisturbed upper part of the sequence was deposited following cessation of spreading (Keen et al., 1974).

Precambrian

The oldest rocks in Baffin Bay are found on the margins, where Precambrian igneous and metamorphic rocks com-

---

Figure 7.21 Generalized depth-to-basement, Baffin Bay, based on Map 1707A (in pocket). Contour interval is 2 km.

monly form the bedrock immediately adjacent to the coast. Henderson et al. (1981) and Brett and Zarudzki (1979) mapped the offshore extension of Precambrian rocks along the coast of West Greenland. These rocks outcrop at the seafloor along a zone extending from 64°20'N to 68°N. This zone is up to 40 km wide in the south and narrows to about 2 km in the north. The surface of the Precambrian basement has a regional westerly dip which in West Greenland Basin is interrupted by the Kangamiut Structural High. This ridge is more than 90 km long and 10 km wide and runs in a north-south direction. In the offshore eastern part of West Greenland Basin, complex block faulting affects the Precambrian.

Tectonic trends in Precambrian basement of West Greenland generally lie north-south. This is shown in some major faults which extend for more than 100 km. Presumably this pattern could have controlled the orientation of Mesozoic-Cenozoic rifting and drifting in Baffin Bay. Locally Precambrian rocks may also occur in apparently fault related structures farther seaward on the shelf. Precambrian rocks were also encountered in the Kangamiut 1 (3700 m) and the Nukik 1 (2343 m) wells on the West Greenland Shelf. The basement rocks encountered in Kangamiut at 3700 m consist of kaolinized gneiss of probable Archean age (Rolle, 1985). These rocks are cut by a chloritized metadolerite dyke that is thought to be equivalent to Early Proterozoic dyke swarms found onshore.

Paleozoic

The dominant Phanerozoic rocks on the shelves of Baffin Bay and Davis Strait are of Late Cretaceous and Tertiary age. Older rocks also occur. Ordovician rocks underlie much of Southeast Baffin Shelf between Frobisher Bay and Cumberland Sound. This has been confirmed by the recovery of Upper Ordovician (Caradocian) bedrock at five localities (MacLean et al., 1977; MacLean et al., 1978). On the basis of seismic reflection, magnetic and gravity data, Ordovician strata also appear to extend north to Cape Dyer. Thus, a core of sandstone and banded carbonate obtained off Padloping Island in 1985 may be of this age although paleontological data are not yet available. Middle Ordovician to Silurian limestone and dolomite were recovered in dredge samples from the continental margin of southwest Greenland (Johnson et al., 1975). Ordovician rocks are present in three wells on the Labrador Shelf — Freydis B-87, Hopedale E-33, and Indian Harbour M-52. The oldest rocks, Tremadocian-Arenigian, were found in Hopedale E-33 and Indian Harbour M-52. Younger Ordovician rocks, Llanvirnian or Caradocian, occur in both Hopedale E-33 and Indian Harbour M-52.

Upper Paleozoic rocks have not been recovered from Baffin Bay, although reworked Carboniferous palynomorphs are present in all the wells drilled in West Greenland Basin and in Gudrid H-55 and Verrazano L-77 wells on the Labrador Shelf.

Cretaceous

The oldest Mesozoic bedrock in the region is in Cumberland Sound, south of Cape Dyer, where MacLean and Williams (1983) recovered a dark grey shale of Barremian-Cenomanian age. The age of this nonmarine shale was confirmed through further sampling by MacLean et al. (1986a), who mapped the extent of these strata. The oldest marine Mesozoic sediments lie east of Cumberland Sound where a sandstone core is of Albian-Cenomanian age. Dinoflagellates indicate deposition in a shallow, marine environment (MacLean and Falconer, 1979).

On Southeast Baffin Shelf, four subsurface structural ridges that trend northeast-southwest have been identified off Cumberland Sound (MacLean et al., 1982). These ridges lie within a large positive gravity anomaly and on the basis of samples and geophysical data appear to consist of both volcanic and sedimentary rocks. Emplacement of the ridge structures was not complete until post Early Eocene, with subsequent bevelling of the region through erosion. The ridges probably originated with the formation of massive dykes during volcanism. The orientation of the ridges is in accord with the predominant structural grain and they are thought to have resulted from translational motion between the Greenland and North American plates.

Pre-Upper Cretaceous sedimentary rocks may be present on Northeast Baffin Shelf, between Scott and Buchan troughs. There, seismic refraction measurements indicate a structural depression containing some 4 km of rocks with velocities of 2.40 and 4.35 km/s (Jackson et al., 1977). Velocities in these ranges are commonly associated with sedimentary rocks. A velocity of 5.25 km/s from rocks deeper and to seaward is less definitive, being similar to velocities of both Precambrian metamorphic rocks and Paleozoic carbonates (MacLean et al., 1977; Jackson et al., 1979).

The most complete offshore record of Upper Cretaceous-Tertiary sequences in the region is provided by Rolle (1985). He erected several formal lithostratigraphic units, based upon sections penetrated in the exploratory wells on West Greenland Shelf.

The oldest marine rocks encountered were Campanian sandstones and interbedded mudstones, which were named the Narssarmiut Formation (Rolle, 1985). The type section is from 3700 to 3674 m in the Kangamiut 1 well. The formation rests on Precambrian basement and is unconformably overlain by the Ikermiut Formation. This unconformity is the Bylot Unconformity of McWhae (1981). The Narssarmiut Formation is believed to be the equivalent of the Freydis Member of the Cartwright Formation, which occurs in the subsurface of the Labrador Shelf (Rolle, 1985). Rocks of equivalent age are present on the western side of Baffin Bay, on Northeast Baffin Shelf (Fig. 7.22, 7.23, 7.24). Shallow core hole samples from Buchan Trough consist of semi-consolidated, dark grey, calcareous siltstones, that locally grade to silty mudstones and contain abundant glauconite and some siderite. The contained dinoflagellate assemblages indicate a Campanian age and closely resemble assemblages from other Arctic areas, including Bylot Island, Graham Island and West Greenland (MacLean and Williams, 1980; MacLean et al., 1981).

Samples from two localities, 24 km apart, in Home Bay ranged from silty mudstone to argillaceous sandstone and are semi-consolidated. The strata in the northern part of this bay contain abundant dinoflagellates which show affinities with Bylot Island assemblages dated as Campanian (G.L. Williams, pers. comm., 1983). The samples from the southern part of the bay may be coeval (MacLean and Williams, 1983). The mudstones are organic-rich, with

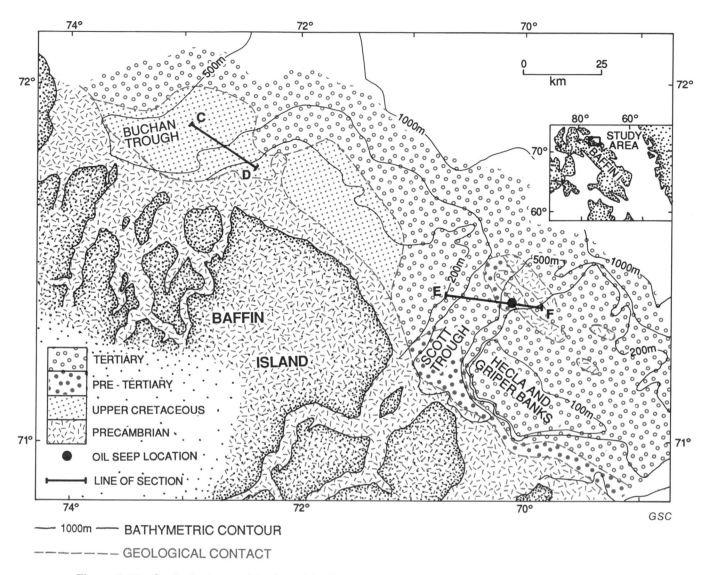

Figure 7.22 Geological map of the Scott Inlet-Buchan Gulf area of the Northeast Baffin Shelf. The Scott Inlet submarine oil seep lies near the southern margin of the Scott submarine trough, 40 km offshore (adapted from MacLean et al., 1981).

high concentrations of amorphogen, and hold promise as a potential source rock. This is also true of the Narssamiut Formation, with which the mudstones are considered to be coeval.

The Campanian rocks at Buchan Trough and Home Bay were deposited in a shallow marine, probably neritic, environment. Locally, these rocks are folded and faulted.

Uppermost Cretaceous rocks may be present in Gjoa G-37 in the northern Labrador Sea. There, a few metres of shale have been assigned a Maastrichtian age (Klose et al., 1982) and tentatively included in the Markland Formation by Balkwill and McMillan (in part 1 of this chapter).

Paleogene

The oldest Tertiary sedimentary sequences are Paleocene as recorded from the West Greenland Basin. A litho- and biostratigraphic framework was established by Rolle (1985) for the offshore portion of West Greenland Basin

from a study of sample lithologies and palynomorph assemblages from exploratory wells located in southern Baffin Bay and northern Labrador Sea (see Fig. 7.18 for location). The oldest Tertiary sediments were included in the Ikermiut Formation, with the type section designated as the interval 3619-1534 m in the Ikermiut No. 1 well (Rolle, 1985). The formation is also present in Kangamiut 1, where it is 149 m thick and in Nukik 2, where it is 193 m thick. The Ikermiut consists of carbonaceous mudstone with some thin siltstones and sandstones. In the Nukik 2 well volcanic fragments are common.

The Ikermiut at the type section is Campanian-Middle Eocene (Rolle, 1985). Where it directly overlies basement, as in the Kangamiut 1 and Nukik 2 wells, it is Paleocene-Early Eocene and Paleocene respectively. The formation was correlated with the Markland and Cartwright formations (Fig. 7.25) of the Labrador Shelf (Rolle, 1985).

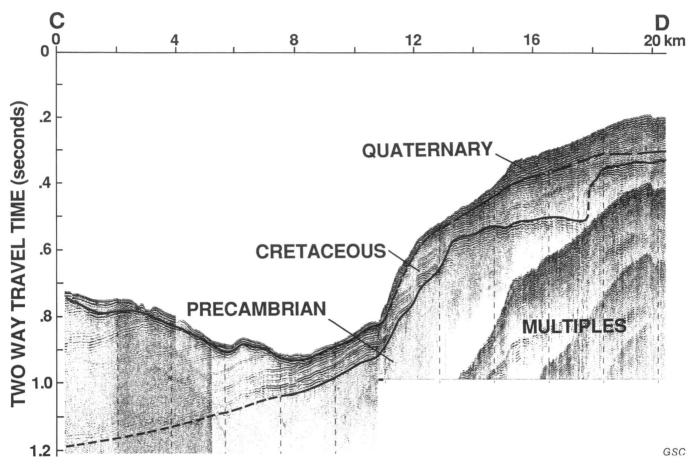

Figure 7.23 Cross-section C-D (see Fig. 7.22 for location) illustrating northwesterly dipping Upper Cretaceous strata and underlying basement rocks at Buchan Gulf (from MacLean et al., 1981).

The Hellefisk Formation appears to be coeval with the Ikermiut. The type section and only known occurrence of the Hellefisk is the interval 2507-1890 m in Hellefisk 1. The formation is predominantly silty mudstone with interbedded calcareous sandstone. In the uppermost part there are thin coal seams and lignite.

The Hellefisk Formation overlies basalt and grades upwards into the overlying Kangamiut Formation. The age, according to Rolle (1985), is Late Paleocene to Middle Eocene. The Hellefisk may be a correlative of the Eureka Sound Formation of Bylot Island.

The Ikermiut Formation grades upwards into the Nukik Formation, the type section of which is the interval 2350-2078 m in Nukik 2. The Nukik is also present in Nukik 1 where it is about 200 m thick and in Kangamiut 1 where it is 65 m thick (2625-2560 m). It probably extends over most of the eastern part of the basin and is absent to the northwest (Rolle, 1985). The Nukik consists of alternating beds of turbiditic sandstone and mudstone, with fining-upward sequences. Glauconite and lignite are present locally. Towards the top there may be shale and massive glauconitic sandstones. The Nukik Formation is Early to Late Eocene towards the east, and Late Eocene to the west. Rolle equated the Nukik to the Gudrid Formation of the Labrador Shelf.

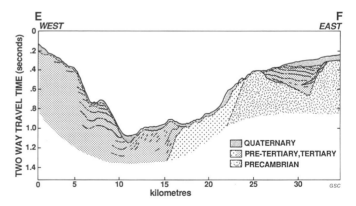

Figure 7.24 Cross-section E-F across the outer part of Scott Trough in the vicinity of the submarine oil seep, 20-25 km along the section (see Fig. 7.22 for location). Seepage apparently occurs through migration of hydrocarbons updip in the strata flanking the basement high or along the contact with those rocks (modified after MacLean et al., 1981; Grant et al., 1986).

Figure 7.25 Correlation chart of Eclipse Trough, Lancaster Sound, Davis Strait, and Labrador Shelf.

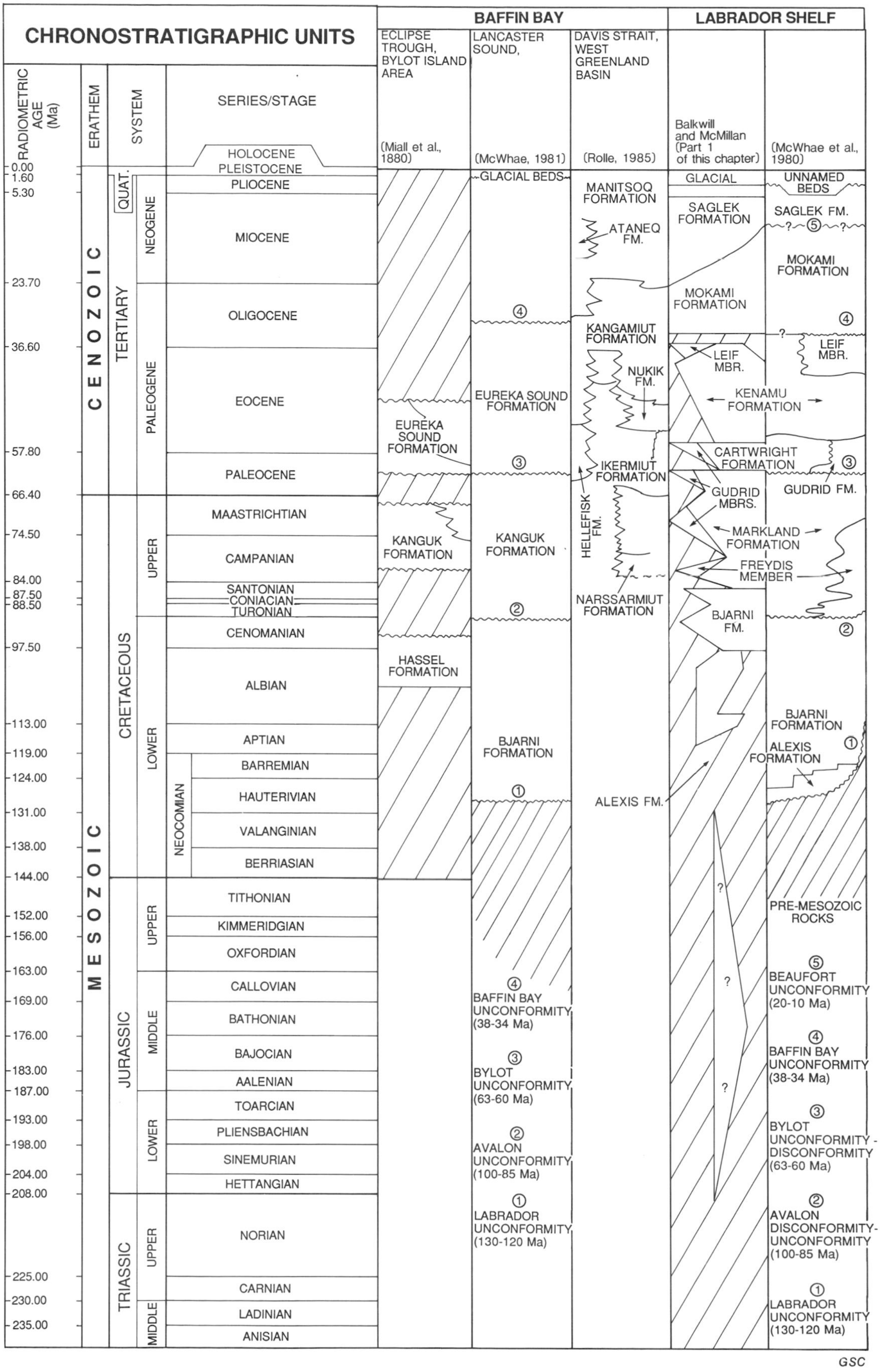
CHRONOSTRATIGRAPHIC UNITS
RADIOMETRIC AGE (Ma)
ERATHEM
SYSTEM
SERIES/STAGE
BAFFIN BAY
ECLIPSE TROUGH, BYLOT ISLAND AREA
(Miall et al., 1880)
LANCASTER SOUND,
(McWhae, 1981)
DAVIS STRAIT, WEST GREENLAND BASIN
(Rolle, 1985)
LABRADOR SHELF
Balkwill and McMillan (Part 1 of this chapter)
(McWhae et al., 1980)
0.00
1.60
5.30
23.70
36.60
57.80
66.40
74.50
84.00
87.50
88.50
97.50
113.00
119.00
124.00
131.00
138.00
144.00
152.00
156.00
163.00
169.00
176.00
183.00
187.00
193.00
198.00
204.00
208.00
225.00
230.00
235.00
CENOZOIC
MESOZOIC
QUAT.
TERTIARY
NEOGENE
PALEOGENE
CRETACEOUS
UPPER
LOWER
NEOCOMIAN
JURASSIC
MIDDLE
TRIASSIC
HOLOCENE
PLEISTOCENE
PLIOCENE
MIOCENE
OLIGOCENE
EOCENE
PALEOCENE
MAASTRICHTIAN
CAMPANIAN
SANTONIAN
CONIACIAN
TURONIAN
CENOMANIAN
ALBIAN
APTIAN
BARREMIAN
HAUTERIVIAN
VALANGINIAN
BERRIASIAN
TITHONIAN
KIMMERIDGIAN
OXFORDIAN
CALLOVIAN
BATHONIAN
BAJOCIAN
AALENIAN
TOARCIAN
PLIENSBACHIAN
SINEMURIAN
HETTANGIAN
NORIAN
CARNIAN
LADINIAN
ANISIAN
GLACIAL BEDS
EUREKA SOUND FORMATION
KANGUK FORMATION
HASSEL FORMATION
EUREKA SOUND FORMATION
KANGUK FORMATION
BJARNI FORMATION
MANITSOQ FORMATION
ATANEQ FM.
KANGAMIUT FORMATION
NUKIK FM.
IKERMIUT FORMATION
HELLEFISK FM.
NARSSARMIUT FORMATION
ALEXIS FM.
GLACIAL
SAGLEK FORMATION
MOKAMI FORMATION
LEIF MBR.
KENAMU FORMATION
CARTWRIGHT FORMATION
GUDRID MBRS.
MARKLAND FORMATION
FREYDIS MEMBER
BJARNI FM.
UNNAMED BEDS
SAGLEK FM.
MOKAMI FORMATION
LEIF MBR.
GUDRID FM.
BJARNI FORMATION
ALEXIS FORMATION
PRE-MESOZOIC ROCKS
④ BAFFIN BAY UNCONFORMITY (38-34 Ma)
③ BYLOT UNCONFORMITY (63-60 Ma)
② AVALON UNCONFORMITY (100-85 Ma)
① LABRADOR UNCONFORMITY (130-120 Ma)
⑤ BEAUFORT UNCONFORMITY (20-10 Ma)
④ BAFFIN BAY UNCONFORMITY (38-34 Ma)
③ BYLOT UNCONFORMITY - DISCONFORMITY (63-60 Ma)
② AVALON DISCONFORMITY-UNCONFORMITY (100-85 Ma)
① LABRADOR UNCONFORMITY (130-120 Ma)
GSC

The youngest Paleogene unit in West Greenland Basin is the Kangamiut Formation. The type section is the interval 2560-1555 m in Kangamiut 1. Reference sections are: Hellefisk 1 (1890-1077Wm); Ikermiut 1 (1534-1160 m); and Nukik 2 (2073-1454 m). Thicknesses therefore vary between 374 m and 1005 m. The Kangamiut consists of shelf sandstones with subordinate siltstone and mudstone. Lignite, glauconite, pyrite and shell fragments occur throughout the formation. The age is Middle-Late Eocene to Oligocene.

Lower Tertiary rocks are also present on the Northeast and Southeast Baffin shelves. On Northeast Baffin Shelf, Upper Eocene-Lower Oligocene rocks have been recovered by dredging. The samples appear to be bedrock which is exposed on the lower part of the south wall of Scott Trough in water depths of about 650 m. The rocks are dark grey, silty and sandy, calcareous concretions and calcareous sandstone with plant remains. Deposition was probably in a shallow, nearshore marine environment (MacLean et al., 1981). The rocks may correlate with the Kangamiut Formation.

Where observed on single channel seismic reflection profiles, Tertiary strata on Northeast Baffin Shelf are generally flat-lying or dip gently eastward, with some folding and faulting.

On Southeast Baffin Shelf, Upper Paleocene-Lower Eocene cores have been recovered (MacLean et al., 1982). Two cores off Cumberland Sound are Early Eocene and Late Paleocene-Early Eocene respectively on the basis of contained palynomorph assemblages. The first is a calcareous siltstone; the second is a dark grey to black, silty mudstone, which contains gas. These appear to equate with the Eureka Sound Formation of Bylot Island.

Paleogene rocks occur in the two wells, Hekja A-72 and Gjoa G-37 in northern Labrador Sea. In Hekja A-72, Paleocene volcanic rocks are overlain by dark grey Paleocene shales and Eocene-Oligocene mudstones and shales, with some silty stringers and occasional coal. This interval, which is up to 2858 m thick, has been assigned to the Cartwright Formation by Balkwill and McMillan (in Part 1 of this chapter). The top of Danian age rocks is at 3530 m.

The top of the Paleocene in the Hekja well is marked by sand, which extends from 3210 to 3286 m. This sand is the reservoir for the wet gas (Klose et al., 1982). The sand is included in the Middle Gudrid member of the Cartwright Formation and provides a detailed description of the lithology of this member in the Hekja well (Balkwill and McMillan in Part 1 of this chapter). The base of the Middle Gudrid is placed at about 3515 m. The member consists of poorly sorted, fine- to coarse-grained, coaly sandstones. The sediment source area has been identified as the Precambrian uplands of Baffin Island (Balkwill and McMillan in Part 1 of this chapter).

The Cartwright Formation is also present between 2337 and 3877 m in Gjoa G-37 according to Balkwill and McMillan (in Part 1 of this chapter). This interval would also be equivalent to the Ikermiut Formation of West Greenland Basin.

The Cartwright Formation is overlain by the Kenamu Formation on the Labrador Shelf. The Kenamu, which is Eocene, is present in the Gjoa G-37 and Hekja A-72 wells. In Hekja, the Kenamu is 850 m thick, extending from 2580 to 1730 m and includes thin coal beds. In Gjoa, according to Balkwill and McMillan (in Part 1 of this chapter), the upper surface of the Kenamu represents the top of an upward coarsening sequence. This unit may be truncated by an unconformity, the Baffin Bay unconformity of McWhae (1981).

Neogene

Neogene sediments presumably underlie the seafloor across much of Baffin Bay. They are present in the West Greenland Basin, where two formations were recognized, the Manitsoq and the Ataneq (Rolle, 1985). The type section of the Manitsoq Formation is the interval 1555-500 m in Kangamiut 1 well. Reference sections are in Hellefisk 1 (1077-779 m) and Nukik 1 (1507-457 m). The formation is an upward-coarsening unit of paralic and fan delta sandstones, with interbedded mudstone common in the lower part. The Manitsoq is Miocene, although questionable Oligocene palynomorphs occur in Hellefisk 1 (Rolle, 1985). The formation conformably overlies the Kangamiut and is overlain by the Ataneq Formation or by boulder clay. Rolle (1985) correlated the Manitoq Formation with the Saglek Formation of the Labrador Shelf.

The youngest unit named by Rolle (1985) is the Ataneq Formation. The type section is from 779-448 m in Hellefisk 1. The Ataneq consists of interbedded fine grained sand, siltstone and mudstone, with occasional coarse grained sand and carbonaceous mudstone. The rocks show some fining upward cycles. Their age, according to Rolle, is Miocene-Pleistocene.

A comparable section of lower Miocene to Recent sediments was drilled at Site 645 of the Ocean Drilling Program on the lower continental slope off southern Baffin Island (Srivastava et al., in press). The hole, drilled in a water depth of 2000 m, bottomed in upper Oligocene-lower Miocene sediments at a depth of 1147 m. The sedimentary sequence recovered is dominated by muddy sandstones and claystones with the exception of the intervals between 75 and 225 m and 770 and 900 m in which silty claystones and clayey siltstones are more abundant. Numerous dropstones exist in the upper 330 m of the section. Their composition is highly variable: granitic, gneissic, and shallow-water limestones or micritic carbonate clasts are most common, but friable sandstone, shale and basalt pebbles are also present. The entire sequence has a pronounced terrigenous character. This is also evident from the relatively high organic content of terrestrial origin in the section drilled, with an average organic content of about 0.8%. The organic matter is predominantly terrestrial above 460 m and a mixture of terrestrial and marine material below 460 m.

Dating of the entire section in Site 645 is difficult because of the sparsity of siliceous and calcareous microfossils, except in the uppermost and lowermost parts of the sequence. Only organic-walled microfossils occur through most of the sequence. The dating is primarily based on dinocysts and benthic foraminifers, with some control based on nannofossils and diatoms. Extensive use is also made of the magnetic stratigraphy. Based on the examination of the core material recovered at this hole the sequence has been divided into three major units (Srivastava et al., in press). The units are:

unit Ia (late Pleistocene to Recent) — alternating beds of calcareous muddy sand and silty mud with scattered dropstones up to cobble size;

unit Ib (early to late Pleistocene) — alternating beds of calcareous silty clay to silty mud with dropstones up to cobble size;

unit II (late Pliocene to early Pleistocene) — noncalcareous silty mud, clayey silt and silty clay with dropstones up to cobble size. This unit also contains scattered iron sulphides;

unit IIIa (middle Miocene to late Pliocene) — poorly sorted muddy sand and sand-bearing silty mud with scattered, predominantly shale pebbles in coarser beds;

unit IIIb (middle Miocene) — muddy sandstones and silty mudstones, interbedded with well laminated calcareous silty claystones;

unit IIIc (early to middle Miocene) — fine- to medium-grained muddy sandstones and silty mudstones. The sandstones are occasionally glauconite-bearing.

Rhythmic sedimentation predominates in units II and I with interbedded dark grey to olive grey silty clay succeeded by light brownish to greyish brown calcareous muddy sands, silty clay or mud (Srivastava et al., in press). Contacts between the units are sharp and bioturbation is minor. These rhythmic cycles signify glacial-interglacial cycles, with light coloured intervals corresponding to interglacial cycles as they contain a coarser detritus including detrital carbonate. Ice-rafted pebbles and cobbles are randomly distributed in both lithologies. The cycles average about 1 m in thickness, equivalent to 8 ka at an average depositional rate of 130 m/Ma at this site for the upper 470 m. Such a period is much shorter than the 41 ka period that has been estimated from studies of oxygen-isotope stratigraphy of shallow piston cores from Baffin Bay (Aksu, 1983). The reason for this difference may be known upon completion of detailed oxygen isotope work on the material from Ocean Drilling Program Site 645. The preliminary results from Site 645 strongly indicate that the glacial cyclicity on the margins of the Baffin Bay region occurred on a shorter timescale than expected.

The onset of major glacial ice-rafting in Baffin Bay, recorded by the first abundance of dropstones and other coarse detritus, took place at least as early as 2.5 Ma (340 m) and probably as early as 3.4 Ma (465 m). The beginning of major glacial activity in this region therefore preceded evidence of ice-rafting in the North Atlantic by at least 1 Ma. However, the isolated occurrences of pebbles and granules in strata as old as late Miocene (605 m) could indicate the presence of at least seasonal sea ice in Baffin Bay as recently as 8 Ma (Srivastava et al., in press).

Based on the correlation of seismic reflection data with the texture and structure observed in the core material at ODP Site 645, two major unconformities were recognized (Srivastava et al., in press). The older occurs at the early to middle Miocene boundary, the younger occurs at the early-late Pliocene boundary and coincides with the onset of glacial activity in the Baffin Bay region. The strata overlying the early-middle Miocene unconformity includes most of unit IIIb material and shows strong characteristics suggestive of pronounced but variable influence of deep currents during deposition. This indicates a southward-directed flow of Arctic water through Davis Strait into the Labrador Sea starting in the middle Miocene.

Other records of Neogene sediments are from Southeast Baffin Shelf. Basal marine shales of the lower Mokami member (of the Mokami Formation) disconformably overlie the Kenamu Formation on Southeast Baffin Shelf (Balkwill and McMillan, in Part 1 of this chapter). The lower Mokami member, of probable Oligocene age, is overlain by the upper Mokami member of the Mokami Formation, which is in part Miocene. Most of the inner and central parts of Southeast Baffin Shelf were emergent in the middle to Late Oligocene (Balkwill and McMillan, in Part 1 of this chapter). During that time, nonmarine muds and peat accumulated in interfluvial lake basins.

The Saglek Formation (Late Oligocene-Pliocene) may cover much of the sea floor of Southeast Baffin Shelf. The Saglek consists of fine- to coarse-grained clastics, with some lignite fragments and broken pelecypod shells. Overlying this formation along Southeast Baffin Shelf are Quaternary sediment sequences.

Igneous rocks

As indicated earlier, subaqueously and subaerially erupted early Tertiary volcanic rocks occur onshore in the Cape Dyer region of eastern Baffin Island and in the Disko Island-Svartenhuk area of western Greenland. Volcanic rocks also occur extensively offshore on parts of the respective continental shelves (Fig. 7.19). These deposits are considered to have been emplaced through leakage along fractures developed during the separation of Greenland from North America.

The distribution of volcanic rocks in southern Baffin Bay and Davis Strait was reviewed by Johnson et al. (1982). On Southeast Baffin Shelf, volcanic rocks have been recovered from shallow drillholes and their areal extent mapped by MacLean et al. (1978, 1982) and MacLean and Falconer (1979). Unfortunately the basalts were too highly altered to provide reliable ages. Basalt cores have also been obtained from the Davis Strait High. This structural high in the middle of the strait is on trend with the subsurface ridge structures on Southeast Baffin Shelf described by MacLean et al. (1982) and Srivastava et al. (1982).

Volcanic rocks are also present in two wells Hekja A-72 and Gjoa G-37 in northern Labrador Sea (Klose et al., 1982; Balkwill and McMillan, Part 1 of this chapter). In Hekja, which was drilled to a depth of 4566 m, the bottom 1021 m consist of olivine tholeiites interbedded with shales and, in the upper part, with limestone and dolomite. The palynomorphs in this interval are Paleocene. The volcanics have yielded K-Ar ages of 119 Ma and 105 Ma (Klose et al., 1982). The age of the volcanics has been accepted as Early Cretaceous (Balkwill and McMillan, Part 1 of this chapter). This could be incorrect, since alteration of the volcanics may obstruct reliable age determinations.

In Gjoa G-37, there are two basalt sequences. The upper one has been dated (K-Ar) as 56 ± 3 Ma or Late Paleocene-Early Eocene. This accords with the age of most of the volcanics elsewhere in Baffin Bay. However, volcanic piles of several ages appear to be represented at Gjoa G-37 and Hekja A-72. There, thick successions of Late Cretaceous and Paleocene basalts overlie Early Cretaceous flows. This is supported by the presence of several prominent reflectors between basement and the mid-Miocene unconformity on Southeast Baffin Shelf. These have been interpreted as Late Cretaceous to Paleocene basaltic flows (Srivastava et al., 1981).

High frequency magnetic anomalies directly northeast of the Hekja well and other areas on Southeast Baffin Shelf follow the elongate positive gravity anomaly. As shown by drilling to the north (MacLean et al., 1978, 1982), these magnetic anomaly highs denote areas underlain by volcanics, primarily basalts.

The most extensive offshore occurrences of volcanic rocks are in West Greenland Basin. Subaerial basalts have been recovered in dredge samples and their areal extent mapped from seismic reflection and magnetic anomaly profiles. These occurrences are seaward of the onshore outcrops in the Svartenhuk, Halvo and Disko Island areas and extend 135 km to the south (Ross and Henderson, 1973; Denham, 1974; Clarke, 1975; Clarke and Pederson, 1976; Brett and Zarudzki, 1979).

Confirmation of in situ basalts offshore was found in the Hellefisk 1 and Nukik 2 wells. The bottom 140 m of the Nukik 2 well are subaqueous basalt flows alternating with hyaloclastites, and underlain by a tholeiitic olivine dolerite (Rolle, 1985). Mobil Oil dated (Ar-Ar) the dolerite as 93.4 ± 4.7 Ma, whereas Hald and Larsen (Rolle, 1985) dated (K-Ar) it as 62 ± 7 and 68 ± 7 Ma. The Early Paleocene age has been regarded as more reliable (Rolle, 1985).

In the Hellefisk 1 well, the bottom 694 m consist of subaerial basalt flows of 3-50 m thick. These basalts have been dated (K-Ar) as 63.3 ± 12.6, 54 ± 5.4 and 53.1 ± 5.3 Ma (Rolle, 1985). This would indicate a Late Paleocene to Early Eocene age, although Rolle stated it was Late Paleocene.

A plot of the occurrences of the Paleocene basalts suggests that there is a broad belt of volcanic rocks trending northeast-southwest from Disko Island to east of Frobisher Bay. This would include all of the Davis Strait High. If Johnson et al. (1982) are correct, the belt also expands southward, to include most of the central part of the northern Labrador Sea. The southern boundary may be marked by the Cartwright Fracture Zone.

Basalt dredge samples have also been recovered from the continental shelf and slope off southwest Greenland (Johnson et al., 1982). Some of these samples have been dated as Jurassic, but others appear to be Tertiary.

Clarke (1970) was the first to realize that the Baffin Bay Tertiary basalts belong to a single petrological province. Subsequent studies of the offshore wells have confirmed this (Johnson et al., 1982).

EVOLUTION

Baffin Bay is the northwestern extension of the Atlantic Ocean and Labrador Sea, and its evolution is related to those regions. The opening of the North Atlantic in the Jurassic (Keen et al., Chapter 2; Wade and MacLean, Chapter 5) resulted in mild tectonic activity and volcanism in the Baffin Bay area (Rolle, 1985).

Stretching, block faulting and rifting of the crust between Greenland and North America first occurred in the early Cretaceous (Srivastava, 1978). This led to graben formation in the Labrador Sea and Baffin Bay regions. In Baffin Bay, Lower Cretaceous continental to marine clastics were deposited unconformably (Labrador Unconformity) on Precambrian and possibly Paleozoic rocks. The Lower Cretaceous clastic rocks were succeeded unconformably by marine Upper Cretaceous sediments, which are coeval with marine sediments of the Labrador Sea.

Active seafloor spreading migrated from south to north (Wade and MacLean, Chapter 5). In the southern Labrador Sea, seafloor spreading commenced in the Campanian (anomaly 34) whereas in the northern Labrador Sea, it began in the Maastrichtian (anomaly 31). During this phase the continental crust of Baffin Bay is thought to have been thinned and stretched, but no oceanic crust was formed. Initial opening in Baffin Bay was about a pole of rotation in northern Baffin Bay and took place during the Paleocene (anomaly 25; Rice and Shade, 1982).

The major phase of seafloor spreading in Baffin Bay was in the Early Tertiary (Fig. 7.26). This was coincident with active seafloor spreading in the Norwegian Sea. Rotation was about a pole in Hudson Bay and oceanic crust was formed over a 130 km wide distance in Baffin Bay (Srivastava and Tapscott, 1986; Rice and Shade, 1982). This was accompanied by stretching of the lithosphere causing the formation of grabens in the Hudson Strait, Cumberland Sound, Eclipse Trough and Jones Sound areas and lateral movement along the Ungava Transform Fault.

The seafloor spreading model for Baffin Bay is supported by the gravity and magnetic data. There is a pronounced gravity low which trends north-south in the centre of Baffin Bay (Ross and Henderson, 1973; Srivastava, 1978). In the vicinity of 72°N, the low broadens, separating into two lobes which are aligned northwest-southeast. The low denotes the former axis of spreading in the bay, in an analogous manner to the low marking the extinct Labrador Sea Ridge (Srivastava, 1978; Jackson et al., 1979). A Late Precambrian orthogonal fracture system trending northwestward and northeastward, as well as faults developed during the Paleozoic, apparently influenced much of the subsequent faulting and spreading history of the region (McWhae, 1981). For example, the position of the axis of spreading may have been determined by the location of a major sinistral shear zone developed between Canada and Greenland during the Grenville Orogeny (Rolle, 1985).

Shipborne magnetic data delineate a series of northwest-trending anomalies in the centre of Baffin Bay. By correlation with the Labrador Sea, these are interpreted to be anomalies 13 through 21 and indicate a spreading rate of 0.3-0.4 cm/a (Jackson et al., 1979). The direction of the lineations and their low amplitudes suggest spreading obliquely to the axis.

The Mesozoic-Cenozoic rift-drift history can be used to explain the origin of the secondary grabens and major fault patterns in and adjacent to Baffin Bay. As discussed under the section Tectonic Setting, there is a major fracture zone, the Ungava Transform Fault, which runs southwest from Disko Island to Hudson Strait. This fault was interpreted to be one arm of a triple junction, with the other arms being the Hudson Strait Graben and the Labrador Sea Ridge (Hood and Bower, 1975). This Ridge-Ridge-Fault junction was unstable, so that migration took place along the Ungava Fault. Such migration may have led to the formation of the Frobisher Bay and Cumberland Sound grabens.

A stable Ridge-Ridge-Fault triple junction model was postulated for the northern end of Baffin Bay (Burke and Dewey, 1973). It has been assumed that Lancaster Sound was the failed arm, Baffin Bay the ridge, with the transform fault running along Nares Strait (Hood and Bower,

1975). If correct, then Jones Sound could have originated in an analogous fashion to Cumberland Sound.

Baffin Bay underwent considerable vertical as well as lateral movement during the Mesozoic-Cenozoic (Keen et al., Chapter 2). On eastern and northeastern Baffin Island relative elevations of Paleocene volcanic rocks and upper Eocene sediments indicate upward movement relative to the shelf of about 600 m. The relatively uniform sediment cover across the bay is interpreted as indicative of high sedimentation rates subsequent to cessation of rifting (Keen et al., 1974). Elevation of Baffin Island would have provided a source for the Neogene clastic sediments of the bay, as would the relatively soft shelf sediments of Late Cretaceous-Early Tertiary age.

Any model for the evolution of Baffin Bay must take into account glaciation and the corresponding relative sea-level changes. The fiords of Baffin Island and their offshore submarine equivalents extending across the shelf were certainly molded into their present configuration by ice action. It has been postulated, however, that the fiords and canyons developed initially along existing Tertiary drainage systems (Fortier and Morley, 1956; Ives and Andrews, 1963; Pelletier, 1966). This would seem to support the idea that the sources for much of the Baffin Bay Neogene rocks were the surrounding land masses.

CRETACEOUS AND TERTIARY PALEO-OCEANOGRAPHY

The oldest Mesozoic sedimentary rocks known in the Baffin Bay-Davis Strait region are Barremian-Aptian sequences in Cumberland Sound; they are equivalent to the Bjarni Formation of the Labrador Shelf and are apparently terrestrial. Immediately preceding deposition of these sediments, a phase of tectonism and volcanism represented by the Alexis Formation probably affected the northern Labrador Sea-Baffin Bay region. The oldest marine fossils are Albian-Cenomanian dinocysts (MacLean and Falconer, 1979) from a core taken east of Cumberland Sound. These and marine sediments of questionable Cenomanian-Turonian age from Disko Island are the first indications of a marine transgression in this region during Cretaceous time. This would equate with the worldwide rise in sea level postulated by Vail et al. (1977).

The West Greenland rocks contain Cenomanian-Turonian to Maastrichtian ammonites, which show strong affinities with coeval assemblages from the western interior of North America. This indicates a marine connection between the two areas at that time (Teichert in Ruedemann and Balk, 1939; Rosenkrantz et al., 1942; Birkelund, 1965; Jeletzky, 1950, 1970; Williams and Stelck, 1975). The West Greenland assemblages also contain Campanian-Maastrichtian ammonites with North Pacific and Atlantic affinities, suggesting the existence of connecting waterways between these regions (Birkelund, 1965; Jeletzky, 1970; Williams and Stelck, 1975).

The microfossil evidence is more specific. Planktonic foraminifers in marine Campanian-Maastrichtian shales from Nugssuaq, West Greenland, show Atlantic affinities and were presumably brought in by Atlantic surface water incursions (Gradstein and Srivastava, 1980). The Campanian dinoflagellates include taxa with Atlantic affinities and others that are only known from the McIntyre flora (MacLean and Williams, 1980). As defined by Lentin and Williams (1980) the McIntyre flora are restricted to the Arctic or boreal province. This indicates that a marine connection through Baffin Bay existed between the Atlantic and Arctic, at least during part of the Late Cretaceous.

These findings are supported by the Upper Cretaceous rocks of Northeast Baffin Shelf, including Buchan Trough and Home Bay, and on Bylot Island. Sediments in these areas assigned to Kanguk Formation contain Campanian dinoflagellates which show affinities with coeval assemblages from the North American interior and from Graham and Ellef Ringnes islands in Sverdrup Basin (Manum and Cookson, 1964; McIntyre, 1974). These assemblages were placed in the McIntyre flora (Lentin and Williams, 1980).

The boreal affinities of the Campanian dinoflagellate assemblages from Bylot Island and Buchan Trough support the presence of a northern marine connection between Baffin Bay and the western interior of North America in the Late Cretaceous (Fig. 7.27). This idea was earlier postulated by Teichert in Ruedemann and Balk (1939), Birkelund (1965), and Jeletzky (1970).

The West Greenland foraminiferal and palynological assemblages and the mixed Atlantic-Arctic dinoflagellate assemblages at Home Bay indicate that a marine connection also existed between southern Baffin Bay and the Atlantic in the Late Cretaceous. This connection was presumably through Davis Strait. This is confirmed for the Campanian by the ammonite and foraminiferal data and by the dinoflagellate assemblages in Labrador Shelf wells, which represent transitional Arctic-Atlantic assemblages. The Campanian dinoflagellates in those wells show more affinities with coeval Scotian Shelf-Grand Banks assemblages than those of the McIntyre flora. However, some species known only from the McIntyre flora are found on the Labrador Shelf, but never in high concentrations.

Tertiary paleoceanographic conditions in Baffin Bay can be deduced from Henderson et al. (1976), Miall et al. (1980), MacLean et al. (1981), McWhae (1981), Srivastava et al. (1986), and Rolle (1985). There seems general agreement that there was a major regression in the Paleocene Baffin Bay and Davis Strait. This regression in the Bylot Island section was observed where the Upper Cretaceous Kanguk Formation is unconformably overlain by the Eureka Sound Formation of Late Paleocene age (Miall et al., 1980). The Bylot Unconformity was placed at this horizon (McWhae, 1981). This break was also noted in some of the wells on the West Greenland Shelf (Rolle, 1985). This would conform to the worldwide lowering of sea level as noted by Vail et al. (1977) in Late Maastrichtian-Danian time.

A major marine transgression in the Late Paleocene-Early Eocene led to the deposition of glauconitic sands and organic rich mudstone (Rolle, 1985). The West Greenland faunal assemblages show both North American and Atlantic affinities (Henderson et al., 1976), indicating a continuing connection of the Arctic and Atlantic oceans through Baffin Bay. This would be expected during the drifting phase. However, plate reconstructions indicate a rather narrow passage through Davis Strait which would have limited circulation in the Paleocene sea (Srivastava et al., 1981).

The Early Eocene appears to have been a period of major transgression in Baffin Bay, as indicated by the turbidites in some of the wells of West Greenland Shelf. In the

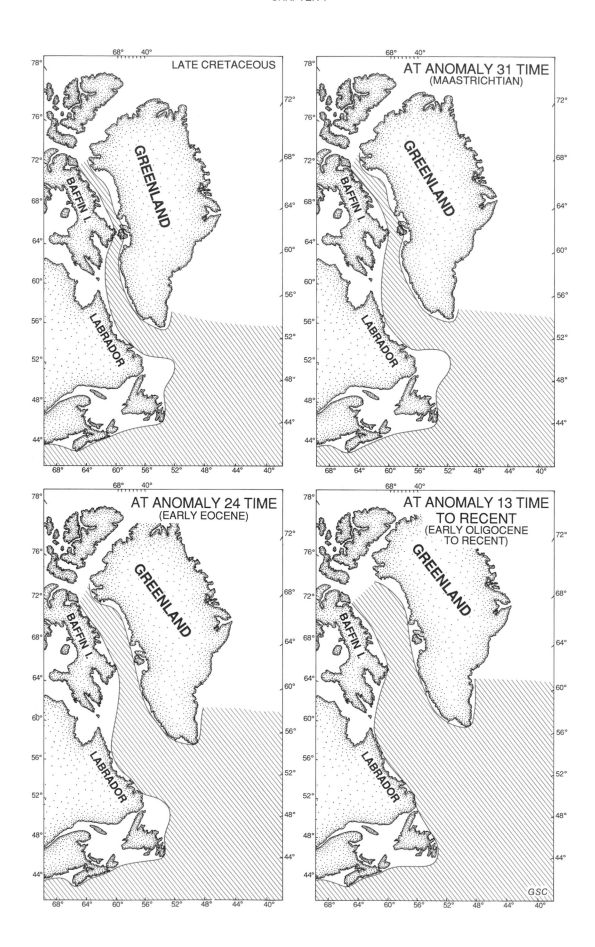

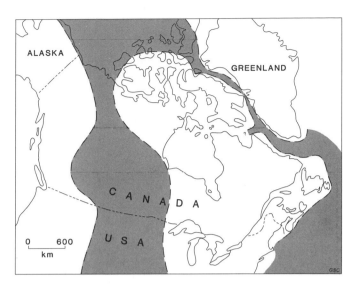

Figure 7.27 Map showing the postulated distribution of Campanian seas. Baffin Bay is connected with the interior of North American through the Arctic, and with the Atlantic by a narrow seaway through Davis Strait. Greenland and North America are shown in their inferred late Cretaceous geographic positions (derived from Jeletzky, 1971; Williams and Stelck, 1975; Gradstein and Srivastava, 1980).

Eocene, the environment became less anoxic, possibly due to the widening and subsidence of Baffin Bay and Davis Strait and establishment of effective oceanic circulation. The greater influx of coarse clastics was related to a more humid Maritime climate (Rolle, 1985). This could have increased erosion on the surrounding landmass. The Eocene marked the onset of the clastic, commonly turbidite, sequences which persisted throughout the remainder of the Tertiary.

Marine incursions occurred in the Late Eocene-Early Oligocene, with some evidence for a major regression in the Late Oligocene (Balkwill and McMillan, Part 1 of this chapter). They noted an unconformity between the lower and upper Mokami members, and stated that most of the inner and central parts of the Baffin shelves were emergent in the Late Oligocene, accompanied by subaerial erosion and the accumulation of nonmarine muds and peat in interfluvial lake basins. Extensive bevelling of the shelf strata subsequent to the early Eocene is also indicated (MacLean et al., 1982). However, Rolle (1985) did not see any evidence on the West Greenland Shelf for a global fall in sea level, as postulated by Vail et al. (1977).

In the Neogene, a thick upward coarsening clastic sequence was deposited over much of the shelves. On West Greenland Shelf this phase is represented by the Manitsoq Formation; on Southeast Baffin Shelf it is in part the Saglek Formation. An increase of granitic fragments in Manitsoq Formation was recorded, which was related to

Figure 7.26 Paleogeography of the Baffin Bay-Labrador Sea region during the Late Cretaceous, Early Paleocene, Early Eocene and Early Oligocene. Hachuring denotes marine environments (modified after Srivastava et al., 1981; Gradstein and Srivastava, 1980).

rejuvenation of the source areas, notably the Greenland Shield and the Davis Strait High (Rolle, 1985).

Lower and upper Saglek units were recognized by Balkwill and McMillan (Part 1 of this chapter). The "lower Saglek" consists of conglomeratic sandstones and is unconformably overlain by the "upper Saglek", also a conglomeratic facies. This unconformity is regarded as Late Miocene on the Labrador Shelf (Grant, 1980). This would accord with the worldwide drop in sea level recognized by Vail et al. (1977) and be equivalent to the Beaufort Unconformity of McWhae (1981).

According to Balkwill and McMillan, the upper Saglek unit is also present on Southeast Baffin Shelf. It is overlain by Quaternary sediments of varying thickness. The Quaternary sediments commonly contain reworked Late Cretaceous palynomorphs, which exhibit affinities with known boreal assemblages.

Cenozoic paleocirculation reconstructions (Berggren and Hollister, 1977) favoured polarward surface circulation from the Atlantic into the Arctic Basin via the Labrador Sea, Davis Strait and Baffin Bay. Microfossil data from the exploratory wells (Labrador Shelf, West Greenland, and the Grand Banks) confirm incursions of Atlantic water into the Labrador Sea and northward during the Paleogene. By the end of the Paleogene, the Labrador Sea-Baffin Bay connection would have widened to its present width from an initially elongate, narrow seaway. Well data indicate that climatic deterioration with cooler water circulation began in the Oligocene-Miocene. Such a trend was also observed at ODP Site 647 in the Labrador Sea where the lower Oligocene sediments change from calcareous to biosiliceous. This signifies an increase in opal and decrease in carbonate production in surface water, a trend which began in the late Eocene and was accompanied by cooling of the surface water (Srivastava et al., in press).

The Neogene paleocirculation of the deeper parts of Baffin Bay has been revealed to some extent by the results from ODP Site 645. In this hole, the lack of siliceous and calcareous biota, the neritic aspect suggested by diatoms and the dominance of organic material of terrestrial derivation indicate that the surface water of the bay remained cool and nutrient free, with perhaps lower than normal salinity from the Miocene to Recent (Srivastava et al., in press). Dissolution and/or diagenesis cannot be ruled out as possible explanations for the poor preservation or absence of calcareous and siliceous biota. However, the presence of some calcareous microfossils and dinocysts having North Atlantic affinities in the lower Miocene sediments indicates relatively warm, northward-flowing waters from the North Atlantic. In the middle Miocene (unit IIIa) occurrence of dinocysts with subarctic or North Atlantic affinities suggests that cool conditions existed in that part of the bay. Rare planktonic foraminifera in middle Miocene and younger strata apparently signify that there were periodic incursions of warm North Atlantic waters. The southward flow of Arctic water masses into the Labrador Sea through Davis Strait presumably extends back to at least the middle Miocene. This is supported by the seismic data from the upper slope (dated at ODP Site 645) of Baffin Bay which show a mid-Miocene unconformity cutting deeply into Paleocene or older strata. The overlying strata contain dune-like structures. Thus, the unconformity may mark the onset of a vigorous southward-directed current in the Baffin Basin, which is coincident with the cooling trend indicated by floral and faunal assemblages in the middle Miocene (Srivastava et al., in press). This further confirms the existence of the cold Labrador Current in the Miocene as postulated by Gradstein and Srivastava (1980).

ECONOMIC GEOLOGY

Baffin Bay has been shown to be a major sedimentary basin with sediments up to about 14 km in thickness east of Lancaster Sound, up to 4 km in the Scott Inlet area of Northeast Baffin Shelf (Jackson et al., 1977), about 8 km offshore western Greenland, and up to 10 km beneath Melville Bay (Henderson et al., 1976). Multichannel seismic data indicate that there are numerous potential structural traps in these sedimentary sequences. Many of the traps appear to be related to block faulting in the basement with subsequent draping of the sediments over the structures, or to shale diapirism.

Three types of hydrocarbon "plays" were identified in the northern Labrador Sea, and by extrapolation to the Southeast Baffin Shelf (Klose et al., 1982). The three types were: wrench-related structures, including anticlines and "flower structures", in the Tertiary section above the volcanics; Lower Cretaceous sandstones draped over or around horst blocks; and Paleozoic reservoirs which could occur as outliers on basement. Data from the wells and shallow core holes show that there are suitable reservoir rocks, such as the Hassel and Kanguk formations, and potential source-rocks, such as the Ikermiut and Kanguk formations. As possible source rocks Lower Cretaceous terrigenous deposits, Upper Cretaceous shales and Lower Tertiary shales containing resinite were suggested (Klose et al., 1982).

Consequently, Baffin Bay may hold considerable promise as a hydrocarbon province. This is borne out in part by the results of exploration in the adjacent northern Labrador Sea-Davis Strait region. The first and only significant discovery was the Hekja A-72 well. This was drilled on a wrench-fault-related basement structure on Southeast Baffin Shelf in 1979 and 1980. The well encountered a sandstone-shale interval between 3210 and 3286 m, which contained gas and condensate. The reservoir interval consists of 44 m of porous, coarse grained sandstone — the Hekja sand — with a permeability of 10 millidarcies. The estimated minimum recoverable reserves are 6.44 Mm^3.

Gjoa G-37 was also drilled on a wrench-fault-related anticline about 215 km eastnortheast of Hekja. It was a dry hole.

Drilling results in West Greenland Basin have been disappointing. All were dry, with drillstem testing being carried out on only one well — Kangamiut 1.

Encouraging indicators of petroleum potential exist on Northeast Baffin Shelf. There, a submarine oil seep at Scott Trough indicates that favourable conditions existed for hydrocarbon generation (Loncarevic and Falconer, 1977; Levy, 1978; MacLean et al., 1981; Grant et al., 1986).

Potential source rocks are known from several areas. Lower Cretaceous terrigenous deposits, the Hassel or Bjarni equivalents, were identified as possible sources for gas (Klose et al., 1982). It was noted that an organic rich

Campanian mudstone, sampled at Home Bay, was a promising petroleum source rock (MacLean and Williams, 1983). In assessing source rock potential, important parameters are: 1. the geothermal gradient; 2. amount of total organic carbon (TOC); 3. the kerogen type; and 4. the thermal maturity. The geothermal gradients are low in West Greenland Basin, where they range from 19.3°C/1000 m in Nukik 2 to 28.9°C/1000 m in Ikermiut 1 (Rolle, 1985). On Southeast Baffin Shelf a geothermal gradient of 31°C to 36°C/1000 m is estimated in Hekja A-72 and 29°/1000 m in Gjoa G-37 (Klose et al., 1982).

The percentage of total organic carbon in the offshore rocks of West Greenland is generally low. It was concluded that the Narssarmiut, Kangamiut, Manitsoq and Ataneq formations have total organic carbon values that are too low (less than the required 0.5%) to be source rocks (Rolle, 1985). The Nukik, Hellefisk and Ikermiut formations have sufficiently high total organic carbon values to be source rocks: in the Nukik it is 0.5 to 1.5%; in the Hellefisk it is 0.5 to 2%; and in the Ikermiut it is 0.5 to 3%.

The wells on Southeast Baffin Shelf show similar percentages. The total organic carbon for the Paleocene in Hekja A-72 is 1.6%, in Gjoa G-37 it is 1.3%.

Kerogen type has a major bearing on source rock potential. Four types were recognized: amorphogen, phyrogen, hylogen and melanogen (Bujak et al., 1977). Amorphogen, organic material of marine origin, is the most likely to be the source of oil. The other three types are terrestrially derived. Phyrogen and hylogen have far less potential for generating oil, whereas melanogen can only result in gas.

The relative percentages of the four types of kerogen in the wells from West Greenland Basin were determined (Croxton, internal report, Grølands Geologiske Undersøgelse 1981). The Nukik Formation contains predominantly hylogen and melanogen, so it would be a gas prone source rock. The Ikermiut Formation contains up to one-third amorphogen and one-third phyrogen, so would appear to be a much more promising oil source as well as a good gas source. There is a possibility, however, that the amorphogen is in reality degraded phyrogen. The Hellefisk Formation contains very little amorphogen, so has minimal oil but some gas potential.

Detailed kerogen analyses are not available for the wells drilled on Southeast Baffin Shelf. Resinite was noted in a 300 m zone centred on the Hekja sand in Hekja A-72 (Klose et al., 1982). Resinite has been identified as a possible major source of oil in the Canadian Arctic (Snowdon, 1980). No data are provided for Gjoa G-37.

Thermal maturity can be determined from the vitrinite reflectance or the thermal alteration index. The oil window falls between vitrinite reflectance values of 0.7 and 1.2 R_o. In the sediments of West Greenland Basin, the vitrinite reflectance values indicate immature section above the Paleocene (Rolle, 1985). An R_o value of 0.5% is recorded from approximately 3200 m in the two wells, Ikermiut 1 and Kangamiut 1. However, there are two different interpretations for Ikermiut 1. According to Chevron (Rolle, 1985) the onset of maturity (R_o 0.7%) is not reached at total depth of 3619 m, and would not occur until 3850 m. Other data indicate that the onset of maturity is at 3200 m and peak generation would be at 3800 m (R_o of 1%) (Rolle, 1985). In Kangamiut 1, there are also two possible interpretations. The first indicates an R_o of 0.7% at 3580 m, the second indicates an R_o of 0.7% at 3700 m.

Greater depth of burial of Paleocene sediments away from the Kangamiut structure, and to a lesser extent away from the Ikermiut structure, suggests that an appreciable thickness of thermally mature mudstone of the Ikermiut Formation may be present in western and southern parts of the West Greenland Basin (Rolle, 1985).

Data for Southeast Baffin Shelf are scant. The top of the zone where liquid hydrocarbons can be generated is at 3300 m (Klose et al., 1982). There, the vitrinite reflectance R_o value is 0.5%. No data are given for Gjoa G-37.

Using the thermal alteration index (TAI), the minimum value for the generation of oil or the onset of maturity is 2- to 2 (Bujak et al., 1977). This applies only to amorphogen (Croxton, internal report, Grønlands Geologiske Undersøgelse 1981). This value is usually reached in Eocene or older sediments. Thermal alteration index values of 2 are reached in the Paleocene of Nukik 2, the Early Eocene of Hellefisk 1, the Paleocene of Ikermiut 1, and the Late Paleocene of Kangamiut 1. It was concluded from this and the kerogen type that the major part of the sequences was not in the oil window (Rolle, 1985).

No data are available on the thermal alteration index for the wells drilled on Southeast Baffin Shelf.

Collation of all the information seems to indicate that Baffin Bay and the surrounding region are gas prone. The potential for oil generally appears to be low, primarily because of the dominance of terrigenous organic material in most of the sediments. The presence of the submarine oil seep at Scott Trough, however, indicates the existence of conditions favourable for oil generation at least in part of this region.

ACKNOWLEDGMENTS

The compilation of this paper would not have been possible without the pioneer studies of M.E. Bower, D.B. Clarke, A.C. Grant, G. Henderson, P.J. Hood, H.R. Jackson, C.E. Keen, N.J. McMillan and F. Rolle. The authors are indebted to B. Cooke and A. Grant, who ably reviewed the manuscript and made numerous constructive criticisms. We are especially grateful to Margie Best for compiling several of the text figures.

REFERENCES

Aksu, A.E.
1983: Holocene and Pleistocene dissolution cycles in deep sea cores of Baffin Bay and Davis Strait: paleoceanographic implications; Marine Geology, v. 53, p. 331-348.

Andrews, J.T., Quennel, G.K., Wray, J.L., and Ives, J.D.
1972: An early Tertiary outcrop in north central Baffin Island, Northwest Territories, Canada; environment and significance; Canadian Journal of Earth Sciences, v. 9, p. 233-238.

Bally, A.W.
1981: Atlantic-type margins; in Geology of Passive Continental Margins: American Association of Petroleum Geologists, Education Course Note Series No. 19, p. 1-1 to 1-48.

Barss, M.S., Bujak, J.P., and Williams, G.L.
1979: Palynological zonation and correlation of sixty-seven wells, eastern Canada; Geological Survey of Canada, Paper 78-24, 1-118 p.

Berggren, W. A. and Hollister, C.D.
1977: Plate tectonics and paleocirculation; commotion in the ocean; Tectonophysics, v. 38, p. 11-48.

Birkelund, T.
1965: Ammonites from the Upper Cretaceous of West Greenland; Meddelser om Grønland, Bd. 179, 193 p.

Bolton, T.E., Sanford, B.V., Copeland, M.J., Barnes, C.R., and Rigby, J.K.
1977: Geology of Ordovician rocks, Melville Peninsula and region, southeastern District of Franklin; Geological Survey of Canada, Bulletin 269, 137 p.

Brett, C.P. and Zarudzki, E.F.K.
1979: Project Westmar; a shallow marine geophysical survey on the West Greenland continental shelf; Grønlands Geologiske Undersøgelse, Rapport 87, 29 p.

Bridgwater, D., Watson, J., and Windley, B.F.
1973: The Archean craton of the North Atlantic region; Philisophical Transactions of the Royal Society of London, Series A, v. 273, p. 493-512.

Bujak, J.P., Barss, M.S., and Williams, G.L.
1977: Offshore east Canada's organic type and colour and hydrocarbon potential; Oil and Gas Journal, v. 75, p. 198-202.

Burke, K. and Dewey, J.F.
1973: Plume generated triple junctions; key indicators in applying plate tectonics to old rocks; Journal of Geology, v. 81, p. 405-433.

Clarke, D.B.
1970: Tertiary basalts of Baffin Bay; possible primary magma from the mantle; Contributions to Mineralogy and Petrology, v. 25, p. 203-224.
1975: Tertiary basalts dredged from Baffn Bay; Canadian Journal of Earth Sciences, v. 12, p. 1396-1405.

Clarke, D.B. and Pedersen, A.K.
1976: Tertiary volcanic province of West Greenland; in Geology of Greenland, ed. A. Escher and W.S. Watt; Grønlands Geologiske Undersøgelse, Copenhagen, p. 365-385.

Clarke, D.B. and Upton, B.G.J.
1971: Tertiary basalts of Baffin Island; field relations and tectonic setting; Canadian Journal of Earth Sciences, v. 8, p. 248-258.

Cutt, B.J. and Laving, J.G.
1977: Tectonic elements and geologic history of the south Labrador and Newfoundland continental shelf, eastern Canada; Bulletin of Canadian Petroleum Geology, v. 25, p. 1037-1058.

Dawes, P.R.
1976: Precambrian to Tertiary of northern Greenland; in Geology of Greenland, ed. A. Escher and W.S. Watt; Grønlands Geologiske Undersøgelse, Copenhagen, p. 248-303.

Dawes, P.R. and Kerr, J.W.
1982: The case against major displacement along Nares Strait; in Nares Strait and the Drift of Greenland; a conflict of plate tectonics, ed. P.R. Dawes and J.W. Kerr; Meddelelser om Grønland, Geoscience 8, p. 369-386.

Dawes, P.R. and Kerr, J.W. (ed.)
1982: Nares Strait and the Drift of Greenland; a conflict of plate tectonics; Meddelelser om Grønland, Geoscience 8, 392 p.

Denham, L.R.
1974: Offshore geology of northern West Greenland (69° to 75°N); Grønlands Geologiske Undersøgelse, Rapport 63, 24 p.

Douglas, R.J.W.
1969: Geological map of Canada, scale 1:5 000 000; Geological Survey of Canada, Map 1250A.

Escher, A. and Watts, W.S. (ed.)
1976: Geology of Greenland; Grønlands Geologiske Undersøgelse, Copenhagen, p. 11-16.

Fortier, Y.O. and Morley, L.W.
1956: Geological unity of the Arctic Islands; Royal Society of Canada Transactions, v. 50, Section III, p. 3-12.

Gradstein, F.M. and Srivastava, S.P.
1980: Aspects of Cenozoic stratigraphy and palaeoceanography of the Labrador Sea and Baffin Bay; Palaeogeography, Palaeoclimatology, Palaeoecology, v. 30, p. 261-295.

Gradstein, F.M. and Williams, G.L.
1976: Biostratigraphy of the Labrador Shelf; Geological Survey of Canada, Open File 349, 39 p.
1981: Sediment ages based on foraminifera and palynomorphs of 9 exploratory wells, Labrador Shelf; Geological Survey of Canada, Open File 826, 5 p.

Grant, A.C.
1972: The continental margin off Labrador and eastern Newfoundland — morphology and geology; Canadian Journal of Earth Sciences, v. 9, p. 1394-1430.
1975a: Structural modes of the western margin of the Labrador Sea; in Offshore Geology of Eastern Canada, Volume 2 ed. W.J.M. van der Linden and J.A. Wade; Geological Survey of Canada, Paper 74-30, v. 2, p. 217-231.

1975b: Geophysical results from the continental margin off southern Baffin Island; in Canada's Continental Margins and Offshore Petroleum Exploration, ed. C.J. Yorath, E.R. Parker and D.J. Glass; Canadian Society of Petroleum Geologists, Memoir 4, p. 411-431.

1980: Problems with plate tectonics: the Labrador Sea; Bulletin of Canadian Petroleum Geology, v. 28, p. 252-278.

1982: Problems with plate tectonic models for Baffin Bay-Nares Strait; evidence from the Labrador Sea; in Nares Strait and the Drift of Greenland; a conflict in plate tectonics, ed. P.R. Dawes and J.W. Kerr; Meddelelser om Grønland, Geoscience 8, p. 313-326.

Grant, A.C. and Manchester, K.S.

1970: Geophysical investigation in the Ungava Bay-Hudson Strait region of Northern Canada; Canadian Journal of Earth Sciences, v. 7, p. 1062-1076.

Grant, A.C., Levy, E.M., Lee, K., and Moffat, J.D.

1986: Pisces IV research submersible finds oil on Baffin Shelf; in Current Research, Part A, Geological Survey of Canada, Paper 86-1A, p. 65-69.

Henderson, G.

1973: The geological setting of the West Greenland basin in the Baffin Bay region; in Earth Science Symposium on Offshore Eastern Canada, ed. P.J. Hood; Geological Survey of Canada, Paper 71-23, p. 521-544.

1976: Petroleum geology; in Geology of Greenland, ed. A. Escher and W.S. Watt; Grønlands Geologiske Undersøgelse, Copenhagen, p. 488-505.

Henderson, G., Rosenkrantz, A., and Schiener, E.J.

1976: Cretaceous-Tertiary sedimentary rocks of West Greenland; in Geology of Greenland, ed. A. Escher and W.S. Watt; Grønlands Geologiske Undersøgelse, Copenhagen, p. 340-362.

Henderson, G., Schiener, E.J., Risum, J.B., Croxton, C.A., and Anderson, B.B.

1981: The West Greenland Basin; in Geology of the North Atlantic borderlands, ed. J.W. Kerr and A.J. Fergusson; Canadian Society of Petroleum Geologists, Memoir 7, p. 399-428.

Hinz, K., Schulter, H-U., Grant, A.C., Srivastava, S.P., Umpleby, D.C., and Woodside, J.

1979: Geophysical transects of the Labrador Sea: Labrador to southwest Greenland; Tectonophysics, v. 59, p. 151-183.

Hiscott, R.N.

1984: Clay mineralogy and clay-mineral provenance of Cretaceous and Paleogene strata, Labrador and Baffin shelves; Bulletin of Canadian Petroleum Geology, v. 32, p. 272-280.

Hoffman, P.

1987: Tectonic subdivision of the Churchill Province; in Current Activities Forum, Program with Abstracts, Geological Survey of Canada, Paper 87-8, p. 8.

Hood, P.J. and Bower, M.E.

1970: Aeromagnetic profile from Cape Cargenholm, Baffin Island to Red Head, West Greenland; in Report of Activities, Part B, Geological Survey of Canada, Paper 70-1B, p. 37-39.

1973: Low-level aeromagnetic surveys of the continental shelves bordering Baffin Bay and the Labrador Sea; in Earth Science Symposium on Offshore Eastern Canada, ed. P.J. Hood; Geological Survey of Canada, Paper 71-23, p. 571-597.

1975: Aeromagnetic reconnaissance of Davis Strait and adjacent area; in Canada's Continental Margins and Offshore Petroleum Exploration, ed. C.J. Yorath, E.R. Parker and D.J. Glass; Canadian Society of Petroleum Geologists, Memoir 4, p. 433-451.

Hyndman, R.D.

1973: Evolution of the Labrador Sea; Canadian Journal of Earth Sciences, v. 10, p. 637-644.

1975: Marginal basins of the Labrador Sea and the Davis Strait hot spot; Canadian Journal of Earth Sciences, v. 12, p. 1041-1045.

Ioannides, N.S.

1986: Dinoflagellate cysts from some Upper Cretaceous-Lower Tertiary sections, Bylot and Devon Islands, Arctic Archepelago; Geological Survey of Canada, Bulletin 371, 99 p.

Ives, J.D. and Andrews, J.T.

1963: Studies in the physical geography of north-central Baffin Island, Northwest Territories; Geographical Bulletin, v. 19, p. 5-48.

Jackson, G.D. and Davidson, A.

1975: Bylot Island map-area, District of Franklin; Geological Survey of Canada, Paper 74-29, 12 p.

Jackson, G.D. and Taylor, F.C.

1972: Correlation of major Aphebian rock units in the northeastern Canadian Shield; Canadian Journal of Earth Sciences, v. 9, p. 1650-1669.

Jackson, G.D., Davidson, A., and Morgan, W.C.

1975: Geology of the Pond Inlet map-area, Baffin Island, District of Franklin; Geological Survey of Canada, Paper 74-25, 33 p.

Jackson, H.R., Keen, C.E., and Barrett, D.L.

1977: Geophysical studies on the eastern continental margin of Baffin Bay and in Lancaster Sound; Canadian Journal of Earth Sciences, v. 14, p. 1991-2001.

Jackson, H.R., Keen, C.E., Falconer, R.K.H., and Appleton, K.P.

1979: New geophysical evidence for seafloor spreading in central Baffin Bay; Canadian Journal of Earth Sciences, v. 11, p. 2122-2135.

Jeletzky, J.A.

1950: *Actinocomax* from the Upper Cretaceous of Manitoba; Geological Survey of Canada, Bulletin, 15, p. 1-27.

1971: Marine Cretaceous biotic provinces and paleogeography of Western and Arctic Canada: illustrated by a detailed study of Ammonites; Geological Survey of Canada, Paper 70-22, 92 p.

Jenkins, W.A.M.

1984: Ordovician rocks in the Eastcan et al. Freydis B-87 and other wells in offshore Atlantic Canada; Canadian Journal of Earth Sciences, v. 21, p. 864-868.

Johnson, G.L., McMillan, N.J., Rasmussen, M., Campsie, J., and Dittmer, F.

1975: Sedimentary rocks dredged from the southwest Greenland continental margin; in Canada's continental margins and offshore petroleum exploration, ed. C.J. Yorath, E.R. Parker and D.J. Glass; Canadian Society of Petroleum Geologists, Memoir 4, p. 391-409.

Johnson, G.L., Srivastava, S.P., Campsie, J., and Rasmussen, M.

1982: Volcanic rocks in the Labrador Sea and environs and their relation to the evolution of the Labrador Sea; in Current Research, Part B, Geological Survey of Canada, Paper 82-1B, p. 7-20.

Keen, C.E.

1979: Thermal history and subsidence of rifted continental margins — evidence from wells off Nova Scotia and Labrador shelves; Canadian Journal of Earth Sciences, v. 16, p. 505-522.

Keen, C.E. and Barrett, D.L.

1972: Seismic refraction studies in Baffin Bay; an example of a developing ocean basin; Royal Astronomical Society Geophysical Journal, v. 30, p. 253-271.

Keen, C.E., Keen, M.J., Ross, D.I., and Lack, M.

1974: Baffin Bay; small ocean basin formed by seafloor spreading; American Association of Petroleum Geologists Bulletin, v. 58, p. 1089-1108.

Keen, M.J., Johnson, J., and Park, I.

1972: Geophysical and geological studies in eastern and northern Baffin Bay and Lancaster Sound; Canadian Journal of Earth Sciences, v. 9, p. 689-708.

Kerr, J.W.

1967: A submerged continental remnant beneath Labrador Sea; Earth and Planetary Science Letters, v. 3, p. 283-289.

1981: Stretching of the North American plate by a now dormant Atlantic spreading centre; in Geology of the North Atlantic Borderlands, ed. J.W. Kerr, A.J. Fergusson and L.C. Machan; Canadian Society of Petroleum Geologists, Memoir 7, p. 245-278.

1982: History and implications of the Nares Strait conflict; in Nares Strait and the Drift of Greenland; a conflict of plate tectonics, ed. P.R. Dawes and J.W. Kerr; Meddelelser om Grønland, Geocience 8, p. 37-49.

King, A.F. and McMillan, N.J.

1975: A mid-Mesozoic breccia from the coast off Labrador; Canadian Journal of Earth Sciences, v. 12, p. 44-51.

Klose, G.W., Maltere, E., McMillan, N.J., and Zinkan, C.G.

1982: Petroleum exploration offshore southern Baffin Island, northern Labrador Sea, Canada; in Arctic Geology and Geophysics, ed. A.F. Embry and H.R. Balkwill; Canadian Society of Petroleum Geologists, Memoir 8, p. 233-244.

Kristoffersen, Y.

1978: Sea-floor spreading and the early opening of the North Atlantic; Earth and Planetary Sciences Letters, v. 38, p. 273-290.

Kristoffersen, Y. and Talwani, M.

1977: Extinct triple junction south of Greenland and the Tertiary motion of Greenland relative to North America; Geological Society of America Bulletin, v. 88, p. 1037-1049.

Larsen, L.M., Rex, D.C., and Secher, K.

1983: The age of carbonatites, kimberlites and lamprophytes from southern West Greenland; recurrent alkaline magmation during 2500 m.y.; Lithos, v. 16, p. 215-221.

Laughton, A.S.

1972: The southern Labrador Sea — a key to the Mesozoic and Early Tertiary evolution of the North Atlantic; in Initial Reports of the Deep Sea Drilling Project, Volume 12, ed. A.S. Laughton et al.; United States Government Printing Office, Washington, D.C., v. 13, p. 1155-1179.

Lentin, J.K. and Williams, G.L.
1980: Dinoflagellate provincialism with emphasis on Campanian peridiniaceans; American Association of Stratigraphic Palynologists, Contributions Series, n. 7, 47 p.

LePichon, X., Hyndman, R.D., and Pautot, G.
1971: Geophysical study of the opening of the Labrador Sea; Journal of Geophysical Research, v. 76, p. 4724-4734.

Levy, E.M.
1978: Visual and chemical evidence for a natural seep at Scott Inlet, Baffin Island, District of Franklin; in Current Research, Part B, Geological Survey of Canada, Paper 78-1B, p. 21-26.

Loncarevic, B.D. and Falconer, R.K.H.
1977: An oil slick occurrence off Baffin Island; in Report of Activities, Part A, Geological Survey of Canada, Paper 77-1A, p. 523-524.

MacLean B.
1978: Marine geological/geophysical investigations in 1977 of the Scott Inlet and Cape Dyer-Frobisher Bay areas of the Baffin Island Continental Shelf; in Current Research, Part B, Geological Survey of Canada, Paper 78-1B, p. 13-20.

MacLean, B. and Falconer, F.K.H.
1979: Geological-geophysical studies in Baffin Bay and Scott Inlet-Buchan Gulf and Cape Dyer-Cumberland Sound areas of the Baffin Island Shelf; in Current Research, Part B, Geological Survey of Canada, Paper 79-1B, p. 231-244.

MacLean, B. and Williams, G.L.
1980: Upper Cretaceous rocks in Baffin Bay; Geological Association of Canada, Annual Meeting, Halifax, 1980, Program and Abstracts, 69 p.
1983: Geological investigations of Baffin Island Shelf in 1982; in Current Research, Part B, Geological Survey of Canada, Paper 83-1B, p. 309-315.

MacLean, B., Falconer, R.K.H., and Clarke, D.B.
1978: Tertiary basalts of western Davis Strait; bedrock core samples and geophysical data; Canadian Journal of Earth Sciences, v. 15, p. 773-780.

MacLean, B., Falconer, R.K.H., and Levey, E.M.
1981: Geological, geophysical and chemical evidence for natural seepage of petroleum off the northeast coast of Baffin Island; Bulletin of Canadian Petroleum Geology, v. 29, p. 75-95.

MacLean, B., Jansa, L.F., Falconer, R.K.H., and Srivastava, S.P.
1977: Ordovician strata on the southeastern Baffin Island shelf revealed by shallow drilling; Canadian Journal of Earth Sciences, v. 14, p. 1925-1939.

MacLean, B., Srivastava, S.P., and Haworth, R.T.
1982: Bedrock structures off Cumberland Sound, Baffin Island Shelf; core sample and geophysical data; in Arctic Geology and Geophysics, ed. A.F. Embry and H.R. Balkwill; Canadian Society of Petroleum Geologists, Memoir 8, p. 279-295.

MacLean, B., Williams, G.L., Jennings, A., and Blakeney, C.
1986a: Bedrock and surficial geology of Cumberland Sound, Northwest Territories; in Current Research, Part B, Geological Survey of Canada, Paper 86-1B, p. 605-615.

MacLean, B., Williams, G.L., Sanford, B.V., Klassen, R.A., Blakeney, C., and Jennings, A.
1986b: A reconnaissance study of the bedrock and surficial geology of Hudson Strait, Northwest Territories; in Current Research, Part B, Geological Survey of Canada, Paper 86-1B, p. 617-635.

MacLean, B., Woodside, J.M., and Girouard, P.
1984: Geological and geophysical investigations in Jones Sound, District of Franklin; in Current Research, Part A, Geological Survey of Canada, Paper 84-1A, p. 359-365.

Manchester, K.S. and Clarke, D.B.
1973: Geologic structure of Baffin Bay and Davis Strait as determined by geophysical techniques; in Arctic Geology, ed. M.G. Pritcher; American Association of Petroleum Geologists, Memoir 19, p. 536-541.

Manum, S. and Cookson, I.C.
1964: Cretaceous microplankton in a sample from Graham Island, arctic Canada, collected during the second "Fram"-Expedition (1898-1902), with notes on microplankton from the Hassel Formation, Ellef Ringnes Island; Schrifter utgitt av Det Norske Videnskaps-Akademi i Oslo I, Mat-Naturv. Klasse, Ny Series IT, p. 1-35.

McIntyre, D.J.
1974: Palynology of an Upper Cretaceous section, Horton River, District of Mackenzie, Northwest Territories; Geological Survey of Canada, Paper 74-14, 57 p.

McMillan, N.J.
1973: Shelves of Labrador Sea and Baffin Bay, Canada; in Future Petroleum Provinces of Canada, ed. R.G. McCrossan; Canadian Society of Petroleum Geologists, Memoir 1, p. 473-515.

McWhae, J.R.H.
1981: Structure and spreading history of the northwestern Atlantic region from the Scotian Shelf to Baffin Bay; in Geology of the North Atlantic Borderlands, ed. J.W. Kerr and A.J. Fergusson; Canadian Society of Petroluem Geologists, Memoir 7, p. 299-332.

McWhae, J.R.H. and Michel, W.T.E.
1975: Stratigraphy of Bjarni H-81 and Leif M-48, Labrador Shelf; Bulletin of Canadian Petroleum Geology, v. 28, p. 112-129.

McWhae, J.R.H., Elie, R., Laughton, K.C., and Gunther, P.R.
1980: Stratigraphy and petroleum prospects of the Labrador Shelf; Bulletin of Canadian Petroleum Geology, v. 28, p. 460-488.

Meneley, R.A.
1986: Oil and gas fields in the east coast and arctic basins of Canada; in Future Petroleum Provinces of the World, ed. M.T. Halbouty; American Association of Petroleum Geologists, Memoir 40, p. 143-176.

Menzies, A.W.
1982: Crustal history and basin development of Baffin Bay; in Nares Strait and the Drift of Greenland; a conflict in plate tectonics, ed. P.R. Dawes and J.W. Kerr; Meddelelser om Grønland, Geoscience 8, p. 295-312.

Miall, A.D., Balkwill, H.R., and Hopkins, W.S. Jr.
1980: Cretaceous and Tertiary sediments of Eclipse Trough, Bylot Island area, Arctic Canada, and their regional setting; Geological Survey of Canada, Paper 79-23, 20 p.

Miller, A.K., Youngquist, W., and Collinson, C.
1954: Ordovician cephalopod fauna of Baffin Island; Geological Society of America, Memoir 62, 166 p.

Parrott, R.J.E. and Reynolds, P.H.
1975: Argon ^{40}/Argon^{39} geochronology: age determinations of basalts from the Labrador Sea area; Geological Society of America, Abstracts with Proceedings, v. 7, p. 835.

Pelletier, B.R.
1966: Development of submarine physiography in the Canadian Arctic and its relation to crustal movements; in Continental Drift, ed. G.D. Garland; Royal Society of Canada, Special Publication 9, p. 77-101.

Powell, R.J. and Baum, G.R.
1982: Eocene biostratigraphy of South Carolina and its relationship to Gulf Coastal Plain zonations and global changes of coastal onlap; Geological Society of America Bulletin, v. 93, p. 1099-1108.

Rashid, M.A., Purcell, L.P., and Hardy, I.A.
1980: Source-rock potential for oil and gas of the East Newfoundland and Labrador areas; in Facts and Principles of World Oil Occurence, ed. A.D. Miall; Canadian Society of Petroleum Geologists, Memoir 6, p. 589-608.

Rice, P.D. and Shade, B.D.
1982: Reflection seismic interpretations and seafloor spreading history of Baffin Bay; in Arctic Geology and Geophysics, ed. A.F. Embry and H.R. Balkwill; Canadian Society of Petroleum Geologists, Memoir 8, p. 245-265.

Rolle, F.
1985: Late Cretaceous-Tertiary sediments offshore central West Greenland; lithostratigraphy, sedimentary evolution and petroleum potential; Canadian Journal of Earth Sciences, v. 22, p. 1001-1019.

Roots, W.D. and Srivastava, S.P.
1984: Origin of the marine magnetic quiet zones in the Labrador and Greenland seas; Marine Geophysical Research, v. 6, p. 395-408.

Rosenkrantz, A. and Pulvertaft, T.C.R.
1969: Cretaceous-Tertiary stratigraphy and tectonics in northern West Greenland; American Association of Petroleum Geologists, Memoir 12, p. 883-898.

Rosenkrantz, A., Noe-Nygaard, A, Gry, H. Munck, S., and Lauren D.
1942: A geological reconnaissance of the southern part of the Svartenhuk Peninsula, West Greenland; Meddelser om Grønland, v. 135, 72 p.

Ross, D.I. and Henderson, G.
1973: New geophysical data on the continental shelf of central and northern West Greenland; Canadian Journal of Earth Sciences, v. 10, p. 485-497.

Ruedemann, R. and Balk, R. (ed.)
1939: Geology of North America, Volume I; Berlin, Gebrüder Borntraeger, 643 p.

Sanford, B.V., Grant, A.C., Wade, J.A., and Barss, M.S.
1979: Geology, eastern Canada and adjacent areas; Geological Survey of Canada, Map 1401A (1:2,000,000).

Snowdon, L.R.
1980: Resinite — a potential petroleum source in the Upper Cretaceous-Tertiary of the Beaufort-Mackenzie Basin; in Facts and Principles of World Petroleum Occurrences, ed. A.D. Miall; Canadian Society of Petroleum Geologists, Memoir 6, p. 509-521.

Srivastava, S.P.

1978: Evolution of the Labrador Sea and its bearing on the early evolution of the North Atlantic: Royal Astronomical Society, Geophysical Journal, v. 52, p. 313-357.

1985: Evolution of the Labrador Sea and its implications to the motion of Greenland along Nares Strait; Tectonophysics, v. 114, p. 29-53.

1986: Geophysical maps and geological sections of the Labrador Sea; Geological Suvey of Canada, Paper 85-16, 11 p.

Srivastava, S.P. and Falconer, R.K.H.

1982: Nares Strait; a conflict between plate tectonic predictions and geological interpretation; in Nares Strait and the Drift of Greenland; a conflict in plate tectonics, ed. P.R. Dawes and J.W. Kerr; Meddelelser om Grønland, Geoscience 8, p. 339-352.

Srivastava, S.P. and Tapscott, C.R.

1986: Plate kinematics of the North Atlantic; in The Western North Atlantic Region, ed. P.R. Vogt and B.E. Tucholke; Geological Society of America, The Geology of North America, v. M,p. 379-404.

Srivastava, S.P., et al.

in press: Preliminary report, ODP Leg 105. ODP publication, Texas A & M University, Preliminary results of Leg 105. (in press)

Srivastava, S.P., Falconer, R.K.H., and MacLean, B.

1981: Labrador Sea, Davis Strait, Baffin Bay; geology and geophysics — a review; in Geology of the North Atlantic borderlands, ed. J.W. Kerr and A.J. Fergusson; Canadian Society of Petroleum Geologists, Memoir 7, p. 333-398.

Srivastava, S.P., MacLean B., Macnab, R.F., and Jackson, H.R.

1982: Davis Strait; structure and evolution as obtained from a systematic geophysical survey; in Arctic Geology and Geophysics, ed. A.F. Embry and H.R. Balkwill; Canadian Society of Petroleum Geologists, Memoir 8, p. 267-278.

Stouge, S. and Peel, J.S.

1979: Ordovician conodonts from the Precambrian shield of southern West Greenland; Grønlands Geologiske Undersøgelse, Rapport 91, p. 105-109.

Talwani, M. and Eldholm, O.

1977: Evolution of the Norwegian-Greenland Sea; Bulletin Geological Society of America, v. 88, p. 969-999.

Taylor, F.C.

1971: A revision of Precambrian structural provinces in northeastern Quebec and northern Labrador; Canadian Journal of Earth Sciences, v. 8, p. 579-589.

1981: Precambrian geology of Canadian North Atlantic borderlands; in Geology of the North Atlantic Borderlands, ed. J.W. Kerr and A.J. Fergusson; Canadian Society of Petroleum Geologists, Memoir 7, p. 11-30.

Trettin, H.P.

1969: Lower Paleozoic sediments of northwestern Baffin Island, District of Franklin; Geological Survey of Canada, Bulletin 157, 70 p.

1975: Investigations of Lower Paleozoic geology, Foxe Basin, northeastern Melville Peninsula, and parts of northwestern and central Baffin Island; Geological Survey of Canada, Bulletin 251, 177 p.

Umpleby, D.C.

1979: Geology of the Labrador Shelf; Geological Survey of Canada, Paper 79-13, 34 p.

Vail, P.R., Mitchum, R.M., Todd, R.G., Widmier, J.H., Thompson, S., Sangree, J.B., Bubb, J.N., and Huttelid, W.G.

1977: Seismic stratigraphy and global changes in sea level; in Seismic Stratigraphy — Application to Hydrocarbon Exploration, ed. C.E. Payton; American Association of Petroleum Geologists, Memoir 26, p. 49-212.

Van der Linden, W.J.M.

1975: Crustal attenuation and seafloor spreading in the Labrador Sea; Earth and Planetary Science Letters, v. 27, p. 409-423.

Vogt, P.R., Perry, R.K., Feden, R.H., Fleming, H.S., and Cherkis, N.Z.

1981: The Greenland-Norwegian Sea and Iceland environment; geology and geophysics; in The Ocean Basins and Margins, the Arctic Ocean, ed. A.E.M. Navin, M. Churkin and F.G. Stehli; Plenum Press, New York and London, p. 493-598.

Wade, J.A., Grant, A.C., Sanford, B.V., and Barss, M.S.

1977: Basement structure eastern Canada and adjacent areas; Geological Survey of Canada, Map 1400A (1:2 000 000).

Wanless, R.K., Stevens, R.D., Lachance, G.R., and Delabio, R.N.

1974: Age determinations and geological studies, K-Ar isotopic ages, Report 12; Geological Survey of Canada, Paper 74-2, 72 p.

Watt, W.S.

1969: The coast-parallel dike swarm of Southwest Greenland in relation to the opening of Labrador Sea; Canadian Journal of Earth Sciences, v. 6, p. 1320-1321.

Watts, A.B.

1981: The U.S. Atlantic continental margin: subsidence history, crustal structure and thermal evolution; in Geology of Passive Continental Margins; American Association of Petroleum Geologists Education Course Note Series No. 19, p. 2-1 to 2-75.

Williams, G.D. and Stelck, C.R.

1975: Speculations on the Cretaceous paleogeography of North America; in The Cretaceous System in the Western Interior of North America, ed. W.G.E. Caldwell; Geological Association of Canada, Special Paper 15, p. 1-20.

Williams, V.E.

1986: Palynological study of the Continental shell sediments of the Labrador Sea; Ph. D. Thesis, University of British Columbia, 216 p.

Workum, R.H., Bolton, T.E., and Barnes, C.R.

1976: Ordovician geology of Akpatok Island, Ungava Bay, District of Franklin; Canadian Journal of Earth Sciences, v. 13, p. 157-178.

Authors' addresses

H.R. Balkwill
Petro Canada Resources
P.O. Box 2844
Calgary, Alberta
T2P 3E3

N.J. McMillan
Institute of Sedimentary and Petroleum Geology
Geological Survey of Canada
3303-33rd Street N.W.
Calgary, Alberta
T2L 2A7

B. MacLean
Atlantic Geoscience Centre
Geological Survey of Canada
Bedford Institute of Oceanography
P.O. Box 1006
Dartmouth, Nova Scotia
B2Y 4A2

G.L. Williams
Atlantic Geoscience Centre
Geological Survey of Canada
Bedford Institute of Oceanography
P.O. Box 1006
Dartmouth, Nova Scotia
B2Y 4A2

S.P. Srivastava
Atlantic Geoscience Centre
Geological Survey of Canada
Bedford Institute of Oceanography
P.O. Box 1006
Dartmouth, Nova Scotia
B2Y 4A2

Printed in Canada

MARGIN EVOLUTION

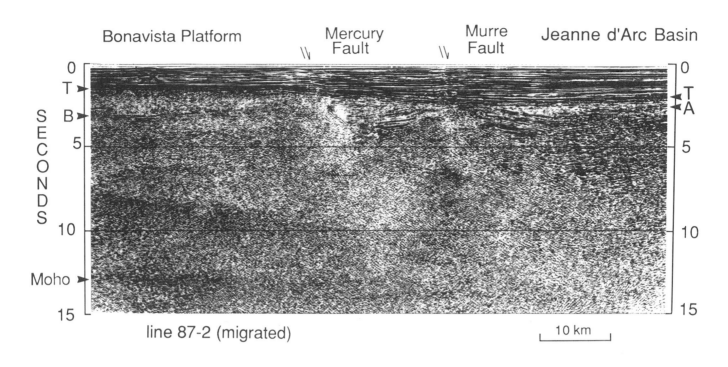

Bonavista Platform   Mercury Fault   Murre Fault   Jeanne d'Arc Basin

line 87-2 (migrated)

10 km

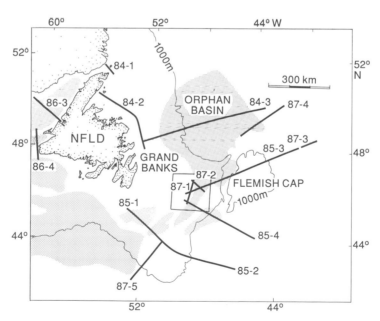

MARGIN EVOLUTION IMAGED IN DEEP SEISMIC REFLECTION STUDIES

Deep seismic reflection line 87-2 shot in 1987. This line runs northwest to southeast across a part of the Jeanne d'Arc Basin, tying to the south with a deep line shot in 1985 (85-3). The data image the Mercury-Murre fault system which bounds the Jeanne d'Arc Basin and which may be the result of Cretaceous reactivation of earlier (Paleozoic) thrusts. Two 'bands' of crustal reflections beneath the northwestern portion of the line are clearly imaged; the lower band of the two is interpreted as Moho. Reproduced from de Voogd et al., in press, in Seismic Probing of Continents and their Margins, Tectonophysics, special issue.

Chapter 8

ASPECTS OF NORTH ATLANTIC PALEO-OCEANOGRAPHY

Chapter 8

ASPECTS OF NORTH ATLANTIC PALEO-OCEANOGRAPHY

F.M. Gradstein, L.F. Jansa, S.P. Srivastava,
M.A. Williamson, G. Bonham Carter and B. Stam

INTRODUCTION

At about the end of Triassic time North and South America, Africa and western Europe were parts of the landmass Pangea, which had been assembled during late Paleozoic. What is now known as southern Europe and Asia faced Tethys, the equatorial ocean. The northward drift of Africa, India and Australia has obliterated much of Tethys and so its latitudinal extent is poorly known (Stöcklin, 1984). Tethys may have extended eastward to Panthalassa, the Pacific "superocean" which surrounded Pangea.

The Atlantic Ocean was born in the Middle Jurassic, when the North American and African continents started separating along the newly formed Mid-Atlantic Ridge. Rifting and spreading progressed in a zipper-like fashion slowly northward, with opening in the Early Cretaceous between Iberia and the Grand Banks, in the latest Cretaceous in the southern Labrador Sea, and in the Early Tertiary in the northern Labrador Sea, Baffin Bay, and the Norwegian Sea.

Seafloor spreading led to a different distribution of sedimentary facies in the North Atlantic Ocean by comparison with other oceans. In the Pacific, for example, ocean floor was carried across oceanic climatic zones, beneath water masses with different biological and chemical characteristics (Berggren and Hollister, 1974). Consequently, the facies distribution in this ocean is complex. Spreading in the Atlantic did not in general cross climatic zones, and its sediment facies are dominated by the effects of sinking of the oceanic crust with time and the changes in the carbonate compensation depth. Terrigeneous sediment in the Atlantic was transported largely down the continental slopes before the mid-Tertiary, but contour currents have provided a mechanism for erosion, transportation and distribution in deep water along the margins since that time.

The Atlantic Ocean provides a natural laboratory for testing the temporal relationships between biota, lithofacies, climate and paleogeography for several reasons. The stratigraphic and paleontological record is relatively complete for the last 200 Ma; several groups of microfossils evolved rapidly, so that a high resolution is possible in the biostratigraphy; and the climatic gradient has increased with time. The western Atlantic margin has rotated through more than 15° counterclockwise into its present-day position since the Jurassic. As a result, a strong latitudinal gradient developed, and this was enhanced during the last 40 Ma, since the start of cooling in the southern oceans. The North Atlantic climate, equable, and sub-tropical to temperate in Mesozoic time, changed north of 50°N to temperate and sub-glacial in the last 10 Ma. These climatic changes are reflected in the type and nature of sediments and microfossil communities preserved on the ocean floor.

Advances in our knowledge and understanding of the depositional history of the Mesozoic and Cenozoic of the North Atlantic stem from extensive marine surveys, the drilling during the Deep Sea Drilling Project of many legs — notably 11 (Hollister et al., 1972), 12 (Laughton et al., 1972), 43 (Tucholke et al., 1979), 44 (Benson et al., 1978), 48 (Montadert et al., 1979), 76 (Sheridan et al., 1983) and 79 (Hinz et al., 1984) — and exploration wells on the continental margins. The history of sampling and of stratigraphic investigations for the western North Atlantic has been documented previously by Gradstein and Srivastava (1980) and Gradstein (1986) and is discussed in Chapters 5, 6, and 7.

This chapter is a study of four aspects of the evolution of the North Atlantic Ocean, including the Labrador and Norwegian seas: (1) paleogeography and plate kinematics; (2) the development of lithofacies and climate since the Jurassic; (3) the relationship between subsidence, sedimentation and tectonic events during the Cretaceous and Cenozoic of the margin of the northwestern Atlantic, where we have detailed information on age, lithology, and former water depths; and (4) the relationship between Atlantic paleogeography, lithofacies and the distribution of selected foraminifers in six broad time-slices for the last 200 Ma. Emphasis is on Mesozoic paleobiogeography, which has been much less explored than that of the Cenozoic. The concept of the unified and dynamic interrelationships between changes in geography, lithofacies, climate and fossil distribution provide an insight into ocean circulation, which is driven by winds and gradients in temperature and salinity and shaped differently by topography and the Coriolis force in the western and eastern basins.

Gradstein, F.M., Jansa, L.F., Srivastava, S.P. Williamson, M.A., Bonham-Carter, G., and Stam, B.
1990: Aspects of North Atlantic paleo-oceanography, Chapter 8 in Geology of the Continental Margin of Eastern Canada, M.J. Keen and G.L. Williams (ed.); Geological Survey of Canada, Geology of Canada, no. 2, p. 351-389 (also Geological Society of America, the Geology of North America, v. I-1).

NORTH ATLANTIC PALEOGEOGRAPHY

The marine magnetic anomaly patterns, which form mirror images on each side of the mid-ocean ridges (Fig. 8.1), confirm that the North Atlantic Ocean and its adjacent seas formed by seafloor spreading, when North America, Africa, Eurasia and Greenland separated during Mesozoic and Cenozoic time. Evolution of these ocean basins is recorded by the magnetic anomalies and by the fracture zones. Calibration of these anomalies with geological time from Deep Sea Drilling sites (Cox, 1973; Berggren et al., 1985a, b; Kent and Gradstein, 1985) enables the anomalies to be used as isochrons, and so paleogeographic changes in the ocean basins can be delineated. Fracture zones connecting different segments of the spreading centres are tracers of the direction of motion of the plates. Thus, using the anomalies and fracture zones, former positions of adjacent plates can be reconstructed. The poles of rotation for North America and Africa and for North America, Greenland and Eurasia have been used to reconstruct the past positions of the continents surrounding the North Atlantic Ocean (Klitgord and Schouten, 1986; Srivastava and Tapscott, 1986).

The magnetic anomoly pattern in the southern part of the North Atlantic (Fig. 8.1a) shows that the region evolved largely as a two plate system, though a few "microplates" must have been involved near the Gulf of Mexico (Klitgord and Schouten, 1986). In the northern North Atlantic (Fig. 8.1b), however, the situation was very different because of simultaneous spreading in the Norwegian Sea, Labrador Sea and Arctic Ocean, notably involving the Arctic Islands and Greenland. Thus the evolution of the North Atlantic is a result of the interaction between a number of plates, whose spatial arrangement has changed several times during the past 100 Ma. The evolution of these oceanic basins will be described from their initial configuration to the present one.

Jurassic motion

Magnetic anomaly patterns in the southern North Atlantic (Fig. 8.1a) trace active seafloor spreading back to about the time of anomaly M-25 (157 Ma, Oxfordian). A strip about 100 km wide in the western Atlantic west of M-25, however, shows no clear magnetic stripes, so certain assumptions have to be made in trying to determine the positions of the continents at earlier times. The reconstruction given by Klitgord and Schouten (1986) is prefered here, because it is better constrained by geophysical data than previous versions. Figure 8.2a shows a reconstruction from Klitgord and Schouten (1986); this suggests that initial rifting between plates in Triassic to Early Jurassic time may have been responsible for the creation of some of the rift basins, which extend from the Gulf of Mexico to the Bay of Biscay and contain evaporites. True seafloor spreading north of the Bahamas did not start until the late Middle Jurassic (Sheridan et al., 1983). A small spreading segment between the southern Grand Banks and southwestern Iberia may have led to creation of seafloor in the region of the Tagus Abyssal Plain, west of Portugal, before being abandoned due to a shift in its spreading centre. Little or no oceanic connection seems to have existed between Tethys and the Atlantic Ocean prior to Middle Jurassic time.

Late Jurassic-Cretaceous motion

A narrow oceanic seaway, connecting the Gulf of Mexico with Tethys, may have been established by the Middle Jurassic; this widened and deepened in the Late Jurassic (Fig. 8.2b). Reorganization of the plate boundaries between South America and North America took place from Middle to Late Jurassic time, and led to a confused pattern of the spreading geometry in this region. Except for a shift in the spreading in the Tagus Abyssal Plain mentioned above, spreading seems to have continued more-or-less uniformly, at a rate of about 2 cm/a, between Africa and North America until the Early Cretaceous. The central Atlantic was by then sufficiently wide for a broad marine connection to exist between Tethys and the Gulf of Mexico.

At about the time of anomaly M-11 (Neocomian, 133 Ma; Fig. 8.2c) plate motions changed in several parts of the Atlantic. Rifting commenced between South America and Africa, and between Iberia and the Grand Banks of Newfoundland. This probably gave rise to the formation of the Benue Trough in Central Africa (Burke and Dewey, 1974) and to enhanced differential subsidence in sedimentary basins such as the Jeanne d'Arc (see subsidence curves for the well Gabriel C-60, Fig. 8.6b) on the Grand Banks. It is not certain how far north this rifting progressed in the North Atlantic, but an indication of it may be seen in the regional subsidence and in the increase in differential subsidence in the North Sea rift in the Early Cretaceous.

Active seafloor spreading began in the North Atlantic between Iberia and the Grand Banks and in the South Atlantic between South America and Africa at about the time of anomalies M-0 to M-4 (111 to 118 Ma, Hauterivian-Aptian). This is the time when the central Grand Banks experienced the tectonic reactivation resulting in the formation of the "breakup" (Avalon) unconformity, which separates deformed Jurassic and Lower Cretaceous sediments from the overlying, undeformed Upper Cretaceous and Cenozoic wedge (see Chapter 5). Iberia moved with Africa and away from Eurasia at this time, creating the Bay of Biscay. Thus, spreading in the southern part of the North Atlantic was linked to that in the northern part and the Bay of Biscay by a ridge-ridge-ridge triple junction at the mouth of the Bay of Biscay between the time of anomaly M-4 and the time of anomaly 33 (75 Ma, Campanian). North of the Bay of Biscay, spreading continued between Newfoundland and the British Isles and through Rockall Trough into the Arctic Ocean until anomaly 34 (85 Ma, Santonian), time. Another triple junction formed south of Greenland at this time, when spreading shifted to the west of Rockall Trough and active spreading commenced in the Labrador Sea.

The northern plate boundary between Africa and North America remained located in the Bay of Biscay until anomaly 10 (30 Ma, Oligocene) time, but motion along this boundary changed considerably during the Cenozoic. The ridge-ridge-ridge triple junction at the mouth of the Bay of Biscay changed to ridge-ridge-transform triple junction at anomaly 33 time. A similar change took place in the southern North Atlantic at this time, when the Caribbean spreading centre was abandoned. Some motion between Eurasia and Greenland probably took place before active seafloor spreading started, at the time of anomaly 24 (56 Ma, Paleocene), but not enough to create any significant amount of seafloor or recognizable magnetic anomalies.

Cenozoic motion

Major changes occurred in seafloor spreading in the Cenozoic, forming deep water connections between the Arctic and the North Atlantic oceans. Spreading continued in the Labrador Sea at a rate of 1.9-2.5 cm/a until anomaly 25 (59 Ma, Paleocene) time, when there was a major reorganization of the plates. Spreading shifted to the Norwegian and Greenland seas and to the Eurasian Basin; relative motion between Eurasia and Iberia, which was moving with Africa at that time, changed, resulting in deformation of the Eurasian plate immediately north of Iberia. This motion seems to have propagated northward leading to compression and to strike slip motion along the north Biscay margin, and subduction is postulated along the North Spanish Trough. Between the time of anomaly 25 and anomaly 10, along the Eurasian and Iberia-Africa plates' boundary, the Pyrenees Mountain chain formed on land, while King's Trough, the Azores-Biscay Rise, and the North Spanish Trough formed on the ocean side (Fig. 8.1b). The Tertiary basalts of western and eastern Greenland, Davis Strait, and the Greenland-Scotland region were extruded at the time of anomaly 25, producing sills which could form major barriers for free exchange of bottom water between the Arctic and North Atlantic oceans.

It is not certain what amount of motion took place in Davis Strait and Baffin Bay during the period of active seafloor spreading in the Labrador Sea. It may have been largely translational. This uncertainty is due mainly to the fact that although Baffin Bay may well be underlain by oceanic crust, the inferred marine magnetic anomalies show a confused pattern and are difficult to correlate between widely spaced tracks (see Keen et al., Chapter 2). The complex pattern may be the result of "overprinting" due to later magmatism or to thick sedimentary blanketing, or be the result of intricate transform motion. Detailed magnetic measurements made in central Baffin Bay show some lineations, however, and these are described in Chapter 2. A small gravity low, similar to that observed over the extinct Labrador Sea Ridge (Srivastava, 1978), has also been observed in central Baffin Bay (Jackson et al., 1979).

In spite of the lack of direct evidence for seafloor spreading in the Baffin Bay area, some information about its origin can be obtained from the paleogeographic reconstruction of Greenland relative to North America. This is based on the assumption that North America and Greenland acted as rigid plates throughout the development of the Labrador Sea. The plate reconstructions show significant opening of the southern Labrador Sea in the Late Cretaceous to Eocene, of the northern Labrador Sea in the Paleocene to Eocene, and of Baffin Bay in the Eocene (Fig. 8.2d (M-34), Fig. 8.2e (M-21), and Fig. 8.2f (M-13)) (Hamilton, 1983). Hamilton has given an excellent account of the tectonic problems related to the opening of Baffin Bay and the interested reader is referred to this summary.

Several shifts in the centre of spreading took place in the Norwegian-Greenland Sea from anomaly 24 time to anomaly 7 time (56 to 26 Ma, Paleocene to Oligocene). With a shift in the direction of spreading at about anomaly 20 time (46 Ma, Eocene) a rift started to develop between Greenland and the Jan Mayen Ridge resulting in its separation from Greenland. With the end of spreading in the Labrador Sea just before anomaly 13 (36 Ma, Oligocene) time, the motion between Svalbard and Greenland, which had been of a strike-slip nature until then, changed to

extensional and Svalbard separated from Greenland. Spreading has since continued across the Nansen-Gakkel Ridge in the Arctic Ocean and across the Knipovich, Mohns, Kolbeinsey, Reykjanes and Mid-Atlantic ridges to the south. Iberia started to move with Eurasia at about the time of anomaly 10 (30 Ma, Oligocene), when the boundary between Eurasia and Africa moved to the south along the Azores-Gibraltar Fracture Zone.

NORTH ATLANTIC PALEOGEOGRAPHY AND LITHOFACIES

This section presents a broad overview of the regional sedimentation history during the Mesozoic and Cenozoic for the central and northern North Atlantic. Figures 8.3a to g (in pocket) illustrate the paleogeography and facies in the Mesozoic. These maps were compiled from published literature and field studies. Principal references are listed in Table 8.1.

The paleogeographic maps span relatively broad time intervals (such as Early Jurassic, Middle Jurassic, etc.). Because of the length of these intervals, time restricted facies changes are sometimes under represented. An example is the Early Jurassic map for the Grand Banks where, during the Pliensbachian, shallow water limestone changes rapidly into deep water shale, although the paleogeographic map shows the dominance of shallow water limestones.

Another limitation is in the plate reconstructions. The currently available reconstructions are relatively crude for plotting detailed facies distribution. The reconstructions do not account for differential stretching of the continental crust which results in continental overlaps that seemingly conflict with local geological data. In this study a problematic overlap is between Iberia and the Grand Banks, with Galicia Bank partially overlapping Flemish Cap (Fig. 8.2b). Another area is the northern Labrador Sea, where the continental overlap is about 250 km and hinders paleogeographic lithofacies reconstruction.

In summation, we do not have the same coverage of geological data for all the regions. This is particularly true of the outer parts of the continental margins, where there is often an absence of data.

Late Triassic

The Triassic rift basins extend northward from the Gulf of Mexico and the eastern United States, through the Bay of Fundy in eastern Canada to the Grand Banks, across the Atlantic to the Celtic Sea and the North Sea, to the Greenland-Norwegian rift and Svalbard in the Barent Sea. The sedimentary basins of western Europe were transgressed from the south by Tethys in the Middle Triassic. This shallow sea deposited carbonates at the fringes with Tethys, whereas the northern part of the proto-Atlantic rift system remained the site of terrestrial deposition. Transgression also led to a brief period of marine deposition in central east Greenland and Svalbard, where shallow marine clastics were deposited (Clemmenson, 1980; Jacobson and van Veen, 1984). During the early Carnian regional regression, probably eustatically induced, marine Muschelkalk deposition in western Europe came to an end and was followed by a period of evaporite deposition (Ziegler, 1982). During Carnian-Norian time the marine incur-

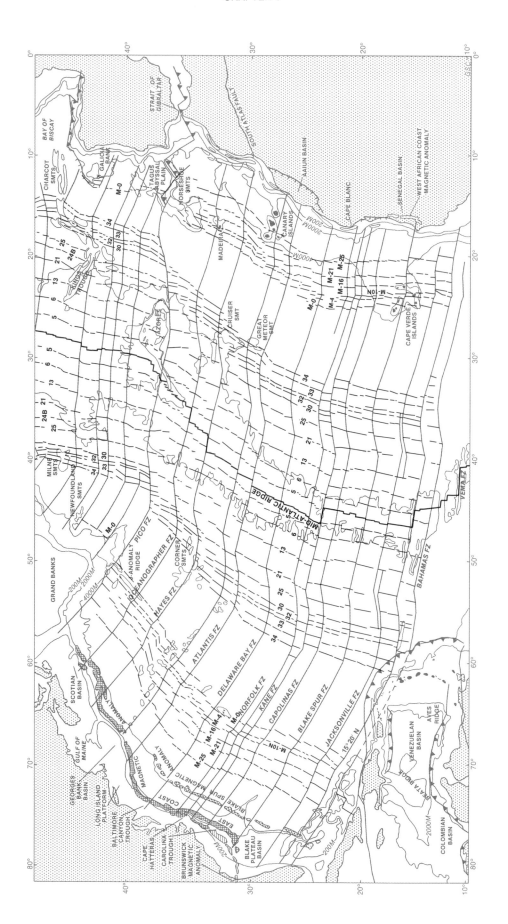

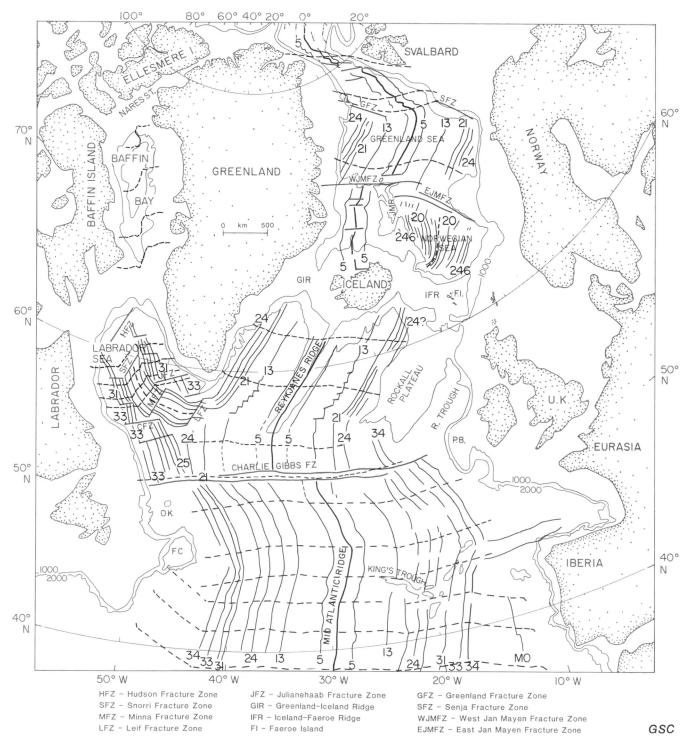

Figure 8.1. Marine magnetic anomaly patterns and position of major spreading ridges and fracture zones.

a. Southern part of the North Atlantic Ocean

b. Northern part of the North Atlantic Ocean. OK is Orphan Knoll, FC is Flemish Cap, and PB is Porcupine Basin.

HFZ – Hudson Fracture Zone	JFZ – Julianehaab Fracture Zone	GFZ – Greenland Fracture Zone
SFZ – Snorri Fracture Zone	GIR – Greenland-Iceland Ridge	SFZ – Senja Fracture Zone
MFZ – Minna Fracture Zone	IFR – Iceland-Faeroe Ridge	WJMFZ – West Jan Mayen Fracture Zone
LFZ – Leif Fracture Zone	FI – Faeroe Island	EJMFZ – East Jan Mayen Fracture Zone

GSC

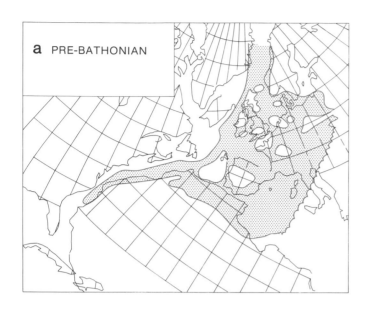

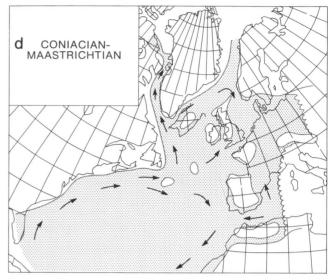

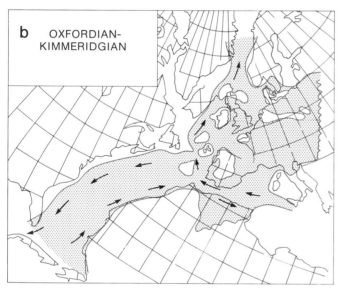

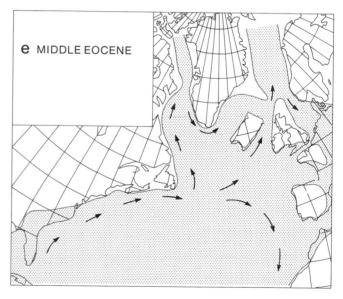

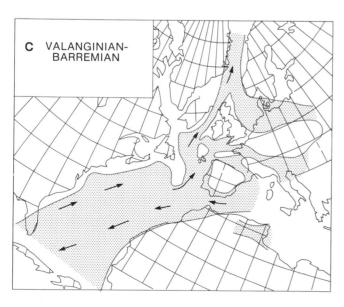

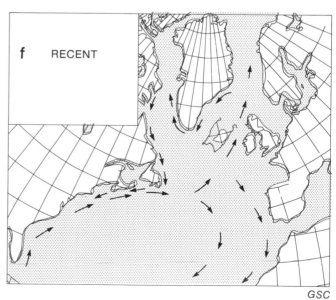

GSC

Table 8.1 Principal literature used for compilation of the lithofacies maps in Figure 8.3 (in pocket).

Area	Main sources of data
Eastern North America	Amato and Simonis (1980), Austin et al. (1980), Eliuk (1978), Given (1977), Jansa and Wade (1975), Jansa and Wiedman (1982), Mattick et al. (1981), McIver (1972), Poag (1982), Ryan and Miller (1981), Schlee et al. (1976), Wade (1977)
Northwest Africa	Adams (1979), Ambroggi (1963), Busson (1970), Butt (1982), Choubert et al. (1966), Du Dresnay (1971, 1979), Malod (1980), Manspeizer et al. (1978), Monbaron (1981), Salvan (1974), Van Houten (1977), Wildi (1981), Wildi et al. (1977)
Central North Atlantic Basin	Initial reports of the Deep Sea Drilling Project in the North Atlantic; Bernoulli (1972), Bernoulli and Jenkyns (1974), de Graciansky et al. (1985), Dean et al. (1978), Jansa et al. (1979), Lancelot et al. (1972), Ogg et al. (1983), Thiede (1979)
Iberia	Berthou and Lanverjat (1979), Biju-Duval et al. (1977), Garcia (1982), Garcia-Moudejar et al. (1985), Mouterde and Ruget (1975), Pujalte (1982), Ramalho (1971), Rocha (1977), Stam (1986), Wilson (1979), Wilson and Exton (1979)
Northwestern Europe	Stevaux and Winnock (1974), Soler et al. (1981), Ziegler (1978, 1982)
Labrador and Baffin Bay	Gradstein and Srivastava (1980), Johnson et al. (1982), MacLean et al. (1986), McWhae et al. (1980), Rolle (1985), Umpleby (1979)
Arctic and Sverdrup Basin	Balkwill et al. (1983)
Eastern Greenland	Birkelund et al. (1974), Clemmenson and Surlyk (1976), Surlyk (1973, 1978, 1984), Surlyk and Clemmenson (1983), Surlyk et al. (1981)
Norway margin and Spitsbergen	Aasheim and Larsen (1984), Westre (1984), Jacobson and van Veen (1984), Karlsson (1984), Larsen (1984), Larsen and Skarpness (1984), Olaussen et al. (1984), Talwani and Eldholm (1977), Zakharov et al. (1981)
Barents Sea	Faleide et al. (1984), Hinz and Schlüter (1978), Matishov (1977), Mork and Bjoroy (1984), Mork et al. (1982), Steel and Worsley (1984)

sions reached the eastern Grand Banks, where more than 2000 m of evaporites were deposited on top of, or intercalated with, extensive terrigenous redbeds (Jansa et al., 1980). Evaporite deposition progressed southward, with evaporites of late Norian to Hettangian age occurring in the Scotian Basin (Barss et al., 1979). That the diapiric structures off Morocco are formed by salt was proved by deep sea drilling (Hinz et al., 1984); by extension, the diapirs of the Slope Diapiric Province of the Scotian margin must also be evaporites. Spores in the salt off Morocco are of the same age as salt in the Scotian Basin (E. Davies, pers. comm., 1983).

Figure 8.2. Paleogeography of the plates and extension of the sea for the North Atlantic realm.
a. Pre-Bathonian (closure)
b. Oxfordian-Kimmeridgian (163 to 152 Ma), Late Jurassic (M-25)
c. Valanginian-Barremian (138 to 119 Ma), Early Cretaceous (M-11)
d. Coniacian-Maastrichtian (87.5 to 74.5 Ma), Late Cretaceous (M-34)
e. Middle Eocene (52 to 40 Ma) (M-21)
f. Recent (post 35.5 Ma) (post M-13)

Closing the North Atlantic, using the western and eastern salt provinces as boundaries (Hinz et al., 1982), suggests that the North Atlantic rift during the Hettangian was about 350 km wide and 900 km long, and interconnected to the north through a system of grabens and half-grabens with northwestern Europe (Fig. 8.3a, in pocket). The marine communication with Tethys was either through a rift in what is now the Bay of Biscay or through rifts in western Europe, or both. A connection through northern Africa has been suggested by Busson (1970). Evaporites in east Greenland and Norway (the Halten-banken), which are more than 600 m thick (Aasheim and Larsen, 1984), indicate that during the Late Triassic the polar sea was transgressing southward but did not reach the North Sea rift (Clemmenson, 1980).

The majority of the Late Triassic rift basins were located in the equatorial and sub-equatorial climatic zones, which resulted in a hot arid climate and weak and variable atmospheric circulation. The northern part of this rift system was affected by "trade winds" (Parrish and Curtis, 1982), and surface water driven by wind and salinity differences circulated towards the southwest, parallel to the basin axis (Jansa, 1986). The paleocirculation regime in the Late Triassic and earliest Jurassic was comparable to that of a narrow estuary, with complete vertical mixing; the evidence of this lies in the highly oxidized clastics intercalated with the evaporite beds.

Early Jurassic

Evaporite deposition in the central North Atlantic extended into the Early Jurassic (Hettangian) off Morocco, beneath the Grand Banks and in the Scotian Basin off Nova Scotia, the Baltimore Canyon Trough east of and in the Aquitaine Basin (Barthe and Stevaux, 1971; Jansa and Wade, 1975; Holser et al., in press). Thus the main facies change occurred in the Sinemurian, which is used as the lower limit for the Early Jurassic lithofacies map. Igneous activity, ranging from 212 to 180 Ma (Norian to Bajocian), extended from Georgia to the Grand Banks and the Bay of Biscay Rift; continental tholeiites were emplaced as flows, sills or dykes in the rift basins (Stevaux and Winnock, 1974; Smith et al., 1975; Manspeizer et al., 1978; McHone and Butler, 1984; Pe-Piper and Jansa, 1986). This period of volcanism is in a broad sense associated with tectonic movements and appears to mark a period of intensified rift tectonics and crustal extension. The tectonism was related by Wade (1977) to the Early Cimmerian tectonic disturbance, a disturbance which led to the development of an unconformity, separating the Triassic from the Jurassic depositional cycle (see Wade and MacLean, Chapter 5). This tectonic disturbance is also observed in northwestern Europe (Ziegler, 1978) and extends to the Norwegian continental shelf (Larsen and Skarpnes, 1984).

In the Sinemurian, a marine cycle followed the evaporites and redbeds on the Grand Banks, in the conjugate Portugese basins and elsewhere in western Europe. Hallam (1981) has suggested that this facies change arose on account of an eustatic rise in sea level, which caused widespread transgression and the building of carbonate platforms under a warm, arid climate. On the Grand Banks this facies includes the Murre carbonates (Jansa et al., 1976), homotaxial to the Coimbra Beds of Sinemurian and Early Pliensbachian age in Portugal (Fig. 8.3b; Exton and Gradstein, 1984). Off Morocco, grey to dark grey claystones of possible deep water origin (Hinz et al., 1984) may be representative of a coeval deep water facies in the incipient North Atlantic basin (Fig. 8.3b).

Continued transgression led to the displacement of the carbonates of the Grand Banks, Portugal, the Aquitaine Basin, the Western Approaches and the Celtic Sea by deeper neritic marls and marine shales (Ziegler, 1982). Farther to the north — in Germany, the North Sea and the Irish Sea — mainly shallow marine clastics were laid down. Marginal marine clastic deposits with common coal seams in the Hettangian-Sinemurian become more marine towards the top of the Early Jurassic off Norway (Aasheim and Larsen, 1984); this suggests an open marine connection, with a shallow epeiric sea connecting the Polar Sea to the shelf sea of northwestern Europe.

Deltaic deposition dominated most of the eastern Sverdrup Basin (Balkwill et al., 1983) with littoral and neritic shales deposited to the west. This indicates the presence of a basement high which may extend up to Svalbard (Steel and Worsley, 1984) and Franz Josef Land, east Greenland (Fig. 8.3b). The coarsening upward Toarcian sediments in the Haltenbanken area (Karlsson, 1984) suggest that the shallow marine connection to the Polar Sea severed (see below), which may account for the widespread

occurrence of a bituminous shale facies in western Europe. This facies includes the Posidonien Schiefer of Germany (Riegraf, 1985), the Jet Rock of England and the Schistes-Carton of northern France. No equivalent facies are known from the Grand Banks and Portugal, although Pliensbachian bituminous shales and Toarcian mudstones and shaly limestones are found in southwestern and central Portugal (Exton and Gradstein, 1984); bituminous shales of Toarcian age have been found in Peniche, in central Portugal, overlain by carbonate fan deposits (Wright and Wilson, 1984). The occurrence of dark grey shales with minor bituminous shale intercalations in the deep basin off Morocco indicate that the basin was deep and poorly ventilated.

The southern extension of this Early Jurassic basin is uncertain but Lower Jurassic marine deposits are unknown from the Senegal Basin, the Blake-Bahama Basin off the southeastern United States or in Florida, so that the edge of the basin was probably near a line from Senegal to Florida (Templeton, 1971; Klitgord et al., 1984). The paleogeographic map of the Early Jurassic (Fig. 8.3b) shows that shelf carbonates dominated the southern part of the basin, and fine grained clastics with coal dominated the northern part; these features suggest climatic control of sediment deposition. A humid, temperate climate is indicated by the sediment distribution patterns for northern Europe and the Arctic, with southern Europe and the central North Atlantic being in a warm, subtropical climatic zone.

Middle Jurassic

The Aalenian to Bajocian was a period of tectonic instability, accompanied by regression, erosion and volcanism, and by major changes in the depositional and oceanographic regimes. The Middle Jurassic regression is well documented in the Scotian Basin, where Bajocian continental clastics, the Mohican Formation, prograded over the carbonate platform of the Abenaki Formation (Fig. 8.3c; see also Chapter 5). A similar change occurred in northwestern Morocco, where it was accompanied by basaltic volcanism and local development of an angular unconformity (Monbaron, 1982). Shoaling in the same period is recorded in Mexico (Longoria, 1984), on the Grand Banks (Jansa and Wade, 1975) and Georges Bank (Amato and Simonis, 1980; Wade and MacLean, Chapter 5). In Portugal carbonate platforms and reefs are found (Rocha, 1977; Stam, 1986), similar to those in the middle Atlas in Morocco. Synchronous tectonic uplift in the central North Sea and parts of the Norwegian margin led to deep erosion of Lower Jurassic and older strata (Ziegler, 1982). Continental clastics and minor coal beds were deposited in northern Europe and paralic sands with coal debris, offshore of central Norway (Karlsson, 1984; Fig. 8.3c). The early Middle Jurassic paleogeography suggests that a marine connection between northwestern Europe and the Polar Sea could have been temporarily disrupted (Olaussen et al., 1984). Data from the Sverdrup Basin suggest that regression was delayed; there it is notable for the widespread deposition of glauconitic sandstones and some basin margin erosion during the Bathonian to possibly early Oxfordian (Balkwill et al., 1983).

This widespread Middle Jurassic tectonism (the "mid-Cimmerian" tectonic phase of Ziegler, 1978) led to or accompanied continental separation and initiation of seafloor spreading in the central North Atlantic. The oldest oceanic crust encountered by drilling is in the Blake-Bahama Basin, where it is overlain by radiolarian-rich, silty clays and marls of middle Callovian age (Sheridan et al., 1983). In the Callovian, the ocean was not anomalously shallow. If this oceanic crust formed on a mid-ocean ridge at a normal depth of 2.7 km it would by now have subsided to its present depth of 5 km, taking into account the effects of loading by sediment and water. The uncertainty over whether the crust is continental or oceanic in the strip 200 km wide between the Blake Spur Magnetic Anomaly and the East Coast Magnetic Anomaly, along the western edge of the Blake-Bahama Basin, precludes unequivocal dating of the initial opening of the Atlantic Ocean. An estimate made using reasonably conservative assumptions of velocity of continental drift (Sheridan et al., 1983) suggests that significant seafloor spreading started in the Bathonian. If the central Atlantic rift subsided several hundreds of metres below sea level in the Sinemurian and Bajocian-Bathonian oceanic crust formed at a normal depth of 2.7 km, then the initial subsidence of the central North Atlantic Basin was about 10 cm/ka. Westermann (1984) has proposed that a shallow marine connection was established in post-Bajocian time between the deep western Tethys (central North Atlantic Ocean) and the central American corridor to the northeast, and the deep Jurassic superocean of the Pacific to the southwest.

Late Jurassic

Transgressions during the Bathonian, Callovian and late Oxfordian to Kimmeridgian led to widespread marine carbonate and clastic deposition around the North Atlantic, the Gulf of Mexico and throughout most of northwestern Europe (Fig. 8.3d). For example, detailed micropaleontological analyses of sequences in Portugal, in the Grand Banks basins and in the Scotian Basin show "deepening upward" trends in the middle Bathonian to Callovian and in the Callovian to early Kimmeridgian (Stam, 1986); this agrees with the sedimentological evidence (Jansa and Wade, 1975; Gibling and Stewart, in press). Each of the sedimentary basins developed on the North Atlantic continental margins has its own individual characteristics with regional trends being frequently interrupted or overprinted by local trends.

In general the Late Jurassic margins of the central North Atlantic, including the Gulf Coast of the United States, were areas of extensive development of carbonate platforms; examples are the Smackover and Abenaki formations (Fig. 8.3d; Jansa, 1981; Jansa and Wiedman, 1982). The same facies of Callovian-Berriasian age is extensively developed along Northwest Africa in the Tarfaya and Essaouira basins and on the Mazagan Plateau (von Rad and Sarti, 1986). Northwestern Europe remained an area of mainly shallow-water marine shale and minor limestone deposition, locally alternating in a cyclic manner (Talbot, 1973). Deep water marine shales were deposited in a widening Greenland-Norway rift zone (Surlyk and Clemmenson, 1983; Karlsson, 1984), with deposition of neritic clastic sediments continuing farther north to Svalbard (Mork and Bjoroy, 1984) and the Sverdrup Basin (Balkwill et al., 1983).

Economically significant hydrocarbon source rocks formed in early Kimmeridgian time in the North Sea,

southern England and off mid-Norway. This facies extended to the northern Grand Banks, where it is also an important source rock, and is probably represented in central Portugal by the shales of the Tojeira Formation. Tyson et al. (1979) have given a plausible model for the facts leading up to deposition of the oil shale facies. These authors, like Talbot (1973), drew attention to the cyclic alternation of coccolith limestones and clay-oil shales in southern England. The phytoplankton bloom is a symptom of widespread anerobic conditions in a stratified water column. Preservational factors exert major control on the dark shale facies. According to Tyson et al. (1979), "the development of widespread stagnant conditions in Northwestern Europe during the Kimmeridgian was influenced both by paleogeography and the global rise in sea level. The lower Kimmeridgian probably marked the maximum extent of the Jurassic shelf areas, and the increase in depth of the water column must have separated the mixed surface waters from the sea bottom, creating a stagnant, potentially anaerobic layer". The broad expanse of the Kimmeridgian shelf seas and widespread tectonic upheaval (Ziegler, 1982) together may have created many local "shelf" basins (embayments, etc.), largely dependent on periodic convection and turbulent mixing in the surface waters, with a corresponding tendency for stagnation below wave base. Following mass mortality during stagnation, renewed convective mixing increased the fertility and productivity of the surface waters, resulting in plankton blooms. These in turn increased the organic content of the bottom waters. What caused this periodic ($\sim$14 000a) return to thermal stratification in an equable, subtropical climate is not clear. Tyson et al. (1979) favoured a combination of subtle changes in local rates of subsidence, primary production, circulation patterns and climate to upset the balance between aerobic and anerobic conditions. A similar set of circumstances may have caused the periodic mass mortality of planktonic foraminifers in the dark shales of the Tojeira Formation in the Montjunto Basin of Portugal (Stam, 1986).

The Late Jurassic evolution of the deep central part of the North Atlantic Basin is better constrained by data than that of the Early and Middle Jurassic evolution. The oceanic character of the deep basin is confirmed by the tholeiitic basalts — drilled in numerous sites of the Deep Sea Drilling Project, such as 105, 376 and 534 — which are overlain by pelagic deposits. The Upper Jurassic rocks in the deep basin consist of two distinct sequences: 1) older reddish pelagic marls, variegated claystones and marly limestones, similar to the Rosso et Aptico facies of the Italian Jurassic; and 2) overlying white pelagic nannofossil limestones, of late Tithonian to Hauterivian age, which are comparable to the Maiolica Formation of the present Mediterranean realm (Bernoulli, 1972; Bernoulli and Jenkyns, 1974; Jansa et al., 1979; Ogg et al., 1983). Turbiditic beds are common, particularly near the continental margins, with thick debris flow beds on the seaward side of carbonate platforms (Benson et al., 1978; Hinz et al., 1984; Jansa et al., 1984).

In the Late Jurassic, the major change in the deep-water lithology in reddish marly limestones to white, deep-water limestones took place during the Tithonian (Fig. 8.3d). This lithological transition can be mapped seismically using reflector C (J_1) in the western North Atlantic (Jansa et al., 1979) and may have been caused by a change in the carbonate budget in the oceans. Evidence from the margins of the Atlantic and Tethys oceans (described below) shows that the growth of shelf and reef carbonates slowed and was progressively restricted by increasing input of terrigenous clastic during the Jurassic.

Offshore eastern North American, marginal-marine clastics began to displace the Jurassic shallow-water carbonates after the Callovian, and these clastics finally prograded right over the carbonate platforms during the Early Cretaceous (Fig. 8.3d; Schlee et al., 1979; Jansa, 1981). A similar change from a regime of carbonates to one of siliciclastics was observed along the northwest African margin (von Rad and Sarti, 1986) and in the Lusitanian Basin of Portugal and northwestern Spain. In Spain, Ziegler (1982) related this change to the gradual arching of the Iberian Meseta.

This restriction of carbonate shelf sedimentation may have led to a relative enrichment of calcium carbonate in the oceans themselves, with a concurrent increase in nannofossil productivity, resulting in increased deposition of abyssal limestones. Why the formation of shallow-water carbonates stopped during the Late Jurassic-Early Cretaceous is not well understood, although a combination of regional vertical tectonic movements and sea level changes, such as the well documented Berriasian fall in sea level, may have been responsible. Probably the most important factor for the facies change affecting the northern part of the carbonate platforms was the northward motion of continental plates. Carbonate shelf deposition is limited to between 30°N to 30°S, with most of Europe and the central North Atlantic passing out of this carbonate depositional belt during the Early Cretaceous. The erosion of a well-known upward bend of the landward edge of the subsiding continental margin as occurred during early seafloor spreading (Beaumont et al., 1982), may have enhanced clastics supply. Studies of sediment budgets would be helpful.

Early Cretaceous

Major block faulting and tilting took place in eastern Greenland and on the Norwegian shelf at the end of the Jurassic or at the beginning of the Cretaceous (Aasheim and Larsen, 1984; Surlyk, 1984). The same tectonic event, probably a response to crustal stretching, may have been responsible for the local uplift and tilting of continental blocks in western Europe, in the Bay of Biscay, along the Grand Banks, in Portugal and off Morocco. For example, sedimentation rates decreased by factors of five or more on parts of the central Grand Banks and in the Scotian Basin. The discovery of shallow marine carbonates of Tithonian age on Galicia Bank, overlain by successively deeperwater clastics of Early Cretaceous age, confirms that the Atlantic seaway between the Grand Banks and Iberia started to subside in the Early Cretaceous (Ocean Drilling Program Leg 103 — Boillot et al., 1986). Actual opening took place in M-4 to M-0 time (Hauterivian-Aptian). The same tectonic event may also be reflected in the initiation of rifting in the Labrador Sea, which was accompanied by the deposition of volcaniclastics, intercalated with basalt flows with ages ranging between 139 and 104 Ma (Berriasian and Albian) (Fig. 8.3e, Umpleby, 1979; McWhae et al., 1980; Balkwill et al., 1989). The Lower Cretaceous clastic fill in the Labrador rift zone, located beneath the present-

day shelf, is nonmarine. The terrigenous sedimentation here maintained pace with subsidence (Gradstein and Srivastava, 1980).

A relatively small amount of the world's continental areas was covered by sea in the Early Cretaceous, and so it is generally assumed that eustatic sea level then was low by comparison with sea level in the Late Jurassic and the mid-Cretaceous. The combination of this low-stand of sea level and tectonic activity triggered extensive clastic deposition along the Atlantic continental margin as shown in Figure 8.3e. We have already pointed out that this led to the progradation of marginal marine and fluviatile clastics over the carbonate platforms from the Baltimore Trough northward to the Grand Banks and from Morocco to Portugal. Coals and oolitic limestones found in the basins of Portugal and in the Scotian Basin point to a warm, temperate climate, possibly similar to that of Florida now. In western Europe the widespread Neocomian terrigenous clastics, accompanied by minor carbonates, are generally referred to as the "Wealden" facies.

Deltaic clastic sediments built out several major depocentres, which on the eastern Canadian margin are found in the Newfoundland Basin and parts of the Scotian Basin. The original sedimentation rates were locally greater than 15 cm/ka. Submarine fans developed in front of deltaic depocentres such as those in the Scotian Basin, the Baltimore Trough, and in the Aaiun and Tarfaya basins off northwest Africa (Jansa and Macqueen, 1978; Van Hinte et al., 1985; von Rad and Sarti, 1986). Abyssal sedimentation rates in the central Atlantic during the Early Cretaceous are a factor of five less than along the margin. The white pelagic limestones continued into the Barremian, but dark marls, enriched in organic matter, intercalated with carbonates increase in thickness upwards in the section. The transition from limestone to dark shale in the western Atlantic constitutes seismic reflector ß, separating the Blake-Bahama and Hatteras formations (Jansa et al., 1979).

Middle Cretaceous

Several major tectonic events occurred close to the Barremian-Aptian boundary and affected deposition on the continental margins, the shelves and the deep ocean basin of the North Atlantic (Fig. 8.3f). The most significant is that for the first time the axis of the Mid-Atlantic Ridge extended northward between the Grand Banks of Newfoundland and Iberia and separated Flemish Cap, east of the Grand Banks, from Galicia Bank, west of Spain (Boillot et al., 1986). An incipient spreading axis probably continued northward with a triple junction formed in the mouth of the Bay of Biscay. One of the arms caused initial opening of the Bay of Biscay with the third arm probably continuing into the Rockall Trough, west of Ireland. In these areas where oceanic crust was just beginning to form, paleodepths were shallow, between 1 and 2 km. At the southern part of the eastern Canadian margin the Barremian (at about 120 Ma) represents the culmination of the regression already described, a time when mainly fluviatile clastics were deposited up to the edges of the continental shelf. The Aptian transgression which followed led to the deposition of shallow-water marine shales over the entire shelf from the Gulf Coast north to the Grand Banks off Newfoundland. After a brief regressive period in ?late

Aptian to early Albian time, slow transgression continued with shallow marine and deltaic sands being deposited on the shelves off eastern North America (Jansa and Wiedmann, 1982). The development in the southern North Sea and north Germany was different; the Valanginian and Barremian was a time of gradual transgression, with a temporary regression during the early to mid-Aptian (Ziegler, 1982). This variation reflects the influence of local tectonism on sediment evolution, with local subsidence exceeding sea level lowering. The occurrence of mid-Cretaceous transgressive shales and minor clastics along the Norwegian and Greenland margins (Birkelund et al., 1974; Surlyk, 1978; Aasheim and Larsen, 1984; Larsen and Skarpnes, 1984; Westre, 1984) indicates the continuation of margin subsidence, with neritic deposits laid down over most of the margins and with deeper-water, terrigenous facies deposited in the central rift (Fig. 8.3f). As previously mentioned, the middle Cretaceous was a time of intense tectonism, which culminated in the development of extensive unconformities and deep erosion in the late Aptian and early Albian. Erosion cut deep, locally exposing Lower Jurassic rocks (Jansa and Wade, 1975), and peneplained tilted basement blocks, not only on the shelf but also on the deeper parts of the continental margin, where blocks are truncated by submarine erosion. This is found in the Bay of Biscay, on the Newfoundland Ridge, off the Galicia Bank and in the West Shetland Basin (Grant, 1979; Montadert et al., 1979a, b; Ziegler, 1982; de Graciansky et al., 1985; Boillot et al., 1986). This tectonism is an expression of the "Austrian" tectonic phase (Ziegler, 1982), which is the last important tectonic phase in the southern segment of the northern North Atlantic. This tectonism most probably resulted from a rearrangement of plate stresses as continental spreading extended northward into the north Iberia-Grand Banks-Bay of Biscay-southern Rockall Trough regions. The tectonism was accompanied by extensive mid-plate alkaline volcanism, recorded from the Baltimore Canyon Trough north to the Grand Banks (Jansa and Pe-Piper, 1985), and extending towards northwestern Europe (Dixon et al., 1981; Fig. 8.3f).

A major change in sediment type and composition occurred in the deep, central North Atlantic Basin during the Barremian and Aptian. The pelagic carbonates were progressively replaced by non-calcareous, dark grey, organic-rich shales, frequently referred to as the "black shale" facies of the Hatteras Formation (Jansa et al., 1979). Deposition of this lithofacies continued into the Cenomanian. It is very widespread, having been confirmed by drilling in the central North Atlantic, the South Atlantic, the Mediterranean and the Pacific (Bernoulli, 1972; Thiede and van Andel, 1977; Dean et al., 1978; Arthur and Natland, 1979). In the North Atlantic this facies extends up to the Goban Spur and the Bay of Biscay (Fig. 8.1b; de Graciansky et al., 1985). The absence of carbonates in these oceanic black shales indicates that they were mostly deposited below the level of the calcium carbonate compensation depth, but similar deposits enriched in organic carbon also occur on the deeper parts of the continental margins, where they are developed as marls.

Several theories have been proposed for the origin of these mid-Cretaceous black shales (Fischer and Arthur, 1977; Thiede and van Andel, 1977; Dean et al., 1978; Habib, 1982). They include basin stagnation, changes in circulation, high input of organic matter into the basin, and diagenetic changes in the sediments of the basin. An excellent summary is provided by Reyment and Bengtson (1985).

The black shales are a potential source of hydrocarbons, although those discovered are thermally immature (Katz, 1983). The terrestrial organic matter within the shales makes them a potential source of gas, although only a few levels have yielded significant quantities of gas in laboratory tests. Hydrogen-rich, marine organic matter within the shales is concentrated only locally in the Cape Verde Basin, offshore of west Africa (Tissot et al., 1980) near the Cenomanian-Turonian boundary, so that the potential of the shales as sources of liquid hydrocarbons is poor.

Late Cretaceous

A well defined triple junction at the mouth of the Bay of Biscay separated the North American, Iberian-African and European continental plates. Narrow oceanic basins formed in the Bay of Biscay, Rockall Trough and Labrador Sea (Fig. 8.2d, 8.3g). For the first time a shallow marine connection extended north of the Labrador Sea via Baffin Bay into the Sverdrup Basin and the Polar Sea. Another arm connecting the North Atlantic to the Polar Sea was through the widening epeiric seaway between Greenland and Norway. There is a distinct geographic lithofacies differentiation: marls and chalks are predominantly deposited in the epeiric seas of Europe (Ziegler, 1981), Iberian Peninsula and in northwestern Africa; fine grained marls or clastics dominate the western margins of North America (except Gulf Coast), the Greenland-Norway seaway and the Arctic (Fig. 8.3g).

Global sea level reached a maximum in the Late Cretaceous and estimates for the elevation above present sea level range from about one hundred to several hundreds of metres (Hardenbol et al., 1981). In the majority of the sedimentary basins around the Atlantic this change in sea level is reflected in a continuation of the transgression which began in the Aptian. Because of the prolonged erosion of the hinterland around the Atlantic since the birth of that ocean in the Late Triassic and Jurassic, or even earlier (Late Carboniferous-Permian), the geographic relief was low. The combined effects of high sea level and low relief caused drastic reduction in the amount of clastic sediments entering the oceans. Glauconitic mudstones, marls and chalks were deposited in shelf seas (Fig. 8.3f), and the rate of sediment accumulation in the deeper parts of the North Atlantic basin decreased remarkably. From the late Cenomanian to the Maastrichtian, variegated, noncalcareous clays were deposited in the deep basin at a rate of less than 0.3 cm/ka (Jansa et al., 1979). In Maastrichtian time, the calcium carbonate compensation depth in the central Atlantic Ocean dropped, and a distinct deep water chalk — the Crescent Peaks Member of the Bermuda Formation, some 2 to 46 m thick — was deposited; this extends into the Bay of Biscay. In Deep Sea Drilling sites adjacent to the eastern Canadian margin, such as site 111 (50°26′N, 46°22′W, Orphan Knoll) and site 384 (40°22′N, 51°40′W, J-anomaly Ridge), there is an hiatus between Albian or Cenomanian and Campanian or Maastrichtian strata.

On the eastern Canadian shelf, the Late Cretaceous saw the beginning of widespread blanketing by transgressive sediments over older strata, which in some places were tectonically deformed. For the first time much of what are now the outer shelf of the Grand Banks and the outer part of the Scotian Shelf sank into deep water (Gradstein et al., 1975). This progressive deepening was the result of higher global sea level stand and decreased clastic supply, not the result of margin tectonics.

Two distinct transgressive pulses are recognizable on the eastern Canadian shelf. The first one occurred during the Turonian and the second mainly in the Campanian. Chalks and limestones, rich in nannoplankton, were deposited during these transgressive periods, younger by almost one stage in the Newfoundland Basin than to the south in the Scotian Basin (Doeven, 1983). On the J-anomaly Ridge, southeast of the Grand Banks, the Cretaceous-Tertiary boundary beds have been preserved (Thierstein and Okada, 1979) in marked contrast to the substantial hiatus in the Campanian, Maastrichtian and Paleocene records on the continental margin (Doeven, 1983). This hiatus may have been caused by erosion or non-deposition on account of a local or global fall in sea level at the Cretaceous-Tertiary boundary. This apparent fall in sea level may be related to continental separation north of the Charlie-Gibbs Fracture Zone — the "Laramide" tectonic phase.

Tertiary, south of the Labrador Sea

The Tertiary sedimentary history of the margin off eastern Canada south of the Labrador Sea has been poorly studied, mainly because the Tertiary sediments have not been considered prospective in the search for hydrocarbons. Generally, all the Tertiary sediments on the Scotian Shelf and Grand Banks have been grouped into a single formation (McIver, 1972; Jansa and Wade, 1975), the Banquereau, despite the fact that major sedimentary changes and disconformities are recorded in wells and seismic sections (Poag, 1982; Gradstein and Agterberg, 1982). The Tertiary sediments thicken towards the present day shelf edge and in places are more than 2.5 km thick. Relatively thin Paleocene sediments, deposited in neritic to bathyal water depths, are overlain by much thicker Eocene and Oligocene strata, representative of deeper waters. The overlying Neogene was deposited in shallower waters. Miocene sediments near the edge of the southern Grand Banks may be more than 1 km thick.

The predominant Tertiary lithology is mudstone, reflecting terrigenous input, accompanied by minor sands deposited mainly during the Paleocene and Miocene. Chalk, of Paleocene and Early to Middle Eocene age, was deposited only locally and was confined to the outer continental margin with its higher pelagic productivity and reduced supply of terrigeneous sediments. The Eocene was also a period of zeolitic claystone deposition. Radiolaria and diatom-rich beds occur scattered throughout the Cenozoic rocks and may reflect local upwelling along the margin, particularly in the Late Paleocene and Early Eocene and in the Late Oligocene and Early Miocene (Thomas and Gradstein, 1981). The interval containing the widespread hiatus between the marine shelf deposits of the Miocene and the glaciomarine clastics of the late Pliocene and Pleistocene is not generally well sampled. This hiatus

is equivalent to part or all of the standard planktonic foraminiferal zone *Neogloboquadrina acostaensis*, and to the interval within or immediately above the benthic foraminiferal zone of Ceratobulimina contraria (Gradstein et al., 1985).

Gradstein and Agterberg (1982) have drawn attention to the major and consistent gap in mid-Tertiary beds on the edge of the Scotian Shelf and the southern Grand Banks. The missing interval largely corresponds to the standard planktonic foraminiferal zones *Cassigerinella chipolensis* and *Globigerina ampliapertura* of Early Oligocene age (Fig. 8.4). Both the lower and upper stratigraphic boundaries of the gap probably vary in time, and locally part of the Eocene and the Oligocene-earliest Miocene are missing. Gradstein and Agterberg believed that the gaps are the result of erosion during Early Oligocene coastal offlap, reflecting a major eustatic fall in sea level, followed by coastal onlap of the sea due to continued subsidence. Miller et al. (1984) supported this model. They suggested that on the margins off both western Europe and the eastern United States, early Oligocene (ca. 31 Ma) lowering of sea level, eustatically induced, triggered erosion and canyon cutting. In mid-Oligocene time, sea level rose locally on account of increased margin subsidence. The issue of stratigraphic gaps and their causes is discussed in the section on Subsidence and Sedimentation.

In the abyssal western North Atlantic slow deposition, on average less than 0.1 cm/ka of variegated claystones, continued from the Late Cretaceous into the Early Tertiary. The sediments are enriched in siliceous components, such as radiolarians, diatoms and siliceous sponge spicules, and in zeolites and volcanic debris (Jansa et al., 1979). Chert, responsible for seismic reflector Ac, is largely confined to the Late Paleocene and Early Eocene (see Tucholke and Mountain, 1979).

The mode of chert formation has been disputed, but most hypotheses invoke a combination of deep circulation with upwelling of cool, nutrient-rich water and intensified volcanism. This cool, nutrient-rich water is thought to have originated in high latitudes and to have surfaced in upwelling zones along a west-flowing circum-global current through Tethys, the North Atlantic and the Pacific oceans.

The effects of deep currents on deep-sea sediments increased in the Eocene to Miocene, giving rise to drift deposits and hiatuses. For example, in the eastern Atlantic and the Labrador Sea, the seismic reflector R4 indicates a change from predominantly pelagic sedimentation to the pelagic, hemipelagic and terrigenous drift deposits (Miller et al., 1982; Roberts et al., 1984; Kidd and Hill, 1986), approximately dated as Oligocene. The same increase in the effects of deep currents is generally linked to the erosion of the western Atlantic abyssal plain and continental rise, with greater erosion closer to the rise where more section is missing. According to Tucholke and Mountain (1979), the stratigraphically deepest seismic expression of these erosional effects is represented by seismic horizon A^u which, south of Cape Hatteras, North Carolina, cuts through a variety of beds as old as Early Cretaceous. The extent of this seismic reflector suggests that the erosion was the result of a southerly flowing, westward intensified, abyssal boundary current, which in effect may have been a forerunner of the modern Western Boundary Undercurrent. The youngest sediments below A^u may be Late

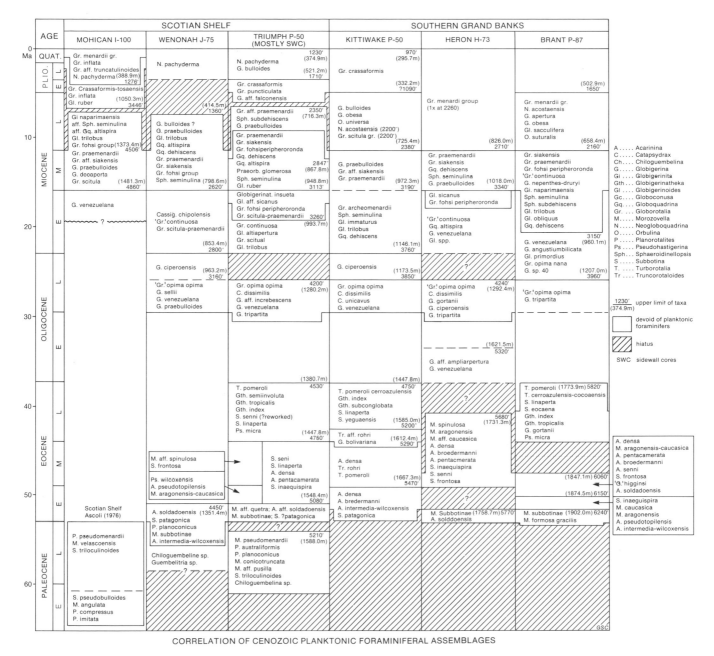

Figure 8.4. Biostratigraphic evidence for Early Oligocene disconformity on the Scotian Basin (after Gradstein and Agterberg, 1982). SWC = Sidewall core.

Eocene and sediments as old as Early Miocene may overlie it. The absence of the Oligocene suggests erosion during that time.

We believe that the thick prism of shallow-water deposits of Miocene age along the western margins of the Labrador Sea and western Atlantic, may have been the principal sediment source for the precursor of the Western Boundary Undercurrent. Sculpturing and plastering of the western continental rise — the effects of which can be seen in the spurs such as Sackville Spur off the northern Grand Banks and the Blake Outer Ridge — started in the Miocene. The Blake Outer Ridge has been extensively sampled and it has been established that it comprises hemipelagic

muds, deposited from nepheloid layers carried by contour currents (Heezen et al., 1966; Hollister et al., 1972; Sheridan et al., 1983). Sedimentation rates on this ridge reached 5-10 cm/ka.

On the basis of acoustic evidence, gas hydrates had been predicted within the sediments of the Blake Outer Ridge. The ridge and its sediments lie within the predicted window for the stability of gas hydrates in terms of temperature and pressure. This acoustic evidence was confirmed by drilling at site 533 (31°16′N, 74°52′W) of the Deep Sea Drilling Project. The ^{13}C isotopes and the C_1/C_2 ratios down this hole indicate that the gas of the hydrates was generated by normal diagenesis of organic matter within

365

the sediments. No evidence was found to suggest that the gas was a product of thermal cracking.

Cretaceous-Tertiary, Labrador Sea and Baffin Bay

The Labrador margin is underlain by up to 5 km of Cretaceous and Cenozoic sediments. These are mainly clastic and were deposited during three phases in the geological history of the Labrador Sea (see Chapters 2 and 7): Cretaceous — rifting; Maastrichtian to Eocene — seafloor spreading; Oligocene to Recent — the phase following active seafloor spreading. Proximal parts of the clastic wedge once extended over the area now occupied by the marginal channels off Labrador, but the sediments of this region were eroded and deposited seaward during and after the Late Miocene.

The western segment of the Cretaceous rift graben, under the present-day Labrador Shelf, has been sampled by exploratory wells. The oldest rocks of the Mesozoic rift consist of Neocomian basaltic volcaniclastics of continental origin, the Alexis Formation. Laterally and upwards this "intra-montane basin" unit grades into mid-Cretaceous coarse sands with some shale and lignite, collectively termed the Bjarni Formation, which are interpreted as deposits of an upper delta plain with braided rivers and swamps. The Bjarni fills the irregularities in the basement. The sands are hydrocarbon prospects (see Balkwill et al., Chapter 7 and Campbell and Bell, Chapter 12). The most northern occurrence of Barremian-Cenomanian nonmarine mudstones was recorded from Cumberland Sound (MacLean et al., 1986).

Labrador Sea marine sedimentation started in the mid-Cretaceous, when a seaway was formed during the Albian-Turonian high stand of sea level. Albian to Campanian shallow marine clastic rocks have been sampled as far north as the Southeast Baffin Shelf.

The timing of the main early transgressive event reflected in the sediments closely agrees with the onset of spreading of the southern Labrador Sea, during anomalies 34-32 (86 to 70 Ma, Santonian to Maastrichtian) time (Fig. 8.1, 8.2). The Maastrichtian-Paleocene shale facies beneath the present shelf is regarded as homotaxial with the oldest oceanic deposits, not yet drilled, in the newly formed Labrador Sea. Several unconformities in this unit are useful for seismic mapping (see Balkwill et al., Chapter 7). Deep seismic reflection studies have shown that in Maastrichtian-Eocene time, considerable differential relief existed over the Labrador and Northeast Newfoundland shelves. The grabens of this compartmented region contain fluviomarine and carbonate poor terrigenous sediment, rapidly deposited at original rates of 10 to 20 cm/ka. Sediments are mostly shales and mudstones, with mid-Paleocene to lower Eocene quartzose and feldspathic sands (the Gudrid sandstones) and some shale and detrital coal. The Gudrid sandstones are a commercial target for hydrocarbons and have tested wet gas. The facies delineated in seismic interpretations vary from delta plain to prodelta turbidites, probably depending on the distribution updip and downdip (Umpleby, 1979; McWhae et al., 1980).

An essentially Eocene sequence, the Kenamu Formation, is predominantly shale, with a laterally discontinuous sand unit at the top, the Leif Member. The shale is generally of an outer neritic to upper bathyal origin, because the arenaceous foraminiferal assemblage is diversified, and because locally planktonic foraminifers, benthic foraminifers such as *Pleurostomella*, and stilostomellids are found; thin micritic limestone beds indicate interruptions in the supply of clastic sediments.

The Maastrichtian to Eocene shales locally reflect conditions of somewhat restricted bottom circulation, which accounts for the general abundance and diversity of the agglutinated foraminifers. In more distal deposits, sampled in wells farther offshore, the assemblage resembles the so-called "flysch-type" assemblages in the Tertiary Central and Viking grabens of the North Sea, the Upper Cretaceous and Eocene facies of the Carpathian foredeeps and the Maastrichtian to Paleocene facies known from the southern Trinidad foredeeps (Gradstein and Berggren, 1981; Kaminski et al., in press).

The end of seafloor spreading in the Labrador Sea just before the time of anomaly 13 (36 Ma, Oligocene), near the Eocene and Oligocene boundary, coincides with the general change from deeper to shallower marine conditions in the region of the present Labrador Shelf. This change in environment is shown by the disappearance of the neritic and bathyal assemblages just described, which were replaced by a calcareous benthic assemblage of low diversity belonging to the foraminiferal zones *Turrilina alsatica*, *Uvigerina dumblei*, *Spiroplectammina carinata*, and *Ceratobulimina contraria*. These assemblages contain very few pelagic foraminifers. Neogene sediments are coarser grained than those below, and seismic data show that they are up to 2000 m thick. Several disconformities within the Neogene have been recognized, both biostratigraphically and seismically (see Chapter 7), and have been correlated with interruptions in deposition during Oligocene and Late Miocene time.

The sediments of the deeper parts of the southern Labrador Sea are known from drilling by the Deep Sea Drilling Project at sites 111 and 112, and from site 647 of the Ocean Drilling Program. Site 111 was drilled on the isolated seamount Orphan Knoll, at the eastern margin of Orphan Basin. Site 112 was drilled near a basement ridge beneath the central Labrador Sea. The oldest sediments recovered there are about 56 Ma (Paleocene), in agreement with the results of drilling at site 647 on anomaly 24 (56 Ma, Paleocene), just to the southeast.

The drilling at these sites provided data to establish the patterns of shallow- and deep-water circulation. As discussed earlier, seismic reflector R^4 at site 112, dated approximately as Oligocene, reflects a change from more pelagic to drift generated deposition. The reflector heralds more vigorous deep circulation of waters from high southern and northern latitudes. The northern source was probably in the region of the Norwegian Sea (Norwegian Sea overflow water). Baffin Bay is an unlikely source of cold, deep water because the source was probably in the region of the Norwegian Sea (Norwegian Sea overflow water) as deduced from the extent of the reflector R^4 in the eastern Labrador Sea and the eastern Atlantic. Furthermore, the Canadian Arctic may not have been cold enough in Oligocene time: sites 111 (50°26'N, 46°22'W) and 112 (54°01'N, 46°36'W) clearly show the transition from subtropical and temperate to subpolar pelagic foraminiferal taxa in mid-Pliocene time, indicating northern hemisphere polar glaciation (Poore and Berggren, 1974). As discussed later, few wells drilled on the eastern Canadian margin have a significant planktonic record younger than the Middle Miocene. This is due to shallowing, the Late Miocene hiatus (Gradstein and Agterberg, 1982), and increased cooling, which led to the onset of the cold Labrador Current, a surface current with relatively low salinity.

The Mesozoic and Cenozoic depositional history of Baffin Bay is poorly known. Although there are seismic data, only one hole has been drilled in the bay, at site 645 (70°28′N, 64°40′W) of the Ocean Drilling Program, and this ended in Miocene. Arguments concerning the mechanism of formation of this "small ocean basin", through spreading (Keen and Peirce, 1982), or through foundering (Grant, 1982), are thwarted by the lack of stratigraphic information. Oceanic crust in Baffin Bay is overlain by up to several thousand metres of sediments and so is virtually inaccessible through drilling. Targets could be established on the western slope of Baffin Bay which would provide stratigraphic control for its oceanic history (Gradstein et al., 1984; J. Peirce, pers. comm., 1984). Turonian and Danian shallow marine, shaly sediments underlie continental basalts at Nugssuaq and at adjacent localities in West Greenland. Upper Cretaceous (Senonian), upper Eocene-lower Oligocene and Pleistocene marine sediments overlie basalts on southeastern Baffin Island (see also Chapter 7).

Clues to the relationship between Baffin Bay and other regions in the Late Cretaceous-Paleocene are given by the microand macrofossil records. Williams and Stelck (1975) suggested that a Late Cretaceous marine seaway extended from the western interior epicontinental marine realm into the area of Baffin Bay. Mid-Cretaceous sediment distributions in the Arctic Islands suggest propagation of shelf seas southward into the Baffin Bay area (Balkwill et al., 1983; Fig. 8.3f). By (late) Campanian time, when a less endemic ammonite fauna appeared in West Greenland (Birkelund and Perch-Nielsen, 1976), there may have been a marine connection from the Atlantic to the Arctic through the Baffin Bay area. This change in endemism coincides with the initial opening of the Labrador Sea (anomalies 34-28 (86 to 64 Ma, Santonian to Paleocene) time). The presence of Campanian or Maastrichtian and Danian planktonic foraminifers in the Nugssuaq Shales of western Greenland, brought by incursions of Atlantic rather than Arctic surface water, provide evidence of the direct connection in the latest Cretaceous and the Danian of Baffin Bay and the North Atlantic (Gradstein and Srivastava, 1980). Water-mass conditions, although not tropical, may have been temperate; this agrees with the conclusions by Floris (1972), based on the evidence from scleractinian corals, concerning local temperate climatic conditions at that time.

SUBSIDENCE AND SEDIMENTATION

Subsidence and sediment burial curves are useful tools in geological analysis. Such curves can explain and graphically illuminate details of geological history. We use this tool to relate tectonic, sedimentation and paleo-oceanographic events along the Canadian Atlantic margin.

Subsidence, the result of processes in the lithosphere and asthenosphere (Keen and Beaumont, Chapter 9) is defined as the vertical motion of "basement" at a site

below the sediment cover, corrected for downward motion caused by sediment loading. Following Watts and Steckler (1981) the unloaded basement depth Y is given by

$$Y = S* \frac{p_m - p_s}{p_m - p_w} + \frac{w_x + w_m}{2} + \frac{d_x + d_m}{2} - \frac{p_w}{p_m - p_w} \cdot \frac{d_x + d_m}{2} \quad (1)$$

where p_m, p_s and p_w are the mean density of the mantle, sediment and seawater respectively, wx the minimum and wm the maximum estimate for the paleowater depth, sl_x the minimum and sl_m the maximum estimate for height of sea level above or below the present level and S* the original (decompacted) sediment thickness. The mean density of the sediment p_s is calculated with

$$p_s s = \frac{[F \cdot p_w + (1 - F) \cdot p_g] \cdot S}{S*} \quad (2)$$

in which F is the porosity calculated from sonic velocities or laboratory measurements on cores (Stam et al., 1987), p_g is the grain density, S is the thickness/depth before decompaction.

The subsidence equation is applied using the "backstripping method"; for each package of sediment the value of Y is calculated, starting with the youngest package which is stripped off, and the basement depth prior to its deposition is calculated.

The "burial curve" is defined here as the path followed by a particular age level in a well site through time, from its original depth of deposition to its present-day burial depth. We work with restored thicknesses. Decompaction was achieved by sliding each lithological unit up its own porosity-depth curve, calculated from sonic velocity logs. The burial depth B_d at any given time is a function of the thickness of the restored sediment column, the water depth at the time of deposition, and (if used) the eustatic sea level height relative to the present-day level:

$$B_d = S* \frac{w_x + w_m}{2} + \frac{d_x + d_m}{2} \quad (3)$$

In a passive continental margin driving force, vertical motion is generally downward, the result of crustal extension and thermal decay of the deep crust and upper mantle. In this account we will review the relation between plate tectonic events, "basement" subsidence, restored sedimentation and burial rates in Jurassic, Cretaceous and Cenozoic basins along the Canadian Atlantic margin. Representative drill sites were selected for which we have information on age, lithology and sonic travel time, and paleo-waterdepths inferred from fossil assemblages. The Fortran 77 programs DEPOR and BURSUB, developed to generate the numerical and graphical interpretations, are explained and listed in Stam et al. (1987). Figures 8.5a and 8.6a show original sedimentation, burial history and subsidence rates for the wells Murre G-67 in Jeanne d'Arc Basin and Mohican I-100 in southern Scotian Basin. Murre ended in Devonian metamorphic "basement" which is unconformably overlain by lower Jurassic strata. In Murre more than 75% and in Mohican more than 50% of burial took place during the first 50 Ma of sedimentation in Jurassic time. The average rate of sedimentation during that time was about 5 cm/ka. The tectonic instability of the Toarcian to Bajocian (near 185 Ma on the curves) and the sea level

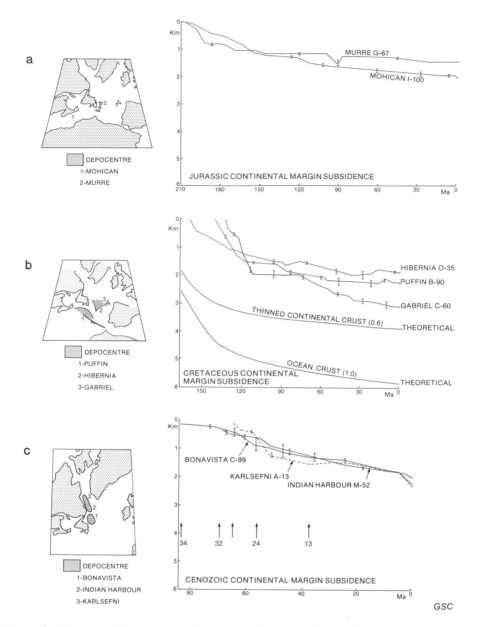

Figure 8.5a. Subsidence of basement in the two wells on the Grand Banks-Scotian Shelf.

Figure 8.5b. Modes of subsidence for the three Grand Banks wells since Late Jurassic-Early Cretaceous time, as compared to oceanic and to thinned continental crust with 60% dyke injection.

Figure 8.5c. Subsidence of basement in the three wells on the Labrador-Northeast Newfoundland shelves; also shown are the principal marine magnetic anomaly events in the adjacent ocean.

fall show as an inflection to lower rates of subsidence, with a resulting fall in sedimentation rates and with shallowing. The deep erosion in Aptian-early Albian time over the Grand Banks is clearly shown at the Murre site (Fig. 8.6a). The abrupt decrease in porosity at the unconformity between 100 (Albian) and 150 (Tithonian) Ma indicates that several hundreds of metres of lower Cretaceous sediments were removed by this erosion. The Turonian increase in water depth may be both eustatic and tectonic in origin. The Late Cretaceous-Tertiary hiatus in Mohican I-100 is the result of local canyon cutting and slumping

along the slope, which started in the Oligocene. From the abundance of Miocene pelagic foraminifers in Mohican and from regional evidence, it is inferred that sedimentation did not keep up with subsidence and deeper-water conditions resulted. The absence of the *Neogloboquadrina acostaensis, Globorotalia margaritae* and *G. crassaformis* standard planktonic foraminiferal zones may be the result of erosion and nondeposition, induced by the late Miocene (Andalusian) eustatic sea level drop of several tens of metres (Berggren and Haq, 1976).

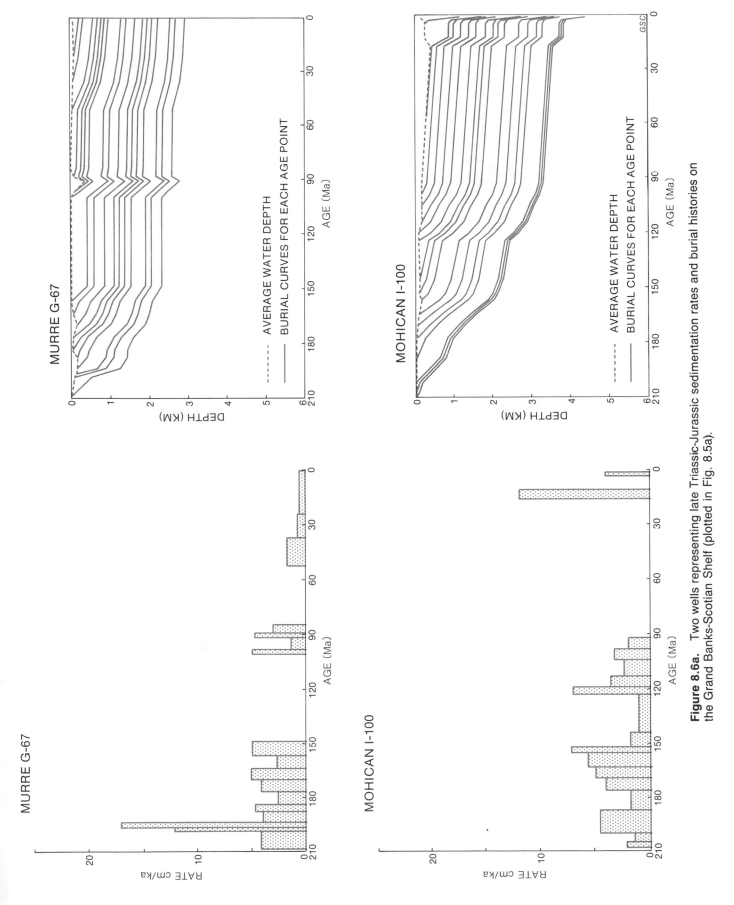

Figure 8.6a. Two wells representing late Triassic-Jurassic sedimentation rates and burial histories on the Grand Banks-Scotian Shelf (plotted in Fig. 8.5a).

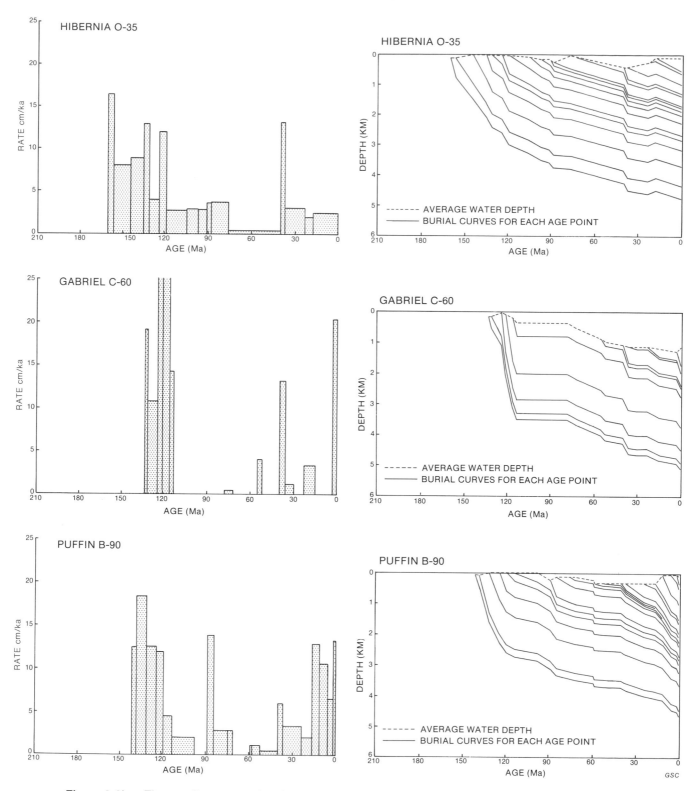

Figure 8.6b. Three wells representing Cretaceous sedimentation rates and burial histories on the Grand Banks (plotted in Fig. 8.5b).

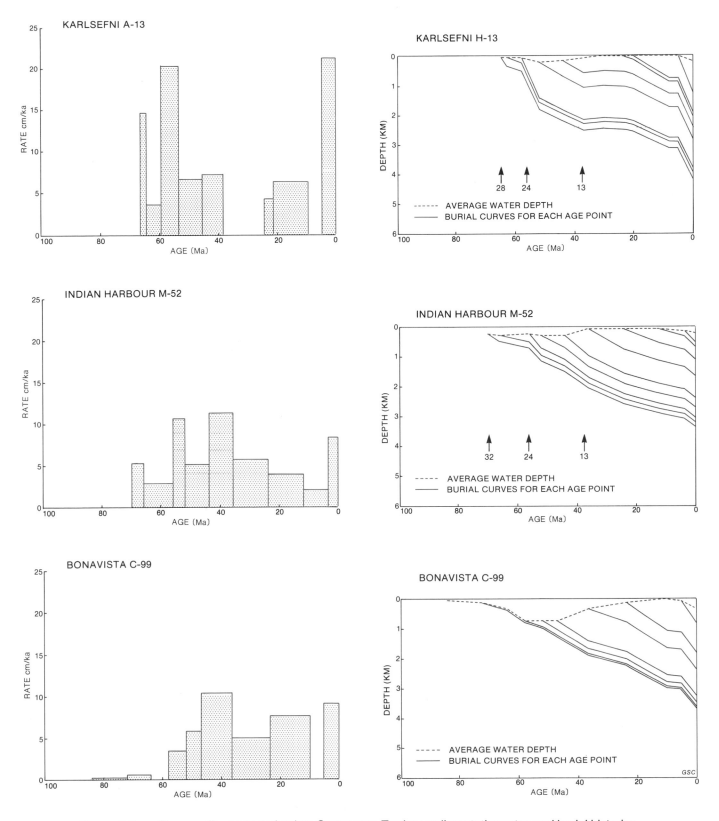

Figure 8.6c. Three wells representing late Cretaceous-Tertiary sedimentation rates and burial histories on the Labrador and Northeast Newfoundland shelves (plotted in Fig. 8.5c); also shown are the principal marine magnetic anomaly events in the adjacent ocean.

After correction for the effects of sediment and water loading and for changes in water depth and sea level relative to the Recent, the tectonic subsidence curves (Fig. 8.5a) show an overall exponential decrease with time; early rapid subsidence (7 cm/ka) gave way to lesser rates. Such exponential decay curves are generally thought to be the result of a response to thermal contraction of the subsedimentary lithosphere as it cools following initial rifting. This rifting occurred in the Murre G-67 and Mohican I-100 during the Late Triassic to Early Jurassic. The sudden steepening of the Early-Middle Jurassic subsidence curve in Murre may be related to extensional faulting; the well is situated in a fault bounded basin.

The Grand Banks of Newfoundland is underlain by several sedimentary basins. The three wells chosen to illustrate Cretaceous burial and subsidence reflect different tectonic settings in different basins. Puffin B-90, in Scotian Basin, is near the transform margin of the Grand Banks, where large translations occurred; Hibernia O-35, in Jeanne d'Arc Basin, is on the edge of a continental graben, which has subsided since the Early Jurassic; Gabriel C-60, located in Flemish Pass, the passage between the Grand Banks and the Flemish Cap is the closest of the three wells to the oceanic regime between the Grand Banks and Iberia. Rifting started here in the Late Jurassic to Early Cretaceous. None of the wells penetrated basement, which is probably of Paleozoic age.

At all three sites, a major Lower Cretaceous clastic wedge formed (Fig. 8.6b), with a depositional rate of 10-25 cm/ka, when shallow water sedimentation kept pace with subsidence. A major sand influx occurred around 120 Ma (Barremian), which is one of the oil reservoirs in the Hibernia area.

This sand influx is seen in the plots of sedimentation rates in Hibernia O-35, Gabriel C-60 and Mohican I-100, and it reflects the general regressive shallowing seen along the margin. During the late Early Cretaceous, Late Cretaceous and Tertiary, subsidence slowed, but because of the low rate of sedimentation the sea deepened (Fig. 8.6b). Gabriel C-60, the well most distal from the continent, was even more sediment starved and so the deepest water conditions are found here, with deposition occurring only intermittently during the major sedimentary cycles of the late Eocene, about 40 Ma, and the Neogene, about 20 Ma. The peak in Quaternary sedimentation is due to glacial deposition.

At all three wells the Senonian to Middle Eocene (80-40 Ma) was a period of low sedimentation. This is true for all Atlantic margins, on account of high sea level, a hinterland of low relief, and a limited supply of clastic sediments. In the Gabriel well, located in a slope environment, the hiatuses of the Oligocene and the Late Miocene may relate to the increased activity of the forerunner of the Western Boundary Undercurrent. The peak in sedimentation near 40 Ma (late Eocene) in Gabriel could be due to drift deposition, at the time of the reflector R⁴. Stratigraphic resolution in the Puffin B-90 and Hibernia O-35 wells, both in shallower water, is low, on account of poor sample quality and we cannot relate gaps in the record and eustatic events unequivocally.

The subsidence curves in Figure 8.5b are compared with the thermal subsidence predicted for oceanic crust and for a thinned continental crust where 60% has been replaced by igneous rocks, as may occur during rifting (Royden et al., 1980; Hardenbol et al., 1981).

The general form of the burial history of these three wells shows rapid early subsidence (3-10 cm/ka; average 5 cm/ka), presumably reflecting thermal processes (see Chapter 9). This stage corresponds to rifting and the earliest formation of oceanic crust between the Grand Banks and Iberia, north of the Azores Fracture Zone. A second period of rapid subsidence associated with renewed high rates of sedimentation may be largely the result of sediment loading. Detection of widespread changes in sea level and in patterns of circulation may be feasible during the second period of subsidence, because the rate of subsidence was relatively low. The upward bump in the burial and subsidence curves for Puffin B-90 around 90 Ma (Turonian-Coniacian), may reflect the relative buoyancy of the salt structure on which the well is drilled.

A final example of the use of burial history for geological basin analysis is drawn from the study by Gradstein and Srivastava (1980) on the tectonic and stratigraphic events in the Labrador Sea. If margin subsidence can be partly interpreted in terms of a simple thermal cooling model of the sort now well established theoretically and empirically for basins on oceanic crust, then regional transgressions and regressions on the one hand and seafloor rifting and incipient spreading on the other should be correlative. Although this simplistic notion must be applied with caution — the effects of local events may overwhelm the effects of regional and global events — correlations can be made for the Labrador Sea and its margins. This may be because the geological history of the Labrador Sea is relatively simple.

Figure 8.6c shows the late Mesozoic and Cenozoic depositional history for three well sites, all of which ended in Precambrian or Paleozoic "basement" rocks, along a southeast to northwest transect of the western margin of the Labrador Sea. The geological history recorded in the wells — Karlsefni H-13, Indian Harbour M-52 and Bonavista C-99 — reflects the history of seafloor spreading in the Labrador Sea. Opening started in the south at about 70 Ma (Maastrichtian, magnetic anomalies 34-32) and at about 65 Ma (early Paleocene, anomaly 28) in the north; a shift in the centre of spreading took place at about 58 Ma (late Paleocene, anomalies 25-24), and spreading stopped at about 37 Ma (anomaly 13). Subsidence and significant sedimentation started with opening, but subsidence and sedimentation were most rapid (6-12 cm/ka) at the time of reorganization of spreading at 52-57 Ma (Fig. 8.5c, 8.6c). Eocene sedimentation rates, in the order of 5 cm/ka, did not keep up with subsidence, possibly because the hinterland had been worn down. On the mid-Labrador Shelf, an abrupt decline in sedimentation coincides with termination of the opening of the Labrador Sea. The early part of the three subsidence curves resembles exponential crustal cooling (Keen, 1979). In several wells the Oligocene (represented by the *Turrilina alsatica* Zone) and Upper Miocene (represented by the upper part of the *Ceratobulimina contraria Zone*) rocks are either very thin or are absent; we postulate that the major Oligocene and Late Miocene falls in eustatic sea level (Vail et al., 1977) contributed to these phenomena.

Subsequent younger tectonic movements, possibly in combination with sediment loading (Fig. 8.6c), may have caused the renewed late Cenozoic high sedimentation rates in the northern wells, a trend that from seimostratigraphic studies (Grant, 1980) appears to be enhanced northward along the Labrador Shelf. Cooke (1929), in his classical paper on the physiography of the Canadian Shield, noted the young tectonic activity on land. He inferred that the Canadian Shield as a whole was uplifted above its present altitude and tilted to the northwest in "Pliocene" time, followed by glacial depression and some post-glacial re-elevation (see also McMillan's (1973) review of river bed drainage through time). These observations on young tectonic activities agree with the findings of Fillon et al. (1978) concerning several successive Pleistocene deep shelf and slope terraces along the margin of the Labrador Sea. These terraces tilt downward to the north, parallel to shallow subsurface reflectors that dip northward towards a sedimentary basin off Hudson Strait.

In conclusion, we note that the composite Cenozoic stratigraphic section of the Labrador Sea margin (see also fig. 3 in Gradstein and Srivastava, 1980) is continuously marine, with the deepest, bathyal conditions in the Eocene. The formation of the Labrador Sea in the latest Cretaceous, Paleocene and Eocene coincides with the principal transgression of the margin. Sedimentation rates were generally high and greater than 10 cm/ka following the Maastrichtian, except in the Oligocene and Late Miocene when the rate at which sea level fell exceeded the rate of subsidence, and regression resulted. The region of the Labrador Shelf and the adjacent landmass has been tectonically active since the later part of the Neogene.

NORTH ATLANTIC PALEOBIOGEOGRAPHY AND PALEOCIRCULATION

In Jurassic-Early Cretaceous time the North Atlantic was essentially a tectonically restricted and equatorially oriented ocean between Tethys in the east and the Pacific in the west. During Late Cretaceous-Cenozoic time the North Atlantic became a latitudinally oriented, broad open ocean basin, with influx of southern and northern polar waters at surface and depth.

The study of the distribution patterns of fossil organisms is pertinent when assessing the dynamic changes in plate configuration, the development of the oceanic basins, and the changes in climate through time. Not only do the faunal distributional patterns provide a direct means for modelling surface and deep water circulation, but they also

help to solve ambiguities in paleogeography where geology and geophysics fail. Examples of this are the early marine connection in Baffin Bay, the extensions of Tethys, and the nature of the early seaways between Iberia and the Grand Banks.

The gross distributional changes in Atlantic benthic and planktonic foraminifers and a few other selected groups of microfossils from the Jurassic to the early Neogene are highlighted here. The emphasis is on the Mesozoic and the distributions are placed in the dynamic perspective appropriate to the changing scene. Foraminifers are particularly suitable for such a study, because the order contains pelagic and bottom dwelling families sensitive to oceanographic conditions in a reasonably well understood manner. There is also an abundance of species, many of which are widespread and occupy distinct niches.

A number of micropaleontological studies have addressed Atlantic biogeography during the Mesozoic and Cenozoic in some detail. The main contributions are listed in Table 8.2.

The microfossil distribution patterns in six time slices are shown in Figures 8.7a to f. The time slices are: (a) Early Jurassic, with the Atlantic closed; (b) Middle to Late Jurassic; (c) Early Cretaceous; (d) Late Cretaceous (Coniacian to Maastrichtian); (e) Middle Eocene; (f) Middle Miocene.

Late Triassic

As discussed previously the majority of the Late Triassic rift basins of the incipient North Atlantic were located in the equatorial and subequatorial climatic zones. This resulted in a hot and arid climate and weak and variable atmospheric circulation. The northern part of this rift system was affected by "trade winds". Surface water, driven by wind and salinity differences, circulated towards the southwest parallel to the basin axis. The rift regime in the Late Triassic and earliest Jurassic was comparable to a several hundred kilometre wide estuary (Jansa, 1986). The sediment fill of oxidized clastics and evaporites indicates a non-stratified water column.

Early Jurassic

There are two main types of Early Jurassic foraminiferal assemblages (Exton and Gradstein, 1984). The first type appears to be cosmopolitan, is dominated by nodosariids,

Table 8.2 Principal studies used for reconstruction of Mesozoic and Cenozoic paleobiogeography and paleocirculation of the North Atlantic.

Period/Era	Main sources of data
Jurassic:	Dilley, 1973; Westermann and Riccardi, 1976; Gradstein, 1977; Jaffrezo, 1980; Copestake et al., 1981; Gradstein and Sheridan, 1983; Exton and Gradstein, 1984; Riegraf et al., 1984; Westerman, 1984; Stam, 1986.
Cretaceous:	Douglas and Sliter, 1966; Dilley, 1973; Berggren and Hollister, 1974; Ascoli, 1977; Jaffrezo, 1980; Burnhill and Ramsay, 1981; Hart et al., 1981; Doeven, 1983; Williamson, 1987.
Cenozoic:	Berggren and Hollister, 1974; Haq et al., 1977; Gradstein and Srivastava, 1980; Gradstein and Berggren, 1981; Berggren and Schnitker, 1983; King, 1983.

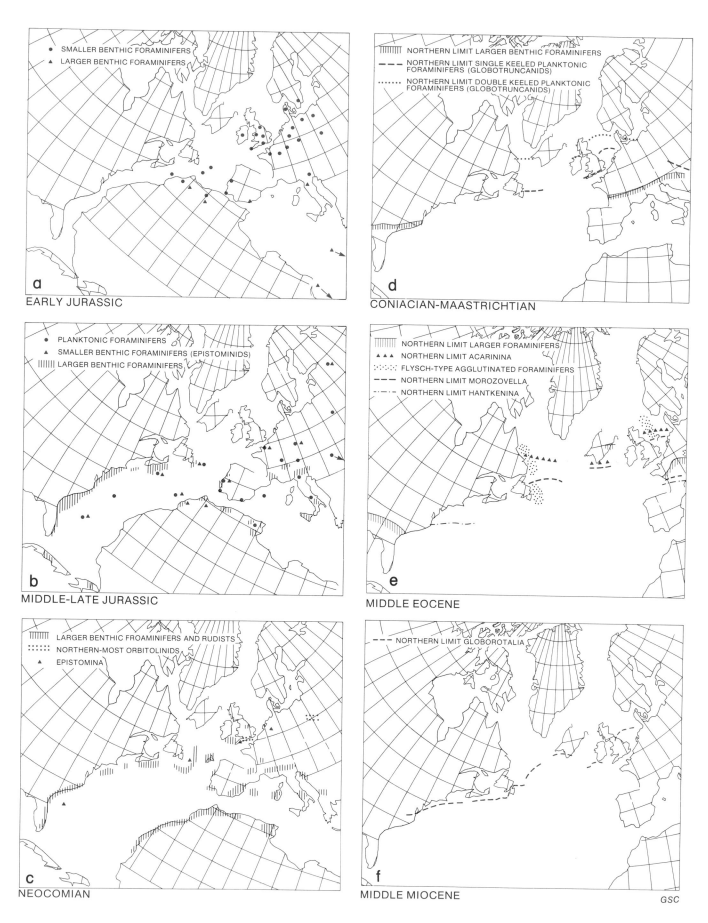

a EARLY JURASSIC

- SMALLER BENTHIC FORAMINIFERS
▲ LARGER BENTHIC FORAMINIFERS

b MIDDLE-LATE JURASSIC

- PLANKTONIC FORAMINIFERS
▲ SMALLER BENTHIC FORAMINIFERS (EPISTOMINIDS)
|||||| LARGER BENTHIC FORAMINIFERS

c NEOCOMIAN

||||||| LARGER BENTHIC FROAMINIFERS AND RUDISTS
·········· NORTHERN-MOST ORBITOLINIDS
▲ EPISTOMINA

d CONIACIAN-MAASTRICHTIAN

||||||| NORTHERN LIMIT LARGER BENTHIC FORAMINIFERS
– – – NORTHERN LIMIT SINGLE KEELED PLANKTONIC FORAMINIFERS (GLOBOTRUNCANIDS)
·········· NORTHERN LIMIT DOUBLE KEELED PLANKTONIC FORAMINIFERS (GLOBOTRUNCANIDS)

e MIDDLE EOCENE

||||||| NORTHERN LIMIT LARGER FORAMINIFERS
▲ ▲ ▲ NORTHERN LIMIT ACARININA
·········· FLYSCH-TYPE AGGLUTINATED FORAMINIFERS
– – – NORTHERN LIMIT MOROZOVELLA
–·–·– NORTHERN LIMIT HANTKENINA

f MIDDLE MIOCENE

– – – NORTHERN LIMIT GLOBOROTALIA

GSC

and has a species similarity level of more than 70%. It is known from the northern and southern hemispheres — for example from Alaska to Australia. The assemblage occurs along the margins of Tethys and in the epeiric seas to the north and south, and it is widely represented in the shelf seas from the Grand Banks, Portugal and western Europe (Fig. 8.7a). There are some indications that there was a simple depth zonation in Jurassic benthic foraminifers, despite the lack of any steep thermal gradient and thermal stratification (see below). Bathyal or deeper deposits contain more primitive arenaceous benthic foraminifers together with the nodosariid assemblage; such an assemblage was found in the Deep Sea Drilling Project Site 547, in an early rift graben off Morocco (Riegraf et al., 1984). The shallow nodosariid dominated fauna is best represented in shale facies.

In a previous section it was pointed out that climatic control may have led to carbonates being abundant along the margins of Tethys in the equatorial belt (Fig. 8.7a) and this carbonate facies harbours the second type of assemblage of Early Jurassic foraminifers. The assemblage contains larger benthic foraminifers, with complex wall structures, such as *Lituosepta*, *Lucasella* and *Orbitopsella*. It is quite diversified, and includes genera in common with the nodosariid fauna such as *Ammobaculites*, *Ophthalmidium* and *Textularia*, as well as less widespread siphonate valvulinids, large megalodont and lithiotid bivalves and dasycladacean algae.

From a circulation point of view the Atlantic embayment (Fig. 8.2a) probably experienced a certain amount of mixing and turnover, but the limited western extension of Tethys did not allow for a globe-girding, equatorial circulation system. There is no indication of major geographic or climatic barriers, which would limit access of bottom dwellers to the string of basins that dotted the pre-breakup continents.

Middle and Late Jurassic

Quantitative analysis by Stam (1986) has shown that there is an ecological zonation in benthic foraminifers in Middle and Late Jurassic "shelf" basins which, at least in Portugal and on the Grand Banks, can be related to water depth. A shallower nodosariid assemblage grades in deeper water into an assemblage with nodosariids, epistominids and arenaceous taxa accompanied by planktics included in *Globuligerina*. *Ophthalmidium carinatum*, *Paalzowella feifeli*, *Spirrilina elongata*, *S. infima* and *S. tenuissima* preferred relatively shallow water, up to about 50 m. *Epistomina mosquensis*, *Ophthalmidium strumosum*, *Pseudolamarckina rjasanensis* and the agglutinated taxa like *Ammobaculites* spp., *Bigenerina* spp., *Reophax* spp., *Trochammina* spp. and *Textularia* spp. preferred relatively

deep water and a muddy substrate, from about 200 to 250 m or possibly more. *Discorbis* spp., *Eoguttulina* spp., *Lenticulina* spp., *Lenticulina muensteri* and *Nodosaria/Dentalina* spp. filled the niche in between, from about 50 to 150 m.

Foraminiferal assemblages on the Grand Banks are similar to coeval assemblages of Portugal, and many of the taxa are widespread along the Atlantic margin and the ancient European shelf seas. The analysis illustrates the "Old World" affinity of the microfauna of the eastern American margin (Fig. 8.7b), in agreement with a geography of shallow surface connections at the northern end of the young Atlantic Ocean, or with a distribution of shallow water benthic foraminifers which could "float" across deep-water passages.

There is a typical low-latitude microfauna, associated with the photic zone, however, and known to be more dependent on shallow marine connections than the benthic fauna just described. It contains larger foraminifers like *Alveosepta*, *Anchispirocyclina*, *Feurtilia*, *Pfenderina* and *Pseudocyclammina* that occur in what was then the sub-equatorial belt of the Caribbean, the Gulf of Mexico, the eastern North American Atlantic seaboard to the Grand Banks, the Mediterranean, North Africa and east Asia. In Europe such an assemblage occurs as far north as southern France. In the Tethys of the Mediterranean region many more foraminiferal species and many algal components, not found along the Canadian margin, occur. This reflects Canada's position along the more northern rim of this low-latitude, subtropical belt. Nevertheless, the overall distribution pattern reflects the low-latitude and contiguous shallow margins of the Tethys-Atlantic ocean seaway (Dilley, 1973; Gradstein, 1977; see also Fig. 8.7b, c).

The abyssal Middle to Late Jurassic environment supported a benthic foraminiferal assemblage that showed striking differences from epicontinental assemblages. This has been seen in Deep Sea Drilling Project sites 100 (24°41'N, 73°48'W), 105 (34°54'N, 69°10'W), 261 (12°57'S, 117°54'E), 367 (12°29'N, 20°03'W) and 534 (28°20.6'N, 75°23'W). The oceanic biofacies had a stronger representation in arenaceous foraminifers, like the modern biofacies of the ocean floor, belonging to a dozen or so families and with a variable admixture of epistominids, opthalminids and spirrilinids. The average size of tests is 150 μm or less, well below the size of the tests of forms in epicontinental basins. Preliminary observations suggest a low communality and patchiness at the species level between samples. The assemblage is frequently accompanied by radiolarians, calcispherulids, aptychi and *Saccocoma*. Similar deep-water benthic foraminiferal communities are known from ODP Site 261 in the Indian Ocean and the DSDP sites 100, 105, 367 and 534. This suggests an essentially cosmopolitan abyssal microfauna. The benthic affinities may reflect similar deep, bottom-water characteristics, due to circulatory exchange, and similar substrates in the different Jurassic oceans.

From the pelagic fossil record and the paleogeography we believe that exchange of surface water in the Middle and Late Jurassic — between Tethys in the east, the incipient North Atlantic Ocean, and probably the Pacific — was unimpeded and was relatively stable. Such a circulation is shown by the distribution of diversified "Old World" assemblages of Middle and Late Jurassic nannofossils and radiolarians, and by the "filament-type" facies at

Figure 8.7. Distribution of selected groups of marine microfossils (mainly foraminifers), North Atlantic, based on contributions listed in Table 8.2.
a. Early Jurassic (208 to 187 Ma)
b. Middle-Late Jurassic (187 to 144 Ma)
c. Neocomian (144 to 119 Ma)
d. Coniacian-Maastrichtian (88.5 to 66.4 Ma)
e. Middle Eocene (52 to 43.6 Ma)
f. Middle Miocene (16.6 to 11.2 Ma)

DSDP Site 534, in the Blake-Bahama Basin (Sheridan et al., 1983), the filaments being derived from a floating pelecypod. The "filament-type" was even recorded from silicified limestone laminae between individual basalt pillows of oceanic "basement" in Site 534. Coeval Callovian beds in the Mediterranean are also rich in these filaments. The presence of Oxfordian planktic foraminifers at Site 534 is in agreement with their occurrence in Oxfordian limestone blocks dredged from the Moroccan lower slope (Renz et al., 1975), and to a peak in their abundance in Oxfordian strata in Portugal and in the basin margins of the Mediterranean. Clearly the central Atlantic, however narrow, was originally subject to surface water exchanges.

The assemblage of Saccocoma, calcispherulid and aptychi at the top of the Jurassic red claystones at site 534 is well known from other ocean drilling sites like 100, 105 and 367 in the western and eastern central Atlantic. It is typical of the pelagic facies of Tethys and attests again to the free surface-water exchange in the expanding ocean basin.

A reasonable model of surface circulation is based on predictions of observations of wind and current patterns in the equatorial belt. The reconstruction postulated by Ager (1975) is used here. In its near equatorial position and with its northeast to southwest orientation, the embryonic North Atlantic formed an ideal passageway for the easterly trade winds of the Jurassic. We suggest that during the earliest stages, the surface currents were wind driven from Tethys through the North Atlantic to the Pacific, and into to Tethys again with a flow only to the west.

We speculate too that in the late Callovian-Oxfordian, the North Atlantic widened to a point where the equatorial countercurrent was able to create a return flow along the southeastern edge of the North Atlantic, which continued into the equatorial countercurrent of the southern edge of Tethys (Fig. 8.2b, c). This equatorial current pattern persisted, we believe, until the central Atlantic margin drifted north of 30° latitude in the Early Cretaceous, and then the effects of westerly winds led to the clockwise North Atlantic gyre, and the beginning of the Gulf Stream.

Biogeographic studies on Jurassic mollusks (Hallam, 1975; Westermann and Riccardi, 1976) show only an increasing latitudinal differentiation of faunas from the Middle to the Late Jurassic. There is little or no evidence in the equatorial belt of distinct provinces in the eastern Pacific and western Tethys (Mediterranean), as far back as the earliest Middle Jurassic. On the evidence provided by Middle and Upper Jurassic marine epicontinental deposits in Cuba and Mexico (Barr, 1974), and by Upper Jurassic marine sediments in the Gulf of Mexico, Hallam (1975) and others favour a central Atlantic pathway as early as the Bajocian. Rifting may have led to a pre-Callovian ocean pathway, and it is reasonable to assume this to be the Bajocian-Bathonian pathway.

It is more difficult to speculate on the Jurassic bottom circulation in the Atlantic Ocean Basin. The limited record in DSDP sites 534 and 547, where dark sediments of Callovian-Oxfordian age are found and the Kimmeridgian-Tithonian Cat Gap Formation is reddish in colour, suggests that oxygen ventilation was more limited before than after this time. There is evidence for Callovian-Oxfordian in situ, however, bottom dwelling fauna, and possibly contourite-induced sedimentation, suggesting some flow of bottom water. In the Kimmeridgian-Tithonian water mixing was sufficient to supply oxygen and maintain generally oxidizing conditions. Because the deep-water circulation today is controlled mainly by the sinking of cold, oxygen-rich surface waters in high latitudes, and since the poles were probably ice-free until at least Early Tertiary time, it has been argued that Mesozoic circulation was sluggish (Reyment and Bengtson, 1985). Salinity, however, may have been equally important globally or regionally in inducing vertical mixing. The relatively warm, salty shelf waters that formed by evaporation may have dominated the water masses as suggested by Brass et al. (1982). These authors argued that an effective source of warm, saline bottom water is a basin where evaporation is not sufficient for salt to be deposited. Based on this line of reasoning — the warm Jurassic climate, an ocean bordered by shallow basins in which a variety of sediments were being deposited other than salt, and westerly trades — all may have helped to induce deep circulation in the Atlantic.

Cretaceous

The Late Jurassic geography, climate, circulation and distribution of biota such as foraminifers, nannoplankton and radiolarians continued into the Early Cretaceous. For example, early Cretaceous benthic foraminifers show wide uniform variations in geographical distribution patterns along the margins of the central North Atlantic and along the northern and southern margins of Tethys (Fig. 8.7c). Early to mid-Cretaceous foraminiferal associations recovered from the Jeanne d'Arc and Scotian basins (Ascoli, 1977; Williamson, 1987) and of a predominantly marginal marine to outer neritic character, show more affinity with the low to mid latitude assemblages described from Canada's conjugate margins — northwestern Africa and western Europe — and with central Europe, than with the high latitudes boreal associations of the western Canada basins and the Arctic. In the North Atlantic, four main taxonomic groups can be distinguished:

1) Robertinaceans with *Conorboides hofkeri, C. lamplughi, C. valendisensis, Epistomina caracolla, E. carpenteri, E. cretosa, E. hechti, E. ornata, E. spinulifera and E. tenuicostata.*

2) Gavellinellids with *Gavelinella ammonoides, G. cenomanica, G. intermedia and G. sigmoicosta.*

3) Sculptured lenticulinids with *Lenticulina crepidularis, L. eichenbergi, L. guttata, L. nodosa, L. saxonica and L. sigali;*

4) Smaller agglutinated taxa with *Ammobaculites subcretaceous, Arenobulimina macfadyeni, Dorothia gradata, Falsogaudryinella tealbyensis, Gaudryina dividens, Spiroplectinata lata and Textularia bettenstaedti.*

The majority of these taxa are not known from the basins of western Canada and the Arctic, but are widespread along Tethys and western Europe, for example in the Celtic Sea, southern England, North Germany, Aquitaine, Tunisia, Morocco, Rumania, Trinidad and Asia Minor.

The distribution of rudists and the larger benthic foraminifers of the photic zone, like *Anchispirocyclina, Choffatella, Orbitolina* and *Pseudocyclammina* the genus *Trocholina,* as far north as the northern Grand Banks and southern France, reflects the subtropical climatic conditions, the availability of carbonate platforms, and the contiguous shallow marine connections along the outer parts of Tethys. In the Aptian-Albian, the larger foraminifer *Orbitolina* occurs in the Gulf of Mexico, Florida, as far north as Flemish Cap, Portugal, northern Spain, northern Italy and Austria. In the Cenomanian there are isolated occurrences of *Orbitolina* even farther north in Europe (Fig. 8.7d), before it became extinct. The accompanying neritic and benthic assemblage of epistominids, nodosariids and rotalids is also widely distributed on the Atlantic margins of the Old and New World. The planktonic foraminifers became stratigraphically useful in the Aptian and Albian, when increasing diversification took place in this group. The causes of this evolutionary "explosion", after a stasis of 60 Ma, or more, are not known. The greatest faunal diversity at present is found in the tropical belts, and that is where most Cretaceous genera are found. Keeled or spinose genera like *Planomalina*, *Schackoina* and *Ticinella* are common in the Gulf Coast, Caribbean and central North Atlantic, and the Tethyan region of the Mediterranean, just reaching the Grand Banks with a paleolatitude of 35°N. Genera such as *Globigerinelloides* and *Hedbergella* are more cosmopolitan, and reach as far north as the present North Sea.

The widespread distribution of black shales in the oceanic basins in Hauterivian-Albian time has often led to the conclusion that the circulation was sluggish and the sediment-water interface deficient in oxygen. As pointed out previously, the black shale facies may have developed at different places for different reasons, and oxygen deficiency is only one factor among many.

The oxygen levels of moderate- and deep-water depths in the mid-Cretaceous oceans may have been delicately balanced between surplus and deficiency (Reyment and Bengston, 1985). Small changes in the flux of organic matter or in the rate of deep-circulation may have caused anoxia within the oxygen-minimum zones of middle waters or the bottom. Higher global sea level and warm, equable climates probably influenced rain fall, the production of terrestrial vegetation and run-off to the oceans. The result could have been an increased influx of terrigenous sediment and organic matter (to ocean basins) into a relatively narrow Atlantic during the Hauterivian and Albian. The rapid rate of supply of terrigenous organic matter to a basin that was already poorly oxygenated, but not necessarily anoxic, could have led to even greater oxygen deficiencies in some basins; this would have allowed the preservation of any marine matter that was produced and supplied to the deep ocean basins.

During the mid-Late Cretaceous, separate Old and New World foraminiferal faunas developed. The western Atlantic (New-World-American) larger benthic foraminifers, with few exceptions, became different from the Old World (European and African) larger benthic foraminifers. The fauna also developed to the south of their northern limit in the Early Cretaceous, because climatic belts contracted as latitudinal temperature gradients increased and the land masses moved north. The low-latitude, shallow benthic community of the Early Cretaceous lost its contiguous shallow connection in the North Atlantic between Canada and Europe. By Turonian time North America had rotated anti-clockwise by 5 to 10° rela-

tive to Africa, bringing the Grand Banks to 35-40°N (Firstbrook et al., 1979). In Jurassic time the banks lay at 30°N.

Among the Cretaceous planktonic foraminifers high diversity occurred in the tropical belts, and there were no specific high-latitude forms, only eurythermal cosmopolitan species. Single-keeled *Globotruncana* and various pseudotextulariids are indicators of low-latitudes and warm surface waters. In shallow ecosystems *Globigerinelloides* and *Rugoglobigerina* were among the remaining taxa in high latitudes.

There is no difference in composition between eastern and western Atlantic pelagic faunas, and only the latitudinal extent of the groups differ. Along the American margin, the northern limit of single keeled Cenomanian-Senonian rotaliporids and globotruncanids was on the Grand Banks, then at a latitude of about 35°N, which represents the northern limit of sub-tropical conditions. Double-keeled forms occur on the southern Labrador Shelf and in the Campanian-Maastrichtian, *Globigerinelloides* and *Rugoglobigerina* occurred as far north as Baffin Bay (a latitude then of 55°N to 65°N). Evidently, watermasses of the Senonian Atlantic Ocean reached Baffin Bay but were cooler to the north. Along the European margin, Cenomanian-Senonian single-keeled planktonic foraminifers occurred in southern England, in the southern North Sea, and even in the northern North Sea, to then at a latitude of 50°N: from these northern waters Burnhill and Ramsay (1981) recorded *Globotruncana imbricata*, *G. renzi*, *G. tricarinata*, *Praeglobotruncana hagni*, *P. stephani*, *Rotalipora cushmani*, *R. greenhornensis* and *R. reicheli*. This northern shift of the faunas along the eastern half of the Atlantic realm may be due to the influence of the embryonic Gulf Stream, which flowed across the Grand Banks towards western Europe and displaced pelagic fauna northward.

Doeven (1983) has looked at the possible onset of systematic cooling of Late Cretaceous watermasses along the northwestern Atlantic margin, using the distribution patterns of nannoplankton as a guide. From the relative frequencies of higher latitude assemblages — dominated by *Arkhangelskiella cymbiformis*, *Kamptnerius magnificus*, *Micula "staurophora"* and *Nephrolithus frequens* — and the more tropical *Watznaueria barnesae*, he concluded that systematic cooling may have started in the late Campanian and increased in the late Maastrichtian.

Tertiary

There is a considerable volume of literature on Cenozoic biogeography and circulation, as reconstructed from the distribution of plants, vertebrates and microfossils (Berggren and Hollister, 1974; Dawson et al., 1976; Haq et al., 1977; Gradstein and Srivastava, 1980; Berggren and Schnitker, 1983). The details of the reconstructions are complex, particularly those concerning the onset of more vigorous, deep marine circulation following the role of changing gateways and the increasing temperature gradients as functions of depth and latitude. The main elements of the Cenozoic biogeography and circulation are described followed by an account of a recent mathematical analysis of microfossil patterns along a latitudinal transect offshore eastern Canada which illustrates these elements.

Findings on Nugssuaq, West Greenland, of rich molluscan, echinoid and coral fauna, a planktonic foraminiferal assemblage and a nannoplankton assemblage, all of Danian age, indicate temperate climatic conditions in the Paleocene as far north as 75°. The presence in the Eureka Sound Formation on Ellesmere Island, which is northwest of Nugssuaq, of Early Eocene vertebrates like lizards, crocodile, flying lemur, small primates and tapir suggests a mean temperature in the coldest month above 10-12°C. All these animals show adaptation to warm conditions and to long twilight and dark conditions of the high latitudes. These findings agree with the Paleogene paleobotanical record in Greenland and Svalbard, which also indicate warm temperate climatic conditions.

In the North Atlantic Ocean, including the Labrador and Norwegian seas, there was a simultaneous northward incursion of low-latitude morozovellids (Fig. 8.7e) and subbotinid-acarininid planktonic foraminiferal assemblages during the Early to early Middle Eocene. This is interpreted as an indicator of a climatic optimum, during an overall decline in Cenozoic temperatures. Such a finding agrees with the record in the Arctic Islands, mentioned above. The Gulf Stream must have extended at least as far as 50°N in the Labrador Sea. In Europe a similar record is found even farther north, as would occur with the modern Gulf Stream. For example, the northern limit of temperate warm acarininids with *A. broedermanni*, *A. densa*, *A. pentacamerata*, *A. wilcoxensis* and some morozovellids, including *M. aragonensis caucasica*, *M. formosa gracilis* and *M. subbotinae* is on Rockall Bank in the western North Atlantic, in southern England and in the southern North Sea (Fig. 8.7e). The larger foraminifers such as *Nummulites*, which are typical of the photic zone on the one hand and Tethys on the other, are found a full 30° farther north in the shallow eastern Atlantic basins than they are along the North American margin. The Tertiary larger foraminiferal taxa are almost completely different on each side of the Atlantic, so that this latitudinal difference is not due to an offset of the Gulf Stream.

It was pointed out previously that virtually identical agglutinated benthic assemblages, characteristic of the Alpine-Carpathian flysch basins, occur in the Paleogene and Early Miocene of the Central and Viking grabens of the North Sea, the Late Cretaceous and Eocene slopes off Labrador and Newfoundland, and the Maastrichtian and Paleocene foredeep facies of southern Trinidad. The assemblages extend into the turbidite facies of the Norwegian Sea, and it is predicted here, will be found in central Baffin Bay. The assemblages reflect carbonate poor, fine grained terrigenous clastic deposits of bathyal or deeper basins. The lack of endemism shows that bottom-dwelling, deeper-marine biota dispersed freely in the Atlantic borderlands formed after the Late Cretaceous.

The global Eocene-Oligocene cooling accompanying the build-up of the Antarctic ice sheet led to an impoverished Atlantic planktonic record; this is demonstrated by the oxygen isotope content in calcareous foraminifers. Relatively high latitude globigerinid and nannofossil assemblages repeatedly extended far into lower latitudes. Deep-currents intensified, particularly so when in early Miocene time the Norwegian-Greenland ridge was breached sufficiently to allow cold Norwegian water to overflow into the Atlantic. This is the time when "drift" deposits became more extensive.

A further cooling in the Miocene and Pliocene is reflected in the migration of the warm-temperate planktonic faunal belt southward. Nevertheless, in both the Canadian Atlantic margin, in the southern Labrador Sea and in the eastern North Atlantic incursions of tropical planktonic foraminifers are found (Fig. 8.7f), with *Globigerinoides*, *Globorotalia*, *Orbulina* and occasionally *Pulleniatina* until about mid Pliocene time (3-5 Ma). At that time there was an abrupt replacement of the fauna by subpolar *Neogloboquadrina atlantica*, *N. pachyderma* and *Globigerina bulloides*, due to polar glaciation in the northern hemisphere. Glacial ice rafting in the Labrador Sea has been found as early as almost 3 Ma.

Spatial distribution of Cenozoic foraminifers

The spatial distribution of Cenozoic foraminifers in the northwestern Atlantic Ocean from well data has been analyzed mathematically by Bonham-Carter et al. (1986). The purpose of the study, which uses correspondence analysis, was to investigate any faunal gradients and see if these can be related to oceanographic changes over the Labrador Shelf, the Grand Banks and the Scotian Shelf. Ranking and scaling (RASC) of the data allowed the recognition of ten reliable assemblage zones, which can be grouped into six well-defined time slices: Paleocene-early Eocene; early to middle Eocene; middle to late Eocene; Oligocene; early to middle Miocene and late Neogene (Gradstein et al., 1985).

Correspondence analysis is an ordination technique that seeks to find the spatial distribution of co-occurring taxa. Samples along a transect (e.g. wells) are ordered according to the weighted averages of the presence or absence of species. The algorithm used is iterative, and stabilizes on a solution where taxa occur in order of ascending scores and samples also occur in ranked order by scores. The technique was applied by Bonham-Carter et al. (1986) both for the Tertiary as a whole and for each of the six time slices; it clearly shows geographical trends in the faunal distribution varying with time and latitude. Events occurring in fewer than two wells, or events with a "spotty" geographic range in the wells ordered according to their score were omitted. This left 52 taxa out of 206. Figure 8.8 shows the score for "communality" in the wells arranged according to their geographic locations. There is an almost perfect latitudinal gradient from north to south, with, as expected, deep water wells off the northern Grand Banks similar to the wells of the Scotian Shelf. This reflects the "southern" influence of the Gulf Stream around the Grand Banks. This preliminary result does not indicate how geographic distribution varies with time, the reason why the analysis was also performed for each of the six time slices. Each time slice will now be discussed in turn, beginning with the oldest.

Paleocene-Early Eocene

The most important biogeographic feature is the restriction of the planktonic taxa *Morozovella aequa*, *M. aragonensis*, *M. subbotinae*, *Planorotalites australiformis* and *P. pseudomenardii* to the Scotian Shelf and southern Grand Banks, with some scattered occurrences in the more offshore northern Grand Banks wells. The trend clearly reflects the influence of temperate, open oceanic water

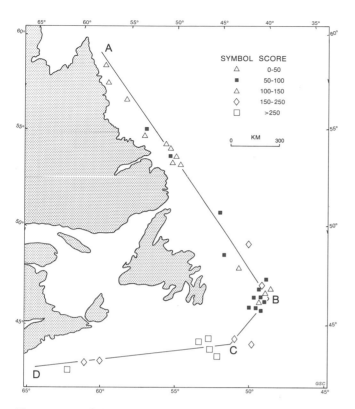

Figure 8.8. Schematic compositional change of Cenozoic foraminiferal assemblages from the Scotian Shelf to the Grand Banks to the Labrador Shelf, as detected by correspondence analysis (after Bonham-Carter et al., 1986). Ranking of the wells is based on scores that reflect the weighted averages of the presence or absence of species.

masses, probably the embryonic Gulf Stream. Zonal benthic taxa are ubiquitous, and include *Gavellina beccariformis*, *Rzehakina epigona* and *Spiroplectammina* aff. *navarroana*.

Early to Middle Eocene

There are more ubiquitous benthic and planktonic taxa than earlier and the lower latitude *Acarinina* aff. *broedermanni*, *A. densa*, *Morozovella caucasica* and *M. spinulosa* range as far north as the Grand Banks. Spotty occurrences outside this analysis are known from Labrador, in agreement with the pronounced warming trend discussed earlier.

Middle-Late Eocene

The deep marine terrigenous mudstone sequence over the Labrador Shelf and the northern Grand Banks created a typical assemblage not found consistently or at all to the south, including *Ammobaculites* aff. *polythalamus*, *Ammosphaeroidina* sp. 1, *Cibicidoides alleni*, *C. batjes*, *Haplophragmoides kirki*, *H. walteri*, *Karreriella conversa* and *Plectofrondicularia* sp. 1. Several other taxa were found only in Labrador Shelf wells. The southerly planktonics are more restricted and include *Globigerina gortanii*, *G. senni*, *G. tripartita*, *Globigerinatheka index* and *G. tropicalis*.

Oligocene

There is a small number of widespread taxa, which make up the body of the *Turrilina alsatica* Zone. Some pelagic taxa and deep-water planktonics are restricted to southern wells only, which is in agreement with the shallower facies sampled in the northern wells.

Early to Middle Miocene

A particularly large group with deep-water benthic forms and warmer-water planktonic taxa, including *Globigerinoides*, *Globoquadrina*, *Globorotalia* and *Orbulina* is found well south; this reflects deep water and the strong influence of the Gulf Stream in Miocene time on the Scotian Shelf and the southern Grand Banks. About 9 taxa, including *Alabamina wolterstorfi*, *Ceratobulina contraria*, *Epistomina elegans*, *Globigerina praebulloides*, *Globorotalia scitula praescitula*, *Guttulina problema*, *Gyroidina girardana*, *Spiroplectammina carinata* and *Uvigerina dumblei* are ubiquitous and useful for widespread correlation. Taxa restricted to northerly wells are under-represented during this time, which is the result of low productivity.

Late Neogene

Widespread shallow benthic taxa predominate, including *Asterigerina gurichi*, *Cassidulina spp.* and *Uvigerina canariensis*. Few wells of the Canadian margin have a significant post-Middle Miocene planktonic record. This is the result of further shallowing due to building of the Cenozoic progradational clastic wedge, hiatuses, and the increasing cooling which led to the onset of the Labrador Surface Current, which is cold and of low salinity. This current presently flows south over the Labrador Shelf, Grand Banks and Scotian Shelf and has an indigenous fauna with dominant *Neogloboquadrina pachyderma* and minor *Globigerina bulloides* and *G. quinqueloba*. The last influx of temperate and tropical taxa is seen in the southern Labrador Sea and on the Labrador Shelf in mid-Pliocene time, as discussed earlier. Since then colder-waters have dominated.

In summary, the Cenozoic biogeography supports the strong incursions of relatively warm Atlantic waters into the southern Labrador Sea and probably to the north. The influence of cooler Atlantic water prevailed in the Oligocene and Miocene, with the Scotian Shelf still swept by the Gulf Stream. It was not until the Late Miocene that there was evidence of a Labrador Current hugging the Canadian shelves. The glacial mode of surface flow from the Arctic towards the Atlantic through the Labrador Sea became fully established only after mid-Pliocene time.

CONCLUSIONS

The dynamic interrelation through Mesozoic and Cenozoic time of major events caused by plate tectonics, subsidence and sedimentation histories of oceans and margins, apparent sea level fluctuations, climatic changes and paleocirculation as reflected in biota distribution, provide a conceptual and unifying earth science framework. Seemingly unrelated and distant facts, gathered by individual scientists, gain new meaning and help to explain and predict trends in the litho-, aqua- and biosphere of earth.

Table 8.3 Major paleo-oceanographic and tectonic events through Mesozoic and Cenozoic time, in the North Atlantic.

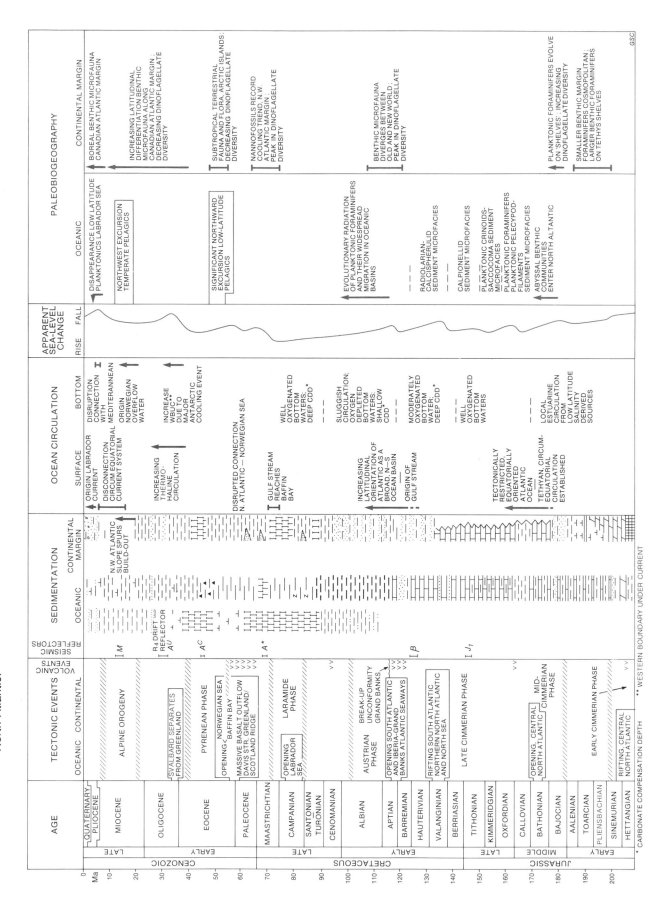

Several key events stand out in the 220 Ma history of the North Atlantic and its borderlands (see also Table 8.3):

1. Late Triassic-Early Jurassic rift grabens, largely in a subequatorial position, filled with redbeds and evaporites. The widespread late Sinemurian to Pliensbachian transgression of Tethys blanketed the rift grabens with carbonates.

2. Middle Jurassic ocean opening between North America and Africa was followed by mid-Cretaceous opening between the central North Atlantic and southwest Europe, late Cretaceous opening in the Labrador Sea and early Tertiary opening of the Norwegian Sea and Baffin Bay.

3. Rates of margin subsidence and sedimentation were driven by thermal contraction of the sub-sedimentary lithosphere as it cooled following initial rifting; the rates were subsequently modified by sediment loading and faulting. Along the Canadian Atlantic and Labrador Sea margins there was a first order relation between the timing and rate of exponentially decreasing initial subsidence and initial rapid sedimentation (in the order of 5-15 cm/ka). This was followed by a second sedimentation pulse of a lesser rate, the result of loading.

4. The type of sedimentation along the Atlantic continental margins was largely controlled by the relief and type of hinterland, the relief of the seafloor (sills, basins, etc.), water depth tied to subsidence and transgression-regression trends and the position of margins relative to the climatic belts.

   A carbonate platform facies formed around the central North Atlantic during the middle-late Jurasssic: this resulted from subequatorial climatic conditions, rising sea level and a low hinterland. For poorly understood reasons, one of which was probably the gradual drift north of the latitudes of photic zone carbonate production, massive clastic deltas and submarine fans replaced the platform facies near the Jurassic-Cretaceous boundary. This was the same time that the centre of carbonate deposition shifted in the deep central Atlantic. The low sea-level stand in the Early Cretaceous enhanced clastics supply. High sea level and low relief in the mid-Cretaceous caused a dramatic reduction of clastic sediments entering the ocean. Glauconitic mudstones, marls and chalks predominated along the margins. Widespread Maestrichtian-Paleocene, Early Oligocene and Late Miocene gaps in the shelf sedimentary record were the result of apparent sea level fall in the order of tens of metres.

5. Atlantic surface and deep-water circulation, as controlled by ocean opening, wind stress and water density differences due to vertical and horizontal salinity and temperature differences modified dramatically through time. The circulation in Late Triassic-Early Jurassic rift basins was probably of a local nature and with a southwest drift. A globe-girding equatorial circulation system originated in the Middle-Late Jurassic ocean, initially creating a counterclockwise equatorial gyre in the North Atlantic. When the central North Atlantic margins drifted north of 30° latitude in the Early Cretaceous, the westerly winds led to the development of the clockwise North Atlantic gyre known as the Gulf Stream. The Gulf Stream was responsible for low-mid latitude planktonic fauna in the middle and Upper Cretaceous rocks of the northern Grand Banks and the North Sea, with incidental incursions in Campanian-Maestrichtian time as far north as Baffin Bay (65°N). During the climatic optimum in the Early to early Middle Eocene, the Gulf Stream reached as far north as 50-55° along the western side of the ocean during an overall Cenozoic decline in temperature. The onset of the cold, low salinity Labrador current can be traced back to the Late Miocene; this current became fully established after the middle Pliocene, when there was a dramatic change in benthic foraminiferal assemblages along the Atlantic margin.

   Atlantic deep-bottom circulation in the Mesozoic was probably sluggish, although generally deep water masses remained well mixed, except in the Callovian-Oxfordian and Aptian-Cenomanian when immature dark shales formed. Deep-current circulation intensified in the Early Miocene, when the Greenland-Scotland Ridge was breached sufficiently to allow cold Norwegian overflow water in the North Atlantic. This was accompanied by more extensive drift deposition. The thick prism of Miocene sediments along the western margins of the Labrador Sea and Atlantic Ocean may have been the principal sediment source for the precursor of the Western Boundary Undercurrent. This was the time when the spurs and continental rises built out at rates of 5-10 cm/ka.

6. Low to mid-latitude benthic microfauna showed depth stratification in the Jurassic and Early Cretaceous. The shallow-water component was tethyan in nature and inhabits its northern margins. The abyssal microfauna is as far as known cosmopolitan in Tethys. Separate Old and New World shallow microfaunas originated in middle-Late Cretaceous time, when the only Atlantic shallow-water connections were at higher latitudes. The cosmopolitan, flysch-type, agglutinated foraminiferal fauna invaded the rapidly subsiding North Sea and East Newfoundland and Labrador basins during Maastrichtian through Paleocene time, when thick, deep marine, terrigenous mudstone sequences were laid down. This fauna disappeared when shallow water conditions were re-established in Oligocene-Miocene time, enhanced by Oligocene sea level drop.

ACKNOWLEDGMENTS

D. Gillis (Vancouver, British Columbia) and M Fearon (Halifax, Nova Scotia) provided valuable programming support. L. Jansa gratefully acknowledges the contribution to Figure 8.3 by many colleagues during Mesozoic field studies in western Europe and northwest Africa.

REFERENCES

Aasheim, S.M. and Larsen, V.
1984: The Tyrihans Discovery: preliminary results from well 6407/1-2; in Petroleum Geology of the North European Margin, ed. A.M. Spencer et al., Proceedings, North European Margin Symposium, Norwegian Petroleum Society; Graham and Trotman, London, p. 285-291.

Adams, A.E.
1979: Sedimentary environements and palaeography of the western High Atlas, Morocco, during the Middle and Late Jurassic; Palaeogeography, Palaeoclimatology and Palaeoecology, v. 28, p. 185-196.

Ager, D.V.
1975: The Jurassic World Ocean (with special reference to the North Atlantic); in Proceedings Jurassic Northern North Sea Symposium, Stavanger; Norwegian Petroleum Society, p. 1-43.

Amato, R.V. and Simonis, E.K.
1980: Geologic and operational summary, COST G-2 well, Georges Bank area, North Atlantic OSS; United States Geological Survey, Open File Report, n. 80-269, 116 p.

Ambroggi, R.
1963: Étude géologique du versant meridional du Haut Atlas occidental et de la Plaine du Souss; Notes et Mémoires du Service Géologique du Maroc, n. 157, 321 p.

Arthur, M.A. and Natland, J.H.
1979: Carbonaceous sediments in the North and South Atlantic: the role of salinity in stable stratification of Early Cretaceous basin; in Deep Drilling Results in the Atlantic Ocean: Continental Margins and Paleoenvironment, ed. M. Talwani, W.W. Hay and W.B.F. Ryan; American Geophysical Union, Maurice Ewing Series 3, p. 375-401.

Ascoli, P.
1977: Foraminiferal and ostracod biostratigraphy of the Mesozoic-Cenozoic Scotian Shelf, Atlantic Canada; in Proceedings, First International Symposium on Benthonic Foraminifera, Halifax 1975, Part B; Maritime Sediments, Special Publication no. 1, p. 653-771.

Austin, J.A., Uchupi, E., Shaughness, D.R. III, and Ballard, R.D.
1980: Geology of New England passive margin; American Association of Petroleum Geologists, v. 64, no. 4, p. 501-526.

Balkwill, H.R., Cook, D.G., Detterman, R.L., Embry, A.F., Hakansson, E., Miall, A.D., Poulton, T.P., and Young, F.G.
1983: Arctic North America and northern Greenland; in The Phanerozoic Geology of the World, II The Mesozoic B., ed. M. Moullade and A.E.M. Nair; p. 1-31; Elsevier Science Publishers, The Netherlands.

Barr, K.W.
1974: The Caribbean and plate tectonics: some aspects of the problem; Verhandlungen der Naturforschenden Gesellschaft in Basel, v. 84, no. 1, p. 45-67.

Barss, M.S., Bujak, J.P., and Williams, G.L.
1979: Palynological zonation and correlation of sixty-seven wells, eastern Canada; Geological Survey of Canada, Paper 78-24, 118 p.

Barthe, A. and Stevaux, J.
1971: Le Bassinà evaporites du Lias inferieur de l'Aquitaine; Bulletin du Centre de Recherches de Pau, v. 5, p. 363-370.

Beaumont, C., Keen, C.E., and Boutilier, R.
1982: A comparison of foreland and rift margin sedimentary basins; Philisophical Transactions of the Royal Society of London, Series A, no. 305, p. 295-317.

Benson, W., Sheridan, R.E., et al. (editors)
1978: Initial Reports of the Deep Sea Drilling Project, Volume 44; United States Government Printing Office, Washington, D.C., v. 44, 1005 p.

Berggren, W.A. and Haq, B.U.
1976: The Andalusian stage (Late Miocene): biostratigraphy, biochronology and paleoecology; Palaeogeography, Palaeoclimatology and Palaeoecology, v. 20, p. 67-129.

Berggren, W.A. and Hollister, C.D.
1974: Paleogeography, paleobiogeography and the history of circulation in the Atlantic Ocean; in Studies in paleo-oceanography, ed. W.W. Hay; Society of Economic Paleontologists and Mineralogists, Special Publication 20, p. 126-186.

Berggren, W.A. and Schnitker, D.
1983: Cenozoic marine environments in the North Atlantic and Norwegian-Greenland Sea; in Structure and development of the Greenland-Scotland Ridge, ed. M. Bot; Plenum Publishing Corporation, New York, p. 495-548.

Berggren, W.A., Kent, D.V., and Flynn, J.
1985a: Paleogene chronology and chronostratigraphy; in Geochronology and Geologic Time Scale, ed. N.J. Snelling; Geological Society of London, Memoir 10, p. 211-260.

Berggren, W.A., Kent, D.V., and Van Couvering, J.A.
1985b: Neogene geochronology and chronostratigraphy; in Geochronology and Geologic Time Scale, ed. N.J. Snelling; Geological Society of London, Memoir 10, p. 141-195.

Bernouilli, D.
1972: North Atlantic and Mediterranean Mesozoic facies: a comparison; in Initial Reports of the Deep Sea Drilling Project, Volume 11, ed. C.D. Hollister and J.I. Ewing; United States Government Printing Office, Washington, D.C., v. 11, p. 801-871. Bernouilli, D. and Jenkyns, H.C.

1974: Alpine, Mediterranean and central Atlantic Mesozoic facies in relation to the early evolution of the Tethys; inin Modern and Ancient Geosynclinal Sedimentation, ed. R.H. Dott Jr. and R.H. Shaver; Society of Economic Paleontologists and Mineralogists, Special Publication n. 19, p. 129-160.

Berthou, P.Y. and Lanverjat, J.
1979: Essai de synthèse paléogéographique et paléobiostratigraphique du Bassin occidental Portugais au cours du Cretace superieur; Ciencias da Terra, Lisboa, v. 5, p. 1231-144.

Biju-Duval, B., Dercourt, J., and Le Pichon, X.
1977: From the Tethys Ocean to the Mediterranean seas: a plate tectonic model of the evolution of the western Alpine system; in Structural History of the Mediterranean basins, ed. B. Biju-Duval and L. Montadert; XXVe Congrès-Assemblée plenière de la commission Internationale pour l'Exploration Scientifique de la Méditerranée, p. 143-164.

Birkelund, T. and Perch-Nielsen, K.
1976: Late Paleozoic-Mesozoic evolution of central East Greenland; in Geology of Greenland, ed. E. Eacher and W.S. Waters; Gronlands Geologiske Undersögelse, p. 305-339.

Birkelund, T., Perch-Nielsen, K., Bridgwater, D., and Higgins, A.K.
1974: An outline of the geology of the Atlantic coast of Greenland; in The Ocean Basins and Margins, Volume 2, ed. A.E.M. Nairn and F.G. Stehli; Plenum Publishing Corporation, New York, v. 2, p. 125-159.

Boillot, G., Winterer, E.L., Applegate, J., Baltuck, M., Bergen, J.A., Comas, M., Davies, T.A., Dunham, K., Evans, C.A., Girardeau, J., Goldberg, D., Haggerty, J., Jansa, L.F., Johnson, J.A., Kasahara, J., Loreau, J.P., Luna, E., Meyer, A.W., Moullade, M., Ogg, J., Sarti, M., Thurow, J., and Williamson, M.A.
1986: ODP Leg 103 drills into rift structures; Geotimes, v. 31, p. 15-17.

Bonham-Carter, G.F., Gradstein, F.M., and d'Iorio, M.A.
1986: Distribution of Cenozoic foraminifera from the northwestern Atlantic margin, analyzed by correspondence analysis; Computers and Geosciences, v. 12, no. 4B, p. 621-635.

Brass, G.W., Saltzman, E., Sloan, J.L., Southam, J.R., Hay, W.W., Holser, W.T., and Peterson, W.H.
1982: Ocean circulation, plate tectonics and climate; in Climate in Earth history, ed. W.H. Berger and J.C. Crowell; United States National Academy of Sciences, p. 83-89.

Burke, K. and Dewey, J.F.
1974: Two plates in Africa during the Cretaceous?; Nature, v. 249, p. 313-316.

Burnhill, T.J. and Ramsay, W.V.
1981: Mid-Cretaceous palaeontology and stratigraphy, central North Sea; in Proceedings, Second Conference on Petroleum Geology of the Continental Shelf of Northwest Europe, ed. L.V. Illing and G.D. Hobson; Institute of Petroleum, Heydon and Son, London, p. 245-254.

Busson, G.
1970:   Le Mesozoique saharien, Tom I et II; Centre National de la Recherche scientifique, Paris, 811 p.

Butt, A.
1982:   Micropaleontological bathymetry of the Cretaceous of western Morocco; Palaeogeography, Palaeoclimatology and Palaeoecology, v. 37, p. 235-275.

Choubert, G., Faure-Muret, A., and Hottinger, L.
1966:   Le Bassin Cotier de Tarfaya; Tom 1. Notes et Memoires du Service Geologique du MAROC; Rabat, 319 p.
1971:   La série stratigraphique de Tarfaya (Maroc sud-occidental) et le problème de la naissance de l'océan Atlantique; Notes du Service géologique du Maroc, v. 31, p. 29-40.

Clemmenson, L.B.
1980:   Triassic rift sedimentation and paleogeography of central East Greenland; Geological Survey of Greenland, Bulletin no. 136, 72 p.

Clemmenson, L.B. and Surlyk, F.
1976:   Upper Jurassic coal-bearing shoreline deposits, Hochstitter forland, east Greenland; Sedimentary Geology, v. 15, p. 193-211.

Cooke, H.C.
1929:   Studies of the physiography of the Canadian Shield; Transactions of the Royal society of Canada, v. 3, n. 25(IV), p. 91-120.

Copestake, P., Johnson, B., Coleman, B., Shipp, D., and Murray, J.W.
1981:   Jurassic; in Stratigraphical atlas of fossil foraminifera, ed. D.G. Jenkins and J.W. Murray; British Micropaleontological Society, Ellis Horwood Ltd., p. 81-148.

Cox, A.
1973:   Plate Tectonics and Geomagnetic Reversals; Freedman and Company, San Francisco, 720 p.

Dawson, M.R., West, R.M., Langston, W., and Hutchison, J.H.
1976:   Paleogene terrestrial vertebrates: northernmost occurrence, Ellesmere Island, Canada; Science, v. 192, p. 781-782.

Dean, W.E., Gardner, J.V., Jansa, L.F., Cepek, P., and Seibold, E.
1978:   Cyclic sedimentation along the continental margin of northwest Africa; in Initial Reports of the Deep Sea Drilling Project, Volume 41, ed. Y. Lancelot et al.; United States Government Printing Office, Washington, D.C., v. 41, p. 965-991.

de Graciansky, P.C., Poag, C.W., Cunningham, R. Jr., Loubere, P., Masson, D.G., Mazzullo, J.M., Montadert, L., Muller, C., Otsuka, K., Reynolds, L.A., Sigal, J., Snyder, S.W., Townsend, H.A., Vaos, S.P., and Waples, D.
1985:   The Goban Spur transect: geologic evolution of a sediment-starved passive continental margin; Geological Society of America Bulletin, v. 96, p. 58-76.

Dilley, F.C.
1973:   Larger foraminifera and seas through time; in Organisms and Continents Through Time, ed. N.F. Hughes; Paleontology, Special Paper 12, p. 155-168.

Dixon, J.E., Fitton, J.G., and Frost, R.T.C.
1981:   The tectonic significance of post-Carboniferous igneous activity in the North Sea Basin: Petroleum Geology of Continental Shelf of Northwest Europe; Institute of Petroleum, London, p. 121-137.

Doeven, P.H.
1983:   Cretaceous nannofossil stratigraphy and paleoecology of the northwestern Atlantic; Geological Survey of Canada, Bulletin 356, 69 p.

Douglas, R. and Sliter, W.V.
1966:   Regional distribution of some Cretaceous rotaliporidae and globotruncanidae (foraminiferida) within North America; Tulane Studies in Geology, v. 4, n. 3, p. 89-131.

Du Dresnay, R.
1971:   Extension et dévelopement des phénoménes recifaux jurassiques dans le domaine atlasique marocain, particuliérement au Lias moyen; Bulletin de la Societé géologique de France, v. 13, p. 46-56.
1979:   Sediments jurassique du domaine des chaines atlasiques du Maroc; in Symposium Sedimentation jurassique d'européen, Paris, 1977; Association Sedimentologique français, Publication Spéciale, n. I, p. 345-365.

Eliuk, L.S.
1978:   The Abenaki Formation, Nova Scotia Shelf, Canada — a depositional and diagenetic model for a Mesozoic carbonate platform; Canadian Petroleum Geology Bulletin, v. 26, p. 424-514.

Exton, J. and Gradstein, F.M.
1984:   Early Jurassic stratigraphy and micropaleontology of the Grand Banks and Portugal; in Jurassic-Cretaceous Biochronology and Paleogeography of North America, ed. G.E.G. Westermann; Geological Association of Canada, Special Paper 27, p. 13-30.

Faleide, J.I., Gudlangsson, S.T., and Jacquart, G.
1984:   Evolution of the western Barents Sea; Marine and Petroleum Geology, v. 1, p. 123-150.

Fillon, F.H., Folinsbee, R.A., and Palmer, R.
1978:   Deep shelf and slope terraces off northern Labrador; Nature, v. 273, no. 5665, p. 743-746.

Firstbrook, P.L., Funnell, B.M., Hurley, A.M., and Smith, A.G.
1979:   Paleoceanic reconstructions 160-0 Ma; United States National Science Foundation, National Ocean Sediment Coring Program, University of California, California, 41 p.

Fischer, A.G. and Arthur, M.A.
1977:   Secular variations in the pelagic realm; in Deep Water Carbonate Environments, ed. H.E. Cook and P. Enos; Society of Economic Paleontologists and Mineralogists, Special Publication 25, p. 18-50.

Floris, S.
1972:   Scleractinian corals from the Upper Cretaceous and Lower Tertiary of Nugsuaq, West Greenland; Bulletin Gronlands Geologiske Undersógelse, v. 100, p. 1-132.

Garcia, A.
1982:   El Cretacico de Espana; Universidad Comparteuse de Madrid, 680 p.

Garcia Moudejar, J., Hines, F.M., Pujalte, V., and Reading, H.G.
1985:   Sedimentation and tectonics in the western Basque-Cantabrian area (northern Spain) during Cretaceous and Tertiary times; Guidebook to Excursion no. 9, p. 308-392.

Gibling, M.R. and Stuart, C.J.
in press: Translational slides and the geometry of a carbonate continental slope in the Middle Jurassic of Portugal; Sedimentary Geology.

Given, M.M.
1977:   Mesozoic and Early Cenozoic geology of offshore Nova Scotia; Canadian Petroleum Geology Bulletin, v. 25, p. 63-91.

Gradstein, F.M.
1977:   Biostratigraphy and biogeography of Jurassic Grand Banks foraminifera; in Proceedings, First International Symposium on Benthonic Foraminifera, Halifax 1975, Part B; Maritime Sediments, Special Publication 1, p. 557-583.
1986:   Northwestern Atlantic Mesozoic biostratigraphy; Chapter 3 in The Western Atlantic Region, ed. P.R. Vogt and B.E. Tucholke; Geological Association of America, The Geology of North America, v. M, p. 507-526.

Gradstein, F.M. and Agterberg, F.P.
1982:   Models of Cenozoic foraminiferal stratigraphy, northwestern Atlantic margin; in Quantitative Stratigraphic Correlation, ed. J.M. Cubitt and R.A. Reyment; J. Wiley and Sons Ltd., New York, p. 119-170.

Gradstein, F.M. and Berggren, W.A.
1981:   Flysch-type agglutinated foraminifera and the Maestrichtian to Paleogene history of the Labrador and North Seas; Marine Micropaleontology, v. 6, p. 211-268.

Gradstein, F.M. and Sheridan, R.E.
1983:   On the Jurassic Atlantic Ocean and a synthesis of results of Deep Sea Drilling Project Leg 76; in Initial Reports of the Deep Sea Drilling Project, Volume 76, ed. R.E. Sheridan and F.M. Gradstein; United States Government Printing Office, Washington, D.C., v. 76, p. 913-945.

Gradstein, F.M. and Srivastava, S.P.
1980:   Aspects of Cenozoic stratigraphy and paleoceanography of the Labrador Sea and Baffin Bay; Palaeogeography, Palaeoclimatology, and Palaeoecology, v. 30, p. 261-295.

Gradstein, F.M., Agterberg, F.P., Brower, J., and Schwarzacher, S.
1985:   Quantitative stratigraphy; Reidel Publishing Company, Dordrecht and Unesco, Paris, 598 p.

Gradstein, F.M., Srivastava, S.P., Jansa, L.F., Miller, K., Mudie, P.J., Peirce, J., Grant, A.C., Piper, D.J.W., and Aksu, A.
1984:   Ocean crust and high latitude paleoceanography in the Labrador Sea; Proposal, Ocean Drilling Program, 30 p.

Gradstein, F.M., Williams, G.L., Jenkins, W.A.M., and Ascoli, P.
1975:   Mesozoic and Cenozoic stratigraphy of the Atlantic continental margin, eastern Canada; Canadian Society of Petroleum Geologists, Memoir 4, p. 103-131.

Grant, A.C.
1979:   Geophysical observations bearing upon the origin of the Newfoundland Ridge; Tectonophysics, v. 59, p. 71-81.
1980:   Problems with plate tectonics: the Labrador Sea; Bulletin of Canadian Petroleum Geology, v. 28, no. 2, p. 252-2173.
1982:   Problems with plate tectonic models for Baffin Bay-Nares Strait: evidence from the Labrador Sea; in Nares Strait and the Drift of Greenland: A Conflict in Plate Tectonics, ed. P.R. Dawes and J.W. Kerr; Meddelelser om Grønland, Geoscience, v. 8, p. 313-326.

Habib, D.
1982:   Sedimentary supply origin of Cretaceous black shales; in Nature and Origin of Cretaceous Carbon-rich Facies, ed. S.O. Schlanger and M.B. Cita; Academic Press, London, p. 113-127.

Hallam, A.
1975:   Jurassic Environments; Cambridge University Press, Cambridge, 269 p.
1981:   A revised sea level curve for the early Jurassic; Journal of Geological Society of London, v. 138, p. 735-743.

Hamilton, W.
1983:   Cretaceous and Cenozoic history of the northern continents; Annals of the Missouri Botanical Garden, v. 70, p. 440-458.

Haq, B.U., Premoli-Silva, I., and Lohman, G.P.
1977:   Calcareous plankton paleobiogeographic evidence for major climatic fluctuations in the Early Cenozoic Atlantic Ocean; Journal of Geophysical Research, v. 82, no. 27, p. 3861-3876.

Hardenbol, J., Vail, P.R., and Ferrer, J.
1981:   Interpreting paleoenvironments, subsidence history and sea level changes of passive margins from seismics and biostratigraphy; Oceanologica Acta, v. 4, suppl. 1981, n. SP, p. 33-44.

Hart, M.B., Bailey, H.W., Fletcher, B., Price, R., and Sweicicki, A.
1981:   Cretaceous; in Stratigraphical Atlas of Fossil Foraminifera, ed. D.G. Jenkins and J.W. Murray; British Micropaleontological Society, Ellis Horwood Ltd., p. 149-225.

Heezen, B.C., Hollister, C.D., and Ruddiman, W.F.
1966:   Shaping of the continental rise by deep geostrophic contour currents; Science, v. 152, p. 502-508.

Hinz, K. and Schlüter, H.U.
1978:   The geological structure of the western Barents Sea; Marine Geology, v. 26, p. 199-230.

Hinz, K., Dostmann, H., and Fritsch, J.
1982:   The continental margin of Morocco: seismic sequences, structural elements and geological development; in Geology of the Northwest African Continental Margin, ed. U. von Rad, K. Hinz, M. Sarntheim and E. Seibold; Springer-Verlag, Berlin, p. 34-60.

Hinz, K., Winterer, E.L. et al. (editors)
1984:   Initial Reports of the Deep Sea Drilling Project, Volume 79; United States Government Printing Office, Washington, D.C., v. 79, 934 p.

Hollister, C.D. and Ewing, J.I. et al. (editors)
1972:   Initial Reports of the Deep Sea Drilling Project, Volume 11; United States Government Printing Office, Washington, D.C., v. 11, 1077 p.

Holser, W.T., Jansa, L.F., Peretsman, G.S., and Wade, J.A.
in press: Evaporite deposits of the North Atlantic Rift; in Triassic-Jurassic Rifting and the opening of the Atlantic Ocean, W. Manspeizer, ed., Elsevier Science Publishers, The Netherlands.

Jackson, H.R., Keen, C.E., Falconer, R.K.H., and Appleton, K.P.
1979:   New geophysical evidence for seafloor spreading in Central Baffin Bay; Canadian Journal of Earth Sciences, v. 16, p. 2122-2135.

Jacobson, V.W. and van Veen, P.
1984:   The Triassic offshore Norway north of 62°; in Petroleum Geology of the North European Margin, ed. A.M. Spencer et al.; Proceedings, North European Margin Symposium, Norwegian Petroleum Society; Graham and Trotman, London, p. 317-327.

Jaffrezo, M.
1980:   Les formations carbonatées des Corbières (France) du Dogger à l'Aptien, micropaléontologie stratigraphique, biozonation, paléoécologie: Extension des résultat à la Mésogée; Ph.D. thesis, Université Pierre et Marie Curie, Paris, 165 p.

Jansa, L.F.
1981:   Mesozoic carbonate platforms and banks of the eastern North American margin; Marine Geology, v. 44, p. 97-117.
1986:   Paleoceanography and evolution of the North Atlantic Ocean to basin during the Jurassic, in The Western North Atlantic Region, P.R. Vogt and B.E. Tucholke, ed., Geological Society of America, The Geology of North America, v. M, p. 603-613.

Jansa, L.F. and Macqueen, R.W.
1978:   Stratigraphy and hydrocarbon potential of the central North Atlantic Basin; Geoscience Canada, v. 5, no. 4, p. 176-183.

Jansa, L.F. and Pe-Piper, G.
1985:   Early Cretaceous volcanism on the northeastern American margin and implications for plate tectonics; Geological Society of America Bulletin, v. 96, p. 83-91.

Jansa, L.F. and Wade, J.A.
1975:   Geology of the continental margin off Nova Scotia and Newfoundland; in Offshore Geology of Eastern Canada, Volume 2, Regional Geology, ed. W.J.M. Van der Linden and J.A. Wade; Geological Survey of Canada, Paper 74-30, v. 2, p. 51-106.

Jansa, L.F. and Wiedmann, J.
1982:   Mesozoic-Cenozoic development of the Eastern North American and Northwest African continental margins: a comparison; in Geology of the Northwest African Continental Margin, ed. U. von Rad, K. Hinz, M. Sarntheim and E. Seibold; Springer-Verlag, Berlin, p. 215-269.

Jansa, L.F., Bujak, J.P., and Williams, G.L.
1980:   Upper Triassic salt deposits of the western North Atlantic; Canadian Journal of Earth Sciences, v. 17, p. 547-559.

Jansa, L.F., Enos, P., Tucholke, B.E., Gradstein, F.M., and Sheridan, R.E.
1979:   Mesozoic-Cenozoic sedimentary formations of the North American Basin, western North Atlantic; in Deep Drilling Results in the Atlantic Ocean: Continental Margins and Paleoenvironments, ed. M. Talwani, W. Hay, and W.B.F. Ryan; American Geophysical Union, Maurice Ewing Series 3, p. 1-58.

Jansa, L.F., Gradstein, F.M., Harris, I.M., Jenkins, W.A.M., and Williams, G.L.
1976:   Stratigraphy of the Amoco 10E Murre G-67 well, Grand Banks of Newfoundland; Geological Survey of Canada, Paper 75-30, 14 p.

Jansa, L.F., Steiger, T.H., and Bradshaw, M.J.
1984:   Mesozoic carbonate deposition on the outer continental margin off Morocco; in Initial Reports of the Deep Sea Drilling Project, Volume 79, ed. K. Hinz and E.L. Winterer; United States Government Printing Office, Washington, D.C., v. 79, p. 857-891.

Johnson, G.L., Srivastava, S.P., Campsie, J., and Rasmussen, M.
1982:   Occurrences of volcanic rocks in the Labrador Sea and environs and their relation to the evolution of the Labrador Sea; in Current Research, Part B, Geological Survey of Canada, Paper 82-1B, p. 7-20.

Kaminski, M.A., Gradstein, F.M., Berggren, W.A., Geroch, S., and Beckmann, J.P.
in press: Flysch-type agglutinated foraminiferal assemblages from Trinidad: taxonomy, stratigraphy and paleobathymetry; in Proceedings, II Conference on Agglutinated Foraminifera, ed. F. Rögl and F.M. Gradstein; Austrian Geol. Bundes anstalt, Vienna, 1986.

Karlsson, W.
1984:   Sedimentology and diagenesis of Jurassic sediments offshore mid-Norway; in Petroleum Geology of the North European Margin, ed. A.M. Spencer et al., Proceedings, North European Margin Symposium, Norwegian Petroleum Society; Graham and Trotman, London, p. 389-396.

Katz, B.J.
1983: Organic geochemical character of some Deep Sea Drilling Project cores from Legs 76 and 44; in Initial Reports of the Deep Sea Drilling Project, Volume 76, ed. R.E. Sheridan et al.; United States Government Printing Office, Washington, D.C., v. 76, p. 463-469.

Keen, C.E.
1979: Thermal history and subsidence of rifted continental margins — evidence from wells on the Nova Scotian and Labrador shelves; Canadian Journal of Earth Sciences, v. 16, p. 505-522.

Keen, C.E. and Peirce, J.W.
1982: The geophysical implication of minimal Tertiary motion along Nares Strait; in Nares Strait and the Drift of Greenland: A Conflict in Plate Tectonics, ed. P.R. Dawes and J.W. Kerr; Meddelelser om Grønland, Geoscience, v. 8, p. 327-337.

Kent, D.V. and Gradstein, F.M.
1985: A Cretaceous and Jurassic geochronology; Geological Society of America Bulletin, v. 96, p. 1419-1427.

Kidd, R.B. and Hill, P.R.
1986: Sedimentation of Feni and Gardar sediment drifts; in Deep Sea Drilling Project, Leg 94, ed. R.B. Kidd, W. Ruddiman et al.; United States Government Printing Office, Washington, D.C., p. 1217-1244.

King, C.
1983: Cainozoic micropaleontological biostratigraphy of the North Sea; Report of the Institute of Geological Sciences, no. 82/7, p. 1-40.

Klitgord, K.D. and Schouten, H.
1986: Plate kinematics of the Central Atlantic; in The Western North Atlantic Region, ed. P.R. Vogt and B.E. Tucholke; Geological Society of America, The Geology of North America, v. M, p. 351-378.

Klitgord, K.D., Popenoe, P., and Schouten, H.
1984: Florida: a Jurassic transform plate boundary; Journal of Geophysical Research, v. 89, p. 7753-7772.

Lancelot, Y., Hathaway, J.C., and Hollister, C.D.
1972: Lithology of sediments from the western North Atlantic, Leg XI, Deep Sea Drilling Project; in Initial Reports of the Deep Sea Drilling Project, Volume 11, ed. C.D. Hollister et al.; United States Government Printing Office, Washington, D.C., v. 11, p. 901-950.

Larsen, H.C.
1984: Geology of the East Greenland shelf; in Petroleum Geology of the North European Margin, ed. A.M. Spencer et al., Proceedings, North European Margin Symposium, Norwegian Petroleum Society; Graham and Trotman, London, p. 329-339.

Larsen, R.M. and Skarpnes, O.
1984: Regional interpretation and hydrocarbon potential of the Traenabanken area; in Petroleum Geology of the North European Margin; Norwegian Petroleum Society (Graham and Trotman publishers), p. 217-236.

Laughton, A.S., Berggren, W.A. et al. (editors)
1972: Initial Reports of the Deep Sea Drilling Project, Volume 12; United States Government Printing Office, Washington, D.C., v.12, 1212 p.

Longoria, J.F.
1984: Mesozoic tectostratigraphic domains in East-Central Mexico; in Jurassic-Cretaceous Biochronology and Paleogeography of North America, ed. G.E. Westerman; Geological Association of Canada, Special Paper 27, p. 65-77.

MacLean, B., Williams, G.L., Sanford, B.V., Klassen, R.A., Blakeney, C., and Jennings, A.
1986: A reconnaissance study of the bedrock and surficial geology of Hudson Strait, Northwest Territories; in Current Research, Part B, Geological Survey of Canada, Paper 86-1B, p. 617-635.

Malod, J.A.
1980: La marge atlantique marocaine au Nord de Casablanca; Revue de Géologie Dynamique et de Géographie Physique, v. 22, p. 201-212.

Manspeizer, W., Puffer, J., and Cousminer, H.
1978: Separation of Morocco and eastern North America: A Triassic-Liassic record; Geological Society of America Bulletin, v. 89, p. 901-920.

Matishov, G.G.
1977: Relief, morphotectonics and principal features of the evolution of the Barents Sea Shelf; Oceanology, v. 17, p. 322-326.

Mattick, R.E., Schlee, J.S., and Bayer, K.C.
1981: The geology and hydrocarbon potential of the Georges Bank-Baltimore Canyon Trough area; in Geology of the North Atlantic Borderlands, ed. J.W. Kerr and A.J. Fergusson; Canadian Society of Petroleum Geologists, Memoir 7, p. 461-486.

McHone, J.G. and Butler, J.R.
1984: Mesozoic igneous provinces of New England and the opening of the North Atlantic Ocean; Geological Society of America Bulletin, v. 95, p. 757-765.

McIver, N.L.
1972: Cenozoic and Mesozoic stratigraphy of the Nova Scotia shelf; Canadian Journal of Earth Sciences, v. 9, p. 54-70.

McMillan, N.J.
1973: Shelves of Labrador Sea and Baffin Bay, Canada; in Future Petroleum Provinces of Canada, ed. R.G. McCrossan; Canadian Society of Petroleum Geologists, Memoir 1, p. 473-517.

McWhae, J.R.H., Elie, R., Laughton, K.C., and Gunther, P.R.
1980: Stratigraphy and petroleum prospects of the Labrador Shelf; Bulletin of Canadian Petroleum Geology, v. 28, p. 460-488.

Miller, K.G., Gradstein, F.M., and Berggren, W.A.
1982: Late Cretaceous to Early Tertiary agglutinated benthic foraminifera in the Labrador Sea; Micropaleontology, v. 28, no. 1, p. 1-30.

Miller, K.G., Mountain, G.S., and Tucholke, B.E.
1984: Oligocene glacio-eustasy and erosion on the margins of the North Atlantic; Geology, v. 1, p. 10-13.

Monbaron, M.
1981: Sédimentation, tectonique synsédimentaire et magmatisme basique: l'évolution paléogéographique et structurale de l'Atlas de Behi Millal (Maroc) au cours du Mesozoique; ses incidences sur la tectonique tertiaire; Ecologae Geologiae Helvetiae, v. 74, n. 3, p. 625-638.
1982: Un relief auté-Bathonien enfovi sur la ride du Ibel La'bbadine (Haut Atlas Central, Maroc): conséquenses pour la chronologie de l'orogenèse atlasique; Bulletin Vereinigung der Schweizerischen Petroleum-Geologen und -Ingenieure, v. 48, p. 9-25.

Montadert, L., de Charpel, O., Roberts, D., Guennoc, P., and Sibuet, J.
1979a: Northeast Atlantic passive continental margins: rifting and subsidence processes; in Deep Drilling Results in the Atlantic Ocean: Continental Margins and Paleoenvironments, ed. M. Talwani, W. Hay and W.B.F. Ryan; American Geophysical Union, Maurice Ewing Series 3, p. 154-186.

Montadert, L., Roberts, D.G. et al. (editors)
1979b: Initial reports of the Deep Sea Drilling Project, Volume 48; United States Government Printing Office, Washington, D.C., v. 48, 1183 p.

Mork, A. and Bjoroy, M.
1984: Mesozoic source rocks on Svalbard; in Petroleum Geology of the North European Margin, ed. A.M. Spencer et al., Proceedings, North European Margin Symposium, Norwegian Petroleum Society; Graham and Trotman, London, p. 371-382.

Mork, A., Knarud, R., and Korsley, D.
1982: Depositional and diagenetic environments of the Triassic and Lower Jurassic of Svalbard; Canadian Society of Petroleum Geologists, Memoir 8, p. 371-398.

Mouterde, R. and Ruget, C.
1975: Esquisse de la Paléogéographie du jurassique inférieur et moyen au Portugal; Bulletin Society Géologique de France, v. 18, p. 779-786.

Ogg, J.G., Robertson, A.H.F., and Jansa, L.F.
1983: Jurassic sedimentation history of Site 534 (western North Atlantic) and of the Atlantic-Tethys Seaway; in Initial Reports of the Deep Sea Drilling Project, Volume 76, ed. R.S. Sheridan and F.M. Gradstein; United States Government Printing Office, Washington, D.C., v. 76, p. 829-884.

Olaussen, S., Dalland, A., Gloppen, T.G., and Johannessen, E.
1984: Depositional environment and diagenesis of Jurassic reservoir sandstones in the eastern part of Troms I area; in Petroleum Geology of the North European Margin, ed. A.M. Spencer et al., Proceedings, North European Margin Symposium, Norwegian Petroleum Society; Graham and Trotman, London, p. 61-79.

Parrish, J.T. and Curtis, R.L.
1982: Atmospheric circulation, upwelling, and organic-rich rocks in the Mesozoic and Cenozoic Eras; Palaeogeography, Palaeoclimatology, and Palaeoecology, v. 40, p. 31-66.

Pe-Piper, G. and Jansa, L.F.
1986: Triassic olivine-normative diabase from Northumberland Strait, eastern Canada: implications for continental rifting; Canadian Journal of Earth Sciences, v. 23, p. 1013-1021.

Poag, C.W.
1982: Stratigraphic reference section for Georges Bank Basin depositional model for New England passive margin; Bulletin American Association of Petroleum Geologists, v. 66, p. 1021-1041.

Poore, R.Z. and Berggren, W.A.
1974: Pliocene biostratigraphy of the Labrador Sea: calcareous plankton; Journal of Foraminiferal Research, v. 4, n. 3, p. 91-108.

Pujalte, V.
1982: Transito Jurassico-Cretacico, Berriasiense, Vlanginiense, Hauteriviense y Barremiense; in El Cretacico de Espana, Universidad Complutense de Madrid, p. 51-62.

Ramalho, M.M.
1971: Contribution à l'étude micropaléontologique et stratigraphique du Jurassique supérieur et du Crétacé inférieur des environs de Lisbonne (Portugal); Servicos geologicos de Portugal, Memoria 19, 212 p.
1985: Considérations sur la biostratigraphique du Jurassique supérieur d l'Algarve Oriental (Portugal); Comunicacoes Servicos geologicos de Portugal, v. 71, p. 41-50.

Renz, O., Imlay, R., Lancelot, Y., and Ryan, W.B.F.
1975: Ammonite-rich Oxfordian limestones from the base of the continental slope off northwestern Africa; Eclogae Geologicae Helvetiae, v. 68, no. 2, p. 431-448.

Reyment, R.A. and Bengtson, P.
1985: Mid-Cretaceous events, report on results obtained from 1974-1983 by IGP Project no. 58; Publications Paleontological Institution, University of Uppsala, Special Volume 5, 132 p.

Reyre, D.
1966: Sedimentary basins of the African coast: Symposium on the Post-Cambrian Sedimentary Coastal Basins of West Africa; Association of African Geological Surveys, Paris, 304 p.

Riegraf, W.
1985: Mikrofauna, Biostratigrafie und Fazies im unteren Toarcium Südwestdeutschlands und Vergleiche mit benachbarten Gebieten; Tübingen Mikropaläont. Mitt., n. 3, 232 p.

Riegraf, W., Luterbacher, H., and Leckie, R.M.
1984: Jurassic foraminifers from the Mazagan Plateau, Deep Sea Drilling Project Site 547, Leg 79 off Morocco; in Initial Reports of the Deep Sea Drilling Project, Volume 79, ed. K. Hinz, E.L. Winterer et al.; United States Government Printing Office, Washington, D.C., v. 79, p. 671-702.

Roberts, D.G., Bachman, J., Morton, A.C., Murray, J.W., and Keene, J.B.
1984: Evolution of volcanic rifted margins: synthesis of Leg 81 results on the west margin of Rockall Plateau; in Initial Report of the Deep Sea Drilling Project, Volume 81, ed. D.G. Roberts, D. Schnitker et al.; United States Government Printing Office, Washington, D.C., v. 81, p. 883-911.

Rocha, B.R.
1977: Estudo estratigrafico e paleontologico do Jurassico do Algarve occidental; Universidade Nova De Lisboa, Ciencias da Terra, v. 2, 178 p.

Rolle, F.
1985: Late Cretaceous-Tertiary sediments offhsore central West Greenland: lithostratigraphy, sedimentary evolution and petroleum potential; Canadian Journal of Earth Sciences, v. 22, p. 1001-1019.

Royden, L., Sclater, J.G., and Von Herzen, R.P.
1980: Continental margin subsidence and heat flow: important parameters in formation of petroleum hydrocarbons; American Association of Petroleum Geologists Bulletin, v. 64, no. 2, p. 173-187.

Ryan, W.B.F. and Miller, E.L.
1981: Evidence of a carbonate platform beneath Georges Bank; Marine Geology, v. 44, p. 213-228.

Salvan, H.M.
1974: Les séries salifères du Trias marocain: caractères généraux et possibilités d'interprétation; Bulletin de la Society Géologique de France, v. 16, p. 724-731.

Schlee, J.S., Behrend, J.C., Grow, J.A., Robb, J.M., Mattik, R.E., Taylor, P.T., and Lawson, B.J.
1976: Regional geologic framework off northeastern United States; American Association of Petroleum Geologists Bulletin, v. 60, p. 926-951.

Schlee, J.S., Dillon, W.P., and Grow, J.A.
1979: Structure of the continental slope off the eastern United States; Society of Economic Paleontologists and Mineralogists, Special Publication, v. 27, p. 95-117.

Sclater, J., Hellinger, S., and Tapscott, C.
1977: The paleobathymetry of the Atlantic Ocean from the Jurassic to the Present; Journal of Geology, v. 85, p. 509-552.

Sheridan, R.E., Gradstein, F.M. et al. (editors)
1983: Initial Reports of the Deep Sea Drilling Project, Volume 76; United States Government Printing Office, Washington, D.C., v. 76, 947 p.

Smith, R.C. II, Rose, A.W., and Lanning, R.M.
1975: Geology and geochemistry of Triassic diabase in Pennsylvanian; Geological Society of America Bulletin, v. 86, p. 943-955.

Soler, R., Lopez Vilchez, J., and Riaza, C.
1981: Petroleum geology of the Bay of Biscay; in Proceedings, Secon Conference on Petroleum Geology of the Continental Shelf of Northwest Europe, ed. L.V. Illing and G.D. Hobson; Institute of Petroleum, Hoydson and Son, London, p. 474-484.

Srivastava, S.P.
1978: Evolution of the Labrador Sea and its bearing on the early evolution of the North Atlantic; Geophysical Journal of the Royal Astonomical Society, v. 52, p. 313-357.

Srivastava, S.P. and Tapscott, C.R.
1986: Plate kinematics of the North Atlantic; in The Western North Atlantic Region, ed. P.R. Vogt and B.E. Tucholke, Geological Society of America, The Geology of North America, v. M, p. 379-404.

Stam, B.
1986: Quantitative analysis of Middle and Late Jurassic foraminifera from Portugal and its implications for the Grand Banks of Newfoundland; Utrecht Micropaleontological Bulletin, no. 34, 167 p.

Stam, B., Gradstein, F.M., Lloyd, P., and Gillis, D.
1987: Algorithms for porosity and subsidence history; Computers and Geosciences, v. 13, no. 2, p. 317-349.

Steel, R.J. and Worsley, D.
1984: Svalbard's post-Caledonian strata — an atlas of sedimentational patterns and paleogeographic evolution; in Petroleum Geology of the North European Margin, ed. A.M. Spencer et al., Proceedings, North Atlantic European Margin Symposium, Norwegian Petroleum Society; Graham and Trotman, London, p. 109-135.

Stevaux, J. and Winnock, E.
1974: Les bassins du Trias et du Lias inférieur d'Aquitaine; Bulletin Service Géologique France, v. 16, no. 6, p. 679-695.

Stöcklin, J.
1984: Orogeny and Tethys evolution in the Middle-East: an appraisal of current concepts; in Proceedings, 27th International Geological Congress, Moscow, Volume 5, Tectonics of Asia; Scientific Press, Utrecht, v. 5, p. 65-84.

Surlyk, F. and Clemmenson, L.B.
1983: Rift propagation and eustacy as controlling factors during Jurassic inshore and shelf sedimentation in northern east Greenland; Sedimentary Geology, v. 34, p. 119-143.

Surlyk, F., Clemmensen, L.B., and Larsen, H.C.
1981:   Post-Paleozoic evolution of the East Greenland continental margin; in Geology of the North American Borderland, ed., J.W. Kerr, and A.J. Ferguson. Canadian Society of Petroleum Geologists, Memoir 7, p. 611-645.

Surlyk, J.
1973:   The Jurassic-Cretaceous boundary in Jameson Land, East Greenland; in The Boreal Lower Cretaceous, ed. R. Casey and P.F. Rawson; Museum de Minéralogie et de Géologie de l'Université de Copenhague, Geological Journal, Special Issue 5, p. 81-100.
1978:   Mesozoic geology and palaeogeography of Hochstetter Forland, East Greenland; Geological Society of Denmark Bulletin, v. 27, p. 73-87.
1984:   Fan-delta to submarine fan conglomerates of the Volgian-Valanginian Wollaston Foreland Group, east Greenland; in Sedimentology of Gravels and Conglomerates, ed. E.H. Koster and R.J. Steel; Canadian Society of Petroleum Geologists, Memoir 10, p. 359-382.

Talbot, M.R.
1973:   Major sedimentary cycles in the Corallian beds (Oxfordian) of southern England; Palaeogeography, Palaeoclimatology, Palaeoecology, v. 14, p. 293-317.

Talwani, M. and Eldholm, O.
1977:   Evolution of the Norwegian-Greenland Sea; Geological Society of America Bulletin, v. 88, p. 969-999.

Templeton, R.S.M.
1971:   The geology of the continental margin between Dakar and Cape Palmas; in The Geology of the East Atlantic Margin, ed. F.M. Delany; Great Britain Institute of Geological Sciences, Report 70/16, p. 47-60.

Thiede, J.
1979:   History of the North Atlantic Ocean: evolution of an asymmetric zonal paleoenvironment in a latitudinal ocean basin; in Deep Drilling Results in the Atlantic Ocean: Continental Margins and Paleoenvironment, ed. M. Talwani, W. Hay and W.B.F. Ryan; American Geophysical Union, Maurice Ewing Series 3, p. 275-296.

Thiede, J. and van Andel, T.H.
1977:   The paleoenvironment of anaerobic sediments in the Late Mesozoic South Atlantic Ocean; Earth and Planetary Science Letters, v. 33, p. 301-309.

Thierstein, H.R. and Okada, H.
1979:   The Cretaceous-Tertiary boundary event in the North Atlantic; in Initial Reports of the Deep Sea Drilling Project, Volume 43, ed. B.E. Tucholke and P.R. Vogt; United States Government Printing Office, Washington, D.C., v. 43, p. 601-617.

Thomas, F.C. and Gradstein, F.M.
198 Tertiary subsurface correlations using pyritized diatoms, offshore eastern Canada; in Current Research, Part B, Geological Survey of Canada, Paper 81-1B, p. 17-23.

Tissot, B., Demaison, G.J., and Masson, P.
1980:   Paleoenvironment and petroleum potential of the mid-Cretaceous black shales in the Atlantic basins; American Association of Petroleum Geologists Bulletin, v. 64, p. 2051-2063.

Tucholke, B.E. and Mountain, G.S.
1979:   Seismic stratigraphy, lithostratigraphy and paleosedimentation patterns in the North American basin; in Deep Drilling Results in the Atlantic Ocean: Continental Margins and Paleoenvironments, ed. M. Talwani, W. Hay and W. Ryan; American Geophysical Union, Maurice Ewing Series 3, p. 58-86.

Tucholke, B.E., Vogt, P.R. et al. (editors)
1979:   Initial Reports of the Deep Sea Drilling Project, Volume 43; United States Government Printing Office, Washington, D.C., v. 43, 1115 p.

Tyson, R.V., Wilson, R.C.L., and Downie, C.
1979:   A stratified water column environmental model for the type Kimmeridge clay; Nature, v. 277, no. 5695, p. 377-380.

Umpleby, D.C.
1979:   Geology of the Labrador Shelf; Geological Survey of Canada, Paper 79-14, p. 1-34.

Vail, P.R., Mitchum, R.M., and Thompson, S.
1977:   Seismic stratigraphy and global changes of sea level, Part 4: Global cycles of relative change of sea level; in Seismic Stratigraphy — Applications to Hydrocarbon Exploration, ed. C.E. Payton; American Association of Petroleum Geologists, Memoir 26, p. 83-97.

Van Hinte, J.E., Wise, S.W., Biart, B.N.M., Covington, J.M., Drugg, W.S., Dunn, D.A., Farre, J., Habib, D., Hart, M.B., Haggerty, J.A., Johns, M.W., Lang, T.H., Meyers, P.A., Miller, K.G., Moullade, M.R., Mountain, G.S., Muza, J.P., Ogg, J.G., Okamura, M., Sarti, M., and von Rad, U.
1985:   DSDP Site 603: first deep penetration (> 1000 m) of the continental rise along the passive margin of eastern North America; Geology, v. 13, p. 392-396.

Van Houten, F.B.
1977:   Triassic-Liassic deposits, Morocco and eastern North America: a comparison; American Association of Petroleum Geologists, v. 61, no. 1, p. 79-99.

von Rad, U. and Sarti, M.
1986:   Early Cretaceous events in the evolution of the eastern and western North Atlantic continental margins; Geologische Rundschau, v. 75, n. 1, p. 139-158.

von Rad, U., Hinz, K., Sarnthein, M. and Seibold, E. (editors)
1982:   Geology of the Northwest African Continental Margin; Springer-Verlag, Berlin, 703 p.

Wade, J.A.
1977:   Stratigraphy of Georges Bank Basin: interpreted from seismic correlation to the western Scotian Shelf; Canadian Journal of Earth Sciences, v. 14, p. 2274-2283.

Watts, A.B. and Steckler, M.S.
1981:   Subsidence and tectonics of Atlantic-type continental margins; Oceanologica Acta, v. 4, suppl. 1981, no. SP, p. 143-153.

Westermann, G.E.G.
1984:   Summary of symposium paper on Jurassic-Cretaceous biochronology and paleogeography of North America; Geological Association of Canada, Special Paper 27, p. 307-315.

Westermann, G.E.G. and Riccardi, A.C.
1976:   Middle Jurassic ammonite distribution and the affinities of the Andean faunas; Primer Congreso Geologico Chileno, v. 1, p. 23-39.

Westre, S.
1984:   The Askeladden gas find — Troms 1; in Petroleum Geology of the North European margin; Norwegian Petroleum Society (Graham and Trotman publishers), p. 33-39.

Wildi, P., Nold, M., and Uttinger, J.
1977:   La Dorsale calcire entre tetouan et Assifane (Rif interne, Maroc); Eclogae Geologicae Helvetiae, v. 70, p. 371-415.

Wildi, W.
1981:   Le Ferrysch: cône de sédimentation détrique en eau profonde à la bordure nord-ouest de l'Afrique au Jurassique moyen à supérieur (Rif externe, Maroc); Eclogae Geologicae Helvetiae, v. 74, p. 481-527.

Williams, G.D. and Stelck, C.R.
1975:   Speculations on the Cretaceous paleogeography of North America; in Cretaceous System in the Western Interior of North America, ed. W.G.E. Caldwell; Geological Association of Canada, Special Paper 13, p. 1-20.

Williamson, M.A.
1987:   Quantitative biozonation of the Late Jurassic and Early Cretaceous of the East Newfoundland Basin; Micropaleontology, v. 33, n. 1, p. 37-65.

Wilson, R.C.L.
1979:   A reconnaissance study of Upper Jurassic sediments of the Lusitanian Basin; Ciencias da Terra, Lisboa, v. 5, p. 53-84.

Wilson, R.C.L. and Exton, J.
1979:   Excursion to the Mesozoic of the Lusitanian Basin, west central Portugal; Published by the Open University, 80 p.

Wright, P.V. and Wilson, R.C.L.
1984: A carbonate submarine fan sequence from the Jurassic of Portugal; Journal of Sedimentary Petrology, v. 54, no. 2, p. 394-412.

Zakharov, Y.A., Surlyk, F., and Dalland, A.
1981: Upper Jurassic-Lower Cretaceous Buchia from Andøy, northern Norway; Geological Museum of the University of Copenhagen, Contributions to Palaeontology, no. 302, p. 260-269.

Ziegler, P.A.
1975: Geologic evolution of the North Sea and its tectonic framework; American Association of Petroleum Geologists Bulletin, v. 59, p. 1073-1097.
1978: Northwestern Europe: tectonics and basin development; Geologie en Mijnbouw, v. 57, p. 589-626.
1981: Evolution of sedimentary basins in northwest Europe; in Proceedings, Second Conference on Petroleum Geology of the Continental Shelf of Northwest Europe, ed. L.V. Illing and G.D. Hobson; Institute of Petroleum, Heydon and Son, London, p. 3-39.
1982: Geological atlas of western and central Europe; Shell Internationale Petroleum Maatschappij B.V., Elsevier Scientific, New York, 130 p.

Authors addresses

F.M. Gradstein
Atlantic Geoscience Centre
Geological Survey of Canada
Bedford Institute of Oceanography
P.O. Box 1006
Dartmouth, Nova Scotia
B2Y 4A2

L.F. Jansa
Atlantic Geoscience Centre
Geological Survey of Canada
Bedford Institute of Oceanography
P.O. Box 1006
Dartmouth, Nova Scotia
B2Y 4A2

S.P. Srivastava
Atlantic Geoscience Centre
Geological Survey of Canada
Bedford Institute of Oceanography
P.O. Box 1006
Dartmouth, Nova Scotia
B2Y 4A2

M.A. Williamson
Shell Canada Limited
P.O. Box 100, Station 'M'
Calgary, Alberta
T2P 2H5

G. Bonham Carter
Geological Survey of Canada
601 Booth Street
Ottawa, Ontario
K1A 0E8

B. Stam
Syria Shell Petroleum Development B.V.
Rawda Str. 61
P.O. Box 3663
Damascus
Syria

Chapter 9

GEODYNAMICS OF RIFTED CONTINENTAL MARGINS

Chapter 9

GEODYNAMICS OF RIFTED CONTINENTAL MARGINS

C.E. Keen and C. Beaumont

INTRODUCTION

Scope of chapter

This chapter provides a review of geodynamic models of rifted continental margins. The models have been developed to explain some aspects of the observed geological data within the framework of physical processes acting within and below the lithosphere. These processes control the evolution of the margin and may be related to the driving forces of plate tectonics. Thus, this chapter differs in its approach from others in this volume in that the emphasis is on the processes involved in the evolution of the margins and on the procedures for determining those processes, with little discussion of the observational data, except as they affect modelling. This is perhaps timely, for there are few places to which the geologist can turn for an account of these models and for assistance in determining the factors which control the evolution of major geological features. Geodynamic modelling has mostly been the preserve of the geophysicist, and one goal of this chapter is to present the topic in a manner which will be useful to the geologist and geophysicist alike.

While the emphasis is on processes, a brief summary of the observational data is also presented, highlighting those features most critical in geodynamic studies. The reader is also encouraged to look elsewhere in this volume for detailed accounts of these observations. Other pertinent reviews include those by Jansa and Wade (1975); Hinz et al. (1979); Umpleby (1979); McWhae (1981); Wade (1981); and Haworth et al. (1985). We shall use these observations on the geology and geophysics of rifted margins, offshore eastern Canada, to illustrate the capabilities of the geodynamic models, their sensitivity to changes in geological variables, and their strengths and weaknesses in predicting the observed geological phenomena. The models have global applications, and so we shall discuss other rifted continental margins where they are more illustrative of particular aspects of margin evolution.

Finally, it is impossible to describe in equal detail all the various processes which have been proposed as occurring during the evolution of rifted continental margins. Hypotheses, which do not at present yield testable quantitative model predictions, are therefore not described in detail.

Classification and evolution of continental margins

Passive or Atlantic-type continental margins are formed during continental break-up or rifting, which eventually forms divergent plate margins as new oceanic lithosphere is created between the rifted parts of the continent. Their evolution is distinct from that of convergent continental margins at which subduction of oceanic lithosphere and accretion of lithosphere onto the stable continent take place. Passive margins can be divided into two categories: rifted margins formed during divergent plate motion, and transform or sheared margins created by transform motion between the separating plates or between newly formed oceanic crust and the continent. The rifted and transform segments of a passive margin are therefore analogous to the ridge-transform segments of a mid-ocean ridge.

Passive margins contain evidence of two phases in their evolution (Fig. 9.1): a rift phase which occurs before the final break-up of the continent, and a drift or post-rift phase which occurs after the onset of sea-floor spreading adjacent to the rifted continent. Thus contemporary examples of the rift phase may be features such as the East African Rift System, or the Basin and Range Province of the western United States. The Red Sea and Gulf of California are examples of young margins, now in the early part of the post-rift phase. These relatively young margins and continental rifts provide important clues to the early evolution of older passive margins; information which models should reproduce.

Passive margins are tectonically active during the rift phase, and exhibit normal faulting, elevation changes, sedimentation, volcanism, and high heat flow. The post-rift phase is one of lithospheric cooling, thermal subsidence, and the development of major sedimentary basins. Thus passive margins can be viewed as one class of sedimentary basins, with many features in common with other basin types (Bally and Snelson, 1980). In particular, there are many cratonic sedimentary basins, like those of the North Sea, whose early development was similar to that of passive margins but where rifting stopped before

Keen, C.E. and Beaumont C.,
1990: Geodynamics of rifted continental margins, Chapter 9 in Geology of the Continental Margin of Eastern Canada, M.J. Keen and G.L. Williams (ed.); Geological Survey of Canada, Geology of Canada, no. 2, p. 391-472 (also Geological Society of America, The Geology of North America, v. I-1).

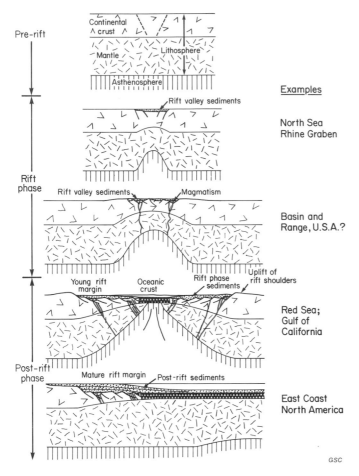

Figure 9.1. Schematic illustration of the evolution of a rifted continental margin. Examples of the evolutionary stages are given. Red areas denote volcanism and sedimentation which took place during the rift stage.

divergent margins; many of the offshore basement structures and fundamental lineaments are related to Paleozoic tectonics. Thus, the timing and geometry involved in the creation of the offshore margins is directly related to the plate tectonic history of the region (see Chapter 2). However, while plate tectonics provide a useful framework for descriptions of rifted margins, it does not address the question of the nature of the deep seated processes which control their development.

Role and nature of geodynamic models

The crustal structure and near-surface geological history of sedimentary basins occupying the rifted margins reflect the fundamental processes acting within and below the lithosphere. These processes caused the initiation of the basins and their subsequent evolution. The role of geodynamics is to provide the link between the observational data and these causative processes, and to show how the processes can explain the observed evolution of the basin.

Quantitative modelling is an integral part of most geodynamic studies. Modelling takes the form of hypothesis testing, in which one proposes that certain processes are responsible for the observed geological behaviour. The consequences of this hypothesis are then predicted by solution of the appropriate physical equations. These predictions are then tested against the observations. If there is good agreement between the predictions and the observations, the initial hypothesis may be correct. If the converse is true then the hypothesis is not valid. This is the essence of geodynamic modelling. It is important to recognize hypothetical geodynamic processes which have not been tested by the comparison of quantitative model predictions with observations. Without these rigorous tests the proposed processes remain highly speculative, and no rational basis exists for discriminating between them. Furthermore, without quantitative model studies there is no means of testing the sensitivity of the models to variations in the geological and physical processes and the values of the parameters used.

Benefits of a practical nature can also come from quantitative model predictions. This is particularly true in the assessment of petroleum generation within the sediments of these rift margin basins. Because the model predictions include the thermal and subsidence histories of the sediments, estimates can be obtained of the degree of organic maturity of strata of different ages. This may become a particularly valuable tool to those concerned with petroleum exploration in areas where little other evidence is available. An example is beneath the continental slopes off eastern Canada.

Role and nature of the lithosphere

If we are to describe lithospheric processes we must be able to describe the basic properties of the lithosphere itself. There are two aspects of the behaviour of the lithosphere which are especially important in geodynamic studies — its thermal and its mechanical behaviour.

The concept of the lithosphere as a thermal boundary layer is central to thermal aspects of geodynamic modelling. The thermal boundary layer roughly corresponds to the plate of plate tectonics, which moves over the underlying asthenosphere. The lithosphere comprises the earth's

lithospheric rupture and complete continental break-up could occur. Other kinds of basins occur in onshore and offshore eastern Canada, formed within the predominantly compressional environment during the Paleozoic evolution of the Appalachian Orogen. These basins include the Appalachian foreland basin (part of which is the Anticosti Basin within the Gulf of St. Lawrence) which was formed as a result of overthrusting during ocean closure, and the Magdalen Basin, an extensional basin probably in part formed by transcurrent motion along a sigmoidal fault system (see Chapter 2). The geodynamics of these basins are not described in this chapter. Their development is important, however, as it provides some interesting contrasts to and similarities with the development of passive margins.

The development of the rifted margins of eastern Canada can also be viewed in terms of the Wilson cycle, in which oceans are formed by rifting, grow through sea-floor spreading, and eventually close by subduction, the creation of active margins, and continental accretion and collision (see Chapters 1 and 2). The Paleozoic was a time of ocean closure and accretion, which superimposed foreland basins over ancient passive margins, remnants of which are preserved in the Appalachian Orogen. This earlier history laid the foundations for the creation of the present

crust and uppermost mantle, and heat is transferred mainly by conduction through the earth's surface. In thermal equilibrium, its thickness is defined by two isotherms; the temperature at the earth's surface and at the lithosphere-asthenosphere boundary (Sclater et al., 1980). If the thermal equilibrium is perturbed, heat flow near the earth's surface will change, and the elevation of the lithosphere may also vary because of density changes induced by thermal contraction or expansion. As the thermal anomaly decays through heat diffusion the lithosphere will return to its equilibrium state, in a time interval characterized by its thermal time constant. The main parameters which affect the thermal behaviour of the lithosphere are its equilibrium thickness, its average thermal conductivity, and the temperature at its base. Its thickness is fairly well defined for oceanic regions, but there is considerable controversy concerning its thickness in continental regions.

The sediments deposited in basins act as an external load on the lithosphere and the lithosphere responds by subsiding under this load. Thus the total subsidence of a basin is the sum of two parts: the subsidence due to thermal and other deep-seated processes, known as the tectonic subsidence; and the subsidence due to loading of the basin with sediments and water. An important part of modelling the evolution of basins is correctly describing the mechanical response of the lithosphere to these loads. This introduces the concept of the mechanical or rheological lithosphere which can support loads and transmit stress.

The mechanical properties of the lithosphere are not well understood. They are probably complex, on account of the large temperature and compositional changes which occur within it. Different parts of the lithosphere therefore respond in different ways to applied external stresses or loads (Beaumont, 1979; Goetz and Evans, 1979; Courtney and Beaumont, 1983). Temperature is a major factor in determining the rheology of the lithosphere. The cold, outer parts behave as a brittle, elastic body, whereas the warmer regions may exhibit viscous flow. The coupling between temperature and mechanical response requires the use of a coupled thermo-mechanical model to describe the behaviour of the lithosphere. The mechanical behaviour may then be time dependent, if the temperature within the lithosphere is changing. This will be described in more detail later. We note, however, that the question of how well the properties of the lithosphere can be defined is an important one in constructing geodynamic models and in assessing the validity of the model predictions.

MARGIN EVOLUTION — OBSERVATIONS ON THE EASTERN CANADIAN MARGIN

A plate tectonic overview

The Phanerozoic plate tectonic history of offshore eastern Canadian is one of plate divergence in the late Precambrian-early Paleozoic, followed by ocean closure, subduction and accretion throughout the rest of the Paleozoic. Paleozoic convergent tectonics led to the development of the Appalachian Orogen (Williams, 1979). The Mesozoic-Cenozoic was a time of renewed plate divergence which saw the creation of the present rifted and transform margins off eastern Canada. The margins north of the Appalachians, off Labrador and Baffin Island, were tectonically inactive during the Paleozoic, and the present margins were formed within the Precambrian craton.

Vestiges of the early Paleozoic passive margin, which lay west of the Iapetus Ocean, are preserved on the western edge of the orogen. This margin formed within crust of the Precambrian Grenville Province. Overthrusting and westward transport of material led to the destruction of that margin during ocean closure in the middle Ordovician (Williams and Stevens, 1974). This was accompanied and followed by the accretion of several distinct terranes or zones, now situated east of the ancient passive margin (Williams and Hatcher, 1983). Terrane accretion progressed in several pulses until the late Paleozoic, but the plate tectonic setting of the terranes with respect to North America is unclear.

The formation of rift basins in the Triassic signalled the beginning of a new phase of ocean opening. Triassic rifting occurred on the present Scotian margin and on the Grand Banks due to incipient plate motions between Africa and North America. This created a rifted margin off Nova Scotia, and a transform margin south of the Grand Banks. Final separation between Africa and Nova Scotia occurred in the early Middle Jurassic, but transform motion continued until the mid Cretaceous (Fig. 9.2; Haworth and Keen, 1979). In mid-Cretaceous time the separation of Iberia and North America formed the margin east of the Grand Banks (Keen et al., 1977; Tucholke and Ludwig, 1982). Early Cretaceous rifting, which accompanied this event, was also observed beneath the margins farther north, but rifting of these margins was not complete until Late Cretaceous. Plate motions between North America and Europe created the margins northeast of Newfoundland, and motion between Greenland and North America was responsible for the margins of the Labrador Sea and Baffin Bay (Srivastava, 1978). Thus, contemporary margins off eastern Canada exhibit a variety of ages from Middle Jurassic to Late Cretaceous, and a diversity in geological and geomorphological characteristics as a result of the plate tectonic motions that produced them.

Contemporary margins off eastern Canada

Architecture and development of the sedimentary basins

The sedimentary basins, which now occupy the margins off eastern Canada, form a chain a depocentres strung latitudinally along the margins (see Chapters 2, 4, 5, 6 and 7). Between the basins lie platforms, regions in which the sediment cover is relatively thin. The boundaries between basins and platforms commonly coincide with landward prolongations of oceanic transform faults and also with older continental lineaments. The Dover Fault-Charlie-Gibbs Fracture Zone which marks the northern edge of the Orphan Basin and the Grenville Front-Cartwright Fracture Zone are good examples of the nature of some of these boundaries (Fig. 9.2, 9.3, 2.2).

The landward side of the basins is usually marked by a hinge zone, seaward of which the thickness of sediments increases rapidly. Landward of the hinge zone a thin sedimentary section commonly onlaps the continental interior as with the Scotian Basin. On some margins, however, this inner region is uplifted. For example, the hinge zone of the Labrador and Baffin Island margins lies beneath the inner shelf, inland of which a steep, faulted coastline exhibits uplifts of 500 to 800 m (see Chapter 7).

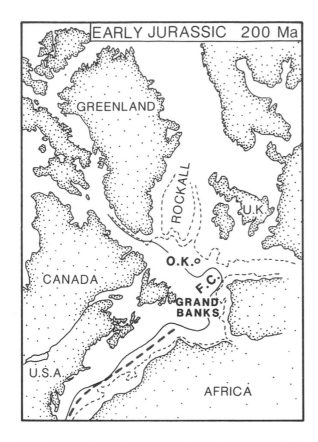

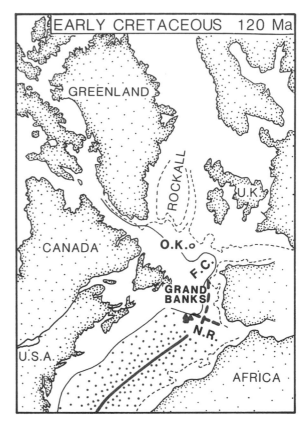

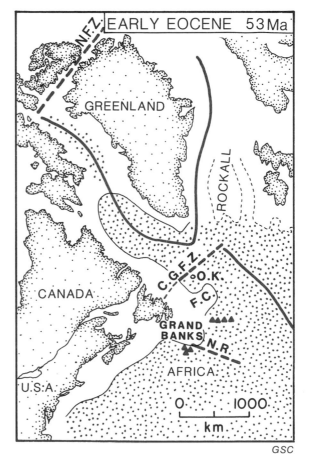

GSC

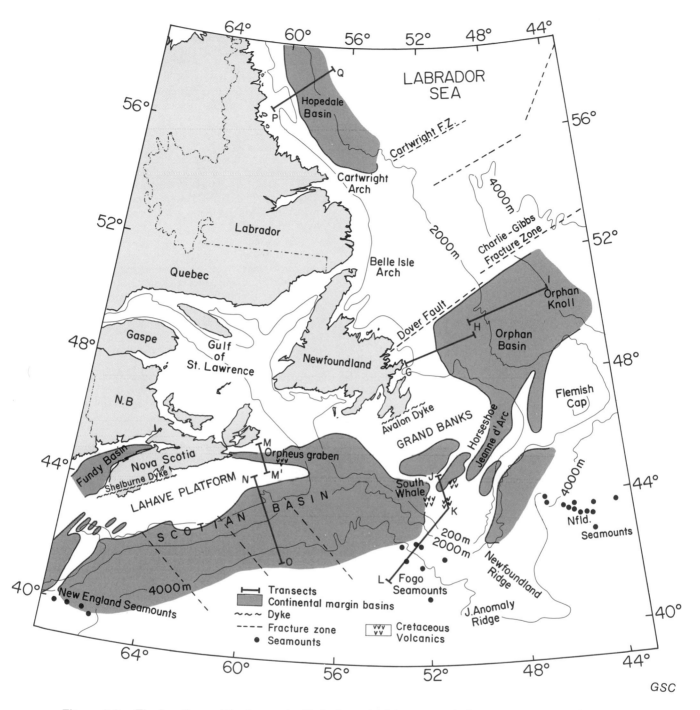

Figure 9.3. The locations of the transects, Early Jurassic dykes, oceanic fracture zones near the margins, and Cretaceous volcanism are shown. The transects are shown in Figure 9.5.

Figure 9.2. A sketch of 4 stages of opening of the Atlantic Ocean. Red lines denote active mid-ocean ridges. Red stipple indicates areas of oceanic crust. Triangles are seamounts. Dashed red lines represent fracture zones. The age of each stage is indicated. The abbreviations are: O.K. = Orphan Knoll; F.C. = Flemish Cap; N.R. = Newfoundland Ridge; N.F.Z. = Nares Strait Fracture Zone; and C.G.F.Z. = Charlie-Gibbs Fracture Zone.

The seaward edge of the basins is not sharply defined; it simply merges with the deep sea sediments of the oceanic basins (King and Young, 1977; Jansa et al., 1979). There are exceptions to this. The most prominent of these are the continental fragments of Orphan Knoll and Flemish Cap (Fig. 9.3), which are continental basement highs situated between the basins and oceanic crust. More subdued outer basement highs (Scheupbach and Vail, 1980) may also occur along some segments of rifted continental margins, but are not well defined by the data.

The basement rocks of the sedimentary basins in places exhibit normal faulting. This is particularly clear beneath the Labrador margin (McWhae, 1981), beneath Orphan Basin (Grant, 1975), and beneath Georges Bank Basin (Fig. 2.3), south of Nova Scotia (Klitgord et al., 1982). These faults form an en-echelon pattern, down-thrown towards the ocean, and are now covered by sediments. In contrast, the sedimentary basins on the Grand Banks are elongate, fault bounded grabens which are isolated from each other, except for a thin cover of upper Mesozoic and Cenozoic sediments (Jansa and Wade, 1975). Other regions, including the platforms, exhibit little evidence of extensive normal faulting. Some faults, however, may be too deeply buried by sediments to be detected, and this may be true of much of the Scotian Basin.

The geometry of the normal faults below their contact with the overlying sediments is unknown. They may be listric faults which sole out along horizontal detachment zones and thus indicate thinning of the upper crust (Montadert et al., 1979). However, this has yet to be demonstrated.

Volcanism is a common occurrence during the rift stage of margin evolution. Early Jurassic volcanic rocks are found near the coasts of Nova Scotia and eastern Newfoundland, and may occur beneath the sediments of the offshore basins (Haworth and Keen, 1979). Northeast of Newfoundland, a granite aplite of Jurassic age has been sampled, and along the adjacent coast lamphropyre dykes and mafic intrusions have been described (Strong and Harris, 1974). All are Jurassic. Basalts were subaerially extruded on the Labrador margin during rifting in the Early Cretaceous (Umpleby, 1979; see Chapter 7). This volcanism appears to have been most intense early in the rift phase. The volcanism may have continued with equal intensity in later phases but in regions now overlain by thick sedimentary sequences. Farther north, the Paleocene volcanism in the Davis Strait region may herald the onset of seafloor spreading in Baffin Bay (Srivastava et al., 1981).

Post-rift volcanism has occurred on the Grand Banks and in the Orpheus Graben on the Scotiann margin (Gradstein et al., 1977; Jansa and Pe-Piper, 1985). This volcanism is of Early to mid-Cretaceous age, synchronous with the rift phase volcanism of the Labrador margin. Extensive volcanism on oceanic crust encircles the southeastern Grand Banks (Fig. 9.3). These volcanic features include the Fogo Seamounts, the Newfoundland Seamounts, the Newfoundland Ridge, and the J-Anomaly Ridge (Keen et al., 1977; Sullivan and Keen, 1978; Tucholke and Ludwig, 1982).

Both syn-rift and post-rift sediments fill the deep basins. The syn-rift sediments are nonmarine or shallow marine deposits. For example, on the Scotian margin the oldest sediments are nonmarine Triassic redbeds, which are generally found between fault blocks. These are overlain by shallow marine sediments of Late Triassic and Early Jurassic age, including extensive salt deposits (Argo Formation) and carbonates (Jansa and Wade, 1975; Wade, 1981; Jansa et al., 1980; Wade, 1981). North of the Grand Banks, most of the syn-rift deposits comprise both nonmarine and shallow marine, clastic sediments (Umpleby, 1979).

The duration of the rift phase can be estimated from the ages of the syn-rift volcanic rocks and sediments. Rifting was a lengthy process off Labrador and northeastern Newfoundland, extending over 40 to 60 Ma (see Chapters 6 and 7). Off Nova Scotia the duration of rifting was about 20 to 30 Ma. The Grand Banks is anomalous because of the variety of plate motions which affected the region over about 90 Ma.

The transition from syn-rift to post-rift sediments is usually marked by a change in depositional environment and sometimes by a regional unconformity, commonly called the "break-up unconformity". On the Labrador margin, the margin northeast of Newfoundland, and the Grand Banks the break-up unconformity is well developed. Off Nova Scotia there is no unconformity (but see Chapter 4), but there is a change in depositional environment reflecting deeper water and more open marine conditions at the beginning of the post-rift phase. This corresponds to the change from salt to carbonate deposition. On the margins north of the Grand Banks, the break-up unconformity is of mid to late Cretaceous age, and separates nonmarine and shallow marine, syn-rift sediments from younger deepwater sediments.

It is not clear that these break-up unconformities can always be associated with tectonic uplift and erosion late in the rift phase. Eustatic sea-level changes could equally well be responsible. However, when viewed within a global perspective, the random age distribution and frequency of these events on passive margins suggest that they cannot all be attributed to eustatic sea level effects alone; at least some must have a regional tectonic origin (Falvey and Middleton, 1981).

Sediments associated with the post-rift phase were generally deposited in a marine environment. On the Scotian margin the early post-rift sediments are mainly carbonates. These formed carbonate banks and build-ups whose growth was controlled by the balance between carbonate supply, margin subsidence, and sea-level changes (Jansa, 1981). These Jurassic and lower Cretaceous carbonates now mark the position of the paleo-shelf edge. In the late Jurassic and early Cretaceous, the carbonate banks were drowned by an increased influx of clastic sediments, and the latter dominate the later sedimentary history of the Scotian margin. On both the Scotian margin and the Grand Banks, salt diapirism has in places deformed these post-rift sediments. Diapirism is particularly intense within the Diapiric Slope Province at the foot of the Scotian Slope (Fig. 2.3). North of the Grand Banks the post-rift sediments are mainly clastic (Umpleby, 1979).

In this brief discussion of syn- and post-rift sedimentation, the Grand Banks segment of the margin has been largely ignored because of the complexity of that region, resulting in part from the multiple plate tectonic events which affected it. The history of sedimentation in this region is described in detail elsewhere in Chapter 6.

The post-rift subsidence history of the margins off Labrador and Nova Scotia shows a general decrease in the rate of subsidence since rifting ended. The amount of subsidence increases approximately linearly with $\sqrt{\text{time}}$ during the first 60 Ma or so following break-up, and follows an exponentially decreasing path thereafter (Fig. 9.4; Keen 1979; Royden and Keen, 1980). The data are somewhat "noisy", particularly those for the Labrador margin. This may be caused by the variable paleowater depths which have been inferred from the faunal data (Gradstein and Williams, 1976, 1981) and other modifying factors discussed later in this chapter. The syn-rift subsidence of the margins is not well known except on the Labrador Shelf where some deep wells have sampled the complete sedimentary section down to basement. Both syn- and post-rift subsidence histories are illustrated in Figure 9.4. The syn-rift subsidence is most rapid early in the rift phase. Similar behaviour has been described for the Australian margins (Falvey and Middleton, 1981).

Geophysical characteristics of the rifted margins

Crustal seismic refraction measurements have been made along a number of transects of the margins, from continental to oceanic crust (Keen and Keen, 1974; Jackson et al., 1975; Keen et al., 1975; Keen and Hyndman, 1979; Keen and Barrett, 1981; Haworth et al., 1985; see Chapter 2). Interpretations of the crustal structure across the margins are shown in Figure 9.5. There are several aspects of these cross-sections which require discussion:

1) The crystalline continental crust thins across the rifted margins, by factors of 2 to 4 over horizontal distances of 100 to 400 km. This is the most prevalent and conspicuous feature of the crustal structure at many rifted margins. Thinning appears to be most intense beneath the regions of greatest subsidence. Hence, the thinnest continental crust is normally found near the ocean-continent boundary, but exceptions do occur in regions such as the Orphan Basin (Fig. 9.5).

2) The lowermost crust beneath the rifted margins appears to consist of a layer with high seismic P wave velocities of about 7.2 to 7.4 km/s. This layer is about 5 to 10 km thick and lies directly above the crust-mantle boundary. Off eastern Canada, this layer has been observed beneath the rifted margins of Labrador, northeast Newfoundland, and Nova Scotia. It has also been observed at other rifted margins, off the eastern United States (LASE Study Group, 1986); off Australia (Falvey and Middleton, 1981), and off northwest Africa (Goldflam et al., 1980). This lower crustal layer may be localized beneath the ocean-continent boundary, as suggested by the Nova Scotian margin transect (Fig. 9.5), but in some regions (e.g. northeast of Newfoundland) the lateral extent of this layer beneath the continent is uncertain.

3) The nature and width of the ocean-continent transition region is still unclear. In part this ambiguity stems from the lack of a clear definition of this term. Some have suggested that the transition includes the entire region underlain by thinned continental crust, sometimes called "rift stage" crust, extending from the

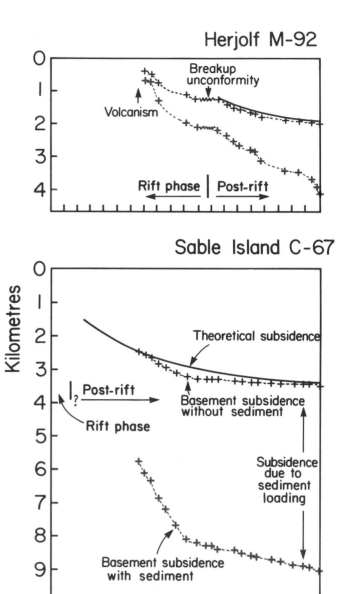

Figure 9.4. Subsidence curves for two wells, Herjolf M-92 in Hopedale Basin, Labrador margin and Sable Island C-67, Scotian Basin. The crosses are observations derived from biostratigraphic control. Two curves are shown for each well: the subsidence of basement including that due to sediment loading (red), and the subsidence with the effects of sediment loading removed (black). For the latter, a computed subsidence curve is shown for comparison (solid line), which assumes that the post-rift subsidence is due to lithospheric cooling, with a thermal time constant of 62 Ma. The position of the breakup unconformity and the timing of volcanism are shown for the Herjolf M-92 well.

hinge zone to the region where oceanic crust can be defined (e.g. Hutchinson et al., 1983). Others, including the authors, prefer to limit the definition to a generally

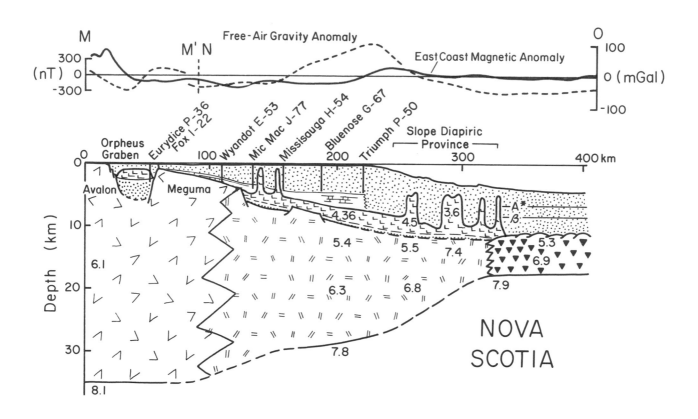

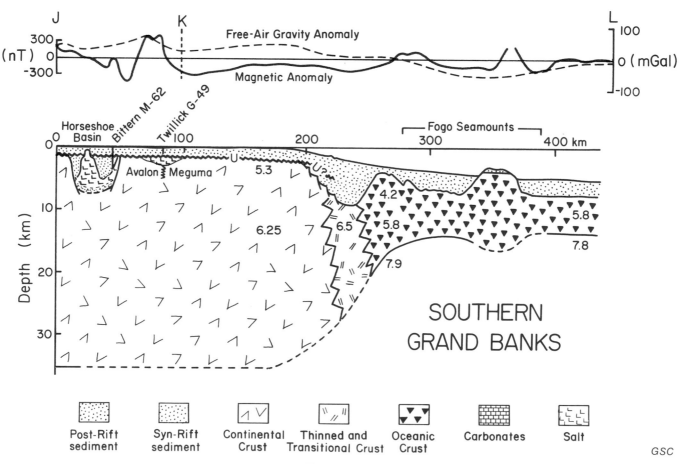

Post-Rift sediment   Syn-Rift sediment   Continental Crust   Thinned and Transitional Crust   Oceanic Crust   Carbonates   Salt

GSC

Figure 9.5a

Figure 9.5b

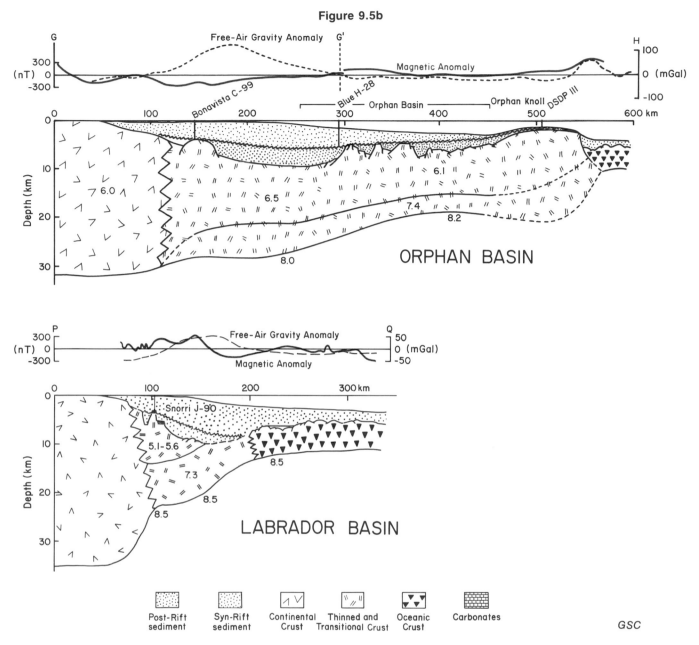

Post-Rift sediment   Syn-Rift sediment   Continental Crust   Thinned and Transitional Crust   Oceanic Crust   Carbonates

GSC

Figure 9.5. Four transects of the crustal structure of the margins (Fig. 9.3) with corresponding gravity and magnetic anomalies. Numbers on transects are seismic velocities in kilometres/second. Deep wells near the transects have been projected onto the transect and are indicated by vertical black lines with well names above. Subhorizontal wavy lines (red) mark breakup unconformities in the sedimentary section such as the "U" unconformity in transect JL. Dashed lines indicated uncertainty in depth to a boundary.

narrower region, in which crustal properties suggest that the crust has not only been thinned but also extensively intruded and possibly modified by metamorphism during rifting.

The basic problem in defining the transition zone is that seismic velocities and other geophysical signatures do not yield a unique interpretation. Deep penetration, high resolution seismic data which could discriminate between normal faults in continental basement and the characteristic diffraction pattern produced by the oceanic basement reflector, are a highly desireable future addition to present techniques.

Some of the implications of the thinned crust and the high velocity lower crustal layer need further discussion. First, we note that it is unlikely that the thinning is caused mainly by sub-aerial erosion, because more than 15 km of crust has gone. While there is evidence of some erosion during rifting, remnants of older sediments and other near surface crustal rocks which

401

predate rifting have been sampled above the thinned regions. It is therefore unlikely that erosion can account for these observations; this suggests that the crust is either thinned from below, or thinned by stretching.

The high velocity lower crustal layer is subject to a variety of interpretations. In many cases it may also occur beneath the adjacent continent, and so may not be directly related to the process of margin development. In other regions, such as off Nova Scotia, it is not found beneath the continent. In such regions the layer has been interpreted either to reflect a phase change from greenschist to amphibolite facies (Falvey, 1974), or to reflect continental crust which has been underplated or intruded by basaltic magma during rifting (Keen et al., 1975; van der Linden, 1975; Sheridan et al., 1979; Haworth et al., 1985).

The free air gravity anomalies across the margins exhibit a characteristic signature, consisting of a positive anomaly over the outer continental shelf and a negative anomaly near the foot of the continental slope (Fig. 9.5, 9.6). There is a correlation between margins with the largest positive gravity anomalies and those with the deepest sedimentary basins. Platform regions exhibit relatively small gravity anomalies. The gravity anomalies must be explained in terms of the density distribution across the margin and the degree of regional, as opposed to local, isostatic support of these density variations.

The gravity field, then, mimics to some degree the lateral dissection of the margins into basins and platforms. At the boundary between platforms and basins there is commonly a disruption in the trend and amplitude of the anomaly pattern (see Chapter 2). This is clearly illustrated by the gravity near the Dover Fault-Charlie-Gibbs Fracture Zone and at the boundary between the LaHave Platform and Scotian Basin (Fig. 9.6). These disruptions may reflect fundamental changes at depth, but so far they have not been studied in a quantitative manner.

The magnetic anomaly patterns (Chapter 2) are in general more difficult to interpret. There are several outstanding features which deserve mention here. The East Coast Magnetic Anomaly (ECMA) is a prominent, positive magnetic lineament which runs sub-parallel to the Scotian margin and off the margin of the United States to the south (Klitgord and Berhendt, 1979). This anomaly is believed by many to mark the ocean-continent transition (e.g. Emery et al., 1970; Keen et al., 1975). An analogous magnetic feature was observed northeast of Newfoundland (Fenwick et al., 1968) but does not occur on other margins, for reasons which are unclear at present.

There are offsets in the trend of the East Coast Magnetic Anomaly which coincide with those in the gravity field. These may mark the locations of oceanic fracture zones which can be traced into the continental margin and which commonly coincide with basin-platform boundaries. Thus both magnetic and gravity anomalies are useful for defining tectonic boundaries and lineaments on the margins.

Seaward of the Labrador and Scotian margins lie regions of subdued magnetic anomalies: the magnetic quiet zones. Some, like that off Nova Scotia, can be explained by an absence of magnetic reversals during the period of sea-floor spreading in the region (Barrett and Keen, 1976). Others, like that off Labrador, may result from the great depth to the magnetic basement, from an overprinting of the magnetic anomalies by later volcanism, or from high sedimentation rates which led to intrusion rather than extrusion of basaltic magma. Whatever the cause, these quiet zones obscure the early sea-floor spreading history adjacent to the margins.

The present heat flow through the margins has only been measured off Nova Scotia (Lewis and Hyndman, 1976; Hyndman et al., 1979; Reiter and Jessop, 1985). Heat flow on the continental shelf has been measured using bottom-hole temperatures logged in deep wells. The accuracy of these measurements is uncertain. Generally the heat flow is compatible with that measured on mainland Nova Scotia, about 60 ± 14 mW/m^2, and is fairly uniform across the margin to the continental rise. The heat flow is comparable to that found in other continental regions of late Paleozoic age (Sclater et al., 1980). Considerable, apparently random, variation were observed, but how much was due to errors in measurement is uncertain. Other sources of variation may include fluid migration and the presence of salt diapirs (Lewis and Hyndman, 1976; Hyndman et al., 1979; Keen, 1983).

MODELS

Conceptual models of rifting

The observations, briefly reviewed in the preceding section, show that the first order features of rifted margins are thinned crust, brittle, near-surface extensional faulting, and both syn- and post-rift subsidence. In contrast, transform margins exhibit little thinning of the continental crust adjacent to the ocean basin (see Chapter 2). Given these characteristics, what conceptual models offer an explanation? Many fundamentally different hypotheses concerning deep seated lithospheric processes have been offered. These are summarized in Figure 9.7 and are briefly reviewed here.

Stretching from stress within the lithosphere

Stretching of the lithosphere during rifting results in lithospheric thinning and upwelling of hot asthenosphere below the thinned region (Fig. 9.7A; McKenzie, 1978; Royden and Keen, 1980; Beaumont et al., 1982a; LePichon et al., 1982; Sawyer et al., 1982a,b; Steckler and Watts, 1982). There is normally an initial subsidence during rifting to accommodate isostatic adjustment caused by the redistribution of mass. This subsidence will occur provided that the ratio of initial crustal thickness to initial lithospheric thickness is greater than about 0.15; otherwise uplift will occur. After rifting has ceased there will be further subsidence as the lithosphere cools and returns to thermal equilibrium. It is generally assumed in the stretching model that the lithosphere will extend by a factor ß and that this will produce thinning of the lithosphere by ß (Fig. 9.8). If values of ß can be determined from observational data, then the thermal and subsidence histories may be quantitatively predicted.

Thermal and mechanical convective thinning

Rifting the lithosphere by thinning it from below, or active rifting, requires the presence of an upwelling convective

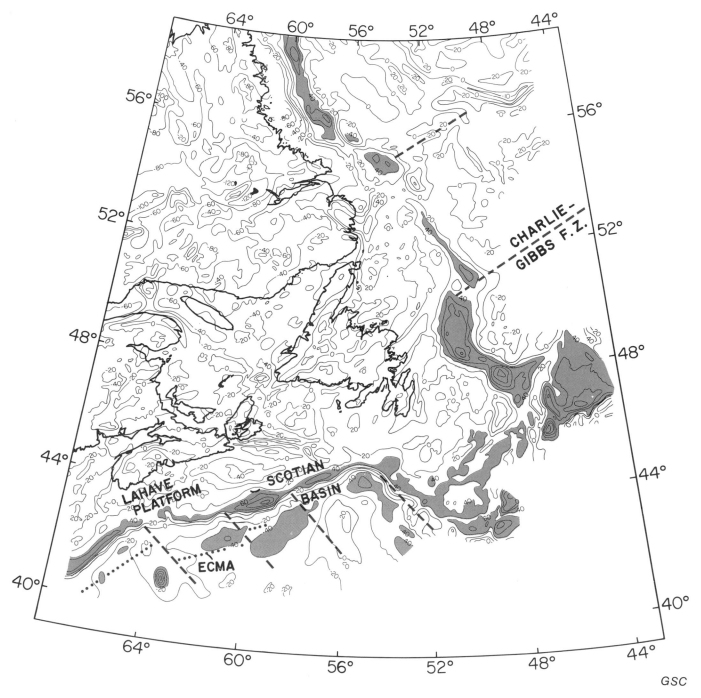

Figure 9.6. Free-air gravity anomaly map, with a 20 mGal contour interval (after Map 1708A, in pocket). Shelf edge gravity anomalies above 40 mGal are shaded in red. Gravity lows below -40 mGal near the foot of the slope are shown in grey tone. Fracture zones, inferred from gravity and magnetic data, are shown as red dashed lines. The East Coast Magnetic Anomaly (ECMA) is shown as a red dotted line.

plume at the base of the lithosphere (Sengor and Burke, 1978; Spohn and Schubert, 1982). The thinning process occurs either as a result of increased heat input at the base of the lithosphere, which displaces the solidus (Fig. 9.7B), or mechanical thinning in which material from the base of the lithosphere is removed by the flow. The former mechanism has been quantitatively described by Spohn and Schubert (1982) and the latter by Keen (in press). The thinning process causes uplift by as much as several kilometres during rifting but, unlike the stretching process, there will be little extension of the near-surface basement rocks, although faulting may occur. The base of the lithosphere must rise to the crust-mantle boundary before crustal thickness can be reduced by this process.

Metamorphic phase changes

Metamorphic phase changes in the lower crust to more dense rock types have been suggested to account for the subsidence observed on most margins (Falvey, 1974; Artyushkov, 1981; Falvey and Middleton, 1981; Artyushkov and Sobolev, 1982; Neugebauer and Spohn, 1982). Falvey (1974) suggested that a change from greenschist to amphibolite facies occurs (Fig. 9.7,C-1) with an associated density increase of about 10% and a seismic velocity increase from about 6.5 to 7.3 km/s. In contrast, Artyushkov (1981) suggested that the basalt-eclogite phase change occurs in the lower "basaltic" crust (Fig. 9.7,C-2) and that the heavy eclogite breaks away from the upper crust and sinks through the sub-crustal lithosphere. This leaves a thinned crust which will subside because of the replacement of the lower crust by more dense mantle.

Of these mechanisms, stretching of the lithosphere during rifting has received the most attention and quantitative models of the subsidence and thermal histories of several rifted margins based on this hypothesis have been presented (Royden and Keen, 1980; Royden et al., 1980; LePichon and Sibuet, 1981; Beaumont et al., 1982a; Sawyer et al., 1982a, b; Steckler and Watts, 1982). The advantage of this model is that it explains a number of the important properties of rifted margins. The alternatives to stretching, thinning of the lithosphere from below, and phase changes are attractive in some respects. We note, however, that phase changes require an increased geothermal gradient in the lithosphere, and so must be combined with either the stretching or the active rifting processes. The main objection to both of the mechanisms involving phase changes is that they assume fairly uniform initial compositions for the lower continental crust. It is difficult to imagine that this is a valid assumption, given the variety of ages and of pre-rift tectonic activity characterizing the regions now forming the margins. Furthermore, the time required to complete these phase transitions is not well known. This time may be of the order of 100 Ma for the gabbro-eclogite transformation (Neugebauer and Spohn, 1982); and this is too long to explain the observations on rifted margins.

There are also second order processes which may occur at passive margins. These may be important but require a significant role to be played by either stretching or convective thinning mechanisms. These are discussed in the following sections.

Gravity induced ductile flow in the lower crust

Ductile flow of the lower continental crust toward the ocean may occur during and following continental break-up (Bott, 1971, 1982; Bott and Dean, 1972). The flow (Fig. 9.7D) occurs as a result of hydrostatic pressure differences acting across the ocean-continent transition (Vetter and Meisner, 1979). This mechanism will thin the continental crust beneath the margin and cause subsidence, but it requires a pre-existing rift zone or rifted margin.

Partial melting

Partial melting and segregation of basaltic magma may occur as as result of the reduced pressures within the upwelling asthenosphere (Beaumont et al., 1982a; Foucher et al., 1982). This magma may migrate to crustal levels and intrude or underplate the continental crust, or alternatively may be retained in the asthenosphere, to be released at the time of final continental break-up.

Erosion of the upper crust

If uplift of a margin occurs during rifting, there may be substantial erosion of the upper crust. This will thin the crust and eventually allow the margin to subside below sea level (Sleep, 1971).

The processes causing rifting and break-up are probably closely related to the driving forces of plate tectonics. The importance of either stretching or convection below the lithosphere is directly analogous to the contributions of two possible classes of driving forces for plate tectonics. One class is concerned with stresses generated and acting within the plates themselves, and this is equivalent to stretching at continental margins. The other group is concerned with various forms of convection in the mantle below the lithosphere, directly analogous to the active rifting model. Ultimately, the forces that drive plate tectonics are almost certainly convective in origin, but it is important to determine whether "in plate" or "sub-plate" forces dominate in a rift zone.

Stretching models

The uniform extension model

Kinematic stretching models are the only ones for which we have a more-or-less complete set of model predictions to compare with observations. They assume that unspecified "far field" forces are responsible for stretching and necking of the lithosphere and attempt to represent the consequences of this extension, without properly understanding the physics of the process. Thus, it is assumed that the response of the lithosphere to extensional forces can be represented by a number of parameters.

The simplest and most generally applied kinematic model is the uniform extension model first described by McKenzie (1978). That model (Fig. 9.8, 9.9) involves equal stretching of both the crust and sub-crustal lithosphere by a factor ß which may vary laterally, across the stretched region. If the mass of the lithosphere is conserved, all thicknesses will also thin by ß. Asthenosphere, at constant temperature (Tm) is assumed to rise passively into space created below the thinned region. If this process is adiabatic, so that no heat is lost during stretching, the geothermal gradient within the lithosphere and the surface heat flow also increase by ß. This model has been termed the instantaneous stretching model because of the assumption that there is no heat loss. In a geological context, this implies that rifting is rapid compared to the time for significant cooling to occur.

Surface elevation changes during stretching result from the isostatic response caused by the replacement of the lower lithosphere by asthenosphere and of the crust by mantle. The replacement of low density crust by more dense mantle will cause subsidence of the thinned region. The replacement of cool mantle lithosphere by hotter, less dense asthenosphere will cause uplift. These two effects are therefore opposite in sign, and when combined may produce uplift or subsidence, depending on the parameter values used for quantities such as crust and mantle densities, and initial crustal and lithospheric thicknesses. The

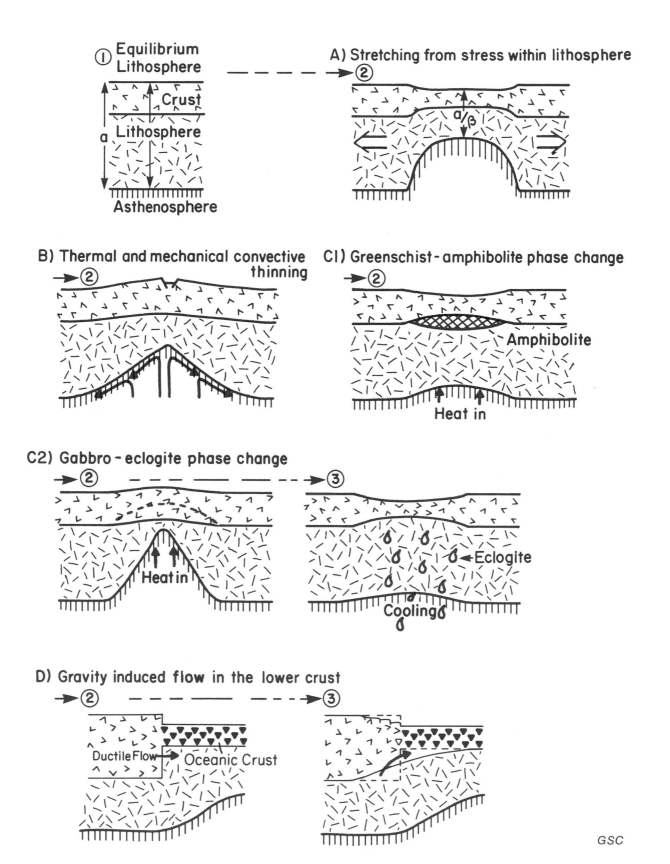

Figure 9.7. Some proposed models of rifting. Circled numbers indicate the stage of the process: stage 1 refers to an equilibrium state before rifting; stage 2 illustrates the rifting process; stage 3 in models C2 and D shows the effects late in the rift stage or early in the post-rift stage. The most important processes are highlighted in red.

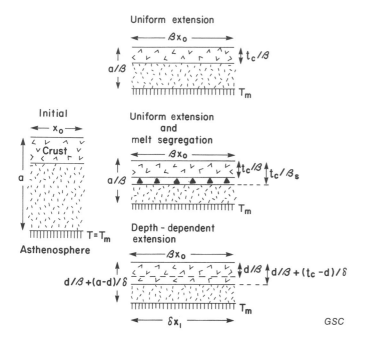

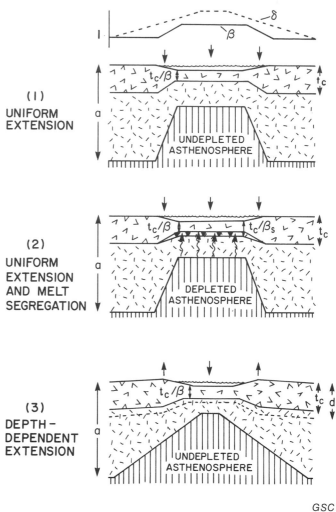

Figure 9.8. One-dimensional extension models. The initial lithospheric structure is shown on the left. In the uniform extension model, the entire lithosphere is extended from an initial width (x_o) to βx_o. The uniform extension and melt segregation model also involves extension by β, but the crust is thickened by the addition of basaltic material (solid triangles), for a final thickness of t_c/β_s. Depth-dependent extension involves different amounts of extension in the upper and lower parts of the lithosphere, separated at depth d. Above d the lithosphere is extended by β, below d by δ.

Figure 9.9. Two-dimensional extension models, showing the variation in extension across the rift zone. The initial subsidence or uplift is shown and the sense of vertical motion indicated by arrows. The process of melt migration and addition to the continental crust is indicated by wavy arrows. The thickness of the melt added to the crust is indicated by inverted solid triangles. The models are discussed in more detail in the text.

change in surface elevation at the time of stretching is known as the *initial subsidence* and is usually computed assuming an Airy, or local, isostatic compensation process. Most equations for describing subsidence and thermal history can be found in Table 9.6.

After stretching is complete, the lithosphere cools by conduction toward its thermal equilibrium state. This results in thermal contraction and post-rift subsidence, known as the *thermal subsidence* (S_c). Subsidence increases linearly versus $\sqrt{time}$ during the first thermal time constant following stretching, and thereafter exhibits an exponentially decreasing rate. This time dependence is typical of any diffusively cooling layer. The thermal time constant is a useful parameter for scaling the time dependent processes of the post-rift phase, and can be expressed as $\tau = a^2/\pi^2 k$, where a is the equilibrium thickness of the lithosphere, and k is its thermal diffusivity. The *tectonic subsidence*, S_T, is the sum of S_I and S_c. It is the total subsidence due to the rifting process.

The post-rift cooling can be computed by solving the equation for heat diffusion in a layer with constant temperatures on its upper and lower boundaries (Fig. 9.8) and with the initial condition being the temperature distribution after stretching (McKenzie, 1978). Thermal contraction and thus thermal subsidence can be found from the resulting temperature as a function of depth and time (see Table 9.6).

During the post-rift cooling phase lithospheric thickness increases as its base — thermally defined — deepens and returns to equilibrium. The crust, which was also thinned by stretching, however, remains thinned because its properties are determined by composition, not temperature. This is important because it allows us to estimate ß from present variations of crustal thickness across the margins.

Both initial and thermal subsidence, as well as the temperature distribution within the lithosphere, depend on the initial properties of the lithosphere and on the value of ß. All model predictions are dependent on these parameter values. Any subsidence predicted by the model will also be amplified by the sediment and water load.

If stretching is slow and occurs over times comparable with the thermal time constant of the lithosphere, heat will be lost by conductive cooling during extension and the 'instantaneous' stretching model will not be applicable. Jarvis and McKenzie (1980) investigated how the model predictions will change if finite rates of extension are specified. The effect is to increase the initial subsidence by conductive cooling during stretching and to decrease correspondingly the post-rift thermal subsidence, so that the total subsidence remains the same. Similarly, the surface heat flow during rifting will decrease for slow extension by comparison with that predicted by the instantaneous stretching model. The instantaneous stretching model remains a good approximation to the finite extension rate model unless the duration of rifting approaches the thermal time constant, about 60 Ma for typical lithosphere 125 km thick.

Another model (Royden et al., 1980) emphasizes the brittle cracking of the lithosphere, as opposed to necking, and the intrusion of magma into the cracks as the lithosphere is stretched. The predictions of this model are similar to those of the uniform stretching model except that the crust is not thinned. Only during rifting and in the first 10 Ma or so thereafter are near surface temperatures and heat flow greater than those of the corresponding uniform stretching model, because magma at the temperature of the asthenosphere reaches the surface. The additional heat input, however, is soon lost by conductive cooling.

This model, which considers the lithosphere to respond to extensional forces by brittle failure, and the stretching model in which the lithosphere's response is one of ductile necking, may be considered as end members of a range of possible kinematic models that describe the behaviour of the lithosphere when stretched.

We do not use the intrusion model in studies of rifted margins, but instead have developed variations of the uniform stretching model which better represent particular features of margin development. Some aspects of these models, however, do reflect the concepts embodied in the intrusion model. Two models, in addition to the uniform, instantaneous stretching model, have been applied in these continental margin studies. They are the uniform extension-melt segregation model and the depth dependent extension model. Like the uniform extension model they both assume rifting is the response of the lithosphere to far field extensional forces.

The uniform extension and melt segregation model

The uniform extension and melt segregation model (Fig. 9.8-9.10) is similar to the uniform extension model, except that it allows for the effects of partial melting in the asthenosphere, and the segregation and migration of basaltic magma to crustal levels. The basaltic magma may underplate the thinned continental crust, to form a discrete lower crustal layer, or it may intrude the lower crust. In either case, the model is more realistic than the uniform extension model because it accounts for the observations of high seismic velocities in the lower crust. It also provides a better description of the transition from continental to oceanic crust. As before, the lithosphere is stretched by ß, but, in addition basaltic melt in proportion to the amount

of stretching migrates to the base of the crust. The underplating makes the total thickness of the stretched crust $t_c/ß_s$, where $ß_s = t_c/[t_{oc} + (t_c-t_{oc})/ß]$ (Fig. 9.10), by comparison with $t_c/ß$ for the uniform stretching model. The dependence of melt volume on ß is based on the physically reasonable assumption that the amount of partial melting increases as hydrostatic pressure in the asthenosphere decreases. Thus a greater amount of melt is generated as thinning increases. At the ocean-continent boundary the greatest amount of melt is generated, equal in thickness to the thickness of the oceanic crust, t_{oc}. Also at that boundary $ß \to \infty$, and there is complete rupture of the continental lithosphere. This approach provides a smooth transition from continent to ocean and a realistic description of the processes which are likely to occur there.

When interpreted in terms of the uniform extension-melt segregation model, measurements of crustal thickness no longer give a direct measure of ß, the amount of stretching. Instead the quantity $ß_s$ is determined, but ß can be found from the expression for $ß_s$, given above, if t_c and t_{oc} are known. The melt segregation results in small changes in density, which are included in the calculation of initial subsidence. The thermal subsidence is almost the same as that predicted by the model with uniform extension.

The depth dependent extension model

The depth-dependent extension model (Fig. 9.8, 9.9) differs from the uniform extension model in that it assumes decoupling of the lithosphere at depth d. Stretching above and below d may be by differing amounts. The model differs most from the uniform extension model when $d = t_c$. This assumption is commonly made to emphasize the difference. In this case, the crust is thinned by a factor ß and the sub-crustal lithosphere is thinned by δ. This model

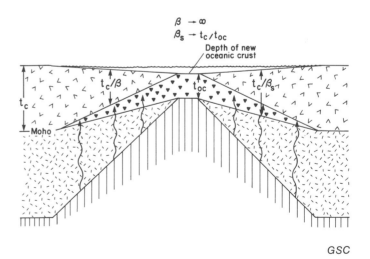

GSC

Figure 9.10. The uniform extension and melt segregation model, showing the zone affected by melt production in the asthenosphere, its migration and addition to the thinning crust. This illustrates the smooth transition from continental to oceanic crust. The model also illustrates the relationship between ß and ß_s described in the text. Patterns are as used in Figures 9.7-9.9.

407

predicts either initial uplift or initial subsidence during rifting, depending on the relative values of ß and δ (Fig. 9.9). While values of ß can, as before, be estimated from variations in crustal thickness, evidence no longer exists for the values of δ which differ from ß. This problem arises because the sub-crustal lithosphere returns to its equilibrium thickness during the post-rift stage. Values of δ therefore are usually estimated from the requirement for initial uplift in certain regions of the model, as determined from the observations.

The total post-rift thermal subsidence predicted by this model for a given ß value is similar to that of the uniform extension model. However, if values of δ are chosen such that there will be initial uplift rather than subsidence, no early post-rift sediments will be deposited and the consequences of erosion of uplifted crust must be included.

This two-layer stretching model represents an attempt to include the first order rheological properties of the lithosphere. We expect that the stretching response will be different between the upper, cool, brittle region of the lithosphere and the lower, hot, ductile regions. The upper region will extend by faulting and relative movements across these faults. At greater depths ductile flow will occur. The ease of ductile flow will increase as temperture increases. The depth-dependent extension model crudely represents the differing response of the brittle and ductile regions by allowing two stretching factors, ß and δ respectively. The transition between the two regions will be a zone of high shear, and can be interpreted as a décollement at the bottom of a region of normal faulting in the crust. The parameter δ will itself vary with depth but there is little utility in adding more and more parameters, whose values are not independently known. A more useful approach is to investigate the dynamics of rifting and to include the effects of a temperature dependent rheology. This is described later.

One of the constraints on the depth-dependent extension model is that the total amount of extension when summed across the rift zone must be the same in the upper, ß(x), and lower, δ(x), parts of the lithosphere. This means that regions where ß(x) is larger than δ(x) must be offset by regions where the converse is true. Regions where ß is small and δ > ß are characterized by significant uplift, whereas regions of δ > ß exhibit large initial subsidence (Fig. 9.9). These characteristics arise because of the opposing effects of crustal thinning and asthenospheric upwelling in determining the isostatic balance in the rift zone, as described earlier. Thus depth-dependent extension predicts that regions of both uplift and subsidence should co-exist within the rift zone, if mass is to be conserved. There have been other suggestions for conserving mass. These include the possibility that the extended lower lithosphere initially occupied a different horizontal interval than the upper lithosphere. If δ > ß, this implies that the initial width of the δ-stretching zone is narrower than that of the ß-stretching zone (Beaumont et al., 1982a; Hellinger and Sclater, 1983).

Thermomechanical models of post-rift evolution

Rationale for a thermomechanical model

The kinematic models of rifting just described predict the initial and post-rift subsidence in the absence of the ther-

mal effects of blanketing by sediments, and loading by sediments and water. These effects could be approximately included on a point-by-point basis. Instead of following this approach, we have developed a thermomechanical model that traces the post-rift evolution of a complete cross-section of a continental margin and which includes flexure of the lithosphere when loaded, sediment compaction, and conductive heating of the sediment pile. The initial conditions for the thermomechanical model are based on predictions of the kinematic rifting models.

The models are two-dimensional and predict the form of cross-sections of the margins, against which observations on the margins of eastern Canada and other margin archetypes can be compared (Fig. 9.11). The amount of crustal extension, ß, is estimated from seismic measurements of the present crustal thickness assuming that prior to rifting the crust had a uniform thickness equal to the present thickness at the landward end of the section. Values of ß will therefore vary along the cross-section (ß = ß(x)), from a value of ß = 1 where no stretching has occurred beneath the landward end of the section to a value of ß = ß$_{max}$ for uniform extension beneath the seaward end of the profile. Thus, we are modelling the evolution of large scale features of these margins. We are not concerned with minor lateral variations in structure.

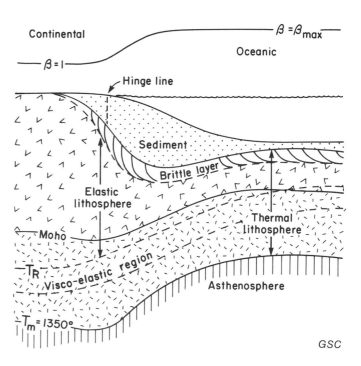

Figure 9.11. A schematic illustration of the model used to describe rifted or Atlantic-type margins. Various regions of the model are shown: sediment, brittle layer, elastic lithosphere, thermal lithosphere, the isotherm T$_R$ and its relationship to the visco-elastic region, the crust, subcrustal lithosphere, and asthenosphere. The hinge line indicates where the basin deepens significantly. The distribution of stretching ß = ß(x) is shown to increase from ß = 1 (unstretched continental crust) to ß = ß$_{max}$ (oceanic crust).

The rifting process controls the post-rift evolution of the margins. The estimates of ß are used in the instantaneous kinematic models of stretching and, together with parameter values describing the initial state of the lithosphere, allow the post-rift thermal and subsidence histories to be traced by the thermal part of the model. During rifting, the thermal state of the lithosphere is perturbed and the thermal gradient is raised above its ambient value in proportion to the amount of extension, ß. Thermal equilibrium is restored by post-rift conductive cooling of the lithosphere, which is accompanied by thermal contraction and thermal subsidence, also included in the model.

If there was no loading of the thermally subsiding lithosphere by sediment and water, further refinement of the model would be unnecessary. However, the response of the lithosphere to the surface loads requires that the mechanical properties of the lithosphere be included in the model. We shall show that a reasonable approximation of the mechanical properties of the lithosphere in this case is an elastic layer, which supports the surface loads. This representation implies that the lithosphere exhibits a finite strength and will produce a flexural response to loads. At the time of rifting we have assumed a local, Airy isostatic compensation process because the lithosphere is hot and weak. As cooling proceeds the lithosphere becomes stronger and so the mechanical behaviour of the lithosphere must reflect its increasing strength.

The thermomechanical model

The thermal part of the model is based on one dimensional solutions for conductive cooling of the thermal boundary layer. The one dimensional, time dependent equation of heat transport is:

$$K \partial^2 T / \partial z^2 = \rho c (\partial T / \partial t + v_z \partial T / \partial z) - A$$

where T = temperature, K = thermal conductivity, ρ = density, A = radioactive heat generation, and c = specific heat. The term in v_z is required to describe the heat advected by isostatic subsidence of the lithosphere at velocity v_z. The initial conditions are obtained from the stretching models for a specified ß. The boundary conditions are $T = 0°C$ on the upper boundary and $T = T_m$ at $z = a$, the base of the equilibrium lithosphere (Fig. 9.8). A finite difference approximation is used to obtain the numerical solution, with a spatial step size of 0.5 km and a time step of 0.1 Ma. These one-dimensional solutions are found at intervals along the cross-section, where ß values vary. Linear interpolation between the one-dimensional solutions gives the temperature distribution as a function of lateral and vertical position.

The model has two regions, sediments and lithosphere, which exhibit different thermal properties. Sediments are deposited at 0°C and are then considered part of the model to be conductively heated or cooled. The effects of radiogenic heat production in the sediments and crust can also be included.

The thermal subsidence, $w(\Delta t)$, due to thermal contraction of the lithosphere for the time interval Δt is given by,

$$w(\Delta t) = a_v \int [T(z,t) - T(z,t + \Delta t)] dz$$

where a_v is the volume coefficient of thermal expansion and the integral is taken over the entire lithosphere plus the sedimentary section. There is a small additional subsidence, related to the contraction of the finite difference grid (Beaumont et al., 1982a).

The thermal evolution is accompanied by mechanical effects which, though secondary, have important consequences for margin evolution, as can be judged by comparison with local isostatic models. The lithosphere, the earth's thermal boundary layer, behaves as a mechanically strong, competent region that can undergo flexure during isostatic adjustment to surface loads. The importance of flexural effects is most simply considered as a function of the flexural rigidity, $D = E d_L^3 / 12(1 - \sigma^2)$, where E is the average Young's modulus of the lithosphere, d_L is its mechanical thickness, and σ is Poisson's ratio. The flexural parameter, $a \propto D$ (Walcott, 1970), is proportional to the distance to which a load can drag down (downflex) the lithosphere against the buoyancy forces exerted by the relatively much more fluid asthenosphere or mantle. The dependence of the flexural parameter on d_L means that a ranges from about 10 km for oceanic ridges where the mechanically strong part of the lithosphere is very thin to about 100 km for shield regions in continents, where the lithosphere is thermally old.

Rifted continental margins cannot be charaterized by one value of the flexural rigidity. On the continental side, where there is little or no extension, the lithosphere remains strong giving a a large value, whereas in a highly stretched region thinning of the lithosphere and fracture of the upper crust both contribute to making the lithosphere mechanically weak. Thinned regions cool as they age, in much the same manner as oceanic lithosphere (Fig. 9.12a) and the mechanical strength returns.

No simple analytical mathematics exists to predict the flexure and vertical deformation of a lithosphere that has properties which vary in time and space. We have used a two-dimensional finite element model to determine the isostatic response to loading by water and sediments (Beaumont et al., 1982a) but a finite difference approach (Bodine, 1981) is equally valid.

The finite element grid represents the rheological lithosphere, that part of the lithosphere which remains elastic and undergoes flexure. What region is this? It is the region below the one which has failed by faulting during extension and above that which is sufficiently hot to undergo significant viscous creep on the timescales of margin evolution, 10-100 Ma. Because viscosity is an exponential function of temperature, the ability of the lithosphere to creep will change very rapidly with depth in the lithosphere.

In Figure 9.12 the viscosity, η, as a function of depth and the thermal age of the lithosphere is shown. A region where $\eta > 10^6 \eta_b$ will not creep significantly on the timescales of margin evolution unless plastic failure occurs; therefore, such regions can be considered to be elastic and undergo flexure when loaded. Regions where $\eta < 10^3 \eta_b$ will creep so rapidly that they appear fluid on the timescales of margin evolution and can be modelled as such. The intervening region is transitional and will show significant creep which can be modelled as a viscoelastic process (Courtney and Beaumont, 1983). This extrinsic zoning of the lithosphere is primarily a function of temperature and is not an intrinsic property: the whole lithosphere could equally well be modelled as a temperature-dependent viscoelastic material (Courtney, 1982).

It is not always necessary to include explicitly the viscoelastic transition in models. Consider the cases of young stretched lithosphere beneath a continental margin and

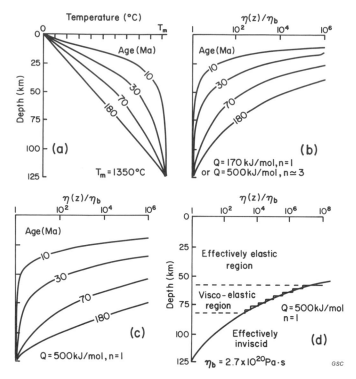

Figure 9.12. The viscosity-temperature relationship. Panel a shows how the temperature changes with time in a cooling lithosphere. Panels b and c show the corresponding viscosity-depth functions for different values of activation energy (Q) and for Newtonian and non-Newtonian flow (n = 1 or n = 3). η_b is the basal viscosity, the viscosity at the base of the lithosphere (T = T_m). It is assumed that strain rates are constant. Panel d shows how a simple zonation of the lithosphere can be derived from a viscosity-depth function, as described in the text. This is only valid for assessing the response of the lithosphere to surface loads. The viscosity-temperature relationship is described in more detail in the section on "Improved Models" in this chapter.

young oceanic lithosphere. The viscoelastic transition layer in these examples is thin enough to be ignored. Furthermore, cooling is proceeding sufficiently rapidly that it effectively freezes the region in which creep would occur in a thermally stable environment, so that the extrinsic effects of creep do not appear in the geological record of oceanic lithosphere or in the record of rifted margin evolution. This is true for a significant part (~ 100 Ma) of their evolution (Courtney and Beaumont, 1983). Added to this is the fact that sedimentation rates on margins usually decrease with age, in part because the thermal subsidence is also waning. Therefore, under normal circumstances there is little potential for loads on margins to elicit a flexure that has observable characteristics of viscoelastic flow (Beaumont, 1981). One possibility would be an old sediment-starved margin which becomes the site of rapid sediment deposition.

Modelling of the rheological properties of rifted margins is therefore relatively easy. The lithosphere can be divided into three zones: the passive faulted upper brittle layer, the effectively elastic rheological lithosphere, and the low viscosity fluid-like basal zone (Fig. 9.11). Only the

rheological lithosphere need be represented in the finite element model. Its base is determined by an isotherm which we term the relaxation isotherm, T_R, corresponding to the negligibly thick viscoelastic transition zone. Its value cannot be specified *a priori* because it is a function of the mineralogy and the activation energy for creep, Q, which are not precisely known.

It must now be evident why a coupled thermomechanical model is used. The thermal evolution determines the tectonic subsidence and the position of the relaxation isotherm. The mechanical model then determines the flexural response to water and sediment loads which fill and isostatically amplify tectonic subsidence. Feedback from sediment blanketing and erosion modify the cooling history, thermal contraction, and tectonic subsidence.

Sedimentation and bathymetry

A sediment budget and the physical properties of the sediments are required as input to the models. When modelling cross-sections for comparison with observations, this information is usually found from well data on the cross-section. This includes the biostratigraphy, depositional environment, lithologies and well logs. The sediments must be restored to their original thickness at the time of deposition by decompaction. They can then be added to the model by specifying their thickness and density as a function of position and model timestep. We term this method of adding sediment the 'specified thickness' method.

Methods used for correcting for compaction by Van Hinte (1978). We use the one described in detail by Sclater and Christie (1980) which expresses porosity as a function of depth of burial by:

$$\Phi = \Phi_o \exp(-hz)$$

For different lithologies, values of parameters h and 'Φ_o' are determined from well logs. Some examples are given later in this chapter.

The model compacts the sediments as they are added so that the final predicted thickness is equal to that observed. This approach of specifying the thickness of the sediment loads is called the specified thickness method. It predicts the model paleobathymetry for comparison with observations. The success of a model is judged on the acceptability of the predictions of paleo- and present bathymetry and not on the sediment thickness itself, because this is predetermined.

An alternative but complementary approach to sediment loading is to add sediment for each time increment until a desired bathymetry is achieved; this is the 'paleoprofile' method. The sediments are added in an uncompacted form but are compacted by the model. When used in this way the model predicts the synthetic stratigraphy of the margin section for comparison with observations.

Other properties of the sediments are also important to the model predictions. In particular the thermal properties of the sediments, their thermal conductivities and their capacity for radiogenic heat production, are important for the calculation of the thermal histories of the sediments. These properties have only a minor influence on subsidence, but are very important with respect to the thermal maturation of the sediments. Consequently, from the perspective of those engaged in hydrocarbon exploration, the model will only be of real use if it can be shown to provide accurate temperature histories for the sediments as well as accurate subsidence histories. The thermal aspects of the models from the viewpoint of hydrocarbon maturation are considered in detail in another section of this chapter, after the basic model predictions are tested against observational data.

Modelling procedures

The computational procedures used in the coupled thermomechanical model may be summarized as follows. The required input variables are:

1) the variations in $\beta(x)$ and $\delta(x)$;
2) the value of T_R;
3) the values of the thermal, mechanical, and sedimentological parameters; and
4) the sediment budget in either of the forms 'specified thickness' or 'paleoprofile'.

Calculations are performed by stepping the models through time in model timesteps usually chosen to be 10-20 Ma. The procedure is as follows:

1) At $t = 0$, extension occurs, resulting in the initial subsidence as predicted by local isostatic adjustment. This depression is then filled with a combination of sediment and water to simulate loading of the continental margin just after rifting. Isostatic adjustment to this load is calculated using the mechanical model described above.

2) A time interval Δt elapses during which the lithosphere cools and subsides as predicted by the thermal model; the position of the isotherm T_R also changes. A further load of water and sediment is then added. Isostatic adjustment is again calculated by the mechanical model, adjusted for the new depth of T_R.

3) This process is continued over the number of time steps necessary to simulate the evolution of the margin. The depths to the seafloor and to the basement, the position of the M discontinuity, the temperature distribution, and the gravity anomaly across the margin, are computed after each time step.

RESULTS FROM THERMOMECHANICAL MODELLING

Introduction

The variability of margin structure prompts the question: can thermomechanical models in which β, δ, and sedimentation are the main parameters explain such diversity? The question is addressed here first by predicting variations in style for model margins in which β and sedimentation take particularly simple yet systematically changing distributions. The sensitivity of model results to other model parameter values is then reviewed. Results from four specific margin transects complete this section. Emphasis is placed on the intercomparison of model results as well as the comparison of models with observations. We show that it is possible to propose a first-order classification of margins based on β and on sedimentation.

Dependence of margin style on the distribution of β and on sediment supply

The archetypal model results (Fig. 9.13-9.21) are included to illustrate how $\beta(x)$ (the stretching profile) and the

amount of sediment available influence the character of a rifted continental margin. All models have exactly the same lithospheric properties, the standard properties (Table 9.1), except for $\beta(x)$ which takes a linear, convex or concave form, so named because the basin-basement interface takes the named shape with increasing distance x across the 240 km wide stretched transition from continental to oceanic crust. A measure of the crustal thickness, $1-1/\beta$ or γ, also varies in the named manner (convex or concave) when viewed from below (Fig. 9.13-9.21).

The model bathymetry is that of a typical margin having a shelf, shelf break, slope and rise. The bathymetry for each model is held constant with time and the effects of differences in sediment supply are modelled by placing the shelf break 40, 120, or 240 km seaward of the point where stretching begins. This means that in the absence of flexure the shelf width of the models would vary from 40 to 240 km, reproducing the change from a nearly starved margin to a delta.

Many margins fall within the range of these models, so they are useful in fingerprinting the style of given examples. The range could be extended to include a narrower transition zone between ocean and continent, more complicated forms of $\beta(x)$, and prograding sediment wedges. Some of these properties are included in the specific case studies discussed in this section.

The models are designed to investigate whether the necking process during rifting leaves its imprint on the character of the margin during post-rift evolution. The analogy of lithospheric necking during extension with that of a drawn metal rod suggests various necking profiles, the most simple of which, linear β, has uniformly increasing attenuation across the margin to a point where break-up and infilling by oceanic crust occurs. Extension that progresses incrementally, so that successive amounts of stretching are proportional to the thickness of the lithosphere, results in a concave-β distribution; a distribution that is characteristic of ductile or malleable materials. Conversely, brittle materials may give a convex-β distribution because the point of failure tends to nucleate to one location, the oceanic edge of the rift, following limited distributed stretching. The analogies are oversimplifications, but serve to explain the rationale for the choice of β distributions.

Although we do not know which of these necking processes is preferred, or even if there is a preferred mode of extension, it is probable that dynamical models will predict attentuation that will conform with at least one of these profiles. Can we detect which profile is appropriate for a given margin transect? Beaumont et al. (1984) presented results for models of moderately sedimented margins (Fig. 9.14, 9.17, 9.20) and argued that, all things being equal, the character of the sediment thickness distribution, the depth of Moho, and the gravity anomaly are good fingerprints of $\beta(x)$, and that these fingerprints are modified in a predictable manner during margin evolution. The β distribution also has a significant effect on the temperature history of the sediments, suggesting that it is a useful parameter to know when making general hydrocarbon maturation assessments.

The fingerprints of β distribution remain even when the added variable of sedimentation is included. Some important points emerge.

1) Deep sedimentary troughs (sediment thickness 15 km) only occur where the shelf break and slope have prograded over oceanic crust or over strongly attenuated continental crust (Fig. 9.15, 9.18, 9.21). Deep sedimentary troughs can occur for any ß distribution but, for a given shelf width, the trough will be widest and most spoon-like for concave-ß (compare Fig. 9.15 and 9.21). Furthermore, to have a deep sedimentary trough on a convex-ß margin more progradation must have occurred than on other margins.

Table 9.1. Standard parameter and property values for kinematic rifting and thermomechanical models

Layer	Parameter	Symbol	Value	Units
Water	Density	ρ_w	1030	kg/m^3
Sediments	See Table 9.5			
Crust	Pre-rift thickness	t_c	35*	km
	Density	ρ_c	2819.882	kg/m^3
	Thermal conductivity	K	3.099	W/(m·°C)
			7.407×10^{-3}	cal/(cm·s·°C)
	Specific heat at constant volume times density	c_p	3.877×10^6	J/(m^3·°C)
			0.9266	cal/(cm·s·°C)
	Radioactive heat production	A	2.092	µW/m^3
			5×10^{-13}	cal/(cm·s)
	Volume coefficient thermal expansion	$\propto$	3.2×10^{-5}	/°C
	Depth of radioactive layer of uniform density	D	7.5	km
Sub-crustal lithosphere	Pre-rift thickness	a-t_c	125-35 = 90	km
	Density	ρ_o	3330	kg/m^3
	Thermal conductivity	K	3.099	W/(m·°C)
			7.407×10^{-3}	cal/(cm·s·°C)
	Specific heat at constant volume times density	c_p	3.877×10^{-6}	J/(m^3·°C)
			0.9266	cal/(cm^3·°C)
	Volume coefficient thermal expansion	α	3.2×10^{-5}	/°C
Asthenosphere	Density	ρ_o	3186	kg/m^3
	Temperature	T_m	1350	°C
	Thermal conductivity	K	3.099	W/(m·°C)
			7.047×10^{-3}	cal/(cm·s·°C)
	Specific heat at constant volume times density	c_p	3.877×10^{-6}	J/(m^3·°C)
			0.9266	cal/(cm^3·°C)
	Volume coefficient thermal expansion	$\propto$	3.2×10^{-5}	/°C
Rheological lithosphere	Relaxation isotherm or equivalent elastic core	T_R	250	°C
	Young's modulus	E	2×10^{11}	Pa
	Poisson's ratio	σ	0.25	
	Density of underlying fluid	ρ_f	3186	kg/m^3

Note: *Crustal thickness is 35 km unless otherwise stated.

2) Relatively starved margins (shelf widths $\gtrsim$ 40 km) have only thin sediments (Fig. 9.16) or no sediments (Fig. 9.19) beneath the 'shelf' region if ß is linear or convex. Because there is little sediment in this region to flexurally downwarp the adjacent unstretched continent, no significant hinge line develops separating flexurally from tectonically subsided regions. Conversely, the hinge line is well developed even for a poorly sedimented model with concave-ß (Fig. 9.13). This is because there is a proportionately larger sediment load within one flexural wavelength of unstretched crust by comparison with the models with linear-and convex-ß. Progradation beyond one flexural wavelength does not increase subsidence landward of the hinge line (compare Fig. 9.13, 9.14, and 9.15). In fact there is a subtle uplift because the hinge zone is on the peripheral bulge of the sediments beneath the outer shelf. Subsidence of the hinge line, which is a function of T_R, is a maximum of 2 km for these models (T_R = 250°C). In an equivalent manner, the width of the subsided zone landward of the hinge line ($\gtrsim$ 130 km in these models) increases with T_R. A sharp hinge line fingerprints a concave-ß distribution with a relatively narrow transition zone.

3) Flexural subsidence also occurs for linear-ß models, which have weak hinge zones, and for convex-ß models. In the latter case the flexurally downwarped region is superimposed on the tectonically subsided region and there is no sedimentary evidence of a hinge line (Fig. 9.20, 9.21).

4) For models with the fixed paleobathymetry shown (Fig. 9.13-9.21), most of the sediments beneath the shelf and slope are syn-rift (below 0 Ma stratigraphic horizon) or accumulates within one lithospheric thermal time constant of the rifting event (sediments between the 0 and 50 Ma stratigraphic horizons). Sedimentation rates decline as cooling and thermal contraction wane such that in the interval $2\tau - 3\tau$ little sediment accumulates (sediment between the 135 and 185 Ma stratigraphic horizons). At this stage there must be progradation if significant sedimentation is to occur.

5) The models predict offlap of sediments in the hinge zone because the centre of mass of the sediment load migrates seaward with time. This tendency would be further emphasized in models with prograding sediment profiles. The flexural strength of the lithosphere beneath the hinge zone remains constant because these are uniform stretching models; therefore, there is no flexurally related change in the width of the hinge zone.

6) Differential compaction between carbonates and clastic sediments is responsible for the development of sedimentary highs beneath the outer shelf seen clearly in Figure 9.15. Note that significant highs develop only after 50 Ma, when the clastics, deposited between 25 and 135 Ma after rifting, compact.

7) Sediment temperatures are related to sediment thickness, age of the margin and sediment lithology. Only general conclusions can therefore be drawn from these models which do not consider lithologies more complex than a change from dominantly sandstones beneath the shelf to dominantly shales beneath the slope, with some carbonates deposited beneath the outer shelf from 25 to 135 Ma. The significantly thicker sediments in concave-ß models lead to the highest temperatures at the sediment-basement interface and these highs occur in the low conductivity shales. At the opposite extreme, convex-ß models are unlikely to develop large volumes of mature syn- and post-rift sediments beneath the shelf unless the shelf is as wide as the transition zone.

8) The gravity anomalies arise from three sources (Beaumont et al., 1982a): basin shape including distributions of sediment and water; Moho position; and a thermal contribution (resulting from perturbations induced by thermal expansion, which are important in the early stages of margin evolution). Large positive anomalies sit astride the shelf break (e.g. Fig. 9.15) and are reinforced when this position also coincides with a strong lateral thinning of the crust (Fig. 9.21). These highs would be smaller were the shelf edge more rounded. The flanking negative anomalies (e.g. Fig. 9.14, 9.17, 9.20) are from flexurally downwarped areas most clearly identifiable above the hinge zone (e.g. Fig. 9.13, 9.14, 9.15, 9.17). Their existance in the convex-ß models (Fig. 9.21) confirms the flexural aspect of the subsidence beneath the shelf. For narrower shelves (Fig. 9.19, 9.20) the load is less, the flexural low is smaller and the shelf edge positive high moves inboard to overwhelm the negative lobe. The landward positive lobes of the flexural anomaly occur over the peripheral bulge (an effect which would be much smaller were the peripheral bulge eroded), and in many cases reinforce the shelf-edge positive anomaly. The sequence shown in Figures 9.13 to 9.15 demonstrates how the flexural and shelf-edge positive lobes separate as the shelf becomes wider. The same effect occurs in the linear-ß models (Fig. 9.16-9.18) but is less spectacular than the concave-ß models because there is less flexure.

9) The effect of increasing T_R would be correspondingly to increase the amplitude and wavelength of the flexural lobes in the gravity anomaly (Beaumont et al., 1982a).

Depth-dependent extension

The need for depth-dependent extension is usually based on the observed uplift of rift shoulders during rifting. The uniform extension and uniform extension and melt segregation models do not produce uplift for the standard set of parameter values. The results of an end member of the family of depth-dependent extension models are presented in this section to illustrate the maximum uplift and subsidence obtainable with the standard parameter values. The model (Fig. 9.22) is designed to explain in a simplified manner some aspects of the evolution of the Norwegian margin of the Greenland Sea. It ignores evidence of pre-Tertiary extension and presumes an extreme form of instantaneous depth-dependent extension at about 60 Ma. Detachment at the Moho allows sub-crustal lithosphere to be pulled from beneath the continent without extending the overlying crust. Adjacent regions of the crust are stretched above the unextended but moving subcrustal lithosphere. Subcrustal extension is thereby balanced by the adjacent crustal stretching. The thinned crust would remain as extended continent and not become oceanic in character because the underlying sub-crustal lithosphere is not thinned. The model assumes that sufficient sediments are available to fill subsided areas to the constant paleobathymetry shown. Other model characteristics are the same as those used in the archetypes.

Table 9.2 Physical properties used in extension and melt model calculation

	Meaning	Value
ρ_l	density of basaltic melt	2600 kg/m³
ρ_b	density of basaltic rock	2862 kg/m³
ρ_c	average crustal density	2862 kg/m³
ρ_m	average mantle density	3237 kg/m³
ρ_a	density of asthenosphere	3186 kg/m³
ρ_w	density of water	1000 kg/m³
f_o	maximum degree of partial melting	22%
T_m	temperature at base lithosphere	1350°C
α	coefficient of thermal expansion	3.2×10^{-5}/°C
t_c	initial crustal thickness	36 km
a	initial lithosphere thickness	125 km
β_c	critical value for onset of partial melting	1.63
γ	adiabatic gradient - asthenosphere	0.5°C/km

Uplift of 1.5 km occurs above the sub-crustal stretching zone on extension. Erosion could easily amplify the uplift to create mountain peaks 4-5 km high. Pre-rift sediments would similarly be uplifted as shown and, if eroded, would form an angular unconformity beneath onlapping post-rift sediments (inset Fig. 9.22), a feature seen on some seismic sections along the Norwegian margin (Eldholm and Sundvor, 1980). The thermal time constant for cooling, contraction and subsidence of this region is that of the whole lithosphere, not just the crust, therefore, the thermal uplift persists, decaying in this example with a time constant of 63 Ma. Surface heat flow in this region remains unperturbed on extension, rises to a maximum of approximately twice the normal value after about 5 Ma (the crustal thermal time constant), and then decays to one and one-half the normal value after 60 Ma.

Tectonic subsidence of the adjacent region of crustal stretching is virtually all syn-rift. The small post-rift thermal subsidence is the result of lithospheric cooling because the overlying crust has been thinned. It would be temporary were the lithosphere to thicken correspondingly by accretion to its base. Margins of this type would typically have large thicknesses of syn-rift sediments and little post-rift sediments; the total eventual subsidence, however, would remain the same as in a corresponding uniform extension model. It is difficult to test whether the Voring Plateau in the Norwegian Sea is a region of this type because it has remained sediment starved. Clues to recently extended regions of this type are that the tectonic subsidence would be larger than anticipated for their thermal age, and the heat flow would be nearly normal. The model would not apply to the Basin and Range, because that region has undergone no broad-scale subsidence.

Figure 9.22 illustrates an extreme case of extension being transferred laterally from different lithospheric levels along detachment or shear zones most likely within the crust. A less extreme case, perhaps with a higher level detachment surface, which would model most of the known geological and geophysical characteristics of the Norwegian margin could easily be found. Such models are not particularly useful without better information on the actual existence of the hypothetical detachments. However, we shall utilize less extreme cases of depth-dependent extension to explain post-rift coastal plain onlap in the next four sections of this chapter.

Depth-dependent stretching is also introduced to account for reduced amounts of syn- and early post-rift subsidence, by comparison with uniform extension models. Changing other parameter values would not achieve both the correct early and final amounts of subsidence. Another option, that of making the length of the extension and rifting period finite (Jarvis and McKenzie, 1980), will not work in cases where our instantaneous rifting models already delay this event as much as possible, thereby minimizing the tectonic subsidence at anytime during the model's evolution. Under these circumstances finite rate-uniform extension is not equivalent to instantaneous-depth dependent extension.

The difference between the depth-dependent and uniform extension models is greatest when the detachment between the upper and lower layer in the former model of stretching coincides with the Moho. Other choices reduce the ability of the depth-dependent model to decrease syn-rift subsidence and to cause crustal uplift when other parameter values remain unchanged. When there is no erosion, a depth-dependent model only modifies the model stratigraphy by comparison with a uniform extension model or a uniform extension and melt-segregation model. It does not change the long term tectonic subsidence, which is primarily a function of t_c, ß, and the density distribution in the lithosphere.

Figure 9.13. Evolution of a 240 km wide transition zone uniform extension model in which the values of ß vary with position in a concave manner. ("Concave" means that the curve of ß against distance from the origin on the continent side is concave downwards). The model has the same paleobathymetry throughout time with a 40 km wide shelf in the absence of flexure. The panels, from top to bottom, show: ß distribution; crustal thinning, $\gamma = (1-1/\beta)$; free air gravity anomaly 185 Ma after rifting; the crust of the 185 Ma old margin with Moho position and temperature distribution (in red); stratigraphy and lithology of the 185 Ma old basin; the stratigraphy of the basin at 50, 25 and 0 Ma, respectively; the crust of the present margin with Moho position and temperature distribution (in red). See Table 9.1 for other model properties. Patterns indicate carbonates, sandstones and shales.

Figure 9.14. Evolution of a 240 km wide transition zone, concave-ß model that has a 120 km wide shelf in the absence of flexure. The panels and other properties are as described in Figure 9.13.

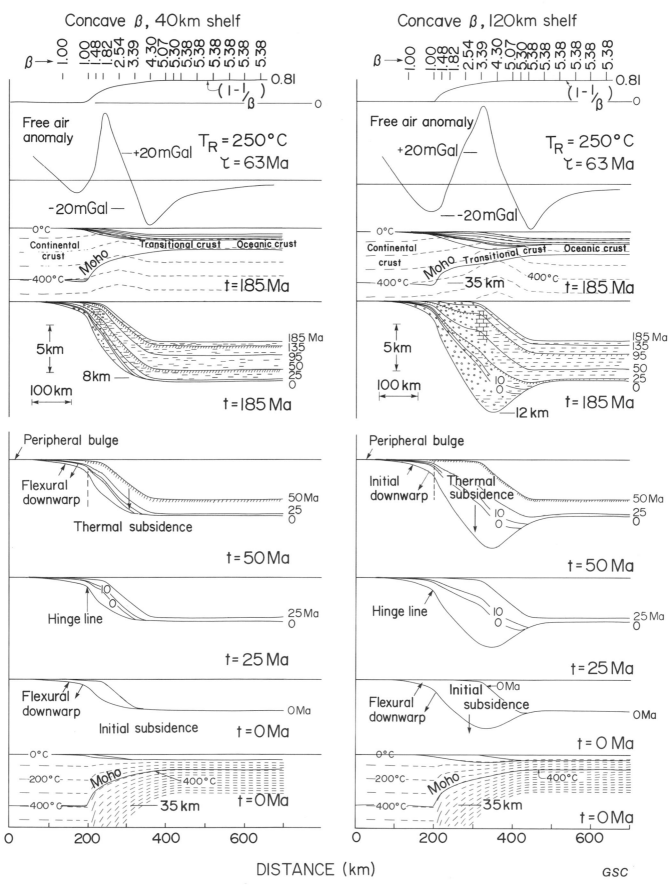

Figure 9.13

Figure 9.14

DISTANCE (km)

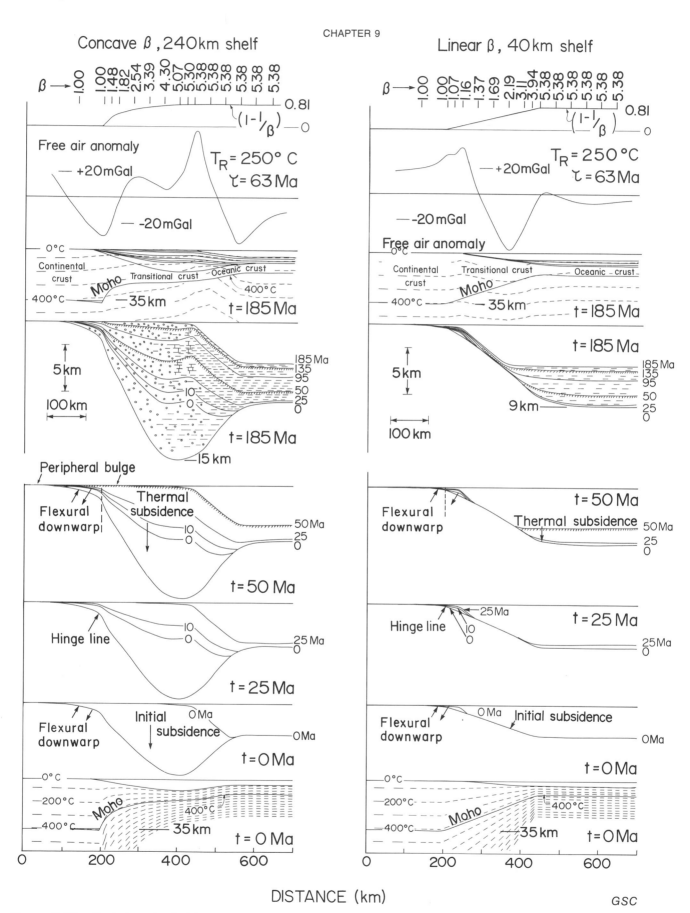

Figure 9.15. Evolution of a 240 km wide transition zone, concave-ß model that has a 240 km wide shelf in the absence of flexure. The panels and other properties are as described in Figure 9.13.

Figure 9.16. Evolution of a 240 km wide transition zone, linear-ß model that has a 40 km wide shelf in the absence of flexure. The panels and other properties are as described in Figure 9.13.

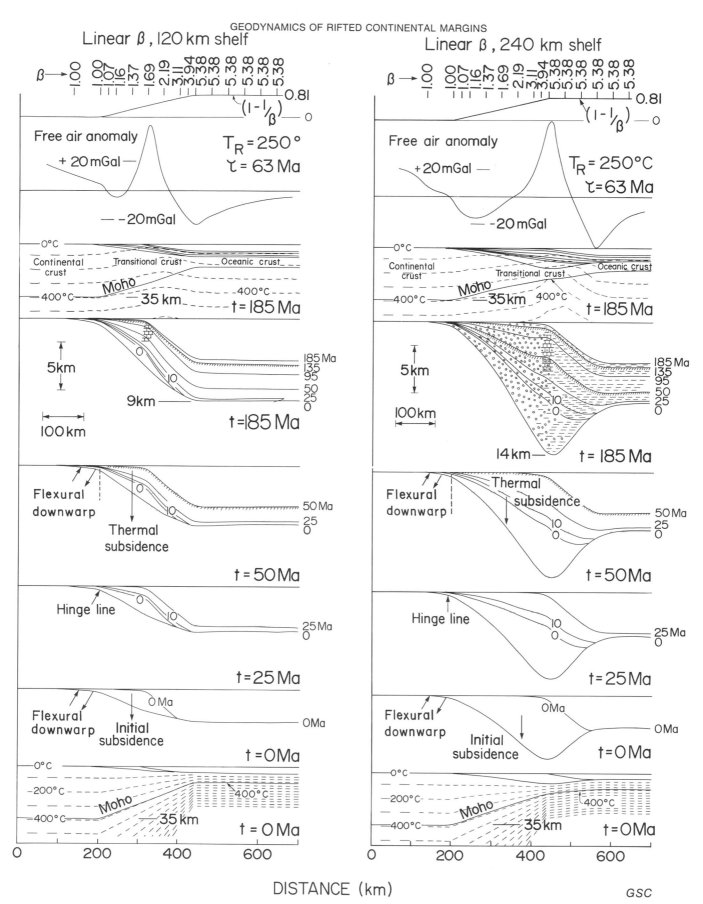

Figure 9.17. Evolution of a 240 km wide transition zone, linear-ß model that has a 120 km wide shelf in the absence of flexure. The panels and other properties are as described in Figure 9.13.

Figure 9.18. Evolution of a 240 km wide transition zone, linear-ß model that has a 240 km wide shelf in the absence of flexure. The panels and other properties are as described in Figure 9.13.

417

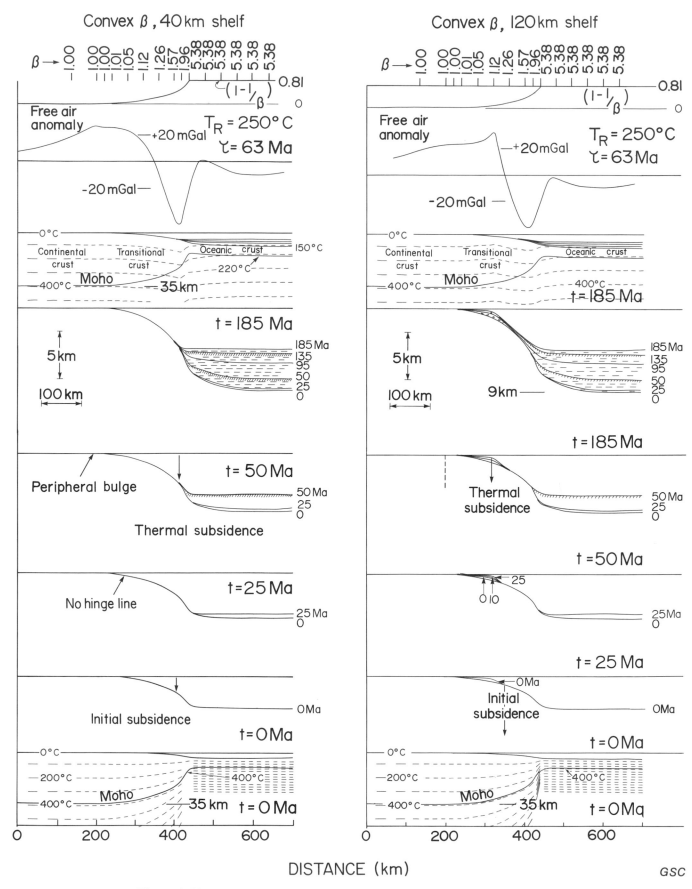

Figure 9.19

Figure 9.20

DISTANCE (km)

Dependence of margin characteristics on other model parameters

Most studies using the stretching model have employed similar parameter values so that the results can easily be compared (e.g. McKenzie, 1978; Royden et al., 1980; Royden and Keen, 1980; LePichon and Sibuet, 1981; Beaumont et al., 1982a,b; Sawyer et al., 1982a,b). However, this has led to a general lack of attention to the importance of realistic variations in parameter values, such as the densities and initial thicknesses of the crust and lithosphere, coefficients of thermal expansion, and equilibrium temperature distribution in the lithosphere. Small variations, particularly in the densities and thicknesses can have a large effect on the tectonic subsidence predicted by the models (eg. Dewey, 1982). We shall briefly examine this sensitivity for the uniform extension model; similar results would be obtained for the melt segregation-uniform extension and the depth-dependent extension models.

The range of realistic parameter values can vary quite widely. We have chosen a range of crustal densities between 2700 and 2900 kg/m^3, a range of mantle densities between 3100 and 3450 kg/m^3, initial crustal thicknesses (t_c) between 25 and 55 km, and initial thicknesses (a) of the lithosphere between 100 and 250 km. Values of S_I, the initial subsidence, and of S_c (∞), the total post-rift thermal subsidence (t $\rightarrow$ ∞), were calculated using these ranges of parameters. The results (Fig. 9.23a,b) show that changes in S_I of several kilometres occur as a result of reasonable perturbations in parameter values. S_m is the depth to newly formed oceanic lithosphere (Fig. 9.23). The total thermal subsidence, $S_c(\infty)$, is sensitive only to the initial thickness of the lithosphere. $S_c(\infty)$ is also a function of T_m, the temperature at the base of the lithosphere (Table 9.6). Similarly, both S_I and $S_c(\infty)$ will vary with changes in other parameters, such as thermal conductivity, coefficient of thermal expansion, and initial temperature distribution, but these variations will probably be less than those due to the densities and thicknesses of the lithosphere.

The least well known of the parameters is the initial thickness of the lithosphere. This affects both S_I and S_c, and also the thermal time constant of the lithosphere. Parsons and Slater (1977) determined values of lithospheric thickness for the oceanic lithosphere of 125 ± 10 km, corresponding to a thermal time constant of 62 ± 7 Ma. This result is supported by most of the relevant observations in the oceans. Some continental studies, however, favour a much greater lithospheric thickness, about 250 km for old continents (e.g. Jordan, 1981). If this were so, there would be initial uplift, not subsidence, during rifting. The results

(Fig. 9.23a) show that uplift will occur for small ratios of crustal to lithospheric thickness of about 0.15. The thermal time constant for a 250 km lithosphere is 248 Ma as opposed to 62 Ma for a 125 km lithosphere. Sclater et al. (1980) have argued that a thermal time constant of about 60 Ma was observed for cratonic sedimentary basins, and therefore the thicknesses of continental and oceanic lithosphere were similar. Similar thermal time constants were also observed beneath many rifted continental margins. For these reasons we have chosen a 125 km lithosphere to represent the initial conditions in our models.

Several studies have used the concept of a limiting ß value to constrain parameter values (Royden and Keen, 1980; LePichon and Sibuet, 1981; Beaumont et al., 1982a; Dewey, 1982). This concept is based on the premise that there will be a maximum value of ß beyond which the stretching process will be superseded by upwelling of basaltic magma and the creation of new oceanic lithosphere. Le Pichon and Sibuet (1981) and Dewey (1982) suggested this value, $ß = ß_{max} \sim 4$. In order that the transition from ocean to continent be relatively smooth, the initial subsidence at $ß = ß_{max}$ must equal the depth of newly formed oceanic lithosphere at the mid-ocean ridges. This depth is 1.7 km when the water load is removed. The requirement for S_I ($ß_{max}$) = 1.7 constrains a combination of parameter values to provide this result. In the uniform extension models discussed previously, $ß_{max} = 5.38$ was used together with the standard parameter values shown in Tables 9.1 and 9.6.

This concept of a "$ß_{max}$" is useful in modelling rifted continental margins, when the models must extend across the ocean-continent transition onto oceanic lithosphere and a uniform extension model is to be used. A fairly good approximation for the oceanic region is provided when ß = $ß_{max}$. Because values of $ß_{max}$ are large, they give a good approximation to the oceanic thermal subsidence, which is more properly modelled with $ß \rightarrow \infty$. Furthermore $ß_{max}$ provides the correct initial depth of the oceanic lithosphere and of oceanic crustal thickness (6.5 km, if $ß_{max} = 5.38$, and $t_c = 35$ km). When we are not primarily concerned with the detailed behaviour of the oceanic region, this is a reasonable approximation. However, both the model with melt segregation-uniform extension ($ß \rightarrow \infty$) and the model with depth-dependent extension ($\delta \gg ß$) provide better predictions of the thermal subsidence in the oceanic region.

The important model parameters during the post-rift phase are ß, δ, and the thicknesses a and t_c which, together with the densities ρ_c and ρ_o, control the overall tectonic subsidence. The rate of post-rift subsidence is determined by a and the thermal properties of the lithosphere (K). T_R determines the importance of flexure and, therefore, the form of the gravity anomalies.

The effects of some model parameters can be separated from others (e.g. Fig. 9.23) but in general the choice of parameter values is non-unique. We have therefore adopted a standard set of values (Tables 9.1 and 9.6) and vary these only when the models fail. Our modelling philosophy asks whether or not the stretching of a standard lithosphere can explain the observations.

Beaumont et al. (1982a) investigated the effect of varying T_R from 0 to 450°C. On the basis of both the width and amplitude of the hinge zone and the gravity anomalies

---

Figure 9.19. Evolution of a 240 km wide transition zone, convex-ß model that has a 40 km wide shelf in the absence of flexure. ("Convex" means that the curve of ß against distance from the origin on the continent side is convex downwards.) The panels and other properties are as described in Figure 9.13.

Figure 9.20. Evolution of a 240 km wide transition zone, convex-ß model that has a 120 km wide shelf in the absence of flexure. The panels and other properties are as described in Figure 9.13.

predicted, $T_R \sim 250\,°C$ was the preferred value for the cross-section of the Scotian Basin. They also discussed the interpretation of T_R in terms of the thickness of an elastic core region within the lithosphere, a point that is considered in more detail under 'Discussion and Synthesis'. A similar range of T_R values was used in the detailed modelling of the cross-sections presented here.

The temperature history of the sediments is determined by a combination of the lithospheric heat flux, radiogenic heat, and thermal properties of the sediments. The thermal history is only considered in detail for the Scotian Basin.

Temperature at the base of the lithosphere in the models is held at $1350\,°C$, so that the equilibrium reduced heat flux through the lithosphere is $33\ mW/m^2$. This value is not changed in the modelling over and above the effects of stretching and thermal blanketing by the sediments. It should be remembered, however, that there is a trade-off between the reduced heat flux and the thermal properties of the sediments with regard to sediment temperature.

Variability of the values of the radiogenic heat production and thermal conductivity in the sediments is not known. We suspect that thermal conductivity, in particular, will vary with location even for the same lithology, implying that the thermal calculations will not be accurate unless we know these values.

Normal compaction of the sediments with increasing depth of burial is included in the modelling, but some other effects such as salt withdrawal and diapirism, overpressuring and faulting are not. However, their importance is assessed when comparing model stratigraphy with observations.

Sea-level changes are not modelled, largely because there is no consensus on the magnitude of long term Mesozoic and Cenozoic change, the Vail et al. (1977) supercycle (Watts and Thorne, 1984; Hallam, 1984), and because the models discussed here are not designed to resolve short term events, the Vail et al. (1977) higher order cycles. However, tectonic and flexural subsidence, which lead to sedimentation patterns like those resulting from sea-level change, are discussed and the inherent ambiguity between basement subsidence and sea-level rise is stressed once again.

Scotian Basin

The Scotian Basin section was used as an example of models of margin evolution by Beaumont et al. (1982a). The present model (Fig. 9.24, 9.25, 9.60) is similar to the original except that the ß and δ stretching profiles have been refined and the thermal properties of the sediments modified on the basis of measurements and our improved understanding of their thermal history (see the section on Thermal History for more detailed information).

The observed section is based on stratigraphy from exploratory wells (Jansa and Wade, 1975; Given, 1977; Barss et al., 1979, 1980; Wade 1981) and from multichannel seismic reflection profiles (Fig. 7, in pocket), and seismic refraction data which provide information on the variation of crustal properties and those of the deeper sedimentary section not clearly defined by the multichannel reflection data (Dainty et al., 1966; Keen et al., 1975; Keen and Hyndman, 1979; Keen and Cordsen, 1981; Keen and Haworth, 1985; Fig. 9.31).

Some of the wells have been projected relatively large distances onto the cross-section (see Fig. 9.55) and the section is not normal to the strike of the margin. Forcing the model to agree with the projected well data causes some small-scale irregularities in the model stratigraphy and the Moho position which may not occur along the straight-line section. The diapirs in the two salt provinces have been ignored and the stratigraphy interpolated across them.

The specified thickness depth-dependent extension model assumes that $t_c = 35\ km$ on the basis of the measured crustal thickness at the landward end of the section. ß increases approximately linearly across the 260 km wide transition zone. The model should therefore be compared with the simple linear-ß models (Fig. 9.17, 9.18) to see the effects of modifying model parameter values. In particular, the results show the differences between the "paleoprofile" and "specified thickness" approaches to synthetic stratigraphy.

Depth-dependent extension was used to reproduce the Jurassic-Cretaceous onlap landward of the Mic Mac J-77 well by the gradual subsidence of thermally uplifted crust beneath the hinge zone. This should be compared with the equivalent uniform extension model (Fig. 9.17) which does not show progressive onlap. High values of δ, implying highly attenuated sub-crustal lithosphere, also minimize the bathymetry of the shelf region during the Jurassic when it was a carbonate bank. Neither the onlap nor the Jurassic paleobathymetry is completely satisfactory. The observed onlap is not as uniform as that predicted. Absence of Middle Jurassic sediments in the Wyandot E-53 well causes a depression in the model inner shelf at this time, which is then filled by locally thickened, Upper Jurassic sediments (Fig. 9.25d). It is difficult to avoid this problem, seen clearly in the 175 and 160 Ma panels of Figure 9.60, because Callovian age sediments have not been identified in Wyandot E-53.

Figure 9.21. Evolution of a 240 km wide transition zone, convex-ß model that has a 240 km wide shelf in the absence of flexure. The panels and other properties are as described in Figure 9.13.

Figure 9.22. Evolution of a model that employs an extreme form of depth-dependent extension in which subcrustal extension in the region 100-300 km is balanced against crustal extension in the region > 300 km. A detachment surface at the Moho separates the two regions. The model shows the maximum likely crustal uplift and syn-rift subsidence and is similar in some respects to the Norwegian margin. The panels, from top to bottom, show: the ß and δ distributions and corresponding thinning of crust and subcrustal lithosphere (1-1/ß) and (1-1/δ); the free air gravity anomaly for the model after 60 Ma; the crustal cross-section and temperature distribution in red after 60 Ma; the sedimentary basin and adjacent uplift after 60, 30, and 0 Ma (the figures are drawn to emphasize what may happen to pre-existing sediments and the inset illustrates the effect of erosion); the crustal cross-section and temperature distribution at the end of rifting assuming that syn-rift sediments mostly fill the basin. This model has: $a = 125\ km$, $t_c = 35\ km$, $T_R = 250\,°C$ and the sediments are a mixture of sandstone and shale.

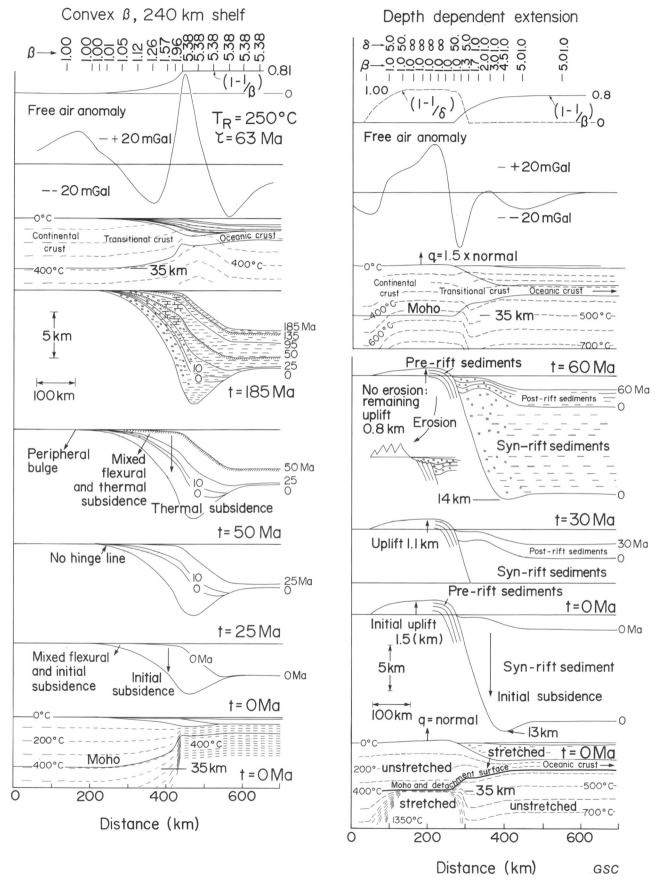

Figure 9.21

Figure 9.22

GSC

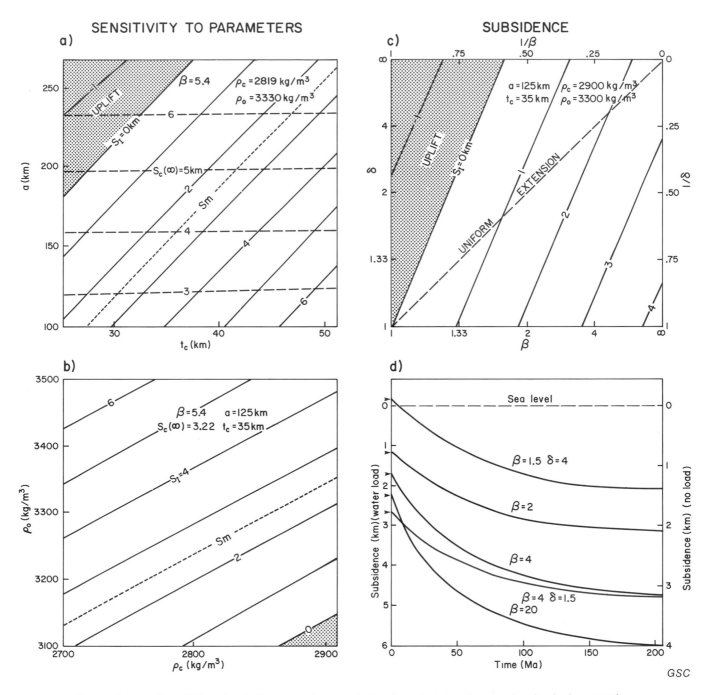

Figure 9.23. Sensitivity of subsidence (when loaded with water) to changes in physical properties (panels a and b) and to changes in the amount of extension given by ß and δ, (panels c and d). Panel a shows the sensitivity of the initial subsidence (black lines) and the total thermal subsidence (red lines) to changes in lithospheric and crustal thickness (a and t_c, respectively). Panel b shows sensitivity of initial subsidence to changes in the densities of crust and mantle (ρ_c and ρ_o, respectively). The dashed lines (S_m) in panels a and b represent the depth of new oceanic lithosphere. Panel c shows the amount of initial subsidence or uplift for the depth-dependent extension model, as a function of ß and δ. Panel d shows the subsidence versus time for uniform (black) and depth-dependent (red) extension models for various values of ß and δ. The initial subsidence at t = 0 Ma is given by the arrows. The subsidence is shown when loaded by water and with no load. In panels a to c values of key parameters held constant are shown at the top of each panel.

The outer shelf was probably too deep (~ 800 m) at the end of the Jurassic (Fig. 9.25d), suggesting either that our estimates of the thickness of syn-rift and Jurassic sediments beneath the outer shelf are too low, or more likely that withdrawal of salt from beneath the shelf to form diapirs had thinned the pre-Cretaceous section. If this is correct, withdrawal of a layer of salt (Argo Formation) about 1 km thick must have been nearly complete by the end of the Early Cretaceous, since model predictions of bathymetry are acceptable from that time (see Fig. 9.60). It is important to remember that a specified thickness model uses the presently observed sediment distribution. It does not take into account earlier phases of sediment movement. The clue to these movements is unacceptable paleobathymetries.

Uniform extension models predict unacceptable pre-Cretaceous bathymetry for the shelf, even when the salt is restored to a reasonable initial thickness; therefore, it is likely that extension varies with depth. The ß and δ values for the inner shelf and hinge zone (Fig. 9.25) are not unique. This model is an end member in which there is no erosion of crust raised above sea level on rifting. To reproduce the same stratigraphy and paleobathymetry when crust is eroded would require that δ be increased to prevent onlap, onlap would be assisted by erosion, and ß decreased because erosion, like stretching, creates space for sediments.

Onlap ended by the beginning of the Late Cretaceous (Fig. 9.25). Evidently, thermal subsidence of the hinge zone was waning by this time and flexure was insufficient to maintain onlap. This effect parallels that of the simple uniform extension models and can be seen in the other cross-sections examined in detail. We agree with Watts (1982) and Watts and Thorne (1984) that flexure and thermal subsidence of syn-rift uplifts can combine to produce an onlap-offlap cycle, which in this case could be the cause of the Vail et al. (1977) Jurassic supercycle. That is, the long-term properties of the stratigraphy are explained without changes in sea level. A series of supercycles will emerge if we choose to analyze the early stratigraphy from rifted margins of all ages (Watts, 1982). That the supercycles correlate in absolute time, as well as with the thermal age of the basin, may be a coincidence of worldwide plate reorganizations which serve to synchronize phases of basin creation.

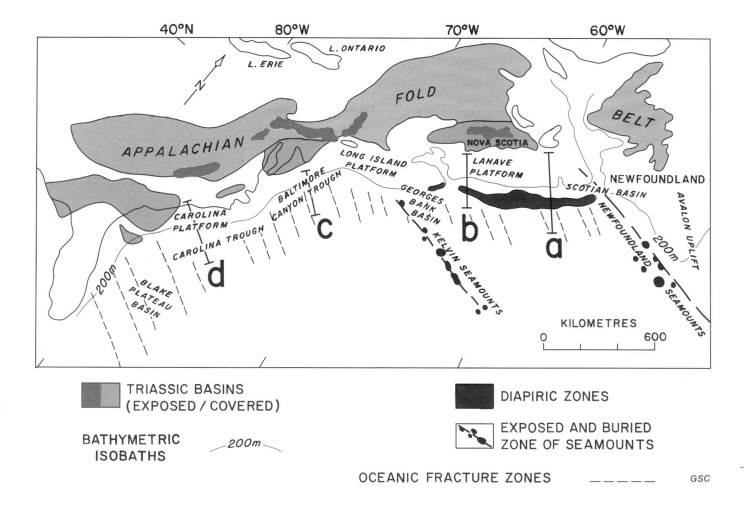

Figure 9.24. Location of the four cross-sections along the east coast: a) the Scotian Basin, b) the LaHave Platform, c) the Baltimore Canyon Trough, and d) the Carolina Trough.

It is shown in the modelling for the other cross-sections that the time when onlap ceases is sensitively related to the ß and δ stretching profiles beneath the inner shelf and hinge zone, erosion of uplifts, and the effects of pre-existing topography which may not be related to the rifting process. To determine the amplitude of a superimposed eustatic sea level rise during this onlap phase, as proposed by Watts and Thorne (1984), is difficult. Their model, which includes a 120 m rise in sea level from the Jurassic, culminating in the Late Cretaceous, predicts an end to the first onlap cycle at the end of the Cretaceous followed by a step down in the Paleocene. Closer inspection of the stratigraphy of the U.S. coastal plain, using data from Brown et al. (1972) and Watts and Thorne (1984, their profiles 1-4, Fig. 2), shows that the timing of offlap at the end of the first cycle varies from Early to Late Cretaceous. It is by no means synchronous along the margin. Our results suggest that the onlap cycle and its termination can equally well be modelled without a rise in sea level. Sea level may have changed but the change cannot be unambigously determined from the stratigraphy.

We return to a more detailed examination of thermal history in a later section.

LaHave Platform

As its name implies, the LaHave Platform region, offshore southwestern Nova Scotia has a platformal cross-section (Fig. 9.26a), with seismically well-defined, uniformly dipping basement and sedimentary strata beneath the platform but less well known deep structure farther offshore. The well control in this section is good, Mohican I-100 being the only well that is sufficiently along strike to require special consideration when comparing model predictions with observations. The cross-section shows the stratigraphy by continuous lines where known or confidently inferred, and as dashed lines elsewhere. The section is similar in style to the section along USGS line 32 off North Carolina (discussed later), and has a similar free air gravity anomaly.

The models assume that prior to rifting the crust and lithosphere beneath this section were the same as for the Scotian Basin section some 200 km to the east. This is not known to be correct, but it is a reasonable starting point for a comparison of margin development. The model (Fig. 9.26) assumes depth-dependent extension and has a 100 km wide crustal transition zone extending from midway across the shelf to mid-way down the slope. The effect of sub-crustal extension, characterized by δ, which extends farther landward than the crustal extension, characterized by ß, is to cause syn-rift basement uplift of the region which later became the shelf, and to reduce the paleobathymetry of the region landward of oceanic crust by comparison with an equivalent uniform extension model, when the margin was young. For the purposes of illustration the model is the opposite end member to the Scotian Basin model in that it assumes all uplifted basement was eroded before onlap of sediments onto the shelf. The amount eroded ($\gtrsim 2$ km) is shown by the distance from the dashed line to the surface (Fig. 9.26e).

Model sediment was added in a decompacted form according to the present distribution where its thickness is known, approximately landward of the well Acadia K-62. Elsewhere the sediment was added so that the paleobathymetry of the model slope and rise is similar to the present bathymetry. The model may therefore be regarded as a "constant paleobathymetry" model for the slope and rise and a "specified thickness" model for the shelf. Apart from a short interval in the Middle Jurassic, the model predicts a realistic shelf, shelf-break and upper slope paleobathymetry, and the predicted subsidence history at the well locations is in accord with that inferred from the well data except for the Tertiary in the wells of the outer shelf.

The simplicity of the model is appealing. Progressive sedimentary onlap of the shelf during the Jurassic occurs naturally, largely in response to thermal subsidence of the eroded region. Offlap occurs during the Tertiary because the lithosphere beneath the shelf achieves thermal stability. Sedimentation on the outer shelf is possible since that region continues to be flexurally downwarped by sediment loads beneath the slope and rise. The model predicts that the shelf break remained in the same position throughout.

Lithologies were chosen in accordance with those from the wells and from equivalent formations in other locations on the margin (Jansa and Wade, 1975). In particular, the Late Jurassic configuration is suitable for the development of a carbonate bank. Lower Jurassic sediments beneath the slope are assumed to be dominated by salt. The diapirs, seen on seismic sections at the base of the slope, are also assumed to be salt and are modelled as a salt province which was deposited in accordance with the stratigraphy shown in the figures. Presumably, salt movement was sufficiently seaward of the shelf to have had no significant effect on the stratigraphy beneath the shelf. Elsewhere, clastic sand-shale lithologies are assumed for the sediments.

The failings of the model (Fig. 9.27) are instructive because they indicate geological events which affected margin stratigraphy and modified otherwise simple predictions. The seismic data of the outer shelf and slope suggest four major reflectors A-D which do not coincide closely with model stratigraphy, shown as solid lines. A series of reflectors form dashed line A. One interpretation suggests that these represent the collapsed position of the uppermost Jurassic carbonates resulting from salt migration. The configuration of the reflectors that form line A is incompatible with a margin that had simple paleobathymetry. If the salt were withdrawn from beneath the upper slope to form a salt province during the Cretaceous, as shown, the predicted end of the Jurassic (144 Ma) horizon could be downfaulted to position A. Reflector B

Figure 9.25. Comparison of model results with observations for the Scotian Basin. Panel a) observed cross section. Sedimentary horizons are defined from seismic reflection data, tied to borehole data where possible. See text for further details. Panels b), c), d), and e) model cross sections show stratigraphy and lithology at the times indicated. Underscored stratigraphic horizons are: end Jurassic, end Early Cretaceous, end Late Cretaceous and present. Panel f) shows the ß and δ distributions and equivalent crustal and sub-crustal lithospheric thinning (1-1/ß) and (1-1/δ).

Figure 9.26. Comparison of model results with observations for the La Have Platform. Underscored stratigraphic horizons are end Jurassic, end Cretaceous and present. Patterns and description are as in Figure 9.25.

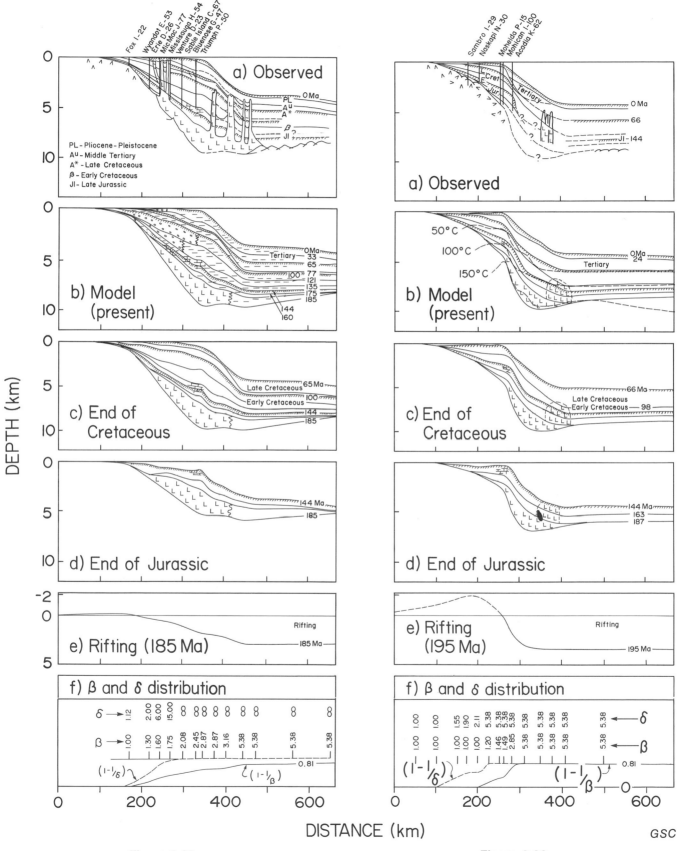

Figure 9.25

Figure 9.26

may correspondingly be the sagged position of the stratigraphic horizon representing the end of the Albian (98 Ma).

Salt withdrawal in the form of event 1 could explain reflectors A and B, but reflectors C and D are probably evidence of a major Tertiary erosional event, termed "event 2". Normal sedimentation during the Paleogene would have produced an end Oligocene horizon shown in Figure 9.27 at 24 Ma. Erosion of the lower and mid-Tertiary sediments, perhaps by contour currents, resulted in downcutting to reflector C. Reflector D occurs within the post-erosional infilling (probably Miocene and more recent), which brings the margin to its present bathymetry. Timing of erosional event 2 as Oligocene is speculative, but its existence is confirmed by a major Tertiary unconformity within the wells Moheida P-15, Mohican I-100, and Acadia K-62. For the purpose of interpretation of the Tertiary sedimentary section, the projected position of Mohican I-100 should be moved seaward as shown. This is equivalent to noting that erosion extended farther landward at the location of Mohican I-100, some 15 km west of the modelled section. Events 1 and 2 could be included in the thermomechanical model but there is little to be gained by such an exercise in sediment addition and removal. What is more important is that the events were found to be necessary by comparison with a model in which simple bathymetric profiles were used. An erosional event, like event 2, is considered for illustrative purposes in the model of the Carolina Trough.

Attempts to reproduce the shelf stratigraphy, using uniform extension models with geologically instantaneous rifting events, were not successful because the onset of subsidence of the regions of the mid- and inner shelf occurred too early. This early subsidence either resulted in immediate post-rift onlap of the platform or unrealistic sediment and paleobathymetric distributions.

The model shown might be improved slightly by extending the crustal stretching region an additional 50 km landward and eroding less of the uplifted basement. Such a model would conform more closely to the convex-ß archetype for platforms. Comparison of the LaHave platform model and observed cross-section (Fig. 9.26) with the convex-ß, 120 km shelf model (Fig. 9.20) shows that the LaHave platform is clearly of this form but that the crustal transition region is a little narrower than for the archetype. It is unlikely that a deep trough of sediments exists beneath the region of the slope because the shelf edge has not prograded far enough seaward (compare Fig. 9.20 and 9.21). The apparent hinge line beneath the outer shelf is too deep to be a hinge separating flexural and tectonically subsided regions. Its presence is largely the result of projecting the position of Mohican I-100 in a normal direction onto the cross-section. Alternative projections (for example preserving distance from the shelf break) would have de-emphasized the hinge, and the 'jog' in the γ-profile (Fig. 9.26f) would largely disappear. If the model lithologies are correct and the sediments have the same conduc-

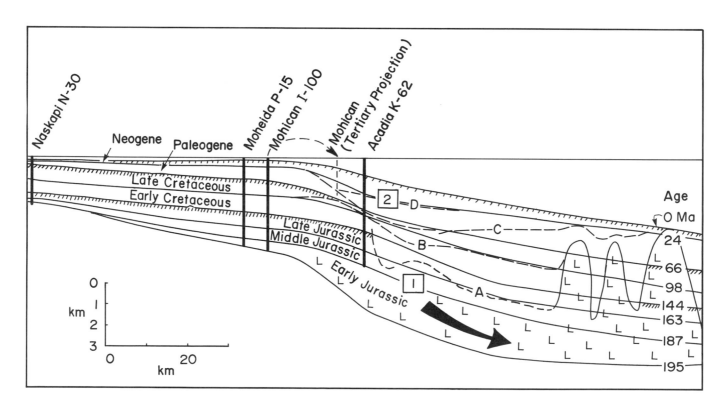

GSC

Figure 9.27. Detail of the model results from Figure 9.26 (solid lines) compared with prominent seismic reflectors (dashed lines A,B,C,D) for the outer shelf and slope regions of the LaHave Platform. See text for explanation of events 1 ans 2 which may have caused the difference between observed and model stratigraphy.

tivities as those of the Scotian Basin, the results (Fig. 9.26) indicate that only the relatively thin Jurassic sediments below the outer shelf and slope have temperatures exceeding 100°C. This result should be compared with the correspondingly much larger volumes of sediments beneath model sections of the Scotian Basin and Baltimore Canyon Trough (see Fig. 9.59, 9.28).

Baltimore Canyon Trough — USGS line 25

The interpreted cross-section along the USGS multichannel seismic line 25 off southern New Jersey (Fig. 9.28) is based on that of Grow (1980), Poag (1980), and Schlee and Grow (1980), with additions to include more recent drilling data (Libby-French, 1984) and seismic results from the LASE project (LASE Study Group, 1986; Fig. 9.27). The interpretation has been discussed in detail by these authors and others (Steckler and Watts, 1978; Poag, 1979) and is not repeated here. We point out that drilling did not extend below Upper Jurassic rocks, however, so that neither the total depth of the basin nor the nature and timing of sedimentation before the Late Jurassic are well known. In particular, the depth of the base of the syn- and post-rift sediments in the deepest part of the trough may be from 15-19 km depending on the thickness of pre-rift sediments. Sawyer et al. (1982a,b) have also modelled this cross-section using a stretching model.

The free air gravity anomaly is subdued, suggesting that flexure is relatively less important than on the Scotian margin. This lack of flexure is in keeping with a margin that was strongly stretched during rifting and received most of its sediment during rifting or soon after, when the lithosphere was still very weak.

Several features of this cross-section that are common to all transects off the New Jersey coast (USGS lines 2, 6, and 25) and that require explanations within the context of the thermomechanical model are:

1) the sharp hinge line and the shallow depth of the basin landward of the hinge line;

2) the deep spoon-shape of the basin;

3) the relationship between the spoon-shape of the basin, the thickness of the underlying crust, and inferred estimates of crustal extension;

4) the great thickness of Jurassic and older sediments by comparison with post-Jurassic sediments;

5) the shallowing of Jurassic stratigraphic horizons beneath the slope close to, and seaward of, the COST-B3 well;

6) the 'sag' in the position of the Jurassic reflectors beneath the middle of the shelf; and

7) the increase in rate of sediment accumulation on the shelf since the end of the Oligocene.

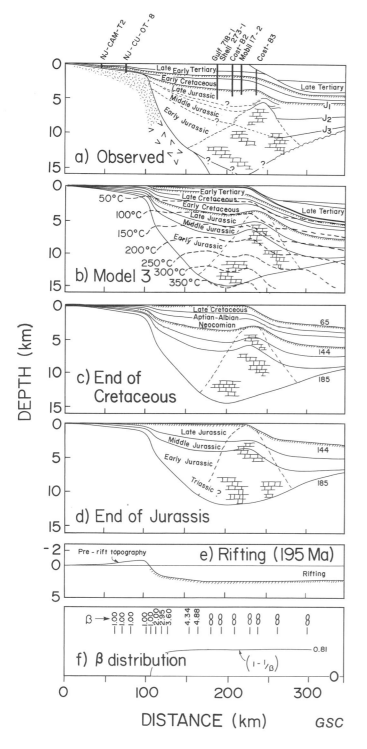

Figure 9.28. Comparison of model 3 (panels b-e) with observations (panel a) for USGS line 25 in the Baltimore Canyon Trough. Model cross sections show stratigraphy and carbonate bank at present, end Cretaceous, end Jurassic and rifting (195 Ma), respectively. Panel b also shows the predicted temperature distribution. Panel f shows the ß distribution and corresponding lithospheric thinning (1-1/ß). In this model a = 125 km, t_c = 38 km, T_R = 250°C. This is a uniform extension and melt segregation model with an oceanic crustal thickness of 6.5 km. Sediment lithologies are sandstone and shale except in the region of the carbonate bank. A small amount of pre-existing topography (1 km) is assumed to have existed landward of the hinge line; paleobathymetry remained fixed except in the late Tertiary when increasing sedimentation on the continental rise led to a decrease in bathymetry in that region.

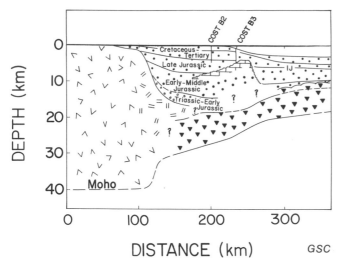

Figure 9.29. Cross-section of the crust and overlying sedimentary basin along USGS line 25 in the Baltimore Canyon Trough. The crustal structure is based on results from LASE (Large Aperture Seismic Experiment; LASE Study Group, 1986). Patterns as in Figure 9.5.

Instead of trying to duplicate the cross-section exactly by loading the model with the observed sediment load, we illustrate some important points using models with simple paleobathymetric profiles. In this approach we are in essence asking: to what extent can the observed section be explained by constant paleobathymetry that is the same as that today?

USGS line 25 models 1 and 2 (see Fig. 9.30) demonstrate that uniform extension models provide a good match for the major features of the sedimentary section (Fig. 9.28a), if the Jurassic outer shelf and upper slope sediments are mainly carbonates. Under these circumstances, the 'sag' in the Jurassic reflectors at mid-shelf and their rise beneath the outer shelf and slope (Fig. 9.28a) can be accounted for by differential compaction between the limestones and surrounding continental clastic sediments. These features evolve naturally without the need for paleobathymetric changes if the sediments below the slope are relatively more resistant to compaction. No major migration of the shelf edge is needed. This behaviour is similar to that seen in the equivalent archetype (Fig. 9.15).

The maximum depth (14-18 km) of the syn- and post-rift sediments is bracketed by varying the initial thickness of the continental crust from 35 to 40 km. The evidence available, although poor, suggests that 40 km may be a reasonable estimate of initial thickness (Taylor et al., 1980). Although the $t_c = 40$ km model predicts a deeper trough, in agreement with the seismic refraction results, it overestimates the more accurately known depth to basement beneath the continental rise; this is a common feature of the uniform extension model which represents oceanic crust by highly stretched continental crust. The results from a model with similar ß(x) but with uniform extension and melt segregation model (model 3, Fig. 9.28) are much better in this respect. Model 3 had $t_c = 38$ km but the subsidence of oceanic crust, located seaward of COST-B2 in this model, is independent of t_c in the melt segregation model.

Both magnetic anomaly, and reflection and refraction evidence (Fig. 9.29), leave little doubt that oceanic crust, or oceanic-like crust, extends landward beneath the continental shelf to a point near the COST-B2 well. Some interpretations of reflection line 25 (e.g. Schlee and Grow, 1980, their Fig. 5) and magnetic anomaly modelling of the sections along USGS lines 2, 6, 10 and 3 (Klitgord and Behrendt, 1979) suggest that the deepest part of the trough lies landward of the oceanic crust. This is possible because when $t_c > 35$ km, both the initial and final tectonic subsidence of highly stretched continental crust (ß > 5) are greater than that of normal oceanic crust. A basement ridge in the form of a 3-5 km step-up from continental to oceanic crust is predicted if it is possible to extend continental crust substantially without intruding it with basaltic melt. Figure 9.30 (model 1) illustrates this change in predicted basement depth (change A to B), when a uniform extension model is replaced by a uniform extension and melt segregation model in which there is an abrupt change from extended continental to oceanic crust at the 200 km position. Steps of this kind are most likely to occur where the continental crust was thick before stretching and where the crust is greatly stretched — circumstances also associated with deep 'spoon-shaped' basins. The raised areas of oceanic crust may be vulnerable to decapitation and obduction as ophiolites during compression and attempted subduction of the rifted continental margin.

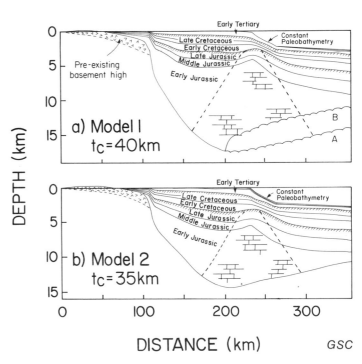

Figure 9.30. Model results showing the predicted cross-section along USGS line 25 in the Baltimore Canyon Trough for 195 Ma old uniform extension models 1 and 2 (a = 125 km, $T_R = 250°C$, $t_c = 40$ km (Model 1), $t_c = 35$ km (Model 2)) and having constant paleobathymetry equal to the present bathymetry. Both models had a pre-existing basement high equal to that of the Arabian Platform. Sediment properties and distribution are the same as those of the model 3 (Fig. 9.28). Panel a shows the effect of changing from a uniform extension model (A) to a uniform extension and melt segregation model (B) at the 200 km position.

COASTAL PLAIN EXTENSION USGS LINE 25

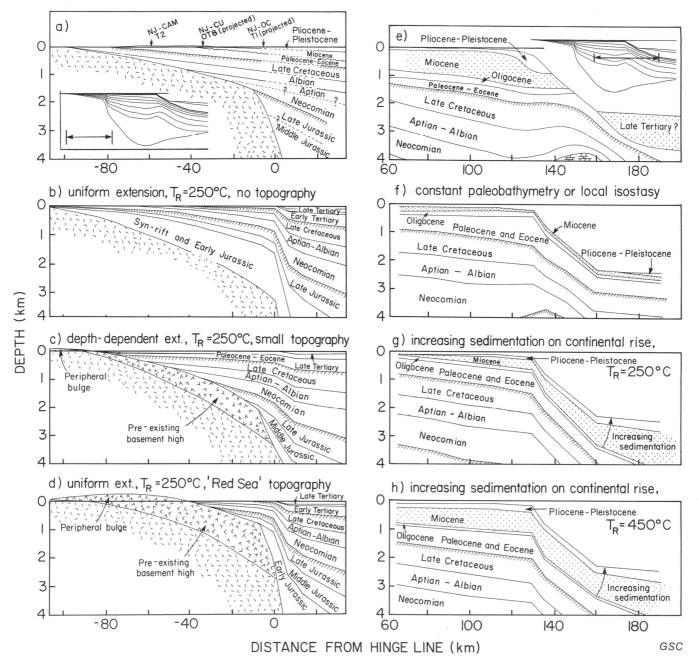

Figure 9.31. Comparison of details of model results (panels b-d, f-h) with observations (panels a, e) along USGS line 25 for the hinge line and shelf edge regions. Insets in panel a and e show relative position of panels a-d and e-h to the slope, respectively. Panels b, c, and d show the relative effects of pre-existing topography and depth-dependent extension on sedimentation landward of the hinge line. Panels f, g, and h illustrate how changing amounts of sedimentation on the continental rise can flexurally influence sedimentation on the outer shelf and continental slope once thermal subsidence has waned. These panels show that increasing sedimentation on the continental rise can produce sedimentation patterns on the shelf similar to those caused by a rise in sea level. See text for a more detailed description.

A uniform extension and melt segregation model ($t_c = 40$ km, Fig. 9.34) gives the best agreement with the LASE estimates of crustal thickness and depth to the Moho (Fig. 9.29). Even in this model the Moho is not as deep as the seismic results suggest; however, the oceanic crust beneath this section may be thicker than the 6.5 km used in the model. The model results are presented as though the melt underplates the stretched crust to emphasize its contribution to the total crustal thickness. An equivalent model of uniform extension predicts the discontinuity following the bold dashed line in Figure 9.34. This depth is much too shallow (compare with Fig. 9.29) and this suggests that melt segregation is an important process. A case for melt segregation can be made for this example because the great depth of the basin requires a high value of ß, yet the seismic thickness of the crust is too large for uniform extension models.

The models emphasize the strongly concave nature of the ß distribution, a result in accord with a deep spoon-shaped basin that subsided by more than 12 km within 50 Ma of rifting (Fig. 9.28d).

All the acceptable models predict relatively thin Cretaceous and Tertiary shelf sediments. This partly reflects the decrease in thermal subsidence with time but is also related to the superimposed thermal blanketing effect of the thick syn-rift and Jurassic sediments. The late stage tectonic subsidence is reduced by comparison with a starved model approximately in proportion to the thickness of older sediments. Both models of Figure 9.30 have the same characteristics except for the difference in t_c, yet the model with the overall deepest basin (model 1) predicts a post-Jurassic section on the shelf thinner by about 500 m than in model 2, and there are no post-Eocene shelf sediments.

Figure 9.28b also illustrates the predicted temperature distribution in the sediments if they are assumed to have the same properties as those of the Scotian margin. We have no geochemical evidence with which to test these predictions, but the predicted present temperature gradient beneath the outer shelf is in agreement with the observations from the COST-B2 (Scholle, 1977) and COST-B3 (Scholle, 1980) wells, about 23°C/km, but is about 15% higher than that predicted by Sawyer et al. (1982b). The discrepancy is presumably a result of differing assumed thermal properties of the sediments.

Several factors may combine to produce the hinge zone subsidence: 1) uplift from lateral heat flow at this margin may be important because the transition zone is narrow; 2) lithospheric decoupling across the narrow transition zone may have prevented early flexural onlap; 3) pre-existing topography, perhaps related to the rifting process but not properly understood, may have had to be downwarped before onlap could occur; and 4) depth-dependent extension may have uplifted the surface. Figure 9.31 shows that sediment thickness landward of the hinge line is less than that expected even for a $T_R = 250$°C model, and it is the reduced subsidence and the overall form of onlap and offlap that require explanation.

The effect of lateral heat flow is to produce a transient uplift which delays sedimentation but does not reduce its ultimate thickness. In the present case, it can only offer a partial explanation by way of delaying onlap until the Late Jurassic-Early Cretaceous. Decoupling of the continental and oceanic lithospheres near the hinge line during the Jurassic may have occurred, but we have no evidence to prove it. It offers an explanation for delayed flexure landward of the hinge line but is not predicted by the thermomechanical model which would have cooled significantly by the Middle to Late Jurassic. We consider the most likely explanation for the sharp hinge line and small coastal plain in this region, by comparison with that farther south, to be pre-existing basement topography combined with uplift from depth-dependent extension that had to be flexurally downwarped before onlap could occur. This explanation accounts both for the progressive nature of the initial onlap, an effect not seen when the surface is initially flat, and for the reduced sedimentation.

Figure 9.31 shows a comparison of various of these possible effects on sedimentation landward of the hinge line. Panel a shows the observed cross-section. Panel b shows that a uniform extension model with no pre-existing topography and which ignores lateral heat flow, predicts onlap almost immediately following rifting. It predicts the correct width for the downflexed zone, but the hinge zone is too deep, most of the sediments are Jurassic, and Tertiary sediments are very thin. Panel d shows that if a topographic high, like that of the Arabian Shield adjacent to the Red Sea, existed landward of the Baltimore Canyon hinge line, onlap would be progressive and would be delayed until sufficient flexure had occurred to depress topography below the depositional baseline. The sediment wedge is too small, however, and insufficient onlap is predicted, even if the peripheral bulge in the basement is eroded. Panel c shows the combined effect of low amplitude (1 km maximum) pre-existing topography plus uplift caused by depth-dependent extension. In this limiting model, the lithosphere below 35 km depth in the hinge zone and seaward of that position is extended by an infinite amount, whereas the crust landward of the hinge line remains unextended. Crustal extension elsewhere is the same as that for the other models. The two effects combine to give initial uplift that is very similar to that of the present topography of the Arabian Shield. The thermal uplift from depth-dependent extension decays as the margin cools, thereby allowing a larger final sediment wedge than that of panel d and in much better agreement with observation, than the model of panel b, in that the sediments are largely Cretaceous and Tertiary in age.

The strongest argument in favour of a varying component of pre-existing topography is the doubling in width of the coastal plain along strike from New York to Delaware, a region in which the margin seaward of the hinge line has uniform properties and for which models would otherwise predict uniform onlap. Flexure along this segment is probably uniform; pre-existing topography probably increased to the north. Unfortunately, we cannot assume that the models start from a flat surface.

Watts (1981), who used a lithosphere with the form of a uniform elastic plate that increased in thickness with time as it cooled, suggested that progressive onlap of the coastal plain was in response to the associated increase in flexural rigidity. Landward of the hinge line, the lithosphere retains its initial flexural characteristics, however, and our results give a coastal plain of almost constant width, except when there are thermal uplifts or pre-existing topography. This agrees with Watts et al. (1982, their Fig. 15).

Offlap of sedimentation is not necessarily in response to falling sea level; it also occurs when the basin depocentre migrates seaward and the flexural response follows the depocentre. All of our models of line 25 (Fig. 9.28, 9.30) for example, predict this behaviour landward of the hinge line. Any margin that has near constant paleobathymetry throughout its development will undergo offlap after about 2 lithospheric cooling time constants, and a rise in sea level is generally required to prevent this offlap. The offlap between Late Cretaceous and Miocene, a common feature of many cross-sections of the east coast of the U.S.A. (Brown et al., 1972), may reflect this tendency.

The converse, onlap and coastal aggradation during margin evolution, cannot be uniquely attributed to a rise in sea level. Sedimentation may be an important clue to sea level change in the manner suggested by Vail et al. (1977) and Vail and Hardenbol (1979), but flexure from increased sedimentation on the continental rise can create the same form of onlap. Figure 9.31 illustrates how this effect can explain a thick Miocene section along line 25 (panel e). Panels f, g and h show enlargements of the outer shelf, slope, and rise for models which have: (f) constant paleobathymetry equal to that observed today (like those in Fig. 9.30), in which case thermal subsidence and sedimentation have all but ceased by the mid-Tertiary and there is no thick Miocene section; (g) a decrease in paleobathymetry on the continental rise of 400-500 m during the Miocene and Plio-Pleistocene ($T_R = 250°C$); and (h) the same decrease in paleobathymetry as (g) but $T_R = 450°C$.

Panel f shows that in the case of constant paleobathymetry, or equivalently in the case of a local isostatic model, a sea level rise would be necessary to produce a thick Miocene section on this old rifted margin. However, panels g and h show that an increase in sediment influx, which initially bypasses the shelf and accumulates on the rise, can downflex the shelf and allow increased sedimentation there too. The strength of the rise-shelf flexural coupling increases with T_R and with the age of the margin. Even in the case $T_R = 250°C$, it can be significant.

Interpretation of seismic line 25 and other lines suggests that the upper Tertiary sediments on the continental rise of the east coast of the U.S.A. are thick (>2 km), and they could therefore give rise to increased comtemporary shelf sedimentation of the magnitude observed if $T_R = 450°C$. These results do not demonstrate that the thick Miocene section and associated onlap is solely flexural, but that increased sedimentation rates on the continental rise will give the same shelf sedimentation as a sea level rise. It is important to consider the complete sediment distribution when making inferences concerning the effects of a rise in sea level.

Carolina Trough — USGS line 32

The Carolina Trough, offshore North and South Carolina, and its landward continuation, the Carolina Platform and coastal plain, have a uniform linear structure along their 450 km length (Grow and Markl, 1977; Klitgord and Behrendt, 1979; Klitgord and Grow, 1980; Dillon et al., 1983). USGS multichannel seismic line 32 (Dillon et al., 1983; Hutchinson et al., 1983) is sited near the southern end of the trough adjacent to the Blake Outer Ridge, a region of post-Oligocene sedimentation that partly covers the southern end of the trough (Bryan, 1970). The trough

is terminated in the south at the Blake Spur Fracture Zone; no other major fracture zone offsets the structure along its length (Klitgord and Behrendt, 1979).

Comparison of cross-sections of the margin at several positions along the trough (Klitgord and Grow, 1980; Dillon et al., 1983; Hutchinson et al., 1983) shows the Mesozoic development to have been similar and that the section along line 32 (Fig. 9.32a) differs from that along other seismic lines only because of the draping by recent sediments.

The deepest part of the trough, 60-80 km wide, is thought to contain salt because there are diapirs that form a linear chain seaward of the Jurassic shelf edge (Dillon et al., 1983). On line 32 the gently dipping basement can be traced seaward from beneath the platform to the inferred position of the salt, where a strong reflector at a depth of 11-12 km may mark the top of the salt. Reflectors do occur at greater depth beneath the trough but their interpretation is uncertain. Basement cannot be followed beneath the paleo-shelf and slope (Fig. 9.32a, Hutchinson et al., 1983, Fig. 4), but oceanic basement can be traced landward to a position near the prominent diapir where its depth is also 11-12 km. It is unlikely that basement is much deeper than 12 km in the region where it cannot be traced.

A paleoslope, interpreted to be formed of truncated Jurassic and Cretaceous sediments, is clearly seen beneath the present continental slope. This interpretation is confirmed by the lines farther to the north. The present shelf edge has evidently retreated over 100 km from its original position. We follow Hutchinson et al. (1983) in interpreting the Jurassic and Early Cretaceous shelf edge to have been a carbonate bank or reef which could partly account for the steepness of the paleoslope, now about 16°. This slope should be compared with the 9° slope of the present Blake Escarpment to the south. During the Late Cretaceous and Early Tertiary, clastic sediments prograded across the shelf and draped the slope and rise. This interpretation is subject to the correct identification of the J_1, ß and A^u reflectors beneath the present slope and rise (Klitgord and Grow, 1980). The mid-Tertiary (A^u) unconformity (Tucholke and Mountain, 1979) is thought to represent a major, widespread Late Eocene to Miocene erosional event, which may have been responsible for the truncation of the Jurassic-Cretaceous shelf, and extends across most of the section (Fig. 9.32a). The overlying thick layer of post-Oligocene sediments is the northern flank of the Blake Outer Ridge, already mentioned, which is much thinner to the north, allowing a clearer interpretation of the underlying Mesozoic section.

Growth faulting (Fig. 9.32a) occurs along the length of the Carolina Trough. It is interpreted to result from withdrawal of salt from beneath the paleoshelf (Dillon et al., 1983) but there are no offshore wells to confirm this interpretation. Those onshore along the projection of line 32 (e.g. NCNHOT15, Brown et al., 1972) are shallow ($\gtrsim 500$ m) but serve to confirm the Aptian-Albian onlap of the coastal plain at the Cape Fear Arch. They are separated by 40 km of shelf from the landward end of line 32. The Esso Hatteras Light No. 1 well, 250 km north of line 32, penetrated basement at 3 km and shows an Early Cretaceous onlap (Brown et al., 1972). Its projected location (approximately 250 km position, Fig. 9.32a) has only 1 km of sediment above the break-up unconformity, demonstrating the influence of the Cape Fear Arch on reducing the thickness of shelf and coastal plain sediments.

The crustal structure beneath the margin is not known. Hutchinson et al., (1983) summarized data on crustal thickness beneath the coastal plain and suggested crustal thickness variations based on a locally compensated gravity model. In our modelling, we have been guided by the similarity of the Carolina Trough structure to that of the LaHave Platform and by Hutchinson et al. (1983).

Features of line 32 that require explanation within the context of the modelling are:

1) Whether the interpreted stratigraphy can be explained by the subsidence of a stretching model;

2) The form of the stretching profile;

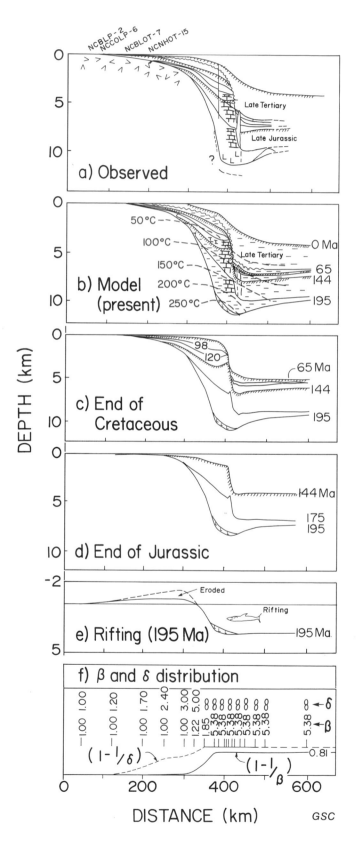

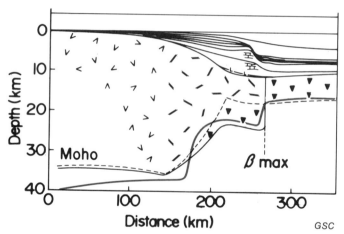

Figure 9.33. An alternative interpretation of the model results (solid black line) shown in Figure 9.34d (dashed line), compared to the inferred cross-section based on observations. The red line represents observations by Hutchinson et al. (1983). The region of the model just landward of oceanic crust is interpreted to consist of basaltic magma (solid inverted triangles) underplating the continental crust. Patterns as in Figure 9.5.

Figure 9.32. Comparison of model 3 results (panels b, c, d, e) with observations (panel a) for USGS line 32 in the Carolina Trough. Model cross sections show stratigraphy and carbonate bank at present, end Cretaceous, end Jurassic, and rifting (195 Ma), respectively. Panel b shows the predicted temperature distribution. Panel f shows the β and δ distributions and corresponding crustal and subcrustal lithospheric thinning, (1-1/β) and (1-1/δ) respectively. A depth-dependent extension model with standard parameter values was used. Sediment lithologies are sandstone and shale except in the region of the carbonate bank. Underscored horizons are latest Jurassic, latest Cretaceous, and present.

3) The degree to which the paleoslope has been truncated;

4) Possible bounds on the amount of sediment eroded to produce the unconformity Au;

5) The effect of salt withdrawal on margin stratigraphy; and

6) The origin of the progressive sedimentary onlap of the Carolina Platform.

The depth-dependent extension model (Fig. 9.32 and 9.34), which uses the standard set of parameter values (Tables 9.1 and 9.5), has subcrustal stretching which extends about 200 km farther landward than crustal stretching (Fig. 9.32f). Both the ß and δ profiles have a simple form.

The basement beneath the Carolina Platform was uplifted by up to 900 m on rifting. Erosion is assumed to reduce rapidly the maximum topography to 400 m (Fig. 9.32e) thereby partially creating the space necessary for sediments to accumulate landward of the zone of crustal stretching. The observed Jurassic — Cretaceous onlap of the eroded basement is accurately reproduced by this model (compare Fig. 9.32 panels c, d, e to a) as the combined effect of thermal subsidence and flexural downwarping, without the need for changes in sea level. As in other cases uniform extension models fail to reproduce the progressive onlap. The model is intermediate to, and probably more realistic than, those for the Scotian Basin and LaHave Platform, in that uplifted crust is partly eroded (Fig. 9.32e). Acceptable end members having no erosion or having total erosion of uplifted basement could be developed. Such models would have modified ß and δ profiles beneath the shelf by comparison with the model presented. For example, a model with less erosion would require crustal stretching to reach farther into the continent and would have a convex-ß style.

The ß-distribution of the model is determined by the need for the basin to deepen seaward of the 300 km position (Fig. 9.32a) and to be 11-12 km deep beneath the trough. Uniform extension or depth-dependent extension models can only achieve sufficient depth using the standard parameter values if the crust beneath the trough is oceanic, or continental crust thinned to an equivalent thickness. Consequently, the predicted crustal transition zone is narrow, only 75 km wide (Fig. 9.34). That the stretching follows a convex-ß style in the transition region follows directly from the shape of the basement profile, a feature that is well determined.

The paleoprofile method of adding sediments was used, subject to the additional constraint that the model stratigraphy conforms to the interpreted section (Fig. 9.32a; Hutchinson et al., 1983). Could realistic paleobathymetries and the correct form of coastal onlap be achieved while still reproducing the final stratigraphy? The model certainly reproduces the present stratigraphy. Its earlier evolution suggests the following interpretation. The outer shelf was a carbonate bank from the Middle Jurassic until

Figure 9.34. Comparison of model results on a crustal scale for the four cross-sections modelled in detail (see Fig. 9.24). There is considerable variation in the style of these sections, largely due to differences in the stretching profiles and sedimentation (see text for further details). Patterns as in Figure 9.5.

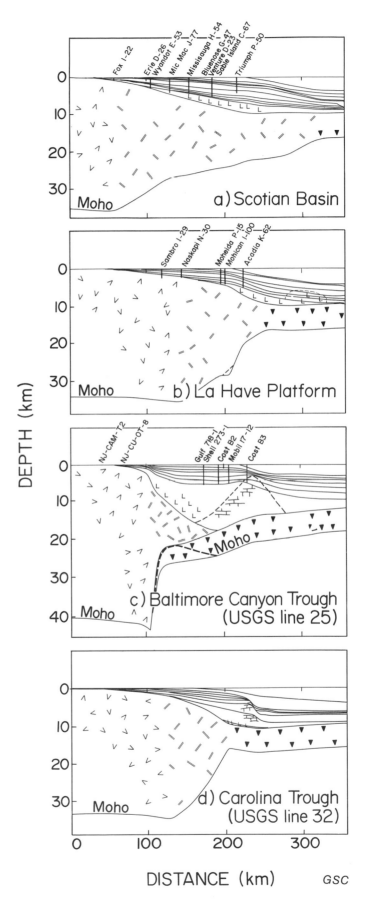

Table 9.3 Matrix thermal conductivities and heat production values for 32 sedimentary rock samples from the Nova Scotia Shelf

Sample Description Formation, Well and Sample Depth (m)		K (W/m°K)	ρ (g/cm3) or (Mg/m3)	Heat Prod. (μW/m3)	Th/U
BANQUEREAU:					
Sachem D-76	(1256)	3.19	2.39	0.34	1.87
Citnalta I-59	(1231)	2.82	2.08	0.62	2.32
Oneida O-25	(1196)	2.04	2.05	0.68	1.39
Cohasset D-42	(595)	1.90	2.61	1.28	0.85
Averages		2.48 ±0.6			1.61
DAWSON CANYON:					
Adventure F-80	(831)	1.05	2.06	1.04	4.55
Citnalta I-59	(1552)	1.32	2.18	0.92	3.60
Cohasset D-42	(1227)	1.82	2.17	0.87	2.66
Oneida O-25	(1417)	2.27	2.39	0.84	2.79
Averages		1.62 ±0.5			3.40
LOGAN CANYON:					
Adventure F-80	(1020)	1.78	2.50	1.14	2.04
Intrepid L-80	(2361)	1.71	2.43	1.32	3.92
Citnalta I-59	(1920)	1.87	2.32	1.02	3.51
Primrose F-41	(1804)	1.99	2.36	0.70	2.19
Averages		1.84 ±0.1			2.92
MISSISSAUGA:					
Intrepid L-80	(3457)	1.72	2.53	1.38	4.31
Citnalta I-59	(3507)	1.94	2.38	1.49	4.12
Demascota G-32	(2632)	2.55	2.56	0.72	4.26
Cohasset D-42	(2940)	2.58	2.42	0.79	4.37
Averages		2.20 ±0.4			4.27
MIC MAC:					
Intrepid L-80	(4108)	1.45	2.53	1.80	4.17
Citnalta I-59	(4338)	1.57	2.46	1.84	4.07
Naskapi N-30	(1731)	1.96	2.78	1.35	4.05
Bluenose G-47	(4583)	1.64	2.70	1.45	3.90
Averages		1.65 ±0.2			4.05
VERRILL CANYON:					
Demascota G-32	(3406)	1.02	2.70	1.80	4.57
Marmora C-34	(3998)	1.86	2.62	1.54	4.09
Eagle D-21	(4659)	1.81	2.63	1.65	3.82
Oneida D-25	(2833)	1.43	2.40	1.55	4.69
Averages		1.53 ±0.4			4.20
ABENAKI:					
Intrepid L-80	(2970)	2.15	2.45	0.30	1.02
Citnalta I-59	(4668)	1.35	2.30	0.52	3.79
Demascota G-32	(3708)	1.08	2.43	0.64	2.88
Cohasset D-42	(3633)	1.90	2.48	0.50	2.48
Averages		1.62 ±0.5			2.54
MOHICAN:					
Heron* H-73	(2672)	1.76	2.45	0.17	1.59
Mohican I-100	(3809)	1.87	2.47	0.95	3.80
Naskapi N-30	(2141)	2.06	2.44	0.92	4.66
Oneida O-25	(4124)	1.39	2.61	1.52	4.88
Averages		1.77 ±0.3			3.73
Average K over all formations: 1.84 ± 0.5 W/m°K					

Note: Numbers in brackets are sample depths in metres. Occasionally samples over a range of 200 to 300 m were combined. In this case the average depth is shown. ρ is wet sample density. Heat Production is the value at zero porosity.

*Heron is located on the Grand Banks.

Table 9.4. Mackenzie and McKenzie (1983) estimates of reaction constants

Reaction	E(kJ/mol)	A(/s)	γ
Sterane Isomerization at C-20	91	$k_2 = 0.007$ $k_1 = 0.006$	1.174
Hopane Isomerization at C-22	91	$k_2 = 0.025$ $k_1 = 0.016$	1.564
Steroid Hydrocarbon Aromatization	200	$k = 1.8 \times 10^{14}$	

E = activation energy; A = frequency factor; k_1 = back reaction rate coefficient; k_2 = forward reaction rate coefficient; $\gamma = k_2/k_1$

about the end of the Neocomian, thereby explaining the steepness of the paleoslope (Fig. 9.32c, d) and the reverse landward dip of reflectors on the outer paleoshelf. Carbonates can form a steep bank and differential compaction between the carbonates and the surrounding clastics creates the reverse dip (see Fig. 9.15). Note that this reverse dip ends above the carbonates in Figure 9.32a, b. The model shelf edge and slope at the end of the Cretaceous looked similar to the present Blake-Bahama Plateau at the Blake Escarpment.

By the end of the Cretaceous, clastic sediments had prograded across the model shelf, spilled over the edge, and begun to pile against the base of the steep slope. How much sediment was added from this time until the erosional event that created the A[u] reflector is not known and we have modelled end member sediment distributions to determine what effects may remain. The main effect of significant infilling, for example to a paleobathymetry like that of the Scotian Basin today, is to compact significantly

Table 9.5: Parameter and property values for sedimentary layers of the models

	Sandstone	Shale	Limestone	Salt
Matrix density (ρ_{sg}) kg/m^3	2650	2700	2710	2160
Compaction constant (h) (/m)	360	650	160	∞
Surface porosity ($\emptyset_0$) (%)	62	60	24	0
Thermal conductivity (K) Beaumont et al. (1982a)				
W/(m·°C)	4.184	1.883	2.929	5.858
cal/(cm·s·°C)	10×10^{-3}	4.5×10^{-3}	7×10^{-3}	14×10^{-3}
Model A				
W/(m·°C)	2.761	1.255	1.925	5.858
cal/(cm·s·°C)	6.6×10^{-3}	3.0×10^{-3}	4.6×10^{-3}	14×10^{-3}
Model B				
W/(m·°C)	2.552	1.130	1.757	5.858
cal/(cm·s·°C)	6.1×10^{-3}	2.7×10^{-3}	4.2×10^{-3}	14×10^{-3}
Specific heat (c)				
J/(kg·°C)	1088	837	1004	854
cal/(g·°C)	0.26	0.20	0.24	0.204
Radiogenic heat production (A)				
(μW/m^3)	0.8368	1.046	0.8368	0
cal/(cm^3·s)	2×10^{-13}	2.5×10^{-13}	2.0×10^{-13}	0

the underlying sediments and raise their level of thermal maturity. Drilling is required to test this prediction. The modelling results certainly suggest that interpreting the reflector as an unconformity is consistent with a Tertiary deposition-erosion-deposition cycle. However, it would have required erosional processes to operate on the shelf, slope, and rise.

Other models, in which the erosional event significantly cuts back a much less steep Jurassic-Cretaceous slope, predict stratigraphic horizons which are truncated by the A^u horizon in the neighbourhood of the diapir. Such truncated reflectors were not seen on line 32 or others from the Carolina Trough; therefore, it is unlikely that the erosional event which created A^u also converted a previously gently-sloping paleoslope to its present steep form. Erosion that steepened the carbonate bank from about 9° to about 15° is, however, possible.

Sediments above the A^u unconformity are assumed to be Miocene or younger. Model results suggest that, like the Baltimore Canyon Trough, there was little room for sediments on the shelf so late in the margin's evolution. Evidently, a component of flexural coupling that allows the load of the thick slope and rise prism to depress the shelf may be necessary. Models in which the elastic region of the lithosphere is between the 0° and 250°C isotherms fail to give sufficient coupling at this stage, because the lithosphere beneath the trough is hotter than 250°C (Fig. 9.32b). If the elastic region is assumed to be between the 200° and 450°C isotherms, coupling is restored and the model gives sufficient flexure. This choice of isotherms is not unique but it does suggest that the elastic core is deeper than a literal interpretation of $T_R = 250°C$ would suggest.

The model predicts a Jurassic and Early Cretaceous outer shelf that is about 800 m deep, probably too deep to be consistent with a growing carbonate bank or reef. The apparently excessive depth may be explained by salt withdrawal from that region. If salt had been withdrawn during the Cretaceous, stratigraphic horizons older than the end of the Cretaceous would deepen and growth faulting (Dillon et al., 1983) would develop. Models that reproduce present stratigraphy reproduce the post-salt withdrawal positions of horizons. The difference between model shelf paleobathymetry and that considered to be reasonable can therefore be used to estimate the timing and amount of salt withdrawal. The results strongly suggest continued withdrawal at least until the end of the Cretaceous. The cumulative total, 75 km³ per km length normal to section at line 32, is a factor of 5 larger than the estimate from Dillon et al. (1983). Their estimate of 4400 km³ withdrawn and 4100 km³ intruded as salt domes is, however, averaged along the length of the Carolina Trough and there is a concentration of diapirs near line 32. It is not clear whether the two results are compatible, given that Dillon et al. regarded their estimate as a lower limit and ours is an upper limit. Our estimate amounts to a 900 m thick layer over the 80 km wide trough.

The crustal cross-section (Fig. 9.34) predicted by the depth-dependent model (Fig. 9.32a) does not agree with that proposed by Hutchinson et al. (1983) in Figure 9.33, nor does the model gravity anomaly agree with that observed. The position of the major thinning is in reasonable agreement with Hutchinson et al. (1983) but their region of relatively thick 'rift-stage crust' below the trough is not predicted by our model. A uniform extension or depth-dependent extension model cannot give sufficient subsidence of this region if the crust was standard and remains as thick as shown by Hutchinson et al. (1983). The two models can be reconciled if melt segregation is included. If the crust beneath the trough (Fig. 9.33) is interpreted to be stretched continent (ß ~ 5) which has been underplated or intruded by segregated melt in proportion to ß, the Moho will match that predicted by Hutchinson et al. (1983). The step-up of the Moho seaward of the trough, labelled $ß_{max}$, can be interpreted as the position where the stretched crust rifted and creation of oceanic crust started. As Hutchinson et al. (1983) demonstrated, this interpretation correctly predicts the position of the East Coast Magnetic Anomaly. Our model predicts that the region of 'underplating melt' will not contribute to the anomaly because its temperature exceeds 350°C. The subsidence of the trough when underplated with melt will not differ significantly from that of the equivalent depth-dependent model because subsidence is largely insensitive to ß when it is $\gtrsim 5$. The gravity anomaly of the melt-segregation model agrees with observations much better than the depth dependent model although the minor low over the shelf, inferred to arise from low density sediments in a graben (Hutchinson et al., 1983, Fig. 8) is not reproduced.

Discussion and synthesis

A comparison of model results for the four cross-sections of eastern North America (Fig. 9.34) demonstrates the diversity of styles, even among simple margins in which there is a regular decrease in crustal thickness across the transition zone. This diversity can be explained within the context of lithospheric stretching models. The models account for all of the known first-order observations from these sections and some of the second-order properties. Crustal thickness variations are not known for the Carolina Trough or LaHave Platform, and so these models have yet to be tested. The results for the Scotian Basin and Baltimore Canyon Trough agree with observations, if reasonable departures from the model assumption of a uniformly thick, pre-rift crust are acknowledged.

Variations in the styles seen in Figure 9.34 can be attributed mainly to variations in ß across the transition zone and to variations in sedimentation. Apart from subtleties, the models are seen to fall within the range of variations predicted by the archetypal models (Fig. 9.13-9.21).

The Scotian Basin has a relatively wide linear-ß crustal transition on which there has been moderate sedimentation but where the shelf edge has only advanced over crust thinned to about one third of its original thickness. It is therefore intermediate to the archetypes in Figures 9.17 and 9.18.

The LaHave Platform may either be interpreted as a linear-ß model with a narrow transition region or a convex-ß model with a transition region of similar width to that of the Scotian Basin. There is much less sediment than in either the Scotian Basin or the Baltimore Canyon and the shelf edge has prograded over crust thinned to half its unextended thickness. It is therefore like the section in Figure 9.20.

By contrast, the Baltimore Canyon section has a narrow transition region and may be interpreted as concave-ß or linear-ß depending on whether the crust beneath the thickest sediment is truly oceanic or highly extended crust as previously discussed. Although the shelf has prograded no further in absolute distance than for the Scotian Basin, there is a thick sedimentary spoon and the edge of the shelf is over crust no more than one quarter of its unextended thickness. The Baltimore Canyon section is therefore intermediate to those in Figures 9.14 and 9.15.

The Carolina Trough section is similar to the section for the LaHave Platform, except that the shelf break has advanced a little farther. It was probably very similar to the LaHave section until the time of what is interpreted to be a major phase of upper Tertiary sedimentation. The additional sediments have prograded over thinner crust and, consequently, started to create a small trough. The section is therefore intermediate to those in Figures 9.20 and 9.21.

How do other margins fit within this classification scheme? The sections in Figure 9.5, for example, suggest the following interpretations. The southern Grand Banks is a poorly sedimented margin with a narrow transition zone, as would be expected for a transform margin. The ß distribution is most similar to that of the Baltimore Canyon and, were the shelf edge to prograde a further 100 km, a similar deep spoon basin would develop. The Labrador section is in many respects like a narrower version of the Scotian Basin. A linear-ß distribution with the shelf edge having prograded to where ß = 3 would predict the major features of this section. The Orphan Basin section suggests a wide linear-ß transition zone where the necking did not go to completion. Instead, a piece of less attenuated crust remains beneath Orphan Knoll and the transition to oceanic crust occurs to the east of it. Orphan Basin may have undergone two separate events, with nearly orthogonal stretching, and the non-monotonic ß distribution may be a result of their superposition (see Chapter 2).

The models all have a low value of T_R (250°C), or equivalently a 250°C core, indicating that the lithosphere beneath these margins is flexurally weak. This result is based on the low amplitudes of the flexural components of the observed gravity anomalies and the small hinge zones. Lithospheric weakness can, in part, be explained by the thinning of the lithosphere during extension. Interpretation of T_R as the depth at which lithospheric rocks become weak and can creep over a period of geological time of 10 to 100 Ma is, however, apparently not reconcilable with laboratory experiments (summarized by Kirby, 1980), suggesting that creep occurs at temperatures about 750°C or greater. The large flexural strength of the lithosphere beneath foreland basins (Beaumont, 1981; Karner and Watts, 1982; Quinlan and Beaumont, 1984) also demonstrates that creep cannot occur at temperatures as low as 250°C. Beaumont et al. (1982a) suggested that T_R/(geothermal gradient) be interpreted as the thickness of the elastic core of the lithosphere, the zone below that of brittle failure and above the region of creep. If the upper region of the crust is considered to be without strength as a result of faulting during stretching, then the elastic region of the lithosphere must be beneath this zone and the value of T_R increased so that the thickness of the elastic region remains the same. For this region the depth to T_R from the base of the sediments is best interpreted as the effective thickness of the elastic part of the lithosphere and the absolute value of T_R given less emphasis.

The only direct evidence for this interpretation of T_R from the modelling comes from the Carolina Trough, and perhaps from the Baltimore Canyon Trough results, where models with T_R = 250°C were less successful than models with an elastic core 250°C thick, but buried at a greater depth.

The models have considerable implications for the subsidence and temperature history of syn- and post-rift sediments. Less can be said about the fate of the largely unknown pre-rift sediments. Sediments beneath a flexural hinge zone will be preserved in an undisturbed state unless, as is commonly the case, there is pre- or syn-rift uplift and erosion. Sediments above regions of crustal extension will be preserved on the subsided parts of blocks produced by the brittle failure of the upper regions of the crust. Where ß is small and δ large, the fault block system may be uplifted and eroded. Where ß ≥ 1.60 the surface will subside no matter what the concurrent behaviour of δ, provided that it is typical lithosphere that is being extended (see Fig. 9.23). This simple interpretation implies that pre-rift sediments are presently preserved beneath mature margins where the average thickness of the overlying sediments is ≳ 4 km.

Classification of margins by style is a useful and perhaps necessary step before the style variations can be explained. Are they a consequence of inherited lithospheric structure or thermal conditions, or do they reflect along-strike alternation from active to passive rifting? Do style variations correlate with the position of hot spots during rifting? Do the style changes occur abruptly at the prolongations of oceanic transform faults or are they more diffuse? How do style variations of conjugate margins compare? Is there a difference in the way different style margins respond to continental collision? The thermomechanical model is useful because it helps us recognize these style variations.

IMPROVED MODELS OF RIFTING

Limitations of the simple kinematic models

Although the models presented in the last section are able to reproduce most of the broad scale features of the margins investigated, a number of problems remain, particularly with the kinematic stretching models. Among the most serious are: 1) the inability of the models to describe the rift phase properly, 2) the problem of correctly describing uplift of the shoulders of the rifted zones, 3) the occurrence of major unconformities within the sedimentary section, in particular the break-up unconformity, and 4) the variable degree of volcanism observed beneath the margins. These problems are addressed in this section. Before doing so, however, it is necessary to stress that our kinematic models have assumed that the lithosphere will deform in a certain way when stretched, although there is no physical justification for this assumption. The lithosphere may not extend in a way that conforms to the various ß and δ distributions that we have found acceptable in our models. Moreover any process, not necessarily stretching, which results in changes in crustal and subcrustal lithosphere thicknesses in accord with the acceptable ß and δ distributions, is also an acceptable rifting process.

This fundamental limitation of approaching rifting through kinematic modelling demonstrates the need for dynamical models which describe the underlying physical processes of the rift phase. Although the dynamical models are in their infancy, we believe that they are of sufficient importance to be included here. The models do not give accurate predictions of the rifting process. They do, however, provide insight concerning the significance of the ß and δ distributions that we have used and whether or not they are compatible with lithospheric stretching.

Dynamical models of rifting

Statement of the problem

In principle, we should be able to determine the way the lithosphere will deform when extensional, far field forces are applied to its ends. We should also be able to compute the resulting changes in the thermal regime of this deforming body, and so find the thermal and subsidence histories without having to make arbitrary assumptions about its response to extension.

The two main barriers to constructing dynamical models are our lack of knowledge of the rheology of the lithosphere and the computational problems involved in obtaining numerical solutions. It is accepted by most that the lithosphere can be divided into an upper, cool brittle layer and a lower, hotter ductile layer, but more complex brittle-ductile layering has also been proposed (Fig. 9.35). These complexities arise because rheology will vary with composition, with the applied stress, and with temperature. Even with a simple model of the rheology, for example a single elastic or viscous layer, three, second order partial differential equations must be solved at each point in the deforming body. This is accomplished through the numerical techniques of finite difference or finite element approximations for the partial differential equations. To obtain a solution in other cases, it is often necessary to simplify the rheology while ensuring that the essence of the lithosphere's behaviour is retained. How successfully this can be achieved depends on the nature of the problem to be solved. In the following discussion we assume that a model comprising an upper brittle layer and a lower ductile layer (Fig. 9.35a) is sufficient to describe the first order behaviour of the lithosphere.

Rheology of the lithosphere

The brittle region of the lithosphere (Fig. 9.35a) lies within the crust and its thickness is probably about 20-40 km. This is the maximum depth of most intra-plate earthquakes (Chen and Molnar, 1983) and the depth at which normal faults are thought to sole out into a décollement zone (Bally et al., 1981). Its thickness is probably related to composition, temperature distribution, and the amount of fluid present in fractures. This region will deform by faulting or by plastic flow, depending on the stress applied, the temperature and the confining pressure.

Several different kinds of brittle deformation have been proposed for extensional regions. Listric normal faults have been mapped on one rifted margin (Fig. 9.35; Montadert et al., 1979), and their presence has been inferred beneath many others. It has been suggested that these faults represent the primary mode of deformation and thinning within the upper brittle layer in extensional regions (Bally et al., 1981; Bally, 1982; Jackson and McKenzie, 1983). However, the amount of thinning that can be accommodated by such faults is uncertain. LePichon et al. (1982), by analysis of the geometry of listric faults, have presented a case for extension and thinning by

a factor of about 4. Others have argued that the same listric faults can thin the brittle layer only by about 20%, much less than is suggested as occurring during rifting (Chenet et al., 1982). This issue is a complex one, for there may be an additional internal plastic deformation of the individual fault blocks which cannot always be observed. Other styles of faulting have also been suggested to accommodate extension. These include low angle detachment faulting, described by Wernicke and Burchfiel (1982), which may accommodate large amounts of extension and thinning and may allow depth-dependent extension to occur. In this case, large allochthonous extensional terranes, which may be displaced tens of kilometres laterally, are decoupled from the underlying lithosphere by low angle décollement zones. These are analogous to thin-skinned allochthons in compressional orogens.

The main problem in numerical modelling of the upper brittle region is that there is no simple way of determining in an a priori manner the locations at which faulting will occur. One approach would be to specify a random distribution of faults, but in reality many young faults develop over older zones of weakness and so are not randomly distributed. A second problem is that the relative role played by plastic deformation, as opposed to faulting, is unknown (Fletcher and Hallet, 1983; Jackson and McKenzie, 1983). This question is partly one of scale. If the faults are sufficiently close together, compared to the overall dimensions of the structure being studied, an approximation of the upper layer as a continuum which deforms plastically is valid. However, if the faults are large and widely separated, the resulting deformation cannot be represented by continuum physics. Thus the nature of deformation in the upper brittle layer remains an unresolved and contentious issue.

Below the brittle upper region, the lithosphere deforms by ductile creep. Knowledge of the rheology in this region comes from laboratory studies of the deformation of rocks representative of the composition of the lower crust and upper mantle (e.g. Weertman, 1970; Ashby and Verall, 1977; Goetz and Evans, 1979; Kirby, 1980). These studies suggest that viscous flow is the primary mode of deformation below the brittle region. The creep law for viscous flow can be expressed as $\dot{\varepsilon}_{ij} = (\sigma^n_{ij} - P\delta_{ij})/2\eta$ where $\dot{\varepsilon}$ is the strain rate tensor, P is pressure, δ is the Kronecker delta, η is viscosity, and σ is the stress tensor. Values of parameter n dictate whether the flow law is linear, Newtonian (n = 1), or is nonlinear, power law in stress (n > 1) in which case the effective viscosity is dependent on the strain rate. Values of n = 3 are compatible with the laboratory observations.

The viscosity of the lithosphere is highly temperature dependent, and can be expressed by the relationship

$$\eta(T) = \eta_b \dot{\varepsilon}^{(1-n)/2n} exp[\frac{Q}{nRT_m}(\frac{T_m}{T} - 1)]$$

Figure 9.35. Rheology and deformation of the upper lithosphere. Panels a to c illustrate some of the models which have been proposed for the crust. Panels d and e illustrate two of a wide range of extensional fault geometries. Panel f shows a seismic reflection record across part of the northern margin of the Bay of Biscay (after Montadert et al., 1979). Red stipple denotes sediments of syn-rift age. Reflector S is interpreted to be a décollement zone.

where Q is the activation energy, η_b is the basal viscosity, and T_m the temperature at the base of the lithosphere. Temperatures (T) are in Absolute units. $\dot{\varepsilon}$ is the second invariant of the strain tensor (Parmentier et al., 1976; Crough, 1977). Thus the viscosity of the lithosphere varies by many orders of magnitude with depth (Fig. 9.12) and it will change with time as the geothermal gradient in the lithosphere changes. Values of Q, the activation energy, may vary from about 500 kJ/mol to about 150 kJ/mol,

depending on composition and water content. Values for wet olivine are about 350 kJ/mol, and those for dry olivine are 500 kJ/mol (Kirby, 1980).

There is no agreement on which flow mechanism, Newtonian or power law, predominates within the lithosphere. The main difference between the two types of flow lies in the magnitude of viscosity change across the lithosphere (Fig. 9.12) and in the dependence of viscosity on strain rate in the case of power law flow.

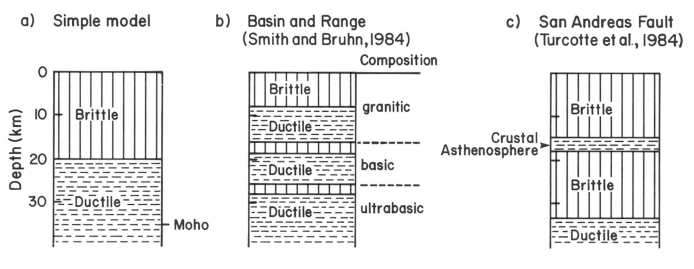

a) Simple model   **b) Basin and Range (Smith and Bruhn, 1984)**   **c) San Andreas Fault (Turcotte et al., 1984)**

Layered rheologies due to composition and temperature changes

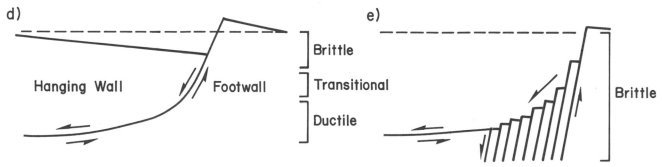

Fault geometries that may generate a listric fault image (Smith and Bruhn, 1984)

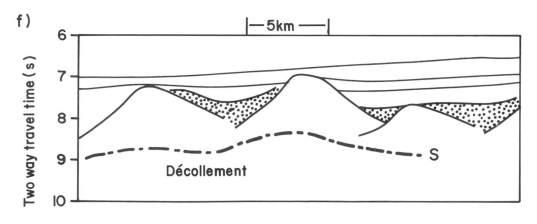

The lower lithosphere is commonly modelled as a viscous material; in fact, it may be more properly described by a viscoelastic rheology. A purely viscous substance cannot transmit stress, whereas a viscoelastic material will transmit stress in the same manner as an elastic solid but it will also creep like a viscous fluid. In problems which involve large deformations of the lower lithosphere, the elastic deformation is not significant, and can be modelled equally well by a viscous rheology. However, the manner in which stress is distributed within the lithosphere is an important consideration in determining the resultant deformation, so in this respect the use of a viscoelastic rheology is preferable.

Dynamical models

Several studies in the literature illustrate elements of the dynamics of rifting (e.g. Kusznir and Bott, 1977; Vierbuchen et al., 1982; England, 1983). We describe here only the dynamical models of Keen (1985; in press), for which results are presented later in this section.

Keen (1985; in press) has described the dynamic evolution of rift zones in terms of their subsidence and thermal histories, using a two layer rheological model of the lithosphere (Fig. 9.36). The upper 40 km thick layer corresponds to the brittle layer and is assumed to deform according to the uniform extension model. The lower layer corresponds to the ductile region, and was characterized by a temperature dependent viscosity, with $n = 3$, and $Q = 250$ kJ/mol. The effect of strain rate on viscosity was ignored. The asthenosphere was modelled as constant viscosity fluid (viscosity, η_b), below the equilibrium depth of the lithosphere. It was included in the models to allow for flow in that region resulting from horizontal and vertical motions of the overlying lithosphere (Fig. 9.36). Thus the model explicitly allows the replacement of mantle lithosphere by asthenosphere, a feature not contained in other studies. The deformation of the viscous region was found by solution of the appropriate equations for viscous flow.

The temperature and therefore the viscosity distribution in the lithosphere changed in reponse to the computed deformation. The model included a number of time steps, starting from the equilibrium state of the lithosphere. At each time step the deformation within the viscous region of the model was computed, and the temperature and viscosity distributions in the lithosphere were updated, using the computed flow velocities. These new temperatures were then used to compute the isostatic elevation changes, in a manner similar to that for the kinematic models. Thus S_I, the initial subsidence, could be computed at each time step during the rift stage. Boundary conditions included a constant rate of extension throughout the lithosphere at the sides of the rift zone, initial width $2\lambda_o$, and a free boundary at the base of the asthenosphere. The specified extension rate (V_o) provided the driving force for extension. The driving velocity was set to zero after an interval Δt_r but model evolution was followed to determine its post-rift thermal and subsidence behaviour.

Two additional effects of the viscous flow were described: 1) The dynamic pressure and stress due to viscous flow were computed along the top and bottom boundaries of the viscous layer. They may have an important effect on the elevation changes during rifting. 2) The gravitational body forces resulting from changes in density within the viscous region of the model were included in the calculations. These density changes are caused by the lateral temperature variations produced by the deformation. The body forces are shown to perturb the flow and for certain parameter values cause vigourous convection beneath the thinning lithosphere. This flow can have important implications for the deformation of the lower lithosphere and elevation changes. Neither of these two factors is included in the kinematic models.

Finite and episodic rates of stretching

The first step towards a better description of the rift phase is to consider non-instantaneous kinematic models of stretching. Consider the situation in Figure 9.36 which depicts stretching as a process which occurs at a constant rate (V_o). The unstretched sides of the rift zone, initially of width $2\lambda_o$, move away from each other and create a rift zone which is characterized by $\beta(x,t)$ and $v_x(x,t)$. For the uniform stretching model, $\partial v_x / \partial z = 0$; there is no change of v_x with z (Jarvis and McKenzie, 1980). For kinematic models, $v_x(x,t)$ may be specified, although dynamical models may not entirely support the assumed form of v_x. In Figure 9.37, $\beta(x,t)$ and the initial subsidence resulting from three different velocity functions are shown. Stretching distributions such as the linear β distribution used in the instantaneous models each result from a different v_x function. Furthermore, for constant V_o, the time dependence of β is proportional to the initial width of the rift zone; rapid stretching will occur over narrow rifts. The most useful prediction is the shape of the initial subsidence curves, which show decreasing subsidence with time since rifting began. This kind of behaviour has been observed on several margins, including the Labrador margin (Fig. 9.4). Falvey and Middleton (1981) used this characteristic of initial subsidence curves on the Australian margins to argue in favour of a phase change in the lower crust during rifting; however, the results presented here suggest that simple stretching models which include finite rates of extension can satisfy the observations.

Very few measurements of the subsidence during rifting are available. The shape and magnitude of the subsidence curves could, in principle, be used to estimate the unknown parameters λ_o and V_o. In practice, observations on a single margin cross-section are sparse and it would be pure speculation to attach too much significance to the results. The subsidence curves also suggest an explanation for the occurrence of break-up unconformities on some margins; the decrease in initial subsidence with time may create an interval of little or no subsidence late in the rift phase. However, the additional subsidence due to cooling during a prolonged rift phase has not been included in these calculations, so this would only occur if rifting was rapid and if the basin was completely filled with sediments.

This simple illustration of finite rifting rates adds another dimension to studies of rifted margins and is one that has not been explored. More complex situations may occur, however, in which rifting is a diachronous process as stress is concentrated over different zones of various width. If the results of England (1983) are correct, then we should expect the lithosphere to grow stronger as stretching proceeds. In that case one might expect the stresses to act on the weaker, unstretched regions at the sides of the initial rift zone, and so rifting would progress outwards with time.

Episodic extension is another process which might also affect the rift history of the margins. Instead of a constant rate of extension, there may be several "instantaneous" stretching events during the rift phase which are separated from each other by periods of simple lithospheric cooling. If the stretching episodes are numerous and suffi- ciently closely spaced in time, the result will resemble a continuous stretching event. When the episodes are separated by times which are long enough to allow significant cooling to occur, the result is a rift stage subsidence history which exhibits a series of discontinuities. Figure 9.38 shows the initial subsidence, including cooling effects, for

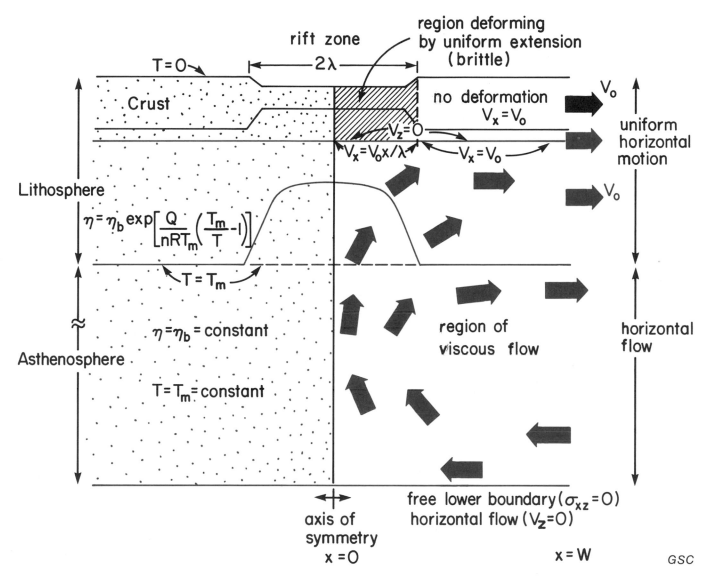

Figure 9.36. Model showing important parameters, the regions of brittle deformation and viscous flow, and the boundary conditions used in dynamical models, the results of which are described in detail in the text. The model comprises the lithosphere and asthenosphere (total depth 700 km; and total half width, x = W = 700 km). The brittle region comprises the crust and upper mantle down to a depth of 40 km (black stipple). This region is assumed to deform according to the uniform extension model. The area with red stipple represents the region of viscous flow. It is for this region that the dynamics of rifting have been described, as indicated by the large red arrows representing viscous flow. Viscosity (η) is temperature dependent in the viscous lower lithosphere (see equation). In the asthenosphere viscosity is held constant, at the basal viscosity, η_b. Temperature (in general T) at the base of the lithosphere and in the asthenosphere is constant at T_m. The width of the rift zone is specified by 2λ, initially $2\lambda_o$. The sides of the lithosphere move with velocity V_o. Below the lithosphere, flow at the sides of the asthenosphere is horizontal. At the boundary between the brittle and viscous regions, velocity boundary conditions specify constant horizontal velocity outside the rift zone ($x > \lambda$) and a linear change in velocity inside the rift zone, given by $v_x = V_o x/\lambda$.

441

a series of stretching episodes, each of which is treated as an instantaneous event. The times between intervals vary, from $\tau/2$ to $3\tau/2$ where τ is the thermal time constant, taken here as 62.8 Ma. These curves show that relative uplift of the rift basin can be achieved if there is a long delay between episodes and if the preceding episode has thinned the crust by a factor of 2 or more. Recall that in the discussion of model sensitivity to parameter values, we noted that the ratio of crustal to lithospheric thickness was a critical parameter in determining whether uplift or subsidence would occur. Thus if the crust is sufficiently thinned during the first stretching event and the time between events is long enough to allow the lithosphere to thicken considerably toward thermal equilibrium, the ratio of crustal to lithospheric thickness may predict relative uplift on the next stretching event (Fig. 9.38). A time interval equal to or greater than one thermal time constant is sufficient to give uplift during the second stretching episode, provided that values of ß were large enough during the first episode. Time intervals of about $\tau/2$ do not allow enough cooling to occur and result in initial subsidence during the second rifting event.

These multiple stretching histories could produce reactivation of listric faults or the creation of a new generation of listric faults, overprinting earlier generations. Several superpositions of extensional fault systems are observed in regions such as the Basin and Range of the western United States (Proffet, 1977). Also such a history would predict the tilting and truncation of sediments deposited between rifting events as they became affected by renewed faulting. There might also be uplift and erosion under these circumstances.

Some of these effects are not clearly observed in marine regions; in particular, several generations of extensional faults have not been mapped. Two stage rifting, however, might explain the large unconformity (or series of unconformities) observed on the Grand Banks, which span the Cretaceous. The Grand Banks were affected by Jurassic rifting to the south, during which time half grabens were formed. Later the region was affected by rifting to the east, during the Early to mid-Cretaceous. The time between these events was about 80 Ma. The unconformity may be associated with the second rifting event and may be due to uplift as a result of renewed stretching. Erosion of the uplifted region could increase the total uplift by a factor of 2 or more and prolong the time spent above sea level. This would decrease the depth of the post-rift basin formed since the uplift. Post-rift sedimentation and subsidence are small over most of the Grand Banks, being about 1 to 2 km. This would appear to provide a satisfactory explanation for the subsidence history of the region. However, evidence of the first phase of stretching suggests that it was confined

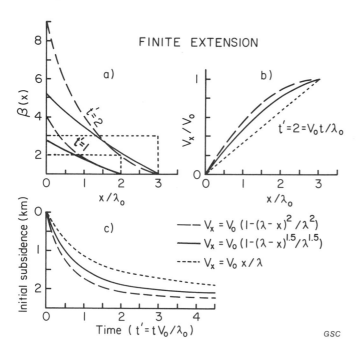

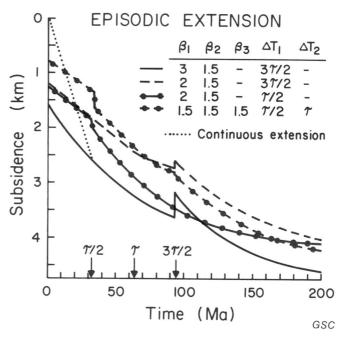

Figure 9.37. Kinematic results for the uniform extension model with finite rates of extension. For each panel three curves are shown for different horizontal velocity functions applied across the rift zone. These functions are shown in panel b, as a function of horizontal distance, and the corresponding equations are also given. Distance is normalized to the initial half-width of the rift zone (λ_0) outside of which $v_x = V_0$. Panel a shows how ß changes with position for the three velocity functions. Results are given for two times. Panel c shows the initial subsidence as a function of time during rifting.

Figure 9.38. Subsidence as a function of time since rifting, for instantaneous, episodic extension models. The initial (t = 0) subsidence in each case is the displacement from the 0 position on the vertical scale. Four models are shown. The ß values for each stretching episode are given in the figure. These ß values are cumulative; that is, the total value after all extension events have occurred is found by multiplying ß1 by ß2 (and ß3). Times (ΔT), expressed as fractions of the thermal time constant at which episodes occur after the first stretching event at t = 0, are also shown for each model. The dotted line represents continuous extension during rifting, over a time interval of $\tau/2$ and with a final ß value of 3.

to narrow half grabens, and so the simplest model would predict that the second phase uplift should also be confined to those areas. In fact, the uplift was a widespread event affecting the entire Grand Banks region. Therefore the multi-stage rift process is an attractive model to apply to the Grand Banks, but requires that the first phase of stretching must have been widespread and the evidence later removed during uplift and erosion. The uplift late in the rift stage on the Labrador margin (Fig. 9.4) cannot be explained by two stage rifting because the events are too close together to create uplift, assuming that we start with lithosphere that has a 62.8 Ma cooling time constant.

Results of the dynamical stretching models

Lithospheric thinning and small scale convection

The shape of the lithosphere-asthenosphere boundary as the lithosphere thins is shown in Figure 9.39 for several models with different parameter values. For high basal viscosities ($\eta_b \gtrsim 10^{21}$ Pa·s) the results give values of ß which are the same for the lower and upper parts of the lithosphere, supporting the uniform extension model of McKenzie (1978).

For low viscosity ($\eta_b \sim 2 \times 10^{19}$ Pa·s) models, however, small scale convection occurs near the base of the lithosphere. Convection is induced by the horizontal temperature and density gradients, generated by lithospheric thinning. Cold material is carried down into the asthenosphere and hot asthenosphere flows up to replace it. This process will itself thin the lithosphere, so that the lower lithosphere is thinned more than the upper lithosphere, and it will occur when ß is sufficiently large to create the necessary temperature differences and when the viscosity is low. When $\eta_b = 2 \times 10^{19}$ Pa·s convection can thin the lower lithosphere from ß=2 to ß=3 and results in the same thermal and mechanical conditions as the kinematic depth dependent extension model (Fig. 9.39).

In addition to the requirements on ß and viscosity, the extension rate, duration of the rift phase, and width of the rift zone are important variables in determining the deformation and subsidence induced by small scale convection (Fig. 9.39).

Slow extension (0.1 cm/a for 40 Ma) would give a final ß value of 2 if there was no small scale convection. With small scale convection, further thinning of the lower lithosphere occurs so that δ=3 and δ>ß. For these model parameters, the flow due to small scale convection is of the same order of magnitude as that due to extension. Small scale convection continues well into the post-rift stage but its vigour decreases as conductive cooling of the lithosphere increases the viscosity and reduces lateral temperature gradients. One lithospheric thermal time constant after extension stops, small scale convection may still have an effect on surface elevations. During this time further thinning occurs, thereby increasing δ to values greater than 5. This mechanical thinning, however, is offset to some extent by conductive cooling. The lower lithosphere is not only thinned but the zone of deformation is widened as material at the sides of the rift zone is carried down into the asthenosphere. Convection is most vigorous at the sides (x = λ, Fig. 9.40) because horizontal temperature gradients are greatest there. Thinning the lower lithosphere beyond the region of stretching in the upper

lithosphere is equivalent to the depth-dependent extension model where δ>ß=1; therefore, the sides of the rift zone will be uplifted.

A comparison of the subsidence history with and without small scale convection is shown in Figures 9.41 and 9.42. For slow extension rates there is relatively less subsidence during rifting with small scale convection. The most striking difference, however, is the retardation of the post-rift subsidence, so that with small scale convection there may be relative uplift during the early post-rift stage. Near the edges of the rift zone, uplift occurs both during and after rifting. The shoulders of the rift zone may be uplifted by about 700 m, and this effect persists for at least 60 Ma after rifting has ceased.

Rapid rates of extension (1 cm/a for 4 Ma) give the same ß value of 2 as the slow extension model. The deformation of the lower lithosphere during rifting (Fig. 9.39) is not significantly different in this case for models with and without small scale convection. The flow due to extension dominates the flow due to convection, or equivalently, the duration of rifting is too short to allow significant convective thinning. After extension stops, however, the lower lithosphere continues to thin to values of δ = 5 over one thermal time constant whan small scale convection occurs. The deformation of the lower lithosphere is similar in shape to that produced by slow extension. Differences between models with fast and slow extension result primarily from the fact that fast extension has proceeded adiabatically, with no conductive heat loss. Therefore, there is more thermal energy to support small scale convection during the post-rift stage. This explains why the uplift of the rift shoulders is somewhat greater in this case and may exceed 1 km (Fig. 9.41).

Vigorous convection occurs where lateral temperature gradients are greatest, near the edges of the rift zone. Consequently, for rift zones which are wide by comparison with lithospheric thickness, maximum lithospheric thinning may occur at the sides of the rift (Fig. 9.39) and not beneath its centre.

Dynamic stress

Another important result from the dynamical models, and not included in the kinematic models, is the demonstration of the significance of dynamic stress acting on the upper surface of the viscous layer. This stress will cause uplift of the surface layer which must be added to the initial subsidence S_I to obtain the actual elevation during rifting. Dynamic elevation changes are proportional to η_b and to the rate of extension. The dynamic stress vanishes when extension stops, unless there is significant small-scale convection during the post-rift period. Similar dynamical effects result when problems involving large scale mantle convection are considered (e.g. Jarvis and Peltier, 1982).

These stresses appear to cause uplift during rifting (Fig. 9.43). However, our models are not sufficiently reliable to provide accurate numerical estimates. The present estimate of 13 km for $\eta_b = 2 \times 10^{19}$ Pa·s and $V_o = 1$ cm/a is obviously unrealistic. There are several reasons why the present models are inadequate in this respect. First, the dependence of viscosity on strain rate was not included in the calculations. This may lower the effective values of η_b. Second, some of the initial and boundary conditions used in the model calculations may be wrong or oversimplified.

For example, the effect of radiogenic heat production on the temperature distribution has been ignored. This alone could reduce the viscosity in the lithosphere by an order of magnitude. Finally, the effects of rheological layering or the presence of a crustal asthenosphere in the upper lithosphere would significantly affect these results. These and other simplifications make it difficult to estimate the magnitude of dynamic uplift. It is imperative to recognize the importance of this attribute, however, and to allow for the fact that it may significantly modify elevation changes. It could, for example, dominate the initial subsidence and account for net uplift of the rift zone during rifting rather than subsidence.

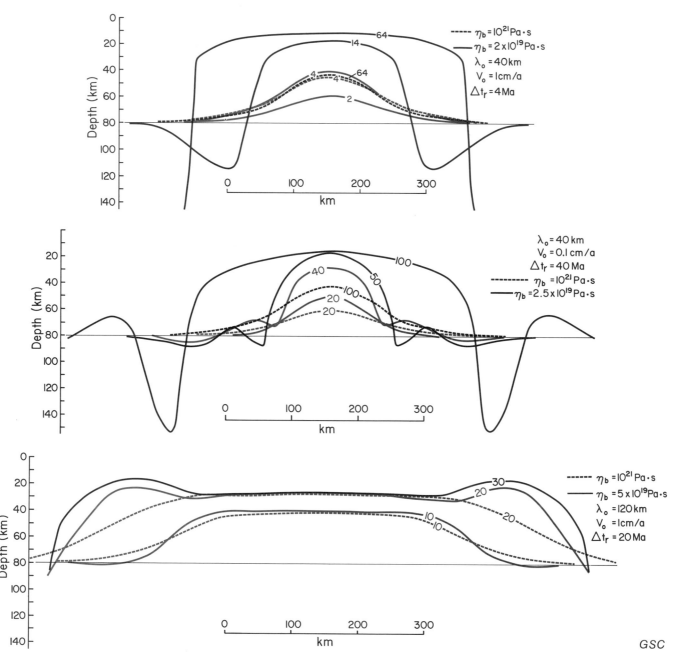

GSC

Figure 9.39. Deformation of the lithosphere-asthenosphere boundary for three dynamical models of rifting. The model parameters are shown adjacent to each model result. Two sets of curves are shown on each drawing, one for a high basal viscosity (dashed lines) for which the deformation resembles that predicted by kinematic models and one for a low basal viscosity (solid lines) which differs from kinematic models for reasons described in the text. The numbers on the curves indicate millions of years (Ma) after the start of rifting. Red curves show the deformation during rifting, black curves show that during the post-rift phase. The horizontal line through each model is the equilibrium depth of the lithosphere-asthenosphere boundary.

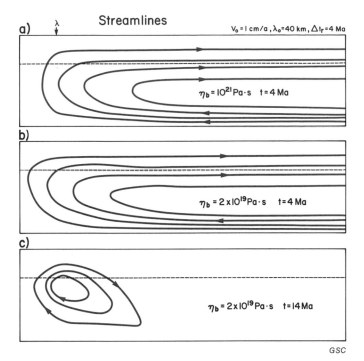

a) **Streamlines**

$V_o = 1 \, cm/a$, $\lambda_o = 40 \, km$, $\Delta t_r = 4 \, Ma$

$\eta_b = 10^{21} \, Pa \cdot s$ $t = 4 \, Ma$

b)

$\eta_b = 2 \times 10^{19} \, Pa \cdot s$ $t = 4 \, Ma$

c)

$\eta_b = 2 \times 10^{19} \, Pa \cdot s$ $t = 14 \, Ma$

GSC

Figure 9.40. Streamlines illustrating the flow in the viscous part of the lithosphere and asthenosphere. The dashed line represents the equilibrium position of the lithosphere-asthenosphere boundary. The arrow above panel a is the final width of the rift zone. Model parameters are also shown above the panels. Panels a and b show the flow during rifting for high (a) and low (b) values of basal viscosity. Panel c shows the flow 10 Ma after rifting has stopped (t = 14 Ma), for the model with low basal viscosity.

Summary of dynamical model results

A summary of the important elements of the dynamical model results is shown in Figure 9.44. In terms of the observations on rifted continental margins, relative uplift during the rift stage could be due to either dynamic stress or to small scale convection (see also Yuen and Fleitout, 1985). The latter also provides a physical explanation for depth dependent kinematic models. Relative uplift that depends on the extension rate and other fundamental properties of the rifting environment, which may themselves change with time, gives us a means of explaining why rift tectonics exhibit such a wide diversity of characteristics. The presence of a breakup unconformity, for example, may signal thermal convection and relative uplift late in the rift stage. Uplift of a rift zone at the onset of rifting may imply dynamic uplift due to the initiation of flow. The shift in the locus of maximum thinning, which occurs near the edge of the rift zone for wide rifts, is consistent with comparisons of conjugate margins; this suggests that basins were once adjacent to platforms or promontories (e.g. Jansa and Wiedmann, 1982). Thus, while we wish to emphasize the simplicity of the models compared to reality and the danger of applying the model results directly to observations, the general physical processes which dynamical models describe are extremely important in understanding how the kinematic models may be modified and why they do not always explain important observations on rifted margins.

Uplift of the landward side of the margin

One of the major problems in reconciling the predictions of the stretching models with observations is that uplift of the shoulders of rift basins and of the landward side of the rifted margins is a well documented feature of many regions. Uplift of the landward sides of the Red Sea, where rifting occurred in the mid-Tertiary, reaches more than 1 km. Similarly, uplifted regions surround the young Gulf of California (Curray et al., 1981). The Rhine Graben, a presently active continental rift, exhibits uplift of the graben shoulders by as much as 1 km; this uplift may have been greater in the past (Illics, 1981). The landward side of the Tertiary margins of Baffin Bay and Norway exhibit uplift (Srivastava et al., 1981) of 1 to 2 km.

One of the main questions regarding these uplifted regions is when the uplift occurred (Sengor and Burke, 1978). In some regions broad scale doming may be a precursor to rifting. Other regions, such as the Rhine Graben, exhibit syn-rift uplift of the rift shoulders. Still others, such as the landward side of the Baffin Bay margins, appear to have been uplifted after rifting had stopped in that region (Srivastava et al., 1981; see Chapter 4). The distribution of uplift can also be problematic. Is subsidence of rift basins superimposed on a broad regional uplift, or is it only the rift shoulders which are uplifted?

Finally there is the question of the permanence of uplift. In general, peripheral uplift will persist if its cause is due to isostatic adjustment to deformation during rifting, whereas thermally induced uplifts will decay with time. In previous sections the more general questions of uplift of the entire rift zone have been addressed, and depth-dependent extension models have been used to explain uplift of the landward parts of rifted margins. We present below some of the other possible mechanisms for uplift of the rift shoulders.

Lateral heat transfer

Lateral heat flow from the rift zone toward the continent will cause uplift during and following rifting. This heat transport occurs because of the juxtaposition of the cold continent against the relatively warm rift zone. If the rift zone is very wide and ß values vary slowly across it, the lateral heat flow will be small. If its width is much greater than the thickness of the lithosphere, heat will mainly be lost by vertical rather than horizontal conduction. If there are significant heat losses by lateral heat transport, the uplift of the interior region will be matched by additional subsidence of the rift basin. This is only true for conductive, as opposed to convective heat transport.

Peripheral uplift due to conductive heat transfer has been discussed by Beaumont et al. (1982a), among others. It is illustrated in Figure 9.41 where uplift of the rift shoulders is due to conduction only, provided that viscosities are high ($\eta_b \sim 10^{21}$ Pa·s). These model results show that uplift due to lateral heat conduction is small, less than about 300 m. This could be amplified by factors of 2 to 3 by erosion of the uplifted region, but it is more likely to be offset by flexural subsidence in response to sediment loading.

Uplift of the rift shoulders due to small scale convection may reach 1 km in magnitude (Fig. 9.41), and more if erosion occurs. For slow rates of extension, most of the uplift will occur during the rift phase, while for rapid extension,

445

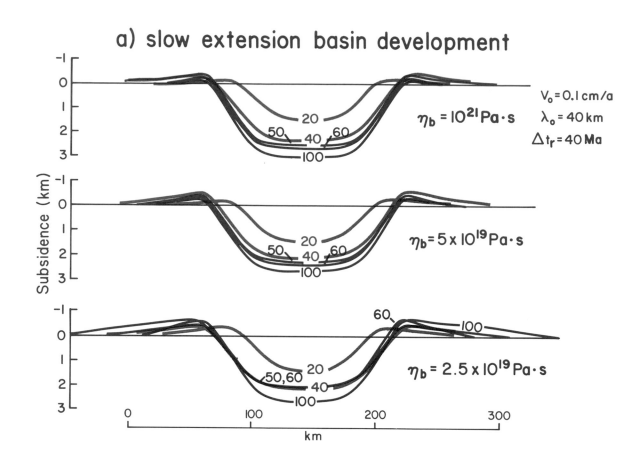

a) slow extension basin development

$V_o = 0.1 \, cm/a$
$\lambda_o = 40 \, km$
$\Delta t_r = 40 \, Ma$

$\eta_b = 10^{21} \, Pa \cdot s$

$\eta_b = 5 \times 10^{19} \, Pa \cdot s$

$\eta_b = 2.5 \times 10^{19} \, Pa \cdot s$

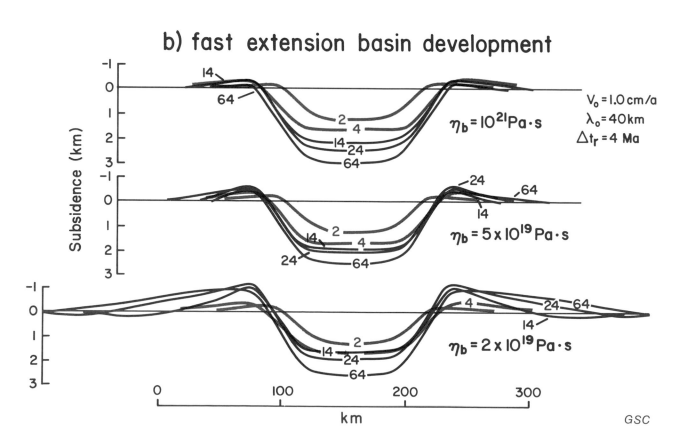

b) fast extension basin development

$V_o = 1.0 \, cm/a$
$\lambda_o = 40 \, km$
$\Delta t_r = 4 \, Ma$

$\eta_b = 10^{21} \, Pa \cdot s$

$\eta_b = 5 \times 10^{19} \, Pa \cdot s$

$\eta_b = 2 \times 10^{19} \, Pa \cdot s$

GSC

uplift is most pronounced during the post-rift phase. The uplift will persist over periods of about one thermal time constant and then slowly decay. This kind of process can explain not only syn-rift, but post-rift uplift of the kind observed on eastern Baffin Island. In that region marine sediments of syn- and early post-rift are now found 600 m above sea level, and furthermore the topographic uplift of Baffin Island is similar to that illustrated in Figure 9.41 for rapid extension rates. A similar process has also been suggested to explain the uplift of the Norwegian coastline (Fleitout et al., 1983).

Uplift due to faulting and flexure

Elevation changes due to isostatic adjustment during rift phase deformation may play an important role in uplift of the rift shoulders. Consider first a single normal fault like that shown in Figure 9.35d. The redistribution of mass due to fault displacement causes a change in elevation due to isostatic adjustment. In this case, the footwall will be uplifted by an amount proportional to the hanging wall subsidence. Calculations by Jackson and McKenzie (1983) suggest that the ratio of footwall uplift to hanging wall subsidence is about 0.1, provided the footwall is not buried beneath sediments. This uplift occurs because the fault unloads the footwall, allowing it to rise above its initial elevation. If we consider a rift zone underlain by a single fault of this kind, then the edge of the rift will be uplifted about 1 km for a 10 km deep basin. Jackson and McKenzie (1983) have suggested that this kind of uplift may be responsible for the raised islands in the Aegean, a region of active extension, and that similar faults may bound the ranges in the Basin and Range of the western United States.

Comparable uplift may occur at rifted continental margins either by the isostatic adjustment across major normal faults near the hinge zone, or by the regional isostatic response of the lithosphere to distributed thinning of the crust. The latter was discussed by Beaumont et al. (1982b). Stretching and necking of the lithosphere leads to regional isostatic readjustment. If the lithosphere maintains finite strength, flexure of the lithosphere will occur. Near the edges of the rift zone where the lithosphere becomes thick, there will be flexural upwarp of the unextended region in response to buoyancy and gravitational forces. The uplift may be about 1 km and, like the fault controlled uplift, will be permanent.

Isostatic adjustment due to flexure and faulting during rifting produces significant and permanent uplifts of the rift shoulders. Thermal uplift may occur during rifting or in the post-rift period and will eventually decay. These temporal differences suggest that the relative importance of these mechanisms can be distinguished by careful study of the stratigraphic record. For example, the presence of

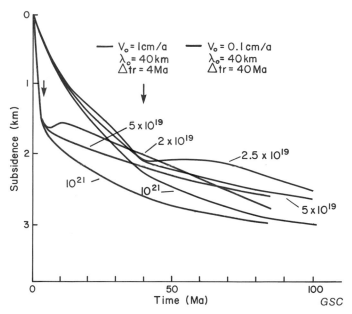

Figure 9.42. Subsidence of the centre of the basins for fast extension (in red) and slow extension (in black). Arrows denote the end of the rift phase. Numbers associated with the curves are the values of basal viscosity (Pa·s).

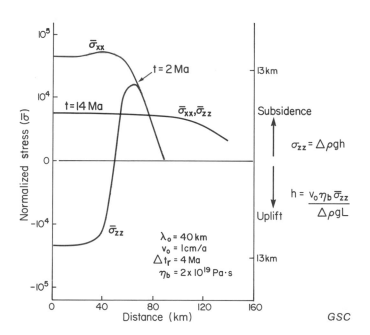

Figure 9.43. Dynamic stresses on the upper surface of the viscous layer generated by the flow shown as a function of distance from the centre of the rift zone. Model parameters are shown. The red curves are for t = 2 Ma, during the rift phase. The black curve is for t = 14 Ma, 10 Ma after rifting stopped. The right hand axis shows the vertical motions which could be induced by the vertical stress. The simple equations relating stress to elevation (h) are shown to the right of the diagram.

Figure 9.41. Development of the sedimentary basins for two dynamical models of rifting: slow extension rate (a) and rapid extension rate (b). The model parameters are shown. For each of the two models, results are shown for three basal viscosities, given next to each drawing. Numbers on the basin depths indicate time in millions of years (Ma) since rifting began. Red lines represent basin depths during rifting; black lines represent basin depths in the post-rift period.

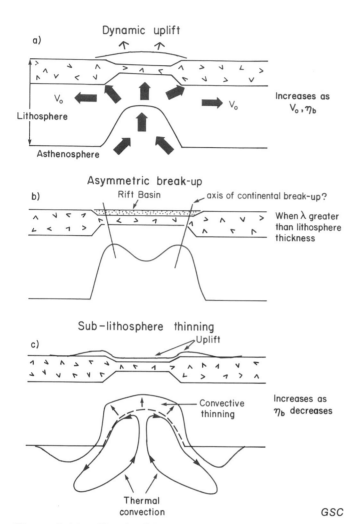

Figure 9.44. Sketch of the three processes predicted by dynamic models of extension which are not predicted by the kinematic models. Red lines highlight the processes involved.

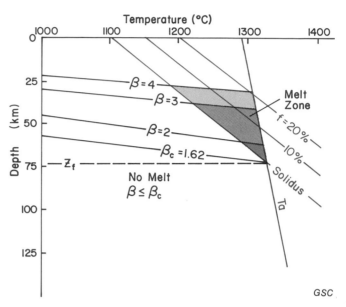

Figure 9.45. Temperature versus depth in the lower part of the lithosphere. Black lines show the temperatures predicted by the uniform extension models for various values of ß. The red lines are the degree of partial melting predicted for a pyrolite mantle; for example, $f = 20\%$ gives the depths and temperatures at which 20% of the mantle rocks will form melt. T_a is the mantle adiabat. If the base of the lithosphere is below depth Z_f, no melt is formed. The shaded region is where partial melting is predicted, and the solidus intersects the geotherms. Different shadings correspond to different regions in which melt will form as ß increases from $ß_c$ to 2, 2 to 3, and 3 to 4.

syn-rift marine sediments at elevations of 600 m on eastern Baffin Island suggests post-rift uplift, compatible with convective heat transfer. This margin is of early Tertiary age, and the decay of the thermal uplift is not yet apparent. This too is compatible with the model results. The best fitting kinematic model of the region of the Baltimore Canyon Trough would suggest that a combination of depth dependent extension and pre-existing, permanent topography, perhaps due to flexure or faulting during rifting, best fits the stratigraphy in that region. Recall that depth dependent extension is the kinematic equivalent of small scale convection in the dynamical models, so that we require a combination of the thermal and isostatic processes discussed in this section to account for the stratigraphy landward of the hinge line. However, the effects of erosion, sea level changes, and flexure due to sediment loading make separation of these various processes difficult in many other regions.

The role of partial melting

Any form of lithospheric thinning may be accompanied by partial melting of mantle asthenosphere. This melt may be the source of volcanism observed on some rifted margins, when substantial lithospheric thinning occurs. So far in this chapter we have not discussed how melt is formed, although some of the models assume that melt production, segregation and migration do occur. Here we describe some simple models of melt production and some of the observational evidence supporting this process.

Consider the uniform extension model in which extension and lithospheric thinning occur by an amount ß. As the lithosphere thins, asthenosphere rises beneath the thinned region. If the process is rapid enough to be considered adiabatic, then the stretching lithosphere and upwelling asthenosphere will experience a decreased pressure at constant temperature. The decreased pressure enables partial melting of the more volatile, basaltic fraction of mantle rocks. The degree of partial melting will depend on the pressure decrease, and this is related to the thinning by ß. This is illustrated in Figure 9.45, where the solidus and degree of partial melt is shown for a pyrolite mantle composition, superimposed on the temperature distribution in the lower lithosphere and asthenosphere for several values of ß. The solidus intersects the adiabatic thermal gradient for the asthenosphere (T_a) at a depth of about 75 km, so no melt is produced until the lithosphere-asthenosphere boundary reaches this critical depth (Z_f) allowing us to define a critical ß value for the onset of melting, $ß_c$. The total amount of melt can be obtained by integrating over the melt zone, the shaded region in Figure 9.45. The numerical calculations are described in detail by Foucher et al. (1982). The total amount of melt available can be expressed as the equivalent thickness of a basaltic layer:

$$h_b = \frac{\rho_l}{\rho_b} \frac{f_o}{2} \beta_c \, \alpha \left[\frac{1}{\beta_c} - \frac{1}{\beta} \right]^2 ; \beta \geq \beta_c \text{ (see Table 9.2)}$$

The subsidence during rifting is modified by partial melting. The creation of the less dense basaltic magma tends to produce relatively less initial subsidence than the uniform extension model without melt for the same β value. The difference in initial subsidence can be computed from:

$$S_I = S_I(\text{no melt}) - h_b(\rho_b - \rho_c)/(\rho_a - \rho_w)$$

In this expression loading by water is assumed. S_I is the initial subsidence for uniform extension without melt (Table 9.6). The second term is the effect of partial melting. The initial subsidence and equivalent thickness of basalt are shown in Figure 9.46, for a constant rate of extension and assuming no heat loss during rifting. Parameter values given in Table 9.2 have been used to obtain these results. The maximum thickness of basalt is 5.5 km as $\beta \to \infty$, a result equivalent to the creation of oceanic crust.

The initial subsidence with partial melting is not only less than that of the uniform extension model, but subsidence shows a more marked decrease with time. The melt curves suggest that there will be no further subsidence for $\beta > 3$. This may create a suitable environment for the development of a break-up unconformity.

What happens to the melt once it has formed? There are two possible end member models (Fig. 9.47). In the first, the melt segregates and migrates through the lithosphere to solidify at crustal levels. The melt may underplate the continental crust or intrude it, as in the uniform extension-melt segregation model. Alternatively, the melt may be retained in the asthenosphere. In the latter case the initial subsidence would be less, because the melt has the lowest density. The case for migration of melt is supported by the results of crustal seismic studies in the Baltimore Canyon Trough (LASE Study Group, 1985). In that region, a lower crustal layer is found with a velocity of about 7.2 km/s, which is continuous with the lower oceanic crust farther seaward. This supports the melt segregation model in which there is a gradual change from continental to oceanic crust as more basaltic melt is produced. Similar deep crustal layers are found on the margins off eastern Canada.

If the melt is retained in the asthenosphere (Fig. 9.47), it may migrate to surface levels at the time of final continental break-up. This might produce large quantities of basaltic material near the site of the ocean continent boundary, and could be responsible for margins such as the Voring Plateau and Rockall Plateau. The association of dipping seismic reflectors with lava flows on these and many other margins may suggest that such processes are widespread (Hinz, 1981; Mutter et al., 1982). The Fogo Seamounts along the southern margin of the Grand Banks could have formed in a similar manner (see Chapter 2).

THERMAL HISTORY AND MATURATION OF MARGIN SEDIMENTS

Previous sections focussed on the structural, subsidence and sedimentary history of continental margins. We now turn our attention to the thermal history of the sediments. Four aspects contribute to the temperature: 1) lithospheric syn-rift heating and post-rift cooling, which determine the basal heat flow into the sediments; 2) the thermal properties of the sediments, in particular their thermal conductivity, which determines how good an insulator the blanketing sediments become; 3) heat production from radiogenic elements in the sediments and upper crust, which increases the sediment temperatures; and 4) subsidence, which controls the depth to a given sediment horizon. We assume that heat is transferred by conduction and that fluid convection or the flow of fluids expelled during compaction do not carry sufficient heat to be significant. This is not always true for all types of sedimentary basins, as has been shown by Oxburgh and Andrews-Speed (1981), Andrews-Speed et al. (1984), Garven and Freeze (1984a, b), Beaumont et al. (1985), and Majorowicz et al. (1984). The validity of the assumption for our present examples is supported, however, by comparison of observations with model predictions.

The temperature history of sediments is potentially important because it may be possible to relate the process of conversion of organic matter to petroleum (or sediment maturation) to temperature history. The ability to predict

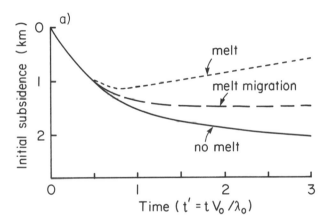

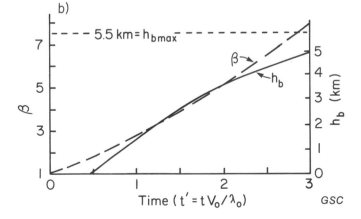

Figure 9.46. Curves of the initial subsidence (a) and the amount of extension and basalt produced (b) versus time. These results were computed for a constant extension rate (V_o). In panel a the simple uniform extension model with no melt production is compared with two cases where melt production is included, as described in the text.

maturation within a sedimentary basin from sparse data — for example, seismic stratigraphy, isolated wells, and some knowledge of thermal conductivity of the sediments — would assist oil and gas exploration, particularly in frontier areas. We illustrate the importance of thermal history with examples from the Scotian Basin where sufficient data are available to test the model predictions.

Model predictions of thermal history

Heat flow in the sediments

Simple kinematic models predict the thermal history of the sediments with an accuracy which depends on how well the model parameters describe the thermal behaviour of the lithosphere, and on the choice of thermal properties for the

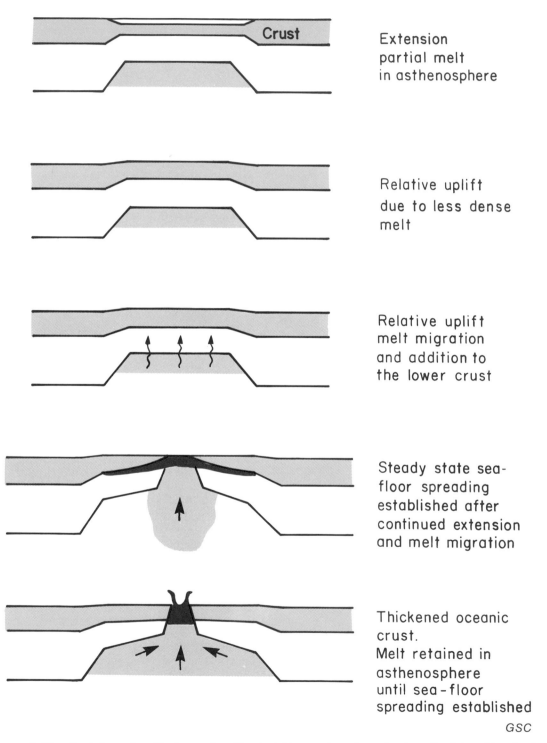

Crust

Extension
partial melt
in asthenosphere

Relative uplift
due to less dense
melt

Relative uplift
melt migration
and addition to
the lower crust

Steady state sea-
floor spreading
established after
continued extension
and melt migration

Thickened oceanic
crust.
Melt retained in
asthenosphere
until sea-floor
spreading established

GSC

Figure 9.47. Evolution of a rifted margin with stretching and melt production. Partial melting in the asthenosphere is shown as light red shading and the basaltic layer formed by melt segregation, migration and solidification is shown in solid red.

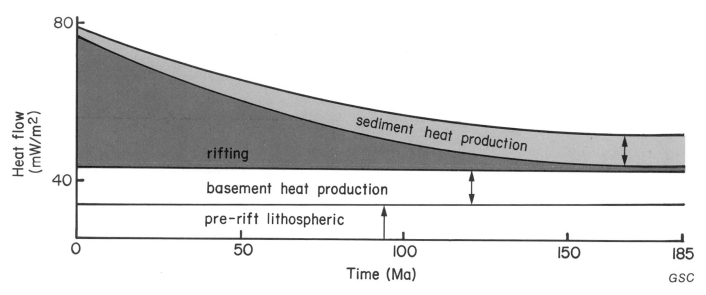

Figure 9.48. The relative contributions to total surface heat flow as a function of time since rifting for a uniform extension model with ß = 2 (after Keen and Lewis, 1982).

sediments. The thermal behaviour of the lithosphere depends on the equilibrium heat flow through the base of the lithosphere and on the increase in that heat flow during rifting. In kinematic models (Fig. 9.8), the equilibrium heat flow is specified by $Q_o = KT_m/a$ where K is the mean thermal conductivity, T_m the basal temperature, and "a" the thickness of the lithosphere. Parameter values were chosen so that $Q_o = 33$ mW/m², a value consistent with estimates from worldwide heat flow studies (Sclater et al., 1980) and with detailed heat flow measurements in Atlantic Canada (Hyndman et al., 1979). In addition to this constant equilibrium heat flow, high heat flow is produced during rifting by lithospheric stretching (Fig. 9.48). For the instantaneous kinematic uniform extension model, stretching by ß increases the heat flow to $ßQ_o$. After rifting, the lithosphere cools and the heat flow decays toward thermal equilibrium with a time constant of τ (62 Ma, Fig. 9.48). Thus several time constants after rifting, the lithospheric heat flow approaches Q_o.

The lithospheric heat flow responds differently to different rifting processes. Figure 9.49 illustrates the lithospheric heat flow versus time for several instantaneous kinematic models and for one dynamic model, all of which have been described previously in this chapter. There are significant differences between the uniform extension and depth-dependent kinematic models, even when the total subsidence, as τ→∞, is the same (ß = 2 models, Fig. 9.49). Both models exhibit an instantaneous rise in heat flow on stretching, but the depth-dependent extension model shows an increase in heat flow in early post-rift time. This is due to the greater amount of stretching and higher heat flow in the lower lithosphere (δ > ß). The dynamic model illustrates some of the changes in thermal response to a long rift phase. Perhaps the most important attribute of all these curves is that, despite significant differences in early heat flow, these differences disappear about one thermal time constant after rifting. Only those sediments deposited before this time could experience markedly different thermal histories.

Heat production in the upper crust significantly increases the equilibrium heat flow. Studies of heat flow versus heat production in eastern North America, including Atlantic Canada, suggest that crustal heat production can be explained by a 7.5 km thick upper layer, with constant heat production of 2.1 μW/m³ (Hyndman et al., 1979). This characterizes the unstretched continental region adjacent to the Scotian margin. When the crust is stretched during rifting, the thickness of the basement heat-producing layer is thinned by ß and its contribution

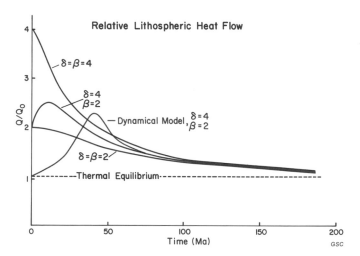

Figure 9.49. The relative heat flow versus time for models having various values of the extension parameters ß and δ. The red curve is the heat flow for a dynamical model described in the text, with parameters $V_o = 0.1$ cm/a, $\Delta t_r = 40$ Ma, $\lambda_o = 40$ km and $\eta_b = 2.5 \times 10^{-19}$ Pa·s. This model gives effective values for ß and δ of 2 and 4, respectively. In all cases only the lithospheric heat flow is shown; there is no contribution from heat production in the crust or sediments.

to total surface heat flow is decreased. Thus, on an old sediment starved margin which is approaching thermal equilibrium like the northern margin of the Bay of Biscay, heat flow should be significantly less in stretched as opposed to unstretched regions (Foucher and Sibuet, 1980).

A thick sedimentary section will, in part, compensate for the thinner heat producing crustal layer because some of the common lithologies exhibit significant heat production (Keen and Lewis, 1982; Fig. 9.48). Measurements of heat production on samples from deep exploratory wells suggest that heat production in the sediments of the Scotian Basin will contribute 15% of the total surface heat flow (Fig. 9.48). This is a relatively small factor, but important when sediment maturity is considered.

The heat flow thus consists of four contributions, all of which are sensitive to the model parameter values. Two of these contributions are time variant over the post-rift period — the additional heat flow due to stretching and heat production in the sediments (Fig. 9.48). The latter is time varying because its contribution increases as the sediment thickness increases. It is clear that on rifted margins, it is not correct to assume that heat flow remains constant with time as some workers have done in estimating sediment maturity (e.g. Robbins and Rhodehamel, 1976).

Thermal conductivity

The temperature and temperature gradients in the sediments are given by

$$T(z,t) = T_{surface} + \int_0^z [Q(z,t)/K(z)] \, dz$$

where Q is the total heat flow at depth (z) and time (t). K is the thermal conductivity of the sediments and this varies with porosity and lithology. The thermal conductivity is as important as the heat flow in model prediction of sediment temperature. Values of the bulk conductivity in a column of sediment at a single location were calculated using a simple approach (Beaumont et al, 1982a). Each lithology is assigned a grain matrix conductivity (Tables 9.3, 9.5). The sediments added in each time interval may comprise several lithologies, so that the geometric mean of matrix values is used, according to the sediment composition. The porosity versus depth for each lithology is given by an equation of the form $\Phi = \Phi_0 e^{-hz}$. The parameters Φ_0 and h can be obtained from well logs of density or sonic velocity. We found that sonic velocity logs gave consistent estimates of h and results for several formations are shown in Figure 9.50. Estimates of the sea floor porosity (Φ_0) are not well determined by this method, so instead we used values of Φ_0 reported in the literature for various sediment types. The sediment matrix conductivities assume zero porosity. To obtain representative porous sediment conductivities, the Maxwell model of thermal conductivity was used (Beck, 1976). This model physically corresponds to solid grains dispersed through water and relates sediment conductivity at given porosity to matrix conductivity.

Determination of accurate matrix conductivities is critical for good model predictions. Values can be assumed from a variety of measurements reported in the literature, but values quoted for a "shale", for example, could vary by a factor of 2, and the wrong choice would seriously bias the thermal history. Therefore measurements of matrix conductivity were made on 32 samples from 14 deep exploratory wells in the Scotian Basin, with four samples taken from each of the major formations (Table 9.3). These

values, with a mean of 1.88 W/m°C, are significantly lower than 'commonly quoted' conductivities.

An example of the sensitivity of sediment temperatures to some of the sediment thermal properties is shown in Figure 9.51, which compares observed (Issler, pers. comm., 1984) and predicted temperatures for the well, Bluenose G-47. As stated above, the 'commonly quoted' conductivities used by Beaumont et al. (1982a), are clearly incorrect. They predicted geothermal gradients of about 16°C/km, consistently lower than those observed in Bluenose G-47 and in the other wells. Addition of radiogenic heating in a near-surface heat-producing crustal layer, 7.5 km deep, and also within the sediment column raises the geothermal gradient significantly, but the predicted values are still too low. Much better results are obtained using the measured thermal conductivities and these results match the observed temperatures. The importance of good control on the thermal properties of the sediments is clear. For depths of 4 km, changes in the chosen values will alter predicted sediment temperatures by more than 20°C and this will significantly change the resulting estimates of sediment maturity (Fig. 9.51).

Predicting sediment temperatures

Once the heat flow and the thermal conductivity are specified, the sediment temperatures can be predicted as a function of time and depth. The most common procedure is to start with a model whose rift parameters satisfy the subsidence history and other observed data, such as crustal thickness, as described earlier in this chapter. The subsidence history is important; even if heat flow was high, the sediments will only experience high temperatures and high sediment maturity if they are deeply buried. For example, many depth dependent extension models exhibit higher heat flow (Fig. 9.49) but less subsidence than uniform extension models during the early post-rift period. The model with highest heat flow will not necessarily create more mature sediments during that period, because the sediments will be closer to the surface. However, after about one thermal time constant, the heat flow has decayed sufficiently for there to be little difference between various rift models. Thus during the later post-rift period, subsidence and rates of sedimentation effectively control thermal history.

For a given location, a time-depth-temperature history for sedimentary strata can be predicted from the model (Fig. 9.52). The temperature history versus depth is displayed as isotherms which are closely spaced immediately after rifting (high heat flow) but, which for about the last 100 Ma, have remained at a similar, wider spacing (Fig. 9.52). Superimposed on the temperature history are the curves of subsidence for strata of different ages. The intersections of a subsidence curve and an isotherm gives the temperature, time and depth of a particular sedimentary stratum. Thus the entire thermal history can be illustrated.

How good are the predicted temperatures? While some parameters are relatively well known, the overall accuracy of the model predictions must be tested. The simplest method is to compare the predicted temperatures to corrected bottom hole temperatures logged in the wells. Equivalently, one can compare measured and predicted surface heat flow, if good measurements are available. However, other means must be found to test past temperatures.

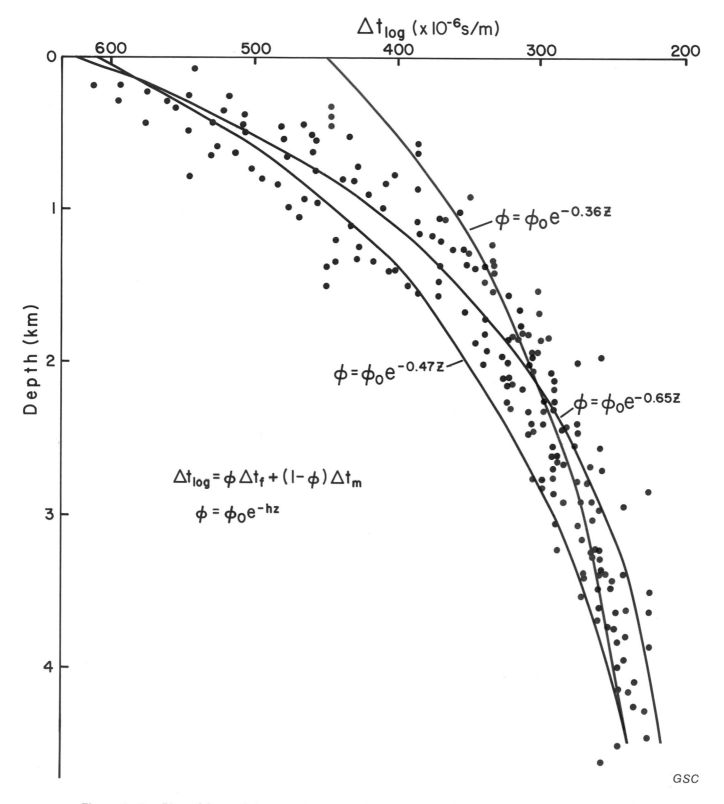

Figure 9.50. Plots of the sonic log transit time (Δt) versus depth. Sedimentary units composed primarily of shale and of sandstone are shown as black and red dots, respectively. The solid curves are theoretical best fits to the data, assuming that the porosity can be expressed as an exponential function of depth. The compaction constant (h, see text) can be derived from these curves as indicated on the diagram. Values for the seafloor porosity (Φ_o) are not well defined because of the greater scatter of data points in the uppermost 1 km. Values for Φ_o corresponding to the curves shown are about 89 and 56% for shale and sandstone, respectively.

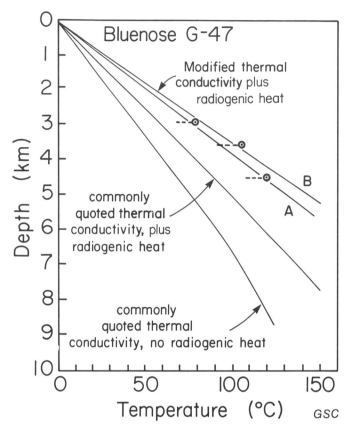

Figure 9.51. Comparison of predicted and observed (red dots) present temperature versus depth for the Bluenose G-47 well, Scotian Shelf, illustrating the influence of sediment thermal conductivity and radiogenic heat production. Parameter values for models A and B are given in Table 9.5.

Predicted indices of sediment maturity have been derived which are easily computed from the time-depth-temperature history, such as that shown in Figure 9.52a. Of these, Lopatin's Time Temperature Index (TTI; Waples, 1980) is the most common. TTI is computed assuming that the rate of reaction in organic matter will double for each 10°C increase in temperature (Hood et al., 1975). Lopatin's method divides the thermal history into i time segments, in each of which the sediment resides for a time Δt_i at a temperature between T_i and $T_i + 10°C$. Lopatin's TTI is then computed from:

$$TTI = \sum_i 2^{T_i/10} \Delta t_i$$

Remember that TTI is computed from a model thermal history and is not a measureable quantity. Rather it must be calibrated against measureable indices of sediment maturity, such as vitrinite reflectance, discussed in the next section. Issler (1984) made a detailed study of observed R_o values versus TTI for the Scotian Basin. The empirical relationship he derived assuming a constant heat flow is:

$$\log TTI = 6.1841 \log R_o + 2.6557$$

An example of model TTI values is given in Figure 9.52b, where TTI versus time is shown for strata 100 to 160 Ma

old whose thermal histories are shown in Figure 9.52a. Not only do these maturation curves give predictions of present sediment maturity but they also show the maturation history. This is useful in determining the earliest time that petroleum generation could occur and therefore when petroleum could begin to migrate from source rock to reservoir.

Geochemical constraints on thermal histories

While it is generally agreed that maturation is related to temperature, it is not clear that the predicted temperature history is sufficiently accurate to allow us to predict sediment maturity. Therefore, we need a means of checking the accuracy of predictions of thermal history. Predictions of past conditions cannot be easily tested because no suitable, accurate geothermometer exists.

Among the more common geothermometers used to measure the maturity of sediments in wells off eastern Canada are vitrinite reflectance (R_o, Bostick, 1973) and the thermal alteration index (TAI; Barss et al., 1980). Only vitrinite reflectance provides quantitative data, however, which can be related to thermal history.

Most chemical reactions in kerogen, the fraction of organic matter insoluble in the usual organic solvents, are assumed to obey the Arrhenius equation: $k = A\exp(-E/RT)$ where k is the rate coefficient of reaction, A is the frequency factor, E is the activation energy, R is the ideal gas constant, and T is the absolute temperature. Sediment maturity is then proportional to the integrated reaction rate over time: $M \propto \int k(t) \, dt$. Thus, R_o and other indices of maturity are functions of the integrated temperature-time history of the sediments. Values of R_o do not indicate whether the sediments have been heated for a long time at a low temperature, or for a short time at a much higher temperature. However, the geological setting commonly helps in determining qualitatively the likely time-temperature path. For a given thermal history, the usual method of comparing measured and predicted R_o is to compute R_o values from the thermal history. The computed R_o values are generally obtained from a set of empirically calibrated curves, which give R_o as a function of time and temperature. These curves are derived from the Arrhenius equation, assuming reactions are first order, and using values of A and E obtained from known thermal histories or laboratory experiments (Bostick, 1973). There are several problems with using R_o as a basis for testing model predictions. Vitrinite is a complex organic compound, a maceral of coal, and may therefore exhibit a range of reflectance behaviour with temperature, due to its compositional variability. The reflectance scale is empirical and must be calibrated against presumed temperature histories. Stable isotopes, conodont colouration, inorganic geochemical indicators, and thermal alteration indices are no better than vitrinite reflectance. Any method that relies on the equilibria of the various phases constituting the inorganic matter is potentially suspect, because the very existence of an equilibrium state for a given P-T condition depends on the availability of chemical species that may be limiting in the reactions. This may also be true for complex organic compounds.

A different approach is to use the kinetics of specific molecular reactions. Thermally activated reactions in organic molecules, if simple, may provide constraints on temperature history against which theoretical predictions

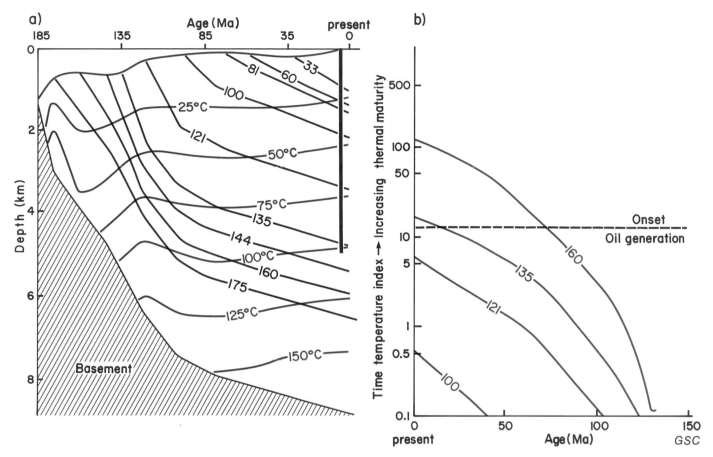

Figure 9.52. Prediction of sediment maturity from a given thermal history. Panel a shows the thermal history of a number of sedimentary units, deposited at the times (in Ma) indicated on the solid black curves. The latter depict the subsidence, or burial history, of these units. The red lines are isotherms. The vertical black line is the present position of a well penetrating these sediment beds. Panel b shows Lopatin's Time Temperature Index computed from the thermal histories for sediments deposited at 100, 121, 135 and 160 Ma. The horizontal line indicates the onset of sediment maturity, when petroleum generation is expected (after Keen and Lewis, 1982).

can be tested. In principle, the kinetic parameters of a reaction, E and A, are measured. The degree to which the reaction has progressed in the sediment column is then predicted by integrating the reaction equations using the model thermal history. The amount of reaction in samples is then measured and theory and observation compared. If we are confident that we know kinetic parameters with sufficient accuracy, the comparison, when applied to a suite of samples, allows the model thermal history to be accepted or rejected. Below we discuss the application of this technique using simple aromatization and isomerization reactions of specific hydrocarbons as our constraint on model temperature histories.

The aromatization and isomerization (A-I) reactions and the thermal history of the Scotian Margin

At low temperatures the breakdown of organic constituents in sediments is complex, with microbial activity contributing as much as the effects of temperature. The reactions that occur in the saturated alkanes and aromatic hydrocarbons at temperatures above 50°C, however, are mainly in response to increases in temperature. Both the reactants and products of these reactions can be identified because enzyme biosynthesis of the parent molecules gave them characteristic architectural forms which are inherited by their breakdown products. The relative amounts of reactant and product of simple thermally activated reactions can be used as a measure of the thermal maturity of the host sediment (Mackenzie and Maxwell, 1981).

Three such reactions were used in a study of sediments from the Scotian Basin (Fig. 9.53): (A) the conversion of natural product derivative sterane with an R-stereochemistry at its Carbon-20 (C-20) site to the equivalent S form; (B) a similar side-chain stereochemistry conversion at the C-22 site in a hopane; and, (C) the conversion of a monoaromatic (single aromatic ring) steroid to its tri-aromatic form. These are the a to b reactions in each of the A, B, C panels (Fig. 9.53). The upper parts of the A and B panels show the ancestral molecules of the sterane and hopane. The reactions and the nomenclature for the molecules are discussed in more detail by Mackenzie et al. (1982, 1985).

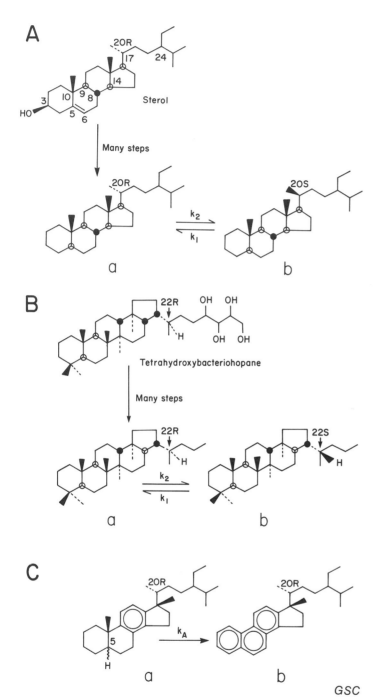

A

Sterol

Many steps

a   b

B

Tetrahydroxybacteriohopane

Many steps

a   b

C

a   b

GSC

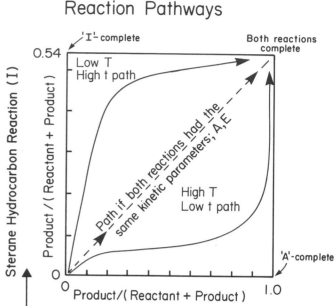

Reaction Pathways

'I'-complete   Both reactions complete

0.54

Low T
High t path

Path if both reactions had the same kinetic parameters; A,E

High T
Low t path

'A'-complete

0   Product/(Reactant + Product)   1.0

Sterane Hydrocarbon Reaction (I) — Product / (Reactant + Product)

Aromatic Steroid Reaction (A)   GSC

Figure 9.54. The A-I diagram. Reactions start in the lower left corner of the diagram and proceed to completion in the upper right corner. The axes are labelled by progress of the reaction toward completion or equilibrium. Reaction pathways in the diagram are diagnostic of the temperature (T) histories of the samples. Histories involving large elapsed time (t) in a relatively cool (~95°C) environment favour progress of the isomerization reactions toward completion before that of the steroid aromatization; therefore, paths are in the upper left part of the figure. Conversely, histories involving short elapsed time in a relatively hot environment (>100°C) favour the rapid completion of the steroid aromatization; therefore, paths are in the lower right part of the diagram. Kinetic parameters E and A are Activation energy and Frequency factor, respectively.

Figure 9.53. A) Representations of the molecules of a sterol, found in living organisms, and the two isomeric steroid hydrocarbons found in sediments which are used to determine the extent of isomerization, a and b. The lines represent carbon-carbon bonds and the carbon atoms lie at the line intersections. All carbon atoms have four bonds, and where these are not shown, bonds to hydrogen atoms are implied. The hexagons are cyclohexane rings which are not planar. Chiral centres are shown in two different ways, by dots or drawing a solid triangle (or a dotted line) with the centre at one apex. A solid (open) dot represents a carbon atom above (below) the plane of the paper, and with a carbon-hydrogen bond pointing out of (into) the plane of the paper. A solid triangle (dotted line) shows a -CH$_3$ group above (below) the plane of the paper. The configuration at

one chiral centre (C-24) is not indicated because the two isomers were not resolved by the GC-MS system used. Of the 256 possible arrangements of the eight chiral centres shown only two are present after early diagenesis. Hydrogen exchange then occurs at the site marked 20 by removal and then reattachment of the hydrogen atom.
B) Representations of a hopanoid molecule found in living organisms (tetrahydroxybacteriohopane) and the two isomeric hopanes found in sediments were used to determine the extent of isomerization, a and b.
C) (a) represents two monoaromatic steroid hydrocarbons, which are isomeric at C-5 (shown by the sinuous C-H bond), with the aromatic ring shown by an inscribed circle. The numbers identify the carbon atoms. With increasing temperature hydrogen and a methyl group are lost to produce a triaromatic hydrocarbon (b). The reaction is assumed to be irreversible under geological conditions.

It is sufficient to state here that the reactions start with the 20R and 22R isomers of the sterane and hopane, and the monoaromatic steroid. At elevated temperatures, ~65°C for the isomerizations and ~90°C for the aromatization, the thermally activated reactions start to convert reactant to product. Possible complications from catalysis are: removal and addition of product and reactant, alternate reaction pathways, contamination, and impregnation. These complications are discussed by Mackenzie and McKenzie (1983) and by Beaumont et al. (1985). The isomerization is particularly simple: a carbon-hydrogen bond is broken and a hydrogen reattached at the same site with either the R or S stereochemistry. For these reversible reactions a dynamic equilibrium is established between the R and S forms which depends on the ratio of the forward and reverse reaction rates (γ). The free energies of the two forms are not the same and therefore $\gamma \neq 1.0$. The aromatization is more complex, involving the loss of 7 hydrogen and 1 methyl substituents and is irreversible.

Progress of the reactions is measured by the concentration ratios: 20S/(20R + 20S) for the sterane, which progresses from 0 to 0.54 in the temperature range 65-130°C; 22S/(22R + 22S) for the hopane, which progresses from 0 to 0.61 over a similar temperature range; and, T/(M + T) (where M and T are the mono- and tri-aromatic steroids), which progresses from 0 to 1.0 over the temperature range 90-130°C.

Steranes, hopanes, and steroids with from 26-35 carbon atoms, reflecting variations in side-chain length, are common in most organic-rich sediments (organic carbon content $\geq$ 1%). Consequently, there are many choices of specific reaction to follow. The choice of C29 species for the aromatization and sterane isomerization and C32 species for the hopane isomerization is discussed by Mackenzie and McKenzie (1983), who also described the extraction techniques and the techniques for analysis by gas-chromatography-mass spectrometry to measure the ratios listed above.

Mackenzie and McKenzie (1983) also discussed the kinetics of the reactions and equations relating reactant and product concentrations. It is assumed that the reactions are first-order and that the reaction rates vary with temperature according to the Arrhenius law. The activation energies (E) and frequency factors (A) (Table 9.4) for each reaction have been estimated by several methods, including comparison of model and observed reaction extents in basins where the thermal history of the analyzed sediments is considered to be well known. Eight sedimentary basins formed in crustal stretching environments have been considered (Mackenzie and McKenzie, 1983). More recently, the results of laboratory experiments have been incorporated (Abbott and Maxwell, 1985).

A, E, and γ for each of the reactions are the fundamental parameters necessary to predict the extent of reaction for a model time-temperature history. The effect of differing values of kinetic parameters for the isomerization reactions versus the aromatization reactions can be seen by plotting the reactions against one another in an A-I plot (Fig. 9.54). Paths within the diagram trace progress of the reactions from start to completion. Relatively low temperatures for long periods of time favour the isomerization reactions, whereas the converse favours aromatization. The basis for this difference can be seen from Arrhenius's plots of the reactions in which the straight lines for the two types

of reaction cross as temperature increases, thereby allowing the aromatization to be most rapid at high temperature. Paths followed by a suite of samples in an A-I diagram can be used to partly separate the effects of temperature and time. For example, rapid burial in a region with a high geothermal gradient can easily be distinguished from slow burial in a region of low geothermal gradient (Mackenzie and McKenzie, 1983). Conventional maturation indices cannot provide this separation.

The reaction extents have been measured in 55 samples from 7 wells, or well groupings, in the Scotian Basin, chosen so that the results could be compared with the thermomechanical model results (Fig. 9.55). Illustrative results from the Mic Mac J-77, Venture D-23 and Sable Island C-67 wells are presented here. A complete discussion can be found in Mackenzie et al. (1985). It is assumed that the thermo-mechanical model correctly predicts the subsidence and heat flux through the lithosphere at each of the well locations. Only sediment conductivities and radiogenic heat production were allowed to vary in order to obtain agreement between the present temperature distribution and corrected bottom-hole temperatures (Fig. 9.56-9.58). The corresponding time-temperature histories were then used to predict the extent of reactions and the results compared with measured samples (A-I plots panel d, Fig. 9.56-9.58). The effect of assumed values of sediment thermal conductivity and radiogenic heat production can be seen for the Bluenose G-47 well (Fig. 9.51). Values used

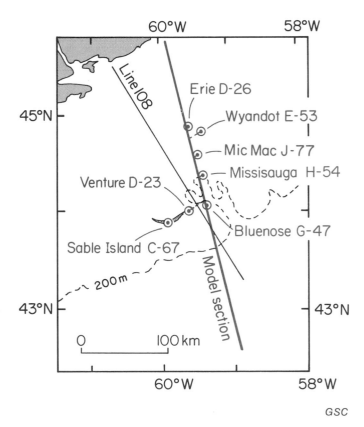

GSC

Figure 9.55. Wells on the Scotian margin from which A-I samples were taken in relation to the modelled cross-section.

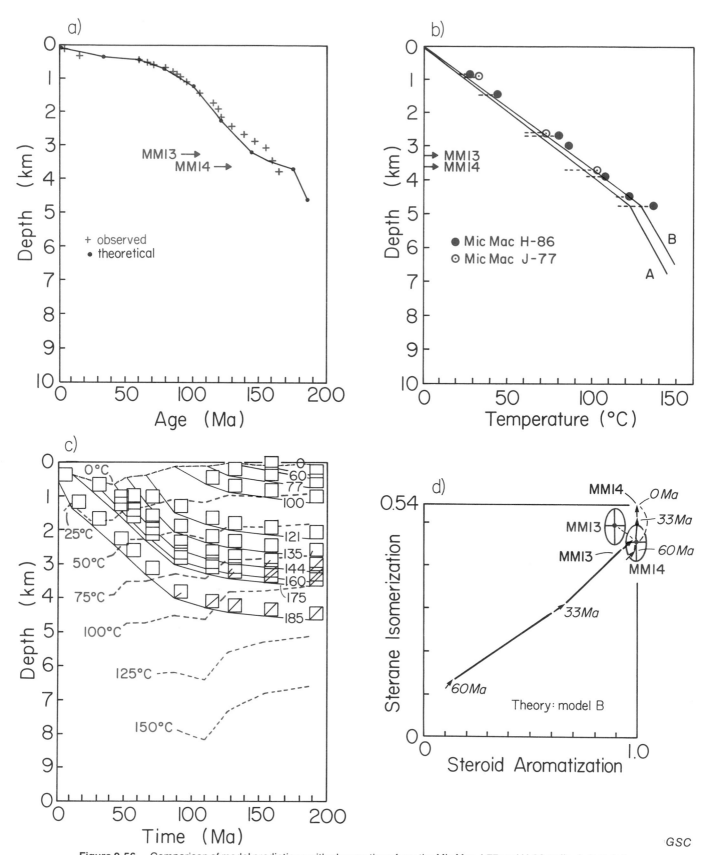

Figure 9.56. Comparison of model predictions with observations from the Mic Mac J-77 and H-86 wells. A description of symbols and a more detailed explanation are given in the text. Panel a compares the present age-depth relationships; b compares the corrected bottom-hole temperatures with those of models A and B (both panels a and b show the depth from which the A-I samples were taken); c illustrates the predicted subsidence, paleobathymetry and temperature histories together with the development of the A-I (Sterane) reactions (age of stratigraphic boundaries in Ma); d compares the observed (cross surrounded by an analytical error ellipse) and predicted (arrow head) amounts of A-I (Sterane) reactions, respectively.

GSC

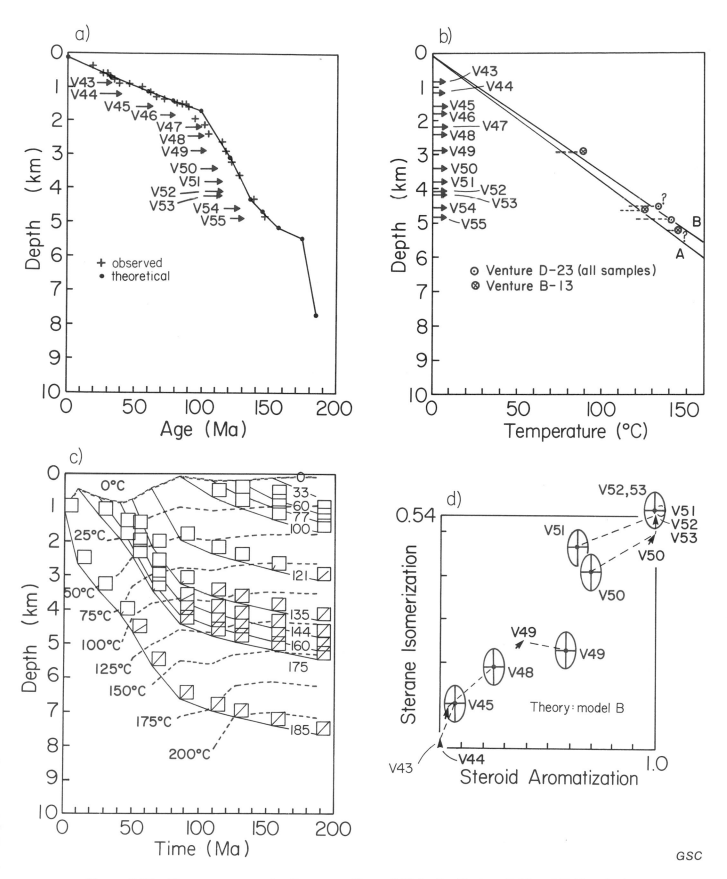

Figure 9.57. The same composite diagram as Figure 9.56 for the Venture D-23 and B-13 wells (see text and Fig. 9.56 for description).

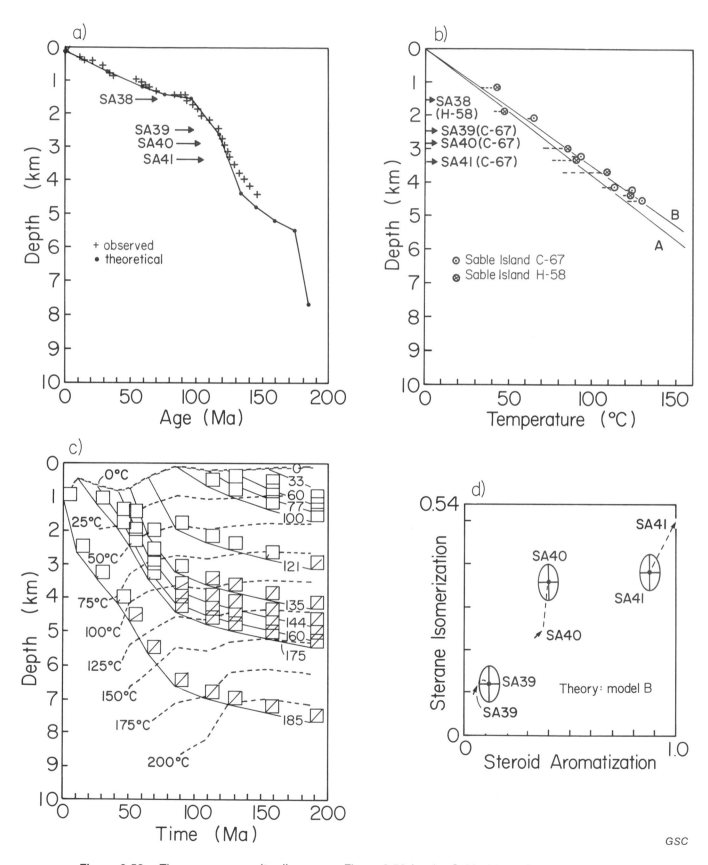

Figure 9.58. The same composite diagram as Figure 9.56 for the Sable Island C-67 and H-58 wells (see text and Fig. 9.56 for description).

by Beaumont et al. (1982a) give too low a geothermal gradient, whereas those used in models A and B (Table 9.5) for the constituent lithologies give good agreement. These values are also in good agreement with those measured for samples from the Scotian margin (Table 9.3).

The a panels (Fig. 9.56-9.58) compare the observed and theoretical present age-depths for the wells and show the depths from which the A-I samples were taken. The Decade of North American Geology timescale (Palmer, 1983) was used to convert to absolute age.

The corresponding b panels compare the predicted temperatures from models A and B with the observed corrected bottom-hole temperatures. The sizes of the corrections, which revise the observed temperatures upward to correct for the cooling of drilling mud circulation (Issler, 1984), are shown by horizontal dashed lines. Both models are in reasonably good agreement with the observations, which indicate a uniform gradient within the sediments. The predicted near-surface temperatures may be as much as 5°C too low and both models may predict slightly low temperatures for the Mic Mac H-86 well.

The c panels show the subsidence, temperature and A-I reaction histories predicted for each well. The solid lines trace the subsidence history of the model B stratigraphic horizons as a function of time since rifting. Their present depths are labelled with the age in millions of years. The corresponding changes in temperature distribution with time (dashed lines) partly reflect changing paleobathymetry shown by the depth of the 0°C isotherm, and are also related to basal heat flux, sediment lithology and compaction, and radiogenic heat production. The small boxes are A-I diagrams that refer to the time-depth-temperature locations of their bottom left corners. The straight lines in the boxes join the predicted reaction end points to the origin; they do not show the reaction path in the diagram.

The plots are useful in that they illustrate progress of the reactions which can then be related to the onset of maturity. For example, in the Mic Mac J-77 and H-86 wells, reactions in 185 Ma old sediment are predicted to have started 80 Ma after rifting and to be complete by 130 Ma. Reactions are currently underway in sediments that are 135 ± 10 Ma old at a depth of about 2.8 ± 0.5 km. The reactions, once started, are very sensitive to temperature and time and, for the Scotian margin, typically traverse the A-I diagram in the depth range of 1 km. This sensitivity means that even to have captured the reactions in progress within a sample, irrespective of their precise relative amounts, provides a good measure of the approach to the onset of maturity.

The d panel compares the observed sample (dot surrounded by an analytical error ellipse circle) and corresponding predicted (arrow head) states of the reactions when taken in pairs and plotted as A-I diagrams. These diagrams are of the same form as Figure 9.54. The discrepancy between model B predictions and observations is shown by a dashed line.

In Mic Mac samples MM13 and 14 reactions are nearly complete, as predicted, and there is sufficient space to show the predicted progress of the reactions from 60 to 33 Ma and then to the present by a series of three arrows joined by a bold solid line. Note the large difference in amount of reaction during this period for the two samples; reactions for MM14, the deeper, were approaching completion at 60 Ma. During the last 60 Ma, the thermal gradient has

remained almost constant (Fig. 9.56c), but the sample temperatures have increased by about 10°C due to blanketing by the 400 m of sediments deposited. Both temperature and time are contributing to the reactions; late stage burial plays an important role in determining the depth to mature sediments. Observed and predicted results for both samples are in good agreement, as are those for the hopane isomerization (not shown); the reactions being insensitive to small errors in their early temperature history that result from differences between the observed and predicted subsidence history (Fig. 9.56a).

The Venture D-23 well was studied in greater detail because it is important in relation to the Venture gas field. The 13 samples show an interesting pattern of results that reflect both the effects of in situ reactions in the sediments and the consequences of impregnation by what appears to have been oil migrating from depth. The model accurately predicts the present age-depth curve and temperature-depth observations (Fig. 9.57a, b). Figure 9.57d indicates that virtually no A-I (sterane) reactions should have occurred in samples V43-V47, all of which come from depths where the temperature is low. Correspondingly, reactions in samples V51-V55, which come from depths of 4 km or more, should be nearing or have gone to completion. Figure 9.57d confirms these predictions with the exception of three samples, V44, V46, and V47 (not shown, but discussed by Mackenzie et al., 1985), which come from a depth range of 1.3-2.3 km in regions adjacent to oil staining in the well cores. These sample results, which indicate too high a level of maturity, are best interpreted in terms of mixing of partly mature or mature migrating hydrocarbons, in which the A-I reactions were probably complete, with indigenous hydrocarbons, in which the reactions had not started or were only just starting (Mackenzie et al., 1985). Samples V43 and V45 were evidently not impregnated in this way and samples V48-V53 show reasonably good correspondence between observation and theory.

The results for the samples SA39-SA41 from Sable Island C67 (Fig. 9.58) again show good correspondence between theoretical and observed stratigraphy and present temperature, particularly for model B. The samples all come from depths for which reactions are predicted to be in progress (Fig. 9.58c) and the observations confirm this prediction. Sample SA38 from the well Sable Island H58 was contaminated by migrating oil, but otherwise the theory and observation are in good agreement.

Temperature and maturation of the Scotian Margin sediments

The results from all the wells that were part of the A-I study are best summarized by projecting the temperature and reaction distributions on the model cross section (Fig. 9.59). The temperature distribution (panel a) is for model B, which agrees best with observations where available. At depths greater than 4 km, and in all areas below the continental slope and rise, the results are theoretical predictions based on the good agreement elsewhere and the assumption that shale is the dominant lithology beneath the slope and rise. Panel b predicts that the A-I reactions are currently underway in a thin zone, 1 km thick, which crosses stratigraphic horizons. Its depth has proved to be correct where drilling results are available. Beneath the slope and rise the zone position has been predicted using the theoretical temperature history and the reaction kinetics.

Much more work is necessary to relate the basin temperature history to oil and gas maturation. The present results only serve to calibrate and give confidence to the theoretical temperature predictions. Given a sufficient suite of results of this kind, it will be possible to recalibrate the time-temperature index (TTI) to vitrinite reflectance relationship with the intent of determining a universal calibration (Waples, 1980; Issler, 1984). Such results will also help in quantifying the relationship between other geochemical indicators and temperature and time.

The A-I reactions used in this study are precursors to oil and gas generation. On the basis of the knowledge (Mackenzie and Maxwell, 1981) that the onset of petroleum generation closely follows the completion of the reactions, it is possible to map an approximate distribution of the top of the zone of significant petroleum generation (Fig. 9.59b) for the cross-section of the Scotian margin. This distribution is approximate because it considers only the largest scale structure of the basin. It does not include small-scale perturbations that may occur due to local variations in lithology, sediment thickness or diapirism by salt and shale.

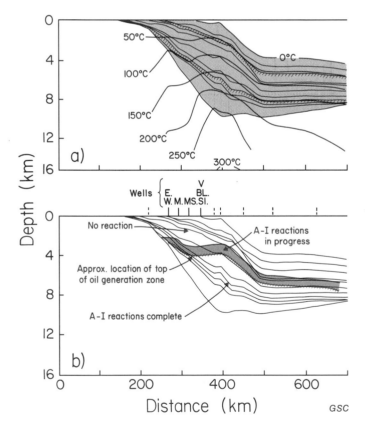

Figure 9.59. Model B predictions of present temperature distribution of the Scotian margin along the model cross-section (panel a) and of the regions of the section in which the A-I (Sterane) reactions are presently underway (panel b). Panel b also shows an approximate position for the top of the petroleum generation zone. The letters represent well names whose locations are shown in Figure 9.55; W-Wyandot E-53; E-Erie D-26; M-Mic Mac J-77; MS-Missisauga H-54; SI-Sable Island C-7; BL-Bluenose G-47; V-Venture D-23.

The evolution of maturation for the cross-section (Fig. 9.60) is based on predicting the position of the base of the A-I reaction zone (underscored line) and the temperature distribution from model B. Powell (1982) proposed that the Verrill Canyon Formation is the most likely source rock in the Scotian Basin. The calculations confirm that the Verrill Canyon and its landward equivalents (shown shaded, Fig. 9.60) are largely mature seaward of the Missisauga H-54 well. This maturity has been achieved over an extended interval starting in the Early Cretaceous. Significant parts of the landward end of the section entered the oil generation zone during the Tertiary (Mackenzie et al., 1985).

Salt diapirism and sediment maturity

Salt diapirs are common throughout the Scotian Basin (Wade, 1981), and several have been drilled in the search for petroleum. Their potential importance in petroleum exploration arises, in part, because of their high thermal conductivity with respect to other sedimentary strata (about 5.8 W/m°C compared to 4 W/m°C, Table 9.5). Thus, these diapirs may act as conduits for conductive heat transfer to the surface, and the high geothermal gradients and heat flow in sediments immediately above them may create a favourable environment for hydrocarbon generation (Klemme, 1975; Dow, 1978). In Figure 9.61 a geothermal gradient map is shown (after Issler, 1984), which delineates several localized "hot spots". Most of these are associated with salt diapirs.

Keen (1983) studied the changes in sediment temperature in the vicinity of two salt diapirs, the Primrose and West Sable structures (Smith, 1975; Rashid and McAlary, 1977). The intent of that study was to determine if the observed high levels of sediment maturity over both these features could be related to the presence of high conductivity salt structures (Rashid and McAlary, 1977; Powell and Snowdon, 1979; Powell, 1982). It was concluded that the mere presence of salt diapirs would not significantly change the levels of sediment maturity. The reason is illustrated in Figure 9.62 for the Primrose structure. Although the isotherms and hence temperatures are somewhat higher over the diapir than at the same depth away from it, the sedimentary strata are also elevated over the diapirs. Therefore sediments over the diapir experience similar temperatures to those in contemporaneous sediments not affected by its presence. Similar results were obtained for the West Sable structure. However, in the case of the Primrose diapir, petroleum and mature source rocks have been found at depths of only 1500 m, directly over the diapir; this is an unusual condition not found elsewhere in the Scotian Basin (Rashid and McAlary, 1977; Powell and Snowdon, 1979).

Figure 9.60. Model B predictions of the temperature and maturation history of the Scotian Basin cross-section. Solid black lines are the chronostratigraphic horizons, red lines show the positions of the isotherms, and the black underscored line is the predicted location of the top of the petroleum generation zone. The shaded area shows the Middle Jurassic-Lower Cretaceous Verrill Canyon Formation and coeval strata. The ß and δ distributions are the same as those for the model discussed previously (Fig. 9.25). Wells are identified in Figure 9.59.

If high sediment maturity is not caused by the presence of highly conductive salt, what other mechanism could provide the necessary high temperatures? Keen (1983) suggested that there may be a zone of fracturing in the sediments adjacent to the salt structure, allowing fluid migration to the top of the diapir from deeper, hotter levels. Simple calculations suggest that such a mechanism is at least feasible. The anomalous high geothermal gradients in a zone several hundred metres thick just above the Primrose structure suggest that it might be fruitful to measure the regional hydrogeological setting and investigate in detail geochemical properties near diapirs. Given the large number of diapirs, particularly beneath the continental slope, such studies could help identify other diapirs above which mature source rocks may be present and help determine the cause of these over-mature regions.

Conclusions and future directions in thermal modelling

Considerable progress has been made in testing model predictions of thermal history and sediment maturity against observations. The development of more sensitive geothermometers, such as the A-I reactions described here,

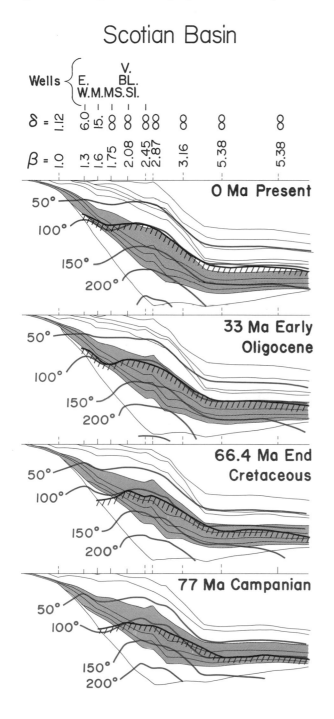

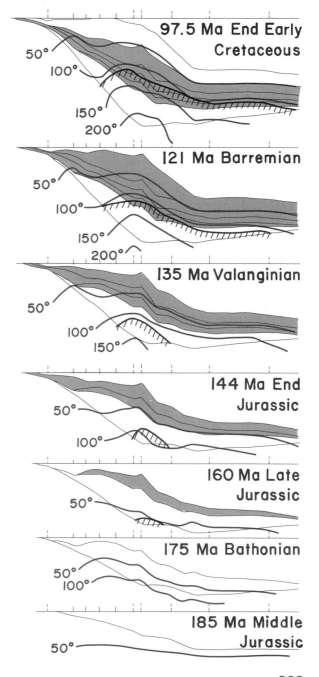

is an important element in this aspect of the modelling and such data should become more easily accessible in future. The need for more measurements of physical properties, such as thermal conductivity, is clearly illustrated in the large differences in sediment temperatures predicted using 'commonly quoted' and measured conductivities.

We can now demonstrate that the predictions of thermal history are compatible with observations in the sediments. We have chosen to study the broad scale features of the temperature distribution, an exception being the diapirs described above; detailed studies within known petroleum fields have not been conducted. The primary reason for this is that predictions of thermal history and sediment maturity as an exploration tool are probably most useful in frontier areas where relatively little is known of the region studied.

However, several effects known to be important within petroleum prospects off eastern Canada need further consideration. In particular, fluid migration may significantly affect the results obtained from the numerical models. The most direct way to determine if fluid migration is at present an important means of heat transfer is to examine the distribution of geothermal gradients, as Issler (1984) has done for the Scotian Basin. His results (Fig. 9.61) showed

that the gradients vary from about 2 to 3.4 °C/100 m. Much of this variation can be explained by the following: 1) the presence of salt diapirs as discussed earlier, 2) variations in radiogenic heat production in the sediments, and, 3) contrasts in thermal conductivity between basement and sediment and between different sedimentary units. Issler (1984) concluded that the flow of fluid at depth is not an important factor, given the linearity of the observed gradients and the absence of any anomalous gradients, not explained by the variations described above. However, we cannot extrapolate this conclusion into the past.

The transitory nature of present day thermal conditions means that it cannot be assumed that they hold for arbitrary lengths of time in the past. Thus the dynamic nature of fluid migration makes it very difficult to assess its importance. A useful study might be to investigate the behaviour with depth of maturation indices such as vitrinite reflectance or A-I reactions, to determine anomalous variations, perhaps indicative of non-linear geothermal gradients and fluid migration in the past.

Overpressured zones may have an important influence on sediment thermal history. Such zones are common off eastern Canada and are associated with petroleum-rich areas such as the Hibernia and Venture fields (see Chapter

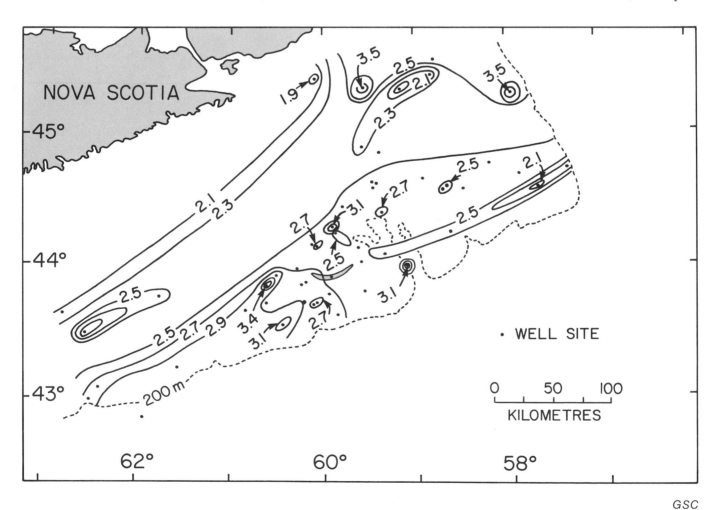

GSC

Figure 9.61. Geothermal gradient for the Scotian Shelf (after Issler, 1984). Contour interval is 0.2°C/100 m. Values were derived from well temperature logs, corrected for drilling effects.

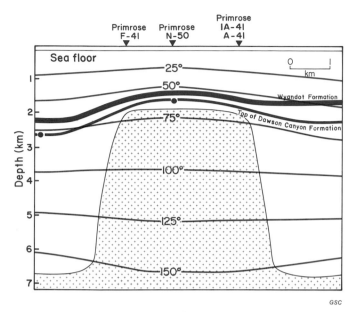

Figure 9.62. Present thermal distribution over the Primrose salt diapir (after Keen, 1983). Isotherms are shown in red at 25°C intervals. Some key Upper Cretaceous sedimentary units (top of the Dawson Canyon Formation and Wyandot Formation) for which maturation was predicted are shown. The dots are the positions where maturity was computed. The locations of the Primrose wells penetrating the diapir are given above the diagram.

6). The zones may exhibit low thermal conductivities due to their higher porosity and therefore higher geothermal gradients. These effects have not been included in the model predictions presented in this chapter, in part, because our understanding of overpressured regions is limited, and also because the intent of the models is to investigate regional, rather than local, effects. It is important to mention this limitation of the present models, if only to point out the need for future work in this area.

CONCLUSIONS

In this chapter we have attempted to illustrate how a family of proposed rifting models — the lithospheric stretching model and its relations — has been developed to provide numerical predictions of a variety of observational properties of rifted continental margins. We have tried to indicate where the models are deficient or incomplete and how some of these deficiencies might be overcome in future. Perhaps more importantly, we have determined the sensitivity of each observed parameter to changes in each of the main attributes of the models.

The main conclusion is that models of lithospheric stretching appear to satisfy most of the observed properties of continental margins and are therefore prime candidates for the processes which control their development. What produces these extensional forces, however, is still unclear; until this critical issue is addressed the relationship between lithospheric rifting and the global driving forces of plate tectonics will remain speculative. Furthermore, it is important to recognize that we have not proved the hypothesis that lithospheric extension is the driving force of continental rifting. Rather, we have shown that it is consistent with the observations presently available. The models are only as good as the real data with which their predictions are compared and new data, incompatible with the present models, may require the development of a new or modified hypothesis.

Nevertheless, the models represent real progress towards an integrated approach to understanding one of the earth's major structural features. The fact that we require the models to predict such a wide variety of observations — gravity anomalies, sedimentary stratigraphy, and thermal history, for example — makes successful models more likely to be a unique representation of the thermal and mechanical processes in the lithosphere. The great variability in observed properties at rifted margins can also be satisfied. This variability indicates the need to study more than one or two margin segments if one is to truly test an hypothesis of the rifting process. Conversely, the models themselves are the best proof of the fundamental relationship between the near surface geological development of the sedimentary rift basins and the underlying changes in the deep crust and mantle. One cannot begin to understand the development of any sedimentary basin without considering the changes in deep structure which must accompany their formation and development. Geodynamic modelling has increased our awareness of these relationships and has provided a powerful and rigorous framework within which to assess hypotheses of basin development.

Future studies will require better observations of crustal structure, rift phase sedimentation and faulting, and will require more accurate geothermometers. Our knowledge of the physical properties of the lithosphere must also be improved, particularly beneath the continents. The mechanical properties of the lithosphere are particularly important. The dynamics of rifting must be explored in much more detail, and it will be this which may clarify the links between lithospheric stretching and the global driving forces on which rifting ultimately depends.

ACKNOWLEDGMENTS

We are indebted to Bill Kay who helped us put this chapter together in a readable form, and to John Manuel for his assistance with thermomechanical model computations. G. Quinlan read the first version of the manuscript and made many helpful suggestions.

Table 9.6. Equations describing subsidence and thermal history for the instantaneous kinematic stretching models

Initial Subsidence: The initial subsidence (S_I) assumes no heat loss during extension. It is computed from the isostatic balance of a column of lithosphere (and asthenosphere) before and just after extension, using an Airy model of isostasy. The surface of the pre-stretched lithosphere is assumed to be at sea level ($z = 0$). We define the following quantities:

$$\rho_c = \rho_c(1 - a\overline{T}_c); \rho_o = \rho_o(1 - a\overline{T}_o); \rho'_o = \rho_o(1 - aT_m) \ and$$

$$\overline{T}_c = \frac{T_m}{2} \frac{t_c}{a} ; \overline{T}_o = \frac{T_m}{2}(1 + \frac{t_c}{a})$$

Where ρ_c, ρ_o, ρ'_o are the average densities of the crust, subcrustal lithosphere, and asthenosphere, respectively. $\overline{T}_c$ and $\overline{T}_o$ are the average crustal, and subcrustal lithospheric temperatures. See Table 9.1 for a definition of parameters and the section on 'Models', for their descriptions .

For the uniform extension model, assuming no loading by either water or sediment.

$$S_I = \{a - \frac{[\overline{\rho}_c t_c + \overline{\rho}_o (a - t_c)]}{\rho'_o}\}(1 - {}^1/\beta)$$

For the uniform extension-melt segregation model, we define another density $\rho_u = t_{oc} \rho_c + (a - t_{oc} - S_m)/(a - S_m)$. ρ_u is the density of undepleted asthenosphere, chosen so that the initial subsidence equals the average depth of the mid-ocean ridges ($S_m = 1.78$ km) as $\beta \to \infty$. t_{oc} is the thickness of oceanic crust. The initial subsidence is then given by:

$$S_I = \{a - \frac{[\overline{\rho}_c t_c + \overline{\rho}_o (a - t_c)]}{\rho'_u}\}(1 - {}^1/\beta)$$

where $\rho'_u = \rho_u(1 - aT_m)$, the average density of asthenosphere at T_m. For the depth-dependent extension model,

$$S_I = \{a - (t_c - d)\overline{\rho}_{c2} - (a - t_c)\overline{\rho}_o\}(1 - {}^1/\delta) + d({}^1/\delta - {}^1/\beta) - d\frac{\overline{\rho}_{c1}}{\rho'_o}(1 - {}^1/\beta)$$

where the zone above depth, d, extends by β, below d by δ. We have assumed d lies within the crust, so two mean crustal densities are required;

$$\overline{\rho}_{c1} = \rho_c(1 - a\overline{T}_{c1}); \overline{T}_{c1} = \frac{T_m}{2} \frac{d}{a} \ for \ z < d \ and$$

$$\overline{\rho}_{c2} = \rho_c(1 - aT_{c2}); \overline{T}_{c2} = \frac{T_m}{2}(\frac{d}{a} + \frac{t_c}{a}) \ for \ d \leq z \leq t_c$$

Temperature Distribution The solution of the one-dimensional equation for conductive heat transfer has the form:

$$T^*(z,t) = \sum_{n=1}^{\infty} A_n \sin\left(\frac{n\pi z}{a}\right) exp(-\kappa a_n^2 t)$$

where the boundary conditions are; $z = o$, $T = T_m$; $z = a$, $T = 0$. T^* is the temperature excess over the equilibrium, pre-rift temperature and $\alpha_n = \pi^2 n^2/a^2$. The form of the coefficients, A_n, is

$$A_n = \frac{2}{a} \int_o^a [T^*(z,o)\sin(\frac{n\pi z}{a})]dz$$

and the form of $T^*(z,o)$ the initial temperature after stretching is known. It is a function of the equilibrium temperature distribution $T_o(z)$ and β (and δ). Thus its form will differ for the uniform and depth dependent extension models.

Table 9.6. (cont.)

By evaluation of coefficients A_n, $T^*(z,t)$ can be obtained. The surface heat flow, Q, is found by evaluating:

$$Q = K\partial T/\partial z\big|_{z=a} = K\partial T_0/\partial z\big|_a + K\sum_{n=1}^{\infty} A_n \frac{n\pi}{a} exp(-\kappa a_n^2 t)$$

$$= Q_0 + K\sum_{n=1}^{\infty} A_n \frac{n\pi}{a} exp(-\kappa a_n^2 t)$$

Q_0 is the equilibrium heat flow, and κ is the thermal diffusivity.

Thermal Subsidence: The elevation above the final equilibrium level at $t \to \infty$ is given by:

$$u(t) = a\int_0^a T^*(z,t)dz$$

The thermal subsidence S_c is given by:

$$S_c(t) = u(o) - u(t)$$

Therefore:

$$u(t) = a\sum_{m=0}^{\infty} 2A_{2m+1} \frac{a}{(2m+1)\pi} exp(-\kappa a_n^2 t)$$

Note that for large t, the exponent becomes large. For n = O

$$\kappa a_o^2 t = \kappa \pi^2 t/a^2 = t/\tau \quad where\, \tau \equiv a^2/\pi^2\kappa$$

If $t >> \tau$

$$u(t) \sim \frac{2aA_o a}{\pi} exp(-t/\tau)$$

Where τ is the thermal time constant of the lithosphere.

Evaluation of the coefficients, A_n, leads to somewhat unwieldy algebraic equations and are not repeated here. Instead, to indicate the parameters involved in the thermal subsidence, we show the asymptotic thermal subsidence (as $t \to \infty$).

For uniform extension, and uniform extension-melt segregation models,

$$S_c(\infty) = \frac{aT_m}{(2-aT_m)}\{a(1 - {}^1/\beta) - S_I\}$$

For the depth-dependent model,

$$S_c(\infty) = \frac{aT_m}{(2-aT_m)}\{a(1 - {}^1/\delta) - S_I + d({}^1/\beta - {}^1/\delta)(2 - \frac{d}{a})\}$$

Most of the equations given in this table can also be found in Beaumont et al. (1982a).

REFERENCES

Abbott, G. and Maxwell, J.R.
1985: The kinetics of specified organic reactions in the zone of catagenesis; Philosophical Transactions of the Royal Society of London, Series A, v. 315, no. 1531, p. 107-120.

Andrews-Speed, C.P., Oxburgh, E.R., and Cooper, B.A.
1984: Temperatures and depth-dependent heat flow in western North Sea; American Association of Petroleum Geologists Bulletin, v. 68, p. 1764-1781.

Artyushkov, E.V.
1981: Physical origin of crustal movements on passive margins; Oceanologica Acta, v. 4, SP Geology of Continental Margins Symposium, p. 167-170.

Artyushkov, E.V. and Sobolev, S.V.
1982: Mechanism of passive margin and inland sea formation; in Studies in Continental Margin Geology, ed. J.S. Watkins and C.L. Drake; American Association of Petroleum Geologists, Memoir 34, p. 689-701.

Ashby, M.F. and Verrall, R.A.
1977: Micromechanisms of flow and fracture and their relevance to the rheology of the upper mantle; Philosophical Transactions of the Royal Society of London, Series A, v. 288, p. 59-95.

Bally, A.W.
1982: Musings over sedimentary basin evolutions; Philosophical Transactions of the Royal Society of London, Series A, v. 305, p. 325-338.

Bally, A.W. and Snelson, S.
1980: Realms of subsidence; in Facts and Principles of World Petroleum Occurrence, ed. A.D. Miall; Canadian Society of Petroleum Geologists, Memoir 6, p. 9-14.

Bally, A.W., Bernoulli, D., Davis, G.A., and Montadert, L.
1981: Listric normal faults; Oceanologica Acta, v. 4, SP Geology of Continental Margins symposium, p. 87-101.

Barrett, D.L. and Keen, C.E.
1976: Mesozoic magnetic lineations. The Magnetic Quiet Zone and seafloor spreading in the northwest Atlantic; Journal of Geophysical Research, v. 81, p. 4875-4884.

Barss, M.S., Bujak, J.P., Wade, J.A., and Williams, G.L.
1980: Age, stratigraphy, organic matter type and colour, and hydrocarbon occurrences in 47 wells, offshore eastern Canada; Geological Survey of Canada, Open File 714, 6 p.

Barss, M.S., Bujak, J.P., and Williams, G.L.
1979: Palynological zonation and correlation of 67 wells, eastern Canada; Geological Survey of Canada, Paper 78-24, p. 1-118.

Beaumont, C.
1979: Rheological zonation of the lithosphere during flexure; Tectonophysics, v. 59, p. 347-366.
1981: Foreland basins; Geophysical Journal of the Royal Astronomical Society, v. 65, p. 291-329.

Beaumont, C., Boutilier, R., and Keen, C.E.
1984: Marginal models; in Petroleum Geology of the North European Margin, ed. A.M. Spencer et al.; Norwegian Petroleum Society, p. 171-186.

Beaumont, C., Boutilier, R., Mackenzie, A.S., and Rullkotter, J.
1985: Isomerization and aromatization of hydrocarbons and the paleothermometry and burial history of the Alberta Foreland Basin; American Association of Petroleum Geologists Bulletin, v. 69, p. 546-566.

Beaumont, C., Keen, C.E., and Boutilier, R.
1982a: Evolution of rifted continental margins; camparison of models and observations for the Nova Scotia margin; Geophysical Journal of the Royal Astronomical Society, v. 70, p. 667-715.
1982b: A comparison of foreland and rift margin sedimentary basins; Philosophical Transactions of the Royal Society of London, Series A, v. 305, p. 295-317.

Beck, A.E.
1976: An improved method of computing the thermal conductivity of fluid-filled sedimentary rocks; Geophysics, v. 41, p. 133-144.

Bodine, J.H.
1981: The thermo-mechanical properties of oceanic lithosphere; Ph.D. thesis, Columbia University, New York, U.S.A., 332 p.

Bostick, N.H.
1973: Time as a factor in the thermal metamorphism of phytoclasts; Congrès International de Stratigraphie et de Géologie du Carbonifère Septième, Krefeld, Aug. 23-28, 1971, Compte Rendu, v. 2, p. 183-193.

Bott, M.H.P.
1971: Evolution of young continental margins and formation of shelf basins; Tectonophysics, v. 11, p. 319-327.
1982: Origin of lithosphere tension causing basin formation; in The Evolution of Sedimentary Basins, ed. P. Kent, M.H.P. Bott, D.P. McKenzie and C.A. Williams; Philosophical Transactions of the Royal Society of London, v. A305, p. 319-324.

Bott, M.H.P. and Dean, D.S.
1972: Stress systems at young continental margins; Nature, v. 235, p. 23-25.

Brown, P., Miller, J.A., and Swain, F.M.
1972: Structural and stratigraphic framework and spatial distribution of permeability of the Atlantic Coastal Plain, North Carolina to New York; United States Geological Survey Professional Paper, v. 796, 79 p.

Bryan, G.M.
1970: Hydrodynamic model of the Blake Outer Ridge; Journal of Geophysical Research, v. 75, p. 4530-4537.

Chen, W.P. and Molnar, P.
1983: Focal depths of intracontinental and intraplate earthquakes and their implications for the thermal and mechanical properties of the lithosphere; Journal of Geophysical Research, v. 88, p. 4183-4214.

Chenet, P., Montadert, L., Gairaud, H., and Roberts, D.
1982: Extension ratio measurements on the Galicia, Portugal and north Biscay continental margins; Implications for evolutionary models of passive continental margins; in Studies in Continental Margin Geology, ed. J.S. Watkins and C.L. Drake; American Association of Petroleum Geologists, Memoir 34, p. 703-715.

Courtney, R.C.
1982: Rheology of the oceanic and continental lithosphere; M.Sc. thesis, Dalhousie University, Halifax, Nova Scotia, 237 p.

Courtney, R.C. and Beaumont, C.
1983: Thermally activated creep and flexure of the oceanic lithosphere; Nature, v. 305, p. 201-204.

Crough, S.T.
1977: Isostatic rebound and power law flow in the asthenosphere; Geophysical Journal of the Royal Astronomical Society, v. 50, p. 723-738.

Curray, J.R., Moore, D.G., Kelts, K., and Einsele, G.
1981: Tectonics and geological history of the passive continental margin at the tip of Baja, California; in Initial Reports of the Deep Sea Drilling Project, Leg 64, ed. J.R. Curray, D.G. Moore et al.; United States Government Printing Office, Washington, D.C., p. 1089-1116.

Dainty, A.M., Keen, C.E., Keen, M.J., and Blanchard, J.E.
1966: Review of geophysical evidence on crust and upper-mantle structure of the eastern seaboard of Canada; in The Earth Beneath the Continents, ed. J.S. Steinhart and T.J. Smith; American Geophysical Union Monograph, v. 10, p. 349-369.

Dewey, J.F.
1982: Plate tectonics and the evolution of the British Isles; Journal of the Geological Society of London, v. 139, p. 371-412.

Dillon, W.P., Popenoe, P., Grow, J.A., Klitgord, K.D., Swift, B.A., Paull, C.K., and Cashman, K.V.
1983: Growth faulting and salt diapirism: their relationship and control in the Carolina Trough, eastern North America; in Studies in Continental Margin Geology, ed. J.S. Watkins and C.L. Drake; American Association of Petroleum Geologists, Memoir 34, p. 21-46.

Dow, W.G.
1978: Petroleum source beds on continental slopes and rises; American Association of Petroleum Geologists Bulletin, v. 62, p. 1584-1595.

Eldholm, O. and Sundvor, E.
1980: The continental margins of the Norwegian-Greenland Sea: Recent results and outstanding problems; Philosophical Transactions of the Royal Society of London, Series A, v. 294, p. 77-86.

Emery, K.O., Uchupi, E., Phillips, J.D., Bowin, C.O., Bunce, E.T. and Knott, S.T.
1970: Continental rise off eastern North America; American Association of Petroleum Geologists Bulletin, v. 54, p. 44-108 and p. 1120-1139.

England, P.C.
1983: Constraints on extension of continental lithosphere; Journal of Geophysical Research, v. 88, p. 1145-1152.

Falvey, D.A.
1974: The development of continental margins in plate tectonic theory; Australian Journal of Petroleum Exploration, v. 14, p. 95-106.

Falvey, D.A. and Middleton, M.F.
1981: Passive continental margins; evidence for a pre-breakup deep crustal metamorphic subsidence mechanism; Oceanologica Acta, v. 4, SP Geology of Continental Margins Symposium, p. 103-114.

Fenwick, D.K.B., Keen, M.J., Keen, C.E., and Lambert, A.
1968: Geophysical studies of the continental margin northeast of Newfoundland; Canadian Journal of Earth Sciences, v. 5, p. 483-500.

Fleitout, L., Froidevaux, C.M., and D.A. Yuen
1983: Dynamics of the continental lithosphere and its associated stress fields; Inter-Union Commission on the Lithosphere, XVIII General Assembly of the International Union of Geodesy and Geophysics, Programme and Abstracts, Hamburg, Germany, August 1983, p. 26-27.

Fletcher, R.C. and Hallet, B.
1983: Unstable extension of the lithosphere; a mechanical model for basin and range structure; Journal of Geophysical Research, v. 88, p. 7457-7466.

Foucher, J.-P. and Sibuet, J.C.
1980: Thermal regime of the northern Bay of Biscay continental margin in the vicinity of the D.S.D.P. Sites 400-402; Philosophical Transactions of the Royal Society of London, Series A, v. 294, p. 157-167.

Foucher, J.P., LePichon, X., and Sibuet, J.C.
1982: The ocean-continent transition in the uniform lithospheric stretching model; role of partial melting in the mantle; Philosophical Transactions of the Royal Society of London, Series A, v. 305, p. 27-43.

Garven, G. and Freeze, R.A.
1984a: Theoretical analysis of the role of groundwater flow in the genesis of stratabound ore deposits. Part 1: mathematical and numerical models; American Journal of Science, v. 284, p. 1085-1124.
1984b: Theoretical analysis of the role of groundwater flow in the genesis of stratabound ore deposits. Part 2: quantitative results; American Journal of Science, v. 284, p. 1125-1174.

Given, M.M.
1977: Mesozoic and early Cenozoic geology of offshore Nova Scotia; Bulletin of Canadian Petroleum Geology, v. 25, p. 63-91.

Goetz, C. and Evans, B.
1979: Stress and temperature in the bending lithosphere as constrained by experimental rock mechanics; Geophysical Journal of the Royal Astronomical Society, v. 59, p. 463-478.

Goldflam, P., Hinz, K., Weigel, W., and Wissmann, G.
1980: Some features of the northwest African margin and magnetic quiet zone; Philosophical Transactions of the Royal Society of London, Series A, v. 294, p. 87-96.

Gradstein, F.M. and Williams, G.L.
1976: Biostratigraphy of the Labrador Shelf; Geological Survey of Canada, Open File 349, 39 p.
1981: Stratigraphic charts of the Labrador and Newfoundland shelves; Geological Survey of Canada, Open File 826, 5 p.

Gradstein, F.M., Grant, A.C., and Jansa, L.F.
1977: Grand Banks and J-Anomaly Ridge; a geological comparison; Science, v. 197, p. 1074-1076.

Grant, A.C.
1975: Structural modes of the western margin of the Labrador Sea; in Offshore Geology of eastern Canada, Volume 2, Regional Geology, ed. W.J.M. Van der Linden and J.A. Wade; Geological Survey of Canada, Paper 74-30, p. 217-231.

Grow, J.A.
1980: Deep structure and evolution of the Baltimore Canyon Trough in the vicinity of the COST No. B-3 well; in Geological Studies of the COST No. B-3 well, United States Mid-Atlantic Continental Slope Area, ed. P.A. Scholle, United States Geological Survey Circular 833, p. 117-125.

Grow, J.A. and Markl, R.G.
1977: IPOD-USGS multichannel seismic reflection profile from Cape Hatteras to the mid-Atlantic ridge; Geology, v. 5, p. 625-630.

Hallam, A.
1984: Pre-Quaternary sea-level changes; Earth and Planetary Science Annual Review, v. 12, p. 205-243.

Haworth, R.T. and Keen, C.E.
1979: The Canadian Atlantic margin; a passive continental margin encompassing an active past; in Crustal Properties Across Passive Margins, ed. C.E. Keen; Tectonophysics, v. 59, p. 83-126.

Haworth, R.T., Williams, H., and Keen, C.E.
1985: Transect D1: North Appalachian mountains acros Newfoundland to south Labrador Sea: North Continent-Ocean Transects Program, Decade of North American Geology, Geological Society of America, Centennial Continent/Ocean Transect No. 1.

Hellinger, S.J. and Sclater, J.G.
1983: Some comments on two layer extensional models for the evolution of sedimentary basins; Journal of Geophysical Research, v. 88, p. 8251-8270.

Hinz, K.
1981: A hypothesis on terrestrial catastrophes: Wedges of very thick oceanward dipping layers beneath passive continental margins; Their origin and significance; Geologisches Jahrbuch, Reihe E, Heft 22, p. 3-28.

Hinz, K., Schluter, H.V., Grant, A.C., Srivastava, S.P., Umpleby, D., and Woodside, J.
1979: Geophysical transects of the Labrador Sea; Labrador to southwest Greenland; in Crustal Properties Across Passive Margins, ed. C.E. Keen; Tectonophysics, v. 59, p. 151-183.

Hood, A., Gutjahr, C.C.M., and Heacock, R.L.
1975: Organic metamorphism and the generation of petroleum; American Association of Petroleum Geologists Bulletin, v. 59, p. 986-996.

Hutchinson, D.R., Grow, J.A., Klitgord, K.D., and Swift, B.A.
1983: Deep structure and evolution of the Carolina Trough; in Studies in Continental Margin Geology, ed. J.S. Watkins and C.L. Drake; American Association of Petroleum Geologists, Memoir 34, p. 129-152.

Hyndman, R.D., Jessop, A.M., Judge, A.S., and Rankin, D.S.
1979: Variations of heat flow in the Maritime Provinces of Canada; Canadian Journal of Earth Sciences, v. 16, p. 1154-1165.

Illies, J.H.
1981: Mechanism of graben formation; Tectonophysics, v. 73, p. 249-266.

Issler, D.R.
1984: Calculation of organic maturation levels for offshore eastern Canada — implications for general application of Lopatin's method; Canadian Journal of Earth Sciences, v. 21, p. 477-488.

Jackson, H.R., Keen, C.E., and Keen, M.J.
1975: Seismic structure of the continental margins and ocean basins of southeastern Canada; Geological Survey of Canada, Paper 74-51, 13 p.

Jackson, J. and McKenzie, D.
1983: The geometrical evolution of normal fault systems; Journal of Structural Geology, v. 5, p. 471-482.

Jansa, L.F.
1981: Mesozoic carbonate platforms and banks of the eastern North American margin; Marine Geology, v. 44, p. 97-117.

Jansa, L.F. and Pe-Piper, G.
1985: Early Cretaceous volcanicity on a northeastern American margin and its implications for plate tectonics; Geological Society of America Bulletin, v. 96, p. 83-91.

Jansa, L.F. and Wade, J.A.
1975: Geology of the continental margin off Nova Scotia and Newfoundland; in Offshore Geology of Eastern Canada, Volume 2, Regional Geology, ed. W.J.M. Van der Linden and J.A. Wade; Geological Survey of Canada, Paper 74-30, p. 51-105.

Jansa, L.F. and Wiedmann, J.
1982: Mesozoic-Cenozoic development of the eastern North American and northwest African continental margins; a comparison; in Geology of the Northwest African Continental Margin, ed. U. von Rad and K. Hinz; Springer-Verlag, New York, p. 215-269.

Jansa, L.F., Bujak, J.P., and Williams, G.L.
1980: Upper Triassic salt deposits of the western North Atlantic; Canadian Journal of Earth Sciences, v. 17, p. 547-559.

Jansa, L.F., Enos, P., Tucholke, B.E., Gradstein, F.M., and Sheridan, R.E.
1979: Mesozoic-Cenozoic sedimentary formations of the North Atlantic basin, western North Atlantic; in Deep Drilling Results in the Atlantic Ocean: Continental Margins and Paleoenvironment, ed. M. Talwani, W. Hay and W.B.F. Ryan; Maurice Ewing Series 3, American Geophysical Union, p. 1-57.

Jarvis, G.T. and McKenzie, D.P.
1980: Sedimentary basin formation with finite extension rates; Earth and Planetary Science Letters, v. 48, p. 42-52.

Jarvis, G.T. and Peltier, W.R.
1982: Mantle convection as a boundary layer phenomenon; Geophysical Journal of the Royal Astronomical Society, v. 68, p. 385-424.

Jordan, T.H.
1981: Continents as a chemical boundary layer; Philosophical Transactions of the Royal Society of London, Series A, v. 301, p. 359-373.

Karner, G.D. and Watts, A.B.
1982: Isostasy at Atlantic-type continental margins; Journal of Geophysical Research, v. 87, p. 2923-2948.

Keen, C.E.
1979: Thermal history and subsidence of rifted continental margins — evidence from wells on the Nova Scotia and Labrador shelves; Canadian Journal of Earth Sciences, v. 16, p. 502-522.
1983: Salt diapirs and thermal maturity, Scotian Basin; Bulletin of Canadian Petroleum Geology, v. 31, p. 101-108.
1985: The dynamics of rifting; Deformation of the lithosphere by active and passive driving forces; Geophysical Journal of the Royal Astronomical Society, v. 80, p. 95-120.
in press: Some important consequences of lithospheric extension; Journal of the Geological Society of London.

Keen, C.E. and Barrett, D.L.
1981: Thinned and subsided continental crust on the rifted margin of eastern Canada; crustal structure, thermal evolution and subsidence history; Geophysical Journal of the Royal Astronomical Society, v. 65, p. 443-465.

Keen, C.E. and Cordsen, A.
1981: Crustal structure and seismic stratigraphy of the rifted continental margin off eastern Canada: Ocean bottom seismic refraction results off Nova Scotia; Canadian Journal of Earth Sciences, v. 18, p. 1523-1538.

Keen, C.E. and Haworth, R.T.
1985: D-3 Rifted continental margin off Nova Scotia: offshore eastern Canada; Decade of North American Geology, Geological Society of America, Centennial continent/ocean Transect No. 3.

Keen, C.E. and Hyndman, R.D.
1979: Geophysical review of the continental margins of eastern and western Canada; Canadian Journal of Earth Sciences, v. 16, p. 712-747.

Keen, C.E. and Keen, M.J.
1974: The continental margins of eastern Canada and Baffin Bay; in The Geology of Continental Margins, ed. C.A. Burk and C.L. Drake; American Asociation of Petroleum Geologists, Continuing Education Series No. 5, p. 381-389.

Keen, C.E. and Lewis, T.
1982: Radiogenic heat production from the continental margin of eastern North America; Implications for petroleum generation; American Association of Petroleum Geologists Bulletin, v. 66, p. 1402-1407.

Keen, C.E., Hall, B.R., and Sullivan, K.D.
1977: Mesozoic evolution of the Newfoundland Basin; Earth and Planetary Science Letters, v. 37, p. 307-320.

Keen, C.E., Keen, M.J., Barrett, D.L., and Heffler, D.E.
1975: Some aspects of the ocean-continent transition at the continental margin of eastern North America; Geological Survey of Canada, Paper 74-30, p. 189-197.

King, L.H. and Young, I.F.
1977: Paleocontinental slopes of the east coast geosyncline (Canadian Atlantic Margin); Canadian Journal of Earth Sciences, v. 14, p. 2553-2564.

Kirby, S.H.
1980: Tectonic stresses in the lithosphere; constraints provided by the experimental deformation of rocks; Journal of Geophysical Research, v. 85, p. 6353-6363.

Klemme, H.D.
1975: Geothermal gradients, heat flow and hydrocarbon recovery; in Petroleum and Global Tectonics, ed. A.F. Fischer and S. Judson; Englewood Cliffs, N.J., Princeton University Press, p. 251-304.

Klitgord, K.D. and Behrendt, J.C.
1979: Basin structure of the U.S. Atlantic margin; in Geological and Geophysical Investigations of Continental Margins, ed. J.S. Watkins, L. Montadert and P. Dickenson; American Association of Petroleum Geologists, Memoir 29, p. 85-112.

Klitgord, K.D. and Grow, J.A.
1980: Jurassic seismic stratigraphy and basement structure of western Atlantic magnetic quiet zone; American Association of Petroleum Geologists Bulletin, v. 64, p. 1658-1680.

Klitgord, K.D., Schlee, J.S., and Hinz, K.
1982: Basement structure, sedimentation and tectonic history of the Georges Bank Basin; in Geological Studies of the COST No. G-1 and G-2 Wells, United States Outer Continental Shelf, ed. P.A. Scholle and C.R. Wenkam; United States Geological Survey, Circular 861, p. 160-193.

Kusznir, N.J and Bott, M.H.P.
1977: Stress concentration in the upper lithosphere caused by underlying visco-elastic creep; Tectonophysics, v. 43, p. 247-256.

LASE Study Group
1986: Deep Structure of the US East Coast passive margin from large aperture seismic experiments (LASE); Marine and Petroleum Geology, v. 3, p. 234-242.

LePichon, X. and Sibuet, J.C.
1981: Passive margins; a model of formation; Journal of Geophysical Research, v. 86, p. 3708-3720.

LePichon, X., Angelier, J., and Sibuet, J.C.
1982: Subsidence and stretching; in Studies in Continental Margin Geology, ed. J.S. Watkins and C.L. Drake; American Association of Petroleum Geologists, Memoir 34, p. 731-741.

Lewis, J.F. and Hyndman, R.D.
1976: Ocean heat flow measurements over the continental margins of eastern Canada; Canadian Journal of Earth Sciences, v. 13, p. 1031-1038.

Libby-French, J.
1984: Stratigraphic framework and petroleum potential of northeastern Baltimore Canyon Trough, mid-Atlantic outer continental shelf; American Association of Petroleum Geologists Bulletin, v. 68, p. 50-73.

Mackenzie, A.S. and Maxwell, J.R.
1981: Assessment of thermal maturation in sedimentary rocks by molecular measurements; in Organic Maturation Studies and Fossil Fuel Exploration, ed. J. Brooks; Academic Press, London, p. 239-254.

Mackenzie, A.S. and McKenzie, D.P.
1983: Isomerization and aromatization of hydrocarbons in sedimentary basins formed by extension; Geological Magazine, v. 20, p. 417-528.

Mackenzie, A.S., Beaumont, C., Boutilier, R., and Rullkotter, J.
in press: Aromatization and isomerization of hydrocarbons and the thermal evolution of the Nova Scotia continental margin; Philosophical Transactions of the Royal Society of London, Series A.

Mackenzie, A.S., Brassell, S.C., Eglinton, G., and Maxwell, J.R.
1982: Chemical fossils — the geological fate of steroids; Science, v. 217, p. 491-505.

Majorowicz, J.A., Jones, F.W., Lam, H-L., and Jessop, A.M.
1984: Regional variations of heat flow differences with depth in Alberta, Canada; Geophysical Journal of the Royal Astronomical Society, v. 81, p. 479-487.

McKenzie, D.P.
1978: Some remarks on the development of sedimentary basins; Earth and Planetary Science Letters, v. 40, p. 25-32.

McWhae, J.R.H.
1981: Structure and spreading history of the northwestern Atlantic region from the Scotian Shelf to Baffin Bay; in Geology of the North Atlantic Borderlands, ed. J.W. Kerr and A.J. Ferguson; Canadian Society of Petroleum Geologists, Memoir 7, p. 299-332.

Montadert, L., de Charpal, O., Roberts, D., Guennoc, P., and Sibuet, J.C.
1979: Northeast Atlantic passive continental margins; rifting and subsidence processes; American Geophysical Union, Maurice Ewing Symposium Series 3, p. 154-186.

Mutter, J., Talwani, M., and Stoffa, P.
1982: Origin of seaward dipping reflectors in oceanic crust off the Norwegian margin by "subaerial sea-floor spreading"; Geology, v. 10, p. 353-357.

Neugebauer, H.J. and Spohn, T.
1982: Metastable phase transitions and progressive decline of gravitational energy; aspects of Atlantic-type margin dynamics; in Dynamics of Passive Continental Margins, ed. R.A. Scrutton; American Geophysical Union, Geodynamics Series, v. 6, p. 166-183.

Oxburgh, E.R. and Andrews-Speed, C.P.
1981: Temperature, thermal gradients, and heat flow in the south western North Sea; in Petroleum Geology of the Continental Shelf Shelf of North West Europe, ed. L.V. Illing and G.D. Hobson; London Institute of Petroleum, p. 141-151.

Palmer, A.R.
1983: The Decade of North American Geology 1983 geologic time scale; Geology, v. 11, p. 503-504.

Parmentier, E.M., Turcotte, D.L., and Torrance, K.E.
1976: Studies of finite amplitude non-Newtonian thermal convection with application to the earth's mantle; Journal of Geophysical Research, v. 81, p. 1839-1846.

Parsons, B. and Sclater, J.G.
1977: An analysis of the variation of ocean floor bathymetry and heat flow with age; Journal of Geophysical Research, v. 82, p. 803-827.

Poag, C.W.
1979: Stratigraphy and depositional environments of Baltimore Canyon Trough; American Association of Petroleum Geologists Bulletin, v. 63, p. 1452-1466.

1980: Foraminiferal stratigraphy, paleoenvironments, and depositional cycles in the outer Baltimore Canyon trough; in Geological Studies of the COST No. B-3 Well, United States Mid-Atlantic Continental Slope area, ed. P.A. Scholle; United States Geological Survey, Circular 833, p. 44-65.

Powell, T.G.
1982: Petroleum geochemistry of the Verrill Canyon Formation; a source for Scotian Shelf hydrocarbons; Bulletin of Canadian Petroleum Geology, v. 30, p. 167-179.

Powell, T.G. and Snowdon, L.R.
1979: Geochemistry of crude oils and condensates from the Scotian Basin; offshore Eastern Canada; Bulletin of Canadian Petroleum Geology, v. 27, p. 453-466.

Proffett, J.M.
1977: Cenozoic Geology of the Yerington district, Nevada, and implications for the nature and origin of basin and range faulting; Geological Society of America Bulletin, v. 88, p. 247-266.

Quinlan, G. and Beaumont, C.
1984: Appalachian thrusting, lithospheric flexure, and the Paleozoic stratigraphy of the eastern interior of North America; Canadian Journal of Earth Sciences, v. 21, p. 973-996.

Rashid, M.A. and McAlary, J.D.
1977: Early maturation of organic matter and genesis of hydrocarbons as a result of heat from a shallow piercement salt dome; Journal of Geochemical Exploration, v. 8, p. 549-570.

Reiter, M. and Jessop, A.M.
1985: Estimates of terrestrial heat flow along offshore eastern Canada by using petroleum bottom hole data; Canadian Journal of Earth Sciences, v. 22, p. 1503-1517.

Robbins, E.I. and Rhodehamel, E.C.
1976: Geothermal gradients help predict petroleum potential of Scotian Shelf; Oil and Gas Journal, v. 74, p. 143-145.

Royden, L. and Keen, C.E.
1980: Rifting process and thermal evolution of the continental margin of eastern Canada determined from subsidence curves; Earth and Planetary Science Letters, v. 51, p. 343-361.

Royden, L., Sclater, J.G., and Van Herzen, R.P.
1980: Continental margin subsidence and heat flow, important parameters in formation of petroleum hydrocarbons; American Association of Petroleum Geologists Bulletin, v. 64, p. 173-187.

Sawyer, D.S., Swift, B.A., Sclater, J.G., and Toksoz, M.N.
1982a: Extensional model for the subsidence of the northern United States Atlantic continental margin; Geology, v. 10, p. 134-140.

Sawyer, D.S., Toksoz, M.N., Sclater, J.G., and Swift, B.A.
1982b: Thermal evolution of the Baltimore Canyon Trough and Georges Bank Basin; in Studies in Continental Margin Geology, ed. J.S. Watkins and C.L. Drake; American Association of Petroleum Geologists, Memoir 34, p. 743-762.

Scheupbach, M.A. and Vail, P.R.
1980: Evolution of outer highs on divergent continental margins; National Research Council, Geophysics Study Committee, Continental Tectonics; National Academy of Sciences, Studies in Geophysics, p. 50-60.

Schlee, J.S. and Grow, J.A.
1980: Seismic stratigraphy in the vicinity of the COST No. B-3 well; in Geological Studies of the COST B-3 well, United States Mid-Atlantic Continental Slope Area, ed. P.A. Scholle; United States Geological Survey Circular 833, p. 111-116.

Scholle, P.A.
1977: Geological studies of the COST No. B-2 well, U.S. Mid-Atlantic outer continental shelf area; United States Geological Survey Circular 750, 71 p.

1980: Geological studies of the COST No. B-3 well, U.S. Mid-Atlantic continental slope area; United States Geological Survey Circular 833, 132 p.

Sclater, J.G. and Christie, P.A.F.
1980: Continental stretching; an explanation of the post Mid-Cretaceous subsidence of the central North Sea Basin; Journal of Geophysical Research, v. 85, p. 3711-3739.

Sclater, J.G., Jaupart, C., and Galson, D.
1980: The heat flow through oceanic and continental crust and the heat loss of the earth; Review of Geophysics and Space Physics, v. 18, p. 269-311.

Sengor, A.H.C. and Burke, K.
1978: Relative timing of rifting and volcanism on earth and its tectonic implications; Geophysical Research Letters, v. 5, p. 419-421.

Sheridan, R.E., Grow, J.A., Behrendt, J.C., and Bayer, K.C.
1979: Seismic refraction study of the continental edge of the eastern United States; Tectonophysics, v. 59, p. 1-28.

Sleep, N.H.
1971: Thermal effects of the formation of Atlantic continental margins by continental break-up; Geophysical Journal of the Royal Astronomical Society, v. 24, p. 325-350.

Smith, H.A.
1975: Geology of the West Sable structure; in Canada's Continental Margins and Offshore Petroleum Exploration, ed. C.J. Yorath, E.R. Parkes, and D.J. Glass; Canadian Society of Petroleum Geologists, Memoir 4, p. 133-154.

Smith, R.B. and Bruhn, R.L.
1984: Intraplate extensional tectonics of the Eastern Basin and Range; inferences on structural style from seismic reflection data, regional tectonics, and thermal-mechanical models of brittle-ductile deformation; Journal of Geophysical Research, v. 89, p. 5733-5762.

Spohn, T. and Schubert, G.
1982: Convective thinning of the lithosphere; a mechanism for the initiation of continental rifting; Journal of Geophysical Research, v. 87, p. 4669-4681.

Srivastava, S.P.
1978: Evolution of the Labrador Sea and its bearing on the early evolution of the North Atlantic; Geophysical Journal of the Royal Astronomical Society, v. 52, p. 313-357.

Srivastava, S.P., Falconer, R.K.H., and MacLean, B.
1981: Labrador Sea, Davis Strait, Baffin Bay; geology and geophysics — a review; in Geology of the North Atlantic Borderlands, ed. J.W. Kerr and A.J. Ferguson; Canadian Society of Petroleum Geologists, Memoir 7, p. 333-398.

Steckler, M.S. and Watts, A.B.
1978: Subsidence of the Atlantic-type continental margin off New York, Earth and Planetary Science Letters, v. 41, p. 1-13.

1982: Subsidence history and tectonic evolution of Atlantic-type continental margins; in Dynamics of Passive Continental Margins, ed. R.A. Scrutton; American Geophysical Union, Geodynamics Series, v. 6, p. 184-196.

Strong, D.F. and Harris, A.
1974: The petrology of Mesozoic alkaline intrusives of central Newfoundland; Canadian Journal of Earth Sciences, v. 11, p. 1208-1219.

Sullivan, K.D. and Keen, C.E.
1978: The nature of the crust in the vicinity of the Newfoundland Ridge; Canadian Journal of Earth Sciences, v. 15, p. 1462-1471.

Taylor, S.R., Toksoz, M.N., and Chaplin, M.P.
1980: Crystal structure of the northeastern United States; contrasts between Grenville and Appalachian Provinces; Science, v. 208, p. 595-597.

Tucholke, B.E. and Ludwig, W.J.
1982: Structure and origin of the J Anomaly Ridge, western north Atlantic Ocean; Journal of Geohphysical Research, v. 87, p. 9389-9407.

Tucholke, B.E. and Mountain, G.S.
1979: Seismic stratigraphy, lithostratigraphy, and paleosedimentation patterns in the North American Basin; in Deep Drilling Results in the Atlantic Ocean; Continental Margins and Paleoenvironments, ed. M. Talwani; American Geophysical Union, Maurice Ewing Series, v. 3, p. 58-86.

Turcotte, D.L., Liu, J.Y., and Kulhawy, F.H.
1984: The role of an intracrustal asthenosphere on the behaviour of major strike-slip faults; Journal of Geophysical Research, v. 89, p. 5801-5816.

Umpleby, D.C.
1979: Geology of the Labrador Shelf; Geological Survey of Canada, Paper 79-13, 34 p.

Vail, P.R. and Hardenbol, J.
1979: Sea-level change during the Tertiary; Oceanus, v. 22, p. 71-79.

Vail, P.R., Mitchum, R.M., Todd, R.G., Widmier, J.M., Thompson, S., Sangree, J.B., Bubb, J.N., and Hatlelid, W.G.
1977: Seismic stratigraphy and global changes of sea level; in Seismic Stratigraphy – Applications to Hydrocarbon Exploration, ed. C.E. Payton; American Association of Petroleum Geology, Memoir 26, p. 49-212.

Van der Linden, W.J.M.
1975: Crustal attenuation and sea-floor spreading in the Labrador Sea; Earth and Planetary Science Letters, v. 27, p. 409-423.

Van Hinte, J.E.
1978: Geohistory analysis — application of micropaleontology in exploration geology; American Association of Petroleum Geologists Bulletin, v. 62, p. 201-222.

Vetter, U.R. and Meisner, R.O.
1979: Rheologic properties of the lithosphere and application to passive margins; Tectonophysics, v. 59, p. 367-380.

Vierbuchen, R.C., George, R.P., and Vail, P.R.
1982: A thermal-mechanical model of rifting with implications for outer highs on passive continental margins; in Studies in Continental Margin Geology, ed. J.S. Watkins and C.L. Drake; American Association of Petroleum Geologists, Memoir 34, p. 765-778.

Wade, J.A.
1981: Geology of the Canadian Atlantic margin from Georges Bank to the Grand Banks; in Geology of the North Atlantic Borderlands, ed. J.W. Kerr and A.J. Fergusson; Canadian Society of Petroleum Geologists, Memoir 7, p. 447-460.

Walcott, R.I.
1970: Isostatic response to loading of the crust in Canada; Canadian Journal of Earth Sciences, v. 7, p. 2-13.

Waples, D.W.
1980:   Time and temperature in petroleum formation: Application of Lopatin's method to petroleum exploration; American Association of Petroleum Geologists Bulletin, v. 64, p. 916-926.

Watts, A.B.
1981:   The U.S. continental margin: subsidence history, crustal structure and thermal evolution; in Geology of Passive Continental Margins; History, Structure, and Sedimentologic Record, Education Cruise Notes Series, No. 19, American Association of Petroleum Geologists, Tulsa, Oklahoma, 75 p.
1982:   Tectonic subsidence, flexure and global changes in sea-level; Nature, v. 297, p. 469-474.

Watts, A.B. and Thorne, J.
1984:   Tectonics, global changes in sea-level and their relationship to stratigraphical sequences at the U.S. Atlantic continental margin; Marine and Petroleum Geology, v. 1, p. 319-339.

Watts, A.B., Karner, G.D., and Steckler, M.S.
1982:   Lithospheric flexure and the evolution of sedimentary basins; in The Evolution of Sedimentary Basins, ed. p. Kent et al.; Philosophical Transactions of the Royal Society of London, v. A305, p. 249-282.

Weertman, J.
1970:   The creep strength of the Earth's mantle; Geophysics and Space Physics Review, v. 8, p. 145-168.

Wernicke, B. and Burchfiel, B.C.
1982:   Modes of extensional tectonics; Journal of Structural Geology, v. 4, p. 105-115.

Williams, H.
1979:   The Appalachian Orogen in Canada; Canadian Journal of Earth Sciences, v. 16, p. 792-807.

Williams, H. and Hatcher, R.D.
1983:   Appalachian suspect terranes; in Contributions to the Tectonics and Geophysics of Mountain Chains, ed. R.D. Hatcher Jr., H. Williams and I. Zietz; Geological Society of America, Memoir 159, p. 33-53.

Williams, H. and Stevens, R.K.
1974:   The ancient continental margin of eastern North America; in Geology of Continental Margins, ed. C.A. Burk and C.L. Drake; Springer-Verlag, New York, p. 781-796.

Yuen, D.A. and Fleitout, L.
1985:   Thinning of the lithosphere by small-scale convective destabilization; Nature, v. 313, p. 125-128.

Authors' addresses

C.E. Keen
Atlantic Geoscience Centre
Geological Survey of Canada
Bedford Institute of Oceanography
P.O. Box 1006
Dartmouth, Nova Scotia
B2Y 4A2

C. Beaumont
Department of Oceanography
Dalhousie University
Halifax, Nova Scotia
B3H 4J1

Printed in Canada

QUATERNARY STUDIES

A view from the CSS Hudson of a Baffin Island fiord. The instrument housing on the deck is the "fish" for the Huntec Deep-tow seismic system. Several examples of high-resolution seismic profiles obtained with this system appear in this volume. Photo courtesy of Bedford Institute of Oceanography Photo Services.

Chapter 10

QUATERNARY GEOLOGY

Chapter 10

QUATERNARY GEOLOGY

D.J.W. Piper, P.J. Mudie, G.B. Fader, H.W. Josenhans, B. MacLean, and G. Vilks

with contributions by: A.E. Aksu, C.L. Amos, D.E. Buckley, S.M. Blasco,
P.R. Hill, I. Hardy, D.A. Hodgson, C.F.M. Lewis, R.A. Myers,
B.R. Pelletier, D. Praeg, R. Klassen,
C.T. Schafer, J.P.M. Syvitski, and J.-S. Vincent

INTRODUCTION

D.J.W. Piper

Quaternary rocks on land have long been treated differently from the rest of Phanerozoic rocks. They are, for example, the subject of a separate volume in Geology of Canada. The bulk of the readily accessible Quaternary sedimentary sequence is terrestrial and will not ultimately be preserved in the geological record. The time scale of major changes in facies is of the order of 10 ka, and for the last 30-40 ka good chronostratigraphic correlation is possible through radiocarbon dates. Because of their proximity to the present day, the terrestrial nature of the deposits, and the high resolution of time information, the study of Quaternary deposits has always required close interactions with other disciplines, particularly archeology, geomorphology, paleobiology, and climatology.

The study of the Quaternary of the oceans is more like the study of pre-Quaternary sediments, and its methods and problems will be more familiar to geologists working on older rocks than are those of traditional Quaternary geology. The deep ocean generally contains a continuous record of Quaternary sedimentation that will be preserved in the geological record. The stratigraphic record on continental shelves, like that at the margin of any craton, is less complete, but nevertheless is more continuous than almost all exposed sections on land. The marine record contains a wealth of data for stratigraphic correlation. Seismic reflection profiling allows rapid lithostratigraphic correlation. Biostratigraphic control is provided by the evolutionary record of marine microfossils; sequential variations in the microfossil assemblages permit interpretation of changes in environmental conditions through time; and pollen transported from the land may allow correlation with terrestrial stratigraphy. There are extensive event

markers such as major ash horizons, paleomagnetic reversals, and the record of essentially synchronous oceanic changes in oxygen isotopic ratios imprinted in deep-sea marine microfossils. On continental shelves, marine strata interfinger with tills deposited from grounded ice. The marine Quaternary record has *de facto* become the type section for all studies of Quaternary sediments beyond the limit of conventional radiocarbon dating of about 40 ka.

The present episode of polar glaciation apparently began in the southern hemisphere with Oligocene glaciation of the Antarctic mountain ranges as the continent approached the south pole. This glaciation became much more extensive by the Late Miocene. Progressive changes in ocean-floor topography as the Gondwana continents drifted away from Antarctica allowed cold bottom waters generated on the Antarctic continental shelves to change the circulation pattern, overall temperature and geochemistry of the world ocean through the Tertiary (Kennett, 1982). In the northern hemisphere, the Late Miocene was also a time of cooling when glaciers were established in Alaska and probably elsewhere. Ice-rafted sand grains are contained in Arctic Ocean sediments as old as 4.5 Ma. Clear evidence of significant ice rafting first occurs in Baffin Bay, the Labrador Sea and the Norwegian Sea about 3.4-3.0 Ma. The first major growth of the Laurentide ice sheet, which accounted for about 45% of the northern hemisphere ice volume, took place within the Pleistocene. Glacial ice first extended across the Scotian Shelf about 0.8 Ma.

The Labrador Sea and Baffin Bay are, together with the Norwegian-Greenland Sea and the Bering Sea, one of three seaways between the Arctic Ocean and the world ocean. The Labrador Sea was flanked by the two largest Pleistocene northern hemisphere ice sheets, one of which has persisted on Greenland through the Holocene. Many theories of the onset of glaciation see the passage of storm tracks along this seaway as the means of nourishing these two large ice sheets with moisture. The marine areas off eastern and arctic Canada are thus pivotal in our understanding of Late Cenozoic glaciation.

Piper, D.J.W., Mudie, P.J., Fader, G.B., Josenhans, H.W., MacLean, B., and Vilks, G.,
1990: Quaternary Geology, Chapter 10 in Geology of the Continental Margin of Eastern Canada, M.J. Keen and G.L. Williams (ed.); Geological Survey of Canada, Geology of Canada, no. 2, p. 475-607 (also Geological Society of America, The Geology of North America, v. I-1).

The significance of the Quaternary geology of the East Coast Offshore is not limited to what it can tell us of the history of the Laurentide and adjacent ice sheets. The well-studied and accessible Canadian continental shelf provides insights into the glacial geology of less accessible waters off Antarctica. Biostratigraphic and environmental interpretations of microfossils developed off eastern Canada have been applied to other high latitude areas. The termination of large ice sheets at 44°N latitude a few hundred kilometres from the Gulf Stream only 40 000 years ago produced glaciological and meteorological conditions not represented in the world today, but have important implications for latest Proterozoic and other extensive glaciations in the past. The safe and economic development of offshore hydrocarbons depends on a proper engineering understanding of Quaternary sediments — engineers "soils" — offshore; the exploitation of placer minerals and aggregates offshore will also rely on Quaternary marine geology.

The data base on the Quaternary of offshore eastern Canada as of 1985 could only partially resolve controversies about the timing and magnitude of Quaternary glaciations.[†] Seismic reflection profiles provide a basic interpreted lithostratigraphy for most continental shelf and some deep sea areas. There are, however, few long boreholes to allow direct sampling of the early Quaternary stratigraphic section (Fig. 10.1). Although large numbers of piston cores have been collected, they generally sample only the latest part of the Quaternary record (<25 ka).

The nature of the marine Quaternary record is different from that on land, so that correlating the two is difficult. Many terrestrial type sections represent discontinuous deposition, are difficult to correlate regionally, do not contain useful biostratigraphic material for correlation over long distances, or are not well dated. In eastern Canada, most land areas are underlain by resistent irregular bedrock and were areas of ice accumulation and thus erosion. In contrast, continental shelf areas are largely floored by soft rocks and are areas of thick sediment accumulation. Seismic reflection profiling permits regional correlation, and marine sediments contain microfossil material suitable for both stratigraphic correlation and environmental interpretation.

Marine areas between or adjacent to Canada and Greenland contain a wealth of information on the history of Quaternary glaciation. Brief summaries of Arctic marine areas are therefore included in this volume because they record the geological history of the outer margin of the Laurentide and its peripheral ice sheets. At the time of writing, only preliminary data were available from Ocean Drilling Program sites in Baffin Bay and the Labrador Sea; those sections may in the future become the stratigraphic standard for the eastern Canadian margin.

CHRONOLOGICAL CONTROL

Introduction and terminology

D.J.W. Piper

Chronological control on marine Quaternary sediments is provided by biostratigraphic methods, radionuclide dating

techniques, and oxygen isotope chronology. The application of these methods to the Quaternary marine sediments adjacent to Canada is discussed in the following sections.

The standard stratigraphic stages for the Quaternary of North America were defined on land: Wisconsinan applies to the last major glaciation, preceded by the Sangamonian Interglacial and Illinoian Glaciation. Standard stages based on marine oxygen isotope chronology provide a much more precise nomenclature for Late Quaternary marine stratigraphy (Fig. 10.2). They are numbered from one corresponding to the Holocene, with even numbers representing periods of greater ice extent, and odd numbers times of interglacials or major interstadials. The terrestrial and marine stages have been variously correlated by different authors; in this chapter the usage of Harland et al. (1982) and Fulton (1984) is followed in applying the term Sangamonian to the entire oxygen isotope stage 5. The term Early Wisconsinan corresponds to isotopic stage 4 (dated at about 75-65 ka), Middle Wisconsinan to stage 3 and the early part of stage 2 (65-23 ka) and Late Wisconsinan to the latter part of stage 2 and the beginning of stage 1 (23-10 ka). Postglacial is used as a local stratigraphic term for sediments that accumulated following ice retreat. Wisconsinan is applied only to areas affected by Laurentide or Atlantic Canada ice; the term Foxe glaciation applies to the corresponding "last glaciation" on Baffin Island.

Biostratigraphic correlation and biochronology

P.J. Mudie and G. Vilks

The Late Cenozoic sections sampled in offshore wells and pelagic marine sequences have been dated biochronologically, whereby geological time units are defined according to irreversible processes of biological evolution (Fig. 10.3). Few such biostratigraphic sequences are known from thick Pliocene and Quaternary marine sections off eastern Canada and at present, data are insufficient to permit definite correlation of regional faunal and floral range zones with standard biochronologies proposed for the North Atlantic (e.g. Berggren, 1981a; Suc and Zagwijn, 1983; Baldauf, 1984; Berggren et al., 1985). Furthermore, because the standard chronologies are largely based on European stratotypes and Deep Sea Drilling Project (DSDP) sites from sub-tropical to temperate regions of the North Atlantic, biochronological correlation with high latitude DSDP sites is not yet well established (Srinivasan and Kennett, 1981). Nevertheless, limited biochronological data from the Fogo Seamounts (Piper, 1975a; Alam and Piper, 1977; Alam et al., 1983), from DSDP Sites 111, 112 and 113 (Laughton et al., 1972), from Davis Strait cores (Mudie and Aksu, 1984; Aksu and Mudie, 1985a), and from eastern Canadian wells (Williams and Bujak, 1977a, b), suggest the stratigraphic ranges of planktonic foraminifera, calcareous nannofossils (coccoliths and discoasters), diatoms, dinoflagellate cysts and pollen from the eastern Canadian offshore are broadly correlatable with the high latitude biochronology established for DSDP Site 611 (Ruddiman, 1987). Thus, the tentative correlation chart for deep sea sediments off eastern Canada (Fig. 10.3) is calibrated against the magnetochronology and biochronological datums (first and last occurrences) of guide fossils at DSDP Site 611.

In most parts of the eastern Canadian offshore the only Quaternary biostratigraphic data are from piston cores

---

[†] See Addendum page 606.

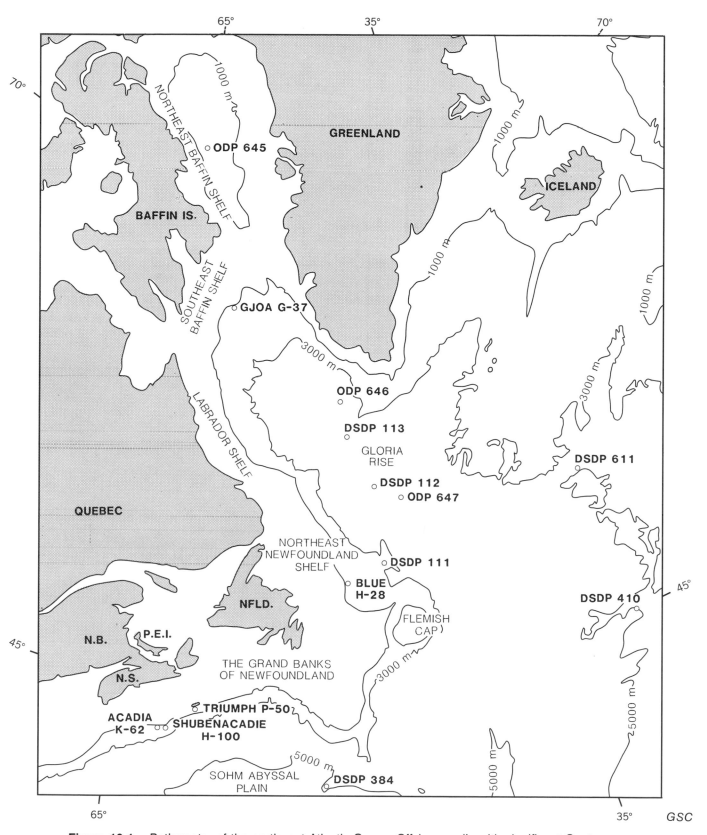

Figure 10.1. Bathymetry of the northwest Atlantic Ocean. Offshore wells with significant Quaternary stratigraphic sequences are indicated. For more detail see Map 850-A (in pocket).

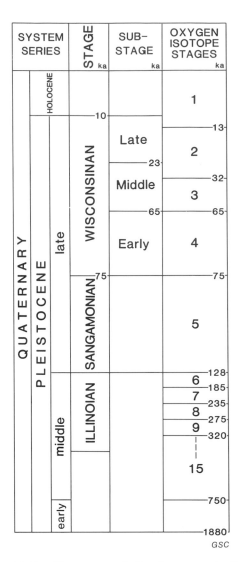

Figure 10.2. Summary of Quaternary stratigraphic nomenclature used in this chapter (after Fulton, 1984, but with Early-Middle Quaternary boundary placed at the base of the Brunhes magnetochron).

that span a geologically short time interval, generally less than 50 ka. Few evolutionary changes are evident in the marine biota over such a period. Therefore, biostratigraphic time scales for the Late Pleistocene and Holocene are based mainly on correlation of superpositional sequences of microfossil* assemblages with radiometric datums (Fig. 10.4). These assemblages of species reflect changes in the environment. The biostratigraphic boundaries are correlated following the principles of ecostratigraphy, whereby species assemblages may re-enter the stratigraphic column as ecological conditions change. Such boundaries are time-transgressive over distances of hundreds of kilometres.

---

* The term microfossil as used in this chapter refers to palynomorphs as well as siliceous and calcareous microfossils.

During the Quaternary the perturbations in the marine environment of the continental shelves were induced by and influenced the glacial-interglacial cycles through a series of feedback mechanisms. From the ecostratigraphic point of view the most important changes were in water temperature and salinity, but for some taxa turbidity, sedimentation rates, proximity to glacial ice and changes in water depths were also significant. Ubiquitous fossils of faunas and floras that are sensitive to these environmental parameters are commonly used to establish stratigraphic horizons (Vilks, 1981).

One of the major shortcomings of the ecostratigraphic zonation of Quaternary sediments is the diachronous aspect of changes in the environment, mainly across the latitudes and towards the offshore. Therefore, in addition to understanding paleoenvironmental events, absolute dating of these events is necessary. Dating inaccuracies, however, are caused by mixing of indigenous and transported fossils due to reworking of fossiliferous sediments, by dissolution of calcareous or siliceous microfossils (Aksu and Mudie, 1985a), and by the oxidation of agglutinated foraminifera (Scott and Medioli, 1980; Scott et al., 1984b). Correlation of marine pollen assemblages with onshore pollen stratigraphy that is controlled by radiocarbon dating (Fig. 10.5) commonly provides the most reliable means for relative dating of postglacial hemipelagic mud sequences (Vilks and Mudie, 1978; Mudie, 1980). Therefore, palynological correlation has been used as a primary dating tool in compiling the biostratigraphic chart (Fig. 10.4) for microfossils in Late Wisconsinan to recent sediments on the Canadian margin from Nova Scotia (44°N) to central Labrador (56°N).

Radiometric dating methods
D.J.W. Piper

A variety of radionuclides are available for dating sediments of Quaternary age: the problems of their application to marine sediments of eastern Canada are briefly reviewed here. Full descriptions of the methods can be found in a number of standard texts and review papers (e.g. Rutter, 1985; Wilson et al., 1984).

[14]C dating has been widely applied to the dating of sediments younger than about 60 ka. Until the development of accelerator mass spectrometry, shells of sufficient size for dating were only rarely found in cores, and almost no shell dates older than 12 ka are available. At the time of writing (1985) accelerator mass spectrometry has been generally available for only about one year: it permits dating of carbonate samples as small as 30 mg, and has already greatly extended our chronologic control (Andrews et al., 1985). Problems of reworking of such small samples have not yet been fully evaluated, however, and at present only dates of up to 30 000 BP are considered reliable by the analytical laboratories.

Most ^{14}C determinations from the eastern Canadian offshore are based on the total organic carbon content of muds. This organic carbon is of diverse origin and, particularly in proglacial sediments, may contain large amounts of reworked carbon. Comparison of shell and total organic carbon dates shows that pre-Holocene total organic carbon dates commonly over estimate the true age because of the effect of dead carbon (Fillon et al., 1981a; Andrews et al., 1985). However, total organic carbon dates commonly show a consistent relationship with subbottom depth (King and Fader, 1986), suggesting that within a single sediment facies the proportion of dead carbon may remain approximately constant. The proportion of particles of reworked carbon greater than 10 μm can be estimated from standard palynological preparations (Nambudiri et al., 1980), and appropriate corrections made to the radiocarbon age assuming that this size fraction is representative of all the carbon present. Fluorescence microscopy may provide an additional method of discriminating dead carbon, but the origin of very fine carbon-rich particles is extremely difficult to determine.

Total organic carbon dates appear reasonably reliable for most Holocene (postglacial) marine muds with a relatively high organic carbon content (>2% dry weight). In many cases, they are the only dates available for older sediments: here they must be treated with great caution since they provide only an estimate of maximum age.

Uranium series dating (Schwarcz and Blackwell, 1985) provides a means of dating over the last 350 ka. The method has been applied to pelagic carbonates, corals, molluscs, wood and other materials; in eastern Canada it has been used extensively only in the dating of marine molluscs exposed in land sections (Grant, 1980; Szabo et al., 1981). Shells of sufficient size for analysis are rarely recovered in marine cores, and detrital input of uranium is too variable to apply the method to most marine sediments. 10Be dating has not yet been applied to sediments off eastern Canada, but the method (with a range of several million years) holds promise for early Quaternary sections (Segl et al., 1984).

Short-lived isotopes, notably ^{210}Pb and ^{127}Cs, have been used extensively to date late Holocene events in eastern Canada (Smith and Schafer, 1984). Their range is generally less than 100 a.

Oxygen isotope stratigraphy

A.E. Aksu and D.J.W. Piper

Oxygen isotope ratios preserved in carbonate of marine microfossils provide a record of past fluctuations in temperature and isotopic composition of seawater (in turn dependent on salinity and global ice volume). In addition, the isotopic composition of the carbonate is dependent on the particular species. Most isotopic curves measured in marine sequences are based on determinations from single species generally of foraminifera (planktonic or benthic), on account of their relative abundance. Most mass spectrometers require at least 30 mg of carbonate, or about 20-50 foraminifera tests for species larger than 150μm.

Sequential changes in oxygen isotope ratios with sub-bottom depth in cores (and hence with time) are remarkably similar for most parts of the world ocean away from ice margins, thus permitting a standard oxygen isotope curve to be erected (Shackleton and Opdyke, 1973, 1976; Shackleton et al., 1982). This shows a sequence of alternating ^{18}O enriched and depleted stages of a few tens of thousands of years duration throughout the Late Quaternary, with each stage identified by a number beginning with 1 for the Holocene interglacial (Fig. 10.2). Prior to about 1 Ma, fluctuations in isotope ratios are smaller. A chronology can be applied to this standard curve using radiometrically or biochronologically dated marker horizons such as the base of the Brunhes magnetochron, and using ^{14}C dates for Quaternary sediments younger than 40 ka. Dates have then been interpolated assuming constant sedimentation rates, refined by spectral analysis for Milankovich cyclicity (Hays et al., 1976).

The application of oxygen isotope stratigraphy relies on correlation of a local isotopic curve to the standard curve of Shackleton and Opdyke (1976). Several factors limit the resolution with which this can be carried out. Only in an instantaneously mixed ocean would changes in oxygen isotope ratios be synchronous: in practice, both evaporation of sea water and input of fresh water from the continent are concentrated in certain areas. The mixing time for a large meltwater spike from the continent into the world ocean is about a thousand years, but poorly mixed marginal seas may retain an anomalous isotopic composition.

The isotopic record measured in deep water benthic foraminifera is less dependant on oceanic temperature fluctuations because the temperature of deep water has probably fluctuated little during the Quaternary. The record preserved in planktonic foraminifera is more strongly influenced by temperature changes (up to 10°C) that may not be synchronous with ice volume changes (Ruddiman and McIntyre, 1984). The standard Quaternary oxygen isotope curve is regarded as principally reflecting global changes in ice volume (Berger, 1981).

Several factors other than temperature limit the accuracy with which the measured isotopic record represents changes in oceanic isotopic composition. Bioturbation results in a smoothing of the isotopic record, so that peak amplitudes are dependant on sedimentation rate, mixing depth and intensity of bioturbation. Dissolution of carbonate tests of foraminifera is known to be selective towards both individuals and species that lived in shallower water, where ^{18}O is depleted. As a result, dissolution results in an anomalously heavy isotopic signal. Because several tens of foraminiferal tests are required to make an oxygen isotope determination, the bulk analyses are influenced by any transported or reworked specimens. Analyses of resedimented microfossils can be used only in exceptional circumstances (Vilks et al., 1985).

It is frequently difficult to correlate the isotopic record obtained from cores from oceanic areas off eastern Canada to the standard isotopic curve (Fillon and Duplessy, 1980; Aksu, 1983a; Alam et al., 1983; Scott et al., 1984a; Schafer and Scott, 1985). The range of available species is limited, and both dissolution and resedimentation are widespread. Many areas, particularly the Arctic Ocean and Baffin Bay, are poorly mixed with the world ocean and are strongly influenced by glacial meltwater. As a result, independant dating methods are generally essential to confirm isotopic correlations.

Although isotopic stratigraphy is generally applied only to deep water sediments, it has recently been applied to continental shelf areas off eastern Canada (Corliss et al., 1982; Scott et al., 1984a). In these areas, the constraints of reworking and poor mixing with global ocean water are more severe. However, regional isotopic stratigraphies based on local variations in isotopic composition of seawater may prove a powerful correlation tool in ice-marginal settings lacking other means of correlation.

STAGES / BIOZONES

Radiometric age (Ma)	Geological age	Magneto-chronology	δ18O Marine climatic stages	North America A	North America B	North west Europe	Mediterranean	Planktonic foraminifera	Calcareous nannofossils	Diatoms	Dinocysts	Pollen
0.06	Holocene / LATE	Bruhnes	5	Wisconsinan	Wisconsinan	Weichselian	Tyrrhenian		NN21 Emiliana huxleyi	(LAD) Rhicurv. ostris	Multispinula minuta	Ambrosia Rumex
			6	Sangamonian	Sangamonian	Eemian						
			7	Illinonian		Saalian	Milazzian		NN20 Gephyrocapsa oceanica	Pseudoeunotia doliolus	(FAD)	(LAD) Carya
	MIDDLE		8 12	Yarmouthian complex	Illinonian	Holsteinian Elsterian		N22				
			15	Kansan		Cromenian	Sicilian		NN19 Pseudoemiliania lacunosa	W Nitzchia reinholdii E ?	Spiniferites elongatus	(LAD) Juglans Pseudotsuga
0.73			16 17	Aftonian complex	Yarmouthian complex			Globorotalia truncatulinoides (FAD)				
0.88	PLEISTOCENE	J	22 23	Nebraskan	Kansan	Menapian	Emilian				Spiniferites frigidus (FAD)	
0.94 1.00	EARLY			Irvingtonian I warm and cold phases	Aftonian Waalian		Calabrian		NN18-17 Calcidiscus macintyrei and/or Discoaster pentaradiatus	W E	(LAD) Filisphaera filifera Impagidinium multiplexum Operculodinium israelianum	(LAD) Tsugaepollenites igniculus
		O			Nebraskan	Eburonian					(LAD)	
1.72											Operculodinium janduchenei	Osmunda spp.
1.88		R				Tiglian		PL6 Globorotalia inflata (FAD)		Nitzchia marina		
2.00		M	low high ■ = warmer	Blancan V	Regional phases not formally recognized for North Atlantic	Pretiglian		PL3-5 Sphaeroidinellopsis seminulina			Amiculasphaera umbracula	
2.48	LATE						Piacenzian		Discoaster brouwei		Selenopemphix nephroides	(FAD) Graminaceae Cyperaceae
2.92 3.00 3.01 3.05 3.15		K M	Gauss	Blancan IV		Reuverian		Globorotalia altispira Globorotalia miocenica (LAD)	NN16 Discoaster surculus		(LAD) Achomosphaera ramulifera Invertocysta lacrymosa (FAD)	(LAD) Podocarpus Liquidambar Nyssa Cedrus
3.40	PLIOCENE			Blancan III				PL2 (LAD) Globorotalia margaritae	NN15 Reticulofenestra pseudoumbilica	Nitzchia jouseae	Filisphaera filifera Spiniferites membranaceus	(LAD) Taxodium Sequoia ?Bombacaceae
3.86 3.98 4.00		C N	Gilbert	Blancan II				PL1 (FAD) Globorotalia margaritae	NN14 Discoaster asymmetricus		(LAD) Achomosphaera andalousiensis	
4.16 4.26	EARLY	S				Bruns-sumian	Zanclian		NN13 Ceratolithus rugosus		Reticulatosphaera stellata	
4.41 4.49		T		Blancan I				Globigerina nepenthes (LAD)			Nematosphaeropsis aquaeducta	
4.59											Lingulodinium machaerophorum	(FAD) Artemisia Taraxacum
4.79									NN12 Ceratolithus tricornialatus	Thalassiosira convexa		
5.00											(LAD) Nematosphaeropsis oblonga	
5.41								Globorotalia conomiozea (FAD)			Impagidinium japonicum	(LAD) Gleichenidites Quercoidites
5.70	MIOCENE / LATE					Susterian	Messinian		NN11 Discoaster quinqueramus		Impagidinium velorum Operculodinium wallii	Alnipollenites spp.
6.00 6.07												

GSC

Figure 10.3. Tentative Late Cenozoic zonation for North Atlantic deep sea, high latitude regions (compiled by P.J. Mudie) — See Addendum.

Radiometric ages are those generally accepted for the standard magnetochronostratigraphic intervals (Harland et al., 1982); polarity subchrons are indicated by the following letters: J = Jaramillo, O = Olduvai, R = Reunion, K = Kaena, M = Mammoth, C = Cochiti, N = Nunivak, S = Sidufjall, T = Thvera.

Oxygen isotope stratigraphy is from Shackleton and Opdyke (1976), Harland et al. (1982) and Shackleton and Hall (1984).

Late Miocene-Holocene stages show two commonly accepted chronologies for North American stages: (A) from Repenning (1984) and (B) from Harland et al. (1982, p. 42); stages for the Northwest European stratotypes in the Netherlands and Germany are compiled from Harland et al. (1982) and Suc and Zagwijn (1983); stages for the western Mediterranean are compiled from Suc and Zagwijn (1983) and Berggren (1981a). Note that there is still much disagreement regarding the subdivision of the Pleistocene in the Mediterranean; see other schemes given by Harland et al. (1982, p. 42). There is also disagreement regarding formal geological subdivisions for the Pleistocene, e.g. the 1983 Decade of North American Geological Time Scale correlates the Calabrian Stage with the whole of the Pleistocene. The Early, Middle and Late subdivisions of the Pleistocene are those commonly used in recent Deep Sea Drilling Project (DSDP) studies according to the boundary ages assigned by Berggren (1981a). There is also considerable disagreement regarding definitions and ages of the Mediterranean and pre-Illinoian North American stages, as clearly demonstrated by Cooke (1973). Some authors (e.g. Repenning, 1983) have cited new evidence from western North America which suggest that the Kansan and Nebraskan tills may be as young as 0.44 Ma (isotope stage 12) and 1.2 to 0.78 Ma (isotope stage 16), respectively.

Planktonic foraminiferal biozones use the zone numbers and names employed for DSDP Leg 94, based on Berggren and van Couvering (1974) and Berggren (1981a). The zone names reflect the FAD (first appearance datum) or LAD (last appearance datum) of the listed guide species. Details of the assemblage composition for DSDP Leg 12 sites in the Labrador Sea are given with the lithostratigraphic descriptions of sites 111, 112 and 113 (Laughton et al., 1972), and correlation with the standard temperate-tropical North Atlantic zones of Bolli, Blow, Jenkins and other workers is discussed in detail by Srinivasan and Kennett (1981). A finer subdivision of zone N22 was attempted for DSDP Sites 111 and 112, using the dominance of *Globorotalia* (= *Neogloboquadrina*) *atlantica* in the Late Pliocene and *G.* (= *N.*) *pachyderma* in the Pleistocene (Laughton et al., 1972, p. 173). Recently, Berggren (1981b, p. 152) has proposed a more complicated North Atlantic subarctic zonation in which the Pliocene is marked by the range zone of *N. atlantica*, the Pliocene is subdivided into an Early Pliocene *N. pachyderma* (d) (= dextral or right coiling) acme zone, followed by a Late Pliocene *N. atlantica* (d) acme zone. Berggren (1981b) also subdivided the Pleistocene into an Early Pleistocene *N. pachyderma* (d) acme zone and a Late Pleistocene *N. pachyderma* (s) (sinistral, or left coiling) acme zone.

Calcareous nannofossil zonations are essentially the same as those of Bukry (1981, p. 338) who has correlated his data with the standard Mediterranean zones of Martini (1971). Bases and tops of zones are mostly based on FAD and LAD of the listed guide fossils. In Labrador Sea Ocean Drilling Program (ODP) Site 646, *Emiliania huxleyi* is common to abundant in Wisconsinan and Holocene sediments (Mudie, unpublished data), therefore an extension of the top of the NN21 zone is shown. Many correlation charts select *Discoaster brouweri* as the main index species for the Late Pliocene; the range of this species extends from the base of NN16 to the top of NN18.

Diatom zones are described by Baldauf (1984). However, the dates of guide species FAD given by Baldauf for the Rockall Plateau are very different from those assigned for DSDP Site 611, which is located about 1000 km farther west (Mudie, 1987). These differences are indicated on the correlation chart by oblique dashed lines, marked W and E to indicate the ages assigned at DSDP Site 611 and Rockall Plateau, respectively.

The *Rhizosolenia curvirostris* (LAD) zone added to the top of the chart was not recognized at DSDP Site 611, but it occurs in Upper Quaternary sediments at ODP Site 646, and this tropical guide fossil (Baldauf, 1984) may have a longer range in the eastern Labrador Sea.

Dinocyst zones are from the range chart of Mudie (1986) for DSDP Site 611, and subsequent more detailed study of Middle-Upper Quaternary sediments from Davis Strait (Aksu and Mudie, 1985a). At present, few of the dinocyst range zones shown here coincide exactly with those proposed by Williams and Bujak (1977a) for eastern Canadian offshore wells. This largely reflects the scanty recovery of palynomorphs from the Pliocene-Pleistocene sections in the wells, and the common occurrence of reworked palynomorphs in Neogene sediments off Eastern Canada.

Pollen zones are based on detailed studies of pollen assemblages in Middle-Late Quaternary cores from the Fogo Seamounts (Mudie, unpublished data) and Davis Strait (Mudie and Aksu, 1984; Aksu and Mudie, 1985a), from observed pollen and spore ranges in DSDP Site 611 (Mudie, 1986), from eastern Canadian offshore well stratigraphies of Williams and Bujak (1977a) and from ranges reported for Norwegian Sea DSDP Leg 38 sites (Koreneva et al., 1976). Note the following: 1) The youngest range zone shown refers to the late Holocene European weed zone that is marked by the FAD in eastern Canada of *Ambrosia psilostachya* and *Rumex acetosella*, which were introduced to the Maritime Provinces and Newfoundland about 150-300 BP (Schafer and Mudie, 1980). 2) The LAD of *Carya* is strongly diachronous: in Davis Strait (Mudie and Aksu, 1984), it disappears near the top of isotopic stage 7 but in Nova Scotia (de Vernal et al., 1983) and on the Fogo Seamounts (Mudie, unpublished data) its last common occurrence is isotopic stage 5e, although it also occurs rarely (probably through long distance dispersal) in the middle Holocene of Nova Scotia. 3) The FAD of *Gramineae and Cyperaceae* refers to the first common occurrence of these taxa which subsequently reoccur at frequent intervals associated with glacial stages during the Late Pliocene- Pleistocene, and also reappear as part of the European weed zone associated with land clearance in the late Holocene. The evolutionary FAD of *Gramineae*, however, is much older (at least Paleocene).

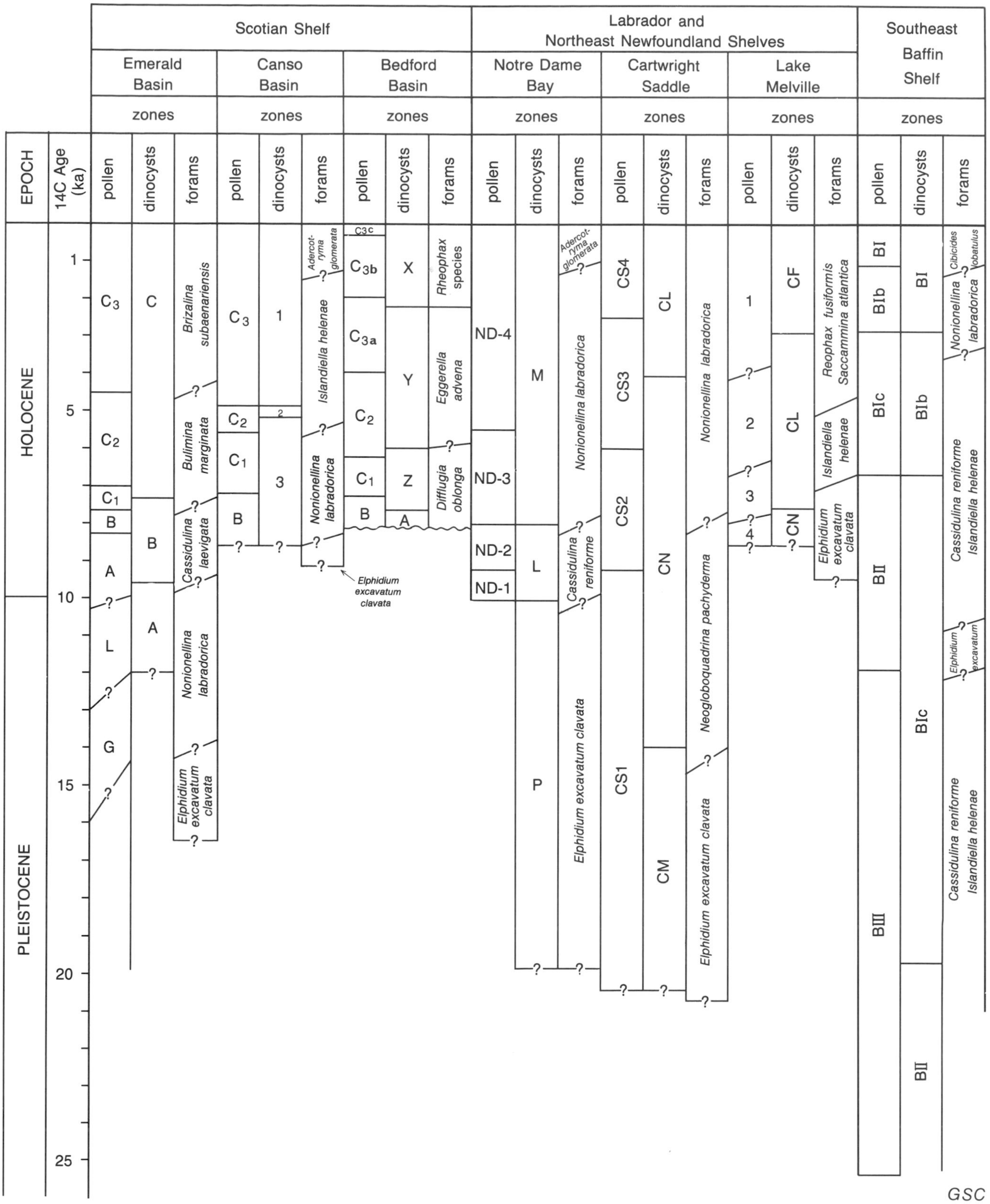

		Scotian Shelf							Labrador and Northeast Newfoundland Shelves									Southeast Baffin Shelf		
		Emerald Basin			Canso Basin			Bedford Basin			Notre Dame Bay			Cartwright Saddle			Lake Melville				
		zones			zones			zones			zones			zones			zones			zones		
EPOCH	14C Age (ka)	pollen	dinocysts	forams	pollen	dinocysts	forams	pollen	dinocysts	forams	pollen	dinocysts	forams	pollen	dinocysts	forams	pollen	dinocysts	forams	pollen	dinocysts	forams

Chart content (biostratigraphic zonation by column):

Emerald Basin — pollen: C_3, C_2, C_1, B, A, L, G; dinocysts: C, B, A; forams: *Brizalina subaenariensis*, *Bulimina marginata*, *Cassidulina laevigata*, *Nonionellina labradorica*, *Elphidium excavatum clavata*

Canso Basin — pollen: C_3, C_2, C_1, B; dinocysts: 1, 2, 3; forams: *Adercotryma glomerata*, *Islandiella helenae*, *Nonionellina labradorica*, *Elphidium excavatum clavata*

Bedford Basin — pollen: C_{3c}, C_{3b}, C_{3a}, C_2, C_1, B; dinocysts: X, Y, Z, A; forams: *Rheophax species*, *Eggerella advena*, *Difflugia oblonga*

Notre Dame Bay — pollen: ND-4, ND-3, ND-2, ND-1; dinocysts: M, L, P; forams: *Adercotryma glomerata*, *Nonionellina labradorica*, *Cassidulina reniforme*, *Elphidium excavatum clavata*

Cartwright Saddle — pollen: CS4, CS3, CS2, CS1; dinocysts: CL, CN, CM; forams: *Nonionellina labradorica*, *Neogloboquadrina pachyderma*, *Elphidium excavatum clavata*

Lake Melville — pollen: 1, 2, 3, 4; dinocysts: CF, CL, CN; forams: *Reophax fusiformis*, *Saccammina atlantica*, *Islandiella helenae*, *Elphidium excavatum clavata*

Southeast Baffin Shelf — pollen: BI, BIb, BIc, BII, BIII; dinocysts: BI, BIb, BIc, BII; forams: *Nonionellina labradorica*, *Cibicides lobatulus*, *Cassidulina reniforme*, *Islandiella helenae*, *Elphidium excavatum*, *Cassidulina reniforme Islandiella helenae*

EPOCH: HOLOCENE, PLEISTOCENE

14C Age (ka) scale: 1, 5, 10, 15, 20, 25

GSC

Figure 10.4. Summary of Late Wisconsinan and Holocene microfossil zones on the continental shelves of eastern Canada (Tables 10.1 to 10.5 provide a key to the lettered zones). The time scale for this chart is based on radiocarbon dates for the boundaries of onshore pollen zones established by Livingstone and Livingstone (1958), Livingstone (1968), Railton (1973, 1975), and Green (1976) for the Nova Scotia region; by Macpherson (1982) for the Newfoundland region; by Jordan (1975) and Short and Nichols (1977) for the Labrador region; and by Mudie and Short (1985, and reference therein) for Baffin Island. Wherever possible, independent dates have also been obtained for the marine reference sections, in order to confirm the validity of the pollen zone correlations. These dates are listed in publications which describe the marine pollen, dinoflagellate and foraminiferal zones in detail, mainly Scott et al. (1984b) for the Scotian and Northeast Newfoundland shelves, Vilks and Mudie (1978, 1983) for the Labrador Shelf; and Mudie and Short (1985) and Praeg et al. (1986) for the Southeast Baffin Shelf. Details of the biozone assemblage composition are also given in these publications, and their salient characteristics are given in sections of this chapter which describe regional stratigraphies. For Lake Melville, pollen zones 1 to 4 correspond to the zones shown for southeast Labrador in Fig. 10.5, as follows: 1 = *Picea*; 2 = *Picea, Abies*; 3 = *Picea, Alnus*; 4 = shrub tundra. Dinocyst zones CN and CL for Lake Melville are the same as for Cartwright Saddle; zone CZ contains a mixture of species characteristic of CL (Cartwright Saddle) and Zone Z (freshwater indicators) for Bedford Basin.

Other dating and correlation methods

D.J.W. Piper, P.J. Mudie and A.E. Aksu

Paleomagnetic stratigraphy is commonly used in studies of deep sea sediment cores containing continuous sedimentary sequences more than 0.7 Ma old to establish correlations with the standard magnetostratigraphy of Harland et al. (1982) (Fig. 10.3). Unfortunately, off eastern Canada, sedimentation rates are so high that few piston cores completely penetrate the Brunhes magnetochron (Aksu, 1985a).

Most work off eastern Canada has therefore concentrated on the recognition of correlatable excursions within the late Brunhes polarity interval. Aksu (1983b) recognized a widespread excursion in Baffin Bay which he dated as isotopic stage 5 or 6, and tentatively correlated with the Blake event. Both Stow (1977) and Alam et al. (1983) recog-

nized a low inclination event in cores from the Grand Banks and Scotian margins that appeared to be of similar age to the Lake Mungo event of about 25 ka. On the Northeast Newfoundland Shelf a low inclination excursion of early Holocene age was recognized in several cores (Piper et al., 1978; Mudie and Guilbault, 1982). In all of these cases, magnetic measurements have served only to add confidence to a correlation and chronology established by other methods. Furthermore, the events are not always detectable from all cores in a region.

Particularly in high latitudes, detailed paleomagnetic analysis of rapidly accumulating sediments allows recognition of secular variations on a scale of a few hundreds of years. This method has been widely used in the correlation of lake sediments and is applicable to marine environments, at least for the last 10 ka. Measurements of

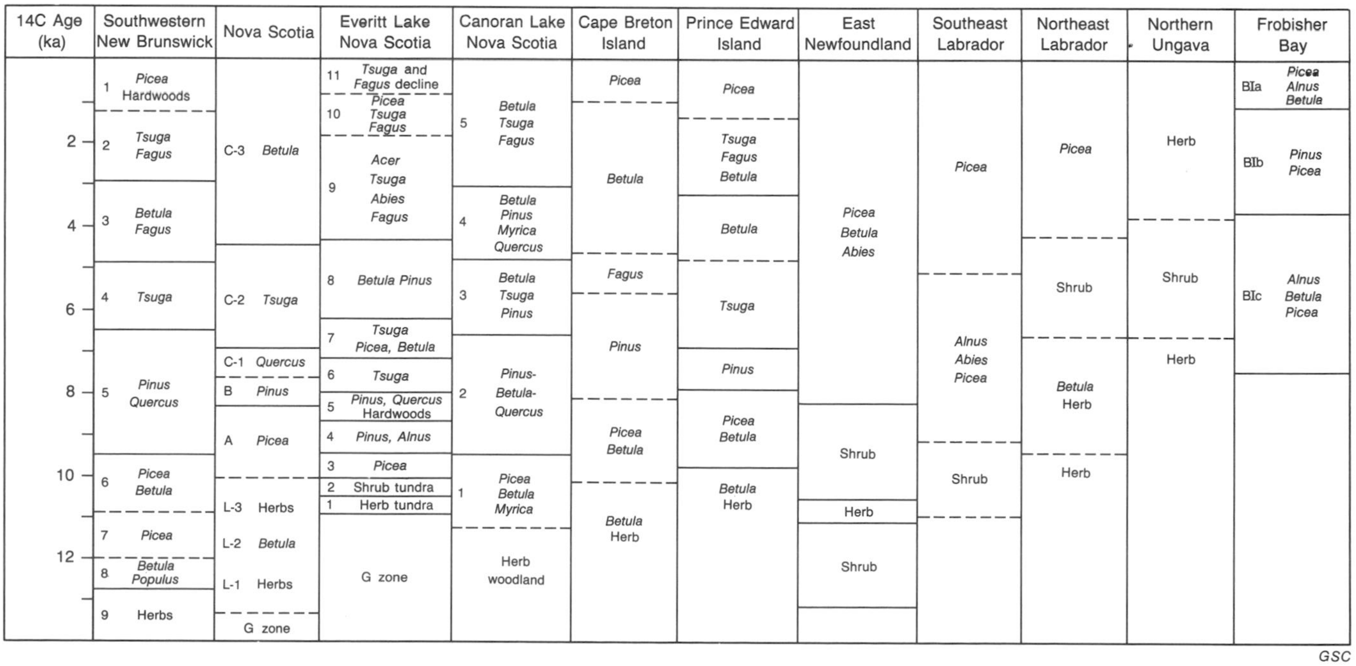

GSC

Figure 10.5. Summary pollen zonation for eastern Canada based on data summarized in Mudie (1980), Anderson (1985), and Mudie and Short (1985).

485

paleomagnetic intensity have been used to substantiate the ^{14}C chronology in Frobisher Bay (Osterman and Andrews, 1983); and to correlate between shelf and fiord core sections (Jennings, 1985; Andrews et al., 1986).

Volcanic ash horizons in Labrador Sea (Chough, 1978; Fillon and Duplessy, 1980; Schafer et al., 1985) and Baffin Bay (Aksu, 1983a) have proved to be useful event markers for stratigraphic correlation in deep water cores. Ruddiman and Glover (1972, 1975) recognized three distinct ash horizons in North Atlantic pelagic sediments, dated at approximately 9.8 ka, 57.5 ka and 340 ka (Ruddiman and McIntyre, 1984). The widespread distribution of coarse shards and their association with ice-rafted debris suggests that the ash was transported as debris in icebergs and sea ice. Binns (1972) suggested a source in Iceland or Jan Mayen. Aksu (1981) showed that the lower two ash horizons were almost exclusively rhyolitic, whereas the horizon dating from 9.3 ka also included dacite and basalt. Brown ash found on raised beaches in Ellesmere Island and dated at about 5 ka by Blake (1970) is compositionally distinct and has not been recognized in marine sediments.

Geochronology through amino acid racemization and epimerization (Rutter et al., 1979; Blackwell, 1983) is based on temperature-dependant chemical changes that take place in amino acids after the death of an organism. Amino acids within calcareous skeletal material (such as molluscs and foraminifera) appear to be closed to the environment, and the early stages of racemization can be analyzed by first order kinetic reactions. Although several amino acids are available, the isoleucine/alloisoleucine reaction is most widely used. The success of the technique as a chronostratigraphic tool depends on accurate estimation of the temperature history of the fossils (with particular attention to warm temperatures), the determination of the species-dependant Arrhenius frequency factor, and the determination of the genus-dependant activation energy. Furthermore, it is necessary to calculate the relationship between temperature and the forward epimerization rate constant for a given species.

In high latitudes, where post-depositional temperatures have been buffered by ice, molluscs with similar amino acid ratios can be used to define "aminozones" that are probably of similar age. Mollusc shells in raised marine deposits in Baffin Island and the Hudson Bay Lowlands (Andrews et al., 1983; Brigham, 1983; Andrews and Miller, 1984; Miller, 1985) have been used to provide a tentative correlation back to the Pliocene. For similar reasons, the method can be applied to deep water areas below the thermocline, where determinations have been made from monospecific samples of planktonic and benthic foraminifera and shell fragments in deep water sediments (Bada and Schroeder, 1975; Miller et al., 1983; Sejrup et al., 1984; Macko and Aksu, 1986).

Thermoluminescence dating of mineral grains measures the amount of thermoluminescence in quartz or other minerals resulting from irradiation by U- and K-bearing minerals in sediment since a sample was last exposed to sunlight. It can potentially be applied to deposits in the age range of 1 ka to 1-2 Ma (Dreimanis et al., 1978; Huntley et al., 1985). Thermoluminescence appears to be the most promising method for dating Quaternary sediments lacking organic materials, and it is one of very few methods available for absolute dating in the range of 50 ka to 1 Ma (Wintle and Huntley, 1980). Thermoluminescence tech-

niques may also be used for dating fossiliferous calcareous and siliceous marine sediments if special techniques are applied (Berger et al., 1984). At present, however, although series of thermoluminescence dates are usually in correct chronological order, caution is needed in accepting the validity of the absolute age. This is because different minerals, such as quartz, feldspar and calcite, respond variably according to age, exposure history and burial history, and more theoretical work is still needed to determine the best laboratory method for preparing different samples and measuring their thermoluminescence properties.

METHODS IN MARINE QUATERNARY GEOLOGY

D.J.W. Piper

Brief descriptions of some methods used in marine Quaternary studies are given in this section; more detailed accounts of these techniques are available in a number of textbooks.

Accurate positioning of data has until recently been a major problem in marine geology. Although there is, unfortunately, no marine equivalent of the airphoto on land, marine navigation methods have steadily improved over the last 30 years. In most east coast areas of Canada south of the Arctic Circle, ship positioning to within a few hundred metres has been possible for the last 10 years.

Positioning the ship, however, does not necessarily position the data. Equipment that is towed behind or lowered over the side of a ship may drift significantly in deep water or where currents are strong. In many cases, the position of towed instruments is known only from the length and orientation of the cable. Positioning systems using high-frequency acoustic signals can also be used to accurately locate the towed body. In deep water, acoustic equipment such as echosounders or seismic profiling systems survey a large area of the seafloor, resulting in a loss of resolution of detailed seabed information.

Seismic reflection profiling

Seismic reflection profiling is the most important technique that sets apart marine Quaternary studies from those on land. The echo sounder illustrates the basic principle of the technique. A sound signal is transmitted through the ocean, reflects off the seabed, and is received by a hydrophone. The time taken for the sound to travel to the seabed and back (two-way travel time) is recorded graphically. By using a sequence of sound signals as a ship moves across the seabed, a graphic record of the shape of the seabed is obtained, and knowing the speed of sound in seawater, the depth to the seabed is determined.

For echosounding, a high-frequency acoustic signal (in the range of 5-200 kHz) is used, usually generated by an electromagnetic transducer (or pinger) that can also serve as a transceiver. This high frequency signal provides good spatial resolution, but is attenuated rapidly; although it will penetrate water effectively, it will scarcely penetrate seabed sediments. Discrimination of fine from coarse sediment at the seabed is possible with some systems. Pingers using lower frequencies of a few kiloHertz (such as the standard 3.5 kHz profiler) will penetrate up to about 50 m of muddy surficial sediments.

In seismic reflection profiling, a more powerful and lower frequency sound source is used, with the intention of obtaining signals from reflectors beneath the seafloor. The sources used most widely for Quaternary work are the airgun, which uses the rapid release of a charge of high-pressure air; the sparker, in which sound is created by discharge of high voltage electricity; and the boomer, in which two parallel plates are rapidly separated electromechanically. These systems yield a range of frequencies from a few hundred to a few thousand Hertz. The airgun and sparker are more powerful than the boomer, but they produce bubbles which oscillate before they burst or collapse yielding a complex bubble pulse source signal. These complex source signals result in similarly complex reflected signals, which often do not allow resolution of fine structure in the sediment. The reflected signals are usually received on a series of hydrophones towed in an "eel" behind the ship. Signal-to-noise ratio is improved by summing the signals from a number of hydrophones, by appropriate filtering to remove unwanted noise, and by towing slowly. A variety of artifacts are produced by seismic reflection profiling (Fig. 10.6), including multiple parallel reflections resulting from the bubble pulse and ringing, hyperbolic reflections (diffractions) from point sources, and bottom multiples. Penetration and resolution can be improved by use of a multichannel recording system, in which reflections are separately recorded on a number of hydrophone groups: this allows comparison of reflected signals from a number of different shots that have been reflected to different hydrophones from the same depth within the sediments (common depth point — CDP). Digital recording of such data allows computer processing that can determine the acoustic velocity of different layers, stack returns from the same common depth point, and remove artifacts due to source signal complexity and multiples.

The most widely used tool for high resolution seismic reflection profiling on the east coast continental shelves is the Huntec Deep Towed Seismic (DTS) system (Hutchins et al., 1976; King and Fader, 1976). This system uses a boomer source towed several tens of metres below the sea surface to reduce ship and wave noise and water column attenuation and to improve spatial geometry of reflecting signals. Heave compensation is also provided to eliminate the effects of towfish motion on the graphic record. The boomer seismic signature is very sharp (0.2 ms) and repeatable. The system can resolve reflections of less than 25 cm spacing to a sub-bottom depth of tens of metres. A combination of air gun and echosounder data in conjunction with the high resolution boomer profiles makes possible interpretation of surface morphology, sediment character and depth of the unconsolidated sediment cover. A similar deep water boomer system (SeaMor), with slightly lower resolution, has recently been developed (Hutchins et al., 1985).

Where Quaternary features have a distinct geomorphological or textural expression at the seabed, they can be imaged using sidescan sonar. This works essentially like a sideways-looking echosounder, and gives an image analagous to a low angle oblique aerial photograph. This image can be orthorectified to yield an image more similar to that in a vertical air photograph. Range and resolution in sidescan sonographs depend on sidescan fish altitude, signal frequency (which may be between 12 and 500 kHz — Fig. 10.7) and the uniformity of the water column.

Coring and other sampling

Simple grab samplers (van Veen and Shipek) have provided numerous surficial samples off eastern Canada, which can be used for textural and petrological studies. However, most samples used for marine Quaternary stratigraphy are obtained by corers which are lowered by cable from a ship and penetrate the seafloor under their own weight (Bouma, 1969). The simplest corer, the gravity corer, consists of a tube containing a plastic liner, a weight at the top of the tube, a valve to minimize sediment loss once a core is collected, and a catcher at the bottom of the corer to stop sediment from falling out. Using weights up to 100 kg, the corer may penetrate one to two metres in soft mud, and a few centimetres in compact sand. The box corer works on the same principle, but has a box instead of a tube, which requires a more complex core catching device; it can obtain a larger sample, but with usually less penetration than a gravity corer.

The piston corer is similar to a gravity corer, but it has a heavier weight (up to 1500 kg) and a piston device inside the barrel that reduces resistance to penetration. A small gravity corer (trigger weight corer) attached to the piston corer is used to activate the piston. If the piston does not start to move until after the corer has started to penetrate the sediment, then the top section of sediment bypasses the cutting head and will not be sampled. The gravity corer used as a tripping device, however, should sample this surface sediment. Conventional piston corers will penetrate 12 m in mud, and 2 to 8 m in alternating sands and muds. They cause little sediment compaction, whereas gravity corers commonly result in considerable sediment shortening. Corers are now being developed with a planned penetration of up to 50 m. Piston corers do not satisfactorily penetrate either compact sand or till.

To penetrate sand, a vibrocorer is used. This is a weighted corer in which the head is vibrated to aid penetration; this can result in disturbance of sediment. To sample till, a small seabed auger or drill is usually required; where till is exposed at the seabed, a large clamshell grab is an effective sampling tool.

With conventional over-the-side technology, the upper 12 m of the Quaternary section can be sampled in areas of muddy seabed, with lesser penetration where coarser sediments are present. Although seismic reflection profiling can be used to recognize areas where older sediments are exposed at the seabed and may be sampled, only the Holocene and Late Wisconsinan sections are sampled in most offshore areas. Many samples contain artifacts or disturbances resulting from the method by which they were collected (Stow and Aksu, 1978).

Obtaining deeper subsurface samples usually requires a dedicated drill ship or platform. Some shallow boreholes (100 m) have been drilled for geotechnical purposes connected with hydrocarbon developments. In the upper few hundred metres of exploratory wells, cuttings samples are not collected and logging is not undertaken; however, in areas having a thick Quaternary section some Lower Pleistocene samples have been recovered. Deeper stratigraphic horizons recognized on seismic reflection profiles may also be traced laterally and sampled where they are exposed or come close to the seafloor. Long composite sections have been built up in this way from piston cores. The hydraulic piston corer and extended core barrel developed by the Deep Sea Drilling Project allow long, relatively

A) 40in³ Airgun (25 foot streamer)

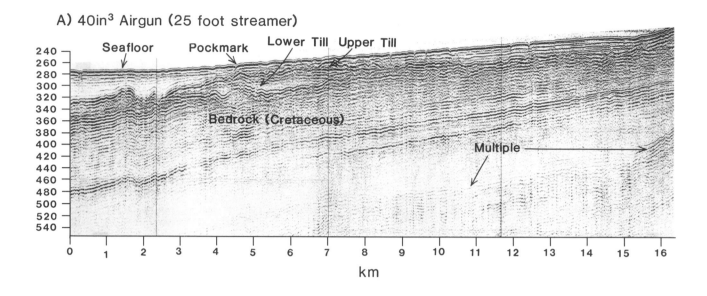

B) Huntec (DTS) boomer (internal hydrophone)

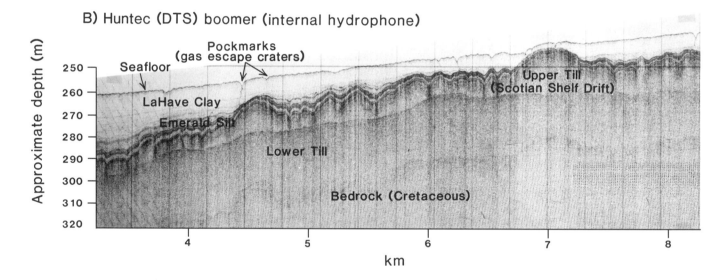

C) MS 26-B echosounder (14.25 kHz)

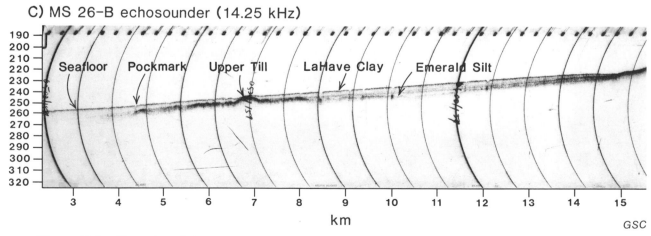

GSC

Figure 10.6. Examples of single channel air gun profile, Huntec DTS profile and 14 kHz MS26-B echosounder profile showing acoustic character of each type of seismic reflection profiling system.

undisturbed cores to be collected from a drill ship, and are used by the Ocean Drilling Program.

OCEANOGRAPHIC AND CLIMATIC SETTING OF QUATERNARY GLACIATION ON THE EASTERN CANADIAN MARGIN

P.J. Mudie

Surface water circulation

Surface water currents off eastern Canada (Fig. 10.8) originate now from two main sources: polar water from the western Arctic Ocean, and temperate water from the North Atlantic Drift (Hachey, 1961; Lazier, 1982). The North Atlantic Drift is a warm (16-18°C) and saline (35-36‰) northern extension of tropical Gulf Stream water that occupies most of the southern and eastern North Atlantic Ocean. Off the Scotian Shelf, rings of warm water from the North Atlantic Drift periodically move onto the outer Scotian Shelf (Houghton et al., 1978) and contribute to the Warm Slope Water on the Scotian Margin. Between latitudes 45°N and 60°N, branches of the North Atlantic Drift flow north around Flemish Cap; these and other branches merge to form the complex Irminger Current System south of Greenland and Iceland, which consists of temperate (6-10°C) water. The Irminger Current water mixes with polar East Greenland Current water, and flows northward into eastern Baffin Bay as the subarctic West Greenland Current with temperatures of 4-6°C and salinity of 34-35‰. In the Norwegian Sea, the North Atlantic Drift continues northwards along the western European margin, and forms a relatively warm water mass (3°C, 35‰) as far north as the Barents Shelf in the eastern Arctic Ocean. There, winter cooling and ice formation finally result in its descent into the Arctic Ocean Basin where it forms the Arctic Atlantic Water 150 m beneath the Arctic Surface Water.

Most of the surface water off northeastern Canada originates as overflow of Arctic Surface Water through Nares Strait and Lancaster Sound. This polar water is cold (0 to −2°C) and of low salinity (28-32.5‰) and flows southwards along the margin of eastern Baffin Island as the Baffin Current. In the shallow Davis Strait region, there is considerable mixing of this polar water and temperate North Atlantic water. The resultant Labrador Current flows southwards along the eastern Canadian continental margin. Off Labrador and Newfoundland, the surface waters of the Labrador Current show a strong easterly gradient from the polar Labrador Shelf water (−0.5 to 2.5°C, 32-34‰) to relatively warm and saline (0-5°C, 34.5-34.8‰) Outer Labrador Current water that fills most of the Labrador Sea above 800 m depth (Lazier, 1982).

Circulation of surface water on the eastern Canadian continental shelves is complex due to variability in shelf topography, seasonal runoff, meltwater flux and periodic invasion of more saline, warmer offshore surface or deep water (Trites, 1982; Lazier, 1985). An important low salinity Hudson Bay component influences the inner Labrador Shelf but the arctic character of the shelf current is greatly diminished south of the Grand Banks. Runoff from the Gulf of St. Lawrence also lowers the salinity of surface water on the inner shelf off Newfoundland and eastern

Nova Scotia. The general surface circulation on the Scotian Shelf is cyclonic, with the Nova Scotia Current (4-8°C, 32‰) flowing southwest along the inner shelf and a reverse flow of warmer water (8-16°C, 32-34‰) entrained by the North Atlantic Drift along the continental margin (Scott et al., 1984b).

Deep water circulation

The deep water (>800 m) off eastern Canada (Fig. 10.9) also has two main sources: overflow from the Norwegian Sea and downwelling of Labrador Sea surface water. Labrador Sea Water is formed off Hudson Strait by mixing and cooling of outer Labrador Current water by strong northerly (arctic) winds. The resultant cold, saline water (3.2°C, 34.88‰) sinks to a depth of 1200-1800 m and flows southwards and eastwards throughout the subarctic regions of the North Atlantic Ocean.

Norwegian Sea overflow is cold, saline water (2-3°C, 34.94‰) formed by cooling of surface water in the Northeast Atlantic. Most of this dense water flows over the Scotland-Iceland Ridge and westwards along the flanks of the submarine ridges south of Greenland at a depth of 2000-3000 m. This water forms the North Atlantic Deep Water between 1800 and ca. 4000 m depth in the Labrador Sea and western North Atlantic Ocean (Worthington, 1976). The fast-flowing layer between 2000 and 3000 m in the Labrador Sea and at greater water depths south of the Grand Banks and Scotian Shelf is referred to as the Western Boundary Undercurrent (Heezen et al., 1966). Below this water mass in the Labrador Sea, is a thin (ca. 50 m) layer of North Atlantic Bottom Water which is colder, less saline water (1.8°C, 34.92‰) derived from Norwegian Sea overflow through the Denmark Strait.

On the continental margin off Nova Scotia two deep water layers underlie the North Atlantic Deep Water below a depth of ca. 4000 m (Richardson et al., 1981; Weatherly and Kelley, 1982). From ca. 4000-4900 m, a cold, relatively low salinity water mass (ca. 1.6 to −1.0°C, 34.65‰) composed of Antarctic Bottom Water (AABW) flows rapidly (35-73 cm/s) southwestward as the Western Boundary Undercurrent. From ca. 4900-5000 m, there is a thin bottom layer of denser (34.65-34.89‰) cold water. The average flow rate (9 cm/s) of this bottom water is much slower than the Antarctic Bottom Water, but flow direction is variable and "abyssal storms" appear to promote periodic rapid mixing of this water mass (Hollister et al., 1984).

In Baffin Bay, two deep water masses underlie the surface layer (0-300 m) of mixed Arctic and Atlantic water from the West Greenland Current (Collin and Dunbar, 1964; Aksu, 1983a). Baffin Bay Atlantic Water (ca. 300-1300 m) has temperature and salinity characteristics (0-2°C, 34.3-34.5‰) intermediate between the relatively warm, low salinity surface water mass (0-4°C, 31-33.7‰) and a bottom layer of very cold, saline (0 to −0.4°C, 34.4-34.5‰) Baffin Bay Bottom Water (ca. 1300-2400 m). The intermediate water probably originates from surface water cooling in Baffin Bay, and the bottom layer is formed by sinking of deep Arctic Ocean Atlantic Water which enters Baffin Bay via Nares Strait (Tan and Strain, 1980; Top et al., 1980).

a

GLORIA LONG-RANGE

SEAMARC 1 MID RANGE

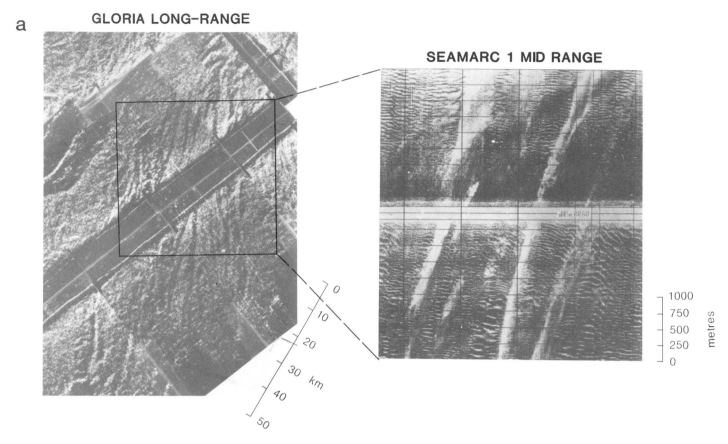

0
10
20
30 km
40
50

1000
750
500
250
0
metres

b

70 kHz SIDESCAN SONOGRAPH

100 kHz SIDESCAN SONOGRAPH

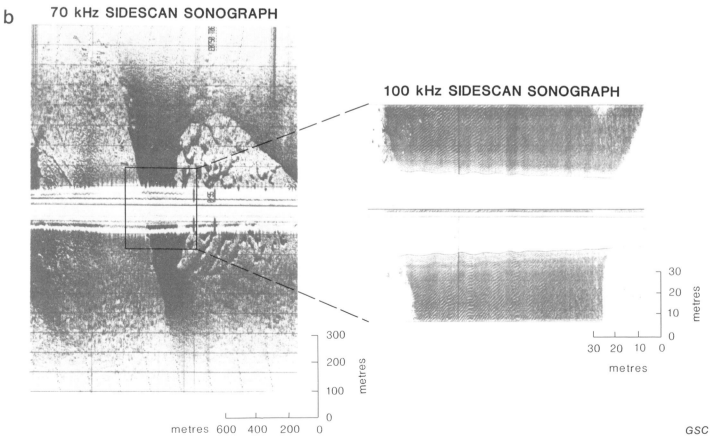

300
200
100
0
metres

metres 600 400 200 0

30
20
10
0
metres

30 20 10 0

metres

GSC

Atmosphere-ocean interaction and the initiation of glaciation

The flow of surface currents in the North Atlantic is closely related to the zonal position of the jet stream (circumpolar vortex) in the upper troposphere (Herman and Goldberg, 1985). Conditions that widen the jet stream path result in large undulations corresponding to atmospheric pressure centres between latitudes 40°N and 80°N. Cold, dry polar air and warm, moisture-bearing southerly winds are subsequently directed abnormally far south and north, respectively. At present, exceptionally severe winters are associated with semi-stationary highs centred over the Aleutian Islands and Iceland. The causes of these "blocking highs" is uncertain.

Computer models, which attempt to simulate historical changes in global weather patterns on the scale of decades, presently fail to provide a good fit with the observed data, and much attention is now being directed towards improving these models by incorporating more data on ocean-atmosphere related parameters, e.g. sea surface temperature, sea ice extent, ocean albedo and arctic haze.

Onset of glacial conditions may be linked to the development of blocking highs. These may be promoted by events which disrupt horizontal air flow, including uplift of land masses, Plinian-type volcanic eruptions, formation of ice fields on land or sea, and tectonic or solar events that decrease the thermal gradient between tropical and polar regions and widen the path of the jet stream. Onset of glacial conditions also requires a reduction of insolation, such that winter snowfall or sea ice growth is not balanced by summer melting. Cyclical variations in the Earth's orbital parameters (eccentricity, obliquity, and precession/seasonal attitude) satisfactorily account for many of the inferred changes in insolation (Berger, 1978); however, other interacting factors, such as isostasy, must be involved to explain the dominance of the 100 ka cycle (Peltier and Hyde, 1984).

Late Cenozoic climatic cooling

Few data exist from which to reconstruct the specific events associated with the Late Cenozoic onset of glacial conditions in eastern Canada. Exploration wells on the eastern Canadian margin provide general information on Miocene environments (Gradstein and Williams, 1976; Williams and Bujak, 1977a; Gradstein and Srivastava, 1980), but undisturbed samples of Upper Neogene and Quaternary sediments are rarely recovered because the upper parts of the wells are not sampled during drilling. Shelf sediments also lack planktonic microfossils (foraminifers, nannofossils and radiolaria) which are needed for correlation with standard global biochronologies (Berggren, 1981a). Future studies of benthic foraminifers and palynomorphs from exploratory wells on

the continental slope (Piper et al., 1987) may, however, provide insight into the evolution of the Late Cenozoic climate in eastern Canada when compared to paleoclimatic data from stratotypes in Europe and the North Atlantic.

In conjunction with global data, however, some conclusions can be drawn regarding the probable sequence of events that terminated in the Late Quaternary climates of eastern Canada. Exploration well data (Williams and Bujak, 1977b) show that dinocyst genera with modern subtropical distributions, e.g. *Polysphaeridium* (as *Hemicystodinium*) *zoharyi*, were present on the Scotian Shelf in the Late Miocene. By the middle to Late Pliocene, these floral elements were displaced eastwards into ocean regions below the present path of the North Atlantic Drift and its northern extension to Baffin Bay (de Vernal et al., 1986). *Polysphaeridium zoharyi* presently occurs in both shallow and deep subtropical to warm temperate waters. The seaward displacement of this species therefore cannot be attributed only to global lowering of relative sea level (Vail et al., 1977). It is more likely that the eastward floral migration indicates major changes in western North Atlantic ocean circulation starting in the Late Miocene. Although warm temperate floras disappear from Alaska, the Canadian Arctic, Greenland and Spitsbergen in the Late Miocene or earlier (Hills and Matthews, 1974; Funder et al., 1985; Nelson and Carter, 1985), pollen of subtropical floras, e.g. *Taxodium*, *Podocarpus* and *Liquidambar*, persist in sediments from the Labrador Shelf and Labrador Sea until at least the Late Pliocene (Fig. 10.3).

Paleoecological and oxygen isotope records from deep sea sediments in the South Atlantic and Central Pacific (Shackleton and Kennett, 1975; Woodruff et al., 1981; Shackleton et al., 1982) suggest that the Cenozoic glaciations were initiated in the Southern Hemisphere during the Middle Miocene (16-13 Ma) when the Antarctic Circumpolar Current began to intensify and the East Antarctic ice sheet expanded to cover western Antarctica. Absence of a landmass centred on the North Pole accounts for the lack of concurrent ice sheet formation in the Northern Hemisphere. Pollen records in northern Oregon (Taggart and Cross, 1980) indicate the onset of pluvial-arid or warm-cold climatic cycles by 14 Ma, and polar marine floras first appear in the Norwegian Sea (Thiede et al., 1986) at this time. By 10-9.5 Ma, highland glaciers existed in western Alaska (ca. 70°N) and subtropical floras in eastern Iceland (61°N) were replaced by sequences of boreal and subarctic floras that suggest climatic oscillations with a periodicity of about 40 ka (Mudie, 1983; Mudie and Helgason, 1983). In northwestern Wyoming (45°N), pollen from highland lake sediments dated at about 8.2 Ma show alternating pluvial and arid cycles, with wet intervals lasting from 1 to 11 ka, and longer dry intervals lasting from 2 to 210 ka (Barnosky, 1984). Unfortunately, few comparable ocean records are available for this critical period of climatic change because hiatuses (e.g. reflectors R_3 and R_2 of Keller and Barron, 1982) are widespread in deep sea sediments. These hiatuses probably indicate stronger bottom currents as deep water cooled by polar ice began to flow towards the equator from high latitude oceans. Drift deposits on the Eirik Ridge in the Labrador Sea began to form at about 7 Ma, probably in response to these strong bottom currents (Arthur et al., 1986). This is discussed in Chapter 8.

Figure 10.7. Comparison of (a) GLORIA long-range and SEAMARC I mid-range sidescan sonographs of gravel waves and sand ribbons on Eastern Valley of Laurentian Fan (GLORIA from Masson et al., 1984); (b) BIO 70 kHz and Klein 100 kHz sidescan sonographs of areas of wave-formed bedforms from Grand Banks.

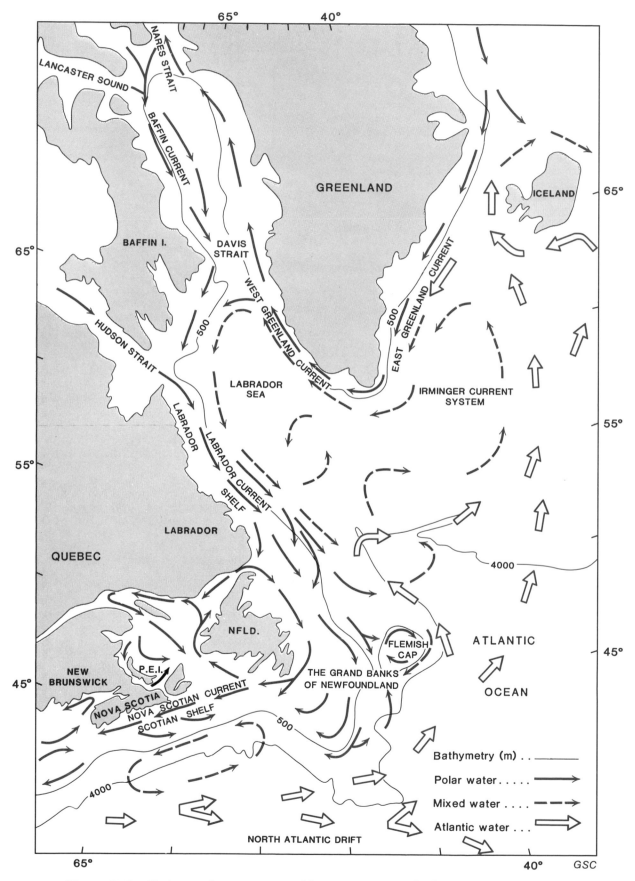

Figure 10.8. Modern surface oceanographic current patterns in the Northwest Atlantic.

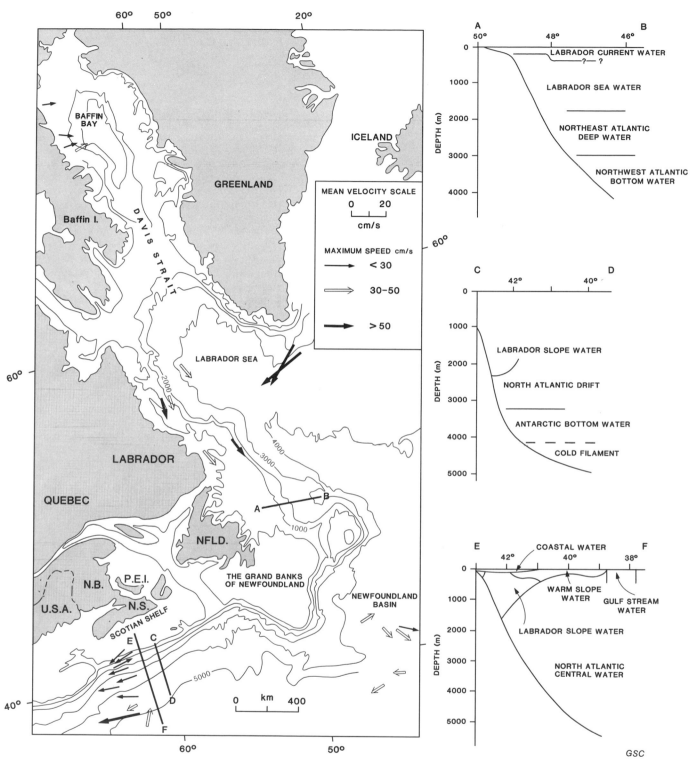

Figure 10.9. Series of oceanographic sections of the continental margin of eastern Canada showing water mass distribution. Major flow paths of deep bottom water are indicated; length of arrow indicates mean velocity and style of arrow the maximum velocity. (After Carter and Schafer, 1983; Gatien, 1976; and Thomas, 1985).

In general, the evidence points towards the inception of local glaciers in the western Northern Hemisphere during the Late Miocene, accompanied by cooling of surface ocean waters on the western margin of the North Atlantic north of 45° latitude, and by the elimination of warm temperate floras from coastal Alaska and Arctic islands north of southwestern Banks Island at 72°N (Hills and Matthews, 1974; Nelson and Carter, 1985). The oldest tillites in Iceland are dated 6 to 4.8 Ma, which broadly corresponds with the second major expansion of the Antarctic ice sheet and the termination of tropical water exchange through the Tethys and Panama Seaways at ca. 7 Ma and 5 Ma, respectively (Wise, 1981; Keller and Barron, 1982). Terrestrial floras in eastern Canada and western Europe, and marine biota in the eastern North Atlantic south of the Iceland-Faroes Ridge (ca. 55°N) however, do not record an equivalent climatic cooling of glacial stage magnitude until ca. 3.4 Ma (eastern Canada) or 2.5 Ma (eastern Atlantic).

Detailed marine records of climatic changes in eastern Canada during the Pliocene and Early Pleistocene are sparse, although deep sea records obtained during the Ocean Drilling Program Leg 104 (Norwegian Sea) and Leg 105 (Labrador Sea-Baffin Bay) will provide extensive new data in the near future (de Vernal et al., 1986; Thiede et al., 1986; Arthur et al., 1986). Important constraints for climatic models, however, are set by the following datums.

1) Ice rafted pebbles and gravel occur in hemipelagic sediments of Early Pliocene age (ca. 4 Ma) on the Alpha Ridge in the Central Arctic Ocean (Mudie and Jackson, 1985).

2) Pollen and other plant deposits in the Canadian Arctic Islands (Hills and Matthews, 1974), and from northern Alaska, 71°N (Nelson and Carter, 1985) indicate a north-south gradient from High Arctic forest-tundra to Low Arctic warm temperate forests between 70° and 80°N from the Late Miocene to the end of the Pliocene (ca. 5-1.9 Ma). The presence of fossil trees implies summer temperatures of at least 10°C, and raised peat bogs in Greenland indicate much higher precipitation than now. During this time, glaciers must have been restricted to mountain ranges and highlands in the circum-Arctic region. In mountain ranges of Alaska and the Sierra Nevada, tillites and tills have ages ranging between 3.1 and 2.72 Ma (Cooke, 1973).

3) Ice-rafted debris first occurred in Baffin Bay and the northeastern Labrador Sea at 3.4 Ma, and it subsequently appeared about 0.5 Ma later (at 2.8-3 Ma) in the southern Labrador Sea, Norwegian Sea, and central North Atlantic (Deep Sea Drilling Project Sites 611 and 116) and the Fogo Seamounts southwest of the Grand Banks (Piper, 1975a). This interval also corresponds to the time of the earliest evidence of glacial ice fluctuations from the benthic foraminiferal isotopic record in the Pacific Ocean (Shackleton and Opdyke, 1977), to the opening of the Bering Strait, and to the first occurrence of Pacific molluscs in Alaska and the North Atlantic (Repenning, 1983).

4) Ice-rafted debris first occurred at about 2.4 Ma in the eastern North Atlantic (DSDP Site 400, 47°23'N 09°12'W) and subtropical North Atlantic (DSDP Site 607, 41°00'N 32°57'W). This datum appears to mark the inception of continental ice sheet growth throughout the Northern Hemisphere, and it coincides with the southward retreat of western European subtropical floras and the start of alternating cycles of boreal forest (interglacial) and tundra or steppe (glacial) vegetation in Europe and Asia.

5) Sediments, plant deposits, molluscs and marine mammals at Ocean Point on the Alaskan coast (Repenning, 1983; Nelson and Carter, 1985) and coastal areas of Peary Land, northern Greenland (Funder et al., 1985) indicate that the Arctic Ocean was not covered by permanent ice at the start of the Pleistocene (2-1.7 Ma). At Ocean Point, the Pliocene subarctic marine deposits are overlain by extensive Lower Pleistocene fluvial sands. By 0.7 Ma, however, low arctic tundra-shrub vegetation had replaced the subarctic forest tundra. Overlying Illinoian Stage and younger Pleistocene sediments show alternating cycles of tundra steppe (polar desert) and tundra-shrub (sub arctic-low arctic) vegetation.

6) The oldest till deposits dated for the Canadian Arctic Archipelago have a minimum age of 0.73 Ma (Banks Glaciation) and they are probably correlative with the maximum influx of glaciogenic sediments to the Alpha Ridge during the Late Pliocene to Middle Pleistocene (Clark et al., 1984).

7) On the central Scotian Slope, rates of hemipelagic sediment accumulation apparently increased from about 5 cm/ka in the Miocene and Early Pliocene to about 35 cm/ka during the Late Pliocene, followed by a slight decrease to 20 cm/ka during the Early Pleistocene (Piper et al., 1987). Late Pleistocene sedimentation rates range between 10 and 40 cm/ka. The major increase in sedimentation in the Late Pliocene and Early Pleistocene is consistent with palynological evidence from Arctic Canada and from Baffin Bay (ODP Site 645; de Vernal et al., 1986) which suggests that there was increased runoff and fluvial erosion in the Early Pleistocene, probably marking the start of ice sheet growth and glacial climatic conditions in northeastern Canada. According to Piper et al. (1987), however, changes in sea level were a major influence on sedimentation rates and glaciers did not cross the Scotian Shelf and deposit till on the Scotian Slope before about 0.8 Ma.

PALEOENVIRONMENTAL INTERPRETATION OF QUATERNARY DEPOSITIONAL ENVIRONMENTS

Acoustic and lithological data

D.J.W. Piper and G.B. Fader

Detailed high resolution seismic reflection profiling, core sampling and subsequent microfossil and sedimentological investigations have resulted in standard criteria for the paleoenvironmental interpretation of Quaternary offshore facies. High resolution seismic reflection profiles are interpreted principally on the basis of the amplitude, continuity, relief and spacing of reflections (Fig. 10.10), and the structural style of these reflections in relationship to other facies (Fig. 10.11).

Acoustic facies characterized by incoherent reflections and abundant diffractions generally represent coarse unstructured sediment, including diamictons (tills) and massive sands and gravels. Some muddy slumps exhibit a similar character but tend to be acoustically more transparent. In many parts of the continental shelf, bedrock is

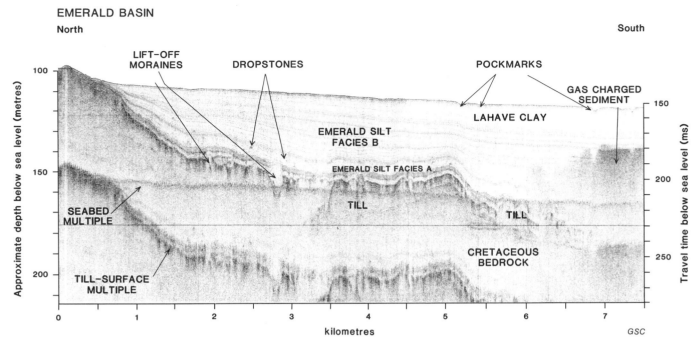

EMERALD BASIN

North

South

Figure 10.10. Typical Huntec DTS profile from Emerald Basin, Scotian Shelf, showing the acoustic character of the principal glacial and postglacial facies. These facies are typical of those found on the continental shelves off eastern Canada. For full explanation of facies, see text. Profile is located in Figure 10.15.

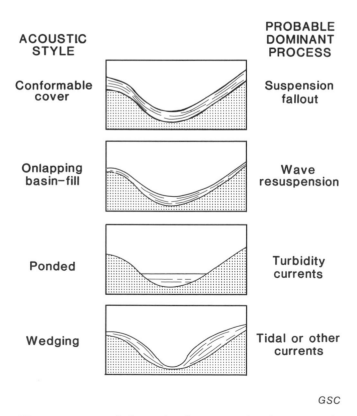

Figure 10.11. Schematic diagrams showing acoustic depositional style of various fine grained sediment facies in coastal and shelf basins (modified from Barrie and Piper, 1982).

overlain by an acoustic facies of incoherent reflections, which locally shows well-defined lateral intertonguing relationships with sediments identified from cores as stratified sub- or proglacial muds. Samples within this facies are compact, poorly sorted, gravelly sandy muds containing no marine microfossils (except within 1 m of upper contacts). This facies is therefore generally identified as till deposited from grounded ice (Josenhans et al., 1986; King and Fader, 1986). The abrupt lateral contacts with fine grained sediments and lack of marine microfossils preclude deposition of this facies as a diamict from floating ice. A similar acoustic facies, but with a ponded style, occurs in basins in coastal embayments, and was interpreted as massive or steeply bedded sands and gravels (Kontopoulos and Piper, 1982b).

Areas of thick marine sand (known, for example, from boreholes on Banquereau and Sable Island Bank) show some continuous coherent reflections, which may be subhorizontal or take the form of large-scale crossbedding. Thick sequences of finer grained sediments are more acoustically transparent. They are characterized by continuous coherent reflections, which tend to be more closely spaced and of higher amplitude in sediments with sand or silt laminae and rather weak and rare in bioturbated clayey lithologies. In general, sequences with high rates of sedimentation show more conformable depositional style; a ponded style reflects slower deposition under the influence of periodic wave or current resedimentation. More powerful current activity results in sediment build-ups (Fig. 10.11).

A general environmental interpretation of the principal acoustic facies found on eastern Canadian continental shelves can be made from the detailed studies of King (1980), Barrie and Piper (1982), Josenhans et al. (1986), and

King and Fader (1986), in which core samples provide ground truth for acoustic data. Regionally extensive till sheets overlie bedrock on most shelf areas. The till tongues (King and Fader, 1986) that interfinger with the overlying stratified sediments at basin margins (Fig. 10.12) and on the upper continental slope (Piper et al., 1987) are typically 10 km in length and a few tens of metres thick. Most till tongues are rooted within larger bodies of till, in some cases with several tongues stacked one above the other (Fig. 10.13). The till roots may form prominent ridges (Fig. 10.13), some of which appear on the seabed as linear moraines. King and Fader (1986) demonstrated that the development of a till tongue results from migration of the grounding (buoyancy) line of an ice sheet, with till deposited from grounded ice, and the intertonguing stratified sediment deposited either seaward of the ice margin or from beneath floating ice.[†]

[†] See Addendum

The formation of a till tongue represents an advance followed by a retreat of the grounding line, which may be due to glacial advance and recession, or to vertical changes in sea level or to isostatic adjustments. Variations in thickness measured on seismic reflection profiles show that the depositional rate of the till can be more than five times that of the stratified sediments. These regional linear moraines were previously regarded as normal ice-front recessional moraines (King et al., 1972). However, because they form the roots to the till tongues and also encircle basin and trough areas of the shelf, they must also be subglacial features and are termed "regional subglacial iceshelf moraines" by King and Fader (1986). Where exposed at the seabed, the surface of the moraines has been modified by iceberg furrowing (Fig. 10. 12).

In basinal areas, particularly on the Scotian Shelf, the upper surface of the buried till sheet in many places is covered by parallel ridges of till, typically 40 m apart and

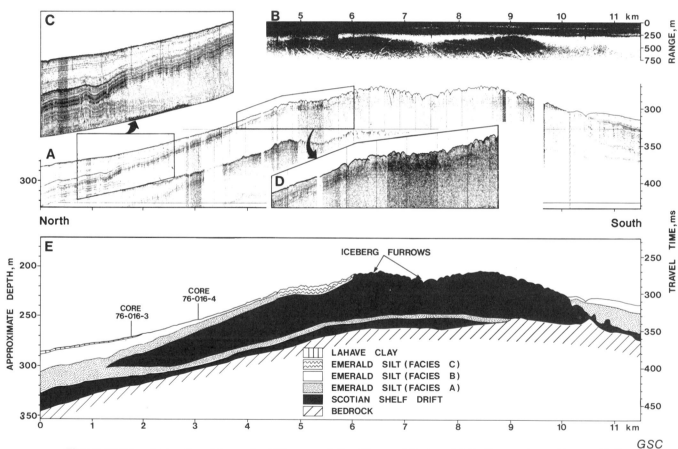

Figure 10.12. Acoustic evidence for till tongues (after King and Fader, 1986). Figure shows Huntec DTS seismic reflection profile (A), sidescan sonogram (B), enlarged sections of the Huntec DTS profile (C and D), and geological interpretation (E) across Sewell Ridge in the Gulf of Maine (location is shown in Fig. 10.15). Emerald Silt facies A is interbedded with till of the moraine ridge (Fundian moraine) and extends under the moraine for a distance of 8 km, where it pinches out against the bedrock surface (in E). Near the top of the moraine, facies A grades over a distance of 1.5 km to Emerald Silt facies C, which has an acoustic character of continuous-discontinuous coherent reflections (in D). The surface of the till of the moraine is covered with iceberg furrows up to 5 m deep (in A and B). The wedge-shaped body of till which interfingers with Emerald Silt facies A is referred to as a till tongue; its distal termination is shown in profile C. The positions of the piston cores are indicated and the type section for the Gulf of Maine area is located 1.1 km south of core 76-016-3. The morphology and position of the bedrock surface in E was interpreted from an adjacent airgun seismic reflection profile.

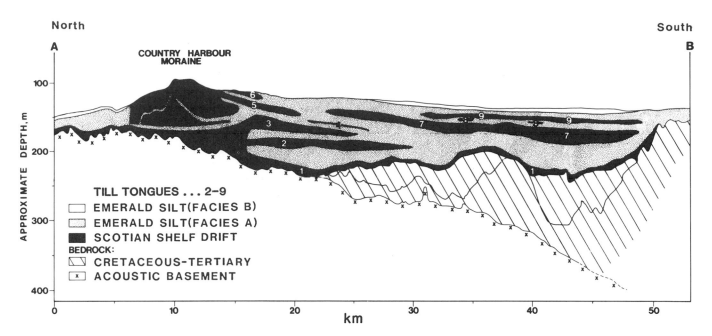

Figure 10.13. Interpretation of seismic profiles across northern Emerald Basin, showing development of multiple till tongues south of the Country Harbour Moraine (after King and Fader, 1986). Till tongues 2-9 are interbedded with Emerald Silt facies A. Till tongue 4 does not occur along this profile and the position indicated only represents its stratigraphic horizon. This moraine ridge is composed entirely of glacial materials and is not located on a bedrock high. Note the continuous deposits of Emerald Silt immediately above till tongue 3, which extend beneath the entire moraine across the section. Figure 10.15 shows location of profile.

up to 20 m high (Fig. 10.14). Stratified sediments occur between the ridges and stratification can be traced into the ridges, showing that the till ridges and stratified sediments are synchronous facies equivalents (Fig. 10.14). Seismic reflection profiles show that these ridges are not formed sequentially (for example during progressive recession and stabilization of an ice margin), but rather are essentially synchronous over a large area of basin floor. The synchroneity of stratified sediment and till deposition indicates that they occur during initial lift-off (buoyancy) of an ice sheet, and thus have a somewhat similar origin to the till tongues. The spacing of the ridges must be controlled by some systematic irregularity in the base of an ice sheet, perhaps due to fracturing. The till ridges are morphologically similar to De Geer moraines, but because King and Fader (1986) regarded them as synchronous over a large area, and different in origin from many De Geer moraines, they referred to them descriptively as "lift-off moraines".

The acoustically stratified sediments that directly overlie till, such as the Emerald Silt of the Scotian Shelf, tend to have a conformable depositional style and pass upwards into stratified sediments with a slightly more ponded morphology. Point source hyperbolic reflections, probably due to boulders, are common. This acoustic facies shows considerable regional variation in relationships to other facies and in internal characteristics (which are discussed in the regional sections later in this chapter); these data suggest that in some areas the facies developed beneath a floating ice shelf, whereas elsewhere it represents rapid proglacial sedimentation in open water (King and Fader, 1986). Where intensely scoured by ice-

bergs, the proglacial sediments may appear acoustically unstratified (Praeg et al., 1986; Josenhans et al., 1986).

Postglacial basinal muds, such as the LaHave Clay of the Scotian Shelf, have a slower rate of accumulation and exhibit a much more ponded depositional style. Acoustically, they tend to be very transparent with very weak continuous coherent reflections.

Microfossil assemblages
P.J. Mudie

Microfossil assemblages (particularly foraminifera and dinoflagellate cysts) are good indicators of depositional environments. Interpretation of the fossil assemblages is based on the distribution of modern species. Interpretations of paleoenvironmental conditions, such as temperature, salinity and water depth, were formerly made by empirical correlation between the modern distribution of selected microfossil species and the dominant characteristics of the overlying water. These empirical correlations should be treated with caution because they may be biased either by a limited amount of control sample data from the eastern Canadian region, or by invalid assumptions regarding the modern age of surface sediments sampled without high resolution seismostratigraphic control. Recent studies have used statistical tests to evaluate the correlation between microfossil assemblage composition and modern environmental parameters, with data carefully selected to include only surface samples known to represent modern sediment deposits (Mudie, 1982; Mudie et al., 1984). Statistically significant correlations between pollen and spore assemblages and onshore vegetation

southwest

northeast

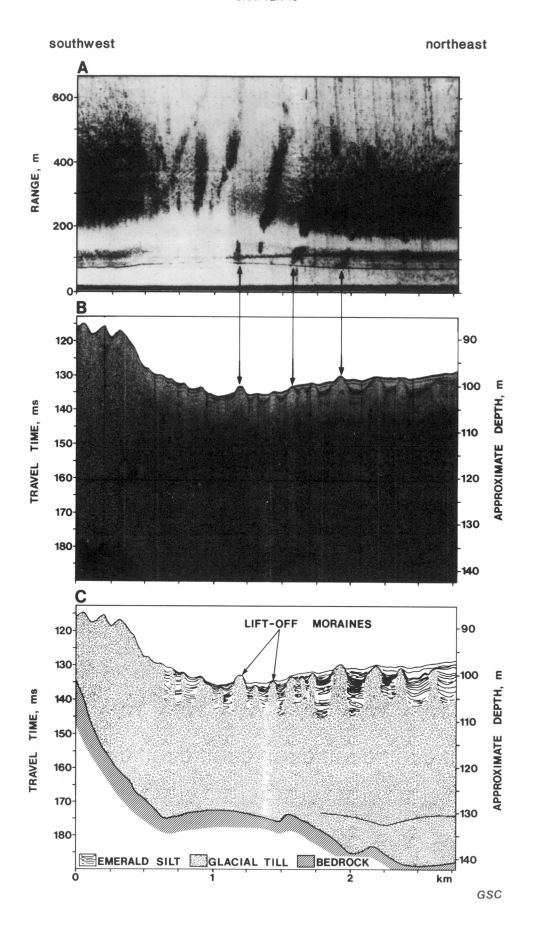

LIFT-OFF MORAINES

EMERALD SILT   GLACIAL TILL   BEDROCK

GSC

regions have been established for the continental shelf from southern Nova Scotia to northern Baffin Bay (Mudie, 1982; Mudie and Short, 1985) as have significant correlations between dinoflagellate cyst assemblages and surface water temperature and salinity for eastern Canada (Mudie and Keen, 1983), Baffin Bay (Mudie and Short, 1985) and for the North Atlantic Ocean (Harland, 1983). Correlations between benthic foraminiferal assemblages, water depth and bottom water characteristics (temperature and salinity) have also been established for the Scotian Shelf and Slope (Williamson et al., 1984), for the Labrador Shelf, Davis Strait, Hudson Bay and the Beaufort Sea (Mudie et al., 1984), and for the Baffin Shelf (Osterman, 1982). Quantitative correlation between planktonic foraminifera and sea surface temperature in the Labrador Sea has been attempted by Fillon and Williams (1984) but it is now evident (Aksu and Mudie, 1985a; Chough et al., 1985) that some of the samples used for this study represent redeposited sediment of uncertain Quaternary age.

Detailed lists of diagnostic microfossils and their paleoenvironmental significance are provided in Tables 10.1 to 10.5. The simple guidelines given below can be used, however, for rapid assessment of paleoenvironments represented by the microfossil content of a marine sediment sample.

Interglacial (including Holocene) sediments

Microfossils and organic particles are common to abundant in interglacial sediments except where strong currents prevail (sandy facies) or where sedimentation rates are very high (deltaic facies and some slump deposits). In general, interglacial microfossil assemblages show a distinctive change in composition from nearshore to offshore environments, as described below. Superimposed on this transverse gradient are zonal changes, which can only be recognized by analysis of species composition, using the data listed in Tables 10.2 to 10.5.

Estuarine and deltaic environments are characterized by relatively high numbers (>5000/g) of palynomorphs and a low diversity of benthic foraminifers, often including many small arenaceous species. The ratio of marine dinoflagellates to pollen and spores (D/P) is much less than 1.0; woody plant fragments are abundant and thin peat beds or organic pseudovarves are often present. Planktonic microfossils (foraminifers, radiolarians and silicoflagellates) are usually absent. Thecamoebians are common and they indicate a strong fluvial influence, especially when associated with freshwater palynomorphs such as *Pedias-*

trum. Assemblages found in Holocene sediments of Bedford Basin (Fig. 10.15) (Miller et al., 1982), Hamilton Inlet (Vilks and Mudie, 1983) and Frobisher Bay (see Fig. 10.35) (Osterman, 1982) provide good examples of these paralic biofacies in temperate, subarctic and arctic regions, respectively.

Neritic shelf environments are much more variable in microfossil composition, according to distance from shore and water depth, with strong contrasts between basin and bank areas. Shelf biofacies are generally distinguished by numerous and highly diverse calcareous benthic foraminifers, a D/P ratio of ca. 1.0 and a high proportion of amorphous organic material. Diatoms are generally common, but planktic foraminifers and radiolaria are rare except in deep water areas of the outer shelf. The ratio of arenaceous to calcareous benthic foraminifers usually decreases from inner to outer shelf environments. The Holocene assemblages described for Emerald Basin, Canso Basin, Notre Dame Bay and Cartwright Saddle (Scott et al., 1984b), the inner Labrador Shelf (Vilks et al., 1982, 1984) and the Southeast Baffin Shelf (Praeg et al., 1986) provide good examples of these variable shelf biofacies on the eastern Canadian margin.

Continental slope environments are also variable in microfossil composition, depending on water depth, temperature and salinity characteristics of the bottom water masses and the intensity of winnowing by bottom currents. In general, however, all the slope environments are distinguished by a dominance of planktonic microfossils, abundant benthic foraminifera, rare occurrences of coccolithophorids, and relatively low concentrations of palynomorphs and organic particulates (kerogen). The D/P ratio is usually greater than 1.0, and usually increases downslope to greater than 2.0 on the continental rise. Good examples of the downslope trends in microfossil assemblages are provided by data from the Northeast Newfoundland Slope (Carter et al., 1979; Carter and Schafer, 1983) and the Scotian Slope (Thomas, 1985; Williamson, 1985). Some indications of the downslope trends in palymorphs are given by Mudie (1980, 1982) for the Scotian Slope, and by Mudie and Short (1985) for the slopes of Baffin Bay.

Bathyal oceanic enviroments are strongly dominated by planktonic foraminifera and calcareous nannofossils in temperate and subarctic waters, and by siliceous microfossils and benthic foraminifera in silled high latitude basins, e.g. Baffin Bay, where carbonate dissolution inhibits the preservation of planktonic foraminifera. In oceanic environments, south of the Arctic Ocean, palynomorph assemblages are relatively low (<2000/g), the D/P ratio is usually greater than 2.0, and particulate organic matter is rare. Good examples of typical oceanic microfossil assemblages are documented for the boreal southern Grand Banks region (Alam, 1979; Alam et al., 1983) and for the subarctic area of Davis Strait (Aksu and Mudie, 1985a). Some data on foraminifera and radiolaria in Labrador Sea sediments are provided by Fillon and Duplessy (1980) and by Fillon et al. (1981b). Arctic Ocean assemblages have been less well described, but they appear to represent a unique fauna dominated by planktonic and calcareous benthic foraminifera (Aksu, 1985b; Scott et al., 1986), with common pteropods and sponge spicules but rare siliceous microfossils and coccoliths. Arctic Ocean palynomorphs are also rare (<1000/g), the D/P ratio is usually less than 1.0 and species diversity is very low (Mudie, 1985).

Figure 10.14. Acoustic evidence for "lift-off moraines" (after King and Fader, 1986). Figure shows sidescan sonogram (A), Huntec DTS seismic reflection profile (B), and interpretation of Huntec DTS profile (C) across an area of "lift-off moraines" from the northwestern Grand Banks of Newfoundland (location of section is shown in Fig. 10.15). The sidescan sonogram (A) shows that the features are linear ridges and not isolated mounds or hummocks. The "lift-off moraines" range in height from 8-10 m and are spaced from 0.1 to 0.25 km apart. Note the consistent character of the Emerald Silt reflections throughout the field of "lift-off moraines" in profile B.

Table 10.1. Pollen assemblage zones on the Scotian Shelf

Pollen assemblage zones used by Livingstone (1968) and by Livingstone and Livingstone (1958) to subdivide palynostratigraphies for lake sediments in Nova Scotia. Similar zones are applicable to the Scotian Shelf.

Zone	Sub-zone	Pollen assemblage characteristics	Paleoenvironment
G		Very low pollen concentrations (< 100 grains per cm^3); variable representation of *Betula* (birch), *Pinus* (pine), *Picea* (spruce) and *Quercus* (oak) some or all of which may be reworked.	Glacial drift prior to revegetation or slumped postglacial sediment.
L		Low pollen concentrations (< 1000 grains per cm^3), high % NAP.	Late-glacial climatic phase.
A		High concentrations of *Picea, Abies* (fir) and *Pinus*; maximum % *Picea*, high % *Betula*; *Quercus* pollen present.	Closed boreal forest; cool, moist climate like that now in southern Quebec highlands.
B		Very high concentrations of *Pinus*; high % *Picea* and *Abies*; maximum % *Pinus*.	Closed boreal forest; climate warmer and drier like that now in northern Maine.
C		Mixed temperate hardwoods and *Tsuga* (hemlock) tree pollen assemblage; presence of *Quercus, Acer* (maple), *Ulmus* (elm), *Fraxinus* (ash); *Tsuga* common.	Mixed boreal-deciduous forest; relatively warm climate.
	C1	*Quercus* pollen maximum.	Warm climate.
	C2	*Tsuga* pollen maximum.	Warmer and moister than present.
	C3	Decline in % *Tsuga* and *Pinus*, increase in % *Picea* and *Betula*.	Climate cooler.
	C3c	Lower pollen concentration; increase in % *Picea* and % NAP (non-tree pollen), especially Gramineae (grasses), *Rumex* (sorrel/dock-weed) and Compositae (ragweeds and daisies).	Historical forest clearance.

Table 10.2.   Microfossil assemblage zones on the Scotian Shelf

---

1. Dinocyst assemblage zones

A: Emerald Basin (Mudie, 1980).

Zone	Assemblage characteristics	Paleoenvironment
C	*Brigantedinium simplex* *Operculodinium centrocarpum*	Mixed coastal, subarctic and warm slope waters.
B	*Operculodinium centrocarpum* *Spiniferites*	Euryhaline, relatively warm shelf water
A	*Operculodinium centrocarpum* *Piperodinium perplexum* *Tectatodinium pellitum* *Multispinula minuta*	Subarctic, with upwelling of deep slope waters.

B: Canso Bank Basin (Scott et al., 1984b)

Zone	Assemblage characteristics	Paleoenvironment
1	*Operculodinium centrocarpum* *Brigantedinium* *Multispinula minuta*	Relatively cold and fresh inner shelf water.
2	*Operculodinium centrocarpum* *Multispinula minuta*	Relatively warm surface waters.
3	*Operculodinium centrocarpum* *Multispinula minuta* *Spiniferites*	Deep, shallow-silled coastal basins, some addition of warmer slope waters.

C: Bedford Basin (Miller et al., 1982)

Zone	Assemblage characteristics	Paleoenvironment
X	*Operculodinium centrocarpum* *Bitectatodinium tepikiense; Spiniferites*	Deep estuarine waters, temperate to arctic.
Y	*Brigantedinium simplex;* Dinocyst C	Euryhaline, marginal marine.
Z	*Peridinium limbatum* *Peridinium wisconsinense* *Peridinium cinctum*	Fresh water.
A	Dinocyst A; *Gonyaulax tamarensis*	Brackish, cold or cool temperate water.

---

2. Foraminifera assemblage zones

A: Emerald Basin

Zone	Assemblage characteristics	Paleoenvironment
Brizalina subaenariensis	*Brizalina subaenariensis* *Virgulina fusiformis* *Pullenia osloensis* *Cassidulina laevigata laevigata* Arenaceous spp. *Globigerinita uvula*	Slight cooling of surface waters.
Bulimina marginata	*Bulimina marginata* *Cibicides pseudoungeranus* *Höglundina elegans* *Pullenia bulloides Globigerina bulloides*	Strong slope water influence.

Table 10.2. (cont'd.)

2. Foraminifera assemblage zones		
Cassidulina laevigata laevigata	*Cassidulina laevigata laevigata* *Chilostomella oolina* *Globobulimina turgida* *Globorotalia inflata* *Orbulina universa*	Relatively strong Gulf Stream influence, with warmer surface and bottom waters.
Nonionellina labradorica	*Nonionellina labradorica* *Islandiella helenae* *Globobulimina auriculata* *Cassidulina reniforme* *Neogloboquadrina pachyderma*	Labrador Current dominates. Temperature close to 0°C, salinity 33 - 34‰.
Elphidium excavatum f. *clavata*	*Elphidium excavatum* f. *clavata* *Cassidulina reniforme* *Neogloboquadrina pachyderma*	Glacial ice margin Lowered salinity

B. Canso Bank Basin (Scott et al., 1984b)

Zone	Assemblage characteristics	Paleoenvironment
Adercotryma glomerata	*Adercotryma glomerata* *Islandiella helenae* *Rheophax scorpiorus* *Recurvoides turbinatus*	Inner shelf, Nova Scotia Current 1°C - 2°C 32 - 32.5‰
Islandiella helenae	*Islandiella helenae* *Nonionellina labradorica* *Cassidulina reniforme* *Elphidium excavatum* f. *clavata*	Inner Labrador Current 1.49 - 3.9°C 33.2 - 34.9‰
Nonionellina labradorica	*Nonionellina labradorica* *Globobulimina auriculata* *Islandiella helenae*	Outer Labrador Current 3.5 - 3.9°C 34.8 - 34.9‰
Elphidium excavatum f. *clavata*	*Elphidium excavatum* f. *clavata* *Nonionellina labradorica* *Islandiella helenae*	Early postglacial

C. Bedford Basin (Miller et al., 1982)

Zone	Assemblage characteristics	Paleoenvironment
Rheophax spp.	*Fursenkoina fusiformis* *Haynesina orbiculare* *Elphidium excavatum* group	Deep estuarine.
Eggerella advena	*Eggerella advena* *Elphidium bartletti* *Haynesina orbiculare* *Elphidium excavatum* group	Marginal marine, euryhaline.
Difflugia oblonga	*Difflugia oblonga* *Centropyxis aculeata*	Fresh water.

Table 10.3. Microfossil assemblage zones in Notre Dame Basin

1: Palynozones (Macpherson, 1982; Scott et al., 1984b)

Zone	Assemblage characteristics	Paleoenvironment
ND-4	*Picea, Abies, Betula, Pinus*	Forest.
ND-3	*Picea, Betula, Abies, Alnus*	Forest.
ND-2	*Betula, Picea, Alnus, Salix*	Arctic-Subarctic
ND-1	Cyperaceae, Gramineae, *Salix*	Tundra.

2: Dinocyst assemblage zones (Scott et al., 1984b)

Zone	Assemblage characteristics	Paleoenvironment
M	*Multispinula minuta* *Brigantedinium* *Operculodinium centrocarpum* *Spiniferites*	Subarctic, neritic.
L	*Multispinula minuta* *Brigantedinium* *Leiosphaera* sp. A	Offshore Labrador Current.
P	Cyst type P *Multispinula minuta* *Brigantedinium* *Dubridinium*	Periglacial, arctic.

3: Foraminifera assemblage zones (Scott et al., 1984b)

Zone	Assemblage characteristics	Paleoenvironment
Adercotryma glomerata	*Adercotryma glomerata* *Spiroplectammina biformis*	Inner Labrador Current, cold.
Nonionellina labradorica	*Nonionellina labradorica* *Cassidulina reniforme* *Elphidium excavatum* f. *clavata* *Islandiella helenae*	Outer Labrador Current.
Cassidulina reniforme	*Cassidulina reniforme* *Islandiella helenae* *Elphidium excavatum* f. *clavata*	Cold (1.5°C) Salinity 31-34‰
Elphidium excavatum f. *clavata*	*Elphidium excavatum* f. *clavata* *Cassidulina reniforme* *Islandiella helenae* *Fursenkoina fusiformis*	Glacial marine.

Table 10.4. Microfossil assemblage zones in Cartwright Saddle

---

1: Palynozones (Jordan, 1975; Short and Nichols, 1977).

Zone	Assemblage characteristics	Paleoenvironment
CS4	*Picea, Betula, Alnus, Abies*	Neoglacial cooling.
CS3	*Picea*	Boreal forest; Optimum climate.
CS2	*Betula, Alnus*	Shrub-tundra.
CS1	*Sphagnum, Betula*	Arctic.

2: Dinocyst assemblage zones (Scott et al., 1984b)

Zone	Assemblage characteristics	Paleoenvironment
CL	*Brigantedinium* *Multispinula minuta* *Leiosphaera* sp. A *Dubridinium*	Relatively cold inner Labrador Current.
CN	*Brigantedinium* *Operculodinium centrocarpum* *Nematosphaeropsis labyrinthea*	Relatively warm, increased mixing with offshore.
CM	*Brigantedinium* *Multispinula minuta* *Leiosphaera* sp. A	Cold, arctic water, similar to present northern Baffin Island.

3: Foraminifera assemblage zones

Zone	Assemblage characteristics	Paleoenvironment
Nonionellina labradorica	*Nonionellina labradorica* *Nonionellina auriculata* *Islandiella helenae* *Globobulimina auriculata*	Outer Labrador Current, slight cooling.
Neogloboquadrina pachyderma	*Neogloboquadrina pachyderma* *Cassidulina reniforme* *Elphidium excavatum* f. *clavata*	Outer Labrador Current.
Elphidium excavatum f. *clavata*	*Elphidium excavatum* f. *clavata* *Nonionellina labradorica* *Cassidulina reniforme* *Nonionellina auriculata*	Proglacial.

Table 10.5. Microfossil assemblage zones on the Southeast Baffin Shelf

1: Palynozones (Mudie and Short, 1985; Praeg et al., 1986)

Zone	Assemblage characteristics	Paleoenvironment
BIa	*Picea, Alnus, Betula*	Relatively mild, wet climate with shrub tundra
BIb	*Pinus, Picea*	Neoglacial cooling and decline in shrub tundra
BIc	*Alnus, Betula, Picea*	Climatic optimum (relatively warm, wet)
BII	*Pinus, Picea, Betula*	High Arctic tundra
BIII	*Pinus*, non-aboreal pollen and re-worked pre-Quaternary palynomorphs	Glacial

2: Dinocyst assemblage zones (Mudie and Short, 1985; Praeg et al., 1986)

Zone	Assemblage characteristics	Paleoenvironment
BIa	*Multispinula minuta* *Brigantedinium* spp.	Cold arctic surface water
BIb	*Operculodinium centrocarpum* *Multispinula minuta* *Brigantedinium* spp.	Mixed arctic and subarctic water
BIc	*Operculodinium centrocarpum* *Nematosphaeropsis labyrinthea*	Maximum influx of subarctic water
BII	Cyst type P	Glacial/periglacial, arctic conditions

3: Foraminiferal assemblage zones (Osterman, 1982; Praeg et al., 1986)

Zone	Assemblage characteristics	Paleoenvironment
Cibicides lobatulus	*Cibicides lobatulus* and *Islandiella helenae*	Cold Arctic surface water
Nonionellina labradorica	*Nonionellina labradorica*	Subarctic and arctic waters - similar to modern Labrador Shelf environment
Cassidulina reniforme and *Islandiella helenae*	*Cassidulina reniforme* *Islandiella helenae*	High diversity zone characterising ice retreat
Elphidium excavatum f. *clavata*	*Elphidium excavatum* f. *clavata*	Ice margin
Cassidulina reniforme and *Islandiella helenae*	*Cassidulina reniforme* *Islandiella helenae* *Elphidium excavatum* f. *clavata*	Cold meltwater

Glacial marine sediments

Microfossil assemblages in glacial marine deposits are mostly characterized by sparse population of low species diversity; Quaternary palynomorphs are commonly absent. Basal tills are usually barren or contain only rare fragments of poorly preserved foraminifera which are probably redeposited and of no direct paleoenvironmental significance. These tills often contain only reworked pre-Quaternary palynomorphs. Proglacial sediments in shelf and coastal environments usually contain low diversity benthic foraminifers, dinocyst and diatom assemblages, with populations usually fluctuating substantially between sample intervals. Meltwater events (e.g. at the isotopic stage 1-2 boundary) are also often marked by barren intervals, but may include rare pollen. Good examples of these sequences are described for cores from Notre Dame Bay (see Fig. 10.35) (Mudie and Guilbault, 1982; Scott et al., 1984b) and the Southeast Baffin Shelf (Osterman, 1982; Mudie and Short, 1985; Praeg et al., 1986). In deep ocean areas, glacial sediments usually contain large amounts of ice-rafted debris. These deposits commonly contain planktonic foraminifers but other microfossils are usually rare, and palynomorphs usually include many reworked pre-Quaternary taxa (Aksu and Mudie, 1985b; Mudie and Short, 1985). Deep-sea fine grained turbidites often contain only rare thin beds of planktic foraminifers and palynomorphs (Stow, 1977; Chough, 1978; Mudie and Short, 1985) although some such sediments also contain variable amounts of reworked benthic foraminifers (Thomas, 1985).

Organic carbon and nitrogen isotopes
A.E. Aksu

Carbon isotopic data provide information on the source of organic matter such as marine versus terrestrial and autotropic versus heterotrophic origins (Macko, 1983). Similarly nitrogen isotopic data provide information on the origin and diagenetic history of sedimentary organic matter. Differences in nitrogen isotope composition are dependent on the source of the nitrogen (Mariotti et al., 1983), and fractionation by nitrogen fixation or by nitrate uptake (Peters et al., 1978; Macko et al., 1983). Such differences can be used to delineate different sedimentary environments. As an example of the use of carbon isotopes, two Baffin Bay cores show variations in organic carbon isotopic ratios ranging from -20 to $-29‰$ during the last 250 000 years (Lobsiger, 1979). Comparison of the organic carbon isotopic data with oxygen isotope curves (Aksu, 1983a) suggests that the heavier carbon isotopic values correlate with interglacials, possibly reflecting warmer surface waters in the photic zone or increased contributions of marine organic material. Similarly the lighter carbon isotopic values may reflect colder surface waters or increased contributions of terrestrial organic carbon. These glacial-interglacial trends are similar to those observed in Quaternary sediments of the Gulf of Mexico (Rogers and Koons, 1969). Recent studies of isotopes of both organic carbon and nitrogen in Baffin Island fiords (Macko et al., 1985) have attempted to identify the mixing of marine and terrestrial organic matter, marine macrophytes and products of salt marshes.

THE SOUTHEAST CANADIAN REGION
D.J.W. Piper and G.B. Fader
Scotian Shelf and Gulf of Maine

Because of accessibility and the long history of hydrocarbon exploration, the Quaternary geology of Canada's continental margins is best known off Nova Scotia (Fig. 10.15) and this area has been a testing ground for applying new methodologies. As early as 1931, F.P. Shepard recognized the glacial origin of many of the sediments on the continental shelf. L.H. King and his coworkers, in the 1960s, developed methods for systematic mapping and interpretation of acoustic stratigraphic units on the continental shelf that led to the development of the Huntec deep-tow, high-resolution seismic-reflection systems. At the same time, D.J.G. Nota, D.H. Loring, D.J. Stanley and D.J.P. Swift investigated the sedimentology of surficial sediments on the continental shelf and slope. Fluctuations in sea level, marked by raised beaches and contemporary evidence for submergence, have long been a focus of glacial investigations in the Maritime Provinces and led to studies of lowered stands of sea level offshore. The exploration and production of offshore hydrocarbons have provided a stimulus to acoustic and geotechnical engineering studies.

Physiographic setting and general distribution of Quaternary sediments

Pre-Wisconsinan deposits of Tertiary or Quaternary age are extremely rare on land in the Maritime Provinces. A series of tilted erosion surfaces have been distinguished in Atlantic Canada (Grant, in press), the oldest of which were thought to date from the Cretaceous (King, 1972), although sediment budgets (Mathews, 1975) suggest that most are of late Tertiary age.

Glacial tills of variable thickness cover much of the land area, except for the highest regions such as northern Cape Breton Island which may not have been glaciated in the Wisconsinan (Grant, in press). A regional southeasterly trend of ice-flow features (except in western Newfoundland, where flow appears to have been towards the Gulf of St. Lawrence) appears to date from the Early or Middle Wisconsinan. Late Wisconsinan ice flow was apparently from local centres and was strongly influenced by drawdown of ice into the present nearshore marine areas (Grant, in press).

Early workers such as Johnson (1925) recognized the morphological similarity between Georges Bank or the outer banks of the Scotian Shelf and the cuestas of the Atlantic Coastal Plain to the south. Shepard (1930, 1931) suggested that the straight-sided submarine valleys of the Laurentian Channel and Bay of Fundy were not the result of faulting, but of glacial erosion. The overdeeping of basins such as those in the Gulf of Maine and Scotian Shelf was interpreted as also resulting from glacial erosion. Such shelf areas contrast strongly with those that lie beyond the Quaternary ice limits to the south off the eastern United States, where the shelf steadily and smoothly deepens oceanwards, though interrupted by relict valleys and drowned beach ridges (Emery and Uchupi, 1973).

Three main physiographic divisions have been delineated on the Scotian Shelf (King and MacLean, 1976). The inner shelf (Fig. 10.16) slopes gently seawards, its overall trend a continuation of the most prominent of the

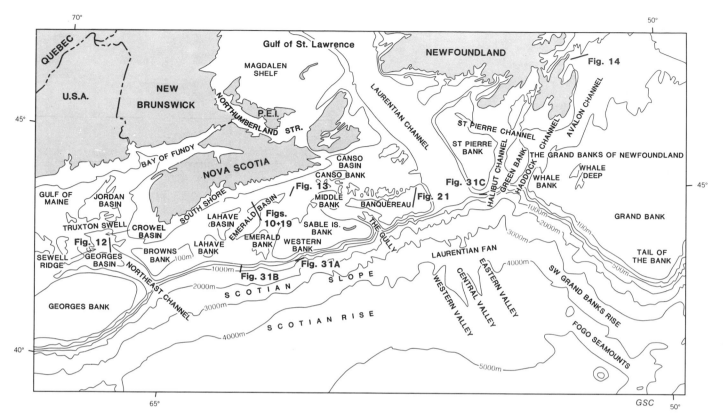

Figure 10.15. Scotian and Grand Banks continental margins. Locations of Figures 10.10, 10.12, 10.13, 10.14, 10.19, 10.21, and 10.31 are shown.

terrestrial peneplains. On a small scale (tens of metres) it is irregular, with overdeepened basins and valleys that are strongly controlled by bedrock. Similar features on the adjacent land appear to result from differential glacial erosion of bedrock in which sub-ice drainage has been important in the development of the prominent valley systems (Piper et al., 1986). The preservation of the peneplain, however, indicates that significant glacial erosion was only local.

On the middle shelf, deep basins occur in the softer strata of the Mesozoic-Cenozoic continental shelf sequence near where they are in contact with resistant Paleozoic strata of the inner shelf. Some basins, such as LaHave Basin, lie in the path of former major ice streams, and their basin-like form is ascribed to glacial erosion (King et al., 1974).

The outer shelf is marked by shallow banks (rising above sea level at Sable Island) on which Tertiary strata commonly occur at shallow depth. The outer parts of southwestern Georges Bank (Knott and Hoskins, 1968), Sable Island Bank and Banquereau, however, appear to be broad depositional wedges of Quaternary sediment, deposited on a south-dipping Tertiary bedrock surface. This surface is over 200 m below sea level on southern Sable Island Bank and Banquereau and 70 m beneath the southwestern edge of Georges Bank off Great South Channel. A complex series of anastomosing and locally overdeepened channels is incised in the Tertiary sediments to depths of up to 550 m beneath Sable Island Bank and Banquereau. These resemble tunnel valleys cut by subglacial meltwater. The

overlying sediment wedge probably acquired its form from deposition of glaciomarine or fluvioglacial sediments modified by marine regressions and transgressions.

The line of outer banks is cut by deep, broad flat transverse troughs, the most prominent being Northeast Channel and Laurentian Channel. These transverse troughs are not marked by any major indentation of the shelf break. Seismic reflection profiles indicate remnants of a former fluvial drainage system beneath the troughs; subsequent glacial modification resulted in straight steep walls, flat overdeepened floors and the presence of hanging tributary valleys. Other valleys that dissect the outer banks of the eastern Scotian Shelf, notably the Gully and the valleys on the north edge of Banquereau, are much more irregular than the transverse troughs in both plan and cross profile. King et al. (1974) suggested that they developed fluvially in a cuesta landscape (Fig. 10.16), although the smaller more irregular valleys are probably subglacial erosion features (R. Boyd, pers. comm., 1985).

Deep filled channels cut Tertiary strata at several places on the continental slope and on the outer shelf, notably on Banquereau and Sable Island Bank and between Western Bank and Emerald Bank (where almost 1.5 km of strata were eroded — Barss et al., 1979). The great depth of these channels suggests that they were cut by a largely submarine process involving headward erosion of submarine canyons; the Gully may represent an unfilled analogue. Some appear continuous with the anastomosing channels cut into Tertiary bedrock beneath the outer banks and may thus result in part from erosion by subgla-

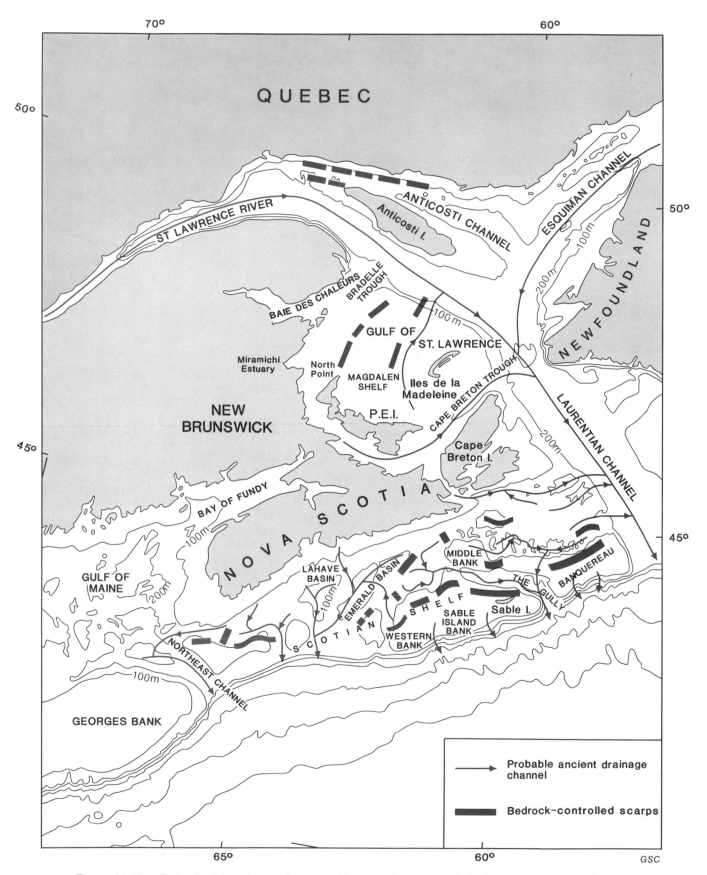

Figure 10.16. Relict fluvial landscape features of Late Tertiary and Early Pleistocene age on the Scotian Shelf and Gulf of St. Lawrence (after King et al., 1974, and Loring and Nota, 1973).

cial meltwater. The possibility of glacial erosion, however, cannot be completely excluded. The age of the channels is not well constrained: they cut Pliocene strata and the great thickness of fill suggests that they must be essentially Late Pliocene or Early Pleistocene in age.

Lithostratigraphy

The type section for the Scotian Shelf

The Quaternary lithostratigraphy for the Scotian Shelf was defined by King (1970) principally on the basis of acoustic data and shallow samples (Fig. 10.17 and Table 10.6). This stratigraphic scheme was subsequently applied to the Gulf of Maine (Fader et al., 1977; Fader, 1984) and the Grand Banks (Fader et al., 1982). Different lithostrati-

graphic sections have been observed in the nearshore zone and on the outer parts of Sable Island Bank and Banquereau. First the type section and then the regional variations are described.

The Scotian Shelf Drift overlies bedrock over much of the shelf (Fig. 10.12, 10.13) and is interpreted as a till deposited from grounded ice (King and Fader, 1986). It is thin in shallow water where it was eroded during the Late Pleistocene to Holocene transgression, and reaches maximum thicknesses of 200 m elsewhere on the shelf. It occurs on most of the outer banks, and to water depths of 500 m on the upper continental slope. There is, however, only limited evidence for till on the outer parts of Banquereau and Sable Island Bank. Possible diamicts have been intersected in some boreholes in this area.

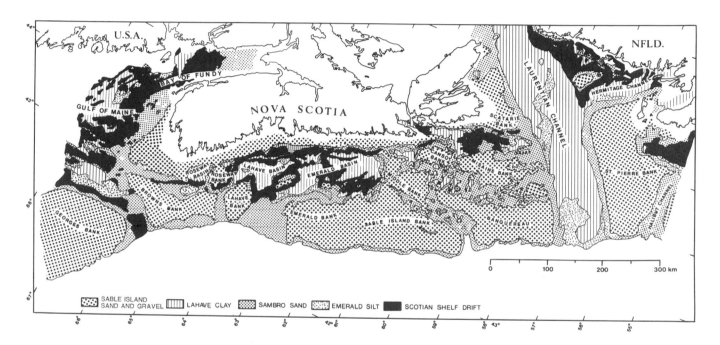

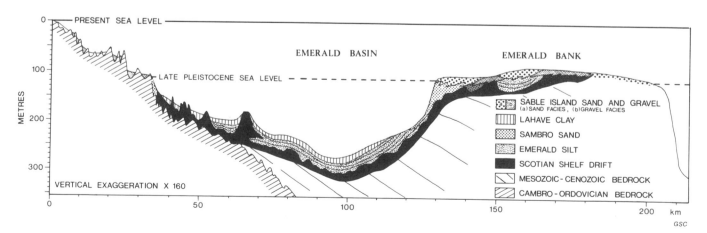

Figure 10.17. (a) Surficial geology of the Scotian Shelf (from King and Fader, 1986). (b) Schematic northwest-southeast cross-section across Emerald Basin and Emerald Bank showing the distribution of surficial sediment formations.

Table 10.6. Quaternary lithostratigraphy of the Scotian Shelf (modified from King and Fader, 1986, Table 1)

Formation	Lithology and distribution	Thickness	Acoustic character	Origin
LaHave Clay	Greyish brown, soft, silty clay grading to clayey silt, confined mainly to basins and depressions of shelf.	0-70 m	Generally transparent without reflections. Some weak continuous coherent reflections in base of section becoming stronger in nearshore sandy facies.	Derived by winnowing of glacial sediments on banks and transported to basins. Time equivalent of Sable Island Sand and Gravel and Sambro Sand on banks.
Sable Island Sand and Gravel	Fine to coarse, well-sorted sand grading to sub-rounded to rounded gravels. Unconformably overlies Emerald Silt and Scotian Shelf Drift in water depths less than 120 m.	0-50 m, generally a veneer	Highly reflective seabed. Generally closely spaced, continuous, coherent reflections if deposit is of sufficient thickness to resolve.	Derived from Emerald Silt and Scotian Shelf Drift through reworking during Holocene transgression. Time equivalent of LaHave Clay in basins.
Sambro Sand	Silty sand grading locally to gravelly sand and well-sorted sand.	0-20 m, generally a veneer	Similar to Sable Island Sand and Gravel.	Deposited sublitorally with respect to the Late Wisconsin low sea level of 100-120 m. Time equivalent to basal LaHave Clay and upper Emerald Silt facies B.
Emerald Silt facies C	Not well sampled.	0-100 m	Discontinuous coherent reflections; transitional between Emerald Silt facies A and glacial till.	Deposition at grounding line.
Emerald Silt facies B	Dark greyish brown, poorly sorted clayey and sandy silt with some gravel. Poorly developed rhythmic banding.	0-40 m	Medium to low amplitude, continuous coherent reflections, and to some degree a ponded sedimentational style.	Proglacial deposition.
Emerald Silt facies A	Dark greyish brown, poorly sorted clayey and sandy silt, some gravel. Well developed rhythmic banding.	0-100 m	High amplitude continuous coherent reflections, highly conformable to substrate irregularities.	Deposition from beneath ice shelf. Time equivalent to parts of Scotian Shelf Drift.
Scotian Shelf Drift	Very dark greyish brown, cohesive glacial till comprised of poorly sorted sandy clay and silt with variable gravel.	0-100 m	Incoherent reflections, sometimes with scattered point-source reflections.	Deposition from grounded ice sheet.

Table 10.7. Summary stratigraphic correlation of Quaternary sediments on east coast offshore shelves

	Sediments strongly influenced by ice sheets			Sediments showing little or no influence by ice sheets	
	Lithology and thickness				
Region	Glacial till	Glaciomarine poorly sorted silts	Muddy sands and gravels	Basinal muds (may contain ice rafted detritus in higher latitudes)	Sands and gravels
Gulf of Maine Bay of Fundy Scotian Shelf	Scotian Shelf Drift <100 m	Emerald Silt <140 m	Sambro Sand <20 m, generally a veneer	LaHave Clay <70 m	Sable Island Sand and Gravel <60 m, generally a veneer
Northumberland Strait	Pomquet Drift <40 m	Malagash Mud 15 m Henry Island Sediment <80 m	Buchtouche Sand and Gravel (in water depths 60-80 m) <10 m, generally a veneer	Pugwash Mud <20 m	Egmont Sand Buchtouche Sand and Gravel (in water depths 60-80 m) <35 m
Gulf of St. Lawrence	FORMATION NAMES NOT ASSIGNED				
Grand Banks of Newfoundland	Grand Banks Drift <60 m	Downing Silt <90 m	Adolphus Sand <10 m, generally a veneer	Placentia Clay <30 m	Grand Banks Sand and Gravel <20 m, generally a veneer
Northeast Newfoundland Shelf	FORMATION NAMES NOT ASSIGNED				
Labrador Shelf	Labrador Shelf Drift <300 m	Qeovik Silt <50 m	Sioraq Sand and Gravel <10 m, generally a veneer	Makkaq Clay <30 m	
Southeast Baffin Shelf	Baffin Shelf Drift <300 m	Davis Strait Silt <70 m		Tiniktartuq Silt and Clay <10 m	Resolution Island Lag <50 cm
Northeast Baffin Shelf	Baffin Shelf Drift <50 m	Davis Strait Silt <10 m		Tiniktartuq Silt and Clay	Cape Aston Sand and Gravel <5 m
Age	Most Wisconsinan. Probably some earlier tills on Northeast Newfoundland, Labrador and Baffin shelves	Middle to Late Wisconsinan (locally earliest Holocene)	Late Wisconsinan sub-littoral deposits off southeast Canada		Latest Wisconsinan to Holocene

Few samples are available that penetrate more than the top few tens of centimetres of the Scotian Shelf Drift. They show a wide range of grain sizes (Fig. 10.18), from gravelly sand with only minor mud, to muds with only minor sand and gravel. The surface of the till has been heavily scoured by icebergs that eroded sediment, allowing it to be sorted and redeposited. Few samples are available to compare systematically the lithologies of the Scotian Shelf Drift with those of tills on land. However, the widespread occurrence of North Mountain Basalt and red sandstone and siltstone clasts on the Scotian Shelf and upper slope suggests that parts of the Scotian Shelf Drift correlate with the Red Head Till on land (Grant, in press).

The Emerald Silt overlies and interfingers with the Scotian Shelf Drift. It is a poorly sorted silt that is acoustically well stratified. King and Fader (1986) recognized two main acoustic facies of the Emerald Silt (Fig. 10.19). Facies A consists of high-amplitude, continuous, coherent reflections that are generally conformable to and draped over irregularities in the underlying till. The contact with the Scotian Shelf Drift is marked by lift-off moraines on basin floors, and Emerald Silt facies A interfingers with till tongues at basin margins. This facies is overlain, disconformably at the edges of basins, by Emerald Silt facies B, which has medium to low amplitude, continuous coherent reflections that are locally conformable. In the upper part of the section, however, facies B is more ponded, with onlap features at basin flanks. Point-source hyperbolic reflections (probably due to boulders) occur in both facies, but appear to be more common in facies B (Fig. 10.10). Facies A consists of mud with prominent alternating bands 1-3 cm thick of silty mud and clayey mud, with minor amounts of dispersed sand and gravel. Foraminifera are rare (10-100/g) and exclusively *Elphidium excavatum*. Facies B has a similar bulk composition, but banding is less prominent and it features silty laminae, some bioturbation and pyritization. It also contains mollusc shells and foraminifers which become more abundant and more diverse upwards.

In shelf basins, the Emerald Silt is overlain by up to 30 m of LaHave Clay, an acoustically transparent postglacial mud that is derived from reworking of glacial sediments during the Holocene transgression. The LaHave Clay generally has a ponded relationship with the subsurface. It consists of bioturbated olive grey mud, which

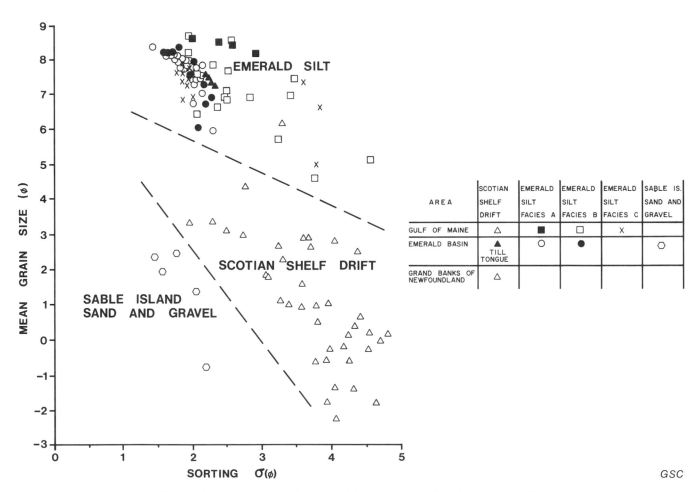

GSC

Figure 10.18. Textural characteristics of sediment facies from the Scotian Shelf and Gulf of Maine (after King and Fader, 1986). The samples of till (Scotian Shelf Drift) are very poorly sorted. The samples from the till tongue in Emerald Basin fall within the Emerald Silt field, together with both Emerald Silt facies A and B samples from the same area. Representative samples of Sable Island Sand and Gravel are plotted for comparison and demonstrate their better sorting.

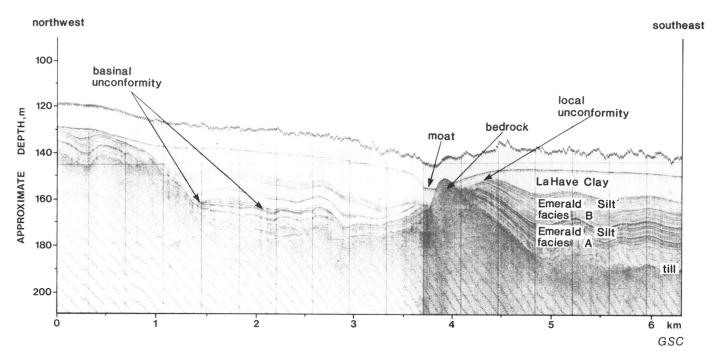

Figure 10.19. Huntec DTS seismic reflection profile showing Emerald Silt facies (after King and Fader, 1986). A basinal unconformity occurs near the top of Emerald Silt facies A and is expressed at the 1.5 km mark as a truncation of continuous coherent reflections. In many areas it becomes disconformable. Note the occurrence of a moat surrounding the bedrock high. These features are widespread and are believed to be formed by a combination of lower sedimentation rates and erosion associated with bottom currents. Figure 10.15 shows profile location.

becomes siltier towards basin margins, where correlative graded beds suggest that much of the sediment is deposited episodically during storms (Kontopoulos and Piper, 1982a).

At basin margins, both the Scotian Shelf Drift and Emerald Silt have been erosionally truncated at water depths of 100 to 135 m (Fig. 11, 12, 29, 31 of King and Fader, 1986), and are overlain in deeper water by a muddy sand unit called Sambro Sand, and in shallower water by sorted sand and gravel of the Sable Island Sand and Gravel (Fig. 10.18). The LaHave Clay onlaps this unconformity. The Sable Island Sand and Gravel was developed by reworking of older glacial sediment during the Holocene transgression. Similar facies also occur in deeper water in areas of contemporary strong current. The Sambro Sand represents either contemporary or relict sublittoral reworking or deposition.

Sable Island Bank and Banquereau

Over much of southern Sable Island Bank and Banquereau, Quaternary sediments are much thicker than elsewhere on the outer banks, ranging from 100 to 200 m in thickness. They overlie southward-dipping, regularly bedded Tertiary sediments. The boundary between the "Quaternary" sediments and the Tertiary Banquereau Formation (see Chapter 3) is not well constrained biostratigraphically but is marked by an erosional unconformity which is cut by a network of deep channels (Fig. 10.20a) up to 550 m below present sea level (R. Boyd, 1985, pers. comm.). There is a second widespread unconformity (1 in Fig. 10.21) generally at depths of 60 to 70 m below

sea level over much of Sable Island Bank and Banquereau (R. Boyd, 1985, pers. comm.; Amos and Knoll, 1987) that is exposed at the bank margins in water depths of about 110 m. This unconformity has shallow channels filled with gravel and sand and is correlated with the Late Wisconsinan low stand of sea level and the subsequent transgression. Both acoustic data and cores indicate that sediments above this unconformity are the Sable Island Sand and Gravel of King (1970). Complex offshore sand ridges and shoreface connected ridges (Fig. 10.21) are developed in places in the upper part of this formation.

Amos and Knoll (1987) identified a deeper prominent reflection (2 in Fig. 10.21) generally 20 m below reflector 1, that is locally cut by channel-like features. The sequence above reflector 2 consists of alternating silts and muds and appears to be a coarse facies of Emerald Silt. Borehole samples are only available for the upper 15 m of section below reflector 2: gravels, sands and possible diamicts overlie sands. The entire sequence sampled below reflector 2 contains shell fragments. The lower, unsampled part of the "Quaternary" section on Banquereau is 80 m thick and is acoustically stratified.

On the eastern margin of Sable Island Bank, R. Boyd (pers. comm., 1986) has mapped a contact between Emerald Silt in the deeper waters of the Gully with till on the shallower flanks of Sable Island Bank. The till appears to interfinger laterally with glacial outwash. This suggests that at one stage during the Wisconsinan, an ice tongue occupied the Gully, but Sable Island Bank was unglaciated.

513

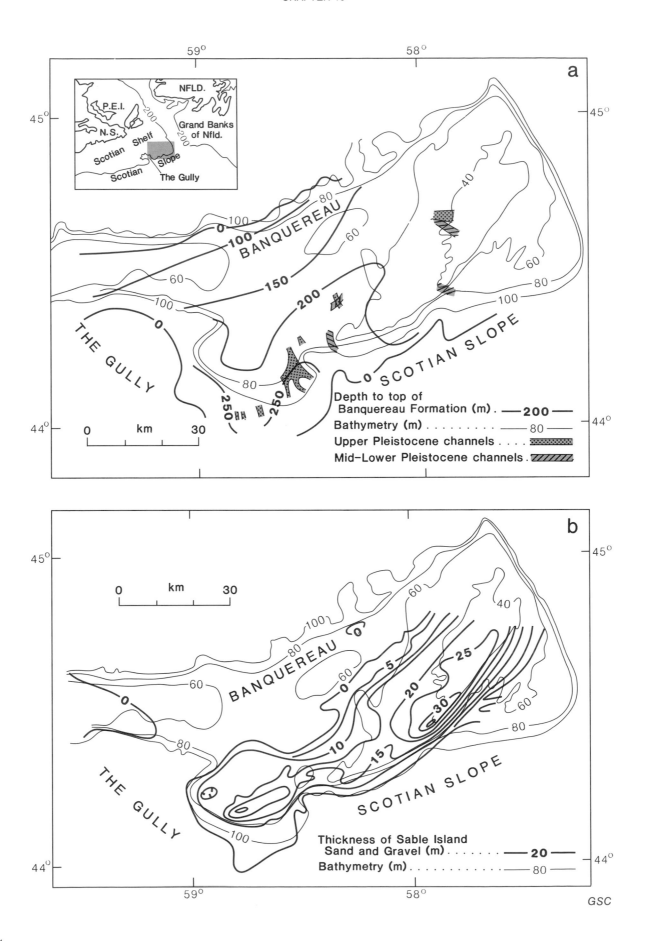

GSC

Gulf of Maine and Georges Bank

In the Gulf of Maine, glacial materials are thickest in Georges Basin, Northeast Channel and Great South Channel. Georges Bank appears to be a relict Tertiary cuesta, with Tertiary rocks occurring at less than 10 m beneath the seafloor and outcropping locally. Northeast Channel and Great South Channel are glacially overdeepened transverse troughs.

Scotian Shelf Drift underlies Browns Bank, Georges Basin, Northeast Channel, Sewell Ridge, Truxton Swell and the approaches to the Bay of Fundy (Fig. 10.15), and ranges up to 140 m in thickness. The tills in Northeast Channel, forming the Browns Moraine, can be traced to till tongues at the shelf break. They stratigraphically underlie till tongues of the Fundian Moraine north of Georges Basin. Both moraine systems are sub-glacial grounding line moraines similar to those on the Scotian Shelf, and are separated and overlain by thin deposits of Emerald Silt facies A. North of the Fundian Moraine, a thick section of Emerald Silt facies B is overlain by a thin development of facies A, associated with a Late Wisconsinan ice advance that formed the Truxton Moraine on Truxton Swell.

Great South Channel appears partially filled with stratified sediment of probable proglacial origin. On the basis of gravel distribution on Georges Bank (Pratt and Schlee, 1969), Schlee (1973) suggested that glacial ice extended only over the northern margin of Georges Bank. High-resolution seismic reflection profiles are available only from the northeastern part of the bank: they indicate small areas of till-like and glaciomarine deposits near the shelf break on the eastern part of the bank.

Seismic reflection profiles (Knott and Hoskins, 1968) show glaciotectonic features on the continental shelf off New England which resemble those seen on land in the moraines on Long Island, and indicate an ice advance at least 30 km seaward of the prominent moraine system extending from Long Island through Block Island, Martha's Vineyard and Nantucket Island. Leaves in clay stratigraphically below till on Martha's Vineyard are dated at 15.3 ka (Kaye, 1964). Till recovered in cores from 41°N in Great South Channel has been dated as Late Wisconsinan (Bothner and Spiker, 1980). Oldale and Eskenasy (1983) sampled tills and interbedded marine sediments on Nantucket Island, that they interpreted to represent deposits of both the Illinoian and Wisconsinan glaciations.

The Late Wisconsinan low stand of sea level is interpreted to have reached a depth of 110 m around Georges Bank, and the shallow areas of the bank have a complex distribution of gravelly and sandy sediments, locally with prominent bedforms (Amos and King, 1984) (see Chapter 11). LaHave Clay is restricted to Georges, Crowell and Jordan basins.

The nearshore zone

The most complete nearshore lithostratigraphy in the Nova Scotian region is found in the Lunenburg area of the South Shore of Nova Scotia (Piper et al., 1986). A discontinuous till sheet (the "late" till) probably of Late Wisconsinan age, can be traced about 5 km offshore. Beyond this, acoustic profiles show a complex sedimentary sequence (Fig. 10.22) overlying an older, dissected till (the "early" till) correlated with the Middle Wisconsinan Scotian Shelf Drift of the continental shelf.[†] The oldest sediment overlying "early" till is acoustically transparent and draped over the till surface. Cores show that it comprises an upward fining sequence of gravel through sand to laminated mud deposited in a proglacial environment. It is overlain by acoustically stratified sediment that generally fills depressions and may comprise sands and gravels that grade laterally northwards into the "late" till. A major unconformity above these stratified sediments probably results from coastal planation following the Late Wisconsinan lowering of sea level, and the "late" till ice advance may be related to this sea level lowering. Acoustically stratified sediments above the unconformity consist of gravels and sands passing upward into laminated muds, deposited in an ice-margin environment as Late Wisconsinan ice retreated and sea level rose. Holocene sands and muds have subsequently accumulated in basins. Sea level indicators suggest that relative sea level has risen by about 35 m over the past 11 ka. Scott and Medioli (1982) suggested that there was a Late Wisconsinan high stand at −27 m; Piper et al. (1986) have found little evidence elsewhere on the Atlantic coast for a Late Wisconsinan high stand, and interpreted the old shallow marine sediments at this elevation as Middle Wisconsinan.

The Holocene sediments of the area east of Halifax (Eastern Shore) have been investigated in detail by Boyd and his coworkers (Boyd and Penland, 1984; Hall, 1985). Holocene coastal retreat has released large quantities of sediment to the coastal zone from drumlin erosion. This has resulted in the progradation of barrier beach complexes. Subsequent overwash and failure of the barriers occur with rising sea level as drumlin sources are exhausted.

Local studies of Late Wisconsinan and Holocene sediment sequences have been made in the Country Harbour area (Hopkins, 1985), Chedabucto Bay (MacLean et al., 1976) and off southeast Cape Breton Island (Wang and Piper, 1982). These studies show sediment evolution similar to that inferred from the South and Eastern shores.

In Minas Basin and the eastern Bay of Fundy, glacial sediments overlie a bedrock surface cut by deep channels up to 60 m below present sea level (Dames and Moore, 1968; Swift and Lyall, 1968). This surface is overlain by glacial till and a thick sequence of proglacial sands and silts. The upper part of the proglacial sequence can be traced into raised Late Wisconsinan deltas on the north side of the Minas Basin (Swift and Borns, 1967), that date from about 14 ka. Postglacial sediments show that the Minas Basin was non-tidal until about 6300 BP (Amos, 1978); since then there has been a progressive increase in tidal range (Scott and Greenberg, 1983).

Figure 10.20. (a) Contour map of the depth of the unconformity between the Banquereau Formation and the "Quaternary" on Banquereau. Also shown are the location of channels cutting this section (from Amos and Knoll, 1987). (b) Isopach map of Holocene sediments on Banquereau (from Amos and Knoll, 1987).

[†] See Addendum

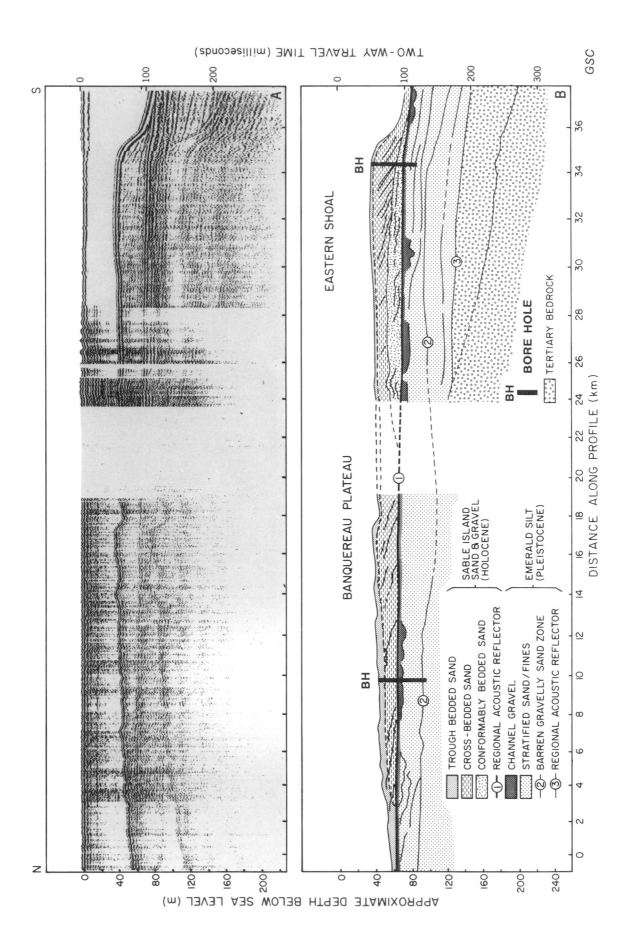

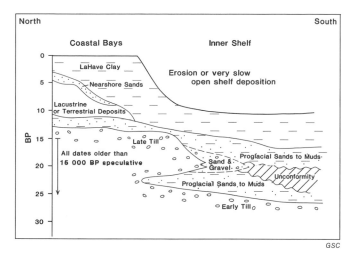

Figure 10.22. Stratigraphic interpretation of acoustic facies in the coastal region of the South Shore, Nova Scotia (after Piper et al., 1986).

Quaternary chronology of the Scotian Shelf

The age of the unconformity between "Quaternary" formations and the Banquereau Formation on the Scotian Shelf is not well defined. Hardy (1975) identified the Plio-Pleistocene boundary at 262 m below seabed in the Sable Island C-67 well, which appears to lie beneath the unconformity (R. Boyd, 1985, pers. comm.). In the Triumph P-50 well, Gradstein and Agterberg (1982) identified the Early to Late Pliocene boundary at about 420 m sub-bottom, but a Plio-Pleistocene boundary could not be recognized. On the upper Scotian Slope, the foraminiferal identification of the base of the Quaternary in the Acadia K-62 well indicates that the main phase of slope canyon-cutting, presumably correlated with the major channels on the Scotian Shelf unconformity, dates from the Late Pliocene and Early Pleistocene (Piper et al., 1987).

Although in terrestrial sections along the coastline a raised beach of probable Sangamon age (stage 5e) has been recognized (Grant, in press), no Middle to Upper Pleistocene sediments of pre-Wisconsinan age have been dated on the Scotian Shelf.

Late Quaternary chronology of the Scotian Shelf is based on biostratigraphic correlation and radiocarbon dating. Pollen, dinoflagellate cyst and foraminiferal ecostratigraphic assemblage zones have been established in the Emerald Silt and LaHave Clay formations of Emerald and Canso basins, and in the coastal equivalents of these formations in Bedford Basin (Table 10.2). In the postglacial sediments in all three basins, pollen chronologies provide the stratigraphic framework for the other zonal bound-

aries (Fig. 10.5). The pollen chronology of the marine basins is based on correlation with palynostratigraphic records of Nova Scotia lakes (Livingstone and Livingstone, 1958; Livingstone, 1968; Railton, 1975; Green, 1976) (Table 10.2). Radiocarbon dating of marine samples provides a more tentative chronological control for the glacial sediments, and confirms the pollen chronology for postglacial sediments (Scott et al., 1984b). The term "early postglacial" is used for sediments older than Holocene (10 ka) that contain "interglacial" rather than "glacial" microfossil assemblages, as defined previously. As a chronological term, the "early postglacial" is diachronous, probably ranging in age from 15 ka offshore to 12 ka nearshore.

Biostratigraphic zonation
P.J. Mudie and G. Vilks

In Emerald Basin, early postglacial and early to middle Holocene assemblages of dinoflagellate cysts reflect the strong influence of the slope water and the warm Gulf Stream (Fig. 10.23); the assemblage changed to one with a greater subarctic and coastal influence during the past 4 ka (Mudie, 1980; Scott et al., 1984b; and Table 10.2). The foraminiferal zones include a late glacial assemblage, with *Elphidium excavatum* f. *clavata* and *Neogloboquadrina pachyderma* (left coiling) as major species (Vilks and Rashid, 1976; Scott et al., 1984b). The *Nonionellina labradorica* zone coincides with the beginning of the postglacial marine environment when water was still cool and salinities slightly reduced. The *Cassidulina laevigata laevigata* zone during the early Holocene includes *Globorotalia inflata* and *Orbulina universa* indicating a relatively pronounced Gulf Stream (warm water) influence. The *Bulimina marginata* zone contains several continental slope species indicating increasing slope water influence as the relative sea level rose to its present height. During the last 4 ka the *Brizalina subaenariensis* assemblage indicates that a slight cooling had taken place both in surface and bottom waters: diversities of planktonic foraminifers are lower and arenaceous species increase.

The Canso Basin assemblage zones (Table 10.2) reflect changes in the inner shelf waters which are characterized by lower salinity and temperature than in the waters of the basins of the central shelf. *Operculodinium centrocarpum* and *Multispinula minuta* dominate the dinocyst assemblages at least as early as 8 ka. The presence of diverse *Spiniferites* species and *Bitectatodinium tepikiense* in Zone 3 suggests a warmer interval during the middle Holocene (6.4-5.5 ka) and the increase of *Brigantedinium* in the late Holocene indicates cooling and freshening of the waters during the last 4-5 ka.

The most prominent foraminifer in Canso Basin (Table 10.2) is the inner shelf species *Islandiella helenae* (= *I. teretis* of Scott et al., 1984b). Zonal boundaries are defined by the addition of other species, which suggest minor fluctuations in the environment. At the bottom of the section the presence of *Elphidium excavatum* f. *clavata* could indicate late glacial meltwater emanating from the Gulf of St. Lawrence. Between approximately 8.5 and 5.5 ka, the *Nonionellina labradorica* zone suggests the presence of the warmer and more saline outer Labrador Current waters. The overlying *I. helenae* and *Adercotryma glomerata* assemblages indicate a trend of cooling and freshening of the water towards the present time. This cooling trend in Canso Basin started earlier (ca. 4.8 ka) than in Emerald

Figure 10.21. Airgun seismic profile (A) and interpretation (B) across Eastern Shoal, Banquereau, showing acoustic stratigraphy and borehole control (from Amos and Knoll, 1987). 1 and 2 are regional reflectors described in text; 3 is a regional unconformity at the top of the Banquereau Formation. Location of profile is shown in Figure 10.15.

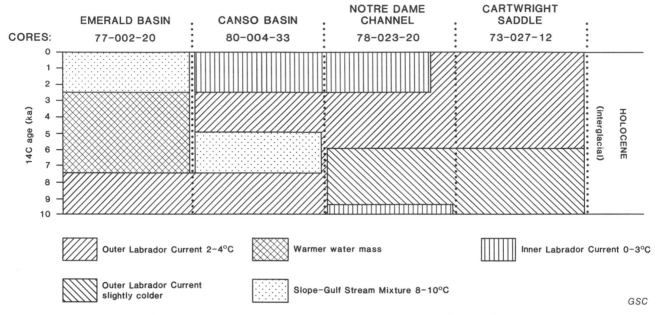

Figure 10.23. Inferred water mass distribution in the Holocene on the Scotian Shelf, Northeast Newfoundland Shelf and southern Labrador Shelf (from Scott et al., 1984b).

Basin (ca. 3 ka), presumably reflecting the greater influence of offshore waters in Emerald Basin since deglaciation.

Bedford Basin is a silled inlet in an area of marine transgression. An early postglacial freshwater phase until about 6 ka is indicated by freshwater dinoflagellate species (Table 10.2) and thecamoebians (Arcellacea; *Difflugia* and *Centropyxis* spp.) (Miller et al., 1982). From that time to 2 ka, a marginal marine environment is indicated by the presence of euryhaline foraminiferal species, such as *Eggerella advena* that tolerates salinities between 27 and 33.4 ‰ (Mudie et al., 1984), and by dinocyst assemblages (*Brigantedinium simplex* — cyst sp. C) that are characteristic of temperate deep salt wedge estuaries (Mudie, 1980). During the last 2000 years a deep estuarine environment is indicated by the presence of agglutinated foraminifera (*Reophax* spp.) and the *Operculodinium centrocarpum* — *Bitectatodinium tepikense* dinocyst assemblage.

Radiocarbon dating of glacial sediments

The stratigraphic sequence on the outer part of Banquereau has been dated by 25 shell radiocarbon dates (Fig. 10.24). Since the shells are detrital, they only provide maximum ages, but the large number of dates do appear internally consistent. The channeled reflector within the proglacial sequence (reflector 2) is dated at about 20 ka; there are no dates between 16 and 8 ka, and sediments above the Late Wisconsinan-Holocene transgressive surface (reflector 1) yield dates of less than 8 ka.

Seventy pre-Holocene radiocarbon dates are available from the basins of Scotian Shelf and Gulf of Maine. Almost all are based on total organic carbon. Four accelerator dates on small shell samples from the LaHave Clay and Emerald Silt facies B in Emerald Basin, in the age range of 8 to 26 ka, agree to within ± 2 ka with the total organic carbon dates (Fig. 10.25). It is therefore assumed that the total organic carbon dates reasonably represent the true

age of the samples.[†] Extrapolation of the oldest dates, assuming constant sedimentation rate, suggests that in Emerald Basin deposition of Emerald Silt facies A began around 47 ka, and facies B accumulated from about 32 to 14 ka. Elsewhere on the shelf similar ages are indicated by the total organic radiocarbon dates (King and Fader, 1986). Both shell and total organic radiocarbon dates are available for the Scotian Slope to the south of Emerald Basin (Hill, 1984; Piper et al., 1985a). These indicate that sedimentation of coarse glaciogenic detritus occurred as recently as 14 ka.

The age of the terrace developed at 115 m below sea level, which corresponds to the boundary between the Emerald Silt and LaHave Clay, is constrained by radiocarbon dates in Emerald Basin to between 15 and 14 ka (King and Fader, 1986).

History of Late Quaternary sea level change

Features such as raised beaches and submerged forests in many parts of Atlantic Canada are evidence of substantial postglacial changes in relative sea level. These changes are principally the result of loading beneath ice sheets, the development of a peripheral crustal bulge beyond the ice sheet margin, changes in these loadings through time, and changes in the total volume of the world ocean as ice sheets retreated.

Much geological evidence exists for a 110-120 m lowering of sea level on the Scotian Shelf, and a 90-110 m lowering on the Grand Banks of Newfoundland. A widespread unconformity at these depths is marked in places by an erosional terrace, above which most till and glaciomarine sediment has been removed. This unconformity cuts the Emerald Silt and is locally overlapped by the Sable Island Sand and Gravel and the LaHave Clay, thus confirming its

---

[†] See Addendum

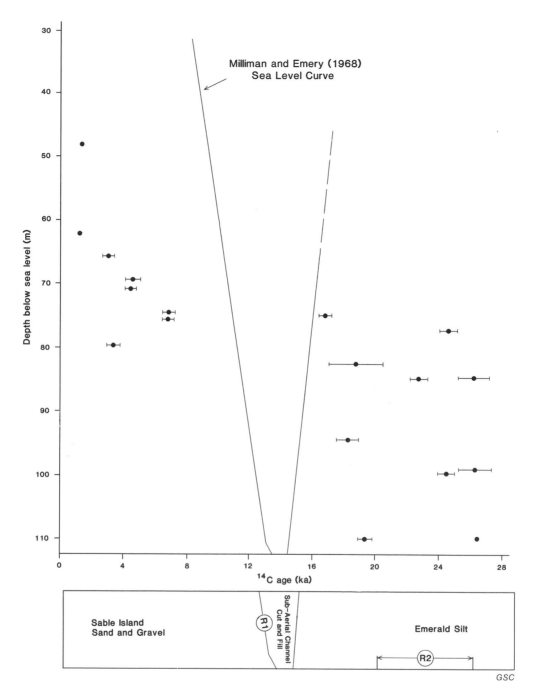

Figure 10.24. Shell radiocarbon dates from boreholes on Banquereau compared with Milliman and Emery sea level curve (from Amos and Knoll, 1987). Lower panel shows relationship to lithostratigraphy: R1 and R2 are regional reflectors shown in Figure 10.21.

Late Wisconsinan age. The unconformity can be traced towards shallower water, consistent with its proposed transgressive origin. The physical properties of sediments that underlie the unconformity in water depths of less than about 110 m on the outer shelf suggest subaerial exposure. The sediments differ from equivalent sediments in deeper water in that shells have been leached, water content is less, the sediments are harder to penetrate (King and Fader, 1986), and on the Grand Banks a paleosol occurs

(Barrie et al., 1984; Segall et al., 1985). The textural characteristics of the Sable Island Sand and Gravel overlying the unconformity are similar to modern coastal sediments derived from erosion of till (Letson, 1981).

The terrace and associated geological features representing the lowered stand of sea level are found in progressively shallower water depths northwards. This trend appears to be the result partly of isostatic rebound (which is greater towards the north), and partly of the

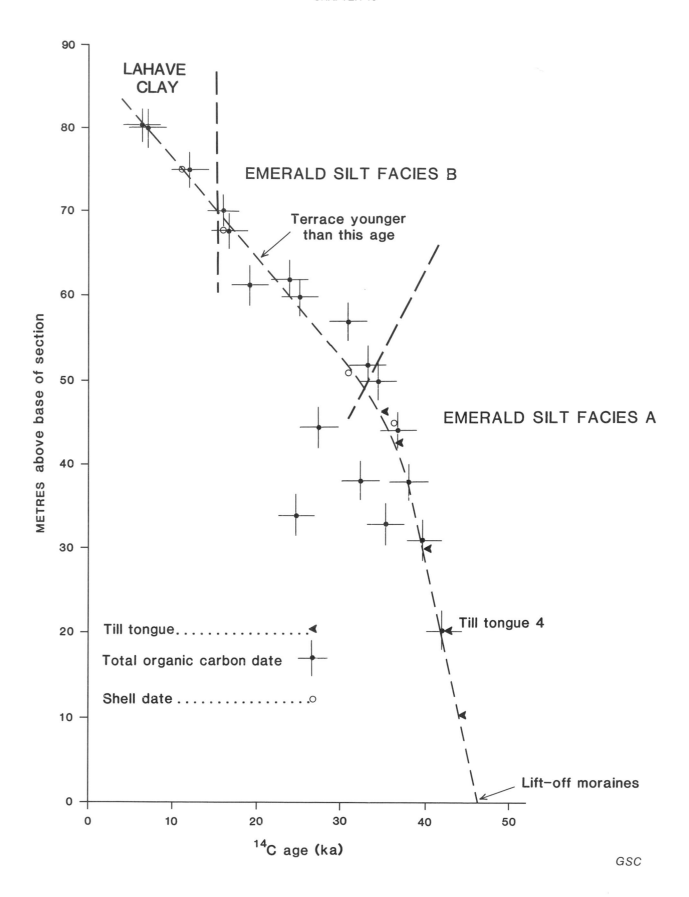

diachronous nature of the terrace, which becomes younger northwards as the postglacial transgression moved landwards. The terrace can be traced to water depths of less than 40 m at the entrance to the Bay of Fundy (Fader et al., 1977), 55 m on the inner shelf off Lunenburg (Piper et al., 1986), and 90 m off the south coast of Newfoundland (Fader et al., 1982).

Quinlan and Beaumont (1981, 1983) modelled the isostatic response of the earth to ice-loading effects, and provided a good theoretical explanation of relative sea level changes in the Atlantic Provinces of eastern Canada for the last 10 ka. They defined four relative sea level zones (Fig. 10.26). In zone A there has been a continuous fall in relative sea level since deglaciation, as a result of isostatic rebound. In zones B and C, shoreward migration of the peripheral bulge as ice retreated resulted first in a fall and then a rise in relative sea level, with the fall greater in zone B and the rise greater in zone C. In zone D there has been a continuous rise in sea level since deglaciation, mainly as a result of the increase in the volume of ocean water. The geographic location of these zones is dependant on the particular ice distribution that is modelled. The rheological models are less constrained by data in Late Wisconsinan time; they suggest a maximum relative sea level lowering on the Scotian Shelf of 75 m, which is inconsistent with the geological evidence for a lowering by 110-120 m.

Little is known about the history of relative sea level on the Scotian Shelf prior to the major Late Wisconsinan lowering. The standard oxygen isotope curve and sea level studies in many parts of the world (Kennett, 1982, p. 272) suggest that global ice volumes as great as those in the Late Wisconsinan last occurred in isotopic stage 6 (Illinoian), and that fluctuations of sea level of many tens of metres probably occurred throughout the Wisconsinan. The Early Wisconsinan ice advance across the Scotian Shelf would have had a significant isostatic effect which presumably would have disappeared by the time of the Late Wisconsinan sea-level minimum. Geological evidence from the South Shore of Nova Scotia (Piper et al., 1986) and Banquereau (Amos and Knoll, 1987) points to relatively high sea levels at times during the Middle Wisconsinan. Fluctuations in sea level at this time, in response to changes in global ice volume, may have played an important role in promoting the recession of ice from the continental shelf.

Figure 10.25. Shell and total organic radiocarbon dates for sediments of Emerald Basin (after King and Fader, 1986). Sedimentation curve is based on ^{14}C ages and seismostratigraphic analyses of Huntec DTS data for Emerald Basin, Scotian Shelf. Extrapolation of dates suggests that initial ice lift-off occurred at approximately 46 ka. Till tongues 2-9 (see Fig. 10.13) were developed during deposition of Emerald Silt facies A. Till tongue 4, the main tongue of the Scotian Shelf moraine complex, was deposited at about 42 ka. Near the top of Emerald Silt facies A the sedimentation rate decreases and remains more or less constant until 8 ka (see Addendum).

Synthesis of glacial history

No direct information is available on the pre-Wisconsinan glacial history of the Scotian Shelf, except at the extreme edge of the shelf where the more continuous record of deep water facies begins. The degree of glacial erosion on the Scotian Shelf, and the stratigraphic record in deep water, suggest that there were major pre-Wisconsinan ice advances across the shelf.

Isotopic stage 5e (Sangamonian) is represented by a raised coastal terrace a few metres above present sea level. Preserved organic deposits on land (de Vernal et al., 1983) suggest that the later part of isotopic stage 5 was not a time of severe glaciation in Atlantic Canada (Grant, in press). The major advance of grounded ice across the Scotian Shelf (Fig. 10.27) is therefore probably of Early Wisconsinan age (isotopic stage 4), corresponding to the Red Head Till of Nova Scotia, tentatively dated between 38 and 75 ka. At its maximum, ice may have been flowed from ice domes on the Scotian Shelf northwards across Nova Scotia, as suggested by glacial striae on land, but no evidence of such flow is preserved in the present marine areas. Ice may not have covered the southern parts of Sable Island Bank and Banquereau (Fig. 10.28). It is uncertain whether ice extended across the continental shelf as a continuous sheet, or whether it was restricted to a series of major ice lobes crossing the larger basins and troughs (de Vernal et al., 1986).

The age of the widespread sub-glacial channels on the outer banks is unclear. Some may date from pre-Wisconsinan glaciation, but the most recent erosional phase presumably correlates with the Early Wisconsinan advance.

Thinning of the ice and marine incursion into deeper basins on the continental shelf were diachronous, and the precise chronology of ice lift-off is not known. Extrapolation of total organic radiocarbon dates suggests lift-off in Emerald Basin around 47 ka, so that the onset of ice recession or lift-off at the shelf edge must have been even earlier.[†] The available chronology suggests lift-off took place in the Gulf of Maine and central Laurentian Channel by 40 ka. The marine beds at Salmon River (Clarke et al., 1972; Grant, 1980) and on Burin Peninsula (Tucker and McCann, 1980), although they have been correlated with this lift-off event, accumulated while the land was still substantially isostatically depressed. The relatively warm water aspect of these faunas suggests that they are more probably interglacial in origin (Grant and King, 1984).

King and Fader (1986) have demonstrated that Emerald Silt facies A was deposited beneath a floating iceshelf.[†] The synchronous "lift-off moraines" over large areas of flat basin floor indicate that ice was removed by being buoyed upward rather than by recessional retreat. The lack of iceberg scours immediately following till deposition also suggests an ice shelf. Furthermore, the synchroneity of till tongues on opposite basin margins is more easily accounted for if there were continuity of glacial ice from the inner Scotian Shelf to the outer banks (although fluctuations in sea level would also produce correlatable till tongues). Finally, the semi-enclosed basins of the middle shelf would have provided a sheltered environment for an iceshelf to form, although the dynamics of an iceshelf at such a low latitude are not understood.

[†] See Addendum

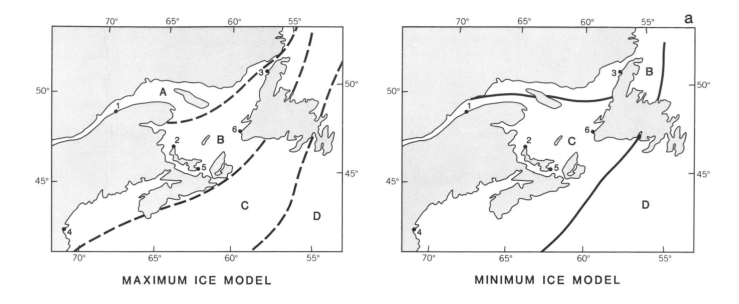

MAXIMUM ICE MODEL

MINIMUM ICE MODEL

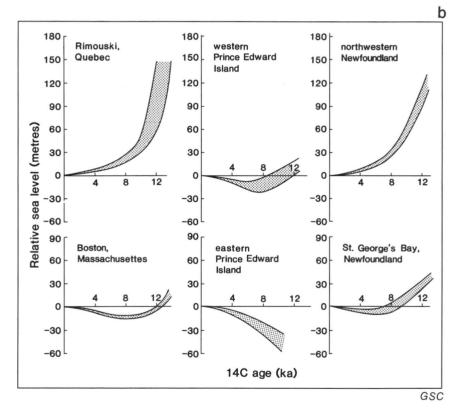

• Data series

1 Rimouski, Quebec

2 Western Prince Edward Island

3 Northwestern Newfoundland

4 Boston, Massachusettes

5 Eastern Prince Edward Island

6 St. George's Bay, Newfoundland

GSC

Figure 10.26. (a) Boundaries of relative sea level zones A to D for "maximum" and "minimum" Late Wisconsinan ice distribution (after Quinlan and Beaumont, 1982). The zones are described in greater detail in the text. (b) Selected relative sea level history curves based on radiocarbon dating (from Quinlan and Beaumont, 1982). Stippled area is envelope including all reliable radiocarbon dates.

The overlying Emerald Silt facies B has a more ponded depositional style, and is characterized by buried iceberg scours. A rather similar acoustic unit on the Labrador Shelf (Qeovik Silt of Josenhans et al., 1986) is also iceberg scoured and was demonstrably deposited from beneath open water. The transition from Emerald Silt facies A to facies B is thus interpreted as a change from sub-ice shelf to proglacial sedimentation. It occurred around 32 ka in Emerald Basin, and a similar chronology is inferred in other areas.[†] In the Gulf of Maine, grounded ice was re-established about 31 to 27 ka and deposited the uppermost tills of the prominent Fundian Moraine (Fig. 10.12). This event does not appear to have correlatives farther to the east.

Drawdown of ice to the Bay of Fundy and Laurentian Channel during the late Middle Wisconsinan broke up the pan-Maritime ice sheet into a series of separate Late Wisconsinan ice centres, which have left a clear terrestrial record (Stea, 1982; Rampton et al., 1984). A strong Late Wisconsinan ice readvance between 20 and 15 ka in the Cape Cod-Long Island area (Schafer and Hartshorn, 1965; Oldale, 1976; Sirkin, 1976) is also represented by grounding of the iceshelf in the Bay of Fundy to form the Truxton Moraine about 17 ka and a minor readvance on the South Shore (Fig. 10.28). The Late Wisconsinan ice margin probably lay not far seaward of the present shoreline of Nova Scotia,[†] and deposits marking this margin in the nearshore region have been largely removed by erosion during the Holocene transgression. Late Wisconsinan tills remain in some coastal sections (Grant, in press), and thick, coarse grained outwash sediments occur locally in the present coastal zone (Piper et al., 1986).

Oxygen isotopes indicate a maximum global ice volume at about 18 ka in the Late Wisconsinan corresponding to a marked low stand of sea level in many parts of the world (Emery and Garrison, 1967). The terrace at 115 m below sea level on the Scotian Shelf appears to correlate with or immediately follow this event (King and Fader, 1986). This low stand of sea level correlates with local readvances of ice margins and the grounding of ice in Bay of Fundy.

It is not clear how ice finally retreated from the coastal zone. Around the Bay of Fundy prominent outwash deltas formed about 14 ka and their petrological composition records the retreat of the ice from the Cobequid Hills (Swift and Borns, 1967; Wightman, 1980). There is little outwash on land along the Atlantic coast, except for ice-contact gravels in some major valleys, and eskers in southwestern Nova Scotia. The ice margin may have been floating in many areas, with ice receding as the sea transgressed. The oldest dates on organic deposits in lakes along the Atlantic coast of Nova Scotia are about 12 ka (Anderson, 1985). Low salinity water, probably related to ice margin conditions, persisted in Emerald Basin and Canso Basin until about 11 ka (Mudie, 1980; Scott et al., 1984b). Ice retreat from the coast of Maine and southwestern New Brunswick may have begun as early as 16 ka but was well underway by 14.5 ka (Smith, 1981; Rampton et al., 1984). Thus ice probably disintegrated gradually between 15 ka and 10 ka within the Maritime region, with a progressive diminution of the associated sedimentation.

On the outer Scotian Shelf, which lies in Quinlan and Beaumont's (1981) zone D, a steady transgression followed the Late Wisconsinan low stand of sea level. Nearshore in zone C, an initial regression was later followed by transgression. The transgression led to the development of barrier complexes on the outer banks (Amos and Knoll, 1987), of which Sable Island is now the only emergent remnant. On the inner Scotian Shelf, most till was removed by coastal erosion during the transgression. The fine grained component of reworked sediment accumulated in shelf basins as the LaHave Clay, at a high rate in the early post-

glacial interval at the end of the Wisconsinan, but more slowly during the Holocene as most shelf areas became submerged. The locus of rapid mud deposition is now in protected basins in the coastal zone fed by quickly eroding drumlins (Piper et al., 1986).

Gulf of St. Lawrence

Physiography

The Gulf of St. Lawrence (Fig. 10.29) is a shallow submerged lowland area of Paleozoic sedimentary rocks surrounded by highlands of the Appalachian and Grenville orogens. The most prominent physiographic feature of the gulf is the submarine trough of the Laurentian Channel, with the tributary Anticosti and Esquiman channels in the northeastern gulf. Although a variety of tectonic origins have at times been proposed for this linear, U-shaped system of channels, it is now accepted that the feature is due to glacial erosional and depositional modification of an earlier fluvial system (King and MacLean, 1970), developed within the gulf along the contact of Lower and Upper Paleozoic strata (Loring and Nota, 1973). In the shallower water areas of the northeastern gulf a drowned cuesta landscape (Fig. 10.16) is developed in Lower Paleozoic bedrock, which also appears to have controlled the position of the glacial troughs (Twenhofel, 1931).

In the southwestern gulf, the broad Magdalen Shelf is underlain at shallow depth by bedrock of Carboniferous age. A prominent cuesta is developed from North Point, Prince Edward Island almost to the Gaspésie peninsula. The Îles de la Madeleine occur at the crest of a broad bedrock dome related to salt diapirism. Major valleys, such as the Baie des Chaleurs, Bradelle and Cape Breton troughs are straight and U-shaped, enter the Laurentian Channel discordantly, and result primarily from glacial erosion. Some smaller sinuous irregular valleys resulted from sub-ice drainage (Loring and Nota, 1966).

Stratigraphy

The acoustic stratigraphy of the gulf is based on sparker and air gun profiles described by Loring and Nota (1973) and Shearer (1973). Their classic early work has not been followed up in recent years with higher resolution studies, so that there is inadequate modern high-resolution seismic reflection data from the gulf to permit detailed comparison with the Scotian Shelf.[†]

Thin till occurs over many of the shallower shelves in the gulf. Thick prograding glaciomarine strata lie along the southwestern edge of the Laurentian Channel and are overlain by proglacial muds, similar to the Emerald Silt of the Scotian Shelf and corresponding to the thick muds of the Champlain Sea in the St. Lawrence Lowlands (Corliss et al., 1982). On the Magdalen Shelf a widespread terrace at -62 to -70 m is correlated with the Late Wisconsinan -115 m terrace on the Scotian Shelf (Loring and Nota, 1973). Well-sorted sandy sediments occur in shallow water above the terrace. Muds similar to the LaHave Clay accumulated in deep-water basins in the Laurentian Trough system (Syvitski et al., 1983).

[†] See Addendum

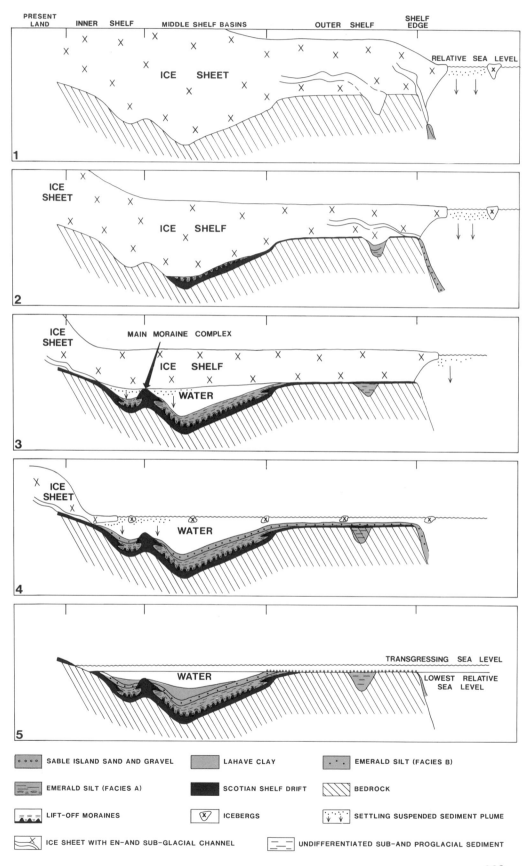

PRESENT LAND   INNER SHELF   MIDDLE SHELF BASINS   OUTER SHELF   SHELF EDGE

1

ICE SHEET

RELATIVE SEA LEVEL

2

ICE SHEET

ICE SHELF

3

ICE SHEET

MAIN MORAINE COMPLEX

ICE SHELF

WATER

4

ICE SHEET

WATER

5

WATER

TRANSGRESSING SEA LEVEL

LOWEST RELATIVE SEA LEVEL

SABLE ISLAND SAND AND GRAVEL

LAHAVE CLAY

EMERALD SILT (FACIES B)

EMERALD SILT (FACIES A)

SCOTIAN SHELF DRIFT

BEDROCK

LIFT-OFF MORAINES

ICEBERGS

SETTLING SUSPENDED SEDIMENT PLUME

ICE SHEET WITH EN-AND SUB-GLACIAL CHANNEL

UNDIFFERENTIATED SUB-AND PROGLACIAL SEDIMENT

GSC

In some deeper water cores, Loring and Nota (1973) found poorly sorted sediment, which they interpreted as till, overlying the proglacial muds. This diamict might well be ice-rafted debris or even poorly sorted, reworked proglacial sediment. They obtained a radiocarbon date of 10 200 ± 440 BP (GSC 1528) on shells immediately below the diamict and one of 8700 ± 290 BP (GSC 1608) on shells close above it.

Both Conolly et al. (1967) and Loring and Nota (1973) recognized an additional "brick red till" within the glaciomarine muds. Stow (1977) also recognized similar brick red diamict on the Laurentian Fan, and suggested an age of around 23 ka on the basis of radiocarbon dating (15 510 ± 530 BP: GX-4780) of an overlying stratum and the recognition of the Lake Mungo magnetic event a short distance below the diamict. Loring and Nota suggested a source for the diamict either on the Magdalen Shelf or in the St. Georges Bay area of western Newfoundland. Foraminifers (Bartlett and Molinsky, 1972) in late glacial strata suggest brackish ice-marginal conditions. Holocene foraminiferal assemblages are similar to those on the eastern Scotian Shelf.

The nearshore zone

Kranck (1971) recognized six Quaternary formations in Northumberland Strait. Pomquet Drift (glacial till) is up to 40 m thick and locally is unconformably overlain by stratified proglacial sediments (Henry Island Sediments) known only from acoustic profiles. Radiocarbon dating (Kranck, 1972) indicated that marine regression took place from deglaciation about 13 ka to about 7 ka, resulting in the establishment of two estuaries, one at either end of the strait. Subsequent transgression resulted in the joining of the estuaries about 5 ka. The Buchtouche Sand and Gravel covers much of the strait and is made of relict sediment up to 15 m thick winnowed during the postglacial regression. The Malagash Mud is an early Holocene marine mud that is presently being eroded by tidal currents. When the two estuaries joined, the modern tidal regime was established in the strait. The Egmont Sand and Pugwash Mud are late

---

Figure 10.27. Schematic diagrams showing the model of development of Scotian Shelf proposed by King and Fader (1986) (See Addendum). The section is oriented north-south across the type area in the northeast part of Emerald Basin and extends from the present shoreline zone to the edge of the continental shelf. The major physiographic divisions are indicated at the top of the diagram and are controlled by the shape of the bedrock surface.

1. Maximum Early Wisconsinan ice advance in isotopic stage 4, probably accompanied by significant erosion by subglacial meltwater. Ice extent on bank tops is uncertain.
2. Early stage of ice lift-off, producing lift-off moraines in Emerald Basin.
3. Ice shelf in Emerald Basin late in isotopic stage 3 during accumulation of Emerald Silt facies A.
4. Calving ice margin with meltwater discharge early in isotopic stage 2 during accumulation of Emerald Silt facies B in Emerald Basin.
5. Late Wisconsinan sea level minimum late in isotopic stage 2, resulting in reworking of shallow bank tops.

Holocene subtidal deposits. The Egmont Sand occurs only in small shallow water areas; the Pugwash Mud occurs in areas where tidal currents are weaker, particularly seaward of major estuaries.

The Baie des Chaleurs, in the northwestern Gulf of St. Lawrence, shows a sequence of glacial till, outwash and glaciomarine sediments unconformably overlain by Holocene sediments (Schafer, 1977). Shell radiocarbon dates provide a chronology for cored sediments directly below the unconformity in which the A/B pollen boundary (Table 10.1, Fig. 10.5) could be dated as about 10.5 ka (Schafer, 1977). Foraminiferal faunas suggest gradual upward shallowing of marine sediments below the unconformity whose surface preserves an intricate deltaic channel system (J.P. Syvitski, pers. comm., 1986). The overlying Holocene sediments are similar to those developed elsewhere in Atlantic Canada during the Holocene transgression (Piper et al., 1983). This sequence represents the effects of a relative sea level history like that of zone B of Quinlan and Beaumont (1981), in which initial regression is followed by transgression (Fig. 10.26). The inflexion point in sea level appears to have occurred about 8 to 9 ka, with a lowering to 20 to 30 m below present datum (Thomas et al., 1973).

A similar geological history was observed in the embayments of the New Brunswick coast between Baie des Chaleurs and Northumberland Strait, including the large Miramichi estuary (Reinson, 1980; Wagner and Schafer, 1980), where prominent barrier systems that developed during the Holocene transgression overlie glacial till and glaciomarine deposits.

Synthesis of glacial history

A tentative glacial history for the Gulf of St. Lawrence can be proposed based partly on an interpretation of the Scotian Shelf data. The age of glacial excavation of the deep troughs is unknown, but the sedimentary record on the Fogo Seamounts indicates a major supply of Carboniferous red sediments during isotopic stage 6 (Alam et al., 1983). Raised beach gravels in the Îles de la Madeleine dating from isotopic stage 5e contain clasts from the Canadian Shield, pointing to an earlier Laurentide glaciation (Grant and King, 1984).

The Îles de la Madeleine have an Early or early Middle Wisconsinan till derived from the Laurentide ice sheet, but were probably unglaciated in later Wisconsinan times (Prest et al., 1976; Grant and King, 1984). Likewise, at least the southwestern edge of Anticosti Island has been ice free since the late Middle Wisconsinan (Gratton et al., 1986). Surficial sediments with a Laurentide provenance are common throughout the gulf (Fig. 10.29). They are mixed with material derived from the Carboniferous bedrock on the Magdalen Shelf (Loring and Nota, 1973). Evidence of grounded ice in the outer Laurentian Channel in the early Middle Wisconsinan (King and Fader, 1986) suggests a widespread grounded Laurentide ice sheet at this time. In the Middle Wisconsinan, a floating ice shelf or iceberg-infested marine embayment may have developed, with a grounding line on Anticosti Island and subglacial streams beneath grounded ice on the Magdalen Shelf building out fan deltas into the Laurentian Channel. Periods of ice break up may be marked by the deposition of brick red diamicts in the outer Laurentian Channel and Laurentian Fan. Proglacial muds, similar to the Emerald Silt, are widespread in the gulf, and modern sedimentation

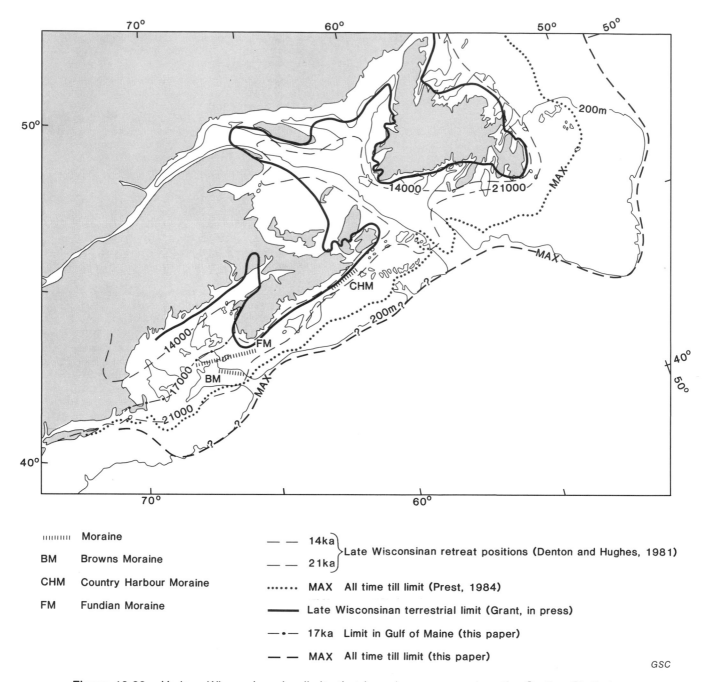

Figure 10.28. Various Wisconsinan ice limits that have been proposed on the Scotian Shelf, (see Addendum).

conditions only developed with the retreat of ice from the shores of the gulf about 12 ka (Prest and Grant, 1969).

Grand Banks of Newfoundland
G.B. Fader and D.J.W. Piper

Physiography

The Grand Banks, off southern and eastern Newfoundland (Map 850-A, in pocket), are a series of shallow outer banks separated by transverse troughs. They are separated from the coast by the deep Avalon Channel and its extension in St. Pierre Channel, and by other irregular inner shelf basins. The largest of the banks is Grand Bank. A marked physiographic change takes place at about 48.5°N (Fig. 10.1) where the shelf becomes substantially deeper and is known as the Northeast Newfoundland Shelf.

Coastal bays and fiords of southern and western Newfoundland are much deeper than corresponding features on the Atlantic coast of Nova Scotia, with water depths in excess of 800 m in Bay D'Espoir. These bays have shallower bedrock sills and their location is controlled by bedrock structure (Fader et al., 1982). The Avalon Channel is

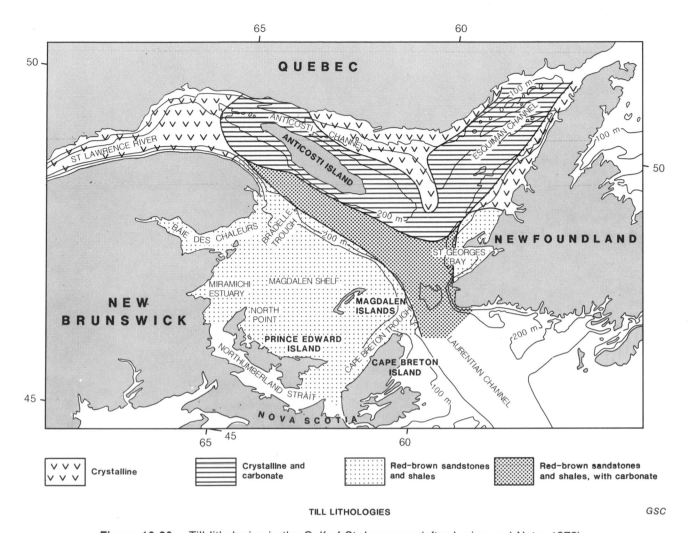

V V V / V V V **Crystalline**	**Crystalline and carbonate**	**Red-brown sandstones and shales**	**Red-brown sandstones and shales, with carbonate**

TILL LITHOLOGIES

GSC

Figure 10.29. Till lithologies in the Gulf of St. Lawrence (after Loring and Nota, 1973).

a deep trough parallel to the coastline off southern Newfoundland and the Avalon Peninsula, that is underlain by Paleozoic sediments (King et al., 1986). Seaward of the Avalon Channel are the transverse troughs of Halibut and Haddock channels and the more isolated Whale Deep and Downing Basin. The Grand Banks are a very broad outer shelf, mostly underlain at shallow depth by Tertiary strata. Remnants of Tertiary cuesta morphology are preserved on the northwestern part of Grand Bank.

Flemish Cap is a submarine knoll in the Atlantic Ocean centred 600 km east of St. John's, Newfoundland. It is roughly circular, about 150 km in diameter at its base, separated from the Grand Banks by Flemish Pass, a submarine saddle some 100 km wide and over 1000 m deep. Seismic refraction studies (Barrett and Keen, 1978) indicate Flemish Cap is underlain by anomalously thin continental crust, with Flemish Pass representing a graben that has been modified by bottom current flow (Kennard, 1982). The top of Flemish Cap is a relatively flat area, 75 km in diameter, with the depth ranging from 126 to 200 m.

Lithostratigraphy

The southern and eastern part of Grand Bank (Fig. 10.30), including the Hibernia area in the northeast, is underlain by Tertiary bedrock at shallow depth (Fader and King, 1981; Fader and Miller, 1986), above which is a sand and gravel unit (Grand Banks Sand and Gravel) that reaches its maximum thickness of 15 m in sand ridges (Barrie et al., 1984). This unit is interpreted as a transgressive deposit similar to the Sable Island Sand and Gravel of the Scotian Shelf. It includes a substantial biogenic component which Müller and Milliman (1973) showed was partly relict Late Wisconsinan material. Slatt (1977) showed that much of the sand and gravel on the outer part of Grand Bank was derived from Tertiary strata; progressive petrological and textural maturity towards the southeast may indicate that much of the sand was derived from glacial outwash from an ice cap lying to the northwest. The sand grains show surface textures indicating reworking in the surf zone (Slatt, 1977). Rounded gravel in the troughs of the sand ridges in some parts of Grand Bank (Fader and Miller, 1986) are largely Lower Paleozoic lithologies from the Avalon Zone of the Avalon Peninsula and inner shelf (King et al., 1986). Thicker Quaternary sections (up to

527

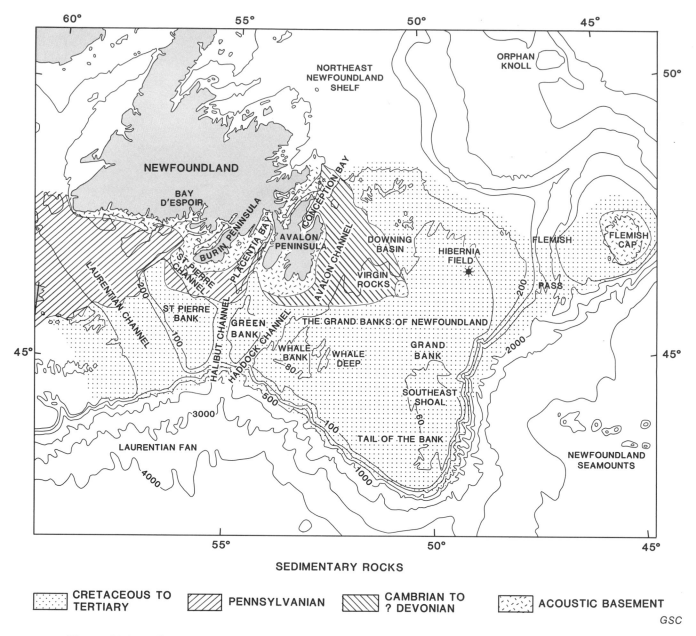

Figure 10.30. Generalized bedrock geology of the Grand Banks of Newfoundland (after Fader and Miller, 1986). See Map 1705A (in pocket) for more detail.

400 m thick) fill channels, most of which are near the eastern edge of the shelf and appear to be headward extensions of submarine canyons on the slope. Filled channels are also numerous beneath St. Pierre, Whale and Green banks (Miller et al., 1983). In the Hibernia area there are a few channels up to 60 m deep, which seismic data suggest are filled with conformable glaciomarine sediment and possibly till. On the southwest edge of Grand Bank (Tail of the Bank to Whale Bank), a surficial sandy mud overlies a 30 m thick complex sequence of probable glaciomarine stratified sediments and till.

Green Bank, Whale Bank and St. Pierre Bank are capped by a megarippled veneer of Grand Banks Sand and Gravel. Haddock and Halibut channels, the transverse

troughs between the banks, are floored by at least three tills interbedded with glaciomarine sediment of probable early Middle Wisconsinan age.[†]

The inner part of Grand Bank is physiographically more complex than its outer part, with the basins of Whale Deep and Downing Basin, the shoals of Virgin Rocks and Eastern Shoals (developed over Precambrian basement), and a highly dissected seafloor northwest of Downing Basin. Over this area the Tertiary bedrock surface is highly irregular, having been cut by channels up to 200 m

---

[†] See Addendum

deep. These channels are probably fluvial developed during Pliocene or Quaternary lowered sea level stands and overdeepened in places by glacial processes. They contain a complex sedimentary fill that on the basis of acoustic evidence includes till (Grand Banks Drift) and interbedded stratified proglacial sediments (Downing Silt). Downing Basin has a thick Late Pleistocene sequence of Downing Silt overlying Grand Banks Drift with lift-off moraines and till tongues similar to those on the Scotian Shelf. The Downing Silt is overlain by thin sandy mud (Placentia Clay) that appears to be a coarse grained equivalent of the LaHave Clay of the Scotian Shelf. Whale Deep has a similar but thinner Late Pleistocene section.

The Avalon Channel is underlain by Paleozoic bedrock and in most places has only a 1 to 5 m thick veneer of till with abundant iceberg scours. Farther west, off Placentia Bay and the south coast of Newfoundland, the Carboniferous bedrock is overlain by a thicker sequence of Grand Banks Drift and Downing Silt (Fader et al., 1982). Unlike the Scotian Shelf, where prominent moraine ridges are widespread, the Grand Banks has few such features. The largest morainic ridge is known as the Burin Moraine along the western flank of Placentia Bay. In this area, a thin development of Downing Silt facies A (analogous to Emerald Silt facies A) suggests that ice shelf conditions persisted for only a short time (King and Fader, 1986). The broad saddles and troughs between the outer banks off southern Newfoundland resulted in the south coast of Newfoundland being more exposed to the open ocean than the more protected middle Scotian Shelf, where an ice shelf persisted much longer.

The least depth on Flemish Cap is 126 m. There granodiorite and Precambrian volcanic rocks outcrop (King et al., 1985). Elsewhere, silty sand and gravel outcrop at the seabed. These sediments show little penetration of seismic energy and have few iceberg scours, suggesting that they may have been overconsolidated. The shallow depth of the cap, its proximity to the glaciated Grand Banks and the possible occurrence of overconsolidated sediment may indicate that Flemish Cap supported its own small ice cap at some time during the Pleistocene.

Chronology

No long cores with systematic biostratigraphic data have been obtained from the Grand Banks. King and Fader (1986) reported some total organic radiocarbon dates from cores in Placentia Bay and in Downing Basin.[†] These cores are well located with respect to seismic stratigraphy, and suggest that ice lift-off had occurred by at least 30 ka and that the thin Downing Silt facies A, representing ice shelf conditions, is older than 22 ka.

Müller and Milliman (1973) and Slatt (1977) obtained radiometric dates from barnacles on the Grand Banks, ranging from 17 100 BP on the outer shelf to modern near Eastern Shoals. They may indicate progressive shoreward deposition of carbonate sediment during the Holocene sea level rise.

Coastal bays of Newfoundland

The coastline of Newfoundland is highly indented, with the development of overdeepened fiords. Several large bays, including Placentia and Conception bays, surround the southeastern part of the island. The location of these fiords and bays is structurally controlled, and some of the coastline corresponds to the margin of Carboniferous basins.

Good seismic stratigraphy is available only from the larger bays, notably Placentia Bay (King and Fader, 1985), where a sequence of Grand Banks Drift, Downing Silt and Placentia Clay is similar to that on the continental shelf. The dates (King and Fader, 1986) suggest that ice retreat occurred in the late Middle Wisconsinan,[†] consistent with the evidence for Late Wisconsinan ice margins on land (Tucker and McCann, 1980). Silts exposed in coastal outcrops at Langlade on the island of Miquelon and on the southern Burin Peninsula (Tucker and McCann, 1980) may date from isotopic stage 5 or may be Downing Silt equivalents. Seismic profiles in the bays of the west coast would provide an excellent opportunity to correlate terrestrial and marine stratigraphy.

Postglacial evolution of coastal bays and fiords has been characterized by falling relative sea level, at least in the early Holocene, along most of the coastline (Quinlan and Beaumont, 1981). Glacial and proglacial sediments were reworked, at least in shallow water, resulting in sedimentological unmixing (Slatt, 1974, 1975; Slatt and Gardiner, 1976; Stehman, 1976), with lag sands and gravels forming in shallow water and muds accumulating in deep basins. Late Holocene relative sea level rise in the south of the island has resulted in some coastal erosion of glacial deposits, and the development of transgressive coastal systems (Forbes, 1984; Brooks et al., 1985).

Synthesis of glacial history

There is good evidence that the entire Grand Banks of Newfoundland were once covered by glacial ice: channels on the outer banks contain strata that acoustically resemble till and proglacial stratified sediment, as well as coarse gravels of Avalon Zone provenance identified on Grand Bank (Fader and Miller, 1986). The age of the glaciation on the outer banks is uncertain; Alam and Piper (1977) suggested it may have been pre-Wisconsinan (isotopic stage 6) on the basis of the age and lithology of sediments accumulating on the nearby Fogo Seamounts. If this is correct, it would account for the maturity of the sands on the outer part of Grand Bank (Slatt, 1977), because they would have undergone periodic transgression and regression throughout the Wisconsinan. On the inner part of Grand Bank, the tills and overlying proglacial sediments are of Wisconsinan age, similar to those on the Scotian Shelf. The tills of Avalon, Haddock and Halibut channels also appear to be of Wisconsinan age and extend across the southwest margin of the Grand Banks to the shelf break.

Deep water areas off southeastern Canada
D.J.W. Piper

Physiography

Deep water areas off southeastern Canada (Fig. 10.15) consist of steep continental slopes seaward of the continental shelf, leading to a lower gradient continental rise, and the

---

[†] See Addendum

almost flat Sohm Abyssal Plain. This "T-shaped" abyssal plain is bounded on the southwest by the New England Seamounts and abyssal hills of the Bermuda Rise, and on the east by the Corner Seamounts. The Fogo Seamounts (Sullivan and Keen, 1977) are a volcanic chain along the Southwest Grand Banks Rise.

The shelf break lies at water depths of 80-100 m off shelf banks, and as deep as 400 m off major saddles and transverse troughs on the shelf. Continental slope gradients are typically in the range of 2 to 4°. Submarine canyons that breach the shelf break (Farre et al., 1983) are common in areas with a shallow shelf break at less than 120 m, and may thus be related to the development of a coastline at the top of the continental slope at times of glacially lowered sea level. Off the major transverse troughs, the upper continental slope is irregular and gullied (Hill, 1983). Areas with the shelf break at intermediate depths are smoother, but also have some slope valley systems (Piper et al., 1985a). In these latter two areas, most gullies and valleys appear to be initiated in about 500 m water depth and may be continuous with the sub-glacially eroded channel system on the outer banks. The walls of larger canyons and valleys are highly dissected into a ridge and gully topography, resembling terrestrial badland topography (Piper et al. 1985a). Areas of continental slope between valleys and gullies are in many places quite smooth; locally slumps and bedding plane slides create a rough topography. Swift (1985a) has shown that slopes seaward of major saddles are rougher and have more continuous valley systems.

Valleys and gullies coalesce on the upper slope, so that only a few large valleys continue to the continental rise. The Laurentian Fan is the only prominent fan-like body on the continental rise; other fans may be present, but have not been investigated in detail. The Western Boundary Undercurrent may play a major role in redistributing sediment along the continental rise and thus modifying turbidite fan morphology (Heezen et al., 1966; Shor et al., 1984).

The Laurentian Fan is similar to many large passive continental margin fans in having a prominent fan-valley system. Two major valleys, Eastern and Western valleys, originate from a zone of gullies on the upper slope, and receive tributary canyons from the Grand Banks Slope to the east. The valleys have asymmetric levees, with the high western levees up to 900 m above the valley floors. This asymmetry is due principally to the action of the Western Boundary Undercurrent (Piper et al., 1984) augmented by Coriolis force. The Eastern Valley is about 20 km wide, and in its lower reaches branches into two distributaries. In the valley termination zone, between the 4500 and 5200 m isobaths, the valleys swing to the east, levee height diminishes rapidly, and the channels open up onto a vast sandy lobe on the northern Sohm Abyssal Plain.

The Sohm Abyssal Plain ranges in depth from 5200 m at the southern edge of the Laurentian Fan to over 5500 m at its southern limit near latitude 32°N. Three major deep sea channel systems lead to the Sohm Abyssal Plain: the fan valleys of the Laurentian Fan from the north, the Northwest Atlantic Mid-Ocean Channel[*] (NAMOC) from the northeast, and an unnamed channel from the northwest that leads from Northeast Channel in the Gulf of Maine. On its southern margins, the Sohm Abyssal Plain onlaps abyssal hills and seamounts to give a very complex bathymetry that has not been mapped in detail.

Late Cenozoic stratigraphic setting

Multichannel seismic data, gathered principally for hydrocarbon exploration, provide a general seismostratigraphic framework for the Quaternary of the continental margin. The widespread erosion, both at the shelf break and in slope valleys (Fig. 10.31), make it difficult to correlate shallow reflectors from one region to another, and the paucity of Quaternary well data makes it difficult to date acoustic markers. Intervalley areas show progradation throughout the Late Pliocene and Quaternary, so that Late Cenozoic seismic stratigraphies (Fig. 10.32) can be established for the western Scotian Slope and Rise (Swift, 1985b), the central Scotian Slope (Piper et al., 1987), the St. Pierre Slope and the Laurentian Fan (Wilson and Piper, 1986).

The best chronology is on the central Scotian Slope, where thick sequences of marine Quaternary sediments in offshore wells on the continental slope provide an opportunity to date Late Pliocene and even Quaternary seismic markers. Gradstein (in Piper et al., 1987) dated the base of the Quaternary in the Acadia K-62 well, and provided a Pliocene stratigraphy for both this well and the Shubenacadie H-100 well (Fig. 10.31). Using multichannel airgun profiles, Piper et al. (1987) have demonstrated that significant canyon cutting on the Scotian Slope began in the Late Pliocene and continued through the Early Quaternary (Fig. 10.32), resulting in decreasing rates of sedimentation on the continental slope as more and more sediment bypassed the slope down the canyons. There is a marked change in style of sedimentation in the middle of the Quaternary sequence (for which there is no biostratigraphic control): in the upper part of the Quaternary at least five stacked till tongues are visible on the upper slope, and these Upper Quaternary sediments thin rapidly downslope.

On the Laurentian Fan and adjacent continental rise a prominent deep reflector (Horizon L, Fig. 10.33), identified by Uchupi and Austin (1979) as marking the approximate base of the Quaternary, is probably of Late Pliocene age on the basis of correlation with the St. Pierre Slope. On the Laurentian Fan, there is an overlying sequence of Lower Pleistocene coarse channel facies, and finer levee-overbank facies up to 2 km thick is deposited from a single fan valley. This valley system built a depositional lobe in about 5000 m water depth, across which the lower levees gradually prograded (Normark et al., 1983). In the Middle Pleistocene the valley pattern on the fan was rearranged,

---

Figure 10.31. Seismic profiles from the Scotian and Southwest Grand Banks slopes showing principal glacial facies. a) Multichannel airgun profile on the western side of Verrill Canyon, showing planar deposition in west, cut and fill in east. Stratigraphy from Piper et al. (1987). b) Shallow mud diapirs on western Scotian Slope. c) Till tongue on slope off St. Pierre Bank.

---

[*] Also known as the Northwest Atlantic Mid-Ocean Canyon

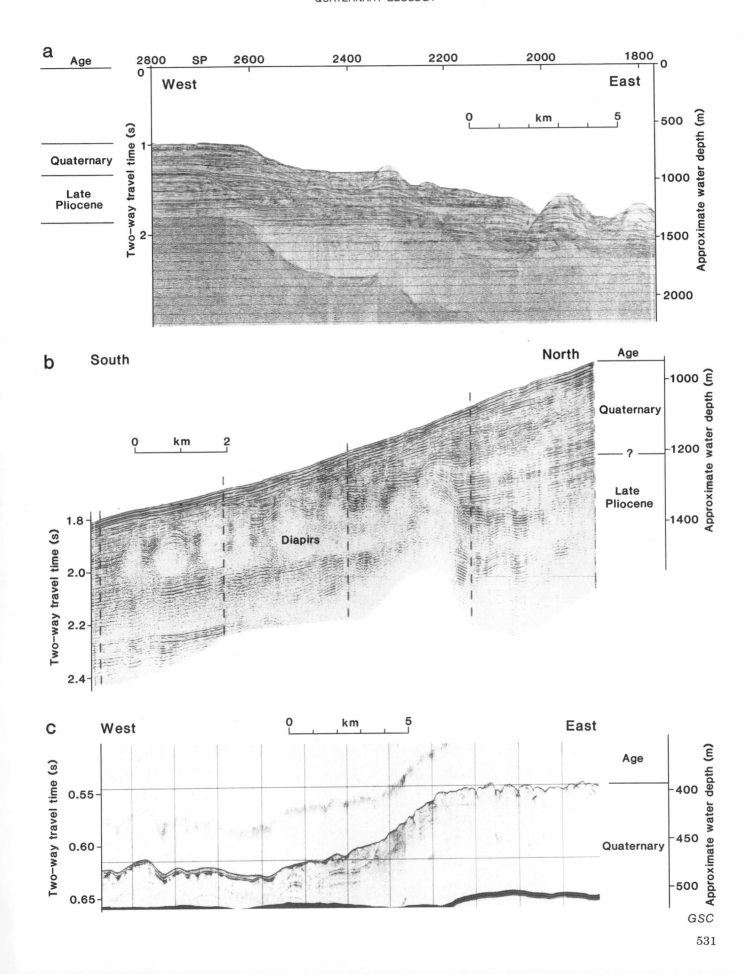

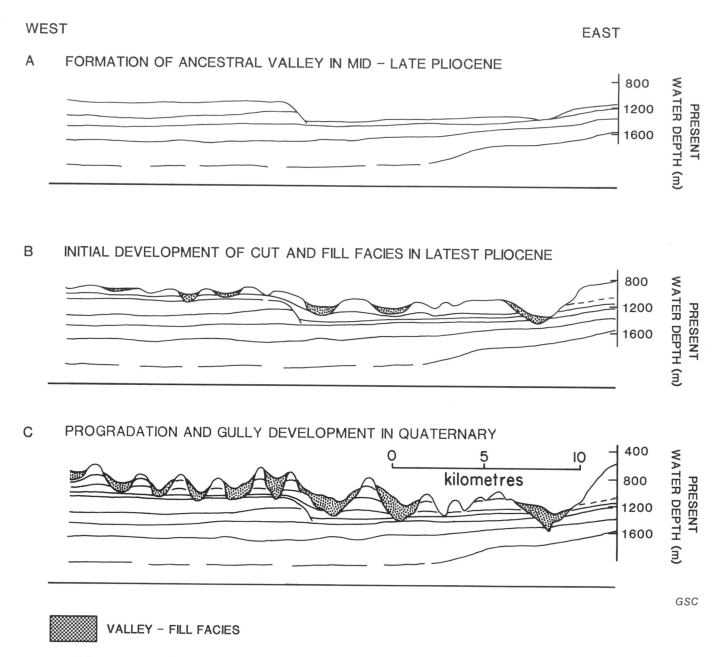

WEST   EAST

A   FORMATION OF ANCESTRAL VALLEY IN MID – LATE PLIOCENE

B   INITIAL DEVELOPMENT OF CUT AND FILL FACIES IN LATEST PLIOCENE

C   PROGRADATION AND GULLY DEVELOPMENT IN QUATERNARY

VALLEY – FILL FACIES

GSC

Figure 10.32. Summary of Late Cenozoic acoustic stratigraphy of the central Scotian Slope (from Piper et al., 1987), showing progressive increase in slope dissection from mid-Late Pliocene to the present.

forming the two main fan valleys present today (Fig. 10.33). This was accompanied by erosional dissection of the upper fan, plugging of parts of the old valley system, and minor deposition on the levees (Piper and Normark, 1982).

Some early seismic reflection profiles across the North Atlantic abyssal plains demonstrated thick accumulations of acoustically stratified sediments (Heezen et al., 1955). These sediments, which are up to 400 m thick in some basins, have been interpreted to be turbidites deposited during Late Cenozoic glacial periods (Laine, 1980; Swift et al., 1986). In DSDP Site 382, on the western margin of the plain, Upper Pliocene and Quaternary turbidites overlie Lower and Middle Pliocene hemipelagic claystones

(Tucholke et al., 1979). The initiation of turbidite deposition probably correlates with the onset of valley cutting on the Scotian Slope.

Lithostratigraphy

Continental slope

In deep water areas, high resolution seismic data are much sparser than on the continental shelf, and almost lacking in water depths greater than 1000 m. Piston cores penetrate only the Late Wisconsinan and Holocene. Two main lithological units have been distinguished (Hill, 1984). Unit I, at the surface, is 1 to 3 m thick and largely of Holo-

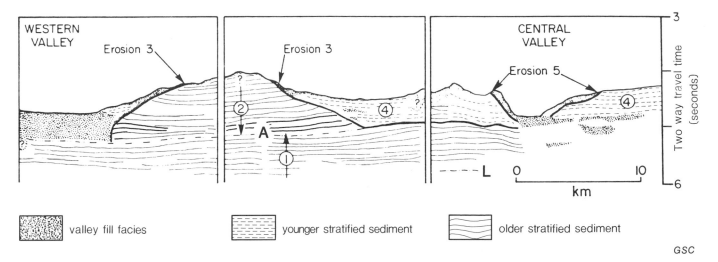

Figure 10.33. Summary of acoustic stratigraphy of the upper Laurentian Fan (from Piper and Normark, 1982), shown on a composite seismic section between the western and central fan valleys. 1. Late Pliocene (?) intervalley sedimentation. 2. Early Pleistocene (?) intervalley sedimentation. 3. Middle Pleistocene erosional event resulting in re-organisation of valley pattern. 4. Middle to Late Pleistocene levee sedimentation. 5. Local Middle to Late Pleistocene valley cut and fill. A and L are correlative reflectors. (One second is approximately equivalent to 1 km).

cene age. This unit grades from sand on the uppermost slope through silt to olive-grey mud in water depths of more than 500 m, and generally ponds in depressions. It consists mainly of reworked shelf sediment, transported by wave and current activity (Hill and Bowen, 1983), and is thus genetically equivalent to the LaHave Clay. The underlying unit II is a complex sequence of reddish and brownish muds and coarser sediments, with sparse microfossil faunas. In areas with slope valleys or gullies, these sediments consist predominantly of proximal sandy turbidites and coarse poorly sorted debris flow deposits (Hill, 1984). Intervalley areas have accumulated laminated muds, many of which appear to be turbidites, but some of which may result from hemipelagic sedimentation dominated by along-slope currents (Hill, 1984). Ice-rafted debris is common in some facies. In some areas, intervalley muds have accumulated several times more rapidly than valley deposits, to give mound-like features on seismic reflection profiles (Piper and Sparkes, 1987). The high sedimentation rates and mound-like features suggest rapid sedimentation from suspension, probably from ice-margin plumes, and by-passing of the continental slope by large amounts of coarse sediment. Sidescan and coring studies have shown that in places, unit II includes large rotational slumps (Piper et al., 1985a) and extensive debris flow deposits. Shale diapirism has affected Wisconsinan sedimentation in places on the mid slope (Fig. 10.31b) (Piper and Sparkes, 1987).

Deeper in the stratigraphic section, lithostratigraphy can only be inferred from seismic reflection profiles (Fig. 10.31, 10.32). The distinction between valley and intervalley sediments recognized in unit II can be applied to many deeper parts of the section. Many intervalley areas have prograded uniformly, with occasional episodes of gullying recognizable in seismic reflection profiles (Piper et al., 1987). Valley areas show a much more complex alternation of cut and fill events, and seismic facies

indicate the presence of coarse valley fill sediments (Fig. 10.31a). Wedges of acoustically unstratified facies interpreted as glacial till underlie the upper slope, thinning downslope and interfingering with stratified sediments (Fig. 10.31c) (Piper et al., 1987). High resolution seismic profiles on the central Scotian Slope show that the shallowest till is laterally equivalent to a gullied horizon about 50 m below seafloor, which is overlain by an unstratified acoustic facies interpreted as sand and gravel filling the gullies (Piper et al., 1985a; Piper and Sparkes, 1987).

The continental slope above the Laurentian Fan consists principally of a chaotic acoustic facies (Meagher, 1984), which shallow cores and submersible observations show to consist of red muds and pebbly muds. Detrital petrology (Stow, 1981) indicates derivation from Lower Paleozoic sediments and the Carboniferous redbeds of the Gulf of St. Lawrence, and the pebbly muds appear to be an ice-rafted facies.

Continental rise

Piston cores (Stow, 1981) and acoustic data (Piper et al., 1985b) from the Laurentian Fan show that the floor of the upper part of Eastern Valley consists of gravel, transported and moulded into large bedforms by the turbidity current triggered by the 1929 Grand Banks earthquake (Piper et al., 1988). Coarse sand is present in the valley termination zone. On the sandy lobe of the northern Sohm Abyssal Plain, a 1 m thick fine sand sheet (dating from 1929: Piper and Aksu, 1987) overlies Holocene pelagic sediments and Upper Wisconsinan turbidite sands, silts and muds (Horn et al., 1971). On the levees of Laurentian Fan, about 1 m of light olive grey hemipelagic muds overlie Late Wisconsinan red-brown turbidite silt-mud couplets (Stow and Bowen, 1980).

The Upper Quaternary sediments of the Scotian and Grand Banks rises are lithologically similar to those of the

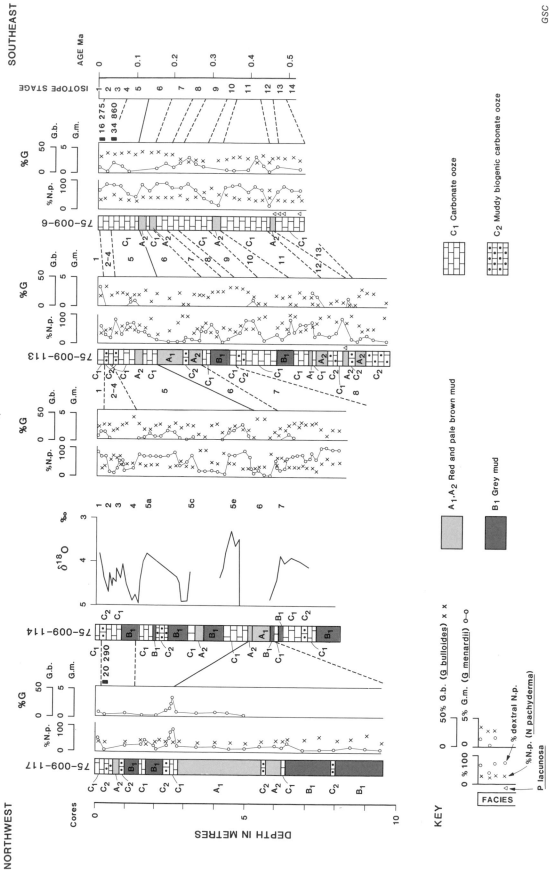

Laurentian Fan (Thomas, 1985). Surface light olive grey muds are 1 to 2 m thick, bioturbated, and contain minor silts (Shor et al., 1984) and rare sands of probable contourite origin (Stow and Lovell, 1979). These overlie 1-2 m of brownish olive-grey mud with some ice-rafted debris. Beneath this are red-brown turbidite muds and silts similar to those on the Laurentian Fan.

The Fogo Seamounts, which lie between the Laurentian Fan and the Grand Banks, are capped by thin Pliocene and Quaternary pelagic sediments, with interglacial biogenic ooze alternating with glacial muds (Alam et al., 1983).

Ice-rafting is widespread in the Late Wisconsinan and Early Holocene of the Scotian Slope and Rise (Piper, 1975b; Stow, 1977, 1978, 1981). In addition to thin "brick red" granular mud horizons near the Laurentian Channel, coarse sand and gravel are scattered throughout the sedimentary sequence, most abundantly on the upper continental slope. Ice-rafted gravels at the end of Laurentian Channel are made up of 70 % red and grey sandstone, limestone and dolomite and 30 % crystalline igneous and metamorphic rock from Gulf of St. Lawrence and adjacent Quebec and Newfoundland. Farther southwest on the Scotian Slope and Rise the clasts are replaced by a granite-quartzite-slate assemblage that was derived from the granites and Meguma Group of Nova Scotia. Comparison of potential source areas and continental margin sediments suggests that sands and silts were dominantly dispersed perpendicularly to the shelf break, possibly from separate ice tongues (Stow, 1981). Clay mineralogy, as a result of probable current transport, shows a general uniformity over the whole Scotian margin with minor variations in kaolinite and montmorillonite content.

Sohm Abyssal Plain
D.E. Buckley

Upper Wisconsinan sediments of the northern Sohm Abyssal Plain consist of turbidite sands and interbedded muds (Horn et al., 1971). At the southern extremity of the Sohm Abyssal Plain, Upper Wisconsinan turbidite muds overlie a thick and continuous layer of sand buried 10 to 13 m below the seafloor (Buckley, 1981). The surface textures of quartz grains in this deposit indicate that the sands were mainly derived from glacial till and were transported more than 1000 km as grain-flows or in suspension in a major turbidity current (Wang et al., 1982). Detrital coal demonstrates that the source of the sands included the area adjacent to the Laurentian Channel on the Scotian Shelf (Hacquebard et al., 1981). Although most sediment probably reached the Sohm Abyssal Plain across the Laurentian Fan, both the Northwest Atlantic Mid-Ocean Channel and the large channel leading from the continental slope off the Gulf of Maine probably contributed sediment to the plain during the Late Pleistocene.

Chronology

The details of the glacial history of the Scotian margin are poorly known. The most reliable chronostratigraphic information comes from deep water sections that contain oxygen isotope and biostratigraphic markers correlative with the deep-water biostratigraphic record established in DSDP holes. Such data (Fig. 10.34) exist for the Fogo Seamounts (Piper, 1975a; Alam et al., 1983). Closer to the continental shelf both biostratigraphic markers and oxygen isotopes are influenced by former ice sheets and are more difficult to interpret. Ice-rafted sediments on the Fogo Seamounts date back to the middle Pliocene (Piper, 1975a), similar to the record in the Labrador Sea (Berggren, 1972). At the margin of the Sohm Abyssal Plain, middle Pliocene biogenic sedimentation changes to Upper Pliocene turbidites at DSDP site 382; on the Scotian Slope, Late Pliocene and Quaternary sedimentation rates are much higher than those for the Late Tertiary (Piper et al., 1986b). A major unconformity separates Quaternary from Upper Tertiary sediments on the Scotian Shelf and Grand Banks. These changes in sedimentation pattern probably reflect frequent lowering of sea level beginning in the Late Pliocene that allowed transport of fluvial sediment to the shelf edge. Seismic reflection profiles from the Scotian Slope (Piper et al., 1987) suggest that the first major advance of ice sheets across the continental shelf occurred in the Middle Pleistocene.

The first direct evidence for glaciation in southeast Canada was found in cores from the Fogo Seamounts at isotopic stage 6, where clays contain abundant glacial sand grains apparently derived from the Grand Banks (Alam and Piper, 1977). The sediment record in the Fogo Seamounts suggests that the isotopic stage 6 glaciation had a much greater sediment yield from the Carboniferous basins around the Gulf of St. Lawrence than any other Pleistocene glaciation, at least since isotopic stage 13 (Alam et al., 1983).

Few cores in the terrigenous sediments of the continental slope and rise appear to penetrate beyond the Late Wisconsinan; the high rates of terrigenous sedimentation resulted in extreme dilution of biogenic material. A series of shell radiocarbon dates from the slope near Verrill Canyon (Mosher, 1986) indicate high sedimentation rates of about 1 m/ka prior to 13 ka, with sediments dating from 18 ka at about 8 m subbottom. The underlying wedges of diamict on the upper slope correlate with the extensive Early Wisconsinan ice advance on the Scotian Shelf, and thus provide a general Wisconsinan stratigraphic marker on the continental slope. The thickness of Wisconsinan

Figure 10.34. Composite lithostratigraphic and biostratigraphic sections of four cores from the Fogo Seamounts (after Alam et al., 1983), showing the decrease in terrigenous mud deposits and reduction in sedimentation rates with distance offshore (i.e. from northwest to southeast). The graphs of planktonic foraminiferal relative abundances also demonstrate the increasing importance of warm water species with distance offshore: % N.p. = *Neogloboquadrina pachyderma*, where crosses denote percentage of total planktonic forams and circles denote *N. pachyderma*; G.m. = % *Globoratalia menardii* + *G. tumida*; G.b. = % *Globigerina bulloides*. Triangles denote the presence of the coccolith species *Pseudoemiliania lacunosa* which has its range top in isotopic stage 12. Oxygen isotopic data ($\delta^{18}O$ in ‰) for Core 114 were obtained from the benthic foraminifera *Uvigerina perigrina* and they indicate glacial-interglacial changes in bottom water conditions; isotopic stages shown for the other cores are interpretations based on lithofacies correlation and changes in the abundance of warm water foraminifera.

sediments on the rise is unknown. Stow (1977) obtained a total carbonate date of 15 510 ± 530 BP (GX-4780) near the base of the biogenic olive-grey sediments on the Scotian Rise, and tentatively identified a magnetic reversal event (?the Lake Mungo event) 1.5 m below this, at the boundary between brownish olive-grey muds with ice-rafted debris and the underlying red-brown turbidite muds. A date of 8955 ± 280 BP (GX-4779) was obtained from the base of the olive-grey biogenic mud sequence on the Laurentian Fan. Interglacial (isotopic stage 5e) sediments were identified in one core from which the Wisconsinan section had been removed by erosion. The immediately underlying sediments were brown-grey muds with abundant gravel clasts. A cyclical sequence of glacial sediments can thus be recognized. Glacial maxima on the continental shelf correspond to times of maximum sand supply to the deep sea. These sands are interbedded with and are overlain by red-brown turbidite muds. The final stages of glacial retreat are marked by brownish olive muds with substantial ice-rafted debris. In areas of shallow shelf break, coarse sediments also accumulated during the Late Wisconsinan minimum stand of sea level. Biogenic olive-grey muds are deposited in interglacials. Turbidite processes appear to have persisted longer into the Late Wisconsinan on the Laurentian Fan than on the Scotian Margin.

Vilks et al. (1985) distinguished between Pleistocene glacial age sediments and the typical interglacial sediments of Holocene age on the Sohm Abyssal Plain. Turbidity currents frequently supplied sediments from the continental margin off eastern Canada during glacial times, but only rare graded sequences are identified in the Holocene section. A thick sand of Middle Wisconsinan age was identified on the distal Sohm Abyssal Plain. Rates of sediment accumulations varied greatly; average rates probably exceeded 1.2 m/ka during part of the Pleistocene and 0.15 m/ka during the Holocene. Sediments deposited during periods of low deposition rates between major turbidite events were probably derived from local seamounts and abyssal platforms. Stanley and Taylor (1981) and Stanley et al. (1981) identified volcanic detritus from local sources in the northwest Atlantic in sediments on the Sohm Abyssal Plain. Biscaye and Eittreim (1977) provided evidence that large quantities of suspended sediments were transported in the nepheloid layer across the northern and central parts of the Sohm Abyssal Plain. The direction of transport of the nepheloid layer is generally determined by the dominant deep ocean currents, such as the Western Boundary Undercurrent, which is capable of carrying fine grained sediments from the Labrador Sea to the Bermuda Rise (Laine, 1980). Oceanographic "storms", such as described by Hollister and McCave (1984) on the Scotian Rise, might also erode some of the areas of pelagic sediment adjacent to the Sohm Abyssal Plain. This would account for the Holocene deposition of carbonate-rich sediments containing subtropical planktonic foraminifers on the southern Sohm Abyssal Plain (Vilks et al., 1985).

THE LABRADOR SEA REGION

Northeast Newfoundland Shelf

D.J.W. Piper, G.B. Fader, and P.J. Mudie

The Northeast Newfoundland Shelf (Fig. 10.35) has two deep outer banks in water depths of 200-300 m, bounded by deep transverse troughs with unusually complex mor-

phology. Warren (1976) ascribed this complexity in part to subglacial meltwater streams. The mid-shelf area includes the St. Anthony Basin, 460 m deep, which appears to be a continuation of the Labrador Marginal Trough. The inner shelf is physiographically complex, reflecting the varied bedrock of the area (Dale and Haworth, 1979).

The Northeast Newfoundland Shelf is considerably deeper than the shelf areas off southern Newfoundland and Nova Scotia. An acoustic stratigraphic sequence has been defined on the inner part of the shelf in Notre Dame Bay (Dale, 1979; Dale and Haworth, 1979). Till is overlain by stratified sediments which in turn are overlain by acoustically transparent muds. Piston cores (Dale, 1979; Mudie and Guilbault, 1982; Scott et al., 1984b) show the following stratigraphic sequence from the top down. Olive-grey mud, locally with ice-rafted debris, corresponds to the surficial acoustically transparent unit whereas the stratified acoustic unit correlates with a 6 m thick sequence of muds in which ice-rafted debris is common, and this sequence overlies 2 m of banded, diatomaceous mud and a thin, stratified stiff till. Unsorted stiff red till, lacking microfossils, was sampled at the bottom of cores. Two total organic radiocarbon dates (25 490 + 1570 -1310 BP, GX6404 and 21 980 ± 1135 BP, GX7763) from near the bottom of the diatomaceous unit, when corrected for dead carbon, suggest an age of 17 to 18 ka (Mudie and Guilbault, 1982). Within the stratified acoustic unit, the pollen record is poor and dinoflagellates are rare or absent, although cyst type P, an organic walled cyst now abundant only in parts of arctic Canada, is common. Benthic foraminifers are represented by the *Cassidulina reniforme* and *Elphidium excavatum* f. *clavata* assemblage zones (Fig. 10.4, Table 10.3). The absence of pollen and dinoflagellates and the abundance of ice rafted debris suggests an ice-proximal depositional site. The banded diatomaceous sediments suggest periodic upwelling of nutrient-rich water at a floating ice margin (Foldvik and Kvinge, 1977). The olive-grey muds, corresponding to the surface acoustically transparent unit, have a maximum estimated age of 10 ka on the basis of total organic radiocarbon dating (9185 ± 359 BP, GX7765 and 9525 ± 315 BP, GX7764) (Mudie and Guilbault, 1982). Within this unit benthic foraminifera (Fig. 10.4) reflect the establishment of the Labrador current and the recent cooling of inner shelf waters. Dinocyst zone L reflects an environment similar to the present day offshore Labrador Shelf, and the uppermost zone M reflects the recent inner shelf cooling (Table 10.3).

The outer shelf is less well known. Reconnaissance seismic profiles indicate that till extends in the troughs to the shelf break. Off Conception Bay the till forms a series of transverse ridges up to 15 m high. Ice scouring is widespread and has disrupted the seabed stratigraphy. Piper et al. (1978) proposed a tentative biostratigraphy from short gravity cores in Bonavista Channel that probably represents a sequence similar to that in Notre Dame Bay. There appears to have been grounded ice on the inner part of the Northeast Newfoundland Shelf in the Late Wisconsinan, and cores from Orphan Basin suggest that ice margin conditions may have existed at the continental shelf edge in Middle Wisconsinan time.

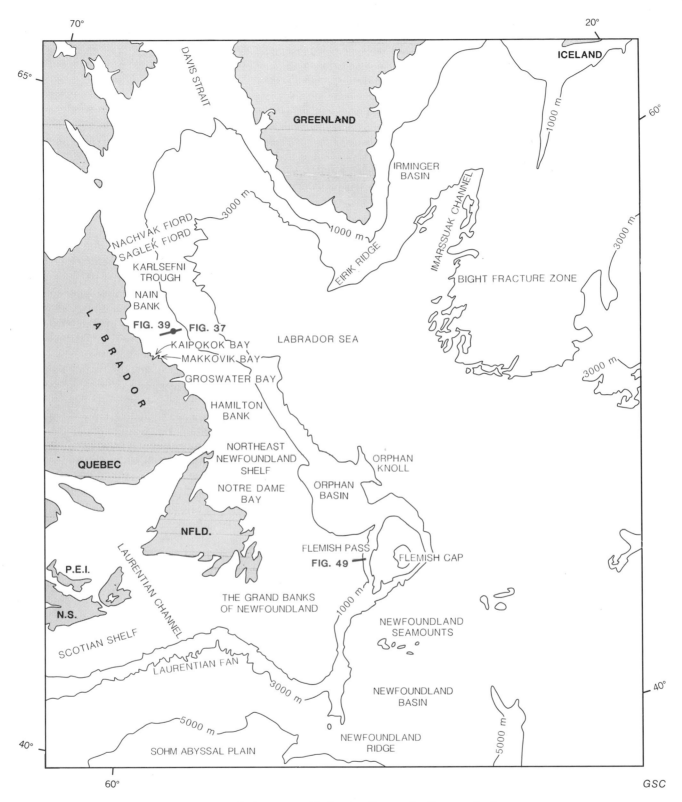

Figure 10.35. Index map of Labrador Sea and adjacent shelf areas.

GSC

Labrador Shelf

H. W. Josenhans

Physiography

The Labrador Shelf (Map 850-A, in pocket) consists of an outer shelf of banks and saddles separated from an irregular inner shelf by a deep marginal trough marking the boundary between the Precambrian rocks of Labrador and the Cretaceous-Cenozoic continental margin sediment wedge (Fig. 10.36). The banks are relatively flat-topped and 120-200 m deep. The saddles are typically 400-500 m deep and shoal seawards from the marginal trough, which reaches maximum depths of 800 m.

Lithostratigraphy

Quaternary acoustic sediment facies are distinguished using criteria similar to those for the Scotian Shelf. Diamicts interpreted as glacial till extend to 600 m water depth at the edge of the continental shelf some 150 km offshore, and are overlain by a sequence of proglacial and postglacial sediments that are thickest in the saddles. Till overlies a sequence of mudstones with a prograding depositional style on seismic reflection profiles (Fig. 10.37). This sequence is known informally as the "prograde sequence" and its acoustic character suggests that it probably consists of preglacial or proglacial deltaic deposits. Correlation with the Labrador Sea basin suggests that the prograde sequence is of Early to Middle Pleistocene age (Myers, 1986). Tertiary strata outcrop locally on the western margin of the banks.

Three distinct tills make up the Labrador Shelf Drift. The Lower Till (Fig. 10.37) is composite, extends across the entire shelf, and passes into stratified proglacial sediments at about 600 m water depth on the upper slope. Lower parts of this composite till are discontinuous, and have been removed by erosion in the deepest parts of the saddles, where the younger tills rest directly on bedrock. The Lower Till appears to be the most highly consolidated of the tills, and has to date not been well sampled.

The Upper Till extends across the inner shelf to the western margins of the outer banks, and extends farther eastwards as lobes through the saddles (3B in Fig. 10.38). The Upper Till is not found in water depths of less than 100 m on the bank tops. The contact with the Lower Till is smooth, suggesting that it resulted from planar glacial erosion. The upper surface of the Upper Till is undulating and iceberg scoured. On the landward side of the marginal trough off northern Labrador and in isolated areas off southern Labrador, a discontinuous linear moraine system is cored by Lower Till and mantled and built up by Upper Till. It may represent a persistent grounding line during ice retreat. The Upper Till is only slightly overconsolidated. It comprises clasts of crystalline rocks, apparently from Labrador, in a finer matrix derived largely from the Tertiary strata of the continental shelf. The upper half metre appears to have been reworked, probably by a calving ice margin or icebergs, and contains rare abraded foraminifers and lithic carbonate clasts.

The Hudson Strait Till (3C in Fig. 10.38) is found only near the mouth of Hudson Strait, where it overlies stratified proglacial silts that rest on the Upper Till. In water depths of less than 610 m the sediments beneath the till are deformed, suggesting that the ice was grounded to that depth. This till contains abundant carbonate clasts throughout.

The Qeovik Silt (Fig. 10.39), overlying the Upper Till, is characterized by a conformable depositional style that mimics the morphology of the underlying till surface. In the lower part of the unit, reflectors are discontinuous, but in the upper part continuous coherent reflectors can be traced for tens of kilometres. The unit has a maximum thickness of 40 m in deep-water areas of the saddles and marginal trough. It pinches out against bathymetric highs on the inner shelf and against the outer banks. It is thicker on the southern side of saddles, probably reflecting regional current flow from the north. The sediment is a poorly sorted, silty sandy mud commonly with coarser ice-rafted debris. Lithic carbonate is a characteristic of the silt, making up 60-80% of the sand sized fraction near Hudson Strait, decreasing to 30-60% on the central Labrador Shelf.

The Makkaq Clay overlies the Qeovik Silt and is well but finely stratified and nearly transparent on acoustic records. It has a ponded style, and is restricted to the deeper parts of the saddles and marginal trough. In Cartwright and Hopedale saddles, it occurs only in water depths greater than 400 m, whereas in Karlsefni Trough it is ponded in water depths as shallow as 175 m. Although generally less than 10 m thick, it locally reaches 30 m thickness. The sediment consists of bioturbated olive grey mud with rare coarser ice-rafted debris. Lithic carbonate is rare.

The Sioraq Sand occurs only on the bank edges and tops. Acoustically it is a weakly stratified to homogenous unit consisting of a fine or muddy sand with some gravel. It forms a thin discontinuous veneer over till on the outer banks. It is derived from a mixture of till and ice-rafted debris reworked by icebergs, storm waves and currents. It is thickest down-current from topographic highs, and it has a higher mud content in water depths greater than 100 m. The Sioraq Sand appears to be coeval with the Makkaq Clay.

Biostratigraphy and chronology

Numerous radiocarbon dates are available for the Labrador Shelf, but they show many inconsistencies.[†] Particular problems arise from the occurrence of reworked dead carbon and the widespread iceberg scouring (and potential for reworking) in the Qeovik Silt. In Cartwright Saddle, total organic radiocarbon dates show a steady increase in age with depth (Vilks, 1980) to a maximum of 21 050 BP about half-way down the Qeovik Silt section. Two total organic radiocarbon dates of about 12 ka (Josenhans et al., 1986) deeper in the section may either have been contaminated or indicate that the dates reported by Vilks were influenced by dead carbon. Off Saglek Fiord, in an ice-scoured sequence of Upper Till and overlying Qeovik

---

[†] See Addendum

Figure 10.36. Distribution of Labrador Shelf acoustic stratigraphic units defined in text. The area designated as unit 1 acoustic basement typically has a veneer of undifferentiated glacial and postglacial sediments less than 10 m total thickness.

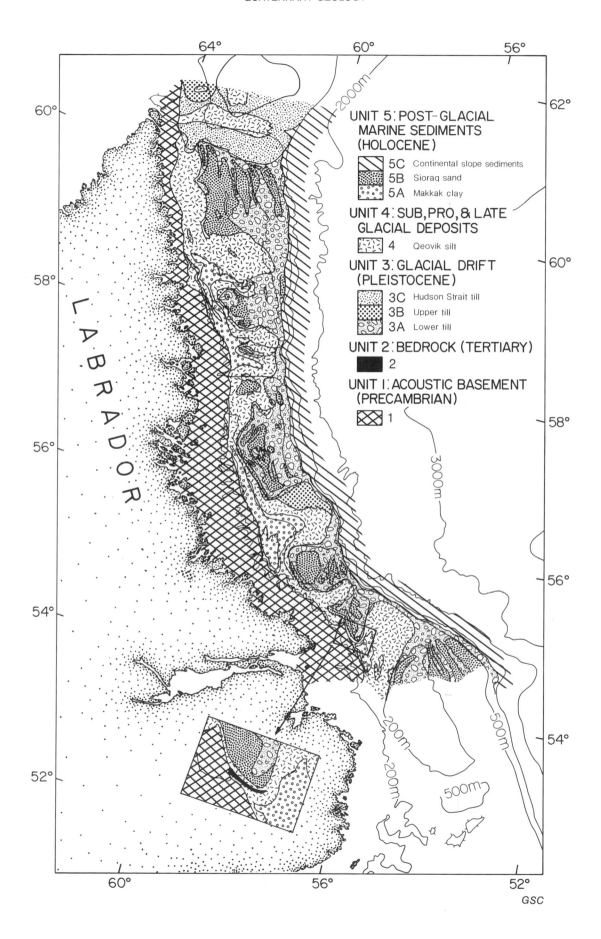

UNIT 5: POST-GLACIAL
MARINE SEDIMENTS
(HOLOCENE)

5C	Continental slope sediments
5B	Sioraq sand
5A	Makkak clay

UNIT 4: SUB, PRO, & LATE
GLACIAL DEPOSITS

4	Qeovik silt

UNIT 3: GLACIAL DRIFT
(PLEISTOCENE)

3C	Hudson Strait till
3B	Upper till
3A	Lower till

UNIT 2: BEDROCK (TERTIARY)

2	

UNIT 1: ACOUSTIC BASEMENT
(PRECAMBRIAN)

1	

LABRADOR

GSC

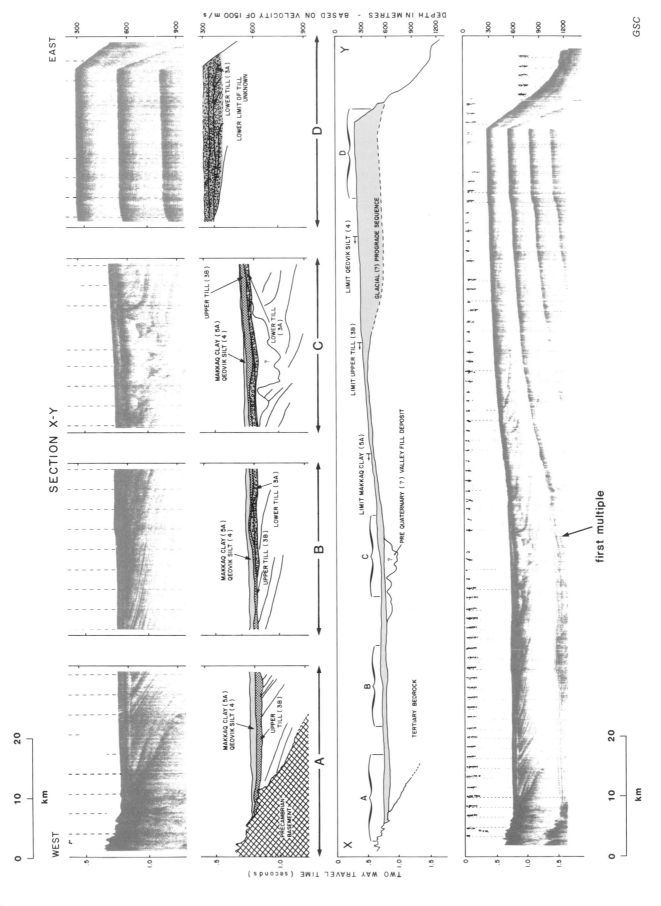

SECTION X-Y

Silt, shells from near the base of the Qeovik Silt yielded a date of 31 400 ± 430 BP (B-11192). The top of the Upper Till, however, gave a total organic radiocarbon date of about 10 ka. A series of total organic radiocarbon dates from Hopedale Saddle range from 20 to 25 ka for the top of the Upper Till to 10 to 15 ka for the lower part of the Qeovik Silt. Throughout the Labrador Shelf, the base of the Makkaq Clay appears to date from about 8 ka (Josenhans et al., 1986).

The biostratigraphic section in Cartwright Saddle (Fig. 10.4, Table 10.4) can be linked to that established farther south on the eastern Canadian margin (Scott et al., 1984b). Pollen is relatively rare within the Qeovik Silt, and dominated by *Sphagnum* and *Betula*, indicating nearby arctic tundra conditions (Vilks and Mudie, 1978). The *Elphidium excavatum* foraminiferal ecozone in the Qeovik Silt indicates proglacial conditions, replaced by Outer Labrador Current Water (with increased abundance of *Neogloboquadrina pachyderma*) in the upper Qeovik Silt. Most microfossil groups show significant changes at the boundary with the Makkaq Clay, with the establishment of the *Nonionellina labradorica* assemblage zone and the appearance of abundant pollen of zone CS2, but the CN dinocyst assemblage zone extends across the boundary. Similar foraminiferal ecozones have been recognized in cores from the central and northern Labrador Shelf.

Coastal inlets and fiords

The coastline of Labrador is highly dissected, with innumerable inlets, islands and shoals. The outer coastline is almost bare of sediment (Vilks et al., 1982), but thick sediment sequences are found in more sheltered waters of the fiords and their nearshore extensions. Detailed studies have been made of Hamilton Inlet (including Lake Melville) in southern Labrador, Makkovik and Kaipokok bays in central Labrador, and Nachvak and Saglek fiords in northern Labrador (Fig. 10.35).

Hamilton Inlet
G. Vilks

The Hamilton Inlet system of Groswater Bay, the Narrows, Lake Melville and Goose Bay extends 250 km inland from the Labrador coastline and is sufficiently large to have influenced the regional Quaternary geology. The surrounding terrain shows evidence that the Hamilton Inlet basin modified the regional westward flow of glacial ice (Fulton and Hodgson, 1979). The axis of the basin contains a narrow trough cut in Cambrian-Precambrian basement that is overdeepened to almost 600 m below present sea level. It is filled with up to 400 m of unconsolidated sediment (Grant, 1975). Outside this trough the sediment is up to 40 m thick. High resolution seismic profiles show that this sediment consists of discontinuous till deposits in isolated bedrock depressions, overlain by intermittently laminated, proximal glaciolacustrine or glaciomarine sediments. These grade distally to continuous sequences of

closely spaced, strong acoustic reflectors within the axial trough probably corresponding to turbidites. The postglacial sediments settle from an effluent plume from the Churchill River that covers the whole of Lake Melville above the pycknocline. This process has produced the acoustically transparent unit conformably draping the sediments below.

Piston cores that penetrated the acoustically transparent unit of postglacial sediments show foraminiferal, lithological and geochemical changes which reflect the processes of deglaciation and environmental changes in response to progressively shallowing sill depths (Vilks and Mudie, 1983). A whole shell ^{14}C date from the top of the stratified late glacial sediments gave a date of 7970 ± 90 BP (TO-200). The stratified glaciomarine sediments are sharply laminated and virtually barren of foraminifera. δ^{13}C values from these sediments are typical of present day soils in the Goose Bay region, suggesting accumulation in a lacustrine environment (Tan and Vilks, 1987). These late glacial muds grade upwards to bioturbated postglacial sediments containing calcareous foraminifera and smaller δ^{13}C deficiency, indicating the addition of marine biogenic carbon. Towards the top of the cores the calcareous foraminifera are replaced by arenaceous species, reflecting the shoaling of the entrance to the lake with isostatic rebound. The salinity of bottom waters of Lake Melville is 4‰ lower than the salinity of the waters of the Labrador Shelf.

Lake Melville contains no massive tills, but does include thick sequences of glaciomarine or glaciolacustrine deposits, suggesting that the Lake Melville basin acted as a depocentre for debris from calving ice and meltwater during deglaciation. The Lake Melville basin appears to have contained fresh water during deglaciation, despite isostatic depression producing a much deeper and wider channel at the entrance to the lake than at the present. It is possible that the estuarine return flow of bottom water was not saline because the whole inner Labrador Shelf contained a wedge of fresh water during the period of maximum meltwater production. In Groswater Bay on the inner shelf, Vilks et al. (1982) also found stratified sediments barren of foraminifera at the bottom of piston cores, possibly indicating freshwater conditions.

Central Labrador fiords
D.J.W. Piper

Quaternary marine geology is well known in only two fiords in central Labrador, Makkovik and Kaipokok bays (Barrie and Piper, 1982; Kontopoulos and Piper, 1982b). The bays have low relief, with maximum water depths of about 100 m. They are divided into several bedrock basins, and are separated from the Labrador Shelf by shallow bedrock sills and a broad zone of shoals and islands. Till deposits on land are thin. Late Wisconsinan ice probably extended at least to the present coastline.

Three main acoustic stratigraphic units can be distinguished in both fiords. Possible glacial till is overlain by features resembling lift-off moraines and by stratified coarse sediment which fills basins and was interpreted as proglacial or ice-margin delta and turbidite deposits. These are overlain by a thick sequence of muds draped over pre-existing topography and correlated with the Qeovik Silt offshore. The muds contain outer-bay to inner-shelf

---

Figure 10.37. Interpreted air gun seismic reflection profile across central Labrador shelf near Hopedale Saddle showing distribution of acoustic stratigraphic units. Figure 10.35 shows profile location.

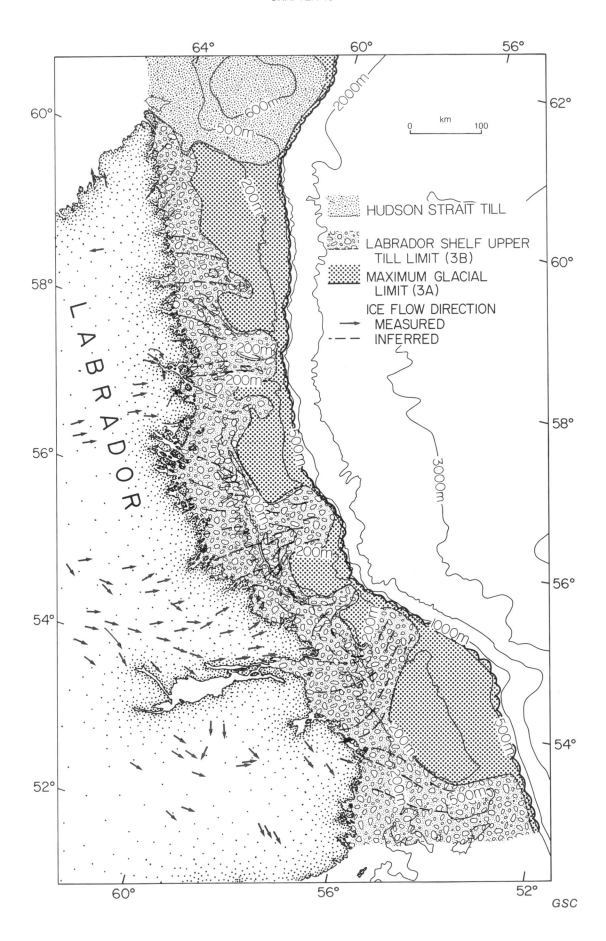

GSC

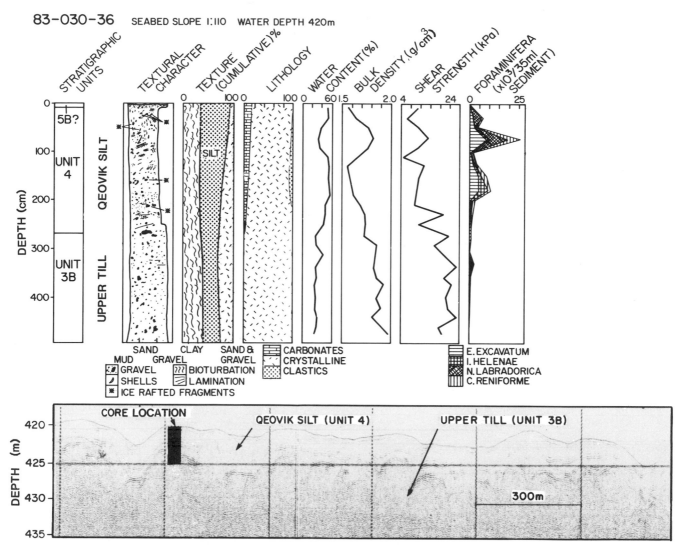

Figure 10.39. Stratigraphy of core 83-030-36 in Hopedale Saddle, through Qeovik silt and Upper till. Accompanying seismic reflection profile shows regional setting. Core location is shown in Figure 10.35. Names of foraminifera taxa given in Table 10.3.

GSC

foraminiferal assemblages, reflecting a highly stratified estuarine circulation with run-off dominated deposition from a surface freshwater plume. Foraminifera from this unit yielded a radiocarbon age of 10 275 ± 225 BP (GX-6345) indicating an ice-free coast at that time. The overlying Holocene basin-fill sediments usually have a ponded acoustic style and are correlated with the offshore Makkaq Clay. The relative importance of sediment supply from run off and from wave reworking of marine sediments varies with age and location within the fiord. A widespread erosional unconformity within the basin muds dated by total organic carbon between 7475 ± 160 BP (GX-5811) and

Figure 10.38. Inferred ice flow directions and lateral extent of major Labrador shelf glacial advances. 3A — Lower till; 3B Upper till; 3C — Hudson Strait till. Terrestrial ice flow data from Vincent (in press a).

5690 ± 280 BP (GX-6346) may be related to increased storm wave action during the Holocene hypsithermal.

Northern Labrador fiords

H.W. Josenhans and D.J.W. Piper

Recent work on land in northern Labrador by Clark (1984) and Evans (1984) has shown evidence for two Wisconsinan advances of the Laurentide ice sheet in this area. The older deposited the Iron Strand drift and the inferred ice profile suggests that the ice extended at least 25-50 km onto Saglek Bank. Marine sediments that overlie the Iron Strand drift appear to be Middle Wisconsinan in age on the basis of radiocarbon dates and amino acid stratigraphy (Andrews and Miller, 1984). The younger advance (the Saglek glaciation of Ives, 1958) built a prominent morainal system at elevations of over 200 m on land, but left higher areas ice free. Clark and Josenhans (1986) suggested that the observed ice profile on land could allow the Saglek glaciers to extend offshore through the saddles to the shelf edge, provided the ice had a low basal shear stress above older marine sediments. The Saglek glaciation appears to be Late Wisconsinan in age, and its deposits are overlain by young glaciomarine sediments offshore and at one coastal locality (Løken, 1962).

Acoustic data from Saglek fiord show from bottom to top: bedrock; a lower till overlying bedrock; more than 50 m of stratified sediment; a 20-40 m thick upper till; and a surface unit of stratified sediment, 40 m thick. The lower till is correlated with the Iron Strand drift and the upper till with grounded ice of the Saglek glaciation, although this chronology remains to be confirmed by detailed studies. No well-defined stratigraphic continuity extends from the fiords to the continental shelf, although isolated sections on seismic records suggest correlation may be possible. No morainal system was observed offshore that might mark the limit of the Saglek glaciation. The till ridge on the landward side of the Marginal Trough does not appear to be a terminal moraine, as both the Lower and Upper tills of the continental shelf can be traced across it.

Synthesis of glacial history

The Lower Till marks one or more major extensions of grounded ice across the entire Labrador Shelf, and is older than Late Wisconsinan. The smooth, sharp contact between the Lower and Upper tills is interpreted to be erosional, resulting from a glacial readvance preceding deposition of the Upper Till, that completely removed the Lower Till on part of the inner shelf in water depths as great as 750 m. This thick ice mass that deposited the Upper Till was largely restricted to the inner shelf and saddles; it does not appear to have extended onto the banks. Deposition of the Upper Till took place during ice retreat while a significant amount of ice was hydrostatically supported, since the till is only slightly overconsolidated and its upper surface is undulatory and ice scoured.

The ages of the Lower and Upper tills remain a major uncertainty.[†] Is the Upper Till of Late Wisconsinan age, thus corresponding to the Saglek glaciation of northern Labrador, or is it of Middle Wisconsinan age, corresponding to the Iron Strand glaciation? In turn, is the Lower Till of Wisconsinan or older age? The evidence favouring a Middle Wisconsinan age for the Upper Till (and hence probably a pre-Wisconsinan age for the Lower Till) includes the consistent total organic radiocarbon chronology of the Cartwright Saddle cores by Vilks (1980) and their biostratigraphic correlation with the Northeast Newfoundland Shelf (Scott et al., 1984b), and the 31.4 ka shell date from near the base of the Qeovik Silt. The evidence favouring a Late Wisconsinan age for the Upper Till (and hence a Middle Wisconsinan age for at least part of the Lower Till) includes the numerous relatively young total organic radiocarbon dates from the Upper Till and lower Qeovik Silt, and the consistent abundance of carbonate detritus in the Qeovik Silt, that is most easily related to deglaciation of Hudson Strait (Josenhans et al., 1986).

The abrupt appearance of detrital carbonate in the Qeovik Silt indicates substantial supply of ice-rafted carbonate sediment immediately following ice recession.

Although carbonate from Hudson Bay might have occurred as englacial material in ice that flowed over Labrador, the lack of carbonate in ablation till on land suggests that Labradorean ice did not traverse a limestone area. Carbonate erratics are found only up to the marine limit, indicating transport by ice rafting, not by glaciers. The most likely source of the lithic carbonate is Hudson Strait, although other possible sources include Ungava Bay, Foxe Basin, and the eastern islands of the Arctic Archipelago. This implies deposition under open water conditions, not from beneath an iceshelf. Ice derived from areas of bedded sedimentary rocks (including limestones) would have eroded and transported much more detritus than ice derived from Labrador, which flowed over resistant crystalline rocks. Thus even a small flux of icebergs calving from sediment-rich ice north of Labrador could have a significant effect on the overall lithological composition of the Qeovik Silt. The erosion of the Qeovik Silt in places suggests that it was deposited under less severe wave and current conditions than those prevailing today, although erosion may have been accentuated by isostatic rebound. The less severe conditions may reflect lesser strength of the Labrador Current prior to the opening of Hudson Strait and the Arctic Island channels and lesser effects of fall storms due to longer periods of sea ice cover.

The transition from Labrador Shelf Drift to Qeovik Silt, when compared with the transition from Scotian Shelf Drift to Emerald Silt, provides some constraints on the possible ice-margin environments represented by these sediments. On the Scotian Shelf, there is an intertonguing relationship between the drift and the silt, implying a floating ice margin. The "lift-off moraines" are thick, implying rapid sedimentation at the ice margin during lift off. This is consistent with the thick ablation till on land, and the evidence of continuous supply of large amounts of englacial detritus to the Scotian margin throughout the Late Wisconsinan. It is difficult to conceive of ice recession on the Labrador Shelf, at least in the saddles, not occurring initially through lift off. Therefore the lack of lift-off moraines may reflect the much lower sediment supply from Labradorean ice, which resulted in only a small amount of sediment being deposited during the early stages of lift off. That sediment would have been easily reworked by iceberg scour. No reliable chronology exists for ice retreat on the Labrador Shelf; it took place by lift off and calving with little associated sedimentation, but whether the process took hundreds or thousands of years is unknown. The Qeovik Silt has a distant provenance (indicated by the abundance of limestone that is absent in Labrador ice), a draped morphology and continuous reflectors; these characters therefore do not imply sub-ice shelf deposition.

The Hudson Strait Till was deposited by a glacier tongue from Hudson Strait that moved eastwards over Qeovik Silt at about 8 ka. Both Fillon and Harmes (1982) and Josenhans et al. (1986) have suggested that this advance was a surge. The ice was grounded to water depths of 610 m, and associated iceberg scours occur to water depths of 650 m. Glacial scour marks on the Qeovik Silt are still preserved on the seafloor, indicating little subsequent erosion or deposition. Collapse and retreat of the surge rapidly led to the opening of Hudson Strait, the establishment of the modern Labrador Current, and the termination of rapid proglacial sedimentation.

[†] See Addendum

Hudson Bay
D.J.W. Piper

Physiography

Hudson Bay (Fig. 10.35) is broadly saucer-shaped, with a gradual increase in depth from the shoreline to about 200 m in the centre of the bay. Long ridges and valleys disrupt the generally concentric pattern of the bathymetric contours; the ridges appear related to bedrock structures and most of the valleys appear to be a continuation of the major river valleys draining into the bay (Pelletier, 1966). A U-shaped trough, 550 m deep, in the northeastern part of the bay was presumably glacially overdeepened.

Stratigraphy and glacial history

At the time of writing (1985), little is known of the Quaternary stratigraphy of Hudson Bay,[†] except for confidential information obtained from several well-site surveys. The shallow water depths over much of the bay suggest that the stratigraphy is generally similar to that in surrounding lowlands (Shilts, 1980; Dredge and Cowan, in press). Currently (1985), several conflicting interpretations prevail for the history of till dispersal and the location of ice centres and divides around Hudson Bay. The classical view of a single domed equilibrium ice sheet centred over Hudson Bay (Flint, 1943; Denton and Hughes, 1981) is inconsistent with dispersal patterns based on till petrology and ice-flow indicators, and with the evidence for more than one Wisconsinan deglaciation of the Hudson Bay Lowlands (Shilts, 1980). Shilts (1980) proposed two main ice centres, one over Keewatin and one over central Quebec. Dyke et al. (1982) proposed a multidomed configuration for the Laurentide ice sheet, in which Hudson Bay was influenced principally by the M'Clintock dome to the northwest, a Hudson dome located over southern Hudson Bay, and the Labrador dome located over central Quebec. Dyke and his colleagues suggested that initial penetration of the sea into Hudson Bay took place along an embayment produced by calving at the confluence of Labrador and Hudson ice. The precise location of this ice divide in southern Hudson Bay would have been very sensitive to the rate of flow of ice through Hudson Strait (Denton and Hughes, 1983).

In the Hudson Bay Lowlands, till is in most places overlain by fluvioglacial deposits, which are probably also present within parts of the bay. Lacustrine sediments of glacial lakes Agassiz and Barlow-Objibway, which lie south of Hudson Bay, were ponded against an ice margin to the north, and may therefore also be present in southern Hudson Bay. Ice scour marks are widespread on land in areas of former glacial lakes; ice scours observed in central Hudson Bay (Whittaker et al., 1985) are probably cut in glaciomarine sediments. Following ice retreat, invasion of the Tyrrell Sea resulted in marine deposits, that have been progressively reworked by falling relative sea level during the Holocene. Marine deposits are exposed in coastal sections, where they are typically 3-4 m thick. The basal strata are gravelly muds with abundant broken mollusc shells, overlain by an upward coarsening sequence of mud to sand (Skinner, 1973). Flights of raised beaches are widespread around Hudson Bay.

[†] See Addendum

The distribution of surficial sediments in Hudson Bay, resulting from this falling sea level reworking late glacial deposits, is described by Pelletier (1969). Bayliss et al. (1970) and Adshead (1973) described the mineralogical characteristics of these sediments, and Leslie (1963, 1965) described the Holocene foraminifera in Hudson Bay.

Hudson Strait and Ungava Bay
B. MacLean, D. Praeg,
H.W. Josenhans and R. Klassen

Physiography

Hudson Strait separates Baffin Island from Labrador and Ungava, and connects Hudson Bay and Foxe Basin with the Labrador Sea (Fig. 10.35). It is 800 km in length and ranges in width from 90 km at its narrowest point to 340 km across Ungava Bay. Water depths greater than 200 m are continuous in a 90 km wide trough that extends from the continental shelf at its eastern margin, through the strait, to the west side of Foxe Basin, with branches into Ungava Bay and northern Hudson Bay (Canadian Hydrographic Service Chart 5.04). An elongate basin with depths to 900 m at the eastern end of this trough (Fig. 10.35) is separated from the Labrador Sea by a narrow, 400-m-deep sill composed of resistant bedrock (mainly Precambrian) lying between northernmost Labrador and Resolution Island.

Hudson Strait and Ungava Bay have large tides, with ranges from a maximum of 12.4 m in the east (Ungava Bay) to 4.9 m in the west (Nottingham Island) (Pilot of Arctic Canada, 1968). Tidal current velocities of 30 to 40 cm/s are common (Drinkwater, 1983).

Stratigraphy

For most of Hudson Strait, Quaternary stratigraphic data are limited to reconnaissance seismic reflection profiles collected in 1985 and several cores. More detailed seismic coverage is available from the outer part of the strait and parts of Ungava Bay. Surficial sediments are generally thin throughout the strait, but accumalations of more than 90 m (Fig. 10.40) and 130 m thick are present in the eastern and western basins respectively (MacLean et al., 1986a). Unstratified sediments 2 to 10 m thick, interpreted as till, are widespread and locally thicken to form moraines. The most prominent moraines are in the western part of the strait, southeast of Nottingham Island (where there are two superimposed tills), near the southern coast 50 km west of Cape Hopes Advance (where they overlie older Quaternary stratified sediments), and near the northern coast at Big Island (where two tills are present). A multiple sequence of up to five tills over 300 m in total thickness lies seaward and in the lee of the bedrock sill at the mouth of Hudson Strait, in the manner of large crag and tail deposits (Fig. 10.41).

Till is succeeded in the eastern and western basins by a massive, acoustically transparent unit (Fig. 10.40). The nature of this sediment has not been established; it may be of debris flow origin, or a lightly compacted watery till (c.f. Gravenor et al., 1984). The massive unit is overlain by stratified sediments that consist of mud, sandy mud and some pebbles. The stratified sediments form two or three units distinguishable by variations in character of the acoustic reflectors and in places by unconformable rela-

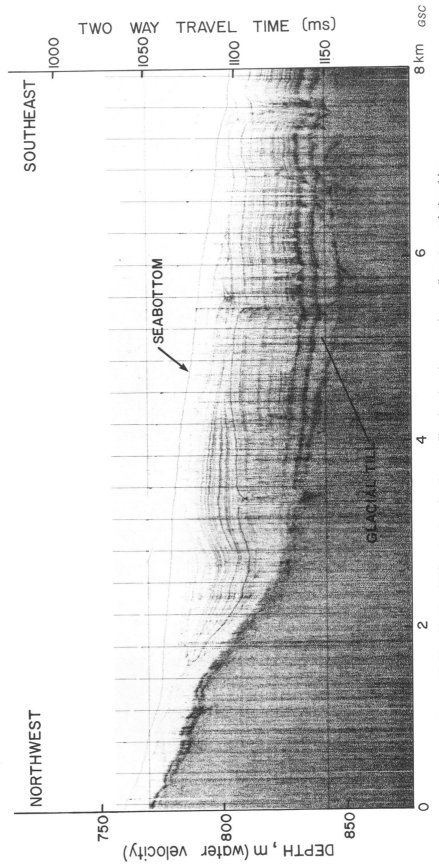

Figure 10.40. Huntec DTS seismic reflection profile showing the complex sedimentary relationships in the eastern Hudson Strait depression. Weakly to strongly stratified sediments overlie unstratified sediments including glacial till. For profile location refer to Figure 10.53.

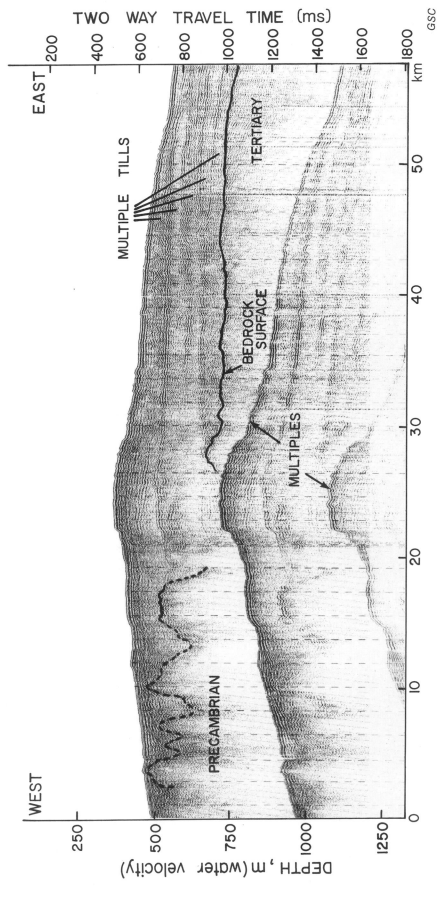

Figure 10.41. Air gun seismic reflection profile showing multiple tills flanking the seaward side of the bedrock sill at the eastern entrance to Hudson Strait. For profile location see Figure 10.53.

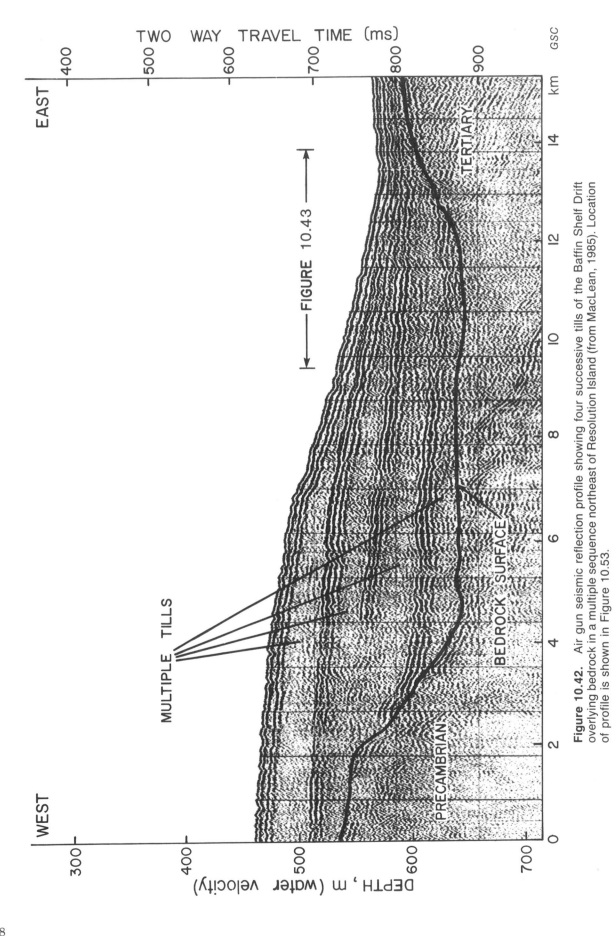

Figure 10.42. Air gun seismic reflection profile showing four successive tills of the Baffin Shelf Drift overlying bedrock in a multiple sequence northeast of Resolution Island (from MacLean, 1985). Location of profile is shown in Figure 10.53.

tions. Shell material at depths of 1-3 m in stratified sediments have been dated at 8730 ± 250 BP and 9100 ± 480 BP (Fillon et al., 1981a; Fillon and Harmes, 1982), and a total organic radiocarbon date of 22 900 ± 420 BP has been obtained at 5.5 m depth.

Sediments composed predominantly of silt and clay also occur in Ungava Bay south of the central plateau (C.L. Amos, pers. comm., 1984) as well as in the narrow bathymetric depression west and southwest of Akpatok Island. Elsewhere in Ungava Bay, seafloor sediments in water depths greater than 200 m appear to consist mainly of muddy sand with a variable amount of gravel-sized components. These sediments commonly form a thin cover up to a few metres in thickness over glacial till or bedrock. In shallower areas close to shore, acoustic data suggest that bedrock is exposed locally or thinly mantled by coarse sediments, reflecting vigorous tidal currents.

Hudson Strait is mainly underlain by sediments deposited in glacial or glaciomarine environments; postglacial muds are mainly restricted to the basins. The pebble fraction of the surficial sediments is principally carbonate rocks, carbonate-cemented sandstone, and mudstone, with lesser gneiss and granite. Ironstone clasts from the circum-Ungava fold belt are present in the eastern reaches of the strait.

Synthesis of glacial history

Local till and moraines in the floor of Hudson Strait, erosionally overdeepened areas, and multiple tills on the shelf seaward from its eastern entrance indicate that grounded glacial ice, presumably associated with dispersal from one or more inland ice centres, has occupied Hudson Strait. Multiple tills are also observed northeast of Resolution Island on the Southeast Baffin Shelf (Fig. 10.42). One or more of those tills may have been associated with the advance of Labrador ice from Ungava (MacLean, 1985) or they may in part represent Hudson Strait events. Striae and clasts on eastern Meta Incognita Peninsula of Baffin Island indicate northeasterly movement of ice in that region and they have been interpreted as resulting from impingement of Hudson Strait ice (Blake, 1966) and inundation by ice flowing out of Ungava Bay and across Hudson Strait from a dispersal centre on Labrador (Miller, 1982; Andrews and Miller, 1983). Limestone-rich, glacial-marine sediment dated at greater than 40 ka on Loks Land at the north side of the entrance to Frobisher Bay has been interpreted as resulting from a pre-Late Wisconsinan advance, either of Labrador ice across the Ordovician limestones of Ungava Bay or of easterly flowing ice from Hudson Bay or Foxe Basin (Osterman et al., 1985).

The Upper Wisconsinan stratified sediments in the deep eastern basin of Hudson Strait indicate that if ice was present in the strait at that time, it was at least partly as a floating shelf. In Ungava Bay, a grounded ice sheet persisted on the shallow seabed surrounding Akpatok Island in the Late Wisconsinan during retreat of a calving ice front from the deeper waters of Hudson Strait, and deglaciation of the island occurred sometime between 9000 and 6270 BP (Løken, 1978). An ice cap on Meta Incognita Peninsula locally expanded in the early Holocene (Osterman et al., 1985), correlating with the well documented Late Foxe (i.e. Late Wisconsinan) Hall moraine on southeast Baffin Island and the corresponding ice advance in Frobisher Bay at about 10.7 ka (Osterman, 1982). The

extent and origin of the moraines observed offshore along the coasts of Hudson Strait are not known. They lie west of Ungava Bay and may relate either to ice flowing into the strait from adjacent land areas, or to ice flowing generally eastward along the strait. The Hudson Strait till on the northern Labrador Shelf, deposited from ice from Hudson Strait or Ungava Bay and dated at about 8 ka, also represents an early Holocene ice advance. Data in Hudson Strait are thus at present (1985) inadequate to assess the importance of the strait as a major outlet of Hudson Bay ice, or the relative importance of local Labrador ice compared with more distant ice sources to the west.

Southeast Baffin Shelf
B. MacLean, D. Praeg, P.J. Mudie, and I.A. Hardy

Physiography

The Southeast Baffin Shelf extends from Hudson Strait in the south to Cape Dyer in the north, and comprises a broad platform up to 230 km wide with rather low relief. Water depths increase from 200 m on the inner shelf to around 500 m at the shelf break, encompassing several small banks and basins. Only an elongate local depression southeast of Cumberland Sound appears to correspond to the marginal channel commonly found on other glaciated shelves. Lemieux Bank, east of this trough, with a minimum depth of 122 m, has ?Pliocene-Quaternary sediment overlying older bedrock; it may be an analogue of outer shelf banks found on southern shelves. The deep basins in Frobisher Bay and Cumberland Sound are grabens, probably overdeepened by glacial erosion. A shallow transverse trough extends across the shelf from the mouth of Cumberland Sound. The unusual depth and character of this shelf in comparison to shelves to the north and south is probably related to the complex tectonic history of Davis Strait, rather than to glacial modification.

Lithostratigraphy

Beneath glacial tills and proglacial sediments on parts of the Southeast Baffin Shelf is a flat-lying sequence of stratified sediments, which is over 100 m thick beneath Lemieux Bank. There is no acoustic evidence that this unit is glacial or proglacial in origin. It overlies dated Paleogene sediments on the shelf, and is probably of Neogene or earliest Quaternary age (MacLean, 1985). It is referred to as the "preglacial unit".

Four glacial and postglacial stratigraphic units have been distinguished acoustically on the Southeast Baffin Shelf (Praeg et al., 1986). The Baffin Shelf Drift is widespread on the shelf overlying bedrock or the "preglacial unit" and in places forms morainal accumulations of one or more tills over 100 m thick (Fig. 10.42). Till has been recognized seaward to at least midway across the southeastern shelf, and it appears to extend to the shelf edge off Cumberland Sound and east of Resolution Island. Gravelly sandy mud of the Davis Strait Silt is prevalent over much of the south-eastern shelf and reaches up to several tens of metres in thickness, overlying bedrock, the "preglacial unit", or Baffin Shelf Drift. Northeast of Resolution Island, acoustically stratified sediments of the Davis Strait Silt interfinger with the uppermost till of a multiple till sequence (Fig. 10.42, 10.43), indicating that the Davis Strait Silt is primarily a glaciomarine sediment. The Davis Strait Silt appears acoustically stratified in several bathy-

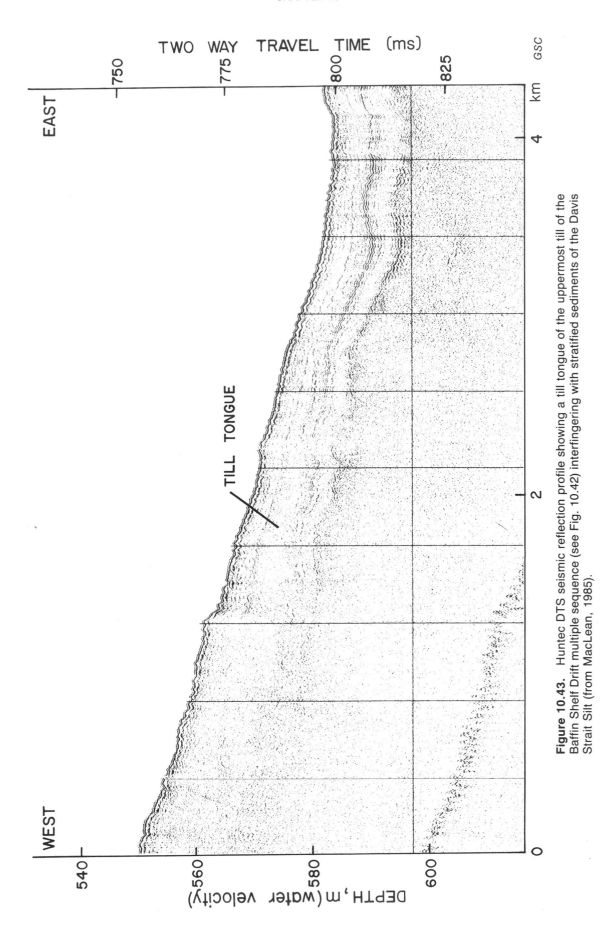

Figure 10.43. Huntec DTS seismic reflection profile showing a till tongue of the uppermost till of the Baffin Shelf Drift multiple sequence (see Fig. 10.42) interfingering with stratified sediments of the Davis Strait Silt (from MacLean, 1985).

metric depressions (e.g. Fig. 10.43), but in most areas is acoustically unstratified due to reworking by grounding icebergs (Fig. 10.44). Iceberg scouring has affected much of the Southeast Baffin Shelf, to a maximum water depth of about 700 m; most scours in deeper water are relict from a time of lowered sea level or larger icebergs. In Cumberland Sound and in a few small localities on the shelf, stratified Davis Strait Silt is overlain in basins by acoustically stratified muds of the Tiniktartuq Silt and Clay (Praeg et al., 1986; MacLean et al., 1986b).

Surficial sediments on much of the Southeast Baffin Shelf are coarser than the underlying material primarily due to the effects of current winnowing, supplemented by ice-rafted debris. This surficial veneer is generally less than 0.5 m thick. On some inner shelf areas, this veneer directly overlies bedrock or discontinuous older Quaternary deposits and is mapped as the Resolution Island Lag.

Chronology of the tills

Limited age control data make shelf-wide interpretation of the glacial chronology of the Southeast Baffin Shelf difficult. However, it is apparent that grounded glacial ice extended onto the shelf during one or more intervals during the Pleistocene, and in places there were repeated advances and retreats. Land evidence (Miller et al., 1977; Andrews and Ives, 1978; Miller, 1980; Osterman et al., 1985) suggests that Late Foxe (equivalent of Late Wisconsinan) ice did not override most Baffin Island coastal areas, but did extend to the outer coast in the Frobisher Bay–Hudson Strait region.

The uppermost till of the multiple sequence northeast of Resolution Island (Fig. 10.42) is inferred to be of Mid Foxe to early Late Foxe age on the basis of a radiocarbon date of 25 170 ± 420 BP (B-8898) on foraminifera from the stratified Davis Strait Silt with which this till interfingers (Fig. 10.44). Within Frobisher Bay, total organic radiocarbon dates of 19 640 ± 480 BP (B-8895) and 14 540 ± 1030 BP (B-8893) were obtained from Davis Strait Silt that overlies and interfingers with till lower in the section (Praeg et al., 1986). These sediments consist of carbonate-rich grey muds with a high planktonic foraminiferal content (core 82-034-69 in Praeg et al., 1986) and may correlate with carbonate-rich sediments (facies A) in Davis Strait. The till apparently predates the Late Foxe advance which deposited the Hall moraine on Hall Peninsula before 10 760 BP (Miller, 1980).

North of Frobisher Bay, a total organic radiocarbon date of 20 180 ± 295 BP (B-7045) was obtained from sediments that overlie till southeast of Cape Mercy. The age of the underlying till is uncertain; on land the last major glacial advance was of early Foxe age.

Biostratigraphy

P.J. Mudie and I.A. Hardy

Biostratigraphic studies on the Southeast Baffin Shelf (Table 10.5) are largely restricted to cores of the Davis Strait Silt. In Frobisher Bay (Osterman, 1982) an *Islandiella helenae* and *Cassidulina reniforme* foraminiferal zone is overlain by sediments in which *Elphidium excavatum* f. *clavata* is dominant (Fig. 10.45). The *E. excavatum*

zone represents the Late Foxe ice maximum of the Hall advance and was interpreted by Osterman (1982) as indicating a floating ice margin. Above this is another *I. helenae* and *C. reniforme* zone, followed by sediments dominated by *Nonionellina labradorica*, which may represent the establishment of a cold coastal Baffin Current about 5 ka. Strengthening of this current led to a surface assemblage dominated by *I. helenae* within Frobisher Bay and *Cibicides lobatulatus* outside. In nearby cores that penetrate deeper into the section, the lowermost sediments that directly overlie or laterally interfinger with Baffin Shelf Drift (Praeg et al., 1986) are almost barren. They are overlain by a *C. reniforme* assemblage coincident with peak abundances of planktonic foraminifera and the dinocyst *Multispinula minuta*. This assemblage is believed to represent a cold meltwater environment. The overlying sediments show a sequence analogous to that described by Osterman (1982).

Sea level changes

Evidence from Baffin Island indicates that large fluctuations in sea level have occurred during the Foxe glaciation (England and Andrews, 1973; Andrews, 1980), but the effect of this offshore is unknown. From the Quaternary record onshore, Andrews (1980) suggested that sea level was lower than present during much of the latter half of the Foxe glaciation whereas from isostatic modelling Quinlan (1985) inferred sea levels above those of the present for the same time interval. Shallow inner shelf areas (<150 m water depth) of the Southeast Baffin Shelf which might have been directly affected by any lowering of relative sea level are as yet largely unexamined, bathymetrically or geologically.

Synthesis of glacial history

The extensive and complex Baffin Shelf Drift points to major glaciations older than Late Foxe extending out onto the Southeast Baffin Shelf and locally reaching the shelf break. The chronology of this older glacial history and the provenance of the tills is unknown, and any correlation with glacial stratigraphy on land is speculative. Extrapolation of radiocarbon dates suggests that the Davis Strait Silt records deposition from Middle Foxe to Late Foxe time. In the Frobisher Bay-Hudson Strait region, this age is consistent with terrestrial glacial chronologies, which indicate the presence of ice offshore that originated in the Hudson Strait–Ungava region (Andrews and Miller, 1984). North of this region, terrestrial evidence suggests that the last glacial advance to extend onto the Baffin Shelf was of Early Foxe age, but there is not yet any chronological control in the marine sequence.

The biostratigraphic zonation of cores from Frobisher Bay provides independent evidence for the Late Foxe readvance, associated with a floating ice margin at least in Frobisher Bay. The cold Baffin Current was established about 5 ka, perhaps reflecting final retreat of ice from the Arctic Island Channels. The Tiniktartuq Silt and Clay reflects a postglacial change in depositional style, probably related to the change in the regional current regime. The coarse surficial sediment lag overlying much of the Southeast Baffin Shelf may also date from this change.

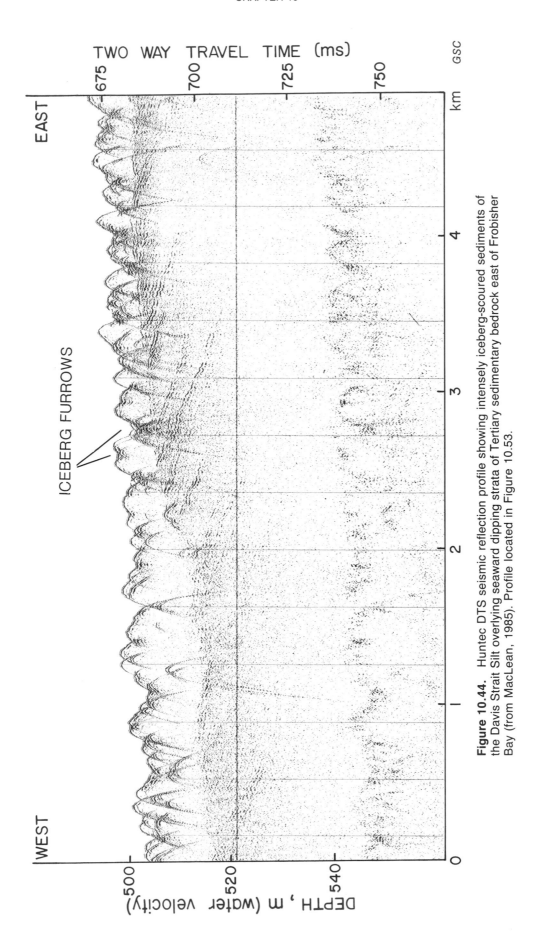

Figure 10.44. Huntec DTS seismic reflection profile showing intensely iceberg-scoured sediments of the Davis Strait Silt overlying seaward dipping strata of Tertiary sedimentary bedrock east of Frobisher Bay (from MacLean, 1985). Profile located in Figure 10.53.

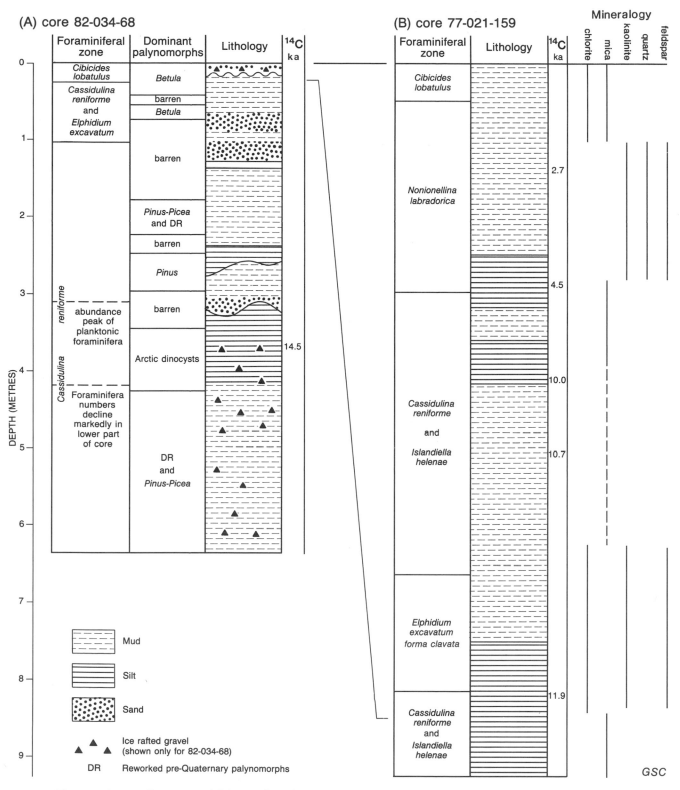

Figure 10.45. Summary of lithostratigraphy and biostratigraphy of cores from the Southeast Baffin Shelf. Core B (77-021-159), from Osterman (1982), provides a detailed section over the last 12 ka. Core A (82-034-68), from Praeg et al. (1986), does not record most of the section in core B (due to either a hiatus in sedimentation or core disturbance) but does record the section prior to 12 ka. Locations of cores are shown in Figure 10.46.

Deep water areas of the Labrador Sea

Physiography

D.J.W. Piper and P.J. Mudie

The Labrador Sea (Fig. 10.35) is a small, tectonically inactive ocean basin which forms a seaway linking temperate waters of the Atlantic Ocean with polar waters of the Canadian Arctic. In the northwest, the broad deep shelf off southeast Baffin Island merges with a 650 m deep sill at Davis Strait which separates the Labrador Sea from Baffin Bay. In the northeast, the ocean basin is bordered by a narrow continental shelf and steep continental slope off southwest Greenland. Off the southern tip of Greenland is the complex deep-water ridge and channel topography (Fig. 10.35) of Eirik Ridge, Imarssuak Mid-Ocean Channel and Gloria Drift. The Labrador Shelf is wide and marked by shallow outer banks cut by deep transverse troughs or saddles. The upper slope is generally smooth, but small gullies that coalesce to form large channels are developed in many areas on the middle and lower slope (Josenhans et al., 1986). The channels cut the continental rise, but are modified by the action of the Western Boundary Undercurrent (Chough et al., 1985; Schafer and Carter, 1986).

The Northwest Atlantic Mid-Ocean Channel (NAMOC) is a deep-sea turbidite channel that extends the length of the centre of the Labrador Sea (Chough and Hesse, 1976). The channel appears to have formed from several tributaries originating in Hudson and Davis straits, and can be traced southward 3000 km to the northeastern Sohm Abyssal Plain (Fig. 10.46). In northern Labrador Sea, this channel flows between 200 m high levees across a broad abyssal plain, but in the south, bedrock ridges rise to the seabed and the channel follows a more complex path, with one short reach flowing along the Charlie-Gibbs Fracture Zone. In the western part of the Newfoundland Basin southeast of Newfoundland, the channel again flows between high levees across an abyssal plain.

The deep water continental margin to the east of Newfoundland can be divided into three main segments (Fig. 10.35). To the east of Grand Bank is a steep continental slope leading to the Newfoundland Basin. This is bounded to the north by the shallow ($\sim$ 200 m) Flemish Cap, separated from the main continental shelf by Flemish Pass, 1000 m deep. Flemish Cap marks the southern edge of Orphan Basin, lying between the Northeast Newfoundland Shelf and Orphan Knoll.

Newfoundland Basin, Flemish Pass and Orphan Basin

D.J.W. Piper, P.J. Mudie, and C.F.M. Lewis

Much of the deep-water continental margin east of Newfoundland is influenced by the Western Boundary Undercurrent, flowing at a depth of 2400 to 2800 m southwards along the western margin of the Labrador Sea (Carter and Schafer, 1983; Schafer et al., 1985). Seismic profiles show sediment drifts of Quaternary age in Orphan Basin, large constructional features both at the northern and southern ends of Flemish Pass, a probable sediment drift south of Flemish Cap in the Newfoundland Basin, and contourite deposits on the southeast Newfoundland Ridge. In addition, current-influenced deposition is documented around the Newfoundland Seamounts in the Newfoundland Basin (Sullivan, 1978). Basin-filling strata, probably turbidites, appear important in both Orphan Basin and the Newfoundland Basin. Orphan Basin underwent an overall Quaternary progradation of the continental slope, interrupted by some erosive phases, but no submarine canyons have been seen. Upper Pliocene and Quaternary sediments are about 1100 m thick at the Blue H-28 well in Orphan Basin, which is located in 1486 m of water (Fig. 10.46). The thickness of Quaternary strata in the Newfoundland Basin is unknown.

DSDP Site 111 on the crest of Orphan Knoll discontinuously sampled a Pleistocene and Upper Pliocene sequence of terrigenous muds with ice-rafted debris (Laughton et al., 1972). Stratigraphic ranges of planktonic foraminifera suggest that the first ice-rafted debris appeared at the site about 3 Ma (Berggren, 1972), but core recovery was insufficient to provide a detailed Late Cenozoic biostratigraphy or chronology.

Core 75-112 (Fig. 10.46) from the Newfoundland Basin (Alam et al., 1983) extends back to isotopic stage 13 (Fig. 10.47). The biogenic carbonate sediments have experienced considerable dissolution, and the core indicates a paleo-oceanographic history which is similar to that of the Fogo Seamounts. Core K9 on the northeast flank of the Newfoundland Ridge (Fig. 10.46) extends only to isotopic stage 5 (Pastouret et al., 1975); the higher sedimentation rate is due to greater detrital input during glacial stages.

A Late Wisconsinan stratigraphy has been established by Alam et al. (1983) for the Southeast Grand Banks Slope and Flemish Pass, and by Carter (1979), Piper et al. (1978) and Schafer et al. (1985) for the western slope of Orphan Basin (Fig. 10.48). The Middle to Late Wisconsinan is marked by sandy turbidites on the Southeast Grand Banks Slope, presumably derived from the shallow shelf edge at times of lowered sea level. The shelf break off the Northeast Newfoundland Shelf is deeper, and in Orphan Basin some turbidites are fine grained and have resulted from slumping of muddy slope sediments (Schafer and Scott, 1985). The early Holocene is marked by microfossils indicating warm surface waters, high planktonic foraminiferal productivity, and a large flux of ice-rafted debris rich in carbonate detritus. The 9800 BP ash horizon (Ruddiman and Glover, 1972) is a useful stratigraphic marker for this time interval in Orphan Basin. The upper Holocene is marked by foraminifers indicating cooler surface waters and an intensification of the Western Boundary Undercurrent on the lower slope and upper rise (Schafer et al., 1985).

In Flemish Pass, lithological and biostratigraphic control for acoustic stratigraphy (Fig. 10.49) is provided by the Gabriel C-60 well (Piper and Sparkes, 1986). Miocene claystones are overlain unconformably by Plio-Pleistocene sands and silts. The lower part of the Plio-Pleistocene sequence on the western margin of Flemish Pass comprises uniform slope-parallel reflectors, similar to those on the Scotian Slope. It is overlain by a stratified sequence cut by shallow slope channels analogous to the Late Pliocene-Early Pleistocene succession on the Scotian Slope. This unit is overlain on the upper slope by thick diamicts or other coarse sediments that pass downslope into a stratified sequence. This sequence is highly dissected by channels that are mostly buried. On the floor of Flemish Pass, this unit thickens rapidly and largely comprises acoustically unstratified material, of either debris flow (Pereira et al., 1985) or contourite origin.

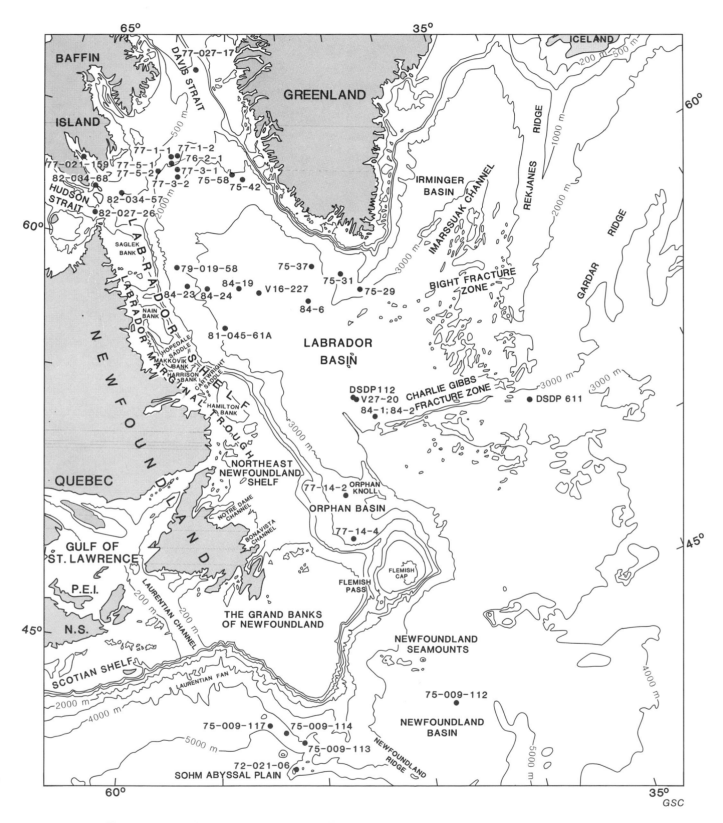

Figure 10.46. Distribution of key Late Quaternary cores shown in Figures 10.47 and 10.48.

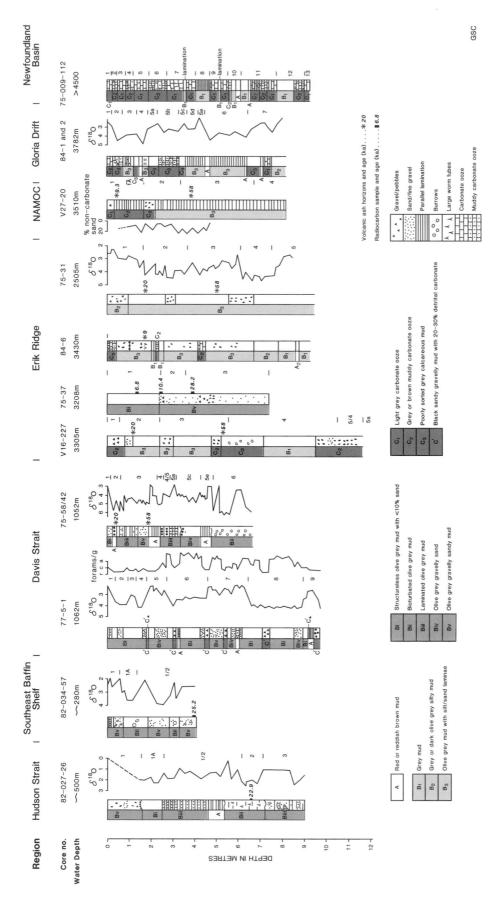

Figure 10.47. Representative cores from deep water areas of the Labrador Sea from Hudson Strait and Davis Strait to the Newfoundland Basin, showing possible lithostratigraphic correlations with major lithofacies recognized for Davis Strait cores (Aksu and Mudie, 1985a) and core 75-009-112 from a abyssal hill in the Newfoundland Basin. Oxygen isotopic curves ($\delta^{18}O$ in ‰) are based on *Neogloboquadrina pachyderma* (sinistral) as reported by Aksu and Mudie (1985a), Fillon and Duplessy (1980), Mudie and Aksu (1984), Scott et al. (1986a) and, for cores 82-027-26 and 82-034-57, from unpublished data of Aksu, Memorial University of Newfoundland. Isotopic stages shown for other cores are correlations made by Fillon and Duplessy (1980) and by Alam et al. (1983) which are supported by microfaunal data and tephrochronology. Core locations are shown in Figure 10.46. For each core: left column shows the lithofacies assignment (see legend and text); right column shows dominant lithology, or for siliciclastic muds, characteristic structures and intraclasts. NAMOC is the Northwest Atlantic Mid-Ocean Channel.

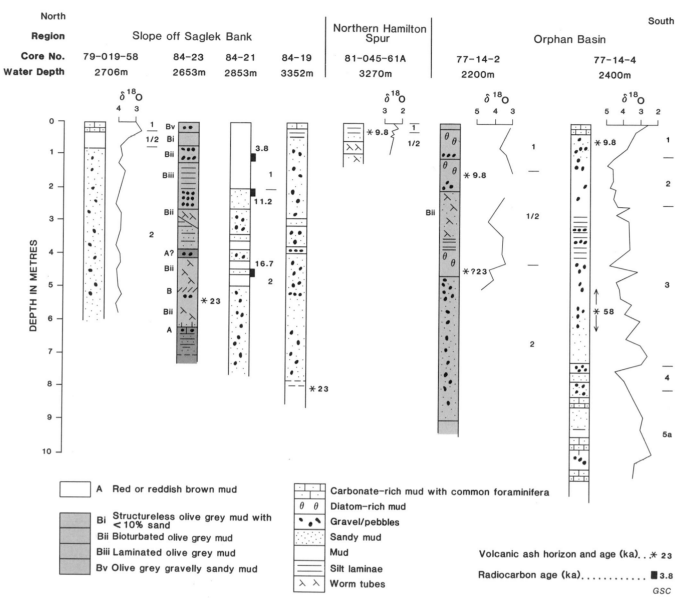

Figure 10.48. Representative cores from the Labrador and Newfoundland continental slope and rise. Note change in lithofacies and δ¹⁸O isotopic values from 61°N to 49°N. Oxygen isotopic curves are based on *Neogloboquadrina pachyderma* (sinistral) as reported by de Vernal (1986) for core 84-21 and by Schafer and Scott (1985); other isotope curves are from unpublished data of Aksu (Memorial University, core 79-019-58). Radiocarbon ages are AMS dates obtained from foraminifera by de Vernal (1986); ages of ash horizons are interpretations of the authors. Core locations are shown in Figure 10.46.

Distinctive lithological suites of ice-rafted debris were recognized in deep-water continental margin sediments off Newfoundland (Pastouret et al., 1975; Alam and Piper, 1981). The ice-rafted debris occurs in cores mostly dating from Middle Wisconsinan to present as coarse sand and pebbles dispersed in hemipelagic or pelagic sediment. The suites are 1) a metamorphic dominated assemblage, derived from Greenland and Baffin Island or from local Labrador and Newfoundland ice; 2) a carbonate dominated suite, derived from the Arctic Islands through Hudson Strait or Baffin Bay, and 3) a red sandstone-siltstone suite derived from the Gulf of St. Lawrence region (Conolly et al., 1967) or Carboniferous basins off Newfoundland. The carbonate suite is typically dominant during the early stages of interglacials and interstadials. Presumably this suite correlates with other finds of Late Wisconsinan car-

bonate ice-rafted debris in Baffin Bay (Aksu and Piper, 1979), the northern Labrador Sea (Chough, 1978), and on the Northeast Newfoundland Shelf (Piper et al., 1978), with detritus transported southward in the Labrador Current. The red sandstone-siltstone suite is restricted to sites south of the Grand Banks of Newfoundland. The clay minerals of these suites are distinctive and variable. During glacial periods when sea level was low, occurrences of illite, chlorite and kaolinite are thought to reflect variations in local source areas on the adjacent shelf (Alam and Piper, 1981). During interglacials with higher sea levels and more widespread distribution of fine sediment by oceanic currents, including transport of ice-rafted debris in the Labrador Current, clay mineral composition (montmorillonite and mixed layer clays) is more uniform over a wider geographic area.

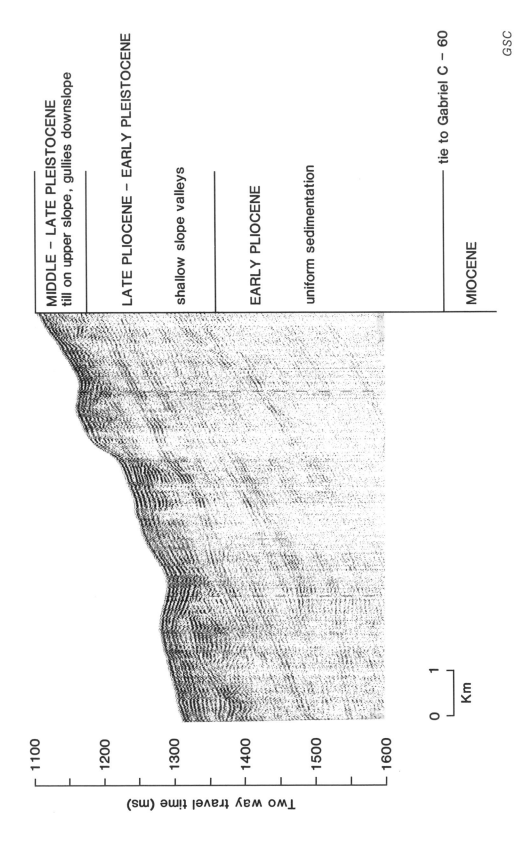

Figure 10.49. Acoustic facies on the western flank of Flemish Pass. Age assignment based on a stratigraphic tie to the Gabriel C-60 well (Piper and Sparkes, 1986).

GSC

Labrador Basin and the Northwest Atlantic Mid-Ocean Channel*

R.A. Myers, D.J.W. Piper and P.J. Mudie

Continental slopes adjacent to the Labrador Basin have complex geology; they are highly dissected, both where the slopes are steep (off Labrador and West Greenland) and where they are gradual (off southeastern Baffin Island and Davis Strait). Late Cenozoic horizons in shelf wells cannot generally be traced with confidence in seismic reflection profiles across the continental slope to the ocean basin. Reflectors observed in the multichannel seismic profiles of Hinz et al. (1979) in the northern Labrador Basin can be traced to the Deep Sea Drilling Project (DSDP) Site 113 and the Ocean Drilling Program (ODP) Site 646, thereby allowing regional interpretation of Quaternary sedimentation patterns. In the southern Labrador Basin (Fig. 10.35), only non-continuous single-channel seismic profiles are available within the ocean basin; hence, regional sedimentation patterns are more difficult to interpret, especially in the area of complex basement topography between the outer Eirik Ridge and Charlie-Gibbs Fracture Zone.

In northern Labrador Basin, three key seismic reflectors can be identified and correlated over much of the basin (Myers, 1986). Seismic ties to Sites 646 and 113 indicate that the deepest reflector (D in Fig. 10.50) corresponds to the Early-Late Pliocene boundary, and the second (B) dates from the base of the Pleistocene. The third reflector (A) is estimated to be of early Middle Pleistocene age. In northeastern Labrador Basin, between the Northwest Atlantic Mid-Ocean Channel (NAMOC) and the Greenland Slope, a flat-lying series of continuous acoustic reflectors is about 1 km thick above reflector A. This sequence is interpreted to be largely turbidites, and it contrasts markedly in acoustic character with the underlying Miocene to Lower Pliocene sediments. The upper 750 m of this turbidite sequence continues westwards into a complex of levee-channel systems which is marked at the seafloor by the Northwest Atlantic Mid-Ocean Channel and shows the characteristic acoustic features of deep-sea turbidite channels (Nelson and Kulm, 1973).

In northwestern Labrador Basin, sediments above reflector D have an irregular acoustic character, including discontinuous lenticular and hyperbolic reflections, indicative of contour current deposition. Above reflector B, these deposits are onlapped by stratified sediments in the vicinity of the Northwest Atlantic Mid-Ocean Channel; however, in the western part of the basin a thin contourite sequence continues up to reflector A. Above reflector A, which appears to form the base of the "prograde sequence" on the outer shelf, lies a thick sequence of stratified sediment in northwestern Labrador Basin, prograded from the shelf edge and cut by channels flowing across the Labrador Slope and Rise. Irregular reflectors indicative of contourite deposition occur in interchannel areas in water depths of 2500 to 2800 m.

In southern Labrador Basin, oceanic basement rises close to the surface in places, and seafloor topography is much more irregular. Eirik and Gloria ridges, and Hamilton and Sackville spurs are large Neogene sediment drifts (Jones et al., 1970; Egloff and Johnson, 1975) and are mantled by Quaternary hemipelagic or contourite deposits. They are onlapped locally by Pleistocene turbidites, as at DSDP Site 112 and ODP Site 647. Although stratigraphic control on many of these drifts is poor, the major sediment accumulation took place in the Neogene. Subsequent Quaternary sedimentation has not significantly modified the overall relief of the larger drifts. In places, such as on the north side of Hamilton Spur, there has been Quaternary erosion of drift deposits.

The best stratigraphic control for the southern Labrador Basin is from ODP Site 646 (Fig. 10.51) on the northwestern flanks of Eirik Ridge (Arthur et al., 1986). The Miocene-Pliocene boundary occurs about 500 m below the seafloor, and Early Pliocene strata are carbonate-rich contourite muds with relatively warm-water microfossils. Near the Early to Late Pliocene boundary (3.4 Ma, 314 m below the seafloor), a pronounced change to predominantly siliceous biota occurs. Major ice-rafted debris was first observed in the Late Pliocene (2.5 Ma, 236 m). Above this horizon the Neogene drift has been generally smoothed by continuous sedimentation of muds with variable but low contents of coarse ice-rafted debris and both siliceous and calcareous microfossils.

ODP Site 647 is located on the southwestern flank of Gloria Drift (Arthur et al., 1986). Upper Pliocene to Quaternary strata disconformably overlie Upper Miocene winnowed pelagic sediments. The oldest Pliocene sediments at 116 m below the seafloor contain ice-rafted debris and are dated at about 2.5 Ma. The overlying strata comprise an alternation of calcite-rich turbidite muds apparently derived from the Northwest Atlantic Mid-Ocean Channel and biogenic-rich muds of contourite origin. A rather similar stratigraphy was encountered at the poorly sampled DSDP Site 113, located on the southwestern margin of Eirik Ridge (Laughton et al., 1972).

Near-surface sediments cored in the eastern Labrador Basin (Fig. 10.47) consist largely of hemipelagic muds with ice-rafted debris (Fillon and Duplessy, 1980; Fillon et al., 1981b; de Vernal et al., 1986). In central Labrador Basin (Fig. 10.46), sedimentation is dominated by turbidite spillover from Northwest Atlantic Mid-Ocean Channel (Chough and Hesse, 1980). The turbidites appear more extensive during glacial stages and interfinger with contourite sediment drift deposits during interglacials (Chough et al., 1985). The North Atlantic ash stratigraphy is believed to be recognizable in the Northwest Atlantic Mid-Ocean Channel area (Chough, 1978), although dating control is sparse. In cores from the channel area, turbidites are more abundant in Wisconsinan intervals than in the Sangamon or Holocene, and detrital carbonate is abundant at some Wisconsinan levels (Chough, 1978; Latouche and Parra, 1979). Detrital petrology suggests further sediment input by bottom currents in the Holocene (Latouche and Parra, 1979).

In the western Labrador Basin, west of the Northwest Atlantic Mid-Ocean Channel turbidite deposits, much of the continental rise has been influenced by the Western Boundary Undercurrent throughout the Late Quaternary (Chough et al., 1985). Representative cores (Fig. 10.47) indicate substantial downslope transport of coarse sediment from the Labrador margin during the Wisconsinan;

---

* Although the term "Canyon" has historical priority over the more accurate term "Channel" for the seafloor bathymetric feature, the entire complex of sediments associated with this valley system and its Pleistocene precursors is generally known as the "North Atlantic Mid-Ocean Channel".

ice rafting was also important, with evidence for local distal turbidite and contourite deposits.

Davis Strait
A.E. Aksu and P.J. Mudie

Multichannel seismic records show that the basement topography of Davis Strait is complex and that it is overlain by only a thin sedimentary cover. It is not possible to trace seismic reflectors from the northern Labrador Sea or the Southeast Baffin Shelf to Davis Strait, and so little is known about the Tertiary history of this area. Detailed studies of several long Quaternary sediment cores from Davis Strait (Aksu, 1981; Fillon and Duplessy, 1980; Fillon and Aksu, 1985) allow tentative correlations to be made with cores from southern Baffin Bay (Mudie and

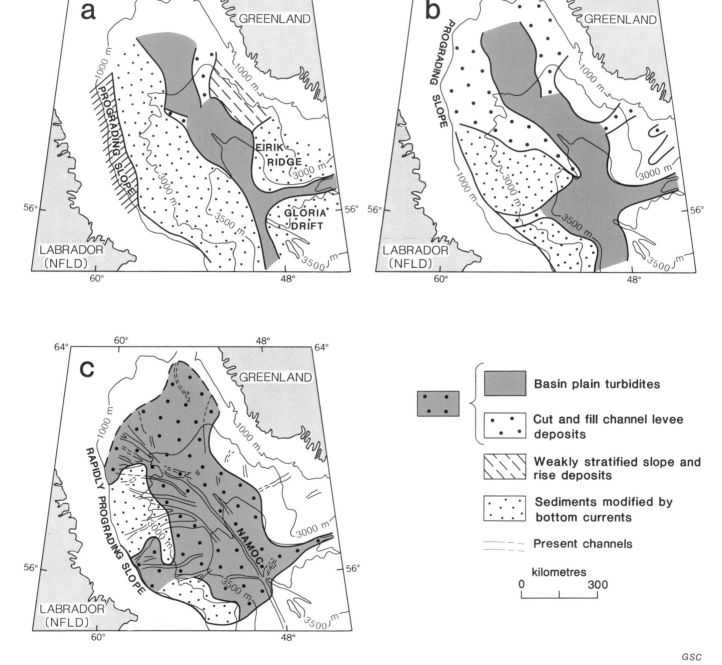

GSC

Figure 10.50. Distribution of sediment facies in the Labrador Sea (from Myers, 1986): (a) reflectors D to B: approximately Late Pliocene: (b) reflectors B to A: approximately Early Pleistocene: (c) reflector A to surface: approximately Middle Pleistocene. NAMOC is the Northwest Atlantic Mid-Ocean Channel.

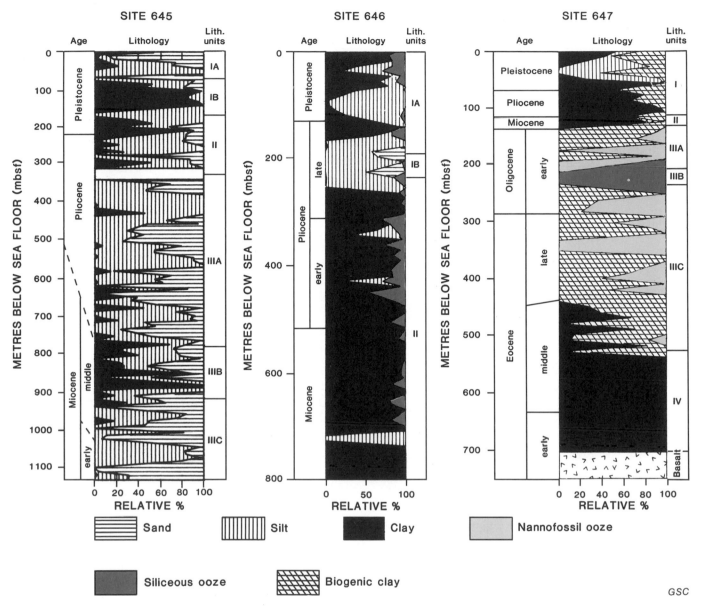

Figure 10.51. Summary stratigraphy of ODP sites 645, 646 and 647 (after Arthur et al., 1986). See Figure 10.1 for site locations.

Aksu, 1984), the Southeast Baffin Shelf (Praeg et al., 1986) and the northern Labrador Sea. Cores from western Davis Strait (Fig. 10.52) contain three lithofacies that can be correlated stratigraphically with facies A, D and C of Baffin Bay. In Davis Strait, facies A consists of yellowish brown, gravelly-sandy mud and fine muds with frequent sand/silt laminae. Lithic carbonate content is characteristically high (50-90%); Paleozoic limestones and dolomites are the main sediment source. Massive beds of gravelly mud indicate deposition by ice rafting; laminated beds and gravelly-sandy muds are probably turbidites and thin-bedded debris flows, respectively. Oxygen isotope data (Aksu, 1983a; Aksu and Mudie, 1985a) show that facies A typically occurs at or near the base of light isotope stages and the sediments probably reflect rapid melting and iceberg calving at these times. The youngest development of

facies A corresponds in core 82-027-26 (Fig. 10.47) to the transition between isotope stages 1 and 2 and overlies sediment with a ^{14}C age of 22 900 ± 410 BP (B-8899).

Facies B in Davis Strait cores consists of olive-grey to dark olive muds or gravelly-sandy mud beds. They appear to be equivalent to facies D of Baffin Bay cores, which is the dominant lithofacies in southern Baffin Bay and northern Davis Strait. In Davis Strait cores, facies B contains less than 10% calcium carbonate, which is mostly of biogenic origin. It includes turbidite sands and muds, ice-rafted gravelly mud, and hemipelagic muds augmented by ice rafting (Aksu and Mudie, 1985a).

Facies C consists of structureless, greyish or brownish black, gravelly sandy muds with 20-30% lithic carbonate and no obvious grading. This lithofacies is believed to rep-

561

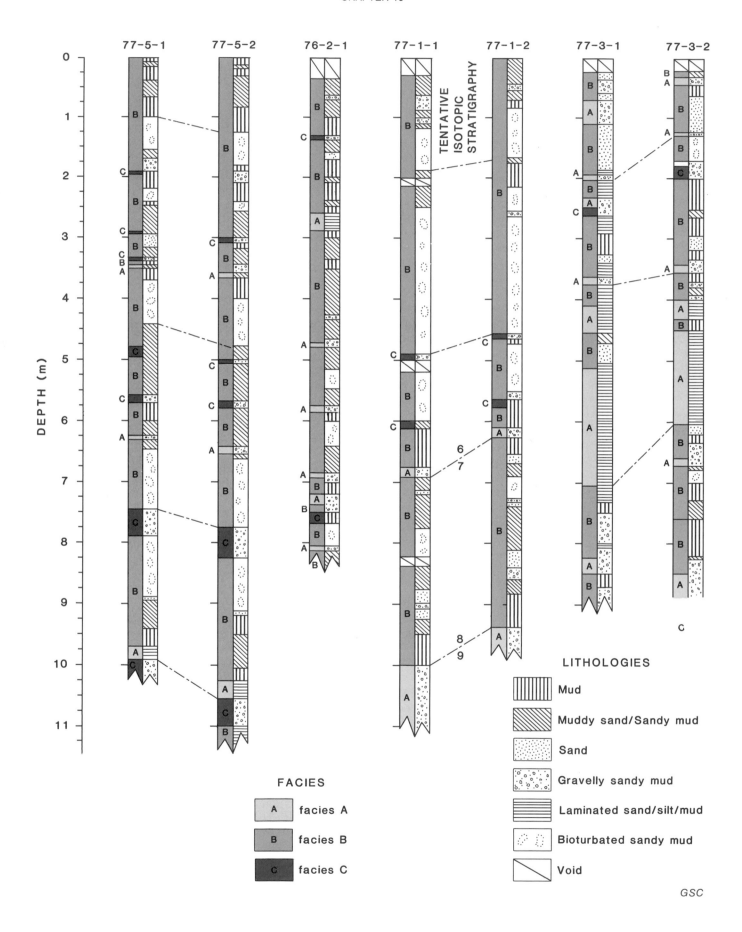

FACIES

A facies A

B facies B

C facies C

LITHOLOGIES

▥ Mud

▨ Muddy sand/Sandy mud

⬚ Sand

⬚ Gravelly sandy mud

▤ Laminated sand/silt/mud

⬚ Bioturbated sandy mud

◩ Void

GSC

resent ice-rafted debris (Aksu and Mudie, 1985a); palyno-morph content suggests that its sources include black Tertiary shales that outcrop on Bylot Island and underlie parts of the Northeast Baffin Shelf (Mudie and Short, 1985; Arthur et al., 1986). In Davis Strait cores, this lithofacies mainly occurs at the top or base of heavy (gla-cial) isotopic stages. Although facies C resembles Baffin Bay facies C in colour and mineral composition, the Baffin Bay lithofacies is graded and is interpreted as a debris flow deposit.

Cores from Davis Strait show relatively poor lithologi-cal correlation (Aksu and Mudie, 1985a) but using multiple criteria, including volcanic ash stratigraphy, microfossils, isotope stratigraphy, ^{14}C, thermoluminescence and amino acid chronologies, a tentative time-stratigraphic frame-work is proposed by which cores can be broadly correlated with core 77-027-17 from southern Baffin Bay and with cores from the Labrador Slope and Rise and central Labrador Sea (Fig. 10.47, 10.52). If this correlation and chronology are correct, mean Late Quaternary sedimenta-tion rates are 3 to 4 cm/ka in western Davis Strait and on the Labrador Slope and Rise, rather lower on Davis Strait sill, and 4 to 9 cm/ka in the Labrador Basin and West Greenland Rise. Oxygen isotope stratigraphies of Davis Strait cores indicate four major glacial-interglacial cycles during the past 400 ka, with amplitudes of about the same range as those reported for the Greenland Sea (Kellog, 1977; Jansen et al., 1983).

Synthesis of glacial history

D.J.W. Piper

The deep-water areas of the Labrador Basin preserve a long record of the history of bottom water circulation, ice rafting, and the supply of glacial sediments from the sur-rounding Greenland and Laurentide ice sheets. The Ocean Drilling Program sites drilled in 1985 have provided a detailed suite of samples from this region, and many cur-rent interpretations may be substantially revised as these samples are analyzed.

The effects of glacially-influenced bottom water circu-lation are recorded in the Miocene disconformities and the Neogene growth of large sediment drifts. The major supply of Upper Pliocene turbidites to the northeastern Labrador Basin at the same time as the onset of major ice rafting is probably related to glaciation in Greenland. The North-west Atlantic Mid-Ocean Channel developed in the Early Pleistocene with sediment from Hudson Strait, but with no significant sediment supply from the Labrador margin until the Middle Pleistocene. Although there was little growth of the major sediment drifts in the Quaternary, the influence of deep water currents in the accumulation of Quaternary sediments was felt over large areas of the Labrador Basin, particularly in the Early Pliocene prior to the major supply of turbidites from the Labrador margin. This bottom current activity also complicates the interpre-tation of Late Quaternary stratigraphy from piston cores.

During glacial maxima, sedimentation in much of the Labrador Basin was dominated by turbidites, but at times of glacial retreat only the Northwest Atlantic Mid-Ocean Channel experienced persistent turbidite sedimentation. Other areas experienced hemipelagic sedimentation domi-nated by bottom currents and this has continued into the Holocene. Ice-rafted sediments are of particular impor-tance in the southwestern Labrador Sea, and ice-rafted lithologies provide a lithostratigraphic link to the stratig-raphy of Baffin Bay.

THE BAFFIN BAY REGION

Baffin Island fiords

J.P.M. Syvitski and D.J.W. Piper

The northeastern coastline of Baffin Island (Fig. 10.53) is highly dissected by fiords, with valley walls up to 1500 m high and maximum water depths of 1000 m. The outer and middle reaches of the fiords have basins separated by bed-rock sills mantled by sediment, whereas the inner fiords are separated into basins by transverse glacial moraines, some of which have become subaerially exposed as relative sea level has fallen in the late Holocene; examples are Ekalugad and Tromso fiords. Some of the fiords draining the Penny Ice Cap still contain large tidewater glaciers; others receive most of their sediment through the sedimen-tological filter of sandur deltas. Most of the fiords have intrafiord cirque or outlet glaciers that advanced into the sea during the late Neoglacial reaching their maximum about 1700 A.D.

The fiords contain sequences of stratified sediments with maximum thicknesses ranging from 40 to over 220 m (Syvitski, 1984; Gilbert, 1985). Some proximal glaciomar-ine sediments (Fig. 10.54) interfinger with till and are locally ice pushed; others have a ponded depositional style and represent gravitational flow deposits adjacent to prograding sandur deltas (Syvitski, 1984). More distal deposits have a more conformable acoustic style. Radiocar-bon dating indicates that the thickness of Holocene sedi-ment in these more distal fiord basins is typically 3 to 4 metres (Andrews et al., 1985). This suggests that the thick stratified sediments are many tens of thousands of years old, and that the last grounded-ice event on the fiord floors must have been of Early Foxe age or older. Moraine distri-bution on land suggests that ice extended to the mouth of Maktak and Coronation fiords in both the Early and Late Foxe (Andrews and Miller, 1984). These fiords contain thick stratified sequences; however, multiple till units have not been recognized. Therefore, it is unclear whether the sequences represent rapid deposition following retreat of Late Foxe ice, or whether they are deposits from a float-ing or grounded Late Foxe ice sheet. If the ice sheet was grounded, it did not disturb older sediments. In four of the fiords studied, end moraines form sills to inner fiord basins, and these sills are of Late Foxe age.

The coastal forelands between the fiords, in places, preserve a thick stratigraphic sequence of raised marine deposits and intercalated tills (Andrews and Miller, 1984). The pre-Foxe sections of the coastal stratigraphic sequences are dated by uranium series and amino-acid racemization (Miller, 1985; Mode, 1986) and suggest that the oldest strata are of Early Pleistocene or even Pliocene (Feyling-Hanssen, 1985) age. Sediments of such age in marine areas have been recovered only in ODP Site 645

Figure 10.52. Correlation of cores from Davis Strait. Iso-topic stratigraphy (after Mudie and Aksu, 1984) is tentative. The facies are described in the text. See Figure 10.46 for core locations.

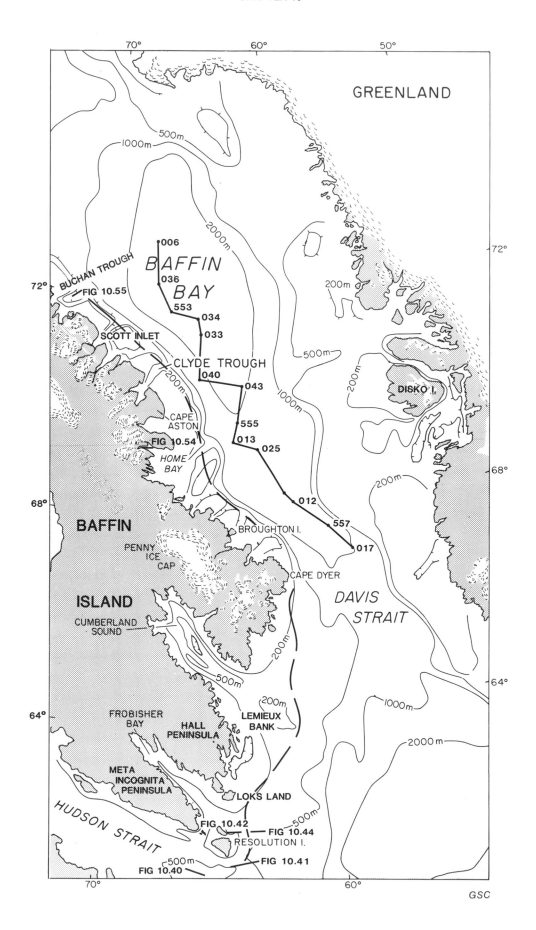

GSC

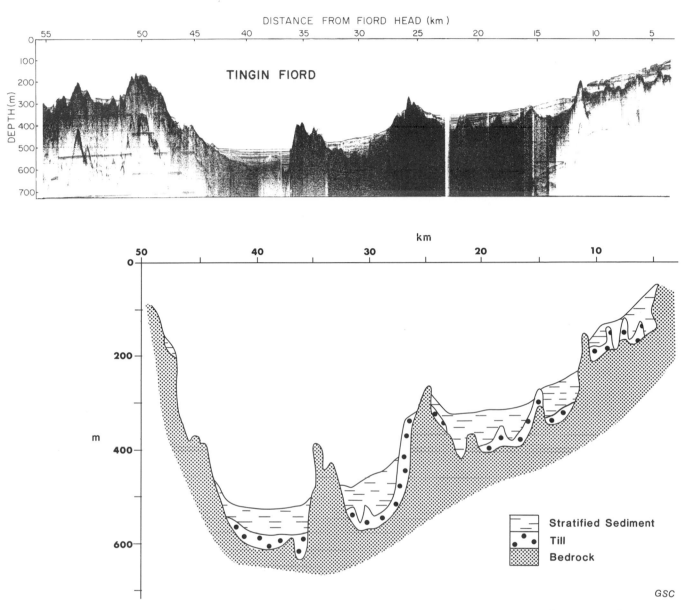

Figure 10.54. Interpretation of Quaternary deposits of Tingin Fiord, Baffin Island (after Gilbert, 1985). For location see Figure 10.53.

Figure 10.53. Index map of the Baffin Shelf. Shows approximate maximum seaward limit of glacial till (heavy discontinuous line) on the Baffin Island Shelf as inferred from air gun and Huntec DTS seismic reflection data (from MacLean, 1984). Numbers and accompanying small lines and dots indicate locations and orientations of profile figures and cores respectively.

in Baffin Bay. During the Early Foxe, outlet glaciers were restricted to the fiords, leaving much of the low coastal forelands ice free. At present no Middle Foxe glacial event has been recognized in the foreland stratigraphy. The Late

Foxe glaciation was less extensive than that of the Early Foxe. The majority of the raised marine sediments are closely associated with tills or coarse ice-proximal sediments, deposited during multiple Quaternary transgression-regression cycles. The youngest cycle dates from the early Holocene and consists entirely of normal marine or ice-distal marine deposits. The fluctuations in relative sea level are inferred to result from glacio-isostatic loading (Andrews, 1980); no offshore data on sea level fluctuations are available at present for correlation.

In northeastern Bylot Island, Klassen (1981, 1985) mapped an extensive series of lateral moraines characterized by a high detrital carbonate content. These were apparently deposited by ice flowing out of Lancaster Sound, and imply a great thickness of glacial ice in the sound. Amino acid ratios and radiocarbon dating suggest that this event was of Early Foxe age.

Northeast Baffin Shelf

D. Praeg and B. MacLean

The Northeast Baffin Shelf in Baffin Bay is much narrower (30-50 km) than the Southeast Baffin Shelf, and has a shelf break around 300 m. It is characterized by banks less than 200 m deep that are shallow extensions of the coastal forelands, separated by transverse troughs up to 800 m deep that extend across the shelf from the mouths of major fiords. The marginal trough common to other glaciated shelves is absent on the Northeast Baffin Shelf. The transverse troughs have been attributed to glacial sculpturing along pre-existing drainage channels (Løken and Hodgson, 1971). The transverse trough off Broughton Island was interpreted by Gilbert (1982) as resulting from Tertiary fluvial deposition along a graben associated with the opening of Baffin Bay, followed by Quaternary glacial erosion and overdeepening.

With the exception of the area between Scott Inlet and Buchan Gulf, limited seismic reflection data are available for the Northeast Baffin Shelf and only a preliminary interpretation of the Quaternary geology is possible. The base of the Quaternary sequence is difficult to distinguish due to widespread conformity with underlying Cretaceous or Tertiary strata but where an unconformity is present, overlying sediments are up to 80 m thick. The relief of the transverse troughs is much greater than the total thickness of Quaternary strata, and bedrock is exposed in places along the trough walls. Glacial till of the Baffin Shelf Drift underlies part of the floors and walls of the troughs with thicknesses up to 30 m, and is overlain by 2-3 m of acoustically stratified, poorly sorted gravelly sandy muds, correlative with the Davis Strait Silt of the Southeast Baffin Shelf. In Buchan Trough sediment of this unit interfingers with glacial till of Baffin Shelf Drift (Fig. 10.55). Poorly stratified basinal muds, correlative with the Tiniktartuq Silt and Clay of the Southeast Baffin Shelf form the floor of the transverse troughs. Inter-trough areas above depths of 300-500 m have been intensely scoured by grounding icebergs, and as a result, the Davis Strait Silt on the upper continental slope and upper trough walls is acoustically unstratified. Baffin Shelf Drift is exposed or thinly mantled by sediment over much of the shelf, and extends to near the shelf edge. On bank tops, in the area between Scott Inlet and Buchan Trough, the Tiniktartuq Silt and Clay locally overlies both Baffin Shelf Drift and Davis Strait Silt in small bathymetric depressions sheltered from

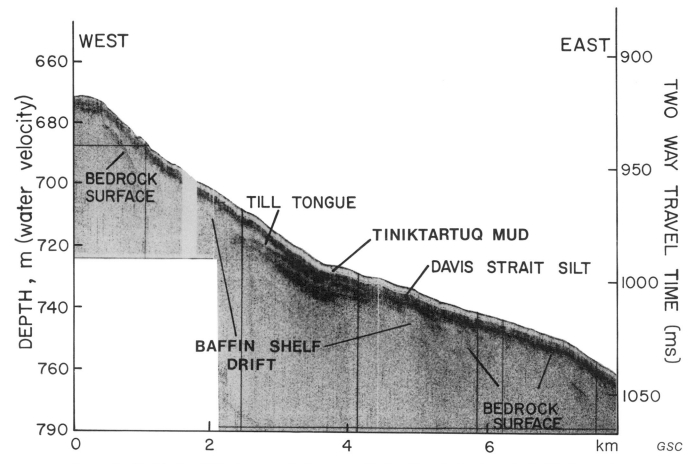

Figure 10.55. Huntec DTS seismic profile from outer Buchan Trough, Northeast Baffin Shelf, showing a till tongue of the Baffin Shelf Drift interfingering with well-stratified sediments of the Davis Strait Silt. The sequence is capped by poorly stratified basinal sediments of the Tiniktartuq Silt and Clay. See Figure 10.53 for location.

iceberg scouring. In water depths of less than 100 m, older Quaternary sediments or locally bedrock are overlain by sands and gravels with up to 30% mud, mapped as Cape Aston sand and gravel; iceberg scours are abundant but shallow in this area, implying a resistant seabed.

Total organic radiocarbon dates from three cores of the Tiniktartuq Silt and Clay in troughs off Narpaing Fiord and Scott Inlet, when corrected for contamination by reworked carbon (Andrews et al., 1985), record deposition since at least 12 ka (Andrews and Osterman, 1984; Jennings, 1985). A similar date of 11 770 ± 550 BP (GX-6280) from the Cape Aston sand and gravel off Cape Aston suggests at least partial synchroneity between this unit and the Tiniktartuq Silt and Clay. Biostratigraphic (foraminiferal) and mineralogical zonation of cores from both fiords and the continental shelf suggests a threefold division. The *Cassidulina reniforme* zone represents a cold meltwater environment from at least 12.3 ka to about 8 ka; the *Melonis zaandami* zone represents relatively warm water conditions from 8 to 7 ka, succeeded by a zone of arenaceous foraminifers representing conditions similar to those now dominated by the cold Baffin Current (Andrews and Osterman, 1984; Jennings, 1985).

The marine stratigraphy supports the terrestrial evidence that the Late Foxe ice advance at 8 to 9 ka was largely restricted to the fiord heads of northeast Baffin Island. Extrapolation of radiocarbon dates from cores of the Tiniktartuq Silt and Clay in Scott Trough (Jennings, 1985) suggests that the top of the underlying Davis Strait Silt is about 16 ka. This suggests a Middle to early Late Foxe age for the underlying Baffin Shelf Drift. Although evidence exists for an advance of similar age on the Southeast Baffin Shelf, the terrestrial glacial chronology suggests that the last ice to reach the Northeast Baffin Shelf was of Early Foxe age (Andrews and Miller, 1984). The number and extent of pre-Foxe glaciations that have affected the shelf is unknown.

The similarity in age and the relative distribution of the Tiniktartuq Silt and Clay and the Cape Aston sand and gravel (Andrews and Osterman, 1984) suggest that both units reflect postglacial erosion and redeposition of sediment. Andrews (1980), from evidence on northeast Baffin Island, proposed that relative sea levels were lower by as much as 80 m during much of the latter half of the Foxe glaciation; Quinlan (1985), however, inferred from isostatic modelling that sea levels were above present level for part of that time. Both lowered sea level and the action of the Baffin Current may have been important in sediment reworking, which was augmented by iceberg scouring.

Baffin Basin

A.E. Aksu and D.J.W. Piper

Physiography

Baffin Bay is a small ocean basin, separated from the Labrador Sea by the shallow Davis Strait. The western continental shelf is narrow and relatively shallow, except where crossed by deep troughs. The Greenland continental shelf is broad and deep, with a shelf break at 300 to 600 m. It is crossed by a few broad transverse troughs which appear to contain much sediment at their seaward end, which have significantly prograded the steep continental slope. In the northern part of the bay, there is no clear shelf

break, and a large sediment wedge appears to have prograded southeast from Lancaster Sound and northern Baffin Bay. The floor of Baffin Basin is a flat abyssal plain with maximum water depths of 2300 m, that has onlapped the continental slope without the development of a clear continental rise.

Neogene-Quaternary stratigraphy

A regional net of industry multichannel seismic profiles have been correlated to the stratigraphy at ODP Site 645 (Arthur et al., 1986). Srivastava et al. (1987) identified a regional unconformity (R-2) which is overlain by Middle Miocene to Lower Pliocene muds showing pronounced but variable influence of contour currents. Isolated ice-rafted granules occur in strata as old as Late Miocene, but the onset of major glacial ice-rafting dates from 3.4 Ma. A second major unconformity (R-1) (Srivastava et al., 1987) represents a major change in glacial sedimentation near the Early-Late Pliocene boundary, and also marks an increase in abundance of ice-rafted debris. The unconformity is overlain by a thick wedge of Upper Pliocene-Quaternary sediment prograded westward from the Greenland margin. Recovered cores (Fig. 10.51) show that the Late Pliocene to Early Pleistocene section (unit 2) consists of silty clays whereas the Early to Late Pleistocene sequence (unit 1b) shows a marked increase in detrital carbonate and clay. The upper 70 m of Upper Pleistocene sediments (Unit 1a) are much siltier, and are rhythmically banded. Insufficient published seismic profiles are available at present to integrate the data from the ODP site in southern Baffin Bay for a synthesis of Quaternary sediment accumulation in the entire bay, and in particular the age of the thick sediment wedge off Lancaster Sound.

Late Quaternary stratigraphy

About 60 piston cores are available from the deeper waters of the Baffin Bay region. On the basis of visual core descriptions, colour and mineralogical analysis, six facies have been distinguished (Aksu, 1981; Aksu and Piper, 1987). Figure 10.56 illustrates the schematic distribution of these facies in time and space. Facies A consists of yellow-brown, gravelly-sandy muds in distinct beds, 5 to 60 cm thick. It occurs predominantly in central Baffin Bay and becomes less abundant and thinner towards the eastern and southern parts of the bay. Most of this facies was deposited by ice rafting. The predominant source of ice-rafted detritus in facies A is carbonate rocks. Carbonate rocks are not found in the coastal areas of Baffin Island and Greenland, so that the source of this facies must be the more distant areas of Paleozoic limestones and dolomites in the eastern Sverdrup Basin and northwest Greenland. Facies B is composed of greyish red, gravelly-sandy muds, in beds 0.3 to 10 cm thick, also deposited through ice rafting. The distribution of this facies is similar to that of facies A, except that it is absent in cores south of 68°N latitude. The mineral assemblages suggest that the source of facies B is Proterozoic and Mesozoic-Cenozoic siliciclastic rocks of Bylot Island, the Sverdrup Basin and Disko Island. Facies C consists of olive-black, graded, gravelly-sandy muds in beds 25 to 125 cm thick (not shown in Fig. 10.56). This facies is the predominant lithology of the slope and rise cores off both Baffin Island and Greenland, but is absent elsewhere. Most of this facies is deposited as debris flows,

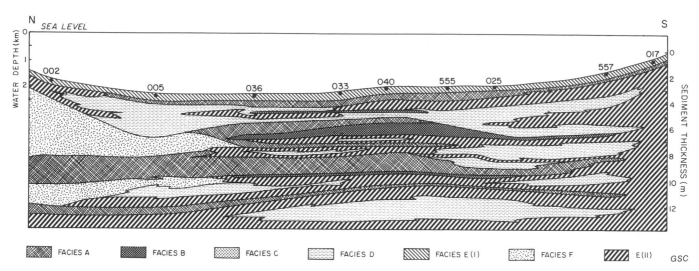

Figure 10.56. Schematic north-south cross-section through Baffin Bay and Davis Strait showing lithofacies based on cores shown in Figure 10.53 (Aksu, 1981). Lithofacies are described in text. Section length is about 750 km and is shown in Figure 10.53.

and the similarities in mineralogy with facies D suggest that facies C is probably the proximal equivalent of facies D. Mineralogically, the sediments in facies C are polycyclic and derived from mixed metamorphic, siliciclastic and carbonate sources. Facies D includes olive-grey gravelly sands, silt-to-mud couplets and muds. It is the dominant lithology in southern Baffin Bay and Davis Strait cores, and becomes less abundant and thinner towards the central bay. It is also the major lithology in cores from the northern bay. Graded gravelly sands and silt-to-mud couplets with complete or partial Bouma sequences suggest that these sediments were deposited by turbidity currents. Highly bioturbated sandy muds with no structural features and with occasional coarse lag deposits and cross to parallel laminations indicate intermittent reworking by bottom currents. Facies E consists of 30 to 40 cm thick beds of brown diatomaceous (Ei) and greenish grey foraminiferal (Eii) mud with as much as 20% ice-rafted sand and gravel. Ei occurs only at the top of all cores examined, and Eii is found at several levels in the cores. Sediments in this facies are bioturbated and are interpreted as hemipelagic augmented by ice rafting. Mineralogical heterogenity observed in all size fractions examined indicates that most outcrops encircling Baffin Bay are potential sources for facies E. Facies F consists of reddish brown, gravelly sandy muds, silt-to-mud couplets and muds. It is the dominant lithology in cores from northwest Baffin Bay and becomes less abundant and thinner towards the central bay, where it exhibits a lateral intercalated contact with facies A, B or D. Structural, textural and fabric data indicate that most of facies F was deposited by debris flows (Aksu, 1984), some of which generated turbidity currents that travelled onto the abyssal plain. Mineralogical data indicate that the Proterozoic and Mesozoic-Cenozoic siliciclastics and the Ordovician-Silurian carbonates of the Arctic Islands are the main source for this facies.

Adjacent cores in Baffin Bay commonly show similar facies sequences, which allows a broad lithological correlation to be established (Fig. 10.57). Several techniques strengthen the lithological correlations and place the observed record into a chronological framework. These include volcanic ash stratigraphy, paleomagnetism, microfossils, oxygen isotope stratigraphy and ^{14}C dating. Oxygen isotopes of the planktonic foraminifera *Neogloboquadrina pachyderma* (sinistral) in cores 040 and 017 (Fig. 10.57) show intervals of alternating light and heavy isotopic composition, with amplitudes much greater than those in the standard oxygen isotope stratigraphy. These cycles are defined as local isotopic stages (Fig. 10.58). The isotopically heavy stages must correspond to glacial stages in the standard (open ocean) isotopic stratigraphy, but the stages with unusually light isotopic composition represent major local melt events, some of which may not correlate with isotopically light periods in the standard isotopic stratigraphy. Radiocarbon dates show that local stages 1 and 2 correspond to standard isotopic stages 1 and 2, but it is uncertain whether this one for one correlation extends all the way back to isotopic stage 10 (Aksu, 1983a), or whether the oldest cored sediments date from isotopic stage 6 (Aksu and Piper, 1979; de Vernal, 1986).

The correlation between the oxygen isotope stratigraphy and the abundance of various microfossils and ice-rafted debris, including volcanic ash, can be used to interpret the paleo-oceanography of Baffin Bay (Aksu, 1983a). During full glacial stages, subarctic water from the south penetrated to about 72°N throughout Baffin Bay, since the southward flow of arctic water was inhibited by glacial and sea ice in the Arctic Island Channels (Fig. 10.59). The early stages of deglaciation were marked by enhanced penetration of subarctic water, but with deglaciation a strong flow of Arctic water was established over the western half of the bay (Fig. 10.59)

Figure 10.57. Summary stratigraphic correlation of piston cores from Baffin Bay. A1 to A3 = Ash levels 1 to 3; P = paleomagnetic reversal; F1/2 to F7/8 = biogenic zone boundaries; local isotopic stages from cores 040 and 017 (Aksu, 1981, 1983a). (For significance of local isotopic stages, see text.) For core locations see Figure 10.53.

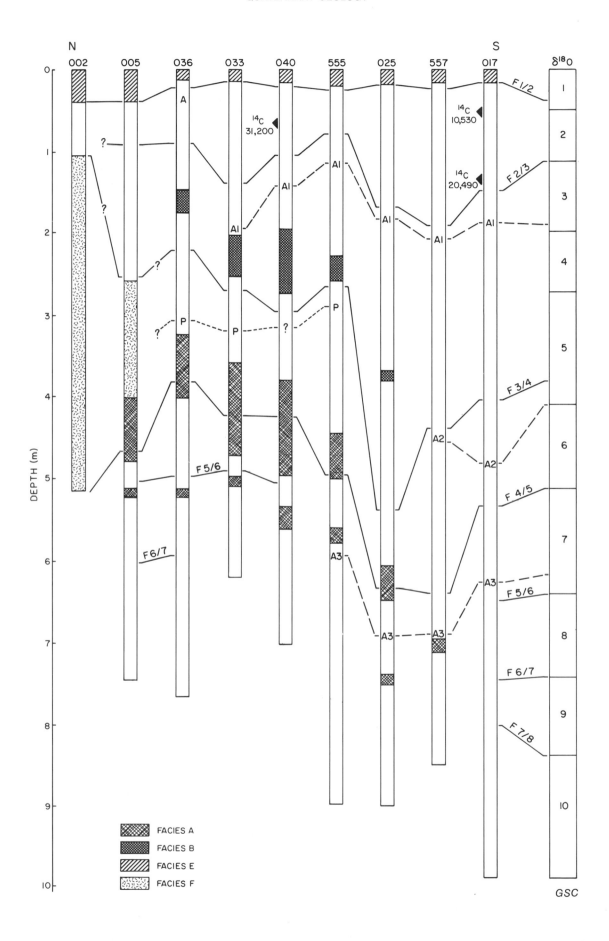

CORE 040

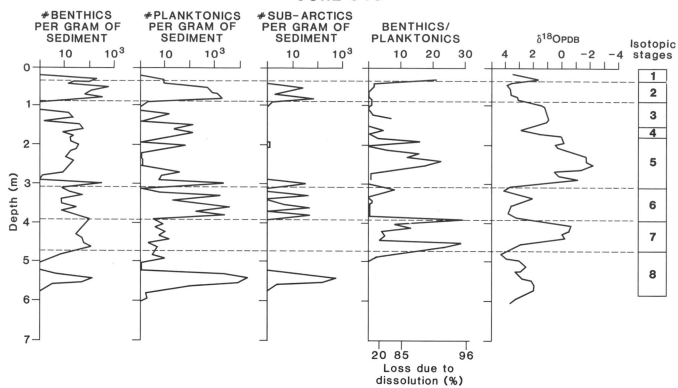

CORE 017

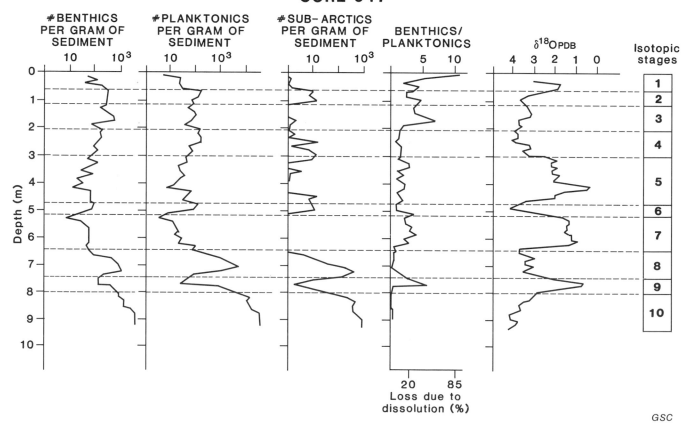

GSC

Figure 10.58. Foraminiferal assemblages and local oxygen isotope stratigraphy in Baffin Bay cores 040 and 017 (Aksu, 1983a). For core locations see Figure 10.53.

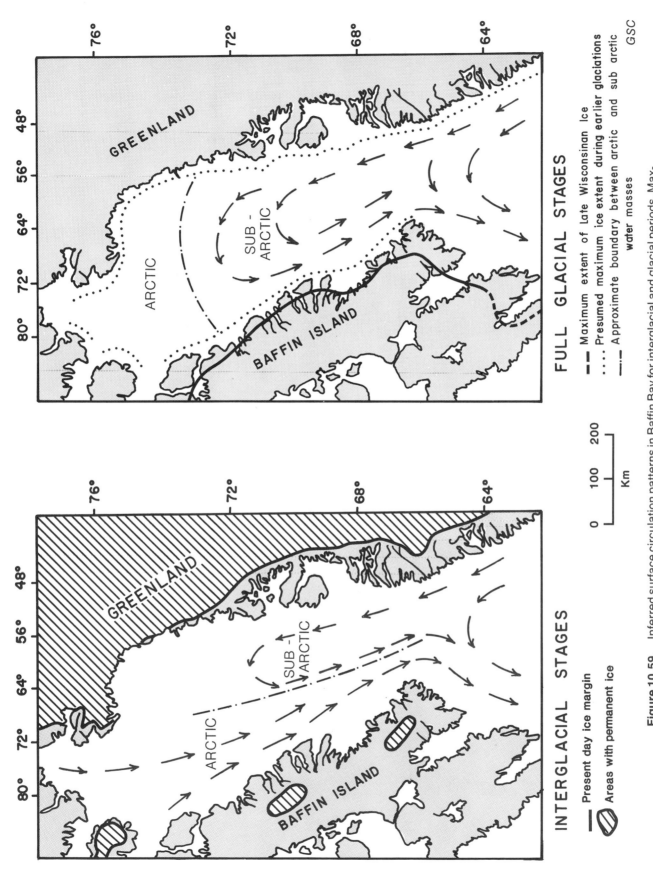

FULL GLACIAL STAGES

ARCTIC

SUB-ARCTIC

GREENLAND

BAFFIN ISLAND

—·— Maximum extent of Late Wisconsinan Ice

········ Presumed maximum ice extent during earlier glaciations

—···— Approximate boundary between arctic and sub arctic water masses

GSC

INTERGLACIAL STAGES

ARCTIC

SUB-ARCTIC

GREENLAND

BAFFIN ISLAND

——— Present day ice margin

⬭ Areas with permanent ice

0   100   200
Km

Figure 10.59. Inferred surface circulation patterns in Baffin Bay for interglacial and glacial periods. Maximum extent of Late Wisconsinan Ice is after Andrews and Ives (1978); presumed maximum ice extent during earlier glaciations is after Weidick (1976).

571

THE ARCTIC OCEAN REGION

Marine areas of the Canadian Arctic Archipelago

G. Vilks, J.-S. Vincent, D.A. Hodgson, B.R. Pelletier, and D.J.W. Piper

The presence of perennial polar ice in the marine channels of the Canadian Arctic Archipelago (Fig. 10.60) interferes with marine geological studies, and as a result, the available information lacks regional coherence.[†] The glacial record on land, however, in the western and northern Arctic Archipelago is one of the longest known in Canada (Craig and Fyles, 1960; Hodgson, in press; Vincent, 1983, in press a).

The earlier history of the marine channels is deduced from regional physiography of the seafloor. Cenozoic faulting is widespread in the Archipelago, and the channels are inherited from a Late Tertiary fluvial drainage system (Fortier and Morley, 1956). The watershed between rivers flowing east to Baffin Bay and those flowing west to the Arctic Ocean was in the vicinity of Barrow Strait (Bornhold et al., 1976).

Successive glacial advances to the inter-island channels produced features such as U-shaped valleys, hanging valleys along the walls of major channels, truncated spurs, hummocky channel bottoms, in places with clear morainal morphology, and the shoaling of valleys towards the Arctic Shelf (Pelletier, 1966, 1980). The history of the Arctic Shelf is less well known, although it may be assumed that it was influenced both by advance of ice sheets and fluctuations in relative sea level (Pelletier, 1966).

The Early Pleistocene Banks Glaciation (Vincent, 1983, in press a) advanced onto the area covering most of Banks Island and extended well onto the Arctic Shelf. It is dated as within the Matuyama reversed magnetic epoch (>0.8 Ma, Vincent et al., 1984), and may be correlated with events in the Arctic Ocean basin (Clark et al., 1984). This glaciation was by far the strongest all time glacial advance in the area and it probably had the greatest effect on the morphology of the inter-island channels and continental shelf. Glacio-isostatic depression resulted in wave cut features more than 30 m above present sea level (Vincent, in press a). In the Middle Pleistocene, the terrestrial record suggests a long relatively warm non-glacial period (Morgan Bluffs Interglacial of Vincent, in press a); analogous Middle Pleistocene conditions have been recognized on the Alaskan Arctic Coastal Plain (Carter et al., 1986). In the late Middle Pleistocene, continental ice advanced again towards the Beaufort Sea (Thomsen Glaciation on Banks Island — Vincent, 1983; Mason River Glaciation on the mainland — Rampton, 1988). This ice did not reach western Banks Island, but extended into Amundsen Gulf and likely down M'Clure Strait. Isostatic depression resulted in marine deposits at 60 m above present sea level in western Banks Island.

During the Wisconsin glaciation, an earlier and a less extensive later glacial advance are distinguished; the age of the earlier advance is uncertain. This earlier glaciation extended in the form of ice streams and ice shelves to the mouth of M'Clure Strait and Amundsen Gulf from the southeast. This ice may be the one responsible for the erratics in the Flaxman Member of the Gubik Formation of the Alaskan Arctic Coastal Plain (Carter et al., 1986). Isostatic depression was in the order of 20 m on western Banks Island. In the late Wisconsinan advance, ice was less extensive in the western Arctic. Glaciers of the Queen Elizabeth Ice complex expanded to limits not yet defined, in some cases at least to fiord mouths (Hodgson, in press). Late Wisconsinan and Holocene emerged marine deposits, documenting glacio-isostatic depression, rise from about 10 m on Prince Patrick Island to over 150 m on Bathurst and Ellesmere islands. On western Banks Island and the southern Beaufort Sea coast marine transgression is still in progress from a low (-150 m) Middle or Late Wisconsinan stand.

Relatively little is known of Quaternary marine sediments in the Canadian Arctic Archipelago.[†] Short cores and bottom grab samples collected through ice comprise mainly silt and clay between the Sverdrup Islands (Horn, 1967), in Hecla and Griper bays (Vilks, 1969), and in M'Clure Strait (Iqbal, 1973). In Prince Gustaf Adolf Sea, Marlowe (1968) found about 10 cm of bioturbated Holocene surficial sediments overlying darker unfossiliferous sediment. To the south, between Melville and Lougheed islands, MacLean and Vilks (1986) also discovered 20-30 cm of brown surface mud underlain by stratified deposits, which are mainly unfossiliferous (Fig. 10.61). Holocene sedimentation rates of a few centimetres per thousand years in the channels were suggested by Vilks (1969). Marlowe (1968) explained the darker subsurface layer by the presence of an ice shelf in the channels. Evidence for an extensive ice shelf over Viscount Melville Sound at 10 000 BP has also been presented by Hodgson and Vincent (1984).

Lancaster Sound is a glacially modified graben with steep flanks and a relatively flat floor with water depths of around 500 m. Seismic reflection profiles suggest substantial thickness of till in western Lancaster Sound. This is exposed at the seabed in Barrow Strait, where it is reworked by bottom currents (Buckley, 1971; Pelletier, 1980), and in places along the flanks of Lancaster Sound (Lewis et al., 1977). Stratified sediments that have accumulated in deeper basins in the sound are 30 m thick east of Barrow Strait, and are up to 200 m thick at the mouth of Lancaster Sound where they merge with deeper water sediments in Baffin Bay. This thickness of stratified sediments suggests that the tills on the floor of the sound are pre-Late Foxe. The carbonate-rich moraine on northeastern Bylot Island (Klassen, 1981, 1985) probably dates from the Early Foxe on the basis of amino-acid ratios (Andrews et al., 1984) and represents a period of grounded ice in Lancaster Sound. This advance correlates with the widespread lithic carbonate horizon of similar age in Baffin Bay.

Jones Sound contains a deep axial trough 500 to 800 m deep bordered by platforms less than 200 m deep. Glacial till up to 40 m thick has been identified in several areas, and is overlain by a few metres of stratified fine grained sediments, attaining 15 m in thickness in the deeper parts of the Sound (MacLean et al., 1984).

[†] See Addendum

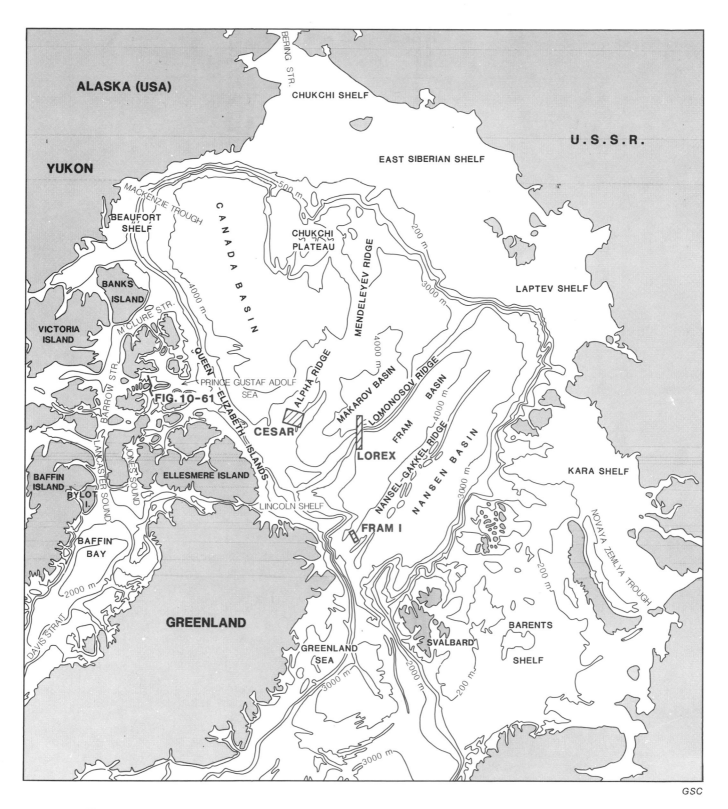

Figure 10.60. Marine physiographic and bathymetric features of the Arctic Ocean region. Detailed study areas (CESAR, LOREX, and FRAM I) are indicated. Canada Basin and Makarov Basin are referred to as the Amerasian Basin, and that Fram Basin and Nansen Basin constitute the Eurasian Basin.

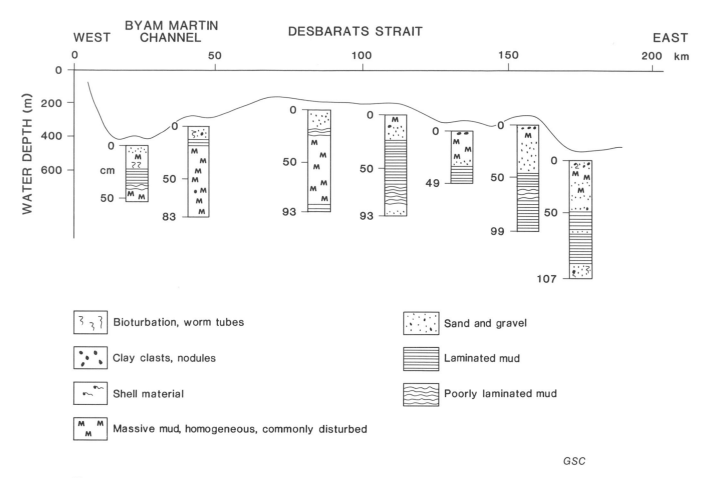

Figure 10.61. Interpreted x-radiographs of short cores for an east-west profile through Desbarats Strait and Byam Martin Channel (from MacLean and Vilks, 1986). For locations of section see Figure 10.60.

Beaufort Sea

P.R. Hill and S.M. Blasco

Of the marine areas bordering the Arctic Ocean (Fig. 10.60), the Quaternary geology of the Beaufort Sea is best known on account of the large amount of work done in support of hydrocarbon exploration, which is made possible by the longer ice-free season in that area. The Beaufort Shelf is divided into an eastern and western part by the deep Mackenzie Trough (Fig. 10.62). The eastern Beaufort Shelf off the Mackenzie Delta consists of a series of deeper transverse troughs separated by shallower "plateaus", with a shelf break at 70-80 m (Fig. 10.62). It is underlain by a thick, prograded, Cenozoic delta sequence. The western Beaufort Shelf off the Yukon is characterized by shallow, shore-parallel troughs and ridges leading to a shelf break at 70-80 m. It is underlain by a relatively thin Quaternary sequence and folded pre-Miocene sediments.

Quaternary sediments are included in the Iperk and Shallow Bay stratigraphic sequences of Dietrich et al. (1985). The Iperk sequence may include Pliocene and even Miocene sediments but the total thickness of Quaternary sediments beneath the Beaufort Shelf probably increases from a few tens of metres near the present coastline to several thousand metres beneath the shelf break. The

sequence consists of interbedded marine, deltaic and fluvial deposits with a general coarsening of lithologies to the east (Young and McNeil, 1984). Growth faults with associated mud diapirs and fluid escape are common. Discontinuous permafrost occurs to subbottom depths of several hundred metres, reflecting periodic emergence of the Mackenzie Delta in the past.

Upper Pleistocene marine and deltaic sediments and thick nonmarine or littoral sands underlie most of the Beaufort Shelf. On the Akpak and Tingmiark plateaus, these sediments comprise 40 m thick, cross-stratified sand sequences, with complex grain-surface textures (Hill and Nadeau, 1985) suggesting a depositional environment of a glacial outwash sandur plain. Shell-bearing marine sediments represent intervals of localized marine transgression. Numerous shallow depressions on the upper surface of this sequence may represent thaw subsidence lakes. The sand sequence is underlain by 40 m of marine and deltaic silts and clays, which in turn overlie a second sand sequence, at least 20 m thick, with characteristics similar to those of the upper sand unit. On the outer shelf and in the Kringalik area, constructional distributary channels with massive sandy mouth bars are distinguished. The Pleistocene sequence on the Kringalik Plateau consists of

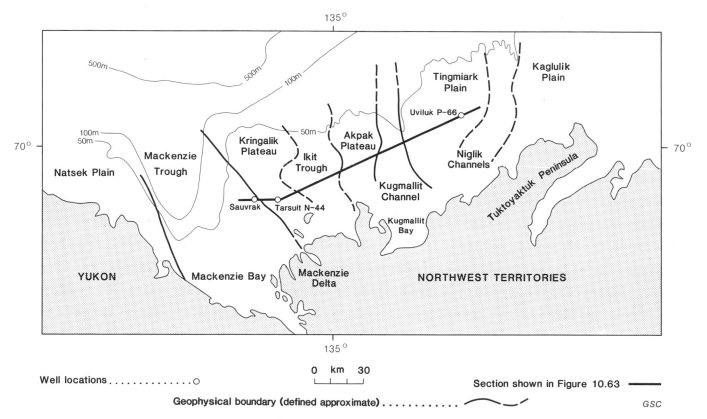

Figure 10.62. Physiographic features of the Beaufort Sea.

predominantly marine and deltaic clays and silts, in contrast to the sandier sequence to the east.

Seismic reflection profiles show that the Ikit and Kugmallit troughs represent broad river valleys, several kilometres wide, that were incised to a depth of 30 m below the general elevation of the shelf. Smaller river channels that have migrated laterally are recognized on the valley floors. These channels give oblique progradational reflectors. A synthesis of the Late Pleistocene sedimentation and its complex relationship with sea level changes is given by Hill et al. (1985).

This Pleistocene deltaic and outwash complex is unconformably overlain (unconformity 1, Fig. 10.63) by a discontinuous unit of stratified sands and muds representing coastal and nearshore facies developed during latest Pleistocene and early Holocene marine transgression. This unit is thickest in the Ikit and Kugmallit troughs, where it is overlain by onlapping Holocene muds up to 30 m thick derived from the modern Mackenzie River (J.R. Harper and S. Penland, pers. comm., 1982).

Stratigraphic correlation is difficult in a sequence with such depositional complexity. The deltaic aspect of many of the sediments means that few marine microfossils are available and most palynomorphs are detrital. Long geotechnical boreholes provide an opportunity to sample the Late Quaternary section, and therefore some preliminary biostratigraphic data are available. A continuous pollen profile in the 60 m long Sauvrak borehole penetrates Holocene sediments to 15 m and indicates that the base of the surficial muds at this site is about 6.5 ka. Few Pleistocene radiocarbon dates are available, the oldest

being a littoral peat from a delta sequence in a borehole at Tarsuit N-44 well site at 130 m below the sea floor that gave an age of 27 380 ± 470 BP (B-5069). A second total organic radiocarbon date of 21 620 ± 630 BP (B-6276) at the base of the marine deltaic sequence on the Tingmiark plain indicates that the upper sandur plain sequence is Late Wisconsinan.

The relative sea level history of the last 27 ka proposed by Hill et al. (1985) shows a continuous rise in sea level from a −150 m Middle Wisconsinan lowering. The marked erosion of deltaic features on the outer shelf and the incision of the Ikit and Kugmallit troughs represent a minor lowering of sea level in the Late Wisconsinan. The Middle Wisconsinan lowering probably requires substantial ice loading at that time within several hundred kilometres of the Mackenzie Delta (Hill et al., 1985), in contrast to the terrestrial geological history proposed by Rampton (1982), who suggested substantial ice retreat at that time. There remains, however, considerable uncertainty about the position and ages of ice limits in the vicinity of the Beaufort coast. Rampton (1982) recognized a "Buckland" glacial limit which extended to just west of Herschel Island and covered most of the Mackenzie Delta and Tuktoyaktuk Peninsula. This limit is inferred to be early Wisconsinan in age, based on subdued moraine morphology and a date of 22 400 ± 240 (GSC 1262; Rampton, 1982) on peat overlying the Buckland drift. This limit represents the farthest documented extent of Laurentide ice in this region. Hughes (1972), however, had previously traced the same limit 450 km south to the western margin of the Bonnet Plume Basin. *Picea* wood from sand underlying till in this

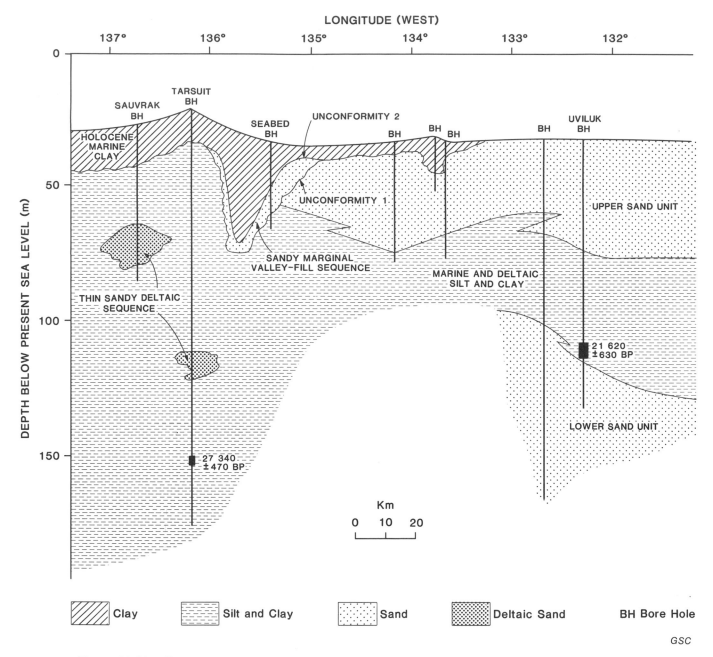

Figure 10.63. East-west transect of the eastern Beaufort Sea continental shelf showing Upper Quaternary lithofacies based on seismic reflection profiles and borehole data. Location of section is shown in Figure 10.62.

area yielded a date of 36 900 ± 300 (GSC 2422) (Hughes et al., 1981), suggesting that the Buckland limit was Middle to Late Wisconsinan.

The Mackenzie Trough is interpreted as a glacially modified valley (Shearer, 1971), filled with over 300 m of Wisconsinan deltaic and possibly glacial deposits. The trough is eroded into folded Tertiary strata and truncates presumed Pleistocene deposits at its western margin.

The Quaternary history of the western Beaufort Shelf off the Yukon coast is much less well known than that of the eastern shelf. The overall Quaternary sequence is thinner, and pre-Upper Wisconsinan strata over most of this part of the shelf appear to have been truncated by the Late Pleistocene-Holocene transgression. Preliminary analysis of seismic data indicates that at least three acoustic units, separated by unconformities, can be identified. The unconformities show low-angle discordance at the margin of Mackenzie Trough, and form sub-horizontal reflectors with no obvious discordance farther to the west. Shallow cores and grab samples indicate that the topmost unit consists of marine silty clay with minor gravel. The gravel forms a surficial lag deposit over much of the western Beaufort Shelf.

Arctic continental shelf and ocean basin

P.J. Mudie

The Arctic Ocean is a small, almost land-locked ocean (Fig. 10.60) which is roughly centred on the North Pole and has only one major connection with the world's major oceans, through the Greenland Sea. Narrow connections exist, however, with the Pacific Ocean through Bering Strait and with the Atlantic Ocean through the Arctic Island Channels. Overflow of Arctic Surface Water through these channels plays an important role in the water circulation and sedimentology of Baffin Bay and the western Labrador Sea (Aksu, 1983a; Aksu and Mudie, 1985a).

More than 90% of the Arctic Ocean is covered by perennial sea ice about 3 m thick, thus navigation by ship is hazardous or impossible in most areas. Geological research has largely been carried out from ice islands (e.g. Fletcher's Ice Island T-3, ARLIS II) or from temporary camps on drifting ice floes (e.g. FRAM, LOREX and CESAR). Consequently, although the general bathymetry of the Arctic Ocean has been mapped, detailed soundings are only available for a few areas: southeastern Alpha Ridge (CESAR) (Jackson, 1985) and the Lomonosov Ridge-Makarov Basin area mapped from LOREX (Weber, 1983).

In general, the Arctic Ocean is flanked by wide continental shelves up to 800 km wide along the Siberian and Eurasian coasts (Chukchi-Kara and Barents Shelf, respectively). The outer continental margin generally descends steeply to about 1500 m, then slopes gently to abyssal plains with an average depth of about 4000 m (Hunkins, 1968). Two major ridge systems traverse the Arctic Basin: Alpha Ridge and Lomonosov Ridge. These ridges separate the three major abyssal plains of the Arctic Ocean: the large Canada Basin to the west; the narrow Makarov Basin in the centre (Siberia and Wrangel abyssal plains of Hunkins, 1968); and the Eurasia Basin to the east. The Eurasia Basin is further subdivided into the Fram and Nansen (or Amundsen) basins by the low rise (1 km) of the Nansen-Gakkel Ridge (also known as the Arctic Mid-Ocean Ridge).

Little is known about the pre-Quaternary history of the thick sediments blanketing most of the Arctic Ocean seafloor. In Canada Basin, more than 6 km of sediments occur off the western Beaufort Shelf (Eittreim and Grantz, 1979). There and north of the Chukchi Plateau are sites of the highest rates of Quaternary sediment deposition: 8.3 cm/ka, compared to an average rate of 2 mm/ka for most of Canada Basin (Clark, 1981). Turbidites make up more than 25% of the cores from water depths of 3 km in these areas of high sedimentation. The mineralogy and distribution of turbidite units suggest that most of them originated on the Canadian continental margin. According to Clark (1981), these turbidites probably result from seismic shocks or oversteepening of slopes due to accumulation of fluvial sediments off the Mackenzie Delta.

The Alpha Ridge has a rugged relief. Small scale irregularities in seabed topography are observed on 3.5 kHz records, and the variable thickness of Plio-Pleistocene sedimentary units (Mudie and Blasco, 1985) suggests that local slumping and erosion have occurred. In general, however, a distinctive sequence of up to 14 Upper Cenozoic lithostratigraphic units (Fig. 10.64), found throughout the area investigated in the CESAR program, can be correlated with cores from most other parts of the Alpha Ridge (Minicucci and Clark, 1983). Although the

age of these sedimentary units is the subject of much debate (Sejrup et al., 1984; Markussen et al., 1985), high resolution paleomagnetic studies (Aksu, 1985a) and palynological correlation with dated northwest European stratotypes and biochronologies from Deep Sea Drilling Project sites in the North Atlantic (Mudie, 1985; Aksu and Mudie, 1985b) strongly support previous age assignments of about 4 Ma for the oldest sedimentary unit (Clark, 1981; Herman, 1974) and confirm that sedimentation rates on the Alpha Ridge are about 1 mm/ka. The uppermost lithostratigraphic units, M to K, consist of bioturbated carbonate muds (with both biogenic and lithic carbonate) that alternate with foraminifer-poor, silty lutites. These sequences were deposited at approximately 0.3 to 0.4 Ma intervals since the end of the Early Pleistocene (Brunhes/Matuyama boundary). The older units, I to A3, are mainly brown arenaceous muds, interlayered with coarse sandy beds (units H, F, C). The mud units contain abundant small ferromanganese micronodules. Units H to A3 contain a low diversity of arenaceous benthic foraminifers and palynomorphs; calcareous and siliceous microfossils are usually absent below unit H.

Bathymetric and shallow seismic reflection profiles over the Lomonosov Ridge near the North Pole (Blasco et al., 1979) show that the ridge is covered by a thin veneer (<1.5 m) of unconsolidated sediments over bedrock that is being eroded by bottom currents. Short cores obtained from the Makarov Basin, Fram Basin and Lomonosov Ridge during the Lomonosov Ridge Experiment (LOREX) contain similar sequences of soft brown silty clay grading downwards to firm, thinly bedded greyish clay, with interlayered grayish silt and olive clay beds at the base (Blasco et al., 1979; Clark et al., 1983). These sequences suggest interbedded pelagic and turbidite facies. The ridge cores have a larger proportion of coarse grained sediment which probably reflects stronger current action and better preservation of calcareous microfossils. Morris (1983) concluded that all the sediments were deposited slowly during the middle and Late Pleistocene and the frequent absence of calcareous foraminifers in the Makarov Basin reflects vertical fluctuations of the lysocline which did not affect the ridge crest fauna. He also proposed a lithostratigraphic correlation of units on the Lomonosov Ridge and Makarov Basin with units M-K on the Alpha Ridge (Fig. 10.64). In contrast, Markussen et al. (1985), who studied short cores (90 cm) from 2990-3820 m in the southeastern Fram Basin (Fig. 10.60), found numerous intervals of abundant planktonic foraminifers, as well as calcareous benthic foraminifera and other calcareous microfossils. An oxygen isotope stratigraphy obtained from *Neogloboquadrina pachyderma* (left-coiling) was correlated with the standard North Atlantic stratigraphy showing that sedimentation rates (1-2 cm/ka) are relatively high.

At present (1985), interpretation of the Quaternary paleoenvironmental history of the Arctic Ocean is controversial because of lack of agreement regarding the age of the lithostratigraphic units and interpretation of oxygen isotopic records, differing emphasis on the environmental implications of coarse grained sediments, and lack of modern analogues for the brown arenaceous mud units. There is general agreement that the widespread lithological correlation between units K-M must largely reflect the importance of glaciogenic transport of clastic sediment (Clark and Hansen, 1983) by sea ice (silt and fine sand) and by icebergs (silt- to cobble-size clasts), and that an ice cover

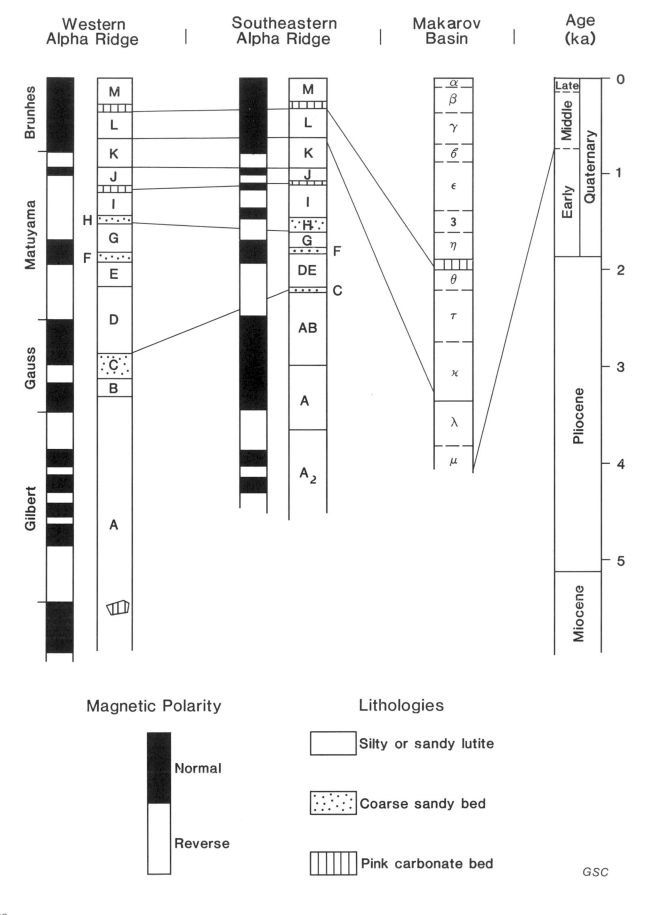

Western Alpha Ridge | Southeastern Alpha Ridge | Makarov Basin | Age (ka)

Magnetic Polarity

Normal

Reverse

Lithologies

Silty or sandy lutite

Coarse sandy bed

Pink carbonate bed

GSC

similar to the present has existed during most of the past 0.7 Ma. However, more detailed interpretations are disputed. For example, attempts have been made to correlate the foraminifer-rich intervals with North American glacial stages (Clark, 1981), with the Banks Island Pleistocene record (Clark et al., 1984), and with the global ice volume curve of Shackleton and Opdyke (Minicucci and Clark, 1983). These studies have led to the conclusion that there has been a warming trend from maximum cold in the Pliocene to increasingly frequent intervals of warmer conditions during the Quaternary. Oxygen isotopic studies of *Neogloboquadrina pachyderma* (left-coiling) in CESAR cores (Aksu, 1985b), however, show that the Alpha Ridge isotopic stratigraphy contains a different chronology of light isotopic peaks compared with the global standard. This difference may be due either to bioturbational mixing of isotopic events in the sediments of the Alpha Ridge, where the sedimentation rate is low, or to a different isotopic record of glacial-interglacial events in the almost land-locked Arctic Ocean. Studies of sediments in which the sedimentation rate is high, from the continental shelves around the Arctic Ocean, for example, are needed to resolve this controversy.

More study is also needed to confirm the interpretation that intervals of coarse sediments in units I-A3 reflect continuous or oscillating periods of thick ice cover (Clark, 1981; Clark et al., 1984; Aksu, 1985b). These units contain rare pebbles and some quartz grains which exhibit glacially-abraded surface features. The older arenaceous brown muds clearly indicate paleoenvironmental conditions or bottom water chemistry different from the carbonate-rich younger sediments. Data are insufficient, however, to determine whether the absence of calcareous microfossils and sparse flora indicate a thicker ice cover (Clark, 1981) or increased density stratification due to increased inflow of low salinity surface water from a deeper Bering Strait entrance (Herman, 1970; Worsley and Herman, 1980). The presence in units DE to A3 of Neogene dinoflagellate cysts that are dominant or common in Upper Miocene-Pliocene Bering Sea sediments (Mudie, 1985) tends to support the latter hypothesis. More study of the taxonomy and paleogeography of microfossils and palynomorphs and of the origin of the coarse grained sediments is needed, however, before any definite conclusions can be drawn regarding the timing of initial glaciation and sea ice formation in the Arctic Ocean. Until these data are available, models that predict an extensive floating Arctic Ocean ice sheet during the latest Pliocene and the entire Pleistocene (Williams et al., 1981) must remain speculative.

Figure 10.64. Summary lithostratigraphy for Arctic Ocean cores from the western Alpha Ridge (Gilbert and Clark, 1982), the southeastern Alpha Ridge (Mudie and Blasco, 1985) and Makarov Basin-Lomonosov Ridge (Morris, 1983). Letters indicate local stratigraphic subdivisions.

SYNTHESIS

Geomorphological evolution
D.J.W. Piper

Glaciated shelf morphology

All the continental shelves of eastern Canada have similar morphological characteristics resulting from glaciation, which distinguish them from most other continental shelves of the world (Shepard, 1972). In most areas, the inner shelf has a very irregular morphology, with numerous small islands, shoals and basins in resistant bedrock — morphological features similar to those on the adjacent land areas. The general surface elevation is commonly a continuation of peneplane surfaces seen on land. Glacially excavated fiords, both shallow and deep, indent the coastline. Where these fiords continue seawards as transverse saddles, the greatest water depths are generally within the fiords, which have shallow sills of bedrock, generally mantled by till.

The middle shelf areas, seaward of the contact of Mesozoic and Tertiary sediments with older bedrock, are characterized by a series of broad basins (as on the Scotian Shelf) or a more continuous marginal trough (as on the Labrador Shelf). The overdeepened character of the middle shelf basins suggests that glacial erosion has played an important role in their formation (Holtedahl, 1970; McMillan, 1978); the occurrence of greatest water depths where saddles cross the middle shelf points to the erosive role of major ice streams.

Most outer shelf areas consist of shallow banks separated by transverse saddles (troughs). On most banks, the relief is developed in Tertiary bedrock, whereas on Sable Island Bank and Banquereau most of the relief on the seaward side results from the deposition of glacial till or proglacial sediment. In many glaciations, ice extended seaward through the saddles, but terminated at the margins of the banks.

The saddles or transverse troughs that cross the continental shelves generally lie seaward of major valley systems on land, and represent the path of major ice streams flowing from the continent. Their greatest depths are generally within coastal fiords or on the middle shelf, and most show a steady decrease in depth towards the shelf break. This decrease is principally the result of less erosion of bedrock, rather than increasing deposition of till.

Sub-glacial meltwater channels are significant geomorphic features on lower latitude shelves, such as the Bay of Fundy, Scotian Shelf and Grand Banks. Most, however, have been subsequently filled by sediment.

Tertiary evolution of continental shelves

The relative importance of glacial erosion — compared with inheritance of a fluvially-dominated landscape from the Tertiary — to the eastern Canadian continental shelves has been debated ever since the early work of Johnson (1925) and Shepard (1930). Seismic reflection profiling and sampling in the Gulf of Maine, Scotian Shelf, Grand Banks and Gulf of St. Lawrence shows that many of the shallower morphological features are underlain by sedimentary bedrock (Tertiary on the Scotian Shelf and Grand Banks, Mesozoic in the Gulf of Maine, Paleozoic in the Gulf of St. Lawrence). The inner shelf areas conform closely to the peneplain surfaces seen on land. The bedrock-controlled residual cuesta landscape was last sculptured by fluvial processes during the Late Pliocene and Early Pleistocene when the geological record in deep water indicates there were low stands of sea level and much fluvial sediment was supplied to the shelf break. Many of the features must date partly from earlier Neogene periods of lowered sea level. Only in the deeper coastal inlets, the overdeepened mid-shelf basins, the transverse troughs and the sub-glacial drainage channels have there been substantial modifications to the fluvially-dominated landscape of the Late Cenozoic. Many of the transverse troughs are along old fluvial valleys. Thick Quaternary sediments have masked the older landscape on some of the outer banks.

On the deeper Labrador and Southeast Baffin shelves, there has been less erosion of what are, presumably, Upper Tertiary sediments. There, seismic reflection profiles show significant aggradation and progradation of preglacial strata, particularly on the Labrador Shelf, in contrast to the erosional unconformity on the shallower southern shelves. The inherited fluvially dominated landscape is thus one that has superimposed on it more depositional features, particularly on the outer shelf. The landward margins of some banks on the Labrador shelf do appear, however, to be old cuestas facing a major strike valley developed along the contact between Mesozoic-Cenozoic continental shelf sediments and Paleozoic-Precambrian basement (see Chapter 7). Tertiary sediments of the transverse troughs were excavated, but it is unclear how much of the morphology of the troughs may be derived from earlier fluvial erosion.

On the Northeast Baffin Shelf, although there is an unconformity of glacial over preglacial strata, it is masked by many tens of metres of Quaternary strata that are the seaward continuation of the foreland deposits of Baffin Island. The lack of a marginal trough off northeastern Baffin Island probably reflects the intense channelling of ice into the fiords along its mountainous coast, and the seaward flow of this ice through the transverse troughs. Ice probably only very rarely extended across the banks of the Northeast Baffin Shelf.

Thus the characterization of the irregular shelves off eastern Canada as typical glaciated shelves (Shepard, 1972) does not imply that glaciation is the dominant process to have shaped the morphology of these continental shelves. Glacial erosion may have produced pronounced relief locally, but much of the irregular morphology of the continental shelf has been inherited from a Late Pliocene-Early Pleistocene fluvial landscape. A similar fluvial landscape developed on the coastal plain and the unglaciated continental shelf of the United States to the south. Glaciation on the Canadian margin resulted in little Late Quaternary sediment accumulation (average 20 m on the Grand Banks, 50 m on the Scotian Shelf), compared with the much thicker sequences on the United States margin.

Large scale tectonic control

The unusually great depth of glaciated shelves is a well known phenomenon (Shepard, 1972) that is generally ascribed to a combination of isostatic loading and glacial erosion. The significant change in water depth at 48.5°N from the shallow southern shelves to the deep northern shelves is difficult to explain by either process. Rather, it apparently reflects fundamental differences in underlying lithosphere evolution, with the boundary marked by features such as the Dover Fault and the Charlie-Gibbs Fracture Zone. If the Labrador and Baffin shelves had been at greater depths during the Late Cenozoic, preglacial sediments would have accumulated on these shelves, so that shelf morphology now would be principally the result of glacial erosion and deposition. On the southern shelves, the lesser water depth and subaerial exposure from time to time would have permitted significant preglacial fluvial erosion, which has been modified only locally by glacial erosion and deposition.

The northward increase in elevation of the coastal regions from the Atlantic provinces to Baffin Island also reflects long-term tectonic evolution (see Chapters 7 and 9). This relief controlled the style of glaciation affecting the continental shelf; alpine glaciation predominated on the northeastern Baffin Shelf, piedmont glaciation on the northern Labrador Shelf, and more continuous icesheets farther south.

The role of sea level changes

Major changes in sea level played an important role in geomorphological evolution. Late Tertiary lowerings of sea level in areas of shallow continental shelf allowed the development of fluvial landscapes and the major headward erosion of submarine canyons. The relative importance of fluvial erosion, headward erosion of submarine canyons, and erosion by sub-ice meltwater or directly by ice in the formation of the deep channels in the preglacial-glacial unconformity of the outer Scotian Shelf and Grand Banks is unclear. A much better knowledge of Late Tertiary and Early Quaternary sea-level changes is necessary to adequately interpret sediment deposition and geomorphological evolution during this period.

Particularly on the shallow southern shelves, changing sea level has also had a major influence on the distribution of glacial ice, the geomorphological evolution of the continental slope, and the development of terraces and associated transgressive sediments. Although the Late Wisconsinan-Holocene history of sea level and its effects are reasonably well understood, we have little knowledge of earlier Wisconsinan sea level changes that may have played a major role in the retreat of ice sheets from the southern shelves and the development of local ice standstills or readvances.

Deep water geomorphic evolution

The geomorphic evolution of deep water areas is dependent on factors similar to those affecting shelf geomorphology: the tectonic framework, preglacial morphology, and the effects of Quaternary glacial erosion and deposition. In deep water areas, deposition is the predominant geomorphic agent, and the supply of sediment and the style of erosion on the continental margin is dependent on conditions on the continental shelves.

Many deep water physiographic features first developed in the Late Neogene. The major sediment drifts of the Labrador Sea are of Miocene to Pliocene age (see Chapter 7). Many of the slope valleys of the Scotian Margin result from Late Pliocene sea-level lowering, and deposition of thick turbidite sequences on the Laurentian Fan and in the northern Labrador Sea began in the Pliocene.

The Quaternary of most of the deep water continental margin is several hundred metres thick, reflecting progradation during fluvial sediment supply in the Early Pleistocene and subsequent Middle and Late Pleistocene glaciation. Major sedimentary deposits lie on the continental rise off the largest transverse troughs on the shelf, notably on the Laurentian Fan off the Laurentian Channel, in the Labrador Sea off Cartwright Saddle, and in northwest Baffin Bay off Lancaster Sound. Sediment accumulation is less pronounced off Hudson Strait, but the Northwest Atlantic Mid-Ocean Channel (Chough and Hesse, 1976) originates in this area and may have facilitated transport of sediment to the south. In general, morphologically distinct deep sea fans are rare on the eastern Canadian continental margin. Much of the fine grained sediment that would normally build up levees and thus stabilize channel and fan development was dispersed over a larger area in nepheloid layers related to bottom currents. In the absence of well-developed channel-levee systems, unusual amounts of sand would have accumulated on the continental slope and upper rise. Where sand was not delivered to the shelf break, a smooth mud blanket was deposited on the continental slope.

Submarine canyons that breach the shelf break (Farre et al., 1983) occur only in areas with a shelf break at 100 m or less on the Grand Banks and Scotian margins, and are probably associated with coastal rip current initiation of turbidity currents (Fukushima et al., 1985) at times of glacially lowered sea level. Canyons coalesce downslope to form submarine valleys. Many areas with a deeper shelf break have a smooth upper slope down to water depths of a few hundred metres succeeded downslope by a region of shallow gullies that originate on the upper slope and probably developed seaward of a grounded ice margin. Some gullies coalesce downslope into larger valleys, notably on the Labrador Slope and Laurentian Fan. Other areas of deep water shelf break have an almost smooth continental slope, as off the Northeast Newfoundland Shelf and Southeast Baffin Shelf.

Late Tertiary and Early Quaternary initiation of glaciation

P.J. Mudie and D.J.W. Piper

The sum of evidence indicates that the periodic widening of the jet stream in response to a decrease in the thermal gradient between equatorial and polar regions is the *prima facie* cause of glacial conditions that characterized the Pleistocene. Glacial-interglacial cyclicity is thereafter governed primarily by changes in the Earth's orbital parameters that determine total and seasonal solar irradiation at different latitudes (Berger, 1978). Off eastern Canada, the development of alpine glaciation in northern Labrador, Baffin Island and Greenland adjacent to a warm eastern Labrador Sea may have played a particularly important feedback role by channelling the tracks of moisture-bearing storms into the Labrador Sea and Baffin Bay (Barry et al., 1975; Crowley, 1984).

A widespread hiatus in Middle to Upper Miocene oceanic sediments probably corresponds to the first development of Antarctic and Arctic bottom water currents following the expansion of the Antarctic ice sheet from 16-14 Ma and the subsidence of the Iceland-Faroes Ridge from ca. 10 — 8 Ma. By 7 Ma, drift deposits began to form around the Eirik Ridge in the Eastern Labrador Sea. Terrestrial plant deposits from the Canadian Arctic Islands and northern Greenland show that there was a southward retreat of temperate forest vegetation between ca. 5 and 1.7 Ma, but boreal trees and peat bogs persisted in the circum-Arctic region until the early Pleistocene (ca. 1.7 Ma).

Dropstones and ice-rafted gravel first occur in the central Arctic Ocean during the Early Pliocene (ca. 4 Ma). However, marine fossils from the circum-Arctic region indicate that the Arctic Ocean was not permanently ice covered before ca. 1.7 Ma. During most of this interval, there was a strong inflow of relatively warm Pacific Ocean water from Bering Strait (Repenning, 1983). Ice-rafted debris was also first evident in Baffin Bay and the northeastern Labrador Sea in the Early Pliocene at 3.4 Ma, and it occurred in the southern Labrador Sea, the central North Atlantic and southwest of the Grand Banks between 3.0 and 2.4 Ma. The petrological character of this ice-rafted debris suggests derivation from both sedimentary and crystalline sources. Alpine glaciers must have prevailed in Ellesmere Island, Greenland or Baffin Island in the late Early Pliocene that calved icebergs into Baffin Bay and probably the Arctic Ocean. The increased extent of ice rafting in the early Late Pliocene corresponds to regional evidence from seismic profiles in both the Labrador Sea and Baffin Bay for greatly increased sediment supply from Greenland. At approximately the same time, on the Labrador, Grand Banks and Scotian slopes, a phase of progressively increasing canyon incision began, allowing sediment to be transferred to deep water by deep sea channels, including the Northwest Atlantic Mid-Ocean Channel. Palynomorph data from both Labrador Sea and Arctic Ocean indicate that the Late Pliocene and Early Pleistocene were times of high discharge of fluvial sediment. The widespread evidence from ice rafting, old tills and pollen records for northern hemisphere glaciation and regional cooling throughout this period suggests that at least parts of Canada were glaciated at this time.

In the Middle Pleistocene, marked changes in marine sedimentation patterns took place in several areas, and these appear to signal a change in style of glaciation. The chronology of these changes is rarely well constrained, so that they may not all be synchronous. The sedimentation pattern in the Arctic Ocean changed to bioturbated carbonate muds and silty lutite; whereas at ODP Site 645 in Baffin Bay, it featured greatly increased amounts of detrital carbonate. Sediments of the Labrador Rise influenced by contour currents gave way to prograding slope muds. Till tongues, evidence of ice sheets crossing the continental shelf, first appear on the upper Scotian Slope. The development of Arctic shrub-tundra vegetation on the Alaskan coast and the oldest till in the Arctic Archipelago (Banks glaciation) probably also date from this time. All these lines of evidence point to more extensive ice cover in the Middle to Late Pleistocene than in the Early Pleistocene.

Stratigraphic synthesis of the glacial successions

D.J.W. Piper

The continental shelves off eastern Canada have received more attention than deeper water areas and provide the closest stratigraphic link to terrestrial stratigraphies. In all the shelves examined in detail, the Quaternary strata consist of a series of glacial sediments developed during ice recession and postglacial sediments, resting on tills. There is thus a broad similarity in lithostratigraphic units established in different geographic areas (Table 10.6). Glacial till is overlain by (and interfingers with) poorly sorted glaciomarine silts with ice-rafted debris; some of this sediment was deposited beneath ice shelves, and some in an open water, proglacial marine environment. Late glacial reworking of these deposits in sub-littoral environments produced muddy sands and gravels that in many areas off southeastern Canada are quite distinct from the sorted sands and gravels formed in the littoral zone during the Holocene transgression. On the deeper shelves in northern latitudes, the effects of the Holocene transgression are less extensive; iceberg scour, ice-rafted debris and reworking of sediment by storms and bottom currents have resulted in accumulation of a Holocene veneer of poorly sorted sediment in many places. Basinal muds have accumulated in sheltered deeper water areas during the Holocene; in high latitudes these have an ice-rafted component. As a result of the differences in glacial history, sea-level changes and water depth, not all the formations associated with one another in Table 10.6 are exact analogues.

Most of the till units on the continental shelf are poorly dated, but are older than Late Wisconsinan.[†] Thus off eastern Canada, maximum Wisconsinan ice volumes probably occurred in isotopic stage 4. This may reflect the important role of northward advection of moisture through the Labrador Sea at times of reduced summer insolation in the initiation of northern hemisphere glaciation in eastern Canada.

Circumstantial evidence in deep water sediments suggest that the stage 6 (Illinoian) glaciation was more intense off eastern Canada than any Wisconsinan glaciation. Microfauna indicate more extreme conditions (Alam et al., 1983; Aksu and Mudie, 1985a) and the Fogo Seamounts show the greatest glacial sediment yield in stage 6 (Alam and Piper, 1977). Well-dated Illinoian depositional or erosional features, however, are not found on the continental shelf, although the Lower Till on the Labrador Shelf, and the deeper parts of the multiple till sections off Hudson Strait may be of this age. The very long chronology seen in coastal sections in Baffin Island suggests that some of the tills on the outer part of the Baffin Shelf may be pre-Wisconsinan.

Little information exists on glaciation in the "Late Sangamonian" of isotopic stages 5d to 5a both offshore and onland in southern Canada (Fulton et al., 1984).

Abrupt changes in oxygen isotopic records in high latitudes (Mudie and Aksu, 1984) are recorded both from stage 5e to 5d, and from 5a to 4. Andrews et al. (1984) have proposed that the first Wisconsinan (Foxe) glaciations in Arctic Canada date from isotopic stage 5: this would include the Ayr Lake stade of Baffin Island, which was the only stade of the Foxe glaciation to reach the continental shelf off northeastern Baffin Island. Isotopic and microfossil data from Davis Strait (Aksu and Mudie, 1985a), however, suggest that interglacial conditions prevailed throughout stage 5, and that stage 6 glaciation was much more severe than that in stages 4 and 2.

The most extensive Wisconsinan glaciation of the Maritime Provinces took place in isotopic stage 4 (Grant, in press), and this is consistent with the radiocarbon evidence for the beginning of recession in isotopic stage 3 of the ice sheet that deposited the Scotian Shelf Drift. If the stratigraphic interpretation of isotopes from the Fogo Seamounts by Alam et al. (1983) is correct, there is sedimentological evidence of glaciation in isotopic stage 5b. Marine incursion has been dated from the latter part of isotopic stage 3 (30 to 40 ka) over wide areas of the continental shelf off eastern Canada,[†] and in adjacent inland seas such as Hudson Bay (Andrews et al., 1983). Although onland abundant evidence exists for a stage 2 glacial advance in eastern Canada (Fulton et al., 1984), only locally (e.g. Gulf of Maine, Notre Dame Bay) is any evidence seen of greater ice extent in marine areas off eastern Canada, despite the pronounced associated lowering of sea level.[†] In the eastern Arctic, the Late Foxe advance dates from isotopic stage 2; ice did not reach the outer coast, but extended to the marine area of Frobisher Bay and possibly Hudson Strait.

Many of the stratigraphic uncertainties in the east coast offshore will be resolved by better knowledge of the deep water and thicker continental shelf sections (such as will be provided by drilling programs). More complete oceanic sections with oxygen isotope records and oceanic microfossils will provide a means of circumventing traditional dating problems in the more proximal glacial environments found on the shelf and on land. Greater attention in offshore sections to detrital petrography will provide better correlation with terrestrial till sheets. More work is needed both on pollen and paleomagnetic stratigraphies to improve stratigraphic correlations between land, the continental shelf and the deep sea. In addition, modern high-resolution seismic reflection profiles are needed in the largely unexplored areas of the Gulf of St. Lawrence[†] and the Northeast Newfoundland Shelf.

The record of ice rafting
C.F.M. Lewis

Ice-rafted detritus is terrigenous sediment that has been released from drifting icebergs or sea ice. According to Ruddiman (1977) "...it is a product of the land, ice, and water realms. Its absolute input in space and time basically defines when, where, and at what rates sediment is dropped from melting ice during passage from land to...ocean. Ice-rafted input may also point to changes both in oceanic circulation and in the size of ice sheets on land." Ice-rafted detritus is originally incorporated into iceberg ice mainly by action of the parental glacier on a continental landmass, but also by deposition from windborne sediment or volcanic ashfalls onto the ice surface. Similarly sea ice may become charged with sediment in the coastal zone by wind action, by slumping from adjacent shore bluffs, by river discharge onto ice, by bottom-surface adhesion during ice formation in shallow nearshore waters, and by suspension freezing (Campbell and Collin, 1958). Sediment may also be acquired by sea-ice pressure ridge keels and iceberg keels in the deeper waters of the continental shelf, during grounding and scouring episodes.

Although ice-rafted detritus comprises a wide range of grain sizes, including clay sizes, it is generally recognized

---

[†] See Addendum

within its host marine sediment by the anomalous presence of coarse, erratic mineral grains and lithic fragments. Coarse ice-rafted detritus grains, too large to be carried by winds or currents, are characteristically dispersed within their host sediment where the larger clasts have commonly induced dropstone structures. The coarse ice-rafted sediment is typically not sorted or graded. Where icebergs are known to be scarce or non-existent, as at present in the Arctic Ocean, Foxe Basin and central Arctic Island Channels, Hudson Bay and the Bay of Fundy, ice-rafted detritus is attributed to rafting by sea ice. On the eastern Canadian continental margin and in the adjacent Atlantic Ocean both icebergs and sea ice coexist and both may transport ice-rafted detritus. Being much larger and longer lasting, icebergs can travel farther than sea ice; thus occurrences of ice-rafted detritus far offshore are usually attributed to iceberg rafting. Otherwise the distinction of sea ice- and iceberg-rafted sediment is generally unclear and rarely accomplished.

Zones of concentrated ice-rafted detritus in a sedimentary sequence imply the presence of drift ice and the influence of distinctive climatic and oceanographic factors such as 1) a colder coastal climate or glacial advance to tidewater that enhances drift-ice production and increases its flux, 2) a decline in surface water temperature that prolongs the lifespan and extends the trajectory of drift ice, 3) an increase in surface current velocity or shift in current position that extends the influence of drift ice into new areas, or 4) a convergence of cold ice-laden currents with warmer water that increases the melt-out rate of ice-rafted detritus. Whether a concentration of ice-rafted detritus represents a 'trajectory' of sediment-charged ice or a 'locus of melting' requires additional information, for example estimates of sea surface temperature based on microfossils co-deposited with the ice-rafted detritus (Ruddiman, 1977; Smythe et al., 1985). The interpretation of transport pathways or oceanic circulation is further aided by consideration of the provenance (Alam and Piper, 1977, 1981), gradients in particle size (Baker and Friedman, 1973), and input rates of the ice-rafted detritus (Ruddiman, 1977; Fillon et al., 1981b). Poorly sorted end members of grain size spectra, thought to be ice-rafted detritus, from surface sediments of the North Atlantic Ocean, Labrador Sea, and Baffin Bay are found predominantly beneath the principal drift paths of modern icebergs and strong oceanic thermal gradients (Fillon and Full, 1984). This finding supports the interpretative principles given above as well as the common practice of using nonbiogenic sand content in deep sea sediments as an indicator of ice-rafted detritus deposition. The interpretation of ice-rafted detritus closer to the margins of a continent where coarse clasts may also originate as ice shelf or ice sheet deposits (King and Fader, 1986) requires additional evidence such as faunal data, regional stratigraphic and chronologic control, provenance information or the presence of ice scour marks to recognize drift ice conditions (Osterman and Andrews, 1973; Jennings, 1985; Josenhans et al., 1986).

Late Pliocene and Quaternary occurrences of ice-rafted detritus

The earliest occurrences of ice-rafted detritus are known from deep sea cores obtained principally by the Deep Sea Drilling Project (Laughton et al., 1972) and the Ocean Drilling Program (Arthur et al., 1986). These show an influx of detrital mineral grains and lithic fragments beginning about 3 Ma in Late Pliocene time (Berggren, 1972; Poore and Berggren, 1974; Poore, 1981) following a general cooling of the North Atlantic Ocean that is indicated by faunal evidence. Traces of ice-rafted detritus may appear much earlier in Baffin Bay (Arthur et al., 1986). This Pliocene influx of detritus is widespread north of latitudes 35° to 40°N in the North Atlantic.

The onset of ice-rafted detritus deposition is marked by distinct changes in sediment composition and sedimentation rates. These changes are particularly clear on Orphan Knoll (DSDP Site 111A) as this location in the western Labrador Sea is elevated and isolated from the effects of turbidity currents and the Western Boundary Undercurrent. Sediment composition changes substantially across the preglacial-glacial boundary, 146 m below seabed, shifting upward from biogenic sediment ($>70\%$ $CaCO_3$) through a transition zone to sandy grey clay ($<20\%$ $CaCO_3$) with rafted pebbles and only scattered foraminiferal zones. Rafted pebble lithologies typically include limestone, quartzite, granite and metamorphics. Clay-size mineralogy also changes at this boundary and is marked by the upward appearance of feldspar, increases in quartz and mica, and decrease in calcite (Laughton et al., 1972). Similar changes occur at other Deep Sea Drilling Project sites except that volcanic rock fragments are more common south of Iceland and adjacent to the Mid-Atlantic Ridge. Ice-rafted detritus in the Labrador Sea cores is commonly diluted by large inputs of current transported material.

A southeastward transect of deep sea cores (Fig. 10.65) from Baffin Bay to the mid Atlantic Ocean illustrates the general reduction in ice-rafted detritus characteristics of oceanic sediment from arctic to temperate climatic zones off eastern Canada. This transect reveals a southward decrease in the fraction of ice-rafted detritus and an increase in biogenic content. Sedimentation rates all increase at the beginning of the Late Pliocene (3 Ma) and again at about 1.5 to 2 Ma suggesting an increase in glacial activity on the continents and ice-rafted detritus input to the ocean in the early Quaternary. At DSDP Site 111A for example, the accumulation rates for noncarbonate sediment are approximately 0.01, 1.7 and 5.6 cm/ka in the preglacial Early Pliocene, glacial Late Pliocene and Quaternary sections respectively (Davies and Laughton, 1972). In general, the onset of ice-rafted detritus deposition occurs earlier and the accumulation rates of ice-rafted detritus are greater towards the northwest, closer to the likely dominant source areas.

Late Quaternary evidence of ice-rafted detritus

The ice-rafted detritus record is best recorded in the upper 2 to 20 m of deep sea sediment. Conolly and Ewing (1965) established the southern limit of Upper Quaternary ice-rafted sediment at about latitude 35°N and showed that the concentrations in glacial marine zones increase from a few grains to about 25 per cent of the sediment volume at about 55°N. This latter value exceeds the present concentration of gravel in Baffin Bay sediments, site of modern ice rafting.

Analysis of the coarse ($>500\mu m$) fraction (Molnia, 1983) from more than 30 piston cores shows quartz as the predominant component in the western Atlantic Ocean,

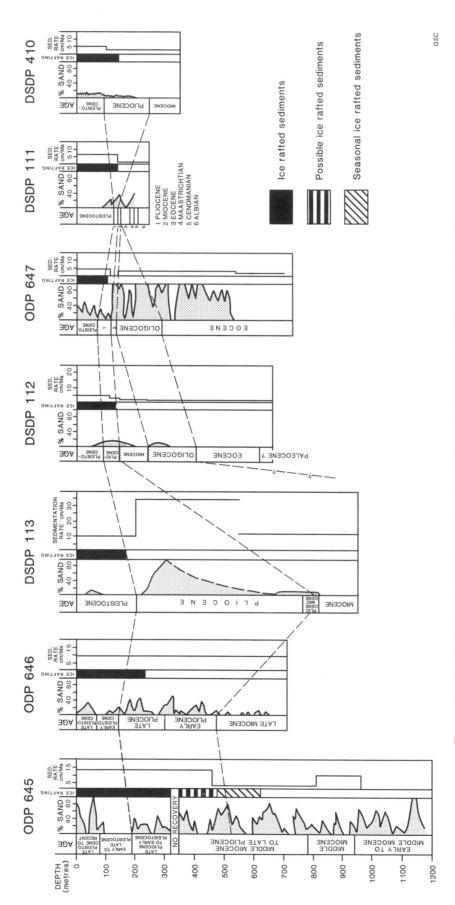

Figure 10.65. Variations in lithology and sedimentation rate, for preglacial Pliocene, glacial Pliocene, and Quaternary sediments in DSDP and ODP wells from Baffin Bay to south-central Atlantic Ocean. For well locations see Figure 10.1.

ranging from less than 20 to more than 50 per cent. The feldspar coarse fraction is relatively uniform, between 8 and 17 per cent throughout the North Atlantic. Granitic rock fragments (<10 per cent) occur most abundantly between Labrador and Greenland whereas the highest concentrations of volcanic rock fragments (about 20 per cent) are centred south of Iceland and the Faeroe Islands. Limestone fragments, locally in excess of 20 per cent of the coarse fraction, were noted in the vicinity of Davis Strait and red sandstone pebbles were commonly observed in the Gulf of St. Lawrence and western North Atlantic regions.

Continental margins show more pronounced concentrations of lithologically distinctive clasts, which also show significant stratigraphic variations. Their distribution in time and space has been reviewed in previous sections. The most distinctive is the concentration of carbonate in Baffin Bay and western Labrador Sea, apparently derived from ice in the eastern part of Sverdrup Basin and in Hudson Strait. Ice-rafted detritus off southeastern Canada commonly includes red sandstones and siltstones derived from Carboniferous and Triassic bedrock. Crystalline ice-rafted detritus off Newfoundland reflects sources in Newfoundland, Labrador, Baffin Island and Greenland, whereas that off Nova Scotia is derived from the adjacent Appalachians.

Between 50 and 55°N volcanogenic ice-rafted detritus sand is about an order of magnitude less abundant than ice-rafted detritus sand of continental origin (Smythe et al., 1985). By tracking these components through the build-up period of the last glacial cycle, Smythe et al. (1985) showed that volcanogenic ice-rafted detritus deposition rates consistently increase eastward whereas the continental ice-rafted detritus deposition rates first decline (115 to 77 ka), then increase eastward (77 to 53 ka).

The deep sea sedimentary record carries at least three major levels of sand-sized, bubble-walled volcanic shards dated at 10.6, 57.5, and 340 ka (Ruddiman and Glover, 1972; Mangerud et al., 1984; Smythe et al., 1985). The ash from each level is interpreted to have initially fallen onto drifting sea ice and icebergs following one or more closely spaced volcanic eruptions (Ruddiman and Glover, 1972, 1975). With their rhyolitic composition pointing to a source area in Iceland or Jan Mayen Island, the dispersal patterns of these ashes demarcate a set of remarkably clear trajectories of ice-rafted sediment. In addition to a major dispersal tongue southeastward from Iceland, both the 10.6 and 57.5 ka ashes have been rafted westward past southern Greenland, through the eastern Labrador Sea northward into Baffin Bay and thence possibly southward along the eastern Canadian continental margin following the pattern shown in Figure 10.66. Observations of the oldest ash layer are reported from the eastern North Atlantic Ocean (Ruddiman and Glover, 1972) and Baffin Bay (Aksu and Piper, 1979).

The mass rates of ice-rafted detritus accumulation during the last glacial cycle can be determined for the central North Atlantic Ocean and Labrador Sea (Ruddiman, 1977; Fillon et al., 1981b). Unlike the continental margin studies the relative comparison of the components of terrigenous detritus (apart from the distinction of volcanogenic and non-volcanogenic debris) has not proved fruitful for ice-rafted detritus investigations (Smythe et al., 1985). From measurements of sand content in 32 cores spaced throughout the subpolar North Atlantic, Ruddiman (1977) estimated and mapped variations in the ice-rafted sand input

rates for six intervals of time spanning the last glacial period, 115 to 13 ka. Fillon et al. (1981b) made similar estimates for eight cores from the eastern and northeastern Labrador Sea over the last 100 ka. The Labrador Sea sand is of mixed glacial terrigenous origin and about one half of it is estimated to have arrived at the core sites by ice rafting.

The geographic pattern of absolute sand input shows relatively low rates in intermediate latitudes between high rates at the northern and southern extremes of the central North Atlantic Ocean. The input rates decline from high values in the Greenland-Iceland region to lower values in the zone of 50 to 60°N latitude, then increase to a broad, east-west elongated ridge of high values south of 50°N. During the last glacial period this zone of high input rates moved south and rotated clockwise from an initial east-southeast trend to an east-northeast orientation. The southern steep gradients coincide with the Polar Front, a zone of sea surface temperature gradients defined by faunal evidence, suggesting the zone of high input rates is a locus of ice-raft melting.

The absolute rates of sand input range over an order of magnitude between 100 and 1000 mg/cm^2/ka during the last glacial period. The total input rates integrated over the subpolar Atlantic increased slightly at 115 ka (at the beginning of isotopic stage 5d), rose markedly at 75 ka (at the beginning of isotopic stage 4) and continued to rise late in the Wisconsinan toward the late glacial maximum at 20 ka. Over the same period ice-rafted detritus input rates were virtually constant in the Norwegian Sea but in the northeastern Labrador Sea they decreased with time. An estimated 9.4×10^{17}g of sand was ice rafted into the western half of the Atlantic Ocean south of 65°N during the Wisconsinan glacial period. This total was about equally divided between the Labrador Sea and the western subpolar Atlantic.

Implications for ocean circulation

An explanation of the observed ice-rafted detritus distribution in space and time requires departure from the present pattern of North Atlantic circulation. In the Late Sangamonian and Early Wisconsinan (stage 5a to the early part of stage 4), high sand input to eastern Labrador Sea at the time of low inputs to the central Atlantic suggests oceanic flow at that time in opposite directions east and west of southern Greenland (Fig. 10.67a). The trajectories of Icelandic ash require southeastward circulation from Denmark Strait. If this flow had been countered to the west by a cyclonic gyre in Labrador Sea as suggested by Fillon et al. (1981b), icebergs calved from glacier termini in eastern Canada would have been retained and drifted northward with warm water from the North Atlantic Drift to melt in the eastern Labrador Sea. This would have given rise to the observed high sand input rates. The northward extension of this flow into Baffin Bay would have supported conditions for hemipelagic sedimentation as documented there. That fraction of bergs and sea ice drifting south from East Greenland and Iceland, which was not advected into the Labrador gyre, would ultimately have been deflected eastward and northeastward by the warm North Atlantic Drift. Melting bergs and sea ice in this southern part of an eastern Atlantic gyre would have released detritus rapidly and given rise to the east-west zone of moderately high sand input rates. The minor trans-

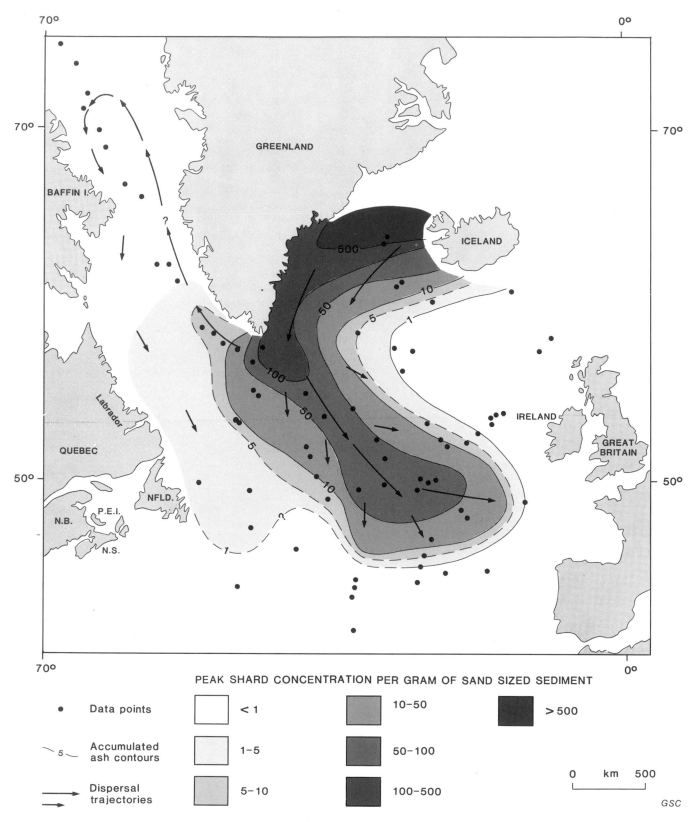

PEAK SHARD CONCENTRATION PER GRAM OF SAND SIZED SEDIMENT

• Data points   < 1   10–50   > 500

∼5∼ Accumulated ash contours   1–5   50–100

→ Dispersal trajectories   5–10   100–500

0   km   500

GSC

Figure 10.66. Ice-rafted ash concentrations and dispersal trajectories at 10.6 ka. Data from Ruddiman and Glover (1975), Piper et al. (1978), Aksu and Piper (1979), Carter (1979), and Fillon and Duplessy (1980).

fer of eastern Canadian drift ice in the Labrador gyre to the eastern Atlantic gyre, inherent in this circulation system, would have sustained the eastward declining gradient of continental debris observed in the zone of moderately high sand input.

If during the Middle and Late Wisconsinan the Labrador gyre weakened, icebergs from eastern Canada would have been advected eastward in a strengthened North Atlantic Drift. Detritus released from melting bergs would have been added to that of the east Greenland bergs giving rise to the high sand input rates mapped in the southern central Atlantic for the Late Wisconsinan (isotopic stage 2) (Fig. 10.67b). This augmented input of drift ice from eastern Canada probably reversed the gradient of continental debris to the observed eastward- increasing trend and could have induced the late glacial southward shift and clockwise rotation of the high sand input zone.

Late Quaternary paleo-oceanography

D.J.W. Piper and P.J. Mudie

The accumulation of major ice sheets on land requires an effective supply of moisture during the earlier parts of glacial stages. It has long been recognized that the waters off eastern Canada, lying between the Greenland and Laurentide ice sheets, may have played a major role in the initiation of northern hemisphere glacial stages (Barry et al., 1975).

The cores of oceanic sediment in the northwest Atlantic contain a record of environmentally sensitive microfossils and sediments that can be precisely correlated and reasonably well dated through oxygen isotope stratigraphy. The environmental significance of particular microfossil assemblages (and to a lesser extent sediments) can be estimated by comparison with assemblages found at the modern seafloor for which environmental conditions are known. Quantitative methods of comparison of "core top" assemblages with those downcore involve the use of transfer functions (Imbrie and Kipp, 1971). Regression analysis shows that the greatest part of the variability in core top assemblages of microfossils from one area to another can be explained by variations in sea-surface temperature, although salinity or nutrient concentrations may control some of the variability for certain groups of fossils. Interpretations based on transfer functions are only reliable if the core top data cover the full range of environmental conditions experienced downcore. Early applications of the transfer function technique (CLIMAP, 1976) were based on inadequate numbers of high latitude and ice-margin core-top samples, and thus resulted in incorrect interpretations of high latitude paleoenvironmental conditions. For example, CLIMAP (1976) predicted that the Labrador Sea was entirely covered by pack ice at 18 ka, in conflict with much qualitative data (Vilks and Mudie, 1978; Aksu and Mudie, 1985a) indicating largely ice-free conditions at that time. These ice-free conditions have been confirmed by subsequent quantitative estimates using CLIMAP techniques (Mudie et al., 1984).

The oxygen isotope record in calcareous microfossils from oceanic sediments has shown clearly that the major variations in ice volume and sea surface temperature during the Quaternary can be correlated with calculated variations in the earth's orbital parameters (Milankovich cycles) (Hays et al., 1976). These variations result in a dominant 41 ka period related to obliquity in insolation at latitudes above 65°N, whereas lower latitudes show a 23 ka dominant period related to precession (Berger, 1978). In addition, there is a strong 95 ka periodicity, in part related to orbital eccentricity but probably also influenced by isostatic effects (Peltier and Hyde, 1984). Complex feedback loops can be expected between insolation and such factors as the growth or decay of ice sheets on land, the development of sea ice, and sea-surface temperatures. Those factors that leave a signature in the marine stratigraphic record can generally be dated by extrapolation, assuming that sedimentation rates were constant, but terrestrial chronologies are generally inadequate to integrate information from land. Ruddiman and McIntyre (1984) showed that estimates of sea-surface temperature from microfossil assemblages have a strong 95 ka periodicity at all latitudes; 23 ka periodicity is seen in latitudes below 54°N, and a 41 ka periodicity is pronounced in higher latitudes. The two longer period sea-surface temperature rhythms, 95 ka and 41 ka, are synchronous with oxygen isotope changes, suggesting regulation by regional atmospheric temperatures. The 23 ka sea-surface temperature rhythm lags behind ice volume by many thousands of years, suggesting that heat transfer by icebergs and meltwater partly regulates mid-latitude sea-surface temperature (Ruddiman and McIntyre, 1981b). Icebergs from Atlantic Canada, Labrador and possibly Hudson Bay would be of particular importance, because they are fed by ice accumulating in low latitudes. The oxygen isotopic record preserved in planktonic foraminifers provides evidence of major periods of meltwater supply from the continent, presumably associated with rapid phases of ice retreat. Phases of rapid supply of ice-rafted debris have also been correlated with times of rapid ice retreat and the break-up of large ice shelves (Ruddiman, 1977; Fillon et al., 1981b).

Data from long, high-latitude, deep-sea cores in the North Atlantic (Jellinek, 1985) and Arctic Ocean (Boyd et al., 1984) provide detailed records of sea-surface temperature changes for the past 1 Ma. These data show that the amplitude of the 95 ka orbital eccentricity component gradually increased through the Middle Pleistocene until about 0.45 Ma, after which very large amplitude oscillations became virtually constant. Superimposed on this dominant power spectrum are other cyclical variations corresponding to changes in obliquity (41 ka) and precession (23 ka), which show more irregular amplitudes after around 0.6 Ma (obliquity) and 0.8 Ma (precession). Furthermore, some detailed North Atlantic records (Jellinek, 1985) reveal the presence of additional spectra, with periods of 54 ka and 31 ka, which appear to be secondary components of the obliquity spectrum. These secondary components imply that there may be important processes operating which translate small amounts of external forcing into larger climatic responses, and indicate that large amplitude spectral signals in deep sea data should not necessarily be correlated with the classical three-component Milankovich cycles with periods of 95, 41 and 23 ka.

Long cores from the Labrador Sea and Baffin Bay provide a record of the environmental changes during the onset and termination of glaciation in eastern Canada since isotopic stage 9 (276 ka). Although similar features are recorded at most interglacial to glacial transitions, the

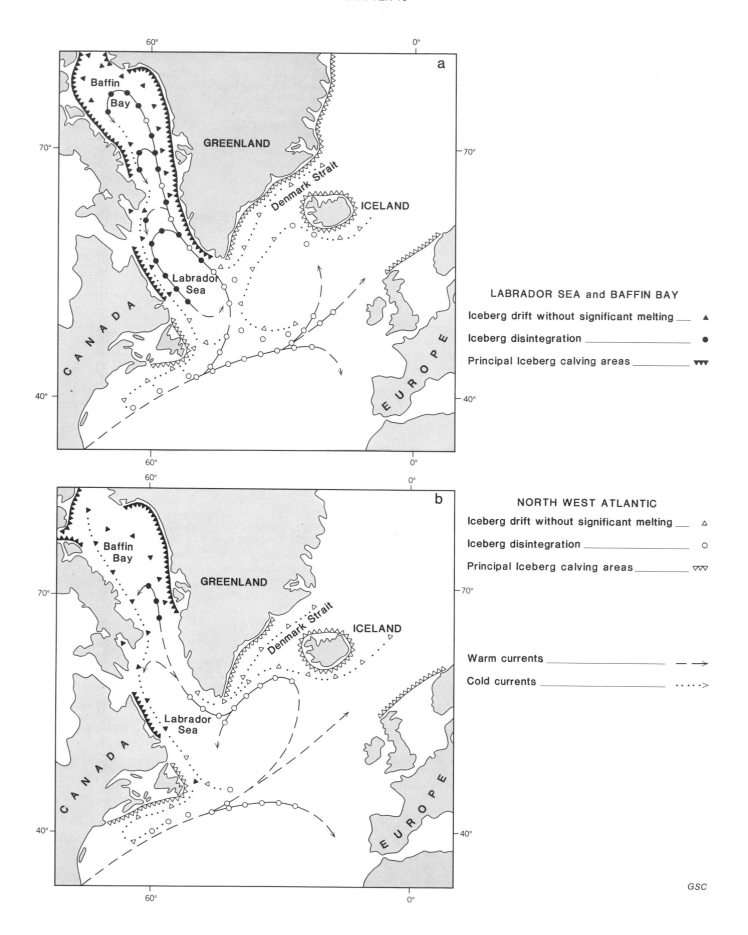

LABRADOR SEA and BAFFIN BAY

Iceberg drift without significant melting _____ ▲

Iceberg disintegration _____ ●

Principal Iceberg calving areas _____ ▼▼▼

NORTH WEST ATLANTIC

Iceberg drift without significant melting _____ △

Iceberg disintegration _____ ○

Principal Iceberg calving areas _____ ▽▽▽

Warm currents _____ – – →

Cold currents _____ ·····>

GSC

clearest record of the onset of glaciation is between inter-glacial stage 7 and glacial stage 6 (the Late Illinoian of continental stratigraphy). During the early part of stage 6, one of the more extreme glacial periods of the Middle Quaternary, at a time when the isotopic record indicates a substantial ice volume on land, warm water persisted in the north Atlantic Ocean (Ruddiman and McIntyre, 1981b and 1984). Warm water is also indicated at this time by microfossil assemblages in the Labrador Sea (Aksu and Mudie, 1985a), and Baffin Bay (Mudie and Aksu, 1984; Aksu, 1985c). These assemblages include high abundances of radiolaria, subarctic planktonic foraminifers and dinoflagellates; warm water faunas occur on the coast of Baffin Island (Feyling-Hanssen, 1985); and boreal *Alnus* and *Picea* pollen are common. This suggests advection of warm water and air into at least the eastern Labrador Sea, Davis Strait and Baffin Bay in the early part of isotopic stage 6. This oceanic configuration with an intense thermal gradient between ice covered land and much warmer ocean creates optimal conditions for ice sheet growth by providing a local source of moisture and channelling the tracks of moisture bearing storms into the Labrador Sea and Baffin Bay. A similar steep thermal gradient, with associated intense storms, would have existed along the southeast Canadian margin, between the ice caps of the Maritime Provinces and the Gulf Stream (Alam et al., 1983). In isotopic stage 6, the transition to much colder fossil assemblages occurs at about the middle of the stage, and may indicate a southward shift of the polar front, the predominance of the colder and dryer westerly Arctic air mass, and a southerly shift of the warm West Greenland Current, leading to extensive sea ice formation in Baffin Bay and the western Labrador Sea. A comparable change from isotopic stage 4 to 2 can be inferred from the distribution of Wisconsinan ice-rafted detritus (see previous section).

Transitions from glacial to interglacial conditions are better known, because of the wealth of information from cores concerning the termination of the Late Wisconsinan glaciation between isotopic stages 2 and 1. Major glacial terminations, such as those from stage 6 to 5e and from 2 to 1, are marked by a very rapid change in global ice volume and a corresponding rise in sea level in most areas. In the North Atlantic Ocean, such major glacial terminations are marked by sediments almost barren of planktonic microfossils, but with abundant ice-rafted detritus, which Ruddiman and McIntyre (1981a) interpreted as resulting from a poorly mixed surface layer of low salinity, glacial meltwater. A similar interval of low planktonic foraminiferal abundances in the Labrador Sea combined with a sharp increase in diatoms and dinoflagellates probably indicates that the local conditions favoured high primary productivity (Aksu and Mudie, 1985b; Mudie and Aksu, 1984). The renewal of oceanic circulation from the Arctic Ocean through the Arctic Island Channels could also have contributed to a nutrient- rich surface layer of low salinity.

During full interglacial periods, such as stage 5e, the northeastern Labrador Sea had surface oxygen isotope values similar to those in the Greenland and Norwegian Seas; this indicates good mixing of oceanic water provided by the East and West Greenland currents. However, a southward depletion in ^{18}O of about 2.5‰ in Baffin Bay and 1‰ in Davis Strait and the northwestern Labrador Sea, reflects the continued meltwater supply from ice caps around Baffin Bay and the Arctic Ocean and mixing of the Baffin and Labrador currents with the West Greenland Current.

The evolution of the Labrador Current during the last deglaciation (stage 2 to 1) is reflected in sediment sequences from Baffin Bay to the Scotian Shelf. The microfossil record from shelf basins on the Labrador, Northeast Newfoundland and Scotian shelves (Scott et al., 1984b) and from the Baffin Shelf (Osterman, 1982; Jennings, 1985) indicates four phases in the Holocene evolution of the Labrador current. Until about 10 ka, shelf waters were dominated by local turbid glacial meltwater. From 10 ka to 7 ka, shelf environmental conditions appear to have been similar to those associated with the modern outer Labrador Current, which is largely supplied with water by the West Greenland Current. At about 7 ka in the south and as late as 5 ka farther north foraminiferal assemblages indicate substantial warming throughout the area from Frobisher Bay (Osterman, 1982) to the Scotian Shelf (Scott et al., 1984b). This is followed by a cooling trend, initiated about 5 ka on the inner shelf and increasing in the surface layer about 2.5 ka. This cooling appears to reflect a greater dominance of the inner part of the Labrador Current. This may result from a slight southward shift of the North Atlantic Drift (Sancetta et al., 1973) in the late Holocene producing a weakening of the West Greenland Current and thus enhancement of the cold Baffin Current. Neoglaciation started about 3.5 ka in Baffin Island, with the most extensive advance terminating in the late 19th century (Andrews et al., 1984). Comparison of pollen, planktonic and benthic microfossil records suggests that warming and cooling first take place in surface waters, with a lag of thousands of years in the temperature response of both bottom waters and the terrestrial pollen record (Balsam and Heusser, 1976; Mudie, 1980; Scott et al., 1984b). This late Holocene cooling and intensification of the Labrador Current on the continental shelf is paralleled by surface water cooling and intensification of the Western Boundary Undercurrent on the continental slope and rise (Schafer et al., 1985).

Glaciomarine sedimentation models

D.J.W. Piper

Much of the Quaternary section off eastern Canada was deposited in glaciomarine environments. An understanding of the sedimentological processes in these environments is important to understand the genesis of the offshore sediments, the character of the glacial conditions that accompanied deposition, and to better understand processes of glaciomarine sedimentation.

The classic paper of Carey and Ahmad (1961), based largely on the study of pre-Quaternary glaciomarine rocks and virtually no knowledge of Antarctica, for twenty years dominated thinking on the origin of glaciomarine sediments. In the last ten years, however, significant new observations have been made on modern glaciomarine environments (Molnia, 1983), particularly in Alaska (Powell, 1984), Svalbard (Elverhoi, 1984), and Antarctica

Figure 10.67. Interpreted paleocirculation patterns in the North Atlantic based on the distribution of ice-rafter debris. (a) isotopic stage 5a and early part of stage 4; (b) Late Wisconsinan (isotopic stage 2) (after Fillon et al., 1981b).

(Orheim and Elverhoi, 1981; Anderson et al., 1983, 1984; Anderson, 1985).

The behaviour of glacial ice depends very much on its thermal characteristics (Sugden and John, 1976; Paterson, 1981), with warm ice (at the pressure melting point) tending to flow faster and have lower basal shear stresses than cold ice. The discharge of ice may be regulated by feedback relationships between the ice thickness, its temperature and velocity. The temperature regime of glacial ice, both above and at the bed, affects the incorporation, distribution and residence time of detritus in a complex manner. Much of the basal movement beneath warm temperate glaciers takes place through deformation of the till substratum (Boulton and Jones, 1979).

The temperature regime of Pleistocene ice sheets and their erosional capacity is uncertain. On the eastern Canadian margin, Pleistocene ice in high latitudes was much of the time topographically restricted to fiords and transverse troughs. In lower latitudes, ice appears to have been more extensive on continental shelves. The southern margin of the Laurentide ice sheet appears to have been characterized by thin, warm ice (Boulton and Jones, 1979). It is therefore difficult to find modern analogues of the ice sheets that terminated in the marine waters of southeastern Canada: Antarctic ice is too cold, and modern midlatitude temperate ice occurs as valley glaciers, not ice sheets. Ice in areas such as Scotian Shelf and Bay of Fundy was characterized by widespread sub-glacial drainage; the complex channel systems resulting from such meltwater have not been recognized on the Labrador and Baffin shelves.

The supply of sediment to the sea by ice is a function of the type of glacier and its flow dynamics (Powell, 1984). Valley and outlet glaciers will contain much more supraglacial debris than continental ice sheets. The style of sediment release at a marine ice margin depends on whether the margin is a tidewater glacier, a calving margin in deep water, or a floating iceshelf.

Powell (1984) distinguished four glaciomarine sedimentation zones. The subglacial zone is the site of deposition from grounded ice that is analogous to subglacial deposition on land. The ice-proximal zone is complex, and includes deposits at the grounding line and immediately seaward. The ice shelf zone occurs where an ice shelf or floating glacier tongue forms seaward of the grounding line. The iceberg zone occurs beyond the limit of continuous ice.

The till recognized acoustically from high resolution seismic profiles on the eastern Canadian continental shelves is believed to be a subglacial, or locally an ice-proximal zone deposit. The geometry of till tongues suggests that the regional morainal ridges represent deposits at a oscillating grounding line (King and Fader, 1986). Samples of tills are frequently overconsolidated. Although dropstone diamictons deposited in the ice shelf zone may be texturally similar to subglacial till, no evidence is apparent in seismic profiles for "till" passing gradually into stratified facies; till tongues have a sharp contact with stratified sediment. Lift off moraines represent the transition from grounded to floating ice (King and Fader, 1986). From study of high resolution acoustic profiles it therefore appears possible to discriminate between till deposited from grounded ice and diamicton deposited beneath floating ice.

Local developments of acoustically transparent facies, in areas such as the deep basins in Hudson Strait and Lake Melville, may represent debris flows, or may be watery till deposited as an undermelt till from ice that at times was just hydrostatically supported (Dreimanis and Lundqvist, 1984).

A complex set of processes have been observed at the grounding line of modern glaciers (Powell, 1984; Elverhoi et al., 1980). If the grounding line is stationary and the ice contains sufficient sediment, a morainal ridge will develop, which in tidewater glaciers may lead to minor advance if the ridge decreases ice exposure to the sea. Grounding line fluctuations may lead to re-erosion of ice proximal sediment (Elverhoi, 1984). In this way, ice-proximal marine faunas may become incorporated in till-like diamictons (Josenhans et al., 1986). The dispersal and melting rate of sediment-rich icebergs will affect the character of ice-proximal sediments, especially if the bergs contain large quantities of supraglacial sediment. Deposition on steep slopes or oversteepening at the grounding line may lead to sediment gravity flows (Kurtz and Anderson, 1979), the finer deposits of which may be indistinguishable from those derived from sandur deltas (Kontopoulos and Piper, 1982b; Syvitski et al., 1986), whereas the coarser diamictons may resemble till. Subglacial meltwater discharge may supply both sand and gravel (deposited as mouth-bar fanglomerates, or resedimented on steep slopes) and mud (as in an interflow or overflow sediment plume). This material is probably volumetrically most important in melting-base, warm-ice, tidewater glaciers (Powell, 1984), and thick ice-proximal fluvial and plume deposits are probably commonest in fiords during the later stages of ice retreat (e.g. Clague and Hicock, 1976; Kontopoulos and Piper, 1982b). It is difficult to use microfossil assemblages to discriminate ice-proximal zone sediments from ice-shelf zone sediments, but macrofauna may prove to be of more value (Syvitski et al., 1989). Abundant microflora, notably diatoms, may indicate upwelling, which may occur at the edge of grounded or floating ice.

Off eastern Canada, thick sequences of glacial till and stratified glaciomarine sediments (Emerald Silt and equivalents) occur largely in areas of soft sedimentary bedrock, where basal ice could entrain a large proportion of fine grained material. On the Scotian Shelf and Grand Banks, the Emerald Silt facies A, which is laterally equivalent to till tongues and morainal ridges, has been interpreted as due to deposition beneath an ice shelf. It has a restricted fauna and drapes pre-existing topography. At present, the stability of warm ice shelves at the southern margin of the Laurentide ice sheet remains uncertain. Ice shelves are most stable where anchored within embayments. They are very susceptible to sea level changes. Falling sea level allows the development of ice rises, which may help dam up and thus stabilize an ice sheet in an embayment. Rise in sea level may remove the anchor points and lead to ice shelf break-up into a calving bay, which in turn leads to rapid recession of the ice sheet. This process was undoubtedly important in the rapid retreat of Late Wisconsinan ice (Denton and Hughes, 1981; Dyke et al., 1982). The gradual fall in sea level due to increasing global ice volume during much of isotopic stage 3 produced conditions that were favourable for the maintenance of ice shelves within the embayments of southeastern Canada. Much more information on changes in relative sea level during the Middle Wisconsinan are needed to assess the ice-shelf theory.[†]

It is also difficult to assess the processes active in areas between the basins in which glaciomarine sediments were preserved. In southeastern Canada, the land record of later Middle and Late Wisconsinan ice suggests it was largely restricted to lobes in lowland areas. Somewhat similar conditions existed along the coast of Baffin Island. Was ice on the Scotian Shelf likewise restricted to lobes filling basins, with the development of periglacial sandur plains on all the bank areas? Or was ice more extensive, covering all but the outermost part of Sable Island Bank and Banquereau? Similar questions can be asked on the Labrador and Baffin shelves, although there the story is further complicated by dating uncertainties.

Furthermore, at the time of writing (1985), the details of processes leading to the formation of features such as till tongues and lift-off moraines are not well understood. They are known from their acoustic signature, and have not been sampled in detail, so that their lithological character is uncertain. They have been studied in greatest detail in the embayments of Emerald Basin and the Gulf of Maine. The variability of these features, particularly in less enclosed environments, needs further study, as does their relationship to features possibly developed by sediment deformation beneath grounded ice, such as the prominent transverse ridges northeast of Conception Bay on the Northeast Newfoundland Shelf. The coastal area of Maine, where features similar to lift-off moraines are exposed on land (Smith, 1981), needs further study as does the style of sedimentation beneath modern ice shelves (Anderson, 1985).

No geometric evidence exists for ice-shelf conditions during the deposition of Emerald Silt facies B, the fauna is more diverse, and the sediments show a more ponded aspect. Few dinoflagellates indicate cold, somewhat fresh and possibly turbid surface water. This sedimentary facies probably accumulated in the iceberg zone, with relatively high rates of meltwater and suspended sediment production. Many mechanisms might produce the distinctive banding in the Emerald Silt facies B that is seen both in acoustic records and cores; probably the most important factor is a low rate of bioturbation resulting from low surface productivity and high sedimentation rates. The banding may have different origins in different localities. At present we cannot propose generalized criteria for distinguishing ice shelf and iceberg zone sedimentation in the Late Quaternary of the east coast offshore.

The thick sediment sequences of the Emerald Silt on the Scotian Shelf, and equivalent strata for example in Hudson Strait, contain widespread disconformity surfaces. It is not clear whether these represent changes in oceanographic conditions, or whether they might result from thin late ice surges with low basal shear stresses.

A marked acoustic, faunal and sedimentological contrast exists between proglacial sediments and overlying basinal muds on the eastern continental shelf. The LaHave Clay is bioturbated and has a more diverse microfossil assemblage. The sediments are ponded and onlapping in basins, not draped over pre-existing topography, thus reflecting a much greater role of near-bottom resuspension (presumably by waves and currents) compared with suspension fall out of sediment. High organic carbon content of the sediment has locally led to the accumulation of considerable biogenic methane (Vilks and Rashid, 1977).

Deep water sedimentation processes
P.R. Hill and D.J.W. Piper

Deep water sedimentation processes off eastern Canada during the Quaternary reflect fewer direct effects of glaciation, but nevertheless there is a striking contrast between Wisconsinan and Holocene processes as a result of increased sediment supply to the deep sea and changes in sea level. Both slumping and turbidity currents are widespread in Quaternary glacial stages, accompanied by a higher rate of hemipelagic sedimentation. In deep water, changes in the depth of the lysocline influence the preservation of carbonate ooze.

Sediment slides

Slides are defined as movements of essentially rigid, internally undeformed sediment along discrete shear planes (Nardin et al., 1979). Sliding occurs when the shear stress resulting from the sediment load exceeds the shear strength of the sediment at the plane of failure. Stability analyses on modern continental slopes, including the St. Pierre Slope (Moran and Hurlbut, 1986) indicate that most slopes are stable under static conditions, but there is widespread evidence for both recent sliding (e.g. the 1929 "Grand Banks" event) and sliding during the Wisconsinan on eastern Canadian continental slopes.

The 1929 "Grand Banks" event was triggered by a powerful earthquake of magnitude 7.2. It is thought that the ground accelerations produced by the earthquake caused dynamic loading of the sediment. The resultant increase in pore water pressure and reduction in effective stress reduced the shearing resistance of the sediment so that failure occurred (Piper et al., 1988). Piper et al. (1985a) postulated a similar origin for a late Wisconsinan slide on the Scotian Slope. In both cases, failure was most pronounced in silty sediments directly downslope from till tongues. These sediments are the most susceptible to failure through cyclical loading (J-M. Konrad, pers. comm., 1986).

Failure, under undrained conditions, may also result from rapid sediment loading. Conditions of rapid deposition may have existed in slope sediments deposited during the Wisconsinan in ice-marginal areas such as seaward of transverse troughs of the Scotian Shelf (Piper and Sparkes, 1987). This type of failure is likely to occur repeatedly within the same region, resulting in very complex sediment facies (Hill, 1984). In contrast, failures due to large earthquakes may be isolated in both time and space.

Sediment failure can also occur under drained conditions, but being dependent on the effective angle of internal friction of the constituent sediment, failure of this sort is restricted to very steep slopes. On the United States mid-Atlantic margin, geotechnical measurements indicate that only slopes greater than 27° would be unstable under these conditions (Almagor et al., 1984). Similar results would be expected from the eastern Canadian margin, so that this mechanism would be restricted to areas such as the steep walls of submarine channels.

The potential for slope failure can be enhanced by a mechanism of in situ creep. This is defined as strain with

---

[†] See Addendum

time under constant loading conditions. Creep may occur in sediments under shear stresses as low as 5% of the material strength and may lead to eventual failure (Bishop and Lovenbury, 1969). This mechanism could lead to the folding and downslope movement of the sediment mass (Hill et al., 1982; Watkins and Kraft, 1978). Possible creep-related folds have been observed on both the Scotian (Piper et al., 1985a) and Beaufort (Hill et al., 1982) slopes. The creep process may play an important role in slope stability by reducing the stress required to cause failure under either drained or undrained conditions.

Debris flows and turbidity currents

Debris flows are intimately related to the process of slope failure. A slide may become sufficiently agitated during downslope transport that the sediment is remoulded and water is incorporated (Hampton, 1970). The remoulding of the sediment results in a loss of strength, so that the potential for debris flow is therefore related to the "sensitivity" of the sediment — the ratio of undisturbed strength to remoulded strength. The debris flow moves downslope as a viscous fluid and large clasts of rock or original sediment, not remoulded, are supported by the mud matrix (Hampton, 1970). Debris flow deposits of Late Pleistocene age have been observed in many areas of the Scotian Slope (Piper et al., 1985a) and Flemish Pass (Pereira et al., 1985), and deposits of this sort were formed during the 1929 Grand Banks earthquake event (Piper et al., 1985b).

Incorporation of water at the upper surface of a debris flow can result in entrainment of sediment in a turbulent suspension (Hampton, 1970). The sediment-water mixture may become sufficiently dense that a turbidity current is generated (Middleton and Southard, 1984). The great abundance of turbidites during glacial intervals is probably related to the failure of rapidly deposited glacial sediments on the upper continental slope (Wright and Anderson, 1982). Some authors have suggested that cold turbid freshwater, flowing directly into the sea, may be sufficiently dense to behave as a turbidity current, but this process has not been convincingly demonstrated. Turbidity currents are also generated by wave induced currents in the heads of shallow-water submarine canyons (Fukushima et al., 1985); this process may have been important on the Scotian and Grand Banks margins at times of lowered sea level.

The grain size of sediment within a turbidity current has an important influence on the behaviour of the current (Bowen et al., 1984). Sandy turbidity currents are fast, may erode older sediment from channels, and tend to deposit large lobes of sediment at the end of the channel system. The presence of gravel (transported by ice rafting or debris flows) will inhibit erosion by such currents. Muddy turbidity currents are generally slow and thick (Stow and Bowen, 1980) and commonly build up levees. Spillover of thicker flows, however, will produce progressive downslope sorting of the turbidite (Flood and Damuth, 1987). Smaller turbidity currents deposit most of their load on the continental slope or rise, and far fewer large currents reach the abyssal plains (Piper and Normark, 1983).

The Wisconsinan glacial pattern of a major Middle Wisconsinan shelf-crossing ice advance, followed by gradual recession, would have produced a parallel pattern of deep water sedimentation. Shelf-crossing ice sheets delivered sand to the upper slope, and this sand in part accumulated on the slope, and in part was transported to deep water, flushing out channels on the slope and rise. During ice retreat on the shelf, abundant suspended sediment was supplied to the continental slope from glacial outwash. Failure of this sediment would have yielded thick muddy turbidity currents that would have built up levees and supplied sediment to nepheloid layers maintained by bottom water circulation. In the Holocene, the lack of sediment supply to the continental slope resulted in an almost complete cessation of turbidity current transport and the accumulation of hemipelagic sediments. Occasional large earthquakes triggered large turbidity currents, which were either muddy or sandy depending on the geology of the epicentral area. The Grand Banks 1929 earthquake, for example, resulted in a very sandy turbidity current (Piper et al., 1988). Major sea level lowering in areas of shallow shelf break may also have triggered sandy turbidity currents for a short time in the Late Wisconsinan.

Bottom current sediment transport

The transport and deposition of sediment by powerful contour-following bottom currents has played an important role in the development of Upper Cenozoic sediment sequences on the eastern Canadian continental margin. Large sediment drifts were built in the Late Miocene and Pliocene in the North Atlantic ocean basin, including the Labrador Sea and the eastern margin of the United States. In Labrador Sea, the growth of drifts slowed in the Quaternary, whereas in places on the United States margin Pliocene drifts were eroded during the Pleistocene, and subsequently received only a thin Holocene sediment veneer. Holocene sedimentological processes associated with bottom currents are described in Chapter 11.

The major asymmetry of the levees of the Laurentian Fan attests to the importance of Pleistocene bottom-current activity in transporting the finer grained components of turbidity currents southwestwards along the continental rise. Indeed, such transport of mud may also be one important factor in preventing the growth of prominent deep sea fans on the eastern Canadian margin. The occurrence of thick continentally-derived mud in glacial intervals on the Fogo Seamounts points to the sedimentological importance of nepheloid layer deposition during glacial maxima; whether the nepheloid layer was fed mainly from turbid ice margin discharge or from turbidity currents is uncertain.

The fluctuations in both the source of bottom water in the Western Boundary Undercurrent and the velocity of the current are not well understood. Several authors (Schnitker, 1974, 1979; Lohmann, 1978; Streeter and Shackleton, 1979; Balsam, 1981) have used Late Pleistocene benthic foraminiferal distributions to infer changes in the distribution of Antarctic Bottom Water and related water, compared with North Atlantic Deep Water. Supply of well oxygenated North Atlantic Deep Water appears to have been unimportant during most glacial stages. The decrease in drift formation in the Labrador Sea in the Quaternary compared with the Pliocene, and the Holocene intensification of the Western Boundary Undercurrent in the Labrador Sea inferred by Schafer et al. (1985) are probably related to changes in circulation of North Atlantic Deep Water. In contrast, however, bottom current activity appears to have been more intense in places on the continental rise off the United States during Pleistocene gla-

Table 10.8. Middle and Late Quaternary sediment budget for eastern Canada and adjacent marine areas

	Area	Mean Thickness	Volume	References and Notes
	x10³ km²	m	x10⁶ km³	
Source areas				
Canadian Shield and internal basins	3600	?	?	1
Shelf basins and troughs	400	200	80	2
Sediment Sinks				
Scotian Shelf, Gulf of Maine, Gulf of St. Lawrence	300	50	15	3
Grand Banks	150	20	3	3
N.E. Newfoundland and Labrador shelves	150	60	9	3
Hudson Strait, Baffin shelves	150	50	7.5	3
Scotian Slope and Rise	180	200	36	4
Grand Banks Slopes and Rises	200	150	30	5
Labrador and N.E. Newfoundland Slope and Rise	300	200	60	6
Baffin Slope	100	50	5	7
Sohm Abyssal Plain	1100	100	110	8
Newfoundland Basin	200	50	10	5
NAMOC West of Orphan Knoll	30	50	1.5	5
Northern Labrador Basin (90%)	120	80	9.6	6
Baffin Bay Basin (50%)	25	100	2.5	7

References and Notes

1. All areas ultimately draining into Baffin Bay, Labrador Sea and the Northwest Atlantic east of Georges Bank according to the ice trajectories of Dyke et al. (1982). This area is bounded by the McClintock ice divide, Hudson dome and the southwest part of the Labrador ice divide.

    Mean thickness of erosion is unknown: balancing the sediment budget is very dependent on uncertain estimates of sediment thickness in the Sohm Abyssal Plain, but suggests mean thickness of erosion of tens of metres (see discussion in text).

2. Area of marginal and transverse troughs (saddles) on the continental shelf, including Hudson Strait and deep water north and southeast of Southampton Island, Lancaster Sound and Jones Sound. Average depth of overdeepening below regional shelf taken as 200 m, which assumes that all of these troughs were valleys prior to glacial overdeepening.

3. Thicknesses based on regional mapping reported in this chapter and shown in Figure 3 (in pocket).

4. Thickness based on Piper et al. (1986b), modified to reflect unpublished regional seismic data.

5. Estimate based on data from Labrador and Scotian margins. NAMOC is Northwest Atlantic Mid-Ocean Channel.

6. Thicknesses from Myers (1986).

7. Thickness extrapolated using unpublished regional seismic reflection profiles from ODP Site 645 (Srivastava et al., 1986).

8. This thickness is critical to the overall balance of the budget. Laine (1980) used a thickness of 320 m, but this includes a substantial amount of Upper Pliocene and Lower Pleistocene sediment. Estimate based on thicknesses on lower Laurentian Fan (Wilson and Piper, 1986) extrapolated seawards with a regional thinning correction applied.

cial stages than either in the Pliocene or the Holocene (e.g. van Hinte et al., 1987).

Pelagic sedimentation

Changes in the style of pelagic sedimentation with changing glacial conditions can be analyzed in terms of the various components of pelagic sediments. Fluctuations in the abundance and source of both ice-rafted detritus and nepheloid transport of mud have been discussed above. Changes in surface water productivity may strongly influence the character of pelagic sediments: for example, the abundance of diatomaceous sediments during ice retreat off eastern Newfoundland (Alam et al., 1983; Mudie and Guilbault, 1982). Changes in the depth of the carbonate compensation zone have played a major role in determining the type of pelagic sediment, with a tendency for greater carbonate dissolution during interglacial periods (e.g., in Baffin Bay, Aksu, 1983a; and in the Newfoundland Basin, Alam et al., 1983).

The volume of deep water sediments
D.J.W. Piper

Several authors (White, 1972; Matthews, 1975; Laine, 1980) have attempted to use the volume of deep sea sediments adjacent to North America as an indicator of the volume of sediment removed by glacial erosion from the North American continent. These estimates have been hampered by the poor age control on deep water sequences in the Sohm Abyssal Plain and Labrador Sea. Some authors (e.g. Laine, 1980; Laine and Bell, 1982) interpreted the data to indicate that hundreds of metres of erosion have taken place on the Canadian Shield, but this has been questioned by others (e.g. Andrews, 1982) because of the evidence for the preservation of preglacial landscapes in many glaciated areas, and the occurrence of only a few shield erratics in the deep sea.

Sediment pathways, and in particular the export of fine grained sediment in the Western Boundary Undercurrent, are not yet well enough known to make a definitive judgement on this issue. However, the weight of evidence favours the proposition that only limited erosional products of the Canadian Shield reached the Atlantic Ocean on account of glaciation. On the continental shelves, pre-glacial landscape features have been preserved, and major glacial erosion is restricted to the basins and troughs at the contact of the Mesozoic-Cenozoic sediment wedge with basement, to the transverse troughs, and to coastal fiords and basins. Most tills sampled on the outer continental shelf have a high proportion of detritus derived from sedimentary rocks of the continental shelf or adjacent land areas. Although data are limited, ice-rafted detritus in deep water also contains a high proportion of detritus of sedimentary origin — not from the shield.

A speculative sediment budget for the Middle and Late Pleistocene is presented in Table 10.8. This time interval is used because of the evidence for continental ice sheets at that time. Earlier, largely alpine glaciation may have eroded large volumes of sediment from the continent, but this erosion would have been concentrated in marginal mountainous areas, not the central part of the Canadian Shield. The ice divides proposed by Dyke et al. (1982) have been used to estimate the area of potential source terrains. It is assumed that transport into the eastern Canadian off-

shore by bottom currents (bringing sediments principally from the Greenland margin) balances loss of sediment by the same mechanism to the continental rise off the United States. Partitioning of sediment in the basins of the Labrador Sea and Baffin Bay between Canadian and Greenland sources is more difficult: we assume that 50% of the Mid to Upper Pleistocene sediment in Baffin Bay and that 90% of the sediment in the Northwest Atlantic Mid-Ocean Channel system are Canadian derived.

The budget is very dependant on the uncertainty in estimates for the Sohm Abyssal Plain. Total Middle to Late Pleistocene (i.e. approximately the last 0.7 Ma) sedimentation is estimated as between 200 and 300 million cubic kilometres. Of this, at least 80 million cubic kilometres would have been supplied from erosion of overdeepened troughs on the continental shelves. The abundance of sedimentary rock detritus in proglacial sediments on the continental margin suggests that the estimate of sediment supplied by such erosion may be low. Even this conservative estimate implies an average of only a few tens of metres of erosion of the terrestrial source areas. If much of this were concentrated in deeply dissected mountainous areas, average erosion of the shield may have been as little as 10 m.

ACKNOWLEDGMENTS

Many geologists have contributed to the compilation of this chapter, by contributing information, and reading, reviewing, and improving individual sections. The co-authors of this chapter have often contributed to sections in addition to those for which they are specifically credited as authors. In addition, A.C. Grant, D.R. Grant, R. Parrott and L. Nicks have reviewed parts of the manuscript and the entire manuscript has been reviewed by J.T. Andrews, H.B.S. Cooke, and J. Stravers. We thank John Zevenhuizen for his work on the Labrador Shelf, Bob Miller on the Scotian Shelf and Grand Banks, Roy Sparkes on continental slopes, and Bob Harmes and Kate Moran on the Beaufort Sea and slope stability. In particular, we recognize the contributions of the officers and crews of the Bedford Institute of Oceanography fleet, and the technicians and engineers in government and industry who have developed and maintained the technology with which we work.

REFERENCES

Adshead, J.D.
1973: Mineralogical studies of bottom sediments from western Hudson and James Bays; Ph.D. thesis, University of Missouri, Columbia, Missouri, 179 p.

Aksu, A.E.
1981: Late Quaternary stratigraphy, paleoenvironmentology and sedimentation history of Baffin Bay and Davis Strait; Ph.D. thesis, Dalhousie University, Halifax, Nova Scotia, 771 p.
1983a: Holocene and Pleistocene dissolution cycles in deep-sea cores of Baffin Bay and Davis Strait; Paleoceanographic implications; Marine Geology, v. 53, p. 331-348.
1983b: A short period geomagnetic excursion recorded in Pleistocene sediments of Baffin Bay and Davis Strait; Geology, v. 11, p. 537-541.
1984: Subaqueous debris flow deposits in Baffin Bay; Geo-marine Letters, v. 4, p. 83-90.
1985a: Paleomagnetic stratigraphy of the CESAR cores; in Initial Geological Report on CESAR — the Canadian Expedition to Study the Alpha Ridge, Arctic Ocean, ed. H.R. Jackson, P.J. Mudie, and S.M. Blasco; Geological Survey of Canada, Paper 84-22, p. 101-114.

1985b: Planktonic foraminiferal and oxygen isotopic stratigraphy of CESAR cores 102 and 103: preliminary results; in Initial Geological Report on CESAR — the Canadian Expedition to Study the Alpha Ridge, Arctic Ocean, ed. H.R. Jackson, P.J. Mudie, and S.M. Blasco; Geological Survey of Canada, Paper 84-22, p. 105-124.

1985c: Climatic and oceanographic changes over the past 400,000 years; evidence from deep-sea cores of Baffin Bay and Davis Strait; in Quaternary Environments: Eastern Canadian Arctic, Baffin Bay and West Greenland, ed. J.T. Andrews; George Allen and Unwin, Boston, p. 181-209.

Aksu, A.E. and Mudie, P.J.
1985a: Upper Quaternary stratigraphy of Davis Strait; Marine Micropalaeontology, v. 9, p. 537-557.

1985b: A minimum 4 million year Arctic Ocean record dated by magnetostratigraphy and palynology; Nature, v. 318, p. 280-283.

Aksu, A.E. and Piper, D.J.W.
1979: Baffin Bay in the last 100,000 years; Geology, v. 7, p. 245-248.

1987: Late Quaternary sedimentation in Baffin Bay; Canadian Journal of Earth Sciences, v. 24, no. 9, p. 1833-1846.

Aksu, A.E., Macko, S.A., and Mudie, P.J.
1986: Paleoclimatic and paleoceanographic history of the Labrador Sea; Abstracts with Programs, 99th Annual Meeting, Geological Society of America, San Antonio, Texas, p. 523.

Alam, M.
1979: The effect of Pleistocene climatic changes on the sediments around the Grand Banks; Ph.D. thesis, Dalhousie University, Halifax, Nova Scotia, 222 p.

Alam, M. and Piper, D.J.W.
1977: Pre-Wisconsinan stratigraphy and paleoclimates off Atlantic Canada and its bearing on glaciation in Quebec; Géographie Physique et Quaternaire, v. 31, p. 15-22.

1981: Detrital mineralogy of deep-water continental margin off Newfoundland; Canadian Journal of Earth Sciences, v. 18, p. 1336-1345.

Alam, M., Piper, D.J.W., and Cooke, H.B.S.
1983: Late Quaternary stratigraphy and paleo-oceanography of the Grand Banks continental margin, eastern Canada; Boreas, v. 12, p. 253-261.

Almagor, G., Bennett, R.H., Lambert, D.N., Forde, E.B., and Shepard, L.S.
1984: Analysis of slope stability, Wilmington to Lindenkohl Canyons, U.S. mid-Atlantic margin; in Seabed Mechanics, ed. B. Derness; Graham and Trotman, London, p. 77-86.

Amos, C.L.
1978: The postglacial evolution of the Minas Basin, N.S.: a sedimentological interpretation; Journal of Sedimentary Petrology, v. 48, p. 965-982.

Amos, C.L. and King, E.L.
1984: Bedforms of the Canadian Eastern Seaboard: A comparison with global occurrences; in Sedimentation on High-Latitude Continental Shelves, ed. B.D. Bornhold and A. Guilcher; Marine Geology, v. 57, p. 167-208.

Amos, C.L. and Knoll, R.G.
1987: The Quaternary sediments of Banquereau, Scotian Shelf; Geological Society of America Bulletin, v. 98, p. 244-260.

Anderson, J.B.
1985: Antarctic glacial marine sedimentation: A core workshop; Geological Society of America, Annual meeting, Orlando, Fl., 66 p.

Anderson, J.B., Brake, C.F. and Myers, N.C.
1984: Sedimentation on the Ross Sea continental shelf, Antarctica; Marine Geology, v. 57, p. 295-333.

Anderson, J.B., Grake, C., Domack, E.W., Myers, N. and Wright, R.
1983: Development of a polar glacial-marine sedimentation model from Antarctic Quaternary deposits and glaciological information; in Glacial Marine Sedimentation, ed. B.F. Molnia, Plenum Publishing Corp., N.Y. and London, p. 233-264.

Anderson, T.W.
1985: Late Quaternary pollen records from eastern Ontario, Quebec and Atlantic Canada; in Pollen Records of Late Quaternary North American Sediments, ed. V.M. Bryant, Jr., and R.G. Holloway; American Association of Stratigraphic Palynologists, p. 281-326.

Andrews, J.T.
1980: Progress in relative sea level and ice sheet reconstructions, Baffin Island, N.W.T., for the last 125,000 years; in Earth Rheology, Isostasy and Eustasy, ed. N.A. Morner; J.A. Wiley and Sons, N.Y., p. 175-200.

1982: Comment on "New evidence from beneath the western North Atlantic for the depth of glacial erosion in Greenland and North America"; Quaternary Research, v. 17, p. 123-124.

Andrews, J.T. and Ives, J.D.
1978: "Cockburn" nomenclature and the late Quaternary history of the eastern Canadian Arctic; Arctic and Alpine Research, v. 10, p. 617-633.

Andrews, J.T. and Miller, G.H.
1983: Quaternary history of the Northeast sector of the Laurentide ice sheet and the mid-Wisconsin sea level problem: Final report to the National Science Foundation, Grant EAR-79-26061; Institute of Arctic and Alpine Research, University of Colorado, Boulder, Colorado, 43 p.

1984: Quaternary glacial and nonglacial correlations for the Eastern Canadian Arctic; in Quaternary Stratigraphy of Canada — A Canadian Contribution to the IGCP Project 24, ed. R.J. Fulton; Geological Survey of Canada Paper 84-10, p. 101-116.

Andrews, J.T. and Mothersill, J.S., and Tabrez, A.R.
1986: Palaeomagnetic record, texture and mineralogy of late Quaternary sediments, Baffin Island fjords; Arctic and Alpine Research, v. 18, p. 361-376.

Andrews, J.T. and Osterman, L.
1984: Late Pleistocene and Holocene paleo-oceanographic changes in the nearshore environment, Baffin Island, Canada: the glacial/interglacial transition: Final report to the National Science Foundation, Institute of Arctic and Alpine Research, University of Colorado, Boulder, Colorado, 100 p.

Andrews, J.T., Jull, A.J.T., Donahue, D.J., Short, S.K. and Osterman, L.E.
1985: Sedimentation rates in Baffin Island fiord cores from comparative radiocarbon dates; Canadian Journal of Earth Sciences, v. 22, p. 1827-1834.

Andrews, J.T., Miller, G.H., Vincent, J-S., and Shilts, W.W.
1984: Quaternary correlations in Arctic Canada; in Quaternary Stratigraphy of Canada — A Canadian Contribution to IGCP Project 24, ed. R.J. Fulton; Geological Survey of Canada, Paper 84-10, p. 127-134.

Andrews, J.T., Shilts, W.W., and Miller, G.H.
1983: Multiple deglaciation of the Hudson Bay Lowlands since deposition of the Missinaibi (last interglacial?) Formation; Quaternary Research, v. 19, p. 18-37.

Arthur, M., Srivastava, S., et al.
1986: High latitude palaeoceanography from the Leg 105 shipboard scientific party; Nature, v. 320, p. 17-18.

Bada, J.L. and Schroeder, R.A.
1975: Amino acid racemization reaction and their geochemical implications; Naturwissenschaften, v. 62, p. 71-79.

Baker, S.R. and Friedman, G.M.
1973: Sedimentation in an Arctic marine environment: Baffin Bay between Greenland and the Canadian Arctic Archipelago; in Earth Science Symposium on Offshore Eastern Canada, ed. P.J. Hood, N.J. McMillan, and B.R. Pelletier; Geological Survey of Canada, Paper 71-23, p. 471-498.

Baldauf, J.G.
1984: Cenozoic diatom biostratigraphy and paleoceanography of the Rockall Plateau region, North Atlantic, Deep Sea Drilling Project Leg 81; in Initial Reports of the Deep Sea Drilling Project, Volume 81, ed. D.G. Roberts et al.; United States Government Printing Office, Washington, v. 81, p. 439-478.

Balsam, W.
1981: Late Quaternary sedimentation in the western North Atlantic: stratigraphy and paleoceanography; Paleogeography, Paleoclimatology, Paleoceanography, v. 35, p. 215-240.

Balsam, W.L. and Heussen, L.E.
1976: Direct correlation of sea surface palaeotemperatures, deep circulation and terrestrial palaeoclimates: foraminiferal and playnological evidence from two cores off Chesapeake Bay; Marine Geology, v. 21, p. 121-147.

Barnosky, C.W.
1984: Late Miocene vegetational and climatic variations inferred from a pollen record in Northwest Wyoming; Science, v. 223, p. 49-51.

Barrett, D.L. and Keen, C.E.
1978: Ocean bottom seismometer studies of the crust near the Orphan Knoll and Flemish Cap continental fragments; EOS, Transactions of the American Geophysical Union, v. 59, p. 322.

Barrie, C.Q. and Piper, D.J.W.
1982: Late Quaternary marine geology of Makkovik Bay, Labrador; Geological Survey of Canada, Paper 81-17, 37 p.

Barrie, V., Lewis, C.F.M., Fader, G.B., and King, L.H.
1984: Seabed processes on the northeastern Grand Banks of Newfoundland: modern reworking of relict sediments; Marine Geology, v. 57, p. 209-227.

Barry, R.G., Andrews, J.T., and Mahaffy, M.A.
1975: Continental ice sheets: conditions for growth; Science, v. 190, p. 979-981.

Barss, M.S., Bujak, J.P., and Williams, G.L.
1979: Palynological zonation and correlation of sixty-seven wells, Eastern Canada; Geological Survey of Canada, Paper 78-24, 118 p.

Bartlett, G.A. and Molinsky, L.
1972: Foraminifera and Holocene history of the Gulf of St. Lawrence; Canadian Journal of Earth Sciences, v. 9, p. 1204-1215.

Bayliss, P., Levinson, A.A., and Klovan, J.E.
1970: Mineralogy of bottom sediments, Hudson Bay, Canada; Bulletin of Canadian Petroleum Geology, v. 18, p. 469-473.

Berger, A.L.
1978: Long term variations in caloric insolation resulting from the Earth's orbital elements; Quaternary Research, v. 9, p. 139-167.

Berger, G.W., Huntley, D.J., and Stipp, J.J.
1984: Thermoluminescence studies on a C-14 dated marine core; Canadian Journal of Earth Sciences, v. 21, p. 1145-1150.

Berger, W.H.
1981: Oxygen and carbon isotopes in foraminifera: an introduction; Paleogeography, Paleoclimatology, Paleoecology, v. 33, p. 3-7.

Berggren, W.A.
1972: Late Pliocene-Pleistocene glaciation; in Initial Reports of the Deep Sea Drilling Project, Volume 12, ed. A.J. Laughton et al.; United States Government Printing Office, Washington, v. 12, p. 953-964.

1981a: Correlation of Atlantic, Mediterranean, and Indo-Pacific Neogene stratigraphies: geochronology and chronostratigraphy: ICGP Project 114, International Workshop on Pacific Neogene Biostratigraphy, Osaka and Kobe, Japan, Nov. 24-29, p. 93-110.

1981b: Neogene planktonic foraminiferal biostratigraphy and biogeography: Atlantic, Mediterranean, and Indo-Pacific regions: ICGP Project 114, International Workshop on Pacific Neogene Biostratigraphy, Osaka and Kobe, Japan, Nov. 24-29, p. 111-160.

Berggren, W.A. and van Couvering, J.A.
1974: The Late Neogene; biostratigraphy, geochronology, and paleoclimatology of the last 15 million years in marine and continental sequences; Paleogeography, Paleoclimatology, Paleoecology, v. 16, p. 1-216.

Berggren, W.A., Kent, D.V., Flynn, J.J., and van Couvering, J.A.
1985: Cenozoic geochronology; Geological Society of America Bulletin, v. 96, p. 1407-1418.

Binns, R.E.
1972: Composition and derivation of pumice on postglacial strandlines in northern Europe and western Arctic; Geological Society of America Bulletin, v. 83, p. 2303-2324.

Biscaye, D.E. and Eittreim, S.E.
1977: Suspended particulate loads and transports in the nepheloid layer on the abyssal Atlantic Ocean; Marine Geology, v. 23, p. 155-172.

Bishop, A.W. and Lovenbury, H.T.
1969: Creep characteristics of two undisturbed clays; Proceedings Seventh International Conference on Soil Mechanics and Foundations Engineering, v. 1, p. 29-37.

Blackwell, B.
1983: Amino acid geochronology: applications to late Cenozoic geology; Geoscience Canada, v. 10, p. 25-27.

Blake, W. Jr.
1966: End moraines and deglaciation chronology in northern Canada with special reference to southern Baffin Island; Geological Survey of Canada, Paper 66-26, 31 p.

1970: Studies of glacial history in Arctic Canada. I. Pumice, radiocarbon dates and differential post-glacial uplift in the eastern Queen Elizabeth Islands; Canadian Journal of Earth Sciences, v. 7, p. 634-664.

Blasco, S.M., Bornhold, B.D., and Lewis, C.F.M.
1979: Preliminary results of surficial geology and geomorphology studies of the Lomonosov Ridge, central Arctic Basin; in Current Research, Part C, Geological Survey of Canada, Paper 79-1C, p. 73-83.

Bornhold, B.D., Finlayson, N.M., and Monohan, D.
1976: Submerged drainage patterns in Barrow Strait, Canadian Arctic; Canadian Journal of Earth Sciences, v. 13, p. 305-311.

Bothner, M.H. and Spiker, E.C.
1980: Upper Wisconsinan till recovered on the continental shelf southeast of New England; Science, v. 210, p. 423-425.

Boulton, G.S. and Jones, A.S.
1979: Stability of temperate ice caps and ice sheets resting on beds of deformable sediment; Journal of Glaciology, v. 24, p. 29-43.

Bouma, A.H.
1969: Methods for the study of sedimentary structures; J. Wiley and Sons, Inc., New York, 458 p.

Bowen, A.J., Normark, W.R., and Piper, D.J.W.
1984: Modelling of turbidity currents on Navy Submarine Fan, California continental borderland; Sedimentology, v. 31, p. 169-186.

Boyd, R. and Penland, S.
1984: Shoreface translation and the Holocene stratigraphic record: examples from Nova Scotia, the Mississippi Delta and eastern Australia; Marine Geology, v. 60, p. 391-412.

Boyd, R.F., Clark, D.L., Jones, G., Ruddiman, W.F., McIntyre, R., and Pisias, N.J.
1984: Central Arctic ocean response to Pleistocene earth-orbital variations; Quaternary Research, v. 22, p. 121-128.

Brigham, J.K.
1983: Stratigraphy, amino acid geochronology and correlation of Quaternary sea-level and glacial events, Broughton Island, arctic Canada; Canadian Journal of Earth Sciences, v. 20, p. 577-598.

Brookes, I.A., Scott, D.B., and McAndrews, J.H.
1985: Postglacial relative sea-level change, Port au Port area, west Newfoundland; Canadian Journal of Earth Sciences, v. 22, p. 1039-1047.

Buckley, D.E.
1971: Recent marine sediments of Lancaster Sound, District of Franklin; Maritime Sediments, v. 7, p. 96-117.

1981: Geological investigation of a selected area of the Sohm Abyssal Plain, western Atlantic: C.S.S. HUDSON Cruise 80-06; Atomic Energy of Canada Ltd., Report TR-168, 38 p.

Bukry, D.
1981: Cenozoic coccoliths from the Deep Sea Drilling Project; in The Deep Sea Drilling Project: A Decade of Progress, ed. J.E. Warme, R.G. Douglas, and E.L. Winterer, E.L.; Society of Economic Paleontologists and Mineralogists, Special Publication No. 32, p. 335-353.

Campbell, N.J. and Collin, A.E.
1958: The discoloration of Foxe Basin ice; Journal of Fisheries Research Board Canada, No. 15, p. 1175-1188.

Carey, S.W. and Ahmad, N.
1961: Glacial marine sedimentation; in Proceedings, First International Symposium on Arctic Geology, Volume 2, ed. G.O. Raasch; p. 865-894.

Carter, L.
1979: Significance of unstained and stained gravel on the Newfoundland continental slope and rise; Journal of Sedimentary Petrology, v. 49, p. 1147-1158.

Carter, L. and Schafer, C.T.
1983: Interaction of the Western Boundary Undercurrent with the continental margin off Newfoundland; Sedimentology, v. 30, p. 751-768.

Carter, L.D., Brigham-Grette, J., and Hopkins, D.M.
1986: Late Cenozoic marine transgressions of the Alaskan Arctic Coastal Plain; in Correlation of Quaternary Deposits and Events around the Margin of the Beaufort Sea: Contributions from a joint Canadian-American Workshop, April 1984; ed. J.A. Heginbottom and J-S. Vincent, Geological Survey of Canada, Open File 1237, p. 21-27.

Carter, L., Schafer, C.T., and Rashid, M.A.
1979: Observations on depositional environments and benthos of the continental slope and rise, east of Newfoundland; Canadian Journal of Earth Science, v. 16, p. 831-846.

Chough, S.K.
1978: Morphology, sedimentary facies and processes of the Northwest Atlantic Mid-Ocean Channel between 61° and 52°N, Labrador Sea; Ph.D. thesis, McGill University, Montreal, Quebec, 167 p.

Chough, S.K. and Hesse, R.
1976: Submarine meandering talweg and turbidity currents flowing for 4000 km in the Northwest Atlantic Mid-Ocean Channel, Labrador Sea; Geology, v. 4, p. 529-533.

1980: The North West Atlantic Mid-Ocean Channel of the Labrador Sea: III headspill vs body spill deposits from turbidity currents on natural levees; Journal of Sedimentary Petrology, v. 50, p. 227-234.

Chough, S.K., Mosher, D.C. and Srivastava, S.P.
1985: Ocean Drilling Program (ODP) site survey (Hudson 84-030) in the Labrador Sea: 3.5 kHz profiles; in Current Research, Part B, Geological Survey of Canada, Paper 85-1B, p. 33-41.

Clague, J.J. and Hicock, S.R.
1976: Sand and gravel resources of Kitimat, Terrace and Prince Rupert, British Columbia; in Report of Activities, Part A, Geological Survey of Canada, Paper 76-1A, p. 273-276.

Clark, D.L.
1981: Geology and geophysics of the Amerasian Basin; in The Ocean Basins and Margins, Volume 5, The Arctic Ocean, ed. A.E.M. Nairn, M. Churkin, and F.G. Stehli; Plenum Press, N.Y. and London, p. 599-634.

Clark, D.L. and Hansen, A.
1983: Central Arctic Ocean sediment texture: a key to ice transport mechanisms; in Glacial-Marine Sedimentation, ed. B.F. Molnia; Plenum Publishing Corp., N.Y. and London, p. 301-330.

Clark, D.L., Morris, T.H., and Blasco, S.M.
1983: Pleistocene sedimentation patterns from the Lomonosov Ridge and Amerasian Basin, Central Arctic Ocean; Geological Society of America, Abstracts with Program, v. 15, p. 545.

Clark, D.L., Vincent, J-S., Jones, G.A., and Morris, W.A.
1984: Correlation of marine and continental glacial and interglacial events, Arctic Ocean and Banks Island; Nature, v. 311, p. 147-149.

Clark, P.
1984: Glacial geology of the Kangalaksiorvik-Abloviak region, northern Labrador, Canada; Ph.D. thesis, University of Colorado, Boulder, Colorado, 248 p.

Clark, P.V. and Josenhans, H.W.
1986: Late Quaternary land-sea correlations, northern Labrador and Labrador Shelf; in Current Research, Part B, Geological Survey of Canada, Paper 86-1B, p. 171-178.

Clarke, A.H., Grant, D.R., and Macpherson, E.
1972: The relationship of *Atractodon stonei* (Pilsbry) (Mollusca, Buccinidae) to the Pleistocene stratigraphy and paleoecology of southwestern Nova Scotia; Canadian Journal of Earth Sciences, v. 9, p. 1030-1038.

CLIMAP Project Members
1976: The surface of the ice-age Earth; Science, v. 191, p. 1131-1137.

Collin, A.E. and Dunbar, M.J.
1964: Physical oceanography in Arctic Canada; Oceanography and Marine Biology Annual Reviews, v. 2, p. 45-75.

Conolly, J.R. and Ewing, M.
1965: Pleistocene glacial marine zones in North Atlantic deep sea sediments; Nature, v. 208, p. 135-139.

Conolly, J.R., Needham, H.D., and Heezen, B.C.
1967: Late Pleistocene and Holocene sedimentation in the Laurentian Channel; Journal of Geology, v. 75, p. 131-147.

Cooke, H.B.S.
1973: Pleistocene chronology: long or short?; Quaternary Research, v. 3, p. 206-220.

Corliss, B.H., Hunt, A.S., and Keigwin, L.D.
1982: Benthonic foraminiferal faunal and isotopic data for postglacial evolution of the Champlain Sea; Quaternary Research, v. 17, p. 325-338.

Craig, B.G. and Fyles, J.G.
1960: Pleistocene geology of Arctic Canada; Geological Survey of Canada, Paper 60-10, 21 p.

Cronin, T.M.
1977: Late-Wisconsinan marine environments of the Champlain Valley (New York, Quebec); Quaternary Research, v. 7, p. 238-253.

Crowley, T.J.
1984: Atmospheric circulation patterns during glacial inception: a possible candidate; Quaternary Research, v. 21, p. 105-110.

Dale, C.T.
1979: A study of high resolution seismology and sedimentology on the offshore late Quaternary sediments northeast of Newfoundland; M.Sc. thesis, Dalhousie University, Halifax, Nova Scotia, 181 p.

Dale, C.T. and Haworth, R.T.
1979: High resolution seismology studies on late Quaternary sediments of the northeast Newfoundland continental shelf; in Current Research, Part B, Geological Survey of Canada, Paper 79-1B, p. 357-364.

Dames and Moore, Inc.
1968: Marine surveys proposed tidal project, Bay of Fundy, New Brunswick and Nova Scotia; Atlantic Tidal Power Programming Board, unpublished report.

Davies, T.A. and Laughton, A.S.
1972: Sedimentary processes in the North Atlantic; in Initial Reports of the Deep Sea Drilling Project, Volume 12, ed. A.S. Laughton et al.; United States Government Printing Office, Washington, v. 12, p. 905-934.

Denton, G.H. and Hughes, T.J.
1981: The last great ice sheets; John Wiley and Sons, New York, 484 p.
1983: Milankovitch theory of ice ages: hypothesis of ice sheet linkage between regional insolation and global climate; Quaternary Research, v. 20, p. 125-144.

de Vernal, A.
1986: Analyses palynologiques et isotopiques de sédiments de la mer du Labrador et de la baie de Baffin: éléments d'une climatostratigraphie du Quaternaire supérieur dans l'est du Canada; Thèse de Doctorat, Université de Montréal, 214 p.

de Vernal, A. and Mott, R.J.
1986: Palynostratigraphie et paléoenvironments du Pléistocène supérieur dans la région du lac Bras d'Or, île du Cap-Breton, Nouvelle Écosse; Canadian Journal of Earth Sciences, v. 23, p. 491-503.

de Vernal, A., Mudie, P.J., Hillaire-Marcel, C. and Aksu, A.E.
1986: Palynology of Pliocene-Pleistocene and recent sediments, ODP Leg 105, Labrador Sea-Baffin Bay: Ocean Drilling Program Initial Reports Leg 105, Volume 1, Geological Association of Canada-Mineralogical Association of Canada Joint Annual Meeting, Program and Abstracts.

de Vernal, A., Richard, P.J.H., and Ochietti, S.
1983: Palynologie et paleoenvironments du Wisconsinien de la région de la Baie Saint-Laurent, Île du Cap-Breton; Géographie physique et Quaternaire, v. 37, p. 307-322.

Dietrich, J.R., Dixon, J., and McNeil, D.H.
1985: Sequence analysis and nomenclature of Upper Cretaceous to Holocene strata in the Beaufort-MacKenzie Basin; in Current Research, Part A, Geological Survey of Canada, Paper 85-1A, p. 613-628.

Dredge, L.A. and Cowan, W.R.
in press: Quaternary geology of the southwestern Canadian Shield; in Chapter 3, Quaternary Geology of Canada and Greenland, ed. R.J. Fulton, Geological Survey of Canada, Geology of Canada, no. 1 [also Geological Society of America, The Geology of North America, v. K-1].

Dreimanis, A. and Lundqvist, J.
1984: What should be called till?; Striae, v. 20, p. 5-10.

Dreimanis, A., Hutt, G., Raukas, A., and Whippey, P.W.
1978: Dating methods of Pleistocene deposits and their problems. I. Thermoluminescence dating; Geoscience Canada, v. 5, p. 55-60.

Drinkwater, K.F.
1983: Moored current meter data from Hudson Strait, 1982; Fisheries and Aquatic Sciences, Canadian Data Report, No. 381, 46 p.

Dyke, A.S., Dredge, L.A., and Vincent, J-S.
1982: Configuration of the Laurentide ice sheet during the Late Wisconsin maximum; Géographie physique et Quaternaire, v. 36, p. 5-14.

Egloff, J. and Johnson, G.L.
1975: Morphology and structure of the southern Labrador Sea; Canadian Journal of Earth Sciences, v. 12, p. 2111-2133.

Elttreim, S. and Grantz, A.
1979: CDP seismic sections of the western Beaufort continental margin; Tectonophysics, v. 59, p. 251-262.

Elverhoi, A.
1984: Glaciogenic and associated marine sediments in the Weddell Sea, fjords of Spitsbergen and the Barents Sea: a review; Marine Geology, v. 57, p. 53-88.

Elverhoi, A., Liestol, O., and Nagy, J.
1980: Glacial erosion, sedimentation and microfauna in the inner part of Kongsfjorden, Spitsbergen; Norsk Polarinstitutt, Skrifter, No. 172, p. 33-59.

Emery, K.O. and Garrison, L.E.
1967: Sea levels 7000 to 20000 years ago; Science, v. 157, p. 684-687.

Emery, K.O. and Uchupi, E.
1973: Western North Atlantic Ocean: topography, rocks, structure, water, life and sediments; American Association of Petroleum Geologists, Memoir 17, 532 p.

England, J.H. and Andrews, J.T.
1973: Broughton Island — a reference area for Wisconsin and Holocene chronology and sea level changes on eastern Baffin Island; Boreas, v. 2, p. 17-32.

Evans, D.J.A.
1984: Glacial geomorphology and chronology in the Selamiut Range/Nachvak Fiord area, Torngat Mountains, Labrador; M.Sc. thesis, Memorial University of Newfoundland, St. John's, Newfoundland, 138 p.

Fader, G.B.
1984: A geophysical survey of Georges Bank, Georges Basin and Northeast Channel area of the Gulf of Maine; Geological Survey of Canada, Open File 978, 3 p.

Fader, G.B. and King, L.H.
1981: A reconnaissance study of the surficial geology of the Grand Banks of Newfoundland; in Current Research, Part A, Geological Survey of Canada, Paper 81-1A, p. 45-56.

Fader, G.B. and Miller, R.O.
1986: Regional geological constraints to resource development - Grand Banks of Newfoundland; Proceedings of the 3rd Canadian Marine Geotechnical Conference, St. John's, Newfoundland.

Fader, G.B., King, L.H., and Josenhans, H.W.
1982: Surficial geology, Laurentian Channel and western Grand Banks of Newfoundland; Geological Survey of Canada, Paper 81-22, 37 p.

Fader, G.B., King, L.H., and MacLean, B.
1977: Surficial geology of the eastern Gulf of Maine and Bay of Fundy; Geological Survey of Canada, Paper 76-17, 23 p.

Farre, J., McGregor, B.A., Ryan, W.B.F., and Robb, J.M.
1983: Breaching the shelfbreak; passage from youthful to mature phase in canyon evolution; in The Shelfbreak: Critical Interface on Continental Margins, ed. D.J. Stanley and G.T. Moore; Society of Economic Paleontologists and Mineralogists, Special Publication No. 33, p. 25-40.

Feyling-Hanssen, R.W.
1985: Late Cenozoic marine deposits of east Baffin Island and east Greenland: microbiostratigrpahy, correlation, age; in Quaternary Environments; Eastern Canadian Arctic, Baffin Bay and West Greenland, ed. J.T. Andrews; George Allen and Unwin, London, p. 354-393.

Fillon, R.H. and Aksu, A.E.
1985: Evidence for a subpolar influence in the Labrador Sea and Baffin Bay, during marine isotopic stage two; in Quaternary Environments; Eastern Canadian Arctic, Baffin Bay and West Greenland, ed. J.T. Andrews; George Allen and Unwin, London, p. 248-262.

Fillon, R.H. and Duplessy, J.C.
1980: Labrador Sea bio-, tephro-, oxygen isotope stratigraphy and late Quaternary paleoceanographic trends; Canadian Journal of Earth Sciences, v. 17, p. 831-854.

Fillon, R.H. and Full, W.E.
1984: Grain size variations in north Atlantic non-carbonate sediments and sources of terrigenous components; Marine Geology, v. 59, p. 13-50.

Fillon, R.H. and Harmes, R.A.
1982: Northern Labrador Shelf glacial chronology and depositional environments; Canadian Journal of Earth Sciences, v. 19, p. 162-192.

Fillon, R.H. and Williams, D.F.
1984: Dynamics of meltwater discharge from northern hemisphere ice sheets during the last deglaciation; Nature, v. 310, p. 674-677.

Fillon, R.H., Hardy, I.A., Wagner, F.J.E., Andrews, J.T., and Josenhans, H.W.
1981a: Labrador Shelf; shell and total organic matter — C^{14} discrepancies; in Current Research, Part B, Geological Survey of Canada, Paper 81-1B, p. 105-111.

Fillon, R.H., Miller, G.H., and Andrews, J.T.
1981b: Terrigenous sand in Labrador Sea hemipelagic sediments and palaeoglacial events on Baffin Island over the last 100,000 years; Boreas, v. 10, p. 107-124.

Flint, R.F.
1943: Growth of the North American Ice Sheet during Wisconsinan age; Geological Society of America Bulletin, v. 54, p. 325-362.

Flood, R.D. and Damuth, J.E.
1987: Quantitative characteristics of sinuous distributary channels on the Amazon Deep-Sea Fan; Geological Society of America Bulletin, v. 98, no. 6, p. 728-738..

Foldvik, A. and Kvinge, T.
1977: Thermohaline convection in the vicinity of an ice shelf; in Polar Oceans, ed. M.J. Dunbar; Arctic Institute of North America, Calgary, p. 247-255.

Forbes, D.L.
1984: Coastal geomorphology and sediments of Newfoundland; inCurrent Research, Part B, Geological Survey of Canada, Paper 84-1B, p. 11-24.

Fortier, Y.O. and Morley, L.W.
1956: Geological unity of the arctic islands; Transactions of the Royal Society of Canada, v. 50, series 3, p. 3-12.

Fukushima, Y, Parker, G., and Pantin, H.M.
1985: Prediction of ignitive turbidity currents in Scripps submarine canyon; Marine Geology, v. 67, p. 55-81.

Fulton, R.J.
1984: Summary: Quaternary stratigraphy of Canada; in Quaternary Stratigraphy of Canada — a Canadian Contribution to IGCP Project 24, ed. R.J. Fulton; Geological Survey of Canada, Paper 84-10, p. 1-5.

Fulton, R.J. and Hodgson, D.A.
1979: Wisconsinan glacial retreat, southern Labrador; in Current Research, Part C, Geological Survey of Canada, Paper 79-1C, p. 17-21.

Fulton, R.J., Karrow, P.F., LaSalle, P., and Grant, D.R.
1984: Summary of Quaternary stratigraphy and history, eastern Canada; in Quaternary Stratigraphy of Canada — A Canadian Contribution to IGCP Project 24, ed. R.J. Fulton; Geological Survey of Canada, Paper 84-10, p. 193-210.

Funder, S., Abrahamsen, N., Bennike, O., and Feyling-Hanssen, R.W.
1985: Forested Arctic: evidence from north Greenland; Geology, v. 13, p. 542-546.

Gatien, M.G.
1975: A study of the slope water region, south of Halifax; MSc thesis, Dalhousie University, Halifax, Nova Scotia, 134 p.

Gilbert, G. and Barrie, J.V.
1985: Provenance and sedimentary processes of ice scoured surficial sediments, Labrador Shelf; Canadian Journal of Earth Sciences, v. 22, p. 1066-1079.

Gilbert, M.W. and Clark, D.L.
1982: Central Arctic Ocean palaeoceanographic interpretations based on Late Cenozoic calcareous dinoflagellates; Marine Micropalaeontology, v. 7, p. 385-401.

Gilbert, R.
1982: The Broughton Trough on the continental shelf of eastern Baffin Island, Northwest Territories; Canadian Journal of Earth Sciences, v. 19, p. 1599-1607.

1985: Quaternary glaciomarine sedimentation interpreted from seismic surveys of fiords on Baffin Island, N.W.T.; Arctic, v. 38, p. 271-280.

Gradstein, F.M. and Agterberg, F.A.
1982: Models of foraminiferal stratigraphy — northwest Atlantic margin; in Quantitative Stratigraphic Correlation, ed. J.M. Cubitt and R. A. Reyment; 26th International Geological Congress, 1980, Wiley and Sons, London, p. 119-166.

Gradstein, F.M. and Srivastava, S.P.
1980: Aspects of Cenozoic stratigraphy and paleoceanography of the Labrador Sea and Baffin Bay; Palaeogeography, Palaeoclimatology, Palaeoecology, v. 30, p. 261-295.

Gradstein, F.M. and Williams, G.L.
1976: Biostratigraphy of the Labrador Shelf, Part I; Geological Survey of Canada, Open File 349, 39 p.

Grant, A.C.
1972: The continental margin off Labrador and eastern Newfoundland: morphology and geology; Canadian Journal of Earth Sciences, v. 9, p. 1394-1430.

1975: Labrador Shelf; Canadian Society of Petroleum Geologists, Memoir 4, 891 p.

Grant, D.
1980: Quaternary stratigraphy of southwestern Nova Scotia: glacial events and sea level changes; Geological Association of Canada and Mineralogical Association of Canada Joint Annual Meeting, Halifax, Field Trip Guidebook 9, 63 p.

in press: Quaternary geology of the Atlantic Appalachian region of Canada; Chapter 5 in Quaternary Geology of Canada and Greenland, ed. R.J. Fulton, Geological Survey of Canada, Geology of Canada, no. 1 [also Geological Society of America, The Geology of North America, v. K-1].

Grant, D. and King, L.H.
1984: A stratigraphic framework for the Quaternary history of the Atlantic Provinces, Canada; in Quaternary Stratigraphy of Canada — A Canadian Contribution to IGCP Project 24, ed. R.J. Fulton; Geological Survey of Canada, Paper 84-10, p. 174-191.

Gratton, D., Dubois, J.-M., Painchaud, A., and Gwyn, H.
1986: L'île d'Anticosta a-t-elle été récemment englacée; Geos, v. 15, p. 21-23.

Gravenor, C.P., von Brunn, V., and Dreimanis, A.
1984: Nature and classification of waterlain glaciogenic sediments, exemplified by Pleistocene, Late Paleozoic and Late Precambrian deposits; Earth Science Reviews, v. 20, p. 105-166.

Green, D.G.
1976: Nova Scotian forest history-evidence from statistical analysis of pollen data; Ph.D. thesis, Dalhousie University, Halifax, Nova Scotia, 155 p.

Hachey, H.B.
1961: Oceanography and Canadian Atlantic water; Fisheries Research of Canada Bulletin, No. 134, 117 p.

Hacquebard, P.A., Buckley, D.E., and Vilks, G.
1981: The importance of detrital particles of coal in tracing the provenance of sedimentary rocks; Bulletin Centre Research Exploration and Production Elf-Aquitaine, 5, p. 555-572.

Hall, R.K.
1985: Inner shelf acoustic facies and surfial sediment distribution of the eastern shore, Nova Scotia; M.Sc. thesis, Dalhousie University, Halifax, Nova Scotia, 197 p.

Hampton, M.A.
1970: Subaqueous debris flow and generation of turbidity currents; Ph.D. thesis, Stanford University, Stanford, California, 180 p.

Hardy, I.A.
1975: Lithostratigraphy of the Banquereau Formation on the Scotian Shelf; in Offshore Geology of Eastern Canda, Volume 2, Regional Geology, ed. W.J.M. van der Linden and J.A. Wade; Geological Survey of Canada, Paper 74-30, v. 2, p. 163-174.

Harland, R.
1983: Distribution maps of recent dinoflagellate cysts in bottom sediments from the north Atlantic Ocean and adjacent seas; Paleontology, v. 26, p. 321-387.

Harland, W.B., Cox, A.V., Llewellyn, P.G., Pickton, C.A.G., Smith, A.G., and Walters, R.
1982: A geologic time scale; Cambridge University Press, 131 p.

Hays, J.D., Imbrie, J., and Shackleton, N.J.
1976: Variations in the Earth's orbit: pacemaker of the ice ages; Science, v. 194, p. 1121-1131.

Heezen, B.C., Ewing, M., and Ericson, D.B.
1955: Reconnaissance survey of the abyssal plain south of Newfoundland; Deep-Sea Research, v. 2, p. 122-133.

Heezen, B.C., Hollister, C., and Ruddiman, W.F.
1966: Shaping of the continental rise by deep geostrophic contour currents; Science, v. 152, p. 502-508.

Herman, J.R. and Goldberg, R.A.
1985: Sun, weather and climate; Dover Publications, Inc., New York, 360 p.

Herman, Y.
1970: Arctic paleo-oceanography in Late Cenozoic time; Science, v. 149, p. 474-477.
1974: Arctic Ocean sediments, microfauna, and the climatic record in Late Cenozoic time; in Marine Geology and Oceanography of the Arctic Seas, ed. Y. Herman; Springer-Verlag, N.Y., p. 283-348.

Hill, P.R.
1981: Detailed morphology and late Quaternary sedimentation of the Nova Scotian slope, south of Halifax; Ph.D. thesis, Dalhousie University, Halifax, Nova Scotia, 331 p.
1983: Detailed morphology of a small area on the Nova Scotian continental slope; Marine Geology, v. 53, p. 55-76.
1984: Sedimentary facies of the Nova Scotian upper and middle continental slope, offshore Eastern Canada; Sedimentology, v. 31, p. 293-309.

Hill, P.R. and Bowen, A.J.
1983: Modern sediment dynamics at the shelf slope boundary off Nova Scotia; in The Shelfbreak: Critical Interface on Continental Margins, ed. D.J. Stanley and G.T. Moore; Society of Economic Palaeontologists and Mineralogists, Special Publication No. 33, p. 265-276.

Hill, P.R. and Nadeau, O.C.
1985: Grain surface textures of late Wisconsinan sands from the Canadian Beaufort Sea Shelf; Journal of Sedimentary Petrology, v. 54, p. 1349-1357.

Hill, P.R., Moran, K.M., and Blasco, S.M.
1982: Creep deformation of slope sediments in the Canadian Beaufort Sea; Geo-marine Letters, v. 2, p. 163-170.

Hill, P.R., Mudie, P.J., Moran, K.M. and Blasco, S.M.
1985: A sea-level curve for the Canadian Beaufort Shelf; Canadian Journal of Earth Sciences, v. 22, p. 1383-1393.

Hills, L.V. and Matthews, J.V. Jr.
1974: A preliminary list of fossil plants from the Beaufort Formation, Meighan Island, District of Franklin; in Report of Activities, Part B, Geological Survey of Canada, Paper 74-1B, p. 224-226.

Hinz, K., Schlüter, H.-U., Grant, A.C., Srivastava, S.P., Umpleby, D., and Woodside, J.
1979: Geophysical transects of the Labrador Sea: Labrador to southwest Greenland; Tectonophysics, v. 59, p. 151-184.

Hodgson, D.A.
in press: The Quaternary geology of the Queen Elizabeth Islands; Chapter 6 in Quaternary Geology of Canada and Greenland, ed. R.J. Fulton, Geological Survey of Canada, Geology of Canada, no. 1 (also Geological Society of America, The Geology of North America, v. K-1).

Hodgson, D. and Vincent, J.S.
1984: A 10,000 yr BP extensive ice shelf over Viscount Melville Sound, Arctic Canada; Quaternary Research, v. 22, p. 18-30.

Hollister, C.D. and McCave, I.N.
1984: Sedimentation under deep-sea storms; Nature, v. 309, p. 220-225.

Hollister, C.D., Nowell, A.R.M., and Jumais, P.A.
1984: The dynamic abyss; Scientific American, v. 250, p. 42-53.

Holtedahl, O.
1970: On the morphology of the west Greenland shelf with general remarks on the marginal channel problem; Marine Geology, v. 8, p. 155-172.

Hopkins, R.
1985: Placer gold potential, Country Harbour, Nova Scotia; Canada Oil and Gas Lands Administration Report, September 1985, Department of Energy, Mines and Resources Canada, 89 p.

Horn, D.R.
1967: Recent marine sediments and submarine topography, Sverdrup Islands, Canadian Arctic Archipelago; Ph.D. thesis, University of Texas, Arlington, Texas, 362 p.

Horn, D.R., Ewing, M., Horn, B.M., and Delach, M.N.
1971: Turbidites of the Hatteras and Sohm Abyssal plains, western North Atlantic; Marine Geology, v. 11, p. 287-323.

Houghton, R.W., Smith, P.C., and Fournier, R.O.
1978: A simple model for cross-shelf mixing on the Scotian Shelf; Journal of Fisheries Research Board of Canada, v. 35, p. 414-421.

Hughes, O.L.
1972: Surficial geology of northern Yukon Territory and northwestern District of Mackenzie, Northwest Territories; Geological Survey of Canada, Paper 69-36, 11 p.

Hughes, O.L., Harington, C.R., Janssens, J.A., Matthews, J.V. Jr., Morlan, R.E., Rutter, N.W., and Schweger, C.E.
1981: Upper Pleistocene stratigraphy, paleoecology, and archaeology of the northern Yukon interior, eastern Beringia: I. Bonnet Plume Basin; Arctic, v. 34, p. 329-365.

Hunkins, K.
1968: Geomorphic provinces of the Arctic Ocean; in Arctic Drifting Stations; Arctic Institute of North America, ed. J.E. Sater; p. 365-376.

Huntley, D.J., Godfrey-Smith, D.I., and Thewalt, M.L.W.
1985: Optical dating of sediments; Nature, v. 313, p. 105-107.

Hutchins, R.W., Dodds, J. and Fader, G.B.
1985: Seabed II: High resolution acoustic seabed surveys of the deep ocean; Proceedings of Society for Underwater Technology, London, England, 27 p.

Hutchins, R.W., McKeown, D. and King, L.H.
1976: A deep tow high resolution mapping system for continental shelf mapping; Geoscience Canada, v. 3, p. 95-100.

Imbrie, J. and Kipp, N.G.
1971: A new micropaleontological method for quantitative paleoclimatology: application to a Late Pleistocene Cribbean core; in The Late Cenozoic Glacial Ages, ed. K.K. Turekian; Yale University Press, New Haven, p. 71-181.

Iqbal, J.
1973: Sedimentology and benthonic foraminifera in M'Clure Strait; (Canadian Arctic Archipelago); M.Sc. thesis, Dalhousie University, Halifax, Nova Scotia, 265 p.

Ives, J.D.
1958: Glacial geomorphology of the Torngat Mountains, northern Labrador; Geographic Bulletin, v. 12, p. 47-75.

Jackson, H.R.
1985: Seismic reflection results from CESAR; in Initial Geological Report on CESAR — the Canadian Expedition to Study the Alpha Ridge, Arctic Ocean, ed. H.R. Jackson, P.J. Mudie, and S.M. Blasco; Geological Survey of Canada, Paper 84-22, p. 19-23.

Jansen, E., Sejrup, H.P., Fjaeran, T., Hald, M., Holtedahl, H., and Skarbo, O.
1983: Late Weichselian palaeoceanography of the southeastern Norwegian Sea; Norsk Geologisk Tidsskrift, v. 63, p. 117-146.

Jellinek, R.
1985: 1.1 million years record reveals major Pleistocene evolution of North Atlantic sea-surface temperature rhythms; Lamont Newsletter, v. 11, p. 2-3.

Jennings, A.E.
1985: Late Quaternary marine sediments from a transect of fiord and continental shelf environments: a study of piston cores from Clark Fiord and Scott Trough, Baffin Island, Canada; M.Sc. thesis, University of Colorado, Boulder, Colorado, 200 p.

Johnson, D.W.
1925: The New England-Acadian Shoreline; Wiley, New York, 608 p.

Jones, E.J.W., Ewing, M., Ewing, J.I., and Eittreim, S.L.
1970: Influences of Norwegian Sea overflow water on sedimentation in the northern North Atlantic and Labrador Sea; Journal of Geophysical Research, v. 75, p. 1655-1680.

Jordan, R.H.
1975: Pollen diagrams from Hamilton Inlet, central Labrador, and their environmental implications for the Northern Maritime Archaic; Arctic Anthropology, v. 12, p. 92-116.

Josenhans, W.H., Klassen, R.A., and Zevenhuizen, J.
1986: Quaternary geology of the Labrador Shelf; Canadian Journal of Earth Sciences, v. 23, p. 1190-1213.

Kaye, C.A.
1964: Outline of Pleistocene geology of Martha's Vineyard, Massachusetts; United States Geological Survey, Professional Paper 501-C, p. C134-C139.

Keller, G. and Barron, J.A.
1982: Paleoceanographic implications of Miocene deep sea hiatuses; Geological Society of America Bulletin, v. 94, p. 590-613.

Kellogg, T.B.
1977: Paleoclimatology and paleoceanography of the Norwegian and Greenland Seas: the last 450,000 years; Marine Micropaleontology, v. 2, p. 235-249.

Kennard, L.H.
1982: Mounds, moats and ridges: seismic evidence for deep current-influenced deposition east of Newfoundland; Joint Oceanographic Assembly, Abstracts, Halifax, Nova Scotia, p. 24.

Kennett, J.
1982: Marine Geology; Prentice-Hall, Inc., Engelwood Cliffs, New Jersey, 813 p.

King, L.H.
1970: Surficial Geology of the Halifax-Sable Island map area; Marine Science Paper 1, Department of Energy, Mines and Resources, Ottawa, Ontario, 16 p.
1972: Relation of plate tectonics to the geomorphic evolution of the Canadian Atlantic Provinces; Geological Society of America Bulletin, v. 83, p. 3083-3090.
1980: Aspects of regional surficial geology related to site investigation requirements; in Offshore Site Investigations, ed. D. A. Ardus; Society for Underwater Technology, Graham and Trotman, London, p. 37-60.

King, L.H. and Fader, G.B.
1976: Application of the Huntec deep-tow high resolution Huntec system to surficial and bedrock studies — Grand Banks of Newfoundland; in Report of Activities, Part C, Geological Survey of Canada, Paper 76-1C, p. 5-7.
1986: Wisconsinan glaciation of the continental shelf, southeastern Atlantic Canada; Geological Survey of Canada, Bulletin 363, 72 p.

King, L.H. and MacLean, B.
1970: Origin of the outer part of the Laurentian Channel; Canadian Journal of Earth Sciences, v. 7, p. 1470-1484.
1976: Geology of the Scotian Shelf; Geological Survey of Canada, Paper 74-31, 31 p.

King, L.H., Fader, G.B., Jenkins, W.A.M., and King, E.L.
1986: Occurrence and regional setting of lower Paleozoic sediments on the Grand Banks of Newfoundland; Canadian Journal of Earth Sciences, v. 23, p. 504-526.

King, L.H., Fader, G.B., Poole, W.H., and Wanless, R.K.
1985: Geological setting and age of the Flemish Cap granodiorite, east of the Grand Banks of Newfoundland; Canadian Journal of Earth Sciences, v. 22, p. 1286-1298.

King, L.H., MacLean, B., and Drapeau, G.
1972: The Scotian Shelf submarine end-moraine complex; 24th International Geological Congress, v. 8, p. 237-249.

King, L.H., MacLean, B., and Fader, G.B.
1974: Unconformities on the Scotian Shelf; Canadian Journal of Earth Sciences, v. 11, p. 89-100.

Klassen, R.A.
1981: Aspects of the glacial history of Bylot Island, District of Franklin; in Current Research, Part A, Geological Survey of Canada, Paper 81-1A, p. 317-326.
1985: An outline of the glacial history of Bylot Island shell-bearing deposits; in Quaternary Environments; Eastern Canadian Arctic, Baffin Bay and West Greenland, ed. J.T. Andrews; George Allen and Unwin, Boston, p. 428-460.

Knott, S.T. and Hoskins, H.
1968: Evidence of Pleistocene events in the structure of the continental shelf off northeastern United States; Marine Geology, v. 6, p. 5-43.

Kontopoulos, N. and Piper, D.J.W.
1982a: Storm-graded sand at 200 m water depth, Scotian Shelf, eastern Canada; Geo-marine Letters, v. 2, p. 77-81.
1982b: Late Quaternary lithostratigraphy and sedimentation, Kaipokok Bay, Labrador; in Current Research, Part B, Geological Survey of Canada, Paper 82-1B, p. 1-6.

Koreneva, E.V., Zaklinskaya, E.D., Bratseva, G.M., and Kartashova, G.G.
1976: Palynology studies of Sites 336, 338, 345, 346, and 348, DSDP Leg 38; in Initial Reports of the Deep Sea Drilling Project, Volume 38, ed. M. Talwani et al.; United States Government Printing Office, Washington, v. 38, p. 1169-1193.

Kranck, K.
1971: Surficial geology of Northumberland Strait; Geological Survey of Canada, Paper 71-53, 10 p.
1972: Geomorphological developments and post-Pleistocene sea-level changes, Northumberland Strait, Maritime Provinces; Canadian Journal of Earth Sciences, v. 9, p. 835-844.

Kurtz, D.D. and Anderson, J.B.
1979: Recognition and sedimentologic descriptions of recent debris flow deposits from the Ross and Weddell Seas, Antarctica; Journal of Sedimentary Petrology, v. 49, p. 1159-1170.

Laine, E.P.
1980: New evidence from beneath the western North Atlantic for the depth of glacial erosion in Greenland and North America; Quaternary Research, v. 14, p. 188-198.

Laine, E.P. and Bell, M.
1982: Reply to Andrews' comment; Quaternary Research, v. 17, p. 125-127.

Latouche, C. and Parra, M.
1979: La sedimentation au Quaternaire — Recent dans le "Northwest Atlantic Mid-Ocean Canyon" - apport des données mineralogiques et geochimiques; Marine Geology, v. 29, p. 137-164.

Laughton, A.S. et al.
1972: Initial Reports of the Deep Sea Drilling Project, Volume 12; United States Government Printing Office, Washington, 1243 p.

Lazier, J.R.N.
1982: Seasonal variability of temperature and salinity in the Labrador Current; Journal of Marine Research, v. 40, p. 341-356.
1985: Arctic runoff in the North Atlantic Ocean; Bedford Institute of Oceanography Review '84, Bedford Institute of Oceanography, Dartmouth, Nova Scotia, p. 21-24.

Leslie, R.J.
1963: Foraminiferal study of a cross section of Hudson Bay, Canada; Geological Survey of Canada, Paper 63-16, 28 p.
1965: Ecology and paleoecology of Hudson Bay foraminifera; Bedford Institute of Oceanography, Dartmouth, Nova Scotia, Report 65-6, 192 p.

Letson, J.R.J.
1981: Sedimentology in southwestern Mahone Bay; M.Sc. thesis, Dalhousie University, Halifax, Nova Scotia, 199 p.

Lewis, C.F.M., Blasco, S.M., Bornhold, B.D., Hunter, J.A.M., Judge, A.S., Kerr, J.W., McLaren, P., and Pelletier, B.R.
1977: Marine geological and geophysical activities in Lancaster Sound and adjacent fiords; in Report of Activities, Part A, Geological Survey of Canada, Paper 77-1A, p. 495-506.

Livingstone, D.A.
1968: Some interstadial and postglacial pollen diagrams from eastern Canada; Ecological Monographs, v. 38, p. 87-125.

Livingstone, D.A. and Livingstone, B.G.R.
1958: Late-glacial and post-glacial vegetation from Gillis Lake in Richmond County, Cape Breton Island, Nova Scotia; American Journal of Science, v. 256, p. 341-359.

Lobsiger, U.
1979: Stable carbon isotope ratios as a bulk parameter to elucidate aspects of the organic carbon cycle in marine systems; Department of Oceanography Report, Dalhousie University, Halifax, Nova Scotia, 50p.

Løken, O.H.
1962: On the vertical extent of glaciation in northeastern Labrador — Ungava; Canadian Geographer, v. 6, p. 106-119.
1978: Postglacial tilting of Akpatok Island, Northwest Territories; Canadian Journal of Earth Sciences, v. 15, p. 1547-1553.

Løken, O.H. and Hodgson, D.A.
1971: On the submarine geomorphology along the east coast of Baffin Island; Canadian Journal of Earth Sciences, v. 8, p. 195-195.

Lohmann, G.P.
1978: Abyssal benthonic foraminifera as hydrographic indicators in the south Atlantic Ocean; Journal of Foraminiferal Research, v. 8, p. 6-34.

Loring, D.H. and Nota, D.J.G.
1966: Seafloor conditions around the Magdalen Islands, southern Gulf of St. Lawrence; Journal of the Fisheries Research Board of Canada, v. 23, p. 1197-1207.
1973: Morphology and sediments of the Gulf of St. Lawrence; Fisheries Research Board of Canada Bulletin, v. 182, 147 pp.

Macko, S.A.
1983: Source of organic nitrogen in mid-Atlantic coastal bays and continental shelf sediments of U.S.: isotopic evidence; Carnegie Institution of Washington Year Book, 1982, p. 390-394.

Macko, S.A. and Aksu, A.E.
1986: Amino acid epimerization in planktonic foraminifera suggests slow sedimentation rates for the Alpha Ridge region of Arctic Ocean; Nature, v. 22, no. 6039, p. 730-732.

Macko, S.A., Estep, M.F., Hare, P.E., and Hoering, T.C.
1983: Stable nitrogen and carbon isotopic composition of individual amino acids isolated from cultured microorganisms; Carnegie Institution of Washington Year Book 1982, p. 404-410.

Macko, S.A., Ivany, D.E., and Pulchan, K.
1985: Organic geochemistry of Baffin Island fjords; Geological Society of America, Abstracts with Programs, v. 17, p. 650.

MacLean, B.
1985: Geology of the Baffin Island Shelf; in Quaternary Environments: Eastern Canadian Arctic, Baffin Bay and West Greenland, ed. J.T. Andrews; George Allen and Unwin, Boston, p. 154-176.

MacLean, B. and Vilks, G.
1986: Marine geological program in the Byam Martin Channel Lougheed Island region, Northwest Territories; in Current Research, Part A, Geological Survey of Canada, Paper 86-1A, p. 769-774.

MacLean, B., Fader, G.B., and King, L.H.
1976: Surficial geology of Canso Bank and adjacent areas; Geological Survey of Canada, Paper 76-15, 11 p.

MacLean, B., Williams, G.L., Jennings, A., and Blakeney, C.
1986a: Bedrock and surficial geology of Cumberland Sound, N.W.T.; in Current Research, Part B, Geological Survey of Canada, Paper 86-1B, p. 605-615.

MacLean, B., Williams, G.L., Sanford, B.V., Klassen, R.A., Blakeney, C., and Jennings, A.
1986b: A reconnaissance study of the bedrock and surficial geology of Hudson Strait, N.W.T.; preliminary results; in Current Research, Part B, Geological Survey of Canada, Paper 86-1B, p. 617-635.

MacLean, B., Woodside, J.M., and Girouard, P.
1984: Geological and geophysical investigations in Jones Sound, N.W.T.; in Current Research, Part A, Geological Survey of Canada, Paper 84-1A, p. 359-365.

Macpherson, E.
1982: Postglacial vegetational history of the eastern Avalon Peninsula, Newfoundland, and Holocene climatic change along the eastern Canadian seaboard; Géographie physique et Quaternaire, v. 36, p. 175-196.

Mangerud, J., Lie, S.E., Furnes, H., Kristiansen, I.L., and Lømo, L.
1984: A younger Dryas ash bed in western Norway, and its possible correlations with tephra in cores from the Norwegian Sea and the North Atlantic; Quaternary Research, v. 21, p. 85-104.

Mariotti, A., Letolle, R., and Sherr, E.
1983: Distribution of stable nitrogen isotopes in a salt marsh estuary; Estuaries, v. 6, p. 304-305.

Markussen, B., Zahn, R., and Thiede, J.
1985: Late Quaternary sedimentation in the eastern Arctic Basin: stratigraphy and depositional environment; Palaeogeography, Palaeoclimatology, Palaeoecology, v. 50, p. 271-284.

Marlowe, J.I.
1968: Sedimentology of Prince Gustaf Adolf Sea, District of Franklin, Polar Continental Shelf Project; Geological Survey of Canada, Paper 66-29, p. 1-83.

Martini, E.
1971: Standard Tertiary and Quaternary calcareous nannoplankton zonation; Proceedings of the 2nd Planktonic Conference, Rome, p. 739-785.

Masson, D.G., Gardner, J.V., Parson, L.M., and Field, M.E.
1984: Morphology of Upper Laurentian Fan using GLORIA long-range sidescan sonar; American Association of Petroleum Geologists Bulletin, v. 69, p. 950-959.

Mathews, W.H.
1975: Cenozoic erosion and erosion surfaces in eastern North America; American Journal of Science, v. 275, p. 818-824.

McMillan, N.J.
1973: Shelves of Labrador Sea and Baffin Bay, Canada; in The Future Petroleum Provinces of Canada — their Geology and Potential, ed. R.G. McCrossan; Canadian Society of Petroleum Geologists, Memoir 1, p. 473-577.
1978: Surficial geology of Labrador and Baffin Island shelves; Geological Survey of Canada, Paper 71-23, p. 451-469.

Meagher, L.
1984: Interpretation of Quaternary and upper Neogene seismic stratigraphy on the continental slope of St. Pierre Bank; Geological Survey of Canada, Open File 1077, 23 p.

Middleton, G.V. and Southard, J.B.
1984: Mechanics of sediment movement; Short Course No. 3, Lecture Notes, Eastern Section of the Society of Economic Paleontologists and Mineralogists, Providence, Rhode Island, March 13-14, 1984, 401 p.

Miller, A.A.L., Mudie, P.J., and Scott, D.B.
1982: Holocene history of Bedford Basin, Nova Scotia; foraminifera, dinoflagellate and pollen records; Canadian Journal of Earth Sciences, v. 19, p. 2342-2367.

Miller, G.H.
1980: Late Foxe glaciation of southern Baffin Island, N.W.T., Canada; Geological Society of America Bulletin, v. 91, p. 399-405.
1982: Glaciation of southeastern Meta Incognita Peninsula, Baffin Island; evidence for a Labradorean ice-dispersal center; in 11th Annual Arctic Workshop, Institute of Arctic and Alpine research, Boulder, Colorado, March 1982, Program and Abstracts, p. 65-67.
1985: Aminostratigraphy of Baffin Island shell-bearing deposits; in Quaternary Environments: Eastern Canadian Arctic, Baffin Bay and West Greenland, ed. J.T. Andrews; George Allen and Unwin, Boston, p. 394-427.

Miller, G.H., Andrews, J.T., and Short, S.K.
1977: The last interglacial-glacial cycle, Clyde Foreland, Baffin Island, Northwest Territories: stratigraphy, biostratigraphy and chronology; Canadian Journal of Earth Sciences, v. 14, p. 2824-2857.

Miller, R.O., Macnab, R., Amos, C.L., and Fader, G.B.
1983: Canadian east coast multiparameter surveys, 1982; in Current Research, Part B, Geological Survey of Canada, Paper 83-1B, p. 331-334.

Milliman, J.D. and Emery, K.O.
1968: Sea levels during the last 35,000 years; Science, v. 162, p. 2824-2857.

Minicucci, D.A. and Clark, D.L.
1983: A Late Cenozoic stratigraphy for glacial-marine sediments of the eastern Alpha Cordillera, central Arctic Ocean; in Glacial-marine Sedimentation, ed. B.F. Molnia; Plenum Publishing Corp., N.Y. and London, p. 331-365.

Mode, W.N.
1986: Pre-Holocene pollen and molluscan records from eastern Baffin Island, Canada; in Quaternary Environments; Eastern Canadian Arctic, Baffin Bay and West Greenland, ed. J.T. Andrews; George Allen and Unwin, Boston, p. 502-519.

Molnia, B.F.
1983: Distal glacial-marine sedimentation: abundance, composition, and distribution of north Atlantic Ocean Pleistocene ice-rafted sediment; in Glacial-Marine Sedimentation, ed. B.F. Molnia; Plenum Press, New York, p. 593-626.

Moran, K. and Hurlbut, S.
1986: Analysis of potential slope instability due to wave loading on the Scotian Shelf; Proceedings of the 3rd Canadian Conference on Marine Geotechnology, St. John's, Newfoundland, p. 503-504.

Morris, T.H.
1983: The stratigraphy and late Pleistocene sedimentological history of the Lomonosov Ridge — Makarov Basin, central Arctic Ocean; M.Sc. thesis, University of Wisconsin, Madison, Wisconsin, 100 p.

Mosher, D.C.
1986: Late Wisconsinan sedimentation on the Scotian Slope near Verrill Canyon; M.Sc. thesis, Memorial University of Newfoundland, St. John's, Newfoundland.

Mudie, P.J.
1980: Palynology of later Quaternary marine sediments, eastern Canada; Ph.D. thesis, Dalhousie University, Halifax, Nova Scotia, 638 p.
1982: Pollen distribution in recent marine sediments, eastern Canada; Canadian Journal of Earth Sciences, v. 19, p. 729-747.
1983: Miocene palynosuccessions: volcanic or glacial cause?; 16th Annual Meeting of American Association of Stratigraphic Palynologists, Programs and Abstracts, San Francisco, Nov. 1983, p. 30.
1985: Palynology of the CESAR cores, Alpha Ridge; in Initial Geological Report on CESAR — the Canadian Expedition to Study the Alpha Ridge, Arctic Ocean, ed. H.R. Jackson, P.J. Mudie, and S.M. Blasco; Geological Survey of Canada Paper 84-22, p. 149-174.
1986: Palynology and dinoflagellate biostratigraphy of DSDP Leg 94, Sites 607 and 611, North Atlantic Ocean; in Initial Reports of the Deep Sea Drilling Project, Volume 94, ed. Ruddiman W.F., Kidd, R.B. and Thomas, E.T.; United States Government Printing Office, Washington, v. 94, p. 785-812.

Mudie, P.J. and Aksu, A.E.
1984: Paleoclimate of Baffin Bay from 300,000-year record of foraminifera, dinoflagellates and pollen; Nature, v. 312, p. 630-634.

Mudie, P.J. and Blasco, S.M.
1985: Lithostratigraphy of the CESAR cores; in Initial Report on CESAR — the Canadian Expedition to Study the Alpha Ridge, Arctic Ocean, ed. H.R. Jackson, P.J. Mudie and S.M. Blasco; Geological Survey of Canada, Paper 84-22, p. 59-99.

Mudie, P.J. and Guilbault, J.-P.
1982: Ecostratigraphic and paleomagnetic studies of late Quaternary sediments on the Northeast Newfoundland Shelf; in Current Research, Part B, Geological Survey of Canada, Paper 82-1B, p. 107-116.

Mudie, P.J. and Helgason, J.
1983: Palynological evidence for Miocene climatic cooling in eastern Iceland about 9.8 Myr ago; Nature, v. 303, p. 689-692.

Mudie, P.J. and Jackson, H.R.
1985: Summary; in Initial Geological Report on CESAR — the Canadian Expedition to Study the Alpha Ridge, Arctic Ocean, ed. H.R. Jackson, P.J. Mudie, and S.M. Blasco; Geological Survey of Canada, Paper 84-22, p. 3-10.

Mudie, P.J. and Keen, C.E.
1983: Dinoflagellate distribution and Quaternary glacial-interglacial records in the northwest Atlantic and Baffin Bay; American Association of Stratigraphic Palynologists Proceedings, Palynology, v. 7, p. 244.

Mudie, P.J. and Short, S.K.
1985: Marine palynology of Baffin Bay; in Quaternary Environments: Eastern Canadian Arctic, Baffin Bay and West Greenland, ed. J.T. Andrews; George Allen and Unwin, Boston, p. 263-308.

Mudie, P.J., Keen, C.E., Hardy, I.A., and Vilks, G.
1984: Multivariate analysis and quantitative paleoecology of benthic foraminifera in surface and late Quaternary shelf sediments, northern Canada; Marine Micropaleontology, v. 8, p. 283-313.

Müller, J. and Milliman, J.D.
1973: Relict carbonate rich sediments on southwestern Grand Bank, Newfoundland; Canadian Journal of Earth Sciences, v. 10, p. 1744-1750.

Myers, R.A.
1986: Late Cenozoic acoustic stratigraphy of the Labrador Sea; M.Sc. thesis, Dalhousie University, Halifax, Nova Scotia.

Nambudiri, E.M.V., Teller, J.T., and Last, W.M.
1980: Pre-Quaternary microfossils — a guide to errors in radiocarbon dating; Geology, v. 8, p. 123-126.

Nardin, T.R., Hein, F.J., Gorsline, D.S., and Edwards, B.D.
1979: A review of mass movement processes, sediment and acoustic characteristics, and contrasts in slope and base-of-slope systems versus canyon-fan-basin floor systems; in Geology of Continental Slopes, ed. L.J. Doyke and O.H. Pilkey; Society of Economic Paleontologists and Mineralogists, Special Publication, No. 27, p. 61-73.

Nelson, C.H. and Kulm, L.D.
1973: Submarine fans and deep-sea channels; in Turbidites and Deep Water Sedimentation; Society of Economic Palaeontologists and Mineralogists, Pacific Section, Short Course, p. 39-78.

Nelson, R.E. and Carter, D.L.
1985: Pollen analysis of Late Pliocene and Early Pleistocene section from the Gubik Formation of arctic Alaska; Quaternary Research, v. 24, p. 295-306.

Normark, W.R., Piper, D.J.W., and Stow, D.A.V.
1983: Quaternary development of channels, levees and lobes on middle Laurentian Fan; American Association of Petroleum Geologists Bulletin, v. 67, p. 1400-1409.

Oldale, R.N.
1976: Notes on a generalized geological map of Cape Cod; United States Geological Survey, Open File Report 76-765, 23 p.

Oldale, R.N. and Eskenasy, D.M.
1983: Regional significance of pre-Wisconsinan till from Nantucket Island, Massachusetts; Quaternary Research, v. 19, p. 302-311.

Orheim, O. and Elverhoi, A.
1981: Model for submarine glacial deposition; Annals of Glaciology, v. 2, p. 123-127.

Osterman, L.E.
1982: Late Quaternary history of southern Baffin Island, Canada: a study of foraminifera and sediments from Frobisher Bay; Ph.D. thesis, University of Colorado, Boulder, Colorado, 380 p.

Osterman, L.E. and Andrews, J.T.
1983: Changes in glacial-marine sedimentation in core HU 77-159, Frobisher Bay, Baffin Island, N.W.T.: a record of proximal, distal and ice-rafting glacial-marine environments; in Glacial-Marine Sedimentation, ed. B.J. Molnia, Plenum Press, New York, p. 451-494.

Osterman, L.E., Miller, G.H., and Stravers, J.A.
1985: Late and mid-Foxe glaciation of southern Baffin Island; in Quaternary Environments; Eastern Canadian Arctic, Baffin Bay and West Greenland, ed. J.T. Andrews; George Allen and Unwin, Boston, p. 520-545.

Pastouret, L., Auffret, G.A., Hoffert, M., Melguen, M., Needham, H.D., and Latouche, C.
1975: Sedimentation sur la Ride de Terre-Neuve; Canadian Journal of Earth Sciences, v. 12, p. 1019-1035.

Paterson, W.S.B.
1981: The physics of glaciers; 2nd edition, Pergamon Press, 380 p.

Pelletier, B.R.
1966: Development of submarine physiography in the Canadian Arctic and its relation to crustal movements; in Symposium on Continental Drift, ed. G.V. Garland; Royal Society of Canada, Special Publication No. 9, p. 77-101.
1969: Submarine physiography, bottom sediments and models of sediment transport in Hudson Bay; Geological Survey of Canada, Paper 68-53, p. 100-135.
1980: Selected physical characteristics of the Lancaster Sound region, geology and physiography; Indian and Northern Affairs Canada, p. 1-25.

Peltier, W.R. and Hyde, W.
1984: A model of the Ice Age cycle; in Milankovitch and Climate, ed. A.L. Berger; Reidel Publ. Co., Amsterdam, v. 2, p. 565-580.

Pereira, C.P.G., Piper, D.J.W., and Shor, A.N.
1985: SeaMARC I midrange sidescan sonar survey of Flemish Pass, east of the Grand Banks of Newfoundland; Geological Survey of Canada, Open File 1161.

Peters, K.E., Sweeney, R.E., and Kaplan, I.R.
1978: Correlation of carbon and nitrogen stable isotope ratios in sedimentary organic matter; Limnology and Oceanography, v. 23, p. 598-604.

Pilot of Arctic Canada, Vol II, 2nd Ed.
1968 Canadian Hydrographic Service, Ottawa, 468 p.

Piper, D.J.W.
1975a: Upper Cenozoic glacial history south of the Grand Banks of Newfoundland; Canadian Journal of Earth Sciences, v. 12, p. 503-508.
1975b: Late Quaternary deep water sedimentation off Nova Scotia and western Grand Banks; in Canada's Continental Margins and Offshore Petroleum Exploration, ed. C.J. Yorath, E.R. Parker, and D.J. Glass; Canadian Society of Petroleum Geologists, Memoir 4, p. 195-204.

Piper, D.J.W. and Aksu, A.E.
1987: The source and origin of the Grand Banks turbidity current inferred from sediment budgets; Geomarine Letters, v. 7, p. 177-182.

Piper, D.J.W. and Normark, W.R.
1982: Acoustic interpretation of Quaternary sedimentation and erosion on the channelled upper Laurentian Fan, Atlantic margin of Canada; Canadian Journal of Earth Sciences, v. 19, p. 1974-1984.
1983: Turbidite depositional patterns and flow characteristics, Navy Submarine Fan, California Borderland; Sedimentology, v. 30, p. 681-694.

Piper, D.J.W. and Sparkes, R.
1986: Shallow sediment instability in the central part of Flemish Pass, East of the Grand Banks of Newfoundland; Geological Survey of Canada, Open File, 1368 p.
1987: Proglacial sediment instability features on the Scotian Slope at 63°W; Marine Geology, v. 76, p. 15-31.

Piper, D.J.W., Farre, J.A., and Shor, A.N.
1985a: Late Quaternary slumps and debris flows on the Scotian Slope; Geological Society of America Bulletin, v. 96, p. 1508-1517.

Piper, D.J.W., Letson, J.R.J., de Iure, A.M., and Barrie, C.Q.
1983: Sediment accumulation in low-sedimentation, wave-dominated, glaciated inlets; Sedimentary Geology, v. 36, p. 195-215.

Piper, D.J.W., Mudie, P.J., Aksu, A.E., and Hill, P.R.
1978: Late Quaternary sedimentation, 50°N, north-east Newfoundland Shelf; Géographie physique et Quaternaire, v. 32, p. 321-332.

Piper, D.J.W., Mudie, P.J., Letson, J.R.J., Barnes, N.E., and Iuliucci, R.J.
1986: The marine geology of the inner Scotian Shelf off the South Shore, Nova Scotia; Geological Survey of Canada, Paper 85-19, 65 p.

Piper, D.J.W., Normark, W.R., and Sparkes, R.
1987: Late Cenozoic stratigraphy of the central Scotian Slope, eastern Canada; Canadian Bulletin of Petroleum Geology, v. 35, p. 1-11.

Piper, D.J.W., Shor, A.N., Farre, J.A., O'Connell, S., and Jacobi, R.
1985b: Sediment slides around the epicenter of the 1929 Grand Banks earthquake; Geology, v. 13, p. 538-541.

Piper, D.J.W., Shor, A.N., and Hughes Clarke, J.E.
1988: The 1929 Grand Banks earthquake, slump and turbidity current; Geological Society of America, Special Paper 229, p. 77-92.

Piper, D.J.W., Stow, D.A.V., and Normark, W.R.
1984: The Laurentian Fan — Sohm Abyssal Plain; Geo-marine Letters, v. 3, p. 144-146.

Poore, R.Z.
1981: Temporal and spatial distribution of ice-rafted mineral grains in Pliocene sediments of the North Atlantic: Implications for late Cenozoic climatic history; in The Deep Sea Drilling Project: A Decade of Progress, ed. J.E. Warme, R.G. Douglas, and E.L. Winterer; Society of Economic Paleontologists and Mineralogists, Special Publication No. 32, p. 505-516.

Poore, R.Z. and Berggren, W.A.
1974: Pliocene biostratigraphy of the Labrador Sea: calcareous plankton; Journal of Foraminiferal Research, v. 4, p. 91-108.

Powell, R.D.
1984: Glaciomarine processes and inductive lithofacies modelling of ice shelf and tidewater glacier sediments based on Quaternary examples; Marine Geology, v. 57, p. 1-54.

Praeg, D.B., MacLean, B., Hardy, I.A., and Mudie, P.J.
1986: Quaternary geology of the southeast Baffin Island continental shelf, N.W.T; Geological Survey of Canada, Paper 85-14, 38 p.

Pratt, R.M. and Schlee, J.
1969: Glaciation on the continental margin of New England; Geological Society of America Bulletin, v. 80, p. 2335-2342.

Prest, V.K.
1984: The Late Wisconsinan glacier complex; in Quaternary Stratigraphy of Canada — A Canadian Contribution to IGCP Project 24, ed. R.J. Fulton; Geological Survey of Canada, Paper 84-10, p. 21-36.

Prest, V.K. and Grant, D.R.
1969: Retreat of the last ice sheet from the Maritime Provinces — Gulf of St. Lawrence region; Geological Survey of Canada, Paper 69-23, 15 p.

Prest, V.K., Terasmae, J., Matthews, J.V., and Lichtifederovich, S.
1976: Late Quaternary history of the Magdalen Islands, Quebec; Maritime Sediments, v. 12, p. 39-59.

Quinlan, G.
1985: A numerical model of post-glacial relative sea-level change near Baffin Island; in Quaternary Environments: Eastern Canadian Arctic, Baffin Bay and West Greenland, ed. J.T. Andrews; George Allen and Unwin, Boston, p. 560-584.

Quinlan, G. and Beaumont, C.
1981: A comparison of observed and theoretical postglacial relative sea levels in Atlantic Canada; Canadian Journal of Earth Sciences, v. 18, p. 1146-1161.

Quinlan, G. and Beaumont, C.
1982: The deglaciation of Atlantic Canada as reconstructed from the postglacial relative sea-level record; Canadian Journal of Earth Sciences, v. 19, p. 2232-2246.

Railton, J.B.
1973: Vegetation and climatic history of southwestern Nova Scotia in relation to a South Mountain ice cap; Ph.D. thesis, Dalhousie University, Halifax, Nova Scotia, 146 p.

1975: Post-glacial history of Nova Scotia; Proceedings of Nova Scotian Institute of Science, v. 27, Supplement No. 3, p. 37-42.

Rampton, V.N.
1982: Quaternary geology of the Yukon coastal plain; Geological Survey of Canada, Bulletin 317, 49 p.

1988: Quaternary geology of the Tuktoyaktuk Coastlands; Geological Survey of Canada, Memoir 423, 98 p.

Rampton, V.N., Gauthier, R.C., Thibault, J., and Seaman, A.A.
1984: Quaternary geology of New Brunswick; Geological Survey of Canada, Memoir 416, 77 p.

Reinson, G.E.
1980: Variation in tidal inlet morphology and stability, northeast New Brunswick; Geological Survey of Canada, Paper 80-10, p. 23-39.

Repenning, C.A.
1983: New evidence for the age of the Grubik Formation, Alaskan North Slope; Quaternary Research, v. 19, p. 356-372.

1984: Quaternary rodent biochronology and its correlation with climatic and magnetic stratigraphics; in Correlation of Quaternary Chronologies, ed. W.C. Mahaney; Geo Books, J.W. Arrowsmith, Bristol, England, p. 1-14.

Richardson, M.J., Wimbush, M., and Mayer, L.
1981: Exceptionally strong near-bottom flows on the continental rise of Nova Scotia; Science, v. 213, p. 897-898.

Rogers, M.A. and Koons, C.B.
1969: Organic carbon 13-C values from Quaternary marine sequences in Gulf of Mexico: a reflection of paleotemperature changes; Transactions of the Gulf Coast Association of Geological Societies, v. 19, p. 529-534.

Ruddiman, W.F.
1977: Late Quaternary deposition of ice-rafted sand in the sub-polar North Atlantic (latitude 40° to 65°N); Geological Society of America Bulletin, v. 88, p. 1813-1827.

Ruddiman, W.F. and Glover, L.K.
1972: Vertical mixing of ice-rafted volcanic ash in North Atlantic sediments; Geological Society of America Bulletin, v. 83, p. 2817-2836.

Ruddiman, W.F. and Glover, L.K.
1975: Subpolar north Atlantic circulation at 9,300 yr. B.P.: faunal evidence; Quaternary Research, v. 5, p. 361-389.

Ruddiman, W.F. and McIntyre, A.
1981a: The North Atlantic Ocean during the last deglaciation; Palaeogeography, Palaeoclimatology, Palaeoecology, v. 35, p. 145-214.

1981b: Oceanic mechanisms for the amplification of the 23,000-year ice volume cycle; Science, v. 212, p. 617-627.

1984: Ice age thermal response and climatic role of the surface Atlantic Ocean, 40°N to 63°N; Geological Society of America Bulletin, v. 95, p. 381-396.

Ruddiman, W.F., Kidd, R.B., Thomas, E.T. et al. (ed.)
1987: Initial Reports of the Deep Sea Drilling Project; United States Government Printing Office, Washington, D.C., v. 94, 1261 p.

Rutter, N.W.
1985: Dating methods of Pleistocene deposits and their problems; Geoscience Canada, Reprint Series 2, 87 p.

Rutter, N.W., Crawford, R.J., and Hamilton, R.D.
1979: Dating methods of Pleistocene deposits and their problems. IV. Amino acid racemization dating; Geoscience Canada, v. 6, p. 122-128.

Sancetta, C., Imbrie, J., and Kipp, N.G.
1973: Climatic record of the past 130,000 years in North Atlantic deep sea core V23-82: correlation with terrestrial record; Quaternary Research, v. 3, p. 110-116.

Schafer, C.T.
1977: Distribution and depositional history of sediments in Baie des Chaleurs, Gulf of St. Lawrence; Canadian Journal of Earth Sciences, v. 14, p. 593-605.

Schafer, C.T. and Carter, L.
1986: Ocean bottom mapping in the 1980's; Sea Frontiers, v. 32, p. 122-130.

Schafer, C.T. and Mudie, P.J.
1980: Spatial variability of foraminifera and pollen in two nearshore sediment sites, St. Georges Bay, Nova Scotia; Canadian Journal of Earth Sciences, v. 17, p. 313-324.

Schafer, C.T. and Scott, D.B.
1985: Micropaleontology, textural and isotopic characteristics of turbidites on the continental slope and rise of Newfoundland; Geological Society of America, Abstracts with Programs, v. 17, p. 63.

Schafer, C.T., Tan, F.C., Williams, D.F., and Smith, J.N.
1985: Late glacial to Recent stratigraphy, paleontology, and sedimentary processes: Newfoundland continental slope and rise; Canadian Journal of Earth Sciences, v. 22, p. 266-282.

Schafer, J.P. and Hartshorn, J.H.
1965: The Quaternary of New England; in The Quaternary of the United States, ed. H.E. Wright and D.G. Frey; Princeton University Press, p. 113-128.

Schlee, J.
1973: Atlantic continental shelf and slope of the United States — sediment texture of the northeastern part; United States Geological Survey, Professional Paper 529-L, L64 p.

Schnitker, D.
1974: West Atlantic abyssal circulation during the past 120,000 years; Nature (London), v. 248, p. 385-387.

1979: The deep waters of the western North Atlantic during the past 24,000 years and the re-initiation of the Western Boundary Undercurrent; Marine Micropaleontology, v. 4, p. 265-280.

Schwarcz, H.P. and Blackwell, B.
1985: Dating methods of Pleistocene deposits and their problems, II Uranium series disequilibrium dating; in Dating Methods of Pleistocene Deposits and Their Problems, ed. N.W. Rutter; Geoscience Canada, Reprint Series 2, p. 9-18.

Scott, D.B. and Greenberg, D.A.
1983: Relative sea-level rise and tidal development in the Fundy tidal system; Canadian Journal of Earth Sciences, v. 20, p. 1554-1564.

Scott, D.B. and Medioli, F.S.
1980: Living vs. total foraminiferal populations: their relative usefulness in paleoecology; Journal of Paleontology, v. 54, p. 814-831.

1982: Holocene relative sea level fall and rise represented in a submarine core from Nova Scotia; Geology, v. 10, p. 278-281.

Scott, D.B., Baki, V., Mackinnon, K., Mudie, P.J., and Cole, F.
1986a: Pleistocene trends of benthic foraminifera in Arctic Ocean CESAR cores: comparison with isotopic and pahynological records; Geological Association of Canada — Mineralogical Association of Canada Joint Annual Meeting, Ottawa, Ontario, Program with Abstracts.

Scott, D.B., Baki, V., Younger, C.D., Mudie, P.J., and Vilks, G.
1984a: Oxygen isotope studies on late-Pleistocene Holocene benthonic foraminifera from the Eastern Canadian margin; Geological Society of America, Abstracts with Programs, v. 16, p. 649.

Scott, D.B., Mackinnon, K.D., Baki, V., Mudie, P.J., de Vernal, A., and Hillaire-Marcel, C.
1986b: Paleoceanography of the Labrador Sea — Baffin Bay subarctic corridor; benthonic foraminiferal, palynological and stable isotopic evidence; 99th Annual Meeting Geological Society of America, Abstracts with Programs, p. 743.

Scott, D.B., Mudie, P.J., Vilks, G., and Younger, D.C.
1984b: Latest Pleistocene-Holocene paleoceanographic trends on the continental margin of eastern Canada: foraminifera, dinoflagellate and pollen evidence; Marine Micropaleontology, v. 9, p. 181-218.

Segall, M.P., Barrie, J.V., Lewis, C.F.M., and Maher, M.L.J.
1985: Clay minerals across the Tertiary-Quaternary boundary, northeastern Grand Banks of Newfoundland: preliminary results; in Current Research, Part B, Geological Survey of Canada, Paper 85-1B, p. 63-68.

Segl, M., Mangini, A., Bonani, G., Hofmann, H.J., Nessi, M., Suter, M., Wolfli, Friedrich, G., Pluger, W.L., Wiechoski, A., and Beer, J.
1984: ^{10}Be-dating of a manganese crust from central North Pacific and implications for ocean palaeocirculation; Nature, v. 309, p. 540-543.

Sejrup, H.P., Miller, G.H., Brigham-Grette, J., Lovlie, R., and Hopkins, D.
1984: Amino acid epimerization implies rapid sedimentation rates in Arctic Ocean cores; Nature, v. 310, p. 772-775.

Shackleton, N.J. and Hall, M.A.
1984: Oxygen and carbon isotope stratigraphy of Deep Sea Drilling Project Hole 552A: Plio-Pleistocene glacial history; in Initial Reports of the Deep Sea Drilling Project, Volume 81, ed. D.G. Roberts and D. Schnitker; United States Government Printing Office, Washington, v. 81, p. 599-609.

Shackleton, N.J. and Kennett, J.P.
1975: Paleotemperature history of the Cenozoic and the initiation of Antarctic glaciation: oxygen and carbon isotope analysis in DSDP Sites 277, 279, and 281; in Initial Reports of the Deep Sea Drilling Project, Volume 29, ed. J.P. Kennett et al.; United States Government Printing Office, Washington, v. 29, p. 743-755.

Shackleton, N.J. and Opdyke, N.D.
1973: Oxygen isotope and paleomagnetic stratigraphy of equatorial Pacific core V28-238: oxygen isotope temperatures and ice volumes on a 10^5 and 10^6 year scale; Quaternary Research, v. 3, p. 39-55.

1976: Oxygen isotope and paleomagnetic stratigraphy of Pacific core V28-239, Late Pliocene to Latest Pleistocene; Geological Society of America, Memoir 145, p. 449-464.

1977: Oxygen isotope and paleomagnetic evidence for early Northern Hemisphere glaciation; Nature, v. 270, p. 216-219.

Shackleton, N.J., Hall, M.A., and Boersma, A.
1982: Oxygen and carbon isotope data from Leg 74 foraminifera; in Initial Reports of the Deep Sea Drilling Project, Volume 74, ed. T.C. Moore, Jr. et al.; United States Government Printing Office, Washington, v. 74, p. 599-612.

Shearer, J.M.
1971: Preliminary interpretation of shallow seismic reflection profiles from the west side of Mackenzie Bay, Beaufort Sea; in Report of Activities, Part B, Geological Survey of Canada, Paper 71-1B, p. 131-138.

1973: Bedrock and surficial geology of the northern Gulf of St. Lawrence as interpreted from continuous seismic reflection profiles; Geological Survey of Canada, Paper 71-23, p. 285-303.

Shepard, F.P.
1930: Fundian faults or Fundian glaciers; Geological Society of America Bulletin, v. 41, p. 659-674.

1931: St. Lawrence (Cabot Strait) submarine trough; Geological Society of America Bulletin, v. 42, p. 853-864.

1972: Submarine Geology, third edition; Harper and Row, New York, 517 p.

Shilts, W.W.
1980: Flow patterns in the central North American ice sheet; Nature, v. 286, p. 213-218.

Shor, A.N., Kent, D.V., and Flood, R.D.
1984: Contourite or turbidite? magnetic fabric of fine grained Quaternary sediments, Nova Scotia continental rise; Geological Society of London, Special Publication 15, p. 257-273.

Short, S.K. and Nichols, H.
1977: Holocene pollen diagrams from subarctic Labrador-Ungava: a vegetational history and climatic change; Arctic and Alpine Research, v. 9, p. 265-290.

Sirkin, L.A.
1976: Block Island, Rhode Island: evidence of fluctuation of the late Pleistocene ice margin; Geological Society of America Bulletin, v. 87, p. 574-580.

Skinner, R.G.
1973: Quaternary stratigraphy of the Moose River Basin, Ontario; Geological Survey of Canada, Bulletin 225, 77 p.

Slatt, R.M.
1974: Formation of palimpsest sediments, Conception Bay, southeastern Newfoundland; Geological Society of America Bulletin, v. 42, p. 853-864.

1975: Dispersal and geochemistry of surface sediments in Halls Bay, north-central Newfoundland: application to mineral exploration; Canadian Journal of Earth Sciences, v. 12, p. 1346-1361.

1977: Late Quaternary terrigenous and carbonate sedimentation on the Grand Bank of Newfoundland; Geological Society of America Bulletin, v. 88, p. 1357-1367.

Slatt, R.M. and Gardiner, W.W.
1976: Comparative petrology and source sediments of Newfoundland fiords; Canadian Journal of Earth Sciences, v. 13, p. 1460-1466.

Smith, G.W.
1981: Kennebunk glacial advance: a reappraisal; Geology, v. 9, p. 250-253.

Smith, J.N. and Schafer, C.T.
1984: Bioturbation processes in continental slope and rise sediments delineated by Pb-210, microfossil and textural indicators; Journal of Marine Research, v. 42, p. 1117-1145.

Smythe, F.W., Ruddiman, W.F., and Lumsden, D.N.
1985: Ice-rafted evidence of long-term north Atlantic circulation; Marine Geology, v. 64, p. 131-141.

Srinivasan, M.S. and Kennett, J.P.
1981: A review of Neogene planktonic foraminiferal biostratigraphy: applications in the equatorial and south Pacific; in The Deep Sea Drilling Project: A Decade of Progress, ed. J.E. Warme, R.G. Douglas, and E.L. Winterer; Society of Economic Palaeontologists and Mineralogists, Special Publication No. 32, p. 395-432.

Srivastava, S.P., Arthur, M., Clement, B., et al.
1987: Site Reports; Proceedings of the Ocean Drilling Program, Volume 105, Part A — Initial Reports; Ocean Drilling Program, Texas A&M University, p. 60-905.

Stanley, D.J. and Taylor, P.T.
1981: Volcanogenic sediment and proximal versus distal provenance in abyssal plains; Marine Geology, v. 43, p. M29-M38.

Stanley, D.J., Taylor, P.T., Sheng, H., and Stuckenrath, R.
1981: Sohm Abyssal Plain; evaluating proximal sediment provenance; Smithsonian Contributions to Marine Science, No. 11, 48 p.

Stea, R.R.
1982: The properties, correlation and interpretation of Pleistocene sediments in central Nova Scotia; M.Sc. thesis, Dalhousie University, Halifax, Nova Scotia, 214 p.

Stehman, C.F.
1976: Pleistocene and Recent sediments of northern Placentia Bay, Newfoundland; Canadian Journal of Earth Sciences, v. 13, p. 1386-1392.

Stow, D.A.V.
1977: Late Quaternary stratigraphy and sedimentation on the Nova Scotian outer continental margin; Ph.D. thesis, Dalhousie University, Halifax, Nova Scotia, 360 p.

1978: Regional review of the Nova Scotian outer margin; Maritime Sediments, v. 14, p. 17-32.

1981: Laurentian Fan: morphology, sediments, processes and growth pattern; American Association of Petroleum Geologists Bulletin, v. 65, p. 375-393.

Stow, D.A.V. and Aksu, A.E.
1978: Disturbances in soft sediments due to piston coring; Marine Geology, v. 28, p. 135-144.

Stow, D.A.V. and Bowen, A.J.
1980: A physical model for the transport and sorting of fine-grained sediment by turbidity currents; Sedimentology, v. 27, p. 31-46.

Stow, D.A.V. and Lovell, J.P.B.
1979: Contourites: their recognition in modern and ancient sediments; Earth Science Reviews, v. 14, p. 251-291.

Streeter, S.S. and Shackleton, N.J.
1979: Paleocirculation of the deep North Atlantic: a 150,000 year record of benthic foraminifera and oxygen – 18; Science, v. 203, p. 168-171.

Suc, J-P. and Zagwijn, W.H.
1983: Plio-Pleistocene correlations between the northwestern Mediterranean region and northwestern Europe according to recent biostratigraphic and paleoclimatic data; Boreas, v. 12, p. 153-166.

Sugden, B.E. and John, B.S.
1976: Glaciers and landscape: a geomorphological approach; Arnold Press, 376 p.

Sullivan, K.D.
1978: Structure and evolution of the Newfoundland Basin; Ph. D. thesis, Dalhousie University, Halifax, Nova Scotia, 294 p.

Sullivan, K.D. and Keen, C.E.
1977: Newfoundland Seamounts: petrology and geochemistry; Geological Association of Canada, Special Paper 16, p. 461-476.

Swift, D.J.P. and Borns, H.W.
1967: A raised fluviomarine outwash terrace, north shore of the Minas Basin, Nova Scotia; Journal of Geology, v. 75, p. 693-710.

Swift, D.J.P. and Lyall, A.K.
1968: Origin of the Bay of Fundy; an investigation from subbottom profiles; Marine Geology, v. 6, p. 331-343.

Swift, S.A.
1985a: Late Quaternary sedimentation on the continental slope and rise off western Nova Scotia; Geological Society of America Bulletin, v. 96, p. 832-841.
1985b: Cenozoic geology of the continental slope and rise off western Nova Scotia; Ph.D. thesis, Woods Hole Oceanographic Institution Technical Paper 85-34.

Swift, S.A., Ebinger, C.J., and Tucholke, B.E.
1986: Seismic stratigraphic correlation across the New England Seamounts, western North Atlantic Ocean; Geology, v. 14, p. 346-349.

Syvitski, J.P.M.
1984: SAFE 1983: Geophysical investigations; in Canadian Data Report of Hydrography and Ocean Sciences, No. 28, J.P.M. Syvitski, compiler; Sedimentology of Arctic Fjords Experiment: HU83-028 Data Report, p. 16-1 to 16-26.

Syvitski, J.P.M., Burrell, D.C., and Skei, J.M.
1986: The fluvial deltaic environment; in Fjords: Processes and Products, Springer, New York, Chapter 3.

Syvitski, J.P.M., Farrow, G.E., Atkinson, R.J.A., Moore, P.G., and Andrews,J.T.
1989: Baffin island fjord macrobenthos: bottom communities and environmental significance; Arctic, v. 42, p. 232-247.

Syvitski, J.P.M., Silverberg, N., Oulette, G., and Asprey, K.W.
1983: First observations on benthos and seston from a submersible in the lower St. Lawrence estuary; Géographie physique et Quaternaire, v. 38, p. 227-240.

Szabo, B.J., Miller, G.H., Andrews, J.T., and Stuiver, M.
1981: Comparison of uranium series, radiocarbon and amino acid data from marine molluscs, Baffin Island, Arctic Canada; Geology, v. 9, p. 451-457.

Taggart, R.E. and Cross, A.T.
1980: Vegetation change in the Miocene Succor Creek flora of Oregon and Idaho; in Biostratigraphy of Fossil Plants, ed. D. Dilcher and T. Taylor; Hutchinson and Ross, New York, p. 185-210.

Tan, F.C. and Strain, P.M.
1980: The distribution of sea-ice meltwater in the eastern Canadian Arctic; Journal of Geophysical Research, v. 85, p. 1925-1932.

Tan, F.C. and Vilks, G.
1987: Organic carbon isotope ratios and paleoenvironmental implications for Holocene sediments in Lake Melville, southeastern Labrador; Canadian Journal of Earth Sciences, v. 24, no. 10, p. 1884-2003.

Thiede, J., Eldholm, O. and ODP Leg 104 Shipboard Scientist Party
1986: Reflector identified, glacial onset seen; Geotimes, March 1986, p. 12-15.

Thomas, F.C.
1985: Lower Scotian Slope benthic foraminiferal faunas past and present, with taxonomic outline; M.Sc. thesis, Dalhousie University, Halifax, Nova Scotia, 150 p.

Thomas, M.L.H., Grant, D.R., and de Grace, M.
1973: A Late Pleistocene marine shell deposit of Shippegan, New Brunswick; Canadian Journal of Earth Sciences, v. 10, p. 1329-1332.

Top, Z., Clarke, W.B., Eismont, W.C., and Jones, E.P.
1980: Radiogenic helium in Baffin Bay bottom water; Journal of Marine Research, v. 38, p. 435-452.

Trites, R.W.
1982: Overview of oceanographic conditions in NAFO subareas 2, 3 and 4 during the 1970-79 decade; Northwest Atlantic Fisheries Organization, Scientific Council Studies, v. 5, p. 51-78.

Tucholke, B.E. et al.
1979: Initial Reports of the Deep Sea Drilling Project, Leg 43; United States Government Printing Office, Washington, 1115 p.

Tucker, C.M. and McCann, S.B.
1980: Late Quaternary events on the Burin Peninsula, Newfoundland, and the islands of St. Pierre and Miquelon, France; Canadian Journal of Earth Sciences, v. 17, p. 1462-1479.

Twenhofel, W.H.
1931: Geology of the Mingan Islands; Geological Society of America Bulletin, v. 42, p. 575-588.

Uchupi, E. and Austin, J.
1979: The stratigraphy and structure of the Laurentian cone region; Canadian Journal of Earth Sciences, v. 16, p. 1726-1752.

Vail, P.R., Mitchum, R.M. Jr., and Thompson, S. III.
1977: Seismic stratigraphy and global changes of sea level, part IV: global cycles of relative changes of sea level; in Seismic Stratigraphy — applications to hydrocarbon exploration, ed. C.E. Payton; American Association of Petroleum Geologists, Memoir 26, p. 83-97.

van Hinte, J.E. et al. (ed.)
1987: Initial Reports of the Deep Sea Drilling Project; United States Government Printing Office, Washington, C.D., v. 93, 1423 p.

Vilks, G.
1969: Recent Foraminifera in the Canadian Arctic; Micropalaeontology, v. 15, p. 35-60.
1980: Postglacial sedimentation on Labrador Shelf; Geological Survey of Canada, Paper 78-28, 28 p.
1981: Late glacial-postglacial foraminifera boundary in sediments of eastern Canada, Denmark and Norway; Geoscience Canada, v. 8, p. 48-55.

Vilks, G. and Mudie, P.J.
1978: Early deglaciation of the Labrador Shelf; Science, v. 202, p. 1181-1183.
1983: Evidence for postglacial paleoceanographic and paleoclimatic changes in Lake Melville, Labrador, Canada; Arctic and Alpine Research, v. 15, p. 307-320.

Vilks, G. and Rashid, M.A.
1976: Post-glacial paleo-oceanography of Emerald Basin, Scotian Shelf; Canadian Journal of Earth Sciences, v. 13, p. 1256-1267.
1977: Methane in the sediments of a sub-arctic shelf; Geoscience Canada, v. 4, p. 191-197.

Vilks, G., Buckley, D.E., and Keigwin, L.
1985: Late Quaternary sedimentation on the Southeast Sohm Abyssal Plain; Sedimentology, v. 32, p. 69-82.

Vilks, G., Deonarine, B., Wagner, F.J., and Winters, G.V.
1982: Foraminifera and mollusca in surface sediments of southeastern Labrador Shelf; Geological Society of America Bulletin, v. 93, p. 225-238.

Vilks, G., Hardy, I.A., and Josenhans, H.W.
1984: Late Quaternary stratigraphy of the inner Labrador Shelf; in Current Research, Part A, Geological Survey of Canada, Paper 84-1A, p. 57-65.

Vincent, J.-S.
1983: La géologie du Quaternaire et la géomorphologie de l'île Banks; Arctique canadien; Commission géologique du Canada, Mémoire 405, 118 p.
in press
a: Quaternary geology of the eastern Canadian Shield; in Chapter 3, Quaternary Geology of Canada and Greenland, ed. R.J. Fulton, Geological Survey of Canada, Geology of Canada, no. 1 [also Geological Society of America, The Geology of North America, v. K-1].
in press
b: The Quaternary geology of the northern Interior Plains; in Chapter 2, Quaternary Geology of Canada and Greenland, ed. R.J. Fulton, Geological Survey of Canada, Geology of Canada, no. 1 [also Geological Survey of Canada, The Decade of North America, v. K-1].

Vincent, J-S., Morris, W.A., and Occhietti, S.
1984: Glacial and nonglacial sediments of Matuyama paleomagnetic age on Banks Island, Canadian Arctic Archipelago; Geology, v. 12, p. 139-142.

Wagner, F.J.E. and Schafer, C.T.
1980: Upper Holocene paleoceanography of inner Miramichi Bay; Maritime Sediments, 16, p. 5-10.

Wang, Y. and Piper, D.J.W.
1982: Dynamic geomorphology of the drumlin coast of southeast Cape Breton Island; Maritime Sediments and Atlantic Geology, v. 18, p. 1-27.

Wang, Y., Piper, D.J.W., and Vilks, G.
1982: Surface textures of turbidite sand grains, Laurentian Fan and Sohm Abyssal Plain; Sedimentology, v. 29, p. 727-736.

Warren, J.S.
1976: The morphology of two transverse channels on the Northeast Newfoundland Shelf; Maritime Sediments, v. 12, p. 19-32.

Watkins, D.J. and Kraft, L.M.
1978: Stability of continental shelf and slope off Louisiana and Texas: Geotechnical aspects; in Framework, Facies and Oil Trapping Characteristics of the Upper Continental Margin, ed. A.H. Bouma, G.T. Moore, and J.M. Coleman; American Association Petroleum Geologists, Studies in Geology No. 7, p. 267-286.

Weatherly, G.L. and Kelley, E.A. Jr.
1982: "Too cold" bottom layers at the base of the Scotian Rise; Journal of Marine Research, v. 40, p. 985-1012.

Weber, J.R.
1983: Maps of the Arctic Basin sea floor: a history of bathymetry and its interpretation; Arctic, v. 36, p. 121-142.

Weidick, A.
1976: Glaciation and the Quaternary of Greenland; in Geology of Greenland, ed. A. Escher and W.S. Watt; Greenland Geological Survey, p. 430-459.

White, W.A.
1972: Deep erosion by continental ice sheets; Geological Society of America Bulletin, v. 83, p. 1037-1056.

Whittaker, S.M., Chevalier, B., and Geerlof, H.
1985: Iceberg scouring in Hudson Bay; Arctic Land-Sea Interaction, 14th Arctic Workshop, Program with Abstracts, p. 91.

Wightman, D.M.
1980: Late Pleistocene glaciofluvial and glaciomarine sediments on the north side of the Minas Basin, Nova Scotia; Ph.D. thesis, Dalhousie University, Halifax, Nova Scotia, 426 p.

Williams, D.F., Moore, W.S., and Fillon, R.H.
1981: Role of glacial Arctic Ocean ice sheets in Pleistocene oxygen isotope and sea level records; Earth and Planetary Science Letters, v. 56, p. 157-166.

Williams, G.L. and Bujak, J.P.
1977a: Cenozoic palynostratigraphy of offshore Eastern Canada; Contributions of Stratigraphic Palynology: Volume 1, Cenozoic Palynology; American Association of Stratigraphic Palynologists Contribution Series No. 5A, p. 14-47.
1977b: Distribution patterns of some North Atlantic Cenozoic dinoflagellate cysts; Marine Micropalaeontology, v. 2, p. 223-233.

Williamson, M.A.
1985: Recent foraminiferal diversity on the continental margin of Nova Scotia, Canada; Journal of Foraminiferal Research, v. 15, p. 43-57.

Williamson, M.A., Keen, C.E., and Mudie, P.J.
1984: Foraminiferal distribution on the continental margin off Nova Scotia; Marine Micropaleontology, v. 9, p. 219-239.

Wilson, E.M. and Piper, D.J.W.
1986: Seismic stratigraphy of the Laurentian Fan; Geological Survey of Canada, Open File 1231, 47 p.

Wilson, G.C., Litherland, A.E., and Rucklidge, J.C.
1984: Dating of sediments using accelerator mass spectrometry; Chemical Geology, v. 44, p. 1-17.

Wintle, A.G. and Huntley, D.J.
1980: Thermoluminescence dating of ocean sediment; Canadian Journal of Earth Sciences, v. 17, p. 348-360.

Wise, S.W.
1981: Deep sea drilling in the Antarctic: focus on Late Miocene glaciation and applications of smear-slide biostratigraphy; in The Deep Sea Drilling Project: A Decade of Progress, ed. J.E. Warme, R.G. Douglas, and E.L. Winterer; Society of Economic Paleontologists and Mineralogists Special Publication No. 32, p. 471-487.

Woodruff, F., Savin, S.M., and Douglas, R.G.
1981: Miocene stable isotope record: a detailed deep Pacific Ocean study and its paleoclimatic implications; Science, v. 212, p. 665-668.

Worsley, T.R. and Herman, Y.
1980: Episodic ice-free Arctic Ocean in Pliocene and Pleistocene time: calcareous nannofossil evidence; Science, v. 210, p. 323-325.

Worthington, L.V.
1976: On the North Atlantic circulation; The John Hopkins Oceanographic Studies No. 6, The John Hopkins University Press, Baltimore, 110 p.

Wright, R. and Anderson, J.B.
1982: The importance of sediment gravity flow to sediment transport and sorting in a glacial marine environment: eastern Weddell Sea, Antarctica; Geological Society of America Bulletin, v. 93, p. 951-963.

Young, F.G. and McNeil, D.H.
1984: Cenozoic stratigraphy of the Mackenzie delta, Northwest Territories; Geological Survey of Canada, Bulletin 336, p. 63.

Revised manuscript received August 1986

ADDENDUM
Added in galley proof, December 1989

D.J.W. Piper

Since the writing of this chapter, new work has rendered some parts obsolete. In particular, radiocarbon dating of molluscs on the Scotian Shelf has shown that total organic carbon dates (Fig. 10.15) are too old typically by a factor of 1.5 to 3; the base of the Emerald Silt is about 18 ka (Gipp and Piper, 1989; King and Fader, 1989). There is still evidence that the isotopic stage 4 ice advance was more extensive (Mosher et al., 1989). Preliminary dating suggests that Late Wisconsin ice was also extensive on the Grand Banks and Labrador Shelf (Josenhans and Zevenhuizen, 1989). The high rates of sedimentation implied by this chronology make the iceshelf sedimentation model for the Scotia Shelf (Fig. 10.27) untenable. The Emerald Silt is a proglacial not a subglacial deposit. Subglacial meltwater was important on the Scotian Shelf (Boyd et al., 1988).

Major surveys have provided data in areas that were previously little known, notably Hudson Bay (Josenhans and Zevenhuizen, in press); the Gulf of St. Lawrence (Josenhans et al., in press; Syvitski and Praeg, 1989); the Arctic Island Channels (MacLean et al., 1989); and the Arctic continental shelf (Hobson et al., 1989). Deep water biostratigraphic zonation (Fig. 10.3) has changed significantly as a result of Leg 105 of the Ocean Drilling Project (Baldauf et al., 1989).

References

Baldauf, J.G., Clement, B., Aksu, A.E., de Vernal, A., Firth, J., Hall, F., Head, M.J., Jarrard, R., Kaminski, M.A., Lazarus, D., Monjanel, A.-L., Berggren, W.A., Gradstein, F., Knuttel, S., Mudie, P.J. and Russell, M.D. Jr.
1989: Magnetostratigraphic and biostratigraphic synthesis of Ocean Drilling Program Leg 105: Labrador Sea and Baffin Bay; in S.P. Srivastava, M. Arthur and B. Clements, (ed.), Proceedings of the Ocean Drilling Program, Leg 105, Vol. B, 935-956.

Boyd, R., Scott, D.B. and Douma, M.
1988: Glacial tunnel valleys and the Quaternary history of the Scotia Shelf; Nature, v. 333, p. 61-64.

Gipp, M.R. and Piper, D.J.W.
1989: Chronology of Late Wisconsinan glaciation, Emerald Basin, Scotia Shelf; Canadian Journal of Earth Sciences, v. 26, p. 333-335.

Hobson, G. and Canadian Ice Island Scientific Party
1989: New features of Canadian Polar Margin; Eos, v. 70, p. 833-840.

Josenhans, H.W. and Zevenhuizen, J.
1989: Quaternary Geology, Labrador Sea; in J.S. Bell, ed., Labrador Sea, East Coast Basin Atlas Series, Atlantic Geoscience Centre, p. 8-17.
In press: Dynamics of the Laurentide Ice Sheet in Hudson Bay, Canada; Marine Geology.

Josenhans, H.W., Zevenhuizen, J., and MacLean, B.
In press: Preliminary seismostratigraphic interpretations from the Gulf of St. Lawrence; in Current Research, Part D, Geological Survey of Canada Paper 90-1D.

King, L.H. and Fader, G.B.
1989: A comparison between the late Wisconsinan history of southwest and northeast Emerald Basin; Geological Survey of Canada, Open File 2060, 14 p.

MacLean, B., Sonnichsen, G., Vilks, G., Powell, C., Moran, K., Jennings, A., Hodgson, D. and Deonarine, B.
1989: Marine geological and geotechnical investigations in Wellington, Byam Martin, Austin and adjacent channels, Canadian Arctic Archipelago; Geological Survey of Canada Paper 89-11, 69 p.

Mosher, D.C., Piper, D.J.W., Vilks, G., Aksu, A.E and Fader, G.B.
1989:   Evidence for Wisconsinan glaciations in the Verrill Canyon area, Scotian Slope; Quaternary Research, v. 31, p. 27-40.
Syvitski, J.P.M. and Praeg, D.B.
1989:   Quaternary sedimentation in the St. Lawrence estuary and adjoining areas, eastern Canada; Géographie physique et Quaternaire, v. 43, p. 291-310.

Authors' addresses

D.J.W. Piper
Atlantic Geoscience Centre
Geological Survey of Canada
Bedford Institute of Oceanography
P.O. Box 1006
Dartmouth, Nova Scotia
B2Y 4A2

G.B. Fader
Atlantic Geoscience Centre
Geological Survey of Canada
Bedford Institute of Oceanography
P.O. Box 1006
Dartmouth, Nova Scotia
B2Y 4A2

B. MacLean
Atlantic Geoscience Centre
Geological Survey of Canada
Bedford Institute of Oceanography
P.O. Box 1006
Dartmouth, Nova Scotia
B2Y 4A2

P.J. Mudie
Atlantic Geoscience Centre
Geological Survey of Canada
Bedford Institute of Oceanography
P.O. Box 1006
Dartmouth, Nova Scotia
B2Y 4A2

H.W. Josenhans
Atlantic Geoscience Centre
Geological Survey of Canada
Bedford Institute of Oceanography
P.O. Box 1006
Dartmouth, Nova Scotia
B2Y 4A2

G. Vilks
Atlantic Geoscience Centre
Geological Survey of Canada
Bedford Institute of Oceanography
P.O. Box 1006
Dartmouth, Nova Scotia
B2Y 4A2

Printed in Canada

Chapter 11

MODERN SEDIMENTARY PROCESSES

Chapter 11

MODERN SEDIMENTARY PROCESSES

C.L. Amos

with contributions by

J.V. Barrie, D.E. Buckley, R.W. Dalrymple, B. D'Anglejan,
R. Davidson-Arnott, G.B. Fader, R. Gillie, J.R. Harper, P.R. Hill,
D.A. Huntley, H.W. Josenhans, M.J. Keen, D.J.W. Piper, J.P.M. Syvitski,
B.B. Taylor, and R.B. Taylor

INTRODUCTION

Sedimentology, during the last 40 years, has become a multi-disciplinary science, due largely to studies of modern sediments and associated processes which have been undertaken to allow correlation with ancient counterparts. The study of modern sedimentary processes has adopted methods and principles from the applied sciences of ocean-ography and engineering. Thus, quantitative, rather than descriptive, relations are becoming prevalent, particularly with respect to sediment transport. This chapter describes the characteristics of modern sediments throughout off-shore eastern Canada and the processes which control their attributes. They are described in terms of the dynamics of sediment behaviour and are related to the var-ious processes present on the continental margin. Facies distributions and the geological significance of modern processes are dealt with in Chapter 10 of this volume.

Modern sedimentary processes

C.L. Amos and M.J. Keen

Modern processes of sedimentation are considered to be the agents observable today that influence the erosion, trans-port or deposition of sediment. These agents may be physi-cal, biological or chemical. On the continental margin of eastern Canada important physical agents are: surface gravity and infragravity wave motion; tidal, wind-driven, inertial or density-driven currents; internal waves; and ice transport and scouring. Biological agents include: infauna living within the sea bed responsible for bioturbation; ses-sile species which cause fouling; and free-swimming fauna responsible for pelletization of suspended material. Changes in water chemistry can affect the flocculation process, important in particle settling, and have diagenetic effects within a substrate leading to alterations in the

geotechnical properties of a sediment and consequently its resistance to erosion.

Each of the above processes has differing and often unknown effects on sediments, dependent upon their grain size. Thus, the first step in the description of modern sedimentary processes of offshore eastern Canada is a description of the distribution and nature of the modern sediments. The textural character of the surface sediments of the region is shown in Figure 11.1A-D for eastern Can-ada. The origin of the observed grain size distribution is not always obvious.

The distribution and character of modern marine sedi-ments are a function of their geological history and the recent events which modify them. How can modern sedi-ment attributes be differentiated from those which are inherited? The surface sediments of the eastern shelves are both autochthonous (principally the sand and gravel fractions) and allochthonous (principally the fine grained sediments); the allochthonous material has resulted from the reworking and dispersion of pre-existing glacially deposited material (King and Fader, 1986). The processes which rework the autochthonous sediments modify in part their fabric, grain-size distribution, mineralogy, and inter-nal structure (Swift and Ludwick, 1976). The relative dom-inance of attributes which are recognizably the result of modern day processes, in comparison to those of the origi-nal sediment, are used to define the sediment state as mod-ern (active), moribund, palimpsest and relict. Unfortunately, the degree of sediment modification is rarely complete and a continuum of states represents different degrees of disequilibrium with the modern regime (Galloway and Hobday, 1983). This is particularly true of continental shelves, such as those off eastern Can-ada, where commonly there is no simple relationship between present shelf processes and the surface shelf deposits (Walker, 1979). This makes it difficult to clearly assign a process to a specific modern sediment attribute.

The differentiation of sediments into modern or relict (Emery, 1968; Curray, 1969) has led to ambiguities in defining the recent sediments of the eastern Canadian margin. Trumbull (1972), for example, called the sediment veneer of Georges Banks relict, because the mineralogy and texture reflect their glacial origin, whereas Swift

Amos, C.L.
1990: Modern sedimentary processes, Chapter 11 in Geology of the Continental Margin of Eastern Canada, M.J. Keen and G.L. Williams (ed.); Geological Survey of Canada, Geology of Canada, no. 2, p. 609-673 (also Geological Society of America, The Geology of North America, v. I-1).

(1976) considered such sediments to be modern on the basis of the bedforms which are forming now. Similar ambiguities arose when the surface sands on Banquereau were called relict on the basis of their fossil fauna (Miller and Scott, 1984) and yet regarded as modern on the basis of the mobility and stratigraphy of the sediment (Amos and Knoll, 1987). Most sediments have both modern and relict attributes, and labelling them as one or the other is an oversimplification which leads to ambiguity. This can be avoided by applying the term "modern" or "relict" only to the attribute to which it refers. Modern attributes only must be determined from a sediment facies for subsequent correlation with ongoing processes.

The key to the interpretation of the distribution and genesis of many modern surface sediments, however, is an understanding of sedimentary response to changing hydraulic conditions. A general hydraulic framework is available to interpret the stability of a sediment under specific conditions of flow – for example, pure wave or current flow (Komar and Miller, 1973; Niedoroda, 1982; Cole and Miles, 1983) – but these relatively simple conditions seldom apply. Generally, the seabed of the continental shelf is subject to the effects of waves and currents in combination. This is particularly true in regions dominated by storms, such as the Scotian Shelf and the Grand Banks. In these regions, the bed response to flow is probably complex and consequently interpretations of sediment stability based on hydraulic character are only speculative.

The theories concerning bottom boundary layer flow and the predicted sediment transport are far more numerous than the observations on which to evaluate such models (Madsen and Grant, 1976; Grant and Madsen, 1979; Seaconsult Marine Research Ltd., 1986). Furthermore, the mechanics of the generation of bedforms, which are important aspects of sediment sorting and transport, are poorly understood. Thus, although wave or current formed bedforms have been identified over a large area of the margin of eastern Canada (Amos and King, 1984), the features, if any, which result from the combined effects of waves and currents are presently unknown. This problem is compounded by the inability to correlate a specific storm event with a particular mapped bedform. This is due to the way mapping is done, largely in periods of fair weather when the features of interest, formed in an earlier storm, are in a state of decay.

The processes leading to deposition of cohesive sediments in environments such as a shelf basin and parts of the continental slope, rise and abyssal plain can be modelled reasonably well (McCave and Swift, 1976; Niedoroda, 1982; Hill and Bowen, 1983; Amos and Mosher, 1985). Erosion or scour – processes affecting the whole margin – are less easily modelled because of the complexities of sediment texture and composition, the physical properties of a seabed such as plasticity, the effects of organic matter, and the material's stress history (McCave, 1984). The majority of these influences are unknown for most of offshore eastern Canada.

The regional setting and distribution of processes
C.L. Amos, R.B. Taylor and P.R. Hill

Ice and storm related processes, characterize most of the margin of eastern Canada. The frequency and intensity of such processes generally decrease with water depth. Thus, the most dramatic changes in sediment facies occur at the shoreface and the least in the quiescent abyssal plains. Along the coastline strong tidal currents prevail in tidal embayments such as the Bay of Fundy, Ungava Bay and Frobisher Bay. More exposed coastlines, such as those of Nova Scotia and Newfoundland, have breaking waves, which produce the rocky and boulder strewn shorelines characteristic of these provinces.

The processes which influence seabed sediments on the inner shelf are currents generated by storm surges or (rarely) tsunamis, surface gravity waves, wind-driven and inertial currents generated by the passage of storms, warm core eddies of slope water which often impinge onto the shelf, and cross-shelf mixing (Smith et al., 1978; Trites, 1982). On the outer continental shelf the dominant phenomena are: impinging oceanic currents; tidal currents which are amplified over shelf-edge banks; breaking internal waves and solitons; storm-driven flows; and, to a lesser extent, surface gravity and infragravity waves (Smith et al., 1978; Pietrafesa, 1984).

On the slope and rise, the dominant phenomena are: breaking internal waves; density flows driven down the slope (Bowen et al., 1984); and the Western Boundary Undercurrent (Carter et al., 1979). On the abyssal plains, the dominant processes are related to deep sea storms which accelerate the deeper parts of the Western Boundary Undercurrent (Hollister and McCave, 1984).

Currents

The presence of thermoclines in surface waters (10 to 40 m depth) and haloclines (20 to 100 m depth) can result in dramatic differences in the magnitude and direction of flow between the sea surface and the sea bed. Thus the distribution of sediments in Figures 11.1A and D bears little relationship to known circulation patterns. This is unfortunate from a sedimentological point of view because the majority of observations collected prior to the 1920s were primarily for purposes of navigation and so restricted to surface waters. They are therefore of dubious value in relation to the genesis of modern sediments.

East of Baffin Island and Labrador the southward flowing, cold Baffin and Labrador currents dominate marine circulation (Fig. 11.2). Near the seabed, these currents are usually less than 0.1 m/s (Petro-Canada, 1982). Currents of such low velocity barely move fine sand and will not cause reworking of local sediments, commonly compacted glacial till (see Chapter 10). The currents will transport fine grained particulate matter, suspended by other processes, to depositional basins on the shelves and to the deeper parts of the margin. The presence of a thin veneer of wave-rippled sand and gravel over much of the eastern Baffin and Labrador shelves (Fig. 11.1C, D; see Chapter 10) illustrates that intermittent wave activity and strong mean currents have been felt by the seabed. Such storm-related events, together with ice rafting, are considered responsible for the genesis of the modern sediments in these regions. In Ungava Bay, Frobisher Bay and Hudson Strait, the oceanographic regime is modified by the locally strong tidal currents (2.5 m/s; Canadian Hydrographic Service, 1978). Yet, this is not reflected in the bottom sediments which are texturally similar to those of the adjacent Baffin shelves. In these cases, seabed sediment texture is controlled by the nature of the parent material from which the modern sediment is derived. The lack of sand reflects the lithology of the underlying glacial till.

The northeast Newfoundland margin and the Grand Banks of Newfoundland have oceanographic features similar to those of the continental margins to the north. Variations in near-bed flow are the result of differences in water depth and gross morphology. In general, conditions near the bed are more active biologically and physically and so there is more reworking than farther north. This trend is even more apparent on the Scotian Shelf.

The prevailing geostrophic flow over the Scotian Shelf is to the southwest at a mean speed of 0.1 m/s. Flows are greatly influenced by the outer banks. Seabed drifters released by Lauzier (1967) showed a westward drift on Banquereau, a northeast drift on Sable Island Bank and a southwest drift on Browns Bank (see Fig. 11.3C). Such near-bed flows are modified by changes in bathymetry (Petrie and Anderson, 1983). This is particularly evident on the margins and tops of the banks near the shelf edge where strong rotary tidal currents are the result of rapid shoaling. Near-bed peak tidal currents on Banquereau, as an example, are 0.4 m/s (Husky/Bow Valley East Coast Project, 1985a, b). Divers observed these currents to be actively scouring and transporting the medium grained sand of the local seabed. Tidal currents of similar magnitude are found around Sable Island (Evans-Hamilton Inc., 1977), on Georges and Browns banks in Northeast Channel (Knebel, 1981) and in the Bay of Fundy. Evidence of active sediment transport such as sand waves and megaripples are found in these regions and are the reworked products of glacially deposited material (King and Fader, 1986).

The surface circulation of the deep-water areas off southeastern Canada is dominated by the warm Gulf Stream. It flows over the Scotian margin in a series of meanders and eddies and thereafter heads northeastward across the open Atlantic. To the north, the Labrador Current, which carries cold water from West Greenland, Hudson Bay and Baffin Bay, flows south along the Labrador Shelf and Slope, across and around the margin of the Grand Banks and onto the Scotian Shelf and Slope. Near-bed residual currents are shown in Figure 11.4. Bottom waters are characterized by southward flowing boundary currents (collectively known as the Western Boundary Undercurrent, WBU) along the slopes and rises off Labrador, Newfoundland and Nova Scotia. The details of the flow of these deep boundary currents is largely unknown, but recent observations have suggested that the so-called Western Boundary Undercurrent is made up of at least two decoupled bottom currents on the Scotian Rise (Hogg, 1983).

Currents over the slope and rise are complex over short periods of time due to the influences of tides, internal waves and sea-floor topography. Over longer periods, water masses tend to show a net drift parallel to the contours of the slope (Fig. 11.5). An exception to this occurs in submarine canyons which may trap shoaling surface waves and internal waves or provide loci for upwelling (Karl et al., 1983). As a consequence, currents are generally directed parallel to the axis in most canyons (Shepard et al., 1979).

Current velocities at the shelf-break are highly variable, with maximum values beneath the cores of strong ocean bottom currents. Hill and Bowen (1983) noted near-bottom velocities between 0.3 and 0.5 m/s at the shelf break on the Scotian Shelf. On the Scotian Rise beneath the Western Boundary Undercurrent, velocities of 0.7 m/s occur (Richardson et al., 1981), and on the Northeast Newfoundland Rise currents with velocities of up to 0.3 m/s occur (Carter and Schafer, 1983). Most slope and rise areas, however, have quieter conditions with current velocities generally below 0.2 m/s (Hill and Bowen, 1983).

Waves

Atlantic Canada is a storm-wave dominated environment with sharp contrasts in seasonal wind, wave and sea ice conditions. Storm waves are generated by cyclonic depressions passing northeastward across the region and also by occasional tropical storms (Owens, 1974a). Adjacent to exposed coasts, wave height isopleths are roughly parallel to the shore (Neu, 1982).

The wave climate is strongly seasonal, with "high energy" storm events in the fall, winter and spring. The largest significant wave height for a normal year is between 8 and 9 m (Fig. 11.3A): the height of the 100-year significant wave is nearly double this with peak periods between 10 and 18 seconds (Fig. 11.3B). Waves are generated by storms in the adjacent North Atlantic and Greenland Sea. Along the Labrador margin, the largest waves approach from the north, whereas in the North Atlantic they approach from the east. At the shelf edge the direction of wave propagation is more complex. In the south, off Nova Scotia for example, storms track parallel to the continental margin creating complex rotary wind patterns. A spectrum of wave conditions are the result and so storm-wave effects on seabed sediments are rarely the same. Coastal exposure to wave energy varies. Storm waves are: low (<2 m) in the high Arctic; moderate (2 to 5 m) in the Gulf of St. Lawrence; and high (>5 m, 3% of the winter season) on the Atlantic coasts of Nova Scotia, Newfoundland and Labrador (Davies, 1980).

Waves in the Gulf of St. Lawrence are of short period, and are locally-generated. They are generally less than 1 m in height, and only exceed this value during short-lived storms. Greenwood and Hale (1980) estimated that 19 storms affect the northeastern New Brunswick shore over an average of 44 days each year. Waves of 5 to 8 m have been reported from other parts of the Gulf (Ploeg, 1971; Forbes, 1984).

In Davis Strait, 6 m waves are common (Nordco, 1978) but in northwestern Baffin Bay the maximum recorded wave height is 6 m. Farther west in Barrow Strait, waves rarely exceed 2 m in height, and within the more northerly (ice-covered) channels waves may not be generated.

The relationship of modern processes to modern sediments

C.L. Amos

Analyses of the relationship between modern processes and sediments have taken place in two types of environment: (1) those where processes are cyclical or constant, such as tidal-dominated environments, and (2) those where processes are random. The most significant results have been obtained from the first type of environment although it is representative of only a small part of the margin of eastern Canada. In storm-dominated environments, which

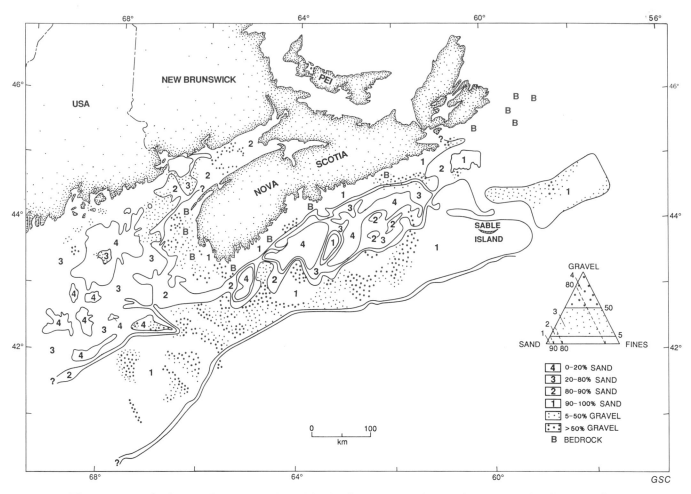

Figure 11.1. Surface sediment texture and bedrock outcrop on the continental margin of eastern Canada. (A) Bay of Fundy and Scotian Shelf; (B) Gulf of St. Lawrence, Grand Banks of Newfoundland and Northeast Newfoundland Shelf; (C) Labrador Shelf, Hudson Strait and Southeast Baffin Shelf; and (D) Northeast Baffin Shelf, Lancaster Sound, Jones Sound and Nares Strait. Bathymetry and major physiographic features are shown in Map 850-A (in pocket).

typify the southern shelves off eastern Canada, the processes which control sediment character are short-lived, unpredictable and intense. The processes and resulting sediment responses observed today may be of little consequence in the fossil record. Therefore, the knowledge of ancient sediments must be utilized to guide the analysis of the modern setting, and the application of this knowledge to refine studies of the past. This process is iterative and essential if studies of modern sedimentation processes are to be more than academic. An example of how this may be achieved is the work on the sedimentary environments of the beaches, bars and barrier islands of the Gulf of St. Lawrence, reviewed by Reinson (1977a). He related the observed modern-day lithostratigraphy to preserved sequences, showing that most modern sequences can be explained in terms of either a regressive barrier model, a transgressive barrier model, or a barrier-inlet model, and not simply in terms of the well-known prograding Galveston Island depositional model (Fig. 11.6) which is merely one example. The barrier-inlet model was based on a study of barrier islands of New Brunswick and shows a different stratigraphic sequence from that of the "classic"

model. Reinson's work on the associated tidal deltas may also prove valuable in differentiating sand wave from tidal delta cross-sets in the ancient record, of importance to paleogeographic reconstructions but still disputed.

The macrotidal Bay of Fundy has often been used for comparative studies with the fossil record. The paper of Dalrymple et al. (1978) on the classification and genesis of flow-transverse bedforms contributed greatly to the understanding and interpretation of fossil counterparts. They found that the scale and type of bedforms faithfully reflected conditions of flow and as such, are valuable as diagnostic tools of modern conditions.

Recent studies of sub-littoral (sub-tidal) deposits from the Chignecto Bay in the Bay of Fundy show a well-preserved 'transgressive tidalite' sequence comprising a number of lithofacies varying vertically and horizontally in a complex fashion (Amos and Zaitlin, 1985; Fig. 11.7). The fining-upwards model, considered diagnostic of tidal deposits, is only a small part of the tidalite sequence, but is often used in the interpretation of ancient counterparts. This is due in part to practical limitations related to recov-

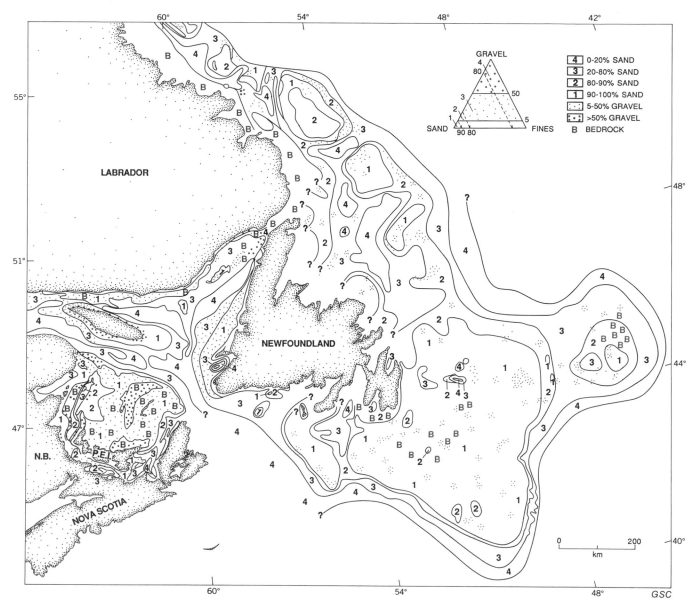

Figure 11.1B

ery of sub-tidal samples, but is also a function of the bias which leads to the belief that what is most apparent today, controlled events in the past. Perhaps a more detailed examination of less obvious sequences of facies in modern tidal deposits would be more productive.

Eastern Shoal, Banquereau is a shelf-edge sand body 35 m high, 20 km wide, and 50 km long, 150 km from the present shoreline. It has been formed in 50 m of water by tidal currents and storm-driven flows accelerated over shelf-edge topographic 'highs'. This feature appears to be a modern analogue to the Upper Cretaceous Shannon sandstone of Montana (Shurr, 1984), which has excellent potential as a reservoir rock for hydrocarbons (Tillman and Martinsen, 1984). Detailed studies of flow characteristics over Banquereau may provide the general mechanisms by which similar reservoir rocks could be formed, even though the specifics of source, grain size or flow magnitude may

vary. Even small-scale (tens of metres) topographic variations cannot be overlooked in paleogeographic reconstructions, as often these variations control the processes by which the sedimentary sequence is formed. This relationship becomes more apparent when it is realized that sediment responds to fluid stress in a highly non-linear fashion. The nature of this response is described in the next section.

Sediment transport and deposition in water
C.L. Amos and B.B. Taylor

The characteristics of sediment responses can be defined as 'cohesive' and 'non-cohesive'. Descriptions of such responses are given in terms of sediment kinematics, defined as 'particle-by-particle motion' or 'mass transport'. Particle-by-particle responses can be considered in terms

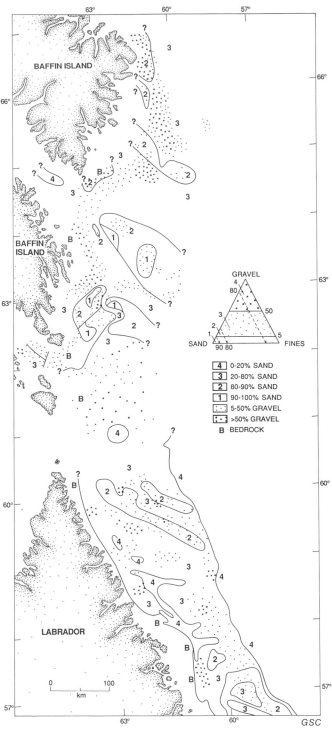

Figure 11.1C

Particle-by-particle: non-cohesive sediment responses

Granular material is usually defined in terms of 'ideal particles' which are described in states of no-motion, bedload transport, or suspension (Blatt et al., 1980). The particular state of a sediment or particle is predicted by reference to competency curves for traction (Vanoni, 1975) or suspension (Bagnold, 1966). These curves delimit thresholds separating phases of sedimentation. Figure 11.8A illustrates the relationship of bottom flow to these phases in its simplest form, subject to invariate, unidirectional flow. The illustrated relationship is controlled by hydraulic and sedimentary variables (Blatt et al., 1980). The hydraulic variables are (1) flow depth, (2) velocity inside the benthic boundary layer, and (3) fluid viscosity and density. Their influence on a granular sediment is complicated by the effects of time-varying turbulence on mean flow (Soulsby, 1983), superimposed wave motion (Thorn, 1979), biological activity (Grant et al., 1982) and the changing form of the seabed due to bedform generation (Davies, 1983; Yalin, 1972; McDowell and O'Connor, 1977). The most critical parameter to the stability of seabed sediments is velocity inside the benthic boundary layer. Isolated velocity measurements have been made in the Bay of Fundy, some coastal sites around Nova Scotia, and in basins of the Scotian Shelf. In tidal regions, predictions of sand transport, even during storms, is known reasonably well. Elsewhere, the structure of the benthic boundary layer is unknown.

Sedimentary variables controlling sediment behaviour are grain size and grain-size distribution, grain shape and density, bedforms and, possibly, packing (Vanoni, 1975). Only the first three parameters are considered in most studies of sediment transport and are usually combined in terms of a 'standard fall velocity' or 'standard fall diameter'. This is in contrast to the surficial geology maps of the east coast, which express surface sediments in phi units derived by sieving or hydrometer analysis. On the Scotian Shelf this is particularly important (James, 1966). Hydraulic sorting has produced stratified sediments reflecting grain size, shape and density, manifested as hydraulically segregated gravel beds, shell horizons and placers. On a larger scale, results of settling tube analysis of samples showed three coarsening-upward cycles (each about 10 m thick) in the Holocene sequence on Sable Island Bank and Banquereau. Despite the dominant signature in the Holocene record, the events or conditions which produced such sorting and stratification are still unknown. This is because measurements of current patterns are of much shorter duration than the period during which the cycles formed. This discrepancy in time scales between process observations and structures can often be large.

The nature and distribution of surficial sands in non-tidal regions are controlled by high-intensity storm events when traction and possibly suspension of sand are presumed to take place. The rate of particle suspension from the bed and the transport rate of the suspended load are controlled by bed stress, particle fall velocity and stresses within the turbulent, near-bed boundary layer, typically 1-2 m thick (Niedoroda, 1982). Such turbulent events and the associated vertical distribution of suspended solids are inherently difficult to measure (Smith and Hopkins, 1972; Vincent et al., 1982). Thus observations and descriptions of this aspect of sediment transport are unavailable for

of bedload motion (rolling or sliding), saltation or suspension; mass transport takes place as slumps, slides, grain flows or turbidity currents. All of these sedimentary responses have either been observed or interpreted in modern sediments of offshore eastern Canada.

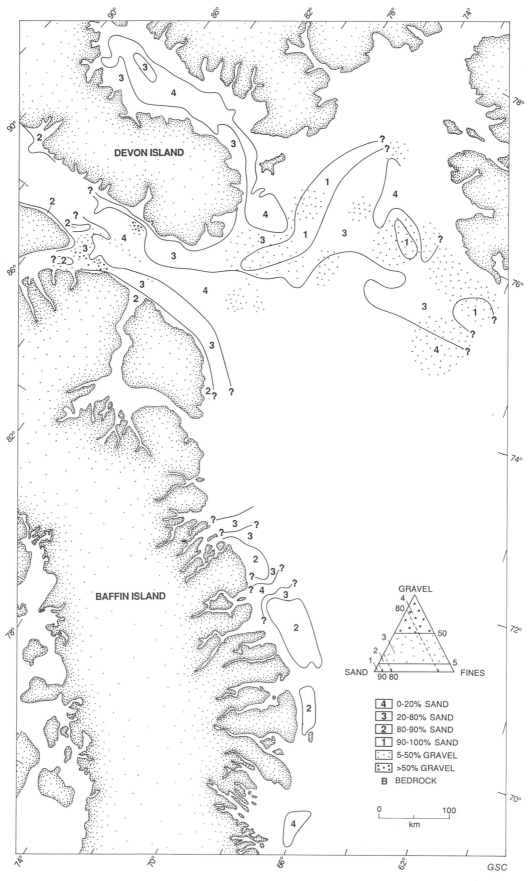

Figure 11.1D

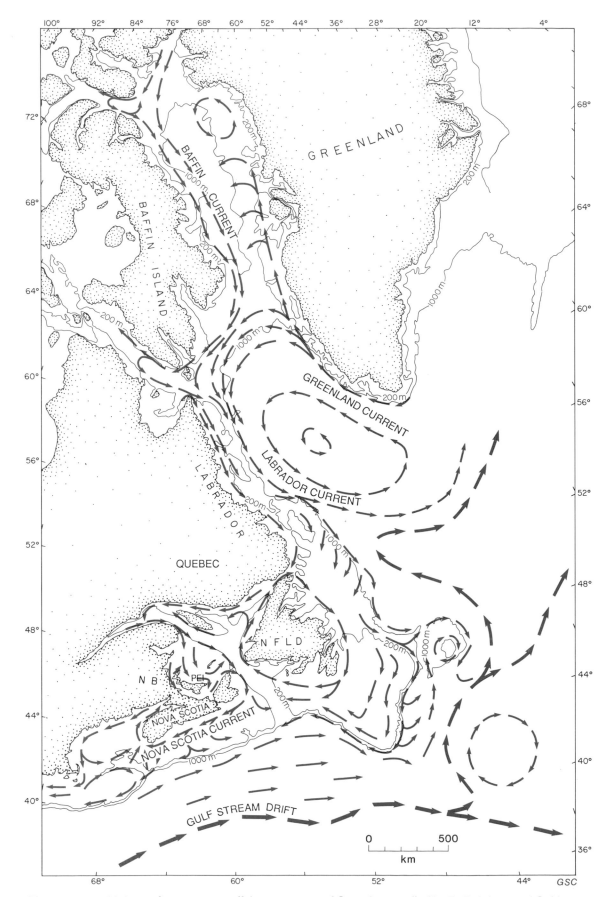

Figure 11.2. Major surface currents off the east coast of Canada compiled by R. Reiniger and C. Mann.

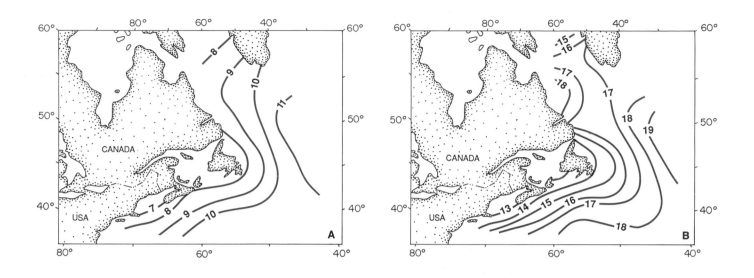

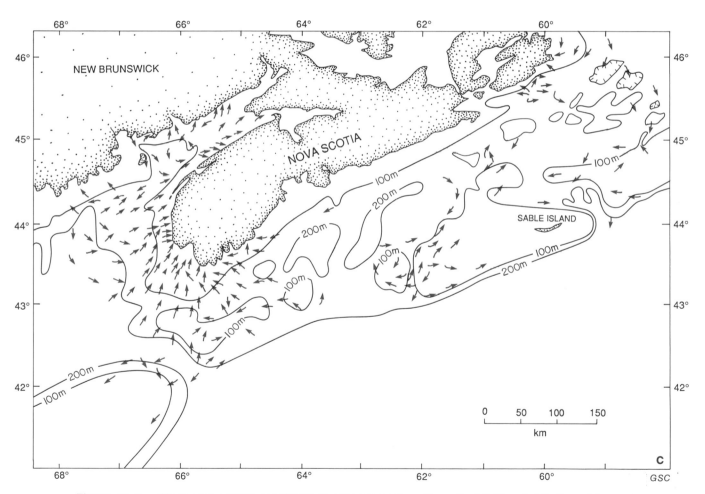

Figure 11.3. Wave and current conditions of offshore eastern Canada. (A) The distribution of largest significant wave height (in metres) for a normal year (after Neu, 1982). (B) The distribution of largest 100-year significant wave height (in metres) (after Neu, 1982). The maximum wave height is approximately 1.8 times greater than the significant. (C) The near-bed currents on the Scotian Shelf and Bay of Fundy, based on recoveries of bottom drifters (after Lauzier, 1967). These currents are markedly different from surface currents shown in Figure 11.2.

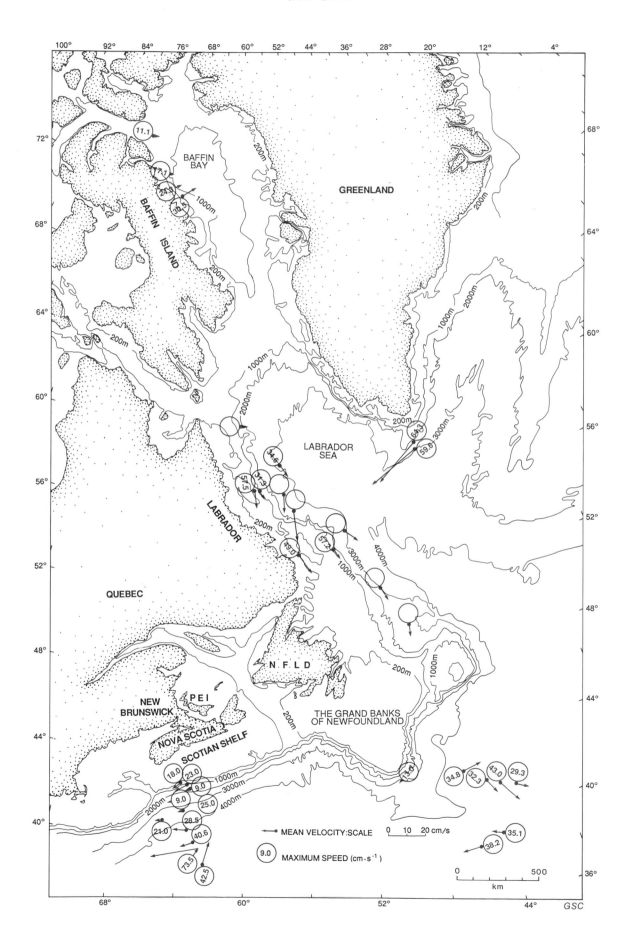

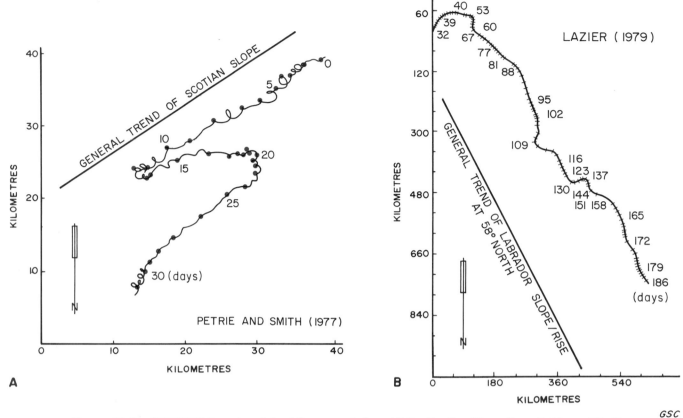

GSC

Figure 11.5. Progressive vector plots of the currents from (A) the Scotian Slope (from Petrie and Smith, 1977) and (B) the Labrador Slope and Rise (from Lazier, 1979). The flow on the Labrador Slope is regular and trends southeast-northwest, parallel with the trend of the Labrador Shelf isobaths. Flow on the Scotian Slope trends generally southwest-northeast, but is more erratic in both magnitude and direction, showing reversals in flow direction lasting up to 10 days.

most regions of the east coast. Exceptions are the Bay of Fundy and some coastal areas around Nova Scotia, New Brunswick and Quebec.

Particle-by-particle: cohesive sediment responses

The relationship between the bulk properties and the responses (in terms of erosion, transport and deposition) of cohesive sediments to environmental processes is not well studied. Detailed measurements are limited and are conflicting in their conclusions (McCave, 1984). Most studies are restricted to flumes and it is doubtful that they can be applied to cohesive sediments of the east coast.

Figure 11.4. Near-bed residual current flow over the slope and rise of the continental margin of eastern Canada. The predominant flow direction is to the south, parallel to the isobaths of the slope. The data were derived from Lazier (1979, 1981), Lively (1979, 1984), Bellfontaine et al. (1982), Levy et al. (1982), Lazier (pers. comm., 1985), and C. Ross (pers. comm., 1985).

Results of Krone (1962, 1978), Partheniades et al. (1968), Creutzberg and Postma (1979), Hydraulic Research Station (1981) and Hill and Bowen (1983) have demonstrated that predictions of deposition rate from suspension are possible, but the estimation of erosion from the bed, once deposited, is extremely complex (Fig. 11.8B). This is due to alterations in the particle bonding and compaction once a bed has formed. On the east coast, this is complicated further by the effects of ice loading and reworking, loading due to migration of bedforms, and bioturbation.

Cohesive sediments are widespread on the continental margin of eastern Canada (see unit 4, Fig. 11.1). In deep basins such as Emerald Basin, or on the continental slope, where deposition is considered continuous, correlations can be made with active processes. However, where intermittent erosion takes place, such as in the Gully on the Scotian Shelf, Placentia Bay, Newfoundland and the Bay of Fundy, the relationship between the surface sediment and the process is less clear. As an example, Amos and Mosher (1985) showed that the critical stress for bed erosion and the erosion rate varies across the intertidal zone of the Bay of Fundy in relation to subaerial exposure, biological activity and degree of compaction. The distribution of mudflats is, thus, not only a product of Postma's settling lag theory (Postma, 1967), but also involves postdepositional changes

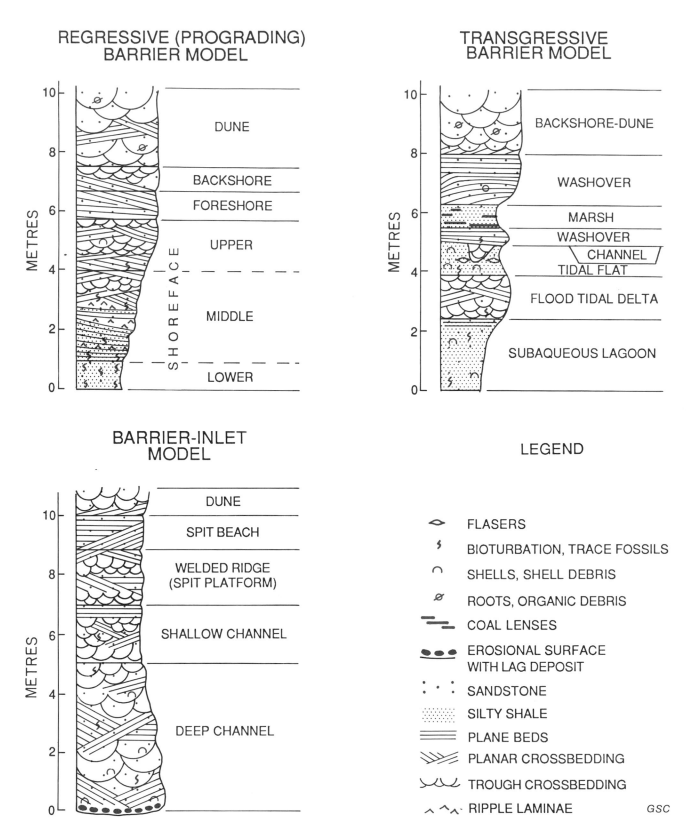

Figure 11.6. Three "end-member" facies sequences defining modern barrier island stratigraphy. The barrier inlet model is based on work in the Gulf of St. Lawrence (after Reinson, 1977a). Sedimentary structures and bioturbation are schematic and are correlated with the environment of deposition.

CHIGNECTO BAY "TIDALITE" TYPE SECTION

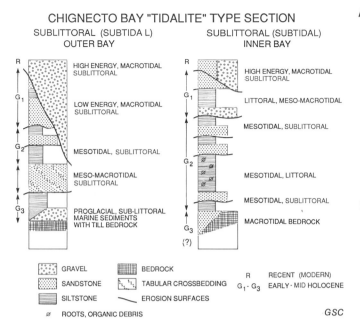

SUBLITTORAL (SUBTIDA L)
OUTER BAY

SUBLITTORAL (SUBTIDAL)
INNER BAY

GSC

Figure 11.7. Two facies type sequences showing the compiled stratigraphy based on the interpretation of cores from Chignecto Bay in the Bay of Fundy (after Amos and Zaitlin, 1985). The sequence shows a complex stratigraphy which becomes coarser grained upwards. The sequences were predominantly formed below low water and differ from fining upward sequences of the intertidal zone.

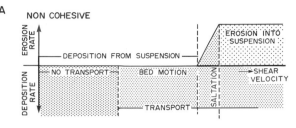

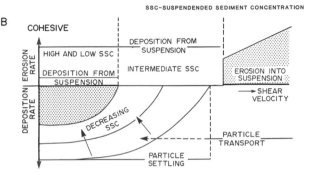

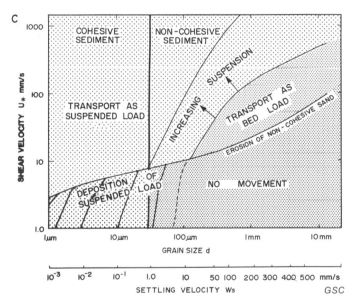

Figure 11.8. Simplified schematics illustrating the relationship of shear velocity (u_*) to deposition, transport and erosion rates for (A) non-cohesive and (B) cohesive sediment types, and (C) the relationship between shear velocity (u_*), grain size (d), and sedimentation phase (transport or deposition; after McCave, 1984).

in the bulk properties of a sediment that are, at present, not predictable. This conclusion is far from satisfactory, given that the Bay of Fundy is probably the most intensively studied marine region of eastern Canada.

Mass transport

Mass transport occurs when sediments become unstable and move downslope under gravity. Many classifications of the various forms of mass transport have been proposed. Prior and Coleman (1983) (Fig. 11.9), divided mass transport into slides, in which the sediments move intact and as undeformed masses over a basal shear surface, and flows, in which the sediments are fluid and hence highly deformed (Middleton and Hampton, 1976). Most authors recognize the term slump as describing the spectrum between these limits (see Cook et al., 1982), in which the sediment is moderately deformed during movement (Dalrymple, 1979).

Slumps are commonly associated with areas of rapid sedimentation, seismic activity, high gas content within the sediments, and high surface wave energy (Moore, 1977). On the eastern seaboard of Canada, seismic activity and wave loading are the dominant modern processes leading to large-scale mass movement of sediment, although rapid sedimentation associated with glacial events was important locally (see Chapter 10). Sediment instability, resulting from a variety of other factors (Fig. 11.10), may arise either from increases in the shear stresses that have to be resisted by the sediments, or from loss of strength of the sediments. In either case, there is a low probability

that mass transport events will take place on the continental margin of eastern Canada (Basham and Adams, 1982, 1983; Jacques/McClelland Geoscience Inc., unpublished report, 1982). Evidence of the mass transport of sediments, seen on seismic profiles, is restricted to relatively steep slopes associated with the continental slope (Laurentian

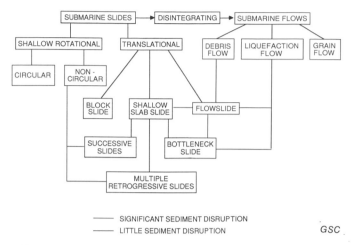

SIGNIFICANT SEDIMENT DISRUPTION

LITTLE SEDIMENT DISRUPTION

GSC

Figure 11.9. Factors contributing to mass movement of marine sediments (Prior and Coleman, 1983). The complexity of the various interactions and the number of factors which influence mass movement are shown. Factors directly influencing flow are outlined in red.

Fan), edges of shelf banks (the Gully) or restricted basins, such as Chignecto Bay in the Bay of Fundy and Saguenay Fiord.

Mass transport: non-cohesive sediment responses

Under static conditions, a slope made up of non-cohesive sediments can attain an inclination equal to the angle of internal friction of the sediments prior to the onset of either a slide or a flow (Terzaghi and Peck, 1967). In the marine environment of eastern Canada, however, cyclic mobility and liquefaction can reduce this inclination. Processes that cause liquefaction are earthquakes, slope instability, upward migration of gas, and pore pressure increases induced by passing waves (Powers and Kinsman, 1953; Allen and Banks, 1972; Christian et al., 1974; Seed and Rahman, 1978). Unlike slumping, this phenomenon has been observed firsthand. Grain flows were seen on the slopes of the lower Gully during PISCES IV dives (Amos, 1989). The flows were active and clearly illustrated a mechanism of sand transfer to the upper slope. The flows were approximately 0.2 m wide and extended in a straight path downslope. During the period of observation one flow was moving at a rate of 100 cm^3/s. The flow had excavated a small trough in the underlying finer grained material. Much larger grain flows have been observed in fiords. They are intermittent and short-lived but can transfer large quantities of sand down the fiord axis (Syvitski et al., 1987).

Liquefaction occurs when the pore water pressure increases so that the effective normal stresses are reduced to zero and the sediment particles are supported by the pore water. Cyclic mobility is the initial stage of progressive effective stress reduction prior to the liquefied state (Pamukcu et al., 1983). Generation of pore water pressure depends on the relative density of the sediment, the induced cyclic shear stress ratio, and the existing pore water pressure. Dalrymple (1979) described the occurrence of small isolated slumps on megaripples in Cobequid Bay,

Bay of Fundy, which he attributed to liquefaction caused by wave impact forces. These, he proposed, are diagnostic of subaerial exposure and could be used in studies of fossil sediments. Liquefaction of sand on the continental shelf is unlikely, due to the relative stability of the parameters leading to this state.

Rapid dissipation of pore water pressure prevents liquefaction, and depends on the sediment stratigraphy, permeability and compressibility (Castro and Poulos, 1977; Seed and Rahman, 1978). The net pore pressure response under cyclic loading is the combined effects of pore water pressure generation and dissipation. Sediments most prone to liquefaction are loose fine sands and coarse silts (Lee and Filton, 1969). These types of sediment are found at the shelf break and in shelf basins. The susceptibility of these seabeds to liquefaction is unknown. Theoretical investigations have addressed wave-seafloor interaction which may lead to liquefaction and cyclic mobility (Schapery, 1974a, b; Coleman et al., 1980; Dumas and Lee, 1980; Kagawa and Kraft, 1980; Dawson et al., 1981) and seismic liquefaction probability, but specific data on the properties of the sediments will be required before the results can be applied to conditions in offshore eastern Canada (Pamukcu et al., 1983).

Mass transport: cohesive sediment responses

Relatively steep slopes can be maintained in cohesive sediments under static conditions. Failures have been reported, however, on slopes as low as 0.25 degrees (Field et al., 1982). Such failures can be attributed in part to the decrease in strength under dynamic loading from natural marine phenomena.

Laboratory and theoretical investigations conducted on the dynamic behaviour of soft saturated clays (Thiers and Seed, 1968; Idriss et al., 1978; Stokoe, 1980; Tsai et al., 1980; Singh et al., 1981) show that the constitutive relations for clays are generally nonlinear and hysteretic in nature. An important point in the behaviour of marine sediments is that cyclic loading experiments on soft saturated clays exhibit progressive moduli reduction and degradation depending on strain amplitude, frequency and duration of loading (Castro, 1975; Castro and Poulos, 1977; Pamukcu et al., 1983). Unfortunately similar experiments have not been repeated on cohesive sediments of the east coast. Even if they were, it is not clear that sediments susceptible to slumping could be identified due to the high number of laminations, any of which could act as slide planes in the event of loading.

Geotechnical examinations of slumped material are useful in defining areas of potential instability, but are not definitive. The disruption of sediment during slumping changes the properties inherent at the time of failure. The distribution of slumps is perhaps more diagnostic of slump potential. Slumps on the continental margin of eastern Canada have been mapped with the potential for slumping defined qualitatively as "high", "medium" of "low" (Jacques/McClelland Geosciences Inc., unpublished report, 1982).

Cohesive sediments susceptible to slumping are found in basinal areas such as LaHave and Emerald basins on the Scotian Shelf; tidal flats such as in the Bay of Fundy, and on the continental slope. Seismic reflection profiles of

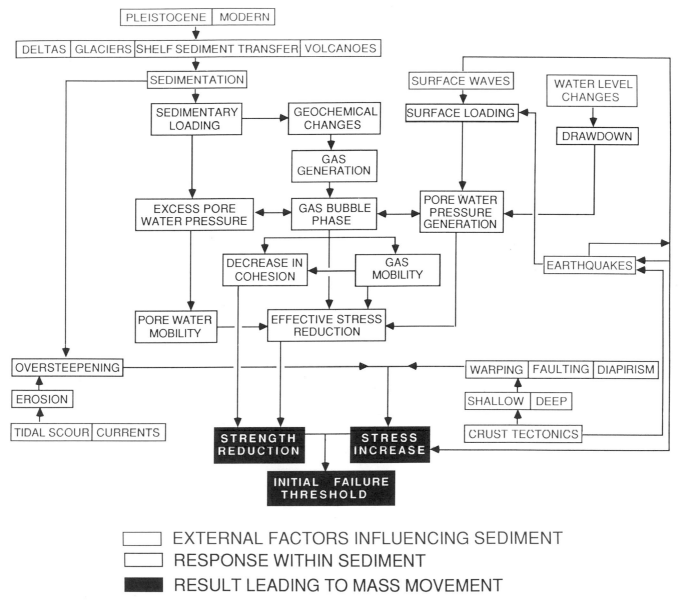

Figure 11.10. The terminology used in the classification of the mass movement of marine sediments (after Prior and Coleman, 1983). Mass movements can be classified as either slides or flows. The morphology of the moved material, together with the degree of liquefaction and sediment disruption are used to subdivide these two groups.

the Scotian and Grand Banks slopes show abundant evidence of slumps and debris flows in cohesive sediments (Stanley and Silverberg, 1969; Piper and Wilson, 1983; Piper et al., 1985a, b). Most of these would appear to be the result of high sedimentation rates associated with glacial events and marine transgression of the bank tops with subsequent seismic shaking providing the triggering mechanism. Modern events, however, do occur, as illustrated by slides and flows observed over a wide area affected by ground shaking in the 1929 earthquake on the continental slope off St. Pierre Bank (Piper and Normark, 1982a,b).

Incorporation of water at the upper surface of a debris flow can result in entrainment of sediment in a turbulent suspension (Hampton, 1970). The sediment-water mixture may become sufficiently dense that a turbidity current is generated (Middleton and Southard, 1978). There are many theoretical and experimental studies of turbidity current dynamics (Bagnold, 1962; Middleton, 1966a,b, 1967; Komar, 1973, 1977; Stow and Bowen, 1980). The ideal turbidity current is made up of a dense head region where sediment is being continuously entrained and more dilute body and tail regions. In reality, it has become useful to distinguish between "dense" and "dilute" turbidity currents to account for the respective coarse- and fine-grained deposits of these flows. The implication of these attributes to the stratigraphy of the offshore east coast is discussed in Chapter 10.

Bedforms

C.L. Amos and R.W. Dalrymple

The interpretation of most marine bedforms depends on a suitable genetic classification system, but unfortunately many bedform classification systems are based wholly on the size or the morphology of the forms, with little respect for process. The concept of an "equilibrium" bed-phase put forward by Southard (1971), and extended by Middleton and Southard (1978), is fundamental to the general interpretation of marine bedforms, and to applications to environments other than alluvial ones. This concept maintains that a given set of flow conditions will generate a reproduceable bed-phase (bedform type) which is in equilibrium with the flow.

A variety of bedforms both parallel and transverse to flow is recognized over much of the eastern seaboard of Canada. These features have a wide range of sizes and morphologies, reflecting many factors: grain size, grain density, sediment distribution, sediment supply, the modern bottom shear stress field, and the former bottom shear stress field.

The majority of bedforms found on the east coast occur in mobile sand, reflecting its abundance in the region (Fig. 11.1). In a recent study of these bedforms, Amos and King (1984) found that the classification scheme of Boothroyd and Hubbard (1975), modified by Dalrymple et al. (1978), adequately defined the flow-transverse, current-generated bedforms. Flow-parallel (or oblique) bedforms recognized on the continental shelf are less clearly defined genetically, but these bedforms include sand ribbons (Kenyon, 1970; McLean, 1981), storm ridges (including shoreface-connected ridges, nearshore ridges and offshore ridges) (Field et al., 1981; Swift et al., 1981) and tidal-current ridges (Off, 1963; Smith, 1969; Huthnance, 1973; Kenyon et al., 1981). The tidal-current ridges are composite features which are generated by the cumulative action of the superimposed megaripples and sand waves. Where sand is abundant, as on Georges Bank, these ridges coalesce to produce larger scale bedforms typical of the southern Canadian continental shelf (King, 1980). A review of the diagnostic characteristics of each bedform type is given by Amos and King (1984).

Table 11.1A gives the approximate range of near-bed velocities appropriate for each type of bedform. In non-cohesive sediments subject to unidirectional flow the following bedforms may occur: current ripples, flat bed (lower), 2-D (dimensional) straight-crested megaripples, sand waves, 3-D (sinuous-crested) megaripples, upper flat bed and sand ribbons. Under purely oscillatory (wave-induced) flow, only wave ripples and flat bed occur. The nature of ripples generated by the combined effect of waves and currents is now known and illustrated in Figure 11.11A. This figure is based on observations made on Sable Island Bank. Side scan sonographs recorded over Banquereau immediately after a major storm show large-scale linguoid features considered to be generated by the combined effects of waves and currents (Amos, 1984). These features, termed 'linguoid megaripples' after Reineck and Singh (1975), are approximately 50 m in width and wavelength, yet have no measureable elevation. Hummocky megaripples, which are also to be considered the result of wave-current interaction, have been recorded on video at exploration sites around Sable Island. These features are 0.3 m high and 1 m in wavelength and are

"fugitive", forming and degrading within hours. Similarly, 2-D megaripples have been observed to form and degrade during the passage of a single winter storm. The seabed is as smooth after the event as it was before. These observations raise questions concerning the value of seeking these bedforms during summer months when the probability of seeing them is lowest. The suite of bedforms transverse to flow (sand waves and megaripples) and parallel to flow (sand ridges and sand ribbons) present in any region (Fig. 11.12) is governed by the processes which are active, whereas the abundance and distribution of these bedforms are governed by the frequency of formation relative to destruction and, most important, by the distribution and availability of bottom sediments. Bedforms are uncommon north of Newfoundland because mobile sediment is scarce, whereas to the south they are widespread because sediment is abundant.

Ripples are in general, ubiquitous in regions underlain by loose sand and in water depths less than about 120 m. The type and orientation of these bedforms vary remarkably over even short distances (e.g. Fig. 11.13A-D). The differences in wavelength and orientation of the ripples present are clear, but the cause of such variations is not clear. Interpretation of paleo-environments from preserved ripple structures may well be difficult on account of the variability in types which can occur in any one environment. Observations made on the Scotian Shelf may help to overcome these difficulties.

On the ice- and storm-dominated shelves of Labrador and northeastern Newfoundland the seabed is dominated by the influence of ice scouring. Bedforms are restricted to the occasional wave-ripple field due to the sparse occurrence of mobile sand (Slatt and Gardiner, 1976; Josenhans, pers. comm., 1986), although megaripples occur at the outer edge of the continental shelf (Fillon, 1976; see section by Barrie and Josenhans in this chapter). Few bedforms have been detected on the shelves off Baffin Island, or on the seafloor of the Arctic Island channels, although isolated sand ribbons have been detected in southern Ungava Bay. This may, in part, reflect the absence of comprehensive surveys of these regions.

The Grand Banks, St. Pierre Bank, and Burgeo Bank, south of Newfoundland, are veneered by clean sand which shows an abundance of 2-D megaripples, sand ribbons, and arcuate equant-type sand waves (Allen, 1982), sand ridges and moribund sand banks (King, 1976; Fader and King, 1981; Lewis and Barrie, 1981). These features were considered by Barrie (pers. comm., 1985) to be active only during winter storms.

Despite the ubiquitous distribution of sand in the Gulf of St. Lawrence, large-scale bedforms are found only in the nearshore regions where various current and wave-generated bedforms are associated with the barrier island complexes of Prince Edward Island (Armon, 1980; Greenwood and Hale, 1980), the Îles de la Madeleine (Loring et al., 1970) and New Brunswick (Reinson, 1977b, 1979). Active bedforms also occur in the fluvial section of the Gulf of St. Lawrence and are interpreted to be megaripples, sharp crested sand waves, and sand ridges (d'Anglejan, 1971a,b; Monahan, 1976).

Banquereau and Sable Island Bank have the thickest sequences of surficial sand found on the east coast. Sand ribbons, moribund 2-D megaripples and both moribund and active storm sand ridges (which were mistakenly

Table 11.1A. Non-cohesive sediment

Bedform	Bounds	Sand			
		Fine cm/s	Medium cm/s	Coarse cm/s	Very Coarse cm/s
Current Ripples	Upper	60	50	35	no ripples
	Lower	13	20	25	
Flat Bed (Lower)	Upper	no flat bed	no flat bed	45	50
	Lower			40	45
2-D Megaripples	Upper	no 2-D	60	60	60
	Lower	megaripples	50	40	40
Sand Waves	Upper	no sand	100	100	100
	Lower	waves	60	50	40
3-D Megaripples	Upper	no 3-D	150	150	no 3-D
	Lower	megaripples	60 cm/s	60	mega's
Flat Bed (Upper)	Upper	85	170	240	295
	Lower	60	150	150	120
Wave Ripples	Upper	70	100	125	200
	Lower	10	13	20	30
Wave Induced Flat Bed	Upper	–	–	–	–
	Lower	70	80	90	100

Table 11.1B. Cohesive sediment

Bedform	Soft Sediment S_v = 0-25 kPa	Stiff Sediment S_v ≥ 25 kPa
	cm/s	cm/s
Megaflutes	12-36	200
Mud Furrows	12-36	200
Mud Waves	20	20

called sand waves by James and Stanley, 1968), are abundantly developed. The only known active bedforms are the shoreface-connected ridges situated on the south flank of Sable Island (Evans-Hamilton Inc., 1972, 1975, 1976), 2-D megaripples located at the base of the Gully (Amos and Asprey, 1982; Amos, 1985) and to the northeast of Sable Island (Amos, 1984) and sand waves in Harky Pass (Boyd, pers. comm., 1985).

The tidal region of the Bay of Fundy-Gulf of Maine exhibits the most extensively developed suite of bedforms discovered on the east coast. The strong tidal currents result in 2-D and 3-D megaripples, sand waves, sand ribbons and tidal-current ridges which are found in a near continuous belt through the Bay of Fundy (Klein, 1970; Fader et al., 1977; Dalrymple et al., 1978), across Georges Bank (Stewart and Jordan, 1964; Twitchell, 1981; Geonautics Limited, unpublished report, 1982), the Northeast Channel (Fader, 1984) and Browns Bank (Drapeau, 1970; Drapeau and King, 1972).

Improved surveying techniques illustrate that non-cohesive bedforms are found in virtually every marine environment. They are not restricted, as previously thought, to shallow water tidal regions – indeed, "gravel waves" have recently been identified on the outer part of the Laurentian Fan (Piper et al., 1985b), and "sediment waves" have been found at the base of the continental slope in approximately 2000 m of water under the Western Boundary Undercurrent (Damuth et al., 1979).

Isolated occurrences of bedforms in cohesive sediment have been found on the eastern Canadian seaboard. The classification of such bedforms and the processes under which they develop are less well known than in the case of non-cohesive sediments, and are less predictable on account of the complex nature of sediment microstructure, sediment shear strength and plasticity. Mud furrows, similar to those documented by Flood (1983), have been recognized in Cumberland Basin, Bay of Fundy by C.L. Amos in 1978 whereas megaflutes (King, 1980), which are thought to be generated by turbidity currents, have been detected in Placentia Bay, Newfoundland (Fader, pers. comm., 1984) and at the base of the Gully. Deep sea furrows (Flood and Hollister, 1980) and mud waves such as those described by Embley et al. (1980) have been recognized on the abyssal plains of the North Atlantic and the Arctic Ocean off Canada (Hall, 1979), in water depths of about 1700 m and greater.

The genesis and classifications of bedforms are still the subjects of dispute. It is not yet clear why and under what initiating conditions they form (Kennedy, 1978). This is particularly true of bedforms which occur in shallow marine environments because of the complex interactions between waves and currents, and the temporally variable flow fields.

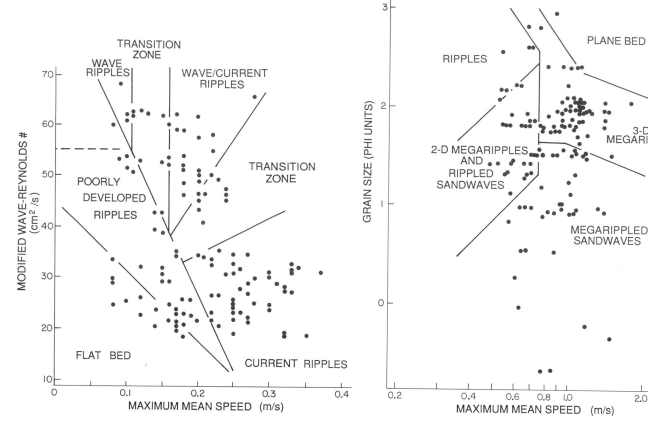

Figure 11.11A. The type of ripples observed to form under combined flows of waves and currents on Sable Island Bank. The depth of water was 22 m; bed grain diameter was 0.23 mm and waves were oblique (45°) to the currents.

Figure 11.11B. The types of bedforms measured in Minas Basin, Bay of Fundy, to occur under varying combinations of tidal current speed and seabed sediment grain diameter.

Current velocities and bedforms

Table 11.1 shows the approximate ranges of "near-bed" current velocities at which bedforms are generated and sustained for different sand sizes of non-cohesive sediments, and for "soft" and "stiff" cohesive sediment. The velocities have been normalized to a height of 1 m above the bed by applying the "Law of the Wall" velocity distribution, assuming a drag coefficient of 3×10^{-3}. The velocity bounds to sand ribbon development are uncertain. A first-order upper limit may be related to the critical fall velocity of sand (Bagnold, 1966). The data on flow-transverse bedforms were abstracted from Dalrymple et al. (1978), Middleton and Southard (1978) and Allen (1982).

The criteria for wave-formed ripples and flat bed have been abstracted from Clifton (1976) and Allen (1982), and are expressed here as the maximum wave orbital velocities defined by Airy Theory, which assumes inviscid flow. The conditions required for the generation of furrows have been derived from Flood (1983); the conditions for the formation of flutes and mud waves are based on the erosion criteria for fine sediments of Terwindt and Breusers (1972) and Young and Southard (1978). The segregation of cohesive sediments into "soft" and "stiff" types has been made on the basis of vane shear strength (S_v).

Instrumentation

D.A. Huntley and C.L. Amos

Instruments used in the study of modern sedimentary processes fall broadly into two classes: those designed to measure properties of sediment and those which measure the physical, chemical or biological processes which influence these properties. Significant advances have been made in the design of field and laboratory instruments which are transforming the study of sedimentary processes from a largely descriptive and qualitative subject into a quantitative science.

A fundamental property of a sediment is settling rate. A variety of techniques is now available to measure this property (Hackett et al., 1986; Syvitski, 1986). Unfortunately, there is no standard method or instrument and so results are not always comparable. Sedimentation tubes are available in most sedimentology laboratories; their inadequacies arise from problems with sample introduction, tube geometry, sample logging rate and sample preparation. No one technique can be used to measure the whole range of sizes found in nature (clays to boulders) and so samples must be separated into broad size ranges for analysis. The results are often then 'meshed' to produce a size histogram of the sediment, and this will usually show discrepancies at the mesh points. Future work is likely to be directed at developing techniques which analyze

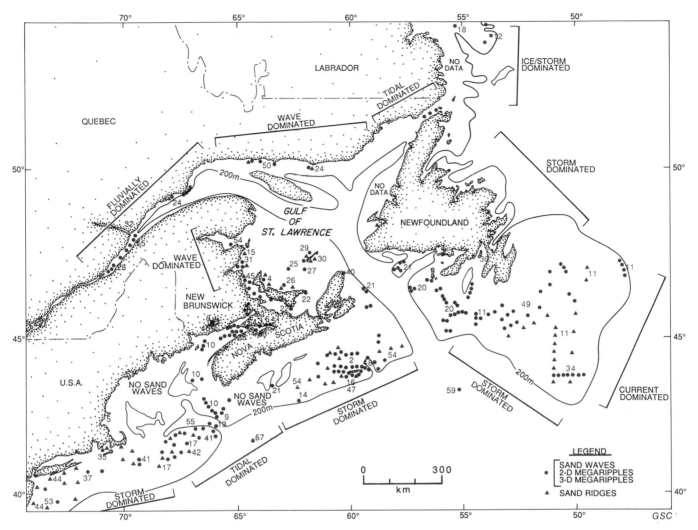

Figure 11.12. The distribution of flow-parallel (sand ridges and sand ribbons) and flow-transverse (sand waves and megaripples) bedforms on the continental shelf of southeastern Canada. The numbers on the diagram refer to the sources of information, complete references are found in the bibliography. 1: Amos and Asprey (1979); 2: Amos and Asprey (1982); 3: Amos and Long (1980); 4: Armon (1980); 5: Cooks et al. (1976); 6: Dalrymple (1977); 7: d'Anglejan (1971a); 8: Donaldson (pers. comm., 1977); 9: Drapeau (1970); 10: Fader et al. (1977); 11: Fader and King (1981); 12: Fillon (1976); 13: Geonautics (1981); 14: Damuth et al. (1979); 15: Huntley (1980); 16: James and Stanley (1968); 17: Jordan (1962); 18: Josenhans (pers. comm. ,1986); 19: King (1970); 20: King (1976); 21: King (1980); 22: Kranck (1971); 23: Lambiase (1977); 24: B.F.N. Long (unpublished data); 25: Loring (1975); 26: Loring and Nota (1966); 27: Loring et al. (1970); 28: Monahan (1976); 29: Owens (1974); 30: Owens and Frobel (1975); 31: Reinson (1977b); 32: C.T. Schafer (pers. comm., 1983); 33: D.H. Loring (pers. comm., 1983); 34: Slatt (1977); 35: Smith (1969); 36: Stehman (1976); 37: Swift and Lyall (1967); 38: Swift et al. (1978); 39: Syvitski et al. (1983c); 40: R.B. Taylor (pers. comm., 1983); 41: Twitchell (1981); 42: Uchupi (1963); 43: Woodward-Clyde Consultants (1982a or b); 44: Knebel (1981); 45: Greenwood and Hale (1980); 46: Boyer et al. (1975); 47: Evans-Hamilton Inc. (1975, 1976); 48: Stanley et al. (1972, 1973); 49: G. Fader and R.O. Miller (pers. comm., 1983); 50: B.F.N. Long (pers. comm., 1983); 51: Knight (1977); 52: Klein (1970); 53: Twitchell et al. (1981); 54: Amos (1978); 55: d'Anglejan (1971b); 56: Stewart and Jordan (1964); 57: Damuth et al. (1979); 58: Amos (1983).

quickly and accurately the size distribution and particle settling rate of an entire sample. Shadow imaging techniques, such as those used to measure the size distribution of dust in the atmosphere of Venus, or the Laser-Diffraction-size analyzer (Syvitski, 1986) appear promising, though no more accurate than existing techniques.

The processes of sedimentation observable in the field and the time scales over which they take place vary, and so the instrumentation needed to measure these processes must be equally varied. For example, processes which significantly influence sedimentation have frequencies which range from seconds (turbulent bursts and sweeps at the sea

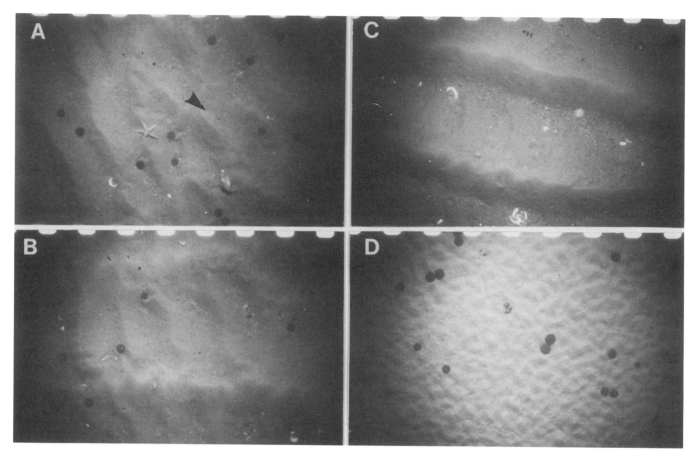

Figure 11.13. BRUTIV photographs of the seabed over Banquereau taken at an elevation of 3 m. The frame size is approximately 2 × 1 m. Frames A-D were taken sequentially at approximate intervals of 25 metres. (A) wave-formed oscillation ripples oriented N-S (the arrow indicates north) (GSC 204702-E); (B) large-scale wave-formed ripples (wavelength = 1 m) with smaller ripples superimposed (GSC 204702-C); (C) well-developed largescale wave-formed ripples (wavelength = 0.6 m) oriented NW-SE (GSC 204702-G); and (D) irregular ripple pattern (brick-brack) (GSC 204702-H).

bed) to years (deep sea circulation) and can operate on scales which range from the size of the bed material (the structure of the viscous sub-layer at the sediment/fluid interface) to circulation cells hundreds of kilometres across. A variety of wave and current sensors have recently become available which are microprocessor-controlled and hence are versatile in terms of sampling strategies. Many of these instruments have "instant-response" electromagnetic or sonic sensors capable of detecting flows of 1 mm/s to an accuracy of 1 mm/s and can be used to 'burst-sample' high-frequency events such as turbulence or wave-induced motion of the water column. Such meters have no moving parts and thus are not subject to mechanical failure and fouling. Innovative sonic sensors such as the hull-mounted AMATEC Straza can measure current velocities remotely throughout a water column and thus problems related to flow interference by the meter itself are avoided. Potential applications of ultrasonic sensors are the measurement of flow velocity and sediment concentration at 10 mm intervals in the so-called seabed boundary layer at rates up to 1 Hz. The product of these measurements is suspended sediment flux, a key parameter in the characterisation of sediment budgets, particularly in estuaries. Unfor-

tunately, the relationship between acoustic backscatter and sediment concentration is highly sensitive to grain size and shape. Advances in the future will be towards overcoming the problems caused by these variations in the natural environment.

An important concept in the study of modern sedimentary processes is that sediment transport varies in proportion to the power expended at the seabed by the overlying flow. Unfortunately no-one has ever measured bed shear stress directly in the field during a stormy, sediment transport event. Shear plates or Preston tubes (which measure bed stress directly) are available for laboratory studies of smooth beds, but these instruments are delicate and must be carefully deployed to prevent flow disturbance. Advances in the future will be towards developing a field instrument capable of measuring directly bed stress over a rough bottom during stormy conditions. As a partial solution to this problem, Caldwell and Chriss (1979) developed a bottom sensor which measures flow within millimetres of the seabed in the viscous sub-layer. Here they argue, the vertical gradient in velocity is related to stress through molecular viscosity. The sensor is equipped with a set of heated bead thermistors which move through the viscous sub-layer on a cantilevered arm at a fixed rate or a rate remotely controlled from the surface. The position of the sensors relative to the bed can be determined to within 1 mm and thus accurate velocity gradients can be determined. Using electromagnetic current meters, Huntley and Hazen (1988) made measurements on Sable Island Bank to verify and refine Grant and Madsen's (1979) method to compute bottom stress under the combined influences of waves and currents. This method is widely used to derive estimates of sediment transport in the marine environment and so the verification of the method on the Scotian Shelf is significant to further predictions of seabed sediment transport. The instrument used by Huntley and Hazen is limited in its use to smooth seabeds and relatively tranquil flow, and the data have to be transmitted via an umbilical to a surface vessel. Further developments will be towards an instrument that can be deployed over a variety of seabed types for long periods of time in order to monitor storm events.

The flow conditions under which bedforms are generated are known reasonably well in the case of small-scale bedforms that can be simulated in a flume. Even so, most flumes are only capable of generating either waves or currents; only a few can generate random waves typical of the marine environment and none to our knowledge can generate random waves and a current at the same time. Consequently, the response of sediment to combined random wave and current action is largely unknown. Significant advances could be made in bedform generation, sediment transport theory and the scour phenomena around seabed structures were such a flume available. Investigations of this sort should be accompanied by detailed and widespread observations of seabed responses under various flow conditions, particularly the most severe events.

The technology of developing underwater cameras has been advancing rapidly during the last 10 years. The camera which photographed the TITANIC has an effective ASA of 250 000 and is capable of imaging 0.3 hectares of the deep sea bed in a single frame using conventional light sources. High resolution, low light video cameras mounted on remotely operated vehicles (ROV's) are also effective tools to observe the sea bed. They can be used under conditions unsuitable for manned submersible operation and at a fraction of the cost. In association with manipulator arms, sampling tools and attitude sensors these instruments can be tailor-made for each application. Two such remotely operated vehicles are UFO, used to monitor scour around the spud cans of the jack-up rig ROWAN GORILLA 1 and JASON Jr. used from ALVIN to inspect the inside of the TITANIC.

Dr. T.M. Chriss (see Huntley et al.,1986) has developed a Traversing Underwater Photogrammetry System (TUPS) which takes stereo-photographs of a 11 m² area of the sea bed from a height of 1 m. The purpose of this instrument is to accurately monitor bed roughness. This may be particularly useful in areas where well-developed bedforms exist, or where the seabed is highly irregular. In such areas significant changes in nearbed flow may produce many of the features observed on sidescan sonar records such as comet marks, sand ribbons, asymmetric specks or flute marks.

The Mesotech 971 colour rotary scanning sonar shows great promise as a mapping tool in the monitoring of seabed scours around seafloor structures and in the measurement of seafloor bathymetry over ranges of 5 to 200 m. A 330 or 675 kHz signal is emitted radially from a single stationary transceiver; displays of the returned pulses are composed into a map of the seabed bathymetry which is displayed on a colour monitor and stored on video. This system has been used with great success to monitor artificial island degradation during storms in the Beaufort Sea and the shape of keels of icebergs on the Grand Banks of Newfoundland. The significance of this system is that it maps an object in real time, is almost instantaneous in the mapping process, and has virtually no data storage limitations.

Advances have taken place in the measurement of bedform type, stability and sediment movement at the seabed. Such measurements are essential to verify and calibrate theories of sediment response, yet no data set exists which adequately measures sediment transport and concommitant physical processes. Multi-parameter sensors such as BASS, Geoprobe, or the University of Washington tripod have been used with some success but have suffered from limitations in data storage or sampling rates. RALPH (Heffler, 1984) was designed and deployed to overcome these limitations (see Fig. 1.8). It too has a high failure rate, but results from a deployment at the Venture discovery site, Sable Island Bank, were excellent and have been successfully used to evaluate ripple genesis and bedload transport under waves and currents. The most significant attributes of this sensor are: its ability to act "intelligently" while deployed and hence to reject unnecessary data; its capacity to store up to 100 Mb of data necessary for long-term deployment; and its capacity to 'burst sample' high-frequency events such as sweeps and bursts of turbulence.

COASTLINES

R.B. Taylor, J.R. Harper and R. Gillie

Coastlines and the shoreface

The coastal zone is a dynamic environment whose stability is affected by a complex array of processes. The shore zone serves the land as a buffer against direct wave attack. It is constantly changing. To maintain a 'dynamic equilibrium' trade-offs must be made between four basic factors: energy input (waves, tides and ice), materials (source, supply), morphology (slope, features), and fluctuations in relative sea level. If one factor changes significantly — greater than normal erosion by waves, for example, without an appropriate balancing adjustment in another factor such as an increase in sediment input, then the 'dynamic equilibrium' and stability of the coast is threatened.

The coastline of eastern Canada covers a broad spectrum of geological, physiographic, and oceanographic environments and includes a wide diversity of shoreline types. The present configuration of the coast reflects the influence of bedrock lithology, structure and tectonic history, the late Pleistocene glaciation and post-glacial changes in relative sea level, and modern oceanographic processes. Owens (1977b) is followed here in subdividing the coastal zone into two regional components, Atlantic and Arctic, and in subdividing these into the parts dominated by rock and those which are not. The regional division reflects the dominance by sea ice, periglacial and cryogenic processes of high latitude shores; this contrasts with the dominance of processes due to wave, tides and currents of lower latitude shores. A summary of the coastal environments of eastern Canada is given in Figure 11.14; Figure 4 (in pocket) illustrates coastal geology. The figure shows coastal relief, slopes, material dominating the coastal regions, and the location of major depositional features, including beaches, deltas, and estuaries.

The classification of shorelines

There are about 115 000 km of shoreline in eastern Canada, if Hudson Bay is included. The coastal environments range from the permanently ice-bound shores of northern Ellesmere Island to the only seasonally ice-affected shorelines of the Maritime Provinces. Coastal classification systems provide a systematic means of categorizing these diverse coastal environments and a means of applying results from site-specific process studies (e.g. Owens, 1977a; Armon, 1979; Rosen, 1979; Taylor et al. 1985) to other similar coastal regions.

A critical component of shoreline classification or mapping is the scale of application (Owens, 1974). The scale of the initial observations — whether from field studies, aerial video tapes, or aerial photographs — constrain the spatial resolution at which the classification can be made. The scale of the final presentation also controls the detail that can be shown. Discussions of classifications cannot be separated from considerations of scale and there is no single classification that encompasses the complete range of scales from the global to the micro-scale. As a result no one classification is appropriate for all applications (King, 1972). Coastal classifications in eastern Canada and the mapping scales at which they were made are descriptive rather than quantitative. Table 11.2 shows that there are significant regional variations. Only regional descriptions of coastal environments have been developed for many parts of Canada, including the Arctic Islands and Hudson Bay (Owens, 1977b).

Terminology varies greatly between individual classifications (see Table 11.2). There is no standard and standards are unlikely to be developed in the near future because of the range in scales of application. In general the terminology used to define "coastal types" in classification and mapping programs in the scale range 1:50 000 to 1:500 000 is comprehensible, but is not consistent or rigorous. For example, Environment Protection Service (EPS)(1980) listed two distinct coastal types: cliffs and pebble/shingle beaches. These coastal types, in fact, commonly occur together. Definitions of coastal types are frequently not given, and this hinders interpretation of results.

Atlantic Canada

The coastline of Atlantic Canada is structurally controlled by the upland rim of the Canadian Shield to the north and the southwest-northeast trends of the Appalachian mountain chain to the south. Geological faults also control the alignment of many shores in the area such as Chedabucto and Aspy bays, Nova Scotia and St. Mary's Bay, Newfoundland. Topographic relief is highest along the northern Labrador coast where it varies from 200 to 1200 m. The maximum coastal relief associated with the uplands of Gaspésie, Anticosti Island, Cape Breton Island, Newfoundland and southern New Brunswick ranges from 200 to 800

m. The coastline elsewhere has a lower relief. Atlantic Canada is described here in terms of differences in coastal character and stability between the wave-exposed, rocky outer Atlantic coast and the more sheltered, depositional shores of the Gulf of St. Lawrence and the upper reaches of the Bay of Fundy. Owens (1977b) has described the region in terms of "morphodynamic" coastal units.

Resistant igneous and metamorphic rocks exposed along the outer coast of Atlantic Canada and the northern Gulf of St. Lawrence give rise to an irregular rocky shoreline (Dubois, 1980) of variable relief: 76% of the Labrador coast is rocky for example (McLaren, 1980). The character of this outer Atlantic coast depends on local relief, rock type, structure and exposure. It varies from low wave-washed skerry topography, with moderately sloping shore ramps and wave-cut platforms, to high steep-walled fiords (Fig. 11.15). Weathering is slow and the rates of coastal retreat are low, in the range, for example, of 0.02 to 50 mm/a (Trenhaile, 1983). Many of the shore platforms observed are thought to date from processes of the late Pleistocene, e.g. the Sangamon Interglacial (Grant, 1980). The outer Atlantic coast is devoid of beaches except where glaciogenic deposits are locally abundant or where locally-derived sediments collect in wave-sheltered environments as cliff-based talus, fluvial deposits, beach veneer or pocket beach wedges (Forbes and Taylor, 1987). Sandy beaches are particularly rare because the parent glaciogenic deposits are coarse and the ambient wave energy is high.

The diversity in form and scale of modern coastal depositional features is related not only to local sources of sediment, but also to spatial variations in the dominance of particular oceanographic parameters such as waves, tides, and sea ice. Atlantic Canada can be divided into three main marine environments: the exposed, wave-dominated outer Atlantic coast; the enclosed, microtidal Gulf of St. Lawrence; and the sheltered, tide-dominated Bay of Fundy (Owens, 1974a, 1977b).

The southern Gulf of St. Lawrence is a broad sedimentary basin of Permo-Carboniferous sandstones and shales overlain by glacial and postglacial marine deposits. The shore is erosional and is retreating at rates in the range of 0.3 to 3.0 m/a (Owens, 1974; Owens and McCann, 1980). Friable bedrock and abundant sandy sediments across the Magdalen Shelf are the primary sources of sediment for the extensive sand barrier beaches found along the shores of northeastern New Brunswick, Prince Edward Island, and the Magdalen Islands. These barrier beaches, tombolos and spits extend for some 350 km. They have been described in detail by: Bryant and McCann, (1973); Armon, (1975, 1979); Armon and McCann, (1977, 1979); Reinson, (1977a); McCann, (1979); Owens, (1979); Drapeau, (1980); and Owens and McCann, (1980). Essentially the barriers have developed across structurally controlled embayments and estuaries; they are transgressive in character except for some locally prograding beach ridges at the southern or downdrift ends of the systems (Fig. 11.15D).

Figure 11.14. The coastal relief, major rivers and shoreline character of eastern Canada (after Dolan et al., 1972).

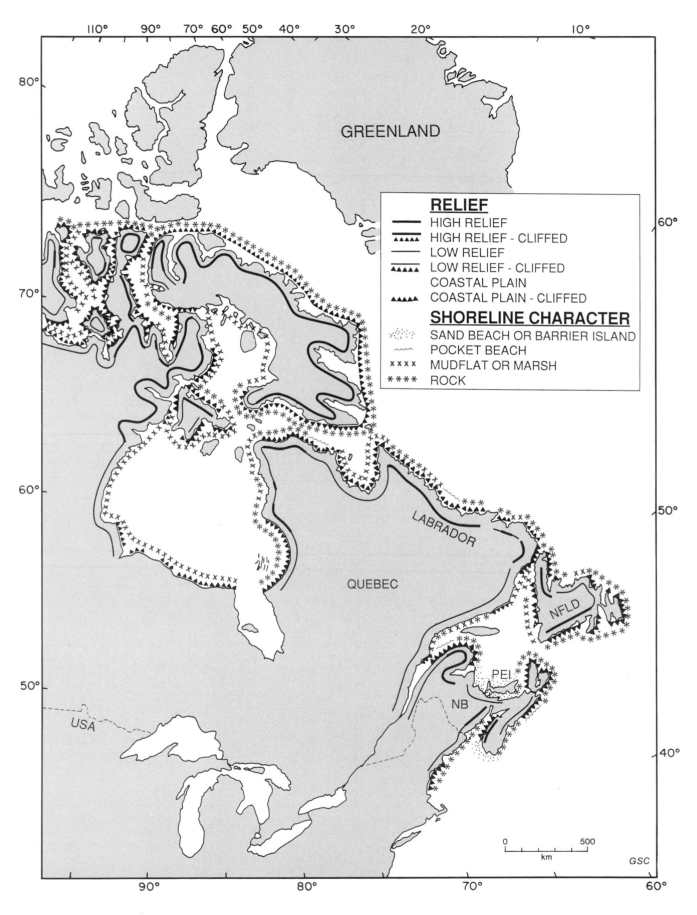

Table 11.2. Coastal classification systems used on Canada's east coast

Region	Scale	Materials	Slope	Wave Exposure	Authors
		|————— Primary Classification Criteria —————|			
Lancaster Sound	1:250 000	X	X		McLaren and Barrie, 1985
Southeast Baffin Island	1:250 000	X	X		Barry et al., 1977
Labrador	1:250 000	X	X		McLaren, 1980
Labrador (local communities)	1:50 000	X			E.H. Owens, P.S. Penland, P.D. Reimer, B. Sawyer and E.R. White, pers. comm., 1982
Northeastern Newfoundland	1:250 000	X	X		E.H. Owens and E.R. White, pers. comm., 1982
Southeastern Newfoundland	1:500 000	X			Environment Protection Service, 1981
	1:250 000	X	X		Woodward-Clyde Consultants, pers. comm., 1981
	1:50 000	X	X	X	Forbes, 1984
Cabot Strait	$\geq$1:10 000	X	X	X	Petro-Canada, unpub. data, 1985
Northern Gulf of St. Lawrence	1:50 000	X			Dubois, 1973, 1983 Dubois et al., 1984, 1985
Southern Gulf of St. Lawrence	1:500 000	X			Environment Protection Service, 1979
Prince Edward Island	1:500 000	X	X	X	Owens, 1979
Cape Breton Island	1:50 000	X			Eastern Ecological Research Limited, 1978
Eastern Nova Scotia	1:350 000	X			Environment Protection Service, 1980
	1:75 000	X			Owens, 1971
	1:50 000	X		X	Munroe, 1982
Bay of Fundy	1:500 000	X	X		Owens, 1977
	1:250 000	X			Welsted, 1974

These barriers are breached by 30 tidal inlets, many of which are used as small craft harbours. Sand dunes vary from 3 to 10 m in relief with the largest occurring on the northern Prince Edward Island shore (McCann, 1979). Wave overwash and wind-induced transport are important processes modifying these shores. Much of the rest of the southern Gulf of St. Lawrence has rapidly eroding, low (5 to 25 m) rock cliffs, fringed by intertidal rock platforms or narrow, mixed sediment beaches.

Wide intertidal flats in Atlantic Canada are associated with areas of larger tidal ranges. They are characterized by sandy bedforms, boulder clusters, or boulder barricades (Forbes, 1984). The boulder forms are best illustrated along the Labrador coast (Rosen, 1979; McLaren, 1980). Extensive salt marshes are restricted to the sheltered bay-head locations with meso to macro tides; examples are the Bay of Fundy, Baie des Chaleurs, and Lobster Bay, southwest Nova Scotia (Munroe, 1982).

The wide variety of beach systems in Atlantic Canada reflects differences in the geometry and supply of source materials, coastal planforms (the shape of the coastline)

and exposure, the varying history of sea level, and the variable oceanographic conditions. The largest depositional systems are supplied by erosional products from locally thick accumulations of glaciogenic deposits. These deposits can recede at mean rates of 0.3 to 1.1 m/a, or up to 3.3 m/a at exposed headland locations (Bowen et al., 1975; Forbes, 1984; Taylor et al., 1985). Most beaches are composed of mixed sediments ranging from sand- to boulder-size clasts and characteristically possess steep reflective beach-face slopes.

Along the Atlantic coasts of Nova Scotia and Newfoundland (zone D of Fig. 11.16) where marine transgression has proceeded at rates of 0.3 to 0.4 m/century over the last 5000 years (Grant, 1980; Quinlan and Beaumont, 1981; see Chapter 10), shore zone deposits have been left below sea level as lag deposits or have been pushed landward as retreating beaches. New onshore sources of sediment have been made available as sea level has risen. The example in Figure 11.15C shows that marine transgression occurred through a drumlin field in Cape Breton and that a finite but repetitive sediment source was made

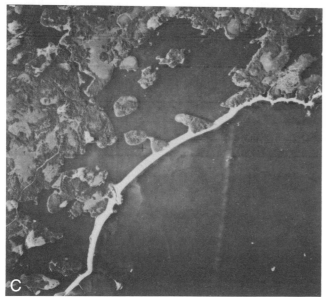

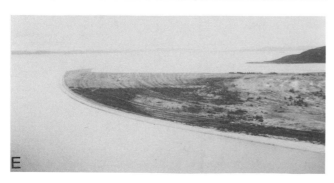

Figure 11.15. Atlantic Canda coastal morphology. (A) High rock cliffs, Avalon Peninsula (boat circled for scale, from Forbes, 1984; BIO FZ 8308); (B) Low cliffs fringed by wide rock platform, Bay of Fundy (GSC 204702-A); (C)) Depositional shore dominated by glaciogenic deposits such as drumlins, Cape Breton Island (from Wang and Piper, 1982) (GSC 204702-B); (D) Spits and barriers from local source material, Butoche Spit, New Brunswick (lighthouse circled for scale) (GSC 204702-C); (E) Raised beach deposits on emergent coast at Sandy Point, Labrador (from McLaren, 1980, GSC 203475-V).

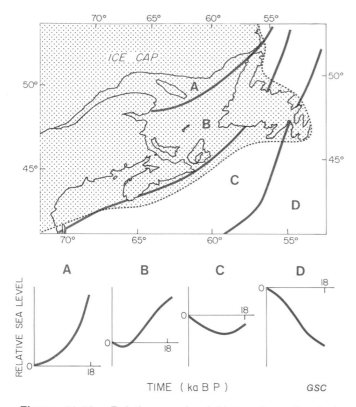

Figure 11.16. Relative sea level history (over the last 18 000 years) in Atlantic Canada. Four zones have been identified: zone A — continuously rising sea level; Zone B — predominantly rising sea level; Zone C — predominantly falling sea level; and zone D — continuously falling sea level. The lower curves show change in sea level with time for each of the zones and the stippled area represents the area of glaciation (after Quinlan and Beaumont, 1981).

available. Spit formation and barrier beach progradation resulted during periods of large sediment supply, but barrier erosion and possible failure occurred when the sediment supply was low (Boyd et al., 1982). Where thick ice-marginal or ground moraine deposits are the source of the supply is more continuous. Other parts of Atlantic Canada have experienced marine regression during early postglacial times; these are zones A, B and C in Figure 11.16. As relative sea level fell, in response to the rise of the land following retreat of glacial ice, older beach deposits were left above the reach of waves, and the migration of the shore zone led to the accumulation of littoral deposits farther seaward. Within parts of the Gulf of St. Lawrence, where sea level trends have reversed with time, both submerged transgressive sequences and older regressive shore deposits are being reworked in the present coastal system (Forbes, 1982).

The size and shape of depositional features are also influenced by coastal planform. Where increased coastal compartmentalization occurs, longshore transport is reduced. This limits the contribution which glaciogenic deposits can make, as in Mutton Bay, Newfoundland (Forbes, 1984). In larger embayments or on exposed shores, where longshore transport continually feeds coastal features, large scale spit or barrier progradation can take

place; Buctouche Spit, New Brunswick, and Flat Island Barrier in St. Georges Bay, Newfoundland are examples.

The duration of seasonal sea ice varies from near zero along the south coast of Nova Scotia to more than six months along the Labrador coast. Sea ice and shorefast ice prevent wave generation in the Gulf of St. Lawrence and the upper Bay of Fundy for more than three months each year. Ice is an important agent in the transport of sediment in the larger tidal settings of the upper Bay of Fundy, the St. Lawrence estuary and along the tidal flats of Labrador (Dionne, 1972; Knight and Dalrymple, 1975; Rosen, 1979).

The Canadian Arctic

The shores of the Canadian Arctic are affected by similar processes to those of lower latitudes. The relative importance of processes involving both marine and terrestrial ice, however, is greater. As a consequence, two coastal types are unique to this polar region — the ice shelf coast of northern Ellesmere Island and the thermokarst embayed shores of the Beaufort Sea.

Present coastal stability in the Arctic reflects the effects of Holocene changes in sea level in much of the eastern Arctic, but recent information from southeastern Baffin Island indicates that relative sea level has risen there as much as 2 m over the last 1500-2000 years (Miller et al., 1980). A more long-lasting rise in relative sea level which began at 20 ka is recorded in the coastal morphology of the Beaufort Sea, where present sea levels are at their highest since the late Wisconsinan, although these levels may be 10 m below the limit of an earlier mid-Wisconsinan transgression (Forbes, 1980). Tide gauge records from Tuktoyuktuk, although not statistically significant, suggest a rise in sea level of approximately 2 mm/a between 1952 and 1975 (Forbes, 1980).

Many shoreline types and coastal environments have been recognized in the Canadian Arctic (Taylor, 1973; Owens, 1977b; Sempels, 1982; Barrie and Associates, 1985). As a consequence of limited wave activity along these shores, the physical coastal characteristics reflect primarily the regional geology and physiography. For example, the shores of the eastern and southern Arctic are dominated by resistant Precambrian igneous and metamorphic rocks, the central Arctic Islands by Paleozoic sedimentary outcrops, and the western Arctic shores by younger sedimentary rocks of mainly Mesozoic and Cenozoic age. Coastal topography varies from the spectacular mountainous terrain of 600 to 2000 m elevation along the shores of Baffin Bay to gently sloping coastal plains in the western Arctic where the relief only occasionally exceeds 100 m. A plateau topography with coastal cliffs of 110 to 600 m elevation exists around many of the central Arctic Islands. The shores of the Arctic mainland and Hudson Bay are dominated by low irregular rocky shores, limestone lowlands with gravel beaches, wetlands, and cliffs of rock and unconsolidated deposits of low to moderate relief.

The eastern Arctic

Ice-capped mountains, steep-walled fiords and tidewater glaciers characterize the western shores of Baffin Bay and eastern Ellesmere Island, whereas a distinctive ice-shelf coast is found along northern Ellesmere Island. Much of the eastern Baffin Island coast was examined during the

Eastern Arctic Marine Environmental Survey project (McCann et al., 1978; Miller et al., 1980; Sempels, 1982; McLaren and Barrie, 1985) and in the Sedimentology of Arctic Fiord Environments program (Syvitski, 1984). Much of the area is occupied by the Davis Highlands, a belt of deeply dissected mountains, that extends from southeastern Baffin Island to the central part of eastern Ellesmere Island. Farther north the Innuitian sedimentary fold belt structurally controls the alignment of large fiord systems, as it does for example in Nansen Sound-Greely Fiord area.

Bedrock shores in the eastern Arctic are characterized by fiords and dominated by steep-walled slopes. Nevertheless, moderately sloping shore ramps, ragged headlands, rock stacks and low wave-washed skerry topography are commonly observed. Shorelines composed of unconsolidated material are restricted to the low coastal forelands, on broad deltaic areas at the heads of fiords, on small fan deltas along the sides of fiords, and in macrotidal environments. Beaches are found where glaciogenic material or relict Pleistocene beaches are abundant. Along the macrotidal shores of southeastern Baffin Island and central-eastern Ellesmere Island wide boulder-strewn intertidal flats are the most striking depositional feature (Gilbert and Aiken, 1981; McCann et al., 1981; Krawetz and McCann, 1986). In Pangnirtung Fiord, Baffin Island, as in many other cases, a nearly continuous boulder barricade fringes the outer margin of the tidal flats. These barricades are the result of a seaward transport of boulders by shore ice during spring breakup (Gilbert and Aiken, 1981).

Along the low coastal forelands of central and northern Baffin Island, extensive sand beaches are fed from rapidly-eroding cliffs of interbedded glacial and marine sedimentary sequences and from large rivers cutting through raised deltaic deposits. At a few locations, such as Pond Inlet, Baffin Island, and southwestern Bylot Island, the forelands consist of Quaternary surficial sediments disconformably overlying well-sorted, poorly lithified Tertiary rock (Syvitski, 1984). The shore cliffs along the forelands range from 5 to 40 m in height (Feyling-Hanssen, 1976). The sandy beaches of these regions have low ridges separated by wide, elevated tidal flats or lagoons, fringed by nearshore bars. Eolian processes become locally significant across the elevated tidal flats during late summer. Coastal lowlands along northern Bylot Island and eastern Devon Island are fringed by continuous sand and gravel or boulder beaches. Large barrier beaches front the ice-proximal sandurs of eastern Bylot Island.

At the heads of fiords and at their side-entry valleys extensive sandur and deltaic deposits overlie a variety of other deposits of variable thickness and distribution. These are marine, proglacial, lacustrine or lagoonal sequences and basal tills. Many of the deltas are fringed by wave-built ridges and are topped by elevated terraces of variable origin. Eolian processes are also important across many of these delta or sandur surfaces (Syvitski, 1984).

The fiords of Baffin Island lie in a region subject to earthquakes. Consequently they are dominated sedimentologically by subaqueous slope failures and sediment gravity flow deposits (Syvitski, 1984).

Ice coasts make up only a small percentage of the total eastern Arctic coastline, yet tidewater glaciers are nearly continuous along the eastern shores of Devon Island and southeastern Ellesmere Island, and ice shelves dominate northern Ellesmere Island (Fig. 11.17). Coastal sediments emerging from beneath glacial ice are quickly reworked by waves, yet are less well-developed than in other parts of eastern Canada. The distinctive ice-shelf coast, which began forming roughly 3000 years ago, may have covered most of northern Ellesmere Island in the early 1900s. Today, by contrast, only a few individual ice-shelves remain, Ward Hunt and Milne being examples. It is postulated that ice-shelves are formed by growth of ice at the bases and surfaces, through the incorporation of multi-year sea ice along the leading edge of the shelf, and through coalescing glaciers (Jeffries, 1982).

The central Arctic Islands

Lancaster Sound, eastern Barrow Strait, Jones Sound and adjacent channels have a well-defined plateau topography deeply dissected by fiords. Scree-banked coastal cliffs of 100 to 600 m elevation dominate the coastline, except where the coastal plain is wide enough to allow the formation of depositional beach features (Fig. 11.18). Steep, reflective gravel beach ridges are most common, with heights which extend to a marine limit of 76 to 120 m above sea level (Blake, 1975; Dyke, 1979). Glacial deposits are not abundant, and sediment is derived from local bedrock. The region has only a limited fetch, a mixed semi-diurnal tidal range of 1.2 to 2.8 m and a short open-water season (44 to 67 days). Shorelines are therefore reworked only during short and infrequent periods of intense wave action, such as occurred in 1969 and 1974 (Taylor and McCann, 1983; Fig. 11.18). Simple depositional features are the norm. Dunes are fringed by wide, shallow marine beaches, small spits, barriers and lagoons. North-facing shores and promontories are subject to intense sea-ice pressures during the annual breakup. Rock falls and debris slides occur periodically. Nonetheless, the gravel shores appear to be relatively stable judging by the evidence of well-preserved raised beach ridges, the oldest of which formed 9000 BP.

The shores of the central Arctic Islands present a transition between the cliffed and coarse-clast shores to the east and the low lying, fine grained coastal plain to the west and north. A distinctive ridge and valley or ria coastal topography is formed by the peninsulas and islands that form along the resistant flanks of the folds and the embayments where the less resistant rock units lay. Extensive deltaic deposits are found at the head of the embayments. Elsewhere beach morphology is simple and sediments are mixtures of sand and gravel. Steep slopes, higher than 3 m, are common in this area. Most consist of angular rock fragments covered by variable thicknesses of colluvium. Meltwater, from semi-permanent snow patches fringing the upper slopes, saturate the lower slopes. Consequently, solifluction, creep and earth flows are common processes redistributing the surficial slope deposits.

The Arctic coastal plain

Fringing the Arctic Ocean is a series of low lying islands consisting of a thick succession of Mesozoic-Cenozoic sedimentary rocks and sand and gravel deposits. Two contrasting sub-environments have evolved within this framework: (1) the emergent northwest Queen Elizabeth Islands, ice-locked for at least eleven months each year and dominated by the actions of sea ice and fluvial processes

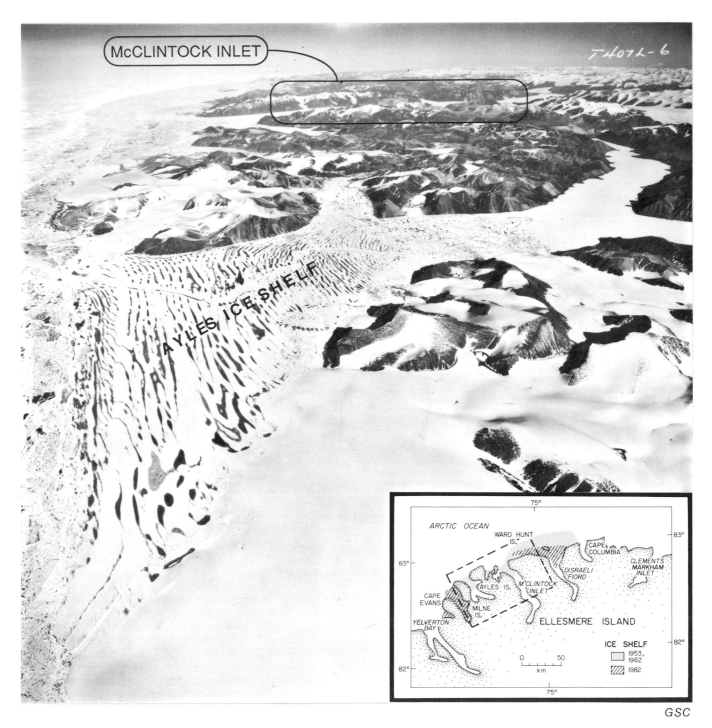

Figure 11.17. Aerial view of Ayles Ice Shelf looking east-northeast toward the Ward Hunt Ice Shelf. The inset illustrates the temporal changes in the extent of the ice shelf (after Jeffries, 1982).

(Fig. 11.19); and (2) the coastline of the southern Beaufort Sea. The Beaufort Sea coastline is presently submerging and has annual open water periods of 3 to 4 months, with a potential wave fetch of over 300 km. Both regions are microtidal (less than 1 m) but storm surges in the Beaufort Sea can raise the tide levels by 2 to 3 m. Such surges lead to large amounts of sediment being transported and to concomitant coastal flooding. In the Beaufort Sea most ice-

seabed interactions occur beyond the 10 m isobath. Hence, the direct effects of ice on coastal stability are less than in the northwestern islands where shore-ice pile-ups and overriding by ice are common, particularly on deltas or north-facing shores.

A gently inclined coastal plain, covered by a dense network of sub-parallel streams forms an apron around many

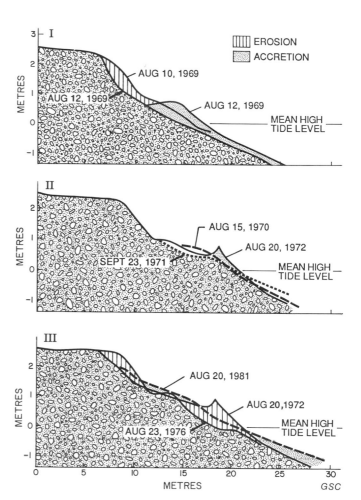

Figure 11.18(A) Plateau cliffs (150 m relief) and flights of emerged beach ridges dominate the shores of Barrow Strait-Lancaster Sound (after Taylor, 1980a, b; GSC 165034). (B) Beach changes for southwest Devon Island same region show little morphological change except during major storm events (August, 1969). Rates of temporal beach changes are shown for 1970-72 and 1972-81 (after Taylor and McCann, 1983).

of the northwest Queen Elizabeth Islands. Relief is generally less than 30 m but exceeds 100 m in places, as on northern Cornwall Island. Material delivered by streams to the coast is unaffected by marine processes, and consequently corresponds closely in mineralogy to the weathered products of the underlying bedrock. Numerous deltas of all sizes protrude offshore, reflecting the inability of waves to redistribute the sediment. Other principal coastal types include (1) featureless sandy plains where fluvial processes dominate but where eolian processes are locally significant; (2) hummocky shores where fine grained earth-flow levees, scars and ice-push features persist; and (3) mixed sediment shores with a wide intertidal zone. Wave-built features are subdued in this region.

The character of the southern Beaufort Sea coast is dominated by the erosion of ice-rich unconsolidated Quaternary sediments and their redistribution into coastal barriers and spits. Four main coastal types exist: (1) cliffs composed of unconsolidated sediments; (2) coastal barriers, with associated lagoons and estuaries; (3) deltas and fan deltas; and (4) breached lake features (Forbes and Frobel, 1985). Coastal cliffs, overlain by peat and composed of variable amounts of icy mud, sand, gravel and till are 5 to 50 m high and reach 100 m at Kay Point (Fig. 11.20). Cliffs constitute over half of the Yukon coast and exist along the many islands fronting the Mackenzie delta. Rates of recession are highly variable. The maximum 5-year average rate is 13 m/a (Forbes and Frobel, 1985).

Rapid rates of retreat are associated with thermo-erosional falls, debris slides, ground ice slumps and surface wash (Harper et al., 1978). Multiple nearshore bars, barrier washover flats and complex lagoon shore bars all attest to the greater wave reworking of these shores (Fig. 11.20B).

The Mackenzie River has produced the largest delta in the region, with an area of 13 000 km² and its discharge has important effects on the sea ice regime and physical oceanography of the Beaufort Sea. Thermokarst lakes cover most of the coastal plain of Richards Island and Tuktoyuktuk Peninsula (Fig. 11.20A). The breaching of these lakes has produced the complex embayed shoreline which is considered to be a distinctive polar coastal type (Fig. 11.20B).

The southern Arctic Archipelago and the mainland

The area is diverse geologically and includes the inland seas of Foxe Basin, Hudson Bay and James Bay and the narrow inter-connecting channels leading west to the Beaufort Sea. With the exception of James Bay, little work has been done on these shores. The major sources of information are the terrain surveys of the late 1950s and early 1960s (Bird, 1967).

Rocks of the Canadian Shield cover much of the mainland coast and extend north into west-central Victoria Island, and Boothia and Melville peninsulas. The upland

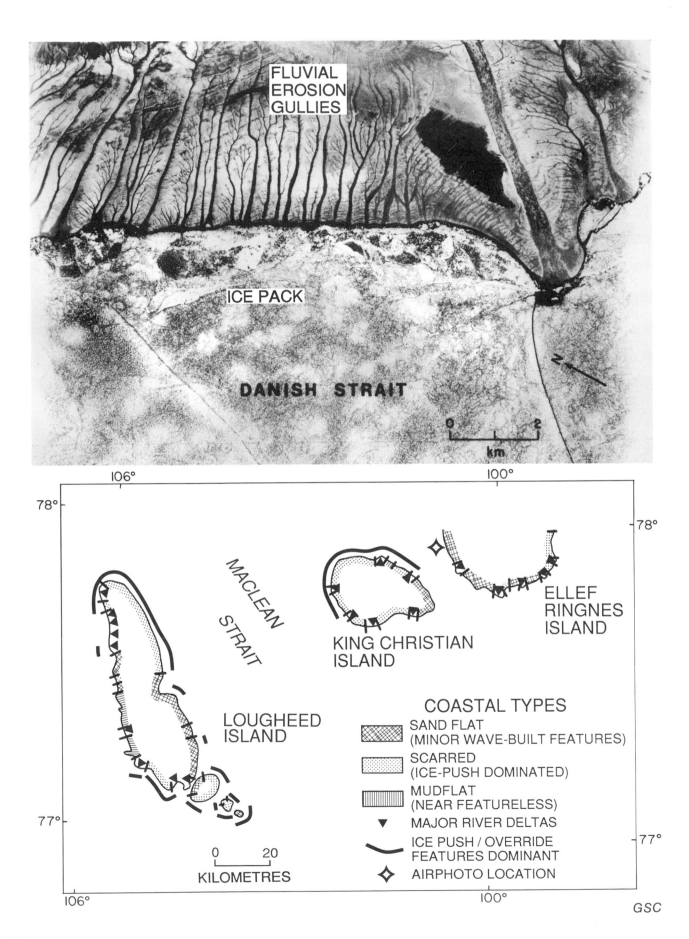

FLUVIAL
EROSION
GULLIES

ICE PACK

DANISH STRAIT

0   2
km

106°   100°

78°   78°

MACLEAN

STRAIT

KING CHRISTIAN
ISLAND

ELLEF
RINGNES
ISLAND

COASTAL TYPES

LOUGHEED
ISLAND

SAND FLAT
(MINOR WAVE-BUILT FEATURES)

SCARRED
(ICE-PUSH DOMINATED)

MUDFLAT
(NEAR FEATURELESS)

▼   MAJOR RIVER DELTAS

ICE PUSH / OVERRIDE
FEATURES DOMINANT

77°   77°

◇   AIRPHOTO LOCATION

0   20

KILOMETRES

106°   100°

GSC

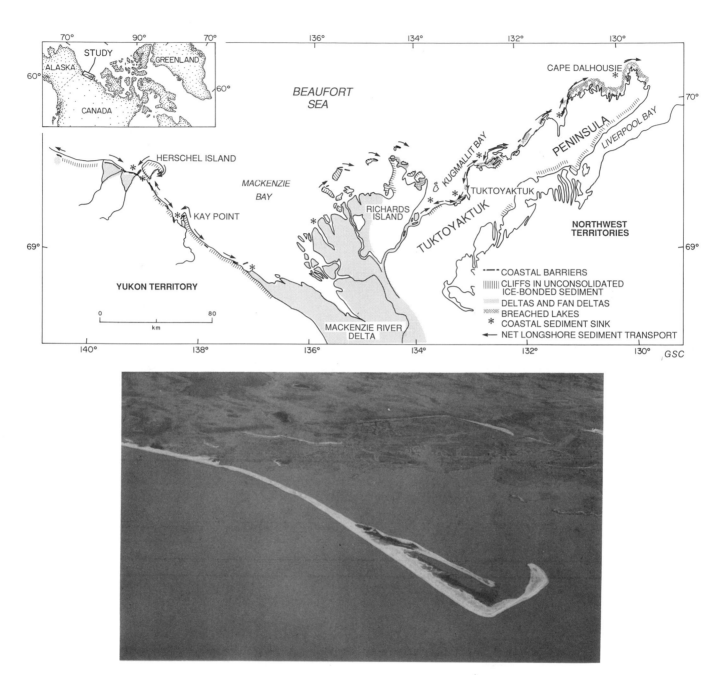

Figure 11.20 (A) Coastal types and direction of sediment transport (arrows) along the Canadian Beaufort Sea. The breached lake shores produce an embayed coast which is unique to polar regions (after Forbes and Lewis, 1984). (B) Coastal depositional features along the Tuktoyaktuk peninsula illustrate the greater role of littoral processes as compared to the northwest Arctic archipelago (GSC 202925-X).

Figure 11.19. The shores of the northwestern Arctic archipelago are ice locked for at least 11 months each year yet are dominated by fluvial and other geomorphic processes. (A) Sandy shores of Ellef Ringnes Island (National Air Photo Library photo A22386-42, 1971 — location marked in B); (B) coastal types in the region reflect the dominance of sea ice and absence of wave action.

and higher cliffed shores coincide with these areas. A distinctive, cuesta rock coast exists around Coronation Gulf, Bathurst Inlet, parts of northern Victoria Island, and Richmond Gulf in southeastern Hudson Bay (Bird, 1967; Guimont and Laverdière, 1980). The physical characteristics of the cuesta shores vary, depending on bedrock dip.

The remaining shores are low lying. These are characterized by irregular rocky headlands and pocket beaches, interspersed between continuous modern and raised gravel beaches, associated with regions of carbonate rock outcrop. Sandy and gravelly shorelines occur adjacent to locally thick accumulations of glaciogenic material in southern Victoria Island. Extensive tidal flats and salt marshes several kilometres wide occur along the Great Plain of Koukdjuak, Foxe Basin, and the Hudson-James Bay lowlands, where numerous large rivers transport large amounts of sediment to these shallow inland seas.

The shores of James Bay are best known because of recent studies by Dionne (1980), Martini et al. (1980) and reports completed for the James Bay hydro-electric project. James Bay is a shallow sea, generally less than 40 m deep, fringed by extensive tidal flats especially in the southern part (Dionne, 1980). The west coast of the bay comprises tidal flats and salt marshes, but well-developed sandy and gravelly beach ridges have formed along the more wave-exposed shores north of Akimiski Island (Fig. 11.21; Martini et al., 1980). By contrast, the eastern shore is irregular and is lined with numerous bedrock-controlled islands and skerries. Wide tidal flats in the embayments are bounded by an inner fringe of salt marsh, commonly 500 m wide (Dionne, 1980). The action of drift ice is particularly impor-

tant in these tidal flat and salt marsh environments and a wide range of sedimentary structures have formed as a result.

The shores of the southern archipelago and mainland Arctic are reworked by littoral processes for less than four months each year. Short periods of intense wave action occur in most years; in Hudson Bay and James Bay these periods are most commonly associated with storm surges. Tides are less than 2 m except in southern Foxe Basin where they are 3 m. Along the Arctic mainland, the irregular configuration of the coast, the numerous small rocky islands, the shallow bathymetry and the swift currents in the narrower straits combine to present hazardous conditions for any shipping in the area.

In summary, knowledge of the regional variations in the high-energy shorelines of eastern Canada is increasing as a result of mapping at a reconnaissance level and of classification surveys of the physical characteristics of shore zones.

Some regions, such as the barrier islands of the Gulf of St. Lawrence, and the sand and gravel beaches in populated areas, have been studied intensively in the last ten years. Most of the studies of these sand and gravel beaches have been site specific, although concentrated research on barrier islands and sedimentation on gravel beaches is contributing to the refinement of coastal models in general. Process related studies in the Arctic are still only descriptive, and we have few sets of long-term observations. Detailed facies models of Arctic sediments have not yet been made and so the application of Arctic studies to the problems in the ancient record are limited.

"Graphic Information Systems" will undoubtedly play an increasing role in coastal classifications. Two prototype systems have been developed for eastern Canada (Sempels, 1982). These systems offer considerable potential in the development of rigorous regional classifications and of hierarchial classifications (e.g. Shepard, 1963; Owens, 1974) that would link classifications from a variety of scales of mapping.

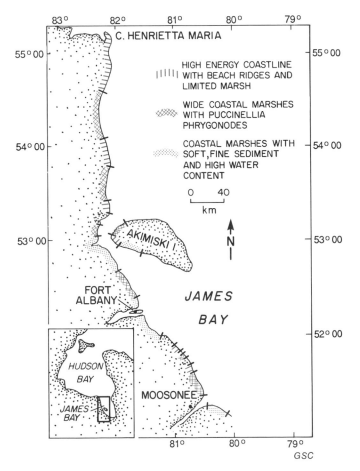

Figure 11.21. The main coastal types observed along the west side of James Bay have been described by Martini et al. (1980). Much of the coast is fringed by extensive tidal flats, however sandy-gravel beach ridges have developed along the more wave-exposed shores north of Akimiski Island.

SANDY BEACHES AND NEARSHORE BARS
R. Davidson-Arnott

The shape of the beach and nearshore zone is controlled by factors such as sediment size and abundance, slope, beach orientation, wave refraction, and the characteristics of the incident waves. On sandy beaches the nearshore slope is gentle and waves may break some distance offshore, giving rise to a wide surf zone. Studies from a number of areas around the world have shown that the profiles of beaches fall into two basic types: reflective and dissipative (Wright and Short, 1984). Under conditions of low swell the nearshore profile is flat and the beach face is steep, leading to considerable reflection of wave energy. However, under conditions with relatively short-period, steep, storm waves the beach is flattened, and sand bars form parallel to the coast resulting in a highly dissipative beach profile (Guza and Inman, 1975).

In areas exposed to both ocean swell and storm waves the beach morphology may be transformed through a series of stages from one profile type to the other in response to changing wave conditions; the dissipative profile is associated with stormy winter months and the reflective profile with the summer months (e.g. Wright and

Short, 1984). In areas of restricted fetch, such as the Gulf of St. Lawrence, bars are a permanent feature of the near-shore profile and the beach profile changes only in response to alternating stormy and quiescent conditions.

Greenwood and Davidson-Arnott (1979) recognized six types of sand bars, of which three are commonly found in the Gulf of St. Lawrence. These are: (1) nearshore bars which form parallel to the shoreline in the nearshore zone and are permanent, equilibrium features; (2) multiple, parallel bars which develop primarily in the intertidal zone, and are also equilibrium features; and (3) migratory swash bars, also called "ridges and runnels" (McCann, 1982).

Nearshore bars develop parallel to the shoreline and are associated with wave breaking and reformation during storms (Fig. 11.22). They are asymmetric in profile with a steep landward-facing slope and a more gentle seaward-facing slope. Bar height, spacing, depth of water over the crest, and the wavelength of crescentic forms all increase offshore. It is usually possible to distinguish between an inner and outer system of bars. The outer system consists of one or two bars which are commonly 1 – 3 m in height and which extend parallel to the shoreline, typically for distances of several kilometres. They generally are situated 150 m to 300 m offshore in water depths (over the crest) of 3-5 m. They may be straight, such as those on the Miramichi Barrier (Greenwood and Mittler, 1979) and the west coast of the Îles de la Madeleine (Owens, 1977a), or crescentic such as those in Kouchibouguac Bay (Greenwood and Davidson-Arnott, 1975) and on the east coast of the Îles de la Madeleine (Owens, 1980). The inner bars are much less continuous alongshore, being broken by rip channels. They also vary in shape, being straight, cuspate, or crescentic, and may be transverse or oblique to the shoreline (Fig. 11.23). They are commonly connected to the shoreline at cusp horns and shoal areas formed on the low tide terrace, producing an alongshore rhythmicity over distances of 100 to 250 m. Bar heights are between 0.5 and 1.5 m and the depth of the water over the crest is between 0.5 and 2.5 m.

Waves, generated in the Gulf of St. Lawrence shoal and break primarily as spilling breakers on the seaward slope and crest of the bars. The waves regenerate in the intervening troughs and the cycle is repeated across the inner bars until the waves reach shore. The intensity of wave-breaking is greatest over the innermost system. Plunging breakers may occur on the shallowest bar crests. Strong rip-cell circulations develop over the inner system; water moves landward across the crests of straight bars and the shoal areas of crescentic bars and moves seaward in the rip channels. Strong feeder currents, parallel to the shore, develop in the troughs in response to this general process (Greenwood and Davidson-Arnott, 1975, 1979). Rip-cell circulation also develops in the outer system of bars, as is shown by the presence of seaward-dipping dune cross-stratification in sediment cores (Davidson-Arnott and Greenwood, 1976; Greenwood and Davidson-Arnott, 1979; Greenwood and Hale, 1980).

Wave action and rip-cell circulation result in changes to the morphology and position of the bars, both normal to the shore and alongshore. These changes are relatively small on the outer bars, which are permanent features of the nearshore (e.g. Greenwood and Davidson-Arnott, 1975; Owens, 1977b). Scour occurs on the crests and tops of the landward slopes during severe storms, while deposition takes place on the seaward side of the crests (Greenwood and Hale, 1980). During less severe storms and lower wave activity the areas of scour and deposition are reversed. This leads to an oscillation of the bar crest about a mean position (Greenwood and Davidson-Arnott, 1979). The inner bars are more mobile because of the shallower water depths and exposure to more frequent wave action (Greenwood and Davidson-Arnott, 1975); the greatest modifications are found in the inner bars of exposed areas, such as the Magdalen Islands (Owens, 1977b).

Davidson-Arnott and Greenwood (1974, 1976) have identified five sedimentary facies associated with nearshore bars. Four of these — the seaward slope, bar crest, landward slope and trough facies — repeat across each bar trough sequence (Fig. 11.22). The rip current facies is characterized by ripple and lunate megaripple crossbedding, dipping seaward, and this occurs in well-defined rip channels in the inner system and across the centres of crescentic bars. Similar sequences of bedforms from the Oregon and New York coasts have been described by Hunter et al. (1979) and Shipp (1984), respectively. Sediments are finer and better-sorted on crests of bars and on the seaward slopes. The troughs, particularly near the base of the bar, are characterized by the presence of coarse sand and shell fragments swept over the bar, and by the accumulation of small amounts of silt and organic matter (Greenwood and Davidson-Arnott, 1972; Davidson-Arnott and Greenwood, 1974, 1976).

Multiple, parallel bars occur in a number of locations along both sides of the Northumberland Strait (Owens and Bowen, 1977; McCann, 1982). They have not been studied in detail but appear to be similar to classic ridge and runnel systems (King and Williams, 1949; Parker, 1975) and to the bars on the coastline of the Straits of Georgia described in detail by Hale and McCann (1982). The bars of Northumberland Strait are low amplitude (0.6 m in height) and symmetrical or slightly asymmetrical. They are developed on nearly horizontal platforms, and the thickness of the sand unit, from which they are formed, is roughly the same as the bar height. Ten or more bars may occur on a single foreshore. They are aligned roughly parallel to the coast and are broken in places by channels formed by currents generated during the falling tide. Like nearshore bars, they are stable equilibrium features of the profile. They do not migrate rapidly or change significantly in position and pattern through time.

Much of the sediment eroded from the beach during storms is returned in the form of swash bars, termed 'ridges and runnels'. They migrate onshore 'welding' onto the beach under low swell and 'fair weather' wave conditions (Davis et al., 1972; Owens and Frobel, 1977). Bars forming below low-tide level may be discontinuous and exhibit a range of shapes such as straight, cuspate or transverse (Sonu, 1968). They are commonly less than 0.7 m in height and 100 to 200 m in length. These bars migrate alongshore under the action of waves propagating obliquely to the bar crest. When the wave approach is perpendicular to the shoreline they move onshore to form a straight-crested ridge and associated landward trough (runnel). Sediment swept over the ridge by wave action generates an avalanche slope adjacent to the runnel. Wave transmitted water returns along the runnel and drains seaward through channels cut in the ridge. This ridge eventually migrates across the runnel to form a continuous

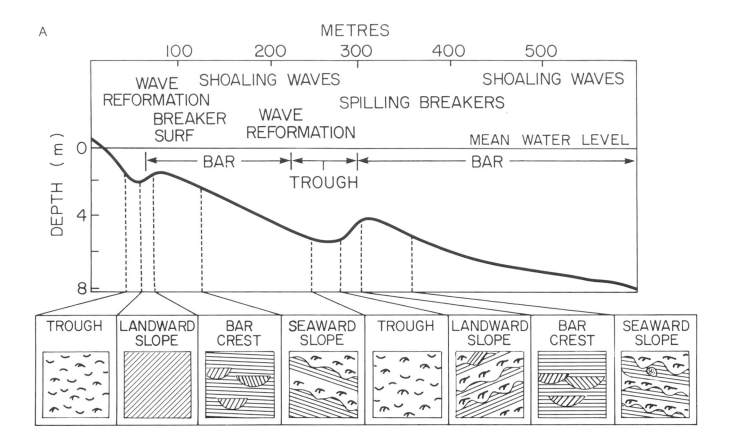

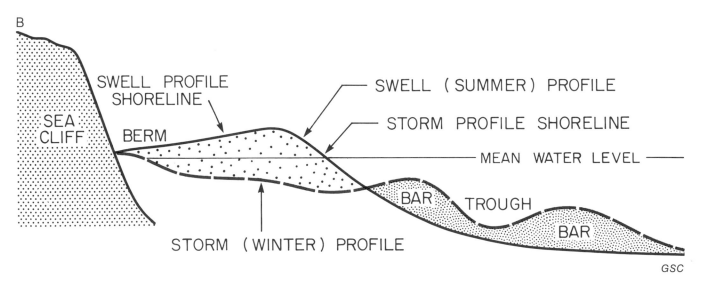

GSC

Figure 11.22. Cross-sections through a barred beach typical of the southern Gulf of St. Lawrence. (A) Sedimentary structures typifying the various parts of the beach. Bar troughs are characterized by small-scale ripple cross laminae. The crest and slopes are characterized by larger-scale, tabular foresets and channel cut-and fill. (B) Summer (swell) and winter (storm) beach profiles of a typical sandy nearshore. In the summer sand moves shoreward, during the winter sand moves seaward.

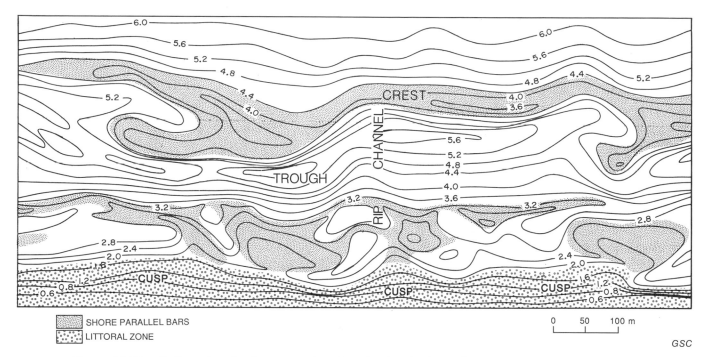

Figure 11.23. Bathymetry of an inner nearshore bar showing rip channels, crescentic crests and cusps. Contours in metres.

berm. Such berms are characterized by a gentle landward slope and a steep swash slope (Davis et al., 1972; Owens and Frobel, 1977). Giant cusps (Komar, 1971), which are rhythmic and highly coherent, become more prominent as the process of bar migration takes place. Internal structures in the berm show a sequence of small-scale ripple cross-laminations formed by current ripples developed in the runnel. These are overlain by steeply-dipping, landward-oriented, tabular cross-stratifications formed by migration of the avalanche slope of the ridge. The unit is capped by sub-horizontal, plane-bed stratification formed by the action of wave swash and backwash (Davis et al., 1972).

The morphology, sedimentology and response to changing wave conditions of nearshore bars on the eastern Canadian seaboard have been described in some detail. Two major sets of problems remain unresolved and are the subject of intensive study. The first is the need to develop simple models to predict and explain the occurrence of barred beaches and to determine the overall controls on the characteristic equilibrium morphology found on a particular beach. Some success has been achieved by using simple empirical equations such as those of Guza and Inman (1975), Wright and Short (1984) and Wright et al. (1985). These empirical approaches, however, do not shed much light on the actual physical processes.

The second set of problems concerns the complex interaction of all the processes controlling sediment transport in the nearshore zone affecting bar shape and behaviour. A large number of hydrodynamic mechanisms have been proposed to account for the formation of bars (e.g. Bowen and Inman, 1971; Carter et al; 1973; Lau and Travis, 1973; Boczar-Karakiewicz et al., 1981; Holman and Bowen, 1982; Heathershaw and Davies, 1985). Despite recent field experiments with electromagnetic current

meters which provide an increased knowledge of water motion in the barred nearshore area (Huntley, 1980; Davidson-Arnott and Randall, 1984; Wright and Short, 1984), the verification of models that predict equilibrium sediment transport patterns has not been possible (Bowen and Huntley, 1984).

ESTUARIES, DELTAS AND FIORDS

Estuaries and embayments
J.P.M. Syvitski and B. d'Anglejan

Estuaries and embayments are two related classes of environment which encompass coastal features that vary greatly in physiography and dimension. Nevertheless, they are often subject to quite similar sedimentary processes because of their common exposure to tides, wave action, fresh-water run-off and ice-flow movements. Generally speaking, the term 'estuary' pertains to water mass character, whereas 'embayment' pertains to physiography.

The highly indented coastline of eastern Canada offers several examples of embayments, varying from broad re-entrants in the coastline to basins having a length-to-width ratio significantly greater than unity. They also differ greatly in size. Major 'first-order' embayments such as Ungava Bay and James Bay, are inland seas. There are also numerous 'second-order' and 'third-order' features (e.g. Rupert Bay, Quebec; Baie des Chaleurs, New Brunswick). In most cases (Bay of Fundy being the exception) only a fragmental view is available of their overall circulation and sedimentation processes. Some are characterized by strong vertical mixing caused by tidal action (e.g. Bay of Fundy; Ungava Bay). Others such as James Bay are subject to high freshwater discharge and thus have the oceanographic character of large estuaries.

Most embayments have distinct 3-dimensional circulation cells because stratification and the Coriolis effect tend to maintain significant lateral pressure gradients. This is noticeable in James Bay, which exports large volumes of fresh water and fine sediments in suspension to Hudson Bay along its eastern shore (Pelletier et al., 1968). Other large bays, which are subject to low fresh-water discharge and large tides and are dominated by sand, have a landward movement of sediment (i.e. Minas Basin, Nova Scotia) (Amos and Long, 1980).

An estuary is defined here as a partially enclosed body of water which has a free connection with the open sea and in which the marine water is measurably diluted with the influx of fresh water from land drainage. Conceptually, an estuary is also defined as that part of a river influenced by the sea. Estuaries have been classified by Pritchard (1956, 1967) and Hansen and Rattray (1966) on the basis of water mass types. Estuaries of eastern Canada are the result of: 1) drowning of river valleys incised during the low sea level period of the Late Pleistocene; 2) tidal cutting of glaciomarine sediments along presently emerging coastlines; 3) processes of glacial excavation common to fiord formation; 4) natural bedrock control and associated diastrophism; and 5) local environments that form along prograding coastlines such as tidal inlets and lagoons. Sediment erosion, transport and deposition are related to the time-dependent and sometimes complex circulation patterns within the estuary. Schubel and Carter (1984) have related the various types of estuary to sediment transport and deposition patterns, showing that major differences in sedimentary character result from even slight changes in water mass circulation. Estuarine circulation systems have been classified principally by the level of stratification within the water column (Bowden, 1967; Partheniades, 1972; Dyer, 1973; Kjerfve, 1978; Officer, 1983). The level of stratification is a simple balance between the buoyancy forces set up by inflowing fresh water and the processes such as those associated with tidal action that work to mix the fresh water with the denser and saltier sea water. Estuary types include: 1) salt wedge, where the river flow dominates with little mixing between the fresh water and the salt water layers; 2) two-layer flow with entrainment (e.g. fiords) where mixing processes across the interfaces between the layers are important; 3) partially-mixed where river flow buoyancy is balanced by tidal mixing; and 4) vertically homogeneous — well-mixed, where mixing processes predominate. These ideal estuaries are usually further complicated by: the Coriolis effect that forces flow to the right in the northern hemisphere; the centrifugal force, important along sinuous inlets; the lateral separation of inflow and outflow currents as a result of complex bathymetry — multiple channels, for example; flow accelerations developed over rough bottoms and through inlet constrictions; pressure gradients developed from meteorological conditions (changing wind structure or fresh-water discharge); surface mixing from strong winds; the breaking of internal waves; and isohaline instabilities developed during the process of salt rejection associated with sea ice development.

There may be a variety of circulation patterns for a particular estuary, the patterns changing with place and time. For example, the St. Lawrence estuary varies seaward from salt wedge to partially mixed, and finally to a fiord type of estuary (d'Anglejan and Smith, 1973). The upper Miramichi estuary seasonally alternates between a salt wedge when fresh-water discharge is high, to a highy stratified two-layer system when the discharge is low (Vilks and Krauel, 1982). River regulation can also cause radical changes in estuarine dynamics and kinematics. The control of the outflow of the Rivière aux Outardes, Quebec, allows tidal mixing to dominate the system; furthermore, regulation has enhanced the influence of ocean swell (Cataliotti-Valdina and Long, 1984). Partially-mixed conditions developed in the Eastmain estuary, in James Bay, when the river run-off was redirected to La Grande basin in 1980 (Lepage, 1984). As a result, levels of turbidity and siltation steadily increased inside the Eastmain estuary. Recent man-made reductions in fresh-water discharge have also led to further penetrations of the tidal intrusion into the Koksoak River which flows into Ungava Bay, a region of high tides (Hydro Quebec, unpublished data).

The effects of estuarine circulation on sediment movement are complex (Fig. 11.24). Sediment particles may be transported in true suspension (wash load), as near-bed layers (fluid mud layers), or indeed as bedload. Particles in suspension may exist as single particles, biological aggregates or as inorganic and organic flocs (Kranck, 1984). In St. Lawrence estuary, the in-situ modal sizes of suspended particles range between 5 and 10 μm (8 to 7 phi), with few particles larger than 31μm (5 phi) (Kranck, 1979). The near-bed transport, essentially the movement of suspended sediment in the bottom boundary layer as individual particles or as turbid dense suspensions, is difficult to monitor although in some estuaries near-bed transport controls the mass movement of silt and fine sand (Parker and Kirby, 1982). At the leading edge of a salt wedge, bedload material accumulates to form mouth bars or tidal bars. Dredging of these deposits may have to be semi-continuous to increase access to port facilities (Schafer, 1973). Hemipelagic sedimentation (i.e. sedimentation dominated by a vertical flux of particles) is commonly observed under fiord-estuarine circulation (e.g. lower St. Lawrence estuary; Syvitski et al., 1983c). Hemipelagic particles include floccules, agglomerates of organic rich particles, and zooplankton-egested fecal pellets; these are particle types that enhance deposition close to the river mouth (Lewis and Syvitski, 1983). Deposits include discrete alternations of sandy silts and organoclays (varves) reflecting the seasonality of snow storage and freshet release (e.g. Saguenay Fiord, Quebec; Schafer et al., 1983). Partially-mixed estuaries tend to be shallow and so their bottom sediments are reworked and resuspended. A zone of high suspended sediment concentration, a "turbidity maximum" is known to occur in some estuaries, such as the upper St. Lawrence estuary (Silverberg and Sundby, 1979) and the Miramichi estuary, New Brunswick (Kranck, 1981). Mass balance calculations generally reveal a net export of sediment out of the partially-mixed estuary (e.g. Miramichi estuary; Winters, 1983). Homogeneous (well-mixed) estuaries, such as the Minas Basin within the Bay of Fundy, have extremely turbid waters due to tidal resuspension. Although bedload transport is more important in these well-mixed estuaries than in others, sediment is largely transported as a horizontal flux of suspended particles, principally controlled by the asymmetries in the flood and ebb tidal currents within the subtidal region (Amos and Long, 1980).

In general, the estuaries of eastern Canada have circulation characteristics typical of salt-wedge types or highly stratified estuaries as defined in the stratification-

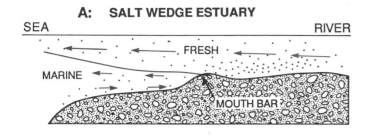

A: SALT WEDGE ESTUARY

SEA — RIVER

FRESH

MARINE

MOUTH BAR

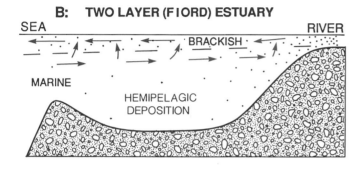

B: TWO LAYER (FIORD) ESTUARY

SEA — RIVER

BRACKISH

MARINE

HEMIPELAGIC DEPOSITION

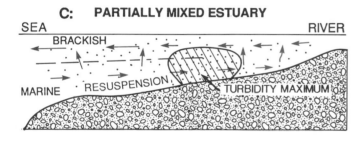

C: PARTIALLY MIXED ESTUARY

SEA — RIVER

BRACKISH

MARINE — RESUSPENSION — TURBIDITY MAXIMUM

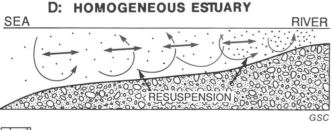

D: HOMOGENEOUS ESTUARY

SEA — RIVER

RESUSPENSION

GSC

[::::] SUSPENDED SEDIMENT

Figure 11.24. Idealized schematics of the major estuary types found along Canada's coastline. A illustrates estuaries characterized by the development of a salt wedge under the fresh riverine water; B is a two-layer estuary typical of fiords; C is a partially mixed estuary with the associated turbidity maximum; and D is a well-mixed estuary such as the Bay of Fundy. Shown are the dominant circulation and turbidity patterns.

circulation classification of Hansen and Rattray (1966). This is a consequence of high run-off during the open water months of the year, and particularly during spring peak discharge which is often very high and which limits, or may even suppress, tidal intrusion into the estuary. The strong two-layer stratification with net ebb dominance leads to a net export of suspended load. Thus, long-term deposition inside the estuary is minimal. The estuaries on the north shore of the Gulf of St. Lawrence behave in this manner, for example the Saint Jean River, Quebec (Cataliotti-Valdina and Long, 1983) and the Miramichi estuary (Vilks and Krauel, 1982; Winters, 1983). Stratification promotes the development of seasonal turbid plumes outside the estuary. Deposition is thus characterized by annual 'doublets' or varves such as those near the mouth of the Eastmain estuary in James Bay (d'Anglejan, 1982). Stratification is well developed under winter-ice at the mouths of large rivers such as La Grande rivière in James Bay and the Grande rivière de la Baleine in Hudson Bay (Ingram, 1981). Due to the lack of wind-induced vertical mixing in these areas fresh-water plumes extend farther offshore in winter. Budgell (1982) found that the neap-spring tidal cycle may alter considerably the stratification of the water mass because of its effect on mixing.

Changes in tidal amplitude linked to the neap-spring cycle modulate the sediment transport process in estuaries such as the Miramichi (Winters, 1983). Resuspension by tidal currents causes turbidity fluctuations to be almost in phase with the peak tidal flows. Tidal advection along the length of the estuary will create an asymmetry in the turbidity with respect to time, with the highest turbidity during the slack period of low water (Schubel et al., 1977). Local turbidity fluctuations in the St. Lawrence estuary are largely controlled by advection because the estuary is relatively deep (d'Anglejan and Ingram, 1976, 1984). By contrast, resuspension of bottom material appears more important in shallower estuaries such as the Miramichi (Winters, 1983).

Many east coast estuaries are fringed by intertidal marshes and mudflats. These are depositional areas of importance in estuaries on low lying coastal plains subject to large tidal ranges. Examples include the St. Lawrence estuary, Rupert Bay and other estuaries along the east and west coasts of James Bay and Hudson Bay; the Koksoak and other river estuaries of Ungava Bay; and the bays and fiords of Frobisher Sound and Cumberland Bay.

In estuaries such as the Bay of Fundy, an equilibrium state is reached, manifested as a logarithmic seaward-decrease of sediment concentration, the results of the balance between the headward motion of sediment produced by tidal asymmetries and seaward mixing due to longitudinal eddy diffusion (Amos and Asprey, 1981). This balance is in a state of continuous adjustment, and sediment may be supplied from offshore to mudflats on broad intertidal platforms, such as those found in Cabbage Willow Bay inside Rupert Bay (Champagne, 1982) or sediment may be flushed out if no sites of deposition are available within the estuary.

Differences in sediment transport and deposition processes among east coast estuaries are not only determined by physical factors but also by the magnitude of the sediment supply and the particle size of the material. Many estuaries were formed on coastal plains built on fine grained deposits produced during early postglacial marine incursions of the shoreline from 12 to 7 ka (for example,

647

the Goldthwaite, Champlain, Laflamme and Tyrrell seas). Isostatic uplift and emergence following retreat of continental ice masses led to erosion of the marine clays and thus made available large supplies of inorganic suspended matter. For example, Kranck and Ruffman (1982) estimated that the total sediment load supplied by rivers flowing into James Bay, and which flow over marine clays, is about half the total load carried by all Canadian rivers emptying into the Atlantic Ocean, including the St. Lawrence. Due to high stratification and flushing of the estuaries, fine grained sediments derived from raised marine deposits are transported into James Bay. There they contribute to the development of large intertidal mudflats adjacent to river entrances, particularly along the west coast (Martini et al., 1980). Extensive intertidal marshes and mudflats are also found at the head of the St. Lawrence estuary. Seasonal depositional patterns and sediment exchanges between the turbidity maximum and less turbid water are important controls on water turbidity and on the transport of suspended sediment out of the estuary (Sérodes, 1980).

Sediment stability and mobility within all the estuaries of the Canadian east coast and Arctic are affected by two major processes. Firstly, rafting by sea ice redistributes shoreline sediment into deeper water. In large estuaries, beds of ice-rafted material have been observed in the St. Lawrence estuary (Syvitski et al., 1983c) and Minas Basin (Amos, 1978). Ice-rafting armours the more easily eroded estuarine sands and muds with a coarser grained gravel component. Secondly, benthic fauna substantially alter the physical properties of the substrate through bioturbation and bio-erosion (Syvitski et al., 1983b). Effects include: 1) increase bed erosion through increased sea-floor roughness and, consequently, near-bed turbulence; 2) the resuspension of bottom sediments directly by stirring or ejection of turbid water upward, or indirectly by inducing changes in the sediments' water content and particle binding, which affect the bed shear stress needed to erode; and 3) bioturbation that will transport sediments to and from the seafloor.

Some of the key influences on estuaries within the Canadian east coast and Arctic include the mean spring tidal range, river discharge, runoff from land, zones of continuous and discontinuous permafrost and areas influenced by glacial meltwater (Fig. 11.25). Large tides occur in two areas: the Bay of Fundy (11 m mean tidal range); and the region around Hudson Strait, including Ungava Bay (10 m mean tidal range). The Bay of Fundy has been studied in detail (Gordon and Hourston, 1983); it is a classic well-mixed homogeneous estuary. The region around Hudson Strait has received little attention but, with the exception of parts of Ungava Bay, it is thought to be well-mixed. Nearby estuaries vary between those which are partially-mixed to fiord-type. Regions of permafrost have a low capacity for ground-water storage and, as a result, estuaries along these coasts are prone to flooding. The influence of flooding on estuary dynamics is not well understood, but may be an important modifier of estuaries that fall within the zone of continuous permafrost that typifies most of the Arctic. The runoff pattern varies systematically from one of desert conditions in the northwest Arctic to one of high runoff towards the Atlantic Provinces. Except for the Saint John River in New Brunswick, small drainage basins typify the Maritime Provinces, and rivers hardly influence local estuaries. The Arctic Archipelago

has both alpine ice fields and ice caps, so that the drainage basins are influenced by glacial meltwater, which, loaded with glacial rock flour, is typically very turbid. This effluent results in high rates of estuarine sedimentation.

Further research is needed to obtain an integrated understanding of estuaries and embayments. Complicated tidal motion, the effects of waves and swells generated over long fetches of open water, sediment transport by longshore currents along irregular coastlines, the importance of ice rafting, and variable particle inputs from a large number of rivers are among the features which are worthy of future research.

Deltas

J.P.M. Syvitski

Deltas result from a radical change in the fluvial hydraulics as river water enters a standing body of water. The effects of this are: 1) bed load deposition as part of the subaerial and intertidal topset deposit; and 2) subtidal sedimentation of the suspended load on the subaqueous portion of the delta – the so-called prodelta environment. A marine delta survives only if sediment supply and accumulation are greater than sediment removal by waves, tidal action, longshore transport or episodic slope failure. During maximum growth, a delta can prograde beyond the normal coastline. The northern shore of the Gulf of St. Lawrence delta is the only major deltaic coastline in eastern Canada (Fig. 11.26). Elsewhere along open coasts the rate of removal is greater than the rate of supply, as it is in James Bay, Hudson Bay and Ungava Bay (d'Anglejan, 1980, 1982). Two plausible reasons have been advanced for this condition. First, bed load is a small percentage (10 to 30 %) of the total sediment supply and is composed of relatively fine grained material. Thus, the coastal stability imparted by delta growth is limited. Second, tidal action is capable of removing much of the suspended load from the coastline. Canada's largest river, the St. Lawrence, is an example of this latter case. Exceptions include: the deltas developing in front of rivers delivering large amounts of sand from proglacial deposits or from exposed moraines (e.g. Grande rivière de la Baleine); and those where a river mouth is protected from direct wave action and longshore transport (e.g. Notaway River in Rupert Bay; Harricana River, south of James Bay).

A number of fiord-valley rivers provide good examples of deltaic progradation on Canada's east coast and Arctic. The reasons for this include: 1) the steeper thalweg (river gradient) of fiord-valley rivers that gives a greater capacity for the transport of coarse grained material, which once deposited is not easily modified by tides and waves; 2) the enclosed nature of these long and narrow inlets which provides an environment of negligible longshore transport (Syvitski and Farrow, 1983); and 3) sedimentation being greatest near the delta due to the nature of fiords which contain deep bodies of water with limited circulation below the estuarine layer (Farrow et al., 1983). Fiord deltas can best be described as "Gilbert-style" deltas with topset, foreset and bottomset deposits. One particularly large delta has developed from the Churchill River that flows into Lake Melville, Labrador (a misnomer because the lake is actually a marine fiord; Vilks and Mudie, 1983). Most of the other large fiord deltas are found, however, at the heads of fiords of the east coast of Baffin Island, an area dominated by turbid glacial meltwater (Knight, 1971;

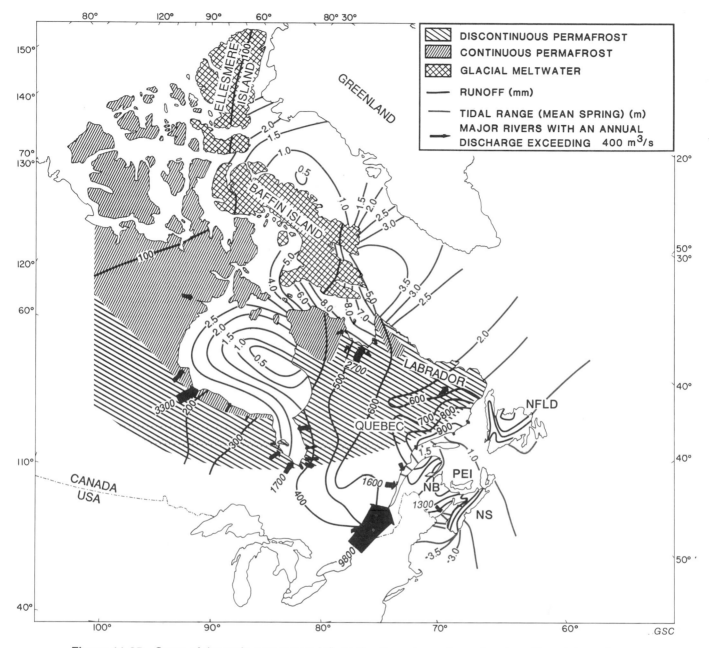

Figure 11.25 Some of the main parameters influencing the estuary dynamics along Canada's eastern and Arctic seaboard, including mean spring tidal range; runoff (significant river discharge indicated in cubic metres per second); and hinterland areas influenced by glacial meltwater, discontinuous or continuous permafrost.

Church, 1972; Syvitski et al., 1983a). These Arctic deltas are commonly referred to as sandurs (sand plain).

Sandurs differ from the deltas of lower latitudes in the strong influence of periglacial processes within a paraglacial framework. The important periglacial characteristics include: 1) the transportation of fluvial sediment in only a few days per season (Church, 1972); 2) large-scale eolian sediment transport on account of extreme winds and lack of vegetation, limited only by the availability of finer grained material (Gilbert, 1983); 3) the substantial movement of glaciofluvial sediment (Gilbert, 1982); 4) the struc-

tural armouring of deltaic tidal flats by boulders brought in by sea ice (McCann et al., 1981); 5) the presence of rock falls, slides and 'dirty' avalanches released along fiord walls in association with the hydrofracturing process (Church et al., 1979); and 6) the rare but impressive transport of water and sediment due to a sudden discharge from ice-dammed lakes (jökulhlaups). A paraglacial framework refers to environments that have a greater-than-normal supply of fluvial sediment. Catchment basins having a "normal" denudation rate would transport and dispose of the same amount of material that is made available by

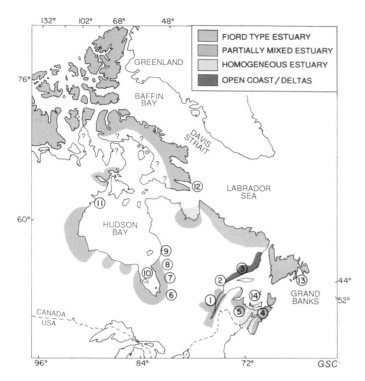

Figure 11.26. The generalized distribution map of major estuary types on the Canadian east coast and Arctic. The numbers refer to estuaries which have been studied in detail: (1) St. Lawrence estuary; (2) Rivière aux Outardes; (3) St. Jean; (4) Minas Basin, Bay of Fundy; (5) Miramichi and Baie des Chaleurs; (6) Rupert Bay; (7) Eastmain; (8) La Grande; (9) Grande rivière de la Baleine, Manitounuk Sound; (10) James Bay; (11) Chesterfield Inlet; (12) Frobisher Bay; (13) Placentia Bay; (14) southern Gulf of St. Lawrence.

weathering processes in the local basin. High sediment yields of the paraglacial environment are a result of the erosion of glacial, proglacial and isostatically raised fluviomarine sediment deposited during and after the last major ice advance. Many Arctic sandurs (sand plains) were affected by a new paraglacial cycle at the onset of the Little Ice Age (circa 1700 AD) increasing further the supply of sediment to the deltas.

Most of the deltas and estuaries of Canada's east coast and Arctic have been affected by significant climatic shifts and changes in sea level during the Late Pleistocene and Holocene. One result has been deltaic deposits, now found uplifted along emerging coastlines and incised as a result of modern fluvial cannibalism. For example, the Baffin sandurs commonly consist of major outwash deposits formed in front of rapidly ablating valley glaciers during the Hypsithermal period (4 to 6 ka); followed by deposits formed as a result of minor delta advances during the warmer stages of the generally cooler Neoglacial Period less than 4 ka (Church, 1978). Half of the annual sediment yield for example of Ekalugad Sandur during the Neoglacial was derived from erosion of the isostatically uplifted Hypsithermal deposits (Church and Ryder, 1972).

Much research remains if we are to understand the pathways of sediment transport in sub-Arctic and Arctic

estuaries and deltas. In particular, the following questions remain to be resolved: 1) what effect does a permafrost substrate have on estuary development and delta progradation? 2) how do long-term as opposed to short-term climatic fluctuations affect sediment yield and thus facies development in estuaries and deltas? 3) how do long-term oscillations in river discharge, and in sea level fluctuations in estuaries and deltas, affect sediment stability in the short term? and 4) can the influence of sea level fluctuations on sedimentary character be distinguished from those of discharge fluctuations when both have been important modifiers in the geometry and hydraulic character of Arctic deltas and estuaries? The answer to the last question may be the most elusive, for the effects of changes in discharge must be decoupled from the effects of changes in sea level even when the phase relationship of the two processes may not be known.

Fiords

J.P.M. Syvitski

Fiords are the deepest of all estuaries. There are approximately 700 "classic" fiords along the Canadian east coast and Arctic. Most are deeper than 200 m, many are deeper than 500 m and some are deeper than 1000 m. Circulation within the upper waters (30-50 m) is usually of the two-layer estuarine type and is related to river runoff, described already. Bottom water circulation depends on sill depth, tidal mixing over the sill, and deep water renewal through periodic exchanges of denser shelf waters with fiord basin waters (Fig. 11.27).

Fiords are commonly silled and there are many examples where the sills have controlled the effects of sea level fluctuations during the Holocene and have changed the estuarine style of circulation. As an example, the Hamilton Inlet sill that partially encloses Lake Melville, was 80 m deep at 7 ka, 50 m deep at 5 ka and is now 28 m deep. This caused a gradual decrease in the bottom water salinity by 5‰ in Lake Melville during the period of shoaling (Vilks and Mudie, 1983). Even more dramatic has been the effect of sea level fluctuations on the estuarine circulation within the Bedford Basin, a Nova Scotian fiord (Miller et al., 1982). The fiord at 8 ka was a cold brackish estuary that with falling sea level changed into a fresh water lake at 7 ka. Sea level began to rise locally, 6 ka, and a deep salt-wedge estuary was produced. This trend has continued to produce the present-day deep-silled estuary.

Much of the sediment accumulation within these over-deepened coastal basins can be related to glacial/proglacial infilling during and just after the last Pleistocene ice advance. Paraglacial deposits may include: 1) a basal till complex (lodgement till, waterlain till, push and dump moraines); 2) proximal glaciomarine sediments dominated by thinly-bedded turbidites alternating with hemipelagic layers; 3) distal glaciomarine sediments that tend to be fine grained and highly bioturbated; and 4) widely varying recent sediments that reflect non-glacial conditions within the east coast fiords of lower latitudes (south of 62°N), and the glacial conditions at the more northerly latitudes as a result of the Little Ice Age (circa 1700 AD).

The northern coast of Ellesmere Island has a number of "frigid" fiords that are both ice-covered year round and enclosed from the sea by the Ward Hunt Ice Shelf; Disraeli fiord at 83°N is an example. Its waters are composed of 45

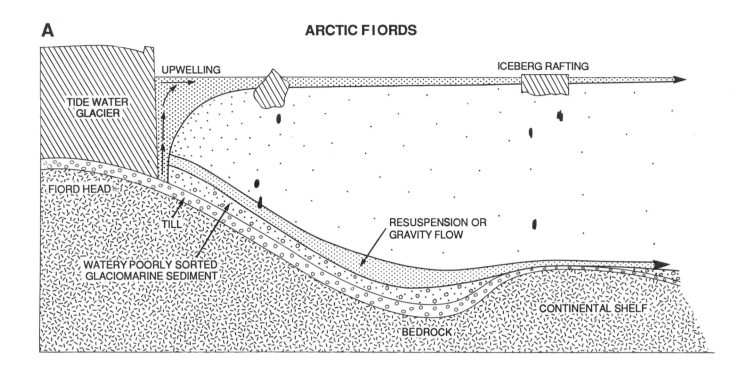

A **ARCTIC FIORDS**

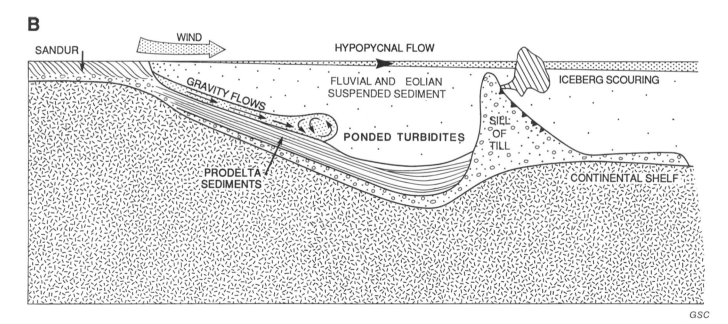

Figure 11.27. Schematics of two idealized Arctic fiord end-members: (A) tide- water glacier non-silled fiord, modelled after Coronation Fiord, Baffin Island; and (B) sandur dominated silled fiord, modelled after McBeth Fiord, Baffin Island.

m of fresh water, enclosed by the ice shelf, lying on top of 135 m of sea water (Keys, 1978). The permanent ice cover prevents mixing by wind, so that, because there is also little tidal mixing, a unique oceanographic condition is maintained. Meltwater from the tidewater glacier at the head of the inlet sinks to the pycnocline where it spreads downfiord losing its glacial flour continuously. The consequence is a quiescent seafloor composed of highly bioturbated silts and clay.

The sea ice of most other Arctic fiords forms seasonally. Salt is released during the fall and winter with the formation of sea ice, and this may stimulate water-column mixing through the initiation of salt-driven circulation, even though wind-driven currents are dampened when ice is present (Gade et al., 1974; Perkin and Lewis, 1978). The melting of the ice cover during the spring, accompanied by freshet runoff, re-establishes stratification, which in turn deteriorates throughout the summer through highly effective wind-induced mixing (Nielsen and Ottesen-Hansen, 1980). The lack of long periods of stratification in the water column has two effects on the patterns of local sedimentation: 1) hemipelagic sedimentation is especially high near river mouths; and 2) relatively stronger bottom currents lead to sediments being ponded and "plastered" in basins and slopes, rather than being "quietly" deposited as a conformable cover. Sea ice is also an important sedimentological agent in most Arctic fiords. The ice actively incorporates sediment during winter freezing along the shores (A.E. Aitken and R. Gilbert, 1981 pers. comm.) and passively carries fluvial, eolian and colluvial material to be subsequently released from the ice during breakup (Berthois, 1969; Knight, 1971).

Many Canadian Arctic fiords are influenced by processes associated with tidewater glaciers and icebergs. In both cases, melting below the waterline can inject significant amounts of fresh water into the fiords. Upwelling around icebergs can increase mixing and thus destabilize the estuarine circulation.

Melting near the wall of a tidewater glacier continues year round and thus contributes to the maintenance of surface stratification (Matthews and Quinlan, 1975; Greisman, 1979). Sedimentation is highest near the fronts of tidewater glaciers with rates commonly being about 1 m/a. The resulting deposits are poorly sorted and have a high water content (Gilbert, 1982). Sediment instability may lead to creep down the proximal slopes of the fiord and deformation of strata (Syvitski et al., 1983c). During the calving of icebergs, the seabed may be disturbed, and the huge waves generated by the impact (called "Tagsaq") can wash material far above the high tide line (Petersen, 1977). A drifting iceberg may remain stable for several days while continuously releasing sediment from its submerged portion. More rapid melting below the waterline eventually changes the centre of gravity of the iceberg which overturns and breaks up. Under such conditions, surface sediment which has been concentrated through melt-out is dumped (for details on iceberg rafting see Ovenshine, 1970). Icebergs may become grounded in shallow portions of fiords, such as prodelta slopes and sills at water depths less than 200 m, reworking the seafloor during the grounding process, and contributing sediment during their period of immobility and ablation (Blake, 1977; Vorndran and Sommerhoff, 1974).

Where the glacier fronts are subaerial, sandur deltas rapidly develop. Where these deltas are actively prograding, the prodelta slopes are crossed by erosive gravity-flow channels, 1 to 5 m deep, 20 to 100 m wide (Syvitski et al., 1983a). These prodelta channels may coalesce in deeper water (Syvitski and Farrow, 1983). Their shallow water position appears controlled by the sandur's flood channels. Most of the annual bedload is transported in a period of a few days during freshet conditions (Church, 1972). This leads to high sedimentation on the foreset beds with slopes between 15 to 35°; sediment instability and subaqueous channel activity result (Gilbert, 1983).

Recent deposits within the basins of Arctic fiords are volumetrically dominated by bioturbated, hemipelagic mud. They also contain significant layers of turbiditic and grain flow-derived sands and occasional gravels (Gilbert, 1983). Some areas contain debris slumps generated from side-entry glaciofluvial sources and tributary fiords. Several fiords have significant submarine channels (up to 20 m deep, 300 m wide and 4 km long) which may indicate the occurrence of rare but powerful turbidity currents or other flows. Research into the sedimentology of these fiords is presently highly active (Lavrushin, 1968; Elverhoi et al., 1980; Powell, 1981; Syvitski and Blakeney, 1983; Syvitski, 1984; Syvitski and Schafer, 1985).

The second largest class of fiords on the east coast of Canada (after Arctic fiords) includes those where sedimentation is low and waves dominate. Such fiords have one or more silled basins, only rarely more than 100 m deep; the exception being the deeper basins of the Newfoundland fiords. These inlets result from lowland continental glaciation over coastal areas underlain by resistant bedrock. Their dominant attributes have been summarized by Piper et al. (1983).

Wave-dominated fiords receive only 5 to 25% of their Holocene sediment from rivers; almost all the remainder is derived from waves reworking older marine sediment or glacial till. Sediment accumulation rates range from 0.5 to 3 mm/a (between 1 and 4 orders of magnitude less than rates in Arctic fiords). The highest sedimentation rates occur in deep basins adjacent to shores where waves are strong. The larger waves arrive as open-ocean swell or storm waves. Cliff retreat rates in glacial sediment may exceed 1 m/a near the fiord mouths, but are as little as 0.25 m/a in the less-exposed inner fiords.

Sediment supply to fiords is variable. In areas undergoing marine transgression, wave-cut platforms are developed through the erosion of till cliffs, and the platforms are gradually submerged by rising sea levels (Barnes and Piper, 1978). The platforms are armoured with gravel, the basin slopes are a mixture of gravel, sand and fines, and adjacent basins are predominantly fine grained. In areas of marine regression, proglacial and younger Holocene sediments are eroded as they reach the zone of wave erosion. The sediment distribution in these areas is similar to the wave-dominated inlets where sea level is rising.

Severe storms are capable of erosion and resuspension of sediment found in water depths of many tens of metres (up to 70 m on the northern exposed slopes of the lower St. Lawrence estuary; Syvitski et al., 1983c). Suspended sediment concentrations remain high in a layer near the bottom for several days after such storms (Barrie and Piper, 1982; DeIure, 1983). Fine sand and silt settle out rapidly, resulting in the deposition of thinly-banded, graded layers on the basin floors (Letson, 1981). The time interval between storm layers varies from 20 to 50 years. The basin slopes accumulate a reservoir of hemipelagic and ice-rafted sediments between these major storms (Piper et al., 1983).

Acoustic surveying can be used to distinguish wave-dominated fiords from those dominated by rivers or tides. Wave resuspension results in onlapping basin-fill units (Fig. 11.28), rather than conformable, ponded or wedged units typical of other depositional settings (Barrie and Piper, 1982; Piper et al., 1983). The complex distribution of sediment facies, that reflect bathymetry and wave exposure is also characteristic of fiords (Slatt, 1974; Stehman, 1976).

Although river-dominated fiords (Fig. 11.29) are perhaps the most widely studied of all fiord systems, they are not a prominent physiographic type on the east coast of Canada. Two exceptions are the Saguenay Fiord, Quebec and Lake Melville, Labrador, both of which receive large quantities of fresh water. The Saguenay River drains an area of about 78 000 km^2 and has a long term mean annual discharge of 1600 m^3/s. The Churchill River that feeds Lake Melville drains an area of 92 500 km^2 with a long term mean annual discharge of over 2000 m^3/s. Both rivers have their flows regulated. During periods of high runoff when reservoirs are high, marine and periglacial sediments, eroded from raised terraces, are transported seaward.

Fresh-water discharge into a fiord-like basin marked by thermohaline stratification is known as "buoyant hypopycnal flow". In this circumstance two zones dominate the fiord (McClimans, 1978; Syvitski et al., 1985): a proximal zone (upper prodelta) in which the energy of the river discharge controls the spreading and mixing of the plume with the surrounding basin water; and a distal zone (lower prodelta) where external agents control transport and mixing. Those external agents include tidal currents, wind, shoreline morphology and the earth's rotation. Mixing between water masses often occurs across sharp, well-defined pycnoclines.

Water temperature and salinity are considered conservative properties of the fiord water masses; they vary linearly along-fiord as the surface layer mixes with ambient basin water. The concentration of suspended particulate matter is, by contrast, non-conservative because of settling. Larger diameter suspended particles in particular behave non-conservatively, while slow-settling fine particles may behave more like a wash load. This results in gradients in the concentration of suspended particulate matter with depth within the zone of estuarine circulation and with distance from the river mouth.

The down-fiord sediment concentration and sedimentation rate decrease exponentially (Syvitski et al., 1985). For example, Smith and Walton (1980) showed that sedimentation rates in the Saguenay Fiord diminish from 23 mm/a near the river mouth to 0.4 mm/a in the deeper outer basin.

The accumulation rate of sediment in a fiord is a consequence of the hemipelagic vertical flux and the sediment accumulation due to input from non-hypopycnal sources (i.e. eolian sources, bedload transport, mass movement and sediment gravity flows, ice rafting, flotation and deep water exchanges) less any net erosion.

Saguenay Fiord is an excellent example of a situation where accumulation rate is a function only of hemipelagic deposition. High sedimentation rates and high concentrations of organic matter within the Saguenay system lead to a concommittant reduction in dissolved oxygen in bottom and interstitial waters. As a result there is little bioturbation and detailed resolution of stratigraphic events is possible (Smith and Walton, 1980; Schafer et al., 1980; Smith and Ellis, 1982; Schafer et al., 1983). The lack of bioturbation results in the preservation of marine varves — the alternation of organo-clay layers deposited in winter with sandy silts deposited in summer. The characteristics of the sediment within the summer layers, dated using ^{210}Pb, have been compared to historical discharge records of the main fiord-valley river. The results satisfactorily show that the sand modal size can be used to predict freshet discharge levels (Schafer et al., 1983).

Future research topics on modern processes in fiords should include both general surveys and specific experiments to compare styles of submarine slope failures within fiords having low to negligible earthquake activity with those of regions of high seismicity such as Baffin Island and Saguenay Fiord. Monitoring experiments might include: (1) inducing failure along the steep fiord-delta foresets to study variations in gravity-flow processes and products, and the possible natural mechanisms normally responsible for such failures; (2) monitoring the separation of bed load and suspended load during peak Arctic discharges with a view to studying facies development; and (3) monitoring the contribution of eolian and ice-rafted sediment to the seafloor using sediment traps.

CONTINENTAL SHELVES
The shelves off eastern Canada
J.V. Barrie and C.L. Amos

The shelves off eastern Canada can be divided into two broad groups based on modern processes which affect sediments: a temperate group, south of 48°N, which is dominated by the effects of winds, waves and currents; and a northern group, north of 48°N, in which the effects of ice rafting and ice scouring dominate. This grouping is, of course, modified locally; for example, the Bay of Fundy and the regions near Hudson Strait are dominated by tides, elsewhere storms and storm-waves predominate. Winter ice can also significantly affect sediment distribution in the temperate group. For example, ice rafting is evident in Minas Basin, Chignecto Bay and in the Gulf of St. Lawrence. The division between the temperate and northern groups, though broad, occurs roughly across the northern part of the Grand Banks. Common to all the shelves are characteristics of the last glaciation which must be separated from Holocene events. On the southern temperate shelves the effects of the Holocene rise in sea level is the dominant postglacial event (see Chapter 10). Most northern shelves are too deep for this to have been significant and, as a consequence, the separation of Holocene from earlier events is much more difficult.

Temperate shelves
C.L. Amos and G.B. Fader

Temperate shelves are those where the dominant modern processes at the seabed are hydraulic. Such processes include tidal currents, waves and storm driven flows. Included in this group are the Grand Banks, Gulf of St. Lawrence, Scotian Shelf, Gulf of Maine and Bay of Fundy.

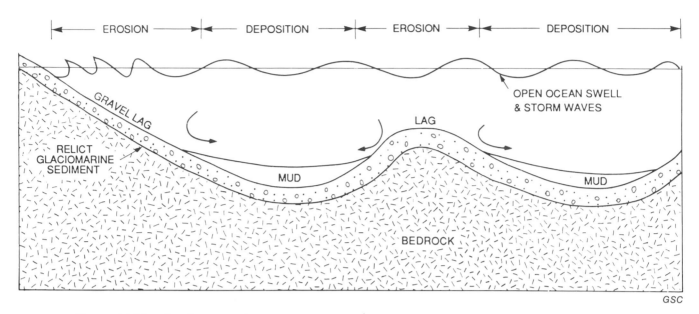

Figure 11.28. A schematic of a wave-dominated fiord end-member found along eastern Canada's southern coastline.

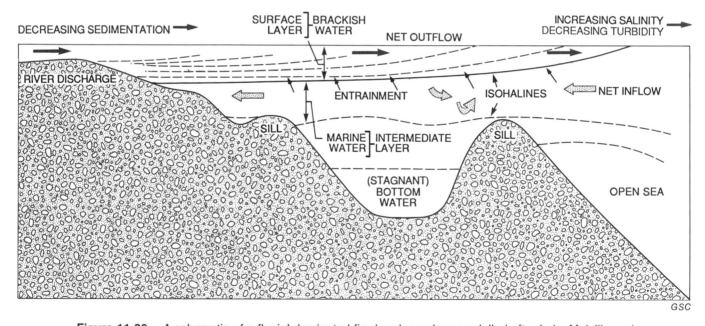

Figure 11.29. A schematic of a fluvial-dominated fiord end-member, modelled after Lake Melville and Saguenay Fiord.

Regional surveys show that about 20% of the Canadian temperate shelves also possess a relict glacial character which do not reflect modern processes (see Chapter 10).

The seabed of the inner shelf of southern shelves is dissected and irregular due to the presence of paleodrainage patterns on Paleozoic and Mesozoic bedrock which have been infilled only in part by glacial and postglacial sediments (King, 1970; King and MacLean, 1976; King and Fader, 1986). The outer shelf, principally underlain by Tertiary sediments, is smoother and separated into a series of isolated banks.

Unconsolidated Recent sediments are widespread on the outer shelf and in the deeper basins separating the banks (see Fig. 11.1A). They are principally derived by winnowing from glacio-marine deposits such as the Emerald Silt or the Sambro Sand (see Chapter 10). The fine grained sediments are taken into suspension during storms (Kontouplos and Piper, 1982; Amos, 1984), transported from the banks and deposited in the adjacent quiescent basins to form the acoustically-transparent LaHave Clay. The coarser material remains as a veneer over the bank surfaces to form the Sable Island Sand and Gravel.

These Quaternary formations have been mapped in detail by King (1970), MacLean and King (1971), Drapeau and King (1972), Fader et al. (1977), MacLean et al. (1977), Fader et al. (1982), and Fader (1984); they are discussed in Chapter 10.

The Quaternary formations of King (1970) can be subdivided into members on the basis of depositional subenvironments. For example, five 50 m boreholes drilled through the Eastern Shoal, Banquereau, revealed the complexity of the Sable Island Sand and Gravel (Amos and Knoll, 1987). The "transgressive gravel lag" described by King (1970) overlies a fluvial sequence dissected by channel cut-and-fill. This gravel lag, locally formed 7 ka, dips seaward at a constant slope of 1:1000 and can be traced under Eastern Shoal. The central core of this shoal comprises conformably-bedded shelly sand which in turn is overlain by up to 20 m of crossbedded sand formed less than 6 ka. Both the environmental interpretation and the ages of the Holocene sequence are similar to those of the New Jersey continental shelf (Stahl et al., 1974; Stubblefield et al., 1984). The large-scale sand bodies of the Scotian Shelf appear to be modern shelf-edge storm ridges, and not degraded submerged barrier islands formed at lower stands of sea level, as was once thought.

The mid-shelf ridges from the Grand Banks are dynamic (Barrie et al., 1984). Cores through 3 m high sand ridges in the region of the Hibernia P-15 well show a sequence of sand and shell horizons (Fig. 11.1B). The base of the ridge sequence is less than 3000 years old. The ages of the crossbedding show that the ridges are migrating southwards, parallel to the shelf contours, although no direct observations of sediment motion have been made. Granulometric studies of surface sediments by McLaren (unpublished report, 1985) support this interpretation and indicate that the process continues in the modern setting.

The nature of the shallow, bank-top seabed on the Grand Banks and the Scotian Shelf varies seasonally. During storm events, wave-induced rippling of sand and gravel will take place to depths of 100-150 m below sea level (Fader and King, 1981). Wind-induced accelerations of the local mean flow, influenced by seabed topography (Pietrafesa, 1984), can produce large-scale features such as sand waves, sand ribbons or sand ridges, "2-D" or "3-D" megaripples and "linguoid" megaripples. Though modern, these features become moribund between storms and are degraded either wholly or in part by "fair weather" wave motion or the effects of bottom browsing organisms (Barrie et al., 1984). Observations made on a daily basis near Sable Island show that 2-D and hummocky megaripples are generated during winter storms. These features appear and are degraded within a 24-hour period, leaving the seabed rippled, but otherwise featureless.

Recent bottom sediments of mid-latitude temperate shelves are reworked and transported by storm-generated currents (Smith and Hopkins, 1972). Butman et al. (1979), working on Georges Bank and the mid-Atlantic shelf off the eastern United States, observed that traction and suspension of sediment usually occurred during severe winter storms. Swift and Freeland (1978) and Lavelle et al. (1976) suggested that such transporting events occur 4-5 times annually across storm-dominated shelves and can be significant even at the shelf edge (Karl et al., 1983). Indeed, Swift et al. (1981), using results from the continental margin of the northeastern United States showed that 95% of sediment motion took place during short-lived storm events. This appears to be true on the Scotian Shelf (Seaconsult Marine Research Ltd., 1986) and the Grand Banks, but not in regions dominated by tidal currents such as the Bay of Fundy, Northeast Channel and Browns Bank, where the processes of sediment transport are virtually continuous (Drapeau, 1970; Dalrymple, 1977; Amos and Long, 1980; Fader, 1984).

The migration of sand over the shallow banks of the shelf is both onshore and offshore, and shows markedly different patterns locally. The concept of net seaward migration of sand through the coastal boundary, proposed for the continental shelf of the United States (Swift, 1976), is not an appropriate one for the eastern Canadian shelves on account of the nature of sediment supply and shelf morphology. On Banquereau for example, sand migration is from west to east, nearly parallel to the coastline, but with a slight seaward component, presumably in the direction of the storm-driven currents. Winnowed gravels cover the seabed in the up-drift direction, whereas Eastern Shoal has formed downdrift in a zone of net accumulation near the shelf break.

Transport across the shelf break, or indeed spillover into large canyons (such as the Gully), is inhibited by the generation of intense currents during storms which are parallel to bathymetric contours (Galt, 1971). These currents act as hydraulic barriers to sediment motion. On Sable Island Bank, net sand transport is also west to east, but with an onshore component. The shoals around Sable Island thus appear to be the downdrift region of sand accretion and in this sense are analogous to Eastern Shoal. So it seems that the shelf-break front and topographically-controlled flow patterns reported by Pietrafesa (1984) seem to be an effective barrier to shelf sediment transport on eastern Sable Island Bank. A belt of fine grained sediment, corresponding to the position of the hydraulic fence, has been observed skirting the bank (Amos, 1985). If Sable Island is analogous to Eastern Shoal: Why is it there? Why is it not submerged as is Eastern Shoal? Was Sable Island created by a catastrophic storm which provided a nucleus for self generation or is it related to ongoing processes in a way, as yet, undetected? As with most large-scale sedimentary features, the period over which they form is too long to adequately monitor the relevant dynamics.

Few direct measurements of bottom sediment mobility have been made on Canadian continental shelves. Those which have are restricted to: (1) time-lapse photography of the seabed near the Venture and Cohasset well sites on Sable Island Bank and at the Hesper well site on Banquereau (for well locations see Fig. 1, in pocket); (2) two radio-isotope sand tracer experiments on Sable Island Bank (Seaconsult Marine Research Ltd., 1986); and (3) a dispersion study using a passive tracer at the Hibernia well site on the Grand Banks. The data from these observations suggest that sediment motion appears restricted to that caused by the migration of wave or current formed ripples.

We know little about the stability of fine grained sediments on the flanks of the banks of the Scotian Shelf; acoustic evidence exists which shows slumping in The Gully and in areas north of Banquereau. The slumps in the Gully are associated with seabed scouring which has produced megaflutes at the base of the bank edges. The winnowed sand derived from scouring has been moulded into active 2-D megaripples which show an offshore transport to the shelf edge. This unique association of bedforms illustrates a "cascading effect" whereby each event is the consequence of a seemingly unrelated, earlier event.

Pockmarks, produced by gas or water venting from the seabed, are abundant in the cohesive sediments of the Scotian Shelf (Josenhans et al., 1978), the Laurentian Channel (Fader et al., 1982), and on the upper slope adjacent to the shelf (Mosher, 1987). They are, however, absent from sandy sediments, where the potential for preservation is lower because the sediment is mobile.

Carbonate-rich sediments have been reported from northern parts of the temperate shelves. By analogy Muller and Milliman (1973) found that an area on the southwestern Grand Banks was enriched in biogenic calcium carbonate; they suggested that the observed barnacles dated from the last low stand of sea level and the Holocene transgression, and suggested that the molluscs, echinoids and foraminifers were modern. Fader and King (1981) described dense shell beds on the Grand Banks. In the Strait of Belle Isle extensive sedimentary bedforms of shell hash have been observed from a submersible (Josenhans and Barrie, pers. comm., 1986).

"Specks", first identified by Evans-Hamilton Inc. (1977), have been recognized on side scan sonograms. These features range in diameter up to 20 m. They are densely packed shell communities (Fig. 11.30) which tend to be circular to oval in shape, and are often aligned in rows on the seabed. The origin and significance of these features are not known, though it is believed they may be associated with the escape of natural gas and with the distribution of the warmer, nutrient-rich slope water mass which occasionally spills onto the shelf providing a source of food to quahogs which comprise the shelf-edge specks.

Although the modern sedimentary character of temperate shelves is well known, the frequency or intensity of the processes which mould the sediments of temperate shelves cannot yet be properly quantified. Unlike in rivers, transport of sediment on shelves is dominated by diffusive processes produced by random fluctuations of high-intensity transient events such as breaking internal waves, infragravity waves or surface-gravity wave action (Boczar-Karakiewicz and Bona, 1986). The sedimentary signature of temperate shelves is controlled by relatively rare events of high intensity, and these are, by their very nature, difficult to monitor.

Northern shelves

J.V. Barrie and H.W. Josenhans

Northern shelves are those of the Arctic Island channels, Baffin Island, Labrador and northeast Newfoundland. The characteristics of surface sediments in these regions are generally dominated by the effects of ice. The effects of wind and waves, however, are significant on some shelves, such as those off Baffin Island and Labrador. In areas of the Arctic — such as Hudson Strait, Davis Strait, Lancaster Sound, Barrow Strait and Peel Sound — tidal influences are also important.

The Labrador and Baffin shelves show no effects of the Holocene transgression except in the nearshore zones, and thus little is known about sea level history from observations in these regions. Surficial sediments are largely relict (Grant, 1971, 1972; Slatt and Lew, 1973; Pelletier,

1979; MacLean, 1982; Josenhans, 1983; Gilbert and Barrie, in press).

Postglacial sediments on the shallow banks of the Labrador Shelf are very thin. The perimeters of these banks below a water depth of 160 m are lined with reworked sands and gravels (Fig. 11.1C), derived presumably from the bank tops (Nordco Ltd., 1982; Gilbert and Barrie, in press) where some modern reworked lag deposits are found (Josenhans and Zevenhuizen, 1984). These deposits of the bank tops, which are termed the Sioraq Sand (Josenhans et al., 1986), are equivalent to the Scotian Shelf Sambro Sand. Thicker deposits of unstratified and stratified silts and clays, constituting the Makkaq Clay (Josenhans et al., 1986), and comparable to the LaHave Clay of the Scotian Shelf, occur in the deeper marginal troughs and saddles (Vilks, 1980; Nordco Ltd., 1982; Josenhans, 1983).

The Baffin shelves are blanketed with relict sandy gravel overlying a smooth erosional surface (Kranck, 1966; Grant, 1971; Baker and Friedman, 1973; Praeg et al., 1986). The details of the origin and distribution of sediments are complex (Fig. 11.1D), and are related to local processes (Perry, 1961; Pelletier, 1966 1979; Lewis et al., 1977; MacLean, 1982).

Many workers have attributed sediment transport by sea ice and icebergs as significant in Baffin Bay, the Labrador Sea and as far south as the Scotian Shelf (Grant, 1965; Baker and Friedman, 1973; McMillan, 1973; Johnson et al., 1975; Piper, 1976; Carter, 1979; Alam and Piper, 1981; Josenhans and Barrie, 1982; Gilbert and Barrie, in press). During the late Pleistocene to early Holocene, ice rafting was responsible for significant mixing of indigenous relict sediment with ice-rafted material (e.g. Baker and Friedman, 1973; Carter, 1979). Gilbert and Barrie (in press) found abundant carbonates on Saglek Bank, including crinoidal calcarenites, that came from Paleozoic rocks of the Arctic Islands and Greenland. By contrast, only one third the amount of carbonate is found farther south on Makkovik Bank on the central Labrador Shelf, reflecting the southerly decrease in the abundance of large icebergs. The sedimentation due to ice rafting is uncertain on account of the year-to-year variability in the flux of ice and icebergs during recent times, and the largely unknown rate of iceberg melting. Furthermore, the volumes of sediment incorporated in or on sea ice and icebergs are generally unknown. McMillan (1973) crudely estimated that only 0.15 m of sediment has accumulated on the Labrador Shelf through ice rafting in the last 15 000 years. Josenhans and Barrie (1982) showed evidence that ice rafting of sediment, although the amounts transported are minor, is a significant factor in the present day surficial sediment budget on the Labrador Shelf. Ice-rafted debris occurs as mound-like features on the seafloor where large accumulations of bouldery sediment dropped from grounded icebergs.

Contemporary iceberg scouring is the principal agent of reworking of surficial sediments on the northern shelves where water depths are less than 230 m (Lewis and Barrie, 1980; Josenhans and Zevenhuizen, 1984). Icebergs calve principally from the glaciers of western Greenland and are carried south with the Baffin and Labrador currents. Grounded icebergs load and consolidate the sediments of the banks. Sea ice seasonally covers much of the area north of the Grand Banks and moves in the direction of currents

Figure 11.30. Photographs taken from PISCES IV over shoreface-connected ridges southwest of Sable Island. The water depth was approximately 40 m. (A) and (B) the shelly coarse sediments in the bed form trough, (C) a circular sand patch referred to as 'specks', and (D) the leading (eastern) edge of an active shoreface-connected ridge. Note the sharp junction between the sands of the lee face and the shelly sand of the trough (A-GSC 204702-K; B-GSC 204702-L; C-GSC 204702-I; D-GSC 204702-J).

and prevailing winds; the coverage by sea ice is on average 100% in the northern areas and 60% on the southern Labrador Shelf (Markham, 1980).

The effect of sea ice on bottom sediments is only slight. Sea ice attenuates surface waves during winter storms and so wave-induced bottom currents which, if generated, would ripple and transport sand, are reduced. Grounded sea ice originating near shore accounts for some ice rafting of sediment — indeed "dirty ice" has been observed in the Arctic Island channels.

The maximum draft of the keels of modern icebergs — their grounding depths — is about 220 m (Hotzel and Miller, 1983). The keels of icebergs which ground on the shallower portions of the shelf excavate linear to curvilinear troughs and pits in the seabed. Embankments of displaced sediment are ploughed to either side of the scour; it is not known if the mechanism of ploughing is shear fail-

ure and lateral displacement, or compression and extrusion of material beneath the keel. Any stratification of sediment is destroyed in most areas by this process and the resulting iceberg 'turbate' (as defined by Vorren et al., 1983) mantles the area to the depth beneath the seabed of the deepest scours, approximately 6 m. Recent or relict iceberg scour marks occur over all the eastern Canadian continental shelves from the Arctic Islands (Lewis et al., 1977; McLaren, 1982) to the Scotian Shelf, down to water depths of 700 m (Parsons, pers. comm., 1985). On the Labrador Shelf complete reworking of all bank tops shallower than 150 m has occurred within the last 10 000 years (Josenhans and Zevenhuizen, 1984). Reworking of sediment on the inner shelf of Baffin Island has been identified in water depths comparable to those of the Labrador Shelf (MacLean, 1984). Although many scour marks are modern, many can only be relict, dating from the Late Wisconsinan

657

(Belderson et al., 1973; King, 1976; Barrie, 1980; Luternauer and Murray, 1983; Lien, 1983; Todd, 1984).

Recent scour marks in some areas are rapidly degraded by bottom currents. The rate of degradation is controlled largely by the strength of wave-induced orbital currents near the seabed (Barrie, 1983), and by the cohesiveness and other physical properties of the sediments into which the scour is cut. In water depths less than 160 m, winnowing of the scour rims is the dominant process of degradation.

Bottom photographs reveal wave-induced ripples over the shallower portions of Nain and Makkovik banks. The presence of sharp-crested megaripples and sand ribbons indicate periods of active, undirectional sediment transport. Sonograms show megaripples with wavelengths of 50 m at the seaward edge of Hamilton Bank (Fillon, 1976). Their crests are roughly parallel to the long axis of the bank and indicate either a downslope or upslope migration. Submersible observations on the outer part of Hamilton Bank, revealed what appeared to be megaripples oriented downslope.

On the Labrador Shelf, the combination of wave-induced motion and flow of the Labrador Current has resulted in a well-sorted gravel which overlies a gravelly, silty clay substrate on some of the shallow banks (Josenhans and Barrie, 1982). It appears that iceberg scouring exhumes material from the subsurface which is subsequently winnowed, leaving behind well-sorted gravel.

Reworking of sediment on the inner part of the Baffin shelves has been identified in depths comparable to those of the Labrador Shelf (MacLean, 1984). Little effort has been made to quantify modern processes on the Baffin and Arctic Islands shelves. Current ripples and megaripples have been seen at the Hekja well site in Davis Strait (250-375 m water depth). These were formed by strong tidal currents which have peak velocities of 0.3 m/s (Barrie, 1983).

In summary, the surficial character of the northern shelves is dominated by the effects of iceberg grounding and ice scour. The effects of hydraulic processes can be seen, but are insignificant by comparison. Future work should address the relationship between bulk sediment properties and iceberg scouring, and the potential for preservation of the scour features.

THE CONTINENTAL SLOPE, RISE AND DEEP SEA

The classification of deep sea environments

P.R. Hill, D.E. Buckley and D.J.W. Piper

The terrigenous depositional environments of the continental margin were classified by Heezen and Menard (1963) on the basis of gradient into continental slope, rise and abyssal plains. On many continental margins the continental slope is cut by submarine canyons, cutting older rocks, and channels, which are in part depositional features. Deep-sea fans are developed on the continental rise and extend onto the abyssal plains. Pelagic sediments of the ocean basins accumulate on abyssal hills, seamounts, and aseismic ridges whose morphology is principally determined by that of the underlying oceanic crust.

The morphology of the continental slope can be considered on a variety of scales from that of the whole margin — thousands of kilometres — to the very local level of small

slides and biogenic mounds — a few metres (Hill et al., 1983). Most sections across the continental margin of eastern Canada show a well-defined shelf break (Vanney and Stanley, 1983), and a concave slope profile with the greatest gradients (up to 6°) on the upper slope. Shelf-break depths are variable, ranging from approximately 200 m on the Scotian margin to 500 m off Labrador, 600 m off Baffin Island and 1000 m off Flemish Cap (Fig. 11.31).

This large scale morphology reflects the underlying geology, Mesozoic-Cenozoic sedimentation and in particular the processes of the late Quaternary slope progradation and erosion (discussed in Chapter 10). The "basement" geology is of minor influence on most eastern margins of Canada, on account of the substantial Mesozoic and Cenozoic sedimentary wedge (Grant, 1975; Jansa and Wade, 1975). Exceptions to this generality, however, are Davis Strait and the margin east of Newfoundland where faulted and foundered basement has extended the margin and reduced slope angles significantly.

Recent side scan surveys of the slope off eastern Canada have indicated that the present-day morphology is closely related to Pleistocene processes. The most detailed work has been completed on the Scotian Slope (Piper et al., 1984; Piper and Sparkes, 1987), while more recent surveys have been carried out on the Labrador Slope (H. Josenhans, pers. comm., 1985). These areas show a complex system of canyons, smaller submarine valleys (gullies) and slides. Farre et al. (1983) have suggested that a complete continuum occurs between slides and slope gullies and shelf-breaching canyons. Valleys develop from continued headward erosion of slide scars and eventually breach the shelf break, at which point they begin to trap sediment transported by shelf processes. Shelf-breaching canyons are relatively rare on the eastern Canadian margin, except on the northeastern Scotian Slope and around the Grand Banks.

Large-scale gullying and sliding are most commonly seen on slopes which are adjacent to the deeper saddle areas of the outer shelves (e.g. "LaHave Channel", Hill, 1983; Laurentian Fan Slope, Piper and Normark, 1982a; Hopedale Saddle and Hudson Strait, H. Josenhans, pers. comm., 1985). Other slope areas which were not directly fed by ice tongues or rivers show either smooth morphologies, such as the slope northeast of Newfoundland (Carter and Schafer, 1983), or a moderate degree of sliding, which results in a mature "ridge and gully" morphology (e.g. Verril Canyon area, Piper et al., 1985a). It is in these latter areas that the model of canyon development proposed by Farre et al. (1983) seems most appropriate.

Most rise areas have not been as closely studied as the slopes. Rise morphology must be influenced by processes on the adjacent slope and, where major systems of canyons, gullies and slides are present, may be related. Channels continue onto the rise directly off the slope, whereas adjacent rise areas are largely smooth and undisturbed.

Discrete submarine fan morphologies have not been observed on the rises of eastern Canada, except on the Laurentian Fan. Several authors have suggested that the absence of fans is the result of sediment transport and reworking by the Western Boundary Undercurrent, but the importance of this process in the development of the continental rise remains controversial (Emery and Uchupi, 1972).

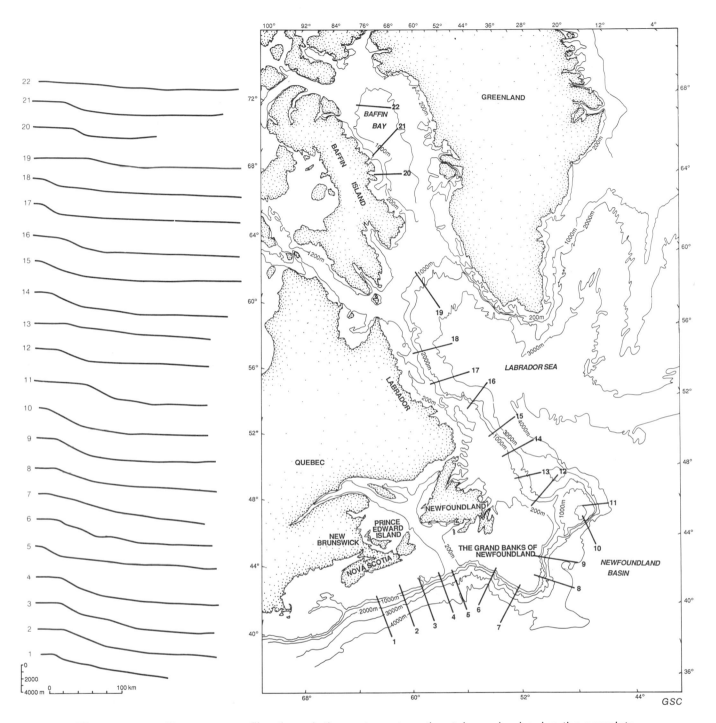

Figure 11.31. Twenty-two profiles through the east coast continental margin showing the complete range in morphologies from Baffin Basin to the Scotian Slope. The profiles run from the shelf-break to the base of the slope.

The Laurentian Fan is like many passive margin fans in having a prominent leveed channel system. The two main valleys on the Laurentian Fan have asymmetric levees up to 900 m high, which lead to a large sandy lobe on the northern Sohm Abyssal Plain. Sediment waves occur at the base of the Scotian Slope. Others have been observed in other rise areas of the eastern Canadian mar-gin, including northern Labrador (Chough et al., 1985) and Hamilton Spur (C.T. Schafer, pers. comm., 1986). These features are considered to be modern and subject to the influences of deep sea 'storms'.

The extensive lower Laurentian Fan has received little attention. The major fan valleys subdivide into shallower (50 m), low-relief channels, two of which can be traced to

659

the Sohm Abyssal Plain (Uchupi and Austin, 1979; Stow, 1981). Between channels, the lower fan has a smooth morphology which merges with the adjacent abyssal plain. Vilks et al. (1985) have noted the presence of turbidites on the abyssal plain as far south as the latitude of Bermuda.

The deeper water environments of slope, rise and canyons have not been studied in detail because of their remoteness. Classification of these vast areas is therefore difficult. Nevertheless, several of studies on the processes acting in these areas have been undertaken (Carter and Schafer, 1983; Hill, 1983, 1984a; Piper et al., 1985b; Schafer et al., 1985). These show that two classes of sediment transport events can be identified: those related to oceanic current processes, and those induced by gravity. These observations may provide the basis for a more rational classification of the deep sea environment than one based purely on morphology.

Deep oceanic basins make up about one third of the area of the North Atlantic (Heezen and Menard, 1963). The floor of the oceanic basin comprises smooth, (nearly) flat-lying plains, seamounts, abyssal hills and scattered aseismic ridges. The dynamics of modern depositional processes on the abyssal plains are surprisingly significant to the character of the local sediments.

Abyssal plains have generally been defined as the part of the ocean floor which extends out from the continental margin where the slope of the floor becomes less than 1:1000 (Heezen and Laughton, 1963). The depth of water over these plains in the North Atlantic ranges from 4500 m to 6000 m. One of the most thoroughly studied abyssal plains is the Sohm Abyssal Plain, located in the northwestern Atlantic adjacent to the continental margin of eastern Canada. This very large T-shaped plain with the stem extending to about 30°N, 57°W was one of the first deep sea areas to be intensively studied by deep-sea echo sounding techniques (Heezen et al., 1955). Results of studies by Ericson et al. (1952), Heezen and Ewing (1952), and Heezen et al. (1954) were that large turbidity currents and submarine slumps were the most significant processes delivering sediments to the abyssal plain.

The slope and rise
P.R. Hill

Slope and rise sediments are derived primarily from the adjacent shelves. Sediment is transported from the shelf to the upper slope during storms (Stanley et al., 1972). The upper slopes of eastern Canada are swept by the southward flowing Labrador Current which may carry storm-suspended sediments over large distances. These sediments are transported obliquely downslope by the effects of the contour-parallel currents and down-slope motion due to gravity (Hill and Bowen, 1983). Most of the sediment is transported in the benthic boundary layer, in so-called "near-bottom nepheloid layers" (McCave, 1972). These layers tend to be metres thick.

There are considerable problems associated with attempts to quantify sediment transport in deep environments. In particular the characterization of bottom boundary layer dynamics and the estimation of bed shear stresses are to be resolved. Both Carter and Schafer (1983) and Hill and Bowen (1983) have attempted to estimate near-bed shear velocities from current velocities, and to relate them to sediment size distribution. Both studies con-

cluded that bed-load transport occurs only during rare (5 per year) "storm" events. Recent data from the HEBBLE project on the Scotian Rise indicate that a single such "storm" can account for erosion and deposition of several centimetres of sediment (Hollister and McCave, 1984).

The products of oceanic bottom currents are broadly contained within the terms "hemipelagites" and "contourites" and are the subject of some controversy (Stow and Piper, 1984), partly because the terminology includes both compositional and genetic criteria. Some thin Holocene sand beds on the Scotian Rise have been defined as contourites (Stow and Lovell, 1979), but most Holocene sediments on slopes and rises off eastern Canada consist of bioturbated pelagic mud not related to gravitational processes (Carter and Schafer, 1983; Hill, 1984a, b; Hollister and McCave, 1984). These sediments can be distinguished from the gravity-driven turbidites on the basis of sediment texture, fabric and petrography (Stow, 1979). When dilute turbidity currents become unconfined, they rapidly decelerate and the suspended sediment may thereafter be transported by bottom currents and assume the appearance of a hemipelagic sediment (Hill, 1984b). Thus single deposits may show gradational characteristics laterally in response to changes in flow conditions.

The work of Hollister and McCave (1984) on the Scotian Rise indicates that the preservation potential of the products of even the strongest current events is very low, due to the low rate of accumulation and high rate of bioturbation. The best methods for quantifying processes in current-dominated parts of the northwest Atlantic appear to be multidisciplinary (sedimentological, paleontological and isotopic methods) (Hollister and McCave, 1984; Schafer et al., 1985).

The downslope movement of sediment under gravity involves a continuum of processes from slow creep with bedding deformation to translational sliding, debris flow and turbidity currents (Nardin et al., 1979). The Laurentian Fan provides evidence for the existence of a turbidity current triggered by the 1929 Grand Banks earthquake. The interpretation that cable breaks were caused by the flow of a turbidity current across the Laurentian Fan (Heezen and Ewing, 1952) was a major step in determining the validity of the process originally proposed by Kuenen and Migliorini (1950). Seamarc side scan surveys of the Laurentian Fan reveal gravel-size sediment waves on its Eastern Valley floor (Piper et al., 1985b), attesting to the high speed of the flow. Recent stratigraphic studies of continental slopes and rises off eastern Canada have shown that gravity-driven processes were much more important during the last glacial interval than in the Holocene.

The presence of canyons and smaller submarine valleys on the slopes and rises of eastern Canada (Hill, 1983; Piper et al., 1984; Piper and Sparkes, 1987; H. Josenhans, pers. comm., 1986), is further evidence of the importance of turbidity currents. The shelf-breaching canyons of the Scotian and Labrador margins are probably supplied with sand by active transport processes on the outer shelf banks. Other smaller valleys (Farre et al., 1983) may have originated from slides but may also be sites of past turbidity currents (Hill, 1983).

The deep sea

D.E. Buckley

Studies of the mechanisms of sediment dispersal from the continental shelves, mainly through deep sea fans, demonstrate that the distal abyssal plains mainly receive fine grained sediments, whereas sands are primarily deposited over the lower slope or rise on a lobate basin plain (Horn et al., 1971; Piper, 1978; Piper et al., 1984). Pilkey et al. (1980), by contrast, have suggested that terrestrial sandy sediments may extend up to 1500 km from the nearest continental margin.

In addition to the Laurentian Fan, the Northwest Atlantic Mid-Ocean Canyon has played an important role in the dynamics of abyssal sediments. This channel, 3800 km long and which extends from Hudson Strait through the Labrador Sea to the northern part of the Sohm Abyssal Plain, has features analogous to subaerial fluvial channels such as overbank or natural levee deposits (Chough and Hesse, 1976, 1980). The channel may have been the pathway of coarse grained terrigenous material which was transported along its entire length during the Pleistocene. This system appears now to be dormant due to the higher stand of sea level.

Vilks et al. (1985) pointed out that sediments deposited on the Sohm Abyssal Plain during periods of low deposition rates between major turbidite events, were probably derived from local seamounts and abyssal platforms. Stanley and Taylor (1981) and Stanley et al. (1981) identified volcanic detritus from local sources in the northwest Atlantic in sediments on the Sohm Abyssal Plain. Biscaye and Eittreim (1977) showed that large quantities of suspended sediments were transported in the nepheloid layer across the northern and central parts of the Sohm Abyssal Plain. The direction of transport of this nepheloid layer is often determined by the dominant deep ocean currents, such as the Western Boundary Undercurrent which is capable of carrying fine grained sediments from the Labrador Sea to the Bermuda Rise. Hollister and McCave (1984) suggested another mechanism for dispersing sediments over the deep ocean basins: "episodic deep sea current pulses". They described these events as oceanographic "storms" which possess sufficient current strength to resuspend large quantities of sediment from the ocean floor and redeposit the material hundreds to thousands of kilometres from the source area. These events could lead to significant erosion on some areas of the Bermuda Rise and would result in sequences of displaced sediments in the deep ocean basins. Such mechanisms may have been responsible for the deposition of sediments containing subtropical planktonic foraminifers during the Holocene on the southern Sohm Abyssal Plain (Vilks et al., 1985).

As new information is gained about the nature of deep sea sediments and the processes that have been responsible for their deposition, new facies models will have to be developed. Indeed, facies models which have been used to interpret ancient deep sea sediments will have to be modified if geologists are to interpret correctly these depositional environments.

SUMMARY

C.L. Amos

Research in modern marine clastic sedimentology off eastern Canada focusses principally on two aspects: the study of sedimentary environments and the associated deposits, and the study of the dynamics of sedimentation. The relationship is sought between a particular process, or suite of processes, and sediment response. Although sediment attributes such as internal structure can be uniquely related to a specific process, the process itself may not be diagnostic of the environment in which the deposit formed. Furthermore, many other sediment properties such as grain size and sorting may be generated under a variety of circumstances, making the interpretation of a single facies ambiguous. Consequently, one has to resort to defining a 'probable stratigraphic sequence', which would be formed by the lateral migration of presently occurring, adjacent sub-environments. To do so, the evolutionary processes are speeded up and projected linearly into the future. But dominating events on the east coast (such as storms or ice-related processes) are inherently random. So there will never be a perfect match between the detailed stratigraphy of modern and ancient deposits. If this is true there must be a limit to the value of studies of recent sediments in application to geological interpretation. How severe is the limitation and has it been reached yet?

It is possible that the point of diminishing returns has been reached in respect to classic stratigraphy and paleogeographic reconstructions based on facies descriptions, but is on a new threshold in the quantification of geological events. This is due to major advances in Quaternary chronology (see Chapter 10), which links geological and modern time scales. This link is becoming more refined, so studies of modern sediment responses will have greater significance to dynamic stratigraphy. The following is a summary of areas and topics where significant advances are yet to be made in the study and application of modern sedimentary processes.

The nature and genesis of shallow marine sands has been reviewed by Walker (1984), who showed that many of the ideas concerning modern sediments can be based on observations made using the rock record. A third aspect must be included — the study of Quaternary stratigraphy — to bridge the gap between modern and ancient sediments. The rock record leaves a product of deposition (the rocks), but little is known of the time-frame of deposition; modern sediments, however, provide evidence for the time-frame and process, but the sequence to be preserved must be inferred; whereas with the Quaternary, the time-frame, the process and the result can be determined. The sedimentologist of the future will be trained in all three aspects.

Some areas worthy of research in modern shelf sedimentology are: the role of infrequent, intense storms in transporting sand seaward across the shelf; the mechanisms which generate hummocky cross-stratification; the likelihood of preservation of nearshore barrier islands, once submerged; and the role of the Holocene marine transgression on shelf sediment facies. The present lack of information is due, in part, to the lack of measurements of shelf sediment transport. Studies by Stubblefield et al. (1984) and Swift et al. (1984) have defined the lithostratigraphy of shelf sequences from the New Jersey continental shelf. These sequences are composed in large part of large-scale bedforms. There is, however, considerable disagreement on the genesis of the ridges and the sedimentary structures which they produce. Are such sand bodies "modern" or "relict" and what are the processes leading to the formation and preservation of such a sequence?

It is difficult to compare observations in the modern marine setting with results of laboratory studies using flumes, for example. There is also a mismatch between the way sediments are described offshore and on land. In the offshore acoustic techniques generally are used to depict the character of the sediments. The most detailed resolution of seismic techniques, however, is only about 10 cm, and acoustic properties are not uniquely correlatable with sediment property. Consequently key elements such as horizontal facies changes and the details of sedimentary structures are often difficult to measure. It is only in sub-environments where large box samples can be recovered that this mismatch does not occur. Unfortunately, sandy substrates cannot be sampled without disturbance when using existing techniques.

The seabed is in a continual state of change due to the ever changing hydraulic conditions. These changes are particularly great on shelves dominated by storms, such as on the margins of eastern Canada. Consequently, bottom stress and the resulting sediment dispersal are both inherently unpredictable and can only be successfully evaluated either deterministically (Martec Limited, unpublished report, 1982) or probabilistically (Gumbel, 1954; Pugh and Vassie, 1980). In tidally dominated environments such as the Bay of Fundy this problem is less severe because tidally modulated bottom shear stresses are continuous and reproduceable. Even within these environments, however, the influences of waves or storm-driven currents superimposed upon the effects of tides can significantly increase sediment mobility (Owen and Thorn, 1978) and change the nature of the bottom sediments. This is also true of the deep sea where intense seabed reworking occurs during short periods. Thus, in almost all environments, the bottom sediments are subject to a number of processes which limit the significance of such terms as "storm" or "tidal" deposits. Initial observations on the Scotian Shelf show a lack of correlation between wind and near-bed flow patterns, but a synthesis of available data on storm-driven currents has yet to be made. Numeric simulation of storm-driven flows does not appear to be a fruitful approach in the prediction of sediment transport, particularly in regions of complex bathymetry. So can direct measures of seabed stability be used?

Concurrent observations of sediment discharge, seabed processes and bed form generation in the marine environment are limited to the nearshore (Bowen, 1980a, b). Only one set of measurements has been made on the eastern Canadian continental shelf (SeaConsult Marine Research Ltd., 1986). Other attempts by Gadd et al. (1978), Heathershaw (1981), Lees and Heathershaw (1981) and Hollister and McCave (1984) have been inconclusive, so that the degree of sediment mobility and the degree of modification of sediments by modern processes has to be inferred from long term geological processes or from bed forms.

McDowell and O'Connor (1977) described numeric methods that may be appropriate to tidal estuaries such as the Bay of Fundy where good results were obtained. On continental shelves, this has not been possible due to an inadequate data base and the inevitable presence of three or four open boundaries. It is in the definition of the open boundaries and in the specification of time sequences that most of the assumptions and simplifications are made, and so confidence limits are very wide (Huntley, 1982). Other errors result from the inability to define adequately the nature and distribution of the seabed sediments. The integration of particle shape, size and density into a 'standard fall velocity', in part, overcomes this problem. But the most widely used sediment transport algorithms use a single modal size and density to express the hydraulic character of the natural sediment (Bagnold, 1963; Yalin, 1963; Engelund and Hansen, 1967). This becomes a problem when the sediment size distributions, such as those in the Minas Basin, are bi- or tri-modal (Long, 1979), and where sediment texture changes over tens of metres such as on the banks of the Scotian and Labrador shelves.

The Atlantic coastline of eastern Canada has suffered major glaciations which have removed much of the sediment overburden. The nearshore surficial sequence which does exist has been studied in detail by Boyd et al. (1987) and by Forbes and Taylor (1987). The stratigraphy delineated bears many similarities to that of non-glaciated regions, despite clear differences in sediment source and regional setting. Studies in the future are needed to examine the detailed stratigraphy of the nearshore zone, its relationship to that of the shoreline and continental shelf, and the diagnostic features which indicate prior glacial activity.

Eastern Canada is rich in ice-dominated environments, such as those of the Labrador Shelf (Barrie and Josenhans, this chapter) and the fiords of Baffin Island (Syvitski, this chapter). The effects of sea ice on the sediments of the Arctic Islands channels are poorly known, as are the influences of icebergs on the facies of shelf sediment.

The processes controlling deep sea sedimentation appear to be infrequent and unpredictable. Studies of Hollister and McCave (1984) off the Scotian Rise reveal a highly active environment subject to deep sea storms which winnow and ripple the seabed. Future work must deal with the problems of monitoring this environment for periods long enough to be representative of the developing facies. Conversely, simulation models of the long term active processes may be a valuable method for defining the deep sea processes of geological significance.

REFERENCES

Aitken, A.E.
1982: Biophysical processes on the intertidal flats of Panquirtung Fiord, Baffin Island, Northwest Territories; M.Sc. thesis, Queen's University, Kingston, Ontario, 229 p.

Alam, M. and Piper, D.J.W.
1981: Detrital mineralogy and petrology of deep water continental margin sediments off Newfoundland; Canadian Journal of Earth Sciences, v. 18, p. 1336-1345.

Allen, J.R.L.
1970: Physical Processes of Sedimentation; George Allen and Unwin, London, 248 p.
1982: Longitudinal bedforms and secondary flows: in Sedimentary Structures: Their Character and Physical Basis, Volume 2, ed. J.R.L. Allen; Elsevier, New York, 2, p. 1-52.

Allen, J.R.L. and Banks, N.L.
1972: An interpretation and analysis of recumbent-folded deformed crossbedding; Sedimentology, v. 19, p. 257-284.

Amos, C.L.
1978: The post glacial evolution of the Minas Basin, Nova Scotia. A sedimentological interpretation; Journal of Sedimentary Petrology, v. 48, p. 965-982.
1983: CSS Dawson cruise report 83-026, Sable Island Bank and Banquereau; Internal Report, Bedford Institute of Oceanography, Dartmouth, Nova Scotia, 7 p.
1984: CSS DAWSON cruise report 84-005, Sable Island Bank and Banquereau; Internal Report, Bedford Institute of Oceanography, Dartmouth, Nova Scotia, 11 p.

1985: PANDORA II cruise report (20-26 May, 1985) — Sable: Internal Report, Bedford Institute of Oceanography, Dartmouth, Nova Scotia, 7 p.

1989: Quaternary sediments and bedforms of the Scotian Shelf observed from the submersible Pisces IV; in Submersible Observations off the East Coast of Canada, D.J.W. Piper (ed.); Geological Survey of Canada, Paper 88-20, p. 9-26.

Amos, C.L. and Asprey, K.W.

1979: Geophysical and sedimentary studies in the Chignecto Bay system, Bay of Fundy; a progress report; in Current Research, Part B, Geological Survey of Canada, Paper 79-1B, p. 245-252.

1981: An interpretation of oceanographic and sediment data from Upper Bay of Fundy; Report Series/B1-R-81-15/September 1981, Bedford Institute of Oceanography, Dartmouth, Nova Scotia, 143 p.

1982: Report on CSS Dawson cruise 82-040, Sable Island Bank; Internal Report, Bedford Institute of Oceanography, Dartmouth, Nova Scotia, 112 p.

Amos, C.L. and King, E.L.

1984: Bedforms of the Canadian eastern seaboard; a comparison with global occurrences; Marine Geology, v. 57, p. 167-208.

Amos, C.L. and Knoll, R.

1987: The Quaternary sediments of Banquereau, Scotian Shelf; American Association of Petroleum Geologists, Bulletin, v. 99, p. 244-260.

Amos, C.L. and Long, B.F.N.

1980: The sedimentary character of the Minas Basin, Bay of Fundy; in The Coastline of Canada; Littoral Processes and Shore Morphology, ed. S.B. McCann; Geological Survey of Canada, Paper 80-10, p. 123-152.

Amos, C.L. and Mosher, D.C.

1985: Erosion and deposition of fine-grained sediments from the Bay of Fundy; Sedimentology, v. 32, p. 815-832.

Amos, C.L. and Zaitlin, B.A.

1985: The effect of changes in tidal range on a sublittoral macrotidal sequence, Bay of Fundy; Geo-Marine Letters, v. 4, p. 161-169.

Amos, C.L., Bowen, A.J., Huntley,D.A., and Lewis, C.F.M.

1988: Ripple generation under the combined influences of waves and currents on the Canadian Continental Shelf; Continental Shelf Research, v.8, p. 1129-1153.

Armon, J.W.

1975: The dynamics of a barrier island chain, Prince Edward Island, Canada; Ph.D. thesis, McMaster University, Hamilton, Ontario, 546 p.

1979: Landward sediment transfers in a transgressive barrier island system, Canada; in Barrier Islands, ed. S.P. Leatherman; Academic Press, New York, p. 65-79.

1980: Changeability in small flood tidal deltas and its effects, Malpeque barrier system, Prince Edward Island; in The Coastline of Canada, Littoral Processes and Shore Morphology, ed. S.B. McCann; Geological Survey of Canada, Paper 80-10, p. 41-50.

Armon, J.W. and McCann, S.B.

1977: Longshore sediment transport and a sediment budget for the Malpeque barrier system, southern Gulf of St. Lawrence; Canadian Journal of Earth Sciences, v. 14, p. 2429-2439.

1979: Morphology and landward sediment transfer in a transgressive barrier island system, southern Gulf of St. Lawrence, Canada; Marine Geology, v. 31, p. 333-344.

Bagnold, R.A.

1962: Auto suspension of transported sediment, turbidity currents; Proceedings of the Royal Society of London, Series A, v. 265, p. 315-319.

1963: Mechanics of marine sedimentation; in The Sea, ed. M.N. Hill; Wiley-Interscience, New York, p. 507-553.

1966: An approach to the sediment transport problem from general physics; United States Geological Survey, Professional Paper 422-I, 37 p.

Baker, S.R. and Friedman, G.M.

1973: Sedimentation in an Arctic marine environment; Baffin Bay between Greenland and the Canadian Arctic Archipelago; Geological Survey of Canada, Paper 71-23, p. 471-498.

Barnes, N.E. and Piper, D.J.W.

1978: Late Quaternary geological history of Mahone Bay, Nova Scotia; Canadian Journal of Earth Sciences, v. 15, p. 586-593.

Barrie, C.Q. and Piper, D.J.W.

1982: Late Quaternary marine geology of Makhovik Bay, Labrador; Geological Survey of Canada, Paper 81-17, 37 p.

Barrie, J.V.

1980: Iceberg/seabed interaction, northern Labrador Sea; Annals of Glaciology, v. 1, p. 71-76.

1983: Sedimentary processes and the preservation of iceberg scours on the eastern Canadian continental shelf; in Proclamations of the of the 7th International Conference on Port and Ocean Engineering under Arctic Conditions, Volume 4 (POAC 1983), Helsinki, Finland, v. 4, p. 635-653.

Barrie, J.V., Lewis, C.F.M., Fader, G.B., and King, L.H.

1984: Seabed processes on the northeastern Grand Banks of Newfoundland; modern reworking of relict sediments; Marine Geology, v. 57, p. 209-227.

Barrie, W.D. and Associates

1985: Coastal geomorphology and processes, northwestern Bathurst Island group, N.W.T. (1982); Geological Survey of Canada, Open File 1146, 106 p.

Barry, R.G., Crane, R.G., Koche, C.W., Locke, W.W., and Miller, G.M.

1977: The coastal environment of southern Baffin Island and northern Labrador-Ungava; Institute of Arctic and Alpine Research, University of Colorado, Boulder, Colorado, 166 p.

Basham, P.W. and Adams, J.

1982: Earthquakes hazards to offshore development on the eastern Canadian continental shelves; in Proceedings of the Second Canadian Conference on Marine Geotechnical Engineering, June 1982, Halifax, Nova Scotia.

1983: Earthquakes on continental margin of eastern Canada – Need future large events be confined to the location of large historical events; United States Geological Survey, Open File Report 83-843, p. 456-467.

Belderson, R.H., Kenyon, N.H., and Wilson, J.B.

1973: Iceberg plough marks in the Northeast Atlantic; Palaeogeography, Palaeoclimatology, Palaeoecology, v. 13, p. 215-224.

Bellefontaine, L., Pritchard, J., and Reiniger, B.

1982: Atlas of Physical Oceanographic Data for the Gulf Stream System — 1972; Canadian Technical Report of Hydrography and Ocean Sciences, No. 15, Atlantic Oceanographic Laboratory, Ocean Science and Surveys, Atlantic Department of Fisheries and Oceans, November 1982, 114 p.

Berthois, L.

1969: Contribution à l'étude sédimentologique du Kangerdlugssuaq, côte ouest du Groenland; Meddelelser om Grønland, v. 187, n. 1, 118 p.

Bird, J.B.

1967: The Physiography of Arctic Canada; Johns Hopkins Press, Baltimore, 336 p.

Biscaye, D.E. and Eittreim, S.E.

1977: Suspended particulate loads and transports in the nepheloid layer on the abyssal Atlantic Ocean; Marine Geology, v. 23, p. 155-172.

Blake, W. Jr.

1975: Radiocarbon age determinations and postglacial emergence at Cape Storm, Southern Ellesmere Island, Arctic Canada; Geografiska Annaler, v. 57, 71 p.

1977: Iceberg concentrations as an indicator of submarine moraines, eastern Queen Elizabeth Islands, District of Franklin: in Current Research, Part B, Geological Survey of Canada, Paper 77-B, p. 281-286.

Blatt, H., Middleton, G., and Murray, R.

1980: Origin of Sedimentary Rocks; Prentice-Hall, Englewood Cliffs, New Jersey, 782 p.

Boczar-Karakiewicz, B. and Bona, J.L.

1986: Wave dominated shelves: A model of sand-ridge formation by progressive, infragravity waves; in Shelf Sands and Sandstones, ed. R.J. Knight and J.R. McLean; Canadian Society of Petroleum Geologists, Memoir 11, p. 160-179.

Boczar-Karakiewicz, B., Paplinska, B., and Winjecki, J.

1981: Formation of sand bars by surface waves in shallow water: Laboratory experiments; Rozprawy Hydrotechniczne, v. 41, p. 111-125.

Boothroyd, J.C. and Hubbard, D.K.

1975: Genesis of bedforms in mesotidal estuaries; in Estuarine Research, Volume 2, Geology and Engineering, ed. L.E. Cronin; Academic Press, New York, p. 217-234.

Bowden, K.F.

1967: Circulation and diffusion; in Estuaries, ed. S.H. Lauff; American Association for the Advancement of Science, v. 83, p. 15-36.

Bowen, A.J.

1980a: Simple models of nearshore sedimentation: beach profiles and longshore bars; in The Coastline of Canada, ed. S.B. McCann; Geological Survey of Canada, Paper 80-10, p. 1-11.

1980b: Basic nearshore processes: Short course lecture notes, n. 4, National Research Council, Ottawa, n. 4, 45 p.

Bowen, A.J. and Huntley, D.A.

1984: Waves, long waves and nearshore morphology; Marine Geology, v. 60, p. 1-13.

Bowen, A.J. and Inman, D.L.
1971: Edge waves and crescentic bars; Journal Geophysical Research, v. 76, p. 8662-8671.

Bowen, A.J., Edmond, D.P., Piper, D.J.W., and Welsh, D.A.
1975: The maintenance of beaches; Technical Report, Institute of Environmental Studies, Dalhousie University, Halifax, Nova Scotia, 582 p.

Bowen, A.J., Normark, W.R., and D.J.W. Piper
1984: Modelling of turbidity currents on Navy submarine fan, California continental borderland; Sedimentology, v. 31, p. 169-185.

Boyd, R., Bowen, A.J., and Hall, R.K.
1987: An evolutionary model for transgressive sedimentation on the Eastern Shore of Nova Scotia, Chapter 4; in Glaciated Coasts, ed. D. Fitzgerald and P.S. Rosen; Academic Press, Toronto, p. 88-114.

Boyd, R., Hall, R.K., and Bowen, A.J.
1982: Transgressive coastal sedimental along the Eastern Shore, Nova Scotia; in Proceedings of the Atlantic Coastal Erosion and Sedimentation Workshop, Halifax, Nova Scotia, p. 15-22.

Boyer, D., Theakston, J., and Tse, S.
1975: Study of sand dunes at Oromocto Island on Saint John River; University of New Brunswick, Fredericton, Department of Civil Engineering, Internal Report CE 6971, 13 p.

Bryant, E.A. and McCann, S.B.
1973: Long and short term changes in the barrier islands of Kouchibouguac Bay, southern Gulf of St. Lawrence; Canadian Journal of Earth Sciences, v. 10, p. 1582-1590.

Budgell, W.P.
1982: Spring-neap variation in the vertical stratification of Chesterfield Inlet, Hudson Bay; Le Naturaliste Canadien, v. 109, p. 709-718.

Butman, B.
1982: Currents and sediment movement on Georges Bank; in Georges Bank: Past, Present and Future of a Marine Environment, ed. G.C. McLeod and J.H. Prescott; Westview Press, Boulder, Colorado, p. 31-59.

Butman, B., Nobel, M., and Folger, D.W.
1979: Long term observations on bottom current and bottom sediment movement on the mid-Atlantic shelf; Journal of Geophysical Research, v. 84, p. 1187-1205.

Caldwell, D.R. and Chriss, T.M.
1979: The viscous sublayer at the seafloor; Science, v. 205, p. 1131-1132.

Canadian Hydrographic Service
1978: Sailing Directions, Arctic Canada; Canada Hydrographic Service, Department of Fisheries and the Environment, Ottawa, Canada. Volume II, 3rd Edition, 298 p.

Carter, L.
1979: Significance of unstained and stained gravel on the Newfoundland continental slope and rise; Journal of Sedimentary Petrology, v. 49, p. 1147-1158.

Carter, L. and Schafer, C.T.
1983: Interaction of the Western Boundary Undercurrent with the continental margin off Newfoundland; Sedimentology, v. 30, p. 751-768.

Carter, L., Schafer, C.T., and Rashid, M.A.
1979: Observations on depositional environments and benthos of the continental slope and rise, east of Newfoundland; Canadian Journal of Earth Sciences, v. 16, p. 831-846.

Carter, T.G., Liu, P.L.F., and Mei, C.C.
1973: Mass transport by waves and offshore sand bedforms; American Society of Civil Engineers, Journal of Waterways, Harbors, and Coastal Engineering Division, WW2, p. 165-184.

Castro, G.
1975: Liquefaction and cyclic mobility of saturated sands; Journal of the Geotechnical Engineering Division, Proceedings of American Society of Civil Engineers, GT6, Paper 11388, p. 511-569.

Castro, G. and Poulos, S.J.
1977: Factors affecting liquefaction and cyclic mobility; Journal of the Geotechnical Engineering Division, Proceedings of American Society of Civil Engineers, GT6, Paper 12994, p. 501-516.

Cataliotti-Valdina, D. and Long, B.F.N.
1983: Évolution du débit liquide et de la charge solide d'un estuaire subboréal, rivière St-Jean, Québec (Côte nord du golfe du St-Laurent); Canadian Journal of Earth Sciences, v. 20, p. 184-194.
1984: Évolution estuarienne d'une rivière régularisée en climat subboréal; la rivière aux Outardes (côte nord du golfe du St. Laurent, Québec); Canadian Journal of Earth Sciences, v. 21, p. 25-34.

Champagne, P.
1982: Morphologie littorale de la baie de Rupert; Le Naturaliste Canadien, v. 109, p. 375-384.

Chough, S.K. and Hesse, R.
1976: Submarine meandering thalweg and turbidity currents flowing for 4000 km in the northwest Atlantic mid-ocean channel, Labrador Sea; Geology, v. 4, p. 529-533.
1980: The northwest Atlantic mid-ocean channel of the Labrador Sea; III Head spill vs. body spill deposits from turbidity currents on natural levees; Journal of Sedimentary Petrology, v. 50, p. 227-234.

Chough, S.K., Mosher, D.C., and Srivastava, S.P.
1985: Ocean Drilling Program (O.D.P.) Site Survey (Hudson 84-030) in the Labrador Sea: 3.5 kHz Profiles; in Current Research, Part B, Geological Survey of Canada, Paper 85-1B, p. 33-41.

Christian, J.T., Taylor, P.K., Yen. J.K.C., and Erali, D.R.
1974: Large diameter underwater pipeline for nuclear power plant designed against soil liquefaction; 6th Annual Offshore Technology Conference, Houston, Texas, v. 2, p. 597-602.

Church, M.
1972: Baffin Island sandurs; a study of arctic fluvial processes; Geological Survey of Canada, Bulletin 216, 208 p.
1978: Paleohydrological reconstructions from a Holocene valley fill; in Fluvial Sedimentology, ed. A.D. Miall; Canadian Society of Petroleum Geologists, Memoir 5, p. 743-772.

Church, M. and Ryder, R.M.
1972: Paraglacial sedimentation; a consideration of fluvial processes conditioned by glaciation; Geological Survey of America, v. 83, p. 3059-3072.

Church, M., Stock, R.F., and Ryder, R.M.
1979: Contemporary sedimentary environments on Baffin Island, Northwest Territories, Canada; debris slope accumulation; Arctic and Alpine Research, v. 11, p. 371-402.

Clifton, H.E.
1976: Wave-formed sedimentary structures; a conceptual model; in Beach and Nearshore Sedimentation, ed. R.A. Davis and R.L. Ethington; Society of Economic Paleontologists and Mineralogists, p. 126-148.

Cole, p. and Miles, G.V.
1983: Two dimensional model of mud transport; Journal of Hydraulic Engineering, v. 109, p. 1-12.

Coleman, J.M., Suhayda, J.N., and Dawson, T.H.
1980: Determination of elastic shear modulus of marine sediments from wave theory and field measurements; in Proceedings of the 12th Annual Offshore Technical Conference, May 5-8, 1980, Houston, Texas, 3811, p. 171-178.

Cook, H.E., Field, M.E., and Gardner, J.V.
1982: Characteristics of sediments on modern and ancient continental slopes; in Sandstone Depositional Environments, ed. P.A. Scholle and D. Spearing; American Association of Petroleum Geologists, Memoir 31, p. 329-364.

Cooks, D.O., Bell, D.L., Willett, C.F., Wilkins, R.L., and Jackimovicz, J.
1976: Surficial sediments and sand and gravel deposits of inner Massachusetts Bay; Maritime Sediments, v. 12, p. 9-16.

Creutzberg, F. and Postma, H.
1979: An experimental approach to the distribution of mud in the southern North Sea; Netherlands Journal of Sea Research, v. 13, p. 99-116.

Curray, J.R.
1969: History of continental shelves; in The New Concepts of Continental Margin Sedimentation 1969, ed. D.J. Stanley; American Geological Institute, p. JC-VI-1 to JC-VI-18.

Dalrymple, R.W.
1977: Sediment dynamics of macrotidal sand bars, Bay of Fundy; Ph.D. thesis, McMaster University, Hamilton, Ontario, 635 p.
1979: Wave induced liquefaction: a modern example from the Bay of Fundy; Sedimentology, v. 26, p. 835-844.

Dalrymple, R.W., Knight, R.J., and Lambiase, J.J.
1978: Bedforms and their hydrodynamic stability relationships in a tidal environment, Bay of Fundy, Canada; Nature, v. 275, n. 5676, p. 100-104.

Damuth, J.E., Tucholke, B.E., and Coffin, M.F.
1979: Bottom processes on the Nova Scotia continental rise revealed by 3.5Khz echo character; EOS, v. 60, p. 855.

d'Anglejan, B.F.
1971a: Submarine sand dunes in the estuary of the St. Lawrence River; Geological Society of America, Abstracts with programs, v. 3, p. 536-537.
1971b: Submarine sand dunes in the St. Lawrence Estuary; Canadian Journal of Earth Sciences, v. 8, p. 1480-1486.
1980: Effects on seasonal changes on the sedimentary regime of a subarctic estuary, Rupert Bay (Canada); Sedimentary Geology, v. 26, p. 51-68.

1982: Patterns of recent sedimentation in the Eastmain Estuary, prior to river cut-off; Le Naturaliste Canadien, v. 209, p. 363-374.

d'Anglejan, B. and Ingram, R.G.
1976: Time-depth variations in tidal flux of suspended matter in the St. Lawrence estuary; Estuarine and Coastal Marine Science, v. 4, p. 1-16.
1984: Near bottom variations of turbidity in the St. Lawrence estuary; Estuarine Coastal and Shelf Science, v. 19, p. 655-672.

d'Anglejan, B.F. and Smith, E.C.
1973: Distribution transport and composition of suspended matter in the St. Lawrence Estuary; Canadian Journal of Earth Sciences, v. 10, p. 1380- 1396.

Davidson-Arnott, R.G.D. and Greenwood, B.
1974: Bedforms and structures associated with bar topography in the shallow-water wave environment, Kouchibouguac Bay, New Brunswick, Canada; Journal of Sedimentary Petrology, v. 44, p. 698-704.
1976: Facies relationships on a barred coast, Kouchibouguac Bay, New Brunswick, Canada; in Beach and Nearshore Sedimentation, ed. R.A. Davis and R.L. Ethington; Society Economic Paleontologists and Mineralogists, Special Publication no. 24, p. 149-168.

Davidson-Arnott, R.G.D. and Randall, D.C.
1984: Spatial and temporal variations in spectra of storm waves across a barred nearshore; Marine Geology, v. 60, p. 15-30.

Davies, A.G.
1983: Wave interactions with rippled sand beds; in Physical Oceanography of Coastal and Shelf Seas, ed. B. Johns; Elsevier, Amsterdam, p. 1-66.

Davies, J.L. (ed.)
1980: Geographical Variation in Coastal Development (2nd Edition); Longman, New York, 212 p.

Davis, R.A. Jr., Fox W.T., Hayes, M.O., and Boothroyd, J.C.
1972: Comparison of ridge and runnel systems in tidal and non-tidal environments; Journal of Sedimentary Petrology, v. 42, p. 412-421.

Dawson, T.H., Suhayda, J.N., and Coleman, J.M.
1981: Correlation of field measurements with elastic theory of sea-floor response to surface waves; 13th Annual Offshore Technical Conference, Paper 3973, p. 201-210.

DeIure, A.M.
1983: The effect of storms on sediment in Halifax harbour, Nova Scotia; M.Sc. Thesis, Dalhousie University, Halifax, Nova Scotia.

Dionne, J.C.
1980: An outline of the eastern James Bay coastal environments; in The Coastline of Canada, ed. S.B. McCann; Geological Survey of Canada, Paper 80-10, p. 311-338.
1972: Caractéristiques des schorres des régions froides, en particulier de l'estuaire du Saint-Laurent; in International Geography 1972 — La Géographie Internationale 1972, 22nd Internation Geographical Congress, 22ᵉ Congrès Internationale Géographie, Papers, v. 2, p. 1027.

Dolan, R., Hayden, B., Hornberger, G., Zieman, J., and Vincent, M.
1972: Classification of the coastal environments of the world, Part I, The Americas; University of Virginia, Department of Environmental Science, Technical Report 1, 163 p.

Drapeau, G.
1970: Sand waves on Browns Bank observed from the shelf diver; Maritime Sediments v. 6, p. 90-101.
1980: Shoreline evolution of the northern end of Iles-de-la-Madeleine; in Proceedings of the Canadian Coastal Conference 1980, Associate Committee for Research on Shoreline Erosion and Sedimentation, National Research Council of Canada, Ottawa, p. 294-308.

Drapeau, G. and King, L.H.
1972: Surficial geology of the Yarmouth — Browns Bank map area; Geological Survey of Canada, Paper 72-24, 6 p.

Dubois, J.M.M.
1973: Essai de classification géomorphologique d'une côte en vue d'une utilisation en génie côtier; Département de Géographie, Université de Sherbrooke, Bulletin de Recherche, n. 10, 96 p.
1980: Géomorphologie du littoral de la côte nord du Saint-Laurent: Analyse Sommaire; in The Coastline of Canada: Littoral Processes and Shore Morphology, ed. S.B. McCann; Geological Survey of Canada, Paper 80-10, p. 215-238.
1983: Géologie des formations en surface et géomorphologie de la zone côtière de la moyenne côte nord du Saint-Laurent (12L, 22I, 22J) avec description de forages; Geological Survey of Canada, Open File 959, 123 p.

Dubois, J.M.M., Desmarais, D., Brouillette, S., Perras, G.L., Tremblay, L., Lariviere, F., Lessard, D., and Lessard, G.
1984: La mer de Goldthwait sur la côte nord du Saint-Laurent: Harrington Harbour (12J), Musquaro (12K), Saint-Augustin (12O), Blanc-Sablon (12P); Geological Survey of Canada, Open File 1045.

Dubois, J.M.M., Gwyn, Q.H.J., Gratton, D., Painchaud, A., Perras, S., Cadieux, R., Saint-Pierre, L. and Bigras, P.
1985: Géologie des formations en surface et géomorphologie de L'Île Anticosti, Québec; Geological Survey of Canada, Open File 1132.

Dumas, F. and Lee, K.L.
1980: Cyclic movements of offshore structures on clay; Journal of the Geotechnical Engineering Division, Proceedings of American Society of Civil Engineers, GT8, Paper 15655, p. 877-897.

Dyer, K.R.
1973: Estuaries; A Physical Introduction; J. Wiley and Sons, London, 140 p.

Dyke, A.S.
1979: Radiocarbon-dated Holocene emergence of Somerset Island, central Canadian Arctic; in Current Research, Part B, Geological Survey of Canada, Paper 79-1B, p. 307-318.

Eastern Ecological Research Limited
1978: Ecological land classification system, Cape Breton Highlands National Park: Environmental components; Parks Canada, Halifax, Nova Scotia.

Elverhoi, A., Liestol, O., and Nagy, J.
1980: Glacial erosion, sedimentation and microfauna in the inner part of Kongsfjorden, Spitsbergen; Norsk Polarinstitutt, Skrifter, v. 172, p. 33-58.

Embley, R.W., Hoose, P.J., Lonsdale, P., Mayer, L., and Tucholke, B.E.
1980: Furrowed mud waves on the western Bermuda rise; Geological Society of America Bulletin, v. 91, p. 731-740.

Emery, K.O.
1968: Relict sediments on continental shelves of the world; American Association of Petroleum Geologists Bulletin, v. 52, p. 445-464.

Emery, K.O. and Uchupi, E.
1972: Western North Atlantic Ocean; American Association of Petroleum Geologists, Memoir 17, 532 p.

Engelund, F. and Hansen, E.
1967: A Monograph on Sediment Transport in Alluvial Streams; Technisk-Vorlag, Copenhagen, 62 p.

Environmental Protection Service
1979: Environmental atlas of the southern Gulf of St. Lawrence; Environment Canada, Marine Environment Branch, Dartmouth, Nova Scotia.
1980: Environmental atlas of eastern Nova Scotia; Environment Canada, Marine Environment Branch, Dartmouth, Nova Scotia.
1981: Environmental atlas of southeastern Newfoundland; Environment Canada, Marine Environment Branch, Dartmouth, Nova Scotia.

Ericson, D.B., Ewing, M., and Heezen, B.C.
1952: Turbidity currents and sediments in the North Atlantic; American Association of Petroleum Geologists Bulletin, v. 36, p. 489-512.

Evans-Hamilton Inc.
1972: Sable Island Sand Transport, Part 1 and Part II; unpublished report, Mobil Oil Canada Ltd., Calgary, Alberta, 2 volumes.
1975: Study of sand waves on Sable Island Bank: Phase I; unpublished report, Mobil Oil Canada Ltd., Calgary, Alberta, 77 p.
1976: Study of sand waves on Sable Island Bank: Phase II; unpublished report, Mobil Oil Canada Ltd., Calgary, Alberta, 67 p.
1977: Final report on a Sable Island data analysis and design study; unpublished report, Mobil Oil Canada Ltd., Calgary, Alberta.

Fader, G.B.
1984: Geological and geophysical study of the Northeast Channel, Georges Bank and Georges Basin area of the Gulf of Maine by Geonautics Ltd.; Geological Survey of Canada, Open File 978.

Fader, G.B. and King, L.H.
1981: A reconnaissance study of the surficial geology of the Grand Banks of Newfoundland; in Current Research, Part A, Geological Survey of Canada Paper 81-1A, p. 45-56.

Fader, G.B., King, L.H., and Josenhans, H.W.
1982: Surficial geology of the Laurentian Channel and the western Grand Banks of Newfoundland; Geological Survey of Canada, Paper 81-22, 37 p.

Fader, G.B., King, L.H., and MacLean, B.
1977: Surficial geology of the eastern Gulf of Maine and Bay of Fundy; Geological Survey of Canada, Paper 76-17, 23 p.

Farre, J.A., McGregor, B.A., Ryan, W.B.F., and Robb, J.M.
1983: Breaching the shelfbreak; passage from youthful to mature phase in submarine canyon evolution; in The Shelfbreak; Critical Interface on Continental Margins, ed. D.J. Stanley and G.T. Moore; Society of Economic Paleontologists and Mineralogists, Special Publications 33, p. 25-39.

Farrow, G.E., Syvitski, J.P.M., and Tunnicliffe, V.
1983: Suspended particulate loading on the macrobenthos in a highly turbid fiord, Knight Inlet, British Columbia: Canadian Journal of Fisheries and Aquatic Sciences, v. 40, p. 273-288.

Feyling-Hanssen, R.W.
1976: The stratigraphy of the Quaternary Clyde Foreland formation, Baffin Island, illustrated by the distribution of benthic foraminifera; BOREAS, v. 5, p. 77-94.

Field, M.E., Gardner, J.V., Jennings, A.E., and Edwards, B.D.
1982: Earthquake-induced sediment failures on a 0.25 degrees slope, Klamath River Delta, California; Geology, v. 20, p. 542-546.

Field, M.E., Nelson, C.H., Cacchione, D.A., and Drake, D.E.
1981: Sand waves on an epicontinental shelf, northern Bering Sea; Marine Geology, v. 2, p. 233-258.

Fillon, R.H.
1976: Hamilton Bank, Labrador Shelf; Postglacial sediment dynamics and paleo-oceanography; Marine Geology, v. 20, p. 7-25.

Flood, R.D.
1983: Classification of sedimentary furrows and a model for furrow initiation and evolution; Geological Society of America Bulletin, v. 94, p. 630-639.

Flood, R.D. and Hollister, C.D.
1980: Submersible studies of deep-sea furrows and transverse ripples in cohesive sediments; Marine Geology, v. 36, p. M1-M9.

Forbes, D.L.
1980: Late-Quaternary sea levels in the southern Beaufort Sea; in Current Research, Part B, Geological Survey of Canada, Paper 80-1B, p. 75-87.

1982: Sources of sand contributing to harbour shoaling at Pte. Sapin, New Brunswick; in Proceedings of the Atlantic Coastal Erosion and Sedimentation Workshop, Halifax, Nova Scotia, p. 1-57.

1984: Coastal geomorphology and sediments of Newfoundland; in Current Research, Part B, Geological Survey of Canada, Paper 84-1B, p. 11-24.

Forbes, D.L. and Frobel, D.
1985: Coastal erosion and sedimentation in the Canadian Beaufort Sea; in Current Research, Part B, Geological Survey of Canada, Paper 85-1B, p. 69-80.

Forbes, D.L. and Lewis, C.P.
1984: Coastal landforms and processes, southern Beaufort Sea; in Marine Science Atlas of the Beaufort Sea, Sediments, ed. B.R. Pelletier; Geological Survey of Canada, Miscellaneous Report 38, p. 4.

Forbes, D.L. and Taylor, R.B.
1987: Coarse-grained sedimentation under para-glacial conditions, Canadian Atlantic Coast Chapter 3; in Glaciated Coasts, ed. D. Fitzgerald and P.S. Rosen; Academic Press, Toronto, p. 52-86.

Gadd, P.E., Lavelle, J.W., and Swift, D.J.P.
1978: Estimates of sand transport on the New York shelf using near-bottom current-meter observations; Journal of Sedimentary Petrology, v. 41, p. 7-18.

Gade, H.G., Lake, R.A., Lewis, E.L., and Walker, E.R.
1974: Oceanography of an arctic bay; Deep-Sea Research, v. 21, p. 547-571.

Galloway, W.E. and Hobday, D.K.
1983: Terrigenous Clastic Depositional Systems; Springer-Verlag, New York, 423 p.

Galt, J.A.
1971: A numerical investigation of pressure induced storm surges over the continental shelf; Journal of Physical Oceanography, v. 1, p. 82-91.

Geonautics Limited
1981: Strait of Belle Isle, Newfoundland, marine borings and surveys, 1981, Volume 2, Marine surveys; unpublished report, Beaver Dredging Company Limited, Lower Churchill Development Corporation.

Gilbert, G.R. and Barrie, J.V.
in press: Provenance and sedimentary processes of ice scoured surficial sediments, Labrador Shelf; Canadian Journal of Earth Sciences.

Gilbert, R.
1982: Contemporary sedimentary environments on Baffin Island, Northwest Territories, Canada; glaciomarine processes in fiords of eastern Cumberland Peninsula; Arctic and Alpine Research, v. 14, p. 1-12.

1983: Sedimentary processes of Canadian arctic fjords; Sedimentary Geology, v. 36, p. 147-175.

Gilbert, R. and Aitken, A.E.
1981: The role of sea ice in biophysical processes on intertidal flats at Pangnirtung (Baffin Island), N.W.T.; Proceedings, Workshop on ice action on shores, Rimouski, Quebec, p. 89-104.

Gordon, D.C. Jr. and Hourston, A.S. (ed.)
1983: Proceedings of the Symposium on the Dynamics of Turbid Coastal Environments; Canadian Journal of Fisheries and Aquatic Sciences, v. 40, 365 p.

Grant, A.C.
1965: Distributional trends in the recent marine sediments of northern Baffin Bay; Bedford Institute of Oceanography, Report 65-9, 74 p.

1971: Distributional trends in the recent marine sediments of northern Baffin Bay; Maritime Sediments, v. 7, p. 41-63.

1972: The continental margin off Labrador and eastern Newfoundland; morphology and geology; Canadian Journal of Earth Sciences, v. 9, p. 1394-1430.

1975: Structural modes of the western margin of the Labrador Sea; in Offshore Geology of Eastern Canada, Volume 2, Regional Geology, ed. W.J.M. van der Linden and J.A. Wade; Geological Survey of Canada, Paper 74-30, p. 217-231.

Grant, W.D.
1980: Quaternary stratigraphy of southwestern Nova Scotia: Glacial events and sea-level changes; Geological Association of Canada, Field Trip Guide Book, Trip 9, 63 p.

Grant, W.D. and Madsen, O.S.
1979: Combined wave and current interaction with a rough bottom; Journal of Geophysical Research, v. 84, p. 1797-1808.

Grant, W.D., Boyer, L.F., and Sanford, L.P.
1982: The effects of bioturbation on the initiation of motion of intertidal sands; Journal of Marine Research, v. 40, p. 659-677.

Greenwood, B. and Davidson-Arnott, R.G.D.
1972: Textural variations in the sub-environments of the shallow-water wave zone, Kouchibouguac Bay, New Brunswick; Canadian Journal of Earth Sciences, v. 6, p. 1347-1358.

1975: Marine bars and nearshore sedimentary processes, Kouchibouguac Bay, New Brunswick; in Nearshore Sediment Dynamics and Sedimentation, ed. J. Hails and A. Carr; J. Wiley and Sons, New York, p. 123-150.

1979: Sedimentation and equilibrium in wave-formed bars: a review and case study; Canadian Journal of Earth Sciences, v. 16, p. 312-332.

Greenwood, B. and Hale, P.B.
1980: Depth of activity, sediment flux, and morphological change in a barred nearshore environment; in The Coastline of Canada; Littoral Processes and Shore Morphology, ed. S.B. McCann; Geological Survey of Canada, Paper 80-10, p. 89-109.

Greenwood, B. and Mittler, P.
1979: Structural indices of sediment transport in a straight, wave-formed nearshore bar; Marine Geology, v. 32, p. 191-203.

Greisman, P.
1979: On upwelling driven by the melt of ice shelves and tidewater glaciers; Deep-Sea Research, v. 26, p. 1051-1065.

Guimont, P. and Laverdière, C.
1980: Le sud-est de la Mer D'Hudson: un relief de cuesta; in The Coastline of Canada, ed. S.B. McCann; Geological Survey of Canada, Paper 80-10, p. 303-309.

Gumbel, E.J.
1954: Statistical theory of extreme values and some practical applications; National Bureau of Standards, Washington, D.C., 51 p.

Guza, R.T. and Inman, D.L.
1975: Edge waves and beach cusps; Journal of Geophysical Research, v. 80, p. 2997-3012.

Hackett, D.W., Syvitski, J.P.M., Prime, W., and Sherin, A.G.
1986: Sediment size analysis system users guide; Geological Survey of Canada, Open File 1240, 25 p.

Hale, P.B. and McCann, S.B.
1982: Rhythmic topography in a mesotidal, low-wave-energy environment; Journal of Sedimentary Petrology, v. 52, p. 415-429.

Hall, J.K.
1979: Sediment waves and other evidence of paleo-bottom currents at two locations in the deep Arctic Ocean; Sedimentary Geology, v. 23, p. 269-299.

Hampton, M.A.
1970: Subaqueous debris flow and generation of turbidity currents; Ph.D. thesis, Stanford University, Stanford, California, 180 p.

Hansen, D.V. and Rattray, D.V. Jr.
1966: New dimensions in estuary classification; Limnology and Oceanography, v. 11, p. 319-326.

Harper, J.R., Owens, E.H., and Wiseman, W.J.
1978:   Arctic beach processes and the thaw of ice-bonded sediments in the littoral zone; Proceedings of the 3rd International Permafrost Conference, 1978, Edmonton, Alberta, Canada, p. 195-199.

Heathershaw, A.D.
1981:   Comparisons of measured and predicted sediment transport rates in tidal currents; Marine Geology, v. 42, p. 75-104.

Heathershaw, A.D. and Davies, A.G.
1985:   Resonant wave reflection by transverse bedforms and its relation to beaches and offshore bars; Marine Geology, v. 62, p. 327-338.

Heezen, B.C. and Ewing, M.
1952:   Turbidity currents and submarine slumps, and the 1929 Grand Banks earthquake; American Journal of Science, v. 250, p. 849-873.

Heezen, B.C. and Laughton, A.S.
1963:   Abyssal plains: in The Sea, Volume 3, ed. M.N. Hill; J. Wiley and Sons, New York, v. 3, p. 312-364.

Heezen, B.C. and Menard, H.W.
1963:   Topography of the deep sea floor; in The Sea, Volume 3, ed. M.N. Hill; J. Wiley and Sons, New York, v. 3, p. 233-280.

Heezen, B.C., Ericson, D.B., and Ewing, M.
1954:   Further evidence for a turbidity current following the 1929 Grand Banks earthquake; Deep-Sea Research, v. 1, p. 193-202.

Heezen, B.C., Ewing, M., and Ericson, D.B.
1955:   Reconnaissance survey of the abyssal plain south of Newfoundland; Deep-Sea Research, v. 2, p. 122-133.

Heffler, D.E.
1984.   RALPH — An instrument to measure seabed sediments; in Current Research, Part B, Geological Survey of Canada, Paper 84-1B, p. 47-52.

Hill, P.R.
1983:   Detailed morphology of a small area on the Nova Scotian continental slope; Marine Geology, v. 53, p. 55-76.
1984a: Sedimentary facies of the Nova Scotian upper and middle continental slope, offshore eastern Canada; Sedimentology, v. 31, p. 293-310.
1984b: Facies and sequence analysis of Nova Scotian slope muds: Turbidite vs. "Hemipelagic" Deposition, Fine-grained Sediments; in Deep Water Processes and Products, ed. D.A.V. Stow and D.J.W. Piper; Geological Society of London, Special Publication no. 15, 659 p.

Hill, P.R. and Bowen, A.J.
1983:   Modern sediment dynamics at the shelf-slope boundary off Nova Scotia; in The Shelfbreak; Critical Interface on Continental Margins, ed. D.J. Stanley and G.T. Moore; Society of Economic Paleontologists and Mineralogists, Special Publication, no. 33, p. 265-276.

Hill, P.R., Piper, D.J.W., and Normark, W.R.
1983:   Pisces IV Submersible dives on the Scotian Shelf at 63°W; in Current Research, Part A, Geological Survey of Canada, Paper 83-1A, p. 65-69.

Hogg, N.G.
1983:   A note on the deep circulation of the western North Atlantic; its nature and causes; Deep-Sea Research, v. 30, p. 945-961.

Hollister, C.D. and McCave, I.N.
1984:   Sedimentation under deep-sea storms; Nature, v. 309, n. 5965, p. 220-225.

Holman, R.A. and Bowen, A.J.
1982:   Bars, bumps and holes: models for the generation of complex beach topography; Journal of Geophysical Research, v. 85, p. 457-468.

Horn, D.R., Ewing, M., Horn, B.M., and Delach, M.N.
1971:   Turbidites of the Hatteras and Sohm abyssal plains, western North Atlantic; Marine Geology, v. 2, p. 287-323.

Hotzel, I.S. and Miller, J.D.
1983:   Icebergs; their physical dimensions and presentation and application of measured data; Annals of Glaciology, v. 4, p. 116-123.

Hunter, R.E., Clifton, H.E., and Phillips, R.L.
1979:   Depositional processes, sedimentary structures, and predicted vertical sequences in barred nearshore systems, southern Oregon coast; Journal of Sedimentary Petrology, v. 49, p. 711-726.

Huntley, D.A.
1980:   Edge waves in a crescentic bar system; in The Coastline of Canada; Littoral Processes and Shore Morphology, ed. S.B. McCann; Geological Survey of Canada, Paper 80-10, p. 111-121.
1982:   Boundary layer flow and the physics of sediment transport; in A Short Course on the Stability of Canadian Shelves, ed. J.V. Barrie; C-CORE Publication 82-10, p. 99-172.

Huntley, D.A. and Hazen, D.G.
1988:   Seabed stresses in combined wave and steady flow conditions on the Nova Scotia Continental Shelf: field measurements and predictions; Journal of Physical Oceanography, v. 18, p. 347-362.

Huskey/Bow Valley East Coast Project,
1985a: Rig Response Report ROWAN GORILLA 1, Hesper P-52 location, 44°41′55″N, 57°52′46″W: Unpublished report, MacLaren Plansearch Ltd., Halifax, Nova Scotia.

Huskey/Bow Valley East Coast Project
1985b: Current meter data analysis Hesper P-52 (ROWAN GORILLA 1) draft report #2, December 22, 1984 — March 1, 1985; unpublished report, MacLaren Plansearch Ltd., Halifax, Nova Scotia, 15 p.

Huthnance, J.M.
1973:   Tidal current asymmetries over the Norfolk sandbanks; Estuarine and Coastal Marine Science, v. 1, p. 89-99.

Hydraulic Research Station
1981:   Severn Tidal Power. An assessment of the feasibility of mathematical modelling of sediment transport processes in the estuary; Hydraulic Research Station, Wallingford, United Kingdom; Internal Report EX 969, 31 p.

Idriss, I.M., Dobry. R. and Singh, R.D.
1978:   Nonlinear behaviour of soft clays during cyclic loading: Journal of the Geotechnical Engineering Division, Proceedings of American Society of Civil Engineers, No. GT12, Paper 14265, p. 1427-1447.

Ingram, R.G.
1981:   Characteristics of the Great Whale river plume; Journal of Geophysical Research, v. 86, p. 2017-2023.

James, N.P.
1966:   Sediment distribution and dispersal patterns on Sable Island and Sable Island Bank; M.Sc. thesis, Dalhousie University, Halifax, Nova Scotia, 254 p.

James, N.P. and Stanley, D.J.
1968:   Sable Island Bank off Nova Scotia; sediment dispersal and recent history; American Society of Petroleum Geologists Bulletin, v. 52, p. 2208-2230.

Jansa, L.F. and Wade, J.A.
1975:   Geology of the continental margin off Nova Scotia and Newfoundland; in Offshore Geology of Eastern Canada, Volume 2, Regional Geology, ed. W.J.M. Van der Linden and J.A. Wade; Geological Survey of Canada, Paper 74-30, v. 2, p. 51-105.

Jeffries, M.
1982:   Mammoth pads circle the Arctic Basin; Geos; v. 13, p. 2-5.

Johnson, G.L., McMillan, N.J., Rasmussen, M., Campsie, J., and Dittmer, F.
1975:   Sedimentary rocks dredged from the southwest Greenland continental margin; in Canada's Continental Margins and Offshore Petroleum Exploration, ed. C.J. Yorath, E.R. Parker and D.J. Glass; Canadian Society of Petroleum Geologists, Memoir 4, p. 391-409.

Jordan, G.F.
1962:   Large submarine sand waves; Science, v. 136, no. 3519, p. 839-848.

Josenhans, H.W.
1983:   Evidence of pre-late Wisconsinan glaciations on Labrador Shelf-Cartwright Saddle region; Canadian Journal of Earth Sciences, v. 20, p. 225-235.

Josenhans, H.W. and Barrie, J.V.
1982:   Preliminary results of submersible observations on the Labrador shelf; in Current Research, Part B, Geological Survey of Canada, Paper 82-1B, p. 269-726.

Josenhans, H.W. and Zevenhuizen, J.
1984:   Sea floor dynamics on the Labrador shelf; in Symposium on Sedimentology of Shelf Sands and Sandstones, ed. J.R. Knight; Canadian Society of Petroleum Geologists, p. 80.

Josenhans, H.W., King, L.H., and Fader, G.B.
1978:   A side-scan sonar mosaic of pockmarks on the Scotian Shelf; Canadian Journal of Earth Sciences, v. 15, p. 831-840.

Josenhans, H.W., Zevenhuizen, J., and Klassen, R.A.
1986:   The Quaternary Geology of the Inner Labrador Shelf; Canadian Journal of Earth Sciences, v. 23, n. 8, p. 1190-1213.

Kagawa, T. and Kraft, L.M. Jr.
1980:   Seismic P-Y responses of flexible piles; Journal of the Geotechnical Engineering Division, Proceedings of American Society of Civil Engineers GT8, Paper 15656, p. 889-918.

Karl, H.A., Carlson, P.R., and Cacchione, D.A.
1983:   Factors that influence sediment transport at the shelfbreak; in The Shelfbreak; Critical Interface on Continental Margins, ed. D.J. Stanley and G.T. Moore; Society of Economic Paleontologists and Mineralogists, Special Publications no. 33, p. 219-231.

Kennedy, J.F.
1978:   Bedforms in alluvial channels; in The Encyclopedia of Sedimentology, ed. R.W. Fairbridge and J. Bourgeois; Dowden, Hutchinson and Ross Inc., p. 56-59.

Kenyon, N.H.
1970:   Sand ribbons of European Tidal Sea; Marine Geology, v. 9, p. 25-39.

Kenyon, N.H., Belderson, R.H., Stride, A.H., and Johnson, M.A.
1981:   Offshore tidal sandbanks as indicators of net sand transport and as potential deposits; in Holocene Marine Sedimentation in the North Sea Basin, ed. S.D. Nio, R.T.E. Shuttenhelm and Tj.C.E. Van Weering; Blackwell Scientific, Oxford, p. 257-268.

Keys, J.E.
1978:   Water regime of Disraeli Fiord, Ellesmere Island, Canada; Department of National Defence Research Establishment, Report 792, 58 p.

King, C.A.M.
1972:   Beaches and Coasts, Second Edition; Edward Arnold, London, 570 p.

King, C.A.M. and Williams, W.W.
1949:   The formation and movement of sand bars by wave action; Geographical Journal, v. 112. p. 70-85.

King, L.H.
1970:   Surficial geology of the Halifax-Sable Island map area; Canadian Hydrographic Service, Marine Sciences Paper no. 1, 16 p.
1976:   Relict iceberg furrows on the Laurentian Channel and western Grand Banks; Canadian Journal of Earth Sciences, v. 13, p. 1082-1092.
1980:   Aspects of regional surficial geology related to site investigation requirements — eastern Canadian shelf; in Offshore Site Investigation, ed. D.A. Ardus; Graham and Trotman, London, p. 37-59.

King, L.H. and Fader, G.B.
1986:   Wisconsinan glaciation of the Atlantic continental shelf of southeast Canada; Geological Survey of Canada, Bulletin 363, 72 p.

King, L.H. and MacLean, B.
1976:   Geology of the Scotian Shelf; Geological Survey of Canada, Paper 74-31, 31 p.

Kjerfve, B. (ed.)
1978:   Estuarine Transport Processes; University of South Carolina Press, Columbia, 300 p.

Klein, G. de V.
1970:   Depositional and dispersal dynamics of intertidal sand bars; Journal of Sedimentary Petrology, v. 40, p. 1095-1127.

Knebel, H.J.
1981:   Processes controlling the characteristics of the surficial sand sheet, U.S. Atlantic outer continental shelf; Marine Geology, v. 42, p. 349-368.

Knight, R.J.
1971:   Distributional trends in the recent marine sediments of Tasiujaq Cove of Ekalugad Fjord, Baffin Island, Northwest Territories; Maritime Sediments, v. 7, p. 1-18.
1977:   Sediments, bedforms and hydraulics in a macrotidal environment, Cobequid Bay (Bay of Fundy), Nova Scotia; Ph.D. thesis, McMaster University, 693 p.

Knight, R.J. and Dalrymple, R.W.
1975:   Intertidal sediments from the south shore of Cobequid Bay, Bay of Fundy, Nova Scotia, Canada; in Tidal Deposits, ed. R.N. Ginsburg; Springer-Verlag, New York, p. 47-55.

Komar, P.D.
1971:   Nearshore cell circulation and the formation of giant cusps; Geological Society of America Bulletin, v. 82, p. 2643-2650.
1973:   Continuity of turbidity current flow and systematic variations in deep sea channel morphology; Geological Society of American Bulletin, v. 84, p. 3329-3338.
1977:   Computer simulation of turbidity current flow and the study of deep sea channels and fan sedimentation; in The Sea, ed. E.D. Goldberg, I.N. Cave, J.J. O'Brien and J.H. Steele; v. 6, p. 603-621.

Komar, P.D. and Miller, M.C.
1973:   The threshold of sediment movement under oscillatory water waves; Journal of Sedimentary Petrology, v. 44, p. 169-180.

Kontoupolos, N. and Piper, D.J.W.
1982:   Storm graded sand at 200 m water depth, Scotian Shelf, eastern Canada; Geo-Marine Letters, v. 2, no. 1-2, p. 77-81.

Kranck, K.
1966:   Sediments of Exeter Bay, Baffin Island, District of Franklin; Geological Survey of Canada, Paper 66-8, 60 p.
1971:   Surficial geology of Northumberland Strait; Geological Survey of Canada, Paper 71-53, 10 p.
1979:   Dynamics and distribution of suspended particulate matter in the St. Lawrence estuary; Le Naturaliste Canadien, v. 106, p. 163-173.
1981:   Flocculation and particulate matter dynamics in a partially mixed estuary; Sedimentology, v. 28, p. 107-114.
1984:   The role of flocculation in the filtering of particulate matter in estuaries; in The Estuary as a Filter, ed. V.S. Kennedy; Academic Press, London, p. 159-175.

Kranck, K. and Ruffman, A.
1982:   Sedimentation in James Bay; Le Naturaliste Canadien, v. 109, p. 353-361.

Krawetz, M.T. and McCann, S.B.
1986:   Coastal characteristics, east-central Ellesmere Island, District of Franklin; in Current Research, Part A, Geological Survey of Canada Paper 86-1A, p. 749-754.

Krone, R.B.
1962:   Flume studies of the transport of sediment in esturial shoaling processes; Hydraulic Engineering Laboratory and Sanitory Engineering Research Laboratory Report, University of California, Berkeley, United States Army Corps of Engineers Contract n. DA-04-203, 110 p.
1978:   Aggregation of suspended particles in estuaries; in Estuarine Transport Processes, ed. B. Kjerfve; University of South Carolina Press, Columbia, p. 177-190.

Kuenen, Ph.H. and Migliorini, C.I.
1950:   Turbidity currents as a cause of graded bedding; Journal of Geology, v. 48, p. 91-127.

Lambiase, J.J.
1977:   Sediment dynamics in the macrotidal Avon River estuary, Nova Scotia; Ph.D. thesis, McMaster University, Hamilton, Ontario, 415 p.

Lau, J. and Travis, B.
1973:   Slowly varying Stokes waves and submarine longshore bars; Journal of Geophysical Research, v. 78, p. 4489-4497.

Lauzier, L.M.
1967:   Bottom residual drift on the continental shelf area of the Canadian Atlantic coast; Journal Fisheries Research Board Canada, v. 24, p. 1845-1859.

Lavelle, J.W., Gadd, P.E., Han, G.C., Mayer, D.A., Stubblefield, W.L., and Swift, D.J.P.
1976:   Preliminary results of coincident current meter and sediment transport observations for wintertime conditions on the Long Island inner shelf; Geophysical Research Letters, v. 3, p. 97-100.

Lavrushin, Y.A.
1968:   Features of deposition and structure of the glacial marine deposits under conditions of a fiord-coast; Translations from Lithology and Economic Minerals, v. 3, p. 63-79.

Lazier, J.R.N.
1979:   Moored Current Meter Data from the Labrador Sea 1977-78; Atlantic Oceanographic Laboratory, Ocean and Aquatic Sciences, Department of Fisheries and Oceans, Data Series BI-D-79-3, March 1979, 131 p.
1981:   Moored Current Meter Data from Hamilton Bank 1978-80; Atlantic Oceanographic Laboratory, Ocean and Aquatic Sciences, Department of Fisheries and Oceans, Data Series BI-D-81-7, December 1981, 64 p.

Lee, K.L. and Filton, J.A.
1969:   Factors affecting the cyclic loading strength of soil; American Society of Testing and Materials, Special Technical Paper 450, p. 77-95.

Lees, B.J. and Heathershaw, A.D.
1981:   Offshore sediment movement and its relation to observed tidal current and wave data; Institute of Oceanographic Sciences, Taunton, Report 123, 113 p.

Lepage, S.
1984:   Salt intrusion and circulation changes in the Eastmain River estuary, James Bay, subsequent to a large reduction of the fresh water discharge; M.Sc. thesis, Institute of Oceanography, McGill University, Montreal, Quebec, 173 p.

Letson, J.R.J.
1981:   Sedimentology of southwestern Mahone Bay, Nova Scotia; M.Sc. thesis, Dalhousie University, Halifax, Nova Scotia, 199 p.

Levy, E., Tarbell, S.A., and Fafanoff, N.D.
1982:   A compilation of moored instrument data and associated oceanographic observations, volume 30 (Gulf Stream Extension and Norwegian Sea Overflow Intrusion Experiments) 1979-80; Woods Hole Oceanographic Institute, Technical Report WHOI 82-43, October 1982.

Lewis, A.G. and Syvitski, J.P.M.
1983:   The interaction of plankton and suspended sediment in fiords; Sedimentary Geology, v. 36, p. 81-92.

Lewis, C.F.M. and Barrie, J.V.
1980:   Ice scour studies on the Labrador Shelf: Newfoundland Institute for Cold Ocean Sciences, Research in Labrador Coastal and Offshore Region Workshop, p. 264-265.

1981:   Geological evidence of iceberg groundings and related seafloor processes in the Hibernia discovery area of Grand Bank, Newfoundland; in Proceedings of the Symposium, Production and Transportation Systems for the Hibernia Discovery, ed. W.E. Russell and D.B. Muggeridge; St. John's Petroleum Directorate, p. 146-177.

Lewis, C.F.M., Blasco, S.M., Bornhold, B.D., Hunter, J.A.M., Judge, A.S., Kerr, W.J., McLaren, P., and Pelletier, B.R.
1977:   Marine geological and geophysical activities in Lancaster Sound and adjacent fiords; in Report of Activities, Part A, Geological Survey of Canada, Paper 77-1A, p. 495-506.

Lien, R.
1983:   Iceberg scouring on the Norwegian continental shelf; in Proceedings of the 15th Annual Offshore Technology Conference, Houston, Texas, 4585, v. 3, p. 41-48.

Lively, R.R.
1979:   Current Meter and Meteorological Observations on the Scotian Shelf, December 1975 to January 1978, Volume 1, December 1975 to December 1976; Bedford Institute of Oceanography, Data Series BI-D-79-1, January 1979, 280 p.

1984:   Current meter observations on the Scotian Rise for November 1980 to October 1981; Canadian Technical Report of Hydrography and Ocean Sciences, no. 50, Atlantic Oceanographic Laboratory, Ocean Science and Surveys, Atlantic Department of Fisheries and Oceans, November 1984.

Long, B.F.N.
1979:   The nature of bottom sediments in the Minas Basin system; Bedford Institute of Oceanography, Data Series BI-D-79-4, 101 p.

Loring, D.H.
1975:   Surficial geology of the Gulf of St. Lawrence; in Offshore Gelology of Eastern Canada, Volume 2, ed. W.J.M. Van der Linden and J.A. Wade; Geological Survey of Canada, Paper 74-30, v. 2, p. 11-34.

Loring, D.H. and Nota, D.J.G.
1966:   Seafloor conditions around the Magdalen Islands in the southern Gulf of St. Lawrence; Journal of the Fisheries Research Board of Canada, v. 23, p. 1197-1207.

Loring, D.H., Nota, D.J.G., Chesterman, W.D. and Wong, H.K.
1970:   Sedimentary environments on the Magdalen Shelf, southern Gulf of St. Lawrence; Marine Geology, v. 8, p. 337-354.

Luternauer, J. and Murray, J.W.
1983:   Late Quaternary morphologic development and sedimentation central British Columbia continental shelf; Geological Survey of Canada, Paper 83-21, 38 p.

MacLaren Plansearch Ltd.
1985a: GORILLA 1, Hesper P-52 location, 44°41'55"N, 57°52'46"W; unpublished report, MacLaren Plansearch Ltd., Halifax, Nova Scotia.

MacLaren Plansearch Ltd.
1985b: Current meter data analysis Hesper P-52 (ROWAN GORILLA 1) draft report #2, December 22, 1984 — March 1, 1985; Huskey/Bow Valley East Coast Project, Halifax, Nova Scotia, 15 p.

MacLean, B.
1982:   Investigations of Baffin Island shelf from surface ship and research submersible in 1981; in Current Research, Part A, Geological Survey of Canada, Paper 82-1A, p. 445-447.

MacLean, B. and King, L.H.
1971:   Surficial geology of the Banquereau and Misaine Bank map area; Geological Survey of Canada, Paper 71-52, 19 p.

MacLean, B., Fader, G.B., and King, L.H.
1977:   Surficial geology of Canso Bank and adjacent areas; Geological Survey of Canada, Paper 76-15, 11 p.

Madsen, O.S. and Grant, W.D.
1976:   Quantitative description of sediment transport by waves; Proceedings of the 15th Coastal Engineering Conference, July 11-17, 1976, Honolulu, Hawaii, v. 2, p. 1093-1112.

Markham, W.E.
1980:   Ice Atlas, Eastern Canadian Seaboard; Environment Canada, Atmospheric Environment Service, Toronto, Canada, 96 p.

Martini, I.P., Cowell, D.W., and Wickwave, G.H.
1980:   Geomorphology of southwestern James Bay; a low energy, emergent coast; in The Coastline of Canada, Littoral Processes and Shore Morphology, ed. S.B. McCann; Geological Survey of Canada, Paper 80-10, p. 293-301.

Matthews, J.B. and Quinlan, A.V.
1975:   Seasonal characteristics of water masses in Muir Inlet, a fjord with tidewater glaciers; Journal of the Fisheries Research Board of Canada, v. 32, p. 1693-1703.

Maxwell, J.B., Duck, P.J., Thomson, R.B., and Vickers, G.G.
1980:   The climate of northwestern Baffin Bay; Canadian Climate Centre Report No. 80-2, Atmospheric Environment Service, Downsview, Ontario, p. 105.

McCann, S.B.
1979:   Barrier Islands in the southern Gulf of St. Lawrence Canada; in Barrier Islands, ed. S.P. Leatherman; Academic Press, New York, p. 26-63.

1982:   Intertidal and subtidal wave-formed bars; in Beach and nearshore depositional environments of the Bay of Fundy and Southern Gulf of St. Lawrence, ed. R.W. Dalrymple, C.L. Amos and S.B. McCann; International Association of Sedimentologists, Field Excursion Guidebook, p. 89-107.

McCann, S.B., Dale, J.E., and Hale, P.B.
1981:   Subarctic tidal flats in areas of large tidal range, southern Baffin Island, eastern Canada; Geographie physique et Quaternaire, v. 35, p. 183-204.

McCann, S.B., Reinson, G.E., and Frobel, D.
1978:   Coastline studies, southeastern Baffin Island; in Proceedings of the Arctic Marine Oil Spill Program Seminar, March 15-17, 1978, Edmonton, Alberta, p. 33-43.

McCave, I.N.
1972:   Transport and escape of fine-grained sediment from shelf areas; in Shelf Sediment Transport, Process and Pattern, ed. D.J.P. Swift, D.B. Duane, and O.H. Pilkey; Dowden, Hutchinson and Ross Inc., Stroudsburg, p. 225-248.

1984:   Erosion, transport and deposition of fine-grained marine sediments; in Fine-Grained Sediments, Deep Water Processes and Facies, ed. D.A.V. Stow and D.J.W. Piper; Blackwell Scientific Publications, Oxford, p. 35-69.

McCave, I.N. and Swift, S.A.
1976:   A physical model for the rate of deposition of fine-grained sediments in the deep sea; Geological Society America Bulletin, v. 87, p. 541.

McClimans, T.A.
1978:   Fronts in fjords; Geophysical and Astrophysical Fluid Dynamics, v. 11, p. 23-34.

McDowell, D.M. and O'Connor, B.A.
1977:   Hydraulic Behaviour of Estuaries; Macmillan Press Ltd., London, 292 p.

McLaren, P.
1980:   The coastal morphology and sedimentology of Labrador: a study of shoreline sensitivity to a potential oil spill; Geological Survey of Canada, Paper 79-28, 41 p.

1981:   An interpretation of trends in grain size measures; Journal of Sedimentary Petrology, v. 51, p. 611-624.

1982:   The coastal geomorphology, sedimentology and processes of eastern Melville and western Byam Martin Islands, Canadian Arctic Archipelago; Geological Survey of Canada, Bulletin 333, 39 p.

McLaren, P. and W.B. Barrie
1985:   The coastal morphology and sedimentology of eastern Lancaster Sound and northeast Baffin Island: A study of shoreline sensitivity to a potential oil spill; Geological Survey of Canada, Paper 83-24, 32 p.

McLean, S.R.
1981:   The role of non-uniform roughness in the formation of sand ribbons; Marine Geology, v. 42, p. 49-74.

McManus, D.A.
1982:   Phi and sediment size analysis; discussion; Journal of Sedimentary Petrology, v. 52, p. 1011-1014.

McMillan, N.J.
1973:   Surficial geology of Labrador and Baffin Island shelves; in Earth Science Symposium on Offshore Eastern Canada; Geological Survey of Canada, Paper 71-23, p. 451-468.

Middleton, G.V.
1966a: Experiments on density and turbidity currents I. Motion of the head; Canadian Journal of Earth Sciences, v. 3, p. 523-546.

1966b: Experiments on density and turbidity currents II. Uniform flow of density currents; Canadian Journal of Earth Sciences, v. 3, p. 627-637.

1967:   Experiments on density and turbidity currents III. Deposition of sediment; Canadian Journal of Earth Sciences, v. 4, p. 475-505.

Middleton, G.V. and Hampton, M.A.
1976:   Subaqueous sediment transport and deposition by sediment gravity flows; in Marine Sediment Transport and Environmental Management, ed. D.J. Stanley and D.J.P. Swift; J. Wiley and Sons, London, p. 197-220.

Middleton, G.V. and Southard, J.B.
1978:   Mechanics of sediment movement; Society of Economic Paleontologists and Mineralogists, Short Course No. 3, Tulsa, Oklahoma, 102 p.

Miller, G.H., Locke, W.W.(III), and Locke, C.W.
1980:   Physical characteristics of the southeastern Baffin Island coastal zone; in The Coastline of Canada, Littoral Processes and Shore Morphology, ed. S.B. McCann; Geological Survey of Canada, Paper 80-10, p. 251-265.

Miller, A.A.L., Mudie, P.J., and Scott, D.B.
1982: Holocene history of Bedford Basin, Nova Scotia; foraminifera, dinoflagellate, and pollen records; Canadian Journal of Earth Sciences, v. 19, p. 2342-2367.

Miller, A.A.L. and Scott, D.B.
1984: Late Quaternary biostratigraphy from two shallow boreholes, western Banquereau; Centre for Marine Geology, Dalhousie University, Technical Report 3, 28 p.

Monahan, D.
1976: Morphology and sediments of sand waves in the St. Lawrence estuary; Maritime Sediments, v. 12, p. 1-7.

Moore, D.G.
1977: Submarine slides; in Rockslides and Avalanches, Volume I, Natural Phenomena, ed. B. Voight; Developments in Geotechnical Engineering, v. 14A, p. 563-604.

Mosher, D.C.
1987: Late Quaternary sedimentology and sediment instability of a small area on the Scotian Slope; M.Sc. thesis, Memorial University of Newfoundland, St. John's, Newfoundland, 212 p.

Muller, J. and Milliman, J.D.
1973: Relict carbonate-rich sediments on southwestern Grand Bank, Newfoundland; Canadian Journal of Earth Sciences, v. 10, p. 1744-1750.

Munroe, H.D.
1982: Regional variability, physical shoreline types and morphodynamic units of the Atlantic coast of mainland Nova Scotia; Geological Survey of Canada, Open File 725, 25 p.

Nardin, T.R., Hein, F.J., Gorsline, D.S., and Edwards, B.D.
1979: A review of mass movement processes, sediment and acoustic characteristics, and contrasts in slope and base-of-slope systems versus canyon-fan-basin floor systems; in Geology of Continental Slopes, ed. L.J. Doyle and O.H. Pilkey; Society of Economic Paleontologists and Minerologists, n. 27, p. 61-73.

Neu, H.J.A.
1982: 11-year deep water wave climate of Canadian Atlantic waters; Canadian Technical Report of Hydrography and Ocean Sciences, no. 13, 41 p.

Niedoroda, A.W.
1982: Sediment transport in the marine environment; in Sediment Stability of Canadian Shelves, Short Course, March 9-10, 1982, ed. J.V. Barrie, Memorial University of Newfoundland, Publication n. 82-10, p. 173-278.

Nielsen, T.K. and Ottesen-Hansen, N.E.
1980: Mixing and exchange processes in a small Greenland sill fjord; in Fjord Oceanography, ed. H.J. Freeland, D.M. Farmer and C.D. Levings; Plenum Press, New York, p. 219-225.

Nordco Ltd.
1978: Wave climate study of southern Davis Strait; unpublished report, Esso Resources Canada Limited, 17 p.

1982: Surficial geology of the Labrador Shelf; unpublished report, Petro-Canada Exploration Ltd., 19 p.

Off, T.
1963: Rhythmic linear sand bodies caused by tidal currents; American Association of Petroleum Geologists Bulletin, v. 47, p. 324-341.

Officer, C.B.
1983: Physics of estuarine circulation; in Estuaries and Enclosed Seas, ed. B.H. Ketchum; Elsevier Scientific, Amsterdam, p. 15-42.

Ovenshine, A.T.
1970: Observations of iceberg rafting in Glacier Bay, Alaska and the identification of ancient iceberg-rafted deposits; Geological Society of America Bulletin, v. 81, p. 891-894.

Owen, M.W. and Thorn, M.F.C.
1978: Effect of waves on sand transport by currents; Proceedings of the 16th Coastal Engineering Conference, August 27 to September 3, 1978, Hamburg, Germany, v. 2, p. 1675-1687.

Owens, E.H.
1971: A reconnaissance of the coastline of Chedabucto Bay, Nova Scotia; Canadian Hydrographic Service, Marine Science Paper 4, 24 p.

1974: A framework for the definition of coastal environments in the southern Gulf of St. Lawrence; in Offshore Geology of Eastern Canada Volume 1, ed. B.R. Pelletier; Geological Survey of Canada, Paper 74-30, v. 1, p. 47-76.

1977a: Temporal variation in beach and nearshore dynamics; Journal of Sedimentary Petrology, v. 47, p. 168-190.

1977b: Coastal environments of Canada: The impact and clean-up of oil spills; Environment Canada, Environmental Protection Service, EPS-3-EC-77-13, 413 p.

1979: Prince Edward Island: coastal environments and the cleanup of oil spills; Environment Canada, Environmental Protection Service, Halifax, Nova Scotia, Report EPS-3-EC-79-5, 167 p.

1980: Sediment removal from the beaches of Prince Edward Island; in Proceedings of the Canadian Coastal Conference, April 22-24, 1980, Burlington, Ontario; Associate Committee for Research on Shoreline Erosion and Sedimentation, National Research Council Canada, Ottawa, p. 367-379.

Owens, E.H. and Bowen, A.J.
1977: Coastal environments of the Maritime Provinces; Maritime Sediments, v. 13, p. 1-31.

Owens, E.H. and Frobel, D.H.
1975: Environmental, morphological and sediment size data from two barrier beaches in the Magdalen Islands, Quebec; Bedford Institute of Oceanography, Data Report BI-D-75-8, 447 p.

1977: Ridge and runnel systems in the Magdalen Islands, Quebec; Journal of Sedimentology Petrology, v. 47, p. 191-198.

Owens, E.H. and McCann, S.B.
1980: The coastal geomorphology of the Magdalen Islands, Quebec; in The Coastline of Canada, Littoral Processes and Shore Morphology, ed. S.B. McCann; Geological Survey of Canada, Paper 80-10, p. 51-72.

Pamukcu, S., Poplin, J.K., Suhayda, J.N., and Tumay, M.T.
1983: Dynamic sediment properties, Mississippi Delta: Geotechnical Practice; in Offshore Engineering Conference, April 27-29, 1983, Austin, Texas, p. 111-132.

Parker, W.R.
1975: Sediment mobility and erosion on a multibarred foreshore (southwest Lancashire, United Kingdom); in Nearshore sediment dynamics and sedimentation, ed. J. Hails and A. Carr; John Wiley and Sons, Chichester, p. 151-179.

Parker, W.R. and Kirby, R.
1982: Time dependent properties of cohesive sediment relevant to sedimentation management — European experience; in Estuarine Comparisons, ed. V.S. Kennedy; Academic Press, London, p. 573-579.

Partheniades, E.
1972: Recent investigations in stratified flows related to estuarial hydraulics; Geological Society of America, Memoir 133, p. 29-70.

Partheniades, E., Cross, R.H., and Ayora, A.
1968: Further results on the deposition of cohesive sediments; Proceedings of the 11th Conference on Coastal Engineering, September, 1968, London, England, p. 723-742.

Pelletier, B.R.
1966: Development of submarine physiography in the Canadian Arctic and its relation to crustal movements; in Symposium on Continental Drift, ed. G.V. Garland; Royal Society of Canada, Special Publication, no. 9, p. 77-101.

1979: Review of surficial geology and engineering hazards in the Canadian offshore; Maritime Sediments, v. 15, p. 55-91.

Pelletier, B., Wagner, F.J.E. and Grant, A.C.
1968: Marine geology; in Science, History and Hudson Bay, ed. C.S. Beale, Volume 2; Department of Energy, Mines and Resources, Ottawa, p. 557-613.

Perkin, R.G. and Lewis, E.L.
1978: Mixing in an arctic fjord; Journal of Physical Oceanography, v. 8, p. 873-880.

Perry, R.B.
1961: A study of the marine sediments of the Canadian eastern Arctic Archipelago; Canadian Fishery Research Board Report no. 89, 89 p.

Petersen, G.H.
1977: Biological effects of sea ice and icebergs in Greenland; in Polar Oceans, ed. M.J. Dunbar: Arctic Institute of North America, Calgary, Alberta, p. 319-329.

Petrie, B. and Anderson, C.
1983: Circulation on the Newfoundland continental shelf; Atmosphere-Ocean, v. 21, p. 207-226.

Petrie, B. and Smith, P.C.
1977: Low Refrequency Motions on the Scotian Shelf and Slope; Atmosphere, v. 15, p. 117-140.

Petro-Canada
1982: Labrador initial environment evaluation; unpublished report submitted to Government of Canada and Newfoundland, January 1982.

Pietrafesa, L.J.
1984: Shelfbreak circulation, fronts and physical oceanography; east and west coast perspectives; in Siliclastic Shelf Sediments, ed. R.W. Tillman and C.T. Siemers; Society of Economic Paleontologists and Minerologists, Special Publication no. 33, p. 233-250.

Pilkey, O.H., Locker, S.D., and Cleary, W.J.
1980: Comparison of sand layer geometry on flat floors of 10 modern depositional basins; American Association of Petroleum Geologists Bulletin, v. 64, p. 841-856.

Piper, D.J.W.

1976: The use of ice rafted marine sediments in determining glacial conditions; Revue de Geographie de Montreal, v. 30, p. 207-212.

1978: Turbidite muds and silts on deep sea fans and abyssal plains; in Submarine Canyon and Fan Sedimentation, ed. D.J. Stanley and G. Kelling; Dowden, Hutchinson and Ross, Stroudsburg, p. 163-175.

Piper, D.J.W. and Normark, W.R.

1982a: Acoustic interpretation of Quaternary sedimentation and erosion on the channelled upper Laurentian Fan, Atlantic margin of Canada; Canadian Journal of Earth Sciences, v. 19, p. 1974-1984.

1982b: Effects of the 1929 Grand Banks earthquake on the continental slope off eastern Canada; in Current Research, Part B, Geological Survey of Canada, Paper 82-1B, p. 147-151.

Piper, D.J.W. and Sparkes, R.

1987: Proglacial sediment instability feature on the Scotian Slope at 63°W; Marine Geology, v. 76, p. 15-31.

Piper, D.J.W. and Wilson, E.

1983: Surficial geology of the upper Scotian Shelf Slope west of Verrill Canyon; Geological Survey of Canada, Open File 939, 73 p.

Piper, D.J.W., Farre, J.A. and Shore, A.

1985a: Mid-range side-scan and 4.5 kHz sub-bottom profiles survey of mass-movement features, Scotian Slope at 61°40'W; Geological Society of America Bulletin, v. 96, p. 1508-1517.

Piper, D.J.W., Letson, J.R.J., DeIure, A.M. and Barrie, C.Q.

1983: Sediment accumulation in low-sedimentation, wave-dominated, glaciated inlets; Sedimentary Geology, v. 36, p. 195-215.

Piper, D.J.W., Shor, A.N., Farre, J.A., O'Connell, S.O., and Jacobi, R.

1985b: Sediment slides and turbidity currents on the Laurentian Fan; Sidescan sonar investigations near the epicenter of the 1929 Grand Banks earthquake; Geology, v. 13, p. 538-541.

Piper, D.J.W., Stow, D.A.V. and Normark, W.R.

1984: The Laurentian Fan, Sohm Abyssal Plain; Geomarine Letters, v. 33, p. 141-146.

Ploeg, J.

1971: Wave climate study, Great Lakes and Gulf of St. Lawrence; National Research Council Canada, Mechanical Engineering Report MH-107A 1, p. 1-160.

Postma, H.

1967: Sediment transport and sedimentation in the estuarine environment; in Estuaries, ed. G.M. Lauff; American Association for the Advancement of Science, v. 83, p. 158-179

Powell, R.D.

1981: A model for sedimentation by tidewater glaciers; Annals of Glaciology, v. 2, p. 129-134.

Powers, M.C. and Kinsman, B.

1953: Shell accumulations in underwater sediments and their relation to the thickness of the traction zone; Journal of Sedimentary Petrology, v. 23, p. 229-234.

Praeg, D.B., MacLean, B., Hardy, I.A., and Mudie, P.J.

1986: Quaternary geology of the southeast Baffin Island continental shelf; Geological Survey of Canada, Paper 85-14, 38 p.

Prior, D.B. and Coleman, J.M.

1983: Lateral movements of sediments; in The Offshore Environment and Petroleum Development, ed. P.G. Teleki, L.E. Garrison and N.T. Monney, Ocean Science and Engineering, v. 8, no. 3, p. 113-155.

Pritchard, D.W.

1956: The dynamic structure of a coastal plain estuary; Journal of Marine Research, v. 15, p. 33-42.

1967: Observations of circulation in coastal plain estuary; in Estuaries, ed. G.H. Lauff; American Association for the Advancement of Sciences, Publication no. 83, p. 37-44.

Pugh, D.T. and Vassie, J.M.

1980: Application of the joint probability method for extreme sealevel computations; Proceedings of the Institute of Civil Engineers v. 69, p. 959-975.

Quinlan, G. and Beaumont, C.

1981: A comparison of observed and theoretical postglacial relative sea level in Atlantic Canada; Canadian Journal of Earth Sciences, v. 18, p. 1146-1163.

Reineck, H.E. and Singh, I.B.

1975: Depositional Sedimentary Environments; Springer-Verlag, Berlin, 439 p.

Reinson, G.E.

1977a: Barrier Island Systems; in Facies Models, 1st Edition, ed. R.G. Walker; Geoscience Canada, Reprint Series 1, p. 57-74.

1977b: Examination of bedforms in shallow water using sidescan sonar, Miramichi estuary, New Brunswick; in Current Research, Part B, Geological Survey of Canada, Paper 77-1B, p. 99-105.

1979: Longitudinal and transverse bedforms on a large tidal delta, Gulf of St. Lawrence, Canada; Marine Geology, v. 31, p. 279-296.

Richardson, M.J., Wimbush, M., and Mayer, L.

1981: Exceptionally strong near-bottom flows on the continental rise of Nova Scotia; Science, v. 213, p. 887-888.

Rosen, P.S.

1979: Boulder barricades in central Labrador; Journal of Sedimentary Petrology, v. 49, p. 1113-1124.

Schafer, C.T.

1973: Distribution of foraminifera near pollution sources in Chaleur Bay; Water, Air and Soil Pollution, v. 2, p. 219-233.

Schafer, C.T., Smith, J.M., and Loring, D.H.

1980: Recent sedimentation events at the head of the Saguenay Fjord, Canada; Environmental Geology, v. 3, p. 139-150.

Schafer, C.T., Smith, J.M., and Seibert, G.

1983: Significance of natural and anthropogenic sediment inputs to the Saguenay Fjord, Quebec; Sedimentary Geology, v. 36, p. 177-194.

Schafer, C.T., Tan, F.C., Williams, D.F., and Smith, J.N.

1985: Late Glacial to Recent stratigraphy and sedimentary processes; Newfoundland continental slope and rise; Canadian Journal of Earth Sciences, v. 22, p. 266-282.

Schapery, R.A.

1974a: Wave-sea bottom interaction study (Phase One) Part 1: Theory and results; Mechanics and Materials Research Centre, Texas Engineering Experiment Station, Texas A & M University, 43 p.

1974b: Wave-sea bottom interaction study (Final Report) Part I: Theory and results; Mechanics and Materials Research Centre, Texas Engineering Experiment Station, Texas A & M University, 46 p.

Schubel, J.R. and Carter, H.H.

1984: The estuary as a filter for fine-grained suspended sediment; in the Estuary as a Filter, ed. V.S. Kennedy; Academic Press, London, p. 81-105.

Schubel, J.R., Wilson, R.E., and Okubo, A.

1977: Vertical transport of suspended sediment in upper Chesapeake Bay; in Transport Processes in Estuarine Environments, 7th Baruch Research Symposium, ed. B. Kjerfve; University of South Carolina, Columbia, p. 161-175.

Seaconsult Marine Research Ltd.

1986: Sediment transport; present knowledge and industry needs; Environmental Revolving Funds, Report 027, Ottawa, Ontario, 394 p.

Seed, H.B. and Rahman, M.S.

1978: Wave-induced pore pressure in relation to ocean floor stability of cohesionless soils; Marine Geotechnology, v. 3, p. 123-150.

Sempels, J.

1982: Coastlines of the eastern Arctic; Arctic, v. 35, p. 170-179.

Sérodes, J.

1980: Étude de la sédimentation intertidale de l'estuaire moyen du St-Laurent; Université Laval, Département Génie Civil, Environment Canada, Report n. DGE1-Q, 26 p.

Shea, J.H.

1974: Deficiencies of clastic particles of certain sizes; Journal of Sedimentary Petrology, v. 44, p. 985-1003.

Shepard, F.P.

1963: Submarine Geology; Harper and Row, New York, p. 357.

Shepard, F.P., Marshall, N.F., McLoughlin, P.A., and Sullivan, G.G.

1979: Currents in submarine canyons and other seavalleys; American Association of Petroleum Geologists, Studies in Marine Geology, v. 8, 173 p.

Shipp, R.C.

1984: Bedforms and depositional sedimentary structures of a barred nearshore system, Eastern Long Island, New York; Marine Geology, v. 60, p. 235-259.

Shurr, G.W.

1984: Geometry of shelf sandstone bodies in the Shannon sandstone of southeastern Montana; in Siliciclastic Shelf Sediments, ed. R.W. Tillman and C.T. Siemers; Society of Economic Paleontologists and Mineralogists, Special Publication no. 34, p. 63-83.

Silverberg, N. and Sundby, B.

1979: Observations in the turbidity maximum of the St. Lawrence Estuary; Canadian Journal of Earth Sciences, v. 16, p. 939-950.

Singh, R.D., Dobry, R., Doyle, E.H., and Idriss, I.M.

1981: Nonlinear seismic response of soft clay sites; Journal of the Geotechnical Engineering Division, Proceedings of American Society of Civil Engineers, n. GT9, Paper 16493, p. 1201-1218.

Slatt, R.M.

1974: Formation of palimpsest sediments, Conception Bay, Newfoundland; Geological Society of America Bulletin, v. 85, p. 821-826.

1977: Late Quaternary terrigenous and carbonate sedimentation on Grand Bank of Newfoundland; Geological Society of America, Bulletin, v. 88, p. 1357-1367.

Slatt, R.M. and Gardiner, W.W.

1976: Comparative petrology and source of sediments in Newfoundland fjords; Canadian Journal of Earth Sciences, v. 13, p. 1460-1465.

Slatt, R.M. and Lew, A.B.
1973: Provenance of Quaternary sediments on the Labrador continental shelf and slope; Journal of Sedimentary Petrology, v. 43, p. 1054-1060.

Smith, J.D.
1969: Geomorphology of a sand ridge;Journal of Geology, v. 77, p. 39-55.

Smith, J.D. and Hopkins, T.S.
1972: Sediment transport on the continental shelf off Washington and Oregon in light of recent measurements; in Shelf Sediment Transport Process and Pattern, ed. D.J.P. Swift, D.B. Duane and O.H. Pilkey; Dowden, Hutchinson and Ross Inc., Stroudsberg, p. 143-180.

Smith, J.N. and Ellis, K.M.
1982: Transport mechanism for Pb-210, Cs-137 and Pu fallout radionuclides through fluvial-marine systems; Geochimica et Cosmochimica Acta, v. 46, p. 941-954.

Smith, J.N. and Walton, A.
1980: Sediment accumulation rates and geochronologies measured in the Saguenay Fjord using the Pb-210 dating method; Geochemica et Cosmochimica Acta, v. 44, p. 225-240.

Smith, P.C., Petrie, B., and Mann, C.R.
1978: Circulation, variability and dynamics of the Scotian Shelf and Slope; Journal of the Fisheries Research Board Canada, v. 35, p. 1067-1083.

Sonu, C.J.
1968: Collective movement of sediment in nearshore environments; Proceedings of the 11th Conference on Coastal Engineering, September 1968, London, England, v. 1, p. 373-400.

Soulsby, R.L.
1983: The bottom boundary layer of shelf seas; in Physical Oceanography of Coastal and Shelf Seas, ed. B. Johns; Elsevier, Amsterdam, p. 189-266.

Southard, J.B.
1971: Representation of bed configurations in depth-velocity-size diagrams; Journal of Sedimentary Petrology, v. 41, p. 903-915.

Stahl, J., Koczan, J., and Swift, D.J.P.
1974: Anatomy of a shoreface-connected sand ridge on the New Jersey shelf; implications for the genesis of the shelf surficial sand sheet; Geology, v. 2, p. 117-120.

Stanley, D.J. and Silverberg, N.
1969: Recent slumping on the continental slope off Sable Island Bank, southeast Canada; Earth and Planetary Sciences Letters, v. 6, p. 123-133.

Stanley, D.J., Swift, D.J.P., Silverberg, N., James, N.P., and Sutton, R.G.
1972: Late Quaternary progradation and sand spillover on the outer continental margin off Nova Scotia, southeastern Canada; Smithsonian Contributions to the Earth Sciences, Washington, D.C., no. 8, 88 p.
1973: Recent sand spillover off Sable Island Bank, Scotian Shelf; in Earth Science Symposium on Offshore Eastern Canada, ed. P.J. Hood; Geological Survey of Canada, Paper 71-23, p. 167-194.

Stanley, D.J. and Taylor, P.T.
1981: Volcanogenic sediment and proximal versus distal provenance in abyssal plains; Marine Geology, v. 43, p. M29-M38.

Stanley, D.J., Taylor, P.T., Sheng, H., and Stuckenrath, R.
1981: Sohm Abyssal Plain; evaluating proximal sediment provenance; Smithsonian Contribution to Marine Science, Washington, D.C., no. 11, 48 p.

Stehman, C.F.
1976: Pleistocene and Recent sediment of northern Placentia Bay, Newfoundland; Canadian Journal of Earth Sciences, v. 13, p. 1386-1392.

Stewart, H.B., Jr. and Jordan, G.F.
1964: Underwater sand ridges on Georges Shoal; in Papers in Marine Geology, ed. R.L. Miller; Macmillan, New York, p. 102-114.

Stokoe, K.H. (II)
1980: Dynamic properties of offshore silty samples; in Proceedings of the 12th Annual Offshore Technical Conference, May 5-8, 1980, Houston, Texas, Paper 3771, p. 289-302.

Stow, D.A.V.
1979: Distinguishing between fine-grained turbidites and countourites on the Nova Scotian deep water margin; Sedimentology, v. 26, p. 371-387.
1981: Laurentian Fan; morphology, sediments, processes and growth pattern; American Association of Petroleum Geologists Bulletin, v. 65, p. 375-393.

Stow, D.A.V. and Bowen, A.J.
1980: A physical model for the transport and sorting of fine-grained sediment by turbidity currents; Sedimentology, v. 27, p. 31-46.

Stow, D.A.V. and Lovell, J.P.B.
1979: Contourites: their recognition in modern and ancient sediments; Earth Science Review, v. 14, p. 251-291.

Stow, D.A.V. and Piper, D.J.W. (ed.)
1984: Fine-Grained Sediments; Deep Water Processes and Products; Geological Society of London, Special Publication; Blackwell Scientific, London, 659 p.

Stubblefield, W.L., McGrail, D.W., and Kersey, D.G.
1984: Recognition of transgressive and post-transgressive sand ridges on the New Jersey continental shelf; in Siliciclastic Shelf Sediments, ed. R.W. Tillman and C.T. Siemers; Society of Economic Paleontologists and Mineralogists, Special Publication no. 34, p. 1-23.

Swift, D.J.P.
1976: Continental shelf sedimentation; in Marine Sediment Transport and Environmental Management, ed. D.J. Stanley and D.J.P. Swift; J. Wiley and Sons, New York, p. 311-350.

Swift, D.J.P. and Freeland, G.L.
1978: Current lineations and sand waves on the inner shelf, middle Atlantic Bight of North America; Journal of Sedimentary Petrology, v. 48, p. 1257-1266.

Swift, D.J.P. and Ludwick, J.C.
1976: Substrate response to hydraulic process; grain-size frequency distributions and bedforms; in Marine Sediment Transport and Environmental Management, ed. D.J. Stanley and D.J.P. Swift; J. Wiley and Sons, New York, p. 159-196.

Swift, D.J.P. and Lyall, A.K.
1967: Bay of Fundy; reconnaissance by subbottom profiler; Maritime Sediments, v. 3, p. 67-70.

Swift, D.J.P., McKinney, T.F., and Stahl, L.
1984: Recognition of transgressive and post-transgressive sand ridges on the New Jersey continental shelf; discussion; in Siliciclastic Shelf Sediments, ed. R.W. Tillman and C.T. Siemers; Society of Economic Paleontologists and Mineralogists, Special Publication no. 34, p. 25-36.

Swift, D.J.P., Parker, G., Lanfredi, N.W., Perillo, G., and Figge, K.
1978: Shoreface-connected sand ridges on American and European shelves; a comparison; Estuarine and Coastal Marine Science, v. 7, p. 257-273.

Swift, D.J.P., Young, R.A., Clarke, T.L., Vincent, C.E., Niedoroda, A., and Lesht, B.
1981: Sediment transport in the Middle Atlantic Bight of North America; Synopsis of recent observations; in Holocene Marine Sedimentation of the North Sea, ed. S.D. Nio, R.T.E. Shuttenhelm and Tj.C.E. Van Weering; Blackwell Scientific, Oxford, p. 361-383.

Syvitski, J.P.M. (ed.)
1984: Sedimentology of arctic fjords experiment; Hu 83-028 Data Report, Volume 2; Canadian Data Report Hydrography Ocean Sciences, v. 28, 1100 p.
1986: Modern methods of grain size analysis; Report of the 1st Working Group Meeting, Bedford Institute of Oceanography, Dartmouth, Nova Scotia, Canada, 14 p.

Syvitski, J.P.M., Asprey, K.W., Clattenburg, D.A., and Hodge, G.D.
1985: The prodelta environment; suspended particle dynamics; Sedimentology, v. 32, p. 83-107.

Syvitski, J.P.M. and Blakeney, C.P. (ed.)
1983: Sedimentology of arctic fjords experiment; HU 82-031 Data Report, Volume 1; Canadian Data Report Hydrography Ocean Sciences, v. 12, 935 p.

Syvitski, J.P.M. and Farrow, G.E.
1983: Structures and processes in bayhead deltas; Knight and Bute Inlet, British Columbia; Sedimentary Geology, v. 36, p. 217-244.

Syvitski, J.P.M. and Schafer, C.T.
1985: Sedimentology of arctic fjord experiments (SAFE): 1, Project Introduction; Arctic, v. 38, p. 264-270.

Syvitski, J.P.M., Blakeney, C.P., and Hay, A.E.
1983a: SAFE; HU-82-031 sidescan sonar and sounder profiles; in Sedimentology of Arctic Fjords Experiment: HU-82-031 Data Report, Volume 1; Canada Data Report Hydrography Ocean Sciences, v. 12, p. 16-1 to 16-49.

Syvitski, J.P.M., Burrell, D.C., and Skei, J.M.
1987: Fjords: Processes and Products; Springer-Verlag Publishing Co., New York, 379 p.

Syvitski, J.P.M., Fader, G.B., Josenhans, H.W., MacLean, B., and Piper, D.J.W.
1983b: Seabed investigations of the Canadian east coast and arctic using Pisces IV; Geoscience Canada, v. 10, p. 59-68.

Syvitski, J.P.M., Silverberg, N., Oulette, G., and Asprey, K.W.
1983c: First observations of benthos and seston from a submersible in the lower St. Lawrence estuary; Geographie Physique et Quaternaire, v. 37, p. 227-240.

Taylor, R.B.
1973: Coastal environments and processes in the Canadian Arctic Archipelago; M.Sc. thesis, McMaster University, Hamilton, Ontario, p. 210.
1980a: Coastal environments along the northern shore of Somerset Island, District of Franklin; in the Coastline of Canada, ed. S.B. McCann; Geological Survey of Canada, Paper 80-10, p. 239-250.
1980b: Beach thaw depth and the effects of ice-bonded sediment on beach stability, Canadian Arctic Islands; in First Canadian Coastal Conference, 1980; Associate for Research on Shoreline Erosion and Sedimentation, National Research Council Canada, Ottawa, p. 103-121.

Taylor, R.B. and McCann, S.B.
1983: Coastal depositional landforms in northern Canada; in Shore-lines and Isostacy, ed. D.E. Smith and A.G. Dawson; Institute of British Geographers, Special Publication no. 16, Academic Press, London.

Taylor, R.B., Wittman, S.L., Milne, M.J., and Kober, S.M.
1985: Beach morphology and coastal changes at selected sites, mainland Nova Scotia; Geological Survey of Canada, Paper 85-12, 59 p.

Terwindt, H.J. and Breusers, H.N.C.
1972: Experiments on the origin of flaser, lenticular and sand-clay alternating bedding; Sedimentology, v. 19, p. 75-98.

Terzaghi, K. and Peck, R.B.
1967: Soil Mechanics in Engineering Practice; J. Wiley and Sons, New York, 729 p.

Thiers, G.R. and Seed, H.B.
1968: Strength and stress-strain characteristics of clays subjected to seismic loading conditions: Vibration effects of earthquakes on soils and foundations; American Society for Testing and Materials, Special Technical Paper 450, 17 p.

Thorn, M.F.C.
1979: The effect of waves on the tidal transport of sand; Hydraulic Research Station, Wallingford, Oxon, Notes 21, p. 4-5.

Tillman, R.W. and Martinsen, R.S.
1984: The Shannon shelf-ridge sandstone complex, Salt Creek anticline area, Power River Basin, Wyoming; in Siliciclastic Shelf Sediments, ed. R.W. Tillman and C.T. Siemers; Society of Economic Paleontologists and Mineralogists, Special Publication no. 34, p. 85-142.

Todd, B.J.
1984: Iceberg scouring on Saglek Bank, northern Labrador Shelf; M.Sc. thesis, Dalhousie University, Halifax, Nova Scotia, 166 p.

Trenhaile, A.S.
1983: The development of shore platforms in high latitudes; in Shorelines and Isostasy, ed. D.E. Smith and A.G. Dawson; Academic Press, New York, p. 77-93.

Trites, R.W.
1982: Overview of oceanographic conditions in NAFO subareas 2, 3, and 4 during the 1970-79 decade; North American Fisheries and Oceans Science Council Studies 5, p. 51-78.

Trumbull, J.V.A.
1972: Atlantic continental shelf and slope of the United States — Sand-size fraction of bottom sediments, New Jersey to Nova Scotia; United States Geological Survey, Professional Paper 529-K, 45 p.

Tsai, Chen-feng, Lam, I., and Martin, R.M.
1980: Seismic response of cohesive marine soils; Journal of the Geotechnical Engineering Division, Proceedings American Society of Civil Engineers, no. GT9, Paper 15708, p. 997-1012.

Twitchell, D.C.
1981: Bedform distribution and inferred sand transport on Georges Bank; Geological Survey of Canada, Open File 764, 32 p.

Twitchell, D.C., McClennen, C.E., and Butman, B.
1981: Morphology and processes associated with the accumulation of the fine-grained sediment deposit on the southern New England shelf; Journal of Sedimentary Petrology, v. 51, p. 269-280.

Uchupi, E.
1963: Sediments on the continental margin off eastern United States; United States Geological Survey, Professional Paper 475-C, p. 132-137.

Uchupi, E. and Austin, J.A.
1979: The stratigraphy and structure of the Laurentian core region; Canadian Journal of Earth Sciences, v. 16, p. 1726-1752.

Vanney, J.R. and Stanley, D.J.
1983: Shelfbreak physiography; an overview; in The Shelfbreak, Critical Interface on Continental Margins, ed. D.J. Stanley and G.T. Moore; Society of Economic Paleontologists and Mineralogists, Special Publication no. 33, p. 1-24.

Vanoni, V.A.
1975: Sedimentation Engineering; American Society Civil Engineers, New York, 745 p.

Vilks, G.
1980: Post glacial basin sedimentation on Labrador Shelf; Geological Survey of Canada, Paper 78-28, 28 p.

Vilks, G., Buckley, D.E., and Keigwin, L.
1985: Late Quaternary sedimentation on the southern Sohm Abyssal Plain; Sedimentology, v. 32, p. 69-82.

Vilks, G. and Krauel, D.P.
1982: Environmental geology of the Miramichi Estuary; physical oceanography; Geological Survey of Canada, Paper 81-24, p. 1-53.

Vilks, G. and Mudie, P.J.
1983: Evidence for postglacial paleoceanographic and paleoclimatic changes in Lake Melville, Labrador, Canada; Arctic and Alpine Research, v. 15, p. 307-320.

Vincent, C.E., Young, R.A., and Swift, D.J.P.
1982: On the relationship between bedload and suspended sand transport on the inner shelf, Long Island, New York; Journal of Geophysical Research, v. 87, p. 4163-4170.

Vorndran, U.G. and Sommerhoff, G.
1974: Glaziologisch-glazialmorphologische Untersuchungen im Gebiet des Qôrqup-Auslafsgletschers (Südwest-Grönland); Polarforschung, v. 44, p. 137-147.

Vorren, T.O., Morten, H., Edvardsen, M., and Hanson, O.W.L.
1983: Glaciogenic sediments and sedimentary environments on continental shelves; General principles with a case study for the Norwegian shelf; in Glacial Deposits in North West Europe 1983, ed. Jürgen Ehlers; p. 61-73.

Walker, R.G. (ed.)
1979: Facies Models, First Edition; Geological Association of Canada, Geoscience Canada Reprint Series 1, 211 p.
1984: Facies Models, Second Edition; Geological Association of Canada, Geoscience Canada Reprint Series 1, 317 p.

Wang, Y. and Piper, D.J.W.
1982: Dynamic geomorphology of the Drumlin Coast of southeast Cape Breton Island; Maritime Sediments and Atlantic Geology, v. 18, p. 1-27.

Welsfad, J.E.
1974: Morphological maps of the Fundy coast; Maritime Sediments, v. 10, p. 46-51.

Winters, G.V.
1983: Modelling suspended sediment dynamics of the Miramichi Estuary, New Brunswick, Canada; Canadian Journal of Fisheries and Aquatic Sciences, v. 40, p. 105-116.

Woodward-Clyde Consultants
1982a: A study of accessibility of three small craft larbours, western Newfoundland; Department of Fisheries and Oceans, Canada, St. John's Newfoundland, 89 p.
1982b: Hydraulic and physical character of Placentia, in relation to the fishing industry; Department of Fisheries and Oceans, Canada; St. John's, Newfoundland, 50 p.

Wright, L.D. and Short, A.D.
1984: Morphodynamic variability of surf zones and beaches; a synthesis; Marine Geology, v. 56, p. 93-118.

Wright, L.E., Short, A.D., and Green, M.O.
1985: Short-term changes in the morphodynamic state of beaches and surf zones; an empirical predictive model; Marine Geology, v. 62, p. 339-364.

Yalin, M.S.
1963: An expression for bedload transportation; Journal of Hydraulic Division American Society of Civil Engineers, no. 89, p. 221-250.
1972: Mechanics of Sediment Transport; Pergamon Press, New York, 290 p.

Young, R.N. and Southard, J.B.
1978: Erosion of fine-grained marine sediments; seafloor and laboratory experiments; Geological Society of America Bulletin, v. 89, p. 663-672.

Author's address

C. Amos
Atlantic Geoscience Centre
Geological Survey of Canada
Bedford Institute of Oceanography
P.O. Box 1006
Dartmouth, Nova Scotia
B2Y 4A2

Printed in Canada

Chapter 12

PETROLEUM RESOURCES

Chapter 12

PETROLEUM RESOURCES

J.S. Bell and G.R. Campbell

INTRODUCTION

From both an industrial and an academic standpoint, an understanding of hydrocarbon generation, migration and entrapment in basins is enlightening and beneficial. Exploration can be targeted more effectively, undiscovered resources can be anticipated more accurately and, since the processes involved relate to geological events, understanding them advances our knowledge of basin evolution.

In this chapter, the results of exploration to date are reviewed, and recent scientific studies are summarized on source rock characteristics, maturation, hydrocarbon migration and entrapment. Assessment of both the discovered resources and undiscovered hydrocarbon potential is provided. The discussion focuses on three well-explored regions—the Scotian Shelf and Slope, the Grand Banks of Newfoundland, and Labrador Shelf—and brief reference is made to the Gulf of St. Lawrence and Bay of Fundy areas.

SCOTIAN SHELF AND SLOPE

The area encompassed by the Scotian Shelf and Slope for the purposes of this chapter includes that part of the Scotian Basin (Fig. 12.1) which extends from the mid-line of the Northeast (Fundian) Channel in the Georges Bank area to the mid-line of the Laurentian Channel (Map 850-A, in pocket), and from the edge of Mesozoic-Cenozoic sediments adjacent to Nova Scotia to the 1500 m isobath. The total area is approximately 130 000 km^2 (Fig. 12.1).

Exploration history

Exploration activity by the petroleum industry has been underway for over 30 years. The initial geophysical survey, an airborne magnetometer program, was conducted by Mobil Oil Canada, Ltd., in 1959 in the Sable Island area. This work was followed in 1960 by Mobil's first marine seismic survey. Since then over 300 000 line kilometres of seismic data have been acquired on the Scotian margin by the oil industry.

Drilling began in 1967, with the Sable Island C-67 well (well locations are shown in Fig. 1, in pocket). One hundred and twenty-five wells have been drilled up to the end of July 1987 on the Scotian Shelf and Slope during two cycles of exploration activity (Table 12.1). Over half of the wells

Bell, J.S. and Campbell, G.R.
1990: Petroleum resources, Chapter 12 in Geology of the Continental Margin of Eastern Canada, M.J. Keen and G.L. Williams (ed.); Geological Survey of Canada, Geology of Canada, no. 2, p. 677-720 (also Geological Society of America, The Geology of North America, v. I-1).

drilled, and all the significant discoveries, are concentrated in the immediate vicinity of Sable Island. To date, 83 separate structures have been drilled and 21 significant discoveries have been made. This impressive success rate of 25%, or one-in-four, is indicative of the potential of the area.

The drilling density for the Scotian Shelf and Slope is approximately one well per 1600 km^2 for the region as a whole.

Significant discoveries

Exploration to the end of 1986 has resulted in twenty-one significant discoveries, consisting of seventeen pools of gas and condensate, two oil and gas pools and two oil pools (Table 12.2). To qualify as "significant" within the context of current Federal legislation, each discovery must have: a pay section which is recognizable on logs; an areal extent documented by seismic mapping; and, most importantly, drillstem test results which establish that the reservoir zones are capable of sustained flow.

The various reservoir units containing pay in these discoveries are indicated on the stratigraphic chart (Fig. 12.2) derived from Wade et al. (in press). The most important hydrocarbon reservoirs are the sandstones of the Upper Jurassic Mic Mac Formation and the Lower Cretaceous Missisauga Formation.

The sequence of discoveries illustrates the evolution of exploration concepts for this region (Fig. 12.3, Table 12.3). Shell Canada's Onondaga E-84 well, drilled on a salt-cored structure in 1969, gave the first indication of gas and condensate in this area. Over the next six years, gas and condensate or gas and oil were discovered in five other wells on salt diapirs, in Sable Island E-48 at the west end of the island, in Primrose N-50, and on down-to-the-south fault closure at Thebaud P-84, Intrepid L-80 and Citnalta I-59. The significant portion of the Thebaud pay was found in deep, overpressured reservoirs, now thought to be equivalent to the upper portion of the pay section in the Venture field. However, none of the gas discoveries made in this first cycle of exploration were considered to be large enough for commercial development. The Cohasset oil pool was discovered in 1973 (Cohasset D-42) in a trap with low relief closure overlying Jurassic carbonates.

In June 1979, industry interest was rekindled with the announcement by Mobil Oil Canada, of the results from their Venture D-23 exploratory well located just off the eastern tip of Sable Island. Gas and condensate were identified in six separate overpressured sandstones which were clearly the best reservoir units discovered to that time. Drillstem test results indicated flows of gas and condensate at up to 0.632×10^6 m^3/d of gas and 50.3 m^3/d of condensate. The four delineation wells on the structure

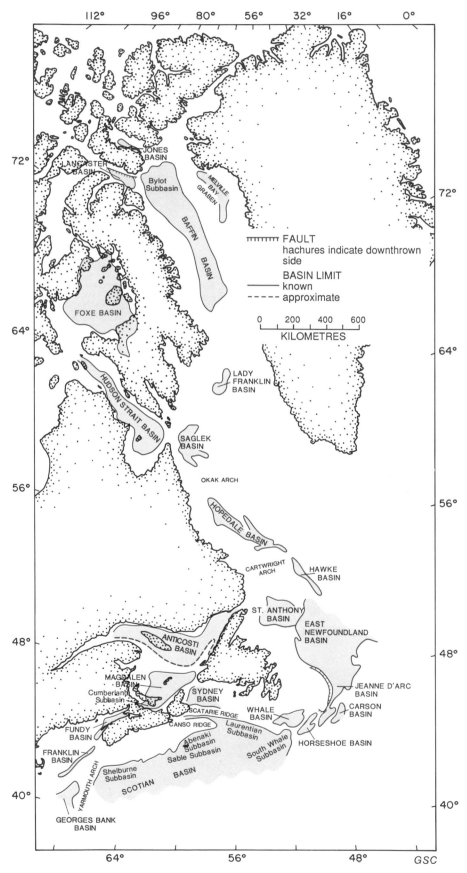

Figure 12.1. Sedimentary basins of offshore eastern Canada.

Table 12.1. Drilling statistics for offshore eastern Canada.

Year	Wells terminated per year (table does not include re-spuds)		
	Scotian Shelf and slope, Gulf of St. Lawrence, Bay of Fundy	Grand Banks, East Newfoundland Basin	Labrador Shelf, Southeast Baffin Shelf
1966	-	2	-
1967	-	-	-
1968	1	-	-
1969	1	-	1
1970	16	-	-
1971	14	4	1
1972	8	9	-
1973	13	15	2
1974	9	9	1
1975	3	3	5
1976	6	-	3
1977	2	-	-
1978	5	-	3
1979	1	3	5
1980	2	2	5
1981	1	6	2
1982	3	4	2
1983	12	4	1
1984	13	10	-
1985	14	14	-
1986	8	7	-
1987	3	3	-

extended the payzone to 18 zones over a 1500 m interval and have confirmed the extent of pay over the area shown in Figure 12.4. According to recent estimates, the Venture field contains on the order of 42×10^9 m^3 of recoverable gas and 64×10^6 m^3 of condensate, almost all of which is in overpressured sandstones of the Missisauga Formation (Wade and MacLean, Chapter 5; Lewis and Keen, Chapter 14). A seismic line through the Venture pool is shown in Figure 12.10.

Since the discovery of Venture, thirteen additional significant discoveries have been made, twelve of gas and condensate, all on fault-bounded prospects, and one of oil (Fig. 12.3). Mobil's activity has been directed to finding additional gas reserves on their Sable Island block to support economic development of the Venture field and as a result, six additional gas pools have been found. Significant discoveries by Mobil in 1985 included three gas and condensate discoveries at West Olympia O-51, West Venture N-91 and West Venture C-62. At West Venture C-62, one of the four zones tested flowed gas at up to 0.95×10^6 m^3/d and 24.3 m^3/d of condensate. West Venture N-91 was spudded on 19 April 1984 and had been drilled to 5547 m when a subsurface blowout occurred. Following repeated attempts to control the well (Lewis and Keen, Chapter 14), the flow was terminated and the well was plugged and abandoned as a significant discovery. Shell Canada has made four recent gas and condensate discoveries southeast of Sable Island. At North Triumph G-43 the results of tests of two zones were reported. Maximum flow rate was 1.05×10^6 m^3/d and 31.8 m^3/d of condensate. Alma F-67, Glenelg J-48 and Husky's Chebucto K-90 gas and condensate discovery of 1984 are all on a linear trend with North Triumph and hold some promise of eventual commercial development due to their similarities and proximity. In

March 1986 attention was drawn to the Cohasset oil pool by the announcement by Petro-Canada and partners (Nova Scotia Resources Ltd. and Canterra Energy) of the test results of Cohasset A-52, the second Cohasset delineation well (Oilweek, 1986). Oil flow rates were the highest ever recorded for any well in eastern Canada. The maximum rate for an individual sand was 1230 m^3/d. The second oil discovery on the Scotian Shelf was made in 1986 at the Shell Panuke B-90 well. A drillstem test of a sandstone interval in the Logan Canyon Formation (thought to be equivalent to the reservoir units of the Cohasset structure) flowed oil at up to 949 m^3/d.

Table 12.2. Discovered resources and hydrocarbon potential, Scotian Shelf.

Significant Discoveries		
Gas and Condensate:	17	
Gas and Oil:	2	
Oil:	2	
Total:	**21**	
	Condensate and Oil 10^6m^3	Gas 10^9m^3
Discovered Resources	21.1	149
Potential	171	512
(%) Discovered	12%	29%

Discovered resources and hydrocarbon characteristics

Estimates of discovered resources for each significant discovery are computed in terms of a "Best Current Estimate". The "Best Current Estimate" comprises those recoverable resources which have been confirmed by logs and testing, and which could be produced using conventional production methods. The extent of the pay area surrounding the well(s) is determined from the interpretation of geophysical, geological and engineering data, and involves a reasonable degree of certainty.

Volume estimates of the discovered resources in individual pools cannot be disclosed due to the confidential nature of the technical data. For all discoveries combined on a "Best Current Estimate" basis, current as of July 1987, the amount of discovered gas is 149.0×10^9 m^3, and

22.1×10^6 m^3 of condensate with some oil for the Scotian Shelf.

Powell and Snowdon (1979) analyzed 36 crude oil and condensate samples from the Scotian Shelf. By comparing n-alkane distributions, pristane-to-phytane ratios and carbon isotope distributions in the saturate and aromatic fractions, they were able to identify three distinct families of crude oils. These three families are largely confined to discrete stratigraphic units: 1) the Mic Mac, Missisauga and Verrill Canyon formations, 2) the Logan Canyon Formation and 3) the Wyandot Formation. Pristane-to-phytane ratios imply that, except for Wyandot Formation samples, all the oils and condensates were at least partly derived from source rocks containing terrestrially-derived organic matter. The oils and condensates in families 1 and 2 are sufficiently similar that a common source is possible.

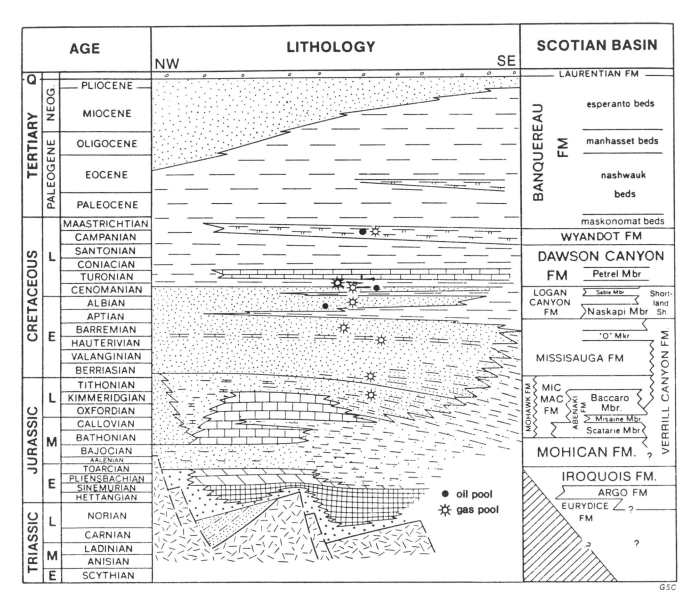

Figure 12.2. Generalized lithology and stratigraphy of the Scotian Shelf and Slope (modified from Grant et al., 1986).

Family 3 was found only in the Wyandot Formation over the Primrose salt diapir (Fig. 12.3) and is believed to represent a locally derived fluid that was generated over a thermal anomaly (Robbins and Rhodelhamel, 1976; Rashid and McAlary, 1977; Purcell et al., 1979).

Although the oil and condensate compositions are significant, particularly since the successful Cohasset A-52 well, the major hydrocarbon resource of the Scotian Shelf is gas. At the present time there are no undisputed analytical techniques for matching natural gases with the source rocks which generated them, and the problem is further complicated because gas composition appears to be a function of source-rock maturity at the time of expulsion (Tissot and Welte, 1984). Kendall and Altebaeumer (1985) analyzed the gas and/or condensate samples from more than 25 wells in the Sable Subbasin of the Scotian Basin collected at depths between 1000 m and 6000 m. Gas associated with the condensates had $\delta^{13}C$ values of methane between -38% and -44%, suggesting a highly mature source (James, 1983; Schoell, 1983).

Source rocks

Shales of the Verrill Canyon Formation (Fig. 12.2) are the most likely source rocks for most of the gas, condensate and oil discovered in the sandstone reservoirs of the Mic Mac, Missisauga, Logan Canyon, and Dawson Canyon formations (Powell, 1982). Currently, the name Verrill Canyon Formation is applied to a thick shale sequence which represents the distal facies of all lithostratigraphic units from the top of the Mohican Formation to the top of the Missisauga Formation. These units range in age from Middle Jurassic to Early Cretaceous. Such a long-ranging sequence is difficult to discuss as a geochemical entity, so the analysis is confined to the middle part of the succession close to the Jurassic-Cretaceous boundary. Powell (1982) analyzed samples from thirteen wells and determined that the shales of the Verrill Canyon Formation contain terrestrially-derived, Type III organic matter (Tissot and Welte, 1984). This substantiated earlier petrographic studies of organic residues separated from cuttings samples (Bujak et al., 1977a,b), which showed that the Verrill Canyon Formation contained abundant herbaceous, woody and coaly material. Upon maturation, these rocks would generate largely gas and condensate. Organic richness appears to be relatively low and almost constant in the wells studied by Powell (1982); total organic carbon values range from 0.55% to 2.25% and average 1.2 %. Kendall and Altebaeumer (1985), however, reported finding a deep, terrestrial source-rock interval with organic carbon content ranging up to 10% in the Venture H-22 well. They also

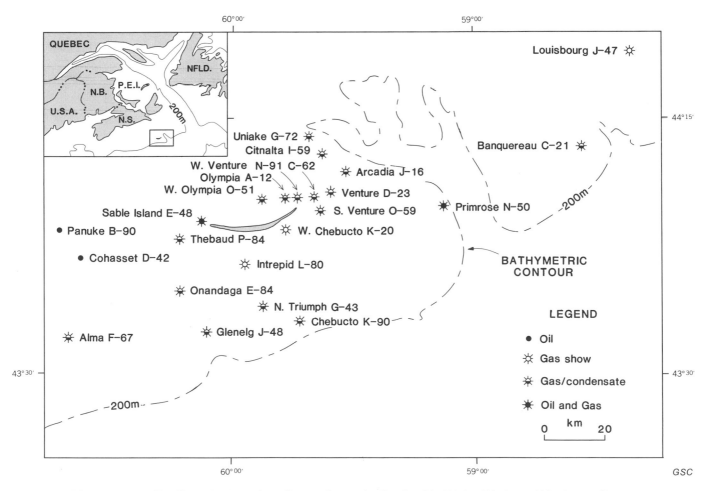

Figure 12.3. Significant hydrocarbon discoveries on the Scotian Shelf (after Wade and MacLean, Chapter 5).

683

noted that the source rock contained mainly vitrinite material with reflectance greater than 1.0 R_o and claimed that it could be correlated analytically with condensates from the same well.

Maturation and migration

A variety of indices have been used to assess or measure organic maturation levels on the Scotian Shelf. These include: 1) geothermal gradients (Robbins and Rhodelhamel, 1976; Cassou et al., 1977; Purcell et al., 1979; Issler, 1982); 2) chemical analysis of gaseous and heavy hydrocarbons (Cassou et al., 1977; Purcell et al., 1979; Hardy and Jackson, 1980); 3) colouration of dispersed organic matter (Bujak et al., 1977a,b; Cassou et al., 1977; Barss et al., 1980); 4) vitrinite reflectance (Hacquebard,

1974, 1975; Davies and Avery, 1984); and, 5) clay diagenesis (Cassou et al., 1977; Hutcheon, 1986). In the absence of sample analysis, organic maturation levels at depth can be inferred by calculation (Lopatin, 1971; Waples, 1980). What is needed is an accurate picture of the burial history and a reliable estimate of the prevailing thermal gradient(s).

As a Type III source rock, the Verrill Canyon Formation is likely to have begun generating significant quantities of gas and condensate when it reached a maturation level equivalent to vitrinite reflectance of 0.7% R_o (Monnier et al., 1983; Powell and Snowdon, 1983). Powell (1982) compiled all the available measured maturation indices and prepared a maturation facies map for the base Cretaceous level (Fig. 12.5). Also shown is the landward limit of the Verrill Canyon shale facies at this level (Given, 1977).

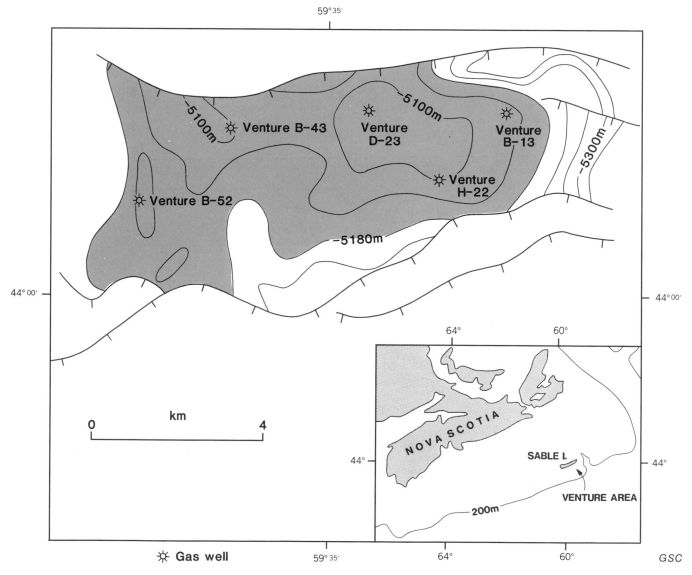

Figure 12.4. Structure map of the Venture Field with area of closure shown in red speckled pattern. Contours are drawn at 40 m intervals on a limestone bed near the top of the Jurassic section (after Meneley, 1981).

Although this figure is somewhat limited in its control, it clearly shows that the landward limit of mature Verrill Canyon shales is concentrated along the rim of the present day Scotian Shelf except in the Sable Subbasin where the shales fill an embayment. Comparison with Figure 12.3 shows that all the major discoveries of gas and condensate lie within, or closely updip, of the mature zone.

Issler (1984) used corrected present day thermal gradients and burial histories of 43 and 37 wells, respectively, to map subseafloor depths to 0.6 and 0.7% R_o levels by following Lopatin's (1971) Time Temperature Index (TTI) procedure. A log plot of 106 sets of TTI and R_o values from 15 wells gave the relationship:

Log TTI = 6.1841 log Ro + 2.6557

with a correlation coefficient of 0.954. Issler (1984) believed that agreement between calculated and actual maturity should be within 10% in most cases. His maps outlined an embayment approximately coincident with the Sable Subbasin where the depth to a given maturation level is locally higher. Nantais (1983) extended the coverage of Issler's original study (Issler, 1982) and calculated the subsea depth of 0.7% R_o for 45 wells on the Scotian Shelf (Fig. 12.6), and documented the same configuration. He interpreted this as reflecting the interplay between variations in heat flow and sediment conductivity. These inferences may be valid for gas generation. Kendall and Altebaeumer (1985) believed that liquids were not expelled until 0.8% R_o vitrinite reflectance levels were reached.

Table 12.3. Drillstem test results for gas and oil discoveries, Scotian Shelf.

Discovery Well (date)	Interval (m)	Condensate, Oil (m³/d)	Gas rate (10⁶m³/d)	Gravity °API	Remarks
Onondaga E-84 (1969)					Untested - log analysis indicates 123 m of gross (gas) pay below 2701 m
Sable Island E-48 (1971) (summary of 30 DST and production tests)	1365-1450		up to 0.19 GOR 102.8	36-41	Production tests - 3 intervals Production tests - 7 intervals
	1454-1634	up to 81.9			Water-bearing
	1637-1682			52-50	Tests of 16 zones
	1682-2320	Condensate at 6.4	up to 0.53		1 inch choke, completion test
	1460-1461.5	457.9	GOR 79.9		
Primrose N-50 (1972) (production tests)	1341-1379	17.5		17.4	Wyandot Formation
	1391-1400	11.2		13.6	Wyandot Formation
	1498-1532	9.0		16.8	Logan Canyon Formation
	1612-1651	55.6 oil	GOR 1258.1		Caprock?
	1643-1650	47.7 oil	GOR 141.8		Caprock?
Thebaud P-84 (1972) (summary: 1 DST and 12 production tests)	3213-3404	some condensate	up to 0.24	47	Production test - 4 zones
	3830-3837	some condensate	0.75	48	Overpressure zone
Cohasset D-42 (1973) (production tests)	1861-1866	35.6 oil	GOR 21.8	49.2	Logan Canyon Formation
	1968-1973	166.9 oil	GOR 12.4	52.9	Logan Canyon Formation
	2248-2255	43.1 oil	GOR 20.4	53.4	Missisauga Formation
Citnalta I-59 (1974) (production tests)	3777-3782	131.0	0.31	45	Missisauga Formation
	3951-3958	70.3	0.17	57.5	Mic Mac Formation
	4054-4049	10.3	0.08	45	Mic Mac Formation
Intrepid L-80	2908-2911	11.9	0.22	51	Naskapi Member of the Logan Canyon Formation
(1974) (DSTs)	2937-2941	3.8	0.14	48	Missisauga Formation
	3383-3389	11.1	0.12	42	Missisauga Formation
	3841-3845	trace	0.05		Missisauga Formation
Venture D-23 (1979) (DSTs)	4414-4419	28.6	0.33	54.2	Normal pressure
	4643-4650	50.4	0.62	50.3	Overpressured
	4899-4910	24.5	0.28	55.5	Overpressured
Olympia A-12 (1982) (DSTs)	4525-4538	36.2	0.25		Press report
	4622-4633	16.9	0.50		
	4640-4648	6.1	0.41		
	4664-4678	75	0.42		
South Venture O-59 (1982) (DSTs)	3962-3932	144.0	0.46		Press report
	3985-3991	96.3	0.48		
	4020-4030	84.7	0.52		
	4209-4212	44.8	0.39		
	4255-4267	113.7	0.38		
	4747-4765	35.8	0.22		
	5035-5050	10.7	0.18		

Nantais (1983) also calculated Ro levels for top of Jurassic sediments from TTI values using Issler's relationship given above (Fig. 12.7). This figure shows maturation levels at approximately the middle of the Verrill Canyon Formation and equivalent stratigraphic levels and, like Powell's (1982) earlier compilation, demonstrates that Verrill Canyon shales are presently mature for gas and condensate generation within the Sable Subbasin and that this is the preferred area for releasing hydrocarbons.

Nantais (1983) used Time Temperature Index (TTI) modelling (Waples, 1980) to map the time (in million of years) when the top Jurassic sediments reached 0.6% R_o (Fig. 12.8). Ideally, a map for 0.7% R_o would have been preferable, but it would have had to be built around far fewer data points. The 0.6% R_o map (Fig. 12.8) involves

inferences from only 22 wells, but their distribution is adequate to delineate a region centred on the Sable Subbasin where maturation occurred earliest. It is reasonable to infer from the configuration that, in the Sable Subbasin, gas and condensate were beginning to be generated from Verrill Canyon shales around mid-Tertiary time. If the bulk of the movement of hydrocarbons was intrastratal and progressed upwards parallel to bedding planes, landward migration would have been feasible regionally on the Scotian Shelf during all of Tertiary time, since structural studies indicate that the Verrill Canyon shales would have been tilted oceanward during that period (Wade and MacLean, Chapter 5). Vertical migration along fractures may also have occurred, particularly if fractures formed in response to the initiation of overpressuring (Drummond,

Table 12.3. (cont.)

Discovery Well (date)	Interval (m)	Condensate, Oil (m³/d)	Gas rate (10⁶m³/d)	Gravity °API	Remarks
Banquereau C-21 (1982) (DSTs)	3565-3596	15.9	0.66		Press report
Arcadia J-16 (1983) (DSTs)	4857-4864 4892-4901 5165-5175		0.15 0.16 0.40		Press report
Glenelg J-48 (1983) (DSTs)	3062-3065 3491-3496 3608-3615 3747-3759 3767-3773 3950-3955	65.0 (condensate) 19.1 (condensate) trace (condensate) 17.6 (condensate)	0.86 0.61 0.10 0.80 0.12 0.13		Press report
					88.1 m³/day water
Uniacke G-72 (1984) (DSTs)	5191-5199 5215-5226 5242-5260	23.4 (condensate) 20.1 (condensate)	0.40 0.35 trace		Press report 18.6 m³/day water 358.0 m³/day water
Alma F-67 (1984) (DSTs)	2872-2890 2911-2916 2978-2984 3026-3032	59.3 (condensate) 24.5 (condensate) 28.9 (condensate)	0.85 0.32 0.52		Press report
Chebucto K-90 (1984) (DSTs)	3352-3357 3798-3815 4227-4238	8.9 (condensate) 25.3 (condensate) 14.0 (condensate)	0.22 0.58 0.42		6.0 m³/day water 80.0 m³/day water 226.6 m³/day water
West Venture C-62 (1985) (DSTs)	4741-4743 4923-4930 5016-5027	24.3 (condensate)	0.95 0.02 trace		Press report 104.9 m³/day water 76.3 m³/day water
West Venture N-91 (1985)					Untested due to underground gas blowout. Deemed a significant discovery.
West Olympia O-51 (1986) (DSTs)	4356-4386 3795-3809	Not reported 31.8	0.60 1.05 0.21		Rate decline during test to 0.53 x 10⁹ m³/day Press report
North Triumph G-43 (1986) (DSTs)	3835-3846	31.8 (condensate)	1.05		
West Chebucto K-20 (1986) (DSTs)	5020-5036	Not reported	0.15		Press report Shallower zone tested only water — Deemed a gas show
Panuke B-90 (1986) (DSTs)	2294-2300	949.0 oil	0.01		Press report No water

GOR = Gas/oil ratios; DST = drill stem test

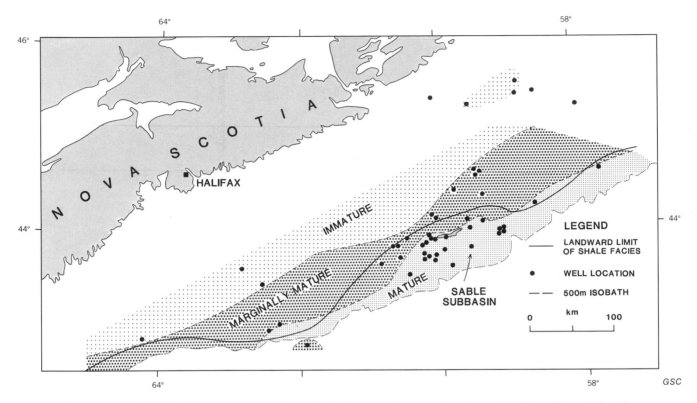

Figure 12.5. Maturation facies map drawn at the base Cretaceous level showing the well control and landward limit of the Verril Canyon Formation shale facies (from Powell, 1982).

1986; Lewis and Keen, Chapter 14; Wade and MacLean, Chapter 5). B.S. Mudford (pers. comm., 1986) suggested that overpressures are now building up to levels approaching fracture pressures (Ervine and Bell, 1987), so it is likely that vertical hydrocarbon migration is occurring at the present time.

Evidence for earlier primary migration is cited by Purcell et al. (1979), who showed that the gas, condensate and oil, presently pooled in many reservoirs on the Scotian Shelf, is contained in rocks which are not mature enough to generate it according to organic matter colouration and gas chromatographic criteria. Kendall and Altebaeumer (1985) cited evidence for secondary migration as well. According to their analytical data, maturation parameters such as carbon isotopic data, heptane and isoheptane values and phenanthrene indices, all suggest that the condensates and gases in the shallowest reservoirs in a single well are the least mature. This situation is believed to have arisen through secondary migration, with the more mature gas and condensate being injected into the deepest reservoirs and displacing earlier generated hydrocarbons, so that the shallower reservoirs now contain the less mature condensates and gas (Kendall and Altebaeumer, 1985). Unpublished vitrinite reflectance studies also point to migration being a factor in hydrocarbon emplacement (M.D. Avery, pers. comm., 1986).

Hydrocarbon entrapment model

The significant hydrocarbon accumulations on the Scotian Shelf occur in growth-faulted rollover anticlines within the Jurassic to Lower Cretaceous sandstones of the Mic Mac and Missisauga formations. Extensive reflection seismic data coupled with paleontological dating (Wade and MacLean, Chapter 5) indicate that growth faulting occurred throughout Jurassic and Cretaceous time. Thus, the essential trap geometry was established early and subsequently enhanced by further faulting and subsidence. Trap integrity relies on the presence of sealing shales interbedded with the reservoir sands and on sealing of key faults in the updip direction. In part, this appears to be due to a favourable sand:shale ratio which limited sand-to-sand communication across faults. Hence, traps with adequate updip seals were ready to receive the migrating hydrocarbons which are thought to have been generated from distal source rocks of the Verrill Canyon Formation from mid-Tertiary time onwards. This combination of geological characteristics, structural history and geochemical evolution is believed to account for the hydrocarbon accumulations on the Scotian Shelf, with the most favourably development in the Sable Subbasin.

Assessment of hydrocarbon potential

Assessments of hydrocarbon potential for each region in Canada are prepared periodically by the Geological Survey of Canada, with technical interpretation, play analyses and pool sizes provided by the Canada Oil and Gas Lands Administration (COGLA). The estimates are prepared using a methodology based on a probabilistic treatment of reservoir parameters, prospect inventory, and prospect characteristics (Lee and Wang, 1983; Procter et al., 1984; Podruski et al., 1988). This subjective probability method

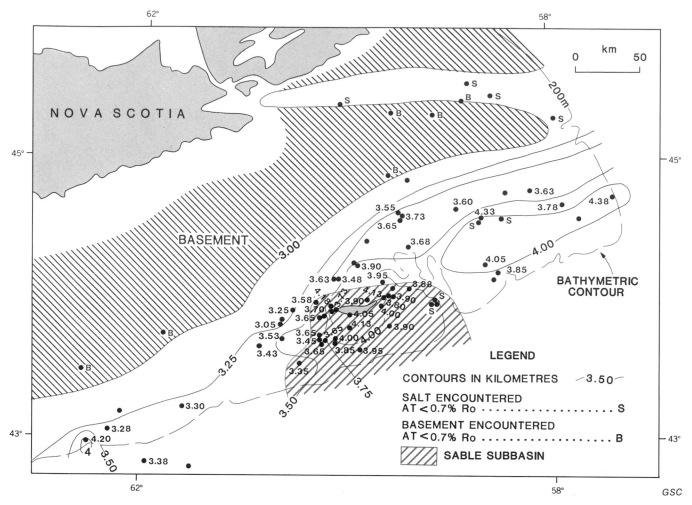

Figure 12.6. Subsea depth (in kilometres) to calculated R_o 0.7% on the Scotian Shelf (Nantais, 1983), indicating the depth in wells at which significant quantities of gas would begin to be generated provided a suitable source rock was present.

incorporates objective data obtained from wells, regional geological studies and seismic surveys, with the subjective judgements based upon the opinions of knowledgeable experts. Analysis is done at the level of individual plays, so that consideration is given to all the potential trapping opportunities which can be envisaged. An alternative approach involves using a discovery process model (Lee and Wang, 1983) in which estimates of play potential and individual pool sizes are derived from the sizes and sequences of discoveries already made.

These assessment exercises result in resource estimates and predicted pool sizes for each play, and aggregate estimates for the combination of all plays. Comparison between the predicted distribution of undiscovered pools and the estimates for the discovered pools provides both a means of checking the input parameters, and also gives an indication of the sizes of possible remaining undiscovered pools.

A resource assessment for the Scotian Shelf and Slope area was completed in 1983 (Wade et al., 1989) and incorporated both subjective probability and discovery process model methods. This study is conceptually current at the

time of writing because no additional trapping regime or plays have been recognized since it was completed. The exercise involved regional geological and geophysical analyses and included compilation of a prospect inventory. All well-derived information was used and augmented by regional seismic interpretations.

Seven plays were recognized based on potential reservoir units and structural style (Fig. 12.9). Plays 1 and 2 involve structural traps created by salt flowage. These include traps related to diapirs which pierce through Cretaceous sediments to the level of the Petrel Member of the Dawson Canyon Formation, and deep-seated salt swells which could potentially create traps in the Abenaki Mic Mac, and Missisauga formations. Fault-related traps (plays 3 and 7, Fig. 12.9), include down-to-the-basin faults at the paleo-shelf/slope break, and deep-seated growth faults involving overpressured sandstone reservoirs. The great potential of this latter play was first recognized in 1979 with the discovery at Venture D-23, but there were earlier positive indications in the 1972 Thebaud P-84 discovery well. An additional structural trapping mechanism is created by drape over basement features (play 4) such

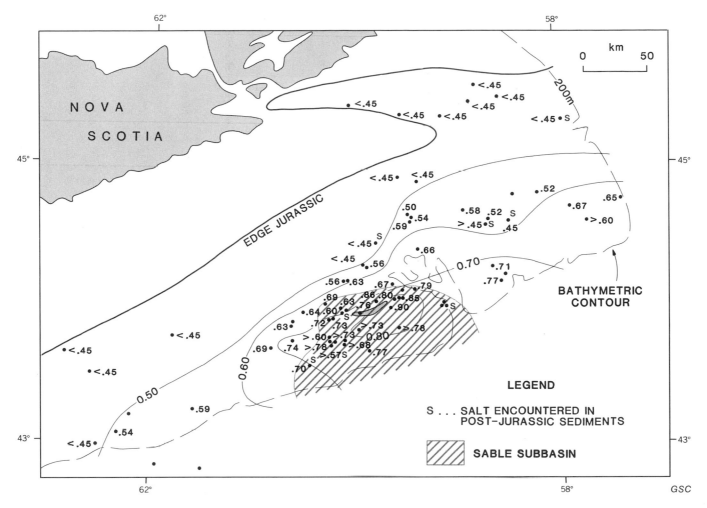

Figure 12.7. %R$_o$ calculated from TTI for the top of Jurassic sediments in wells on the Scotian Shelf (Nantais, 1983) using the relationship Log TTI = 6.1841 Log R$_o$ + 2.6557. Above R$_o$ 0.7% significant quantities of gas are believed to have been generated.

as on the LaHave Platform and Canso Ridge (Wade and MacLean, Chapter 5), areas of high-standing basement extending from onshore Nova Scotia. Oil shows in the Mic Mac Formation at the Erie D-26 and Wyandot E-53 wells are the only encouraging indictions in this play. Two other possible stratigraphic trapping mechanisms are envisaged (plays 5 and 6, Fig. 12.9), one arising from the updip limit of sandstone reservoirs along the northern margin of the Scotian Basin, and the second in the porous Middle-Upper Jurassic carbonates on the western Scotian Shelf.

The reflection seismic line through the Venture discovery illustrates the high quality of seismic data in the area (Fig. 12.10) and the structural style for play 7. Three major down-to-the-basin growth fault zones are apparent, which create structural closures on their downthrown sides.

Based on the results of drilling to date, the most extensively drilled prospects have been the fault-related, normally-pressured and overpressured traps (play 7, Fig. 12.9). Seventeen of the twenty-one significant discoveries are in traps of this type.

The statistical analysis of quantitative data combined with reasonable inferences have yielded the estimates of discovered resources of gas and condensate plus oil given in Table 12.2. The best current estimate of total potential resources on the Scotian Shelf and Slope is 512 × 10^9 m^3 gas and 171 × 10^6 m^3 condensate oil and gas (Wade et al., in press). Approximately 29% of the potential gas and 12% of the potential condensate and oil has been found.

THE GRAND BANKS OF NEWFOUNDLAND AND NORTHEAST NEWFOUNDLAND SHELF

In this section, the shelf area surrounding Newfoundland between the Laurentian Channel to the southwest and the Hawke Saddle to the north is discussed. This shelf area includes the St. Pierre Bank, the Grand Banks of Newfoundland (sensu stricto) and the Northeast Newfoundland Shelf (Map 850-A, in pocket).

The Grand Banks of Newfoundland are underlain by a number of northeast-trending Mesozoic basins and sub-

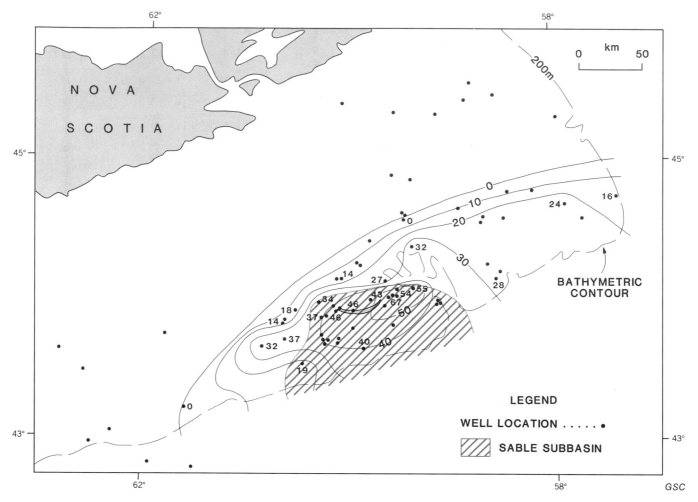

Figure 12.8. Time, in millions of years, since the top of Jurassic beds on the Scotian Shelf reached R_o 0.6% (Nantais, 1983).

basins with petroleum potential: South Whale, Whale, Horseshoe, Carson, and Jeanne d'Arc, as described in Chapters 5 and 6. The Upper Cretaceous-Cenozoic clastic sequence forms a generally undeformed, basinward dipping sedimentary wedge. To date, significant hydrocarbon discoveries have been made in only the Jeanne d'Arc Basin.

Wells and seismic data in the South Whale Subbasin and the Whale, Horseshoe and Carson basins, have confirmed the existence of a prospective Mesozoic reservoir section. In between these basins, lower Paleozoic and metamorphosed Precambrian rocks (Bell and Howie, Chapter 4), are overlain by uppermost Mesozoic and Cenozoic strata of negligible potential. These high-standing areas are barren of mature source rock and the Cenozoic section is too thin to have reached an adequate level of maturity for hydrocarbon generation (Grant and MacAlpine, Chapter 6). Few wells have tested these intrabasinal areas, but a number of wells have been drilled on prospects within the Mesozoic basins.

Drilling began in 1966 when Pan American Petroleum Corporation (now Amoco Production) drilled Tors Cove D-52 in South Whale Subbasin and Imperial Oil (now Esso

Resources Canada) drilled Grand Falls H-09 in the Whale Basin (Fig. 12.11). Between 1968 and 1974, 28 additional wells were drilled to give a total wildcat distribution as follows: South Whale Subbasin - 14 wells, Whale Basin — 10 wells, Horseshoe Basin — 1 well, Carson Basin — 3 wells, and South Bank High — 2 wells. The companies involved were Amoco, Elf, Gulf, Imperial, Mobil and Skelly. No hydrocarbon discoveries resulted, although two hydrocarbon shows occurred in wells drilled in the South Whale Subbasin (Fig. 12.11). This depocentre is discussed in more detail because it is hydrocarbon-bearing and may have a greater potential for commercial pools than drilling has yet revealed.

South Whale Subbasin

Significant shows

The lithological succession in South Whale Subbasin resembles that of the Scotian Shelf. The early operators (Amoco and Imperial, 1973) utilized McIver's (1972) Mesozoic and Cenozoic stratigraphic terminology for the Scotian Shelf and applied Bell's (1944) upper Paleozoic terminology to the underlying section (Fig. 12.11). Recent

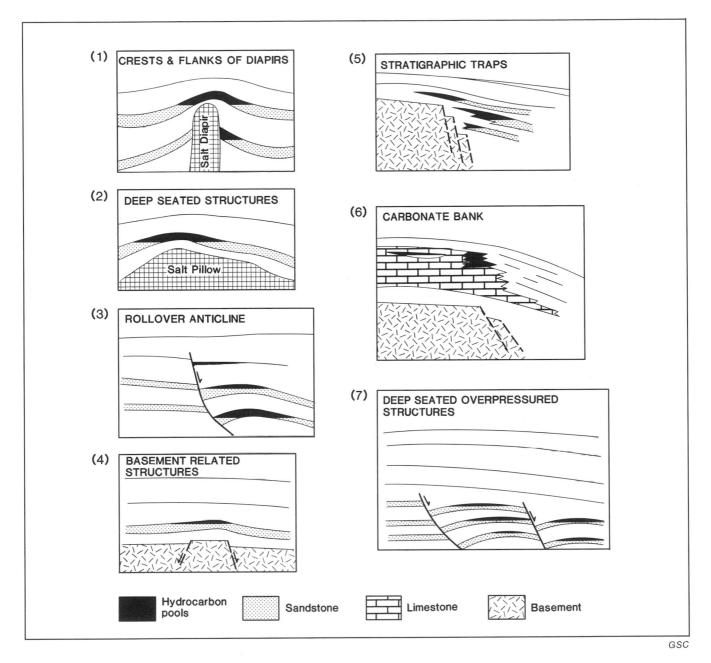

Figure 12.9. Hydrocarbon play types recognized on the Scotian Shelf (Wade et al., in press).

work suggests that some revisions are required. The initial exploration program in South Whale Subbasin was principally directed to both salt diapirs and salt ridges. The results were generally disappointing, although excellent reservoir sandstones of Early Cretaceous age were identified and two hydrocarbon shows were encountered (Fig. 12.12). Twenty-two barrels of oil, together with one hundred and two barrels of salt water were recovered from an Upper Cretaceous limestone, the Petrel Member of the Dawson Canyon Formation, at Heron H-73 (Swift et al., 1975). At this location, the Petrel Member abuts a salt diapir against which there appears to be closure (Swift and Williams, 1980). At the Tors Cove D-52 well gas was recovered from the dolomitic cap rock (?Iroquois Formation) above the Gull salt diapir (Swift and Williams, 1980).

Hydrocarbon characteristics

Gas chromatograph mass spectrometry analysis indicates that the Heron H-73 oil is probably not biodegraded (M. Fowler, pers. comm., 1986). Swift et al. (1975) reported an API gravity of 7°, which is very low for an oil that has not undergone some biodegradation. The pristane/phytane ratio is 0.59, and it appears likely that the oil was derived from a marine Type II source rock deposited in a confined anoxic setting. No analysis of the Tors Cove D-52 gas is available.

The two shows occur in rock sequences which are immature for significant oil or gas generation (Swift and Williams, 1980).

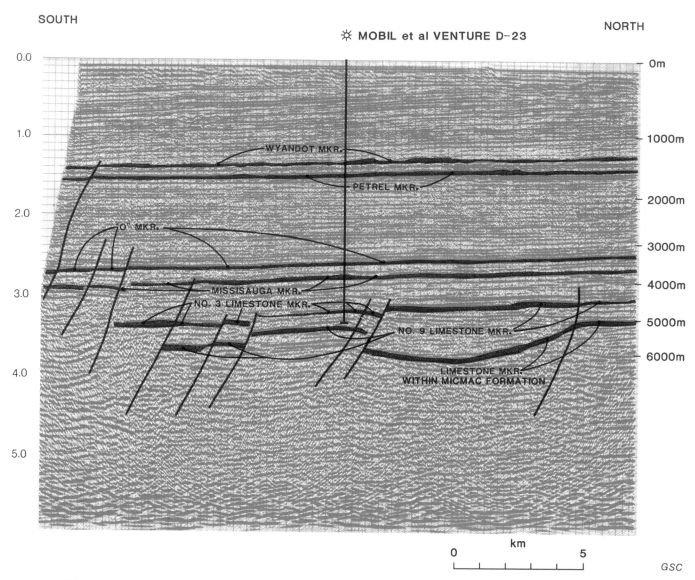

SOUTH   ☀ MOBIL et al VENTURE D-23   NORTH

Figure 12.10. Reflection seismic line shot across the Venture structure, Sable Subbasin. Well location shown in Figure 12.3.

Source rocks

Lower Cretaceous shales lithologically similar to the Verrill Canyon Formation of the Scotian Shelf are present at the base of the Puffin B-90 and Kittiwake P-11 wells in the central part of the South Whale Subbasin. These shales may have sourced gas. To date, no oil source rock has been encountered, although Powell (1985) postulated that Upper Jurassic oil-prone source rocks might occur in the subbasin.

Hydrocarbon entrapment model

There is insufficient information to construct a well-documented hydrocarbon entrapment scenario for the South Whale Subbasin, since the existing wells have been drilled on only a limited number of the known prospect types. However, the two hydrocarbon shows, noted above, occur in traps related to salt diapirs which ceased doming and intruding overlying sediments in late Cenozoic time.

This suggests that some migration has occurred relatively recently.

Asssessment of hydrocarbon potential

The South Whale Subbasin has not been assessed using the current methodology and the most recent seismic mapping. The volume of discovered resources is clearly minimal. As noted above, caprock gas was recovered at Tors Cove D-52 and is assumed to have flowed from a small local accumulation. The Petrel Member reservoir at Heron H-73 is also believed to be of very limited extent, but there are no published estimates of its size.

Hopefully, future exploration will be successfully directed to prospects other than salt structures, and aimed at the Jurassic and Lower Cretaceous sandstones in that part of the basin where a mature Type II Jurassic source rock section may be present.

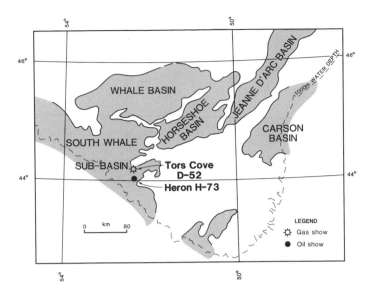

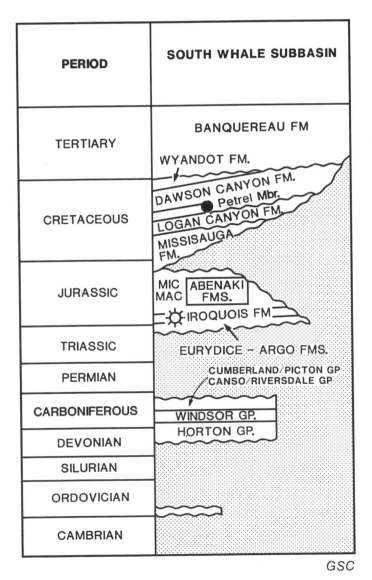

Jeanne d'Arc Basin

Exploration history

Exploration drilling for oil in Jeanne d'Arc Basin and adjacent areas of the northeastern Grand Banks has, at the time of writing, been more successful than in any other area of eastern Canada, particularly with respect to commercially potential oil discoveries. Fifteen significant hydrocarbon pools have been discovered in Mesozoic reservoirs (Fig. 12.13).

Drilling activity in Jeanne d'Arc Basin has continued since 1971, and comprises the entire "second cycle" of exploration in offshore Newfoundland (Table 12.1). Drilling commenced in 1971 with the Amoco-Imperial Murre G-67 well which tested a basement structure in the southern part of the Jeanne d'Arc Basin. Two additional unsuccessful wells, Cormorant K-93 and Spoonbill C-30, were drilled in that area by these partners in 1972 and 1973. In 1972, Mobil and Gulf spudded Adolphus K-41 above a salt-cored diapiric anticline in the centre of Jeanne d'Arc Basin. The following year a deeper well on the same structure, Adolphus 2K-41, was drilled and tested. Oil flowed from a thin sandstone in the Upper Cretaceous at 42.6 m³/d. Between 1973 and 1974, four other wells were drilled in Jeanne d'Arc Basin, which tested the flank of a large salt-cored ridge (Egret K-36, Egret N-46) and basin-margin fault blocks (Flying Foam I-13, Dominion O-23). Unfortunately, all these wells were unsuccessful, although Egret K-36 encountered what appeared to be a good Upper Jurassic oil source-rock sequence (Swift and Williams, 1980) and an excellent Lower Cretaceous reservoir section.

In 1979, Chevron Resources Canada and partners farmed into Mobil and Gulf's Jeanne d'Arc Basin permits and drilled Hibernia P-15 on a rollover anticline which abutted the western faulted margin of the basin. The resulting discovery of oil has so far led to wells being drilled on 30 other structures within and beside Jeanne d'Arc Basin. Thirteen more hydrocarbon pools have been found giving an impressive success rate of over 45% for this phase of exploratory drilling.

Significant discoveries

As noted above, an early indication of the Jeanne d'Arc Basin's oil potential was provided by Adolphus 2K-41. Since then, fourteen significant discoveries have been made consisting of seven oil, five oil and gas, and two containing gas and condensate. Complete drillstem test results are given in Table 12.4.

The Hibernia discovery by Chevron in 1979 was not only the first major oil discovery in the Jeanne d'Arc Basin but also the first on the Canadian east coast. Oil flowed from seven of the eight zones tested, at a maximum individual rate of 592.1 m³/d. Eight of nine delineation wells have been successful in confirming the extent of the pay zones over the structure. However, these wells and the three-dimensional seismic mapping have indicated that

Figure 12.11. Stratigraphy of South Whale Subbasin, southern Grand Banks, and location of the Tors Cove D-52 and Heron H-73 wells which had hydrocarbon shows (after Swift and Williams, 1980).

Table 12.4. Drillstem test results for oil and gas discoveries, Jeanne d'Arc Basin.

Discovery Well (date)	Interval (m)	Oil, Condensate (m³/day)	Gas rate (MMcf/day) (10⁶m³/d)	Gravity °API	Remarks
Hibernia P-15 (1979)	2422-2443	185.4	0.01	32.2	Avalon Formation
	3742-3746	321.3	0.06	34.5	Hibernia Formation
	3805-3822	592.1	0.12	35.5	
	3841-3845	343.4	0.05	34.7	
	3852-3858	422.4	0.05	34.9	
	3898-3905	No flow; recovered salt water			
	4113-4129	127.2	0.01	32.1	Jeanne d'Arc Formation; overpressured reservoir
	4113-4134	89.7	0.01	33.5	
Ben Nevis I-45 (1980)	2378-2446	4 tests; no flow, recovered oil and water			Avalon Formation
	2891-2894	41.5	0.29	48.1	
	4112-4477	6 tests; formation tight, recovered trace oil and gas			Hibernia Formation; overpressured reservoir
	4535-4550	253.7	0.34	38.9	
Hebron I-13 (1981)	1866-1876	121.1	0.01	19.0	Avalon Formation
	1905-1916	110.2	0.003	13.6	
	2923-2940	491.4	0.04	29.0	Hibernia Formation
	3842-3857	848.3	0.08	31.0	Jeanne d'Arc Formation;
	4368-4381	596.5	0.11	36.0	overpressured reservoir
South Tempest G-88 (1981)	3826-3834	23.1	0.05	39.4	Upper Jurassic;
	4041-4049	30.5	0.01	40.7	overpressured reservoir
	4109-4117	198.7	0.14	42.0	
Nautilus C-92 (1982)	3285-3300	334.0	0.05	31.0	Avalon Formation;
	3325-3336	418.1	0.07	31.3	overpressured reservoir
	3982-4001	trace condensate	0.15		'C' member of the Missisauga Formation; overpressured reservoir
North Dana I-43 (1983)	4537-4548	45.3 (condensate)	0.35		Press report
Terra Nova K-08 (1984)	3329-3336	187.0	0.03	32.5	Press report
	3380-3397	597.0	0.07	33.4	
	3410-3423	823.0	0.11	33.4	
	3530-3544	124.0	0.01	N/A	
Trave E-87 (1984)	2144-2150	15.3 (condensate)	0.19		Press report
	2231-2238	86.8 (condensate)	0.51		
South Mara C-13 (1984)	2952-2958	275.7	0.06	34.7	Press report
	2926-2932	104.9 (condensate)	0.40	58.7	
Whiterose N-22 (1985)	2663-2680	107.3 (condensate)	0.61	54	Press report
	2689-2695	25.9 (condensate)	0.03	54	
	2724-2727	no data	0.04		
	3542-3554	87.0	0.01	32	
	3565-3572	57.4	0.01	32	
Beothuk M-05 (1985)[*1]	2740-3061	4 tests; 3 yielded oil Best flow 228.0		31	Press report
Mara M-54 (1985)	1851-1857	98.6	0.003	21.6	Press report
	2403-2408	122.4	0.01	21.5	
	2704-2708	Minor amounts oil and water		11	
West Ben Nevis B-75 (1985)	2002-2015	97.0	0.01	28.1	Press report
	2044-2065	Formation water only			
	2445-2465	340.1	0.02	22.8	
	4498-4507	953.9	0.14	33.7	
North Ben Nevis P-93 (1985)	3062-3067	91.6 (condensate)	0.48		Press report
	3080-3085	625.9	0.05	34.0	
	3091-3095	448.6	0.03	34.0	
Fortune G-57 (1986)	3989-4002	215.4	0.07	35.5	Press report
	4031-4040	107.9	0.01	34.8	
	4401-4453	786.0	0.15	35.5	

*1 Included within Terra Nova discovery.

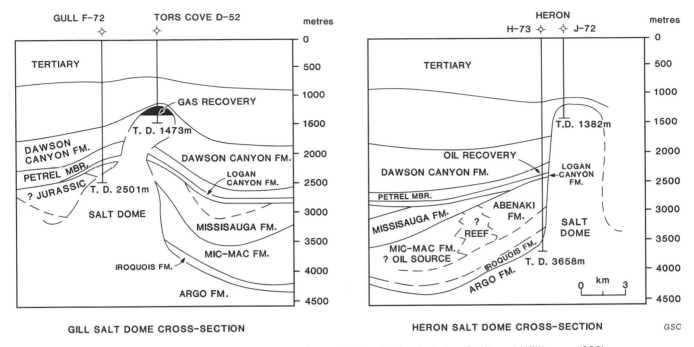

Figure 12.12. Hydrocarbon pools in the South Whale Subbasin (after Swift and Williams, 1980).

the Hibernia field is characterized by considerable stratigraphic and structural complexity. In 1985, Mobil stated that the most likely recoverable reserves are 83.5×10^6 m³.

Eleven of the subsequent discoveries are grouped in a compact area in the vicinity of Hibernia. Of these, eight are associated with a trans-basin fault trend which extends through this area (Grant et al., 1986). This structural zone is a through-going fault complex with both antithetic and down-to-the-basin throws. Immediately east of Hibernia, recent discoveries at the North Ben Nevis P-93 and West Ben Nevis B-75 wells are of interest because of their proximity to the Hibernia pool and earlier finds at the Ben Nevis I-45 and Hebron I-13 wells. Test results were announced in late 1985 by Husky-Bow Valley for the North Ben Nevis P-93 exploratory well, located 25 km east of Hibernia (see Fig. 12.17). Two zones flowed oil with gas and one zone yielded gas and condensate. The deepest test over the interval 3091 to 3095 m flowed oil at 448.8 m³/d with some gas. The second interval flowed at 625.9 m³/d and 0.05×10^6 m³/d through a 28 mm choke. The shallowest interval yielded 0.48×10^6 m³/d of gas with 91.6 m³/d of condensate. In their press release, the companies also stated that the North Ben Nevis discovery would be a good candidate for early development, provided that subsequent delineation drilling confirms both the seismic interpretation and reservoir continuity. At West Ben Nevis B-75, located midway between the significant discoveries of oil at Ben Nevis I-45 and Hebron I-13, oil and gas flowed from three zones. The deepest interval, 4498 to 4507 m, flowed oil at 953.9 m³/d and gas at 0.14×10^6 m³/d. The two shallower intervals flowed at 340.1 m³/d and 97.0 m³/d. Petro-Canada and partners continued work on delineation of their 1984 Terra Nova oil discovery, located at the southeast end of this trend. In 1985, Canterra drilled Beothuk M-05 approximately 7 km south of the Terra Nova K-08 discovery well. Oil was tested from two of three zones at

flow rates as high as 228.0 m³/d. Due to the close proximity of Beothuk and Terra Nova, the two are combined for the purpose of resource calculation. In late 1985, Petro-Canada and partners announced the results of the testing program at the second successful Terra Nova I-97 delineation well. Mobil and partners announced the results of testing at the Mara M-54 discovery, located immediately east of Hibernia. Oil flowed from two of three intervals at the maximum rate of 122.4 m³/d.

On the opposite side of Jeanne d'Arc Basin, Husky-Bow Valley and partners made a gas and condensate discovery with the first well of their farmout at Trave E-87. Their second success was the gas and oil discovery at Whiterose N-22 in 1984. Two successful delineation wells, Whiterose J-49 and Whiterose L-61, have since been drilled. The results of four tests at Whiterose J-49 were reported in late 1985. Oil and gas flowed on two tests; the largest rate was 268.0 m³/d of oil and 0.10×10^6 m³/d of gas from the interval 3093 to 3106 m. Gas and condensate were reported from two zones. The maximum rates, recorded from the interval 3063 to 3067 m, were 18.0×10^6 m³/d of gas and 25.0 m³/d of condensate. For the second delineation well, Whiterose L-61, three zones were tested, but only one yielded hydrocarbons; gas and condensate flowed at rates of 0.69×10^6 m³/d of gas and 69.0 m³/d of condensate.

The most recent discovery in the basin is Husky-Bow Valley's Fortune G-57 well. Test results consist of flows of oil and gas from three tested zones, at the maximum rate of 786.0 m³/d of 35.5°API oil, 0.15×10^6 m³/d of gas. The remaining gas discovery, North Dana I-43, is located on the Outer Ridge Complex, a high-standing structural complex which bounds the eastern margin of Jeanne d'Arc Basin.

In summary, fourteen significant discoveries have been drilled within 100 km of Hibernia, and of these all but two are within the Jeanne d'Arc Basin itself.

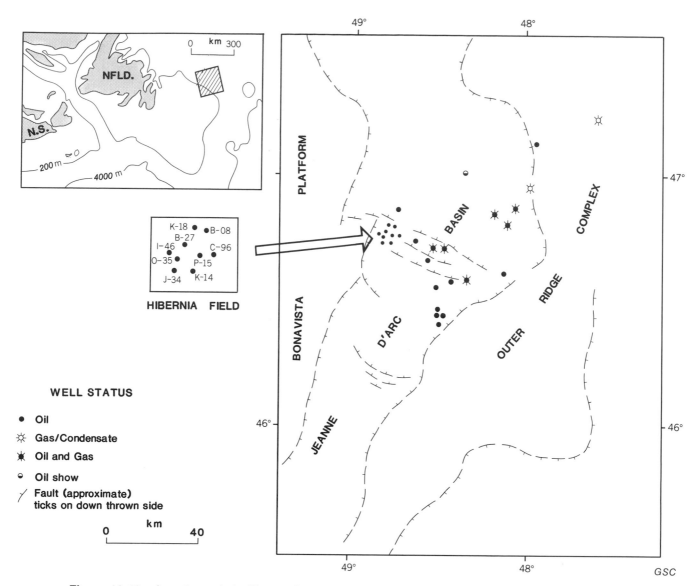

Figure 12.13. Locations of significant oil and gas discovery wells in the Jeanne d'Arc Basin, Grand Banks of Newfoundland.

Discovered resources and hydrocarbon characteristics

Estimates of the discovered resources (recoverable) on a best-current-estimate basis for the fourteen significant discoveries are 169.8×10^6 m^3 of oil with some condensate, and 65.1×10^9 m^3 of natural gas (Table 12.5).

Many of the oils have been subjected to detailed geochemical analyses, but similar information is not available for the gas samples (L.R. Snowdon, pers. comm., 1986). The oils all show geochemical similarities suggesting that they belong to the same genetic family. Relative peak heights and distributions are very similar on saturate fraction gas chromatograms and on triterpane and sterane chromatograms obtained through gas chromatograph mass spectrometer analyses of oils tested from different wells (McAlpine et al., 1986). There is also little variation in the normalized compositions of the C$_7$ compounds as shown by the gasoline range data from oil and condensate

samples recovered from seven wells (see Fig. 6.3 in Chapter 6). Sterane biomarker analyses show a similar clustering. The C$_{27}$:C$_{28}$:C$_{29}$ 5α(H) sterane components of 31 oils from 13 wells show such small compositional variations that derivation from a common source rock is probable (P. Brooks, pers. comm., 1986). The sterane composition points to generation from a typical Type II marine source rock, rich in phytoplanktonic organisms (P. Brooks, pers. comm., 1986).

Source rocks

The Jeanne d'Arc Basin is the only area in offshore eastern Canada which is known to contain mature, rich, oil-prone source rocks. They were first recognized in the Egret K-36 well by Swift and Williams (1980) in a calcareous shale sequence of Kimmeridgian age within what is now termed the Egret Member of the Rankin Formation (Fig. 12.14).

The source-rock beds have a distinctive log signature and Rock-Eval analysis response (McAlpine et al., 1986). Figure 12.15 illustrates the Egret Member's log response in the South Tempest G-88 and Hibernia K-18 wells. The source rock exhibits a relatively high sonic transit time, low density, high porosity and high resistivity compared to adjacent shales. The Rock-Eval analyses are summarized for the same stratigraphic interval in Figure 6.30 in Chapter 6. The parameter T_{max} is a low-focus maturity indicator. The Production Index ($S_1/(S_1 + S_2)$), indicates how much hydrocarbon is present (S_1) relative to the full residual hydrocarbon generation capacity of the sample ($S_1 + S_2$). For Hibernia K-18, ($S_1 + S_2$) approaches 50%. The S_2/S_3 ratio gives a measure of hydrocarbons relative to organically derived carbon dioxide which were released by pyrolysis between 300 and 390°C. High values, such as those of Hibernia K-18, point to Type I or Type II kerogen. This is confirmed by the high Hydrogen Index. Organic carbon content is a measure of source rock richness and the response of the Hibernia K-18 samples is typically high with values commonly ranging between 3 and 9%. High hydrogen indices are characteristic of Type I and Type II source rocks. A typical hydrogen index/oxygen crossplot from Trave E-87 (Fig. 12.16) illustrates that the Egret Member can be classified as a Type II oil-prone source rock.

The geochemical characteristics of the Egret Member at Hibernia K-18 are common to all the correlative intervals in other wells in Jeanne d'Arc Basin and confirm that it is dominantly a Type II marine phytoplankton-rich source rock. It is also becoming clear that this sequence is widely distributed within the Jeanne d'Arc Basin, and that thicknesses in the order of 75 to 100 m are typical (Grant and McAlpine, Chapter 6). Circumstantially, the Egret Member is the obvious source of the oils in the Jurassic and Cretaceous sandstones in Jeanne d'Arc Basin. This is confirmed by the match in geochemical signatures for the oils and the source rock, as shown, for example, in their mass fragmentograms (in Fig. 6.32 of Chapter 6).

As yet, it is not known whether the Egret Member is a basin-wide blanket deposit. It is present around the edge of Jeanne d'Arc Basin in all wells that penetrate the correlative Upper Jurassic section, and the oil at Adolphus 2K-41 was probably derived from the Egret Member in the axial region of the basin (Grant and McAlpine, Chapter 6).

Table 12.5. Discovered resources and hydrocarbon potential, Jeanne d'Arc Basin and Northeast Newfoundland Shelf.

Significant Discoveries		
Oil:	7	
Oil and Gas:	5	
Gas:	2	
Total:	**14**	

	Oil and Condensate $10^6 m^3$	Gas $10^9 m^3$
Discovered Resources	169.8	65.1
Potential	1337.0	345.5
% Discovered	12.7%	18.8%

Present control indicates that the Egret Member is rich in argillaceous limestone in the south, but composed largely of non-calcareous organic shales and siltstones in the north (McAlpine et al., 1986).

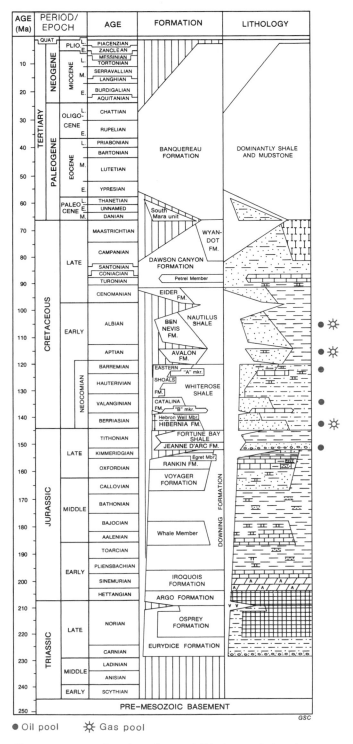

● Oil pool   ☼ Gas pool

Figure 12.14. Stratigraphy and lithology of the Jeanne d'Arc Basin (after Grant and McAlpine, Chapter 6).

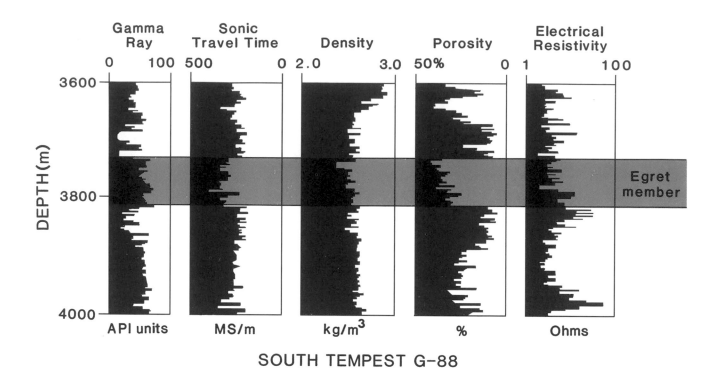

SOUTH TEMPEST G-88

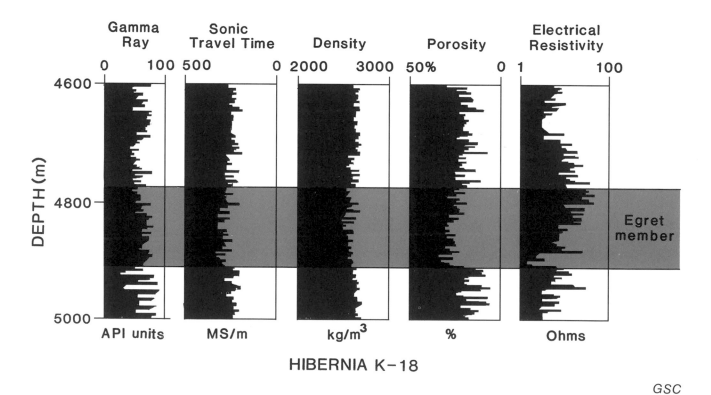

HIBERNIA K-18

GSC

Figure 12.15. Log responses of the Egret Member source rock in the South Tempest G-88 and Hibernia K-18 wells, Jeanne d'Arc Basin (after McAlpine et al., 1986).

Whereas the Egret Member clearly generated the oil trapped in Jeanne d'Arc Basin, the origin of the gas is not so clearcut. Grant and McAlpine (Chapter 6) suggest two possible sources: 1) overmature Egret Member limestones and shales; and 2) Lower Cretaceous shales which have a high organic carbon content. Gas generation from either unit is compatible with the subsidence and deformational history of Jeanne d'Arc Basin, but the problem has not yet been addressed analytically.

Maturation and migration

As a Type II source rock the Egret Member of the Rankin Formation is likely to have generated oil between organic maturity levels equivalent to 0.5 to 1.2% R_o. Figure 12.17 summarises the available well data and vitrinite reflectance information dealing with the distribution and the maturation level at the top of the Egret Member. It is evi-

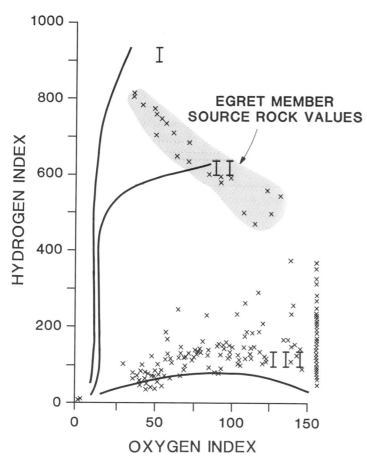

Figure 12.16. Hydrogen index/oxygen index crossplot derived from Rock-Eval pyrolysis analyses of ditch cutting samples from the Trave E-87 well, Jeanne d'Arc Basin. Egret Member source rock values are shaded in red. Type I kerogen largely consists of lipid material and generates oil on maturation. Type II kerogen is formed from marine organic matter deposited in a reducing environment and generates oil on maturation. Type III kerogen is derived from land plants and generates gas and condensate on maturation (Tissot and Welte, 1984).

dent that most of the oil and gas discoveries lie within or updip of the present day mature zone for oil generation (McAlpine et al., 1986). It is also clear that the lack of exploration success in the southernmost part of the basin is most probably due to the absence of this source rock sequence in that area (Powell, 1985; McAlpine et al., 1986).

Von der Dick and Meloche (1986) have undertaken time temperature index modelling of oil generation in Jeanne d'Arc Basin and suggested that it began about 80 Ma in Late Cretaceous time, and that peak generation occurred about 30 Ma in Oligocene time. This is generally compatible with an earlier study by Ervine (1985) which suggested that the Egret Member would not have reached the maturation level for maximum oil generation (0.8 R_o) at the Nautilus C-92 well location until Early Eocene time (Ervine, 1985). If the Egret Member is present in the deepest part of the basin in the vicinity of the Adolphus wells (Fig. 12.17), preliminary calculations suggest that local oil generation could have begun there in mid-Cretaceous time (D.N. Skibo, pers. comm., 1986). If this occurred, and the oil migrated updip prior to trap formation, relict staining might exist. None has been identified, which indirectly supports Von der Dick and Meloche's (1986) proposed timing scenario, since almost all of the oil and gas in Jeanne d'Arc Basin is contained in Upper Jurassic and Lower Cretaceous sandstones in structural traps which formed prior to and during mid-Cretaceous time (Grant and McAlpine, Chapter 6). Hence, charging probably occurred after the development of the mid-Cretaceous Avalon unconformity and associated discontinuities, and after much of the overlying Upper Cretaceous-Tertiary section had been deposited. With the present basin geometry (Fig. 12.18), any other scenario requires special pleading with respect to heat flow history.

The present distribution of mature Egret Member source rocks suggests that, if most of the hydrocarbon-bearing reservoirs were charged in latest Tertiary time, there is no need to invoke lateral migration over long distances (Fig. 12.17). Clearly, however, significant vertical migration has occurred to distribute the oil into reservoirs ranging in age from Late Jurassic to early Tertiary (Mara M-54). Also, the oil in a sandstone interval within the Petrel Limestone at Adolphus 2K-41, must either have been generated and emplaced by vertical migration before or during early Tertiary time, or else migrated some tens of kilometres laterally if it was generated more recently.

McAlpine et al. (1986) and Grant and McAlpine (Chapter 6) made a strong case for the role of vertical migration. They suggested that hydrocarbon-bearing fluids moved upwards periodically along faults and fractures which opened in response to overpressure buildup. They also noted that many of the discovery wells have encountered overpressured zones, and that the Egret Member source rock itself is overpressured in many wells. These overpressure zones approach levels of 100 megaPascals (MPa) at 5 km depth (McAlpine et al., 1986). At these depths, formation fracture pressures and pore pressures appear to converge (Bell et al., 1986), so only relatively small increases in today's formation fluid pressure regimes would be required to initiate fracturing and upward movement of fluids. If this is feasible today, it is likely to have also occurred earlier in the geological record.

Grant and McAlpine (Chapter 6) emphasize that increases in fluid pressure gradient occur stepwise with depth and so cannot be accounted for by simple sediment loading (B.S. Mudford, pers. comm., 1986). Fluid addition at depth is required, and one possible source is hydrocarbon generation. This suggests a charging mechanism involving the following steps: 1) maturation of source rocks; 2) generation of hydrocarbons; 3) fluid pressure increases faster than it can dissipate; 4) the source rocks and overlying rocks fracture, fluids escape along these fractures and pressures are lowered; 5) Cycle 2-3-4 repeats.

Oils from different reservoirs in the same wells exhibit different levels of maturity as is illustrated by plotting the ratios of 20S/20R C_{29} steranes and 14ß17ß/20R C_{29} steranes (Fig. 12.19). Both biomarker ratios would have been zero at the time of deposition of the oil's source rock, and

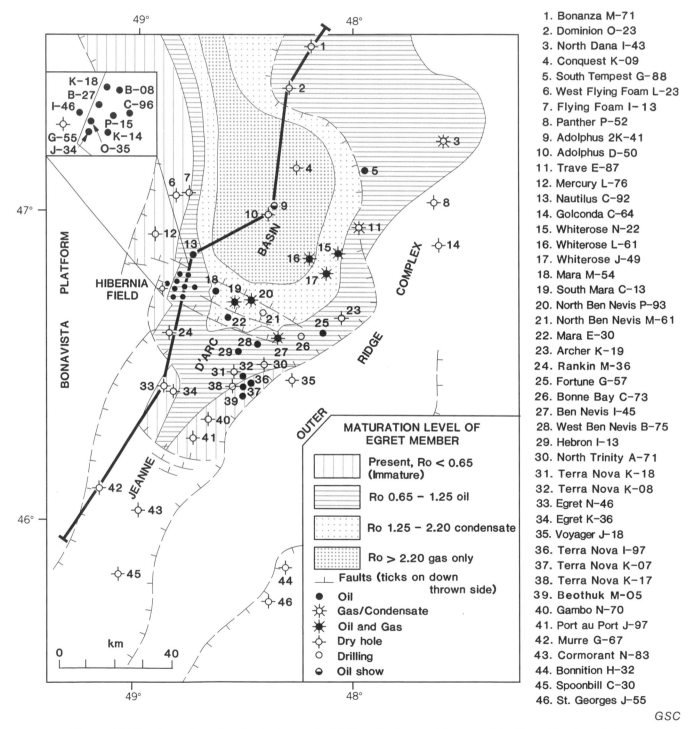

1. Bonanza M-71
2. Dominion O-23
3. North Dana I-43
4. Conquest K-09
5. South Tempest G-88
6. West Flying Foam L-23
7. Flying Foam I-13
8. Panther P-52
9. Adolphus 2K-41
10. Adolphus D-50
11. Trave E-87
12. Mercury L-76
13. Nautilus C-92
14. Golconda C-64
15. Whiterose N-22
16. Whiterose L-61
17. Whiterose J-49
18. Mara M-54
19. South Mara C-13
20. North Ben Nevis P-93
21. North Ben Nevis M-61
22. Mara E-30
23. Archer K-19
24. Rankin M-36
25. Fortune G-57
26. Bonne Bay C-73
27. Ben Nevis I-45
28. West Ben Nevis B-75
29. Hebron I-13
30. North Trinity A-71
31. Terra Nova K-18
32. Terra Nova K-08
33. Egret N-46
34. Egret K-36
35. Voyager J-18
36. Terra Nova I-97
37. Terra Nova K-07
38. Terra Nova K-17
39. Beothuk M-05
40. Gambo N-70
41. Port au Port J-97
42. Murre G-67
43. Cormorant N-83
44. Bonnition H-32
45. Spoonbill C-30
46. St. Georges J-55

GSC

Figure 12.17. Organic maturation in terms of vitrinite reflectance at the top of the Egret Member of the Rankin Formation, Jeanne d'Arc Basin area.

RESOURCES

Oil-soaked carbonate crust from a pock mark on the seafloor in 400m of water off Scott Inlet, Baffin Island. The sample was collected by the submersible PISCES IV, October 1985, and was described by A.C. Grant et al., 1986, in Geological Survey of Canada, Paper 86-1A, p.65-69. *Photo by Roger Bélanger, Bedford Institute of Oceanography Photo Services.*

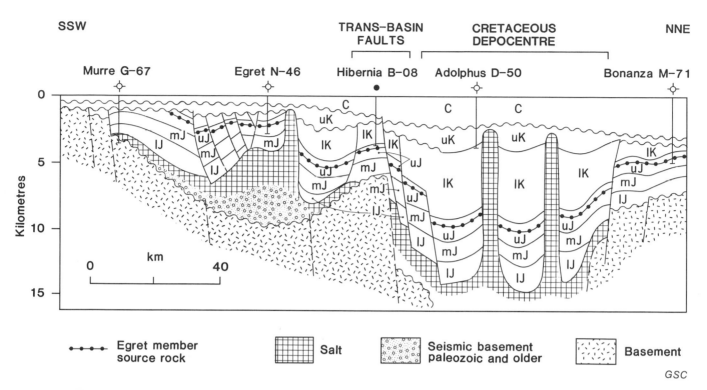

Figure 12.18. Cross-section through Jeanne d'Arc Basin showing truncation of structures against the mid-Cretaceous (Avalon) unconformity. lJ — lower Jurassic, mJ — middle Jurassic, uJ — upper Jurassic, lK — lower Cretaceous, uK — upper Cretacous, C — Cenozoic. The Egret Member is shown as a basinwide deposit (after Avery et al., 1986).

maturity increases upward to the right. The scatter shows that these oils were generated from sources which had reached varying degrees of maturity and this implies a complex migration history involving many episodes of charging individual reservoirs. Snowdon and Krouse (1986) found a bimodal $\delta^{13}C$ carbon isotope content for distillation fractions of crude oil recovered at Hebron I-13. This type of isotope distribution may indicate that the oil was derived from two or more hydrocarbon pulses from a source rock at markedly different levels of maturation. Alternatively, mixing of oils from two or more distinctive source rocks is a possibility (Snowdon and Krouse, 1986).

Hydrocarbon entrapment model

A combination of favourable stratigraphy, structure and timing has led to the hydrocarbon accumulations now trapped in Jeanne d'Arc Basin. A rich oil-prone source rock sequence was deposited in Late Jurassic time. In later Jurassic and Early Cretaceous time it was buried beneath a sequence of sandstone-rich units (reservoirs) separated by shales (top seals). In mid-Cretaceous time, before any significant amount of oil (if any) had been generated from the Upper Jurassic source rocks, down-to-basin faulting occurred which led to the formation of traps in rollover anticlines and rotated fault blocks. Most of the faults appear to have provided adequate lateral seals. Regional uplift, together with some local upwarping induced by salt diapirism, led to widespread subaerial erosion and peneplanation (Avalon Unconformity), but the Upper Jurassic and Lower Cretaceous sandstone reservoirs and the structural traps involving them were largely

preserved. Subsequently, an Upper Cretaceous and Tertiary clastic wedge was laid down and accompanied by subsidence and mild tilting. Fortunately, the beds immediately above the Avalon Unconformity were dominated by shales (seals) and it was only in the southernmost neck of Jeanne d'Arc Basin that the basal beds deposited above the mid-Cretaceous unconformity included sandstones through which leakage could occur.

Late Cretaceous and Tertiary burial provided the thermal conditions for the Upper Jurassic source rock to generate oil, and also possibly gas, which migrated into the Upper Jurassic and Lower Cretaceous sandstone reservoirs. Most of the traps are likely to have been filled during Tertiary time (Von der Dick and Meloche, 1986).

Assessment of hydrocarbon potential

The hydrocarbon potential of Jeanne d'Arc Basin and adjacent Outer Ridge Complex was assessed in 1983. That study recognized that the most important reservoir units were sandstones of Late Jurassic and Early Cretaceous age within Jeanne d'Arc, Hibernia, Catalina and Avalon formations (Fig. 12.14). Seven distinct plays were defined based on the combination of these reservoir units with families of structures (Fig. 12.20). Roll-over anticlinal closures and thickening of reservoir units against the basin-bounding faults are apparent along the western margin of the basin, abutting the Bonavista Platform (play 1). Hibernia is an excellent example of this type of structure. Pillowing of Argo Formation salt may also contribute to axial upwarping. A second play-type (play 2, Fig. 12.20) occurs where the Trans-Basin Fault Zone crosses the southern end of the basin in a northwesterly direction between the Hibernia and Terra Nova wells. The traps are contained in the upthrown and downthrown blocks bounded by down-to-basin listric normal faults and antithetic faults. Other structural plays include horst and graben complexes on the Outer Ridge Complex, involving principally Upper Jurassic sandstones (play 3), and the crest and flanks of salt diapirs in the central and deepest part of the basin (play 4). Large salt swells and salt ridges provide opportunities for closures, and were the target of many of the wells drilled in the basins of the southern Grand Banks (play 6). Large low-relief drape closures, involving potential reservoirs in Upper Cretaceous and Tertiary reservoir rocks have been mapped on regional seismic grids (play 7) and lastly, stratigraphic and unconformity traps are possible along the margin of the basin, or on the flanks of salt ridges (play 5).

The Trans-Basin Fault Zone play (play 2) is the most extensively drilled to date, followed by the basin margin play (play 1). The characteristics of the seismic data and structural style in the Hibernia area are illustrated in Figure 12.21. The Hibernia structure itself is shown abutting the Bonavista Platform, with two of the several fault blocks illustrated.

The results of the assessment (Procter et al., 1984) indicate that there is a 50% probability of more than 1335×10^6 m³ of oil and 345×10^9 m³ of natural gas (Table. 12.5).

EAST NEWFOUNDLAND BASIN

The East Newfoundland Basin is confined by water depth greater than 400 m, and bounded by Cartwright Arch to the north, and the Orphan Knoll and Flemish Cap bathymetric highs to the east and south (Fig. 12.1 and Map 850-A, in pocket).

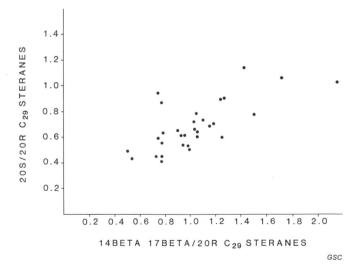

GSC

Figure 12.19. Ratios of 20S/20R C_{29} steranes to C29 14ß17ß20R C_{29} steranes in 31 oils tested from 13 wells in Jeanne d'Arc Basin. Maturity increases upwards to the right. From P.W. Brookes (pers. comm.).

Exploration history

Exploration activity to date has involved principally acquisition and interpretation of seismic data by the major landholders, Shell Canada Resources, Petro-Canada Exploration Inc. and Esso Resources Canada. In 1979, Texaco-Shell et al. Blue H-28 was drilled in 1486 m of water (Fig. 1, in pocket). It was abandoned as a dry hole, but a gas show was reported from a Tertiary claystone and pale fluorescence was noted in a Lower Cretaceous sandstone.

Exploration in this area has been limited due to the extreme water depths which significantly increase the cost and complexity of drilling operations, and due to the lack of a good play with potential in Mesozoic reservoirs, comparable to the plays in adjacent well explored areas.

Assessment of hydrocarbon potential

Estimates for oil and gas potential for this area were prepared in 1978, and have been updated by Procter et al. (1984). The structural style of the basin involves a complex array of basement and Paleozoic fault blocks overlain by undeformed Tertiary clastics (Fig. 12.22). Analysis of biostratigraphic data (Gradstein and Thomas, 1983) indicates that the area in the vicinity of Blue H-28 subsided from very shallow to neritic to bathyl water depth in mid-Cretaceous time, and subsequently gradually deepened in the Late Cretaceous to early Tertiary.

Porous Lower Cretaceous sandstones, which were deposited in shallow neritic depths (Gradstein and Thomas, 1983), were encountered at Blue H-28. Other potential reservoirs tested by the well are Paleozoic limestones and sandstones and Tertiary sandstones. On the flanks of the fault blocks Jurassic sandstone and carbonate reservoirs may also be present.

The likelihood of reservoir sections in this basin is limited by two factors. First, for the Tertiary section, this area is predominently in a distal clastic environment, although fault blocks with positive relief could serve as local sources of sediments. Secondly, there is a risk of truncation of any reservoir section by erosion. At Blue H-28 for example, four major unconformities have been identified (Fig. 12.22), of which the late Early Cretaceous and early Tertiary discontinuities are the most critical.

In addition to the risk of adequate reservoir development, the source-rock characteristics and maturation are an additional concern. Total Organic Carbon at Blue H-28 exceeds 1% in the Cretaceous-Eocene section, with an interval exceeding 2.5% in Upper Cretaceous shales. However, maturation studies reveal that the potential source section is immature. Full maturity is not reached in the well, and beneath the pre-Cretaceous unconformity, the Paleozoic section is overmature (M.P. Avery, pers. comm., 1986).

Although the available geochemical information from the Blue H-28 well is not encouraging, maturation levels could be more favourable on deeper prospects or on structural or stratigraphic traps on the flanks of fault blocks.

Three plays (Fig. 12.23), were assessed for their hydrocarbon potential. Play 1 involves the highly-deformed Paleozoic section in the large horst blocks which are characteristic of the assessment area. Critical risk factors are: the limited possibility for reservoir facies, especially on the high-standing horsts which have undergone several periods of erosion; the presence of porosity within the reservoir; and adequate mature source rocks.

Although high-risk, play 2 is based on the possibility of pre-Cretaceous reservoirs existing on the apexes and flanks of the large structural closures. The critical risk fac-tors are the presence of reservoir facies and adequate source rock. Structure with preserved section between the Paleozoic units and the late Early Cretacous unconformity are potential targets in this play.

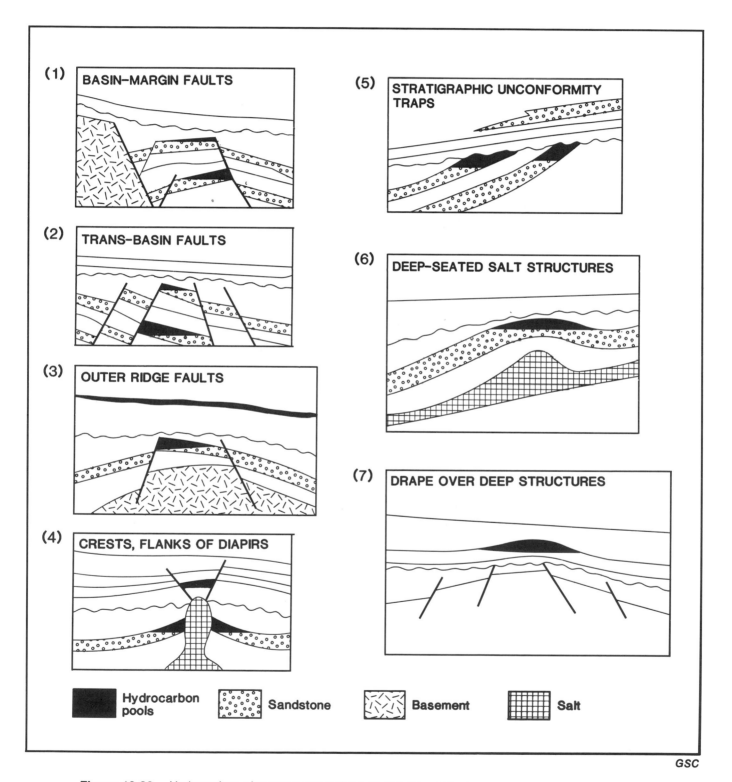

GSC

Figure 12.20. Hydrocarbon play types recognized on the Grand Banks.

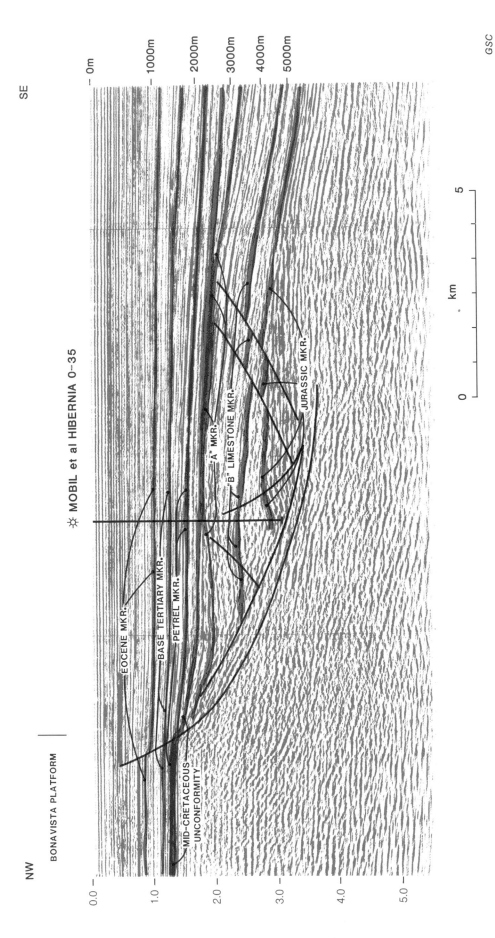

Figure 12.21. Reflection seismic line across the Hibernia structure.

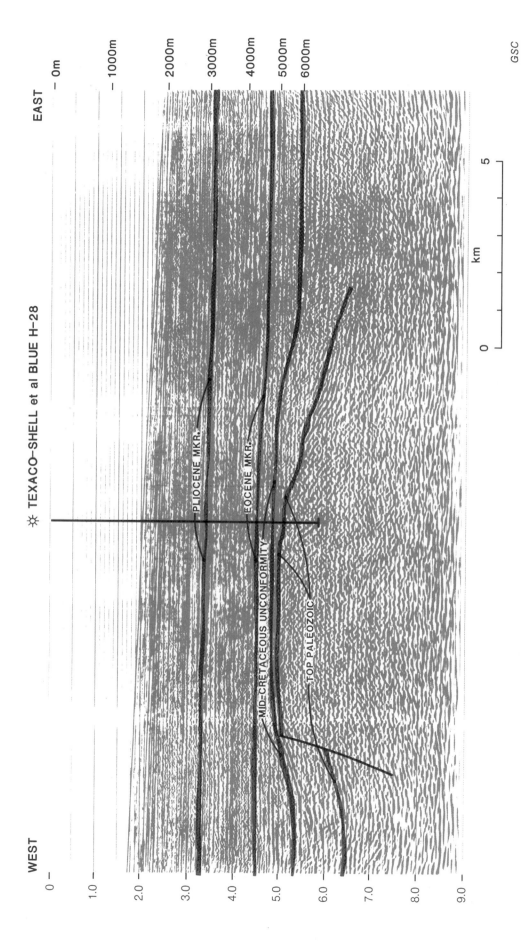

Figure 12.22. Reflection seismic line crossing the Blue H-28 well in the East Newfoundland Basin.

The third play (play 3) concept is similar to that in play 1, but involves Cretaceous-Tertiary reservoirs with the added concept of closure due to drape over large horst blocks. The major risk factors are presence of reservoirs and existence of an adequate, mature source section.

Stratigraphic traps or unconformity traps may occur on the flanks of the fault blocks, either due to limits of deposition or erosion from the early Tertiary or late Early Cretaceous unconformities (Fig. 12.22).

Estimates for potential hydrocarbon resources subdivided by play are shown in Table 12.6. Also shown are the values published by Procter et al. (1984).

LABRADOR SHELF AND SOUTHEAST BAFFIN SHELF

The area covered by the Labrador Shelf extends from the Hawke Saddle in the south to Hudson Strait in the north and encompasses the continental shelf between the coast of Labrador and the 400 m isobath. Southeast Baffin Shelf is located between Hudson and Davis straits and also extends from shore to the 400 m isobath.

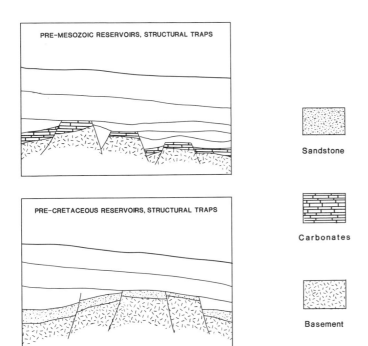

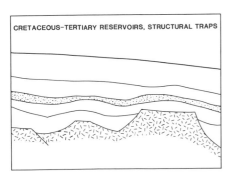

Figure 12.23. Play types, East Newfoundland Basin.

Exploration history

Geophysical exploration of the Labrador Shelf by the petroleum industry began in 1966 with a 14 000 km aeromagnetic survey by Tenneco. In 1968, Tenneco ran a 4000 km reflection seismic program. To date, the industry has acquired over 75 000 km of reflection seismic lines which have provided a good understanding of the tectonic framework, regional geology and play definition.

Exploratory drilling was undertaken from 1971 to 1983 and 31 wells have been completed (Table 12.1). The locations of significant discoveries, shows and other important wells are shown in Figure 12.24. Three wells are considered to be unsuitable for diagnostic tests due to their shallow depth of penetration. The remaining wells tested 25 structures and resulted in six significant discoveries of gas and condensate for an overall success rate of 24%.

The first wildcat well, Tenneco et al. Leif E-38, was drilled in 1971 on what appeared to be a drape structure caused by compaction around the flanks of a basement high. In 1973, Eastcan returned to the prospect and drilled Eastcan et al. Leif M-48, on what is now recognized to be a tilted basement fault block. During their exploration over the next seven years, Eastcan (later Total Eastcan) drilled 15 wells, including the first three significant discoveries. BP Canada drilled an unsuccessful wildcat at Indian Harbour M-52 in 1976. Other operators included Chevron Resources Canada, which drilled two wildcat wells under a farmout arrangement with Paddon Hughes. One of these, Chevron et al. Hopedale E-33, which was drilled in 1978 on a basement horst, resulted in a significant discovery of gas and condensate with reservoirs in both Paleozoic carbonates and the Bjarni Formation sandstone. In 1980, Petro-Canada took over from Total Eastcan as operator for the Labrador Group and has been responsible since then for most of the exploration activity in the area. Eight wildcats were drilled by Petro-Canada between 1980 and 1983; this resulted in a major discovery of gas and condensate at North Bjarni F-06, and recovery of a small quantity of oil from North Leif I-05. Canterra Energy drilled an unsuccessful wildcat well at South Hopedale L-39 in 1983.

Three wildcat wells have been drilled on Southeast Baffin Shelf. Esso and partners drilled Gjoa G-37 in 1979, which was abandoned as a dry hole. Aquitaine (now Canterra Energy) drilled and tested Hekja O-71 in 1979 and 1980, which resulted in a significant discovery of gas and condensate. Canterra's second wildcat well, Ralegh N-18, was abandoned in 1982 as a dry hole.

Table 12.6. Estimates of potential hydrocarbon resources in the East Newfoundland Basin.

Play	Oil ($10^6 m^3$)	Gas ($10^9 m^3$)
Pre-Cretaceous, Structural	181.7	215.2
Cretaceous-Tertiary, Structural	78.4	119.8
Pre-Mesozoic, Structural	15.4	16.5
Total	283.5	362.7
Total (Procter et al., 1984)	270	370

Significant discoveries

The six significant discovery wells, significant shows and drill stem test results are compiled in Table 12.7. The stratigraphic positions of the pay sections are indicated in Figure 12.25.

The first gas and condensate discovery on the Labrador Shelf was at Bjarni H-81 in Lower Cretaceous sandstones of the Bjarni Formation (McWhae and Michel, 1975). The trap was created by onlap and drape of the sedimentary section over a high-standing basement fault block (Fig. 12.26a). Relief and degree of faulting are substantially greater on the seismically-defined surface mapped as the top of the underlying Alexis Formation. The pay distribution is controlled by closure on the top of the lower part of Bjarni Formation and the gas-water contact. The Neutron-Density log through the pay zone in the Bjarni H-81 discovery well indicates that the thickest pay intervals are confined to the upper part of the section, with several thin streaks below. The reservoir section is a poor-quality, arkosic, coarse-to-fine-grained sandstone, with poor to excellent intergranular porosity, which is interbedded with shale. The Bjarni sandstones probably were deposited as the products of erosion of local highs in a continental-shallow marine environment.

Eastcan et al. Gudrid H-55 identified a gas condensate pay zone in a Paleozoic carbonate reservoir. Umpleby (1979) described the reservoir as a micrite, containing oncolites and crinoids, which was subsequently dolomitized and leached to create its intercrystalline porosity. The reservoir section is tilted at 40° and is located at the crest of a horst block. It is draped by shales of the Upper Cretaceous-Paleocene Markland Formation which provide a good seal (Fig. 12.26b). Good porosity values are apparent on the sonic log with the best pay zones confined to two thick intervals in the upper part of the reservoir.

A significant discovery of gas and condensate was made at Eastcan et al. Snorri J-90. The reservoir is a Paleocene sandstone assigned to the Upper Gudrid Member of the Cartwright Formation (Fig. 12.25, 12.26c). Cores show that the sandstone is composed of a fine to very fine grained, feldspathic sandstone which may have been deposited in a shallow subtidal environment. It has good reservoir properties and an average porosity exceeding 20%. The Density-Neutron log through the pay section illustrates a "blocky" log character (Umpleby, 1979). No gas-water contact was observed. The Snorri structure is created by onlap and drape of the Cretaceous and lower Tertiary sedimentary section over a high-standing basement fault block (Fig. 12.26c). An excellent seal above the reservoir section is provided by shales of the lower Tertiary Kenamu Formation. One drillstem test was run across the lower half of the pay zone (Table 12.7) which yielded good flow rates of gas with condensate and no water.

The 1978 wildcat Chevron et al. Hopedale E-33 well identified gas and condensate in two reservoir units, an Ordovician carbonate unit and the Bjarni Formation sandstone. The Hopedale structure is cored by a high-standing basement fault block. Seismic data document onlap by Cretaceous sediments. Differential compaction has created drape and hence structural closure as shallow as the top of the Bjarni/base of the Markland seismic event (Fig. 12.25). At this location, the Bjarni reservoir section is fine grained to pebbly sandstone, poorly sorted, and composed of angular quartz and feldspar and subrounded igneous rock pebbles. Average porosity over the 8 m pay section appears to be 24%, but log quality is poor and unreliable due to hole enlargement. The other reservoir unit, the Ordovician carbonate section, is approximately 24 m thick, and has an average porosity of 8% according to the neutron-density logs. Successful drillstem tests (Table 12.7) were conducted over both reservoir units.

Petro-Canada et al. North Bjarni F-06 was drilled in 1980 and 1981 on a structure immediately north of the Bjarni discovery. Closure was created by differential compaction and consequent drape over a deep-seated basement feature. A core from 2452-2458 m in the Bjarni Formation reservoir section shows that it consists of fine- to coarse-grained, poorly sorted arkosic sandstones with a kaolinitic matrix and cement. These rocks probably accumulated in a continental-shallow marine environment near granitic highs. Neutron-density logs through the pay section and the core samples themselves, illustrate its uniformity and

Table 12.7. Drillstem test results for gas, condensate and oil discoveries, Labrador Shelf and southeast Baffin Shelf.

Well (date)	Interval (m)	Condensate (m³/day)	Gas (10⁶m³/d)	Gravity °API	Remarks
Bjarni H-81 (1974)	2151-2256	15.9 (cond.)	0.37	55	Bjarni Formation
Gudrid H-55 (1974)	2663-2723	18.1 (cond.)	0.57	50	Paleozoic dolomite
	2756-2772	9.5 (cond.)	0.23	50	Paleozoic dolomite
Snorri J-90 (1976)	2493-2502	37.4 (cond.)	0.28		upper Gudrid Member (Cartwright Formation)
Hopedale E-33 (1978)	1948-1959	49.3 (cond.)	0.40	60.1	Bjarni Formation
	1983-1997	79.5 (cond.)	0.55	58.6	Ordovician carbonate
North Bjarni F-06 (1981)	2585-2604		0.20-0.23 (est)		Bjarni Formation (inconclusive test)
North Leif I-05 (1981)	3101-3110	3.6 recovered		33.1	Bjarni Formation Oil Show
Hekja O-71 (1980)	3212-3251	16.9 (cond.)	0.27	54	Paleocene "Hekja" sand

suggest an average 17% porosity. A drillstem test (2579 to 2604 m) run in the Bjarni Formation flowed gas to surface at initial rates of 198 to 226 × 10³ m³/d but the test string plugged, possibly due to the formation of gas hydrate, before accurate, stable flow rates could be measured. Severe weather conditions prevented further testing.

Operators have reported frequent gas shows as they drilled through Cretaceous and Tertiary sandstones and siltstones in wells on the Labrador Shelf. Oil shows, however, have been rare. In Total Eastcan et al. Roberval K-92, oil shows were reported from porous Bjarni Formation sandstones between 3095-3113 m. Wireline logs through this section do not rule out the possibility of oil; however a repeat formation test at 3101 m yielded only mud filtrate and a trace of oil. As a result, the well was not drillstem tested. At Petro-Canada et al. North Leif I-05, oil (3.6 m³) was recovered on a drillstem test over an interval (3101-3110 m) in the Bjarni Formation. Logs indicate that the sandstone is an isolated 10 m unit with low porosity. A cored section (3109-3117 m) exhibited fluorescence and oil bled from isolated intervals beneath the main sandstone unit. A sample obtained from a repeat formation test (RFT) at 3105.5 m contained 2 L of oil and 4 L of mud and filtrate. These results are encouraging and suggest that oil potential may exist for the southern Hopedale Basin on the Labrador Shelf.

On the Southeast Baffin Shelf, the Aquitaine et al. Hekja O-71 well made a significant discovery of gas and condensate (Fig. 12.27). The reservoir section is a 76 m thick Paleocene sandstone (Klose et al., 1982), which may be equivalent in age to the upper Gudrid Member of the Cartwright Formation. The sandstone is poorly sorted, contains associated coals, and originated in a nearshore, perhaps deltaic, environment (Klose et al., 1982). One drillstem test was run over the 3212-3251 m interval and tested wet flowing gas at a rate of approximately 283 × 10³ m³/d (McMillan, 1982).

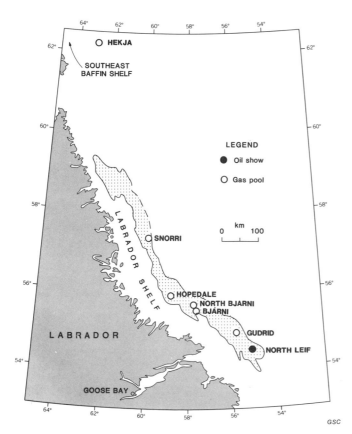

Figure 12.24. Gas pools and oil shows discovered on the Labrador Shelf and Southeast Baffin Shelf. The stippled area outlines Erik Graben, which contains Lower Cretaceous Bjarni Formation sandstones. Outline of Erik Graben from McMillan (1982).

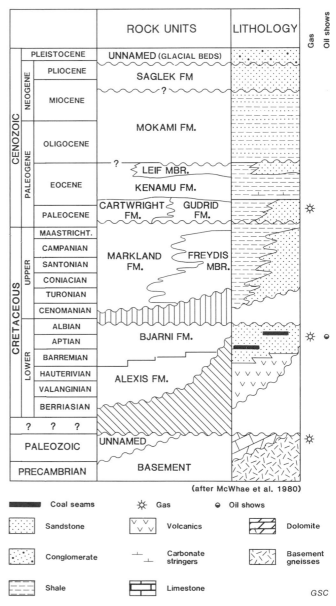

Figure 12.25. Generalized stratigraphy and lithology on the Labrador Shelf. Gudrid Formation is equivalent to upper Gudrid Member of Balkwill et al. (Chapter 7).

Discovered resources and hydrocarbon characteristics

McMillan (1982) has tabulated pay thicknesses, porosity, depth and test results for the Labrador Shelf discovery wells drilled up to 1981. McMillan (1982) estimated that the Bjarni gas pool contained 84.9×10^9 m³. The other discoveries on the Labrador Shelf are judged to be considerably smaller. Estimates of discovered recoverable resources prepared by Canada Oil and Gas Lands Administration are listed in Table 12.8. Larger estimates have been made such as 169.9×10^9 m³ by McMillan (1982) for discovered gas reserves.

On Southeast Baffin Shelf only the Hekja O-71 exploratory well has tested hydrocarbons, but it appears to have encountered a substantial gas-condensate accumulation. Pool size estimates based on seismic extrapolations and the drilled reservoir thickness suggest recoverable gas reserves in the order of 65.1×10^9 m³ (McMillan, 1982).

The compositions of gases recovered during drillstem testing of Labrador Shelf wells are listed in Table 12.9 below (Umbleby, 1979; and operator well history reports). Condensates recovered from Bjarni H-81, Bjarni O-82, Gudrid H-55, Hopedale E-33 and Snorri J-90 have API gravities ranging from 50.0 to 70.8. Compositionally, they appear to be quite similar (Powell, 1979), as shown by the distribution of gasoline range components (Fig. 12.28).

Source rocks

On the Labrador Shelf there are two source-rock sequences which are organically mature enough to have generated the gas and condensate accumulations which have been found. These are the Lower Cretaceous lignite and coal-bearing sequence in the Bjarni Formation (McWhae et al., 1980) and the organic-rich shales of the Upper Cretaceous-Paleocene Markland Formation (Nantais, 1984).

Bjarni Formation lignites and coals have only been encountered in seven wells, but may be widely present in Erik Graben (McMillan, 1982). In Skolp E-07, lignite beds account for 30 to 50 m of the Lower Cretaceous section (Total Eastcan, 1978). Markland Formation shales outcrop widely on the Labrador Shelf and contain largely terrestrially-derived organic matter (see Chapter 7). Bujak et al. (1977a,b) reported a high content of amorphous kerogen. Elemental analyses of the kerogen and gas chromatograms of the hydrocarbons suggest that the shales contain degraded herbaceous gas-prone material (Rashid et al., 1979). The total organic carbon content ranges between 1 and 4% (Rashid et al., 1979).

In Davis Strait, Paleocene shales probably sourced the gas and condensate pool at Hekja O-71. Klose et al. (1982) showed a "rich oil source" interval covering the Paleocene shales below and above the reservoir section at Hekja O-71, but gave no further details other than reporting an average organic carbon content of 1.3%.

Present indications are that the mature source rocks on the Labrador and Southeast Baffin shelves contain liptinite-rich, resinite-poor Type III organic matter (Grant et al., 1986). Organic rich shales such as those of the Markland Formation could also have provided the source for the oil recovered at North Leif I-05.

Maturation and migration

At the present time there are insufficient published data to map maturation-depth configurations across the Labrador or Southeast Baffin shelves. Vitrinite reflectance data from six wells on the Labrador Shelf suggest that Ro levels of 0.7 (at which significant quantities of gas and condensate could be generated from Type III source rocks) occur at depths ranging from 2600 m to 3400 m (Grant et al., 1986). Most of the wells are located on top of positive structures and more mature source rocks are likely to be present downdip on the flanks.

A comprehensive hydrocarbon generation model has not yet been published which estimates when hydrocarbons might have been generated in the deeper off-structure areas. However, it is clear from the preliminary TTI estimates of Nantais (1984) that most of the gas and condensate cannot have been generated prior to latest Tertiary time.

All the hydrocarbon-bearing reservoirs identified on the Labrador Shelf appear to be at maturation levels less than vitrinite reflectance values of 0.7 R_o (Nantais, 1984) or are adjacent to Type III source rocks which are immature for generating significant quantities of gas and condensate (Powell and Snowdon, 1983). Powell (1979) recognized this situation and noted that the gas:oil ratios of the hydrocarbons as well as the high methane content of the gases suggested that vertical migration had occurred. Subsequently, Powell and Snowdon (1983) reported low pristane:nC$_{17}$ ratios for Labrador Shelf condensates relative to extracts from immediately adjacent shales and also cited this as evidence for significant vertical migration.

In contrast, McWhae et al. (1980) believed that the traps were charged with locally derived hydrocarbons and that very little migration needs to have occurred on the Labrador Shelf. They interpreted the hydrocarbon composition as resulting from biogenic degradation and/or early thermal diagenesis of marginally mature source-rocks. If this type of process has occurred, it is, perhaps, surprising that more structures are not filled, since there is no shortage of marginally mature source-rocks on the Labrador Shelf.

At Hekja O-71, on the Southeast Baffin Shelf, the gas and condensate-bearing Paleocene sandstones and surrounding shales exhibit vitrinite reflectance levels of the order of 0.5 R_o (Klose et al., 1982), so some migration is likely to have occurred there as well.

Hydrocarbon entrapment model

On the Labrador and Southeast Baffin shelves the major hydrocarbon discoveries are found in structural traps overlying basement horsts. The basement horsts formed subaerially in Cretaceous time and their relief gave rise to clastic sedimentation which filled the troughs and blanketed the uplifts themselves with fluvial and marine reservoir sandstones. Subsequently, a prograding wedge of uppermost Cretaceous and Lower Tertiary marine sediments was laid down. The sequence included several potential reservoir sandstone intervals, but consists dominantly of marine organic-rich shales, which serve as both source rocks and seals. Further shelf sedimentation in the late Tertiary caused differential subsidence and draped the Upper Cretaceous and Lower Tertiary sediments over the horsts, thus establishing: 1) closed traps involving rift-generated fluvial sandstones abutting and overlying the basement horsts, and 2) anticlinal closure traps above

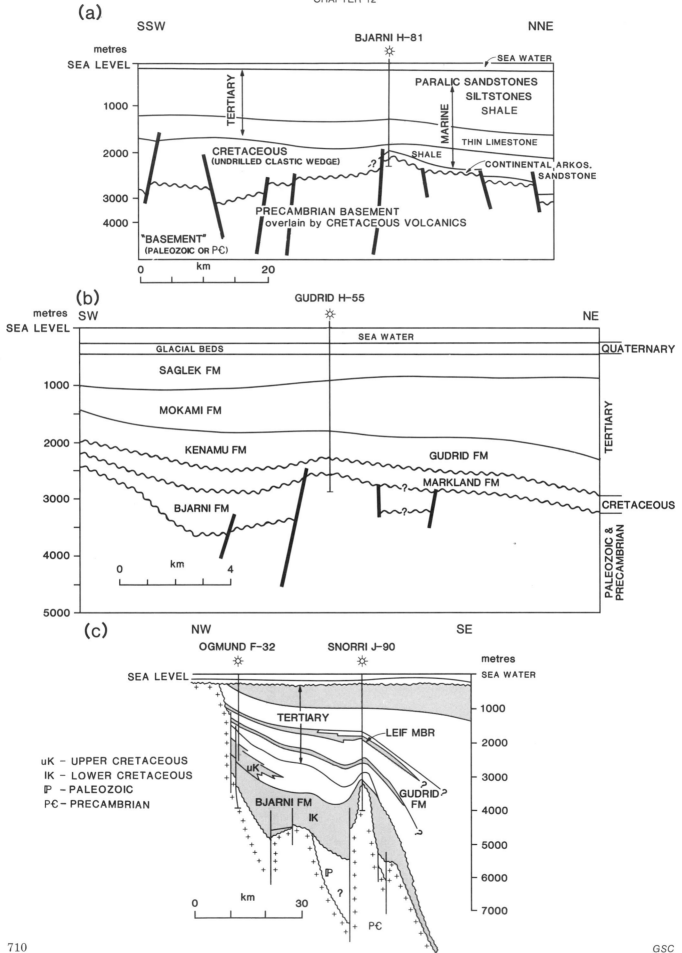

(a)

SSW   NNE

BJARNI H–81

metres
SEA LEVEL

SEA WATER

PARALIC SANDSTONES
SILTSTONES
SHALE

TERTIARY

MARINE

1000

THIN LIMESTONE

2000

CRETACEOUS
(UNDRILLED CLASTIC WEDGE)

SHALE

?

CONTINENTAL ARKOS.
SANDSTONE

3000

PRECAMBRIAN BASEMENT
overlain by CRETACEOUS VOLCANICS

4000

"BASEMENT"
(PALEOZOIC OR PՑ)

0   km   20

(b)

SW   NE

GUDRID H–55

metres
SEA LEVEL

SEA WATER

GLACIAL BEDS

QUATERNARY

SAGLEK FM

1000

MOKAMI FM

TERTIARY

2000

KENAMU FM

GUDRID FM

MARKLAND FM

?

?

3000

BJARNI FM

?

CRETACEOUS

PALEOZOIC &
PRECAMBRIAN

4000

0   km   4

5000

(c)

NW   SE

OGMUND F–32   SNORRI J–90

metres

SEA LEVEL

SEA WATER

TERTIARY

LEIF MBR

1000

2000

uK

3000

uK – UPPER CRETACEOUS
lK – LOWER CRETACEOUS
ℙ – PALEOZOIC
PՑ – PRECAMBRIAN

GUDRID
FM

?

?

BJARNI FM

lK

4000

?

5000

ℙ

6000

?

0   km   30

PՑ

7000

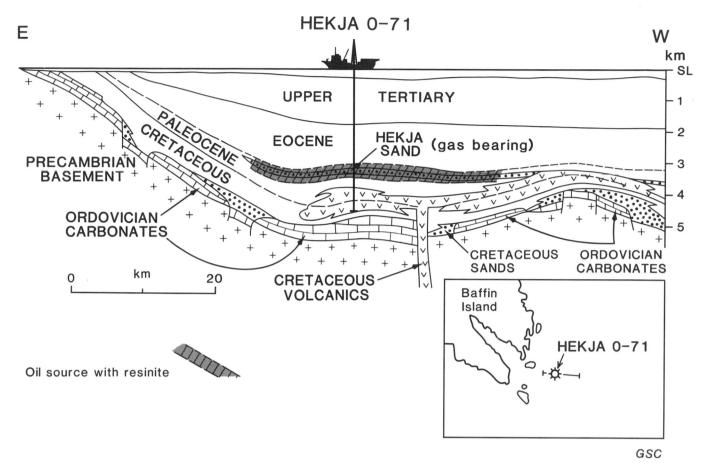

Figure 12.27. Trapping regime at Hekja O-71, Southeast Baffin Shelf (after McMillan, 1982).

them involving lower Tertiary marine sandstones. These trapping configurations evolved between Late Cretaceous and mid-Tertiary time and were not destroyed by subsequent deformation. Some erosion of Lower Cretaceous sandstones above basement horsts may have occurred locally in latest Cretaceous — early Tertiary time.

In late Tertiary time, flanking organic-rich shales became mature enough to generate gas and condensate which migrated into some of the horst-related traps. Proximity to mature source rocks seems to have been a critical factor, since there are several relatively shallow structures with apparently attractive trapping geometries such as in Tyrk P-100, Cartier D-70 and Karlsefni A-13 which are wet. In addition, Tertiary sandstone reservoirs are rather localized and absent, for example, over attractive, deep structures such as Indian Harbour.

At the present time, no sapropelic oil-prone source rock has been identified so there is no hydrocarbon entrapment model involving oil-filled prospects.

Figure 12.26. Trapping regimes recognized in three wells on the Labrador Shelf: (a) Bjarni H-81 (after McWhae and Michel, 1975), (b) Gudrid H-55 (after McWhae et al., 1980), and (c) Snorri J-90 (after McMillan, 1982).

Assessment of hydrocarbon potential

Estimates of the potential of gas and oil resources in five exploration plays (Fig. 12.29) on the Labrador Shelf were made in 1979. Estimates of potential condensate resources were calculated from the gas/condensate ratio observed from drillstem tests. At the time, a regional reflection seismic grid had been interpreted and the geological information from twelve diagnostic wells was available. Recent information has generally supported this geological analysis. However, a shelf-edge fault-play has been delineated by more recent seismic surveys and is discussed below.

In play 1 of Figure 12.29 structural closure exists due to basement horst blocks. Seismic data indicate that the Bjarni Formation onlapped, and eventually covered the basement highs as the basin was being filled (Balkwill et al., Chapter 7). Closure was accentuated by compaction of the sediments on the flanks of the basement features, leading to drape closure at levels as high as the base of the Markland Formation. It is likely that many of the Bjarni Formation closures were subsequently eroded at the crests, following minor readjustments of the basement or sea level changes. Closures are commonly subcircular or elongated with occasional flank faults. There is substantially less faulting at the top of the Bjarni Formation than at the top of the underlying Alexis Formation or the top of basement.

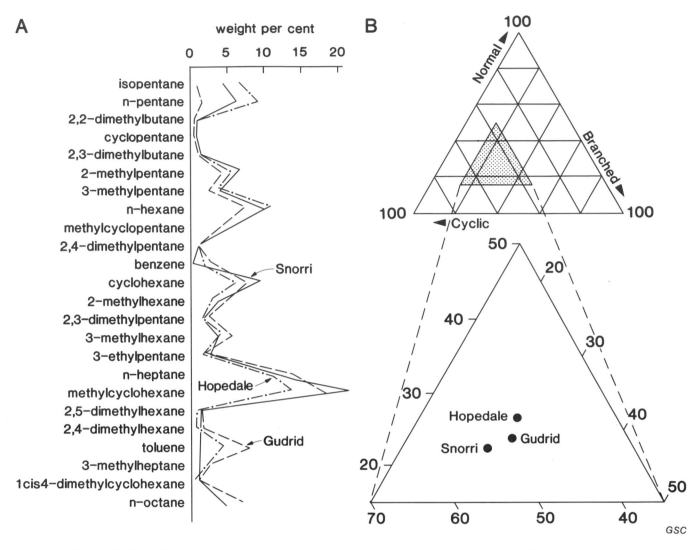

Figure 12.28. Distribution of gasoline range components in the Gudrid, Snorri and Hopedale condensates. (A) Histogram of normalized concentration of gasoline range hydrocarbons. (B) Normalized concentration of hydrocarbon types amongst compounds with seven carbon atoms.

The seal for these Bjarni closures is provided by thick shales in the overlying Cartwright or Markland formations.

Closure on Bjarni Formation structural traps has been present since Late Cretaceous time and has been enhanced by compaction of flanking sediments. Moveover, the closures have not been significantly reduced by subsequent regional tilting or continued subsidence. As a consequence, Bjarni structural traps would have been present at the time of primary migration in late Tertiary time.

Stratigraphic traps could have been created in Bjarni and Freydis sandstones at the limits of deposition on the western margin of the Erik Graben (McMillan, 1982) against the basin-bounding faults, as well as in closed "aprons" surrounding and onlapping basement highs (play 2, Fig. 12.29). Subsidence and compaction of Mesozoic sediments surrounding the structural highs would act to enhance the stratigraphic closure. To ensure trap integrity, the reservoir section would need to be sealed

against the bounding faults and isolated from adjacent porous units to prevent updip migration. For the upper Gudrid Member sandstone reservoir, such stratigraphic traps are possible along the western depositional limit of the unit. Possible stratigraphic traps in each of these reservoirs may have been present since Paleocene time and hence hydrocarbons generated during the late Tertiary could be trapped.

Structures that have potential reservoirs in Cretaceous basal sandstones or carbonates of Ordovician or Silurian age are considered in play 3 (Fig. 12.29). Cretaceous basal sandstones have been identified on the Labrador Shelf as being coeval with the Alexis Formation (Umpleby, 1979). At Snorri J-90, this section is Valanginian to Barremian in age. It is interpreted as being largely derived from volcanic rocks and consists of greywackes, interbedded arkosic sands and silts with coal beds (Umpleby, 1979). Basal sands originating from erosion of Precambrian crystalline rock, such as a granite, are also potential reservoirs.

Porous Paleozoic carbonates are present on several fault blocks in the basin. Structural closure for these prospects is created by basement fault blocks. A seal could be provided by the shales in the overlying Markland and Cartwright formations depending on the relief of the basement block. Alternatively Alexis Formation volcanics could be a viable seal. Structural history indicates that these reservoirs were in trapping configurations when hydrocarbons were generated in late Tertiary time.

In play 4 of Figure 12.29 sandstones of the Paleocene Gudrid Member and the Eocene Leif Member of the Kenamu Formation form closures in prospects created by compaction of the sedimentary section around high-standing basement fault blocks. Any reactivation of block upwarping or subsidence on the flanks would have enhanced this structural relief. An 8 m core section through the upper Gudrid Member sandstones of Snorri J-90 indicates that they are either shallow subtidal deposits (Umpleby, 1979) or part of a deep-sea fan sequence, suggested by the presence of a characteristic Bouma-cycle turbiditic sand-shale sequence (McWhae et al., 1980). The Leif Member sandstone is a relatively clean,

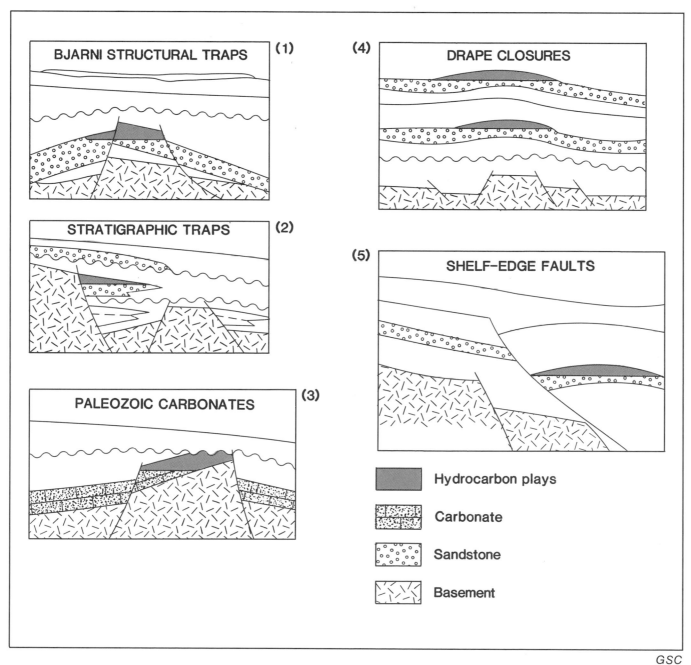

GSC

Figure 12.29. Hydrocarbon play types recognized on the Labrador Shelf.

mature reservoir consisting of fine grained quartzose sandstone, with varying amounts of siltstone and mudstone (McWhae et al., 1980), which was deposited in a deep-water environment in the type area (Umpleby, 1979). Closures in this play are broad, low-relief features that generally are unfaulted. The critical closure direction is directly updip to the west. Seals are provided by the thick shale sections which overlie the reservoir units.

Closed traps of this type, particularly those involving upper Gudrid Member sandstones, are likely to have been in existence during late Tertiary time when hydrocarbons are believed to have migrated. However, several of these features have proved to be wet and there is a risk that the reservoir section is isolated from the mature source rock. This is a particular concern for traps involving the Leif Member sandstone.

The final play type involves rollover or updip closure of Tertiary sandstone reservoirs against down-to-basin listric growth faults (play 5, Fig. 12.29) which are present in the Hopedale and Saglek basins on the Labrador Shelf (Map 1706A, in pocket). These faults moved between Eocene and early Oligocene time and offset beds equivalent to the sand-rich upper Gudrid Member of the Cartwright Formation and Leif Member of the Kenamu Formation (Balkwill, 1987). To date, only two wells have tested this play (Pothurst P-19 and Corte Real P-85) and both were unsuccessful. The play is located on the shelf edge. Reservoir development is a clear risk, but there is a finite possibility that oil-prone source rocks could be present in parts of this sparsely drilled setting.

Resources discovered to date amount to 92.7×10^9 m^3 of gas and 7.3×10^6 m^3 condensate according to prospect analysis undertaken by Canada Oil and Gas Land Administration (Table 12.8). Potential reserves have been estimated by assigning each wildcat well and each discovery to one of the five plays and incorporating assessments of risks with seismically-mapped sizes of drilled and undrilled prospects. Exploration drilling has been unevenly distributed among the plays. Most of the drilling targets have been prospects involving the Bjarni Formation sandstone reservoirs on structural highs. To date this Bjarni Formation structural play contains the bulk of the discovered resources.

Assessments of hydrocarbon potential for the Labrador and Southeast Baffin shelves are given in Table 12.8, and compared with Canada Oil and Gas Lands Administration's estimates of discovered resources.

Table 12.8. Discovered resources and hydrocarbon potential, Labrador Shelf and southeast Baffin Shelf.

Significant Discoveries Gas and Condensate: 6		
	Condensate 10^6m^3	Gas 10^9m^3
Discovered Resources	7.3	92.7
Potential	79.5	538
Average Expectation (Procter et al., 1984)	134.0	745
% Discovered	9.2%	17.2%

GULF OF ST. LAWRENCE

The Gulf of St. Lawrence can be divided into two geological units: the south-dipping, regionally homoclinal, Lower Paleozoic succession of the Anticosti Basin in the north and the Upper Paleozoic succession of the Magdalen Basin in the centre and south. The stratigraphy of both basins is summarized in Chapter 4.

Anticosti Basin

The Anticosti Basin contains a Cambrian-Silurian succession (see Fig. 4.2, 4.3, 4.4 in Chapter 4), which has been subdivided into six unconformity-bounded sequences. The units are exposed onshore on Gaspésie, Anticosti Island, the north shore of the Gulf of St. Lawrence and in western Newfoundland. They can be projected across the area by using information from eight wells drilled on Anticosti Island and seismic reflection data.

Natural oil seepages in western Newfoundland have been known since the early part of the nineteenth century at Parson's Pond, on St. Pauls Inlet and on the Port au Port Peninsula. Howie (1970) noted that some forty wells ranging in depth from 90 to 1220 m have been drilled in the vicinity of these seepages, with several having produced at rates of 0.16 to 0.95 m^3/d. Oil reservoirs include Ordovician limestones of the Humber Arm Supergroup (Port au Port) and Ordovician dolostones of the St. George Group (Parson's Pond, St. Pauls Inlet). Trapping regime information is not available. The oil is likely to have been derived, at least in part, from Ordovician oil shales, which are presently bleeding oil (G. Macauley, pers. comm., 1987).

On Anticosti Island, the Cambrian units are missing and a carbonate-dominated succession of Early Ordovician to Early Silurian age rests unconformably on Precambrian basement (Petryk, 1979) as shown in Figure 12.30. Eight wells were drilled on the island between 1960 and 1974. Gas and oil shows were recorded, but no discoveries were made (Fig. 12.31, Table 12.10). Some of the wells were essentially stratigraphic tests, but others tested structural closures caused by down-to-basin normal faults with little displacement, which offset the Romaine, Mingan and Black River formations, the Trenton Group and basement (Roliff, 1968).

The main hydrocarbon source rock in the Anticosti Basin is the Middle Ordovician Macasty Formation, which is known only from the subsurface. It is equivalent to the Utica Shale in the northeastern United States and contains organic-rich shales with total organic carbon contents ranging from 3 to 5% (Soquip, pers. comm., 1987). The Macasty Formation is present beneath the western part of Anticosti Island, absent at the Sandpoint No. 1 well (Fig. 12.31) on the eastern end of the island, absent in West Newfoundland and Gaspésie, but probably extends to the north beneath the Anticosti Channel. It attains a maximum thickness of 168 m in the Princeton Lake No. 1 well in western Anticosti Island (Fig. 12.31). Specific information on its level of maturation is not available, but regional inferences suggest that, beneath Anticosti Island, the Macasty Formation lies largely within the gas generation window.

Hydrocarbon entrapment in the carbonates underlying the Macasty Formation can be envisaged, since Taconic age normal-faulting could have created traps in these carbonates (Roksandic and Granger, 1981). The Macasty Formation together with the basal calcareous shales of the

Table 12.9. Labrador shelf gas compositions.

Component	Bjarni H-81 (%)	Bjarni O-82 (6 samples) (%)	North Bjarni F-06 (%)	Gudrid H-55 (%)	Hopedale E-33 (3 samples) (%)	Snorri J-90 (11 samples) (%)
C1	83.6	81.41-85.45	83.76	91.2	88.46-88.70	89.82-91.23
C2	8.4	7.88-8.24	9.82	5.86	6.89-7.18	3.38-3.74
C3	3.5	3.04-4.06	2.88	1.3	2.30-2.46	2.15-2.79
C4	1.6	1.07-2.33	1.39	0.54	1.03-1.08	0.94-1.57
CO2	Trace	0.37-0.39	0.55	Trace	0.02	0.48-0.56
N2	1.6	0.14	0.11	Trace	0.08-0.83	0.41-1.98

Vauréal Formation would have provided a seal. Generation of hydrocarbons from the Macasty Formation would then have charged any reservoirs in the stratigraphically underlying carbonates. The problem with this scenario is the poor porosity of the Ordovician carbonates. Timing too, may have been a constraint, although this is difficult to evaluate since there are insufficient data to permit effective time temperature-index modelling of hydrocarbon generation. Also, the extremely limited amount of deformation apparent on seismic reflection profiles suggests that few significant structural traps are likely to be present. Any notable accumulations are likely to be contained in stratigraphic traps exhibiting fracture porosity, or secondary leached porosity, and there are no clearcut geophysical signatures to guide exploration towards them.

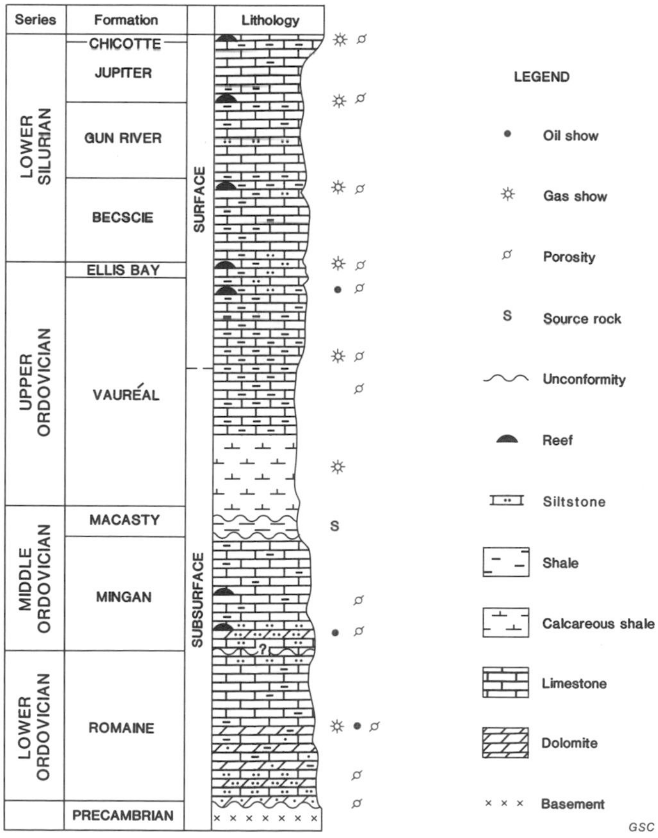

Magdalen Basin

The Magdalen Basin is filled with upper Paleozoic rocks which attain a thickness exceeding 12 000 m in the area east of Îles de la Madeleine. Onshore outcrop data (Howie and Barss, 1975), offshore well information and inferences from seismic reflection lines indicate that the offshore stratigraphy over much of the basin (Fig. 12.32) is likely to be similar to the succession defined onshore (Bell and Howie, Chapter 4), although the units are generally thicker. The western portion of Magdalen Basin contains a relatively undisturbed sedimentary section up to 6000 m thick, whereas the eastern region contains a much thicker section that has been much deformed in the upper part by flowage of the Windsor Group salt. Rift-related vertical faults affecting the Horton Group and younger strata can be mapped seismically along the southeastern edge of the basin, and may be widely developed.

Nine wells were drilled between 1970 and 1983 in the Gulf of St. Lawrence. Except for the Northumberland Strait F-25 well (Fig. 12.33), which was drilled on a basement-cored anticline, all wells tested structural features formed through salt diapirism. The target reservoirs were the porous continental sandstones of the Canso-Riversdale and Cumberland-Pictou groups. The East Point E-49 well (Fig. 12.33) was drilled on a salt-cored anticline and tested dry gas from the base of the Pictou Group. A step-out downdip well, East Point E-47, however, failed to extend the pool, which appears to be of limited extent on the north flank of the structure.

Two significant source rocks of Late Paleozoic age occur in the Maritimes. Oil shales are present in the Albert Formation of the Horton Group in southern New Brunswick (Macauley and Ball, 1982; Altebaeumer, 1985), where they provide the source for the Stony Creek oil and gas field (Williams, 1974). Similar rocks may lie beneath parts of the Gulf of St. Lawrence. Another potential source of hydrocarbons are the thick and widely distributed coal seams which occur in the Upper Carboniferous Cumberland and Pictou groups (Bell and Howie, Chapter 4). The coal deposits are intersected in five wells drilled in the Gulf of St. Lawrence (Hacquebard, 1986). This suggests that an enormous submarine coalfield may exist covering at least 46 000 km² within an area bounded by the coastal Mabou-Inverness coalfield in Cape Breton and the Bradelle L-49 and Brion Island No. 1 wells in the Gulf of St. Lawrence

Figure 12.30. Stratigraphic succession exposed on Anticosti Island and encountered in the subsurface by exploration wells (after Petryk, 1981).

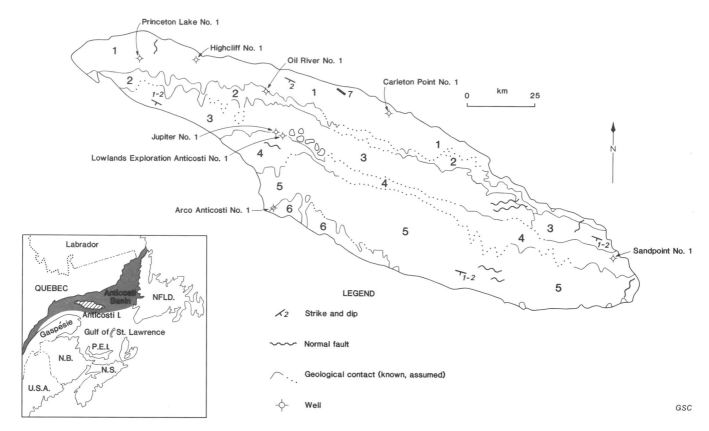

Figure 12.31. Geology of Anticosti Island (after Roliff, 1968 and Petryk, 1979) with well locations. Rock units are labelled as follows: 1 — Vauréal Formation, 2 — Ellis Bay Formation, 3 Becscie Formation, 4 — Gun River Formation, 5 — Jupiter Formation, 6 — Chicotte Formation, 7 — Upper Jurassic dykes.

(Hacquebard, 1986). Such a coalfield would provide a prolific source of gas at maturation levels greater than or equivalent to 0.7 R_o vitrinite reflectance. At Bradelle L-49 (Fig. 12.33), Pictou Group sediments increase in maturation level from 0.73 to 1.16 R_o between 972 and 1859 m (A.M. Vonk, pers. comm., 1986). Onshore at Mabou Mines the average reflectance is 0.62 R_o (Hacquebard, 1986).

If any oil shales are present in the Horton Group beneath the Gulf of St. Lawrence, they are likely to have generated oil and gas during Late Carboniferous or Permian time, depending on their location and the rapidity of their burial. Pictou Group coals probably experienced their deepest burial during Permian or Early Triassic time. Erosion of the upper part of the section has occurred, with approximately 1600 m having been removed at the Bradelle L-49 well location (A.M. Vonk, pers. comm., 1986), but there is no indication that significant Mesozoic sediments were ever present in the Gulf of St. Lawrence. Gas generation from the Pictou coal-bearing section could have occurred throughout most of Mesozoic and all of Tertiary time, according to preliminary time-temperature index modelling. Gas that was probably recently generated was encountered at East Point E-49.

Oil and gas potential in the Gulf of St. Lawrence is not considered large. In the case of oil, any generation is likely to have occurred during Late Paleozoic time and was subject either to leakage or conversion to gas during continued burial. Significant pools are not likely to have been

preserved. There is also a severe decrease in porosity down section (Soquip, pers. comm., 1987) which limits the chances of encountering any substantial gas accumulations. The Canso-Riversdale and Pictou-Cumberland groups contain no thick shale intervals, so there is likely to be a lack of adequate seals. Thus, in a basin containing

Table 12.10. Gas and oil shows in wells drilled on Anticosti Island (Mingan Formation includes Trenton and Black River).

Well	Formation	Gas	Oil
Anticosti No. 1	Vauréal	X	X
	Macasty	X	
	Mingan		X
	Romaine		X
Carleton Point No. 1	Vauréal		X
	Romaine		X
Highcliff No. 1	Mingan	X	X
Oil River No. 1	Mingan	X	
Princeton Lake No. 1	Macasty	X	
	Mingan	X	X
	Romaine		X

a number of large salt-cored anticlines, and other diapirically-generated closures, and a more-than-adequate gas source, several key factors for trapping significant quantities of hydrocarbons are lacking. For these reasons,

Procter et al. (1984) forecast that only 20×10^6 m³ of oil and 40×10^9 m³ of gas are likely to be present at the 50% probability level.

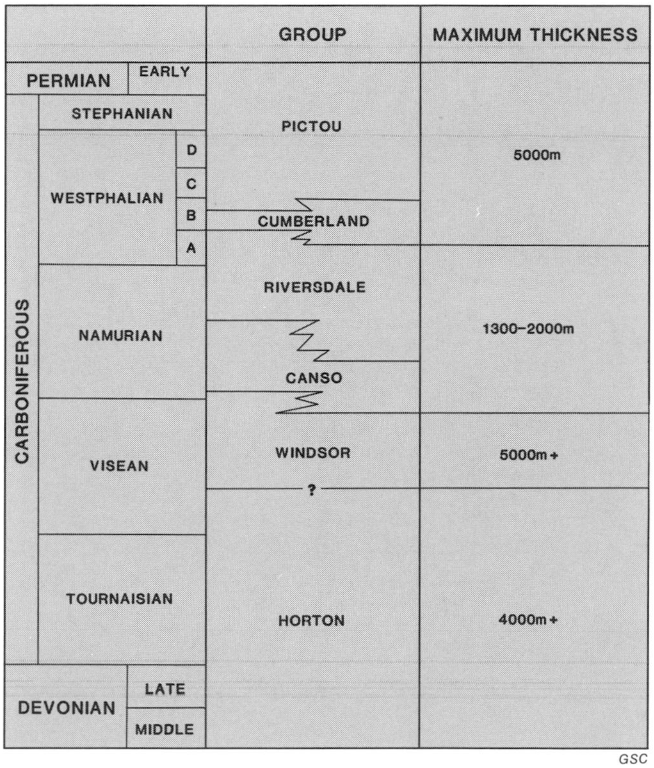

BAY OF FUNDY

The Bay of Fundy is the site of a rift basin filled with Middle Triassic to Lower Jurassic continental sediments and extrusive tholeiitic basalts (Klein, 1962). Two wells, Chinampas N-37 and Cape Spencer No. 1 (Fig. 1, in pocket), were drilled in 1975 and 1983, respectively, on the north flank of the basin, to test faulted anticlines. Both wells were dry. Information bearing on the basin's hydrocarbon potential and possible geochemistry has been presented recently by Brown (1986) and Grierson (1986). The stratigraphic succession in the Bay can be inferred from outcrops in northwestern Nova Scotia and southern New Brunswick (Fig. 12.34). Seismic evidence suggests that the section is close to 3000 m thick in the deepest part of the basin.

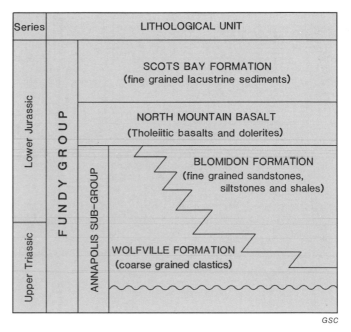

Series			LITHOLOGICAL UNIT		
Lower Jurassic	FUNDY GROUP		SCOTS BAY FORMATION (fine grained lacustrine sediments)		
		ANNAPOLIS SUB-GROUP	NORTH MOUNTAIN BASALT (Tholeiitic basalts and dolerites)		
			BLOMIDON FORMATION (fine grained sandstones, siltstones and shales)		
Upper Triassic			WOLFVILLE FORMATION (coarse grained clastics)		

GSC

Figure 12.34. Stratigraphic succession in the Fundy Basin (after Grierson, 1986).

Figure 12.32. Upper Paleozoic succession in the Gulf of St. Lawrence with maximum thicknesses inferred from seismic interpretation.

			GROUP	MAXIMUM THICKNESS
PERMIAN	EARLY			
CARBONIFEROUS	STEPHANIAN		PICTOU	5000m
	WESTPHALIAN	D		
		C	CUMBERLAND	
		B		
		A		
	NAMURIAN		RIVERSDALE	1300–2000m
			CANSO	
	VISEAN		WINDSOR	5000m +
			?	
	TOURNAISIAN		HORTON	4000m +
DEVONIAN	LATE			
	MIDDLE			

GSC

It is envisaged that hydrocarbons could be trapped in anticlines, in fault-bounded areas of closure and in stratigraphic traps involving continental sandstones and lacustrine shales. The Wolfville Formation sandstones are the most attractive potential reservoirs. Neither of the two wells encountered any source rocks. However, organic-rich lacustrine shales similar to the Lockatong argillite of New Jersey, may have been deposited in the central, undrilled, parts of the basin during the late Triassic and early Jurassic, when the Blomidon, Wolfville and Scots Bay formations were being deposited. Such shales could have reached maturity in axial areas of the basin (Grierson, 1986).

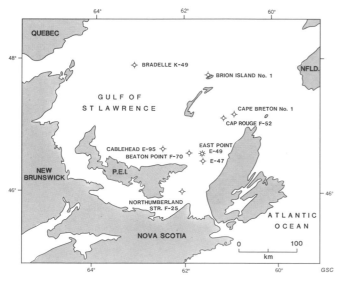

Figure 12.33. Locations of wells drilled in the Gulf of St. Lawrence which tested Upper Paleozoic prospects. Symbols as in Figure 12.17.

717

ACKNOWLEDGMENTS

The authors have benefitted from discussions with numerous colleagues and have been able to refer to a variety of unpublished material. Special thanks are extended to M.P. Avery, D.W. Brown, A.C. Grant, G.C. Grierson, P.A. Hacquebard, R.D. Howie, M.J. Keen, H. Lizotte, G. Macauley, K.D. McAlpine, N.J. McMillan, G. Morrell, J. Plante, R.M. Procter, P.M.R. Robertson, B.V. Sanford, J.A. Wade and G.L. Williams. J.S. Bell is especially grateful to P.W. Brooks, M.G. Fowler and L.R. Snowdon for making their recent geochemical analyses available and explaining their significance. G.R. Campbell is pleased to acknowledge the work of D.R. Smith in the calculation of estimates of discovered resources, and S. Bigelow for assistance with seismic illustrations.

REFERENCES

Altebaeumer, A.M.
1985: Organic geochemical investigation of selected oil shales of the Albert Formation, New Brunswick; Bulletin of Canadian Petroleum Geology, v. 33, p. 427-445.

Amoco Canada Petroleum Company Ltd. and Imperial Oil Ltd.
1973: Regional geology of the Grand Banks; Bulletin of Canadian Petroleum Geology, v. 21, p. 479-503.

Avery, M.P., Bell, J.S., and McAlpine, D.K.
1986: Vitrinite reflectance measurements and their implications for oil and gas exploration in the Jeanne d'Arc Basin, Grand Banks, eastern Canada; in Current Research, Part A, Geological Survey of Canada, Paper 86-1A, p. 489-498.

Balkwill, H.R.
1987: Labrador Basin: structural and stratigraphic style; in Sedimentary Basins and Basin-forming Mechanisms, ed. C. Beaumont and A.J. Tankard; Atlantic Geoscience Society Special Publication 5 and Canadian Society of Petroleum Geologists Memoir 12, p. 17-44.

Barss, M.S., Bujak, J.P., Wade, J.A., and Williams, G.L.
1980: Age, stratigraphic, organic matter type and colour, and hydrocarbon occurrences in 47 wells offshore eastern Canada; Geological Survey of Canada, Open File 714, 58 p.

Barss, M.S., Bujak, J.P., and Williams, G.L.
1979: Palynological zonation and correlation of sixty-seven wells, eastern Canada; Geological Survey of Canada, Paper 78-24, 117p.

Bell, J.S., Podrouzek, A.J. and Ervine, W.B.
1986: Offshore in-situ stress regimes in Eastern Canada; Canadian Society of Petroleum Geologists, Reserves 21 Canada Convention, Calgary, June 1-4, 1986.

Bell, W.A.
1944: Carboniferous rocks and fossil floras of northern Nova Scotia; Geological Survey of Canada, Memoir 238, 277 p.

Brown, D.W.
1986: The Bay of Fundy: thin-skinned tectonics and resultant Early Mesozoic sedimentation; Basins of Eastern Canada and Worldwide Analogues Symposium, Atlantic Geoscience Society Halifax, August 13-15, 1986.

Bujak, J.P., Barss, M.S. and Williams, G.L.
1977a: Offshore eastern Canada: organic type and colour and hydrocarbon potential; Oil and Gas Journal, v. 75, no. 14, p. 198-202.
1977b: Offshore eastern Canada: organic type and colour and hydrocarbon potential; Oil and Gas Journal, v. 75, no. 15, p. 96-100.

Cassou, A.M., Connan, J. and Porthault, B.
1977: Relationship between maturation of organic matter and geothermal effect, as exemplified in Canadian east coast offshore wells; Bulletin of Canadian Petroleum Geology, v. 25, p. 174-194.

Davies, E.H. and Avery, M.P.
1984: A system for vitrinite reflectance analysis on dispersed organic matter for offshore eastern Canada; in Current Research, Part A, Geological Survey of Canada, Paper 84-1A, p. 367-372.

Drummond, K.
1986: Geopressures in Venture and the Sable Island area; Canadian Society of Petroleum Geolgoists, Reserves 21 Canada Convention, Calgary, June 1-4, 1986.

Ervine, W.B.
1985: A synthesis of hydrocarbon maturation data for the East Newfoundland Basin; Geological Survey of Canada, Open File 1170.

Ervine, W.B. and Bell, J.S.
1987: Subsurface in situ stress magnitudes from oil-well drilling records: an example from the Venture area, offshore Eastern Canada; Canadian Journal of Earth Sciences, v. 24, p. 1748-1759.

Grant, A.C., McAlpine, K.D., and Wade, J.A.
1986: The continental margin of eastern Canada: geological framework and petroleum potential; in Future Petroleum Provinces of the World, ed. M.T. Halbouty; American Association of Petroleum Geologists, Memoir 40, p. 177-205.

Given, M.M.
1977: Mesozoic and Early Cenozoic geology of offshore Nova Soctia; Bulletin of Canadian Petroleum Geology, v. 25, p. 63—91.

Gradstein, F.M. and Thomas, F.C.
1983: Stratigraphy and depositional environment of Texaco Blue H-28; Atlantic Geoscience Centre, internal report EPGS-PAL. 1-83, 3p.

Grierson, G.C.
1986: The structural and stratigraphic evolution of the Fundy Basin half-graben; Basins of Eastern Canada and Worldwide Analogues Symposium, Atlantic Geoscience Society Halifax, August 13-15, 1986.

Hacquebard, P.A.
1974: A composite coalification curve of the maritime region and its value for petroleum exploration; in Report of Activities, Part B, Geological Survey of Canada, Paper 74-1B, p. 21-23.
1975: Pre- and post deformation coalification and its significance for oil and gas exploration; Centre National de la Rechercehe Scientifique Paris, 1973, Colloquium Pétrographie de la matière organique des sédiments, p. 225-241.
1986: The Gulf of St. Lawrence Carboniferous Basin; the largest coalfield of eastern Canada; Canadian Institute of Mining and Metallurgy Bulletin, v. 79, no. 891, p. 67-78.

Hardy, I.A. and Jackson, A.E.
1980: A compilation of geochmical data; east coast exploratory wells; Geological Survey of Canada, Open File 694, 10 p.

Howie, R.D.
1970: Oil and Gas Exploration — Atlantic Coast of Canada; American Association of Petroleum Geologists Bulletin, v. 54, no. 11, p. 1989-2006.

Howie, R.D. and Barss, M.S.
1975: Upper Paleozoic rocks of the Atlantic Provinces, Gulf of St. Lawrence and adjacent continental shelf; in Offshore Geology of Eastern Canada, Volume 2, Regional Geology, ed. W.J.M. Van der Linden and J.A. Wade; Geological Survey of Canada, Paper 74-30, v. 2., p. 35-50.

Hutcheon, I.
1986: The relationship of diagenetic mineral reactions to an overpressured zone on the Scotian Shelf; in Basins of Eastern Canada and Worldwide Analogues Symposium Halifax, Aug. 13-15, 1986, Program with Abstracts, p. 56.

Issler, D.R.
1982: Calculation of organic maturation levels from downhole temperatures, burial history curves, Scotian Shelf; B.Sc. thesis, University of Waterloo, Waterloo, Ontario, 129 p.
1984: Calculation of organic maturation levels for offshore eastern Canada - implications for general application of Lopatin's method; Canadian Journal of Earth Sciences, v. 21, no. 4, p. 477-488.

James, A.T.
1983: Correlation of natural gas by use of carbon isotopic distribution between hydrocarbon components; American Association of Petroleum Geologists Bulletin, v. 67, no. 7, p. 1176-1191.

Kendall, S.P. and Altebaeumer, F.J.
1985: Generation and migration of condensates and gas from terrestrial source rocks in the Sable Subbasin, Nova Scotia, Canada; 12th International Meeting on Organic Geochemistry, European Association of Organic Geochemists, Jülich, West Germany, September 16-20, 1985.

Klein, G.D.
1962: Triassic sedimentation, Maritime Provinces, Canada; Geological Society of America Bulletin, v. 73, p. 1127-1146.

Klose, G.W., Malterrre, E., McMillan, N.J. and Zinkan, C.G.
1982: Petroleum exploration offshore soutern Baffin Island, northern Labrador Sea, Canada; in Arctic Geology and Geophysics, ed., A.F. Embry and H.R. Balkwill; Canadian Society of Petroleum Geologists, Memoir 8, p. 233-244.

Lee, P.J. and Wang, P.C.C.
1983: Probablistic formulation of a method for the evaluation of petroleum resources; Journal of the International Society for Mathematical Geology, v. 15, no. 1, p. 349-361.

Lopatin, N.V.
1971: Temperature and geologic time as factors in coalification (in Russian); Akademeya Nauk S.S.S.R. Izvestiya, Seriya Geologicheskaya, no. 3, p. 95-106.

Macauley, G. and Ball, F.D.
1982: Oil shales of the Albert Formation, New Brunswick; Mineral Resources Division, Department of Natural Resources, New Brunswick, Open File 82-12, 173p.

McAlpine, K.D., Bell, S., Avery, M.P. Snowdon, L.R., and Brooks, P.W.
1986: Hydrocarbon generation in the Jeanne d'Arc Basin, offshore Newfoundland; Activities on Oil and Gas in Canada, Geological Survey of Canada Forum, Calgary, February 11-12, 1986.

McIver, N.L.
1972: Cenozoic-Mesozoic stratigraphy of the Nova Scotia Shelf; Canadian Journal of Earth Sciences, v. 9, p. 54-70.

McMillan, N.J.
1982: Canada's East Coast; the new super petroleum province; Journal of Canadian Petroleum Technology, v. 21, p. 1-15.

McWhae, J.R.H. and Michel, W.F.E.
1975: Stratigraphy of Bjarnie H-81 and Leif M-48, Labrador Shelf; Bulletin of Canadian Petroleum Geology, v. 23, no. 3, p. 361-382.

McWhae, J.R., Elie, R., Laughton, K.C., and Gunter, P.R.
1980: Stratigraphy and petroleum prospects of the Labrador Shelf; Bulletin of Canadian Petroleum Geology, v. 29, no. 4, p. 460-498.

Meneley, R.A.
1981: Exploration potential of the Scotian Shelf; Paper presented at Atlantic Margin Energy Conference, Atlantic City, New Jersey, October 4-6, 1981.

Monnier, F., Powell, T.G. and Snowdon, L.R.
1983: Qualitative and quantitative aspects of gas generation during maturation of sedimentary organic matter. Examples from Canadian frontier basins; in Advances in Organic Geochemistry 1981; Proceedings of the 10th International Meeting on Organic Geochemistry; ed. M. Bjory et al.; John Wiley and Sons Ltd., p. 487-495

Nantais, P.T.
1983: A reappraisal of the regional hydrocarbon potential of the Scotian Shelf; Geological Survey of Canada, Open File 1175, 179 p.
1984: Regional hydrocarbon potential of the Labrador Shelf; Geological Survey of Canada Open File 1197, 28 p.

Oilweek
1986: Shell suspends East Coast drilling despite Panuke discovery; Oilweek, October 13, 1986, p. 5.

Petryk, A.A.
1979: Stratigraphie revisée de l'Île d'Anticosti; Ministère de l'Énergie et des Ressources du Québec, DPV-711, 24 p.

Podruski, J.A., Barclay, J.E., Hamblin, A.P., Lee, P.J., Osadetz, K.G., Procter, R.M., Taylor, G.C., Conn, R.F., and Christie, J.A.
1988: Conventional Oil Resources of Western Canada (light and medium density); Geological Survey of Canada, Paper 87-26.

Powell, T.G.
1979: Geochemistry of Snorri and Gudrid condensates, Labrador Shelf: implications for future exploration; in Current Research, Part C, Geological Survey of Canada, Paper 79-1C, p. 91-95.
1982: Petroleum geochemistry of the Verrill Canyon Formation: a source for Scotian Shelf hydrocarbons; Bulletin of Canadian Petroleum Geologists, v. 30, no. 2, p. 167-179.
1985: Hydrocarbon source relationships, Jeanne d'Arc and Avalon Basins, offshore Newfoundland; Geological Survey of Canada, Open File 1094, 12 p.

Powell, T.G. and Snowdon, L.R.
1979: Geochemistry of crude oils and condensates from the Scotian Basin, offshore eastern Canada; Bulletin of Canadian Petroleum Geologists, v. 27, no. 4, p. 453-466.
1983: A composite hydrocarbon generation model: Implications for evaluation of basins for oil and gas; Erdöl und Kohle-Erdgas-Petrochemie vereinigt mit Brennstoff-chemie, v. 36, no. 4, p. 163-170.

Procter, R.M., Taylor, G.C. and Wade, J.A.
1984: Oil and natural gas resources of Canada - 1983; Geological Survey of Canada, Paper 83-31, 59 p.

Purcell, L.P., Rashid, M.A. and Hardy, I.A.
1979: Geochemical characteristics of sedimentary rocks in the Scotian Basin; American Association of Petroleum Geologists Bulletin, v. 62, no. 1, p. 87-105.

Purcell, L.P., Umpleby, D.C. and Wade, J.A.
1980: Regional geology and hydrocarbon occurrences of the east coast of Canada; in Facts and Principles of World Petroleum Occurences, ed. A.D. Miall, Canadian Society of Petroleum Geologists, Memoir 6, p. 551-566.

Rashid, M.A. and McAlary, J.D.
1977: Early maturation of organic matter and genesis of hydrocarbons as a result of heat from a shallow piercement salt dome; Journal of Geochemical Exploration, v. 8, p. 549-569.

Rashid, M.A., Purcell, L.P. and Hardy, I.A.
1979: Source rock potential for oil and gas of the east Newfoundland and Labrador Shelf area; in Facts and Principles of World Petroleum Occurences, ed. A.D. Miall; Canadian Society of Petroleum Geologists, Memoir 6, p. 589-608.

Robbins, E.I. and Rhodelhamel, E.C.
1976: Geothermal gradients help predict petroleum potential of the Scotian Shelf; Oil and Gas Journal, v. 79, no. 9, p. 143-145.

Roksandic, M.M. and Granger, B.
1981: Structural styles of Anticosti Island, Gaspé Passage and eastern Gaspé Peninsula inferred from reflection seismic data; Subcommission on Silurian Stratigraphy, Ordovician-Silurian Boundary Working Group, Field Meeting, Anticosti-Gaspé, Québec 1981, Vol. II: Stratigraphy and Paleontology; ed. P.J. Lespérance, p. 211-221.

Roliff, W.A.
1968: Oil and Gas Exploration, Anticosti Island, Québec; Proceedings of Geological Association of Canada, v. 19, p. 31-36.

Schoell, M.
1983: Genetic Characterisation of Natural Gases; American Association of Petroleum Geologists Bulletin, v. 67, no. 12, p. 2225-2238.

Skibo, D.N., Avery, M.P. and Bell, J.S.
1986: Level of organic maturity measurements and computed thermal geohistory models for the Jeanne d'Arc Basin, offshore Newfoundland: Basins of Eastern Canada and Worldwide Analogues Symposium, Atlantic Geoscience Society, Poster Session, Halifax, August. 13-15, 1986.

Snowdon, L.R. and Fowler, M.G.
1986: Rock-Eval/TOC data from seven wells located within the Jeanne d'Arc Basin, offshore Newfoundland; Geological Survey of Canada, Open File 1382, 40 p.

Snowdon, L.R. and Krouse, H.R.
1986: The stable carbon isotope distribution of distillation fractions of three Canadian Frontier crude oils; Bulletin of Canadian Petroleum Geology, v. 34, no. 3, p. 379-383.

Swift, J.H. and Williams, J.A.
1980: Petroleum source rocks, Grand Banks area; in Facts and Principles of World Petroleum Occurences, ed. A.D. Miall; Canadian Society of Petroleum Geologists, Memoir 6, p. 567-588.

Swift, J.H., Switzer, R.W., and Turnbull, W.F.
1975: The Cretaceous Petrel Limestone of the Grand Banks, Newfoundland; in Canada's Continental Margins and Offshore Petroleum Exploration, ed. C.J. Yorath, E.R. Parker, and D.J. Glass, Canadian Society of Petroleum Geologists, Memoir 4, p. 181-194.

Tissot, B.P. and Welte, D.H.
1984: Petroleum formation and occurrence. A new approach to Oil and Gas Exploration; Springer-Verlag, Berlin, 538p.

Total Eastcan
1978: Skolp E-07, Well History Report; Canada Oil and Gas Lands Administration, Energy, Mines and Resources Canada, 154 p.

Umpleby, D.C.
1979: Geology of the Labrador Shelf; Geological Survey of Canada, Paper 79-13, 34 p.

Von der Dick, H. and Meloche, J.D.
1986: Generation migration and expulsion of hydrocarbons in the Hibernia field; Canadian Society of Petroleum Geologists, Reserves 21 Convention, Calgary, June 1-4, 1986.

Wade, J.A., Campbell, G.R., Procter, R.M., and Taylor, G.C.
1989: Petroleum Resources of the Scotian Shelf; Geological Survey of Canada, Paper 88-19, 26 p.

Waples, D.W.
1980: Time and temperature in petroleum formation: Application of Lopatin's method to petroleum exploration; American Association of Petroleum Geologists Bulletin, v. 64, no. 6, p. 916-926.

Williams, E.P.
1974: Geology and petroleum possibilities in and around the Gulf of St. Lawrence; American Association of Petroleum Geologists Bulletin, v. 58, p. 1137-1158.

Authors' addresses

J.S. Bell
Institute of Sedimentary and Petroleum Geology
Geological Survey of Canada
3303-33rd Street N.W.
Calgary, Alberta
T2L 2A7

G.R. Campbell
Energy, Mines and Resources
COGLA, Resource Evaluation Branch
355 River Road, Tower B
Ottawa, Ontario
K1A 0E4

Chapter 13

MINERAL RESOURCES

MINERAL RESOURCES

P.B. Hale

INTRODUCTION

Non-fuel minerals have been commercially extracted from the oceans, the seafloor and the underlying sediments for several centuries. In eastern Canada such activities date back to about the 1680s when solar evaporation ponds were constructed to obtain sodium chloride from seawater. By the mid-1800s many of the coal mining operations on Cape Breton Island, Nova Scotia, extended under the sea, illustrating another example of exploiting subsea consolidated mineral deposits simply by extending onland mining technology. There have also been numerous temporary operations in Canada to extract sand and gravel from the beaches and shallow nearshore zone, but they do not compare with the type and scale of offshore production common in other maritime countries such as the United Kingdom, France and Japan.

Eastern Canada and the Canadian Arctic have large continental shelves; in eastern Canada there are local concentrations of people living on or near the coast and a long history of onshore marine-related mining and industry. There has been relatively little commercial interest in marine mining, however, except for offshore tunnelling of hardrock deposits such as iron and coal. The reasons for this lack of exploitation are discussed in this chapter, which provides a review of offshore non-fuel mineral resources of eastern Canada and the Canadian Arctic and their past, present and future development.

The first part of the chapter gives an outline of a classification scheme for offshore non-fuel mineral sources and the major factors influencing their exploitability. This is followed by a summary of past commercial activities and the potential for development of minerals from seawater, the deep sea and the shelf. It concludes with a discussion of the future of marine mining in these regions.

Types of non-fuel mineral sources

Based on their geographical distribution and physical characteristics, marine non-fuel minerals can be divided into three general source categories: seawater minerals, deep-sea minerals, and continental shelf minerals (Fig. 13.1).

Hale, P.B.
1990: Mineral resources, Chapter 13 in Geology of the Continental Margin of Eastern Canada, M.J. Keen and G.L. Williams (ed.); Geological Survey of Canada, Geology of Canada, no. 2, p. 721-741 (also Geological Society of America, The Geology of North America, v. I-1).

Seawater minerals

Seawater is a complex solution of many dissolved minerals. The major chemical characteristics of seawater are remarkably uniform from one location to another so that exploitability is influenced by such factors as local climate, availability of other necessary raw materials, cheap energy and market characteristics. Seawater minerals that have been extracted commercially include magnesium, iodine, bromine, and sodium chloride.

Deep-sea minerals

Deep-sea concentrations of manganese nodules in the Pacific, Atlantic and Indian oceans have been investigated from a commercial standpoint since the early 1970s. The metalliferous muds in the Red Sea have been studied extensively and are considered a commercial prospect (Rona, 1983; Amann, 1985). The technical and financial viability of mining and processing the metalliferous sediments has been established and a pilot mining and processing operation is under consideration by the Saudi-Sudanese Red Sea Joint Commission.

Polymetallic sulphide deposits associated with oceanic spreading centres were first discovered in 1978 in the eastern Pacific Ocean (21°N) off Mexico (CYAMEX, 1979). Subsequently, additional occurrences were discovered off the

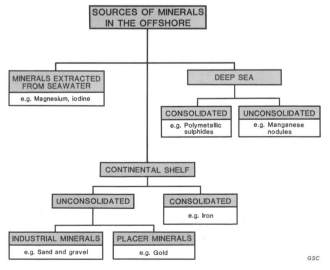

Figure 13.1. Types of non-fuel mineral resources in the offshore.

west coast of North America and along portions of the mid-Atlantic ridge. Because they may be enriched in zinc, copper, manganese, cobalt, gold and silver, they have attracted commercial interest and could be the object of future exploration efforts. They are also providing invaluable information on the origin of onland mineral deposits.

Shelf minerals

The relatively shallow water and proximity to shore of the continental shelves make these regions attractive for the exploration and development of mineral deposits. Consolidated non-fuel mineral deposits of barite (Alaska), iron (Newfoundland), and tin (Great Britain) have been mined from the world's coastal regions for many years. In terms of the value of non-fuel mineral production, and the number of operations, however, the unconsolidated granular deposits (i.e. sand and gravel; high purity silica sand; placer deposits) are more important and have been the focus of attention.

Unconsolidated granular deposits may be grouped into industrial mineral deposits and placer deposits. The former are those in which all or almost all of the dredged material is utilized, such as sand and gravel for construction and calcium carbonate for cement. Mining operations for placer minerals retain only the heavy mineral fraction of the deposit, such as gold, rutile, zircon and diamonds. Both types of deposits are commonly mined by dredging.

In 1977, the last year for which comprehensive global offshore production statistics are available, non-fuel mineral production was worth about $460 million (US) with most of that coming from sand and gravel, tin and calcium carbonate (Glasby, 1979). More recent statistics reveal a steady increase in the proportion of marine-derived sand and gravel in the two major producing countries, the United Kingdon and Japan. The same trend was apparent for offshore tin production until 1981, when the price began to fall and production dropped off accordingly. A global review of mining and exploration for unconsolidated granular deposits has been given by Hale and McLaren (1984).

Criteria for exploitation

« Resources » refer to mineral concentrations, found and unfound, that are of economic interest for the foreseeable future, that is, in most contexts, the next few decades (Canada, Department of Energy, Mines and Resources, 1974; Zwartendyk, internal report, Mineral Policy Sector, Energy, Mines and Resources, 1975, and pers. comm., 1986). An example of a methodology for offshore resource assessment that utilizes existing information is the one developed by the Canada, Department of Energy, Mines and Resources pertaining to the regional geology, physical setting and markets for the commodity (Shelf Working Group, unpublished report, Resource Management Branch, Energy, Mines and Resources Canada, 1980). This provides a practical means of assessing the potential of a geographic region for selected minerals and for raw materials that takes into account both the level of assurance about the quantities estimated to exist and the level of exploitability in economic terms (Fig. 13.2).

The likelihood of existence of deposits is difficult to determine, particularly if field evidence is poor and indirect evidence is used. Such indirect evidence includes the presence of suitable source rocks in coastal drainage basins and appropriate depositional environments. The grade of appropriate commercial deposit and the product specifications are used as guidelines for determining whether or not a mineral concentration qualifies as a resource, i.e., is of economic interest for the foreseeable future. Commercial recovery rates and a reasonable minimum « mine life » provide a basis for evaluating the adequacy of the size of the deposit.

Areas can also be ranked according to the level of exploitability. Economic deposits are those that are exploitable at a profit under existing circumstances because the costs are relatively low and the operating limits, such as water depth and distance from market, are minimal. Marginally subeconomic deposits are deposits which appear not to be economically exploitable at present but may become economic over the next 10 to 20 years. If a deposit exists beyond the bounds established for the subeconomic category, it is unlikely that the deposit would be exploited in the foreseeable future and it is deemed uneconomic.

Each mineral occurrence can be plotted in Figure 13.2 using relative indices for assurance of existence and for level of exploitability. Those falling within the shaded area qualify as mineral resources. Those that have known size and grade, and are considered to be economically exploitable now, are termed « reserves ». Documentation of all mineral deposits and their characteristics would constitute a resource inventory, but there are insufficient data on shelf and deep-sea minerals off eastern Canada and in the Canadian Arctic to establish such an inventory. Information is seldom available on the distribution of deposits, their characteristics such as tonnage and grade, the markets available, and the costs of production.

The first systematic appraisal of the Canadian offshore potential for unconsolidated granular minerals (i.e. sand and gravel, high purity silica sand, and placer minerals) was carried out in 1984. This was, of necessity, subjective and the emphasis was on the presence or absence of a given commodity, together with a few general criteria concerning exploitability (Hale and McLaren, 1984). The approach adopted in this chapter for eastern Canada and the Canadian Arctic is essentially the same, with minor revisions. It is based on a review of information from both published and unpublished geological literature, the CANMINDEX Mineral Occurrence file of the Geological Survey of Canada, the National Mineral Inventory (Mineral Policy Sector, Energy, Mines and Resources), and verbal communication with government and industry geologists.

Various types of dredging are the primary mining techniques used for unconsolidated granular deposits. The largest commercial dredges in the world excavate to a maximum depth of 80 m below sea level. Larger dredges, capable of excavating to greater depths, could be built but this would involve added expense and require time for design and construction. Therefore, it is assumed that offshore mining for surficial materials will be limited to depths of less than 100 m in the next few decades. Occurrences in greater water depths are considered long-term prospects rather than resources. Adoption of the 100 m isobath as the depth limit for resource assessment excludes much of the Arctic and the east coast (Fig. 13.3).

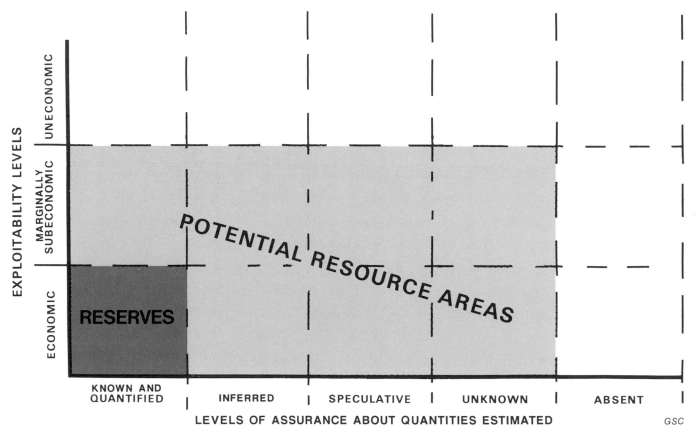

Figure 13.2. Conceptual diagram illustrating the relationship between level of assurance about quantities estimated and economic exploitability in determining what constitutes a "resource" and a "reserve".

Ice imposes an enormous constraint on marine mining operations off the east coast and in the Canadian Arctic. As of 1985 there were no commercial dredging activities during the period of ice cover in the Canadian offshore, which varies widely from one geographic area to another and from one year to the next. The average duration of open water conditions for severe and light ice years (Fig. 13.3) shows that several areas are typically ice-free year round. These areas include Georges Bank, the Bay of Fundy and the Scotian Shelf (for the locations see CHS Map 850-A, in pocket). However, to the north in the Gulf of St. Lawrence, the Labrador Sea and Davis Strait, the duration of open water decreases markedly. Hudson Bay and the Beaufort Sea have open water conditions for only four months of the year in a good year and many of the Arctic Islands' channels are ice-free for less than one month each year.

The duration of open water for each region in Figure 13.3 appears to be rather short because it refers to the period during which ice was absent from the entire coastal area. Some portions of each region will have longer periods of open water.

It is unlikely that a conventional dredging operation would be established in a region having open water for less than four months of the year (based on statistics for "light" ice years). Consequently, most of the Arctic — with the exception of the Beaufort Sea, Lancaster Sound, Hudson Strait and Hudson Bay — is not considered as an area of potential marine mining with conventional dredges. The experience of dredging for aggregates in the Canadian Beaufort Sea has shown that, although the region may be ice-free by mid-summer, ice may delay passage of ships from the west for several weeks, thereby reducing the already short operating window. This has forced many dredges to stay in the Beaufort Sea in winter. This is a costly proposition since the dredges can then operate for only one-third of each year. A similar problem could arise in Lancaster Sound (Fig. 13.3).

The short open water season throughout much of the Canadian Arctic, coupled with the lack of suitable industrial infrastructure and small markets for industrial minerals, imposes such severe constraints that only the high-value placer minerals such as gold, platinum and diamonds are likely to be commercially viable within the foreseeable future. This chapter, therefore, does not address industrial mineral resources in the arctic outside of the Beaufort Sea where potential users already exist. For similar reasons the distribution of low-value placer minerals such as garnet, ilmenite, magnetite and rutile in this area has not been discussed.

SEAWATER MINERALS

Mineral types

The ocean is an unusual ore body in that it is a renewable resource. The minerals dissolved in seawater are being replenished by river runoff at a rate equal to or greater

725

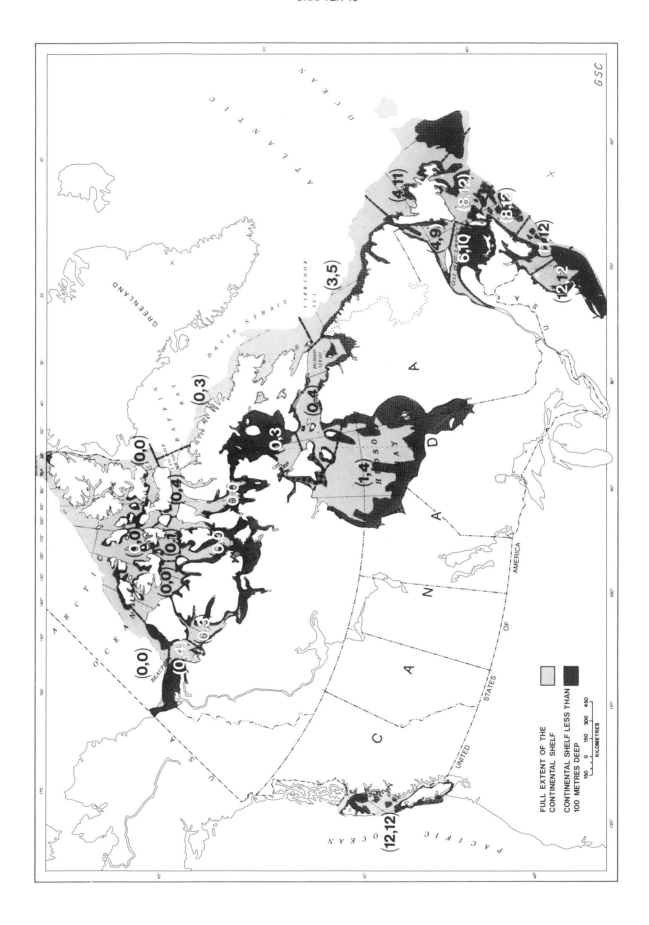

than the present scale of their commercial extraction (Wang and McKelvey, 1976). Of all the 77 elements in seawater, 8 account for more than 99 per cent of the salts; all other 69 elements total less than 1 per cent. As far as the major elements are concerned, seawater is fairly uniform in composition but this is not true for the trace elements.

Isolated gold concentrations as large as 60 mg/t have been found in seawater. This is an ore grade, but the average gold content is only about 11 mg/t, far below that required for economic exploitation using existing technology (North, 1966; Wright, 1969). Areas of high concentration are likely to be associated with hydrothermal activity and stagnant water catchments, which are uncommon conditions off the east or arctic coasts of Canada.

Operations to profitably extract gold or other trace elements such as uranium must efficiently handle large volumes of water. One such approach uses a static recovery system in an active water stream such as the Gulf Stream. The Japanese are most advanced in this technology, having built a pilot-scale uranium extraction plant designed to recover 10 000 g of uranium per year (Mining Journal, 1980; Organization for Economic Co-operation and Development, 1983). Hollister (1980) suggested that offshore oil and gas platforms could provide low-cost facilities for seawater extraction plants to recover uranium, gold and other elements. The presence of onshore reserves in Canada and the projected costs of seawater extraction make it unlikely that such a system will be pursued off the east coast.

The five substances commercially recovered from seawater are: magnesium, iodine, bromine, sodium chloride, and freshwater. The extraction process relies on solar evaporation and is therefore most successful in countries that have hot, dry climates. Solar extraction for salt was attempted on the Atlantic coast of North America in 1680 but failed because of poor weather (Dietz, 1972). Some countries, notably Sweden and Russia, obtain salt from sea water by freezing. The brine is separated from the ice in successive freezing stages to obtain a high concentration for evaporation using artificial heat (Armstrong and Miall, 1946). There are sufficient reserves onland in eastern Canada to meet local needs, however, so there is no need for salt extraction plants.

Magnesium metal and magnesium hydroxide are also recovered from seawater. The metal is widely used in metal products, in the preparation of oxychloride cements, and in the fabrication of rubber, fertilizer and paper. Many of these applications require high quality magnesia which cannot be obtained from most natural sources. In 1978 there were fifteen plants worldwide extracting some two million metric tons of magnesia annually from seawater (Mining Annual Review, 1978). One of the largest and most successful, in Freeport, Texas, provides about 95 per cent

of the United States supply of magnesium metal (Mero, 1965). It utilizes cheap natural gas and lime, in the form of calcareous shells, dredged from the Gulf of Mexico.

In the early 1980s researchers began to consider seawater as a potential source of lithium (Epstein et al., 1981; Sekimachi and Katsuta, 1981), anticipating that a new generation of high energy storage batteries using lithium metal anodes would be in demand. Thermo-nuclear fusion applications may also increase the demand for lithium. Although Canada has adequate resources onland to meet the current demand, seawater extraction may be worth considering in the future.

Canadian operations

A seawater extraction plant to recover deuterium (as a component of heavy water) for use in thermo-nuclear reactors was built at Glace Bay, Nova Scotia, in 1976; a seawater extraction plant to recover magnesium hydroxide to satisfy the needs of the pulp and paper industry and the refactories was built in the mid-sixties at Aguathuna, Newfoundland. The heavy water facilities closed in the spring of 1985, because of the falling demand for deuterium.

The location of a magnesium hydroxide extraction plant is largely independent of oceanographic or climatic factors. The most important needs are the supply of necessary raw materials, inexpensive power and nearby markets. The Aguathuna site was selected, because of its almost inexhaustible supply of dolomitic limestone bordering on the uncontaminated seawater of Port Au Port Bay (Gormley, 1969). It was designed to process about 150 t of magnesium hydroxide per day, based on the use of calcium limestone and seawater, and represented an investment of about $4 million (1969) exclusive of quarrying equipment, storage and shipping. From the beginning it experienced operational and financial difficulties and never operated commercially. Some of its operational problems stemmed from an inconsistent quality of limestone feed (Wolfgang Uebel Ltd., internal report for Newfoundland and Labrador Department of Industrial Development, 1979).

Several magnesium plants around the world use calcareous shells as the source of lime. The chances of finding such deposits off eastern Canada are good-to-excellent. This possibility should, therefore, be kept in mind during any discussions to reopen the Aguathuna facility or to construct a new magnesium extraction plant.

DEEP-SEA MINERALS

Unconsolidated minerals

Manganese nodules and manganese crusts and coatings are the major types of unconsolidated deep seabed deposits that have attracted commercial interest.

Manganese nodules

As noted by Horn et al. (1972, 1973) the paucity of nodule occurrences in the northwestern Atlantic Ocean can be attributed to the large influx of terrigenous sediments from the north and west, as well as to carbonate sedimentation in regions such as the Mid-Atlantic Ridge above the carbonate compensation depth. The only reported occurrence of manganese nodules off eastern Canada is from the

---

Figure 13.3. Map of Canada illustrating the Continental Shelf and waters less than 100 m deep. The numbers in brackets for each region denote the average duration in months of open water for severe and light ice years respectively (compiled from data in Environmental Protection Service, 1978; and Markham, 1981).

Newfoundland Seamounts (Lamont Geological Observatory, manuscript report, 1968). These nodules contain relatively low quantities of nickel, cobalt, and copper (M. Fisk, pers. comm., 1984).

There is at present no economic potential for manganese nodules in the northwest Atlantic.

Manganese crusts and coatings

Manganese crusts and coatings have been reported from topographic highs that are either isolated from major sedimentary influx or are swept by currents such as the Gulf Stream, or both. Bedded manganese crusts, apparently thicker than 10 cm, are reported from the New England Seamounts (Aumento et al., 1968). The location of the seamounts is shown in Map 1706A (in pocket). Chemical analysis indicates relatively low metal content, with the exception of cobalt which is reported to approach one per cent in some cases (Cronan, 1975). The high cobalt content of manganese crusts in relatively shallow water reported by early workers (Menard, 1964; Mero, 1965) has led to speculation that such deposits may be economically viable as cobalt sources. Some preliminary work has been done on processing manganese pavements from the New England Seamounts (Grice and Hancock, 1972). Problems of technology, costs, market and the legal situation will probably inhibit economic development in the next few years.

Manganese crusts are common on the flanks of the mid-Atlantic Ridge (Aumento and Loncarevic, 1969; Phillips et al., 1969; Cronan, 1975). They are low in nickel, copper, iron and manganese, and rarely exceed 0.5% cobalt (Cronan, 1975). In a well-studied area of the ridge near 45°N, Aumento (1969) found that the thickness of manganese crusts increases with distance from the axis of the ridge, approaching 30 cm at a distance of 140 km east of the median valley.

Horowitz and Cronan (1976) noted metalliferous sediments in the basal section of some of the holes drilled by the Deep Sea Drilling Project. They suggested that these may have resulted from the submarine weathering of cold basalt, combined with the formation of ferromanganese oxides that scavenge additional metals from seawater.

Metalliferous sediments

Iron-rich sediments, similar to those found in association with active ocean ridges, have been found in the central valley of the Mid-Atlantic Ridge near 45°N (Cronan, 1972). While the enrichment in some metals is attributed to hydrothermal activity associated with active spreading centres, the sediments are not of economic interest.

Consolidated minerals

Consolidated subsurface mineral deposits have been postulated for some deep-sea regions, based on analogies with certain onland rock sequences and recent discoveries of surface outcrops of sulphide minerals in the vicinity of seafloor spreading centres. Such occurrences have yet to be confirmed.

SHELF MINERALS

Consolidated surface and subsurface mineral deposits

Consolidated mineral deposits exposed on the seafloor have been exploited worldwide to a limited extent. In most cases, this represented an extension offshore of existing onshore operations. Such an example is the barite mining project in Alaska (Stevens, 1970; Thompson and Smith, 1970). In Canada there has not been any commercial mining of outcropping consolidated mineral deposits.

Undersea mining for consolidated subsurface deposits such as coal, iron, tin, nickel, copper, gold and limestone has been carried out since at least the early 1600s and accounts for a significant proportion of the total mineral production in some countries. Japan obtained 52 per cent or 9.7×10^6 t of coal from undersea subsurface mines in 1977 (Earney, 1980). More than 100 undersea mines have been constructed worldwide (Austin, 1967; Cruickshank, 1968). With few exceptions these began as onland mines that extended offshore once the onland resources were depleted.

Eastern Canada has a long history of subsea tunnel mining. The mines extending offshore in the Sydney coal field, Cape Breton Island, Nova Scotia, date back to about 1867, making them one of the longest current undersea mining operations in the world. They extend some 7 km offshore to more than 300 m below sea level and are accessible from adits onshore.

Other subsea mines off eastern Canada are the Wabana Iron Mines, located northwest of St. John's, Newfoundland, which operated from 1895 until 1966. The capacity of the mine at the time it closed was 3 million tonnes per year. More than 75×10^6 t of hematite ore were extracted from the workings, which extended up to 5 km offshore from Bell Island into Conception Bay. The 18 km² of workings descended to 515 m below sea level, at which point the water depth was about 150 m.

At the Wabana mine, two iron ore beds, one above the other, were mined using a modified room and pillar method. The beds have a dip of about 9 degrees seaward or north-northwest. In the later years of mining the long haulage distance from the main shaft to the workings significantly decreased worker productivity per shift. Consequently, costs were high compared with costs of open pit operations. This, combined with problems of marketing the ore, with its relatively low iron and high phosphorus and silicon, led to closure of the mine in 1966.

The histories of the Sydney coal fields and the Wabana iron mines are probably typical of any submarine tunnel- and shaft-mining project that begins as an onshore venture. Both started as small land mines that extended under the sea using standard mining techniques. As they advanced farther offshore, ventilation difficulties and problems of power transmission led to declining returns and, in the case of the Wabana mine, closure. The difficulties with these operations arose in part because of growing inefficiencies associated with increasing distances for transportation.

One may overcome this problem of transportation distance by gaining access to the workings directly from the offshore, a concept that is not new. There is evidence that an artificial island was used as early as 1617 in the Firth of Forth, Scotland, to mine coal beneath the sea (Anonymous, undated, as reported in Austin, 1967). This century the Japanese have constructed artificial islands and sunk shafts through them to gain access to coal seams (Biron, 1961). In addition, they have sunk ventilation shafts on artificial islands. A similar approach could be adopted for mining the offshore coal in the Sydney Basin, Cape Breton Island, although at distances greater than 7 km offshore, the exploitable seams are deep below the surface (greater than 1000 m), making them costly to mine.

Subsea hardrock mining for surface and subsurface mineral deposits is an established industry worldwide. With few exceptions the operations start onshore; there has been little systematic offshore surveying for such deposits, other than in those regions that have mineral deposits onland nearby. Consolidated deposits not exploited no doubt exist in the Canadian offshore. The question that will have to be addressed is whether or not they can be competitive with domestic mines onshore or with imports.

Unconsolidated shelf mineral deposits

Industrial minerals

The unconsolidated industrial minerals that have been mined, or are most likely to be mined, off eastern Canada and in the Canadian Arctic, are sand and gravel, high purity silica sand, and carbonate sand. These high bulk, low value commodities are expensive to transport over large distances.

Sand and gravel is the industrial mineral with the lowest value, that is likely to be dredged from the offshore. Consequently potential sources of marine aggregates have to be appraised in terms of the sustained market requirements associated with urban centres, and the intermittent needs arising from mega-scale construction projects. A "potential economic recovery zone" can be defined for the sustained markets as the area shallower than 100 m and within a 150 km radius of an urban centre (Fig. 13.4). For industrial minerals of higher value the transportation costs are assumed to be less important; hence the limiting criterion adopted is a water depth of less than 100 m.

Silica sand

Silica sand, a material with a high proportion of silica in the form of quartz, is used principally in glassmaking and foundries. Other uses include optical glass, solar cells, fibre optics and the manufacturing of chemicals and insulation products. In 1983 Canada produced 2.3×10^6 t of silica and imported an additional 1.0×10^6 t. The long term prospect for domestic and export markets is considered good, the demand for smelter flux in the foundry industry and for glass and glass fibre manufacturing is expected to increase. This demand may be supplemented by new uses for silica-based products resulting from technological developments.

There has not been a concerted effort to identify silica sand deposits in the Canadian offshore. Nevertheless one commercial venture, Magdalen Silica Inc., has located and delineated two such deposits off the Îles de la Madeleine in the Gulf of St. Lawrence (Fig. 13.5). These deposits contain about 250×10^6 m^3 of recoverable silica sand, which contains 88 per cent quartz and 10 per cent feldspar. The remaining 2 per cent is composed of sea shells, heavy minerals, and limonite coating on the quartz and feldspar grains (Mathieu, 1982; Mathieu and Sirois, internal CANMET Report MRP/MSL 83-111(OP), 1983). The iron and alumina (feldspar) impurities will have to be removed by flotation to render the sand suitable for use as a foundry sand, and a beneficiation process has been devised and demonstrated in a pilot-plant. This work suggests that it is technically possible, and may be economically viable, to process the marine sand. Given a sufficient market and acceptable dredging costs there is a good likelihood that this deposit will come into commercial production.

There are other occurrences of high purity silica sand on Bradelle Bank, northeast of Prince Edward Island, and in the vicinity of the Hibernia oil and gas field on the Grand Banks of Newfoundland (Loring and Nota, 1973; Fader and King, 1981; internal CANMET Report M-3350, 1983; Hale and McLaren, 1984) (Fig. 13.5). Those situated within the Gulf of St. Lawrence have the greatest likelihood of being mined on account of their relatively sheltered, shallow water setting which poses less difficulty for mining.

Calcium carbonate

Calcium carbonate — in the form of shells, coral, and calcareous sand — is mined off several countries around the world including Australia, the Bahamas, Fiji, France, Iceland and the United States. It is used in the construction industry as an aggregate and forms the primary material in the manufacture of Portland cement and lime.

Most of the lime produced in Canada is now consumed in the metallurgical industry, but there is a growing agricultural market for liming of acidic soils that are widespread throughout eastern Canada (MacDonald, 1982). For agricultural applications the choice of liming material (e.g. shells or crushed bedrock) is based on cost, on the ability to raise the soil pH, and on the balance needed between calcium and magnesium in the soil. Where magnesium is required as a crop nutrient, dolomitic limestone is usually recommended. If the magnesium level is adequate, a calcium-rich limestone or shell hash (shells broken into small fragments) is preferable.

Offshore sources of calcium carbonate have been utilized for agricultural purposes in eastern Canada since at least 1928 (Fig. 13.6a) but the practice is not widespread. In many cases the carbonate material is a waste product from the local shell or lobster fishery. There are few examples of detrital carbonate material being recovered from the seafloor for agricultural or other applications in Canada.

Offshore shell beds have been identified in several locations off eastern Canada including the Strait of Belle Isle, Sable Island Bank, Burgeo Bank, St. Pierre Bank and Grand Bank (Nesis, 1965; Fader and King, 1981; Fader et al., 1982). Figure 13.5 illustrates the locations of known shell (carbonate sand) concentrations. In some localities detrital shell material is several tens of centimetres thick and extends over several square kilometres; in other areas, living populations with calcareous shells predominate.

In the Strait of Belle Isle the carbonates take the form of a sandwave complex with bedforms several metres high. This indicates that a considerable quantity of carbonate material is present.

729

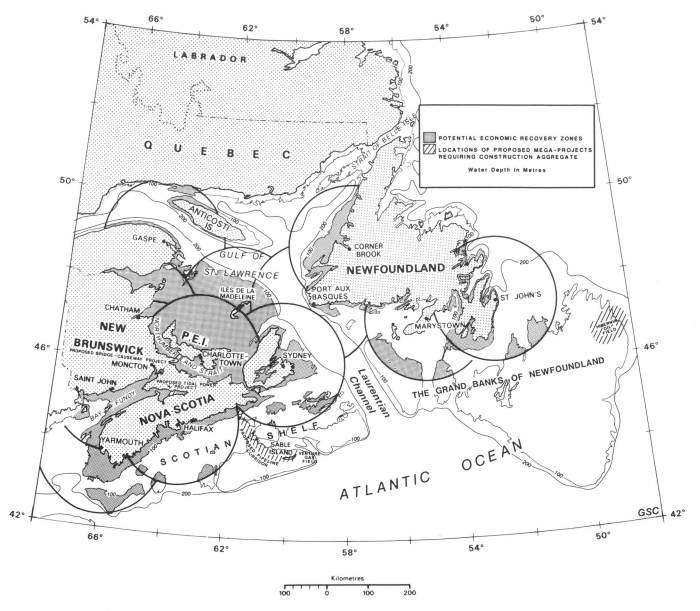

Figure 13.4. Potential urban and mega-project markets for marine aggregates. Circles represent a 150 km radius about an urban centre.

Figure 13.6b is a bottom photograph taken on St. Pierre Bank south of Newfoundland. It illustrates the predominance of dead bivalves concentrated in the troughs of large symmetric, wave-formed ripples. In other localities the shells have been broken down to form small fragments or shell hash (Fig. 13.6c).

Only those deposits situated in relatively shallow water and close to market are likely to be commercially attractive, and the detrital deposits will be of particular interest. Proposals to mine living shell populations would no doubt be opposed, although the possibility does exist for seafood harvesting and carbonate mining in a combined operation. The chances of exploitable carbonate deposits occurring off the east coast are good to excellent.

Sand and gravel

The term sand and gravel refers to naturally occurring, unconsolidated surficial materials from which mineral aggregates may be derived for use in the construction industry. The preferred deposits for most applications are those that are naturally washed and sorted, so that they have a low silt and clay content and blend of the various size-fractions of sand and gravel appropriate to the use. These may be of glaciofluvial, fluvial, lacustrine, or marine origin. If these deposits are absent, glacial till — with its higher content of silt and clay and poorer sorting — may be utilized after suitable processing. As a last resort consolidated bedrock can be processed but this is an expensive operation and may only yield aggregate of poor quality.

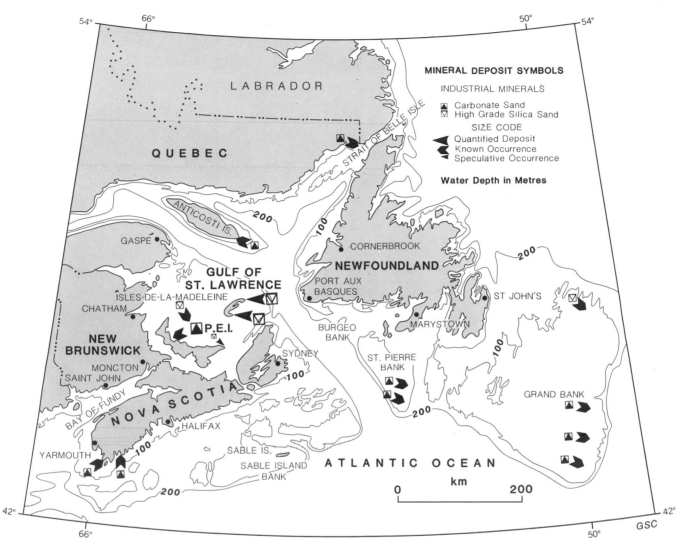

Figure 13.5. Location of calcium carbonate and high-purity silica sand off southeastern Canada.

The production of mineral aggregate for Atlantic Canada in 1984 was about 21.5×10^6 t (Table 13.1) and, although there is some interprovincial transport of material, relatively little was exported or imported.

Granular deposits accounted for 75 to 100 per cent of the total aggregate production for each province. This varies considerably from year to year, however, depending on the nature of the construction projects and the local availabil-

Table 13.1. Aggregate production statistics for Atlantic Canada, 1984

Province	Granular Deposits (tonnes x10³)	(% of Total)	Crushed Stone (tonnes x10³)	(% of Total)	Total (tonnes x10³)
New Brunswick	5 410	75	1 845	25	7 255
Newfoundland	3 715	91	382	9	4 097
Nova Scotia	7 600	85	1 389	15	8 989
P.E.I.	1 156	100	---	--	1 156
Total	17 881	83	3 616	17	21 497

Source: Mineral Policy Sector, Department of Energy, Mines and Resources, Canada

GSC

Figure 13.6. (a) Oyster shells collected along the north shore of New Brunswick for agricultural liming, 1928 (Public Archives Canada/PA 20280); (b) Seafloor on St. Pierre Bank showing detrital bivalve shell material in the troughs of symmetrical ripples (Fader et al., 1982); (c) St. Pierre Bank showing detrital shell hash accummulations (Fader et al., 1982).

ity of unconsolidated materials. The amount of aggregate derived from quarried material may be relatively small, but in regions where naturally occurring unconsolidated materials are rare it is important.

The major use of mineral aggregate is in road construction and maintenance, and in the manufacture of concrete. Consequently, supplies of aggregates are sought along transportation corridors and close to urban centres. Many sources formerly used are now depleted, or have been excluded from exploitation because of environmental concerns and land-use zoning.

In the early 1970s it became apparent that the extraction of sand and gravel from beach foreshores was causing or accelerating shoreline erosion. Further, in some locations the removal of sandy material led to exposure of a coarse cobble lag, making the beaches less desirable for recreational purposes (Bowen et al., 1975; Andries, 1984; Taylor et al., 1985). The Atlantic Provinces have taken steps, therefore, to restrict or prohibit beach mining. This action has placed additional pressure on the existing sources of aggregate on land and increased the need to identify alternate sources of supply (see Chapter 14).

Most of the populated regions in Atlantic Canada are on or near the coast, so that offshore sources could easily supplement supplies onshore. Several countries — including the United Kingdom, Japan and France — possess viable marine aggregate mining industries, and have demonstrated that environmental and fisheries concerns can be accommodated. There is every indication that the same could be accomplished in eastern Canada.

Other major uses of aggregate are related to industrial mega-projects. Future projects could include hydro-electric developments such as a Bay of Fundy Tidal Power Project and expansion of the James Bay Power Project, harbour expansion projects, a bridge or causeway to Prince Edward Island, and offshore oil and gas development (Fig. 13.4).

There have been few sand and gravel dredging operations for purposes other than harbour deepening in eastern Canada. Those that have taken place have generally been small-scale projects of short duration. The largest operation was the provision of container facilities in Halifax Harbour. This project was small by comparison with the sand and gravel dredging activity in the Canadian Beaufort Sea, which started in 1972, in support of offshore oil and gas exploration and was the largest operation of its kind in ice-infested waters. By 1985, 28 artificial islands had been built in water depths of 45 m or less (Fig. 13.7) and more than 30×10^6 m^3 of material had been mined from the seafloor.

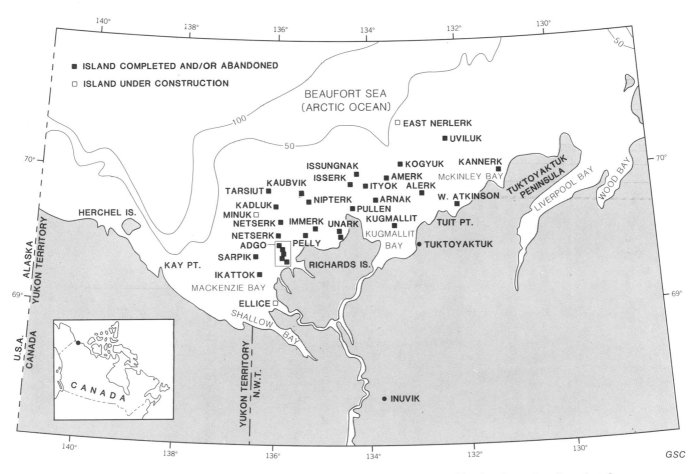

Figure 13.7. Locations of artificial islands that have been constructed in the Canadian Beaufort Sea 1972-1985.

New technologies, such as steel and concrete caissons, have been developed over the last decade to reduce significantly the quantity of material required to construct the artificial islands. When oil and gas production starts, however, much larger and more permanent structures will be required. Each production island could require more than 20×10^6 m^3 of aggregate, with the total quantity of granular material needed approaching 700×10^6 m^3 of which about five per cent could be gravel. The most economic source for this material would probably be the offshore.

Work by industry and government agencies shows that there appears to be enough fine sand for all resource-related construction projects anticipated in the Beaufort Sea in the near future, but not enough gravel-sized material (O'Connor and Associates, internal reports for the Atlantic Geoscience Centre and Northern Renewable Resources Branch, 1983). Four sources of mineable quantities of gravel have been identified on the basis of high resolution geophysical surveys, grab samples, geotechnical boreholes, and vibracores. These constitute a total of 95×10^6 m^3 of which less than 25 per cent is considered to be "proven" reserves. There are also several other localities where exploitable gravel deposits may exist. It appears likely, therefore, that with judicious management there will be sufficient granular material in the Canadian Beaufort Sea to meet future industry needs.

An artificial island has been proposed for the production phase of the Hibernia oil field on the Grand Banks. There the water depth is about 80 m. The island will have to withstand North Atlantic storms and iceberg impacts, and so will have to be massive, constructed of concrete and ballasted with heavy aggregate. About 150 000 m^3 of aggregate will be required for one such "island"; additional quantities of undetermined amount will also be needed to build the onshore facilities and roads. The onshore supply of natural aggregate near the construction site is limited. Preliminary investigations suggest that it will be necessary to crush bedrock or dredge material from the offshore.

The sands and gravels of the shelves off eastern Canada south of about 48°N result from the effects of glaciations and deglaciation in the Pleistocene and Holocene, the changes in sea level which accompanied deglaciation, and the effects of reworking by bottom currents, by waves and, on the northern Grand Banks, by ice. These processes have been described in Chapters 10 and 11, and are not discussed here. The result was to develop sands and gravels on the shallower banks of the shelves. These deposits are now reworked by tidal and storm-induced currents.

North of 48°N conditions were quite different. Only small areas of the shelves were subaerially exposed during and after glaciation. These differences are evident on the Quaternary Geology map (Map 1711A, in pocket), which shows a lack of reworked sands and gravels north of 48°N.

By 15 000 ka, when eustatic sea level reached its lowest position in southeastern Canada, isostatic adjustment of the continental shelf was largely complete (King and Fader, unpublished data, 1985). The ice had virtually disappeared from the shelf and the marine transgression had begun. The low sea-level stand varies in vertical position along the coast as a result of differential isostatic rebound. In the Bay of Fundy low sea-level position occurs at a present depth of 40 m, whereas it ranges from 100-120 m on

the Scotian Shelf and off Newfoundland (Fader et al., 1982). Glacial till and glaciomarine sediments deposited above these depths were reworked during the marine transgression. On the inner shelf where the slope was steeper than the relatively flat outer bank areas, undercutting and local slumping were effective mechanisms for erosion of the glacial sediments. In general the silt and clay fractions have been winnowed leaving well-sorted and rounded residual materials.

What remains on the inner shelf and outer banks are vast areas of exposed bedrock, numerous boulder fields, gravel patches, and areas of well-sorted sand. Beneath the basal transgressive deposits, glacial materials only occur in buried drainage channels and isolated depressions.

Gulf of Maine area. The sand and gravel areas are confined to Georges Bank and Browns Bank and the inner shelf off southwestern Nova Scotia. On Georges Bank the major gravel occurrences occur along the northern flank in a swath more than 5 km wide. Gravel is much more extensive on Browns Bank and consists of varied lithologies. The largest deposits of sand are found in the sandwave and ridge fields of Georges Bank. Sand ridges with widths of 1000-6000 m occur in water depths of less than 70 m and often have superimposed sandwaves and megaripples. The megaripples may range in thickness up to 1.1 m. The sandwaves occur in the shallow, west-central area and reach thicknesses of 17 m. These represnt substantial quantities of sand-sized material and their shallow water occurrence and dynamic aspect make them attractive for aggregate mining.

Near Yarmouth, the largest town in southwestern Nova Scotia, substantial quantities of sand occur in deposits up to 3 m thick on German Bank. Because of the rough, rocky shallow ledges of the coastal zone, 0-10 km offshore, little systematic regional mapping of surficial sediments has been undertaken. Work to date indicates a patchy distribution of coarse sand-fine gravel-sized material in the form of eroded, angular granitic fragments.

Bay of Fundy. The transgressive sand and gravel unit is absent in the Bay of Fundy (Fader et al., 1977). However, the Sambro Sand — a winnowed lag deposit formed by sublittoral, tidal and wave action over the last 8000 years — is present. In the upper Bay of Fundy, within 20 km of proposed tidal project sites, considerable amounts of sand and gravel overlie glaciomarine materials. The floor of Scots Bay has large sand waves which may be active, shifting in response to the high tidal currents of the area. More high resolution seismic reflection data are needed to define the quantity of these materials.

Scotian Shelf. Sand and gravel in this area, which extends from Browns Bank to Banquereau, is confined to a narrow 10-20 km band along the inner shelf and to the surface of the outer banks and all other areas above the −110 to −120 m low sea-level stand. The formation, Sable Island Sand and Gravel, is very thin in some areas such as on Sambro Bank and parts of Emerald Bank, but elsewhere, such as on Sable Island Bank and Banquereau, it may attain thicknesses of over 60 m. As the parent materials of the sand were largely glacial, it consists largely of locally derived resistant metasediments and granitic fragments, especially on the inner shelf. On the outer banks the sand fraction dominates, as the parent materials are mainly coastal-plain rock of Cretaceous-Tertiary age.

Many aggregate deposits have been studied in the vicinity of Halifax. Surveys in Halifax Harbour and Bedford Basin have identified local banks of gravel-sized sediment. Recent sampling indicates thicknesses of up to 2 m. The nearest bank area is Sambro Bank some 80 km distant. The thickness of the sediment beneath the lag gravel is not known. There have not been any systematic surveys for aggregates near the shore. The geological setting and postglacial history are well understood, however, and support the presence of many offshore sand and gravel deposits. A sidescan sonar and submersible survey conducted in 1985 along the inner part of the eastern Scotian Shelf by R. Boyd and D. Forbes identified large areas of gravel waves off Osborne Head.

Offshore Sydney, Nova Scotia, the seabed is composed of approximately equal amounts of sand and gravel. On St. Anns Bank, the gravel consists of subrounded fragments of sandstone and lesser amounts of granitic, volcanic and metamorphic rocks with numerous shell fragments. Sand is concentrated in patches northeast of Sydney, near the seaward edge of St. Anns Bank. These patches are interpreted as isolated concentrations overlying a gravel lag. A field of large sand waves, with wave lengths of 100 m and heights of 3 m, occurs on the southern part of St. Anns Bank. Smaller sand waves occur close to the shore north of Point Aconi, and to the east of Aspy Bay.

Gulf of St. Lawrence. This area was described and mapped by Loring and Nota (1973). North of Prince Edward Island on the Magdalen Shelf, gravel with occasional sand patches and sandy gravels form a thin, discontinuous cover. The gravels occur in water depths between 20 and 70 m and are surrounded by a thicker cover of sands with varying amounts of gravel. As with the Scotian Shelf, the seafloor of the gulf in water depths of less than 100 m was winnowed on account of the Pleistocene-Holocene transgression. Thus, Bradelle and Orphan banks consist of winnowed lag gravels. The gravels consist of mainly reddish brown, friable sandstone, but may also include granites, gneisses and basic igneous rocks, with the largest quantities occurring in the northern part of the shelf adjacent to the Laurentian Channel. The sand occurrences are generally thicker and more continuous. There are, for example, sandwaves on Bradelle Bank which are probably active. Loring and Nota (1973) indicated that the sands of the Magdalen Shelf are largely polycyclic and composed of local erosional products, mainly derived from underlying and intermittently exposed Paleozoic bedrock.

The surficial geology of Northumberland Strait, which separates Prince Edward Island from the mainland, was mapped by Kranck (1971). A lag-type sand and gravel deposit ranging in thickness from less than 1 m to 15 m is widespread in the western half of the strait. To the east, a "blanket" mud predominates, with the exception of a topographic high off East Point, Prince Edward Island, where sandwaves up to 3 m in height have been observed. It is the result of shoreline erosion and modern redistribution of seabed sand. The Buctouche Sand and Gravel overlies the glacial sediments and bedrock above the lowest marine limit and is widespread throughout the strait. The

thickness of the gravel is not well known and bedrock commonly outcrops through the gravel lag.

The Grand Banks of Newfoundland. The Grand Banks of Newfoundland extend from Rose Blanche Bank in the west to Grand Bank in the east and comprise a series of some of the world's largest offshore banks. In the west the smaller banks — Burgeo, St. Pierre and Green — are dominated by gravel clasts with similar lithologies to rocks from the Newfoundland mainland (Fader et al., 1982). Sand occurs in megaripple, sand ribbon, and sand patch deposits. Northern Grand Bank consists of low 4 m sand ridges overlying gravel pavements of well-rounded clasts (Fader and King, 1981). The thickest deposits of sand and gravel are found on the central and southern areas of the Grand Banks (Fader and Miller, 1986). Here large fields of sand ridges up to 15 m thick and with wave lengths of 4 km dominate the morphology of the surface of the banks. Superimposed on the sand ridges are areas of symmetrical megaripples. Their troughs commonly contain gravel with local outcrops of Tertiary bedrock. Along the south coast of Newfoundland the inner shelf area is narrow and exhibits a rough, hummocky morphology, interpreted as outcropping bedrock. Adjacent to the southern area of the Avalon Peninsula, sand is more common, although the deposits are generally thin and patchy.

Offshore from St. John's there do not appear to be any sand deposits. The seabed is very rough and undulating with glacial till exposures.

Placer minerals

Several heavy minerals are known to exist in varying concentrations in the surficial sediments off eastern Canada and in the Canadian Arctic (Fig. 13.8) but, as of summer 1988 none of these minerals has been commercial recovered. Although numerous beaches have been investigated for their placer mineral potential over the past century, offshore exploration has been confined to the Atlantic coast of Nova Scotia and to the north shore of the Gulf of St. Lawrence. This work has been sporadic and has concentrated on placer gold and iron sands.

Gold

All of the provinces in eastern Canada, except Prince Edward Island, have documented gold occurrences onshore and the potential for further gold production. Nova Scotia leads with about 190 occurrences of which 23 are of the placer variety (Ponsford and Lyttle, 1984; Samson, 1984). Total gold production in Nova Scotia until the end of 1985 was about 35×10^6 g: placer operations accounted for about 133 000 g or about 0.4 per cent.

Most of the gold in Nova Scotia occurs in the metasedimentary rocks of the Meguma Group. These rocks have an onshore areal extent of 19 300 km^2 on mainland Nova Scotia. The Meguma Group and Devonian granites have seldom been differentiated in mapping offshore (King and MacLean, 1976). They continue out for about 40 km and cover an area of approximately 25 400 km^2. Of this more than 15 000 km^2 is in water less than 100 m deep. Thus, given suitable mechanisms for liberation and concentration of the gold, the offshore should hold considerable placer potential. Most of the placers onshore occur as

Figure 13.8. Distribution of heavy mineral occurrences in eastern Canada.

alluvial deposits in watersheds flowing to the Atlantic Ocean or as beach placers.

One mechanism, which could have liberated gold from its host rocks, is the action of ice during the Pleistocene. This would have been effective offshore as well as onshore because sea level was about 120 m lower than now. The ice would have abraded, transported and deposited large quantities of material. This mechanism may have liberated gold from the underlying bedrock and made it available for reworking by fluvial, eolian and coastal-marine processes during and following transgression. The end result is a suite of depositional settings, many of which may possess concentrations of placer gold but few of which have been evaluated.

Examples of offshore prospecting

1. Matachewan Canadian Gold Limited. In the late 1960s, Matachewan Canadian Gold Limited became interested in the potential for offshore placer gold and contracted a geophysical and bottom sampling survey in 1968 to assess the placer gold possibilities on the Scotian Shelf (Hunter, 1968; Libby, 1969b,c). Using a 26 m long vessel they obtained 429 km of seismic profiles with a 3.5 kHz sounder and drilled 187 holes (total length 441 m).

Areas for investigation were selected on the basis of favourable geological factors, with the prime targets being buried stream channels, scour basins and submerged beach lines. Nine specific sites, each with an area of about 77 km^2, were selected for drilling using a specially developed jet lift, which incorporated an air-lift pipe together with a high-pressure water jet stream to dislodge the sediments.

The drillhole cuttings were mixed with water on the ship and the heavy minerals separated out in a sluice box. Tailings were retained in order to determine the volume of sample collected and to enable calculation of gold grades.

The analysis of geophysical data and about 226 t of drillhole cuttings led to the identification of three significant gold deposits with a combined total volume of 32 × 10^6 m^3 of gold-bearing alluvium. The largest deposit was off Isaacs Harbour and Country Harbour in water depths of 26-38 m; it lies in the vicinity of a northwest-trending left-lateral fault (Fig. 13.9) and the crest of the Wine Harbour Anticline. The company intended to carry out additional drilling but ceased to exist before any further work was possible, and the deposit has not been exploited.

A second deposit lies in shallow water off the Ovens Peninsula, near the town of Lunenburg, Lunenburg County. An anticline containing gold-bearing strata trends approximately normal to the shore. The beach here was mined for placer gold in the 1860s, and offshore sampling by Matachewan Canadian Gold Ltd. revealed gold in nearly all of their drillholes. The company estimated that 4.6×10^6 m^3 of gold-bearing alluvium lay within 300 m of shore, in a region where some of the highest gold values had been found in the drill core. Accordingly, the company undertook a pilot-scale dredging program to accurately delineate the size and nature of the deposit, hoping that the gold recovered could help offset some of the expenses.

The first gold dredge built and used in the Canadian offshore, the *Sea Gold*, was constructed during the winter of 1968-1969 and put into service the following summer (Fig. 13.10). The system, mounted on a pontoon hull, consisted of a dredge ladder, 17 m long, a dredge pump, and a high-pressure water jet stream to lift the sediment to the surface.

A continuous chain at the bottom of the ladder dislodged the sediments, fed them to the suction intake, and rejected material which was too large (Libby, 1969a). Three sluice boxes were used to obtain a heavy mineral concentrate.

The system was fully operational in 1969, but the water depth off the Ovens Peninsula, the site of the operations, was 2.4 m deeper than it had been the previous year when surveyed. Bedrock exposed at the surface suggested that storms had removed the gold-bearing alluvium during the intervening period.

Metachewan did not develop any commercial placer gold deposits. It did locate several large clam beds, however, which were harvested successfully for several years.

2. Seabright Resources. In 1980 the dramatic rise in the price of gold led Seabright Resources Ltd. to resume investigations of the coastal waters off Isaacs Harbour and Country Harbour (Seabright Resources, 1980; McKay, 1981). The company collected samples with a bucket dredge and conducted a reflection seismic survey to define the texture, mineralogy and geometry of the placer deposits. The samples suggested that the surficial sediment layer in which the gold is prevalent is either glaciofluvial in origin or is a ground moraine. It was interpreted as a flanking lag gravel covering a bathymetric high. This is consistent with the postulated penecontemporaneous deposition of drift and silt around buoyancy contacts of a floating ice sheet, as proposed by King and Fader (unpublished data, 1985). The glacial drift was probably reworked and winnowed leading to subsequent concentration of the heavy mineral fraction and local enrichment of the sediment on isolated topographic highs.

Seabright recovered little if any gold in areas of lag gravel deposits, but found concentrations of fine grained gold elsewhere. In contrast, the earlier investigations by Matachewan Canadian Gold Ltd. had found coarse grained gold in the lag deposits, but only trace amounts elsewhere.

This discrepancy may be attributable to differences in the sampling techniques employed. Seabright used a bucket dredge which could not collect fine interstitial material from areas covered with lag gravel, whereas Matachewan's water jet system favoured recovery of coarse gold.

The results indicate that both coarse and fine gold exist over a widespread area, but uncertainties associated with the sampling programs preclude preliminary estimates of tonnage and grade. Nevertheless, they are sufficiently promising to suggest that additional work is warranted, not only in the Country Harbour area, but all along the Atlantic coast of Nova Scotia underlain by the Meguma Group.

3. Mer Resources Incorporated. Mer Resources Inc. undertook a beach and nearshore sampling program for heavy minerals along the Atlantic coast of Nova Scotia in 1985. Selected beaches were trenched and offshore samples were obtained using a modified Wink vibracorer from a converted fishing boat. Most of the samples had not been analyzed at the time of writing. A cursory examination indicates that gold and other heavy minerals are present, however, in some of the beach and offshore samples.

Iron sands

Concentrations of iron sands in eolian dunes, beaches and nearshore sediments have been mined in several countries around the world, including the Philippines, Japan and New Zealand. Although there is no shortage of iron ore in Canada, selected beach and nearshore occurrences have been investigated since the 1860s (Logan, 1863 and Hunt, 1870 referenced in Gross, 1967; Mackenzie, 1912; Spoerri et al., Mineral Policy Sector, Energy, Mines and Resources, Internal Report 79/9, 1979). The most notable of these occurrences are the extensive accumulations of magnetite-rich sands situated along the north shore of the Gulf of St. Lawrence, in the vicinity of and to the east of the Moisie and Natashquan rivers, Quebec. Other smaller occurrences are scattered along the north shore of the gulf.

In 1904 a promising onshore placer deposit, identified near the Natashquan River mouth, was reported to contain about 800 000 t of 12 per cent magnetite and 6×10^6 t of 6-6.5 per cent magnetite (unpublished Mines Branch files now CANMET, Energy, Mines and Resources Canada). Aconic Mining Corporation constructed a pilot processing plant in the area in 1955 and in 1956 treated 100 000 t of crude sand, obtaining 5000 t of concentrates. These had grades of 65 per cent iron and 3 per cent titanium dioxide, with low sulphur and phosphorus content. These results led the company to drill an additional 188 holes totalling 2260 m and undertake an airborne geophysical survey. In 1958, Aconic announced reserves in excess of 1.4×10^9 t, grading 3.73 per cent iron.

The venture failed however because of the impure magnetite. The coarser magnetite grains commonly contained intergrown hematite or ilmenite or both (R. McLeod, pers. comm., 1985). While this problem could be partially overcome by grinding and reprocessing, it results in a fine grained concentrate which is difficult to pelletize.

The company Sidbec investigated the iron sands again in 1970 as a possible source of low cost iron for steel manufacturing (Frazier and Ayer, 1973). Drilling and offshore seismic and magnetometer surveys revealed iron values as great as 8 per cent, suggesting that the offshore

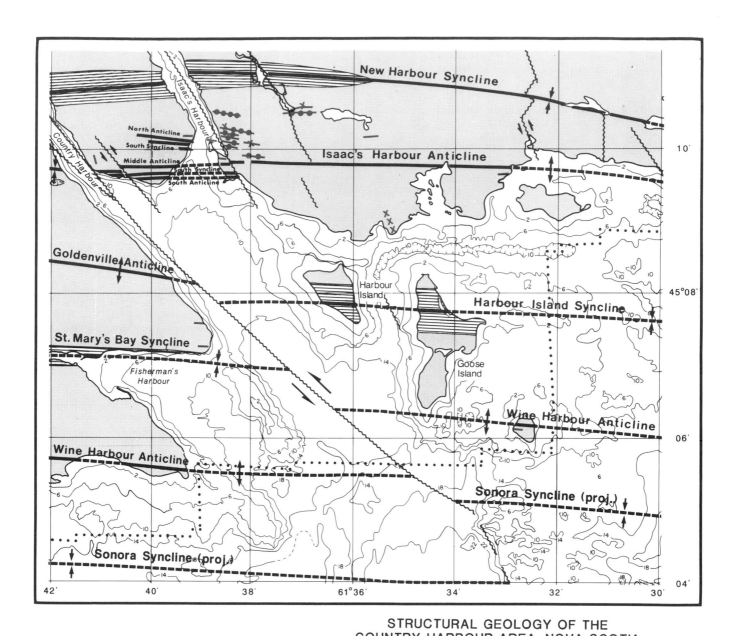

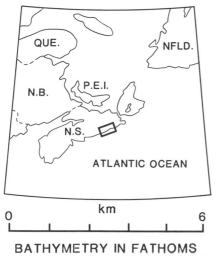

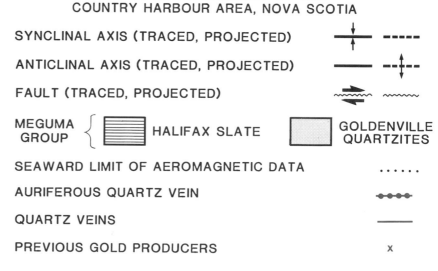

STRUCTURAL GEOLOGY OF THE
COUNTRY HARBOUR AREA, NOVA SCOTIA

SYNCLINAL AXIS (TRACED, PROJECTED)

ANTICLINAL AXIS (TRACED, PROJECTED)

FAULT (TRACED, PROJECTED)

MEGUMA
GROUP { HALIFAX SLATE   GOLDENVILLE
                                QUARTZITES

SEAWARD LIMIT OF AEROMAGNETIC DATA   ......

AURIFEROUS QUARTZ VEIN

QUARTZ VEINS

PREVIOUS GOLD PRODUCERS   x

BATHYMETRY IN FATHOMS

GSC

Figure 13.10. Photograph of the *Sea Gold*, the first offshore gold dredge in Canada built in 1968-1969 for Matachewan Canadian Gold Inc. (photograph courtesy of B. Woolsey).

could be richer than the onshore. Despite this finding no attempt was made to evaluate the offshore reserves because, it was argued, there was no assurance that offshore mineral rights would be granted. However, the operation confirmed the feasibility of using a semi-submersible hydraulic dredge for recovery of the iron. The deposit may yet be exploited as a titanium ore. It could also provide a source of heavy aggregate for ballasting offshore gravity base structures and for use in the manufacture of high density concrete used in coating underwater pipelines.

Figure 13.9. Structural geology of the Country Harbour area, Nova Scotia.

THE FUTURE FOR MARINE MINING OFF EASTERN CANADA AND IN THE CANADIAN ARCTIC

Synthesis of development potential

Minerals that can be exploited from the world's oceans fall into one of three categories: seawater, continental shelf or deepsea. The seawater minerals are in solution; the shelf and deepsea minerals occur as either unconsolidated or consolidated deposits on or beneath the seafloor.

Seawater extraction of minerals appears to hold some promise in eastern Canada. There is a growing need for high quality magnesia which is difficult to obtain from natural sources. The ancillary, high-purity calcium carbonate required to concentrate the magnesia from seawater may be locally available in both onshore and offshore deposits. If the use of lithium expands as projected, we may also see the establishment of seawater extraction plants for this metal. Whereas seawater minerals are a ubiquitous renewable resource, they will only be extracted if onshore sources are either not available or are more costly to develop.

Regional resource assessments by the Department of Energy, Mines and Resources (Canada) suggest that offshore development will be limited to relatively shallow water (100 m) in the next 10 to 20 years. Exploration may take place during periods of ice cover, but marine mining will be confined to the ice-free periods.

The technology to extract minerals from deep water is in the experimental or conceptual stage and will require considerable time, effort, and expense before it can be used for commercial production. Futhermore, the likelihood of polymetallic sulphides or manganese nodules occurring in mineable quantities and grade off eastern Canada and in the Canadian Arctic is remote.

Shelf minerals offer the greatest opportunity for development. Offshore extensions of mineral deposits such as coal and iron ore are already being mined using conventional techniques. Future activity is also likely to be concentrated in offshore extensions of known onshore deposits. There has not been any offshore prospecting for deposits of this type outside these areas.

The unconsolidated mineral deposits in shallow coastal waters will be the focus of activity. Despite large gaps in the geoscientific data base, some areas have a good-to-excellent potential for commercial deposits of both industrial and placer minerals.

Aggregate dredging in the Beaufort Sea to support oil and gas activities will continue. We may also see the development of offshore aggregates and detrital carbonate sand deposits near urban centres and in association with mega-projects in eastern Canada. High-purity silica sand deposits in the Gulf of St. Lawrence have been delineated and, as domestic and foreign markets appear promising, the deposits will probably be exploited before the turn of the century.

Placer minerals, in particular gold and iron sands, will continue to be sought. If the results of exploration programs over the next few years off Nova Scotia are favourable, it is conceivable that gold will be mined from the nearshore by the year 2000.

Constraints and needs to facilitate development

Offshore mineral development has been impeded by the abundance of raw materials onshore, distance to markets or established transportation networks, the general lack of public knowledge and awareness concerning offshore resource potential, and unfavourable economic conditions. There are also concerns about how marine mining might affect the environment and uncertainties regarding the acquisition of offshore mineral rights.

Some of the mineral deposits onshore are nearing depletion or, as with aggregates, have been excluded from exploitation on environmental grounds. Consequently offshore deposits may be appropriate alternative sources in some cases.

A major impediment facing the offshore prospector at the present time is the lack of appropriate geoscientific information, particularly for the coastal zone. This is a difficult region in which to work, so bottom samples and accompanying mineralogical analyses are rare, as are

geophysical records illustrating the characteristics of the surficial sediments and the underlying bedrock. What is required to exploit offshore resources are a better appreciation of the mechanisms which produce placer deposits, regional reconnaissance-scale maps of the inner shelf documenting the distribution and nature of the surficial sediments, geophysical surveys, and appropriate morphogenetic models for placer deposits in the Canadian offshore.

REFERENCES

Amann, H.
1985: Development of ocean mining in the Red Sea; Journal of Marine Mining, v. 5, no. 2, p. 103-116.

Andries, D.M.
1984: The impact of beach protection on beach sand and gravel extraction in Nova Scotia 1968-1983; B.Sc. thesis, Department of Geography, Saint Mary's University, Halifax, Nova Scotia.

Armstrong, E.P. and Miall, L.M.
1946: Raw Materials from the Sea; Chemical Publishing Co., Brooklyn, New York, 196 p.

Aumento, F.
1969: The mid-Atlantic ridge near 45°N, V fission track and ferromanganese chronology; Canadian Journal of Earth Sciences, v. 6, p. 1431-1440.

Aumento, F. and Loncarevic, B.D.
1969: The mid-Atlantic ridge near 45°N. III. Blad Mountain; Canadian Journal of Earth Sciences, v. 6, p. 11-24.

Aumento, F., Lawrence, D.E., and Plant, A.G.
1968: The ferro-manganese pavements on the San Pablo Seamount; Geological Survey of Canada, Paper 68-32, 30 p.

Austin, C.G.
1967: In the rock... a logical approach for undersea mining of resources; Engineering and Mining Journal, August 1967, p. 82-88.

Biron, C.
1961: Undersea coal mining and its application to Zonguldal Coal Basin; Symposium on Coal, Central Treaty Organization, Zonguldak, Turkey, p. 210-242.

Bowen, A.J., Edmond, D.P., Piper, D.J.W., and Welsh, D.A.
1975: The maintenance of beaches; Technical Report, Institute of Environmental Studies, Dalhousie University, Halifax, Nova Scotia, 582 p.

Canada, Department of Energy, Mines and Resources
1974: Towards a mineral policy for Canada: opportunities for choice; Department of Energy, Mines and Resources, Mineral Development Sector, Ottawa, Canada, 56 p.

Cronan, D.S.
1972: The mid-Atlantic ridge near 45°N, XVII: Al, Hg and Mn in ferroginous sediments from the Median Valley; Canadian Journal of Earth Sciences, v. 9, p. 329-323.
1975: Manganese nodules and other ferromanganese oxide deposits from the Atlantic Ocean; Journal of Geophysical Research, v. 80, no. 27, p. 3831-3837.

Cruickshank, M.J.
1968: Mining and mineral recovery; Undersea Technology Handbook/Directory 1968, Compass Publications, Inc. U.S.A., 10 p.

CYAMEX
1979: Massive deep-sea sulfide ore deposits discovered on East Pacific Rise; Nature, v. 277, p. 523-528.

Dietz, R.S.
1972: Mineral resources and power; in Exploring the Ocean World, ed. C.P. Idyll; Thomas Y. Crowell Co., New York, p. 164-195.

Earney, F.C.F.
1980: Petroleum and Hard Minerals from the Sea; Edward Arnold, London, England, 291 p.

Environmental Protection Service
1978: An Arctic atlas; Background Information for developing marine oil spill countermeasures; Fisheries and Environment Canada, Arctic Marine Oilspill Program Report EPS-9-EC-78-1, 475 p.

Epstein, J.A., Feist, E.M., and Zmora, J.
1981: Extraction of lithium from the Dead Sea; Journal of Hydrometallurgy, v. 6, p. 269-275.

Fader, G.B. and King, L.H.
1981: A reconnaissance study of the surficial geology of the Grand Banks of Newfoundland; in Current Research, Part A, Geological Survey of Canada, Paper 81-1A, p. 45-56.

Fader, G.B. and Miller, R.
1986:   Regional geological constraints to resource development — Grand Banks of Newfounland; Proceedings of the Third Canadian Offshore Geotechnical Conference, St. John's, Newfoundland.

Fader, G.B., King, L.H., and Josenhans, H.W.
1982:   Surficial geology of the Laurentian Channel and the western Grand Banks of Newfoundland; Geological Survey of Canada, Paper 81-22, 37 p.

Fader, G.B., King, L.H., and MacLean, B.
1977:   Surficial geology of the eastern Gulf of Maine and Bay of Fundy; Geological Survey of Canada, Paper 76-17, 23 p.

Frazier, D.M. and Ayer, R.D.
1973:   Dredging feasibility of low value iron sands; Proceedings of the Fifth Annual Offshore Technology Conference, Volume 1, April 29-May 2, 1973, Houston, Texas, Paper No. OTC 1761, p. 369-378.

Glasby, G.P.
1979:   Minerals from the sea; Endeavour, New Series, Pergamon Press, p. 82-85.

Gormley, F.J.
1969:   Production of sea water magnesia by Sea Mining Corporation Ltd. at Aguathuna, Newfoundland; unpublished paper, Annual General Meeting, The Canadian Institute of Mining and Metallurgy, Montreal, Quebec, April 21-23, 1969.

Grice, M.A.K. and Hancock, H.A.
1972:   Preliminary results on the processing of manganese pavements from San Pablo Seamount; in Ferromanganese Deposits on the Ocean Floor, ed. D.R. Horn, Lamont-Doherty Geological Observatory, p. 139.

Gross, G.
1967:   Iron deposits in the Appalachian and Grenville regions of Canada; in Geology of Iron Deposits in Canada, Volume 2; Geological Survey of Canada, Economic Geology Report 22, v. 2, 111 p.

Hale, P.B. and McLaren, P.
1984:   A preliminary assessment of unconsolidated mineral resources in the Canadian offshore; Canadian Mining and Metallurgical Bulletin, v. 77, no. 869, p. 51-61.

Hollister, V.
1980:   How to get gold from sea water — at a loss?; Western Miner, p. 68.

Horn, D.R., Delach, M.N., and Horn, B.M.
1973:   Metal content of ferromanganese deposits of the oceans; National Science Foundation, MSF GX 33616, Technical Report No. 3, Washington, D.C.

Horn, D.R., Horn, B.M., and Delach, M.N.
1972:   Distribution of ferromanganese deposits in the world oceans; in Ferromanganese Deposits on the Ocean Floor, ed. D.R. Horn; Lamont-Doherty Geological Observatory, p. 9-17.

Horowitz, A. and Cronan, D.S.
1976:   The geochemistry of basal sediments from the North Atlantic Ocean; Journal of Marine Geology, v. 20, p. 205-228.

Hunter, N.J.
1968:   Geological background for placer exploration on the Scotian Shelf; Nova Scotia Department of Mines, Assessment File no. Offshore 21-W-07, 275 p.

King, L.H. and Fader, G.B.
1986:   Wisconsinan glaciation on the continental shelf, southeast Atlantic Canada; Geological Survey of Canada, Bulletin 373, 72 p.

King, L.H. and MacLean, B.
1976:   Geology of the Scotian Shelf; Geological Survey of Canada, Paper 74-31, 31 p.

Kranck, K.
1971:   Surficial geology of Northumberland Strait; Geological Survey of Canada, Paper 71-53, 10 p.

Libby, F.
1969a: Progress reports — Ovens gold dredging; Nova Scotia Department of Mines, Assessment File no. Offshore 21-W-10, 26 p.

1969b: Searching for alluvial gold deposits off Nova Scotia; Ocean Industry, v. 4, p. 43-46.

1969c: Gold in the sea; Sea Frontiers, v. 5, no. 4, p. 232-241.

Loring, D.H. and Nota, D.J.G.
1973:   Morphology and sediments of the Gulf of St. Lawrence; Bulletin of Fisheries Research Board of Canada, no. 182, 147 p.

MacDonald, K.B.
1982:   Acid soils and agricultural liming practice; Agriculture Canada, Ottawa, Ontario, Publication 1731/E, 17 p.

Mackenzie, G.C.
1912:   The magnetic iron sands of Natashkwan, County of Saguenay, Province of Quebec; Canada Department of Mines, Branch Paper no. 145, 57 p.

Markham, W.E.
1981:   Ice Atlas, Canadian Arctic Waterways; Atmospheric Environment Service, Department of the Environment, Canada, 198 p.

Mathieu, G.
1982:   Comment retabiliser les sables marine; CANMET a démontré comment traiter nos sables marins pour en récupérer de la silice et des feldspaths commerciaux; GEOS, v. 11, no. 4, p. 19-21.

McKay, A.G.
1981:   Sub-bottom profiling survey of the areas off Country Harbour, Nova Scotia; Nova Scotia Research Foundation Corporation, Report 6-81, Project 2707, 42 p.

Menard, H.W.
1964:   Marine Geology of the Pacific; McGraw-Hill, New York, 271 p.

Mero, J.
1965:   The Mineral Resources of the Sea; Elsevier Scientific Publishing Co., New York, 312 p.

Mining Annual Review
1978:   Seawater magnesite; Mining Journal, London, p. 119.

Mining Journal
1980:   Uranium from seawater; Mining Journal, London, p. 93.

Nesis, K.N.
1965:   Biocoenoses and biomass of benthos in the Newfoundland Labrador region; Fisheries Research Board of Canada, Translation Series No. 1375, 75 p.

North, O.S.
1966:   Patents reveal persistent efforts to recover gold from sea water; Engineering and Mining Journal, v. 167, no. 9, p. 195-205.

Organization for Economic Co-operation and Development
1983:   Uranium extraction technology. Current practice and new developments in ore processing; Joint Report, OECD Nuclear Energy Agency and the International Atomic Energy Agency, Washington, OECD Publications and Information Center, 270 p.

Phillips, J.D., Thompson, G., Von Herzen, R.P., and Bowen, V.T.
1969:   Mid-Atlantic ridge near 45°N latitude; Journal of Geophysical Research, v. 74, p. 3069-3077.

Ponsford, M. and Lyttle, N.A.
1984:   Metallic mineral occurrences map and data compilation, eastern, central and western Nova Scotia; Nova Scotia Department of Mines and Energy, Open File Reports 599, 600 and 601.

Rona, P.A.
1983:   Potential mineral and energy resources at submerged plate boundaries; Natural Resources Forum, v. 7, no. 4, p. 329-338.

Samson, J.
1984:   An overview of coastal and marine gold placer occurrences in Nova Scotia and British Columbia; Canada Oil and Gas Lands Administration, Ocean Mining Division, Document 1984-3, 174 p.

Seabright Resources Inc.
1980:   Report on Country Harbour offshore placer deposit; Nova Scotia Department of Mines and Energy, Assessment File 11F/04A, 21-G-61(01).

Sekimachi, T.I. and Katsuta, K.U.
1981:   Method for recovering lithium from sea water; United States Patent No. 4,243,641.

Stevens, J.F.
1970:   Mining the Alaskan seas; Ocean Industry, November 1970, p. 47-50.

Taylor, R.B., Wittmann, S.L., Milne, M.N., and Kober, S.M.
1985:   Beach morphology and coastal changes at selected sites, mainland Nova Scotia; Geological Survey of Canada, Paper 85-12, 59 p.

Thompson, R.M. and Smith, K.G.
1970:   Undersea lode mining in Alaska; Proceedings of the Offshore Technology Conference, Paper OTC 1312, p. 819-826.

Wang, F.F.H. and McKelvey, V.E.
1976:   Marine mineral resources; in World Mineral Supplies Assessment and Perspective, ed. G.J.S. Govett and M.H. Govett; Elsevier Scientific Publishing Co., New York, p. 221-286.

Wright, F.F.
1969:   Minerals of the ocean; in Encyclopedia of Marine Resources, ed. F. Firth; Van Nostrand Reinhold, New York, p. 404-416.

Author's address

P.B. Hale
Mineral Policy Sector
Energy, Mines and Resources Canada
Ottawa, Ontario
K1A 0E4

Chapter 14

CONSTRAINTS TO DEVELOPMENT

Chapter 14

CONSTRAINTS TO DEVELOPMENT

C.F.M. Lewis and M.J. Keen

with contributions by
J. Adams, J.V. Barrie, J.S. Bell, J.D. Brown,
D.E. Buckley, G.B.J. Fader, J. Guigné, I.G. Jones,
H.W. Josenhans, A.S. Judge, M.J. Keen,
C.F.M. Lewis, K.D. McAlpine, N.J. McMillan,
K. Moran, V.H. Noguera, D.J.W. Piper, I. Reid,
D.I. Ross, R.B. Taylor, J.A. Wade, C.M.T. Woodworth-Lynas

THE SETTING: DEVELOPMENTS AND GEOLOGY

The focus of this volume so far has been largely on the geology of the continental margin off eastern Canada. Much of our understanding of this geology has come about because someone needed to know the geological framework for the exploration for hydrocarbons; the processes in the coastal zone to use beaches wisely; and sedimentation in the Bay of Fundy on account of the potential effects of tidal power barrages. The geological framework and geological processes both affect the ways in which we can use the continental margin. Consequently this chapter illustrates some of the interrelationships between geology on the one hand and developments in the coastal zone and the offshore on the other. No attempt is made to present a comprehensive account of all development problems. This chapter is an anthology, rather than a compendium.

The constraints identified do not necessarily prevent or impede development. Some can be benefits. Most of those that are problems, when recognized and understood, can be easily and safely overcome with existing technology and design although often at additional cost. Constraints are hazards for development only when appropriate measures of design, construction or maintenance are not applied because the constraints are not recognized, the constraints are improperly understood, or countermeasures are beyond the capability of present technology.

The sections of this chapter first deal with the coastal zone and then with the open sea. In each section an account is given of the natural constraints to development — the problems posed by geology — and one or more case histories, accounts of problems which have arisen, and what

happened or was done. The constraints are not always "geological" in the strictest sense but when they are not, as for example, in the case of waves in the coastal zone, they are inextricably linked to geological processes. Case histories are not always available with which to tie the perceived geological constraint, but in those cases at least suggestions are given of the practical problems that may arise.

Practical interests in the coastal zone are too diverse to describe separately, so that we have organized the constraints of the coastal zone around its dominant processes. The high seas and high sea levels that affect coastal stability and the geochemical fluxing through estuaries that bear upon pollution are, for example, of particular concern in southeastern Canada and are subjects of individual sections of the chapter. For the Canadian Arctic, the sea ice and permafrost processes that uniquely affect coastal sediments are highlighted.

In contrast to the coastal zone, developments in the open sea are dominated by hydrocarbon exploration and planning for gas and oil exploitation. Consequently the order of introduction for the geological processes and features in the "open sea" portion of the chapter relates to offshore hydrocarbon development: first, those that principally affect exploratory well drilling, and secondly, those that may pose constraints for production structures on the seafloor. The final section of the chapter presents three case histories of experience or planning — oil spills at the shore, pipeline routings for early concepts of Hibernia development, and power cable crossings of the Strait of Belle Isle — that collectively illustrate the role of earth science in decision-making for coastal and offshore developments.

THE COASTAL ZONE

Introduction

The coastal zone is a dynamic environment: the form of the coastline and the materials in the coastal zone constantly change as a result of the effects of waves, winds, tides, currents, ice and longer term changes in sea level. The coast-

Lewis, C.F.M. and Keen M.J.
1990: Constraints to development, Chapter 14 in Geology of the Continental Margin of Eastern Canada, M.J. Keen and G.L. Williams (ed.); Geological Survey of Canada, Geology of Canada, no. 2, p. 743-823 (also Geological Society of America, The Geology of North America, v. I-1).

lines of eastern Canada and the Canadian Arctic range through a broad spectrum of geological, oceanographic and climatological environments and, as was emphasized in Chapter 11, it is conceptually convenient to remember that the southern coastal regions are dominated by the effects of waves and tides, whereas the northern regions are dominated by the effects of sea ice and periglacial and cryogenic processes (Fig. 14.1). Developments in the coastal regions often upset the natural balance between the form of the coastal zone and the processes with which it is interacting dynamically. Examples of this include: exploiting a beach for aggregate where there is no new source of sediment; dredging to maintain a harbour mouth where longshore currents will undo the work; protection of beaches with structures which affect the supply of sediment to regions downdrift; and deforestation or removal of dune vegetation for development.

Wave-dominated coasts: southeastern Canada
R.B.Taylor

High seas and high sea levels

High energy waves generated during storms may cause rapid retreat of the shoreline, changes to beaches, flooding and damage to property (Table 14.1). The effects are greatest when storms coincide with times of ice-free conditions, particularly high tides, and when atmospheric low pressure systems produce storm surges.

Atlantic Canada is affected by storm waves more than the Canadian Arctic on account of the lack of sea ice and the generally greater fetch (Fig. 14.1). The wave conditions in Atlantic Canada vary regionally, seasonally and from year-to-year. The height of the largest annual significant deep-water wave on the Scotian Shelf, on the Grand Banks and in the southern Labrador Sea in the 1970s was about 10 m (Neu, 1982), but during that period there was a steady increase in the mean wave height recorded in the North Atlantic (Neu, 1984). A significant wave height of 12.7 m was recorded, for example, in association with the sinking of the Ocean Ranger semisubmersible drill rig in February 1982 at Hibernia on the northeastern Grand Banks of Newfoundland (Ocean Ranger Royal Commission, 1984). Seasonal variations in wave conditions are the result of seasonal changes in sea ice and in winds. For example, the Atlantic coast experiences intense winter storms, whereas the most severe waves in the Gulf of St. Lawrence occur in the early winter and spring when the Gulf is ice free (Hale and Greenwood, 1980; Brown et al., 1986).

Higher sea levels are caused by tides, onshore winds, storm surges and tsunamis. Higher tides occur at regular intervals each month, and every 4.5 and 18 years. The large tides with the 18 year period, as in 1940-41, 1958-59, and 1976-77, resulted in flooding and destruction of dykes in the Bay of Fundy. Historical evidence from the Bay of Fundy suggests that tides in 1759 and 1869 were even larger than these, reaching 3 m and 2 m respectively above predicted levels (Desplanque, 1979).

Storm surges are produced by a long surface wave that travels with the low pressure system of a storm (Murty, 1984). Surges larger than 0.6 m occur in Atlantic Canada from three to seven times each year (Galbraith, 1979). Variations in the shape of the coastline and the topography of the seafloor alter the effects of surges on the coast, so that the effect of storm surges may be only local. Such was the case in late 1983 when a storm surge badly damaged the harbour facilities and boats anchored at and near Neils Harbour (Fig. 14.2) and Gabarus, Cape Breton Island (Oja 1984; Taylor and Kelly 1984) (Table 14.2).

Tsunamis may also affect water levels at coastlines, as in 1929 in the case of the Grand Banks earthquake. This tsunami generated waves 12 m high at St. Lawrence on the south coast of Newfoundland, and killed 27 people (Doxsee, 1948; Forbes, 1984; Murty, 1984). Other tsunamis have occurred since the 1700s along northern Cape Breton Island and Newfoundland, but they are less well known (Ruffman and Peterson, 1986b).

By contrast with the Atlantic coast of Canada, waves are smaller in most arctic regions because the fetch is reduced by ice, and in the Arctic Islands channels, it is also reduced by geography. For example, storm waves within the central Arctic Islands are less than 2 m in height (McCann, 1973; Taylor, 1978). However, the effects of individual storms are relatively much more important in this region than they are in the south, precisely because of their singularity. For example, when major storms coincide with spring high tide levels in Barrow Strait, beaches can be reworked to elevations of close to 5 m above the level of mean high tide, and the rates of sediment transport can be more than they are during the entire season of open water (Taylor, 1978). Sea ice alters the effects of storm waves. The ice may be driven ashore and this will reduce the levels of wave runup and beach change. Depending on its type, sea ice that is driven ashore can be quickly eroded and tossed up on the beach, or it can ground along the shore, where it may cause severe scouring of the sub-tidal shoreface and interfere with the longshore transport of sediment. The combined action of ice and breaking waves at the coast is a potential threat to buried structures.

In arctic areas such as the Beaufort Sea where the shores are composed of ice-rich sediment, erosion by waves is rapid. Cliff recession has been reported to be as great as 13 m during a single storm (Forbes and Frobel, 1985).

The mobility and replenishment of coastal sediment

The sediments of the coastal zone are both an attractive source of aggregate and a hazard to shipping and structures. In Atlantic Canada the most obvious practical and economic consequence of sediment mobility is the effects on harbours and harbour approaches. Numerous instances are reported each year of harbour entrances filling as a result of storms, trapping fishing boats until the entrance can be dredged. For example, the harbour at Point Sapin, New Brunswick, home port to about 40 boats, has been closed 3 to 4 times per year (Pratte and Willis, 1982; D. Willis, pers. comm., 1987). Numerous types of structures have been erected to attempt to solve this type of problem; they have been designed either to trap sediment before it reaches the harbour entrance or to accelerate its transport across a harbour entrance to the downdrift side (Fig. 14.3).

Figure 14.1. Tidal, wave, and sea-ice conditions in Atlantic Canada and in the Canadian Arctic reflect in part their variety in those regions. Data compiled from Canadian Hydrographic Service (1987), Markham (1980), Maxwell et al. (1980), Lachapelle (1981), and Neu (1982).

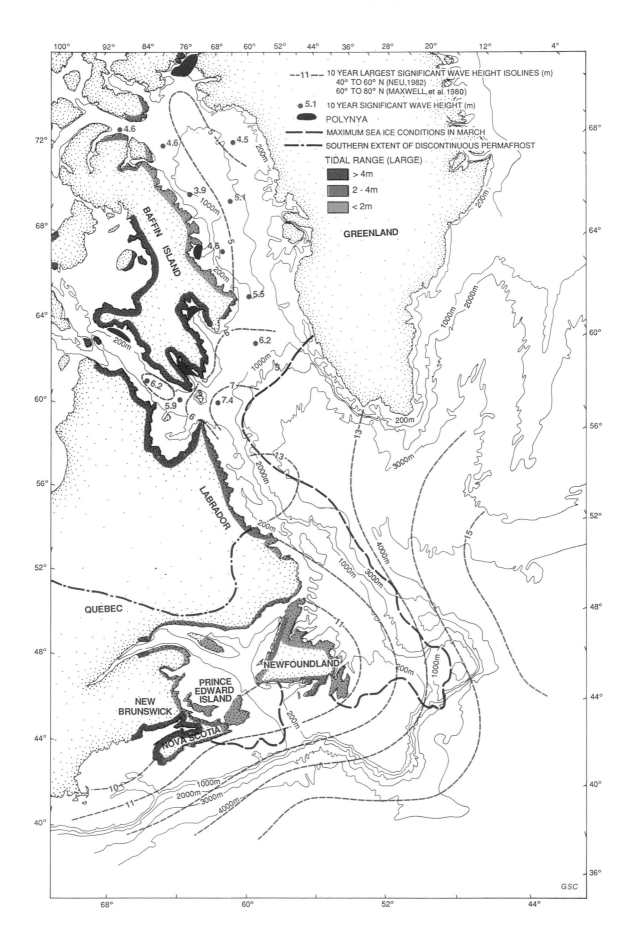

Table 14.1. Examples of storm surges experienced in Atlantic Canada, 1962-1983

Date	Location	Surge Height (m)	Deep Water Wave Height (m)	Effects of Surge	Source of Information
1962-12-31	Halifax	0.83	-		Galbraith, 1979
	Saint John	0.80	-		
1966-12-25	Yarmouth	0.94	-		
1967-02-24	Halifax	1.11	10		
1976-02-02	Yarmouth Saint John	1.48 1.46	12	$10 000 to $15 000 damage in Nova Scotia and New Brunswick	
1982-01-17	Argentia	0.57	10.7	$750 000 damage	Forbes, 1984
	Lamaline	1.30	-	Shores attacked to over 6 m above HHWLT	Brown et al., 1986
	Trepassey	1.30	-		
1983-10-25	North Sydney	0.76	7 to 9	$2 705 000 damage to fishing facilities; shores attacked to 6 m above HHWLT	Oja, 1984; Taylor and Kelly, 1984
	Point Tupper	0.60	-		

HHWLT: Higher High Water Large Tide

However, in nearly all cases some dredging is required to maintain navigable channels. The magnitude of the problem is illustrated by the fact that between 1950 and 1974 some 34 million cubic metres of sediment were dredged from 550 harbours in the Atlantic region (McLean and MacGregor, 1976) (Table 14.2; Fig. 14.3).

The most frequent dredging took place in the harbours for small craft on the Gulf of St. Lawrence. Along much of this coast lagoons and bays are enclosed by barrier islands which provide naturally protected harbours, but the tidal inlets providing access to the harbours are natural sediment sinks. These inlets frequently silt up or shift position, in some cases by as much as 100 m in a year (Reinson, 1980; Reinson and Frobel, 1980). Dredging of inlets may well have adverse effects due to an increase in sedimentation in the inlets and lagoons and loss of sediment from the adjacent barrier beaches, because the sediment normally feeding them has been removed (Reinson and Frobel, 1980).

Beaches are a potentially attractive source of aggregate for manufacturing and construction activities; they are commonly accessible, and the aggregate may be well sorted and clean. As a result they were exploited in Nova Scotia, New Brunswick and Prince Edward Island in the 1950s and 1960s (Fig. 14.4), and the more conventional glaciogenic sources onshore were often ignored (Bowen et al., 1975). Indeed, on Prince Edward Island, beaches were the only local sources of aggregate suitable for the concrete industry (Owens, 1980). Indiscriminate exploitation of beaches for aggregate cannot be sustained; most beaches are not naturally replenished because the supply of new

sediment is less than that removed. Such exploitation leads to destruction of dunes and dune vegetation and accelerates the erosion of the shoreline and coastal retreat (Fig. 14.5). The lower beach crests which result allow storm waves to wash over them and transport sediment into the lagoons and coastal lakes behind. Instability of barrier beaches and inlets leads to flooding of low-lying coastal lands and to the loss of biological habitats and recreational beaches. Several of the once beautiful sandy beaches of Nova Scotia are now merely unstable narrow gravel beach ridges or lag shoals. Such problems have been recognized in all the Atlantic Provinces and, although the various types of legislation have reduced the mining of beaches for aggregate, those beaches which are still mined are experiencing rapid degradation and greater instability (Hunter and Associates, 1982; Taylor, 1982).

An example of coastal management: the eastern shore of Nova Scotia

Background

The previous section described some of the general problems which arise in the exploitation of beaches. In this section, a case history is presented which illustrates the effects of neglect of coastal management. It also demonstrates how geological and geomorphological information is used for planning the proper use of coastal regions and to save badly damaged beaches. The problems of beach damage on the eastern shore of Nova Scotia (northeast of Halifax) arose, at least in part, because there was no comprehensive management policy for the coastal regions of

Figure 14.2. During storms, particularly those which coincide with abnormally high water levels, shores are rapidly eroded, often flooded, and property is damaged. Such was the case in 1983 when a storm surge struck Neils Harbour, Cape Breton Island, pushing the beach landward and moving and destroying buildings and other fishing facilities. The storage shed in foreground is about 4.5 m high.

Nova Scotia. Although the Nova Scotia legislature (1975) allowed beaches to be designated "protected", in practice this only applied to protection from aggregate removal, which is prohibited except where authorized by the appropriate Minister. Much of the coastline above the level of high tide is still owned privately and the landowners are not obliged to apply for land use permits in these cases. Some coastal lands have been developed as provincial parks, or set aside as park reserve, or are owned by the Crown and so in effect are protected anyway.

Geological models concerning the development of beaches and their replenishment help explain much of the damage to beaches resulting from human activities. The eastern shore of Nova Scotia is a transgressive coastline where sea level has been rising for several thousand years by 3 to 4 mm each year (Quinlan and Beaumont, 1981; Scott and Medioli, 1982). The coastline consists of a series of lakes and estuaries oriented perpendicular to the coastline, flanked by spits and tombolos and fronted by barrier beaches (Fig. 14.5). Intervening headlands of glacial

Table 14.2. Sediment mobility and removal rates for selected locations along Northumberland Strait. See Figure 14.4 for locations.

Location	Calculated Net Average sediment Transport (m3/a)[1]	Amount of beach sediment quarried (m3) under permit[2] (1968 to 1974)	Amount of sediment dredged[3] (1950 to 1974)
1. Pte. Sapin	203 932	-	172 719
2. Richibucto Bar	20 974	-	159 717
3. Richibucto Head	-	34 000	
4. St. Eduard de Kent	60 783	40 694	97 342
5. Cocagne	8 412	2 560	100 668
6. Robichaud	27 533	3 359	-

1 Hydrotechnology Ltd. (1980)
2 Airphoto Analysis Associates Consultants Limited (1975)
3 McLean and MacGregor (1976)

Figure 14.3. Since the redesign, in 1961, of the breakwaters at the 50 m wide entrance to Dingwall Harbour, Cape Breton Island, an estimated 47 000 m3 of sediment were dredged from the harbour entrance as opposed to the more than 350 000 m3 removed prior to breakwater construction (McLean and MacGregor, 1976).

deposits, mostly drumlins, act as anchor points for the beaches and are their primary sources of sediment (Taylor et al., 1985; Forbes and Taylor, 1987). This till source is reflected in the composition of the beaches, a mixture of sand and gravel. Although many of the beaches appear to have a large reservoir of sediment, in fact the rates of sediment supply are very slow, so that a single beach would take thousands of years to be replenished. In addition, the relatively small drumlins provide only a limited source of sediment (Boyd and Bowen, 1983), and there is little longshore sediment transport between the different shoreline compartments. The drumlins are presently receding at rates of 0.2 to 3.0 m per year, so that their life spans are only a few hundred years. As the drumlins diminish in size, the adjacent beaches show signs of erosion and often migrate landward through processes such as wave washover and breaching of the barrier beaches, with sediment being transferred to the lagoons and lakes behind. The present beaches of the eastern shore are the products of many evolutionary cycles involving barrier progradation and retreat and destruction as the coastline recedes under the influence of rising sea levels (Boyd et al., 1987). Most of the beaches of this region are in retreat.

Silver Sands Beach, Cow Bay

Silver Sands is one of the many beaches which were threatened because of the removal of aggregate for construction (Fig. 14.6, 14.7). This beach was a well known recreational site but nearly disappeared because about 2 million tonnes of sediment were removed between 1954 and 1971 after which it became protected. By 1960 the western end of the beach had collapsed and the inlet nearby had widened. In 1964, the beach had diminished to about half its original size. A new inlet opened in the mid-1970s, and the beach continued to transgress landward. By the 1980s all that remained of the original beach was a steep gravel storm

ridge, fringed by a veneer of sand covering the lower foreshore and inner nearshore slope. There is no sediment source large enough to replenish the beach: the drumlins which once anchored it have mostly disappeared, and much of the finer sediment eroded from the headlands nearby is swept offshore or landward into the lagoon. This beach was allowed to deteriorate beyond the point of restoration, and it will take many years before the beach rebuilds itself farther landward (Bowen et al., 1975; Taylor et al., 1985).

Conrods and Lawrencetown beaches

Conrods and Lawrencetown beaches were mined for aggregate in the period 1950-1960 but they did not retreat to the same extent as did Silver Sands Beach because the headlands at Conrod Island and Lawrencetown Head were adequate sediment sources for replenishment. (Conrods Beach and Conrod Island as listed in the Gazetteer of Canada for Nova Scotia are commonly known as Conrad's Beach and Conrad Island, respectively.) This abundance of supply is reflected in the existence of relict beach ridges, and a wide modern beach backed by well-developed dunes. These beaches were selected as part of a coastal heritage park system established along the eastern shore (Nova Scotia Department of Lands and Forests, 1984; Fig. 14.8). They were chosen in part because the integrity of the barriers was threatened by pedestrians and vehicles, and in part because the whole coastline is so diverse. Geological surveys have been conducted to establish the relative stability of various parts of the coastal environment and the main pathways of sediment transport (Boyd and Bowen, 1983). As examples, the barrier at the western end of Conrods Beach and the beach flanking the east side of Lawrencetown Head were seen to be unstable, and it was recognized that sand is being lost to lagoons and estuaries by wind and wave washover and through tidal inlets.

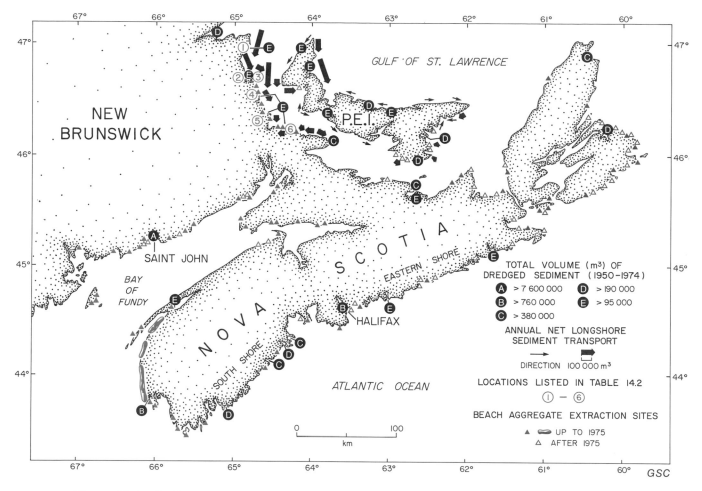

Figure 14.4. Sediment is artificially removed from the coastal zone for two main reasons — dredging to maintain safe navigable channels and beach mining for aggregates. Sites where the greatest dredging took place between 1950 and 1974 are marked along with the location of major beach mining sites. Calculated net sediment transport rates (volume indicated by length of bold arrow) are provided to illustrate the natural mobility and availability of sediment for beach development (after McLean and MacGregor, 1976; Hydrotechnology Ltd., 1980; Hunter and Associates, 1982; Owens, 1980; Andries, 1984).

These observations have been taken into account in the development plan and in controlling access to the beaches, so that the dunes can be revegetated and stabilized and continue to provide a reservoir of sand for natural beach development and evolution.

Shore protection

More elaborate remedial measures than have been described so far may be required at other coastal locations where erosion has been so severe that highways and dwellings are threatened. One approach is to build structures such as seawalls, gabions, groins and breakwaters designed to reflect or dissipate incoming waves. These will cause more problems than they will solve if ill-designed. For example, structures such as groins built perpendicular to the shoreline are designed to slow down the longshore transport of sediment and induce beach progradation, and these work best where the waves approach the coast obliquely. However, in many cases the groins cause increased erosion of shores downdrift because of sediment starvation, as for example at Aspy Bay, Cape Breton Island, Nova Scotia, where shore erosion increased 3 to 3.5 m/a after groins were installed (Nova Scotia Department of Public Works, pers. comm., 1986). A second approach is to deliberately channel sediment from one location to another, past an inlet to a downdrift shore for example, or to artificially nourish eroding beaches. These procedures have to be kept up for many years or the investment in "new" sediment will be quickly lost. The cheapest and easiest solution is not to build near an eroding shoreline.

Ice-dominated coasts in the Canadian Arctic
R.B. Taylor

Sea ice and the coastal zone

Sea ice is a major hazard to structures in the Arctic and a hazard of lesser magnitude in more southerly latitudes.

751

Figure 14.5. An example of the effect of beach mining on natural beach morphology. The removal of backshore dunes reduces beach crest height which often leads to increased wave overwash, as was observed at this beach on Cape Breton Island. Note for scale a small truck (left circle) and a front-end loader (right circle); the unvegetated portion of the barrier (light tone) to the left of the truck is about 75 m wide.

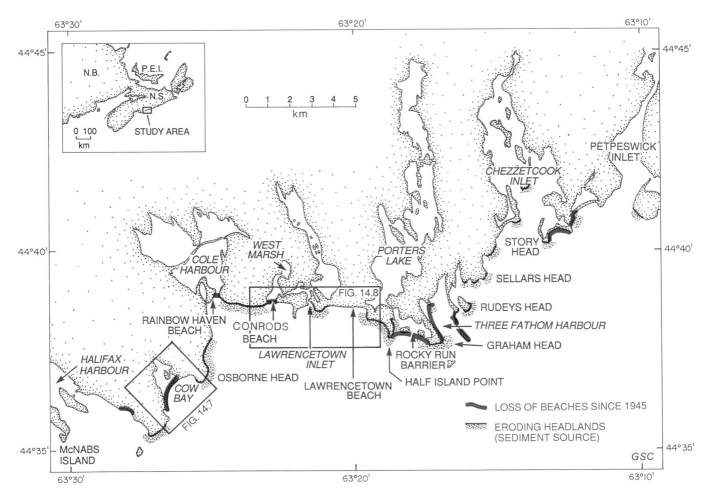

Figure 14.6. Part of the Eastern Shore, Nova Scotia, showing eroding headlands and beaches that changed dramatically or disappeared completely since 1945, in part due to beach mining activities.

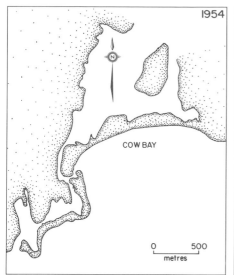

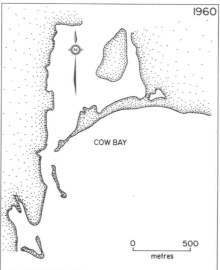

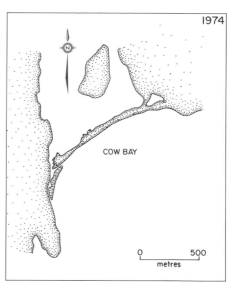

GSC

Figure 14.7. Silver Sands beach in Cow Bay (see Fig. 14.6) was literally trucked away in the late 1950s and early 1960s when beach sediment mining was at its peak. These maps, based on aerial photographs, illustrate the sequence of beach changes between 1954 and 1974. Shorelines from National Air Photo Library, Ottawa, Ontario, Photos A14146-35 (1954, bottom left), A16213-5, and from Maritime Resource Management Service, Amherst, Nova Scotia, Photo 74123-107 (1974, bottom right).

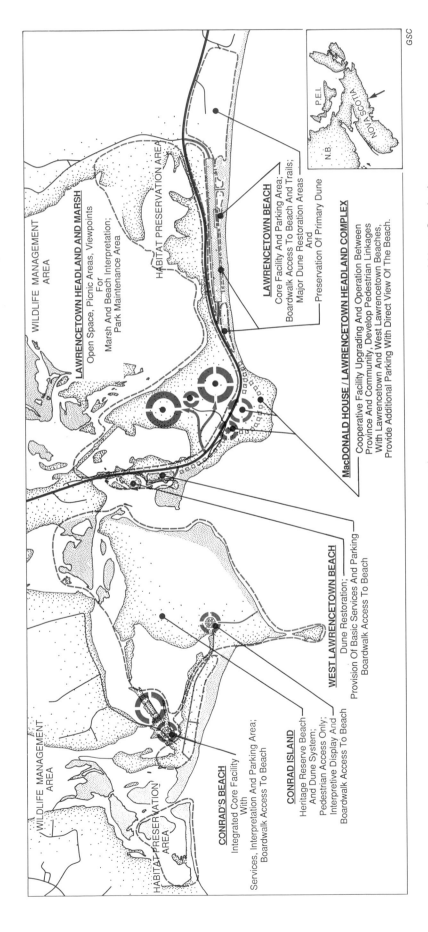

Figure 14.8. Conceptual plans for a coastal heritage park along the Eastern Shore of Nova Scotia, in particular at Conrod's and Lawrencetown beaches (from Nova Scotia Department of Lands and Forests, 1984). Spelling of Conrod's beach and Conrod Island as Conrad's beach and Conrad Island reflects local usage.

This is shown in the coastal zone by features formed by the pushing and melting of ice (Fig. 14.9). Ice floes and brash ice are driven onshore and alongshore by wind and waves. The severity of the effects of ice in the coastal zone depends on: the properties of the ice itself such as its thickness and age; the ice conditions nearshore; the local topography onshore and offshore; the depth of ground thaw; and the driving forces generated by the wind, waves and tides (Kovacs and Sodhi, 1980; Sodhi and Kovacs, 1984).

Ice-push features formed within the zone of normal wave action are ephemeral and are not normally a hazard to structures. This is not true for ice floes which override the beach or hit fixed objects, such as artificial islands or grounded multi-year ice; when this happens, massive ice ridges or shore ice piles form (Fig. 14.10). Ice can override gently sloping terrain or steep coastal bluffs and as it moves inland it bulldozes, crushes or gouges objects in its path. The overriding and pile-up on land can dam streams, disrupt drainage and cause flooding. Where the shore topography is irregular, the ice sheet buckles and forms ice piles. Most shore ice piles develop within 20 m of the water-line and are less than 15 m high. Some ice floes have been pushed more than 100 m inland (Taylor, 1978; Kovacs, 1983). This phenomenon could clearly threaten artificial islands used for drilling exploration wells, many of which are less than 100 m wide.

The overriding and pile-up of shore ice can occur in the fall and winter, but the most dangerous period is in the spring following the breakup of sea ice alongshore. There may be little warning of ice floes being driven onshore (Kovacs, 1983), and ice override may take place in less than 30 minutes (Sodhi and Kovacs, 1984). Piles of ice formed close to mean sea level do not last long — less than one season of open water — but those built beyond the reach of waves can persist for several years (Taylor, 1978, 1980a).

Ice override is difficult to predict; it can occur on most high-latitude shores, and has return periods in the range of many tens to hundreds of years on the Alaskan coast of the Beaufort Sea (Harper and Owens, 1981). Shores more prone to the effects of ice pressure are: the shores of deltas, capes and promontories; shores at the junction of channels where ice movements may be complex; and shores of small islands in the path of sea ice making its annual exodus from the Arctic Archipelago (Taylor, 1978, 1980c; Woodward-Clyde Consultants Ltd., 1980; Barrie and

Associates, 1982). Some small islands such as these have been used as natural laboratories for the study of the forces exerted by sea ice, to gain insight on the effects of ice on offshore drilling structures (Hudson et al., 1981; Metge et al., 1981; Frederking et al., 1983).

Ice ridges are formed where sea ice, driven shoreward, grounds in the nearshore. During buckling and failure, ice fragments are forced upward forming sails as high as 24-30 m. The sail heights are generally much greater than shore ice piles because the frictional and gravitational forces on the moving ice are less offshore than on land. They may extend several kilometres alongshore, or can form as solitary piles of broken ice. The formation of numerous ice ridges at the same location leads to multiple ridges extending offshore or to the development of fields of hummocky ice, particularly along the northern perimeter of the Queen Elizabeth Islands (Hudson et al., 1981).

Thermal constraints in regions of permafrost

Ground-based structures in northern regions of continuous or discontinuous permafrost are generally at risk on account of differential movements induced by the freezing and thawing of interstitial water. In the coastal zone the movements are complicated by the erosion or deposition of sediment and frequent changes in beach morphology, and by the presence of saline pore waters, buried brash ice, fresh water lenses, and fast ice features at the shore. The problems are less severe in more southerly latitudes in Canada, but seasonally frozen ground occurs even there, restricted in the coastal zone to the backshore and the upper parts of intertidal areas. In these southerly areas a frozen crust of sediment or fast ice, or both, may form across the upper beach in winter, but the effects are ephemeral and protect rather than destroy coastal stability (Dionne, 1972, 1985; Knight and Dalrymple, 1976; Owens, 1976; Bourget, 1977).

Frost heave, thrust, thaw, and subsidence naturally occur in the subsurface active layer in the regions of permafrost. Disturbance of the thermal integrity of permafrost and ground ice distorts structures such as pipelines and buildings, and leads to the formation of thermokarst features and the triggering of various processes of mass wasting (Fig. 14.11). Along shorelines that are ice-rich, a combination of thermal and mechanical erosion can result in rapid shoreline retreat. As an example, parts of the coast of the Beaufort Sea are retreating at rates as high as 20 m per year, and rates higher than 5 m per year are common (Harper, 1985). Ice-rich shores are less common in the eastern and central Arctic Islands but, there, other mass wasting processes, such as solifluction, earth flows and retrogressive thaw flow slides, affect the backshore slopes (Hodgson, 1977, 1982; Heginbottom, 1984).

The interface between land and sea in regions of permafrost is a complex environment. It is the transition zone between thick, land-based permafrost and seafloor which is unfrozen or only partially frozen. Permafrost exists beneath the present intertidal zone (Taylor and McCann, 1974), but the distance it extends offshore is not generally well known. Offshore drilling in the western Arctic has shown that there is a sharp boundary between ice-free and ice-bearing sediments within 0.5 km of the present shoreline (Swift et al., 1983). Permafrost forms subaerially, and it appears that the rising sea in the western Arctic has thawed the permafrost beneath former low-lying shores.

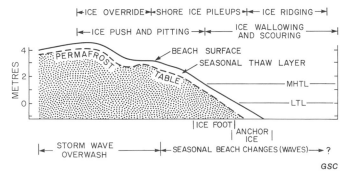

Figure 14.9. Schematic cross-section of an arctic shoreline illustrating the extent and effects of sea-ice movement and reworking by waves in the coastal zone (modified after Harper, 1985) (MHTL: Mean high tide level; LTL: Low tide level).

Figure 14.10. Much of the coastline of eastern Canada is affected by the presence of seasonal sea-ice. Arctic shores, in particular, are adversely affected by sea-ice grounding, ridging and override. Along the northern shore of Somerset Island, Northwest Territories, multiple grounded ice ridges (A) and massive shore ice piles (B), about 9-10 m and 10 m high, respectively, in these examples, are formed to maximum heights of 30 m (GSC 203216-H, 165624).

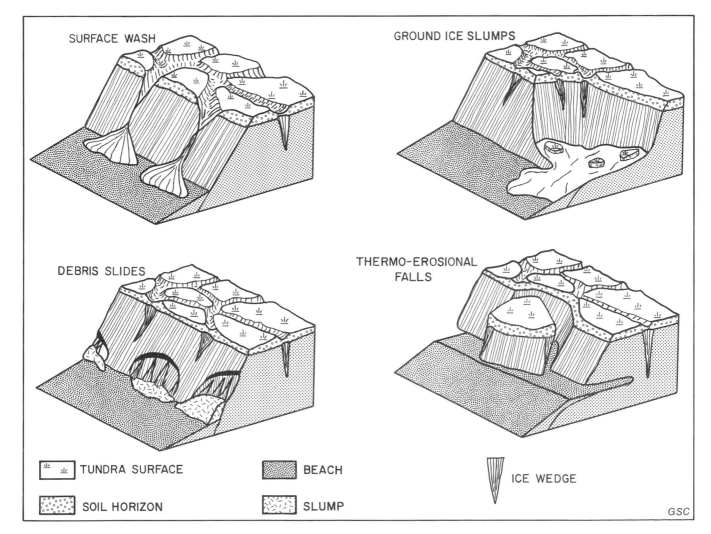

Figure 14.11. Several types of mass-wasting processes affect ice-rich shores in the Arctic Islands. The combination of thermal and mechanical erosion by waves results in rapid shoreline retreat (after Harper, et al., 1978).

By contrast, in the central Arctic, where shores are still emerging in response to glacial unloading, permafrost forms as the coastal zone emerges (Hansell et al., 1983). Consequently, permafrost is not expected offshore beneath the present seafloor. The thickness of coastal permafrost increases with distance inland, and locally aggrades beneath newly formed spits and newly built artificial islands, as a result of the exposure to cold air temperatures (McDonald et al., 1973; Mahar et al., 1983; Taylor et al., 1983).

Subsurface thermal conditions and the characteristics of permafrost beneath the present shore zones depend on climatic, oceanographic, and topographic conditions, as well as on the stability of the shoreline (Owens and Harper, 1977; Harper et al., 1978). The permafrost within the shore zone may be ice-bearing, ice-bonded, contain segregated ice lenses, or be ice free depending on factors such as soil properties and the composition of pore waters. The terminology used to describe the thermal characteristics of the coastal zone is given in Figure 14.12. The thermal regime of coastal zones is complicated and made less predictable by saline pore water, buried brash ice, fresh-water ice lenses, and frequent changes in beach morphology.

The potential complexity can be illustrated by describing the emergent shore zones of the eastern Arctic Islands. The maximum depths of annual thaw can be greater than 1.5 m beneath sand beaches, but they rarely exceed 0.8 m beneath gravel beaches because of different thermal properties of the sediment. Beneath the backshore, above the reach of waves, inland fluctuations in thaw are dominated by climatic factors. The thaw depth usually corresponds to the level of the frost table, normally the level of the 0° isotherm. Rates of thaw in the backshore are more uniform, commonly 1 to 5 cm per day, and are more predictable than are the rates beneath the intertidal and subtidal zones. In these zones the temporal and spatial fluctuations in thaw depth are larger, and the thaw depth may be deeper than the frost table because saline pore water has a lower freezing point than fresh water. When the saline pore water freezes, salts are excluded and brine rich layers form, which may be only partially frozen or unfrozen. These brine rich layers shear easily, and are planes of potential failure (Chamberlain, 1983). Furthermore, variations in the degree of ice-bonding of different sediments result in differential rates of thaw and some zones are more easily eroded by waves (Taylor, 1980b). As an example, a major storm on Bylot Island led to the rapid removal of all unfrozen sediment within the reach of waves and the erosion of hollows in the frozen coarser sediment. Frozen chunks of interbedded finer sediment collapsed and fell into the sea. Ice-bonded sediments may increase the stability of the coastline because of their greater resistance to erosion (Taylor, 1980b) and, although rates of thaw may rise to values of 30 to 70 cm per day during major storms, such rates are not sustained for more than a few days. The presence of saline pore waters may be advantageous to the

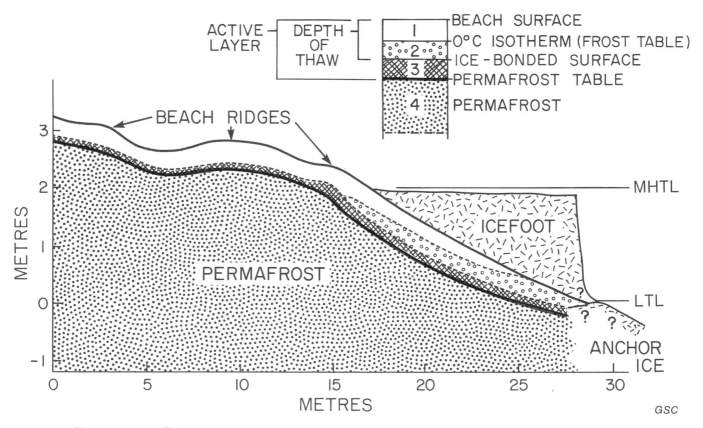

Figure 14.12. Terminology and schematic diagram of the zones of seasonal beach thaw and types of fast ice observed along coarse-clast beaches of the central Arctic Islands (modified after Owens and Harper, 1977) (MHTL: Mean Hight Tide Level; LTL: Low Tide Level).

construction of subsea structures because the smaller proportion of frozen pore waters results in smaller changes in volume as a result of thawing or freezing (Jahns, 1984). For example, Chamberlain (1983) reported that frost heave was reduced by more than 50% in saline subsea sands and clays.

The topography of the backshore influences the thermal regime of the beach. In the case of a barrier beach backed by a lagoon, wave overwash and the sea water on both sides of the beach increase the thaw depth, but the thaw characteristics of foreshore and backshore will be similar: both regions are subject to comparable thermal regimes. Thaw will be delayed where a beach is backed by high relief, on account of increased snow accumulation, increased shade from the sun, and often the growth of thicker fast ice along shore.

Thaw depths reflect changes in beach morphology. The annual thaw depth is relatively constant beneath the backshore, but changes with the thickness of overlying sediment in the intertidal zone, and possibly also in the subtidal zone. For example, when a beach is eroded the thaw depth moves down and when sediment accumulates the thaw depth rises, in this case usually only after the freeze-back cycle of the winter. Consequently, an equilibrium level of thaw is maintained, but irregularities can be introduced by buried brash ice (Taylor, 1980b).

Fast ice protects shores against sea ice, and delays the annual thaw of intertidal sediments. One form of fast ice, the "icefoot" (Fig. 14.12) forms by the accumulation of frozen swash, spray, and cakes of snow and ice within the intertidal zone (McCann and Carlisle, 1972). There are many varieties of "icefoot", including those which form during storms and extend above high tide limit and those which form in nontidal areas such as the Great Lakes. Another form, "anchor ice", is submerged ice attached to the seabed at or seaward of the level of lower low tide; it can be extensive along sandy shores, but is less well developed along gravelly shores (Taylor and McCann, 1976; Taylor, 1980c; Sadler and Serson, 1981). One explanation for its formation is the freezing of fresh-water runoff which flows along the surface of permafrost and is forced up through the seabed by the combined effects of the hydrostatic head and the freezing of surface beach sediment. The thickness to which anchor ice can form or its effects on the thermal regime of the adjacent seabed are not known.

Marine terminals in the Arctic Islands

Permanent marine terminals have not been developed until recently in the Arctic Islands because of the short season for shipping and the small cargoes handled at most centres. The discovery of significant mineral deposits and oil and gas, however, has increased the need for terminals to handle larger vessels for a longer part of the year. Marine terminals have been established at Nanisivik Mines Ltd. of Nanisivik, Baffin Island, and at Polaris Mine on Little Cornwallis Island (Girgrah and Shah, 1978). Feasibility studies have been conducted for several possible sites for liquefied natural gas terminals, the most detailed for Bridport Inlet, Melville Island. Many factors have to be considered when evaluating sites for new terminals in the Arctic: water depths; anchorage; berthing; space for manoeuvering; accessibility; terrain for shore

facilities; sources of aggregate for construction; the type of ice-strengthened vessels needed; and the proximity to the resource being shipped. Activities such as dredging and excavating are expensive in the Arctic, and so should be avoided if possible. At Nanisivik, for example, where water depths were too shallow at the proposed wharf site, dredging was avoided by extending a causeway farther offshore to the new wharf site. This alternative action was only feasible because of the abundance of local aggregate for causeway construction.

The major influence on port design is ice. In winter, sea ice growth will be accelerated by the repeated breakup and refreezing caused by vessels manoeuvering near terminals. At Bridport Inlet it is anticipated that the ice thickness could increase to more than 7 m so that countermeasures have been proposed which involve special ice melting procedures utilizing waste heat from the liquefaction plant (Cammaert et al., 1983). If ice override or pile-up are potential hazards, as they are for artificial islands, berms or other structures have to be built to induce buckling of the ice farther offshore. Such structures lead to a field of ice rubble developing, which protects structures against ice ride-up, and increases the effective diameter of artificial islands (Croasdale, 1983).

In the eastern and northeastern Arctic Islands the fiords and bays provide numerous potential sites for marine terminals should they be needed. There are few natural terminals, however, in the north-central Queen Elizabeth Islands, where the potential for oil and gas is high (Taylor, 1980c). The region is one of multi-year ice, and access by sea year-round demands class 10 ice-strengthened vessels, which are not available. There are few embayments which would provide protection from ice, and those which do exist are usually too shallow. Sites adjacent to the deltas of major rivers may have water which is deep enough but, as they protrude offshore, ice pressures may be severe. Many shores are covered by ice-rich marine silts and clays which are susceptible to disturbance, mass-wasting and thermokarst processes. Gravel shores of the central Arctic and most river deltas may be suitable if the problem of ice override by sea ice can be solved (Barrie et al., 1978; Taylor, 1980c). If marine terminals cannot be established, then oil and gas will have to be sent by pipeline to transshipment terminals farther to the south or east. Indeed, the terminal at Bridport Inlet, mentioned earlier, would be the terminal for a pipeline from the gas field at Drake Point on northern Melville Island.

Pollution and circulation: estuaries

The fate of chemical contaminants
D.E.Buckley

Pollution of the marine environment is caused when contaminants accumulate to levels that lead to undesirable changes in biota, water quality and sediments; pollution will arise locally in a coastal region if contaminants which have been discharged into the sea are not adequately flushed into the open ocean. This may of course lead to more severe problems in the oceans themselves over a longer term (Schaule and Patterson, 1983; Yeats and Bewers, 1987). In order to assess the potential impact of a contaminant on the marine environments, its rate of transport or flux must be estimated across the phase boundaries between sediments and water and across the different segments of its pathways, and its transportation and dispersal in the water as a result of natural circulation must be understood. Most major urban centres are established on bays or estuaries, and understanding the impact of waste discharge on these environments will be determined by the adequacy of the modelling of the hydrodynamic regime (Buckley and Winters, 1983). The metals and processes of interest include transfers of Pb, Cd and Hg, for example, which are not normally abundant in the coastal marine environment and are clearly recognized as contaminants. Occurrences of more common metals such as Fe and Mn are interpreted as a guide to geochemical interactions rather than an indication of contamination.

The fundamental control on the circulation in an estuary or coastal inlet is usually the geomorphological framework. As an example, Halifax Harbour consists of a relatively deep inner basin, Bedford Basin, connected with the open Atlantic Ocean through a relatively narrow and shallow channel. Circulation and flushing is restricted, so that sewage is concentrated in Bedford Basin (Platt et al., 1970; Jordan, 1972; Hargrave et al., 1976; Miller et al., 1982).

Although some river-dominated estuaries of the Atlantic coast of eastern Canada have only relatively small sources of pollution, such as a small urban centre, potentially toxic levels of metals may accumulate and fluctuate under natural conditions. Mercury concentration, due to adsorption of mercury on fine grained sediments deposited in the LaHave River estuary, is affected by seasonal variations in hydrodynamic conditions that determine the efficiency of the estuary in flushing (Cranston, 1976; Cranston and Buckley, 1972).

Metals enter estuaries in at least three distinct phases: (a) as dissolved ions in natural waters or effluents; (b) as part of mineral particles within crystal lattices or adsorbed on surfaces; and (c) as complexes with organic ligands. On entering brackish or marine waters a number of geochemical transformations may take place due to changes in salinity, pH and oxidation-reduction conditions. For example, dissolved ions may form complexes with dissolved organic matter; they may co-precipitate with other metals or salts, or they may adsorb on the surfaces of suspended particulate matter. Metals, which enter the marine area in association with suspended particulate matter, may be absorbed or be exchanged with other metals. Complexed metals in organic compounds may be released to solution or oxidation, may be exchanged, or may simply change coordination with the organic complex. The Miramichi estuary, which is described in a later section, provides several examples of these processes (Buckley and Winters, 1983; Willey and Fitzgerald, 1980).

Different parts of the coastal zone have their own characteristic physical processes, and when establishing the net transport of metals through the coastal zone it is appropriate to estimate the flux across the boundaries between these different regions. The estuary of the St. Lawrence River was divided by Yeats and Bewers (1983) into an upper, middle and lower section, and the flux of dissolved and particulate metals was estimated across each boundary. Yeats and Bewers (1983) showed that less particulate Fe, Co and Mn passes through the lower boundary of the estuary than enters the estuary from the river. The loss in particulate metal flux could be due to desorption from the particulates as well as net reduction in the particulate load (Loring and Nota, 1973).

A similar approach was taken by Buckley and Winters (1983) in estimating the metal fluxes from the Miramichi estuary into the Gulf of St. Lawrence. They calculated the transport of metals through critical sections of the river, and showed that more of the labile (reactive "dissolved") Fe, Mn, Zn and Cu is exported from the estuarine system than enters from the river. The excess Fe appears to come from suspended particulate matter, from which it is desorbed, but the source of the excess Mn, Zn, and Cu is the mud on the bottom of the estuary. By contrast, the annual export of labile Pb and Cd is less than the annual input from the river, and the estuarine bottom muds appear to be a sink for these metals.

The flux of both labile and particulate metals into the Gulf of St. Lawrence from the Miramichi River estuary is much greater for its discharge than is the flux of these metals from the St. Lawrence River into the gulf. The river discharge of the Miramichi is 9.6×10^9 m^3/a, slightly more than 2% of the discharge of the St. Lawrence, 4.4×10^{11} m^3/a, but the flux of metals from the Miramichi is about 8% of the flux from the St. Lawrence. This difference is probably due to the higher concentrations of contaminants and the relatively small areas for geochemical sinks within the estuarine sediments of the Miramichi, as compared with the St. Lawrence. The Miramichi estuarine system is discussed more fully later in this chapter.

It has been noted that a metal deposited in sediments as part of a mineral particle, incorporated in planktonic material or adsorbed on suspended particulate matter, may well not stay there. A variety of processes leads to its recycling. Subsequently, as sediments are buried and isolated from the overlying water, a series of diagenetic processes begin in response to changed oxidation-reduction conditions and cation exchange reactions between the sediments and the associated pore waters (Stoffyn-Egli, 1982; Winters and Buckley, 1986). In nearshore and estuarine sediments Mn deposited in an oxidized form on particulate material is subsequently reduced and dissolved in the pore water and then diffuses through the permeable sediments (Evans et al., 1977; Sundby et al., 1981). In certain cases, the concentration of dissolved metal in the pore water may be several orders of magnitude higher than that in the overlying sea water, producing a significant chemical gradient with depth in the sediments. This may promote a driving force for vertical diffusion and refluxing of metals back into the sea water (Winters and Buckley, 1986).

The Strait of Canso and Chedabucto Bay: causeway construction and industrial development

D.E.Buckley

The Strait of Canso separates Cape Breton Island from mainland Nova Scotia (Fig. 14.13). The Canso Causeway was constructed across the strait in 1954: this cut off the connection between the Gulf of St. Lawrence and the Atlantic Ocean, inadvertently creating an excellent deepwater harbour, which is ice-free throughout the year. The presence of the harbour led to the establishment of industrial plants in the region and to an increase in the urban population. The tanker ARROW spilled about 50 000 barrels of Bunker C fuel oil in 1970 and this oil contaminated about half the shoreline of Chedabucto Bay to the southeast of the Strait of Canso. Consequently, the region is an excellent one to study from the point of view of human impact on the coastal environment. Some of the effects of the causeway and the industrialization are described here, but an account of the effects of the oil spill is given later in this chapter.

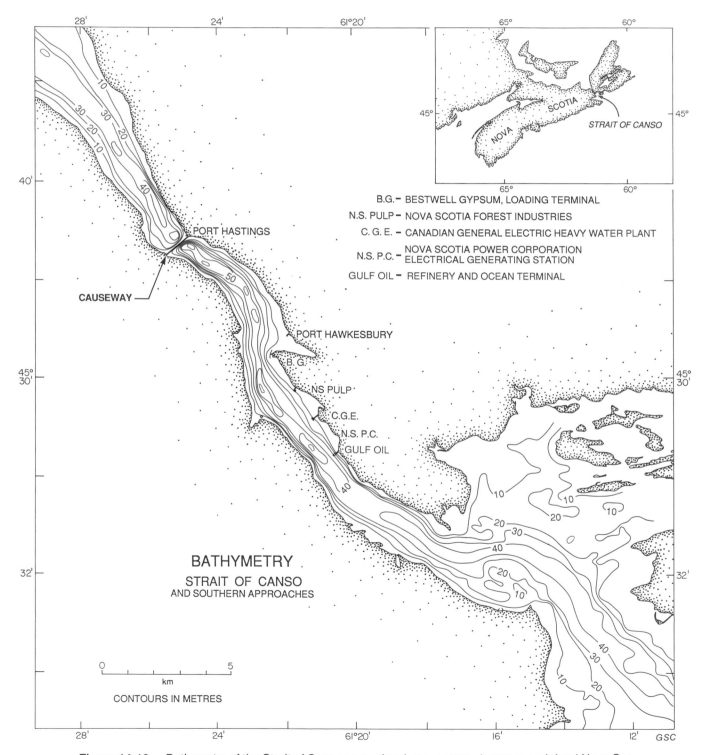

Figure 14.13. Bathymetry of the Strait of Canso area, showing causeway between mainland Nova Scotia and Cape Breton Island and sites of industrial plants (from Buckley et al., 1974).

The strait is a relatively narrow body of water, about 1.5 km wide throughout its length of 27 km. Prior to 1954, the gentle slope in the surface of mean sea level down to the Atlantic created a net outflow of water from the Gulf of St. Lawrence of 1.3×10^{11} m³/a, about one third of the daily discharge of the St. Lawrence River. Currents were fast, about 10 km per hour. The net southeasterly tidal current transported ice in the winter from the gulf through the strait into Chedabucto Bay. The causeway now prevents the discharge of water from the Gulf of St. Lawrence into the Atlantic through the strait, and dams winter ice in the gulf, so that the strait south of the causeway is virtually ice-free. The strong tidal currents have disappeared. The creation of the deep-water harbour led to the establishment of major industries such as: Bestwall Gypsum loading terminal; Nova Scotia Forest Industries pulp and paper plant; a heavy water plant, initially owned by Canadian General Electric; and the Gulf Oil refinery. The combined population of the towns along the strait increased from 2900 to 5700 between 1954 and 1974, and cargo tonnages in the strait increased by a factor of ten between

1967 and 1971. The impact of the causeway construction was investigated in 1973 (Buckley et al., 1974).

The causeway led to the circulation changing from one of vigorous exchange and mixing between the Atlantic and the Gulf of St. Lawrence to a system in which wind-driven circulation dominates in separated bays (Fig. 14.14). Each segment of the strait now has water-masses with distinctive characteristics during much of the year, and different sources and quantities of sediment. The strong tidal currents in the strait before the causeway was built had winnowed fine sediments from the bottom, leaving a lag of relict material. The quieter regime introduced by the causeway has allowed fine sediment to accumulate, at rates in the range of 1 to 2 mm/a. South of the causeway this sediment contains mixtures of urban and industrial wastes. North of the causeway the sediment comes from local sources — the sedimentary strata and glacial till exposed around the shorelines of St. Georges Bay and elsewhere, and from ice-rafting.

Waste material was observed in 1973 to come mainly from the pulp and paper plant on the eastern shore of the

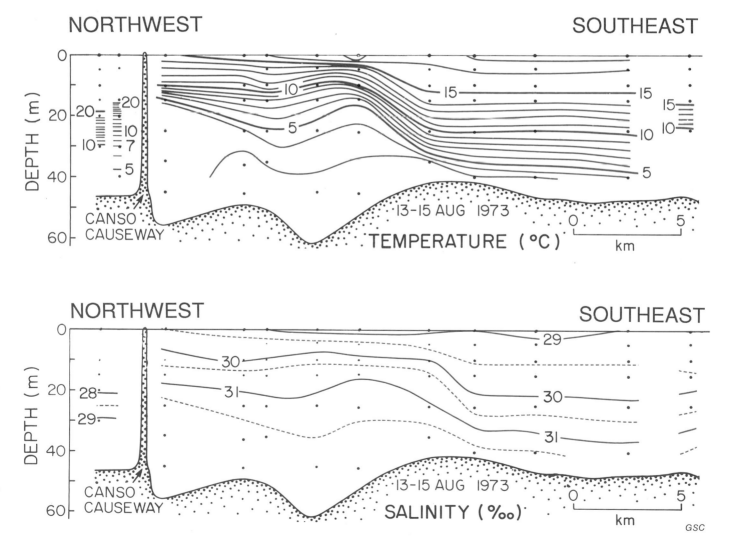

Figure 14.14. Axial profile of temperature and salinity in August 1973 in the Strait of Canso, illustrating distinctive water masses on either side of Canso Causeway (from Buckley et al., 1974).

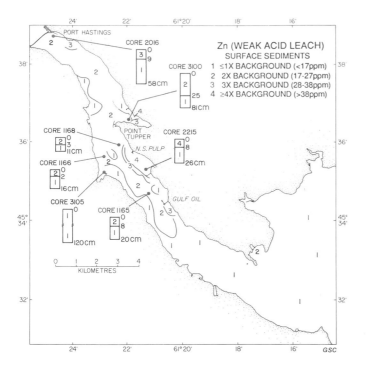

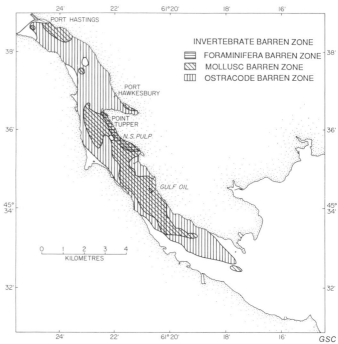

Figure 14.15. Distribution of leachable (weak acid) zinc in surface sediments in the Strait of Canso (from Buckley et al., 1974).

Figure 14.16. Invertebrate barren zones in surface sediments in the Strait of Canso (from Buckley et al., 1974).

strait near Point Tupper. This waste included organic-rich suspended solids and Mn, Fe, Zn and Ni which were dispersed through the surface waters of the strait and carried in the direction of the prevailing winds (Table 14.3). The suspended particulate matter in the waters on the south side of the causeway was as a result richer in organic matter than that on the north side. Significant quantities of these wastes, represented by their leachable zinc content (Fig. 14.15), were deposited in the bottom sediments nearby.

The biological response to the industrialization and to the discharge of wastes was shown by variations in ben-

thonic fauna such as foraminifers, molluscs and ostracodes in surficial sediment samples and in cores; corresponding changes in Zn were used as an indicator of the level of pollution. Molluscs were not found in polluted areas where they had once flourished. The foraminifers, although more tolerant of the increase in environmental stress than the molluscs, could not inhabit the seafloor close to the outfalls of the pulp and paper mill and the heavy water plant, and the diversity of foraminiferal species had decreased over a wide area. Ostracode species appear to have been most sensitive, and were not represented by living specimens in two thirds of the bottom sediments of the strait (Fig. 14.16) (Schafer et al., 1975).

Table 14.3. Representative water quality measurements in surface waters relative to distance from Nova Scotia Forest Industries outfall. Tabulated values denote the mean of a number of determinations.

Distance from Nova Scotia pulp outfall	Mn[a]	Fe[a]	Zn[a]	Ni[a]	POC[b]
0-0.5 km	28.0	3.9	3.13	0.65	5.9
0.5-1.0 km	18.9	1.5	1.03	0.60	3.1
1.0-3.0 km	15.4	1.3	0.81	0.53	3.0
3 km (background)	7.5	0.5	0.90	0.36	2.8

(a) Metal concentrations (µg/L) at natural pH of water.
(b) Particulate organic carbon (mg/L).

The Miramichi: shipping channel design and industrial pollution

C.F.M. Lewis and D.E.Buckley

The Miramichi in New Brunswick illustrates the fate of an estuary that has been long affected by waste products from traditional Maritime activities, the wood and mineral processing industries, and from municipal effluent. These effects came to light through research in the 1970s when questions were raised concerning the environmental impact on lobsters, oysters, salmon and other fishery resources in the Miramichi if dredging was carried out to deepen a shipping channel. The dredging operations were designed to minimize the deleterious effects on fisheries resources while satisfying the need for deeper-draft shipping. The design benefited from enhanced knowledge of estuarine dispersal processes and from an evaluation of contaminant loadings in estuarine sediments caused by the industrial and urban effluents. The sedimentary and geochemical aspects of the estuarine system that controlled or influenced pollution loadings, channel design or dredging operations are summarized here.

The Miramichi estuary in northeastern New Brunswick is a typical funnel-shaped drowned river mouth, separated from the open Gulf of St. Lawrence (Miramichi Bay) by a system of well developed sand barrier islands (Fig. 14.17). The Miramichi River consists of two branches which together drain 1.34×10^4 km^2 with a mean annual runoff of 9.67×10^9 m^3, close to one half of which occurs during the spring freshet. The land of the drainage basin is largely forested, with only minor areas cleared. Several wood processing plants (paper pulp and kraft board) near Newcastle and Chatham, New Brunswick, emit particulate and liquid effluents into the estuary.

The estuary is a recent geological feature, developed on eroded glacial sediments since the last marine transgression about 3.5-4.0 ka (Howells and McKay, 1977). Water depths increase from a maximum of 15 m in pools of the drowned river channel, through a smooth 5-m deep basinal area of Inner Bay (Fig. 14.17) to minimum depths (less than 2 m) over large flood-tidal delta systems landward of the barrier islands. These latter systems were formed by landward transport of littoral sand through inlets by tidal-current processes (Reinson, 1977).

Tides are mixed diurnal-semi-diurnal with an average range of about 1 m at the mouth of the bay. The Miramichi is a typical partially-mixed estuary, with a near-surface seaward drift of brackish water along its southern side and a landward counter drift of more saline water near the bottom on the northern side superimposed on oscillating tidal currents (Bousfield, 1955). The normal annual mean freshwater inflow of 305 m^3/s maintains slight to well mixed stratification in the Inner Bay and highly stratified conditions in the drowned river channel. In spring the monthly mean inflow may peak to six times the annual mean (Ambler, 1976), a condition that restricts penetration of the salt wedge to less than 10 km up the drowned river channel. During summer and winter months when freshwater inflow declines to 10% of the annual mean, the salinity intrusion may extend almost to the head of the tide, some 40 km up the river estuary. Wind mixing of water in the Inner Bay may be significant as salinity stratification increases noticeably under ice-covered conditions from November or December to April.

Five sedimentary environments were recognized and can be related to the physiography of the estuarine system

(Rashid and Reinson, 1979). The meandering drowned river channel contains muddy sediments along its axis, with sands on shoals and inside of meander bends. Muds predominate in central Inner Bay. Surrounding the muds are deposits of sandy mud and muddy sand, grading seaward into sands of the flood-tidal delta deposits.

The barrier island system responds sensitively to changes in sediment supply and morphology. Reinson (1977) showed from historical map evidence that dominant control of barrier development had shifted in historical times from longshore to tidal currents. Furthermore, the creation of an artificial channel inside the main inlet in the late nineteenth century had promoted the scouring of a new channel through an ebb-tidal delta shoal seaward of the barrier.

Pollution loading

The economy of the Miramichi has depended on forest-based industry for more than two centuries, first on sawn-wood then on wood-pulp production. About 18 200 tonnes of organic solids, comprising bark, wood fibre and biosolids, were discharged annually into the lower

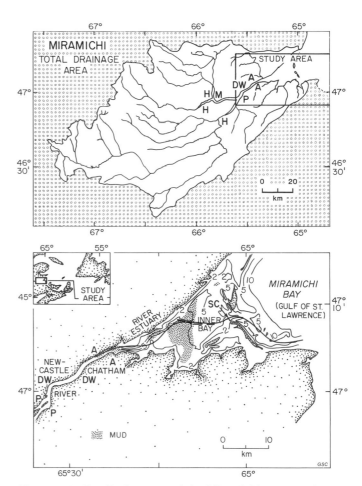

Figure 14.17. Bathymetry of the Miramichi estuary showing watershed area (top), head of tide (H), areas of mud bottom (red stipple), shipping channel (SC), and pollutant sources: M = mining activities, P = pulp and paper industries, DW = domestic waste inputs, A = agricultural areas (after Willey and Fitzgerald, 1980; Philpott, 1978; Vilks and Krauel, 1982).

Miramichi River (Langley, in Philpott, 1978). This discharge, in the same order of magnitude as the natural yield of suspended sediment from the Miramichi watershed, led to an estimated load of 240 290 tonnes (in 1976) of decomposing organic pulp-mill solids in the sediments of the estuary. Environmental concern centred on the possibility that proposed dredging of these deposits would cause dissolved oxygen depletion and release of toxic substances into the water.

Other organic loadings from municipal effluents in the Newcastle-Chatham area of New Brunswick, were considered relatively insignificant from a dredging standpoint as the sewage was treated and the influx was well diluted, being small relative to river flow. However, residual organohalogens, used initially for pesticide spraying (DDT) and wood preserving (PCP), were known in the Miramichi watershed and river. These persistent chemicals could cause mortality or reduced reproductive ability in fish and wildlife if redistributed into the water column from dredged sediment.

Base metal mining operations which extract zinc, lead, and copper were known to have discharged effluents with high loads of these metals into the northwest Miramichi river system prior to 1972 (Philpott, 1978). Mercury may have been discharged incidentally from pulp mills which used bleaching agents containing traces of the metal.

Findings
Several sediment-oriented studies contributed to evaluation of potential sedimentary pollution, improved understanding of estuarine processes, and assessment of the dredging potential and stability of the planned shipping channel. The studies comprised a comprehensive examination of the environmental marine geology of the Miramichi system including its geological setting, sedimentology, geochemistry, oceanography, and paleontology.

Seismic profiling, calibrated by borehole logging (Howells and McKay, 1977), measured the thickness and distribution of fine (mud) and coarse (sand) sediments over hard glacial materials or bedrock and confirmed that the proposed route for the shipping channel was dredgeable. Borehole samples confirmed the presence of wood fibres in the estuarine bottom sediments (Philpott, 1978). Elevated concentrations of Zn and organic carbon in the bottom sediments showed evidence of the advanced state of contamination in Miramichi Bay relative to other bays in Atlantic Canada (Table 14.4). As these high concentrations in surface sediments were substantially greater than background levels measured at depth (15 cm) in Miramichi cores, the trace metals indicated substantial loadings to the estuarine sediments in geologically recent time (Willey and Fitzgerald, 1980). These loadings occurred within the past 200 years as the upper 20 cm of sediment in Inner Bay contain pollen typical of European-type agriculture (Schafer et al., 1977).

Two associations of trace metals were recognized (Willey and Fitzgerald, 1980) in the fine sediment fraction, an inorganic association of total Mn, Pb, Zn, and Cu probably related to mining activities, and an organic carbon association of Fe, Zn and Cu in leachable form that probably originated in the pulp and paper effluent and in municipal sewage. Average metal concentrations were greatest in fine sediments of the river portion of the system (695 μg/g Mn, 282 μg/g Zn, 32 μg/g Cu and 200 μg/g Pb) and decreased seaward by 9-57% in fine sediments of Miramichi Inner Bay (Willey and Fitzgerald, 1980).

Table 14.4. Content of zinc and organic carbon in Miramichi bottom sediments and in other areas of Atlantic Canada (after Willey and Fitzgerald, 1980).

Area	Sediment	n	%OC	Zn(T)	Zn(W)	Reference
Miramichi, New Brunswick	Fine	41	3.4	202	60	Willey and Fitzgerald (1980)
	Coarse	46	6.6	105	22	
	All	46	5.0	153	41	
Placentia Bay, Newfoundland	Muds	12	4.7	78	7	Willey (1976)
	Sands	6	1.4	55	4	
	All	28	3.4	74	6	
Saguenay fiord, Quebec		13	3.31	130	14-29%*	Loring (1976)
St. Lawrence estuary		29	-	112	-	
Gulf of St. Lawrence		71	-	84	-	
Baie des Chaleurs, New Brunswick		24	1.52	97	22	Cranston et al. (1974b)
Canso, Nova Scotia		95	1.66	90	17	Cranston et al. (1974a)
LaHave, Nova Scotia		10	1.13	60	-	Cranston et al. (1975)

NOTES: n = number of samples analyzed; %OC = percentage organic carbon in the sediments; Zn(T) = total zinc in ppm; Zn(W) = weak acid leachable zinc in ppm, except for * which indicates percentage of total zinc that is leachable; - = no reported data.

The organic carbon distribution of the surficial sediments corresponds with the distribution of fine grained sediment, although anomalously high concentrations exist in the sediment coarse fraction, and higher concentrations in general occur in sediments of the drowned river channel than in sediments of the bay portion of the estuary. Coarse, lignin-rich organic matter is attributed to bark and other wood-processing debris. The high quantity of organics in all sediments, and differences in concentrations between river channel and bay sediments, are related directly to the discharge of pulp-mill effluent into the upper reaches of the estuary. The organic carbon isotopic composition ($^{12}C/^{13}C$ ratio) and the carbon-nitrogen ratio of sediments, both indicators of terrestrial organic matter, suggest that land-derived material is the predominant source of organics throughout the estuary (Fig. 14.18). Marine organic material is restricted to the sediments near the estuarine mouth (Rashid and Reinson, 1979).

Paleontological studies revealed further evidence of the natural variability of the estuarine sedimentary system on time scales of several years to decades within the period of contaminant buildup. Between 1965 and 1975 the areal distribution of surface sediment foraminifers became more complex, with the addition of two new assemblages (lower river and transitional assemblages) to the original river and open bay assemblages (Scott et al., 1977). A study

of down core sedimentary and paleontological variations, spanning the period 1860-1976 suggested that low-salinity foraminiferal species and coarse (winnowed) sediment zones are caused by episodes of high river discharge (Schafer and Smith, 1982). Variations in the estuarine tidal circulation induced by changes in barriers and tidal inlets are also a possible contributing factor to the observed variations down core. Thus there appears to be a progressive shift or oscillation in quality of the bottom sediments depending upon small climatic fluctuations and the interplay among the resulting physical influences, particularly the occurrence of high-discharge river events and shoaling or deepening of tidal channels that affect the estuarine bottom circulation regime.

The dynamics of the suspended particulate matter were shown to be a significant process for transporting, depositing and resuspending substances within the estuary. Kranck (1976, 1981) showed that high suspended particulate matter concentrations occur in a well-developed turbidity maximum in the central portion of the estuary (Fig. 14.19) where density stratification, two-layer flow and turbulence prevail. The suspended particulate matter consists of detrital mineral grains, plankton cells and 26 to 87% organic matter (% ash loss in Fig. 14.19), which in part is probably effluent from pulp and paper plants. Most of the suspended particles are so small that without flocculation they probably would be carried out of the estuary. Both flocculation and settling of the highly concentrated suspended sediment, and erosion of the soft unstable bottom indicated by the presence of coarse grains in the suspended particulate matter, are probably simultaneous and continuous processes. Thus the estuarine circulation is double acting; it induces deposition of both dissolved and particulate matter within the estuary itself while enhancing the resuspension and redistribution of material from the sediment surface.

A comprehensive oceanographic and geochemical transport study over two years related the variability in suspended particulate matter and dissolved trace metal loadings (Fe, Mn, Al, Zn, Cu, Pb, Cd) to different freshwater inflows, tidal stages and seasonal effects (Vilks and Krauel, 1982; Buckley and Winters, 1983). The oceanographic study showed that the tide is a prime agent in the Miramichi mixing process; the mean freshwater inflow is only 2% of the tidal prism of 300×10^6 m³. Application of a tidal prism flushing model revealed that the nominal residence time for a contaminant could range from 17 to 43 tide cycles for high (20 percentile) and low (80 percentile) values of freshwater discharge respectively. By analyzing the geochemical data in terms of the tidal flushing model for various stages of freshwater inflow, calculations were made of the annual residence and transport of labile (easily released) and particulate trace metals (Fig. 14.20a, b, c) through the Miramichi estuary.

Wide variations in concentrations of suspended particulate matter and labile metal by more than an order of magnitude are a function of freshwater input rates, tidal prism flushing characteristics, and geochemical interactions within the estuary. Although only 70% of the annual input of suspended particulate matter (86 500 tonnes) is exported from the estuarine system, more of the labile Fe, Mn, Zn and Cu is exported from the system than enters from the river. The source of excess Fe appears to be desorption from suspended particulate matter. The excess Mn, Zn, and Cu is calculated to be from a thin surface layer of bottom muds in both the river estuary and Inner Bay.

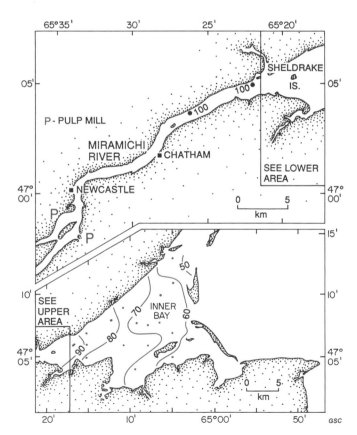

Figure 14.18. Percentage of land-derived (non-marine) organic carbon (based on isotopic composition) showing variation in samples containing more than 90% mud with distance from pulp mills (sample sites in upper diagram, contoured intervals in lower). After Rashid and Reinson (1979) and Philpott (1978).

765

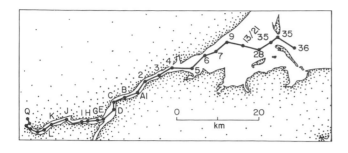

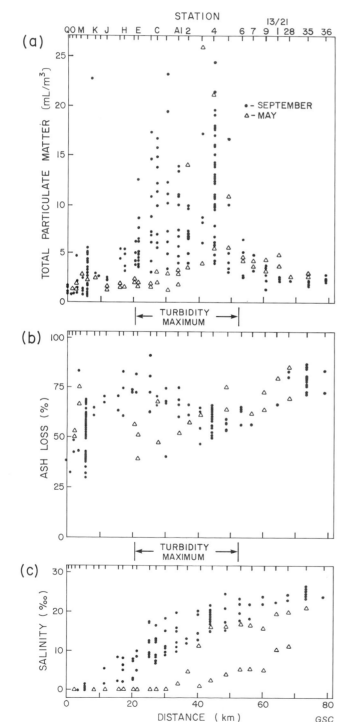

The annual export of labile Pb and Cd is less than the input from the river, and it was therefore concluded that the river estuarine muds are the principal sink for these metals.

During spring flood periods which last for an average of 39 days, about 85% of the annual supply of suspended particulate matter enters the river estuary from the Miramichi River. Also during this time, 30-55% of the annual supply of labile metals Fe, Mn, Zn and Cu enters the system. Much of this spring influx of suspended particulate matter and metal is temporarily stored in the river estuary, and is eventually flushed out of the estuary over the rest of the year. The wide variations in metal concentrations associated with the seasons and tide demonstrate that observations over an annual cycle are critical to properly assess the flux from an estuary or to establish the impact of pollution from a contaminated river or estuary such as the Miramichi. Dredging and construction operations at different times of the year could have greatly different effects depending on the seasonal state of estuarine processes.

Engineering studies associated with the Miramichi Channel Study (Landva, pers. comm., 1976; Willis in Philpott, 1978) showed that failure and creep of bank slopes were significant processes leading to infilling of dredged channels. Consequently the design channel side-slope was reduced to minimize the requirements for maintenance dredging. Physical tests and modelling of the erosion of Miramichi bottom mud under wave and current stress were inconclusive, as had been similar studies in evaluating cohesive sediment erosion elsewhere (Willis, 1977).

Constraints on the dredging design and effects of the dredging

Though the design for enlargement of the shipping channel was dictated by the need for navigability and safe operation of ships, major considerations were given to minimizing the adverse environmental impact (Philpott, 1978). Features of the environmental design included routing of channels to reduce dredging quantity, aligning channels more closely with the natural direction of flow to reduce bottom sediment resuspension, and minimizing increases in saline intrusion or in the level of turbidity in the estuary. Dredging was to be scheduled to reduce impact on the biological cycle of fish stocks in the estuary. Where dredging of highly polluted surface sediment was necessary, the dredge cuts were to be of sufficient thickness to reduce the average concentration of pollutants in the dredge spoil by inclusion of unpolluted subsurface sediment. Specific dredging equipment and techniques were recommended that minimized on-site disturbance and the dredge spoil dumps were localized to avoid fishery resources and to reduce sediment redistribution.

Figure 14.19. Variation of total suspended particulate matter concentration(a), organic fraction of particulate matter expressed as per cent ash loss(b), and salinity(c) along length of the Miramichi estuary showing the position of the turbidity maximum about 20 to 50 km downstream from the limit of salt water intrusion (after Kranck, 1976, 1981; Philpott, 1978).

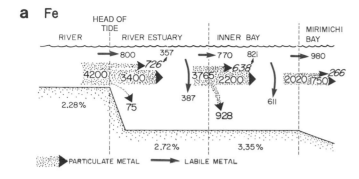

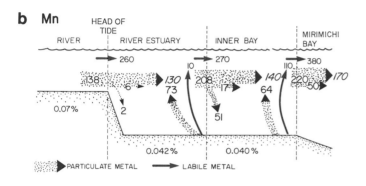

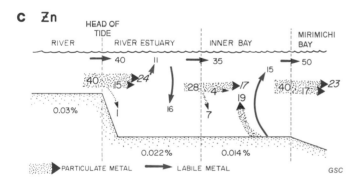

Figure 14.20. Schematic models of the transport and interaction of particulate and labile metals in the Miramichi estuary. Transports are in tonnes per year. Concentration of metals in fine grained bottom muds are shown as percentages. Slanted numbers represent tonnes per year of potential reactive metal (from Buckley and Winters, 1983).

In 1981, three dredges removed about 3.3 million cubic metres, and in 1982, one dredge removed an additional 1.3 million cubic metres of sediment from the 58 km long navigation channel in the Miramichi estuary. The channel depth was increased from 5 to 7.6 m. Approximately one half of the material was dumped in Inner Bay with the remainder divided between a river dump site and a dump site in Miramichi Bay. A monitoring study of water quality, sediments and biota from 1981 to 1984 (MacLaren Plansearch, 1985) revealed that, in spite of the foregoing precautions, some unanticipated dredging effects were

experienced. The tissues of clams, oysters and crabs throughout Inner Bay showed a 20-fold short-term increase in Cd content in 1982. This effect was related to an earlier 10-fold increase in river suspended particulate matter around the principal dredging operation of fall 1981, and to a widespread layer of floc on the sediment surface of Inner Bay in 1982. As the suspended particulate matter was Cd-bearing, this circumstantial evidence was interpreted to imply that overflow losses from the dredges (about 15% of the dredged volume) settled initially in the river but were subsequently transported throughout the whole of Inner Bay in the spring of 1982. These sediments were ultimately exported from the bay after about one year. The benthic biota were therefore contaminated with Cd in 1982, when this material settled to and resided on the floor of the bay. This experience is consistent with the earlier findings that metal concentrations vary widely and are a function of seasonal fluctuations and geochemical interactions within the estuary. However, such large concentrations of suspended particulate matter were not anticipated at the dredging sites, although some generation of suspended particulate matter was expected at the dumping sites.

The monitoring revealed that some dredge spoils were remobilized. Clean sand placed in a part of the river channel, thought to be naturally infilling, showed evidence of erosion (winnowing). In addition, high rates of post-dumping resedimentation, up to 20 cm/a, west of the dump site in Inner Bay, suggest winnowing of this dredge spoil under the influence of an estuarine bottom counter current. This latter sediment movement was not predicted from pre-dredging studies, possibly due to the difficulty in predicting seafloor scour under conditions of combined wave and current stress, but is consistent with the known circulation of the Miramichi estuary.

THE OPEN SEA

Introduction

A great variety of geological phenomena pose practical problems on the continental shelves and slopes and in the deep sea off eastern Canada and in the Canadian Arctic. They have traditionally influenced the fishing industry, defence, the shipping industry and waste disposal in shallow nearshore waters, and more recently have affected exploration for oil and gas. In the future, they are potential constraints to the development of tidal power, to the exploitation of oil and gas and offshore minerals, to the installations of pipelines, power and communication cables, causeways and tunnels, and possibly to the disposal of radioactive waste. The phenomena of interest include: mobile bed forms and current scour; earthquakes; stability of seabed materials under loads and on slopes; boulders and overpressure encountered during drilling; the degradation of gas hydrates and the venting of gas, both shallow and deep; and scour by icebergs. These can be divided into two types — those due to processes active now such as scour by icebergs, and those due to the geological history of the region, such as overpressure and the occurrence of boulder beds. In both cases, solutions to the problems they pose are aided by geological insight into their causes.

Of all the offshore regions, our understanding of the shelves and their constraints is most advanced, particularly for the Scotian Shelf where seabed activities associated with oil and gas exploration, fishing, defence

767

and oceanographic research have been concentrated. More than 20 years ago, L.H. King and colleagues started regional geological mapping of the shelf; this now provides a perspective for generalizing the likely response of the seabed to offshore developments (King, 1980; King and Fader, 1986). The framework, based largely on shelf morphology and sediment stratigraphy, has now been extended with variations throughout most of the continental margin of eastern Canada, as described in Chapter 10. The morphology of the seabed and sediment facies of units within this framework, conditioned by their geological history and the effects of modern processes such as seismicity, waves and currents, and iceberg scouring, appear to control the present physical properties and stability of the shelf seabed (see Chapters 10 and 11).

Few industrial developments now depend on the geology of the continental slope, rise or deep sea off eastern Canada. Only a few wells have been drilled off the shelves, and it may be some years before it is known whether oil or gas may be exploited from these regions. Nevertheless, the time required for the work of L.H. King and colleagues on the Scotian Shelf shows that it will take at least 10 years before our knowledge of the regional geology and of the present processes which operate on the slope and rise will be adequate to plan for exploitation. The principal geological problems for development will likely stem from the instability of sediments on slopes, triggered in some cases by earthquake shaking. Mobile bed forms whose activities are induced by the Western Boundary Undercurrent (WBU) (Carter and Schafer, 1983), for example, and deep sea "storms" (Hollister and McCave, 1984) may well be hazards, but little information is available for the Canadian margin. The technology for a detailed understanding of the slope and rise only became available in the 1980s, so that in 1986 it is possible to give only a sketch of their constraints.

A detailed understanding of the floor of the deep sea is even more remote, though communications cables have been laid and, locally, investigations have been made because of the potential of the deep sea for manganese nodule mining, and for disposal of radioactive and chemical wastes.

Since 1966, seabed use has been dominated by hydrocarbon exploration and by planning for production of oil and gas. The geological constraints for these activities are presented in the following sections, first those constraints that pertain mostly to drilling and, secondly, those that may affect structures on the seabed, mostly for production of hydrocarbons. The first of the following sections includes the influence of boulders, overpressure and gas hydrates. The second describes seabed stability under loads and subsequently outlines the effects of pockmarks and shallow gas, erosion and sedimentation, ice scour, seismicity and earthquake effects, and slope stability. Selected examples of case histories or experiences that illustrate the effects of these constraints are outlined with most topics and in the synthesis section on Earth Science and Decision Making. Geological constraints also influence major offshore developments, not fully discussed here, such as the planning and design of platforms and pipelines for Venture gas production on the Scotian shelf, a gravity base structure for Hibernia oil production on the Grand Banks of Newfoundland, potential tidal barrages for electricity production in the Bay of Fundy and a potential transportation link between Prince Edward Island and New Brunswick across Northumberland Strait.

Constraints for drilling

Boulder beds

N.J. McMillan

Subsurface boulders and cobbles of ice-rafted or glacial origin, have been an expensive impediment to drilling on the Labrador Shelf and on Banquereau, off Nova Scotia. A rig has first to "make hole" in which to set the surface casing, and in these areas boulders and cobbles have jammed the drill bit, causing the drill string to twist off; in some cases, boulders have caved into the hole while it was being reamed out, and have created difficulties for re-entering. No general solution had been found to the problems off Labrador, but on Banquereau the occurrence of boulders within channels associated with what may be a late-Wisconsinan glacial advance (see Chapter 10), offers hope for predicting areas where problems will be found.

Drilling problems associated with boulders occurred at the Leif P-38 wellsite; the first exploratory well drilled on the northeast part of Hamilton Bank on the Labrador Shelf in 1971 (Murray and McMillan, 1982). Boulders and cobbles were encountered when drilling a hole of large

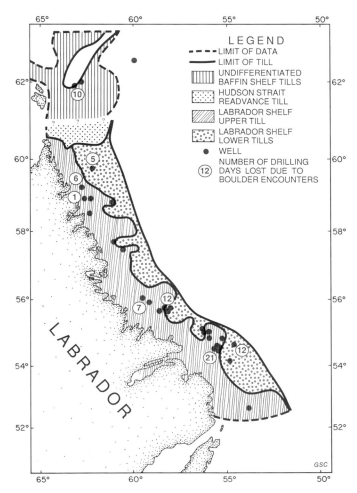

Figure 14.21. Well locations on Labrador and Southeast Baffin shelves (1971-1982) superimposed on a simplified map of surficial glacial geology (adapted from Josenhans et al., 1986 and Praeg et al., 1986). Drilling days lost due to boulder problems are from Murray and McMillan (1982).

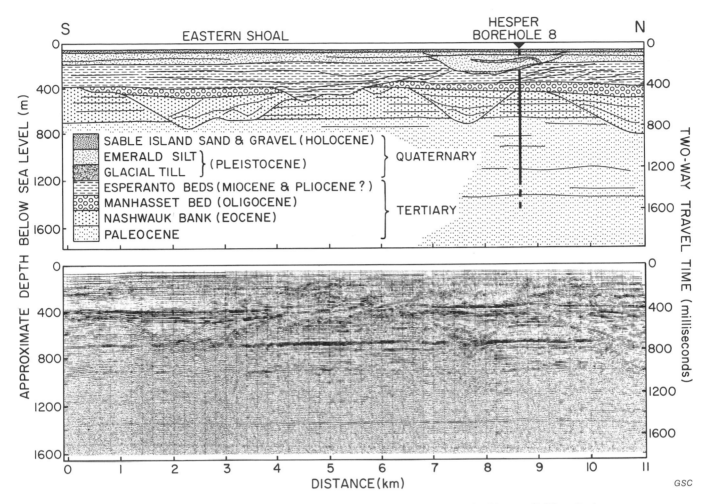

Figure 14.22. Seismic profile from Banquereau through borehole 8 in the Hesper P-52 well site area showing buried channel with boulders in glacial till (from Amos and Knoll, 1987). Well location shown in Figure 1 (in pocket).

diameter (914 mm) in which to set surface casing: these jammed the drill bit, the drill-string twisted off and the guide base lost its level. The drill ship "Typhoon" attempted to start the hole four times, and drilled through a boulder of 2.4 m diameter but eventually the site had to be abandoned, after 21 days had been lost. The well Leif E-38 (see Fig. 1, in pocket) was successfully drilled 900 m south of the first site, although boulders also caused problems at the new site. Dredging and observations from the submersible "Pisces" showed that the sea floor in the vicinity was strewn with boulders of granite, diorite and quartzite 25 to 50 cm in diameter, presumably glacially transported or ice-rafted.

This first experience became a general problem (Murray and McMillan, 1982). Between 1971 and 1982, drilling at 8 of the 29 wells drilled off the Southeast Baffin Shelf and on the Labrador Shelf was delayed because of boulders near the surface, and a total of 74 days was lost. At Hekja A-72 (locations of offshore wells are shown in Fig. 1, in pocket), boulders and strong currents caused the drillship "Ben Ocean Lancer" to abort 10 attempts at spudding before setting casing in 1979. There appears to be no general pattern in the geographic distribution or water depth

of the boulders and cobbles, in the thickness of boulder beds, or in the thickness of unlithified surficial sediments. Indeed, the occurrence of the boulders appears to be characteristically highly variable. However, some of the sites where drilling was hampered lie on the outer shelf in areas underlain only by older tills — unit 3a of Josenhans et al. (1986) (see Chapter 10, and Fig. 14.21). This suggests that the deposition of boulders may be associated primarily with a mid-Wisconsinan or earlier glaciation.

Drilling has been hampered on Banquereau, Scotian Shelf, in areas where boulders were found in buried channels. Drillstems stuck in the hole at Hesper I-52 (Fig. 1, in pocket); delays such as this cost many millions of dollars (C.L. Amos, pers. comm., 1986). Geological investigations there showed that the boulders were confined to the base of a channel associated with a late Wisconsinan glacial advance (see Chapter 10, and Amos and Knoll, 1987), and suggested that the development of sedimentary facies models will be useful in predicting the problems associated with boulders before drilling (Fig. 14.22).

The development of geological models is one tool which will help in circumventing these problems. Detection of individual boulders in the subsurface is not yet possible, although recognition of boulder-bearing till with seismic reflection systems offers some hope. Current developments in acoustic subbottom mapping (Guigne, 1986) may prove to be useful.

Overpressures

V.H. Noguera, J.A. Wade, K.D. McAlpine, and J.S. Bell

Abnormal pressures in the geological section may be above or below normal hydrostatic pressure and, under certain circumstances, they can make hydrocarbon exploration and exploitation hazardous. Pressures greater than hydrostatic are termed overpressures.

Overpressure describes a condition in which subsurface formation fluids, at a given depth, are at a pressure greater than that exerted by a column of water containing 80 000 ppm total dissolved solids, extending from that depth to the surface (Dickinson, 1953). By definition, the normal hydrostatic gradient of this fluid column is equal to 10.52 kPa/m. A formation pressure gradient greater than 10.52 kPa/m is considered abnormal and indicates an overpressured condition. Overpressures cannot be generated or maintained unless restrictions to fluid flow exist that separate the overpressured fluids from normally pressured fluids. Such flow-restricting beds include salt, anhydrite, shales and impermeable sandstones or carbonates. These rock units must have such low permeability that fluid equilibrium is temporarily or permanently retarded in terms of geological time, and predicting their occurrence and distribution is a major factor in locating overpressured zones. Various mechanisms have been proposed for generating overpressures including rapid burial, clay diagenesis, hydrocarbon generation, aquathermal pressuring, osmotic pressuring, and tectonic compression (Bradley, 1975).

Overpressures on Labrador Shelf to Grand Banks of Newfoundland

Overpressuring has been encountered in many of the major depositional regions of the eastern Canadian margin. On the Labrador Shelf, moderate overpressures were encountered locally below approximately 2500 m at the Indian Harbour M-52 well. Moderate overpressures were also encountered at the Pothurst P-19 well, also on the Labrador Shelf. The seal appears to be Tertiary shales and the generating mechanism may be rapid burial during the late Tertiary. Stronger overpressure gradients, 60% higher than normal hydrostatic values, were encountered below 3600 m at the Bonavista C-99 well on Northeast Newfoundland Shelf.

Overpressures have been encountered in several wells in the Jeanne d'Arc Basin on the Grand Banks of Newfoundland. The first eight discovery wells in this basin, including the giant Hibernia oil field, drilled into an overpressured section and three of these wells had to be suspended earlier than planned when formation pressures approached the tolerance limit of the blowout preventers. The overpressures occur mainly below a thick uppermost Jurassic impermeable shale. A pressure gradient of about 31 kPa/m within the overpressured zone is about three times greater than the hydrostatic gradient, on account of volume expansion caused by temperature increases and hydrocarbon generation. Undercompacted shales charac-

terize the overpressured section, implying that rapid burial with restricted dewatering of former muds was the primary generating mechanism. Additional documentation and details of the overpressures in the Jeanne d'Arc Basin area can be found in Chapter 6.

Scotian Shelf overpressures

For the Scotian Shelf, there is a difference of opinion on the cause of the extensive overpressured regimes, in which very high overpressures exist locally within extremely porous sandstones. Drummond (1986) attributed the cause of overpressure to compaction disequilibria and believed that the reservoirs in the Venture field were sealed at an early stage, thereby preserving higher than normal porosity and causing pore fluids to assume much of the overburden load. However, studies by Rodrigue and Meloche (1985) indicated that the overpressured sequences are normally compacted and suggest that overpressuring is a relatively recent phenomenon directly related to hydrocarbon generation. In addition, recent petrographic studies (Noguera, 1987) have revealed that the present porosity in the sandstones is largely secondary in origin, created by deep diagenetic leaching of carbonate cement. The last studies indicated that rapid burial or shale diagenesis is not the cause of the overpressure but suggested that the generating mechanism may be late gas generation into a closed system. Seals appear to be provided by a series of interbedded impermeable shale beds and tight sandstone and limestone units. The overpressures are encountered at depths between 2740 and 4500 m in some wells drilled downdip of the hinge zone in the Scotian Basin (Map 1706A, in pocket). The most studied area with abnormal pressures is the Venture field where gas pools are reservoired in overpressured Lower Cretaceous and Upper Jurassic sandstones.

Figure 14.23 shows a Reservoir Pressure versus Depth plot for five Venture field wells. A geostatic pressure gradient of 22.62 kPa/m and a normal hydrostatic gradient of 10.52 kPa/m define the upper and lower boundary for overpressures. From the onset of overpressures at about 4497 to 5710 m, the pressures increase in three distinct steps, clearly defining a Transition Zone, Low Pressure Gradient Zone and a Very High Pressure Zone. This overpressure is more than 1200 m thick and its base has not been yet encountered.

The Transition Zone (above 46 375 kPa) is interpreted as a zone of upward pore fluid flow as the overpressured fluids try to reach hydrostatic equilibrium by migrating into the overlying normally pressured sequence. This migration or 'leakage' must take place under restricted hydrodynamic conditions probably imposed by the presence of aquitards within and immediately overlying the Transition Zone. These aquitards act as imperfect seals which restrict upward pore fluid flow within the overpressured zone and away from it toward the normally pressured zone. Aquicludes (perfect seals) are not anticipated in the Venture area since this type of seal precludes any upward fluid movement and impedes the development of a transition zone.

In reality, the onset of Venture overpressures develops as a series of small pressure increments, as evidenced by studies by Mobil Oil Canada Ltd. (K.J. Drummond, pers. comm., 1984) and drilling mud weight data. Typically, the hydropressured section of Venture wells is drilled with mud weights in the range of 1078 and 1200 kg/m^3. At the

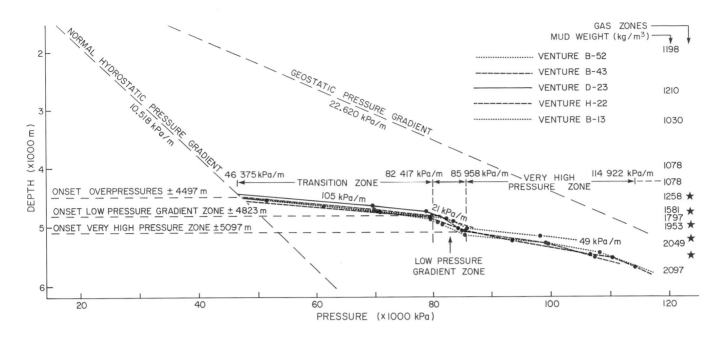

Figure 14.23. Plot of reservoir pressure (kPa) versus depth (m) for five wells in the Venture field, Scotian Shelf.

onset of overpressures, and across the Transition Zone, the mud weight is gradually increased from 1258 to 1581 kg/m³ (Fig. 14.23). These moderate increments in mud weight have proven to be effective in controlling the gently increasing pore fluid pressures within this interval.

The Low Pressure Gradient Zone, which has a gradient of 21 kPa/m, is interpreted as having interconnected permeable reservoirs. The fact that there is no pressure drop in this zone precludes the possibility of increased pore fluid leakage. The underlying Very High Pressure Zone represents an interval of 'hard overpressure' (Fertl, 1976) again characterized by the presence of aquitards as indicated by its steeper pressure gradient. This zone of 'hard overpressure' occurs within a shale-dominated portion of the lithological sequence. The highest pressures recorded in the Venture field are within this zone and consequently it is the zone that offers the greatest drilling risks. Pore pressures in this zone approach, but never quite reach, the upper limiting value imposed by the geostatic pressure (Fig. 14.23). At a depth of 5710 m in the Venture H-22 well, pressures reached 114 922 kPa, the maximum pressure recorded by 1986 in the Venture field. Mud weights of 2049 to 2097 kg/m³ were required to contain these hard overpressures.

Problems and prognosis

The overpressure system in the Scotian Basin has resulted in two blowouts. On 22 February 1984, as reported by COGLA (1984, 1985a), the Uniacke G-72 well, located 20 km north of the eastern end of Sable Island, and drilled with the semisubmersible rig Vinland, encountered abnormally pressured formations containing natural gas and condensate in zones below 5190 m. The lower part of the well had been flow tested and presumed plugged, and preparations to test higher zones containing fluid under normal pressure were under way when the well began to

flow. Several mechanical failures then occurred which led to loss of well control, and the immediate evacuation of the rig. The well was brought under control 10 days after the initial incident. The second well control problem occurred in September 1984, at the West Venture N-91 well (COGLA, 1985b). During preparations for testing, an influx of gas into the drillpipe forced the crew to abort the operation and to evacuate the Zapata Scotian jack-up rig. The subsequent buildup of extremely high pressures in the well burst the casing and allowed gas and salt water from deep formation fluids to flow into low pressure shallow formations. This 'subsurface' blowout was finally brought under control in June 1985.

At the present time there are no plans to attempt to produce gas from this Very High Pressure Zone, either at West Venture or in the Venture field itself. There is a real danger of mechanical failures in this zone, such as occurred in the West Venture N-91 well, which pose a significant constraint to the development of deep reservoirs with hard overpressures. Safe development of reservoirs within the Transition and Low Pressure Gradient zones is well within the capability of current technology, and such a project is in the planning stage with respect to the Venture and Thebaud fields. Exploitation of the fields may result in future lowering of the pressure in the Very High Pressure Zone and make it possible to eventually tap reservoirs within it.

Gas hydrates
A.S. Judge, I.G. Jones and C.F.M. Lewis

Gas hydrates are ice-like compounds of natural gas and water. These solid substances are stable at low temperatures (Fig. 14.24), but may dissociate with heat introduced during drilling or hydrocarbon production operations by circulation of relatively warm drilling fluids or hydrocarbons. Hydrate decomposition normally produces a substantial volume of gas and may result in serious pressure increase and mud gasification within the wellbore. Melting out of ice-like hydrate around the well may cause the casing to become unsupported, further contributing to the danger of loss of control of the well (Davidson et al., 1978; Goodman and Franklin, 1982; Marine Board, 1982).

Hydrate composition and stability

Gas hydrates consist of hydrogen-bonded networks of water molecules arranged in regular cubic lattices. The lattices contain voids that are large enough to host molecules of natural gas, unlike ordinary water ice which crystallizes in the hexagonal system with chambers too small for any molecules larger than hydrogen or helium. Hydrates are of different crystallographic types depending on the hosted gas. One structure, for example, contains small gas molecules such as methane or ethane, and a second contains larger molecules such as propane or isobutane. Methane hydrate is probably the commonest in nature. Massive hydrate has been recovered from holes of the Deep Sea Drilling Project in the Middle America Trench off the west coast of Guatamala and the Blake Bahama Plateau off the east coast of North America (Kvenvolden and Barnard, 1982; Kvenvolden and McDonald, 1983). Hydrate containing heavier hydrocarbons occurs in the Gulf of Mexico (Davidson et al., 1986). Such deposits may be common in association with oil seeps in seafloor sediments.

The stability of gas hydrate is highly non-linear as a function of temperature and pressure (Fig. 14.24); at low pressures it is highly dependent on temperature, at high pressures it is relatively more dependent on pressure. The stability relation is also dependent on the composition of the gas. For example, a hydrate of propane or isobutane is stable at much lower pressures than one of methane. Common components such as carbon dioxide or hydrogen sulphide raise the hydrate formation temperature, whereas the presence of dissolved salts, nitrogen or rare gases in formation water or natural gas depresses the temperature of hydrate formation (Fig. 14.24).

The most favourable sites for hydrates are areas with low subsurface temperatures such as arctic terrestrial sites with permafrost where annual temperatures are less than 0°C, and areas where low temperatures occur in conjunction with high pressures, such as the seabed in deep water (Judge, 1982). As bottom water temperatures are typically low, for example between 0 and −1.8°C, in arctic channels and on the northeastern Canadian continental shelf as far south as the Grand Banks of Newfoundland and, as deeper bottom water temperatures are at most +5°C (Collin and Dunbar, 1964; Grant, 1968; Worthington and Wright, 1970; Muench, 1971; Lemon and Fissel, 1982; Melling et al., 1984), seabed methane hydrates if present would be theoretically stable beneath most water depths greater than about 200 m (Fig. 14.24) in offshore arctic and northeastern Canada. In offshore southeastern Canada, south of the Northeast Newfoundland Shelf and especially on the upper Scotian Slope, where bottom water temperatures are warmer (Fuglister, 1960; Mann et al., 1965), the existence of stable conditions for gas hydrates are expected to be less common.

Increased temperature beneath the seafloor on account of earth heat flow and the geothermal gradient is the principal control for the subbottom depth of potential hydrate formation (Judge, 1982). Under the assumption of a geothermal gradient of 26 mK/m, for example, predictions suggest that methane hydrates may exist to 400 and 850 m subbottom, in 700 and 4000 m of water depth respectively (Taylor et al., 1979; Thurber Consultants Ltd., 1985). The actual occurrence of hydrate and its lower limit will vary depending upon the supply and composition of gas and water, the thermal conductivity and geothermal gradient of the geological section, and the availability of time for hydrate formation.

The base of hydrate zones is commonly recorded on seismic reflection profiles because the higher sound velocity of hydrates (Stoll et al., 1971; Stoll and Bryan, 1979) contributes to an acoustic impedance contrast with hydrate-free sediments below. The base reflection typically follows undulations of the seafloor and may crosscut reflections due to bedding surfaces or other features. Such bottom simulating reflectors have been described and attributed to gas hydrates off the east coast of the United States in water depths of 950 to 4000 m and to subbottom depths of 600 m (Tucholke et al., 1977; Dillon et al., 1983), and in similar environments off the western margin of Central America and elsewhere (Shipley et al., 1979).

Hydrate distribution in the Arctic and offshore eastern Canada

A preliminary investigation of industry seismic records suggests the presence of hydrate to subbottom depths up

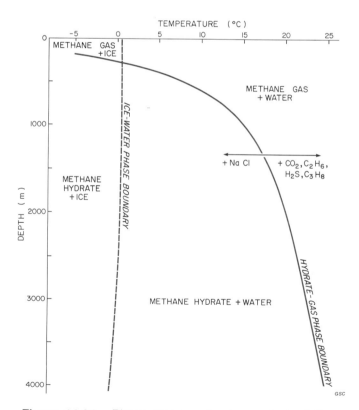

Figure 14.24. Phase diagram showing mutual relations between methane hydrate, ice, water, and methane gas (after Kvenvolden and Barnard, 1983). Arrows signify the direction in which the methane phase boundary shifts in the presence of the indicated components.

to about 500 m northwest of Flemish Cap, on the continental slope east of Northeast Newfoundland Shelf, on Makkovik Bank of the Labrador Shelf and in the Gjoa area of the southern Davis Strait (Fig. 14.25) (Thurber Consultants Ltd., 1985). However, neither bottom-simulating reflections nor hydrates were detected in sediments at deep water sites in Baffin Bay and Labrador Sea by the Ocean Drilling Program (ODP) although considerable free gas was encountered (Leg 105; S.R. Srivastava, pers. comm., 1987).

The bottom-simulating reflection may not uniquely characterize hydrate in Arctic permafrost areas, such as the continental shelf of the Beaufort Sea (Neave et al., 1978), as the sound velocity of water ice is close to that of hydrate (Whalley, 1980) and seismic anomalies due to permafrost and hydrate may be indistinguishable. However, offshore permafrost is not expected in the Arctic Island channels and the northeastern Canadian continental shelf, because the present seabed in these isostatically-emerging areas has never, or only locally, been exposed to

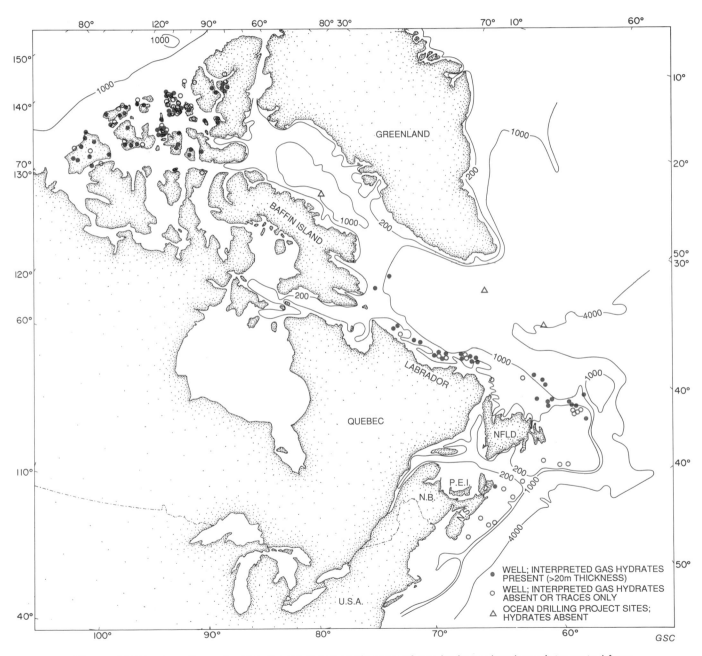

Figure 14.25. Locations at which the presence or absence of gas hydrates has been interpreted from petrophysical evidence in selected oil and gas well logs, and from selected industry seismic profiles (after Hardy Associates (1978) Ltd., 1984; Thurber Consultants Ltd., 1985). Gas hydrates are interpreted to be absent at Ocean Drilling Program (ODP) sites in Baffin Bay and Labrador Sea (S. Srivastava, pers. comm., 1987). Bathymetric contours in metres.

Late Quaternary cold arctic air temperatures (see Chapter 10).

The occurrence of gas hydrate in the Arctic Islands and offshore eastern Canada has also been interpreted, on the basis of petrophysical analysis of downhole electrical logs from 196 selected oil and gas exploration wells in the Sverdrup Basin, Davis Strait, Labrador Shelf, Grand Banks of Newfoundland and Scotian Shelf areas (Fig. 14.25). The controls on hydrate distribution and the associated petrophysical responses are different in the offshore and arctic terrestrial environments. In offshore permafrost areas, where the cold temperature is the most important factor, the main responses are: a low gamma ray reading indicating sand (most inferred hydrates were located in sand zones); cycle skipping on the sonic log (spuriously high velocities that result when thermal invasion and thawing cause borehole walls to wash out); some hole washout on the caliper log; non-correspondence of self-potential and gamma ray logs with tracking of gamma ray and sonic logs and inverse correlation of the caliper and sonic logs; peaks on the mud gas log; and little or no response on the resistivity, density of neutron logs.

In the offshore environment, where high pressure is more significant, the general petrophysical responses are: low gamma ray reading indicating sand (as for the onshore situation); non-correspondence of the self-potential and gamma ray logs; and peaks on the mud gas logs. Two modes of offshore hydrate occurrence have been interpreted, thin disseminated and massive. In thin disseminated hydrate intervals, there is slightly increased resistivity, higher sonic velocity and little response on the density or neutron logs. The petrophysical characteristics of thick massive hydrate intervals include: low resistivity; very low sonic velocity with cycle skipping if the hole is close to its normal drilling diameter; low density; high neutron porosity and a generally enlarged borehole diameter on the caliper log.

Gas hydrate was interpreted to be present with fair to good reliability in 93 out of 148 wells concentrated in the Sverdrup Basin of the Arctic Islands area (Fig. 14.25) (Hardy Associates (1978) Ltd., 1984). Hydrates appear to be widely distributed throughout the area but occur somewhat sporadically in the offshore. Hydrate-bearing intervals up to 160 m thick were interpreted with fair to good reliability up to 700 m below seabottom in water depths to 350 m. The thickest hydrate-bearing intervals (over 1000 m thick at 17 locations) occur at interior sites on islands in the eastern part of the Sverdrup Basin.

On the eastern Canadian continental margin, gas hydrate was interpreted on the basis of petrophysical response in 26 out of 48 wells examined (Fig. 14.25) (Thurber Consultants Ltd., 1985; Judge et al., 1986). However, if hydrates were present, drilling operations were apparently unaffected. Hydrates were inferred in 2 out of 3 Davis Strait wells, extending to 400 and 500 m subbottom in 350 and 970 m water depth. On the Labrador Shelf, hydrate is interpreted in 13 of 19 wells, beneath water depths of 118 to 550 m; the shallow occurrence suggests that relict hydrate may exist locally, related, possibly, to earlier conditions with lower temperature or greater water depth. Hydrate is interpreted to extend up to 550 m subbottom on this shelf. In Flemish Pass and on the Northeast Newfoundland Shelf including the adjacent continental slopes, relatively good quality picks were observed in 9 of 10 wells. The interpreted hydrate-bearing intervals, both massive and disseminated, extend from 530 to 1090 m subbottom, in 160 to 1486 m of water. No hydrate, however, was interpreted on the Grand Banks of Newfoundland in the four wells in the Jeanne d'Arc Basin, where the Hibernia oilfield is located. The petrophysical evidence suggests that hydrate indications are not widely distributed on the Scotian Shelf.

As hydrates may form close to the seafloor in water depths greater than about 200 m at $-1.8°C$, long term variations in bottom water temperature may influence their stability. For example, in the Beaufort Sea a warming trend is believed to have given rise to widespread shallow gas and to high pressure water pockets in the sediments (Weaver and Stewart, 1982). On the eastern Canadian continental margin, warmer waters in the early and mid-Holocene (Scott et al., 1984; see Chapter 10) may have degraded hydrate and released gas, possibly causing underconsolidated surficial sediments and pockmark formation. The late Holocene oceanic cooling off eastern Canada would favour the reformation of seafloor hydrates.

Hydrates as hazards

The presence of hydrates and evidence that they form lenses in sediment similar to water ice (Kvenvolden and McDonald, 1983) suggests the possibility of thaw-settlement problems with bottom-founded structures. Formation of hydrates in production well tubing and in seafloor pipelines may occur under appropriate temperature and pressure conditions and is a consideration in offshore development.

Problems may arise in drilling areas with hydrates because hydrates dissociate from the solid form when heated, releasing large volumes of natural gas. For example, a volume change of about 160-fold is expected when methane hydrate changes phase to gas at the same temperature and pressure. The heating may be caused by circulating drilling mud or by warm hydrocarbons produced from depth. This will lead to two sorts of difficulties: gas in the drilling mud may cause a kick in the well, and the formations around the well may be weakened, so that the casing may buckle (Davidson et al., 1978; Hood, 1980; Goodman and Franklin, 1982; Makogon et al., 1982). A good knowledge of the distribution and properties of hydrate zones is needed for the engineering design of production wells where massive hydrates or hydrate lenses exist. The casing strings may have to be insulated or be of high strength, or special methods may have to be used to bleed off gas produced from hydrates. Conversely, stresses in the well casing will need to be considered when production is curtailed and hydrates reform. Routine drilling procedures in arctic areas where hydrates are expected include: chilling the drilling mud, controlling the mud density closely, and monitoring the mud-gas content (Marine Board, 1982). The significance of hydrates as a constraint for offshore oil and gas production is not well known.

Constraints for offshore structures

Seabed stability under loads

J.D. Brown

Offshore activities are dominated by hydrocarbon exploration and production. These activities include drilling of wells, installation of production structures, and laying of pipelines. Whether these structures can be built and maintained safely and economically depends on the stability of the seabed and the magnitude of wind, wave and ice forces. This section deals with the seabed.

The geological and geotechnical questions raised by these activities are of two kinds: will natural processes cause slumping, erosion and other potentially hazardous events for reasons that are independent of the presence of the structure, and will the latter impose or induce loads and forces on the seabed that will cause instability through inadequate strength or excessive deformation? These broad questions are examined in the context of the types of structures and the typical settings in offshore eastern Canada in which they may be constructed.

Structures

Jack-up rigs. Jack-up rigs are mobile platforms (Fig. 14.26) for drilling wells offshore. They are supported by three or more legs which extend to the seafloor, with the working platform jacked-up on the legs so that it is entirely clear of the water. The so called "air gap" provides sufficient clearance to prevent storm waves from reaching the platform itself. The legs are fitted with bases known as spud cans, which rest directly on or below the seabed. In the course of installation, each of the legs is preloaded to exceed the anticipated maximum load during the well drilling period. The purpose of the preload is to test the foundation stability. In addition, the penetration induced by the preloading, combined in some cases with jetting, embeds the spud cans to depths where they will not be undermined by erosion.

The primary requirement of the foundation is that it should be strong enough to provide support. The most serious hazard associated with preload is "punch-through" (McClelland et al., 1982). If the bearing capacity of a surficial hard layer, for example a paleoweathered crust, is sufficient to allow the unit to elevate, but not sufficient to carry the preload, punch-through will occur as one or more spud cans penetrate the hard layer and plunges rapidly until adequate resistance is encountered at some lower level. Usually only one leg punches through, leaving the platform tilted and possibly in an unworkable condition. In addition, stability problems for a jack-up rig may be caused by scour if the seafloor materials are susceptible to erosion. Scour reduces the depth of leg burial, undermines the spud can, and causes reduced seafloor bearing capacity. Scour in excess of 3 m caused major problems for a jack-up rig operating off Sable Island in 1977 (Song et al., 1979). Differential settlement may occur in time where the seabed properties rapidly vary laterally, for example at the margin of an infilled channel. Other problems may arise if the spud can is lowered near depressions in the seafloor such as pockmarks or the footprint of a previously installed rig.

The influence of environmental forces on a jack-up rig affects the loads it imposes on the seabed, and hence its stability. During a storm, overturning moments caused by wave and wind forces may increase the vertical load on a footing by as much as 35 to 50 per cent of the gravity load. The horizontal footing load during a storm may range from about one tenth to one third the magnitude of the total vertical footing load with wave loads contributing 55 to 65 per cent, wind loads contributing 25 to 35 per cent, and forces generated by a 0.5 m/s current amounting to about 10 per

cent of lateral loading (Jacques Whitford and Associates Limited, 1984). These loads are in addition to the gravity load and must also be borne by the seabed.

Modest water depths, favourable environmental conditions, and economical operating conditions have led to the use of jack-up rigs for exploration drilling on banks of the Scotian Shelf. At most sites the seabed materials provide adequate bearing capacity, but erosion of the surficial sands has been a concern. In weak sediments, where the legs of jack-up rigs are deeply embedded, there may be pull-out problems when the rig is moved.

Pile-supported structures. The vast majority of pile-supported offshore structures are those which employ tubular steel substructures known as templates or jackets, which extend from the seafloor to above the waterline. The jackets are supported on steel-pipe piling driven through the jacket legs into the seabed. Hence the resistance to overturning and vertical and horizontal movement are provided by the interaction of the piles and seabed sediments.

The primary requirements of the foundation sediments are that they should be strong enough to provide support but not so strong that the piles cannot be driven. These conditions can be met at a broad range of sites around the world, notably the Gulf of Mexico where extensive areas are underlain by sediments which are too soft or too loose for a gravity base structure.

The eastern Canadian continental shelf contains many sites suitable for pile supported structures from a foundation standpoint, and one such jacket structure (Fig. 14.26) is proposed for the gas production development in the Venture field on the Scotian Shelf (Mobil Oil Canada Ltd., 1983).

Gravity base structures. A gravity base structure has a large foundation bearing area accompanied by a large mass, so that the resistance to overturning and uplift is provided by the mass of the structure, and the resistance to sliding is provided by frictional or adhesion forces mobilized along the base. It is generally founded directly on the seabed, although it may be founded on a mattress or on a berm. The gravity base structure in turn supports the facilities for drilling and production, often called the "topsides." The primary requirements of the foundation are that it should be smooth and firm. These conditions are met at many sites in the North Sea, where the gravity base structure was first used and where it has found its most widespread application. These conditions are also satisfied on many of the banks of the eastern Canadian continental shelf. A gravity base structure is proposed to support oil production facilities at the Hibernia field in the Jeanne d'Arc Basin on the northeastern margin of the Grand Banks of Newfoundland (Fig. 14.26).

Well-conductor casing. A well-conductor casing supports the wellhead assembly and any loads imposed by the marine riser, including the dynamic loads induced by waves and currents. The casing is thus a large pipe embedded in the seafloor (Fig. 14.26), which is subjected to vertical and horizontal loads, much like a pipe pile in its interaction with the surrounding sediments. The design problem is similar to that of the piles which support jacket structures. The lateral resistance of the seafloor sediment is significant to the design, and the effects of scour and disturbance during conductor installation are important.

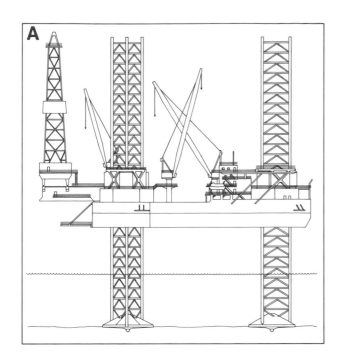

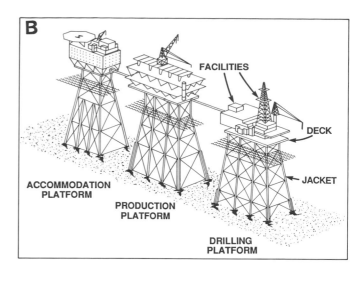

FACILITIES

DECK

JACKET

ACCOMMODATION
PLATFORM

PRODUCTION
PLATFORM

DRILLING
PLATFORM

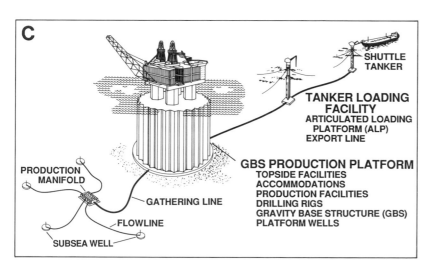

SHUTTLE
TANKER

**TANKER LOADING
FACILITY**
ARTICULATED LOADING
PLATFORM (ALP)
EXPORT LINE

GBS PRODUCTION PLATFORM
TOPSIDE FACILITIES
ACCOMMODATIONS
PRODUCTION FACILITIES
DRILLING RIGS
GRAVITY BASE STRUCTURE (GBS)
PLATFORM WELLS

PRODUCTION
MANIFOLD

GATHERING LINE

FLOWLINE

SUBSEA WELL

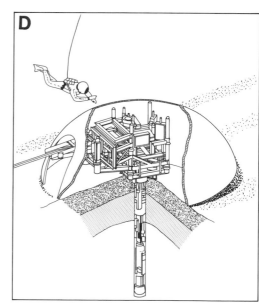

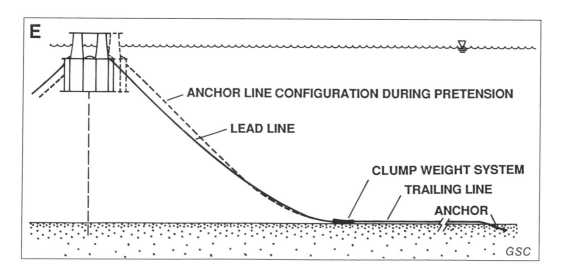

ANCHOR LINE CONFIGURATION DURING PRETENSION

LEAD LINE

CLUMP WEIGHT SYSTEM

TRAILING LINE

ANCHOR

GSC

Pipelines. Both the laying and stability of pipelines must be considered in any discussion of pipelines, since the type of equipment used for installation is at least as significant with respect to the geological and geotechnical setting as the pipeline itself (Palmer, 1980). Pipelines are laid on the seabed unless the hydrodynamic and ice environments or topography dictate burial. Factors related to pipeline installation and stability are discussed by LeTirant (1979) and Herbich (1981). Hazards related to iceberg scouring are discussed later in this chapter. Some of the considerations needed in pipeline routing and the similar problem of cable routing are discussed later in connection with the Hibernia development and the cable crossing of the Strait of Belle Isle.

The primary requirements of the founding sediments are that they provide stability under vertical and horizontal loading and are stable enough to support trenching machines (if used), but are not so dense or stiff that they cannot be trenched. The bottom topography should be gentle enough to accommodate the pipe curvature. Rock outcrops, boulders, shipwrecks and other debris, and mobile bedforms have to be known.

Anchoring systems. Catenary anchoring systems (Fig. 14.26) are generally used to moor floating drilling units. These consist of chain or wire rope, attached to the unit, and of sufficient length to remain tangent with the seafloor even under maximum line tension. The trailing section of this line is secured to the seabed, for example with a fluke or embedded anchor. Such anchors have to penetrate the seabed, and the strength of the surficial sediments is of primary importance. The holding capacity is predicted from empirical relationships among weight, anchor type, chain length, and sediment properties.

Evaluation of seabed stability. The general principles of design and analysis of seabed-founded structures are expressed in physical-mathematical models of limiting equilibrium, consolidation, and elasto-plastic deformation, all of which are employed to describe the stability of the seabed. The constituents of these models include some form of expression of geological features and processes and geotechnical parameters.

Figure 14.26. Sketches of exploration and proposed production structures for offshore eastern Canada. (A) Jack-up rig (from Fee and O'Dea, 1986, p. 212). (B) Pile-supported platforms (from Mobil Oil Ltd., 1983). (C) Gravity base structure (GBS) designed for the Hibernia field with satellite wells, gathering lines and export lines. The sharply corrugated outer caisson wall and internal reinforcement are unique features designed to permit the structure to withstand sea ice and iceberg forces (from Mobil Oil Ltd., 1986). (D) Well conductor casing in seabed, with cover over wellhead control assembly for protection from iceberg collision (artist's conception from Mobil Oil Ltd., 1985). (E) Anchoring system for floating rigs (adapted from Jacques, Whitford and Associates Ltd., 1984).

Geological features (Fig. 2, 3, in pocket) and processes known to affect the seabed stability of the eastern Canadian continental margin include the following: seabed topography and morphology; boulder beds and rock outcrops and lithology; stratigraphy — unit type, thickness and distribution, especially rapidly varying sequences of clay and sand; migrating bedforms; seismicity; major and recent faults; diapirs; slumps or marginally stable sediments; buried channels; depth and frequency of ice scours; shallow gas; gas hydrates; permafrost (possibly limited to western Arctic Island channels); and pockmarks.

The geotechnical and physical parameters that influence seabed stability include the following: sediment density, fabric and composition; pore fluid and gas chemistry; in situ stresses and stress history; drained and undrained shear strength; strength and structure anisotropy; permeability; compressibility; and cyclic load response.

The design of any major structure requires the site-specific identification, and in some cases measurement of, geological features and processses. It also requires that site-specific physical and geotechnical parameters be either measured directly or inferred from site evidence (Ardus, 1980; Matich and German, 1980). Some methods of measuring the geotechnical properties of sediments are mentioned in Chapter 1. For offshore eastern Canada, only two permanent production structures and two sites have been identified at this time (1986): the pile-supported jacket platforms for the Venture field east of Sable Island, and the gravity base structure for the Hibernia field on the Grand Banks. These are the only locations for which detailed investigations have been performed. Site investigations for the Hibernia gravity base structure are described by Long et al. (1986). Foundation behaviour studies are described by Thompson et al. (1986). For the remainder of offshore eastern Canada, general characterizations of sediment behaviour and hence seabed stability can be made on the basis of limited data only.

Geotechnical settings and seabed response to loading. The geological attributes (lithology, age, correlation, and history of development) of the seabed foundation sediments for the eastern Canadian offshore have already been described in Chapter 10 and the modern sedimentary processes which modify them at the seafloor have been described in Chapter 11. The areal distribution of the sediments, bedrock, and features, which constitute the foundation material, is shown in the Maps 1705A and 1711A and Figures 2 and 3 (in pocket). Limited geotechnical information is available, principally on the Scotian Shelf, the Grand Banks of Newfoundland and, to a lesser degree, the Labrador Shelf, other shelves, Arctic Island channels, and the deep sea. Though there are few direct measurements of geotechnical properties, it is possible to infer geotechnical descriptions, as given below. The response of the sediments to loads imposed by either structures or geological processes can be described in general terms. Pockmarks, current scour, seismicity, and slope stability, which may affect foundation response, are discussed elsewhere in this chapter.

Bedrock. In general, resistant crystalline rocks and indurated Paleozoic sediments mostly underlie the inner shelves, but may occur locally farther offshore (Chapters 2, 4, and 10). These rocks would appear to be sound foundation materials, as they are at onshore sites.

The Quaternary sediments of the central to outer shelf regions are underlain by Cretaceous and Tertiary rocks which are of particular significance because they are thick and occur near the seabed in some areas that are actively explored for hydrocarbons. Though commonly referred to as bedrock, these Cretaceous-Tertiary sediments are mostly unlithified and are recognized geotechnically as particulate materials. More resistant materials such as volcanic rocks are found locally on the Baffin shelves (MacLean et al., 1978, 1982). The Tertiary sediments are best known in the Hibernia region of Jeanne d'Arc Basin. There, Quaternary deposits form a thin veneer only a few metres in thickness (Fader and King, 1981), and the characteristics of the Tertiary strata are crucial to the foundation design of the gravity base structure proposed for the Hibernia production site. A typical stratigraphic section shows that sands, originally deposited in a late Tertiary delta (Lewis et al., 1987), dominate the upper 40-45 m of the seabed profile and are underlain by interbedded sands and clays to at least 130 m subbottom depth. The strength and consolidation characteristics of the clays indicate that these Tertiary beds have been overconsolidated by the equivalent of about 60 m of overburden. Cone penetrometer resistance data (Long et al., 1986) show that the upper 40 m of sand is denser, possibly as a result of desiccation and weathering under subaerial conditions (Segall et al., 1985, 1987).

The Tertiary sands and clays are expected to be stable under seismic shaking and other geological processes. Studies of the responses of these sediments to structure loads, which include ice and wave loadings transferred by the structure to its foundation, indicate that the Tertiary sediments at Hibernia provide excellent foundation sites (Thompson et al., 1986). Response to cyclic loading is the least understood of the geotechnical characteristics of these sediments.

Scotian Shelf Drift and equivalents. The Scotian Shelf Drift and its equivalents on other shelves (Table 14.5) are mixed-sediment glacial deposits which lie on pre-

Table 14.5. Geotechnical settings and Quaternary formations for the eastern Canadian Continental Shelf[1,2,3].

	Lithology and Engineering Characteristics	Gulf of Maine Bay of Fundy Scotian Shelf	Northumberland Strait
Sediments showing little or no influence of former ice sheets, but some influence of icebergs on northern shelves	Generally clean, free-draining, well-sorted fine sand to sandy gravel and gravel, commonly dense except in surface remobilized zone, or where deposited on slopes. May contain large boulders. Stable foundation material for all structures but susceptible to wave/current scour. Fine grained component on deeper Baffin shelves may result in properties and response similar to Sambro Sand.	Sand and Gravel (generally a veneer) 60 m	Buctouche Sand and Gravel (in water depths 60-80 m) 35 m
	Cohesive basinal mud of medium to high plasticity containing some sand and gravel due to ice-rafting, particularly in higher latitudes. Soft to firm consistency, normally consolidated and moderately sensitive. Likely susceptible to failure if on steep slopes. Possibly only suited to pile-supported structures.	LaHave Clay 70 m	Pugwash Mud 20 m
	Sand and gravel of variable gradation with substantial silt content. Inferred to be dilatant with short term cohesion and to have wide range of geotechnical properties, so that loading response cannot be generalized	Sambro Sand (generally a veneer) 120 m	Buctouche Sand and Gravel (in water depths 60-80 m) 10 m
Sediments strongly influenced by former ice sheets	Fine grained cohesive glaciomarine sediment with some coarse particles. Generally normally consolidated, and probably quasi-overconsolidated and stiff to hard where interbedded with till, or where previously subaerially exposed as on shallow banks off southeastern Canada. High sand and gravel content on Baffin shelves. Inferred to have widely variable geotechnical properties; loading response cannot be generalized.	Emerald Silt 140 m	Malagash Mud Henry Island Sediment 80 m
	Glacial drift with variable sand and gravel content, generally of low plasticity and permeability due to silt-clay matrix. Inferred to have a wide range of geotechnical properties, from overconsolidated till of high density and shear strength, which is likely to be sound foundation material for all structures, stable under seismic shaking, and resistant to erosion; to nearly normally consolidated sediment, softer and less dense, which although probably stable under seismic shaking, and resistant to erosion, may have limited bearing capacity and stability. Boulders may limit pile penetration.	Scotian Shelf Drift 100 m	Pamquet Drift 40 m

[1] For distribution of Quaternary formations and related information from which geotechnical settings are inferred, see Chapters 10 and 11, and Map 1711A and Figures 2 and 3, in pocket

[2] Engineering characteristics of sediments are interpreted from very limited geotechnical data, mostly from areas south of the Baffin shelves. Sediment stability is inferred and local variations are expected.

[3] Numerals indicate maximum thicknesses of formation

Quaternary bedrock in most areas of the continental shelf (Piper et al. in Chapter 10). In an engineering context, these glacial sediments correspond to tills which comprise sands, gravels, cobbles, and occasional boulders in a silt-clay matrix. Therefore they have the engineering characteristics of clays of low plasticity and permeability. In areas where the till was deposited beneath grounded ice, it probably preserves the high density and undrained shear strength characteristic of over-consolidated terrestrial tills. However, for recessional moraines, lift-off moraines, and till tongues interbedded with Emerald Silt and equivalent glaciomarine sediments elsewhere, this may not be the case, and softer, less dense till may occur in some areas.

Scotian Shelf Drift and its equivalents on other shelves range from over-consolidated basal moraines to nearly normally consolidated ice-deposited sediment. The over-consolidated moraines are expected to be stable under seismic shaking and other geological processes. They will likely provide stable foundations for all types of structures. Penetration of piles into boulder-rich drift could present constraints. Boulders in Labrador tills offshore have caused delays in spudding exploration wells. The normally consolidated drift is expected to be stable under seismic shaking, resistant to erosion, and generally not susceptible to instabilities due to other active geological processes. However, bearing capacity, settlement, stability and movements due to cyclic loading would generally require careful and perhaps extraordinary design methods.

Sable Island Sand and Gravel and equivalents. The Sable Island Sand and Gravel on the Scotian Shelf and its equivalent formations on other shelves (Table 14.5) are wave- and current-worked sands and gravels that occur generally on exposed bank tops and nearshore areas. In an engineering context, Sable Island Sand and Gravel is a clean, free-draining, well-sorted material ranging from uniform fine sand to uniform sandy gravel, generally in a dense state. The surface metre or so in mobile zones is less dense. The lag gravels included in this unit are in the gravel and cobble range. Where the sand has spilled over the banks onto the slopes, it is potentially very loose. Where reworking by currents has been less intense, such as on parts of the Baffin Shelf, the formations are less well-

Grand Banks of Newfoundland	Labrador Shelf	Southeast Baffin Shelf	Northeast Baffin Shelf	Age
Grand Banks Sand and Gravel (generally a veneer)	Not present	Resolution Island Lag	Cape Aston Sand and Gravel	Holocene
				to
20 m		0.5 m	5 m	
Placentia Clay	Makkaq Clay	Tiniktartuq Mud	Tiniktartuq Mud	latest
				Wisconsinan
30 m	30 m	10 m	10 m	
Adolphus Sand (generally a veneer)	Sioraq Sand (generally a veneer)	Not present	Not present	Late Wisconsinan
10 m	10 m			
Downing Silt	Qeovik Silt	Davis Strait Silt	Davis Strait Silt	Mid-Late Wisconsinan (locally earliest Holocene)
90 m	50 m	70 m	5 m	
Grand Banks Drift	Labrador Shelf Drift	Baffin Shelf Drift	Baffin Shelf Drift	Predominantly Wisconsinan (probably some older deposits in depressions and channels of Scotian Shelf and Grand Banks and on Northeast Newfoundland, Labrador and Baffin shelves)
60 m	300 m	300 m	50 m	

sorted, and may contain a fine component that gives some cohesion and an engineering significance similar to that of Sambro Sand.

The Sable Island Sand and Gravel and equivalent formations are expected to be stable under seismic shaking (Jacques/McClelland Geosciences Inc., 1982a, b), but are highly mobile at the seabed in high energy transport regimes. These sands and gravels can provide a stable foundation for all types of structures, but are susceptible to erosion due to increased water velocities associated with currents or waves interacting with a structure.

Sambro Sand, Emerald Silt and equivalents. Sambro Sand on the Scotian Shelf and its equivalent formations on other shelves (Table 14.5) are characterized by a fine grained component. They occur on the bank margins generally below 100 m water depth. In an engineering context, Sambro Sand is a granular sediment of variable gradation that generally contains a substantial silt content. It is inferred to have the drained strength characteristics of a granular material, but the silt content would decrease the permeability and would slow dissipation of excess pore water pressure; this, combined with dilatant behaviour, would give the material an apparent short-term cohesion. These sands are probably not heavily over-consolidated.

Emerald Silt on the Scotian Shelf and its equivalent formations on other shelves (Table 14.5) are fine grained glaciomarine sediments that are commonly found in basins and deep valleys, including saddles, troughs and fiords. In an engineering context, Emerald Silt and its equivalents are a fine grained cohesive material of medium plasticity, containing some coarse particles. Although banded in places with thin very fine sand beds, their engineering properties are probably not strongly affected by the banding. The strength characteristics of the silts depend heavily on their consolidation history and the effects of weathering. On the Scotian Shelf and Grand Banks this material may be partially over-consolidated above the 110 m isobath because of previous subaerial exposure. It is probably over-consolidated where it is interbedded with or underlies till. Because of its over-consolidation, it is probably of stiff to hard consistency. Elsewhere, below 110 m, it may be more normally consolidated. Organic contents in the range 1 to 2.5 per cent, combined with secondary consolidation, give the "normally consolidated" materials some intrinsic cohesion, and they may have soft to firm consistency near the surface.

Sambro Sand and equivalent muddy sands, as well as Emerald Silt and equivalent banded cohesive sediments, can have a wide range of geotechnical properties. Hence their response to loading cannot be generalized in useful terms.

LaHave Clay and equivalents. LaHave Clay on the Scotian Shelf and its equivalents (Table 14.5) are fine grained postglacial sediments that generally occur in basins and valleys, including saddles, troughs, and fiords, of the shelf and coastal zones, where they overlie previous sediments and form the present sea bed. In an engineering context, LaHave Clay and its equivalents are fine grained cohesive materials of medium to high plasticity, containing some coarse particles. The coarse fraction content is greater in northern regions due to the ice-rafted detritus. These sediments are the most recent deposits; this history suggests that they are mainly normally consolidated.

Organic contents of 2.5 to 5 per cent combined with secondary consolidation give the clays some intrinsic cohesion (Rashid and Brown 1975). Near-surface strengths are soft to firm. Sensitivity values, the ratios of undisturbed to remoulded strengths, for these materials are about 4.

LaHave Clay, its equivalent formations and the deep water clays are generally normally consolidated and soft. Seismically induced slope failures may take place on the steeper basin flanks (Jacques/McClelland Geosciences Inc., 1982b). These deposits also occur in areas where pockmarks have been mapped; these features must be regarded as hazards to any construction. The low strength of these sediments makes it unlikely they would be selected for gravity base structures. Pile-supported structures in soft sediments of similar nature have been successfully constructed in the Gulf of Mexico where such deposits are many hundreds of metres thick. Where the soft clays are less than 50 m thick, piles would likely be driven through them to more competent underlying strata.

Slope and deep sea sediments. Geotechnical information for sediments from deeper sites is extremely sparse. Graham and Nixon (1980) described soft, sensitive silty clays, of low to medium plasticity and water contents considerably in excess of the liquid limit, at three sites in Davis Strait in waters 800 to 1000 m deep. Morin and Dawe (1986) investigated piston cores from water depths of 2600 to 3300 m in the Labrador Sea. They described soft silt and clay of low to high plasticity and normal-consolidation below a zone of apparent over-consolidation attributed to cementation. These materials are unlike those found on the shelf areas. A relatively simple load history is suggested by their properties and by their location in deep water. Similar properties are known for the surface sediments of the continental slope and rise off northeast Newfoundland (Schafer and Asprey, 1982), the slope south of St. Pierre Bank (Marsters, 1986), and the Scotian Slope (Mosher, 1987).

Fine grained, impermeable, plastic deep sea sediments are needed for the potential disposal of high level radioactive wastes at sites in the abyssal plains (D.E. Buckley, pers. comm., 1986). The sediments, which are expected to yield under the weight of dropped waste cannisters and to seal radionuclides from the ocean environment, must be homogenous over large areas and stable for at least several hundreds of thousands of years. Although evaluation in 1986 is incomplete, the principal problems identified so far in the Sohm and Nares abyssal plains are potential instabilities related to compaction faults, sandy turbidite sequences and discontinuity of Quaternary sediments in seamount areas (Wang et al., 1982; Auffret et al., 1984; Buckley and Grant, 1985; Vilks et al., 1985).

As discussed in Chapter 10, most sediments on the slope are normally consolidated and stable at high angles of repose; slope failures due to earthquakes are the most likely cause of sediment instability. Loose sediment on the slope may occur as coarse material in transit down submarine canyons that breach the shelf break, or as material in sediment drifts forming under the influence of the Western Boundary Undercurrent. Reservoirs of glacial sand and silt, subject to liquefaction, as occurred off the Laurentian Channel during the Grand Banks earthquake 1929, may have accumulated opposite transverse shelf saddles and on the upper slope below the lower limits of till in water depths of 500-700 m.

Pockmarks and shallow gas

H.W. Josenhans

Damage to structures mounted on the seafloor may arise from the sudden release of gas, which may cause the foundation to collapse (Sieck, 1973; Newton et al., 1980). Shallow gas in near-surface sediments is a constraint for drilling too, as unwanted pressures may be encountered in the wellbore before the conductor casing and blow-out prevention systems are installed. Fluids, which vent at the seafloor, produce two major types of features: pockmarks or conical depressions; and mudlumps or mounds on the seafloor. They form by the expulsion of interstitial water and by locally produced biogenic gas (Nelson et al., 1979); they also form by the dissociation of gas hydrates and by the venting of petrogenic gas, as they are commonly associated with regions where hydrocarbons are known to occur at depth. Indeed, these features have been used as an exploration guide for hydrocarbons (Hovland, 1981). Features similar to mudlumps have been reported from the Southeast Baffin Shelf (Woodworth-Lynas, 1983a) and south of Newfoundland (G.B. Fader, pers. comm., 1986). Mudlumps are not generally common on the shelves off eastern Canada, but may be present on the continental slope (Piper and Sparkes, 1987).

The conical depressions in the seafloor known as "pockmarks" (King and MacLean, 1970) occur in water depths ranging from less than 100 m to more than 4000 m (Nelson et al., 1979; Flood, 1981). Off eastern Canada they have diameters between 1 and 300 m, and depths of up to 15 m (Josenhans et al., 1978; King, 1980). They generally occur in muddy to sandy muddy sediments. Pockmarks are formed by the venting of gas or liquid which entrains sediment at the vent and carries it into suspension (Fig. 14.27). Local slumping within the pockmark enhances their growth and as a result of the action of currents pockmarks can be elongate, the long axis parallel to the direction of the local current. Pockmarks do not have raised rims. The depths of pockmarks are related to their widths and to the angle of repose of the sediment in which they are formed. Thick clays contain wide and deep pockmarks whereas silty and sandy mud sediments have small, more numerous pockmarks. Pockmarks on the Scotian Shelf cover up to one fifth of the basin areas, and as a result a significant amount of material has been eroded (Fig. 14.28). An association with iceberg scours suggests that some pockmarks may be induced by expulsion of interstitial fluids in response to scouring. They are a potential hazard to bottom-founded structures on account of their size and shape and the problems they may pose to foundation design. Little is known about the frequency, magnitude, or pathways of fluid migration through the sediments. Active venting could erode the foundations of structures, and if significant quantities of gas were released could cause fire hazards and possibly affect the buoyancy of floating structures nearby. However, there are differences of opinion on whether gas release affects the stability of floating bodies (W. Bobby, pers. comm., 1987). It is commonly thought that interstitial gas alters the geotechnical properties of sediments and its presence makes these properties difficult to establish (Esrig and Kirby, 1977).

Pockmarks have been found off eastern Canada (see Fig. 2, in pocket) on the Scotian Shelf in water depths of 500 to 1100 m, in the Laurentian Channel in water depths up to 420 m, in the area of Haddock Channel and Placentia Bay, on the slope off St. Pierre Bank in water depths up to 1200 m, and in the Hopedale Saddle of the Labrador Shelf in water depths up to 500 m (MacLean and King, 1971; Josenhans et al., 1978; Fader et al., 1982; Hutchins et al., 1985; Fader and Miller, 1986).

Interstitial gas within surficial sediments can be recognized on high resolution seismic profiles by its effects on reflectivity (Fig. 14.29). The gas increases the acoustic impedance resulting in reflections which appear either anomalously diffuse or sharp. The effect is often so strong

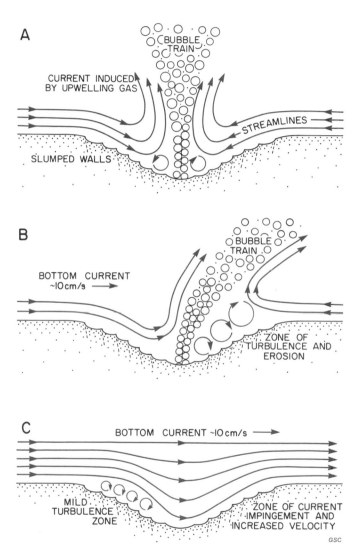

Figure 14.27. (A) Proposed mechanism for pockmark formation by gas venting from the seafloor. Streamlines indicate direction of current flow induced by rising bubbles. Slumping of sediment towards the orifice and the removal of sediment by gas-generated currents results in development of a seafloor depression. (B) Same mechanism as in (A) with the added effect of residual and tidal bottom currents. Deflection of the bubble train and its associated currents could cause turbulence and erosion of the downstream wall of the depression, thereby elongating the pockmark. (C) Elongation of inactive pockmarks by bottom currents (from Josenhans et al., 1978).

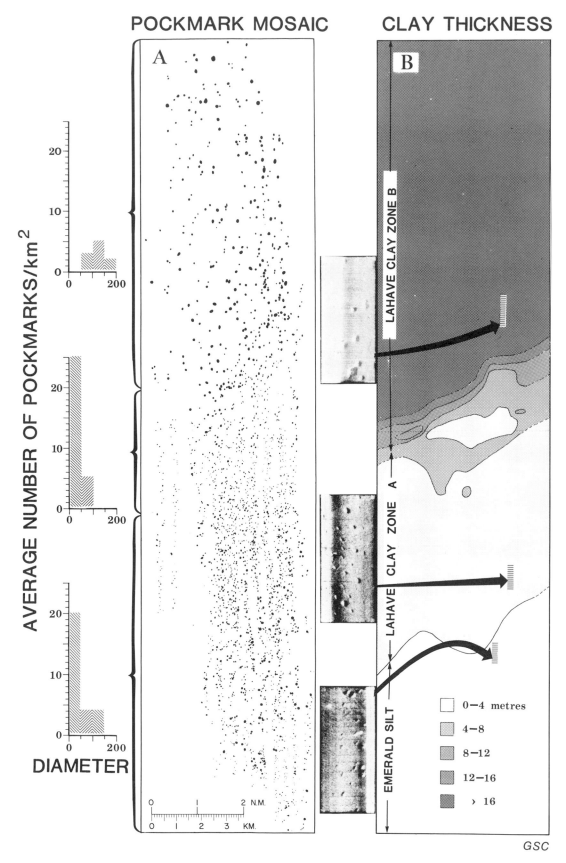

Figure 14.28. Seafloor mosaic (A) from Emerald Basin on the Scotian Shelf showing the incidence of pockmarks on the basin floor and the correlation of their density and size with clay thickness (B) (from Josenhans et al., 1978).

(a)

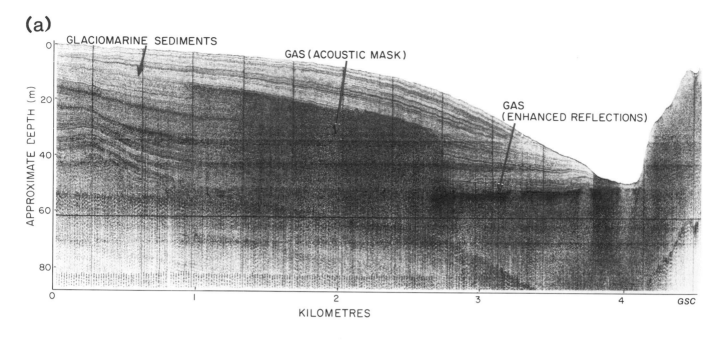

(b)

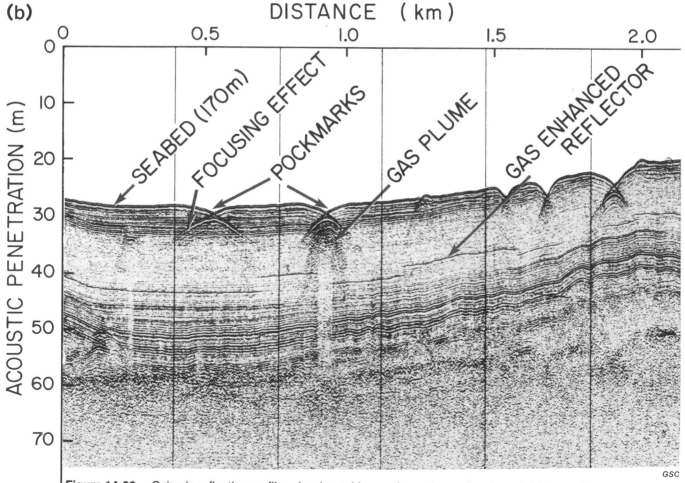

Figure 14.29. Seismic reflection profiles showing evidence of gas-charged sediment. (a) Acoustic mask and enhanced reflections in glaciomarine sediments of Downing Basin, Grand Banks of Newfoundland (from Fader and Miller, 1986). (b) Pockmark with gas plume and enhanced reflector in glaciomarine sediments of northwestern Karlsefni Trough on the northern Labrador Shelf.

that acoustic penetration into sediments beneath the gas is prevented, and the gas appears then to act as a "mask" (Keen and Piper, 1976; Howells and McKay, 1977; Fader and Miller, 1986).

Erosion and sedimentation
J.V. Barrie

Sediment transport is the transfer of sediment grains on the seabed primarily by natural hydrodynamic forces, though it can also result from or be aided by seismic shaking, gravitational stress and bioturbation. Erosion occurs when more sediment leaves an area than enters, and sedimentation results under the reverse conditions. Where an ample supply of mobilized sediment is available for transport through an area, seabed depressions tend to infill and sedimentary bedforms may migrate. Wave action or seismic shaking can cause sediment pore pressure buildup that in extreme cases may lead to seabed liquefaction (loss of shear strength). Four processes — scour, infill, bedform migration, and liquefaction — are forms of seabed instability that require attention in the design and maintenance of facilities such as gravity base production structures, structures supported by piles, pipelines, glory holes (seabed excavations to set wellheads below the influence of scouring ice keels), shipping channels and dump sites.

When an obstruction is put in the way of an equilibrium sedimentary transport system, the hydrodynamics and sediment conditions alter to accommodate the obstruction, usually by increasing the velocity and turbulence of the flow, a condition that may lead to scouring of the seabed. The scour process continues until a new equilibrium is achieved. Scour around a gravity structure tends to undermine the foundation edge, allowing the structure to rock under extreme waves, currents or ice pressures. Repeated rocking may induce pumping, pore pressure buildup and sediment flowage under the foundation leading to unwanted settlement or tilt. An extreme case of rocking erosion was observed at the Christchurch Bay Tower, North Sea, in 8.4 m of water. In the absence of skirts, storm waves and currents undermined the base; this caused free-rocking motion and left the structure with a 4-degree tilt (Dahlberg, 1982).

Erosion around piles and structures diminishes their contact area with the supporting seabed and reduces their resistance to lateral forces arising from waves, currents, winds or ice pressures. For example, scour up to 6 m around piles is reported (van Dijk, 1980) from the Leman Field, North Sea, in 35 m of water, up to 4 m of seabed erosion have been detected in 20 m of water, around the legs of jack-up rigs used off Sable Island on the Scotian Shelf (C.L. Amos, pers. comm., 1986) and up to 2 m of scour occurred around the base of the Frigg TP-1 gravity structure in North Sea (Dahlberg, 1982). If unanticipated, scour could lead to excessive movement and damage of the structure. Erosion and migration of bed forms around pipelines can lead to undermining and spanning causing buckling and fatigue problems, particularly if the vibration caused by current forces coincides with the natural frequency of vibration of the span (Dahlberg, 1982). For example, Philpott Consulting Limited (1986) described scour and spanning of pipe in the Ekofisk-Emden pipeline, North Sea, and in the Bay of Fundy.

Sediment infill or siltation is a direct result of changes in the velocity of near-bed flows and can be induced by marine structures, particularly in the nearshore and estuarine environments. In addition to the well-known problems of siltation of shipping channels and tidal barrages, offshore excavations such as glory holes (Rochelle and Simpson, 1981) are examples of seabed depressions that need to be maintained free of siltation. Migratory bedforms may bury and load seabed installations, particularly pipelines. The larger flow-transverse bedforms such as megaripples and sand waves (discussed in Chapter 11) are important in this regard.

Pore pressure build-up and liquefaction of sediments by wave action or seismic shaking is poorly understood and the available evidence is somewhat circumstantial (Herbich et al., 1984). Seed and Rahman (1977) have proposed an analytical model for estimating the magnitude of residual porewater pressures and the liquefaction potential of seafloor sands under wave loading. Strachan (1984) proposed a method for detecting liquefaction using acoustics, particularly shear waves. Tank model studies of liquefaction are difficult, as the model waves are too small to produce the required stress distribution within the sediments. Porewater pressure measurements made in the field with piezometers are very few (Herbich et al., 1984). Processes of gravity mass transport resulting from liquefaction are described in Chapters 10 and 11; the resulting instabilities are discussed later as a constraint in this chapter. All four processes — scour, infill, bedform migration loading and liquefaction — may occur in vigorous hydrodynamic environments such as the coastal zone and continental shelf.

Considerable uncertainty exists on the explanation of scour formation and the prediction of scour depth, particularly under the combined influence of waves and currents as was shown earlier by the difficulty in estimating the stability of dump sites for dredge spoil in the Miramichi estuary. As a further example, Philpott Consulting Limited (1986) noted that current is the significant agent of scour, and Clark and Novak (1984) have shown from flume studies that the rate of scour formation increases when waves are superimposed on currents. Due to the non-linear dependence of transport on flow velocity, numeric models to predict these phenomena can only estimate first-order values (Weare, 1982), and physical models are difficult to use due to scaling problems of sediment size and bottom roughness, two key parameters. This is particularly true for regions where sediment transport processes are intermittent and of high intensity, such as the storm-dominated Scotian Shelf (Hodgins et al., 1986) and the wave-dominated Grand Banks of Newfoundland. As seabed developments proliferate in sand-rich offshore areas, the need for remedial measures for the sediment transport problem will intensify.

Methods presently used to mitigate scour around structures are varied and consist of techniques such as 1) burial, 2) armouring or backfilling with non-erodible coarse material, 3) filtering or the placement of a permeable layer to reduce current velocity and turbulent flow near the seabed, 4) structural aprons or skirts that prevent bottom flows from penetrating beneath the base of a structure, 5) underpinning to support and anchor pipelines to the seabed, and 6) sacrificial beaches around island structures where there is a lack of suitable armour material (Herbich et al., 1984; Philpott Consulting Limited, 1986). In most cases, measures for counteracting current scour, infill and liquefaction are successful, resulting therefore in few industrial studies of sediment transport and the practice of conservative design which may be more costly (Philpott Consulting Limited, 1986). Little research has been undertaken to evaluate the benefits of shaping or positioning structures to use the natural environment as an aid, such as natural burial of pipelines and infilling of pipeline trenches by bed-load transport. For offshore eastern Canada, evaluation of erosion and sedimentation requires long term monitoring programs to obtain measurements of infrequent, high intensity wave and current events.

Ice scour
C.F.M. Lewis and C.M.T. Woodworth-Lynas

Icebergs calved from glaciers in Greenland and eastern Canadian Arctic are carried south by currents along the coasts of Baffin Island and Labrador to the Grand Banks of Newfoundland and sometimes beyond (Fig. 14.30). Ice islands and sea-ice floes drift from the Arctic Ocean into channels of the Canadian Arctic Archipelago. Ice floes commonly contain pressure-ridges which extend below the bases of the floes as keels. The keels of both icebergs and sea-ice ridges may strike and drag on the seafloor, leaving scour marks in the sediment. Ice scouring reworks and alters properties of the seabed (Silva et al., 1985) and may damage structures and installations such as cables, pipelines and wellheads. This was recognized in the Beaufort Sea as a hazard to development in 1970, where ice scour is due to sea ice and ice islands; and later off eastern Canada, where scour is due to icebergs (see e.g. Shearer, 1971; Pelletier and Shearer, 1972; Harris, 1974; Harris and Jollymore, 1974). Scour by icebergs is emphasized in this section, but the methods of evaluation of the risk of ice scour are in many cases applicable to scour by sea ice as well.

Icebergs

An inventory of up to about 40 000 icebergs is maintained in Baffin Bay by production principally from fast-flowing tidewater glaciers north of Disko Island, western Greenland and in Melville Bugt (Dinsmore, 1972). Some have a mass of as great as 25-30 million tonnes. The currents along the Baffin and Labrador shelves carry many of these southward over the eastern Canadian margin. The average annual flux decreases to the south: about 3000 icebergs pass Hudson Strait, 1000 pass the Strait of Belle Isle and about 400 survive to drift south of 48°N onto the Grand Banks of Newfoundland (Ebbesmeyer et al., 1980). The annual flux is variable; as an example the numbers on the Grand Banks have ranged from zero to over 2000. These differences have been attributed to fluctuations in the calving rates of source glaciers and in the transport from source regions (Dinsmore, 1972; Walsh et al., 1986). Icebergs deteriorate rapidly under the influence of waves and warm surface waters, particularly when sea ice is absent, and so become progressively less stable in southern waters. A typical iceberg 50 m high rolls frequently and survives less than 2 weeks in the North Atlantic Drift south of the Grand Banks (Murray, 1969; Dinsmore, 1972; White et al., 1980). The southward flow of icebergs is seasonal, with greater numbers in the spring and early summer.

Icebergs have a wide range of sizes. Their drafts can be estimated from the water depths in which they ground and from underwater observations (Dinsmore, 1972; Danish Hydraulics Institute, 1979; El-Tahan and El-Tahan, 1982; Hotzel and Miller, 1983; Mobil Oil Canada, 1985). The larger drafts are commonly in the range of 100 to 200 m, but damage has been caused to instruments on the seafloor at a depth of 427 m in Baffin Bay, suggesting that drafts may be very large indeed (Milne, 1969). Icebergs can be tracked by the use of beacons transmitting to satellites, and also by radar. The trajectories show that groundings are numerous (Woodworth-Lynas et al., 1985) (Fig. 14.30), and that large icebergs may spend a substantial part, up to 47%, of their life span aground (Robe, 1980, 1982).

Iceberg scour marks

Markings due to ice scour have been observed on sidescan sonograms and high resolution seismic profiles (Fig. 14.31), from submersibles and by SCUBA divers (Fig. 14.32). They may be curved or linear furrows with parallel ridges or berms at their sides, or appear as elliptical or circular pits. The morphology depends on the force exerted on the seafloor by the ice, dependent itself on factors such as winds, currents and the shape of the iceberg, and by the shape of the keel impinging on the seafloor (Fig. 14.32) (Hodgson et al., 1988). Icebergs which are moving forward and dragging on the bottom create furrows with side berms. An iceberg which is moving forward but is also oscillating vertically produces a chain of craters (Bass and Woodworth-Lynas, 1986). An iceberg which wallows at rest creates a circular or elliptical crater or pit with an encircling berm. Pits may also be formed by bergs which split and increase their draft while rolling (Fig. 14.33, and this process is probably most common when the icebergs are least stable, as they will be during the summer periods of deterioration and at the geographical extremities of iceberg drift (Fig. 14.30) (Barrie et al., 1986; Clark et al., 1986; Hodgson et al., 1988).

The morphology of iceberg scours is affected by the nature of the seafloor. Stiff clays have scour marks which are relatively deep, up to 6 m or more, and which have steep side slopes, up to 60 degrees. Bouldery tills have marks which are shallower, less than 4 m typically, and which have side berms of only modest slopes, less than 15 degrees. The side berms in bouldery tills may consist largely of linear concentrations of boulders from which fine material has been winnowed out. Scours developed in areas of over-consolidated sediments or in pebbly sands generally have low relief, less than 1 m, and the shallowest side slopes, less than 6 degrees (Lewis et al., 1982; Barrie, 1983).

Iceberg scours are abundant on the seafloor if the flux of icebergs with drafts coincident with water depths is high, and if the sediment on the seafloor is cohesive and capable of preserving and accumulating ice scours. As a result, the density of scours is greatest on the northern shelves, where in places the seafloor is completely scoured. By contrast, towards the limit of iceberg travel in the south, modern and Holocene ice scours rarely cover more than 5% of the seabed, as for example on the Grand Banks (d'Apollonia and Lewis, 1981).

Scour marks, once formed, are subject to degradation and modification. Burrowing organisms loosen compacted cohesive sediment and currents winnow fine grained sediment from exposed berms, so that scours may be filled in.

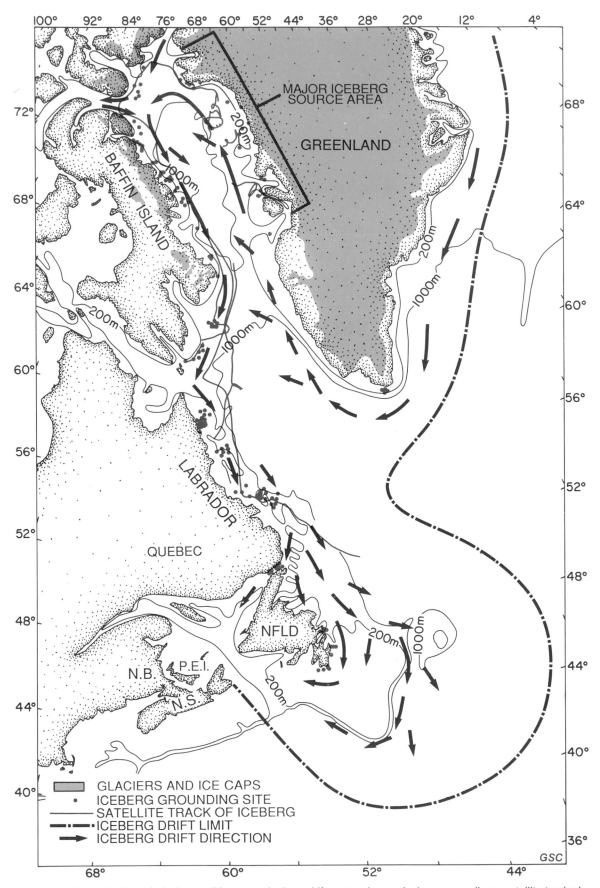

Figure 14.30. Position of glaciers and ice caps, iceberg drift routes, known iceberg groundings, satellite-tracked iceberg trajectories with groundings, and extreme limits of iceberg occurrences (99 percentile). Adapted with additions from Robe (1980, 1982), Markham (1980, 1981), Woodworth-Lynas et al. (1985), El-Tahan et al. (1985), and Gosson (1985).

Currents may cause bedforms to migrate within the scour troughs. New scours may overprint old ones.

The dimensions of iceberg scours have been estimated from the data of sounding, seismic and side-scan records (d'Apollonia and Lewis, 1981; King and Gillespie, 1986)

(Fig. 14.34). For the continental shelf from the Grand Banks of Newfoundland to northern Baffin Island the mean maximum scour depths for 2 km-long sample areas are 1.0, 1.8, and 1.9 m for water depths less than 100, 100-200, and greater than 200 m, respectively. Scour

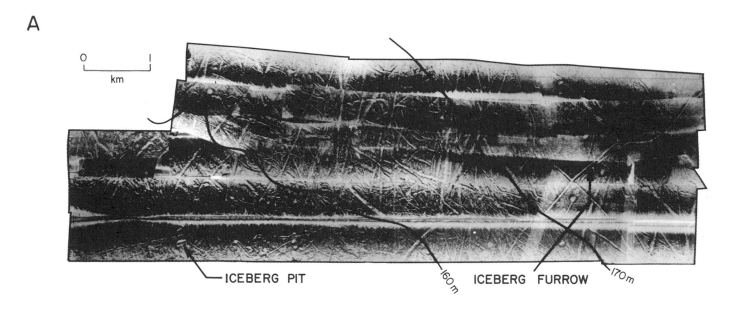

A

ICEBERG PIT 160 m ICEBERG FURROW 170 m

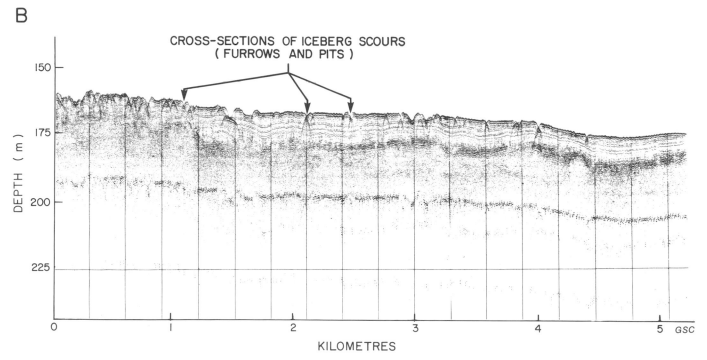

B

CROSS-SECTIONS OF ICEBERG SCOURS
(FURROWS AND PITS)

Figure 14.31. A mosaic of 70 kHz sidescan sonograms(a) and Huntec DTS high resolution seismic profile(b) showing iceberg scours on the seafloor. There is a higher density of ice scours in shallower water, above 170 m, reflecting more frequent scouring by icebergs of lesser draft. The sonogram mosaic is located on the western flank of Karlsefni Trough, on the northern part of the Labrador Shelf. The Huntec seismic profile runs approximately through the centre of the mosaic.

lengths are not well known, because they are usually greater than the width of the sidescan swath used to identify them, commonly 0.4 to 1.5 km, but partial lengths up to about 10 km long have been observed on some individual sonograms or mosaics of sonograms (King 1976; Fader and King 1981; Woodworth-Lynas et al., 1986). Scour trajectories up to 220 km long have been interpreted from radar observations of icebergs themselves (Woodworth-Lynas et al., 1985). Icebergs appear to scour across slopes (Ruffman 1985; Woodworth-Lynas et al., 1985; Todd, 1984; 1986; Woodworth-Lynas et al., 1986). Furrows have been tracked across seabed relief of up to 15 m, and icebergs interpreted to be scouring on the basis of radar observations have crossed relief of up to 45 m. They do this, presumably, by tilting and rotating. The directional trends of iceberg scours reflect the average drift of icebergs, and so reflect the direction of the currents driving them (Fig. 14.30) (Todd, 1984; 1986), although wind and presumably sea-ice influence the trajectories of icebergs as well (Smith and Banke, 1983).

Relict iceberg scours

Scours are recognized as relict if they are superimposed by a modern scour pattern of different orientation or dimensions, and if they are found in areas where icebergs are no longer found, or in areas where modern icebergs no longer

touch the bottom, on account of increase in water depth or decrease in size of icebergs. Relict scours have been found beyond the present limits of common iceberg occurrence in the Laurentian Channel and on the western Grand Banks, on the Scotian Shelf, in the Bay of Fundy and in Hudson Bay (King, 1976, 1980; Whittaker et al., 1985). They have been found in deeper waters off the Baffin and Labrador shelves in water depths up to 750 m, in the Flemish Pass, on the slope off the Grand Banks of Newfoundland up to 650 m, and on the slope off the Nova Scotian slope in depths up to 600 m (Monahan and Macnab, 1975; Hutchins et al., 1985; Pereira et al., 1985; Praeg et al., 1986, 1987). The deepest scours known are relict: furrows 20 and 9 m deep are known from glacial sediments in the Laurentian Channel and the Avalon Channel (d'Apollonia and Lewis 1981; Fader et al., 1982).

The age of relict scours is unknown. Their occurrence beyond the range of present icebergs and their superposition on glacial sediments suggests that they date from periods of breakup of Late Pleistocene ice shelves and marine ice sheets. Relict scour marks are generally absent from the postglacial surfaces of the banks of the Scotian Shelf and the Grand Banks of Newfoundland above about 100 m, presumably on account of erosion during the Late Wisconsinan and Holocene transgression. Few parts of the shelves north of about 48°N were probably ever exposed

Figure 14.32. Underwater photograph of the keel of a small grounded ice island (iceberg) at rest after scouring the seabed adjacent to western Byam Martin Island, central Arctic archipelago (from McLaren, 1982). The berm of displaced sediment beside the ice keel is approximately 80 cm high (arrow).

subaerially during the Pleistocene, and so these shelves were not eroded during the Late Wisconsinan and Holocene transgression, and relict scours may have remained where modern scouring now occurs.

Relict scours obviously do not have the same significance in terms of risk to structures on the seafloor from icebergs as do modern scours. They are nevertheless a potential problem to development on account of roughness which they impart to the seafloor — pipelines will buckle if free spans are too great, for example, and special foundation design may be required for gravity base structures to achieve adequate resistance to horizontal sliding as a result of wave and ice forces (Bea, 1986; Lien, 1986).

Estimating the probability of iceberg impacts

Icebergs scouring the seafloor have damaged communication cables, and the potential for damage has influenced the designs of other seabed facilities. Twenty-five incidents of cable damage from icebergs have been recorded for the Newfoundland, Baffin and southwest Greenland shelves (Fig. 14.30), with more than 90% of these in water depths between 59 and 240 m (Gustajtis, 1979; El-Tahan et al., 1985). The threat of ice scouring has constrained the design of power cable crossings in the Strait of Belle Isle. In the central part of the Arctic Archipelago, tunnels beneath the shore zone out to a water depth of 50 m have been proposed

to protect future gas pipelines from ice scouring (Palmer, 1985). In the Sverdrup Basin the shore crossing of an offshore gas flowline has been protected by burial and artificial freezing of the enclosing sediment as a feasibility study (Palmer et al., 1979; Van Ieperen, 1985).

The design of structures associated with future gas and oil developments offshore is influenced by estimates of potential damage from collisions with ice keels. The evaluation of this risk requires probabilistic estimates of the expected scouring frequency and the distribution of scour depths caused by collisions of ice with the seabed. The effects of transient loading and deformation within sediment beneath the scouring ice keels must also influence buried structures. Methods under development or proposed for estimating the frequency and depth distribution of scouring by sea ice and icebergs are listed in Table 14.6.

Many methods use geological principles in the interpretation of the record from the seabed of past ice scouring to derive frequency-depth relationships. However, most methods suffer from a lack of accurate test information and from a lack of knowledge of the processes which lead to the formation and degradation of ice-scour markings. As an example, present (1986) estimates of scour frequency on the Grand Banks at Hibernia vary by more than two orders of magnitude, from 0.0001 to 0.6 groundings per 100 square kilometres per year (Lewis and Parrott, 1987).

Figure 14.33. Photographs of a spliting 7-million tonne tabular iceberg, 60 m high, on the Labrador Shelf. One part rolled and increased its draught grounding in 137 m water depth. Some pits on the seabed are attributed to catastrophic events like this one (photographs courtesy of D. Diemand C-CORE from Hodgson et al., 1988).

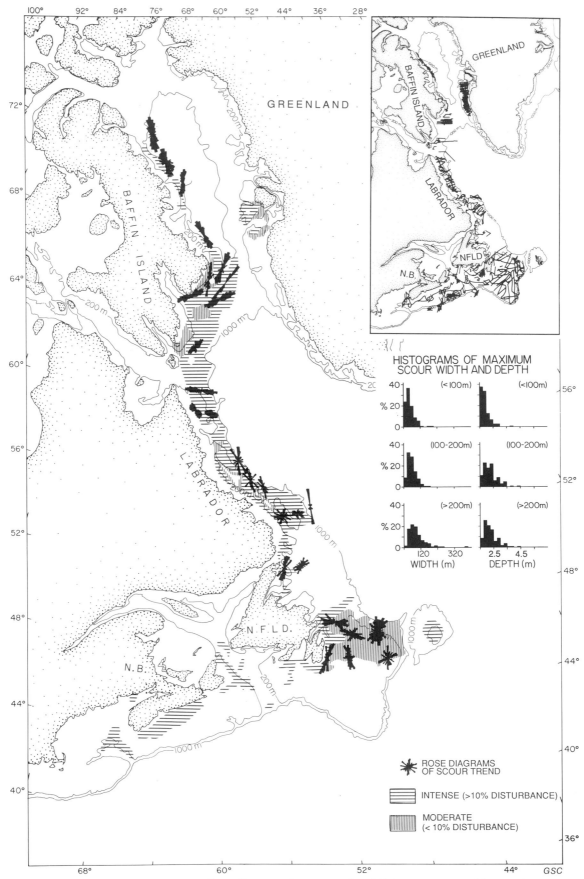

Figure 14.34. Distribution of iceberg scours. Rose diagrams of scour trend and histograms summarizing maximum scour depths and widths in 2 km long sample areas are shown for the continental margin from northern Baffin Island to the northern Grand Banks of Newfoundland for water depths of <100 m, 100-200 m and >200 m. Abstracted from ice scour data bases prepared by d'Apollonia and Lewis (1981), Todd (1984), King and Gillespie (1986), Harris (1974), Harris and Jollymore (1974), King (1976), Lewis et al. (1977, 1980), Brett and Zarudzki (1979), Gustajtis (1979), Barrie (1980), Fader and King (1981), and Lewis and Barrie (1981). Survey lines analyzed for ice scour are shown in the inset map.

Table 14.6. Methods for estimating scour frequency and/or scour penetration depths.

Method	Principle	Application	References
1. Repetitive ice scour mapping	By comparing repetitive maps and profiles of the sea bed, newly formed scours are identified, measured and counted. Return rates are computed for scours of various depths.	Applicable where scours remain identifiable over the mapping period (1 to 10 ± years), i.e. where scouring rates are high relative to scour degradation rates. Generally regarded as a verifying method for other estimates of scour depth and frequency. Widely applied for sea-ice scouring problem in Beaufort Sea.	Hnatiuk and Brown, 1977 Hnatiuk and Wright, 1983 Reimnitz et al., 1977 Barnes et al., 1978 Lewis, 1978 Weeks et al., 1986 Woodworth-Lynas and Barrie, 1985 Lewis and Parrott, 1987
2. Inferred iceberg groundings	Through observation of their trajectory speeds, icebergs are inferred to ground when they are at rest for more than a tidal cycle. Grounding frequency is computed from the number of grounded icebergs as a fraction of observed iceberg flux over the observing period.	Applied to icebergs carried by Baffin and Labrador Currents whose trajectories were monitored by (1) satellite-tracked beacons and (2) offshore drilling and onshore radars.	Robe, 1980, 1982 El-Tahan et al., 1985 Woodworth-Lynas et al., 1985
3. Ice keel draught and flux	From a known annual flux and distribution of the draughts of either sea-ice or iceberg keels, the annual frequency of ice-seabed contacts can be computed for areas of known bathymetry.	Keel depth information for sea ice is obtained from upward beamed seabed or submarine sonars, or is inferred from ridge height distributions.	Pilkington and Marcellus, 1981
		For iceberg scouring, the draught distribution is estimated from direct measurements or from correlations with other better known iceberg parameters (e.g., mass distribution or above-water dimensions).	Gustajtis, 1979, Kollmeyer, 1980 Benedict and Lewis, 1983, Gaskill et al., 1985 d'Apollonia and Lewis, 1986
4. Scour degradation	Based on the premise that if the rate of scour degradation is known for an area, a rate of scour formation can be computed that accounts for the obliterated (infilled) and rescoured scours.	Applied quantitatively for both sea-ice and iceberg scouring. Method is constrained by limited understanding of degradation processes and their rates.	Lewis, 1978 Gaskill et al., 1985 Gaskill, 1986 Weeks et al., 1986
5. Relative and Absolute Scour Dating	The sequence and relative age of intersecting ice scour marks is interpreted from their cross-cutting relationships.	Relative scour dating is applicable to areas of intersecting ice scours only. Domains of up to 12 age-classes of cross-cut scour marks have been determined on Labrador and Baffin shelves.	Woodworth-Lynas, 1983b
	By determining the relative age of ice scours with respect to other seabed features of known age, e.g., a submarine cable, bedforms of known migration rate, fishing trawl marks or faunal populations of known colonization rate, a scouring frequency could possibly be estimated.	Potentially useful where known features exist, but not yet applied.	Fader and King, 1981 Amos and Barrie, 1985
	The relative age of scours is also estimated from their relative state of degradation (ageing).	Applied quantitatively on the basis of submersible observations in both Beaufort Sea and Labrador Shelf.	Shearer and Blasco, 1975, 1986 Josenhans and Barrie, 1982
	The absolute age of a scour event is bracketed by the ages of the scoured sediment and the infilling sediment, determined by conventional methods.	Absolute dating is best suited to older scours with infilled sediment and has been demonstrated for Beaufort Sea and for the Northeast Newfoundland Shelf.	Kenting Exploration, 1975 Mudie, 1986

Table 14.6. (cont.)

Method	Principle	Application	References
6. Paleoscour zone	In areas of cohesive sediment and frequent ice scouring, the base of ice-disturbed sediment (paleoscour zone), is recognized for example on a seismic reflection profile, and indicates a potentially safe depth for structures.	Potentially applicable in the mid-shelf areas of Beaufort Sea where cohesive sediments exist. Base of paleoscour zone is the scour depth expected for a return period equivalent to the full duration of ice scouring and generally indicates conservative (safe but expensive) depth for burial of a pipeline. In areas of relict ice scour, burial of pipe-lines at the base of the paleo-scour zone would be excessively conservative. In the nearshore zone where granular sediments are more common, a paleoscour zone may not be recognized.	M.J. O'Connor and S.M. Blasco, pers. comm., 1982 Pilkington, 1985, 1986
7. Geological constraints	Where the inception of ice scouring is controlled by a geological event of known age, the cumulated scour record is a minimum estimate of scour frequency.	Applied to Grand Banks of Newfoundland and Northeast Newfoundland Shelf where the onset of late Holocene strengthening of cold Labrador Current is correlated with the inception of ice scouring.	Lewis and Parrott, 1987
8. Ice sediment interaction models	Work-energy and force-balance analytical models permit calculation of scour depth and sub-keel pressure distribution for known input values of environmental driving forces, ice feature shapes and sediment physical properties.	Used to suggest maximum scour depths expected for extreme ice or environmental conditions. Potentially these models could generate a distribution of scour depths from given distributions of winds, currents and ice feature dimensions. Currently available models simulate only a limited number of scour processes, ice motions and dimensions.	Kovacs and Mellor, 1974 Chari, 1979, 1986 Chari and Peters, 1981 Fenco Consultants, 1975 Green et al., 1983 Comfort and Graham, 1986 Schoenthaler, 1986

Figure 14.35. A two-storey house swept 3 km to sea from Port au Bras, near Burin, on the south coast of Newfound-land, during the tsunami of 18 November, 1929. The house was subsequently recovered and secured temporarily to the Grand Banks fishing schooner, the 38.6 m long MARIAN BELLE WOLFE from Nova Scotia, which had safely ridden out the tsunami at this anchorage in Little Burin Harbour. The displacement of this coastal dwelling illustrates the unwanted effects of high seas and high sea levels associated with the tsunami of the 1929 Grand Banks earthquake. Photograph from the Still and Moving Image Collection of the Public Archives of Newfoundland and Labrador, St. John's (Official Archives No. A2-149, NA 2149); background research by A. Ruffman, Geomarine Associates Ltd., Halifax.

Several strategies have been proposed to mitigate the risk where it is unacceptably high (Allan, 1986; Jordaan, 1984; Timmermans, 1983). These include: routing of pipelines or site selection of seabed structures in sheltered areas; burial, trenching or excavation and placement of structures beneath the seafloor; strengthening the structure at risk; and deflection or fragmentation of the threatening ice. Examples of plans for pipeline routing and for precautions to be taken to protect power cables from iceberg scour are described later in this chapter as examples of Earth Science and Decision Making.

Earthquakes and seismicity
M.J. Keen, J. Adams, K. Moran, D.J.W. Piper and I. Reid

Seismicity detection and effects

The northern and eastern continental margins of Canada have a relatively high level of seismicity by comparison with most passive margins of the Atlantic-type. Two major earthquakes have occurred this century on the eastern margin, an event in 1929 south of Newfoundland with a magnitude of 7.2, and an event in 1933 in Baffin Bay with a magnitude of 7.3 (Basham et al., 1977; Sykes, 1978; Basham and Adams, 1982). Seismic hazards are clearly potentially significant for offshore development.

The effects of earthquakes which pose hazards offshore and in coastal regions include: ground shaking; surface faulting; subsidence and uplift on a regional scale; seabed liquefaction and effects such as slides, slumps, and turbidity currents; and tsunamis (Fig. 14.35). Adams (1986) has pointed out that acoustic shock waves from earthquakes may also damage floating structures and shipping. Offshore structures must be designed to withstand the effects of earthquakes such as these to attain an annual probability of failure of 10^{-4} or less (Maes, 1986). Consequently, the likelihood of future earthquakes and their effects has to be estimated. A seismotectonic model is needed, a description of the earthquake-generating processes and structures within a region, which defines the spatial, temporal, and magnitude distribution of future earthquakes (Page and Basham, 1985). This leads to estimates of surface faulting, subsidence and uplift, and ground shaking.

Estimates of ground shaking start with the identification of seismic source zones. These are zones within the region of the seismotectonic model where the spatial distribution of the earthquakes can be considered to be uniform. Recurrence relations between frequency and magnitude of the earthquakes in each zone, and the regional relationships between the ground shaking parameters and distance for earthquakes of given magnitudes, then lead to estimates of ground shaking. For any given site or sites in the region, ground shaking is computed and expresses the probability that the peak acceleration or velocity will exceed a certain value, 32% of g for example in the case of acceleration, in a certain period of time, say 50 years. The effects of ground shaking on the foundation materials of the region, including water-saturated sediments offshore, and on structures have then to be predicted. These particular effects will include resonance, flexural failures of structural supports, and seabed movements and their secondary effects such as liquefaction and turbidity currents. From the point of view of design standards, ground

motions with an annual probability of exceedance of 10^{-4} are generally used and ground motion modelling has to lead to prediction of ground motion at the bedrock-sediment interface.

Seismicity offshore eastern Canada

The eastern Canadian network of seismic stations is shown in Figure 14.36a, b. The detection limit and the accuracy

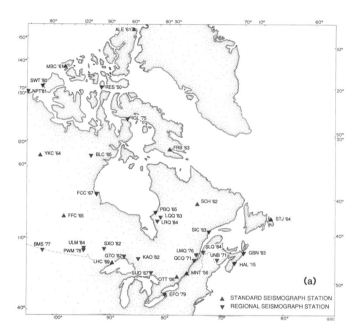

Figure 14.36. (a) Distribution of standard and regional seismograph stations with their installation dates for eastern and central Canada. (b) Standard, regional and telemetered network seismograph stations (1984) for central and southeastern Canada. The positions of stations shown in (a) and (b) and characteristics of the various seismograph systems are described by Munro et al. (1988).

of locating earthquakes offshore has improved over the last few decades as more stations have been added. For example, in Baffin Bay and the Labrador Sea magnitude 5 earthquakes have only been completely detected since 1950 and magnitude 4 since 1968.

All permanent seismic stations are onshore, often in coastal areas with high noise levels compared to inland stations (Fig. 14.36a, b). The coastal stations are typically poorly distributed in terms of azimuth for locating offshore earthquakes, and because no seismographs can be close to such earthquakes only larger offshore ones will be detected. It is difficult to generalize what the detection level has been offshore at any particular time, on account of the changing quality and configuration of seismic stations in eastern Canada and the northeastern United States; for the particular seismic zone south of Newfoundland the record of earthquakes was complete for earthquakes of magnitude 7 and greater from about 1800 until 1930, and thereafter was improved successively so that it is now complete for magnitude 3 and greater (Adams, 1986; Basham et al., 1982).

Examples of the effects of these improvements in terms of changes in sensitivity (new earthquakes located) and in location of old earthquakes are shown in Figure 14.37 (Adams, 1986). Early earthquakes were relocated by more than 100 km in some instances and the more recent ones by as much as 40 km. Earthquake epicentres are shown in Map 1710A (in pocket) and in Figure 14.38. The accuracy of location of any particular earthquake is not shown: in general the locations of earthquakes which occurred before 1964 (open circles) are less certain than the more recent ones. Even with the best land-based readings epicentres may be systematically mislocated by 10 to 15 km because of poorly known velocity and thickness changes at the continental margin. Ocean-bottom seismometers have been used to record micro-earthquakes on the continental slope south of St. Pierre Bank (at the mouth of the Laurentian Channel) (Adams et al., 1984). Similar observations in Baffin Bay provided information on the velocity structure appropriate for that region (Reid and Falconer, 1982; Adams et al., 1984). Experiments with ocean-bottom seismometers to determine lithosphere structure provide useful information on the velocity structure of the margin in general (Keen and Barrett, 1981).

The depths at which the earthquakes occur is generally indeterminate, and assumed to be "mid-crustal", 10-18 km; exact depths can be found using special techniques for the larger events. The record of seismicity in Canada from instrumented stations is only substantial for a relatively short period of 30 to 70 years, too short for the representative level of seismicity to be determined.

However, the epicentres located by the seismic network have been supplemented by searching newspapers and other written documents for the historical record of "felt" earthquakes and of tsunamis from Newfoundland and Nova Scotia (Adams and Staveley, 1985; Ruffman and Peterson, 1986a, b). This historical record has proved to be useful. For example, accounts of the 1929 Grand Banks earthquake and the tsunami generated by the 1755 Lisbon earthquake are numerous, so that there is reasonable certainty that no large earthquakes comparable to the 1929 event occurred off eastern Canada in the last 230 years (Adams, 1986).

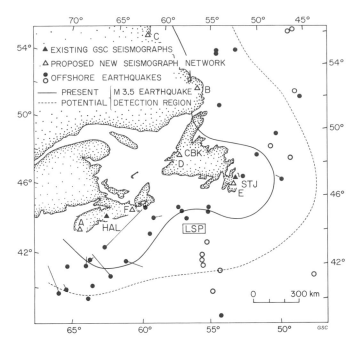

Figure 14.37. Improvements in the detection and location of earthquakes off southeastern Canada. Dots represent locations of offshore earthquakes determined by Wahlstrom and Adams (unpublished data), and in some cases represent a substantial improvement. For such earthquakes, the "tails" join the catalogue location to its revised location (dot). Open dots are new earthquakes found by carefully searching the seismograms from the station at Cornerbrook (CBK); as of 1986 they had not appeared in any catalogue. The box marked "LSP" encloses many earthquakes near the epicentre of the 1929 "Grand Banks" event (see detail in Fig. 14.44). The solid line shows the offshore limit of complete detection of earthquakes of magnitude 3.5 and larger since 1983. The dashed line shows the limit as it would be if the six new stations A through F were established (from Adams, 1986) HAL = Halifax and STJ = St. John's.

The seismicity shown by the instrumental records since 1965 is relatively intense in a number of regions off eastern Canada (Fig. 14.38): Baffin Island; northern Baffin Bay; the northern Labrador Sea; and the continental slope south of St. Pierre Bank (associated with the 1929 event, considered below). A linear set of earthquakes took place in the Labrador Sea, associated spatially and presumably genetically with the buried ridge along the axis of the Labrador Sea. Another linear set is associated with the New England Seamounts. Figure 14.38 shows the relatively high level of seismic activity in the northern Appalachians, in Maine and New Brunswick, and along the St. Lawrence River. Other earthquakes throughout the region occur as a sort of "background", but with improvements in detection levels and in accuracy of location these may also prove to have well-defined geographical and geological associations. Associations might be anticipated with postglacial unloading, with the ocean-continent boundary, and with loading due to sediments, as examples.

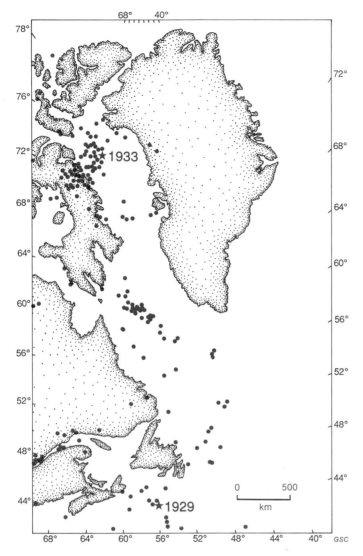

Figure 14.38. Seismicity offshore eastern Canada. Dots represent locations of earthquakes. The major 1929 and 1933 earthquakes are indicated. For more detail see Map 1710A (in pocket).

The seismotectonic associations are poorly known. In the whole area earthquakes can only be firmly associated with well-defined geological features in the cases of the New England Seamounts and the buried mid-Labrador Sea ridge and even in these instances the mechanism producing the events is not known. The regional stress in at least a substantial part of the area is compressive, oriented northeast-southwest, and this is perhaps due to tractions on the base of the lithosphere (Fig. 14.39) (Gough, 1984; Adams, 1985; Podrouzek and Bell, 1985; Adams, 1986; Ervine and Bell, 1987). Superimposed on this regional stress regime — typical of much of North America (Gough, 1984) — are stresses arising from sedimentary loading, glacial unloading, and the mass distribution across the continental margin itself. Earthquakes might be generated from the resultant stress regime imposed on a system of pre-existing faults. This general suggestion is difficult to demonstrate for the offshore where events are recorded relatively poorly and focal mechanisms are

difficult to define, but this explanation has been established on land where the evidence is good. For example in the region of Charlevoix in the St. Lawrence Valley, where the seismicity is intense, earthquakes result from the regional stress acting on a system of Precambrian rift faults. High horizontal compressive stresses are producing thrusts on the preexisting faults (Anglin, 1984). For some earthquakes on the margin off Baffin Island and Labrador, Stein et al. (1979) proposed that stresses arising from glacial unloading would re-activate faults remaining from earlier rifting, and cause normal faulting landward of the 1000 m bathymetric contour and thrust faulting seaward of that contour. This explanation was supported by focal mechanisms reported from seven earthquakes. Quinlan (1984) pointed out that the situation is more complex: in essence glacial unloading might stabilize or de-stabilize a region under stress from other causes (the regional stress, for example). A complete analysis has to be done before it can be said with any confidence that glacial unloading controls the types of faulting observed, and in particular the transition from normal to thrust faulting across the margin. Such a complete analysis has yet to be done, and quantitative explanations are still unavailable for the earthquakes off eastern Canada.

Source zones and seismic hazard

Earthquake source zones have to be established in order to estimate seismic risk; this cannot be done well for the region off eastern Canada because of inadequate information, so that zone boundaries will necessarily be rather arbitrary. The boundaries, which have been defined offshore in order to estimate seismic risk onshore for the National Building Code of Canada (1985), are shown in Figure 14.40, and the relationships between earthquake magnitudes and frequency for these zones are shown in Figure 14.41. These zones could be improved in a number of ways. A separate zone could perhaps be established for the earthquakes of the Labrador Sea associated with the mid-Labrador Sea ridge and for a zone specific to the margin itself as shown by Basham et al. (1983). These suggestions, discussed below, are illustrated in Figures 14.40b, and c, and the recurrence relations in Figure 14.41.

The peak ground motion expected in the future as a result of the seismicity in the source zones is estimated using a method devised by Cornell (1968). These motions are presented as contour maps of the peak horizontal acceleration and velocity that will be exceeded at a probability level of 10% over a period of 50 years, that is with an annual probability of 0.0020) in Figures 14.42 and 14.43.

The source zones shown in Figure 14.40a were devised specifically for the 1985 National Building Code of Canada. They serve this purpose rather well on land, in the sense that the motions onshore are relatively insensitive to changes in the source zones offshore. However, they are not as satisfactory as aids to the design of offshore structures because the rather arbitrary nature of the zones and the other uncertainties discussed already are critically important for offshore sites. Alternative zones are shown in Figures 14.40b and c, and the corresponding recurrence relations in Figure 14.41. These lead to the accelerations and velocities predicted in Figures 14.42b and c, and Figures 14.43b and c (Basham et al., 1983). The different zones partly reflect changes in geographical allocation of earthquakes within the region, as is the case for zone LRX,

795

for example, reflecting the mid-Labrador Sea Ridge. However, some of the changes reflect assumptions which are more controversial. For example, the zone ESX is established by postulating that the seismicity concentrated on the slope south of St.Pierre Bank and in Baffin Bay is representative of seismicity along the whole of the continental margin, not merely of the regions LSP, LSX and BAB themselves. That such a radical proposal can be made reflects the inadequate historical record for the entire margin.

Improvements to the estimation of seismic hazard on the basis of the geological evidence of past earthquakes preserved in the sedimentary record are possible by investigating faults which disturb Holocene sediments, and mass movements of sediments which reflect seismic triggers. Evidence of Holocene faults has to come from high resolution seismic reflection profiles like Huntec DTS. An examination of 2000 km of profiles obtained with this system from the eastern Scotian Shelf and the Laurentian Channel found only two faults reaching the seafloor and

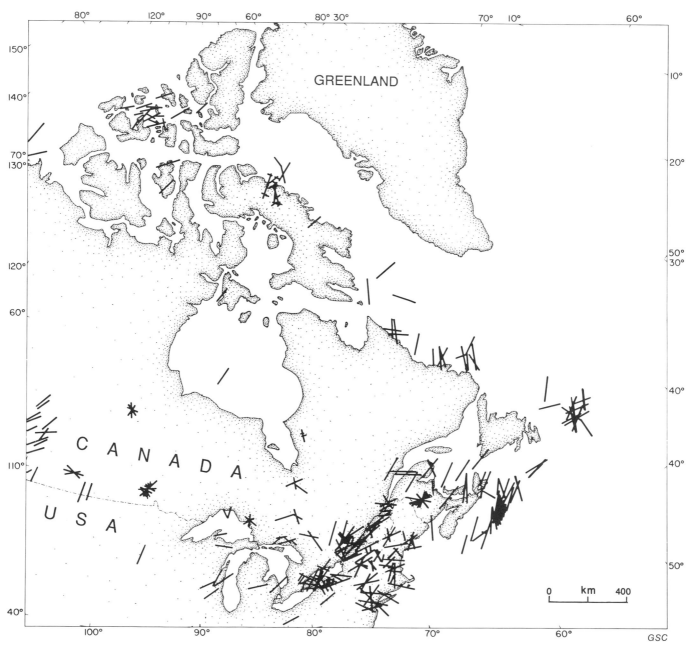

Figure 14.39. Crustal stress in central and eastern Canada. The figure shows the azimuths of maximum horizontal compression as bars. The bars with crosses at each end are the deviatoric extension axes (mostly from normal faulting earthquake mechanisms). The map is a polar projection chosen to reduce the plotted angular discrepancies between azimuths that are parallel on a sphere (from Adams, 1985, updated to November 1986).

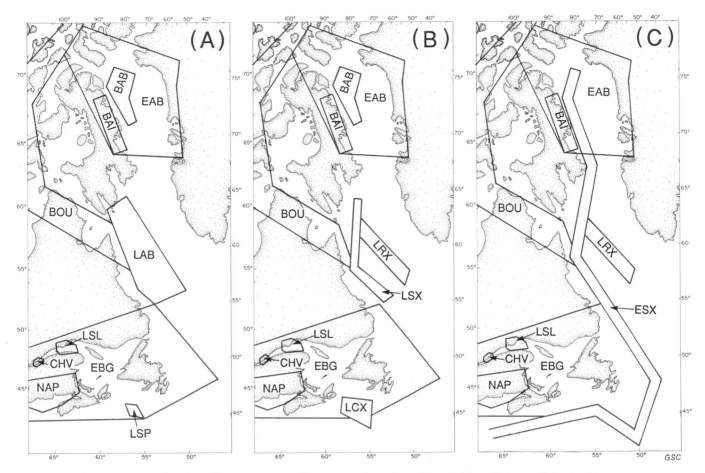

Figure 14.40. Earthquake source zones for eastern Canada and its offshore. A shows "standard" zones used in computations for the National Building Code of Canada. B and C are alternative source zone models (see text). NAP: Northern Appalachians. CHV: Charlevoix. LSL: Lower St. Lawrence. EBG: Eastern background. LSP: Laurentian Slope. LAB: Labrador Sea. BOU: Boothia-Ungava. BAI: Baffin Island. BAB: Baffin Bay. EAB: Eastern Arctic background. LRX: Labrador Sea Ridge, experimental. LSX: Labrador Slope, experimental. LCX: Laurentian Channel, experimental. ESX: Eastern slope, experimental (from Basham et al., 1983).

clearly affecting both bedrock and Holocene sediments (Durling and Fader, 1986). A similar examination of 7000 km of seismic profiles from the Labrador Shelf identified only one fault affecting Holocene sediments and one slump (Josenhans et al., 1986; H. Josenhans, pers. comm., 1986). Slumps and debris flows possibly reflecting seismic triggers are known from Hudson Strait and Scott Inlet and Trough of Baffin Island (MacLean et al., 1982; Syvitski, 1985; B. MacLean and D. Praeg, pers. comm., 1986). The evidence reported, though not conclusive, does not suggest intensive seismicity anywhere on the shelves off eastern Canada.

Unlike the situation for the shelves, evidence for more intensive seismicity is found on the continental slopes. Moran and Hurlbut (1986) have shown that mass movements such as slumps and slides on the upper continental slope off Nova Scotia can be generated by storm-wave loading in only limited regions. Consequently, as evidence of mass movements on the continental slopes is rather widespread, the mass movements are likely to have been triggered seismically. Well-documented evidence of

large-scale mass movements on the continental slopes which might be seismically triggered comes from three areas: the slope off St. Pierre Bank, showing the effects of the 1929 Grand Banks earthquake (see next section); the Scotian Slope, with Late Quaternary slumps and debris flows, suggestive of a large earthquake about 12 000 years ago (Piper et al., 1985a, b; Mosher, 1987); and the Flemish Pass east of the Grand Banks, where a mass flow deposit at least as old as mid-Wisconsinan might have been triggered by an earthquake (Pereira et al., 1985). Piper and Normark (1982) examined seismic reflection profiles from the slope off St. Pierre Bank and from the Laurentian Fan and, because earlier slumps could not be identified from the uppermost tens of metres of sediment, concluded that the return period of large earthquakes comparable to the 1929 event is at least 100 000 years at that site, although less devastating events could be more frequent. Basham and Adams (1982) pointed out in essence that the turbidity current from the 1929 event transported mostly Pleistocene sediments, as observed by Piper and Normark (1982), so that it is not likely that a Holocene failure earlier than

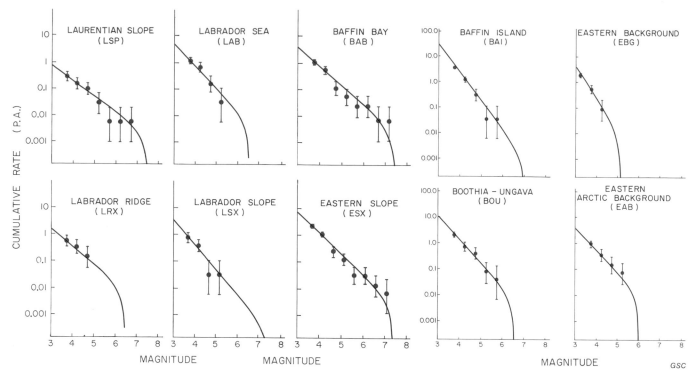

Figure 14.41. Cumulative magnitude recurrence relations for the seismic source zones shown in Figure 14.40 (from Basham et al., 1982, 1983).

the 1929 event occurred. This suggests that the return period has to be more than 10 000 years. Therefore the geological evidence, poor though it is, suggests that very large events are relatively widely spread, not concentrated in one area, and that the indicated return period in the range of 10 000 to 100 000 years is longer than has been assumed in modelling seismicity from instrumental records — 300 years in Figure 14.41 (Basham et al., 1985).

Slope stability
K. Moran, M.J. Keen, D.J.W. Piper, and J. Adams

The hazards and mechanisms of slope failure

One hazard to offshore development is large downslope sediment mass movement. Mass movement was not fully recognized as a problem to offshore structures until mudslides caused the failure of three platforms in the Gulf of Mexico (Bryant and Hall, 1979). These movements probably involved a complex interaction between several mechanisms, but for the sake of simplicity here the various mechanisms are discussed separately.

The terms "slump" and "slide" are both used to describe failure along discrete surfaces. Slumping is a rotational failure generally associated with homogeneous deposits of fine cohesive material, whereas sliding is a translational failure which usually follows a bedding plane and generally occurs in non-cohesive material (Nardin et al., 1979; see Fig. 11.10). Slumps may involve up to 600 km[3] of material (Embley and Jacobi, 1977), but even relatively common events on a small scale, involving as little as 0.5 km[3], are a hazard, as they may displace the upper 50 m of sediment. The most common form of slump-

ing on the seafloor is undrained slumping, where failure either occurs rapidly or takes place in impermeable sediments such as clays where excess pore pressure has not been dissipated. Very few large scale submarine features have sufficient slope to trigger drained failure (Morgenstern, 1967).

The necessary condition for slumping on shallow slopes (less than 10 degrees) is underconsolidation, where the pore pressure is greater than the hydrostatic value. Three mechanisms which may cause this are: high rates of sedimentation (Coleman et al., 1983); gas in the sediment pore water (Whelan et al., 1977); and residual pore pressure following repeated loading, as from storm waves (Strachan, 1984). Slumping is usually initiated by some sort of trigger (Garrison and Bea, 1977). One trigger is oversteepening, and this can lead to failure when deposition occurs at the head of a slope, or erosion takes place at its toe. Retrogressive failure happens when the toe of a slope is removed successively by slumping. Other potential triggers are the dynamic loads of earthquakes and sea ice.

Liquefaction will come about if the sediment structure breaks down as a result of temporarily high pore pressures (Holtz and Kovacs, 1981). Liquefied sediment will flow rather than slump, the nature of the flow depending on the properties of the sediment. In coarse grained dense sediment excess pore pressures are either not generated or are dissipated quickly, whereas in medium grained sediments, fine sands to silts, pore pressures are dissipated more slowly, and the flow can be sustained longer. The duration of these flows is somewhat controversial and is of particular interest because of their probable role in the initiation of many turbidity currents (Middleton, 1969; Otteman and Gillis, 1981; Piper et al., 1985a, b). Flows of fine grained

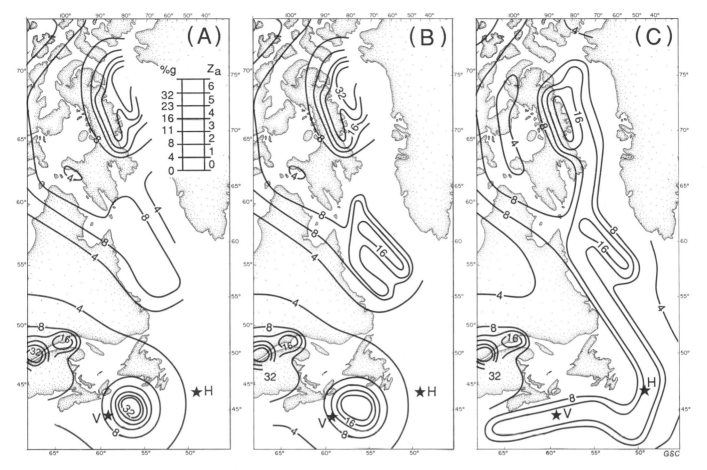

Figure 14.42. Peak horizontal acceleration (Za) for a probability of exceedence of 10% in 50 years computed from the three source zone models shown in Figure 14.40. The legend in A shows the acceleration zones recommended for National Building Code applications on land. Locations of the Venture (V) and Hibernia (H) proposed hydrocarbon production developments are indicated by stars (from Basham et al., 1983). B and C are alternate models.

cohesive sediment or mudflows retain excess pore pressure and therefore are the most common mass flow material.

Turbidity currents are flows of relatively high density and their destructive potential is well known from the 1929 Grand Banks earthquake (Heezen and Ewing, 1952; Piper et al., 1988). However, they are more of a concern in exploitation of hydrocarbons from the lower slope and continental rise than from the continental shelf and upper slope.

Sediment instability on the continental shelf

Though instabilities caused by storm wave loading have been shown to be possible in limited regions of the outer continental shelf off Nova Scotia (Moran and Hurlbut, 1986), the most probable trigger for instabilities on shelf slopes is thought to be earthquake shaking, as on the continental slopes.

Hazards on the continental shelf due to the effects of seismicity will arise from the effects of ground motion and faulting at a particular site, and from mass movements initiated elsewhere. Earthquake loading of sediments results in an increased pore pressure which, in turn, reduces sediment strength. The pore pressure response depends upon the sediment type. Liquefaction occurs when the pore pressure reaches the local lithostatic pressure, so that loose coarse sediments with high permeabilities are more susceptible to liquefaction than are fine grained sediments. These fine grained sediments are more susceptible to fatigue under cyclic loading than are coarse grained sediments, and the fine grained sediments may with time fail under gravity loads following seismic events (Ishihara, 1985). Atkinson et al. (1984) have shown how it is possible to compute the probability of seismically-induced liquefaction as a function of earthquake size, earthquake distance, and the resistance of the sediment expressed in terms of results of engineers' standard penetration tests. Physical properties of sediments are not generally known for the eastern seaboard of Canada, so that the hazard due to liquefaction shall be computed in terms of the most dense sediment necessary to make the risk negligible (Atkinson et al., 1984). It will then be possible at particular sites to use sediment properties measured from static cone penetrometers, for example, to determine quickly if liquefaction is potentially a significant hazard.

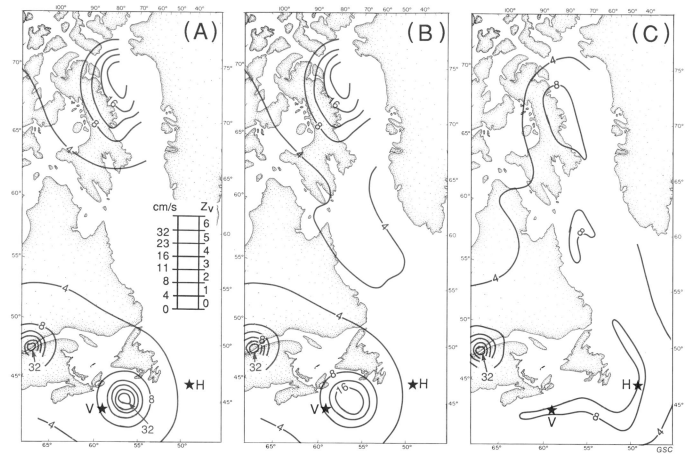

Figure 14.43. Peak horizontal velocity (Zv) for a probability of exceedence of 10% in 50 years computed from the three source zone models shown in Figure 14.40. The legend in A shows the velocity zones recommended for National Building Code applications on land. Locations of the proposed Venture (V) and Hibernia (H) hydrocarbon production developments are indicated by stars (from Basham et al., 1983). B and C are alternate models.

Other studies pertinent to potential instabilities have been based on the results of geological mapping of the sediments on the shelves, reported elsewhere in this volume. Jacques/McClelland Geoscience Inc. (1982a, b) investigated the slopes and the sediment types on the Scotian and Labrador shelves. They classified previously mapped sediments by thickness and type, using engineering properties inferred for the sediments (e.g. "soft clay", "loose silt", "loose sand"). These types were mapped in terms of thicknesses greater or less than 61 m (200 ft) in accordance with engineering practice (American Petroleum Institute, 1981). They recognized that sediments could fail on slopes of less than 1 per cent, but designated only areas where the slopes were greater than 3 or 6 per cent (depending on the sediment type) as regions of potential hazard. Many regions of the shelf are potentially unstable in terms of sediment thickness and type and the local gradients. These findings are not supported, as measured cyclic properties of the sediments in the various classifications are not yet available. The lack of abundant evidence of sediment instability from sediment cores and from the high resolution seismic profiles mentioned previously suggests that their results are conservative and the risk is in fact generally low. This is consistent with esti-

mates made by Atkinson et al. (1984) for the region of Sable Island, if earthquakes similar in size to the 1929 event are much less frequent than every 300 years. Nevertheless, the probability of liquefaction at sites of development cannot be ignored.

Sediment instability on the continental slope: the 1929 Grand Banks Earthquake

The 1929 Grand Banks earthquake with a magnitude of 7.2 caused slope instabilities that severed cables and interrupted trans-Atlantic communications. It also created spectacular geological effects many hundreds of kilometres downslope from its epicentre. Consequently, a separate section is devoted to it here, in part summarizing an account by Piper et al. (1988).

The 1929 event and its aftershocks dominate the Laurentian Slope Seismic Zone (LSP) (Fig. 14.40a, 14.44). Systematic relocation of the larger historical earthquakes and the many smaller recent earthquakes found as a result of improvements to the seismic network show that the events lie within an area 100 km east to west and 35 km north to south (Fig. 14.44). The events are consistent with the hypothesis that current earthquakes are aftershocks of the 1929 event, and with the hypothesis that they appear to lie upon a rupture about 70 km long (Adams, 1986). No surface trace of this postulated rupture has been identified so far in other geophysical investigations. The events lie well to the south of the easterly extension of the Glooscap fault system and we cannot associate them firmly with any known fault system, although they do fall rather generally at the intersection of the Newfoundland Fracture Zone and the rifted margin off Nova Scotia. The earthquakes, however, occurred in the eastern part of the Scotian Basin where the sediments are very thick and the basement to the sediments is not seen in seismic records. The actual depth of the 1929 event is not well known; the depth of an event in 1975 with magnitude 5.2 was 30 km (H. Hasegawa, pers. comm., 1986).

The earthquake occurred at 20 31 53 GMT on 18 November 1929, with an aftershock at about 22 02 00 GMT (Doxsee, 1948). The most recent relocation by Dewey and Gordon (1984) places the epicentre at 44°41.5′N 56°00.4′W, with a value of Ms of 7.2. The earthquake was responsible for 27 of the 28 recorded deaths related to Canadian earthquakes this century, as a result of the tsunami which struck the south coast of Newfoundland. The earthquake caused a remarkable series of cable breaks on the continental slope and rise south of the epicentre which disrupted trans-Atlantic communications for up to six months. The effects of severe seismic shocks on land

were restricted to southeastern Cape Breton Island, where some chimneys fell and highways were blocked by small landslides. One person may have died from the tsunami in Cape Breton (A. Ruffman, pers. comm., 1986). Four ships at sea within 250 km of the epicentre reported severe tremors (de Smitt, 1932).

The tsunami generated by the earthquake coincided with high sea levels generated by a storm and high tide. This coincidence makes it difficult to reconstruct the behaviour of the tsunami itself. Most damage occurred in southwestern Placentia Bay, on the south coast of Newfoundland, particularly in places where the tsunami was funneled by local relief. The tsunami was also detected in Halifax, Nova Scotia, Bermuda and the Azores (Doxsee, 1948). Gussow (1982) suggested that the 1929 event was in fact the slump itself, and not a tectonic earthquake as has been generally supposed. Hasegawa and Kanamori (1987) pointed out that the available geophysical data do not preclude this hypothesis, which would require the slumping of about 550 km^3 of sediment within a few minutes from an area about 200 km across. This volume is about three times that estimated by Piper et al. (1988), and is unlikely on the evidence of the seabed distribution of failures.

Twenty-eight breaks were reported in twelve different cables in the area around and to the south of the epicentre. Some of the breaks were instantaneous and apparently due to sediment failure around the epicentre itself (Heezen and Ewing, 1952), and some occurred sequentially, at times up to 13 hours after the event, interpreted as the effects of the turbidity current (Piper et al., 1988). This turbidity current travelled with velocities of at least 67 km/h on the upper Laurentian Fan and with lower velocities of 32 km/h on the northern Sohm Abyssal Plain, 500 km to the south (Piper et al., 1988).

The epicentre is located on the continental slope north of the Laurentian Fan (Fig. 14.45). The slope west of the epicentre is erosional, the morphology being cut into Pleistocene muds and pebbly mudstones. The valleys of the Laurentian Fan are floored by gravel and sand. East of the epicentre, the uppermost part of the continental slope off St. Pierre Bank is underlain by glacial till, which interfingers downslope with proglacial silts and muds. Both of these lithofacies are overlain by an organic-rich gassy mud, 5 to 10 m thick. Sediment failure in this area has been mapped using mid-range sidescan, high-resolution seismic profiling and observations from a submersible (Piper et al., 1988). The sediments on the uppermost part of the continental slope did not fail during the earthquake, but downslope are truncated by a series of arcuate scarps. Failure of the uppermost 5 to 15 m of soft surficial sediment is widespread on the slope off St. Pierre Bank downslope from these arcuate scarps. Downslope from the arcuate scarps to the west of the Laurentian Channel, the upper part of the Laurentian Fan appears to be largely erosional.

The turbidite generated by the earthquake is mainly sand, and has a total volume of at least 170 km^3. Less than one quarter of this can be accounted for by the volumes of seabed sediment (which is mostly Pleistocene) known as a result of geological mapping to have failed, and Piper et al. (1988) postulated that much of the turbidite was derived by failure of proglacial sands which had accumulated about 50 000 years earlier in the heads of the fan valleys of the Laurentian Fan (see Chapter 10). Surface

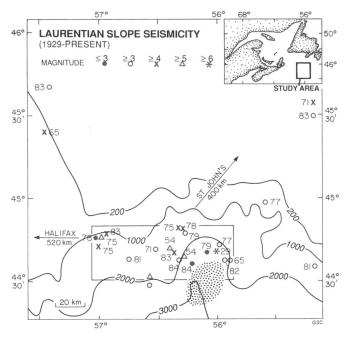

Figure 14.44. Seismicity of the Laurentian Slope Seismic Zone LSP (See Fig. 14.37, 14.40 a for location). Earthquakes are shown with symbols representing their magnitude class, and numbers representing their year of occurrence. "29" represents the best estimate for the 1929 "Grand Banks" earthquake epicentre (after Dewey and Gordon, 1984). Ocean bottom seismometers were deployed in the area for two months in 1983 and the stippled ellipse indicates the approximate location of two poorly-recorded microearthquakes (Adams et al., 1984; from Adams, 1986). Isobaths shown in metres.

failure in the 1929 event was concentrated in the sensitive proglacial silts immediately downslope from till tongues on the upper slope, and on steep valley walls. What was particularly unusual about the 1929 event was the generation of the catastrophic turbidity current, resulting as it did from the coincidence of a large earthquake, a reservoir of potentially liquefiable proglacial sand on a steep slope, and a topography that would funnel and concentrate a turbidity current flow (Piper et al., 1988). Sediment failures in the Holocene related to earthquakes elsewhere on the continental slope have produced turbidity currents, but these were muddy currents likely to be less erosive than sandy currents (Piper et al., 1985a, b; Schafer et al., 1985).

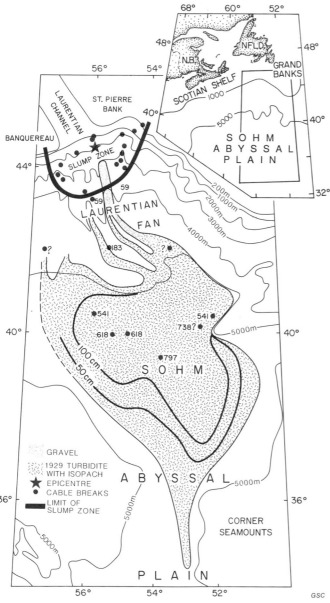

Figure 14.45. Results of 1929 "Grand Banks" earthquake including cable breaks and thickness of turbidite deposit. Epicentre from Dewey and Gordon (1984). Location and time (minutes after main shock) of cable breaks from Doxsee (1948). Limit and isopachs of turbidite on the Sohm Abyssal Plain from Fruth (1965). From Piper et al. (1988).

SYNTHESIS: EARTH SCIENCE AND DECISION MAKING

The role of earth science in coastal and offshore development, apart from resource exploration and evaluation, is often indirect, but nevertheless significant, as illustrated by the three case histories described in this section. Massive spills of oil from wrecked tanker vessels drift ashore to interact with coastal processes, thereby posing questions concerning the effects of the oil and the need for shore cleanup. Much has been learned about the fate of oil at the shore and from controlled oil-spill experiments in inlets of the eastern Canadian Arctic.

Pipeline routing depends, in part, on the suitability of the seabed for the application of trenching and pipelaying technology. An alternate pipeline route across the Grand Banks of Newfoundland was proposed when information from regional geology investigations revealed extensive areas of untrenchable, near-seabed, indurated bedrock.

Planning for construction projects is often an iterative process involving trade-offs between reliability or security for the facility under construction and the difficulty or expense in overcoming natural hazards. This characteristic is well illustrated by marine geological investigations for the engineering of electrical power transmission across the Strait of Belle Isle.

Oil spills on coastal regions of eastern and Arctic Canada

R.B. Taylor

Waste discharge from industrial plants and urban areas is usually a continuing process. An oil spill is different, in that it is an instantaneous event, but it may well have lasting effects. Many spills have affected the coastlines of Canada (Table 14.7), and there is now a wealth of information on the sensitivity of shorelines, on the problems posed by stranded oil, and indeed on the effects of the various methods used for cleaning on the stability of shorelines. The best-known spills in offshore eastern Canada came from the vessels ARROW (1970), GOLDEN ROBIN (1974) and KURDISTAN (1979).

The oil, which has been most commonly spilled on the Atlantic coast of Canada, is the fuel oil Bunker C. Fuel oils of this type congeal when spilled into the cold water typical

Table 14.7. Distribution of Coastal Oil Spills in eastern Canada and the Canadian Arctic from 1976-1980 (from Owens, 1983).

Location	Percent Length of Total Canadian Coastline	Number of Coastal Spills	Percent of Total Spills
Nova Scotia	3.0	43	9.3
New Brunswick	0.9	34	7.3
Prince Edward Island	0.5	5	1.1
Newfoundland	5.3	33	7.1
Labrador	6.0	5	1.1
N.W.T./Yukon	64.4	29	6.2

of eastern Canadian and arctic waters, and form a semi-solid mass which generally floats on or just below the surface of the water. Waves agitate the water and oil into an emulsion of water-in-oil, a 'chocolate mousse', and this blankets beaches. Oil is deposited primarily on the upper foreshore. It may form 'asphalt pavements' or 'bands', which, being resistant to erosion, introduce instabilities into the normal beach profile. The bands of sediment and oil may be alternately exposed and buried by changes in beach morphology (Fig. 14.46), by longshore transport of sediment, and the migration of rhythmic beach forms, such as cusps. Oiled sediments of dunes in the backshore resist the normal transport by wind. Oil may be alternately exposed and buried on account of waves during storms: the waves will tend to erode the upper portion of sandy beaches and expose the oil , but on gravel beaches, pebbles and cobbles are often transported up slope with the result that the oil is buried. Conglomerates of oil and sediment, and oil and organic matter, form clasts, different in size and shape from the normal beach material (Reinson et al., 1980). Clasts of oil and sediment are commonly flat, and accordingly may be easily suspended and carried both onshore and offshore; if they are too large they remain as part of the beach (Fig. 14.47). Oil-sediment conglomerates, because of their low density, collect preferentially in swash lines and near the limit of low tide, occasionally coalescing to form the narrow asphalt pavements and bands mentioned above.

The persistence of oil along a shoreline depends on a variety of factors (Table 14.8). Rocky shorelines are the least sensitive to the effects of spills because oil is not absorbed and buried, as it is on beaches. Sheltered environments such as lagoons and marshlands are generally the most sensitive. However, recent surveys of a salt marsh in eastern Quebec, which experienced an oil spill in 1974, show that these environments can recover naturally in one of two ways (Vandermeulen and Jotcham, 1986). In areas

of high sedimentation the oiled surface is completely buried and revegetated. In areas of low sedimentation, as the oil weathers, it is revegetated from existing root masses beneath the tar layer or by lateral reinvasion. In the case of the spill from the ARROW in Chedabucto Bay, oil spilled in sheltered lagoons showed a very slow rate of degradation and the oil was still visible in some places in 1986. By contrast, in higher energy environments, oil was degraded by normal processes and persisted in significant quantities for only three months (Owens, 1977). From the very nature of accidents at sea, oil spills are commonly associated with storm conditions, times of higher water levels when waves can deposit oil onshore well above the levels of normal high tides, and beyond the reach of normal waves. Degradation by waves will as a consequence be slow. The effects of tides on the persistence of oil are complex. Rates of degradation are most rapid in microtidal environments because waves are concentrated along a narrower band of beach, but the initial thickness of oil deposited will be the greatest. In macrotidal settings waves are dispersed over a wider area but so is the oil; the thinner cover of oil is more susceptible to mechanical degradation as a result of waves and the exposure and submergence on account of the tides. In the Canadian Arctic, oil stranded on beaches persists longer and has greater impact than in more temperate regions on account of the longer duration of seasonal sea ice and permafrost. Beaches will thaw to only shallow depths, so that oil cannot penetrate far, and may be flushed down a beach by ground water above the surface of permafrost. Ice-push can redistribute oiled sediment and move it upslope beyond the reach of waves. Nearshore ice may prevent waves reworking oiled shores.

Controlled experiments to investigate the effects of oil on arctic beaches have been carried out in northern Baffin Island (Owens et al., 1983). These showed that the rate that beaches clean themselves naturally depends on the inten-

Figure 14.46. Oil is commonly deposited on the upper foreshore where it can congeal to form "asphalt pavements", shown partially formed here; or it can become alternately buried and exposed by changes in beach morphology. Note for scale, the 0.5 m long shovel handle.

sity of the waves. The results suggested that where the wave fetch is greater than 25 km, contamination by oil will be reduced naturally to relatively insignificant levels (500 mg of oil per km of shoreline) within 100 days. By contrast, oil stranded on beaches on sheltered shores may persist at significant levels for more than 10 years (Owens et al., 1983). Oil may delay the formation of ice on beaches in the fall. Fast ice will melt more rapidly in spring if oil has been incorporated within it or on it earlier, for example during the previous freeze-up or winter. The deposition of oil on ice-rich ground in areas of permafrost may cause thermal instabilities.

If an underwater blowout of oil and gas occurred in arctic regions, the ice canopy could contain the contaminant and prevent its widespread dispersion; however, the oil would migrate in spring to the surface of the ice where it could spread if not removed. Surface oil slicks are abraded and dispersed in ice infested waters, as during the spill from the KURDISTAN in the waters off Nova Scotia, but the interaction of ice and waves nearshore creates logistical problems during cleanup operations.

Figure 14.47. Congealed oil and sediment conglomerates exhibit different hydrodynamic characteristics in waves than the local sediment. These artificial clasts collect preferentially in swash lines in the wave breaker zone near low tides. The major divisions on the inclined stadia rod, beside the 0.9 m high tripod are each 10 cm long.

Maps and indices showing shoreline sensitivity allow the types of coastlines to be classified and the priorities for protection and cleanup established if a spill occurs. Sensitivities are based on factors such as: shoreline morphology and composition; wave energy levels; sea and air temperature; oil persistence (Table 14.9) (Owens, 1971; Hayes et al., 1978; McLaren, 1980; McLaren and Barrie, 1985; Desmarais et al., 1984).

Stranded oil may significantly affect shoreline stability, through: interference with sediment transport and erosion; binding of sediment and the consequent alteration in sediment hydraulics; destruction of vegetation leading to instability of backshore, marsh and lagoon environments; and the effects peculiar to arctic regions, described above. The impact of a spill depends on the time of its occurrence, in the sense that the impact varies with the presence or absence of fast ice, and the constructional or erosional state of the beach when the oil reaches the shore.

Cleanup procedures themselves may affect beaches. Inappropriate methods can lead to shoreline instability: for example, if oiled sediment is removed from a beach which has no active sediment sources and this sediment is not replaced, the beach will suffer the same fate as beaches which have been improperly exploited for aggregate. The most appropriate method may often be the natural processes of self-cleaning, but public pressure may not allow this.

The Hibernia development: early decisions on pipelines
G.B.J. Fader

The oil and gas of the Hibernia field could be transported to markets in several ways. One method that was considered in early planning involved a pipeline from the field across the continental shelf to Newfoundland. Development plans now specify tanker vessels to transport Hibernia oil ashore (Mobil Oil Canada Ltd., 1985; Canada-Newfoundland Offshore Petroleum Board, 1986), nevertheless early planning for Hibernia oil production clearly illustrates how geological factors influence decisions in the possible routing of a pipeline. With this method of transportation the question arose: "What is an appropriate route?" This question is pertinent because of the problems which could arise from scour by icebergs.

The most direct route leads from the Hibernia field to the Avalon Peninsula (Fig. 14.48) (S. Liesemer, pers. comm., 1980). The western half of the route is underlain by indurated Paleozoic sandstones and siltstones and these are overlain by a thin cover of glacial till, less than 2 m thick (King and Fader, 1980). The seafloor is in places completely covered with iceberg furrows and pits, and in most cases the furrows have cut through the thin veneer of surficial sediments to the underlying bedrock. The pipeline would therefore have to be buried to avoid the hazard posed by iceberg scour. Samples of bedrock suggested that trenching in these indurated rocks would be difficult (King and Fader, 1976). The outer half of the direct route is underlain by Cretaceous and Tertiary bedrock and thin unconsolidated sediments. The Tertiary rocks are relatively soft, and amenable to conventional trenching techniques.

Table 14.8. Factors affecting the persistence of stranded oil on shorelines (after Robillard et al., 1980)

Types of oil	Thickness of oil on shore surface	Depth of oil penetration	Wave energy level at shoreline	Air temperature	Expected persistence	Fetch	Prevailing Winds	Coastal Exposure	Offshore Ice	Energy Level
Light Volatile	Very thin (<1.0 cm)	All oil exposed on shore surface	High Energy levels Exposed coast	High (>25°C)	Days/Week	Long	Onshore	Straight (Open)	Absent	High
↓	↓	↓	↓	↓	↓	↓	↓	↓	↓	↓
Tarry	Thick (>10.0 cm)	All oil buried below beach surface	Low energy: levels: totally sheltered coast	Low (<0°C)	Decades	Short	Offshore	Indented (Sheltered)	Present	Low

The potential problems of the inner part of the direct route led to a proposal to loop any pipeline route to the south, so that as much as possible of the route is underlain by Tertiary and Cretaceous bedrock, at the expense of greater length (King and Fader, 1980; Weir, 1981) (Fig. 14.48). The feasibility of this route from a geological point of view has been confirmed by seismic studies and boreholes (King et al., 1986).

Table 14.9. Examples of relative shoreline sensitivity ratings assigned to shoreline types (A) by McLaren and Barrie (1985) for Eastern Lancaster Sound and northeast Baffin Island; and (B) Owens (1977) for Canadian shorelines in general.

INCREASING PHYSICAL SENSITIVITY	(A)	(B)
	Glacier Coast	Exposed Rock or Cliff Shore
	Rock Coast - steep - moderate - low	Exposed Beaches - mud flats - sand flats
	Unconsolidated Coast - steep - moderate - low	Sheltered Environments - Pocket beaches - Marsh - Lagoons
	Beach Type - Pocket - Continuous - Barrier	
	Beach Material - Boulder - Sand - Gravel - Cobble	
	Intertidal Flats - narrow - wide	

The present plan not to use a pipeline to transport oil ashore from Hibernia was based on the adverse economics of a long route and the technical difficulty in transporting the waxy crude oil found in the Hibernia reservoir; any interruption in flow within the pipes would cause the contained oil to congeal unless the line was heated (D.F. Sherwin, pers. comm., 1987).

The cable crossing of the Strait of Belle Isle
D.I. Ross, H.W. Josenhans, and J. Guigné

Electrical power is generated at Churchill Falls in Labrador and transmitted overland through Quebec to other Canadian provinces and the United States. A link for power between Labrador and the Island of Newfoundland itself would provide power on the island, and provide a market for smaller hydroelectric plants on the lower reaches of the Churchill River, not now developed. The question then arises: how should power be transmitted across the Strait of Belle Isle (Fig. 14.49a).

This question is not a trivial one, because power cables across the Strait have to be protected from the effects of iceberg scour, fishing trawls and strong currents. As an example of the potential problems, 60 to 90 icebergs enter the eastern end of the strait and 2.5 scouring events are expected each year in the cable crossing area (Kollmeyer, 1980). Although the strait is only 15 km wide at its narrowest point, installation of power cables across it and protection of them from these hazards will be constrained by the nature of the bedrock, the nature of the surficial sediments and the morphology of the seafloor. Three options for cable installation have been considered: (1) a tunnel beneath the strait; (2) trenches cut into the bedrock of the sea floor; (3) burial by plough within unconsolidated sediment overlying the bedrock.

The morphology of the strait is relatively complex, and water depths exceed 100 m in the Newfoundland Trough in the centre of the strait (Fig. 14.49a). Bedrock beneath the Strait consists of Precambrian gneisses overlain by a sequence of faulted Cambrian sediments, which outcrop in the strait (Fig. 14.49b) (Geoterrex Ltd., 1975; Green et al., 1982; Bostock et al., 1983). Bedrock on the seafloor is generally covered with sediments such as boulder till, sand

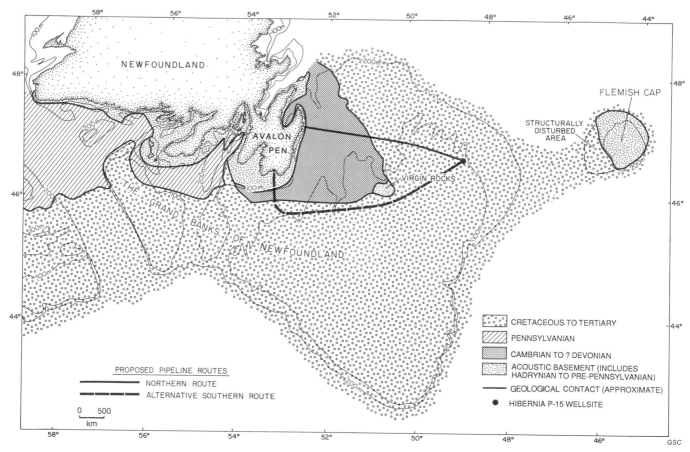

Figure 14.48. Near-surface bedrock geology and proposed northern and alternative southern pipeline routes, considered in the early planning for Hibernia development.

and shell hash. Boulder ridges and morainal ridges form linear ridges parallel to the shoreline. Modern iceberg scours are common on the seafloor of the shallower waters, and relict scours are found in the deeper waters of the Newfoundland Trough. Most of the seafloor is covered by a gravel and boulder lag deposit.

The option of a tunnel is attractive because the problems of currents, waves, trawls and ice scour are avoided, and so it ensures almost complete reliability for power transmission. It could in addition provide a link for transportation from the mainland to the Island of Newfoundland. It was appreciated that the Cambrian sediments might well be water-bearing, and so any tunnel would have to be driven through the Precambrian gneisses, at a minimum depth of 425 m below the seafloor, with access shafts to depths of about 580 m on both sides of the strait (Teshmont Consultants, 1974; SNC-Lavalin Newfoundland Ltd., 1980a). A tunnel would be expensive.

The power cables could be laid in two trenches, each 0.6 m wide, cut 1.5 m into the bedrock of the seafloor beneath any surficial sediments (SNC-Lavalin Newfoundland Ltd., 1980b). Early surveys had suggested that these sediments are thin and could easily be removed to allow trenching of the bedrock, but subsequent geophysical surveys and borehole drilling showed that the thickness of overburden varied significantly across the strait. This later work also showed that numerous till ridges could be a substantial

obstacle to existing trenching equipment and that the flanks of some ridges of till and bedrock were steeper than a trenching tool could negotiate. The sediments and exposed bedrock were examined in detail in selected areas using the submersible PISCES IV and these observations confirmed the geophysical and borehole studies (Zevenhuizen, 1986).

A reassessment of the engineering constraints in the light of this work suggested that the third option, that of ploughing the transmission line into the sediments, might be a viable option. This option has the advantage of being the least costly, but the obvious disadvantage that a cable would be more exposed to hazards, and power more likely to be interrupted in the event of damage. The cable would however be relatively easy to pick up and repair or replace. A route is required where the cable can be ploughed into sediment over at least the shallower portion of the route

Figure 14.49. Cable crossing area, Strait of Belle Isle, showing bathymetry in metres, surficial geological zones and features and possible cable crossing routes (a), and bedrock geological cross-section (b). Sediment cover not shown. (After Geonautics, 1984) (Geological section after Bostock et al., 1983 with fault information from Geoterrex Ltd., 1975.

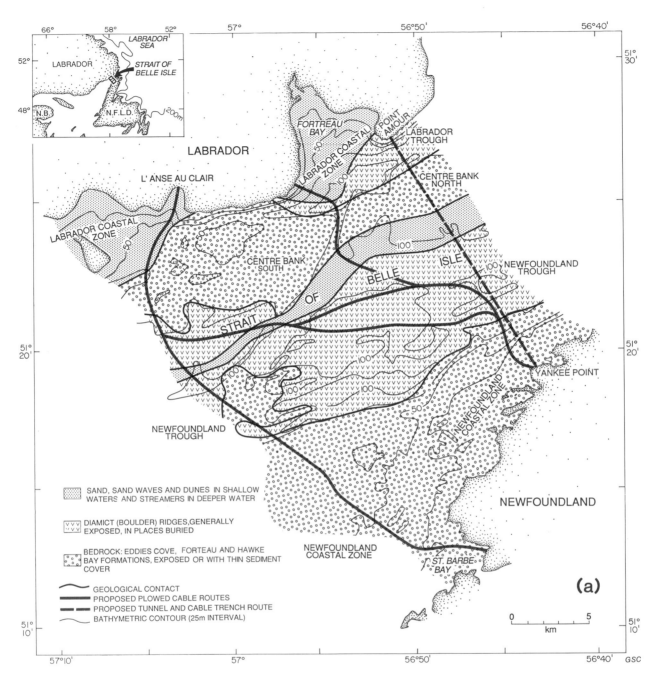

SAND, SAND WAVES AND DUNES IN SHALLOW WATERS AND STREAMERS IN DEEPER WATER

DIAMICT (BOULDER) RIDGES, GENERALLY EXPOSED, IN PLACES BURIED

BEDROCK: EDDIES COVE, FORTEAU AND HAWKE BAY FORMATIONS, EXPOSED OR WITH THIN SEDIMENT COVER

GEOLOGICAL CONTACT

PROPOSED PLOWED CABLE ROUTES

PROPOSED TUNNEL AND CABLE TRENCH ROUTE

BATHYMETRIC CONTOUR (25m INTERVAL)

(a)

0 ——— 5
km

GSC

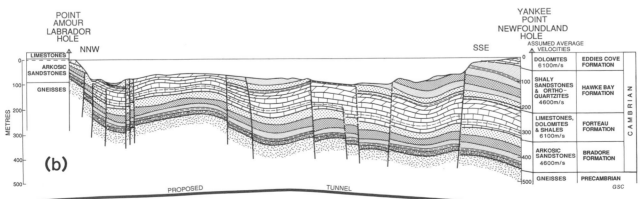

(b)

				ASSUMED AVERAGE VELOCITIES		
	DOLOMITES	6100m/s	EDDIES COVE FORMATION			
	SHALY SANDSTONES & ORTHO-QUARTZITES	4600m/s	HAWKE BAY FORMATION			
	LIMESTONES, DOLOMITES & SHALES	6100m/s	FORTEAU FORMATION			CAMBRIAN
	ARKOSIC SANDSTONES	4600m/s	BRADORE FORMATION			
	GNEISSES		PRECAMBRIAN			

POINT AMOUR LABRADOR HOLE

YANKEE POINT NEWFOUNDLAND HOLE

NNW

SSE

LIMESTONES
ARKOSIC SANDSTONES
GNEISSES

PROPOSED   TUNNEL

GSC

to be protected from icebergs and fishing trawls. In the narrowest region of the strait numerous bouldery till ridges and substantial areas of exposed bedrock, make cable ploughing an unattractive prospect. Farther to the southwest however, the water depth generally increases as does the thickness of sediment, particularly in the shallower coastal regions on the Labrador side. Reconnaissance surveys suggested that, although the resistant till ridges still form a substantial portion of the overburden in this region, their scattered distribution and the overall greater thickness of sediment associated with the wider channel could result in reasonably successful burial of the cable over the major portion of the route. Furthermore, a former river channel, narrow and filled with sediment, was identified crossing the shallow coastal zone offshore from St. Barbe Bay on the Island of Newfoundland which could provide substantial protection for the cable over this exposed nearshore zone (Fig. 14.49a). Geophysical surveys in this southern region of the strait and experiments with a prototype cable plough were followed by observations from PISCES IV one year later (Fig. 14.50). These experiments showed that the bouldery till ridges in this region of the strait do not represent a major obstacle to the plough. Seafloor sediments were penetrated to a depth of 60 cm by the ploughshare over 80% of the total distance traversed. Moreover, the submersible observations did suggest that strong bottom currents winnow all the surface fine material away from an area which has been ploughed and backfill the exposed trench with sand and shell hash, so that a buried cable would probably be protected. Thus, the third option, to plough, became a possibility as a result of geophysical surveys in connection with the second, to trench. The plough option implies acceptance of reliability of less than 100%, with the associated trade-off: lower costs for installation and for replacement of the transmission link.

The engineering of the Power Cable Project in the Strait of Belle Isle has benefited from detailed geological and environmental studies. The results of this work have provided not only new insights into the dynamics of this waterway, but have also provided assessments of the technology appropriate to the project for given levels of reliability and cost. The project has demonstrated the importance of both regional and detailed geological studies in obtaining an understanding of the constraints to engineering scenarios, and has resulted in a data base for future assessments. With the geological and engineering constraints understood, the decision to develop a power link between the Island of Newfoundland and mainland Labrador will be made on the basis of the market for the power, cost of installation and level of reliability required.

SUMMARY

Coastal constraints

The coastal environments of southeastern Canada are diverse, ranging from protected marine waters in fiords, to estuaries influenced by river flow, to exposed coasts dominated by large waves. On the Atlantic coast an annual significant wave height of 10 m is known. This environment is modulated by seasonal storms and variable presence of sea ice in winter and spring. The effects of waves on the shore — flooding, erosion, and coastal sediment transport — are accentuated by storm surges, by exceptionally high tides several times per year and, infrequently, by tsunamis.

The developments in this coastal zone are diverse too, reflecting the industry, habitation, and recreation of its population. Coastal inlets are extensively used as fisheries and fishing harbours. Major inlets support urban development, defence, research, offshore supply, and industries for the processing and trans-shipment of fish, forest, mineral, oil and other products. Shipping interests, which service the industrialized inlets, require developments such as coastal navigational aids, approach channels of adequate depth, and shore structures for wharfage and warehousing. Elsewhere shore property is developed for dwellings, farming , and recreation or tourism. Until recently, beaches were commonly used as a source of sand and gravel aggregate.

The principal geological constraints (Table 14.10) for development of this coast arise from processes controlling the physical stability of the shore, and the chemical quality of inlet sediments. Though parts of the coast are stable due to resistant bedrock, significant reaches of shore that comprise unlithified glacial deposits and pre-Quaternary sandstones are susceptible to shore erosion resulting, in places, in damage to buildings not sheltered by shore protection structures. The eroded coastal sand fraction that drifts alongshore and which has built beaches, spits and barriers, periodically infills shipping channels. This constraint is counterbalanced by dredging; 34 million cubic metres of sediment have been removed from 550 harbours in the Atlantic provinces over a 25-year period. The mining of beach sand, previously a common practice, has been controlled in the last decade and is now recognized as a contributing factor to beach depletion and barrier failure. The eroding Eastern Shore of Nova Scotia illustrates the sensitivity of shore stability. Though the production of sediment is aided here by the present conditions of rising sea level, the supply is insufficient to nourish beaches far downdrift, since the eroding drumlins are a limited source and the sediment is retained locally in the compartmentalized coastline. These processes combined with extensive sediment mining caused Silver Sands Beach, a wide sandy barrier noted as a recreational site, to be reduced over a period of 30 years to a steep narrow gravel storm ridge. The sensitivity of these shores to change is now well recognized; mining is restricted and a nearby reach of drumlin and barrier coast has been protected in a provincial coastal heritage park.

Most major urban and industrial centres are established on bays or estuaries where waste discharge may cause pollution if contaminants are not adequately flushed into the open ocean. Measurable pollution effects were evident just 20 years after construction of a causeway to Cape Breton Island and industrialization of the newly created ice-free, quiet-water inlet, the Strait of Canso. The surface waters there contained waste-related trace metals and organic-rich suspended solids, and the bottom sediments showed evidence of waste buildup and faunal change in response to inlet pollution. Within Atlantic Canada, the Miramichi River and estuarine bottom sediments are among the most polluted with a trace Zn content severalfold greater than other estuaries and bays. This estuary, long a site of wood, pulp, and mineral processing, is also a fishery and a shipping and distribution centre for northeastern New Brunswick. The competing uses of this waterway confronted one another when it became necessary to enlarge a shipping channel to allow passage of ocean-draft

Figure 14.50. Submersible photograph showing residual disturbance of the surface of a gravelly till ridge one year after test plowing. Test trench runs from lower left to upper right of photograph. The fresh (light-coloured) surfaces on disturbed rocks are not yet colonized by benthic organisms. The diameter of the light-coloured cobble at centre is approximately 20 cm.

freight vessels into Miramichi ports. Would dredging recirculate toxic wastes, long-deposited in bottom sediments, and damage the fishery? Oceanographic and river flow studies combined with geochemical, sedimentological and micropaleontological evidence revealed that order-of-magnitude variations in suspended particulate matter and trace metals were a complex function of seasonal freshwater input rates, tidal flushing characteristics and geochemical interactions; for example, some metals are deposited permanently in the bottom sediments, whereas others are stored temporarily during the spring freshet to be flushed from the estuary over the rest of the year. The shipping channel and its associated dredging design took account of these processes and minimized the recirculation of reactive surface sediment by routing where possible to avoid dredging, aligning channels with currents, stabilizing channel banks, minimizing disturbance of surface sediment, and siting dredge spoils for long term stability. Despite these design precautions, some dredge spoils were remobilized and overflow losses from the dredges were widely dispersed, leading to a short-term Cd contamination of the benthic biota.

In contrast to the seasonal influence on the coasts of southeastern Canada, ice and cold climate dominate the coastal processes of northern Canada. The unique constraints (Table 14.10) are instabilities induced by sea-ice movements and permafrost at the shore. Rare storm waves, coincident with open water and thawed beaches, can transport sediment and impose relatively large changes in beach profiles. When sea ice moves shoreward under pressure, particularly following spring breakup, ice floes may raft into grounded ridges nearshore, override the beach to 100 m inland, or buckle and grow into shore ice piles that can persist for several years. These infrequent events are more likely at the shores of capes, deltas, promontories, channel junctions or small islands within channels. Unwanted differential movement of ground-based structures related to permafrost thaw settlement is likely, for example, when surface sediment is disturbed, waves expose the frost table, or shores with massive ground ice recede rapidly. Permafrost effects at the shore are complex, depending on the variable influences of sediment type, topography and morphology, thaw rates, presence of saline interstitial water, and the occurrence of fast ice such as an ice foot or anchor ice. The constraints influence, for example, the development of marine terminals in the Arctic Islands, increasingly required to transship mineral and hydrocarbon resources. Fiords and bays of the eastern and northeastern Arctic Islands provide numerous potential sites. In north-central Queen Elizabeth Islands, where oil and gas potential is high, fewer shores are suitable for port development, as most shores adjoin shallow water and are covered with ice-rich marine silts and clays. Sea ice is a major constraint to navigation, and ice-thickening due to frequent passage of vessels compounds the difficulties.

Public pressure traditionally calls for control and cleanup of oil spilled at sea and washed ashore. The need to predict the fate and effects of spilled oil at the shore has tested the understanding of coastal processes. Oil at the shore is a form of pollution especially damaging to vegetation and wildlife; it may also affect beach stability, coating sediment particles and changing their responses to waves. Cleanup by sediment removal may cause unwanted beach adjustments. Experience with accidental (149 in 5 years) and experimental oil spills shows that the response of oil at the shore is complex and varies with type, thickness and penetration of stranded oil; sediment type; shore morphology; and wave exposure. In arctic waters oil increases the melt rate of sea ice and may cause thermal instabilities if spilled on ice-rich ground. The major factors influencing the residence of oil are now known and have been used to classify much of the eastern Arctic and eastern Canadian shoreline with respect to its sensitivity to oil. This information is used in contingency plans for the control of potential oil spills arising from ongoing and future offshore oil and gas development.

The open sea: geological constraints

Early practical interest in the seafloor, prior to hydrocarbon exploration, was focussed principally on military and fishing operations, and communications. The failure of transatlantic telegraph cables as a result of the 1929 Grand Banks earthquake is well known. Communication cables on the seafloor have also failed due to crushing by icebergs.

Since 1966 seabed use has been dominated by hydrocarbon exploration and by planning for production of oil and gas. The geological constraints for these activities are summarized in Table 14.10.

Boulders and cobbles of probable glacial origin have jammed drill bits, prevented the setting of surface casing, and caused expensive delays, up to 21 days, in drilling progress on the Labrador Shelf and on Banquereau on the Scotian Shelf.

The mechanical integrity of drilling systems may be threatened where subsurface formation fluid pressures significantly exceed pressures expected due to the normal hydrostatic gradient. Moderate overpressures, due to rapid

Table 14.10. Constraints to developments, coastal and offshore eastern Canada

Constraining Process or Feature	Effects for Development	Examples, Comments
High waves in combination with high tides and storm surges; also tsunamis	Physical instability of the shore – flooding, shore erosion, and coastal sediment transport – may damage shore structures and infill shipping channels.	Exposed Atlantic, Gulf of St. Lawrence, and Bay of Fundy coasts.
Geochemical flux	Buildup and release of contaminants in inlet sediments; threatens water quality and fisheries.	Highly developed bays, inlets, estuaries, e.g., Strait of Canso, Nova Scotia, Halifax Harbour, Nova Scotia and Miramichi, New Brunswick.
Sea ice	Thrusting and loading of shore structures by nearshore ice ridging, beach override and shore ice piling. Thick ice constrains shipping.	Arctic Island Channels, especially coastal promontories; most vulnerable in spring.
Permafrost	Thaw settlement may cause strains in shore structures. Ice-rich material at the shore recedes rapidly, undermining potential coastal structures.	Arctic sediment-rich shores, enhanced by wave exposure of frost table.
Coastal oil spills	Contamination of habitat and damage to shore plants and animals. Cleanup by sediment removal may induce unwanted beach adjustment.	Sensitivity of large reaches of coastal zone is evaluated and mapped for oil spill contingency plans.
Boulders, cobbles	In subsurface, boulders may impede drilling for hydrocarbons. On sea bed, boulders may damage fishing trawls.	Labrador Shelf and Banquereau (drilling). Shelf banks (fishing grounds).
Overpressure	Highly (abnormally) pressured formation fluids threaten control of well.	Venture field, Scotian Shelf (2 blowouts); also experienced on Labrador Shelf and Grand Banks of Newfoundland.
Gas hydrate	Oil production could induce rapid gas production and thaw settlement, jeopardizing integrity of well.	Encountered in Arctic Islands and inferred to be widespread below 200 m on eastern Canadian continental margin.
Shallow gas	Poses danger in setting well casing. Alters load-bearing capacity of sediments.	Widespread in fine-grained sediments.
Pockmarks	Potentially unstable foundation sites.	Widespread in shelf basins and on upper slope in fine-grained sediment.

burial of Tertiary shales, are known on the Labrador and Northeast Newfoundland shelves, for example at the Indian Harbour and Bonavista wells. Overpressures are known also in the Jurassic and Lower Cretaceous section of the Jeanne d'Arc Basin on the Grand Banks of Newfoundland and are attributed to rapid burial of former muds and subsequent hydrocarbon generation. The greatest overpressures are known from the Venture Field on the Scotian Shelf below a depth of 4500 m, where overpressured zones pose significant constraints for the development of deep gas reservoirs. The origin of overpressure is controversial, attributed to late gas generation into secondary porosity or to rapid burial and early sealing of pore fluids. The overpressure system in the Scotian Basin has resulted in two well blowouts, one of which required 9 months to bring under control.

Gas hydrates are ice-like compounds of natural gas and water that form at low temperatures, but dissociate when warmed, for example by circulation of drilling fluids. Significant volumes of gas may be released that could cause problems with well control and reduction of support on the well casing. Hydrates are known in the Arctic Island channels and Beaufort Sea and are inferred to occur on the continental margin of eastern Canada mostly north of the Grand Banks of Newfoundland. The significance of hydrates as a constraint for offshore oil and gas production is, in 1986, not well known.

Shallow interstitial gas is recognized as a constraint at the initial phases of drilling before a blow-out preventor can be installed on the well casing. Problems are routinely circumvented by avoiding areas of interstitial gas detected in shallow seismic well-site surveys.

The principal structures used or proposed for oil and gas exploration and production in the eastern Canadian offshore include well conductor casings, jack-up drilling rigs, pile-supported production structures, gravity base production structures, pipelines, and anchoring systems for floating drilling rigs or production platforms. In addition to the gravity loads of structures, the seabed must also support a component of the lateral loads imposed by

Table 14.10. (cont.)

Constraining Process or Feature	Effects for Development	Examples, Comments
Geological features	Channels and canyons are sites of steeper slopes and potential instabilities. Some channels offer smooth routes through rough terrain for cables and pipelines. Buried channels, moraines, weathered zones, and faults mark boundaries of sediments with variable geotechnical properties that could induce differential structure settlement. Rough, irregular bedrock and moraine-ridge outcrops may be troublesome for cable and pipeline routings. Faults and diapirs with Quaternary deformation may indicate areas prone to future movement.	See Chapter 10 for description of features, and Maps 1705A and 1711A and Figures 2 and 3 in pocket for their known distribution.
Erosion and sedimentation	Undermines structures. Infills potential tidal power barrages. May cause unexpected loading or removal of support from pipeline by migrating bedforms. Possible strong currents on slope and rise may constrain future development.	Probable in exposed banks, where abundant sand exists, e.g., Sable Island and Georges Banks, and Bay of Fundy. See Chapter 11 for processes.
Ice scour	Bottom dragging or impacting iceberg or sea-ice ridge keels may collide with and damage seabed structures; also mixes and roughens surficial sediment.	Sea-ice effects limited to less than 50 m in Arctic. Modern iceberg effects may range down to 200-300 m on eastern Canadian shelf.
Seismicity and earthquakes	Shaking and triggering of liquefaction, slides, slumps, turbidity currents and tsunamis that lead to foundation or structure damage and coastal flooding.	Thick normal to underconsolidated sediments on continental slope and shelf basin flanks most susceptible to instability.
Slope stability	Creep and failure cause foundation instability.	Triggered rarely by waves on shelf edge, most likely by earthquakes in underconsolidated sediments on slopes.
Turbidity current	High lateral loading and foundation instability. Permeable turbidites degrade abyssal plain sediments for radioactive waste disposal.	Possible constraint for future development on the lower slope and rise.

environmental forces. As the forces arising from a combination of high waves, sea ice and icebergs are characteristic of the eastern Canadian offshore, and are unique in terms of world experience, exposed structures will likely require innovative design. For example, special reinforcement and a sharply corrugated outer caisson wall uniquely characterize the Hibernia gravity base production platform, designed to withstand impacts by sea ice and icebergs on the northeastern Grand Banks of Newfoundland.

An irregular inner shelf of resistant crystalline rock with scant Quaternary cover offers sound foundation materials for structures but in a rough and exposed setting. An outer shelf of large relatively shallow banks, broken by transverse saddles, is underlain by soft Cretaceous to Tertiary bedrock, which in places is mantled by till (Scotian Shelf Drift and equivalents) and glaciomarine deposits, with a discontinuous cover of loose sediment (Sable Island Sand and Gravel and equivalents) derived from these deposits by wave, current or iceberg reworking. Cretaceous to Tertiary clays and sands are strong and overconsolidated, at sites investigated, suggesting in general that they will be stable foundation materials. The Scotian Shelf Drift and equivalents, where overconsolidated by grounded ice, are expected to be stable under seismic shaking and to provide stable foundations, though boulders within the drift may resist pile penetration. Where normally consolidated as in till tongues, lift-off moraines and recessional moraines, the drift is more likely susceptible to settlement and movement under loading. The Sable Island Sand and Gravel and equivalents can provide stable foundations but are susceptible to scour (erosion) in high energy wave and current regimes.

The surficial sands and gravels tend to contain a fine grained component (Sambro Sand and equivalents) on the margins of the banks. An inner central area of the shelf consists of longitudinal depressions, either trough-like or broad, which together with the transverse saddles are partly infilled by fine grained sediments (Emerald Silt and LaHave Clay and equivalents). The Sambro Sand and similar muddy sands as well as Emerald Silt and equivalents can have a wide range of geotechnical properties and their response to loading cannot be usefully generalized. The LaHave Clay and equivalents are soft and normally consolidated, and are generally more suited to pile-supported rather than gravity base structures. Slope failures may occur on the steeper basin flanks and pockmarks may be a hazard to construction.

Slope failure caused by earthquake shaking is the principal constraint on the continental slope, and is most likely to occur in thick sequences of rapidly sedimented, glacial silt and sand, located seaward of shelf valleys and on the upper slope below the limits of till deposition in 500-700 m water depth.

Pockmarks are seafloor craters, formed by the expulsion of interstitial water or gas, and are known to be common in areas of muddy sediments off eastern Canada, on the shelf and upper slope to water depths of at least 1100 m. Such areas are avoided for siting structures, as their activity or effect on seabed bearing capacity is not well understood.

Wave and current stress can induce seabed instabilities such as scour, infill, bed-form migration, and liquefaction in vigorous hydrodynamic environments such as the coastal zone and continental shelf where mobile sediments are available. Up to 4 m of sand have been scoured from the legs of jack-up drilling rigs on Sable Island Bank. Because sediment transport processes are intermittent and often related to storm waves and currents, they are difficult to predict as theory and data are limited, particularly adjacent to structures. Undercurrents and currents due to deep sea "storms" may be constraints to future development on the continental slope and rise respectively.

Ice scouring, the action of bottom-dragging or grounded icebergs and sea ice ridges, reworks and alters properties of the seabed and may damage structures such as cables, pipelines, and wellheads. Sea-ice ridges affect the nearshore zone and the shallow Arctic Ocean shelf whereas icebergs, mostly from Greenland, threaten the eastern arctic sounds, fiords and the eastern Canadian shelf as far south as the Grand Banks of Newfoundland. Large icebergs, some with drafts as great as 200-300 m, create distinctive pits and furrows 1-2 m deep but locally up to 10 m deep depending on the seabed material. Relict scours of presumed Late Pleistocene age occur throughout the whole eastern Canadian continental margin to water depths as great as 750 m. Seabed roughness caused by ice scouring may induce unwanted pipe bending and reduce sliding resistance for gravity base structures. Seabed structures such as pipelines at serious risk will require protection, possibly by burial to a safe depth, by protective structures, or by siting in sheltered zones of lesser risk. Methods to evaluate the probability of scouring and the mechanisms and depth of sediment deformation are currently under development.

Earthquakes on the northern and eastern Canadian continental margins are relatively common; two major events of magnitudes 7.2 and 7.3 have occurred this century, in 1929 on the continental slope off St. Pierre Bank, south of Newfoundland, and in 1933 in Baffin Bay. The hazards commonly posed for development offshore include ground shaking, seabed liquefaction, slides, slumps, turbidity currents and tsunamis. Acoustic shock waves may damage floating structures and vessels.

The evaluation of seismicity recurrence and effects is difficult for eastern Canada as the period of record is short (100-200 years for historical records and 30-70 years for seismograph records), offshore earthquakes are poorly (selectively) detected and imprecisely located, and earthquake associations with tectonic features and the relative influence of potential mechanisms (glacial unloading, sedimentary loading, mass distribution across ocean-continent boundary, and interaction of a regional stress regime with pre-existing faults) are poorly known. As a result, offshore earthquake source zones, originally defined arbitrarily for estimation of onshore seismic risk, are being re-evaluated. Alternate source zones have been postulated, for example that seismicity concentrated in the large 1929 and 1933 events is representative of seismicity along the whole of the continental margin, not merely within localized epicentral areas. Geological evidence of seismicity in the form of mass sediment movements on the continental slope supports this model by suggesting longer return periods of 10 000 to 100 000 years for large earthquakes. Offshore risk is currently being mapped for various models in terms of the minimum cone penetrometer resistance (measurable geotechnical parameter) needed at a site to withstand the expected ground motion.

Though seabed gradients in excess of 3 per cent are common on the shelf and slope, slumps appear to be more numerous on the continental slope, triggered by earthquakes. The conditions for triggering slope instabilities by large waves occur in only limited areas of the continental margin.

Slope failure by earthquake failure was well illustrated by the spectacular effects associated with the 1929 earthquake in the region of the continental slope off St. Pierre Bank. There, liquefaction and slumping of rapidly-sedimented glacial silt and sand, led to debris flows and a turbidity current, which reached a velocity of at least 67 km/h, causing 28 breaks in 12 different cables that disrupted trans-Atlantic communications for six months. Turbidity currents are the likely major constraint for development on the lower slope and continental rise. Potential use of the Sohm Abyssal Plain for safe burial of radioactive waste is constrained by the presence of sandy turbidites such as the extensive 1929 deposit, because their greater permeability degrades the radionuclide-barrier properties of the surficial sediment sequence.

Earth science and decision making; summary

Selected examples of experience and planning illustrate the significance of geological understanding for coastal and offshore development in eastern Canada. Accidental oil spills cause pollution and alter the response of sediments to waves at the shore. As summarized earlier, prediction of the residence and effects of oil are required for contingency plans of oil spill control and shore cleanup. The effects of cleanup techniques themselves need to be known in terms of shore stability. Like beach mining for aggregate, simple removal of contaminated sediment may lead to unwanted beach depletion and shore failure.

Decisions concerning pipeline routing require understanding and trade-offs among many factors, particularly economics, safety and feasibility, the last factor often requiring a seabed suitable for the technology of pipelaying and pipe protection, as well as for support of the pipeline itself. This trade-off process was well illustrated in the early planning for transportation of hydrocarbons from the Hibernia field when regional geological mapping revealed thin sediment over indurated, untrenchable bedrock along much of the most direct and most economical route across the northern Grand Banks of Newfoundland, a setting exposed to iceberg scour. A route subsequently planned to the south was considered safer, as a pipeline there would suffer less exposure to iceberg scour and, being over softer rock, could feasibly be protected by burial. However, tanker vessels were ultimately selected to transport the oil, due to findings of adverse economics and technical difficulties anticipated in pumping waxy Hibernia crude oil through a long pipeline.

Similar considerations are illustrated by the case of planning for an electrical cable crossing of the Strait of Belle Isle to provide a power link between mainland Labrador and the Island of Newfoundland. Many of the difficulties and hence the cost and reliability for the three engineering scenarios, which have been considered for the protection of the cable from the effects of iceberg scour, fishing trawls, and strong currents, are defined by geological constraints: water-bearing rocks in the case of a tunnel, too high seabed gradients and excessive sediment cover for the cutting of a surface bedrock trench, and long routings for plowing the cable into appropriate surficial sediment.

With these constraints understood, the decision to develop the power link can be made on the basis of the market for the power, cost of installation and level of reliability required.

ACKNOWLEDGMENTS

Many institutions and corporations have helped by providing or referring us to useful information; we are grateful to Canterra Energy Limited, Husky Bow Valley East Coast Project, Mobil Oil Canada Ltd. and the Newfoundland and Labrador Hydro Corporation for sharing their unpublished experiences. Many persons, in addition to the contributors, have helped to formulate or review the contents of this chapter. In particular, we acknowledge the assistance of Basil Cooke, Professor Emeritus of Geology at Dalhousie University; Don Sherwin with Walter Bobby, Neil Jayasinghe, and Brian Power of the Canada-Newfoundland Offshore Petroleum Board; Brian Taylor of Jacques/McClelland Geosciences inc.; and Carl Amos, Don Forbes, Brian MacLean, Bernard Pelletier, David Piper, Dan Praeg, Dirk Tempelman-Kluit and John Wheeler of the Geological Survey of Canada. Paul Durling and David Mosher (GSC) assisted by compiling information for the chapter. The compilation was accomplished with financial assistance from the Offshore Geotechnics Program of the Panel on Energy Research and Development.

REFERENCES

Adams, J.
1985:   Canadian crustal stress data — a compilation to 1985; Earth Physics Branch, Open File 85-31, 81 p.
1986:   Changing assessment of seismic hazard along the southeastern Canadian margin; 3rd Canadian Conference on Marine Geotechnical Engineering, St.John's, Newfoundland, June 1986, v. 1, p. 42-53.

Adams, J. and Stavely, M.
1985:   Historical seismicity of Newfoundland; Earth Physics Branch, Open File 85-22, 73 p.

Adams, J., Reid, I., and Basham, P.W.
1984:   Historical seismicity, 1983 OBS experiment and seismic hazard along the southeastern Canadian margin; Joint program with abstracts, Canadian Geophysical Union, Halifax, p. 67-68.

Airphoto Analysis Associates Consultants Limited
1975:   Beach resources, eastern New Brunswick; unpublished report, Department of Natural Resources, New Brunswick, 215 p.

Allan, D.
1986:   Risk assessment for iceberg scour damage: Labrador Sea and Grand Banks; in Ice Scour and Seabed Engineering; ed. C.F.M. Lewis et al., Environmental Studies Revolving Funds Report No. 049, Ottawa, p. 240-248.

Ambler, D.C.
1976:   Miramichi River navigation channel study; Surface Water and Sediment Investigation, Water Survey of Canada, Department of Fisheries and Environment, Halifax, Nova Scotia, 71 p.

American Petroleum Institute
1981:   Recommended practice for planning, designing and constructing fixed offshore platforms; American Petroleum Institute RP 2a, 94 p.

Amos, C.L. and Barrie, J.V.
1985:   The frequency of ice scouring on the northeastern Grand Banks of Newfoundland using the inter-relationship of scours and bedform migration; in Proceedings of Workshop on Ice Scouring, ed. R. Pilkington; National Research Council of Canada Associate Committee on Geotechnical Research, February 15-19, 1982, Technical Memorandum n. 136, p. 220-221.

Amos, C.L. and Knoll, R.
1987:   The Quaternary sediments of Banquereau, Scotian Shelf; Geological Society of America Bulletin, v. 99, p. 244-260.

Andries, D.M.
1984:   The impact of beach protection on beach sand and gravel extraction in Nova Scotia 1968-1983; B.A. thesis, Geography Department, St. Mary's University, Halifax, 95 p.

Anglin, F.M.
1984:   Seismicity and faulting in the Charlevoix zone of the St.Lawrence Valley; Bulletin of the Seismological Society of America, v. 74, p. 595-603.

Ardus, D.A. (editor)
1980:   Offshore Site Investigation; Graham and Trotman Ltd., London, 291 p.

Atkinson, G.M., Finn, W.D.L., and Charlwood, R.G.
1984:   Simple computation of liquefaction probability for seismic hazard applications; Earthquake Spectra, v.1, p. 107-123.

Auffret, G., Buckley, D., Laine, E., Schuttenhelm, R., Searle, R., and Shephard, L.
1984:   NEA Seabed Working Group Status on site qualification for nuclear waste disposal within deep-sea sediment; Sandia National Laboratories, Albuquerque, New Mexico, Report SAND 83-2037, 64 p.

Barnes, P.W., McDowell, D., and Reimnitz, E.
1978:   Ice gouging characteristics: their changing patterns from 1975-1977, Beaufort Sea, Alaska; Environmental Assessment of the Alaskan Continental Shelf; Annual Reports of Principal Investigators, Volume 11, United States Geological Survey, Open File 78-730, p. 193-229.

Barrie, J.V.
1980:   Iceberg-seabed interaction (Northern Labrador Sea); in Proceed-Proceedings of the Conference on Use of Icebergs: Scientific and Practical Feasibility, Cambridge, April 1-3, 1980, Annals of Glaciology, v.1, p. 71-76.

1983:   Sedimentary processes and the preservation of iceberg scours on the eastern Canadian continental shelf; in Proceedings of the 7th International Conference on Port and Ocean Engineering Under Arctic Conditions, Helsinki, Finland, v. 4, p. 635-653.

Barrie, J.V., Collins, W.T., Clark, J.I., Lewis, C.F.M., and Parrott, D.R.
1986:   Submersible observations and origin of an iceberg pit on the Grand Banks of Newfoundland; in Current Research, Part A, Geological Survey of Canada, Paper 86-1A, p. 251-258.

Barrie, W.B. and Associates
1982:   Coastal geomorphology and processes, northeastern Bathurst Island group, N.W.T.; Geological Survey of Canada, Open File 1146, 106 p.

Barrie, W.B., Bornhold, B.D., Hodgson, D.A., Jubb, R.G., McLaren, P., and Taylor, R.B.
1978:   Coastal reconnaissance for marine terminal planning in the High Arctic, Geological Survey of Canada, Open File 633, 328 p.

Basham, P.W. and Adams, J.
1982:   Earthquake hazards to offshore development on the eastern Canadian continental shelves; in Proceedings of the Second Canadian Conference on Marine Geotechnical Engineering, Halifax, Nova Scotia, June 1982, National Research Council of Canada.

Basham, P.W., Adams, J., and Anglin, F.M.
1983:   Earthquake source models for estimating seismic risk on the eastern Canadian continental margin; Proceedings of the 4th Canadian Conference on Earthquake Engineering, June 15-17, Vancouver, British Columbia, p. 495-508.

Basham, P.W., Forsyth, D.A., and Wetmiller, R.J.
1977:   The seismicity of northern Canada; Canadian Journal of Earth Sciences, v. 14, p. 1646-1667.

Basham, P.W., Weichert, D.H., Anglin, F.M., and Berry, M.J.
1982:   New probabilistic strong seismic ground motion maps of Canada: a compilation of earthquake source zones, methods and results; Earth Physics Branch, Open File 82-33, 205 p.

Basham, P.W., Weichert, D.H., Anglin, F.M., and Berry, M.J.
1985:   New probabilistic strong seismic ground motion maps of Canada; Bulletin of the Seismological Society of America, v. 75, p. 563-595.

Bass, D.W. and Woodworth-Lynas, C.M.T.
1986:   Iceberg crater chains and scour up- and downslope; in Ice Scour Scour and Seabed Engineering; ed. C.F.M. Lewis et al.; Environmental Studies Revolving Funds Report No. 049, Ottawa, p. 122-128.

Bea, R.G.
1986:   Engineering aspects of ice gouging; in Ice Scour and Seabed Engineering; ed C.F.M. Lewis et al.; Environmental Studies Revolving Funds Report No. 049, Ottawa, p. 18-28.

Benedict, C.P. and Lewis, J.K.C.
1983:   Iceberg incursion probabilities into subsea structures; Proceedings of the Seventh International Conference on Port and Ocean Engineering Under Arctic Conditions, Helsinki, Finland, April 5-9, 1983, v. 1, p. 273-279.

Bostock, H.H., Cumming, L.M., Williams, H., and Smyth, W.R.
1983:   Geology of the Strait of Belle Isle area, northwestern Insular Newfoundland, southern Labrador, and adjacent Quebec; Geological Survey of Canada, Memoir 400, 145 p.

Bourget, E.
1977:   Observations on the effects of frost on beach sediments at Rimouski, lower St. Lawrence Estuary, Quebec; Canadian Journal of Earth Sciences, v. 14, p. 1732-1739.

Bousfield, E.L.
1955:   Some physical features of the Miramichi Estuary; Journal of Fisheries Board of Canada, v. 12, p. 342-364.

Bowen, A.J., Edmond, D.P., Piper, D.J.W., and Welsh, D.A.
1975:   The maintenance of beaches; Technical report, Institute of Environmental Studies, Dalhousie University, Halifax, Nova Scotia, 582 p.

Boyd, R. and Bowen, A.J.
1983:   The Eastern Shore Beaches — Cow Bay, Cole Harbour, Conrad's, Lawrencetown and Martinique; final report, Nova Scotia Department of Lands and Forests, 71 p.

Boyd, R., Bowen, A.J., and Hall, R.K.
1987:   An evolutionary model for transgressive sedimentation on the Eastern Shore of Nova Scotia; Chapter 4 in Glaciated Coasts, ed. D. Fitzgerald and P. Rosen; Academic Press, p. 87-114.

Bradley, J.S.
1975:   Abnormal formation pressure; American Association of Petroleum Geologists Bulletin, v. 59, p. 957-973.

Brett, C.P. and Zarudzki, E.F.K.
1979:   Project Westmar: A shallow marine geophysical survey on the West Greenland continental shelf; Gronlands Geologiske Undersogelse, Report no. 87, 27 p.

Brown, R.D., Roebber, P., and Walsh, K.
1986:   Climatology of severe storms affecting coastal areas of eastern Canada; Environmental Studies Revolving Funds, Report No. 20, Ottawa, 233 p.

Bryant, L.M. and Hall, R.A.
1979:   Design for complex foundation configurations and submarine conditions; Eleventh Annual Offshore Technology Conference, Paper n. 3403, p.405-412.

Buckley, D.E. and Grant, A.C.
1985:   Faultlike features in abyssal plain sediments: possible dewatering structures; Journal of Geophysical Research, v. 90, p. 9173-9180.

Buckley, D.E. and Winters, G.V.
1983:   Geochemical transport through the Miramichi Estuary; Canadian Journal of Fisheries and Aquatic Sciences, v. 40, Supplement 2, p. 162-182.

Buckley, D.E., Owens, E.H., Schafer, C.T., Vilks, G., Cranston, R.E., Rashid, M.A., Wagner, F.J.E., and Walker, D.A.
1974:   Canso Strait and Chedabucto Bay: A multidisciplinary study of the impact of man on the marine environment; in Offshore Geology of Eastern Canada, Volume 1, ed. B.R. Pelletier; Concepts and Applications of Environmental Marine Geology, Geological Survey of Canada, Paper 74-30, v. 1, p. 133-160.

Cammaert, A.B., Tanner, R.G., and Tsinker, G.P.
1983:   Design of ice management system for Arctic LNG dock; in Proceedings of the Seventh International Conference on Port and Ocean Engineering Under Arctic Conditions, Helsinki, Finland, April 5-9, 1983, v. 3, p. 242-252.

Canada-Newfoundland Offshore Petroleum Board
1986:   Decision 86.01 Application for approval, Hibernia Canada-Newfoundland benefits plan, Hibernia development plan; Canada-Newfoundland Offshore Petroleum Board, St. John's, Newfoundland, 143 p.

Canadian Hydrographic Service
1987:   Tide and current tables, Volumes 1 to 4: Atlantic Coast and Bay of Fundy, v. 1, 53 p.; Gulf of St. Lawrence, v. 2, 41 p.; St. Lawrence and Saguenay Rivers, v. 3, 39 p.; Artic and Hudson Bay, v. 4, 51 p.: Department of Fisheries and Oceans Canada.

Carter, L. and Schafer, C.T.
1983:   Interaction of the Western Boundary Undercurrent with the continental margin off Newfoundland; Sedimentology, v. 30, p. 751-768.

Chamberlain, E.J.
1983:   Frost heave of saline soils; in Permafrost; Fourth International tional Conference, Proceedings, Washington, D.C.; National Academy Press, p. 121-126.

Chari, T.R.
1979:   Geotechnical aspects of iceberg scours on ocean floors; Canadian Geotechnical Journal, v. 16, p. 379-390.

1986:   Iceberg-scour modelling at Memorial University of Newfoundland; in Ice Scour and Seabed Engineering; ed. C.F.M. Lewis et al.; Environmental Studies Revolving Funds Report No. 049, Ottawa, p. 109-117.

Chari, T.R. and Peters, G.R.
1981: Estimates of iceberg scour depths; in Proceedings of the Symposium: Production and Transportation Systems for the Hibernia Discovery, ed. W.E. Russell and D.B. Muggeridge; Petroleum Directorate, Government of Newfoundland and Labrador, p. 178-188.

Clark, J.I., Landva, J., Collins, W.T., and Barrie, J.V.
1986: The geotechnical aspects of seabed pits in the Grand Banks area; in Proceedings of the Third Canadian Conference on Marine Geotechnical Engineering, June 1986, St. John's, Newfoundland, v. 2, p. 431-456.

Clark, A. and Novak, P.
1984: Local erosion at vertical piles by waves and currents; in Seabed Mechanics, ed. B. Denness; Graham and Trotman, London, p. 248-250.

COGLA
1984: Investigation of events culminating in a blowout of gas and condensate at Shell et al. Uniacke G-72; Board of Investigators, Canada Oil and Gas Lands Administration, Halifax, Nova Scotia, 20 p.

1985a: Annual Report 1984; The Canada Oil and Gas Lands Administration, Ottawa, Ontario, 41 p.

1985b: Investigation of events culminating in a loss of well control at Mobil et al. West Venture N-91; Board of Investigators, Canada Oil and Gas Lands Administration, Halifax, Nova Scotia, 21 p.

Coleman, J.M., Prior, D.B., and Lindsay, J.F.
1983: Deltaic influences on shelf edge instability processes; in Critical Interference on Continental Margins, ed. D.J. Stanley; Society of Economical Paleontologists and Mineralogists, Special Publication n. 33, p. 121-137.

Collin, A.E. and Dunbar, M.J.
1964: Physical oceanography in Arctic Canada; Oceanography and Marine Biology Annual Review, v. 2, p. 45-75.

Comfort, G. and Graham, B.
1986: Evaluation of sea bottom ice scour models; Environmental Studies Revolving Funds Report No. 037; Ottawa, 71 p.

Cornell, C.A.
1968: Engineering seismic risk analysis; Bulletin of the Seismological Society of America, v. 58, p. 1583-1606.

Cranston, R.E.
1976: Accumulation and distribution of total mercury in estuarine sediments; Estuarine and Coastal Marine Science, v. 4, p. 695-700.

Cranston, R.E. and Buckley, D.E.
1972: Mercury pathways in a river and estuary; Environmental Science and Technology, v. 6, no. 3, p. 274-278.

Cranston, R.E., Fitzgerald, R.A., and Winters, G.V.
1974a: Geochemical data from the Strait of Canso and Chedabucto Bay, Nova Scotia; Bedford Institute of Oceanography, Data Series/BI-D-74-3/May 1974, 56 p.

1974b: Geochemical data, Baie des Chaleurs; Bedford Institute of Oceanography, Data Series/BI-D-74-6/October 1974, 22 p.

1975: Geochemical data, LaHave River and Estuary; Bedford Institute of Oceanography, Data Series/BI-D-75-4/February 1975, 33 p.

Croasdale, K.R.
1983: The present state and future development of Arctic offshore structures; in Proceedings of the Seventh International Conference on Port and Ocean Engineering Under Arctic Conditions, Helsinki, Finland, April 5-9, 1983, v. 4, p. 489-518.

Dahlberg, R.
1982: Observation of scour around offshore structures; in Second Canadian Conference on Marine Geotechnical Engineering, Halifax, Nova Scotia, June 1982, National Research Council of Canada.

Danish Hydraulics Institute
1979: Environmental conditions offshore west Greenland, Volume 4; Icebergs; Greenland Technical Organization, 130 p.

d'Apollonia, S.J. and Lewis, C.F.M.
1981: Iceberg scour data maps for the Grand Banks of Newfoundland between 46°N and 48°N; Geological Survey of Canada, Open File 819, 13 p.

1986: Numerical model for calculating spatial distribution and mean frequency of iceberg grounding events; in Ice Scour and Seabed Engineering; ed.C.F.M. Lewis et al.; Environmental Studies Revolving Funds, Report No. 049, Ottawa, p. 221-232.

Davidson, D.W., El-Defrawy, M.K., Fuglem, M.O., and Judge, A.S.
1978: Natural gas hydrates in northern Canada; in Proceedings of the Third International Conference on Permafrost, Volume 1; National Research Council of Canada, Ottawa, p. 937-943.

Davidson, D.W., Gard, S.K., Gough, S.R., Handa, Y.P. Ratcliffe, C.I., Ripmeester, J.A., and Tse, J.S.
1986: Laboratory analysis of a naturally occurring gas hydrate of sediments of the Gulf of Mexico; Geochimica et Cosmochimica Acta., v. 50, p. 619.

Desmarais, G., Daniel, C., and Dubois, J.-M. M.
1984: Geomorphologie et sensieilite physique des cotes aux deversements d'hydrocarbures dans l'estuaire Maritime et le Golfe du Saint-Laurent; Coastal Studies in Canadian Geography, v. 3, p. 2-24.

de Smitt, V.P.
1932: Earthquakes in the North Atlantic as related to submarine cables (abstracts); American Geophysical Union Transactions, p. 103-109.

Desplanque, C.
1979: The periodic reoccurrence of large tides; in Coastal Zone Management Study, Bay of Fundy, New Brunswick; report prepared for Department of Natural Resources, New Brunswick by Hunter and Associates, Mississauga, Ontario, p. 6-15.

Dewey, J.W. and Gordon, D.W.
1984: Map showing recomputed hypocenters of earthquakes in the eastern and central United States and adjacent Canada; United States Geological Survey, Miscellaneous Field Studies, Map MF-1699.

Dickinson, G.
1953: Geological aspects of abnormal pressures in Gulf Coast Louisiana; American Association of Petroleum Geologists Bulletin, v. 37, p. 410-432.

Dillon, W.P., Popenoe, P., Grow, J.A., Klitgord, K.D., Swift, B.A., Paull, C.K., and Cashman, K.V.
1983: Growth faulting and salt diapirism: their relationship and control in the Carolina Trough, eastern North America; in Studies of Continental Margin Geology, ed. J.S. Watkins and C.L. Drake; American Association of Petroleum Geologists Memoir 34, p. 21-46.

Dinsmore, R.P.
1972: Ice and its drift into the North Atlantic ocean; International Commission for the Northwest Atlantic Fisheries, Special Publication no. 8, p. 89-127.

Dionne, J.C.
1972: Characteristiques des schorres des regions froides, en particulier de l'estuaire du Saint-Laurent; Zeitschrift für Geomorphologie, Supplementband 13, p. 131-162.

1985: Formes, figures et facies sedimentaires glacials des estrans vaseux des régions Proides; Palaeogeography, Palaeoclimatology, Palaeoecology, v. 51, p. 415-451.

Doxsee, W.W.
1948: The Grand Banks earthquake of November 18, 1929; Publications of the Dominion Observatory, v. 7, no. 7, p. 324-336.

Drummond, K.J.
1986: Geopressure in Venture and the Sable Island area; Program and Abstracts, Canadian Society of Petroleum Geologists, 1986 Convention, June 1- 4, 1986, Calgary, Alberta, p. 40.

Durling, P.W. and Fader, G.B.
1986: Geological assessment of shallow faults and structural disturbance from the eastern Scotian Shelf and Laurentian Channel area; Geological Survey of Canada, Open File 1371, 27 p.

Ebbesmeyer, C.C., Okubo, A., and Helseth, J.M.
1980: Description of iceberg probability between Baffin Bay and the Grand Banks using a stochastic model; Deep Sea Research, v. 27A, p. 975-986.

El-Tahan, M. and El-Tahan, H.W.
1982: Estimation of iceberg draft; in Conference Record, Oceans 82, Marine Technology Society and Institute of Electrical and Electronic Engineers Council on Ocean Engineering, p. 689-695.

El-Tahan, M., El-Tahan, H., Courage, D., and Mitten, R.
1985: Documentation of iceberg groundings; Environmental Studies Revolving Funds Report No. 07, Ottawa, Ontario, 162 p.

Embley, R.W. and Jacobi, R.D.
1977: Distribution and morphology of large submarine sediment slides and slumps on the Atlantic continental margins; Marine Geotechnology, v. 2, p. 205-228.

Ervine, W.R. and Bell, J.S.
1987: Subsurface in-situ stress magnitudes from oil well drilling records: an example from the Venture area, offshore eastern Canada; Canadian Journal of Earth Sciences, v. 24, p. 1748-1759.

Esrig, M.I. and Kirby, R.C.
1977: Implications of gas content for predicting the stability of submarine slopes; Marine Geotechnology, v. 2, p. 81-100.

Evans, D.W., Cutshall, N.H., Cross, F.A., and Wolfe, D.A.
1977: Manganese cycling in the Newport River Estuary, North Carolina; Estuarine Coastal Marine Science, v. 5, p. 71-80.

Fader, G.B. and King, L.H.
1981: A reconnaissance of the surficial geology of Grand Banks of Newfoundland; in Current Research, Part A, Geological Survey of Canada Paper 81-1A, p. 45-56.

Fader, G.B. and Miller, R.O.
1986: Regional geological constraints to resource development - Grand Banks of Newfoundland; Proceedings 3rd Canadian Conference on Marine Geotechnical Engineering, St. John's, Newfoundland, June 1986, v. 1, p. 3-40.

Fader, G.B.J., King, L.H., and Josenhans, H.J.
1982: Surficial geology of the Laurentian Channel and Western Grand Banks of Newfoundland; Canadian Hydrographic Services, Marine Sciences Paper 21, 37 p.

Fee, D.A. and O'Dea, J.
1986: Technology for Developing Marginal Offshore Oilfields; Elsevier Applied Science Publishers Ltd., New York, 285 p.

Fenco Consultants Ltd.
1975: An analytical study of ice scour on the sea bottom; Arctic Petroleum Operator Association (APOA) Project 69-1, ed. G.R. Pilkington and H. Iyer; Calgary, 185 p.

Fertl, W.H.
1976: Abnormal Formation Pressures; Elsevier, New York, 382 p.

Flood, R.D.
1981: Pockmarks in the Dead Sea (abstract); EOS, v. 62, no. 17, p. 304.

Forbes, D.L.
1984: Coastal geomorphology and sediments of Newfoundland; in Current Research, Part B, Geological Survey of Canada, Paper 84-1B, p. 11-24.

Forbes, D.L. and Frobel, D.
1985: Coastal erosion and sedimentation in the Canadian Beaufort Sea; in Current Research, Part B, Geological Survey of Canada, Paper 85-1B, p. 69-80.

Forbes, D.L. and Taylor, R.B.
1987: Coarse grained beach sedimentation under paraglacial conditions, Canadian Atlantic Coast; Chapter 3 in Glaciated Coasts, ed. D. Fitzgerald and P. Rosen; Academic Press, p. 52-86.

Frederking, R., Sanderson, T., Wessels, E., and Inoue, M.
1983: Ice behavior around a small arctic island; Proceedings of the 7th International Conference on Port and Ocean Engineering Under Arctic Conditions, Helsinki, Finland, April 5-9, 1983, v. 2, p. 875-887.

Fruth, L.S.
1965: The Grand Banks turbidite and the sediments of the Sohm Abyssal Plain; M.Sc. thesis, Columbia University, New York, 258 p.

Fuglister, F.C.
1960: Atlantic Ocean Atlas of Temperature and Salinity Profiles and Data from the International Geophysical Year of 1957-1958; Woods Hole Oceanographic Institution, Atlas Series Volume 1, Woods Hole, Massachesetts, 209 p.

Galbraith, P.W.
1979: Atlantic region storm surge project, preliminary report, MAES 79-2; Atmospheric Environment Service, Bedford, Nova Scotia, 12 p.

Garrison, L.E. and Bea, R.G.
1977: Bottom stability as a factor in platform siting and design; Offshore Technology Conference, Paper no. 2893, p. 127-133.

Gaskill, H., Nicks, L., and Ross, D.
1985: A non-deterministic model of populations of iceberg scour depths; Cold Regions Science and Technology, v. 11, p. 107-122.

Gaskill, H.
1986: Report on a non-deterministic model of population of iceberg scour depths; in Iceberg and Seabed Engineering; ed. C.F.M. Lewis et al.; Environmental Studies Revolving Funds Report No. 049, Ottawa, p. 249-259.

Geonautics Ltd.
1984: Strait of Belle Isle power cable crossing, review of data, March 1984; in Final Report on Strait of Belle Isle Crossing HVDC Transmission Submarine Cable Scheme 1984 Program, Volume 6. Appendix A; Lower Churchill Development Corporation, St. John's, Newfoundland, 29 p.

Geoterrex Ltd.
1975: Seismic survey (4-20 kj digital sparker) in the Strait of Belle Isle; Report to Harrison Bradford and Associates for Lower Churchill Development Corporation, 18 p.

Girgrah, M. and Shah, V.K.
1978: Construction of a deep sea dock in the Arctic; in Proceedings of the Fourth International Conference on Port and Ocean Engineering Under Arctic Conditions, St. John's, Canada, September 26-30., 1977, v. 1, p. 370-381.

Goodman, M.A. and Franklin, L.J.
1982: Thermal model of a new concept for hydrate control during drilling; in Proceedings of the Fourth Canadian Permafrost Conference, Ottawa, Ontario, National Research Council of Canada, p. 349-355.

Gosson, C.M.C.
1985: Canada glaciers; The National Atlas of Canada 5th Edition (Map 1:7 500 000), Geographical Services Division, Surveys and Mapping Branch, Energy, Mines and Resources, Canada.

Gough, D.I.
1984: Mantle upflow under North America and plate dynamics; Nature, v. 311, p. 428-433.

Graham, B.W. and Nixon, J.F.
1980: Some geotechnical properties of seabed samples from Davis Strait, NWT; in Proceedings of First Canadian Conference on Marine Geotechnical Engineering, ed. W.J. Eden; The Canadian Geotechnical Society, Montreal, p. 290-300.

Grant, A.B.
1968: Atlas of oceanographic sections, temperature-salinity-dissolved oxygen-silica, Davis Strait-Labrador Basin-Denmark Strait-Newfoundland Basin 1966-1967; Atlantic Oceanographic Laboratory, Bedford Institute, Report AOL 68-5, Energy Mines and Resources Canada, Dartmouth, Nova Scotia, 80 p.

Green, H.W., Meuleman, A.W., and Dessureault, M.J.
1982: Trenching across the Strait of Belle Isle — marine geotechnical investigations; in Second Canadian Conference on Marine Geotechnical Engineering, June 1982, Dartmouth, Nova Scotia, National Research Council, 12 p.

Green, H.P., Reddy, A.S., and Chari, T.R.
1983: Iceberg scouring and pipeline burial depth; Proceedings of the 7th International Conference on Port and Ocean Engineering Under Arctic Conditions, Helsinki, Finland, 1983, v. 1, p. 280-288.

Guigne, J.
1986: The concept, design and experimental evaluation of an acoustic subseabed interrogator; Ph.D. thesis, University of Bath, England, 2 volumes, 371 p.

Gussow, W.C.
1982: The Grand Bank earthquake of 1929; discussion; Geoscience Canada, v. 9, p. 122-123.

Gustajtis, K.S.
1979: Iceberg scouring on the Labrador Shelf, Saglek Bank; Technical Report, Memorial University of Newfoundland, Centre for Cold Ocean Resources Engineering (C-CORE), Publication no. 79-13, 43 p.

Hale, P.B. and Greenwood, B.
1980: Storm-wave climatology: a study of the magnitude and frequency of geomorphic process; in The Coastline of Canada, ed. S.B. McCann; Geological Survey of Canada, Paper 80-10, p. 73-88.

Hansell, R.I.C., Scott, P.A., Staniforth, R., and Svoboda, J.
1983: Permafrost development in the intertidal zone at Churchill, Manitoba: A possible mechanism for accelerated beach uplift; Arctic, v. 32, no. 2, p. 198-203.

Hardy Associates (1978) Ltd.
1984: Study of well logs in the Arctic Islands to outline permafrost thickness and/or gas hydrate occurrence; Earth Physics Branch, Open File 84-8, 43 p.

Hargrave, B.T., Phillips, G.A., and Taguchi, S.
1976: Sedimentation measurements in Bedford Basin, 1973-74; Environment Canada Fisheries and Marine Service, Technical Report no. 608, 89 p.

Harper, J.R.
1985: Ice interaction with coastal processes; in Short course lecture notes, Coastal processes and engineering, Associate Committee for Research on shoreline erosion and sedimentation, National Research Council, Ottawa, p. 91-114.

Harper, J.R. and Owens, E.H.
1981: Analysis of Ice-Override Potential Along the Beaufort Sea Coast of Alaska; Proceedings of the 6th International Conference on Port and Ocean Engineering under Arctic Conditions, Quebec City, Quebec, Canada, July 27-31, 1981, v. 2, p. 974-984.

Harper, J.R., Owens, E.H., and Wiseman, W.J.
1978: Arctic Beach Processes and the Thaw of Ice-Bonded Sediments in the Littoral Zone; Proceedings of the 3rd International Permafrost Conference, Edmonton, Alberta, Canada, July 10-13, 1978, p. 195-199.

Harris, I.McK.
1974: Iceberg marks on the Labrdor Shelf; in Offshore Geology of Eastern Canada, ed. B.R. Pelletier; Geological Survey of Canada, Paper 74-30, p. 97-101.

Harris, I.McK. and Jollymore, P.G.
1974: Iceberg furrow marks on the continental shelf northeast of Belle Isle, Newfoundland; Canadian Journal of Earth Sciences, v. 11, p. 43-52.

Hasegawa, H.S. and Kanamori, H.
1987: Source mechanism of the magnitude 7.2 Grand Banks earthquake of November 1929: double couple or submarine landslide?; Bulletin Seismological Society of America, v. 77, p. 1984-2004.

Hayes, M.O., Michel, J., and Brown, P.J.
1978: Vulnerability of coastal environments of lower Cook Inlet, Alaska to oil spill impact; in Proceedings of the 4th International Conference on Port and Oceans Engineering under Arctic Conditions, St. John's, Newfoundland, September 26-30, 1977, v. 2, p. 832-843.

Heezen, B.C. and Ewing, W.M.
1952: Turbidity currents and submarine slumps, and the 1929 Grand Banks earthquake; American Journal of Science, v. 250, p. 849-873.

Heginbottom, J.A.
1984: Continued headwall retreat of a retrogressive thaw flow slide, eastern Melville Island, Northwest Territories; in Current Reasearch, Geological Survey of Canada, paper 84-1B, p. 363-365.

Herbich, J.B.
1981: Offshore pipeline design elements; Marcel Dekker, New York, 227 p.

Herbich, J.B., Schiller, R.E. Jr., Watanabe, R.K., and Dunlap, W.A.
1984: Seafloor scour: design guidelines for ocean-founded structures; Marcel Dekker, New York, 320 p.

Hnatiuk, J. and Brown, K.D.
1977: Sea bottom scouring in the Canadian Beaufort Sea; in Proceedings of the Ninth Annual Offshore Technology Conference, Houston, Texas, May 2-5, 1977, v. 3, p. 519-527.

Hnatiuk, J. and Wright, D.B.
1983: Seabottom scouring in the Canadian Beaufort Sea; in Proceedings of the Fifteenth Annual Offshore Technical Conference, Houston, Texas, May 2-5, 1983, v. 3, p. 35-40.

Hodgson, D.A.
1977: A preliminary account of surficial materials, geomorphological processes, terrain sensitivity, and Quaternary history of King Christian and southern Ellef Ringnes islands, District of Franklin; in Report of Activities, Part A, Geological Survey of Canada, Paper 77-1A, p. 485-493.
1982: Surficial materials and geomorphological processes, western Sverdrup and adjacent islands, District of Franklin; Geological Survey of Canada, Paper 81-9, 44 p.

Hodgins, D.A., Huntley, D.A., Liam Finn, W.D., Long, B., Drapeau, G., and Bowen, A.J.
1986: Bottom sediment transport — present knowledge and industry needs; Environmental Studies Revolving Funds Report No. 027, Ottawa, 394 p.

Hodgson, G.J., Lever, J.H., Woodworth-Lynas, C.M.T., and Lewis, G.F.M. eds.
1988: The Dynamics of Iceberg Grounding and Scouring (DIGS) Experiment and Repetitive Mapping of the Eastern Canadian Continental Shelf; Environmental Studies Research Funds Report No. 094, Ottawa, 316 p.

Hollister, C.D. and McCave, I.N.
1984: Sedimentation under deep-sea storms; Nature, v. 309, p. 220-225.

Holtz, R.D. and Kovacs, W.D.
1981: An Introduction to Geotechnical Engineering; Prentice Hall, Inc., Englewood Cliffs, New Jersey, 733 p.

Hood, G.
1980: A review of oil industry experience with gas hydrates in exploratory drilling in the Canadian Arctic; in Proceedings of a Symposium on Permafrost Geophysics, Ottawa, Ontario, National Research Council of Canada, Technical Memorandum 129, p. 159-162.

Hotzel, I.S. and Miller, J.D.
1983: Icebergs: their physical dimensions and the presentation and application of measured data; Annals of Glaciology, v. 4, p. 116-123

Hovland, M.
1981: Characteristics of pockmarks in the Norwegian Trench; Marine Geology, v. 39, p. 103-117.

Howells, K. and McKay, A.G.
1977: Seismic profiling in Miramichi Bay, New Brunswick; Canadian Journal of Earth Sciences, v. 14, p. 2909-2927.

Hudson, R.D., Pilkington, G.R., and Metge, M.
1981: Extreme ice features along the N.W. edge of the Canadian Arctic Archipelago; Proceedings, Workshop on Ice Action on Shores, Rimouski, Québec, p. 15-34.

Hunter, G.T. and Associates
1982: Coastal zone management study, Bay of Fundy, New Brunswick; report prepared for the Department of Natural Resources, New Brunswick, 215 p.

Hutchins, R.W., Dodds, J., and Fader, G.
1985: Seabed II: high-resolution acoustic seabed surveys of the deep ocean; in Advances in underwater technology and offshore engineering, Proceedings of International Conference, Offshore Site Investigation; Graham and Trotman, Ltd., v. 3, p. 69-84.

Hydrotechnology Ltd.
1980: The design and maintenance of harbours in northeast New Brunswick with respect to the alongshore transport of beach sand; Small Craft Harbours Branch, Department of Fisheries and Oceans, Ottawa, Canada, 37 p.

Ishihara, K.
1985: Stability of natural deposits during earthquakes; Proceedings of the Eleventh International Conference on Soil Mechanics and Foundation Engineering, San Francisco, theme lectures; published by A.A. Balkema, Rotterdam, p. 321-376.

Jacques/McClelland Geoscience Inc.
1982a: Shallow materials maps for potential sediment response to earthquakes, continental shelf, offshore Eastern Canada; Geological Survey of Canada, Open File 878, 16 p.
1982b: Seabed stability of the continental shelf of eastern Canada; Geological Survey of Canada, Open File, 130 p.

Jacques, Whitford and Associates Ltd.
1984: The adequacy of available seabed information as input to design criteria and operating constraints for eastern Canada offshore exploratory drilling; Report to the Royal Commission on the Ocean Ranger Marine Disaster, Canada, 60 p.

Jahns, H.O.
1984: Subsea permafrost and petroleum development; in Proceedings of the 4th International Conference on Permafrost, July 17-22, 1983, Fairbanks, Alaska, p. 90-92.

Jordaan, I.J.
1984: Risk and safety assessment for arctic offshore projects; in Arctic Technology and Policy; Proceedings of the Second Annual MIT Sea Grant College Program Lecture and Seminar and the Third Annual Robert Bruce Wallace Lecture, ed. I. Dyer and C. Chryssostomidis; McGraw-Hill, Toronto, Ontario, p. 81-88.

Jordan, F.
1972: Oceanographic data of Halifax Inlet; Bedford Institute of Oceanography, Dartmouth, Nova Scotia, Data Series B1 D-72-8, 82 p.

Josenhans, H.W. and Barrie, J.V.
1982: Preliminary results of submersible observations on the Labrador Shelf; in Current Research, Part B, Geological Survey of Canada Paper, 82-1B, p. 269-276.

Josenhans, H., Barrie, J.V., and Keily, L.
1987: Mass-wasting along the Labrador Shelf margin: submersible observations; Geomarine Letters, v. 7, p. 199-205.

Josenhans, H.W., King, L.H., and Fader, G.B.
1978: A side-scan sonar mosaic of pockmarks on the Scotian Shelf; Canadian Journal of Earth Sciences, v. 15, no. 5, p. 831-840.

Josenhans, H.W., Zevenhuizen, J., and Klassen, R.A.
1986: The Quaternary geology of the Labrador shelf; Canadian Journal of Earth Sciences, v. 23, p. 1190-1213.

Judge, A.
1982: Natural gas hydrates in Canada; in Proceedings of the 4th Canadian Permafrost Conference, ed. H.M. French, March 2-5, 1981, Calgary, Alberta, p. 320-328.

Judge, A.S., Jones, I., and Dawson-Grove, G.E.
1986: Distribution of gas hydrates in the offshore areas of the Canadian east coast (Abstract); in Third Canadian Conference on Marine Geotechnical Engineering, St. John's, Newfoundland, p. 97-98.

Keen, C.E. and Barrett, D.L.
1981: Thinned and subsided continental crust on the rifted margin of eastern Canada: crustal structure, thermal evolution and subsidence history; Geophysical Journal, v. 65, p. 443-465.

Keen, M.J. and Piper, D.J.W.
1976: Kelp, methane, and an impenetrable reflector in a temperate bay; Canadian Journal of Earth Sciences, v. 13, p. 312-318.

Kenting Exploration Services Limited
1975: Ice scour age-dating, Beaufort Sea 1975; Report to Canadian Marine Drilling Limited, p. 29.

King, E.L. and Gillespie, R.T.
1986: Regional iceberg scour distribution and variability on the eastern Canadian continental shelf; in Ice Scour and Seabed Engineering, ed. C.F.M. Lewis et al.; Environmental Studies Revolving Funds Report No. 049, Ottawa, p. 172-181.

King, L.H.
1976: Relict iceberg furrows on the Laurentian Channel and western Grand Banks; Canadian Journal of Earth Sciences, v. 13, p. 1082-1092.
1980: Aspects of regional surficial geology related to site investigation requirements — eastern Canadian Shelf; in Offshore Site Investigation, ed. D.A. Ardus; Graham and Trotman, London, p. 37-59.

King, L.H. and Fader, G.B.
1976: Application of the Huntec deep tow high-resolution seismic system to surficial and bedrock studies — Grand Banks of Newfoundland; in Report of Activities, Part C, Geological Survey of Canada, Paper 76-1C, p. 5-36.

1980: Seabed conditions east of the Avalon Peninsula to Virgin Rocks; Geological Survey of Canada, Open File 723, 5 p.

1986: Wisconsinan glaciation of the Atlantic continental shelf of southeast Canada; Geological Survey of Canada, Bulletin 363, 72 p.

King, L.H. and MacLean, B.
1970: Pockmarks on the Scotian Shelf; Geological Society of America, v. 81, p. 3141-3148.

King, L.H., Fader, G.B., Jenkins, W.A.M., and King, E.L.
1986: Occurrence and regional geological setting of Paleozoic rocks on the Grand Banks of Newfoundland; Canadian Journal of Earth Sciences, v. 23, p. 504-526.

Knight, R.J. and Dalrymple, R.W.
1976: Winter conditions in a macrotidal environment, Cobequid Bay, Nova Scotia; La Revue de Géographie de Montréal, v. 30, no. 1, 2, p. 65-86.

Kollmeyer, R.C.
1980: Iceberg scour probabilities in the Strait of Belle Isle; in Strait of Belle Isle Crossing HVDC Transmission Submarine Cable Scheme, Vol. III, SNC-Lavalin Newfoundland Ltd. Report 11.99.16 to Lower Churchill Development Corporation Limited, 36 p.

Kovacs, A.
1983: Shore ice ride-up and pile-up features: Part 1: Alaska's Beaufort Sea coast; U.S.A. Cold Regions Research and Engineering Laboratory, CRREL Report 83-9, 51 p.

Kovacs, A. and Mellor, M.
1974: Sea ice morphology and ice as a geologic agent in the southern Beaufort Sea; in The Coast and Shelf of the Beaufort Sea, ed. J.C. Reed and J.E. Slater; Arctic Institute of North America, Arlington, VA, p. 113-161.

Kovacs, A. and Sodhi, D.S.
1980: Shore ice pile-up and ride-up: field observations, models and theoretical analyses; Cold Regions Science and Technology 2, p. 209-288.

Kranck, K.
1976: Suspended and bottom sediments of Miramichi Estuary, New Brunswick; Bedford Institute of Oceanography, A.O.L., Environment Canada, Report Series B1-R-76.

1981: Particulate matter grain-size characteristics and flocculation in a partially mixed estuary; Sedimentology, v. 28, p. 107-114.

Kvenvolden, K.A. and Barnard, L.A.
1982: Gas hydrates of the Blake Outer Ridge Site 533 DSDP/IPOD leg 76; in Gas Hydrates in Deep Ocean Sediments, Annual Report; Gas Research Institute, Chicago, p. 335-69.

1983: Hydrates of natural gas in continental margins; in Studies in Continental Margin Geology, ed. J.S. Watkins and C.L. Drake; American Association of Petroleum Geologists Memoir 34, p. 631-640.

Kvenvolden, K.A. and McDonald, T.J.
1983: Gas hydrates of the Middle America Trench DSDP/IPOD leg 84; in Gas Hydrates in Deep Ocean Sediments, Final Report; Gas Research Institute, Chicago, p. 26-59.

Lachapelle, A.
1981: Winds and waves in Lancaster Sound; Proceedings of the 6th International Conference on Port and Ocean Engineering Under Arctic Conditions, July 27-31, 1981, Quebec, v. 2, p. 830-842.

Lemon, D.D. and Fissel, D.B.
1982: Seasonal variations in currents and water properties in northwestern Baffin Bay, 1978-1979; Arctic, v. 35, p. 211-218.

LeTirant, P.
1979: Seabed reconnaissance and offshore soil mechanics for the installation of petroleum structures; Gulf Publishing Co., Houston, Texas, 508 p.

Lewis, C.F.M.
1978: The frequency and magnitude of drift-ice groundings from ice-scour tracks in the Canadian Beaufort Sea; Proceedings of the 4th International Conference on Port and Ocean Engineering Under Arctic Conditions, Memorial University of Newfoundland, St. John's, Newfoundland, September 26-30, 1977, p. 568-579.

Lewis, C.F.M. and Barrie, J.V.
1981: Geological evidence of iceberg groundings and related seafloor processes in the Hibernia Discovery area of Grand Bank, Newfoundland; in Proceedings of the Symposium Production and Transportation Systems for the Hibernia Discovery, St. John's, Newfoundland Petroleum Directorate, Government of Newfoundland and Labrador, 1981, p. 146-177.

Lewis, C.F.M. and Parrott, D.R.
1987: Iceberg scouring rate studies, Grand Banks of Newfoundland; in Current Research, Part A, Geological Survey of Canada, Paper 87-1A, p. 825-846.

Lewis, C.F.M., Blasco, S.M., Bornhold, B.D., Hunter, J.A.M., Judge, A.S., Kerr, J.W., McLaren, P.G., and Pelletier, B.R.
1977: Marine geological and geophysical activities in Lancaster Sound and adjacent fiords; in Report of Activities, Part A, Geological Survey of Canada, Paper 77-1A, p. 495-506.

Lewis, C.F.M., Josenhans, H.W., Fader, G.B., MacLean, B., d'Apollonia, S.J., and Barrie, J.V.
1982: The distribution and shape variability of iceberg scour marks on Canadian continental shelves (abstract); Joint Oceanographic Assembly, Halifax, Nova Scotia, v. 2, p. 40.

Lewis, C.F.M., MacLean, B., and Falconer, R.K.H.
1980: Ice scour abundance in Labrador Sea and Baffin Bay; a reconnaissance of regional variability; First Canadian Conference on Marine Geotechnical Engineering, April 25-27, 1979, Calgary, Alberta, The Canadian Geotechnical Society, Montreal, p. 79-94.

Lewis, C.F.M., Parrott, D.R., and Durling, P.W.
1987: Shallow Tertiary seismostratigraphy and engineering geology of the northeastern Grand Banks of Newfoundland; Geological Survey of Canada, Open File 1437, 18 p.

Lien, R.
1986: Iceberg scouring and its influence on seabed conditions: investigation and proposed model for the Norwegian Shelf; in Ice Scour and Seabed Engineering, ed. C.F.M. Lewis et al., Environmental Studies Revolving Funds Report No. 049, Canada Oil and Gas Lands Administration; Energy, Mines and Resources Canada, Ottawa, p. 87-96.

Long, L.G., Thompson, G.R., Brown, J.D., and Rivette, C.A.
1986: Hibernia site geotechnical characterization; in Proceedings of the Third Canadian Conference on Marine Geotechnical Engineering, June 1986, St. John's, Newfoundland, v. 1, p. 99-116.

Loring, D.H.
1976: The distribution and partition of zinc, copper and lead in sediments of the Saguenay fjord; Canadian Journal of Earth Sciences, v. 13, p. 960-971.

Loring, D.H. and Nota, D.J.G.
1973: Morphology and sediments of the Gulf of St. Lawrence; Fisheries Research Board of Canada, Bulletin 182, 147 p.

MacLaren Plansearch
1985: Environmental monitoring of the dredging of the Miramichi River, Summary Report, 1981-1984; Contract Report to Public Works Canada, Saint John, New Brunswick, 74 p.

MacLean, B. and King, L.H.
1971: Scotian Shelf surficial geology, Banquereau and Misaine Bank; Geological Survey of Canada, Paper 71-52, 19 p.

MacLean, B., Falconer, R.K.H., and Clarke, D.B.
1978: Tertiary basalts of western Davis Strait; bedrock core samples and geophysical data; Canadian Journal of Earth Sciences, v. 15, p. 773-780.

MacLean, B., Srivastava, S.P., and Haworth, R.T.
1982: Bedrock structures off Cumberland Sound, Baffin Island Shelf: core samples and geophysical data; in Arctic Geology and Geophysics, ed. A.F. Embry and H.R. Balkwill; Canadian Society of Petroleum Geologists, Memoir 8, p. 279-295.

Maes, M.A.
1986: Calibration of partial factors in the new Canadian Standard Association — Code for fixed offshore production structures; Environmental Protection Branch, Canadian Oil and Gas Lands Administration, Technical Report no. 9, 81 p.

Mahar, L.J., Wilson, R.M., and Vinson, T.S.
1983: Physical and numerical modeling of uniaxial freezing in saline gravel; Proceedings, Permafrost; Fourth International Conference, Washington, D.C.: National Academy Press, p. 773-778.

Makogon, Yu.F., Tolkachev, M.V., and Topchev, Yu.I.
1982: The drilling of wells that intersect gas hydrate beds; Gazovaya promyshlennost, v. 4, p. 30-32.

Mann, C.R., Grant, A.B., and Foote, T.R.
1965: Atlas of oceanographic sections, temperature-salinity-dissolved oxygen, Northwest Atlantic Ocean, Newfoundland Basin and Gulf Stream, February 1962 — July 1964; Bedford Institute of Oceanography, Report BIO 65-16, Dartmouth, Nova Scotia, 51 p.

Marine Board
1982: Understanding the Arctic Sea-floor for Engineering Purposes; United States National Academy Press, Washington, D.C., 141 p.

Markham, W.E.
1980: Ice atlas, eastern Canadian seaboard; Environment Canada, Atmospheric Environment Service, Toronto, 198 p.

1981: Ice atlas, Canadian arctic waterways; Atmospheric Environment Service, Toronto, Canada, 198 p.

Marsters, J.C.
1986: Geotechnical analysis of sediments from the eastern Canadian continental slope, south of the St. Pierre Bank; M. Eng. project, Technical University of Nova Scotia, Halifax, Nova Scotia, 218 p.

Matich, M.A.J. and German, R.B.
1980: Review of development of offshore site investigation techniques in Canada; in Proceedings of the First Canadian Conference on Marine Geotechnical Engineering, ed. W.J. Eden; The Canadian Geotechnical Society, Montreal, p. 179-197.

Maxwell, J.B., Duck, P.J., Thomson, R.B., and Vickers, G.G.
1980: The climate of northwestern Baffin Bay; Canadian Climate Centre, Report no. 80-2; unpublished manuscript, Atmospheric Environment Service, Downsview, Ontario.

McCann, S.B.
1973: Beach Processes in an Arctic Environment; in Coastal Geomorphology, ed. D.R. Coates; Proceedings of the Third Annual Geomorphology Symposium State University of New York, Binghamton, N.Y., p. 141-155.

McCann, S.B. and Carlisle, R.J.
1972: The nature of the ice-foot on the beaches of Radstock Bay, S.W. Devon Island, N.W.T. in the spring and summer of 1970; Institute of British Geographers, Special Publication 4, p. 175-186.

McClelland, B., Young, A.G., and Remmes, B.D.
1982: Avoiding jack-up rig foundation failures: Proceedings of the Symposium in Geotechnical Aspects of Offshore and Nearshore Structures, Thailand; Geotechnical Engineering (Thailand), v. 13, no. 2, p. 151-189.

McDonald, B.C., Edwards, R.E., and Rampton, V.N.
1973: Position of frost table in the near-shore zone, Tuktoyaktuk Peninsula, District of Mackenzie; Geological Survey of Canada, Paper 73-1, Part B, p. 165-168.

McLaren, P.
1980: The coastal morphology and sedimentology of Labrador: a study of shoreline sensitivity to a potential oil spill; Geological Survey of Canada, Paper 79-28, 41 p.
1982: The coastal geomorphology, sedimentology and processes of eastern Melville and western Byam Martin Islands, Canadian arctic archipelago; Geological Survey of Canada, Bulletin 333, 39 p.

McLaren, P. and Barrie, W.B.
1985: The coastal morphology and sedimentology of eastern Lancaster Sound and northern Baffin Island: a study of shoreline sensitivity to a potential oil spill; Geological Survey of Canada, Paper 83-24.

McLean, A.Y. and MacGregor, C.D.R.
1976: An inventory of historical dredging operations and industrial waste disposal practices in the Atlantic coast region; Canplan Oceanology Ltd., unpublished report, Environment Canada, 66 p.

Melling, H., Lake, R.A., Topham, D.R., and Fissel, D.B.
1984: Oceanic thermal structure in the western Canadian Arctic; Continental Shelf Research, v. 3, p. 233-258.

Metge, M., Danielewicz, B., and Hoare, R.
1981: On measuring large scale ice forces; Hans Island 1980; 6th International Conference on Port and Ocean Engineering under Arctic Conditions (POAC), Québec, Canada, July 27-31, 1981, v. II, p. 629-642.

Middleton, G.V.
1969: Turbidity currents; in The New Concept of Continental Margin Sedimentation, ed. D.J. Stanley; American Geological Institute, Short Course Notes, Philadelphia, Lecture 10, 20 p.

Miller, A.A.L., Mudie, P.J., and Scott, D.B.
1982: Holocene history of Bedford Basin, Nova Scotia: foraminifera, dinoflagellate, and pollen records; Canadian Journal of Earth Sciences, v. 19, no. 12, p. 2342-2367.

Milne, A.
1969: Underwater acoustics in ice covered seas; Man in Cold Water Conference, Montreal, Quebec, May 1969, Oceanology Series no. 1, Department Industry, Trade and Commerce, and McGill University, p. 37-42.

Mobil Oil Canada Ltd.
1983: Venture development project environmental impact statement, v. III a & b: Biophysical Assessment; Mobil Oil Canada Ltd., Halifax, Nova Scotia, v. IIIa, 258 p., v. IIIb, 238 p.
1985: Hibernia development project environmental impact statement, v. IIIa Biophysical Assessment; Mobil Oil Canada Ltd., St. John's, Newfoundland, 258 p.
1986: Overview of the Hibernia development plan, Appendix D; in Canada-Newfoundland Offshore Petroleum Board, Decision 86.01, St. John's, Newfoundland, p. 107-143.

Monahan, D. and Macnab, R.F.
1975: Flemish Cap, Flemish Pass, and the northeastern Grand Banks of Newfoundland morphology; in Offshore Geology of Eastern Canada, Geological Survey of Canada, Paper 74-30, v. II, p. 207-216.

Moran, K. and Hurlbut, S.E.
1986: Analysis of potential slope instability due to wave loading on the Scotian Shelf; Proceedings of the Third Canadian Conference on Marine Geotechnical Engineering, June 1986, St. John's, Newfoundland, p. 503-504.

Morgenstern, N.R.
1967: Submarine slumping and the initiation of turbidity currents; in Marine Geotechnique, ed. A.F. Richards; University of Illinois Press, Chicago, p. 189-220.

Morin, P. and Dawe, C.R.
1986: Geotechnical properties of two deep sea marine soils from Labrador Sea area; in Third Canadian Conference on Marine Geotechnical Engineering, June 1986, St. John's, Newfoundland, v. I, p. 117-137.

Mosher, D.C.
1987: Late Wisconsinan sedimentation on the Scotian Slope near Verrill Canyon; M.Sc. thesis, Memorial University of Newfoundland, St. John's, Newfoundland, 249 p.

Mudie, P.J.
1986: Palynology as a method for dating iceberg scours; in Ice Scour and Seabed Engineering; ed. C.F.M. Lewis et al., Environmental Studies Revolving Funds Report No. 049, Ottawa, p. 233-239.

Muench, R.D.
1971: The Physical Oceanography of the Northern Baffin Region, Baffin Bag — North Water Project, Scientific Report No. 1; The Arctic Institute of North America, Washington, D.C., 150 p.

Munro, P.S., Halliday, R.J., Shannon, W.E., and Schieman, D.R.J.
1988: Canadian Seismograph Operations — 1986; Geological Survey of Canada, Paper 88-16, 20 p.

Murray, J.E.
1969: The drift, deterioration and distribution of icebergs in the North Atlantic Ocean; in Ice Seminar; Canadian Institute of Mining and Metallurgy, Special Volume 10, p. 3-18.

Murray, J.W. and McMillan, N.J.
1982: Drilling problems encountered from boulder beds on the Labrador Shelf and recommendations for resolution: Appendix to: W.H. Mathews, 1982, Glacial history of the eastern seaboard of Canada pertaining to boulder distribution on the continental shelf, an overview; unpublished report, Canterra Energy Ltd., Calgary, Alberta, 43 p.

Murty, T.S.
1984: Storm surges — meteorological ocean tides; Canadian Bulletin of Fisheries and Aquatic Sciences, Ottawa, v. 212, 897 p.

Nardin, T.R., Hein, F.J., Gorsline, D.S., and Edwards, B.D.
1979: A review of mass movement processes, sediment and acoustic characteristics, and contrasts in slope and base-of-slope systems versus canyon-fan-basin floor systems; in Geology of Continental Slopes, ed. L.J. Doyle and O.H. Pilkey; Society of Economic Paleontologists and Mineralogists, Special Publication no. 27, p. 61-75.

National Building Code of Canada
1985: Supplement to the National Building Code of Canada; Associate Committee on the National Building Code of Canada, National Research Council of Canada, Publication no. 23178, 278 p.

Neave, K.G., Judge, A.S., Hunter, J.A., and MacAulay, H.A.
1978: Offshore permafrost distribution in the Beaufort Sea as determined from temperature and seismic observations; in Current Research, Part C, Geological Survey of Canada, Paper 78-1C, p. 13-18.

Nelson, H., Thor, D.R., Sandstrom, M.W., and Dvenvolden, K.A.
1979: Modern biogenic gas-generated craters (sea-floor "pockmarks") on the Bering Shelf, Alaska; Geological Society of America, v. 90, no. 1, p. 1144-1152.

Neu, H.J.A.
1982: 11-year deep water wave climate of Canadian Atlantic waters; Canadian Technical Report of Hydrography and Ocean Sciences no. 13, Department of Fisheries and Oceans, Dartmouth, Nova Scotia, 41 p.
1984: Interannual variation and longer term changes in the sea state of the North Atlantic, from 1970 to 1982; Journal of Geophysical Research, v. 89, no. C4, p. 6397-6402.

Newton, R.S., Cunningham, R.C., and Schubert, C.E.
1980: Mud volcanoes and pockmarks: Seafloor Engineering Hazards or Geological Curiosities; Offshore Technology Conference, May, Houston, Texas, Paper 3729, p. 425-436.

Noguera, V.H.
1987: Geology and diagenetic history of overpressured siliclastic reservoirs in the Lower Missisauga and Mic Mac formations of the Venture field, Scotian Shelf, Nova Scotia; M.Sc. thesis, Department of Geology, Dalhousie University, Halifax, Nova Scotia.

Nova Scotia Department of Lands and Forests
1984: Coastal heritage park system proposal (map); Parks and Recreation Division, Nova Scotia Department of Lands and Forests.

Nova Scotia Legislature
1975: An act to preserve and protect the beaches of Nova Scotia; Bill No. 63, Chapter 6, Acts of 1975, Queens Printer for Nova Scotia, Halifax, p. 33-35.

Ocean Ranger Royal Commission
1984: The loss of the semisubmersible drill rig Ocean Ranger and its crew; Report One, the Royal Commission on the Ocean Ranger Marine disaster, Canada and Newfoundland, Department of Supply and Services, Canada, 400 p.

Oja, E.J.
1984: A conceptual approach to benefit last analysis of storm surge forecasting, a preliminary report; unpublished report, Atmospheric Environment Service, Bedford, Nova Scotia, 21 p.

Otteman, L. and Gillis, J.L.
1981: Deepwater production — is the technology there?; Offshore, January, p. 80-93.

Owens, E.H.
1971: A reconnaissance of the coastline of Chedabucto Bay, Nova Scotia; Canadian Hydrographic Service, Marine Sciences Paper 4, 24 p.

1976: The effects of ice on the littoral zone at Richebucto Head, eastern New Brunswick; Revue de Geographie de Montreal, v. 30, no. 1-2, p. 95-104.

1977: Coastal environments of Canada: the impact and clean-up of oil spills; Fisheries and Environment Canada, Environmental Protection Service, Economic and Technical Review Report EPS-3-EC-77-13, p. 413.

1980: Sediment removal from the beaches of Prince Edward Island; in Proceedings Canadian Coastal Conference, April 22-24, 1980, Associate Committee for Research on Shoreline Erosion and Sedimentation, National Research Council, Ottawa, p. 367-379.

1983: Coastal oil spills and their impact on land; in Stress on land in Canada, ed. W. Simpson-Lewis, R. McKechnie, and V. Neimanis; Lands Directorate, Environment Canada, p. 123-140.

Owens, E.H. and Harper, J.R.
1977: Frost Table and Thaw Depths in the Littoral Zone Near Peard Bay, Alaska; Arctic, v. 30, p. 397-414.

Owens, E.H., Harper, J.R., Forget, C.R., and Robson, W.
1983: Shoreline experiments and the persistence of oil on arctic beaches; in Proceedings 1983 Oil Spill Conference; Prevention, Behaviour, Control, Cleanup, San Antonio, Texas, American Petroleum Institute, p. 261-268.

Page, R.A. and Basham, P.W.
1985: Earthquake hazards in the offshore environment; United States Geological Survey, Bulletin 1630, 69 p.

Palmer, A.C.
1980: Application of offshore site investigation data to the design and construction of submarine pipelines; in Offshore Site Investigation, ed. D.A. Ardus; Graham and Trotman Ltd., London, p. 257-266.

1985: Arctic ice presents unusual problems for pipelines; in Harsh Environment and Deepwater Handbook 1985/1986, Pennwell Publishing Co., Tulsa, Oklahoma, p. 154-157.

Palmer, A.C., Bandais, D., and Masterson, D.
1979: Design and installation of an offshore flowline for the Canadian Arctic Islands; Proceedings of the Eleventh Annual Offshore Technology Conference, Houston, Texas, Paper 3446, p. 765-772.

Pelletier, B.R. and Shearer, J.M.
1972: Sea bottom scouring in the Beaufort Sea of the Arctic Ocean; Section 8; 24th International Geological Congress, Montreal, p. 251-261.

Pereira, C.P.G., Piper, D.J.W., and Shor, A.N.
1985: SEAMARC I Midrange sidescan sonar survey of Flemish Pass, east of the Grand Banks of Newfoundland; Geological Survey of Canada, Open File 1161, 23 p.

Philpott Consulting Limited
(with Acres Consulting Services Limited)
1986: Scour around sea-floor structures: Environmental Studies Revolving Funds Report 017; Canada Oil and Gas Lands Administration, Energy, Mines and Resources Canada, Ottawa, 249 p.

Philpott, K.L.
1978: Miramichi channel study; a Canada-New Brunswick project; Public Works Canada, 284 p.

Pilkington, G.R.
1985: Workshop on ice scouring, February 15-19, 1982; Associate Committee on Geotechnical Research, National Research Council of Canada Technical Memorandum no. 136, 251 p.

1986: Estimating ice scour frequency and risk to buried pipelines; in Ice Scour and Seabed Engineering; ed. C.F.M. Lewis et al., Environmental Studies Revolving Funds Report No. 049, Ottawa, p. 213-220.

Pilkington, G.R. and Marcellus, R.W.
1981: Methods of determining pipeline trench depths in the Canadian Beaufort Sea; Proceedings of the Sixth International Conference on Port and Ocean Engineering Under Arctic Conditions, Quebec, Canada, July 27-31, 1981, v. 2, p. 674-687.

Piper, D.J.W. and Normark, W.R.
1982: Effect of the 1929 Grand Banks earthquake on the continental slope off eastern Canada; in Current Research, Part B, Geological Survey of Canada, Paper 82-1B, p. 147-151.

Piper, D.J.W. and Sparkes, R.
1987: Proglacial sediment instability features on the Scotian Slope at 63°W; Marine Geology, v. 76, p. 15-31.

Piper, D.J.W., Farre, J.A., and Shor, A.N.
1985a: Late Quaternary slumps and debris flows on the Scotian Slope; Bulletin of the Geological Society of America, v. 96, p. 1508-1517.

Piper, D.J.W., Shor, A.N., Farre, J.A., O'Connell, S., and Jacobi, R.
1985b: Sediment slides and turbidity currents on the Laurentian Fan: sidescan sonar observations near the epicentre of the 1929 Grand Banks earthquake; Geology, v. 13, p. 538-541.

Piper, D.J.W., Shor, A.N., and Hughes-Clarke, J.E.
1988: The 1929 Grand Banks earthquake, slump and turbidity current; Geological Society of America, Special Paper 229, p. 77-92.

Platt, T., Conover, F.J., Loucks, R., Mann, K.H., Peer, D.L., Prakash, A., and Sameoto, D.D.
1970: A study of an eutrophicated marine basin; in Food and Agriculture Organization of the United Nations; FAO Technical Conference on Marine Pollution and its effects on Living Resources and Fishing, Rome, Italy, December 9-18, 1970, p. 1-10.

Podrouzek, A.J. and Bell, J.S.
1985: Stress orientations from wellbore breakouts on the Scotian Shelf, eastern Canada; in Current Research, Part B, Geological Survey of Canada, Paper 85-1B, p. 59-62.

Praeg, D.B., MacLean, B., Hardy, I.A., and Mudie, P.J.
1986: Quaternary geology of the southeast Baffin Island continental shelf, N.W.T.; Geological Survey of Canada, Paper 85-14, 38 p.

Praeg, D., MacLean, B., Piper, D.J.W., and Shor, A.N.
1987: Study of iceberg scours across the continental shelf and slope off southeast Baffin Island using the SeaMARC I midrange sidescan sonar; in Current Research, Part A, Geological Survey of Canada, Paper 87-1A, p. 847-857.

Pratte, B.D. and Willis, D.H.
1982: Pointe Sapin harbour — offshore breakwater and sandtrap; in Proceedings of Workshop on Atlantic coastal erosion and sedimentation, Halifax, Nova Scotia, p. 43-49.

Quinlan, G.
1984: Postglacial rebound and the focal mechanisms of eastern Canadian earthquakes; Canadian Journal of Earth Sciences, v. 21, p. 1018-1023.

Quinlan, G. and Beaumont, C.
1981: A comparison of observed and theoretical post-glacial relative sea level in Atlantic Canada; Canadian Journal of Earth Sciences, v. 18, p. 1146-1163.

Rashid, M.A. and Brown, J.D.
1975: Influence of marine organic compounds on engineering properties of a remoulded sediment; Engineering Geology, v. 9, p. 141-154.

Rashid, M.A. and Reinson, G.E.
1979: Organic matter in surficial sediments of the Miramichi estuary, New Brunswick, Canada; Estuarine and Coastal Marine Science, v. 8, p. 23-36.

Reid, I. and Falconer, R.K.H.
1982: A seismicity study in northern Baffin Bay; Canadian Journal of Earth Sciences, v. 19, p. 1518-1531.

Reimnitz, E., Barnes, P.W., Toimig, L.J., and Melchoir, J.
1977: Ice gouge recurrence and rates of sediment reworking, Beaufort Sea, Alaska; Geology, v. 5, p. 405-408.

Reinson, G.E.
1977: Tidal-current control of submarine morphology at the mouth of the Miramichi Estuary, New Brunswick; Canadian Journal of Earth Sciences, v. 14, p. 2524-2532.

1980: Variations in Tidal Inlet morphology and stability, northeast New Brunswick; in The Coastline of Canada, ed. S.B. McCann; Geological Survey of Canada, Paper 80-10, p. 23-39.

Reinson, G.E. and Frobel, D.
1980: Effects of dredging activities on shoreline morphology and stability, northeast New Brunswick; in Proceedings, Canadian Coastal Conference, Burlington; National Research Council, Associate Committee for research on shoreline erosion and sedimentation, Ottawa, p. 394-410.

Reinson, G.E., Frobel, D., Taylor, R.B., and Asprey, K.
1980: Observations on the occurrence of Bunker C oil on the Cape Breton shoreline, May 1979; in Scientific studies during the Kurdistan Tanker incident; Proceedings of a workshop, ed. J.H. Vandermeulen; Bedford Institute of Oceanography, Report Series BI-R-80-3, p. 120-131.

Robe, R.Q.
1980: Iceberg drift and deterioration; in Dynamics of Snow and Ice Masses, ed. Samuel C. Colbeck; Academic Press, Toronto, p. 211-259.
1982: Iceberg drift near Greenland — 1980 to 1982; United States Coast Guard Research and Development Centre, Groton, Connecticut, Report no. CG-D-36-82.

Robillard, G.A., Owens, E.H., Castle, R., and Forget, C.
1980: Arctic shoreline protection and cleanup — how to decide what to do when and where; Proceedings of the Third Arctic Marine Oil Spill Program Technical Seminar, June 3-5, 1980, Edmonton, Alberta, Environmental Protection Service, Environment Canada, Ottawa, p. 342-378.

Rochelle, W.R. and Simpson, D.M.
1981: Methods for protection of sub-sea pipelines and installations; in Proceedings of the Symposium: Production and Transportation Systems for the Hibernia Discovery, February 16-18, 1981, ed. W.E. Russell and D.B. Muggeridge; Newfoundland Petroleum Directorate, St. John's, Newfoundland, p. 253-269.

Rodrigue, G. and Meloche, J.D.
1985: Overpressure genesis within Cretaceous-Jurassic regressive sequences, Scotian Shelf; Geological Association of Canada, Annual Meeting 1985, Program with Abstracts, v. 10, p. 452.

Ruffman, A.
1985: Iceberg "harrowing" as opposed to iceberg "ploughing" (abstract); in National Research Council Associate Committee on Geotechnical Research Workshop on Ice Scouring, ed. R. Pilington, February 15-19, 1982, Addendum.

Ruffman, A. and Peterson, J.
1986a: A review of the historical seismicity of Nova Scotia prior to 1868 with selected later events; Eastern Section, Seismological Society of America, Program with Abstracts, Ottawa, October 1986, p. 44.
1986b: Pre-confederation historical seismicity of Nova Scotia with an examination of selected later events; Geomarine Associates Ltd. Project 85-69, Contract Report to Earth Physics Branch, Department of Energy, Mines and Resources, Ottawa, Ontario, DSS contract No. 0SQ85.00141, 423 p.

Sadler, H.E. and Serson, H.V.
1981: Freshwater anchor ice along an Arctic beach; Arctic, v. 34, no. 1, p. 62-63.

Schafer, C.T. and Asprey, K.W.
1982: Significance of some geotechnical properties of continental slope and rise sediments off northeast Newfoundland; Canadian Journal of Earth Sciences, v. 19, p. 153-161.

Schafer, C.T. and Smith, J.N.
1982: River discharge, sedimentation, and benthic environmental variations in Miramichi inner bay, New Brunswick; Canadian Journal of Earth Sciences, v. 20, p. 388-398.

Schafer, C.T., Cole, F.E., and Wagner, F.J.E.
1977: Relationship of foraminifera distribution patterns to sedimentary processes in the Miramichi Estuary, New Brunswick; in Report of Activities, Part C, Geological Survey of Canada, Paper 77-1C, p. 1-7.

Schafer, C.T., Tan, F.C., Williams, D.F., and Smith, J.N.
1985: Late glacial to Recent stratigraphy, paleontology, and sedimentary processes: Newfoundland continental slope and rise; Canadian Journal of Earth Sciences, v. 22, p. 266-282.

Schafer, C.T., Wagner, F.J.E., and Ferguson, C.
1975: Occurrence of foraminifera, molluscs and ostracods adjacent to the industrialized shoreline of Canso Strait, Nova Scotia; Water Air and Soil Pollution, v. 5, p. 79-96.

Schaule, B.K. and Patterson, C.C.
1983: Perturbation of the natural Pb depth profile in the Surgusso Sea by industrial lead; in Trace Metal in Seawater, ed. C.S. Wong, E. Boyle, K.W. Brulard and E.D. Goldberg; Plenum Press, New York, p. 487-503.

Schoenthaler, L.
1986: Hibernia ice-scour model studies; in Ice Scour and Seabed Engineering; ed. C.F.M. Lewis et al., Environmental Studies Revolving Funds Report no. 049, Ottawa, p. 118-121.

Scott, D.B. and Medioli, F.S.
1982: Micropaleontological documentation for early Holocene fall of relative sea level on the Atlantic coast of Nova Scotia; Geology, v. 10, p. 278-281.

Scott, D.B., Medioli, F.S., and Schafer, C.T.
1977: Temporal changes in foraminiferal distributions in Miramichi River Estuary; Canadian Journal of Earth Sciences, v. 14, p. 1566-1587.

Scott, D.B., Mudie, P.J., Vilks, G., and Younger, D.C.
1984: Latest Pleistocene-Holocene paleoceanographic trends on the continental margin of eastern Canada: foraminiferal, dinoflagellate and pollen evidence; Marine Micropaleontology, v. 9, p. 181-218.

Seed, H.B. and Rahman, M.S.
1977: Analysis for wave-induced liquefaction in relation to ocean floor stability; Report on research sponsored by the National Science Foundation, Report No. UCE/TE-77/02, May 1977, 84 p.

Segall, M.P., Barrie, J.V., Lewis, C.F.M., and Maher, M.L.J.
1985: Clay minerals across the Tertiary-Quaternary boundary, northeastern Grand Banks of Newfoundland: preliminary results; in Current Research, Part B, Geological Survey of Canada, Paper 85-1B, p. 63-68.

Segall, M.P., Buckley, D.E., and Lewis, C.F.M.
1987: Clay mineral indicators of geological and geochemical subaerial modification of near-surface Tertiary and Quaternary sediments on the northeastern Grand Banks of Newfoundland; Canadian Journal of Earth Sciences, v. 24, p. 2172-2187.

Shearer, J.M.
1971: Preliminary interpretation of shallow seismic reflection profiles from the west side of MacKenzie Bay, Beaufort Sea; in Report of Activities, November 1970 to March 1971, Geological Survey of Canada, Paper 71-1B, p. 131-138.

Shearer, J.M. and Blasco, S.M.
1975: Further observations of the scouring phenomena in the Beaufort Sea; in Current Research Part A, Geological Survey of Canada, Paper 75-1A, p. 483-494.
1986: Regional correlation of Beaufort Sea ice scour extreme depth and relative age with environmental factors; in Ice Scour and Seabed Engineering; ed. C.F.M. Lewis et al., Environmental Studies Revolving Funds Report No. 049, Ottawa, p. 167-170.

Shipley, T.H., Houston, M.H., Buffler, R.T., Shaub, F.J., McMillan, K.J., Ladd, J.W., and Worzel, J.L.
1979: Seismic evidence for widespread possible gas hydrate horizons on continental slopes and rises; American Association of Petroleum Geologists Bulletin, v. 63, p. 2204-2213.

Sieck, H.C.
1973: Gas-charged sediment cones post possible hazard to offshore drilling; Oil and Gas Journal, July 16, p. 148, 150, 155 and 163.

Silva, A.J., Dadey, K.A., Josenhans, H.W., and Laine, E.P.
1985: Geotechnical analysis of Labrador Shelf sediments and the influence of ice contact processes; Geological Survey of Canada, Open File 1395, 68 p.

Smith, S.D. and Banke, E.G.
1983: The influence of winds, currents and towing forces on the drift of icebergs; Cold Regions Science and Technology, v. 6, p. 241-255.

SNC-Lavalin Newfoundland Ltd.
1980a: Strait of Belle Isle Crossing HVDC Transmission — Tunnel Scheme; Report No. 11-99-05 to Lower Churchill Development Corporation Ltd., St. John's, Newfoundland.
1980b: Strait of Belle Isle Crossing HVDC Transmission — Submarine Cable Scheme; Report No. 11-99-16 to Lower Churchill Development Corporation Ltd., St. John's, Newfoundland.

Sodhi, D.S. and Kovacs, A.
1984: Forces associated with ice pile-up and ride-up; Proceedings of International Association of Hydraulic Research Symposium on Ice, Hamburg, Germany, August 1984, v. 4, p. 239-262.

Song, K.K., Kloth, H.L., Costello, C.R., and Liesemer, S.V.
1979: Anti-scour method uses air-lift idea; Offshore, v. 39, no. 10, p. 1386-1392.

Stein, S., Sleep, N.H., Geller, R.J., Wang, S., and Kroeger, G.C.
1979: Earthquakes along the passive margin of eastern Canada; Geophysical Research Letters, v. 6, p. 537-540.

Stoffyn-Egli, P.
1982: Dissolved aluminium in interstitial waters of recent terrigenous marine sediments from the North Atlantic Ocean; Geochimica et Cosmochimica Acta, v. 46, p. 1345-1352.

Stoll, R.D. and Bryan, G.M.
1979: Physical properties of sediments containing gas hydrates; Journal of Geophysical Research, v. 84, p. 1629-1634.

Stoll, R.D., Ewing, J.I., and Bryan, G.M.
1971: Anomalous wave velocities in sediments containing gas hydrates; Journal of Geophysical Research, v. 76, p. 2090-2094.

Strachan, P.
1984: Liquefaction prediction in the marine environment; in Seabed Mechanics, ed. B. Denness; Graham and Trotman, London, p. 149-158.

Sundby, B.N., Silverberg, N., and Chesselet, R.
1981: Pathways of Manganese in an open estuarine system; Geochimica et Cosmochimica Acta, v. 45, p. 293-307.

Swift, D.W., Harrison, W.D., and Osterkamp, T.E.
1983: Heat and salt transport processes in thawing subsea permafrost at Prudhoe Bay, Alaska: Permafrost; Proceedings of the Fourth International Conference, Washington, D.C.; National Academy Press, p. 1221-1226.

Sykes, L.R.
1978: Intraplate seismicity, reactivation of pre-existing zones of weakness, alkaline magmatism and other tectonism postdating continental fragmentation; Reviews of Geophysics and Space Physics, v. 16, p. 621-688.

Syvitski, J.P.M.
1985: Subaqueous slope failures within seismically active Arctic fjords; 14th Arctic Workshop, Arctic Land-Sea Interaction, Bedford Institute of Oceanography, Dartmouth, Nova Scotia, November 1985, p. 60-63.

Taylor A., Judge, A., and Desrochers, D.
1983: Shoreline regression: its effect on permafrost and the geothermal regime, Canadian Arctic Archipelago; in Proceedings of the Fourth International Conference on Permafrost, July 17-22, 1983, Fairbanks, Alaska, p. 1239-1244.

Taylor, A.E., Wetmiller, R.J., and Judge, A.S.
1979: Two risks to drilling and production off the east coast of Canada — earthquakes and gas hydrates; in Proceedings Symposium on Research in the Labrador Coastal and Offshore Region, ed. W. Denner; Memorial University of Newfoundland, May 8-10, 1979, p. 91-105.

Taylor, R.B.
1978: The occurrence of grounded ridges and shore ice piling along the northern coast of Somerset Island, N.W.T.; Arctic, v. 31, no. 2, p. 133-149.

1980a: Coastal environments along the northern shore of Somerset Island, District of Franklin; in The Coastline of Canada, ed. S.B. McCann; Geological Survey of Canada, Paper 80-10, p. 239-250.

1980b: Beach thaw depth and the effect of ice-bonded sediment on beach stability, Canadian arctic islands; in Proceedings of the Canadian Coastal Conference, April 22-24, 1980, Burlington, Ontario, p. 103-121.

1980c: Coastal Reconnaissance for Marine Terminal Planning in the Sverdrup Basin, N.W.T.; Geological Survey of Canada, Open File 693, 150 p.

1982: Seasonal shoreline change along Forchu Bay and Framboise Cove, Nova Scotia — A comparison between exploited and natural beaches; in Proceedings of Workshop on Atlantic Coastal Erosion and Sedimentation, November 25, Halifax, Nova Scotia, p. 37-41.

Taylor, R.B. and Kelly, B.J.
1984: Beach observations along the east coast of Cape Breton Highlands National Park, Nova Scotia; Geological Survey of Canada, Open File 1119, 33 p.

Taylor, R.B. and McCann, S.B.
1974: Depth of the "frost-table" on beaches in the Canadian Arctic Archipelago; Journal of Glaciology, v. 13, no. 68, p. 321-322.

1976: The effect of sea and nearshore ice on coastal processes in Canadian Arctic Archipelago; La revue de Géographie de Montréal, v. 30, p. 123-132.

Taylor, R.B., Wittmann, S.L., Milne, M.J., and Kober, S.M.
1985: Beach morphology and coastal changes at selected sites along mainland Nova Scotia; Geological Survey of Canada, Paper 85-12, 59 p.

Teshmont Consultants Ltd.
1974: Gull Island transmission facilities: reference data pertaining to the Strait of Belle Isle; Report for Newfoundland and Labrador Power Commission, 2 volumes.

Thompson, G.R., Foo, S.H.C., and Matlock, H.
1986: Hibernia GBS foundation behaviour; in Proceedings of the Third Canadian Conference on Marine Geotechnical Engineering, June 1986, St. John's, Newfoundland, v. I, p. 141-164.

Thurber Consultants Ltd.
1985: Study of well logs from east coast offshore wells to delineate gas hydrate occurrence; Report to Earth Physics Branch, Department of Energy, Mines and Resources, Ottawa, Ontario, 36 p.

Timmermans, W.J.
1983: Design for offshore pipelines for ice environments; in Design for Ice Forces, ed. S.R. Caldwell and R.D. Crissman; New York, American Society of Civil Engineers, p. 69-98.

Todd, B.J.
1984: Iceberg scouring on Saglek Bank, northern Labrador Shelf; M.Sc. thesis, Dalhousie University, Halifax, Nova Scotia, 172 p.

1986: Iceberg scouring on Saglek Bank northern Labrador Shelf; in Ice Scour and Seabed Engineering; ed. C.F.M. Lewis et al., Environmental Studies Revolving Funds Report No. 049, Ottawa, p. 182-193.

Tucholke, B.E., Bryan, G.M., and Ewing, J.I.
1977: Gas hydrate horizons detected in seismic profiler data from the western North Atlantic; American Association of Petroleum Geologists Bulletin, v. 61, p. 698-707.

Vandermeulen, J.H. and Jotcham, J.R.
1986: Long term persistence of Bunker C fuel oil and revegetation of a north-temperate saltmarsh: Miguasha 1974-1985; in Proceedings of the Ninth Annual Arctic and Marine Oilspill Program Technical Seminar, Edmonton, Alberta, p. 151-166.

van Dijk, R.N.
1980: Experience of scour in the southern North Sea; Seminar Proceedings Scour Around Offshore Structures, Society for Underwater Technology, 7 p.

Van Ieperen, M.
1985: Ice scour protection Drake F-76 flowline bundle; in National Research Council of Canada Associate Committee on Geotechnical Research Workshop on Ice Scouring, February 15-19, 1982, ed. G.R. Pilkington; National Research Council Technical Memorandum 136, p. 48-54.

Vilks, G. and Krauel, D.P.
1982: Environmental geology of the Miramichi Estuary: physical Oceanography; Geological Survey of Canada, Paper 81-24, 53 p.

Vilks, G., Buckley, D.E., and Keigwin, L.
1985: Late Quaternary sedimentation on the southern Sohm Abyssal Plain; Sedimentology, v. 32, p. 69-82.

Walsh, J.E., Wittman, W.I., Hester, L.H., and Dehu, W.S.
1986: Seasonal prediction of iceberg severity in the Labrador Sea; Journal of Geophysical Research, v. 91, no. C8, p. 9683-9692.

Wang, Y., Piper, D.J.W., and Vilks, G.
1982: Surface textures of turbidite sand grains, Laurentian Fan and Sohm Abyssal Plain; Sedimentology, v. 29, p. 727-736.

Weare, T.J.
1982: Mathematical models; in Hydraulic Modelling in Maritime Engineering; Thomas Telford Ltd., London, p. 15-23.

Weaver, J.S. and Stewart, J.M.
1982: In situ hydrates under the Beaufort Sea shelf; in Proceedings of the Fourth Canadian Permafrost Conference, ed. H.M. French, March 2-6, 1981, Calgary, Alberta, p. 312-319.

Weeks, W.F., Tucker, W.B. (III), and Niedoroda, A.
1986: Preliminary simulation of the formation and infilling of sea-ice gouges; in Ice Scour and Seabed Engineering; ed. C.F.M. Lewis et al., Environmental Studies Revolving Funds Report No. 049, Ottawa, p. 259-269.

Weir, F.V.
1981: The ability to protect oil/gas pipelines and sub-sea installations from icebergs; in Proceedings of the Symposium on Production and Transportation Systems for the Hibernia Discovery, February 16-18, 1981, ed. W.E. Russell and D.B. Muggeridge; Petroleum Directorate, Government of Newfoundland and Labrador, p. 279-290.

Whalley, E.
1980: Speed of longitudinal sound in clathrate hydrates; Journal of Geophysical Research, v. 85, p. 2539-2542.

Whelan, T. III, Coleman, J.M., Suhayda, J.N., and Roberts, H.H.
1977: Acoustical penetration and shear strength in gas-charged sediment; Marine Geotechnology, v. 2, p. 147-158.

White, F.M., Spaulding, M.L., and Gominho, L.
1980: Theoretical estimates of the various mechanisms involved in iceberg deterioration in the open ocean environment; United States Coast Guard Report CG-D-62-80, 126 p.

Whittaker, S., Chevelier, B., and Geerlot, H.
1985: Iceberg scouring in Hudson Bay; in 14th Arctic Workshop Abstracts, Arctic Land-Sea Interaction, November 6-8, 1985, Bedford Institute of Oceanography, Dartmouth, Nova Scotia, p. 91.

Willey, J.D.
1976: Geochemistry and environmental implications of the surficial sediments in northern Placentia Bay, Newfoundland; Canadian Journal of Earth Sciences, v. 13, p. 1393-1410.

Willey, J.D. and Fitzgerald, R.A.
1980: Trace metal geochemistry in sediments from the Miramichi Estuary, New Brunswick; Canadian Journal of Earth Sciences, v. 17, no. 2, p. 254-265.

Willis, D.H.
1977: Miramichi channel study hydraulic investigation; Hydraulics Laboratory Technical Report LTR-HY-56, Division of Mechanical Engineering, National Research Council, Ottawa, Ontario, 120 p.

Winters, G.V. and Buckley, D.E.

1986: The influence of $FeSi_3O_3(OH)_8$ on chemical equilibria in pore waters from deep sea sediments; Geochimica et Cosmochimica Acta, v. 50, p. 277-288.

Woodward-Clyde Consultants Ltd.

1980: Coastal geology maps central Sverdrup Basin, N.W.T.; Geological Survey of Canada, Open File 549, 41 p.

Woodworth-Lynas, C.M.T.

1983a: A possible submarine mud volcano from the southeast Baffin Island shelf; Technical Report, C-CORE Publication no. 83-2, 38 p.

1983b: The relative age of ice scours using cross-cutting relationships; Centre for Cold Ocean Resources Engineering, Memorial University of Newfoundland, St. John's, C-CORE Technical Report 83-3, 54 p.

Woodworth-Lynas, C.M.T. and Barrie, J.V.

1985: Iceberg scouring frequencies and scour degradation on Canada's eastern shelf areas using sidescan sonar mosaic techniques; in 8th International Conference on Port and Ocean Engineering under Arctic Conditions, Narssarssuaq, Greenland, September 7-14, 1985, v. 8, p. 419-442.

Woodworth-Lynas, C.M.T., Simms, A., and Rendell, C.H.

1985: Iceberg grounding and scouring on the Labrador continental shelf; Cold Regions Science and Technology, v. 10, p. 163-186.

Woodworth-Lynas, C.M.T., Bass, D.W., and Bobbitt, J.

1986: Inventory of upslope and downslope iceberg scouring; Environmental Studies Revolving Funds Report No. 039, Canada Oil and Gas Lands Administration; Energy, Mines and Resources Canada, Ottawa, 103 p.

Worthington, L.V. and Wright, W.R.

1970: North Atlantic Ocean Atlas of Potential Temperature and Salinity in the Deep Water including Temperature Salinity and Oxygen Profiles from the Erika Dan Cruise of 1962; Woods Hole Oceanographic Institution, Atlas Series Volume 2, Woods Hole, Massachusetts, 6 p. and 58 pl.

Yeats P.A. and Bewers, J.M.

1983: Potential anthropogenic influences on trace metal distributions in the North Atlantic; Canadian Journal of Fisheries and Aquatic Sciences, v. 40, supplement no. 2, p. 124-131.

1987: Evidence for anthropogenic modification of the global transport of Cd; in Cadmium in the Environment; Wiley Press, New York.

Zevenhuizen, J.

1986: Strait of Belle Isle — Pisces IV dives, August 1985 — manned submersible observations of the submarine cable test trench in the Strait of Belle Isle; Geological Survey of Canada, Open File 1286, 43 p.

Authors' addresses

C.F.M. Lewis
Atlantic Geoscience Centre
Geological Survey of Canada
Bedford Institute of Oceanography
P.O. Box 1006
Darmouth, Nova Scotia
B2Y 4A2

M.J. Keen
Atlantic Geoscience Centre
Geological Survey of Canada
Bedford Institute of Oceanography
P.O. Box 1006
Darmouth, Nova Scotia
B2Y 4A2

Printed in Canada

POSTSCRIPT

THE FUTURE

*Staff of the Atlantic Geoscience Centre, Geological Survey of Canada, Bedford Institute of Oceanography,
1987. Photo courtesy of Bedford Institute of Oceanography Photo Services.*

Chapter 15

THE FUTURE:
A VIEW OF MARINE GEOLOGY
AND GEOPHYSICS IN 1987

M.J. Keen

There has been remarkable progress on a global scale in the earth sciences at sea over the last 25 years, and some of the advances in knowledge of the eastern seaboard of Canada and its contiguous ocean basins have been described in this volume. Progress has been driven by exploration of the regions themselves, large parts of which were barely known geologically a quarter of a century ago, and by global conceptual advances.

Offshore eastern Canada is unique in several ways. It spans 40 degrees of latitude, from temperate conditions off Nova Scotia to high arctic conditions off Ellesmere Island. The region includes many different geological settings, with rifted margins and large and small ocean basins developed over 200 million years, and water-covered parts of the Paleozoic Appalachians and intra-cratonic basins. The data base available for large parts of the margin is good because of exploration by the oil and gas industry, the Ocean Drilling Program and the Deep Sea Drilling Project.

What of the future? Advances made since the preparation of this volume have provided new insight and guidance into the geology of the continental margin of eastern Canada. These advances were made as a result of new concepts, the use of new technology, the application of old technology in new areas, and the availability of more detailed data in previously studied areas. Although many were too late to be incorporated in this volume, some are described below.

Deep multichannel seismic lines across the Appalachians northeast of Newfoundland and beneath the Gulf of St. Lawrence have shown that the five tectonostratigraphic zones of that orogen have only three crustal counterparts beneath the surface; this has led to conceptual advances concerning Paleozoic collisions in the Appalachians involving lithosphere delamination (Keen et al., 1986; Stockmal et al., 1987). This deep seismic work has also revealed in a spectacular way the whole of the Carboniferous Magdalen Basin in the Gulf of St. Lawrence, and provided the base for answering questions concerning its origin. Deep seismic lines have shown that the continent-ocean boundary off the Grand Banks can be defined by the occurrence of landward-dipping reflectors in oceanic crust, perhaps reflecting igneous activity associated with early seafloor spreading and underplating of the continental crust. The Moho has been shown to be much more complicated than was once thought on the basis of seismic refraction observations, and it may be a relatively "mobile" feature formed after tectonic activity has affected a region such as the Appalachian Orogen (Peddy and Keen, 1987). The origin of reflectors in the lithosphere, such as those in the lower crust, is as yet obscure; lithological changes are often not sufficient to cause the impedance contrasts needed, and so the role of fluids in the crust is being investigated.

Similar problems will occupy many over the next few years, in order that the complete story of an orogen such as the Appalachians can be told, and the origin of the Moho deciphered.

New aeromagnetic data northeast of Newfoundland have delineated the magnetic anomalies in parts of the northwestern Atlantic much more precisely than previously was possible and have defined the continent-ocean boundary in terms of the magnetic "slope" anomaly. This has not yet been integrated into the definition of the continent-ocean boundary in terms of seismic reflectors as described above. Future studies should allow us to delineate a firm line for this boundary, not a proxy in the form of the 10 km crustal thickness contour (see Map 1706A). The new data have allowed estimates of continental plate reconstructions across the Atlantic, from the Goban Spur to Orphan Knoll for example, which can be compared with extension estimated from modelling of crustal development using the seismic structure as its starting point (S.P. Srivastava, pers. comm., 1987). The aeromagnetic data have also aided in correlating between the Appalachians of Newfoundland and mainland Canada, and are contributing to the delineation of the tectonostratigraphic zones on Cape Breton Island.

The history of the oceanic basins contiguous to the margin off eastern Canada will probably be as well-defined as geophysical data will permit, if a few more well selected aeromagnetic surveys can be flown. The most important gap is Baffin Bay, and aeromagnetic surveys, combined with deep seismic reflection profiles, should resolve the controversies concerning its origin and the questions still surrounding motion along Nares Strait (as discussed in Chapter 7).

Igneous activity is associated with the major changes in seafloor spreading and major rifting events on the margins (see the contribution by Pe-Piper et al. in Chapter 2). Systematic changes in rock type and geochemistry can be distinguished in space and time. Igneous rocks, however, have not yet been fully used to understand processes in the earth's mantle associated with the development of the margin off eastern Canada and the ocean basins. This may change when comprehensive geochemical and isotope information is available, and when theoretical modelling

Keen, M.J.
1990: The future: a view of marine geology and geophysics in 1987, Chapter 15 in Geology of the Continental Margin of Eastern Canada, M.J. Keen and G.L. Williams (ed.); Geological Survey of Canada, Geology of Canada, no. 2, p. 827-832 (also Geological Society of America, The Geology of North America, v. I-1).

of the development of the oceanic basins and margins is more sophisticated.

The precise definition of the history of the oceanic basins will improve our understanding of the relationships between their development and the evolution of the sedimentary basins on the margins. More detailed biostratigraphic zonations based upon graphic correlation or quantitative techniques and improvements in dating of igneous rocks from offshore wells will allow the geochronology of these sedimentary basins to be established (Gradstein et al., 1985). It should be possible to establish clearly the relationships between sedimentological and structural developments within individual basins, and relationships between events over the whole of the continental margin, from basin to basin — although this will be dependent upon a better understanding of eustatic sea level fluctuations recognized in other regions (Haq et al., 1987). Currently it is difficult to establish the relationship between unconformities in northern Baffin Bay and beneath the margin off Nova Scotia, and to relate them unambiguously to either local or global tectonic events.

Deep seismic reflection data have imaged crosssections of the Mesozoic-Cenozoic sedimentary basins of the Grand Banks, and have shown in one case that a reflector interpreted to be the western bounding fault of the Jeanne d'Arc Basin, extends many tens of kilometres into the crust. Is this a general phenomenon? Only more data will clarify this. Such data have already provided clues to the origin of Jeanne d'Arc and Orphan basins, and have been combined with modelling of extension in attempts to determine if they originated by simple or pure shear (Keen and deVoogd, in press; Lister et al., 1986). Are they related by master faults to their potential counterparts on the opposite side of the Atlantic (Tankard and Welsink, 1987)? Is one basin related to another by the mechanism of transfer faults? Only access to data concerning the whole crust will unambiguously resolve the origin of the driving forces responsible for sedimentary basins like those of the Grand Banks, and answer questions concerning the relationships between the development of the ocean basins and the structure and morphology of the margins and the nearby continents. Keen and Beaumont (Chapter 9) have begun this process.

The form of the sedimentary basins on the continental margin of eastern Canada is now reasonably well known. Modelling of their development starting from a premise of extension has been successful in predicting many phenomena, and modelling has become routine in investigating sedimentary basins worldwide. As drilling, however, has been confined to the present continental shelf or the uppermost continental slope, the distal parts of the basins have not been sampled. Furthermore, drilling has only penetrated one third the total thickness of some sedimentary basins. Exploration on the slopes will surely start some time in the next two decades, and begin to fill these gaps in our coverage. Whether or not these areas will prove to be prospective is not certain; source rocks may be more prolific than in proximal areas, but there may be a paucity of reservoir rocks. The origin of overpressured fluids in the basins is not fully understood (see Chapter 14), although an attempt has been made to model the observations made in the region of the Venture field of the Scotian Basin (Mudford, 1988). Extensive occurrences of evaporite diapirs have been mapped in the Scotian Basin (Chapter 5), but their formation and distribution have not been

explained in any general way. How, for example, did the Slope Diapiric Province form? Our knowledge of the Cenozoic on the margin of eastern Canada is still rudimentary: comprehensive studies of sea level changes, climatic evolution, and microfossil evolution have not been completed, and we are ignorant of past microtekite fields and any evolutionary changes associated with them (Keller et al., 1987). Present evidence is restricted to data from the offshore wells and this needs to be expanded.

Some questions concerning sedimentary basins may be answered through results from the Ocean Drilling Program (ODP) on the continental margins. That program and its predecessor, the Deep Sea Drilling Project (DSDP), have answered specific questions such as the age of the magnetic anomaly sequence of the Labrador Sea, the nature and age of regional seismic reflectors, the paleoclimatic events that led to the Pleistocene ice ages, and the time of onset of iceberg rafting in the Labrador Sea and Baffin Bay. ODP will help unravel some of the geological enigmas in offshore eastern Canada through its global research. One example is the Cenozoic evolution of the southern oceans following the separation of the southern continents from Antarctica. The development of the world's oceans cannot be understood without understanding both the northern and southern polar regions. In a similar way, generic information on the distal parts of sedimentary basins of rifted margins can be applied to those of eastern Canada. Within the Appalachians, information provided by the Ocean Drilling Program on the processes of subduction in modern active margins, such as those off Barbados, allows the construction of better models of collisions in the Paleozoic.

In 1987, a part of the continental slope and rise off Georges Bank and the western part of the Scotian Shelf was imaged using the long range sidescan system GLORIA. Future publications will surely have many images from such systems covering all of offshore eastern Canada and the contiguous ocean basins; these will be accompanied by high resolution seismic profiles so that the spatial picture can be related unambiguously to Pleistocene and modern processes. Studies of the Quaternary of the margins have been severely hampered by the lack of this capability. Improvements in seismic reflection instrumentation to provide resolution routinely less than 10 cm would mean that structures of bedforms themselves could be studied, perhaps in real-time, and tied to concurrent studies of the driving forces generated by bottom currents.

Advances coming from the development and use of human-operated and remotely-operated submersibles will be important in future studies. International Submarine Engineering Ltd. of Port Moody, British Columbia, currently the world's largest manufacturer of remotely-operated vehicles (ROV), is presently (1987) building an ROV capable of operating in water depths of 5000 m, with a variety of marine capabilities, one of which will be broadcast-quality video from the ROV to the mother-ship. This should lead to great advances in our knowledge of slopes, rises and mid-ocean ridges.

Improved sampling techniques will facilitate research of the sediments. The "Long Coring Facility" is a system capable in principle of obtaining cores up to 30 m long (Driscoll, 1981). Its first trials (1987) operating from CSS HUDSON on the Scotian Shelf have been successful. A few cores strategically placed on the margin and in the ocean basins will help relate the later Tertiary and Quaternary history of the ocean basins to that of the continent to the west, and to that of the Arctic Ocean Basin to the north. Advances in knowledge of that basin and of the Arctic Island Channels depend almost wholly on technological breakthroughs.

We now have the beginnings of a model for sedimentation during the Quaternary for the margin of eastern Canada, relating the effect of the last ice sheet during Wisconsinan Glaciation and its breakup to morphology and the sediment record (Piper, 1988; see Chapter 10). It appears, for example, that submarine canyons and deep-sea channels are missing in Baffin Bay, but present in the southerly parts of the region, because of the differences in temperature of the bases of ice sheets in northern and southern latitudes. However, we cannot quantitatively account for the deep shelves north of 48.5°N, and have not answered the question of timing and extent of glaciations across the shelves (Piper, 1988). Seismologists and sedimentologists have not satisfactorily determined the rate of return of earthquakes of the magnitude of the 1929 event off the Grand Banks; such knowledge is of practical importance if development of hydrocarbons proceeds offshore eastern Canada, and is important to understanding sedimentation on features such as the Laurentian Fan and the Sohm Abyssal Plain. Pleistocene sedimentation on the shelves has been modelled in terms of deposition associated with the bases of floating or grounded ice shelves, but this model is being vigorously challenged. New data on sedimentation processes beneath the sea ice off Axel Heiberg Island, obtained from the Canadian Ice Island, provide important groundtruth for postulated glacial stage models (Hein and Mudie, in press). The solution to these problems would be helped by observations beneath Arctic and Antarctic ice shelves using remotely operated vehicles. Similar technology would assist us in understanding sedimentation processes at glacier fronts. Do deltas present in those locations shift position on account of movement of the sediment sources, under-ice tunnels, or due to the transport of sediment on the delta itself? What are the effects of water discharged at the seafloor below glacier fronts? Observations with remotely operated vehicles could answer such questions.

This final essay began with observations on the earth as it was, from which we have to attempt to deduce processes, and progressed to an emphasis on the earth as it is now, where we observe and model present processes. This will surely be a dominant theme at all scales of investigations in the next few years. Some neglected fields will receive the attention they deserve. For example, sedimentologists have focused much attention on sands, rather at the expense of the gravels which are distinctive components of the beaches of eastern Canada. D.L. Forbes' work is making amends. We do not yet know the entrainment threshold of gravels — at what values of bottom stress they begin to move. We do not know what triggers the development of major gravel beaches in the Arctic. At another scale in terms of global processes, we have started to map the current state of stress over North America, and to tie these observations to driving mechanisms within the earth but we cannot yet account for the earthquakes on the continental margin of eastern Canada in a satisfactory way. We have tied turbidites of the Laurentian Fan to one recent major earthquake, but have only occasionally observed density currents in real time, and have not yet monitored an actual failure on, say, a delta front, and

established what caused it to fail and what its results were in quantitative terms. We have begun to model the interactions between the oceans and atmosphere, but we cannot reliably predict the consequences of an 8°C rise in temperature in the Arctic.

Observation of the present earth as the key to understanding past processes is not always satisfactory. As an example, the current state of observing and modelling longshore transport and onshore-offshore transport is one of disarray. The physics is not understood. Measurement of physical processes in such a harsh environment is difficult. The effects of bedforms themselves are unknown. Consequently, different approaches are needed to solve practical problems. Holistic approaches have to be adapted to questions concerning the fates of beaches with changes of sea level. If a gravel beach stretches, will it become separated from a source of supply and fail? We cannot predict from first principles what the effect of sea level changes on the coastal zone will be over a timescale of say 100 years, the timescale associated with sea level rise on account of global warming. Consequently, the pragmatic approach of comparing the coastlines of Ireland, where sea level has been stable over the last few thousand years, with the coastline of eastern Canada, where sea level is rising at a rate of about 40 cm per hundred years, is one practical strategy for beginning to answer an urgent global problem. Exploration for minerals as placer deposits in coastal regions and in nearshore regions will undoubtedly accelerate in the next two decades. We are not well equipped to predict their occurrence at present, and any search will be rather pragmatic. Similarly, if there is development of mineral deposits in a coastal region, the effects of exploitation must be predicted.

Progress has been made in understanding processes peculiar to the Arctic, in comprehending, for example, the differences between the ice-bound fiords of Ellesmere Island and the wave-dominated fiords of Nova Scotia. Many arctic phenomena, however, remain to be understood. Small islands in the Arctic are being formed by ice-push; this is significant to the oil and gas industry which constructs artificial islands for drilling platforms. The relationships between permafrost onshore and offshore in the Arctic, except in specific areas such as the coastal regions of the Beaufort Sea (see Chapter 14), remain to be studied.

Work at sea is fun and is demanding and it seems will never end. The reader will have seen that to explore the continental margin and seas off eastern Canada needs all the talents possessed by scholarly and practical men and women.

REFERENCES

Driscoll, A.H.
1981:   The Long Coring Facility, new techniques in deep ocean coring; Oceans, v. 81, p. 404-410.
Gradstein, F.M., Agterberg, F.P., Brower, J.C., and Schwarzacher, W.S.
1985:   Quantitative stratigraphy; D. Reidel Publishing Company, Dordrecht, The Netherlands, 598 p.
Haq, B.U., Hardenbol, J., and Vail, P.R.
1987:   Chronology of fluctuating sea levels since the Triassic; American Association for the Advancement of Science, v. 235, p. 1156-1167.
Hein, F.J. and Mudie, P.J.
in press: Glacial marine sedimentation, Canadian polar margin north of Axel Heiberg Island; Marine Geology.
Keen, C.E. and deVoogd, B.
in press: The continent-ocean boundary at the rifted margin of eastern Canada: new results from deep seismic reflection studies; Tectonics.

Keen, C.E., Keen, M.J., Nichols, B., Reid, I., Stockmal, G.S., Colman-Sadd, S.P., O'Brien, S.J., Miller, H., Quinlan, G., Williams, H., and Wright, J.
1986: A deep seismic reflection profile across the northern Appalachians; Geology, v. 14, p. 141-145.

Keller, G., Herbert, T., Dorsey, R., D'Hordt, S., Johnsson, M., and Chi, W.R.
1987: Global distributions of late Paleogene hiatuses; Geology, v. 15, p. 199-203.

Lister, G.S., Etheridge, M.A., and Symonds, P.A.
1986: Detachment faulting and the evolution of passive continental margins; Geology, v. 14, p. 246-250.

Mudford, B.S.
1988: Modelling the occurrence of overpressures on the Scotian Shelf, offshore eastern Canada; Journal of Geophysical Research, v. 93, p. 7845-7855.

Peddy, C. and Keen, C.E.
1987: Deep seismic reflection profiling: how far have we come?; Geophysics: The Leading Edge, v. 6, no. 6, p. 22-26.

Piper, D.J.W.
1988: DNAG No. 3: Glaciomarine sedimentation on the continental slope off eastern Canada; Geoscience Canada, v. 15, p. 23-28.

Stockmal, G.S., Colman-Sadd, S.P., Keen, C.E., O'Brien, S.J., and Quinlan, G.
1987: Collision along an irregular margin: a regional plate tectonic interpretation of the Canadian Appalachians; Canadian Journal of Earth Sciences, v. 24, p. 1098-1107.

Tankard, A.M. and Welsink, H.J.
1987: Extensional tectonics and stratigraphy of Hibernia Oil Field Grand Banks, Newfoundland; American Association of Petroleum Geologists Bulletin, v. 71, p. 1210-1232.

Author's address

M. J. Keen
Atlantic Geoscience Centre
Geological Survey of Canada
Bedford Institute of Oceanography
P.O. Box 1006
Dartmouth, Nova Scotia
B2Y 4A2

Printed in Canada

APPENDIX

TABLE A1

THE HISTORY OF EXPLORATION OF THE CONTINENTAL MARGIN OF EASTERN CANADA
compiled by M.J. Keen

The main written sources for this table were papers by Drake et al. (1959), Hood, (1971), Keen et al. (1971), MacMillan (1973a), Sherwin (1973), Pelletier (1975), Van der Linden and Wade (1975), Tucker (1976), and Keen (1983). Information from letters, unpublished manuscripts and conversations with C.L. Drake, A. Jackson, L.H. King, D. Sherwin, J.H. Swift, B. Virtue, C. Yorath and many contributors to this volume were very helpful.

The criteria for inclusion of an event or happening were: directly pertinent to the continental margin of eastern Canada, from Georges Bank to Nares Strait; indirectly pertinent, because as a new idea, for example, it affected concepts applied to the continental margin of eastern Canada, or activities in the region; the first exploration of its type; and the first application of a global concept in the region.

The editors would appreciate information on any errors and serious omissions.

1800-1899

1835: Investigations were made in eastern Canada of modern marine invertebrates, some undertaken in connection with studies of the Pleistocene (reported in Whiteaves, 1901).

1849: Lyell (1849) reported on his studies of modern trace fossils and sedimentary structures on mud flats of the Bay of Fundy, and applications to ancient rocks.

1856: J.W. Bailey identified volcanic ash in deep sea sediment east of Newfoundland, and suggested that it might have been dropped from icebergs; Maury suggested that its transport by the Gulf Stream from the West Indies was more likely (Maury, 1859, p.281 et seq.).

1858: The first transatlantic submarine telegraph cable was completed from Trinity Bay, Newfoundland to Valentia Harbour, Ireland, August 5, 1858. The cable was started in the middle of the Atlantic, and two cable ships steamed in opposite directions laying the joined halves (Maury, 1859). The routing of transatlantic cables was one of the first applications of deep-sea geology, and a stimulus to it.

1859: Maury attributed the submerged banks off New England to the accumulation of iceberg rafted debris (Maury, 1859; C.L. Drake, personal communication, 1986).

1867: The mines in the Sydney coal field, Cape Breton Island, Nova Scotia started to tunnel beneath the sea. Extending some 7 km offshore, they are some of the oldest and largest undersea mine workings in the world. (Hale, Chapter 13, this volume).

1868: Sir William Dawson published "Acadian Geology", in which he ascribed many of the Pleistocene features around Nova Scotia to sea-level changes and ice.

1870: Kerr (1870) recognized a terminal moraine across the mouth of Conception Bay, Newfoundland.

1873: HMS CHALLENGER made depth profiles and sampled the sea floor of the Atlantic from side to side, discovering the rise in the middle. HMS CHALLENGER also dredged a large block of granite from the sea floor south of Nova Scotia, identified as Shelburne granite (Gossip, 1873).

1878: United States established a one year summer station at Gloucester, Massachusetts. Fishermen were asked to bring samples of rock from their trawls. As a result, the offshore banks were recognized as an extension of the Atlantic coastal plain of the eastern U.S.A. (Verrill, 1878; Stephenson, 1936; Sherwin, 1973).

1894: Upham reported on rocks recovered from the east coast offshore. "The Fishing Banks are thus to be accounted, like the fiords of our northern coasts, ... as evidence of a great epeirogenic uplift of the northern part of the continent preceding and producing the ice age". (Upham, 1894; C.L. Drake, personal communication, 1986).

1895: Bell pointed out that a pre-glacial delta lies off the entrance to Hudson Strait (Bell, 1895; McMillan, 1982).

1895: The Wabana Iron Mines in eastern Newfoundland began mining hematite. At the time of closing in 1966, the tunnels extended up to 5 km offshore into Conception Bay (Hale, Chapter 13, this volume).

1897: Tarr described the processes of sediment dispersal and sea-bottom sediment disturbance by sea ice and icebergs based on studies along the coasts of northeastern Canada and western Greenland (Tarr, 1897).

1898: First concepts developed on multiple centres and episodes of Pleistocene continental glaciation in the District of Keewatin and Hudson Bay (Tyrell, 1898).

1900-1949

1900: Sampling of the shelf off southwestern Greenland (Boeggild, 1900; McMillan, 1973b).

1903: The first scientific cruise into Hudson Bay to sample the sea floor was conducted (Low, 1906).

1903: Spencer (1903) described the form and location of submarine canyons off Atlantic Canada and proposed that they were cut by continental uplift, which also produced the Pleistocene glaciations. Daly (1936) subsequently proposed that the canyons were cut by turbidity currents.

1912: Wegener published his lectures, later a book, on his concept of continental drift (Wegener, 1915). This had been anticipated earlier in various ways by Snider in 1858, Taylor in 1910, and Baker in 1911 (for discussions of this, see Marvin (1973) and Bullard (1975)).

1924: The German vessel METEOR obtained the first continuous echo sounder profile across the deep ocean basin, clearly demonstrating the scale of irregularities on the ocean floor (Shepard, 1948). Such data were put into systematic form by

Heezen et al. (1959) in a general account of the morphology of the sea floor of the North Atlantic Ocean and its evolution.

1924: Goldthwaite (1924) provided a systematic account of the evolution of the geomorphology of Nova Scotia, including recognition of the summit peneplain and the sculpting of the coastline by glaciers. Johnson (1925) described the development of the famous drumlin coastal scenery in more detail, and King (1972) provided an explanation for the summit peneplane in terms of plate tectonics. (See also Keen and Beaumont, Chapter 9, this volume, for relationships between physiography and geodynamics).

1925: Dahl reported that Tertiary fossils occurred in rocks beneath the offshore east coast (Dahl, 1925).

1928: "Marion" expedition of the U.S. Coast Guard. The bathymetry of the Labrador Sea and Baffin Bay was described, and the characteristics of sediment samples from 27 dredge hauls reported. Widespread carbonate gravels were first recognized (Ricketts and Trask, 1932).

1929: The "Grand Banks" earthquake generated a tsunami which killed 27 people on Newfoundland's south coast. Telephone cables were broken on the continental slope. Later geological studies of the region showed that the earthquake had triggered a turbidity current (see 1952) (de Smitt, 1932; Doxsee, 1948; Piper et al., 1988).

1931: Glacial origin proposed for Laurentian Channel (Shepard, 1931).

1934: Daly (1934) provided a systematic account of post-glacial sea-level changes in Atlantic Canada.

1934: Scientists from Woods Hole Oceanographic Institute began geological sampling on Georges Bank. The work confirmed the presence of Cretaceous and Tertiary sediments in situ (Cushman, 1936; Sherwin, 1973; Stetson, 1936).

1935: M. Ewing and his colleagues began seismic studies of the Atlantic coastal plain off the eastern United States and, after World War II, off Canada (Drake et al., 1959).

1936: Some sediments off the eastern United States were recognized as relict (Shepard and Cohee, 1936).

1936: Density currents were proposed as the explanation for submarine canyons (Spencer, 1903; Daly, 1936).

1941: Bramlette and Bradley noted the widespread dispersal of volcanic ash by ice rafting and also recognized periods of gla-

cial marine sedimentation in the North Atlantic Ocean (Bramlette and Bradley, 1941). Ice-rafted input was quantified and related to the last glacial cycle by Ruddiman (1977).

1943: The first well was spudded offshore eastern Canada by Socony Vacuum and City Services, in Hillsborough Bay, Prince Edward Island: Island Development Company Hillsborough No. 1. It was completed in 1945 at a depth of 4479 m in salt of the Windsor Group; it was for many years the deepest well in Canada (Howie and Cumming, 1963; J.A. Wade, personal communication, 1987).

1949: The Northwest Atlantic Mid-Ocean Canyon (NAMOC) was found from the vessel ATLANTIS, east of Newfoundland. Later exploration showed it to run the length of the Labrador Sea, and to end in the Sohm Abyssal Plain (Ewing et al., 1953; Manchester, 1964; Chough and Hesse, 1976).

1950-1959

1950: Widmer (1950) proposed that a Cabot Strait ice tongue dammed a glacial lake in Placentia Bay, and a later one in Hermitage Bay, Newfoundland. The origin of terraces in this region is still not fully understood, but stratified muds appear to be marine, not lacustrine (King and Fader, 1985).

1950: Scientists at the (then) Lamont Geological Observatory began refraction seismic studies of offshore eastern Canada. The work showed that the "coastal plain" sediments are comparable in thickness to those of the Gulf Coast of the U.S.A., and so worth exploring for oil and gas. Some of the later work, that of 1960 and 1961, was done collaboratively with the Fisheries Research Board of Canada and the Nova Scotia Research Foundation (Officer and Ewing, 1954; Drake et al., 1959; C.L. Drake, personal communication, 1986).

1950s: Airborne and shipborne magnetic field studies were undertaken by agencies from the U.S.A. This work discovered the "East Coast Magnetic Anomaly" (ECMA), and showed that "transcurrent" faulting onshore was associated with changes in depth to basement and with the New England Seamounts offshore at 40°N (Drake et al., 1963).

1950: Seismic refraction observations showed that the "granitic" crust of the continents is absent beneath the oceans, and the oceanic crust is thin (Ewing et al., 1950).

1951: Seismic survey by the Lamont Geological Observatory suggested the presence of Cretaceous and Tertiary rocks on the Grand Banks (Press and Beckmann, 1954).

1951: Marshall Kay published his ideas on geosynclines. As an example, he divided the Appalachian orthogeosyncline into an inner non-volcanic miogeosyncline, and an outer eugeosyncline, which had been actively volcanic and had subsided. Kay's ideas were influential for many years (Kay, 1951; Drake et al., 1959; Williams, 1964).

1952: The "Grand Banks" earthquake of 1929 was shown to have led to the generation of a turbidity current, and the investigations supported Kuenen's hypothesis on the origin of turbidites (Kuenen, 1950; Heezen and Ewing, 1952; Heezen and Drake, 1964).

1955: "Operation Franklin" was conducted by the Geological Survey of Canada in the Arctic Islands. The geological information published by the Survey led as a result to the discovery by industry of many potential hydrocarbon traps in an area not previously explored (Fortier et al., 1963). Permits were granted to companies a few years later, after federal regulations had been established (Canadian Petroleum Association, personal communication, 1986).

1956: The then Dominion Observatory undertook seismic refraction studies in the Gulf of St. Lawrence asking the question: does the circular shape of the southern coastline reflect a meteoritic origin for the Gulf? The answer was: "No" (Willmore and Scheidegger, 1956).

1956: It was proposed that the channels between the Arctic Islands had been formed originally by a Tertiary fluvial system (Fortier and Morley, 1956). The idea that they had been subsequently excavated by glaciers was formulated later (Pelletier, 1962, 1966). The fluvial geomorphology of the central Arctic Islands Channels was confirmed by analysis of detailed bathymetric maps in 1975 (Bornhold et al., 1976).

1957: Ripple marks were found on the continental slope, and the North Atlantic Western Boundary Undercurrent was discovered. The continental margin is shaped by persistent geostrophic currents as well as by intermittent turbidity currents (Elmendorf and Heezen, 1957; Swallow and Worthington, 1957; Heezen et al., 1959).

1958: Aeromagnetic Surveys were begun offshore eastern Canada by the Geological Survey of Canada (Hood, 1971; Keen, 1983).

1958: The Polar Continental Shelf Project (PCSP) was formed on the initiative of the advisory committee on northern development of the Department of Indian and Northern Development and on account of the lack of science capabilities in the region at that time. PCSP was assigned to the Department of Mines and Technical Surveys (G. Hobson, personal communication, 1987).

1958: Mobil Oil Canada applied for offshore permits on 445,000 hectares on and around Sable Island, including the area which would become the Venture field. The Government of Nova Scotia granted provincial permits in 1959 and the Government of Canada granted federal permits in 1960. The company undertook aeromagnetic surveys in 1959 (Canadian Petroleum Association, personal communication, 1986; D.F. Sherwin, personal communication, 1986).

1959: The Geological Survey of Canada began sea magnetic surveys, in conjunction with the Canadian Hydrographic Service. This led to collaborative "multidisciplinary surveys", in which the gravity and magnetic fields were measured as well as bathymetry, starting in 1964 (Bower, 1961; Blandford, 1964; Hood, 1964; Keen, 1983).

1959: The bones and teeth of Pleistocene mammals were dredged from the shelf off New Jersey, showing that sea level had been lower during that epoch, with the shoreline lying to the east of the present one (Richards, 1959).

1959: The continental margin off eastern North America was compared with the miogeosyncline and eugeosyncline of the Appalachians. Seismic refraction and other geophysical observations were interpreted in a way suggesting that the margin consisted of an outer and an inner trough of sediments; the analogy with the Appalachians suggested that the margin would be converted into a mountain chain if the crust beneath the "outer trough" - the eugeosynclinal trough - were thickened, and the sediments of the "inner trough" - the miogeosynclinal trough - were folded and thrusted (Kay, 1951; Drake et al., 1959).

1960 - 1969

1960: Seismic exploration by industry began off the east coast of Canada when Geophysical Services Incorporated performed a seismic survey for Mobil, in the area of Sable Island (Roth, 1983).

1960: The Institute of Oceanography at Dalhousie University, Halifax, Nova Scotia, was founded, under the impetus of F.R. Hayes; it was funded by the National Research Council of Canada. Geophysical activities were led by J.E. Blanchard (Keen, 1983).

1960s: Investigations by the Fisheries Research Board of Canada of the sediments of the Gulf of St. Lawrence and their geochemistry (Loring, 1975).

1960: The first shipboard gravity observations were made off Canada by D. Bower from the USS ARCHERFISH (Geological Survey of Canada, 1986).

1961: The hypothesis of sea-floor spreading was published, explaining the creation and destruction of ocean floors, and the drift of the continents (Dietz, 1961; Hess, 1962).

1961: Carey and Ahmad (1961) proposed a model for glaciomarine sedimentation that forms the basis for many subsequent accounts of Pleistocene glaciomarine sedimentation off eastern Canada (King and Fader, 1985).

1961: Scientists from Lamont Geological Observatory published the first systematic account of both the lithology and biostratigraphy of deep water sediments off southeastern Canada, demonstrating the great changes in sedimentation during glaciation (Ericson et al., 1961).

1961: The first wildcat well in the Arctic Islands, Dome et al. Winter Harbour No. 1 A-09, was drilled on Melville Island to a depth of 3823 m. A minor gas show was encountered at 320 m from hydrates in the Hecla Bay Formation (Canadian Petroleum Association, personal communication, 1986; J.A. Wade, personal communication, 1987).

1961: Magnetic field observations by the Geological Survey of Canada in Hudson Bay using a sea magnetometer suggested that thick sediments lie beneath. These were mapped subsequently by shallow seismic studies. The first sedimentological map of the Bay was produced (Hood, 1964; Leslie, 1964; Grant, 1968).

1962: The Halifax gravity test range was established using bottom gravity measurements (Goodacre, 1964).

1962: Offshore permits were granted in Hudson Bay, to the company Sogepet. A larger filing was made in 1964, 20 million hectares by Aquitaine et al. Companies had filed on land in Hudson Bay in the 1940's and 1950's, but the grants had been rescinded; no exploratory work had been done in connection with these permits (Canadian Petroleum Association, personal communication, 1986; D.F. Sherwin, personal communication, 1986).

1962: Crustal seismic refraction studies by Dalhousie University provided estimates of the thickness of continental crust off Nova Scotia. This was the first of a series of investigations by the group started by J.E. Blanchard (Barrett et al., 1964; G.N. Ewing et al., 1966).

1962: Bedford Institute of Oceanography at Dartmouth, Nova Scotia, was founded by the Government of Canada, and a substantial program of marine scientific research was started off the east coast.

1962: Geological investigations were made by Wood's Hole Oceanographic Institution of the margin off Nova Scotia and Newfoundland, and in the Gulf of Maine. These investigations showed that a shallow "ridge complex" lies beneath parts of the continental slope. This was associated at the time with a deeper "complex linear ridge of crystalline rocks" (Emery et al., 1970), but later studies showed it was formed from diapiric salt structures (Jansa and Wade, 1975a).

1963: Volume III of the Sea was published, summarizing the knowledge on marine geology and geophysics of the time (Hill, 1963).

1963: The hypothesis of sea-floor spreading of Hess and Dietz was supported by the interpretation of magnetic anomalies in the ocean basins in terms of reversals of the earth's magnetic field (Menard, 1986; Morley and Larochelle, 1964; Vine and Matthews, 1963).

1963: The suggestion was made that an inactive mid-ocean ridge lies beneath the Labrador Sea, and this was confirmed by seismic reflection observations which had been made in 1961. Wegener's idea that Nares Strait marks a major fault was also rejuvenated (Drake et al., 1963; Wilson, 1963).

1963: The first marine geophysical work in Baffin Bay and Nares Strait was undertaken from the vessels CCGS LABRADOR and CSS BAFFIN. This work suggested, for example, that the Tertiary basalts of western Greenland might extend offshore, and that Cumberland Sound might be a fault-bounded graben. Both suggestions were confirmed later (Manchester, 1964).

1963: Aeromagnetic surveys of the Labrador Sea and Baffin Bay were begun by the National Aeronautical Establishment and the Geological Survey of Canada. These led to estimates of the thicknesses of sediment beneath the shelves of those regions (Godby et al., 1966; Hood, 1971).

1963: Shell Oil Canada Ltd. acquired about 8 million hectares on the Scotian Shelf.

1963: The highest tides in the world occur in the Bay of Fundy, and the region has been a focus of sedimentological studies of intertidal sediments. Zoning of intertidal sediments was established in the Bay of Fundy in 1963 (Klein, 1963). Many proposals have been made to use the tides of the Bay for generation of power, and proposals initiated in 1969 led to many sedimentological and ecological studies (Pelletier and McMullen, 1972; Dalrymple et al., 1975; Amos and Long, 1980; McCann, 1980).

1964: The publication "Maritime Sediments" was started by B.R. Pelletier, which provided a focus for reconnaissance studies of marine geology in the Atlantic Provinces.

1964: The Appalachians in Newfoundland were shown to be two-sided, with a central mobile belt bounded on either side by Precambrian rocks. These ideas were enhanced with the publication of a modern geological map of Newfoundland (Williams, 1964 and 1967).

1964: The Virgin Rocks, 200 km southeast of St. John's, Newfoundland, were sampled by diving, and quartzites recovered similar to those of the Precambrian Conception Group of Newfoundland. A plaque was put in place, claiming the offshore for Newfoundland (Lilly, 1965).

1964: The Orpheus gravity anomaly was discovered. Later drilling showed that this delineated a Triassic graben (Loncarevic and Ewing, 1967; King and MacLean, 1970a).

1964: Pan American Petroleum Corporation (now Amoco) acquired 12.7 million hectares which covered most of the Grand Banks (D.F. Sherwin, personal communication, 1986; J.H. Swift, personal communication, 1986).

1965: Mobil Oil acquired 5.4 million hectares on the Grand Banks, including what became the Hibernia field (D.F. Sherwin, personal communication, 1986).

1965: Shallow core drilling was undertaken on the Grand Banks, 64 holes (Pan American-Imperial), on the Scotian Shelf, 2 holes (Mobil), and in the Gulf of St. Lawrence, 6 holes (Pan American-Hydro Quebec). The drilling on the Grand Banks confirmed the presence of Cretaceous and Tertiary sediments. The vessel used was the CALDRILL, which had in the same season drilled 6 holes off the USA for the Joint Oceanographic Institutions for Deep Earth Sampling (JOIDES). These holes were part of a trial program for the Deep Sea Drilling Project (Magnusson, 1965; Sherwin, 1973).

1965: Multichannel seismic data were acquired in Hudson Bay by Geophysical Services Incorporated on behalf of Richfield Oil Corp.; studies of the bedrock and surficial geology and crustal structure were undertaken by Canadian universities and government agencies (Pelletier et al., 1968; Ruffman, 1969)

1966: The Appalachians were shown to have formed in the Paleozoic by the opening and closing of an ancient ocean, Iapetus. This defined the "Wilson Cycle" (Wilson, 1966)

1966: The Appalachians were seen in seismic studies to extend offshore from Newfoundland, and their two-sided nature to be reflected in their structure at depth

(Ewing et al., 1966; Sheridan and Drake, 1968; Williams et al., 1970).

1966: A piercement salt dome was discovered beneath the Grand Banks and was drilled by the first wildcat, the Pan Am and Imperial A-1 Tors Cove D-52. A small show of gas was recovered from the caprock of the salt dome, providing the first hint of the petroleum potential in the Canadian offshore (McMillan, 1982; J.H. Swift, personal communication, 1986).

1966: The marginal channels of Labrador were shown by a seismic reflection line to separate crystalline rocks of the Precambrian Shield from sedimentary rocks. Whether or not the channels were caused by faulting or by glacial erosion, or both, could not be seen. This reflection work also suggested that a sedimentary wedge, then of unknown age, lies beneath the Labrador Shelf, seaward of the troughs. These ideas were expanded in later years (Holtedahl, 1950; Grant, 1966 and 1972; Mayhew et al., 1970).

1966: The French Petroleum Company of Canada, Amerada, and Tenneco acquired 6.5 million hectares off Labrador (D.F. Sherwin, personal communication, 1986).

1967: Mobil drilled the first well on Sable Island, Mobil Sable Island No.1, (C-67) to a depth of 4604 m, and encountered gas shows and a small indication of light oil. The cost was $3 million (Mobil, 1968; Appleton, 1983).

1967: Fresh-water peat was reported from the continental shelf off the east coast of North America: "meadows and forests formerly covered the shelf." (Emery et al., 1967).

1967: Plate tectonics was established (McKenzie and Parker, 1967; Morgan, 1968).

1967: King demonstrated the use of acoustic reflection characteristics to differentiate surficial sedimentary facies. This approach is now extensively used in sea-bed geological mapping (King, 1967).

1968: The Deep Sea Drilling Project (DSDP) was initiated (Ewing et al., 1969).

1968: D.J. Stanley and his colleagues carried out studies of sedimentological processes in the Northwest Arm, Halifax (Stanley, 1968), the first of a series of modern studies of the sedimentological and geological evolution of the wave-dominated fiords of eastern Canada (Piper et al., 1983).

1968: A submersible was used for geological research and mapping in the Canadian offshore for the first time. The PISCES-1, owned and operated by Hydrodynamics International, was deployed from the

CCGS LABRADOR at numerous sites in the Arctic Archipelago (Pelletier, 1968).

1968: Matachewan Canadian Gold Limited conducted a survey along the inner Scotian Shelf for placer gold that included geophysics and bottom sampling. Three gold deposits were identified which resulted in construction of the SEA GOLD, the first and only gold dredge to operate in the Canadian offshore. The company did not develop any commercial gold deposits, but did locate and harvest several large clam beds (Libby, 1969).

1969: A sea-water extraction plant for magnesium hydroxide was built at Aguathuna in southwest Newfoundland. It experienced operational and financial difficulties and never operated commercially (Gormley, 1969; Hale, Chapter 13, this volume).

1969: Plate tectonics was applied conceptually to the Appalachians. Modern attempts to relate the Appalachians to their counterparts, the Caledonides, followed in later years (Dewey, 1969; Haworth, 1981).

1969: The East Coast Magnetic Anomaly (ECMA), discovered earlier, was successfully modelled as an edge effect between continental and oceanic crust (Keen, 1969).

1969: Precambrian granodiorite was obtained by diamond drill from Flemish Cap, suggesting that the cap is a continental fragment (Pelletier, 1971).

1969: "Admiral's Finger", a pingo-like feature, was discovered from the vessel CCGS JOHN A. MACDONALD. This led to surveys in the Beaufort Sea in 1970 by the vessel CSS BAFFIN, when 78 such features were discovered, the shallowest with a top at a water depth of only 15.4 m (Shearer et al., 1971).

1969: Surveys contracted by the United States Naval Oceanographic Office discovered possible salt piercement structures beneath the continental rise southwest of the Grand Banks (Watson and Johnson, 1970; Sherwin, 1973).

1969: Industry conducted seismic work in the Bay of Fundy (Appleton, 1983).

1969: Shell Onondaga E-84 was drilled south of Sable Island and was interpreted to contain significant amounts of gas (Grant et al., 1986b).

1969: The first well, Aquitaine et al. Walrus A-71, was drilled in Hudson Bay.

1969: Panarctic made the gas discovery at Drake Point, Melville Island, in the Arctic Archipelago.

1969: The United States tanker S.S. MANHATTAN with the Canadian icebreaker CCGS JOHN A. MACDONALD traversed the Northwest Passage, testing the feasibility of the route for transporting oil to the east.

1970-79

1970: The Canadian Government enacted the Arctic Waters Pollution Prevention Act, a consequence of the voyage of the S.S. MANHATTAN.

1970: The tanker ARROW ran aground in Chedabucto Bay, off Nova Scotia, February 4, 1970, and its oil fouled beaches and damaged habitats.

Multidisciplinary studies subsequently led to comprehensive knowledge of this and other coastal regions (Atlantic Oceanographic Laboratory, 1970; Buckley et al., 1974; Owens et al., 1977; Vilks and Krauel, 1982).

1970: Pockmarks were reported for the first time in the sediments of the Scotian Shelf. They became important in engineering geology in the North Sea (King and MacLean, 1970b).

1970: Deep Sea Drilling Project, Leg 12. Holes were drilled in the Labrador Sea, and on Orphan Knoll northeast of Newfoundland. These holes confirmed the suggestion that the knoll is a continental fragment, and established the date of opening of the Labrador Sea (Grant, 1972; Laughton et al., 1972). These holes also established an age of 3 Ma for the onset of major glaciation in the northern hemisphere (Berggren, 1972).

1970: The CSS HUDSON became the first vessel to circumnavigate the Americas. This led inter alia to the discovery of anisotropy in the oceanic mantle of the eastern Pacific, and to discoveries in the Beaufort Sea and Baffin Bay.

1970: Scour of the sea floor by sea ice in the Beaufort Sea was discovered using side-scan sonar. Ground ice was discovered in sediment cores (Arctic Petroleum Operators' Association, 1971; Shearer, 1971; Yorath et al., 1971; MacKay, 1972). The water depth range of the ice scour occurrences was explained as the long-term result of ice-sea-bed interaction and a rising relative sea level. Subsequently, the ice scours were characterized numerically and their frequency of formation and depth calculated in terms of sea-level change sedimentary processes (Lewis, 1978).

1970: Geophysical work from the vessels CSS HUDSON and CSS DAWSON established that thick sediments lie beneath the northern part of Baffin Bay and beneath Melville Bay, that the basalts of western Greenland extend substantially offshore, and that Baffin Bay is underlain by oceanic crust (Barrett et al., 1971; Keen et al., 1972).

1970: Holocene changes in sea levels in Atlantic Canada were well documented from geological evidence; they are important in considering models of Pleistocene glaciation and deglaciation (Grant, 1970). Modern analytical techniques for studying the loading of the earth were subsequently applied successfully to the problem of changes in relative sea levels associated with deglaciation, and were useful in distinguishing between alternative geological models (Quinlan and Beaumont, 1981).

1970: The company Kenting Limited initiated the "Polarquest" program in the Arctic Archipelago, one of a series of investigations which explored northern waters for the oil and gas industry.

1970: The first of a number of surficial geological maps for the Canadian offshore was published for the Halifax-Sable Island map area. Work on surficial sediments became important for the solution of engineering problems, and for its contribution to our knowledge of Pleistocene geology. The "Emerald Silt" is, for example, an important type section within the Wisconsinan of Atlantic Canada (King, 1970; MacLean and King, 1971).

1970: Sidbec Limited investigated the iron sands off the Natashquan River in the northern Gulf of St. Lawrence as a possible source of iron for steel manufacturing (Hale, Chapter 13, this volume).

1971: One of the first regional syntheses of inner shelf surficial geology was completed for Northumberland Strait (Kranck, 1971). This was followed later in the 1970's by a comprehensive study of the inner Scotian Shelf off the south shore of Nova Scotia (Piper et al., 1986).

1971: The first systematic work was done on the shelf off Baffin Island, in which the major geological units were recognized using geophysical methods. This work was expanded subsequently, and sampling undertaken by rock core drill (Grant, 1975; MacLean et al., 1982).

1971: The opening of the Labrador Sea in two episodes was recognized; Upper Cretaceous to Paleocene, and Paleocene to Eocene. Work of later years gave the spreading history in greater detail (Le Pichon et al., 1971; Hyndman, 1973; Srivastava, 1978).

1971: The first well, Tenneco et al. Leif E-38, was spudded on the Labrador Shelf, reaching a total depth of 1084 m (McMillan, 1982).

1971: Amoco and Imperial resumed drilling on the Grand Banks, and drilled the first deep well on the northern Grand Banks, Amoco Imperial Murre G-67 (Amoco, 1972 and 1973).

1971: The first significant quantity of oil was discovered in the Atlantic offshore, in the well Mobil-Tetco Sable Island E-48. Gas, condensate and oil were recovered on tests of 21 separate zones over a 970 m interval. The well was completed with a potential flow rate of 457.7 cubic meters per day of oil and 36.8 million cubic meters of gas from a 1.5 m interval in the Logan Canyon Formation (Canada Oil and Gas Lands Administration, 1985a; Grant et al., 1986b).

1972: The Atlantic Geoscience Centre, a division of the Geological Survey of Canada, was founded at Bedford Institute of Oceanography, Dartmouth, Nova Scotia. This establishment is responsible on behalf of the Survey for geological and geophysical investigations off eastern Canada.

1972: Stanley and his colleagues developed a model for outer continental margin sedimentation off Nova Scotia, which was perhaps the beginning of modern investigations of deep water sediments in the region (Stanley et al., 1972).

1972: The first measurements of heat flow in the Labrador Sea and Baffin Bay showed "normal" values, consistent with the idea that sea-floor spreading is not active now (Pye and Hyndman, 1972).

1972: Hydrocarbon discoveries were made at two locations on the Scotian Shelf. Oil and gas was discovered at the well Shell Primrose N-50 and gas and condensate at the well Mobil TETCO Thebaud P-84 (Grant et al., 1986b).

1972: The first definitive lithostratigraphic study for the Canadian east coast offshore was published for the Scotian Shelf (McIver, 1972). Other studies followed in later years (Amoco Canada and Imperial Oil Ltd., 1973; Jansa and Wade, 1975a; Given, 1977).

1972: The first artificial island was constructed in the Beaufort Sea during the summer and winter of 1972-73, and the well Imperial Immerk B-48 was drilled from the island during the summer and winter of 1973-74 (Croasdale and Marcellus, 1978).

1973: The Government of Canada published its first estimates of hydrocarbon resources in Canada, following disputes concerning estimates by industry. This has been done fairly regularly since then (Energy, Mines and Resources Canada, 1973).

1973: The first recovery of oil in the Jeanne d'Arc Basin came from the well Mobil Gulf Adolphus 2-K-41 (McMillan, 1982; Canada Oil and Gas Lands Administration, 1985a).

1973: The postulate was made that Davis Strait is a hot spot; this was later supported by geochemical evidence (Hyndman, 1973; Keen and Clarke, 1974).

1974: Iceberg furrows were recognized on the continental shelf northeast of Newfoundland and later on the Scotian Shelf and northern shelves. Relict furrows were recognized in 1976 (Harris and Jollymore, 1974; King, 1976; King and MacLean, 1976; Lewis et al., 1980).

1974: The first oil was discovered in the Arctic Islands, in the well Panarctic et al. Bent Horn N-72 (D.F. Sherwin, personal communication, 1986).

1974: The first discovery of oil and gas was made in the Beaufort Sea, Imperial Adgo F-28 (D.F. Sherwin, personal communication, 1986).

1974: Exploration by industry on the southern Grand Banks ceased, because results had been disappointing (Appleton, 1983).

1974: The first substantial biostratigraphic study for the east coast offshore was published, followed soon after by others (Williams, 1974; Gradstein et al., 1975; Ascoli, 1976).

1975: The publication of the two volumes of the Geological Survey of Canada Paper "Offshore Geology of Eastern Canada" provided a summary of the knowledge of the geology and geophysics off eastern Canada at that time (Pelletier, 1975; Van der Linden and Wade, 1975).

1975: Similarities in the evolution of the Nova Scotian and Moroccan margins during the Mesozoic were first described (Bhat et al., 1975; Jansa and Wade, 1975b).

1975: "Benthonics '75", the first of a continuing series of international symposia on benthonic foraminifera was organized and held in Halifax in August 1975. The proceedings provide a synthesis of the ecology and biology of recent foraminifera of the continental shelves and the paleoecology and biostratigraphy of their fossil counterparts (Ascoli, 1976; Schafer and Pelletier, 1976).

1975: Growing concern for the preservation of beaches led to a detailed investigation of natural development, response to aggregate extraction, and legal framework of sand beaches in Nova Scotia (Bowen, 1975). The predominance of gravel beaches in the region, their distinctive process characteristics, and the pervasive continuing effects of Pleistocene glaciation on beach development in Atlantic Canada were not explicitly recognized until later (Forbes and Taylor, 1987).

1975: Lineations and reversals were discovered in the Magnetic Quiet Zone off Nova Scotia (Barrett and Keen, 1975).

1975: The first well in the Bay of Fundy, Mobil Gulf Chinampas N-37 was drilled to a depth of 3661 meters, with disappointing results (Appleton, 1983).

1975: The first bedrock map of a Canadian offshore region was published (King and MacLean, 1976).

1975: The first use was made of the high resolution seismic system, Huntec Deep-Tow. This represented a major advance in our ability to map surficial sediments in offshore eastern Canada and elsewhere (Hutchins et al., 1976).

1976: Oil slick discovered off Scott Inlet, Baffin Island, and this was thought to be due to a natural seep; this was confirmed by sampling from the submersible PISCES IV in 1986 (Loncarevic and Falconer, 1977; MacLean et al, 1981; Grant et al., 1986b).

1976: A heavy water extraction plant was built at Glace Bay, Nova Scotia. It closed in 1985 due to a falling demand (Hale, Chapter 13, this volume).

1977: The first seismic reflection lines to link southwest Greenland to Labrador were shot (Hinz et al., 1979).

1977: Drilling off Cape Breton Island, Nova Scotia, established the reserves of coal in the Donkin block of the Sydney coalfield (Hacquebard, 1979).

1977: The first of three cruises using the long range sidescan system GLORIA on the eastern margin of Canada was run. Records were collected along the continental slope from the region off Sable Island to Orphan Knoll and also along a line extending to southern Greenland (Parson et al., 1984).

1978: Studies of modern palynology helped show that the Labrador Shelf was deglaciated early, not late, contrary to the suggestions made in the program CLIMAP (Vilks and Mudie, 1978). Syntheses of the Quaternary geology of the Labrador Shelf and the deeper waters further offshore appeared later (Aksu and Mudie, 1985; Josenhans et al., 1986).

1978: McKenzie proposed that rifted margins form by lithospheric stretching (McKenzie, 1978).

1978: The first well was drilled in deep water, 866 m, on the continental slope off Nova Scotia, Chevron et al., Acadia K-62, to a total depth of 5287 m (Chevron et al., 1980).

1978: The presence of Jurassic reefs beneath the Scotian Shelf was described by Eliuk (1978).

1979: The tanker KURDISTAN broke in two, and spilled oil on the shores of Nova Scotia, 15 March, 1979.

1979: Early studies of hydrocarbon geochemistry in association with exploration offshore eastern Canada came to fruition in 1979 and 1980 (Bujak et al., 1977; Powell and Snowdon, 1979; Rashid et al., 1980; Swift and Williams, 1980).

1979: A well was drilled in very deep water, 1486 m, northeast of Newfoundland, Texaco, Shell et al. Blue H-28, to a total depth of 6103 m, with disappointing results (Texaco, 1981).

1979: The first modelling of the margins off eastern Canada using lithospheric stretching was undertaken. It yielded predictions of the thermal maturation of their sediments (Keen, 1979).

1979: A zonation and correlation of sixty-seven wells from the east coast offshore using spores, pollen and dinoflagellates was published (Barss et al., 1979).

1979: The first indications of potentially commercial reserves of gas and condensate in the Atlantic offshore were found in the well Mobil Venture D-23. The well was significant in that it established the presence of major hydrocarbon reserves in a highly overpressured section (Grant et al., 1986b).

1979: The well Chevron et al. Hibernia P-15 established the potential of the Jeanne d'Arc Basin for oil resources. Earlier studies had pointed to the potential of the eastern Grand Banks (Energy, Mines and Resources, 1973; Bujak et al., 1977).

1979: The first exploratory wells were drilled offshore southeastern Baffin Island: Esso H.B.O.G. Gjoa G-37, drilled to a total depth of 3598 m, and Aquitaine et al., Hekja 0-71, drilled to a total depth of 4566 m. Gas resources were discovered estimated to be 65 trillion cubic m (Klose et al., 1982).

1980 — PRESENT

1980: A number of expeditions were mounted by Canada and the U.S.A. to investigate the Arctic Ocean in the 1970's and 1980's; these included the FRAM series, LOREX and CESAR. They showed, inter alia, that the mid-ocean ridge in the Arctic is spreading slowly, that the Alpha Cordillera may be an "oceanic plateau", and that very perplexing cyclic sedimentation dominated the Arctic Ocean in the Cretaceous (Jackson et al., 1982; Jackson et al., 1985).

1980: The first oil was discovered offshore the Arctic Islands in Panarctic et al. Char G-07 (D.F. Sherwin, personal communication, 1986).

1980: The first three-dimensional seismic survey offshore eastern Canada was undertaken, on behalf of Mobil Oil in the Hibernia area (D.F. Sherwin, personal communication, 1986).

1980: Seabright Resources Limited investigated the coastal waters off Isaacs Harbour and Country Harbour, Nova Scotia for placer gold. They found gold and may carry out additional work in the future (Hale, Chapter 13, this volume).

1980: The recognition of the potential damage to the coastlines of eastern Canada from oil spills led to a concentrated effort in the 1970's and 1980's on geological studies of the coastal regime (McCann, 1980; Reinson, 1979; Taylor, 1980).

1981: A study of the carbonate platforms off eastern North America confirmed the northward motion of the North American plate at rates of up to 1.5 cm per year (Jansa, 1981).

1981: The first analysis of sediment facies on the shelf edge, based on detailed coverage of sidescan sonar and related observations, was published for the vicinity of the Hibernia Oil Field (Fader and King, 1981). This study was the basis for further work (Barrie et al., 1984) and for the first compilation of a detailed Quaternary geological map (1:250 000) offshore (Fader et al., 1986).

1982: The Canadian Coastal Sediment Study was initiated as a large-scale multi-year collaborative program to advance understanding of sediment dynamics in the littoral zone (Bowen et al., 1986).

1982: The first systematic multidisciplinary study of the many fjords of Baffin Island was undertaken. They are particularly interesting because many have glaciers at tide-water now. They make an interesting contrast to the river-dominated fiords of temperate British Columbia and wave-dominated fiords of Nova Scotia (Syvitski et al., 1986).

1982: The OCEAN RANGER, a semi-submersible drilling rig, sank during a storm on the Grand Banks while drilling at a location in the Hibernia field, and 84 lives were lost.

1982: The first thermomechanical models were constructed for the east coast offshore. The temperature distribution was predicted from the extension of the lithosphere during rifting, and this was used to derive the mechanical properties of the lithosphere. These were used in turn to derive the response of the lithosphere to loading by sediments and water (Beaumont et al., 1982).

1982: The concept of "suspect terranes" was applied to the Appalachians (Williams and Hatcher, 1982).

1982: The use of aromitization and isomerization in studies of the maturation of sediments was proposed (MacKenzie et al., 1982).

1983: The presence of an extensive zone of overpressure deep beneath the Scotian Shelf was recognized as a major factor affecting the occurrence of gas resources (J.A. Wade, personal communication, 1983).

1984: The first blow-out occurred offshore eastern Canada at the Shell Petro-Canada et al. Uniacke G-72 well (Canada Oil and Gas Lands Administration, 1984a and 1984b).

1984: The well Mobil et al. West Venture N-91 blew out underground; it took 272 days to bring under control, at a cost of more than $170 million (Canada Oil and Gas Lands Administration, 1984a and 1984b).

1984: Substantial elements of the Gulf of Maine boundary dispute between Canada and the U.S.A. were settled by a Cabinet of the International Court of Justice at The Hague.

1984: The first systematic study of the bedforms on the shelves off eastern Canada was published (Amos and King, 1984).

1984: Deep multichannel seismic reflection work across the Appalachians offshore northeastern Newfoundland established the structure of the crust beneath the Appalachians. This was part of the program "Lithoprobe", a multi-disciplinary program of study of the lithosphere (Keen et al., 1986).

1984: The continuation of the Scotian Basin beneath St. Pierre Bank was confirmed by deep multichannel seismic data. (B.C. MacLean and J.A. Wade, personal communication, 1984).

1985: Underplating of the continental crust at rifting was shown to be predicted by thermal modelling of the rifting process, and supported by deep seismic observations (Keen, 1985; LASE, 1986).

1985: Leg 105 of the Ocean Drilling Program (ODP) successfully explored the Labrador Sea and Baffin Bay, confirming the age of opening of the Labrador Sea suggested by magnetic anomalies. The onset of glaciation in Baffin Bay was confirmed at about 3 million years, with significant cooling in Baffin Bay and the Norwegian Sea at about 10 million years, as in Iceland (Mudie and Helgason, 1983; Srivastava, Arthur, Clement et al., 1987).

1985: Mer Resources Limited undertook a beach and nearshore sampling program for heavy minerals along the Atlantic Coast of Nova Scotia. Gold and other heavy minerals were identified and further work is planned (Hale, Chapter 13, this volume).

1985: The NORDCO rock core drill was used successfully on a BIO cruise. The drill is capable of auguring through up to 6 m of overburden prior to coring bedrock (MacLean, 1986).

1985: Deep multichannel seismic reflection work across the Jeanne d'Arc Basin shows that it is in places more than 20 km thick (Keen et al., 1987).

1985: Synthesis of the Quaternary of the shelves off southeastern Canada (King and Fader, 1985).

REFERENCES

Adams, J.
1987: Canadian crustal stress data – a compilation to July 1987; Geological Survey of Canada, Open File 1622, 130 p.

Aksu, A.E. and Mudie, P.J.
1985: Late Quaternary stratigraphy and paleoecology of Northwest Labrador Sea; Marine Micropalaeontology, v. 9, p. 537-557.

Amoco Canada Petroleum Company Ltd.
1972: Murre G-67 Well History Report; by Amoco Canada Petroleum Co., Calgary, Canada Oil and Gas Lands Administration, Ottawa.

Amoco Canada Petroleum Company Ltd. and Imperial Oil Ltd.
1973: Regional geology of the Grand Banks; Bulletin Canadian Petroleum Geology, v. 21, p. 479-503.

Amos, C.L. and King, E.L.
1984: Bedforms of the Canadian eastern seaboard: a comparison with global occurrences; Marine Geology, v. 57, p. 167-208.

Amos, C.L. and Long, B.F.N. 1980: The sedimentary character of Minas Basin, Bay of Fundy; in The Coastline of Canada, ed. S.B.McCann; Geological Survey of Canada, Paper 80-10, p. 123-152.

Appleton, K.P.
1983: Review of drilling and geophysical activities and expenditures; Geological Survey of Canada, Paper 81-6, Part 1, p. 69-73.

Arctic Petroleum Operators' Association
1971: Geological sampling and analytical program — Beaufort Sea; Arctic Petroleum Operators' Association Report no. 4.

Ascoli, P.
1976: Foraminiferal and ostracod biostratigraphy of the Mesozoic-Cenozoic, Scotian Shelf, Atlantic Canada; in Maritime Sediments, Special Publication no. 1, p. 653-771.

Atlantic Oceanography Laboratory
1970: Report of the Task Force — Operation Oil: Clean-up of the Arrow oil spill in Chedabucto Bay; Minister of Transport, Atlantic Oceanographic Laboratory, Bedford Institute, Dartmouth, Nova Scotia.

Barrett, D.L. and Keen, C.E.
1975: Lineations in the magnetic Quiet Zone of the north west Atlantic; Nature, v. 253, p. 423-425.

Barrett, D.L., Berry, M., Blanchard, J.E., Keen, M.J., and McAllister, R.E.
1964: Seismic studies on the eastern seaboard of Canada: the Atlantic coast of Nova Scotia; Canadian Journal of Earth Sciences, v. 1, p. 10-22.

Barrett, D.L., Keen, C.E., Manchester, K., and Ross, D.I.
1971: Baffin Bay: An Ocean: Nature, v. 229, p. 551-553.

Barrie, J.V., Lewis, C.F.M., Fader, G.B., and King, L.H.
1984: Seabed processes on the southeastern Grand Banks of Newfoundland; modern reworking of relict sediments; Marine Geology, v. 57, p. 209-227.

Barss, M.S., Bujak, J.P., and Williams, G.L.
1979: Palynological zonation and correlation of sixty-seven wells, eastern Canada; Geological Survey of Canada, Paper 78-24, 118 p.

Bartlett, G.A. and Smith, L.
1971: Mesozoic and Cenozoic history of the Grand Banks of Newfoundland; Canadian Journal of Earth Sciences, v. 8, p. 65-84.

Beaumont, C, Keen, C.E., and Boutilier, R.
1982: On the evolution of rifted continental margins: comparison of models and observations for the Nova Scotian margin; Geophysical Journal; v. 70, p. 667-715.

Bell, J.S. and Gough, D.I.
1979: Northeast-southeast compressive stress in Alberta; Earth & Planetary Science Letters, v. 45, no. 2, p. 382-475.

Bell, R.
1895: A great pre-glacial river in northern Canada; Scottish Geographical Magazine, v. 11, p. 368.

Berggren, W.A.
1972: Late Pliocene-Pleistocene glaciation; in Initial Reports of the Deep Sea Drilling Project, volume XII, ed. A.S. Laughton et al.; United States Government Printing Office, Washington, v. 12, p. 953-963.

Bhat, H., McMillan, N.J., Aubert, J., Porthault, B., and Surin, M.
1975: North American and African Drift - the record in Mesozoic coastal plain rocks, Nova Scotia and Morocco; in Canada's Continental Margins and Offshore Petroleum Exploration, ed. C.J. Yorath, E.R. Parker, and D.J. Glass; Canadian Society of Petroleum Geologists, Memoir 4, p. 375-390.

Blandford, H.R.
1964: Bay of Fundy survey, August 12 October 30, 1964; Canadian Hydrographic Service, Department of Mines and Technical Surveys, Ottawa, Project 43-3.

Boeggild, O.B.
1900: The deposits of the sea bottom; Danish Ingolf-Expedition, Bianco Luno (F.Dreyer), Printer to the Court, v. 1, pt. 3, p. 1-89.

Bornhold, B.D., Finlayson, N.M., and Monahan, D.
1976: Submerged drainage patterns in Barrow Strait, Canadian Arctic: Canadian Journal of Earth Sciences, v. 13, p. 305-311.

Bowen, A.J.
1975: The maintenance of beaches; Technical Report, Institute for Environmental Studies, Dalhousie University, Halifax, Nova Scotia, 582 p.

Bowen, A.J. et al.
1986: Canadian coastal sediment study; National Research Council Canada, Division of Mechanical Engineering, Hydraulics Laboratory, Technical Report TR-HY-013, 96 p.

Bower, M.E.
1961: Sea magnetometer surveys of the Grand Banks of Newfoundland, Burgeo Bank and St.Pierre Bank; Geological Survey of Canada, Paper 61-30. 11 p.

Bramlette, M.N. and Bradley, W.H.
1941: Lithology and geological interpretation: geology and biology of North Atlantic deep sea cores; United States Geological Survey, Professional Paper 196, p. 1-34.

Buckley, D.E., Owens, E.H., Schafer, C.T., Vilks, G.V., Cranston, R.E., Rashid, M.A., Wagner, F.J.E., and Walker, D.A.
1974: Canso Strait and Chedabucto Bay: a multidisciplinary study of the impact of man on the marine environment; in Offshore Geology of Eastern Canada, Volume 1, Concepts and Applications of Environmental Marine Geology, ed. B.R. Pelletier; Geological Survey of Canada, Paper 74-30, v. 1, p. 133-160.

Bujak, J.P., Barss, M.S., and Williams, G.L.
1977: Offshore eastern Canada's organic type and color and hydrocarbon potential; Oil and Gas Journal, v. 75, no. 14, p. 198-202.

Bullard, E.C.
1975 The emergence of plate tectonics, a personal view; Earth and Planetary Sciences Annual Reviews, v. 3, p. 1-30.

Canada Oil and Gas Lands Administration
1984a: Annual Report 1984; Energy, Mines and Resources Canada, Ottawa.
1984b: Investigation of events culminating in a blow-out of gas and condensate at Shell et al. Uniacke G-72; The Canada Oil and Gas Lands Administration, Halifax, Nova Scotia, 20 p.
1985a: Offshore schedule of wells 1966-1984; Energy, Mines and Resources Canada, Ottawa.

1985b: Investigation of events culminating in a loss of well control at Mobil et al. Venture N-9; The Canada Oil and Gas Lands Administration, Halifax, Nova Scotia, 21 p.

Carey, S.W. and Ahmad, N.
1961: Glacial marine sedimentation; Proceedings of the First International Symposium on Arctic Geology, ed. G.O.Raasch; v. 2, p. 865-894.

Chevron et al.
1980: Acadia K-62, Well History Report: Chevron, Calgary, Canada Oil and Gas Lands Administration, Ottawa.

Chough, S.K. and Hesse, R.
1976: Submarine meandering talweg and turbidity currents for 4000 km in the Northwest Atlantic Mid-Ocean Channel, Labrador Sea; Geology, v. 4, p. 529-533.

Clarke, D.B.
1970: Tertiary basalts of Baffin Bay: possible primary magma from the mantle; Contributions to Mineralogy and Petrology, v. 25, p. 203-224.

Croasdale, K.R. and Marcellus, R.W.
1978: Ice and wave action on artificial islands in the Beaufort Sea; Canadian Journal of Civil Engineering, v. 5, p. 98-113.

Cushman, J.A.
1936: Geology and paleontology of the Georges Bank canyons. Part 4, Cretaceous and Late Tertiary foraminifer; Bulletin Geological Society of America, v. 47, p. 413-440.

Dahl, W.H.
1925: Tertiary fossils dredged off the northeastern coast of North America; American Journal of Science, Series 5, v. 10, p. 213-218.

Dalrymple, R.W., Knight, R.J., and Middleton, G.V.
1975: Intertidal sand bars in Cobequid Bay, (Bay of Fundy); Estuarine Research, v. 2, p. 293-307.

Daly, R.A.
1934: The changing world of the Ice Age; Yale University, Press, 271 p.

1936: Origin of submarine canyons; American Journal of Science, 5th series, v. 31, p. 401-420.

Dawson, J.W.
1868: Acadian Geology (second edition); MacMillan and Company, London, 694 p.

de Smitt
1932: Earthquakes in the North Atlantic as related to submarine cables; Transactions American Geophysical Union, 13th Annual Meeting, Washington, DC, p. 103-109.

Dewey, J.F.
1969: Evolution of the Appalachian/Caledonian orogen; Nature, v. 222, p. 124-129.

Dietz, R.S.
1961: Continent and ocean basin evolution by spreading of the sea floor; Nature, v. 190, p. 854-857.

Douglas, R.J.W. (ed.)
1970: Geology and Economic Minerals of Canada, Fifth edition; Geological Survey of Canada, Economic Geology Report 1, 838 p.

Doxsee, W.W.
1948: The Grand Banks Earthquake of November 18, 1929; Publications of the Dominion Observatory, no. 7, p. 323-335.

Drake, C.L., Campell, N.J., Sander, G., and Nafe, J.E.
1963: A mid-Labrador Sea Ridge; Nature, v. 200, p. 1085-1086.

Drake, C.L., Ewing, M., and Sutton, G.H.
1959: Physics and Chemistry of the Earth; vol. 3, p. 110-198.

Drake, C.L., Heirtzler, J., and Hirshman, J.
1963: Magnetic anomalies off Eastern North America; Journal of Geophysical Research, v. 68, p. 5259-5275.

Eliuk, L.S.
1978: The Abenaki Formation, Nova Scotia Shelf, Canada — a depositional model for a Mesozoic carbonate platform; Bulletin of Canadian Petroleum Geology, v. 26, p. 424-514.

Elmendorf, C.H. and Heezen, B.C.
1957: Oceanographic information for engineering submarine cable systems; Bell System Technical Journal; v. 36, p. 1047-1093.

Emery, K.O., Uchupi, E., Phillips, J.D. Bunce, E.T., and Knott, S.T.
1970: Continental rise off eastern North America; American Association of Petroleum Geologists Bulletin, v. 54, p. 44-108.

Emery, K.O., Wigley, R.L., Bartlett, A.S., Rubin, M., and Barghoorn, E.S.
1967: Fresh-water peat on the continental shelf; Science, v. 158, p. 1301-1307.

Energy, Mines and Resources, Canada
1973: An energy policy for Canada, Phase 1; Department of Energy, Mines and Resources, Ottawa, Ontario.

Ericson, D.B., Ewing, M., Wollin, G., and Heezen, B.C.
1961: Atlantic deep sea sediment cores; Geological Society of America Bulletin, v. 72, p. 193-286.

Ervine, W.R. and Bell, J.S.
1987: Subsurface in-situ stress magnitudes from oil well drilling records: an example from the Venture area, offshore eastern Canada; Canadian Journal of Earth Sciences, v. 24, p. 1748-1759.

Ewing, G.N., Dainty, A.M., Blanchard, J.E., and Keen, M.J.
1966: Seismic studies of the eastern seaboard of Canada: the Appalachian system; Canadian Journal of Earth Sciences, v. 3, p. 89-109.

Ewing, M., Heezen, B.C., Ericson, D.B., Northrop, J., and Dorman, J.
1953: Exploration of the northwest Atlantic mid-ocean canyon; Geological Society of America Bulletin, v. 64, p. 865-868.

Ewing, M., Worzel, J.L., and Burk, C.A.
1969: Introduction; in Initial Reports of the Deep Sea Drilling Project, Volume I; ed. M. Ewing et al., United States Government Printing Office, Washington, v. 1, p. 3-9.

Ewing, M., Worzel, J.L., Press, F., and Hamilton, G.R.
1950: Seismic refraction measurements in the Atlantic Ocean basin, Part 1; Bulletin Seismological Society of America, v. 40, p. 233-242.

Fader, G.B. and King, L.H.
1981: A reconnaissance study of the surficial geology of the Grand Banks of Newfoundland; in Current Research, Part A, Geological Survey of Canada, Paper 81-1A, p. 45-56.

Fader, G.B., Lewis, C.F.M., Barrie, J.V., Parrott, D.R., Collins, W.T., Miller, R.O., and d'Apollonia, S.J.
1986: Quaternary geology of the Hibernia area of northeast Grand Banks; Geological Survey of Canada, Open File 1222, scale 1:250 000.

Falvey, D.A.
1974: The development of continental margins in plate tectonic theory; Australian Petroleum Exploration Association Journal, v. 14, p. 95-106.

Forbes, D.L. and Taylor, R.B.
1987: Coarse-grained beach sedimentation under paraglacial conditions, Canadian Atlantic coast; in Glaciated Coasts, ed. D.M. Fitzgerald and P.S. Rosen, Chapter 3, Academic Press, Orlando, Florida, p. 52-86.

Fortier, Y.O. and Morley, L.M.
1956: Geological unity of the Arctic Islands; Transactions of the Royal Society of Canada, Series 3, v. 50, p. 3-12.

Fortier, Y.O., Blackadar, R.G., Glenister, B.F., Greiner, H.R., Mclaren, D.J., McMillan, N.J., Norris, A.W., Roots, E.F., Souther, J.G., Thorsteinsson, R., and Tozer, E.T.
1963: Geology of the north-central part of the Arctic Archipelago, Northwest Territories (Operation Franklin); Geological Survey of Canada, Memoir 320, 671 p.

Fowler, G.A. and Kingston, P.F.
1975: An underwater drill for continental shelf explorations; Society of Underwater Technology, v. 1, no. 4, p. 18-22.

Geological Survey of Canada
1986: Integration of Atlantic Geoscience Centre marine gravity data into the national gravity data base; Geological Survey of Canada, Open File 1232, 55 p.

Given, M.M.
1977: Mesozoic and early Cenozoic geology of offshore Nova Scotia; Bulletin of Canadian Petroleum Geology, v. 25, p. 63-91.

Godby, E.A., Baker, R.C., Bower, M.E., and Hood, P.J.
1966: Aeromagnetic reconnaissance of the Labrador Sea: Journal of Geophysical Research, v.71, p.511-517.

Goldthwaite, J.W.
1924: Physiography of Nova Scotia; Geological Survey of Canada, Memoir 140, 179 p.

Goodacre, A.K.
1964: A shipborne gravimeter testing range near Halifax, Nova Scotia; Journal of Geophysical Research, v. 69, p. 1-9.

Gormley, F.J.
1969: Production of sea water magnesia by Sea Mining Corporation Ltd. at Aguathuna, Newfoundland; Annual General Meeting, The Canadian Institute of Mining and Metallurgy, Montreal, Quebec, April 21-23, 1969.

Gossip, W.
1873: The Challenger scientific expedition. Visit to Halifax; Transactions Nova Scotia Institute of Science, v. 3, p. 335-337.

Gough, D.I.
1984: Mantle upflow under North America and plate dynamics; Nature, v. 311, p. 428-433.

Gradstein, F.M., Williams, G.L., Jenkins, W.A.M., and Ascoli, P.
1975: Mesozoic and Cenozoic stratigraphy of the Atlantic continental margin, Eastern Canada; Canadian Society of Petroleum Geologists, Memoir 4, p. 103-131.

Grant, A.C.
1966: A continuous seismic profile on the continental shelf off northeast Labrador; Canadian Journal of Earth Sciences, v. 3, p. 725-730.
1968: Some aspects of the bedrock geology of Hudson Bay as interpreted from continuous seismic reflection profiles; in Earth Science Symposium on Hudson Bay, ed. P.J. Hood; Geological Survey of Canada, Paper 68-53, p. 136-143.
1972: The continental margin off Labrador and eastern Newfoundland - morphology and geology; Canadian Journal of Earth Sciences, v. 9, p. 1394-1430.
1975: Geophysical results from the continental margin off southern Baffin Island; Canadian Society of Petroleum Geologists, Memoir 4, p. 411-431.

Grant, A.C., Levy, E.M., Lee, K., and Moffat, J.D.
1986a: Pisces IV research submersible finds oil on Baffin Shelf; in Current Research, Part A, Geological Survey of Canada, Paper 86-1A, p. 65-69.

Grant, A.C., McAlpine, K.D., and Wade, J.A.
1986b: The continental margin of eastern Canada: geological framework and petroleum potential; in Future Petroleum Province of the World, ed. M.J. Halbouty; American Association of Petroleum Geologists, Memoir 40, p. 177-205.

Grant, D.R.
1970: Recent coastal submergence of the Maritime Provinces, Canada; Canadian Journal of Earth Sciences, v. 7, p. 676-689.

Hacquebard, P.A.
1979: A geological appraisal of the coal resources of Nova Scotia; Canadian Institute of Mining and Metallurgy Bulletin, v. 72, p. 76-87.

Hale, P.B. and McLaren, P.
1984: A preliminary assessment of unconsolidated mineral resources in the Canadian offshore; Canadian Mining and Metallurgical Bulletin, September 1984, p. 1-11.

Harris, I.M. and Jollymore, P.G.
1974: Icemarks on the continental shelf northeast of Belle Isle, Newfoundland; Canadian Journal of Earth Sciences, v. 11, p. 43-52.

Haworth, R.T.
1981: Geophysical expression of Appalachian-Caledonide structure on the continental margins of North America; Canadian Society of Petroleum Geologists, Memoir 7, p. 429-446.

Hayes, J.D., Imbrie, J., and Shackleton, N.J.
1976: Variations in the earth's orbit: pacemaker of the ice ages; Science, v. 194, p. 1121-1131.

Heezen, B.C. and Drake, C.L.
1964: Grand Banks Slump; American Association of Petroleum Geologists Bulletin, v. 48, p. 221-233.

Heezen, B.C. and Ewing, M.
1952: Turbidity currents and submarine slumps, and the 1929 Grand Banks earthquake; American Journal of Science, v. 250, p. 849-873.

Heezen, B.C., Tharpe, M., and Ewing, M.
1959: The floors of the ocean; I The North Atlantic; Geological Society of America, Special Paper 65, 122 p.

Heffler, D.E. and Barrett, D.L.
1979: OBS development at Bedford Institute of Oceanography; Marine Geophysical Researches, v. 4, p. 227-245.

Hess, H.H.
1962: History of ocean basins; in Petrologic Studies, ed. A.E.J. Engel, Buddington volume, Geological Society of America, p. 599-620.

Hill, M.N. (ed.)
1963: The Sea; Ideas and Observations: Volume III The Earth Beneath the Sea; John Wiley and Sons, New York, 963 p.

Hinz, K., Schluter, H.-U., Grant, A.C., Srivastava, S.P., Umpleby, D., and Woodside, J.
1979: Geophysical transects of the Labrador Sea; Labrador to southwest Greenland; in Crustal Properties Across Passive Margins, ed. C.E. Keen; Tectonophysics, v. 59, p. 151-183.

Holtedahl, O.
1950: Supposed marginal fault lines in the shelf area off some high northern lands; Geological Society of America Bulletin, v. 61, p. 493-500.

Hood, P.J.
1964: Sea magnetometer reconnaissance of Hudson Bay; Geophysics, v.29, p.916-921.

Hood, P.J. (ed.)
1971: Earth Science Symposium on Offshore Eastern Canada; Geological Survey of Canada, Paper 71-23, 652 p.

Howie, R.D. and Cumming, L.M.
1963: Basement features of the Canadian Appalachians; Geological Survey of Canada, Bulletin 89, 18 p.

Hutchins, R.W., McKeown, D.L., and King, L.H.
1976: A deep tow high resolution seismic system for continental shelf mapping; Geoscience Canada, v. 3, p. 95-100.

Hyndman, R.D.
1973: Evolution of the Labrador Sea; Canadian Journal of Earth Sciences, v. 10, p. 637-644.

Hyndman, R.D., Jessop, A.M., Judge, A.S., and Rankin, D.S.
1979: Heat flow in the Maritime Provinces of Canada; Canadian Journal of Earth Sciences, v. 16, p. 1154-1165.

Issler, D.R.
1984: Calculation of organic maturation levels for offshore eastern Canada — implications for general application of Lopatin's method; Canadian Journal of Earth Sciences, v. 21, p. 477-488.

Issler, D.R. and Beaumont, C.B.
1986: Estimates of terrestrial heat flow in offshore eastern Canada: discussion; Canadian Journal of Earth Sciences, v. 23, p. 2083-2085.

Jackson, H.R. and Koppen, L.
1985: The Nares Strait gravity anomaly and its implication for crustal structure; Canadian Journal of Earth Sciences, v. 22, p. 1322-1328.

Jackson, H.R., Reid, I., and Falconer, R.
1982: Crustal structure near the Arctic Mid-Ocean Ridge; Journal of Geophysical Research, v. 87, p. 1773-1783.

Jackson, H.R., Mudie, P.J., and Blasco, S.M (ed.)
1985: Initial Geological Report on CESAR - the Canadian Expedition to Study the Alpha Ridge, Arctic Ocean; Geological Survey of Canada, Paper 84-22, 177 p.

Jansa, L.F.
1981: Mesozoic carbonate platforms and banks of the eastern North American margin; Marine Geology, v. 44, p. 97-117.

Jansa, L.F. and Wade, J.A.
1975a: Geology of the continental margin off Nova Scotia and Newfoundland; in Offshore Geology of Eastern Canada, ed. J.A. Wade and W.J.M. Van der Linden, Volume 2, Regional Geology; Geological Survey of Canada, Paper 74-30, v. 2, p. 51-105.
1975b: Paleogeography and sedimentation in the Mesozoic and Cenozoic, southeastern Canada; in Canada's Continental Margins and Offshore Petroleum Exploration, ed. C.J. Yorath, E.R. Parker and D.J. Glass; Canadian Society of Petroleum Geologists, Memoir 4, p. 79-102.

Jansa, L.F., Enos, P., Tucholke, B.E., Gradstein, F.M., and Sheridan, R.E.
1979: Mesozoic-Cenozoic sedimentary formations of the North American Basin: western North Atlantic; American Geophysical Union, Maurice Ewing series 3, p. 1-57.

Johnson, D.W.
1925: The New England-Acadian Shoreline; Hafner, New York, 608 p.

Josenhans, H., Zevenhuizen, J., and Klassen, R.
1986: Quaternary geology of the Labrador Shelf; Canadian Journal of Earth Sciences, v. 23, p. 1190-1213.

Kay, M.
1951: North American Geosynclines; Geological Society of America, Memoir 48, 143 p.

Keen, C.E.
1979: Thermal history and subsidence of rifted continental margins — evidence from wells on the Nova Scotian and Labrador shelves; Canadian Journal of Earth Sciences, v. 16, p. 505-522.
1985: The dynamics of rifting; deformation of the lithosphere by active and passive driving forces; Geophysical Journal, v. 80, p. 95-120.

Keen, C.E. and Kay, W.
1986: Deep marine multichannel seismic data from the northeast Newfoundland continental margin – Lithoprobe East; Geological Survey of Canada, Open file 1281.

Keen, C.E. and Peirce, J.W.
1982: The geophysical implications for minimal Tertiary motion along Nares Strait; Meddeleser om Gronland, Geoscience, v. 8, p. 327-337.

Keen, C.E., Boutilier, R., de Voogd, B., Mudford, B., and Enachescu, M.
1987: Crustal geometry and models of the evolution of the rift basins on the Grand Banks off eastern Canada; constraints from deep seismic reflection data: Canadian Society of Petroleum Geologists, Memoir 12, p. 101-106.

Keen, C.E., Keen, M.J., Nichols, B., Reid, I., Stockmal, G.S., Colman-Sadd, S.P., O'Brien, S.J., Miller, H., Quinlan, G., Williams, H., and Wright, J.
1986: Deep seismic reflection profile across the northern Appalachians; Geology, v. 14, p. 141-145.

Keen, M.J.
1969: Magnetic anomalies off the eastern seaboard of the United States; Nature, v. 222, p. 72-74.
1983: The earth sciences at sea: some observations on Canadian accomplishments; Geological Survey of Canada, Paper 81-6, p. 9-18.

Keen, M.J. and Clarke, D.B.
1974: Tertiary basalts of Baffin Bay: geochemical evidence for a fossil hot-spot; in Geodynamics of Iceland and Atlantic Area, ed. L. Kristjansson, Reidel Publishing, Boston, p. 127-137.

Keen, M.J., Johnson. J., and Park, I.
1972: Geophysical and geological studies in eastern and northern Baffin Bay and Lancaster Sound; Canadian Journal of Earth Sciences, v. 9, p. 689-708.

Keen, M.J., Loncarevic, B.D., and Ewing, G.N.
1971: Continental margin of eastern Canada; Georges Bank to Kane Basin; in The Sea: Ideas and Observations on Progress in the study of the Seas; Volume 4, New Concepts of Sea Floor Evolution, Part II, Regional Observations; Wiley-Interscience, New York, v. 4, p. 251-291.

Kennard, L., Schafer, C., and Carter, L.
(in press): Late Cenozoic evolution of Sackville Spur: A sediment drift on the Newfoundland Continental Slope; Canadian Journal of Earth Sciences.

Kerr, J.H.
1870: Ice marks in Newfoundland; Quarterly Journal of the Geological Society of London, v. 26, p. 704-705.

Kidd, R.B. and Hill, P.R.
1986: Sedimentation on mid-ocean drifts; in North Atlantic Paleoceaonography, ed. C.P. Summerhayes and N.J. Shackleton; Geological Society, Special Publication no. 21, p. 87-102.

King, L.H.
1967: Use of a conventional echo sounder and textural analysis in delineating sedimentary facies — Scotian Shelf; Canadian Journal of Earth Sciences, v. 4, p. 691-708.
1970: Surficial geology of the Halifax-Sable Island map area; Ottawa, Department of Energy, Mines and Resources, Marine Science Paper 1, 16 p.
1972: Relation of plate tectonics to the geomorphic evolution of the Canadian Atlantic Provinces; Geological Society of America Bulletin, v. 83, p. 3082-3090.
1976: Relict iceberg furrows on the Laurentian Channel and western Grand Banks; Canadian Journal of Earth Sciences, v. 13, p. 1082-1092.

King, L.H. and Fader, G.B.
1985: Wisconsinan glaciation of the continental shelf, southeastern Atlantic Canada; Geological Survey of Canada, Open File 1126, 114 p.

King, L.H. and MacLean, B.
1970a: Seismic reflection study: Orpheus gravity anomaly; American Association of Petroleum Geologists, Bulletin, v. 54, p. 2007-2031.
1970b: Pockmarks on the Scotian Shelf; Geological Society of America, v. 81, p. 3141-3148.
1976: Geology of the Scotian Shelf; Geological Survey of Canada, Paper 74-31, 31 p.

Klein, G. de V.
1963: Bay of Fundy intertidal sediments; Journal of Sedimentary Petrology, v. 33, p. 844-854.

Klose, G.W., Malterre, E., McMillan, N.J., and Zinkan, G.G.
1982: Petroleum exploration offshore southern Baffin Island, northern Labrador Sea, Canada; Canadian Society of Petroleum Geologists Memoir 8, p. 233-244.

Kranck, K.
1971: Surficial geology of Northumberland Strait; Geological Survey of Canada, Paper 71-53, 10 p.

Kuenen, P.H.
1950: Marine Geology; John Wiley and Sons Inc., New York, 568 p.

LASE
1986: Deep structure of the US east coast passive margin from large aperture seismic experiments (LASE); Marine and Petroleum Geology, v. 3, p. 234-242.

Laughton, A.S. et al. (ed.)
1972: Initial Reports of the Deep Sea Drilling Project Volume XII; United States Government Printing Office, Washington, v. 12, 1243 p.

Le Pichon, X., Hyndman, R.D., and Pautot, G.
1971: Geophysical study of the opening of the Labrador Sea; Journal Geophysical Research, v. 76, p. 4724-4743.

Leslie, R.J.
1964: Sedimentology of Hudson Bay, District of Keewatin; Geological Survey of Canada, Paper 63-48, 31 p.

Lewis, C.F.M.
1978: The frequency and magnitude of drift-ice groundings from ice-scour tracks in the Canadian Beaufort Sea; in Proceedings of the Fourth International Conference on Port and Ocean Engineering under Arctic Conditions, Memorial University of Newfoundland, St. John's, Newfoundland, p. 568-579.

Lewis, C.F.M., MacLean, B., and Falconer, R.K.H.
1980: Iceberg scour abundance in Labrador Sea and Baffin Bay; A reconnaissance of regional variability; in Proceedings of the First Canadian Conference on Marine Geotechnical Engineering, Calgary, Alberta, April 1979, p. 79-94.

Lewis, J.F. and Hyndman, R.D.
1976: Oceanic heat flow measurements over the continental margins of eastern Canada; Canadian Journal of Earth Sciences, v. 14, p. 1031-1038.

Libby, F.
1969: Searching for alluvial gold deposits off Nova Scotia; Ocean Industry, v. 4, p. 43-46.

Lilly, H.D.
1965: Submarine examination of the Virgin Rocks area, Grand Banks, Newfoundland: preliminary note; Geological Society of America Bulletin, v. 76, p. 131.

Loken, O.H. and Hodgson, D.A.
1971: On the submarine geomorphology along the east coast of Baffin Island; Canadian Journal of Earth Sciences, v. 8, p. 185-195.

Loncarevic, B.D. and Ewing, G.N.
1967: Geophysical study of the Orpheus Gravity anomaly; in World Petroleum Congress, 1967, Proceedings, Volume 2, Origin of oil, Geology and Geophysics, Elsevier, New York, v. 2, p. 827-835.

Loncarevic, B.D. and Falconer, R.K.
1977: An oil slick occurrence off Baffin Island; in Report of Activities, Part A, Geological Survey of Canada, Paper 77-1A, p. 523-524.

Loncarevic, B.D. and Woodside, J.M.
1984: Coastal geophysics: gravity measurements in Mahone Bay, N.S. with a shipborne seagravimeter: Canadian Geophysical Union, Program with Abstracts, 20 May — 1 June, 1984, Dalhousie University, Halifax, Nova Scotia, p. 20.

Long, B.
1986: Techniques of tracers; in Sediment Transport and Industry Needs, ed. D.O. Hodgins, D.A. Huntley, W.D. Finn, B. Long, G. Drapeau and A.J. Bowen; Environmental Studies Revolving Funds, Report 027, p. 151-214.

Loring, D.H.
1975: Surficial geology of the Gulf of St.Lawrence; in Offshore Geology of Eastern Canada, Volume 2, Regional

Geology, ed. J.A. Wade and W.J.M. Van der Linden; Geological Survey of Canada, Paper 74-30, v. 2, p. 11-34.

Louden, K.E., Fang, C., and Wright, J.A.
1985: Heat flow and depth versus age in the Labrador Sea; EOS, Transactions of the American Geophysical Union, v. 66, p. 1059.

Louden, K.S., Wallace, D.O., and Courtney, R.C.
1987: Heat flow and depth versus age for the Mesozoic NW Atlantic Ocean: results from the Sohm Abyssal Plain and implications for the Bermuda Rise; Earth and Planetary Science letters, v. 83, p. 109-122.

Low, A.P.
1906: Report on the Dominion Government expedition to Hudson Bay and the Arctic Islands on board the D.G.S. NEPTUNE, 1903-1904; The Queen's Printer, Ottawa, 355 p.

Lyell, C.
1849: Notes on some Recent footprints in Red Mud in Nova Scotia collected by W.B. Webster of Kentville; Quarterly Journal of the Geological Society of London, v. 5, p. 344.

MacKay, J.R.
1972: Offshore permafrost and ground ice, southern Beaufort Sea, Canada; Canadian Journal of Earth Sciences, v. 9, p. 1550-1561.

Mackenzie, A.S., Brassell, S.C., Eglinton, G., and Maxwell, J.R.
1982: Chemical fossils — the geological fate of steroids; Science, v. 217, p. 491-505.

MacLean, B.
1986: Preliminary Report of cruise activities: CSS HUDSON 85-027, September 23-October 28, 1985; Bedford Institute of Oceanography.

MacLean, B. and King, L.H.
1971: Surficial geology of the Banquereau and Misaine Bank map area; Geological Survey of Canada, Paper 71-52, 19 p.

MacLean, B., Falconer, R.K.H., and Levy, E.M.
1981: Geological, geophysical and geochemical evidence for natural seepage of petroleum off the northeast coast of Baffin Island; Canadian Petroleum Geology Bulletin, v. 29, p. 75-95.

MacLean, B., Srivastava, S., and Haworth, R.T.
1982: Bedrock structures off Cumberland Sound, Baffin Island Shelf: core samples and geophysical data; Canadian Society of Petroleum Geologists, Memoir 8, p. 279-295.

Macnab, R., Loncarevic, B.D., Cooper, R.V., Girouard, P.R., Hughes, M.D., and Shouzhi, F.
1985: A regional marine multiparameter survey south of Newfoundland; in Current Research, Part B, Geological Survey of Canada, Paper 85-1B, p. 325-332.

Magnusson, D.H.
1965: Geological report on the Sable Island core-hole program; Mobil Oil Canada Ltd., Calgary, Alberta, 32 p.

Manchester, K.S.
1964: Geophysical investigations between Canada and Greenland; M.Sc. thesis, Dalhousie University, Halifax, Nova Scotia.

Marvin, U.B.
1973: Continental Drift: The Evolution of a Concept; Smithsonian Institution Press, Washington, 239 p.

Maury, M.F.
1859: Physical Geography of the Sea; Harper and Brothers, New York, 6th Edition, 468 p.

Mayhew, M.A., Drake, C.L., and Nafe, J.E.
1970: Marine geophysical measurements on the continental margins of the Labrador Sea; Canadian Journal of Earth Sciences, v. 7, p. 199-214.

McCann, S.B., (ed.)
1980: The coastline of Canada; Geological Survey of Canada, Paper 80-10, 437 p.

McGarr, A.
1982: Analysis of states of stress between provinces of constant stress; Journal of Geophysical Research, v. 87, p. 9279-9288.

McIver, N.L.
1972: Mesozoic-Cenozoic stratigraphy of the Scotian Shelf; Canadian Journal of Earth Sciences, v. 9, p. 54-70.

McKenzie, D.P.
1978: Some remarks on the development of sedimentary basins; Earth and Planetary Science Letters, v. 40, p. 25-32.

McKenzie, D.P. and Parker, R.L.
1967: The North Pacific: an example of tectonics on a sphere; Nature, v. 216, p. 1276-1280.

McMillan, N.J.
1973a: Shelves of Labrador Sea and Baffin Bay, Canada; Canadian Society of Petroleum Geologists, Memoir 1, p. 473-517.
1973b: Surficial geology of Labrador and Baffin Island shelves; in Offshore Eastern Canada Symposium, 1971, ed. P.J. Hood; Geological Survey of Canada, Paper 71-23, p. 451-468.
1982: Canada's east coast: the new super petroleum province; Journal of Canadian Petroleum Technology, v. 21, no. 2, p. 1-15.

Menard, H.W.
1986: The Ocean of Truth; Princeton University Press, Princeton, 353 p.

Mobil Oil Canada Limited
1968: Mobil Sable Island No. 1 (C-67) Well History Report by Mobil Oil Canada Ltd., Calgary; Canada Oil and Gas Lands Administration, Ottawa.

Morley, L.W. and Larochelle, A.
1964: Paleomagnetism as a means of dating geological events; in Geochronology in Canada, ed. F.F. Osborne, Royal Society of Canada, Special Publication no. 8, p. 39-51.

Morgan, W.J.
1968: Rises, trenches, great faults and crustal blocks; Journal of Geophysical Research, v. 73, p. 1959-82.

Mudie, P.J. and Helgason, J.
1983: Palynological evidence for Miocene climatic cooling in eastern Iceland about 9.8 million years ago; Nature, v. 303, p. 689-692.

Officer, C.B. and Ewing, M.
1954: Geophysical investigations in the emerged and submerged Atlantic coastal plain: Part 7. Continental shelf, continental slope, and continental rise south of Nova Scotia; Bulletin Geological Society of America, v. 65, p. 653-670.

Owens, E.H., Leslie, J.A. and Associates
1977: Coastal environments of Canada: the impact and cleanup of oil spills; Fisheries and Environment Canada, Environment Protection Service, Environmental Impact Control Directorate, 214 p.

Parson, L.M., Masson, D.G., Rothwell, R.G., and Grant, A.C.
1984: Remnants of a submerged pre-Jurassic (?Devonian) landscape on Orphan Knoll, offshore eastern Canada; Canadian Journal of Earth Sciences, v. 21, p. 61-66.

Pelletier, B.R.
1962: Submarine geology program, Polar Continental Shelf Project, Isachsen, District of Franklin; Geological Survey of Canada, Paper 61-21, 10 p.
1966: Development of submarine physiography in the Canadian Arctic and its relationship to crustal movements; in Continental Drift, ed. G.D. Garland; Royal Society of Canada, Special Publications, no. 9, p. 77-101.
1968: The submersible PISCES feasibility study in the Canadian Arctic; Maritime Sediments, v. 4, no. 2, p. 69-72.
1971: A granodioritic drill core from the Flemish Cap, eastern Canadian continental margin; Canadian Journal of Earth Sciences, v. 8, p. 1499-1503.
1975: Offshore Geology of Eastern Canada: Volume 1 — Concepts and Applications of Environmental Marine Geology, B.R. Pelletier, ed., Geological Survey of Canada, Paper 74-30, v. 1, 160 p.

Pelletier, B.R. and McMullen, R.M.
1972: Sedimentary patterns in the Bay of Fundy and Minas Basin; in Tidal Power, ed. T.J. Gray and O.K. Gashus, Plenum Press, New York, p. 152-187.

Pelletier, B.R., Wagner, F.J.E., and Grant, A.C.
1968: Marine geology; in Science, History and Hudson Bay, Volume 2, ed. C.S.Beals; Department of Energy, Mines and Resources, Ottawa, v. 2, p. 557-613.

Piper, D.J.W., Letson, J.R.J., de Iure, A.M., and Barrie, C.Q.
1983: Sediment accumulation in low-sedimentation, wave-dominated, glaciated inlets; Sedimentary Geology, v. 36, p. 195-215.

Piper, D.J.W., Mudie, P., Letson, J.R.J., Barnes, N.E., and Iulucci, R.J.
1986: The marine geology of the inner Scotian Shelf off the South Shore of Nova Scotia; Geological Survey of Canada, Paper 85-19, 65 p.

Piper, D.J.W., Shor, A.N., and Hughes Clarke, J.E.
1988: The 1929 Grand Banks earthquake, slump and turbidity current; Geological Society of America Special Paper 229, p. 221-240.

Powell, T.G. and Snowdon, L.R.
1979: Geochemistry of crude oils and condensates from the Scotian Basin, offshore eastern Canada; Bulletin of Canadian Petroleum Geology, v. 27, p. 453-466.

Press, F. and Beckmann, W.
1954: Geophysical investigations in the emerged and submerged Atlantic coastal plain. Part VIII, Grand Banks and adjacent shelves; Geological Society of America Bulletin, v. 65, p. 299-314.

Pye, G.D. and Hyndman, R.D.
1972: Heat-flow measurements in Baffin Bay and the Labrador Sea; Journal of Geophysical Research, v. 77, p. 938-944.

Quinlan, G. and Beaumont, C.
1981: A comparison of observed and theoretical post glacial relative sea level in Atlantic Canada; Canadian Journal of Earth Sciences, v. 18, p. 1146-1163.

Rashid, M.A., Purcell, L.P., and Hardy, I.A.
1980: Source rock potential for oil and gas of the East Newfoundland and Labrador shelf areas; Canadian Society of Petroleum Geologists, Memoir 6, p. 589-608.

Rashid, M.A., Wagner, F.J.E., and Walker, D.A.
1975: Canso Strait and Chedabucto Bay: a multidisciplinary study of the impact of man on the marine environment; in Offshore Geology of Eastern Canada, Volume 1, Concepts and Applications of Environmental Marine Geology, ed. B.R. Pelletier; Geological Survey of Canada, Paper 74-30, v. 1, p. 133-160.

Reinson, G.E.
1979: Barrier island system; in Facies Models, ed R.G. Walker; Geoscience Canada, Reprint Series 1, p. 57-74.

Reiter, M. and Jessop, A.M.
1985: Estimates of terrestrial heat flow in offshore eastern Canada; Canadian Journal of Earth Sciences, v. 22, p. 1503-1517.
1986: Estimates of terrestrial heat flow in offshore eastern Canada: Reply; Canadian Journal of Earth Sciences, v. 23, p. 2085-2086.

Richards, H.G.
1959: Pleistocene mammals dredged off the coast of New Jersey; Geological Society of America Bulletin, v. 70, p. 1769.

Ricketts, N.G. and Trask, P.D.
1932: The "Marion" expedition to Davis Strait and Baffin Bay under the direction of the United States Coast Guard, 1928: Scientific Results, part 1: The Bathymetry and Sediments of Davis Strait; United States Treasury Department, Coast Guard Bulletin no. 19, 81 p.

Roth, M.
1983: Canadian geophysical activity; in The Geosciences in Canada, 1980, Geological Survey of Canada, Paper 81-6, Part 1, p. 73-78.

Ruddiman, W.F.
1977: Late Quaternary deposition of ice-rafted sand in the subpolar North Atlantic (lat. 40° to 65°N); Geological Society of America Bulletin, v. 88, p. 1813-1827.

Ruffman, A.
1969: Seismic investigations of the crust in the Hudson Bay region; in Earth Science Symposium on Hudson Bay, ed. P.J. Hood; Geological Survey of Canada, Paper 68-53, p. 272-291.

Schafer, C.T. and Pelletier, B.R. (ed.)
1976: First International Symposium on Benthonic Foraminifera on Continental Margins; Maritime Sediments, Special Publication no. 1, 790 p.

Shearer, J.M.
1971: Preliminary interpretation of shallow seismic reflection profiles from the west side of Mackenzie Bay, Beaufort Sea; in Report of Activities, Part B, Geological Survey of Canada, Paper 71-1B, p. 131-138.

Shearer, J.M., Macnab, R.F., Pelletier, B.R., and Smith, T.B.
1971: Submarine pingos in the Beaufort Sea; Science, v. 174, p. 816-818.

Shepard, F.P.
1931: Saint Lawrence (Cabot Strait) submarine trough; Geological Society of America Bulletin, v. 42, p. 853-864.
1948: The Earth Beneath the Sea, (First edition); Harper and Brothers, New York, 348 p.

Shepard, F.P. and Cohee, G.V.
1936: Continental shelf sediments off the mid-Atlantic States; Geological Society of America Bulletin, v. 47, p. 441-458.

Sheridan, R.E. and Drake, C.L.
1968: Seaward extension of the Canadian Appalachians; Canadian Journal of Earth Sciences, v. 5, p. 337-373.

Sherwin, D.
1973: Scotian Shelf and Grand Banks; Canadian Society of Petroleum Geologists, Memoir 1, p. 519-559

Spencer, J.W.
1903: Submarine valleys off the American coast and in the North Atlantic; Geological Society of America Bulletin, v. 14, p. 207-226.

Srivastava, S.P.
1978: Evolution of the Labrador Sea and its bearing on the early evolution of the North Atlantic; Geophysical Journal, v. 52, p. 313-357.
1983: Davis Strait; structures, origin and evolution; in Structure and Development of the Greenland-Scotland Ridge - New Methods and Concepts, ed. M.H.P. Bott et al.; Nato Conference Series IV, Marine Sciences, v. 8, p. 159-189.

Srivastava, S.P. and Falconer, R.K.H.
1982: Nares Strait: a conflict between plate tectonic predictions and geological interpretation; in Nares Strait and the drift of Greenland: A Conflict in Plate Tectonics, ed. P.R. Dawes and J.W. Kerr; Meddeleser om Gromland, Geoscience 8, p. 339-352.

Srivastava, S.P., Arthur, M., Clement, B., et al.
1987: Proceedings of the Ocean Drilling Program, Part A, Initial Report, Leg 105, 917 p.

Stanley, D.J.
1968: Reworking of glacial sediments in the North West Arm, a fjord-like inlet on the southeast coast of Nova Scotia; Journal of Sedimentary Petrology, v. 38, p. 1224-1241.

Stanley, D.J., Swift, D.J.P., Silverberg, N., James, N.P., and Sutton, R.G.
1972: Late Quaternary progradation and sand spillover on the outer continental margin off Nova Scotia, southeast Canada; Smithsonian Contributions to Earth Sciences, no. 8, 43 p.

Stein, S., Sleep, N.H., Geller, R.J., Wang, S., and Kroeger, G.C.
1979: Earthquakes along the passive margin of eastern Canada; Geophysical Research Letters, v. 6, p. 537-540.

Stephenson, L.W.
1936: Geology and paleontology of the Georges Bank canyons: Pt. 2, Upper Cretaceous fossils from Georges Bank (including species from Banquereau, Nova Scotia); Geological Society of America Bulletin, v. 47, p. 339-366.

Stetson, H.C.
1936: Dredge-samples from the submarine canyons between the Hudson Gorge and Chesapeake Bay; Transactions of the American Geophysical Union, 17th Annual Meeting, Washington, p. 223-225.

Stockmal, G.S., Colman-Sadd, S.P., Keen, C.E., O'Brien, S.J., and Quinlan, G.
1987: Collision along an irregular margin: A regional plate tectonic interpretation of the Canadian Appalachians; Canadian Journal of Earth Sciences, v. 24, p. 1098-1107.

Swallow, J.C. and Worthington, L.V.
1957: Measurements of deep currents in the western North Atlantic; Nature, v. 179, p. 1183.

Swift, J.H. and Williams, J.A.
1980: Petroleum source rocks: Grand Banks area; Canadian Society of Petroleum Geologists, Memoir 6, p. 567-588.

Syvitski, J., Burrell, D.C., and Skei, J.M.
1986: Fjords: Processes and Products; Springer Verlag, New York, 400 p.

Tarr, R.S.
1897: The Arctic sea ice as a geological agent; American Journal of Science, Series 4, v. 111, p. 223-229.

Taylor, R.B.
1980: Coastal reconnaissance for marine terminal planning in the Sverdrup Basin, Northwest Territories; Geological Survey of Canada, Open File 693, 150 p.

Texaco et al.
1981: Blue H-28 Well History Report by Texaco Canada Ltd., Calgary, Canada Oil and Gas Lands Administration, Ottawa.

Tyrell, J.B.
1898: The glaciation of north-central Canada; Journal of Geology, v. 6, p. 147-160.

Tucholke, B.E. and Fry, V.A.
1985: Basement structure and sediment distribution in the Northwest Atlantic Ocean; American Association of Petroleum Geologists, v. 69, p. 2877-2897.

Tucker, C.M.
1976: Quaternary studies in Newfoundland: a short review; Maritime Sediments, v. 12, p. 61-73.

Upham, W.
1894: The fishing banks between Cape Cod and Newfoundland; American Journal of Science, Series 3, v. 47, p. 123-129.

Upshaw, C.F., Armstrong, W.E., Creath, W.B., Kidson, E.J., and Sanderson, G.A.
1974: Biostratigraphic framework of the Grand Banks; American Association of Petroleum Geologists Bulletin, v. 58, p. 1124-1132.

Van der Linden, W.J. and Wade, J.A. (ed.)
1975: Offshore geology of eastern Canada: Volume 2 Regional Geology; Geological Survey of Canada, Paper 74-30, v. 2, 258 p.

Verrill, A.E.
1878: Occurrence of fossiliferous Tertiary rocks on the Grand Banks and Georges Bank; American Journal of Science, Series 3, v. 16, p. 323-324.

Vilks, G. and Krauel, D.P.
1982: Environmental geology of the Miramichi Estuary: physical oceanography; Geological Survey of Canada, Paper 81-24, 53 p.

Vilks, G. and Mudie, P.G.
1978: Early deglaciation of the Labrador Shelf; Science, v. 202, p. 1181-1183

Vine, F.J. and Matthews, D.H.
1963: Magnetic anomalies over oceanic ridges; Nature, v. 199, p. 947-949.

Watson, J.A., and Johson, G.L.
1970: Seismic studies in the region adjacent to the Grand Banks of Newfoundland; Canadian Journal of Earth Sciences, v. 7, p. 306-310.

Wegener, A.
1915: Die Enstehung der Kontinente und Ozeane; Braunschweig, Vieweg, 212 p.

Whiteaves, J.F.
1901: Catalogue of the Marine Invertebrata of Eastern Canada; Geological Survey of Canada, Ottawa, Ontario, 271 p.

Widmer, K.
1950: Geology of the Hermitage Bay area, Newfoundland; Ph.D. thesis, Princeton University.

Williams, G.L.
1974: Biostratigraphy and paleoecology of the Mesozoic and Cenozoic rocks of the Atlantic shelf; in Report of Activities, Part B, Geological Survey of Canada, Paper 74-1B, p. 150-152.
1975: Dinoflagellate and spore stratigraphy of the Mesozoic-Cenozoic, offshore eastern Canada; in Offshore Geology of Eastern Canada, volume 2, Regional Geology, ed. W.J. Van der Linden and J.A. Wade; Geological Survey of Canada, Paper 74-30, v. 2, p. 107-161.

Williams, G.L. and Brideaux, W.W.
1975: Palynological analysis of Late Mesozoic-Cenozoic rocks of the Grand Banks of Newfoundland; Geological Survey of Canada, Bulletin 236, 162 p.

Williams, H.
1964: The Appalachians in northeastern Newfoundland - a two sided system; American Journal of Science, v. 262, p. 1137-1158.
1967: Island of Newfoundland; Geological Survey of Canada, Map 1231A.

Williams, H. and Hatcher, R.D., Jr.
1982: Suspect terranes and accretionary history of the Appalachian Orogen; Geology, v. 10, p. 530-536.

Williams, H., Kennedy, M.J., and Neale, E.R.W.
1970: The Hermitage Flexure, the Cabot Fault and the disappearance of the Newfoundland Central Mobile Belt; Geological Society of America Bulletin, v. 81, p. 1562-1568.

Willmore, P.L. and Scheidegger, A.E.
1956: Seismic observations in the Gulf of St.Lawrence; Transactions of the Royal Society of Canada, series 3, v. 50, p. 21-38.

Wilson, J.T.
1963: Hypothesis of earth's behaviour; Nature, v. 198, p. 925-929.
1966: Did the Atlantic close and then re-open?; Nature, v. 211, p. 676-681.

Wright, J.A., Keen, C.E., and Keen, M.J.
1984: Marine heat flow along the northeast coast of Newfoundland: Geological Survey of Canada, Paper 84-1B, p. 93-100.

Yorath, C.J., Shearer, J., and Havard, C.J.
1971: Seismic and sediment studies in the Beaufort Sea; in Report of Activities, Part A, Geological Survey of Canada, Paper 71-1A, p. 243-244.

Zoback, M.L. and Zoback, M.D.
1980: State of stress in the coterminous United States; Journal of Geophysical Research, v. 85, p. 6113-6156.

INDEX
(author index follows)

AUTHOR INDEX